2019–2020
FORTY-SECOND EDITION

Ohio School Directory

A State Guide to K-12 Districts, Dioceses, and Schools...

Powered by the Industry's Best Data

- **NEW...8 Additional Administrator Titles!**
- Charter Management Organization Index
- Facebook and Twitter Indicators
- Email Address Availability Highlighted
- Detailed School and District Listings
- Names and Job Titles of Key Personnel
- New Schools and Personnel Index

MDR
A Dun & Bradstreet Division

Copyright 2019 Market Data Retrieval | 6 Armstrong Road, Shelton, CT 06484

Copyright 2019 Market Data Retrieval, a D&B Company. All Rights Reserved. No information furnished hereby may be reproduced or transmitted in any form or by any means, electronic or mechanical, including photocopying and recording, or by any information storage or retrieval system, except as may be expressly permitted by MDR, 6 Armstrong Road, Shelton, CT 06484.

The information in this directory is licensed with the express understanding and agreement that the information will be solely for internal use and will not be used for the creation and/or updating of databases, electronic or otherwise, that are sold or provided to any third party without the express written permission of MDR.

51-Volume National Set   ISBN# 978-1-951295-51-6

Individual Bound State Editions

	ISSN#	ISBN#		ISSN#	ISBN#
Alabama	1077-7393	978-1-947802-68-1	Montana	1077-7652	978-1-951295-25-7
Alaska	1077-7407	978-1-951295-00-4	Nebraska	1077-7660	978-1-951295-26-4
Arizona	1077-7415	978-1-951295-01-1	Nevada	1077-7679	978-1-951295-27-1
Arkansas	1077-7423	978-1-951295-02-8	New Hampshire	1077-7687	978-1-951295-28-8
California	1077-7431	978-1-951295-03-5	New Jersey	1077-7695	978-1-951295-29-5
Colorado	1077-744X	978-1-951295-04-2	New Mexico	1077-7709	978-1-951295-30-1
Connecticut	1077-7458	978-1-951295-05-9	New York	1077-7717	978-1-951295-31-8
Delaware	1077-7466	978-1-951295-06-6	North Carolina	1077-7725	978-1-951295-32-5
District of Columbia	1077-7474	978-1-951295-07-3	North Dakota	1077-7733	978-1-951295-33-2
Florida	1077-7482	978-1-951295-08-0	Ohio	1077-7741	978-1-951295-34-9
Georgia	1077-7490	978-1-951295-09-7	Oklahoma	1077-775X	978-1-951295-35-6
Hawaii	1077-7504	978-1-951295-10-3	Oregon	1077-7768	978-1-951295-36-3
Idaho	1077-7512	978-1-951295-11-0	Pennsylvania	1077-7776	978-1-951295-37-0
Illinois	1077-7520	978-1-951295-12-7	Rhode Island	1077-7784	978-1-951295-38-7
Indiana	1077-7539	978-1-951295-13-4	South Carolina	1077-7792	978-1-951295-39-4
Iowa	1077-7547	978-1-951295-14-1	South Dakota	1077-7806	978-1-951295-40-0
Kansas	1077-7555	978-1-951295-15-8	Tennessee	1077-7814	978-1-951295-41-7
Kentucky	1077-7563	978-1-951295-16-5	Texas	1077-7822	978-1-951295-42-4
Louisiana	1077-7571	978-1-951295-17-2	Utah	1077-7830	978-1-951295-43-1
Maine	1077-758X	978-1-951295-18-9	Vermont	1077-7849	978-1-951295-44-8
Maryland	1077-7598	978-1-951295-19-6	Virginia	1077-7857	978-1-951295-45-5
Massachusetts	1077-7601	978-1-951295-20-2	Washington	1077-7865	978-1-951295-46-2
Michigan	1077-761X	978-1-951295-21-9	West Virginia	1077-7873	978-1-951295-47-9
Minnesota	1077-7628	978-1-951295-22-6	Wisconsin	1077-7881	978-1-951295-48-6
Mississippi	1077-7636	978-1-951295-23-3	Wyoming	1077-789X	978-1-951295-49-3
Missouri	1077-7644	978-1-951295-24-0	Sales Manager's Guide	2150-2021	978-1-951295-50-9

If you have any questions or comments concerning this directory, please write to MDR, 6 Armstrong Road, Shelton, CT 06484, or call us toll-free at 800-333-8802 or collect at 203-926-4800.

MDR's School Directory

TABLE OF CONTENTS

Sample Directory Listings iv
- A complete listing of codes, definitions and data elements used throughout this directory.

Directory Statistics (Yellow Section)

State Statistics A1
- An overview of state statistics showing the distribution of districts, schools and personnel by key indicators.

County Statistics B1
- A county-by-county census of districts and schools and their enrollments.

District Buying Power Index C1
- A complete listing of counties and districts ranked by the amount of money they spend on instructional materials.

New Public Schools and Key Personnel Index (Cream Section) NEW1
- A summary of new public schools that have opened for the current school year, plus Superintendents and Principals who are new to their institution.

District and School Listings (White Section) 1
- Complete information provided for each district and school in the state, organized alphabetically by county.
- Listings within each county are in the following order: County Centers and Schools, Public School Districts and Schools, Catholic Diocesan Offices and/or Schools, Other Private Schools and Regional Centers.

Directory Indices

District Index (Ivory Section) Q1
- A complete listing of districts in alphabetical order for each district type: Public School Districts, Catholic Dioceses, County Centers and Regional Centers.
- Includes number of schools, enrollment, county location and page number.

County Index (Tan Section) R1
- A complete alphabetical listing by county of Public School Districts, Catholic Dioceses, County Centers and Regional Centers.

Supervisory Union Index (Gold Section) S1
- Included for the states of Maine, Massachusetts, New Hampshire and Vermont, where several local school districts are administered by the same administrative personnel located at a Supervisory Union office. The index lists each Supervisory Union followed by their local school districts.

District Personnel Index (Gray Section) T1
- A complete listing, in last name sequence, of all district personnel.

Principal Index (Green Section) U1
- A complete listing, in last name sequence, of all school principals.

District and School Telephone Index (Blue Section) V1
- A complete listing of all districts and schools in the state with their telephone and PID numbers.

District URL Index (Salmon Section) W1
- A listing of districts that have URL addresses.

Charter Management Organization (CMO) Index (Orchid Section) CMO1
- An alphabetical listing, by state-CMO sequence, of Charter Management Organizations.
- Includes CMO number, PID, full address and phone number.

Directory Code Reference Guide located on the bottom of each page.

Sample Directory Listings

MDR's School Directories are your complete reference source, providing comprehensive data on public school districts and schools, Catholic and other independent schools, and regional and county centers in all 50 states and the District of Columbia. Every public school district and school entry in MDR's School Directories is updated each year through telephone interviews conducted with school district personnel. These interviews take place from July to September, capturing the most current school year data available. In addition, information obtained from state, district and school directories is used to verify information contained in MDR's School Directories.

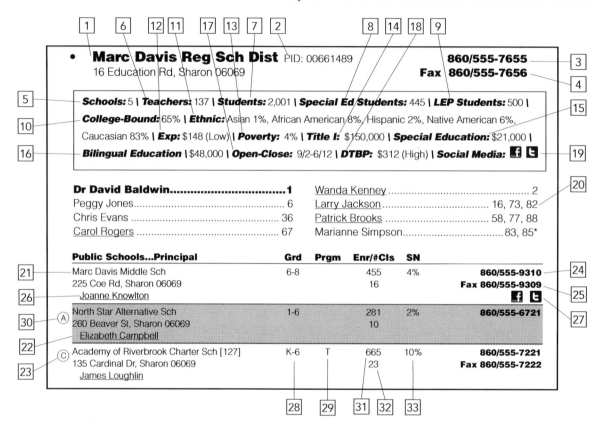

Each directory listing is uniformly organized to reflect the following data as applicable.

Definitions of Codes and Data:

DISTRICT DATA

1 District Name and Address
The physical location address for the superintendent's office is listed. MDR also maintains the mailing address, if different, for each district office. For this alternative mailing address, contact MDR directly at 800-333-8802.

2 District PID Number
Personal Identification Number of the district. Helps identify specific institutions when speaking to an MDR Representative or searching in Education MarketView.

3 Telephone Number
The telephone number of the district's central administration office.

4 Fax Number
The fax number of the district's central administration office. Please use the fax numbers in the directory appropriately.

The FCC prohibits the use of a telephone facsimile machine to send unsolicited advertisements. If you need further clarification of the laws that exist, you can contact the FCC directly at 888-225-5322, or you can visit their website at http://www.fcc.gov.

5 Number of Schools
The number of schools reporting directly to the district. In the case of decentralized large districts (such as Chicago Public Schools), the number of schools reflects those reporting directly to the central school district in addition to those administered directly by each of the subdistrict offices.

6 Number of Teachers
The number of full-time equivalent teachers throughout the district as reported by the U.S. Department of Education.

iv

7 District Enrollment
The projected number of students enrolled in the district for fall 2019.

8 Special Ed Students
The number of students having a written Individualized Education Plan (IEP) indicating their participation in a Special Education Program.

9 LEP Students
The number of Limited-English Proficient students being served in appropriate programs of language assistance (i.e., English as a second language, high-intensity language training, bilingual education).

10 College-Bound Students
The percentage of the district's 12th grade enrollment planning to attend two- or four-year colleges.

11 Student Ethnic Percentages
The student enrollment percentage by ethnic group: Asian, African American, Hispanic, Native American and Caucasian. This information is reported annually by the U.S. Department of Education. Due to rounding, the percentages may not add up to 100%.

12 District Expenditure
The district's expenditure per student for instructional materials. In addition to the actual dollar amount, a level of expenditure is provided as follows:
- High = $300+
- Med = $200-299
- Low = Under $200

13 Poverty Level
This census data reflects the percentage of school-age children in the district from families below the poverty line. Poverty levels are as follows:
- Low = 0-5%
- Med-Low = 6-15%
- Med-High = 16-29%
- High = 30%+

14 Title I
The district's Title I dollar allocation is for the 2018 fiscal year. Funding levels are as follows:
- Highest = $2.5 Million+
- High = $500,000-2.49 Million
- Medium = $150,000-499,999
- Low = Under $150,000

15 Special Education
The sum of federal and state dollars earmarked for special education programs in the district.

16 Bilingual Education
The sum of federal and state dollars earmarked for English Language Acquisition programs in the district.

17 District Opening/Closing Dates
The month and day of the official opening and closing dates of the school district.

18 District Tech Budget Per Pupil
The district's total IT technology budget dollars per pupil. DTBP levels are as follows:
- High = $100+
- Med = $80-99
- Low = $1-79

19 Social Media
The use of Facebook and/or Twitter for information communication, messaging and other content.

20 District-Level Administrators and Job Title Codes
The names of administrative staff with district-wide responsibilities are listed, followed by numeric codes representing their specific areas of responsibility. A full list of job title codes and their descriptions can be found on the bottom of the directory pages.

The names are listed, from left to right, in numeric job title sequence to facilitate identification of individuals responsible for specific administrative areas. In cases where an individual has multiple responsibilities, the job title with the lowest code number is used for sequencing.

An asterisk (*) denotes district administrators who maintain offices at one of the schools in the district rather than at the district office.

Superintendents who are new to the district are printed in **bold** type. Also see our index of new personnel on page NEW1.

An underscore of a district-level administrator indicates an email address at that institution in our database and in Education MarketView.

SCHOOL DATA

21 School Name and Address
The physical location address of the school is listed. MDR also maintains the mailing address, if different, for every school. For this alternative address, contact MDR directly at 800-333-8802.

22 New Schools
The listings of public schools opening for the first time during this school year are shaded for easy identification. Also see our index of new public schools on page NEW1.

23 Charter Management Organization (CMO)
Indicates the CMO number from the CMO Index to which this school reports.

24 Telephone Number
The telephone number of the school's central administration office. Note that in some cases a school district may require that all calls to schools must first go through a central switchboard to be routed to individual schools. In these cases, the central switchboard number is given for all schools affected.

25 Fax Number
The fax number of the school's administration office. Please use the fax numbers in the directory appropriately.

> The FCC prohibits the use of a telephone facsimile machine to send unsolicited advertisements. If you need further clarification of the laws that exist, you can contact the FCC directly at 888-225-5322, or you can visit their website at http://www.fcc.gov.

26 Principal Name
The name of the school principal. When a school has both an elementary and secondary principal, both names are given. The elementary principal is listed first, with the secondary principal listed below.

Principals who are new to their public school are printed in **bold** type. Also see our index of new personnel on page NEW1.

All principals printed with an underscore have an email address at that institution in our database and in Education MarketView.

27 Social Media
The use of Facebook and/or Twitter for information communication, messaging and other content.

28 School Grade Span/Voc, Special, Adult Schools
The lowest and highest grades taught in the school. Schools with dedicated programs in the areas of vocational, special and adult education are designated as Voc, Spec and Adult, respectively.

29 School Program Codes
In addition to the grades taught within the school, schools that have special curriculum programs are indicated with these codes following the school grade span.

- A = Alternative Program: Identifies traditional schools that also provide a special setting/curriculum for students who do not function well in traditional classroom settings.
- G = Adult Classes: Identifies schools that offer adult education classes.
- M = Magnet Program: Identifies traditional schools that also offer an enriched curricula in a special subject area to qualified students.
- T = Title I Schoolwide: Identifies public schools that have a Title I Schoolwide program, allowing greater spending flexibility.
- V = Career & Technical Education Programs: Identifies schools that offer Career & Technical Education programs.

30 Other School Types
Schools that are unique in the curriculum they offer or in the way they operate are indicated to the left of the school name.

- (A) = Alternative School: Identifies schools that provide instruction exclusively for students who do not function well in traditional classroom settings.
- (C) = Charter School: Public schools that have certain freedoms from state and local regulations and policies, having more administrative independence.
- (M) = Magnet School: Identifies schools where all students are offered enriched curricula. Students qualify for admission by competitive exams.
- (Y) = Year-Round School: Schools that operate 12 months a year.

31 Student Enrollment
The projected number of students enrolled for fall 2019.

32 Number of Classrooms
The number of classrooms within a school. The number of classrooms prints below student enrollment when known.

33 Student Need
Percentage of students eligible for the free and reduced-price lunch program at the school.

Ohio

A Dun & Bradstreet Division

STATE STATISTICS

DISTRICT PERSONNEL BY JOB FUNCTION

Job Code	Job Description	Total	Enrollment Under 2,500	Enrollment 2,500-9,000	Enrollment 10,000+
1	SUPERINTENDENT	759	475	161	18
2	BUS/FINANCE/PURCHASING	772	479	187	32
3	BUILDINGS AND GROUNDS	550	375	147	22
4	FOOD SERVICE	517	336	162	17
5	TRANSPORTATION	543	344	172	20
6	ATHLETIC	525	360	152	12
7	HEALTH SERVICES	223	142	69	12
8	CURRIC/INSTRUCT K-12	501	275	163	22
9	CURRIC/INSTRUCT ELEM	93	54	22	10
10	CURRIC/INSTRUCT SEC	98	63	22	9
11	FEDERAL PROGRAM	629	429	152	17
12	TITLE I	152	109	39	4
13	TITLE V	37	25	10	2
15	ASST SUPERINTENDENT	184	38	91	20
16	INSTRUCTIONAL MEDIA SERVICES	399	280	94	8
17	CHIEF OPERATIONS OFFICER	18	4	8	6
18	CHIEF ACADEMIC OFFICER	22	7	9	6
19	CHIEF FINANCIAL OFFICER	93	57	28	8
20	ART K-12	8	0	3	5
21	ART ELEM	1	1	0	0
22	ART SEC	1	1	0	0
23	MUSIC K-12	17	1	10	6
24	MUSIC ELEM	0	0	0	0
25	MUSIC SEC	2	0	2	0
26	BUSINESS EDUCATION	7	3	4	0
27	CAREER & TECH ED	115	63	30	13
28	TECHNOLOGY EDUCATION	20	13	7	0
29	FAMILY/CONSUMER SCIENCE	18	14	4	0
30	ADULT EDUCATION	64	45	14	5
31	CAREER/SCH-TO-WORK K-12	121	80	33	7
32	CAREER/SCH-TO-WORK ELEM	0	0	0	0
33	CAREER/SCH-TO-WORK SEC	21	19	2	0
34	EARLY CHILDHOOD ED	130	44	39	13
35	HEALTH/PHYS EDUCATION	62	33	20	9
36	GUIDANCE SERVICES K-12	191	138	47	3
37	GUIDANCE SERVICES ELEM	78	68	9	1
38	GUIDANCE SERVICES SEC	173	156	16	1
39	SOCIAL STUDIES K-12	8	1	3	4
40	SOCIAL STUDIES ELEM	0	0	0	0
41	SOCIAL STUDIES SEC	1	1	0	0
42	SCIENCE K-12	11	2	5	4
43	SCIENCE ELEM	1	0	0	1
44	SCIENCE SEC	1	0	0	1
45	MATH K-12	20	4	9	6
46	MATH ELEM	0	0	0	0
47	MATH SEC	0	0	0	0
48	ENGLISH/LANG ARTS K-12	9	2	4	3
49	ENGLISH/LANG ARTS ELEM	1	0	0	1
50	ENGLISH/LANG ARTS SEC	0	0	0	0
51	READING K-12	24	14	9	1
52	READING ELEM	7	6	0	1
53	READING SEC	1	1	0	0
54	REMEDIAL READING K-12	40	24	16	0
55	REMEDIAL READING ELEM	7	6	1	0
56	REMEDIAL READING SEC	1	1	0	0
57	BILINGUAL/ELL	230	117	95	15
58	SPECIAL EDUCATION K-12	581	338	169	18
59	SPECIAL EDUCATION ELEM	16	9	5	1
60	SPECIAL EDUCATION SEC	44	37	6	0
61	FOREIGN/WORLD LANG K-12	9	4	3	2
62	FOREIGN/WORLD LANG ELEM	0	0	0	0
63	FOREIGN/WORLD LANG SEC	2	1	1	0
64	RELIGIOUS EDUCATION K-12	2	0	0	0
65	RELIGIOUS EDUCATION ELEM	0	0	0	0
66	RELIGIOUS EDUCATION SEC	0	0	0	0
67	SCHOOL BOARD PRESIDENT	681	477	161	18
68	TEACHER PERSONNEL	172	39	84	23
69	ACADEMIC ASSESSMENT	371	251	98	15
70	RESEARCH/DEVELOPMENT	14	2	6	5
71	PUBLIC INFORMATION	137	41	70	17
72	SUMMER SCHOOL	39	27	9	3
73	INSTRUCTIONAL TECH	660	428	158	17
74	INSERVICE TRAINING	94	33	32	9
75	MARKETING/DISTRIBUTIVE	16	12	4	0
76	INFO SYSTEMS	256	132	93	15
77	PSYCHOLOGICAL ASSESSMENT	124	66	41	4
78	AFFIRMATIVE ACTION	22	8	12	2
79	STUDENT PERSONNEL	202	68	97	18
80	DRIVER ED/SAFETY	3	1	2	0
81	GIFTED/TALENTED	183	67	75	9
82	VIDEO SERVICES	110	84	25	1
83	SUBSTANCE ABUSE PREVENTION	305	230	63	7
84	ERATE	140	102	35	3
85	AIDS EDUCATION	118	95	18	4
88	ALTERNATIVE/AT RISK	249	165	66	6
89	MULTI-CULTURAL CURRICULUM	4	0	1	3
90	SOCIAL WORK	20	8	12	0
91	SAFETY/SECURITY	205	87	100	18
92	MAGNET SCHOOL	9	1	7	1
93	PARENTAL INVOLVEMENT	28	8	15	2
95	TECH PREP PROGRAM	37	14	19	4
97	CHIEF INFORMATION OFFICER	8	3	3	1
98	CHIEF TECHNOLOGY OFFICER	20	8	7	4
270	CHARACTER EDUCATION	49	29	19	1
271	MIGRANT EDUCATION	39	21	15	1
273	TEACHER MENTOR	161	117	38	5
274	BEFORE/AFTER SCH	64	33	24	7
275	RESPONSE TO INTERVENTION	104	54	36	4
277	REMEDIAL MATH K-12	3	1	1	1
280	LITERACY COACH	48	24	21	3
285	STEM	94	54	32	6
286	DIGITAL LEARNING	165	101	57	6
288	COMMON CORE STANDARDS	280	180	94	6
294	ACCOUNTABILITY	81	34	34	10
295	NETWORK SYSTEM	317	200	83	9
296	TITLE II PROGRAMS	206	121	76	9
297	WEBMASTER	46	31	13	2
298	GRANT WRITER/PTNRSHIPS	218	123	80	9
750	CHIEF INNOVATION OFFICER	0	0	0	0
751	CHIEF OF STAFF	4	0	2	1
752	SOCIAL EMOTIONAL LEARNING	13	7	3	2

DISTRICTS BY EXPENDITURE AND ENROLLMENT

Expenditure	Total	Under 2500	2500-9999	10,000+
Low (Under $200)	308	197	98	13
Medium ($200 - 299)	198	150	46	2
High ($300+)	151	131	17	3
TOTAL DISTRICTS	657	478	161	18

SCHOOLS BY LEVEL AND TYPE

School Level	Total	Public	Private	Catholic
Elementary	2,345	1,896	151	298
Middle/Junior	560	553	5	2
Senior	855	777	20	58
K-12 (Combined)	287	133	141	13
Adult/Special/Voc Ed	236	211	23	2
TOTAL SCHOOLS	4,283	3,570	340	373

Ohio School Directory — COUNTY STATISTICS

COUNTY		DISTRICTS	SCHOOLS	ELEM ENROLL[1]	MIDDLE/JHS ENROLL[2]	SENIOR ENROLL[3]	TOTAL ENROLL[4]	% OF STATE	K-5[5]	K-6	K-8	5-8[6]	7-9[7]	7-12[8]	K-12[9]	OTHER[10]
ADAMS	PUBLIC	3	14	3,086	307	2,463	6,034		2	4	0	1	0	6	0	1
	NONPUBLIC	0	1	79	0	35	114		0	0	0	0	0	0	0	0
	TOTAL	3	15	3,165	307	2,498	6,148	0.3	2	4	0	1	0	6	0	1
ALLEN	PUBLIC	10	38	7,133	3,549	4,984	17,211		12	2	3	7	1	9	1	3
	NONPUBLIC	0	11	1,424	0	640	2,064		0	1	4	0	0	2	4	0
	TOTAL	10	49	8,557	3,549	5,624	19,275	1.0	12	3	7	7	1	11	5	3
ASHLAND	PUBLIC	5	18	2,781	1,252	2,366	7,486		6	1	0	3	0	5	0	3
	NONPUBLIC	0	3	335	0	0	335		0	0	3	0	0	0	0	0
	TOTAL	5	21	3,116	1,252	2,366	7,821	0.4	6	1	3	3	0	5	0	3
ASHTABULA	PUBLIC	8	34	6,604	2,865	4,395	14,189		14	3	0	5	2	7	0	3
	NONPUBLIC	0	3	233	0	192	425		0	0	0	0	0	1	2	0
	TOTAL	8	37	6,837	2,865	4,587	14,614	0.8	14	3	0	5	2	8	2	3
ATHENS	PUBLIC	6	20	3,772	1,093	2,625	7,704		3	6	0	1	2	4	1	3
	NONPUBLIC	0	0	0	0	0	0		0	0	0	0	0	0	0	0
	TOTAL	6	20	3,772	1,093	2,625	7,704	0.4	3	6	0	1	2	4	1	3
AUGLAIZE	PUBLIC	6	15	3,534	1,317	2,781	7,578		5	1	1	2	0	4	2	0
	NONPUBLIC	0	2	202	0	17	219		0	0	1	0	0	0	1	0
	TOTAL	6	17	3,736	1,317	2,798	7,797	0.4	5	1	2	2	0	4	3	0
BELMONT	PUBLIC	8	24	3,895	2,314	3,024	9,418		7	1	0	6	0	7	1	2
	NONPUBLIC	0	8	699	0	166	865		0	0	4	0	0	1	3	0
	TOTAL	8	32	4,594	2,314	3,190	10,283	0.5	7	1	4	6	0	8	4	2
BROWN	PUBLIC	5	14	2,649	1,081	2,256	6,835		4	1	1	3	0	4	0	1
	NONPUBLIC	0	1	103	0	0	103		0	0	1	0	0	0	0	0
	TOTAL	5	15	2,752	1,081	2,256	6,938	0.4	4	1	2	3	0	4	0	1
BUTLER	PUBLIC	11	81	29,695	10,514	18,753	58,879		28	21	0	5	8	17	1	1
	NONPUBLIC	0	16	3,115	0	1,061	4,176		0	1	10	0	0	2	2	1
	TOTAL	11	97	32,810	10,514	19,814	63,055	3.3	28	22	10	5	8	19	3	2
CARROLL	PUBLIC	2	6	1,194	689	867	2,865		2	0	0	1	0	4	0	0
	NONPUBLIC	0	1	42	0	18	60		0	0	0	0	0	0	1	1
	TOTAL	2	7	1,236	689	885	2,925	0.2	2	0	0	1	0	4	1	1
CHAMPAIGN	PUBLIC	5	12	3,344	1,394	2,024	6,816		4	0	0	3	0	3	2	0
	NONPUBLIC	0	1	57	0	25	82		0	0	0	0	0	0	1	0
	TOTAL	5	13	3,401	1,394	2,049	6,898	0.4	4	0	0	3	0	3	3	0

[1] **Elem Enroll** is the school by school total of enrollments in K-4, K-5, K-6, K-8 schools, elementary and middle/JHS students in K-12 schools and students in special ed schools. Public enrollments include public and county-operated schools.
[2] **Middle/JHS Enroll** is the school by school total of enrollments in 5-8 and 7-9 public schools. Public enrollments include public and county-operated schools. Private middle/JHS enrollments are included in Senior Enroll.
[3] **Senior Enroll** is the school by school total of enrollments in 7-12 and 9-12 schools, the secondary students in K-12 schools and students in vocational ed schools. Public enrollments include public and county-operated schools. For private schools, Senior Enroll includes middle/JHS enrollment plus senior enrollment.
[4] **Public Total Enroll** columns are not the sum of school building enrollments. They are projected district-wide Fall enrollments provided to MDR by each school district office, plus county-operated school enrollments.
[5] **K-5** includes pre-kindergarten, kindergarten, K-3, K-4, K-5 schools.
[6] **5-8** includes schools with low grades of 4, 5, 6 and high grades of 7, 8, 9 (e.g., 4-8, 5-8, 6-8, 6-9).
[7] **7-9** includes schools with low grades of 7, 8 and high grades of 7, 8, 9 (e.g., 7-7, 7-8, 7-9, 8-9).
[8] **7-12** includes 7-12, 8-12, 9-12, 10-12, etc.
[9] **K-12** includes schools with both elementary and secondary grades.
[10] **Other** includes special ed, vocational ed and adult schools.
***Public State Totals** for all columns can exceed the sum of the counties because state totals include state-operated schools and their enrollments

School Year 2019-2020   800-333-8802   OH—B1

COUNTY STATISTICS — Market Data Retrieval

COUNTY		DISTRICTS	SCHOOLS	ELEM ENROLL[1]	MIDDLE/JHS ENROLL[2]	SENIOR ENROLL[3]	TOTAL ENROLL[4]	% OF STATE	K-5[5]	K-6	K-8	5-8[6]	7-9[7]	7-12[8]	K-12[9]	OTHER[10]
CLARK	PUBLIC	8	41	10,782	2,661	6,232	20,677		8	16	0	3	4	9	0	1
	NONPUBLIC	0	8	1,156	0	696	1,852		1	1	2	0	0	1	3	0
	TOTAL	8	49	11,938	2,661	6,928	22,529	1.2	9	17	2	3	4	10	3	1
CLERMONT	PUBLIC	10	48	13,239	5,944	8,124	28,940		18	6	0	7	1	10	1	5
	NONPUBLIC	0	10	2,654	0	88	2,742		0	1	7	0	0	0	2	0
	TOTAL	10	58	15,893	5,944	8,212	31,682	1.7	18	7	7	7	1	10	3	5
CLINTON	PUBLIC	4	16	3,363	1,800	1,950	7,750		8	0	0	4	0	0	0	0
	NONPUBLIC	0	1	24	0	11	35		0	0	0	0	0	0	1	0
	TOTAL	4	17	3,387	1,800	1,961	7,785	0.4	8	0	0	4	0	4	1	0
COLUMBIANA	PUBLIC	12	40	7,069	2,326	5,396	15,936		10	4	0	5	1	10	3	7
	NONPUBLIC	0	5	489	0	200	689		0	1	0	0	0	1	3	0
	TOTAL	12	45	7,558	2,326	5,596	16,625	0.9	10	5	0	5	1	11	6	7
COSHOCTON	PUBLIC	4	12	2,219	686	1,937	5,296		1	4	0	1	1	3	0	2
	NONPUBLIC	0	2	96	0	17	113		0	1	0	0	0	0	1	0
	TOTAL	4	14	2,315	686	1,954	5,409	0.3	1	5	0	1	1	3	1	2
CRAWFORD	PUBLIC	6	16	3,266	1,103	1,822	6,532		5	1	0	3	0	4	2	1
	NONPUBLIC	0	4	244	0	19	263		0	0	3	0	0	0	1	0
	TOTAL	6	20	3,510	1,103	1,841	6,795	0.4	5	1	3	3	0	4	3	1
CUYAHOGA	PUBLIC	33	323	70,779	22,290	49,177	153,615		105	14	77	27	9	76	4	11
	NONPUBLIC	0	113	25,316	0	11,413	36,729		3	3	70	1	0	20	13	3
	TOTAL	33	436	96,095	22,290	60,590	190,344	10.1	108	17	147	28	9	96	17	14
DARKE	PUBLIC	7	18	3,693	1,530	2,678	7,949		4	3	0	3	0	6	1	1
	NONPUBLIC	0	4	300	0	48	348		0	0	2	0	1	0	1	0
	TOTAL	7	22	3,993	1,530	2,726	8,297	0.4	4	3	2	3	1	6	2	1
DEFIANCE	PUBLIC	5	16	2,934	1,262	1,948	6,292		4	2	0	3	1	5	0	1
	NONPUBLIC	0	2	275	0	0	275		0	0	2	0	0	0	0	0
	TOTAL	5	18	3,209	1,262	1,948	6,567	0.4	4	2	2	3	1	5	0	1
DELAWARE	PUBLIC	5	45	15,701	7,618	9,873	34,786		26	1	0	7	1	7	0	3
	NONPUBLIC	0	10	2,425	0	248	2,673		2	0	4	0	0	0	4	0
	TOTAL	5	55	18,126	7,618	10,121	37,459	2.0	28	1	4	7	1	7	4	3
ERIE	PUBLIC	8	26	4,975	2,483	4,864	13,531		6	6	0	3	2	6	2	1
	NONPUBLIC	0	5	893	0	194	1,087		0	1	2	0	0	0	2	0
	TOTAL	8	31	5,868	2,483	5,058	14,618	0.8	6	7	2	3	2	6	4	1
FAIRFIELD	PUBLIC	8	45	11,884	5,122	7,876	25,246		20	5	0	6	2	10	0	2
	NONPUBLIC	0	5	1,084	0	380	1,464		1	0	2	0	0	1	1	0
	TOTAL	8	50	12,968	5,122	8,256	26,710	1.4	21	5	2	6	2	11	1	2

[1] **Elem Enroll** is the school by school total of enrollments in K-4, K-5, K-6, K-8 schools, elementary and middle/JHS students in K-12 schools and students in special ed schools. Public enrollments include public and county-operated schools.
[2] **Middle/JHS Enroll** is the school by school total of enrollments in 5-8 and 7-9 public schools. Public enrollments include public and county-operated schools. Private middle/JHS enrollments are included in Senior Enroll.
[3] **Senior Enroll** is the school by school total of enrollments in 7-12 and 9-12 schools, the secondary students in K-12 schools and students in vocational ed schools. Public enrollments include public and county-operated schools. For private schools, Senior Enroll includes middle/JHS enrollment plus senior enrollment.
[4] **Public Total Enroll** columns are not the sum of school building enrollments. They are projected district-wide Fall enrollments provided to MDR by each school district office, plus county-operated school enrollments.

[5] **K-5** includes pre-kindergarten, kindergarten, K-3, K-4, K-5 schools.
[6] **5-8** includes schools with low grades of 4, 5, 6 and high grades of 7, 8, 9 (e.g., 4-8, 5-8, 6-8, 6-9).
[7] **7-9** includes schools with low grades of 7, 8 and high grades of 7, 8, 9 (e.g., 7-7, 7-8, 7-9, 8-9).
[8] **7-12** includes 7-12, 8-12, 9-12, 10-12, etc.
[9] **K-12** includes schools with both elementary and secondary grades.
[10] **Other** includes special ed, vocational ed and adult schools.

Public State Totals for all columns can exceed the sum of the counties because state totals include state-operated schools and their enrollments

Ohio School Directory — COUNTY STATISTICS

COUNTY		DISTRICTS	SCHOOLS	ELEM ENROLL[1]	MIDDLE/JHS ENROLL[2]	SENIOR ENROLL[3]	TOTAL ENROLL[4]	% OF STATE	K-5[5]	K-6	K-8	5-8[6]	7-9[7]	7-12[8]	K-12[9]	OTHER[10]
FAYETTE	PUBLIC	2	8	2,319	1,137	1,280	4,862		3	0	0	2	0	2	0	1
	NONPUBLIC	0	0	0	0	0	0		0	0	0	0	0	0	0	0
	TOTAL	2	8	2,319	1,137	1,280	4,862	0.3	3	0	0	2	0	2	0	1
FRANKLIN	PUBLIC	17	328	93,127	32,959	53,470	188,190		154	34	11	39	14	58	3	15
	NONPUBLIC	0	74	16,822	0	5,661	22,483		8	3	36	1	0	7	12	7
	TOTAL	17	402	109,949	32,959	59,131	210,673	11.2	162	37	47	40	14	65	15	22
FULTON	PUBLIC	8	21	3,238	1,885	2,333	8,597		6	1	0	5	0	6	1	2
	NONPUBLIC	0	2	201	0	0	201		0	0	2	0	0	0	0	0
	TOTAL	8	23	3,439	1,885	2,333	8,798	0.5	6	1	2	5	0	6	1	2
GALLIA	PUBLIC	3	14	2,188	933	1,624	4,752		6	1	0	3	0	3	0	1
	NONPUBLIC	0	1	86	0	34	120		0	0	0	0	0	0	1	0
	TOTAL	3	15	2,274	933	1,658	4,872	0.3	6	1	0	3	0	3	1	1
GEAUGA	PUBLIC	6	20	3,673	2,247	3,906	9,974		8	2	0	4	0	5	1	0
	NONPUBLIC	0	6	1,337	0	745	2,082		0	0	4	0	1	1	0	0
	TOTAL	6	26	5,010	2,247	4,651	12,056	0.6	8	2	4	4	1	6	1	0
GREENE	PUBLIC	8	38	10,669	4,785	6,899	22,935		20	1	0	6	0	7	1	3
	NONPUBLIC	0	8	1,785	0	1,018	2,803		0	1	4	0	0	1	2	0
	TOTAL	8	46	12,454	4,785	7,917	25,738	1.4	20	2	4	6	0	8	3	3
GUERNSEY	PUBLIC	3	15	2,183	1,096	1,296	5,257		6	0	0	3	0	4	0	2
	NONPUBLIC	0	1	110	0	0	110		0	0	1	0	0	0	0	0
	TOTAL	3	16	2,293	1,096	1,296	5,367	0.3	6	0	1	3	0	4	0	2
HAMILTON	PUBLIC	23	183	57,350	13,785	37,686	112,366		49	52	12	13	7	34	8	8
	NONPUBLIC	0	88	21,251	0	11,084	32,335		2	2	54	1	0	14	10	5
	TOTAL	23	271	78,601	13,785	48,770	144,701	7.7	51	54	66	14	7	48	18	13
HANCOCK	PUBLIC	9	35	5,861	2,102	3,993	12,174		12	2	0	5	1	7	4	4
	NONPUBLIC	0	3	618	0	23	641		0	0	2	0	0	0	1	0
	TOTAL	9	38	6,479	2,102	4,016	12,815	0.7	12	2	2	5	1	7	5	4
HARDIN	PUBLIC	5	12	2,413	267	1,424	4,289		0	2	0	0	1	3	3	3
	NONPUBLIC	0	0	0	0	0	0		0	0	0	0	0	0	0	0
	TOTAL	5	12	2,413	267	1,424	4,289	0.2	0	2	0	0	1	3	3	3
HARRISON	PUBLIC	2	7	1,081	90	749	2,066		1	2	0	0	0	1	2	1
	NONPUBLIC	0	1	46	0	20	66		0	0	0	0	0	0	1	0
	TOTAL	2	8	1,127	90	769	2,132	0.1	1	2	0	0	0	1	3	1
HENRY	PUBLIC	4	10	2,044	602	1,616	4,199		3	1	0	2	0	3	1	0
	NONPUBLIC	0	3	388	0	0	388		0	0	3	0	0	0	0	0
	TOTAL	4	13	2,432	602	1,616	4,587	0.2	3	1	3	2	0	3	1	0

[1] **Elem Enroll** is the school by school total of enrollments in K-4, K-5, K-6, K-8 schools, elementary and middle/JHS students in K-12 schools and students in special ed schools. Public enrollments include public and county-operated schools.
[2] **Middle/JHS Enroll** is the school by school total of enrollments in 5-8 and 7-9 public schools. Public enrollments include public and county-operated schools. Private middle/JHS enrollments are included in Senior Enroll.
[3] **Senior Enroll** is the school by school total of enrollments in 7-12 and 9-12 schools, the secondary students in K-12 schools and students in vocational schools. Public enrollments include public and county-operated schools. For private schools, Senior Enroll includes middle/JHS enrollment plus senior enrollment.
[4] **Public Total Enroll** columns are not the sum of school building enrollments. They are projected district-wide Fall enrollments provided to MDR by each school district office, plus county-operated school enrollments.
[5] **K-5** includes pre-kindergarten, kindergarten, K-3, K-4, K-5 schools.
[6] **5-8** includes schools with low grades of 4, 5, 6 and high grades of 7, 8, 9 (e.g., 4-8, 5-8, 6-8, 6-9).
[7] **7-9** includes schools with low grades of 7, 8 and high grades of 7, 8, 9 (e.g., 7-7, 7-8, 7-9, 8-9).
[8] **7-12** includes 7-12, 8-12, 9-12, 10-12, etc.
[9] **K-12** includes schools with both elementary and secondary grades.
[10] **Other** includes special ed, vocational and adult schools.

*Public State Totals for all columns can exceed the sum of the counties because state totals include state-operated schools and their enrollments

School Year 2019-2020

COUNTY STATISTICS — Market Data Retrieval

COUNTY		DISTRICTS	SCHOOLS	ELEM ENROLL[1]	MIDDLE/JHS ENROLL[2]	SENIOR ENROLL[3]	TOTAL ENROLL[4]	% OF STATE	K-5[5]	K-6	K-8	5-8[6]	7-9[7]	7-12[8]	K-12[9]	OTHER[10]
HIGHLAND	PUBLIC	5	18	3,285	1,600	2,149	7,404		6	1	0	4	0	5	0	2
	NONPUBLIC	0	2	85	0	0	85		1	0	1	0	0	0	0	0
	TOTAL	5	20	3,370	1,600	2,149	7,489	0.4	7	1	1	4	0	5	0	2
HOCKING	PUBLIC	1	7	1,482	1,174	1,105	3,945		5	0	0	1	0	1	0	0
	NONPUBLIC	0	2	124	0	0	124		1	1	0	0	0	0	0	0
	TOTAL	1	9	1,606	1,174	1,105	4,069	0.2	6	1	0	1	0	1	0	0
HOLMES	PUBLIC	2	16	1,878	598	1,127	4,056		5	3	2	2	0	2	0	2
	NONPUBLIC	0	0	0	0	0	0		0	0	0	0	0	0	0	0
	TOTAL	2	16	1,878	598	1,127	4,056	0.2	5	3	2	2	0	2	0	2
HURON	PUBLIC	7	24	4,659	1,842	2,738	9,525		8	2	0	4	1	7	1	1
	NONPUBLIC	0	9	1,034	0	295	1,329		1	2	5	0	0	1	0	0
	TOTAL	7	33	5,693	1,842	3,033	10,854	0.6	9	4	5	4	1	8	1	1
JACKSON	PUBLIC	3	12	2,409	1,143	1,333	5,200		6	0	0	2	0	2	1	0
	NONPUBLIC	0	2	209	0	41	250		0	0	1	0	0	0	0	1
	TOTAL	3	14	2,618	1,143	1,374	5,450	0.3	6	0	1	2	0	2	1	1
JEFFERSON	PUBLIC	6	23	4,332	1,805	3,336	9,960		7	5	0	2	1	4	2	2
	NONPUBLIC	0	4	522	0	422	944		0	1	0	0	1	1	1	0
	TOTAL	6	27	4,854	1,805	3,758	10,904	0.6	7	6	0	2	2	5	3	2
KNOX	PUBLIC	6	19	3,753	1,438	2,915	8,840		8	1	1	2	0	4	1	2
	NONPUBLIC	0	3	235	0	3	238		0	0	2	0	0	0	1	0
	TOTAL	6	22	3,988	1,438	2,918	9,078	0.5	8	1	3	2	0	4	2	2
LAKE	PUBLIC	10	57	13,228	6,767	10,546	31,587		28	0	1	11	0	10	1	6
	NONPUBLIC	0	12	3,398	0	1,089	4,487		0	1	6	0	0	1	3	1
	TOTAL	10	69	16,626	6,767	11,635	36,074	1.9	28	1	7	11	0	11	4	7
LAWRENCE	PUBLIC	8	25	4,579	2,142	2,814	9,886		8	0	1	6	0	8	0	2
	NONPUBLIC	0	3	192	0	127	319		0	1	0	0	0	0	1	0
	TOTAL	8	28	4,771	2,142	2,941	10,205	0.5	8	1	1	6	0	9	1	2
LICKING	PUBLIC	11	52	13,639	6,415	8,573	29,280		25	2	0	11	1	10	1	2
	NONPUBLIC	0	9	1,000	0	424	1,424		0	0	2	0	0	1	5	1
	TOTAL	11	61	14,639	6,415	8,997	30,704	1.6	25	2	2	11	1	11	6	3
LOGAN	PUBLIC	5	14	2,603	1,672	2,398	7,071		4	1	0	3	0	4	0	2
	NONPUBLIC	0	1	195	0	78	273		0	0	0	0	0	0	1	0
	TOTAL	5	15	2,798	1,672	2,476	7,344	0.4	4	1	0	3	0	4	1	2
LORAIN	PUBLIC	15	86	18,215	9,530	14,497	46,045		40	4	2	17	3	16	1	3
	NONPUBLIC	0	15	4,035	0	761	4,796		0	0	9	0	0	1	5	0
	TOTAL	15	101	22,250	9,530	15,258	50,841	2.7	40	4	11	17	3	17	6	3

[1] **Elem Enroll** is the school by school total of enrollments in K-4, K-5, K-6, K-8 schools, elementary and middle/JHS students in K-12 schools and students in special ed schools. Public enrollments include public and county-operated schools.
[2] **Middle/JHS Enroll** is the school by school total of enrollments in 5-8 and 7-9 public schools. Public enrollments include public and county-operated schools. Private middle/JHS enrollments are included in Senior Enroll.
[3] **Senior Enroll** is the school by school total of enrollments in 7-12 and 9-12 schools, the secondary students in K-12 schools and students in vocational ed schools. Public enrollments include public and county-operated schools. For private schools, Senior Enroll includes middle/JHS enrollment plus senior enrollment.
[4] **Public Total Enroll** columns are not the sum of school building enrollments. They are projected district-wide Fall enrollments provided to MDR by each school district office, plus county-operated school enrollments.
[5] **K-5** includes pre-kindergarten, kindergarten, K-3, K-4, K-5 schools.
[6] **5-8** includes schools with low grades of 4, 5, 6 and high grades of 7, 8, 9 (e.g., 4-8, 5-8, 6-8, 6-9).
[7] **7-9** includes schools with low grades of 7, 8 and high grades of 7, 8, 9 (e.g., 7-7, 7-8, 7-9, 8-9).
[8] **7-12** includes 7-12, 8-12, 9-12, 10-12, etc.
[9] **K-12** includes schools with both elementary and secondary grades.
[10] **Other** includes special ed, vocational ed and adult schools.

*Public State Totals for all columns can exceed the sum of the counties because state totals include state-operated schools and their enrollments

Ohio School Directory — COUNTY STATISTICS

School Year 2019-2020 — 800-333-8802 — OH—B5

COUNTY		DISTRICTS	SCHOOLS	ELEM ENROLL[1]	MIDDLE/JHS ENROLL[2]	SENIOR ENROLL[3]	TOTAL ENROLL[4]	% OF STATE	K-5[5]	K-6	K-8	5-8[6]	7-9[7]	7-12[8]	K-12[9]	OTHER[10]
LUCAS	PUBLIC	8	117	30,317	5,872	16,503	56,450		21	16	41	5	4	19	2	9
	NONPUBLIC	0	33	7,825	0	4,007	11,832		1	1	19	0	0	3	9	0
	TOTAL	8	150	38,142	5,872	20,510	68,282	3.6	22	17	60	5	4	22	11	9
MADISON	PUBLIC	5	17	3,406	1,362	1,887	7,446		5	2	0	2	2	4	0	2
	NONPUBLIC	0	2	219	0	37	256		0	0	1	0	0	0	1	0
	TOTAL	5	19	3,625	1,362	1,924	7,702	0.4	5	2	1	2	2	4	1	2
MAHONING	PUBLIC	15	60	13,615	4,967	9,449	29,309		13	3	11	7	1	17	4	4
	NONPUBLIC	0	11	2,143	0	1,106	3,249		0	0	7	0	0	2	1	1
	TOTAL	15	71	15,758	4,967	10,555	32,558	1.7	13	3	18	7	1	19	5	5
MARION	PUBLIC	6	24	4,998	2,041	3,385	10,412		11	0	0	4	0	5	2	2
	NONPUBLIC	0	2	133	0	10	143		0	0	1	0	0	0	1	0
	TOTAL	6	26	5,131	2,041	3,395	10,555	0.6	11	0	1	4	0	5	3	2
MEDINA	PUBLIC	8	46	12,375	5,756	8,662	28,611		24	2	1	7	2	7	0	3
	NONPUBLIC	0	4	886	0	43	929		0	0	3	0	0	0	1	0
	TOTAL	8	50	13,261	5,756	8,705	29,540	1.6	24	2	4	7	2	7	1	3
MEIGS	PUBLIC	3	10	1,621	739	1,048	3,293		3	0	1	2	0	3	0	1
	NONPUBLIC	0	1	35	0	14	49		0	0	0	0	0	0	1	0
	TOTAL	3	11	1,656	739	1,062	3,342	0.2	3	0	1	2	0	3	1	1
MERCER	PUBLIC	6	18	3,898	1,463	2,461	7,405		5	1	2	3	1	6	0	0
	NONPUBLIC	0	1	175	0	0	175		0	1	0	0	0	0	0	0
	TOTAL	6	19	4,073	1,463	2,461	7,580	0.4	5	2	2	3	1	6	0	0
MIAMI	PUBLIC	10	35	8,715	2,932	5,372	17,437		15	2	1	3	2	6	4	2
	NONPUBLIC	0	6	980	0	202	1,182		0	2	3	0	0	0	1	0
	TOTAL	10	41	9,695	2,932	5,574	18,619	1.0	15	4	4	3	2	6	5	2
MONROE	PUBLIC	1	10	1,332	0	750	2,318		0	1	4	0	0	4	0	1
	NONPUBLIC	0	1	113	0	0	113		0	0	1	0	0	0	0	0
	TOTAL	1	11	1,445	0	750	2,431	0.1	0	1	5	0	0	4	0	1
MONTGOMERY	PUBLIC	17	132	33,372	11,765	22,675	73,377		49	30	5	11	8	23	0	6
	NONPUBLIC	0	30	6,207	0	1,999	8,241		2	4	13	1	0	2	6	2
	TOTAL	17	162	39,579	11,765	24,674	81,618	4.3	51	34	18	12	8	25	6	8
MORGAN	PUBLIC	1	5	950	272	541	1,763		0	3	0	0	1	1	0	0
	NONPUBLIC	0	0	0	0	0	0		0	0	0	0	0	0	0	0
	TOTAL	1	5	950	272	541	1,763	0.1	0	3	0	0	1	1	0	0
MORROW	PUBLIC	4	12	2,539	1,052	1,464	5,424		3	0	0	3	1	3	1	1
	NONPUBLIC	0	2	69	0	100	169		0	1	0	0	0	1	0	0
	TOTAL	4	14	2,608	1,052	1,564	5,593	0.3	3	1	0	3	1	4	1	1

[1] **Elem Enroll** is the school by school total of enrollments in K-4, K-5, K-6, K-8 schools, elementary and middle/JHS students in K-12 schools and students in special ed schools. Public enrollments include public and county-operated schools.
[2] **Middle/JHS Enroll** is the school by school total of enrollments in 5-8 and 7-9 public schools. Public enrollments include public and county-operated schools. Private middle/JHS enrollments are included in Senior Enroll.
[3] **Senior Enroll** is the school by school total of enrollments in 7-12 and 9-12 schools, the secondary students in K-12 schools and students in vocational ed schools. Public enrollments include public and county-operated schools. For private schools, Senior Enroll includes middle/JHS enrollment plus senior enrollment.
[4] **Public Total Enroll** columns are not the sum of school building enrollments. They are projected district-wide Fall enrollments provided to MDR by each school district office, plus county-operated school enrollments.
[5] **K-5** includes pre-kindergarten, kindergarten, K-3, K-4, K-5 schools.
[6] **5-8** includes schools with low grades of 4, 5, 6 and high grades of 7, 8, 9 (e.g., 4-8, 5-8, 6-8, 6-9).
[7] **7-9** includes schools with low grades of 7, 8 and high grades of 7, 8, 9 (e.g., 7-7, 7-8, 7-9, 8-9).
[8] **7-12** includes 7-12, 8-12, 9-12, 10-12, etc.
[9] **K-12** includes schools with both elementary and secondary grades.
[10] **Other** includes special ed, vocational and adult schools.

Public State Totals for all columns can exceed the sum of the counties because state totals include state-operated schools and their enrollments

COUNTY STATISTICS — Market Data Retrieval

COUNTY		DISTRICTS	SCHOOLS	ELEM ENROLL[1]	MIDDLE/JHS ENROLL[2]	SENIOR ENROLL[3]	TOTAL ENROLL[4]	% OF STATE	K-5[5]	K-6	K-8	5-8[6]	7-9[7]	7-12[8]	K-12[9]	OTHER[10]
MUSKINGUM	PUBLIC	7	33	7,269	2,851	4,645	15,432		7	8	0	4	2	8	0	4
	NONPUBLIC	0	5	521	0	128	649		0	0	3	0	0	1	1	0
	TOTAL	7	38	7,790	2,851	4,773	16,081	0.9	7	8	3	4	2	9	1	4
NOBLE	PUBLIC	2	4	1,261	0	404	1,700		0	0	2	0	0	2	0	0
	NONPUBLIC	0	0	0	0	0	0		0	0	0	0	0	0	0	0
	TOTAL	2	4	1,261	0	404	1,700	0.1	0	0	2	0	0	2	0	0
OTTAWA	PUBLIC	6	14	2,888	1,186	1,997	6,112		4	0	1	3	0	4	2	1
	NONPUBLIC	0	3	538	0	67	605		0	1	1	0	0	0	1	0
	TOTAL	6	17	3,426	1,186	2,064	6,717	0.4	4	1	2	3	0	4	3	1
PAULDING	PUBLIC	3	9	1,801	295	1,011	3,305		1	3	0	0	0	2	0	0
	NONPUBLIC	0	1	56	0	0	56		0	1	0	0	0	0	0	0
	TOTAL	3	10	1,857	295	1,011	3,361	0.2	1	4	0	0	0	2	0	0
PERRY	PUBLIC	4	14	2,644	1,246	1,710	5,995		6	1	0	3	0	4	0	0
	NONPUBLIC	0	2	261	0	0	261		0	0	0	0	0	0	0	0
	TOTAL	4	16	2,905	1,246	1,710	6,256	0.3	6	1	0	3	0	4	0	0
PICKAWAY	PUBLIC	4	20	4,683	2,061	2,706	9,858		9	1	0	4	1	4	0	1
	NONPUBLIC	0	2	264	0	86	350		0	0	1	0	0	0	1	0
	TOTAL	4	22	4,947	2,061	2,792	10,208	0.5	9	1	1	4	1	4	1	1
PIKE	PUBLIC	5	13	2,331	926	1,724	5,366		4	1	0	2	0	3	1	2
	NONPUBLIC	0	1	32	0	13	45		0	0	0	0	0	0	1	0
	TOTAL	5	14	2,363	926	1,737	5,411	0.3	4	1	0	2	0	3	2	2
PORTAGE	PUBLIC	13	50	9,878	4,450	7,142	21,828		23	2	0	10	1	12	0	2
	NONPUBLIC	0	5	762	0	43	805		0	0	3	0	0	0	2	0
	TOTAL	13	55	10,640	4,450	7,185	22,633	1.2	23	2	3	10	1	12	2	2
PREBLE	PUBLIC	5	16	2,773	1,093	1,970	6,121		5	2	0	3	0	5	0	1
	NONPUBLIC	0	0	0	0	0	0		0	0	0	0	0	0	0	0
	TOTAL	5	16	2,773	1,093	1,970	6,121	0.3	5	2	0	3	0	5	0	1
PUTNAM	PUBLIC	9	21	3,224	695	1,986	5,853		6	2	2	2	0	5	0	0
	NONPUBLIC	0	3	420	0	0	420		0	0	3	0	0	0	4	0
	TOTAL	9	24	3,644	695	1,986	6,273	0.3	6	2	5	2	0	5	4	0
RICHLAND	PUBLIC	10	43	7,760	4,061	5,984	18,586		18	2	2	7	2	9	0	3
	NONPUBLIC	0	9	1,381	0	432	1,813		0	2	4	0	0	1	2	0
	TOTAL	10	52	9,141	4,061	6,416	20,399	1.1	18	4	6	7	2	10	2	3
ROSS	PUBLIC	8	25	4,847	2,719	2,911	11,384		8	1	0	6	1	7	0	2
	NONPUBLIC	0	2	434	0	69	503		0	0	1	0	0	0	1	0
	TOTAL	8	27	5,281	2,719	2,980	11,887	0.6	8	1	1	6	1	7	1	2

[1] **Elem Enroll** is the school by school total of enrollments in K-4, K-5, K-6, K-8 schools, elementary and middle/JHS students in K-12 schools and students in special ed schools. Public enrollments include public and county-operated schools.

[2] **Middle/JHS Enroll** is the school by school total of enrollments in 5-8 and 7-9 public schools. Public enrollments include public and county-operated schools. Private middle/JHS enrollments are included in Senior Enroll.

[3] **Senior Enroll** is the school by school total of enrollments in 7-12 and 9-12 schools, the secondary students in K-12 schools and students in vocational ed schools. Public enrollments include public and county-operated schools. For private schools, Senior Enroll includes middle/JHS enrollment plus senior enrollment.

[4] **Public Total Enroll** columns are not the sum of school building enrollments. They are projected district-wide Fall enrollments provided to MDR by each school district office, plus county-operated school enrollments.

[5] **K-5** includes pre-kindergarten, kindergarten, K-3, K-4, K-5 schools.

[6] **5-8** includes schools with low grades of 4, 5, 6 and high grades of 7, 8, 9 (e.g., 4-8, 5-8, 6-8, 6-9).

[7] **7-9** includes schools with low grades of 7, 8 and high grades of 7, 8, 9 (e.g., 7-7, 7-8, 7-9, 8-9).

[8] **7-12** includes 7-12, 8-12, 9-12, 10-12, etc.

[9] **K-12** includes schools with both elementary and secondary grades.

[10] **Other** includes special ed, vocational ed and adult schools.

Public State Totals for all columns can exceed the sum of the counties because state totals include state-operated schools and their enrollments.

OH–B6 800-333-8802 School Year 2019-2020

Ohio School Directory — COUNTY STATISTICS

COUNTY		DISTRICTS	SCHOOLS	ELEM ENROLL[1]	MIDDLE/JHS ENROLL[2]	SENIOR ENROLL[3]	TOTAL ENROLL[4]	% OF STATE	K-5[5]	K-6	K-8	SCHOOLS BY GRADE SPAN 5-8[6]	7-9[7]	7-12[8]	K-12[9]	OTHER[10]
SANDUSKY	PUBLIC	5	22	3,491	1,973	2,324	10,588		11	0	0	4	0	4	0	3
	NONPUBLIC	0	5	507	0	224	731		0	2	0	0	0	1	2	0
	TOTAL	5	27	3,998	1,973	2,548	11,319	0.6	11	2	0	4	0	5	2	3
SCIOTO	PUBLIC	11	28	5,414	2,298	3,944	11,867		6	5	0	5	0	9	1	2
	NONPUBLIC	0	5	238	0	177	415		0	1	1	0	0	1	2	0
	TOTAL	11	33	5,652	2,298	4,121	12,282	0.7	6	6	1	5	0	10	3	2
SENECA	PUBLIC	6	16	3,625	678	2,601	8,046		4	2	0	1	0	3	4	2
	NONPUBLIC	0	2	510	0	160	670		0	0	1	0	0	0	1	0
	TOTAL	6	18	4,135	678	2,761	8,716	0.5	4	2	1	1	0	3	5	2
SHELBY	PUBLIC	8	16	4,364	1,303	2,603	8,527		6	1	0	1	0	2	6	0
	NONPUBLIC	0	3	308	0	246	554		0	0	1	0	0	1	1	0
	TOTAL	8	19	4,672	1,303	2,849	9,081	0.5	6	1	1	1	0	3	7	0
STARK	PUBLIC	20	115	28,203	11,672	21,727	62,896		55	6	3	16	4	23	2	6
	NONPUBLIC	0	21	3,223	0	944	4,167		4	1	9	0	0	1	6	0
	TOTAL	20	136	31,426	11,672	22,671	67,063	3.6	59	7	12	16	4	24	8	6
SUMMIT	PUBLIC	15	120	29,936	14,608	21,067	65,819		60	12	0	18	4	23	2	1
	NONPUBLIC	0	39	7,599	0	3,879	11,478		2	4	22	0	0	4	4	3
	TOTAL	15	159	37,535	14,608	24,946	77,297	4.1	62	16	22	18	4	27	6	4
TRUMBULL	PUBLIC	20	63	13,369	4,141	8,384	26,613		16	8	6	8	2	19	2	2
	NONPUBLIC	0	6	747	0	373	1,120		2	0	1	0	0	0	2	1
	TOTAL	20	69	14,116	4,141	8,757	27,733	1.5	18	8	7	8	2	19	4	3
TUSCARAWAS	PUBLIC	9	43	7,052	2,985	5,022	15,977		19	4	0	6	0	8	3	3
	NONPUBLIC	0	4	339	0	192	531		0	2	0	0	0	1	1	0
	TOTAL	9	47	7,391	2,985	5,214	16,508	0.9	19	6	0	6	0	9	4	3
UNION	PUBLIC	3	17	3,898	1,485	2,369	7,862		7	1	0	2	1	5	0	1
	NONPUBLIC	0	3	619	0	0	619		0	1	2	0	0	0	0	0
	TOTAL	3	20	4,517	1,485	2,369	8,481	0.5	7	2	2	2	1	5	0	1
VAN WERT	PUBLIC	4	11	2,103	471	1,682	4,454		2	1	0	1	0	2	3	2
	NONPUBLIC	0	1	100	0	0	100		0	1	0	0	0	0	0	0
	TOTAL	4	12	2,203	471	1,682	4,554	0.2	2	2	0	1	0	2	3	2
VINTON	PUBLIC	1	5	951	461	572	2,100		3	0	0	1	0	1	0	0
	NONPUBLIC	0	0	0	0	0	0		0	0	0	0	0	0	0	0
	TOTAL	1	5	951	461	572	2,100	0.1	3	0	0	1	0	1	0	0
WARREN	PUBLIC	9	45	20,007	6,228	12,137	38,750		18	10	0	2	6	8	0	1
	NONPUBLIC	0	12	2,570	0	1,080	3,650		1	0	3	0	0	1	7	0
	TOTAL	9	57	22,577	6,228	13,217	42,400	2.3	19	10	3	2	6	9	7	1

[1] **Elem Enroll** is the school by school total of enrollments in K-4, K-5, K-6, K-8 schools, elementary and middle/JHS students in K-12 schools and students in special ed schools. Public enrollments include public and county-operated schools.

[2] **Middle/JHS Enroll** is the school by school total of enrollments in 5-8 and 7-9 public schools. Public enrollments include public and county-operated schools. Private middle/JHS enrollments are included in Senior Enroll.

[3] **Senior Enroll** is the school by school total of enrollments in 7-12 and 9-12 schools, the secondary students in K-12 schools and students in vocational ed schools. Public enrollments include public and county-operated schools. For private schools, Senior Enroll includes middle/JHS enrollment plus senior enrollment.

[4] **Public Total Enroll** columns are not the sum of school building enrollments. They are projected district-wide Fall enrollments provided to MDR by each school district office, plus county-operated school enrollments.

[5] **K-5** includes pre-kindergarten, kindergarten, K-3, K-4, K-5 schools.

[6] **5-8** includes schools with low grades of 4, 5, 6 and high grades of 7, 8, 9 (e.g., 4-8, 5-8, 6-8, 6-9).

[7] **7-9** includes schools with low grades of 7, 8 and high grades of 7, 8, 9 (e.g., 7-7, 7-8, 7-9, 8-9).

[8] **7-12** includes 7-12, 8-12, 9-12, 10-12, etc.

[9] **K-12** includes schools with both elementary and secondary grades.

[10] **Other** includes special ed, vocational and adult schools.

*Public State Totals for all columns can exceed the sum of the counties because state totals include state-operated schools and their enrollments

School Year 2019-2020 — 800-333-8802 — OH–B7

COUNTY STATISTICS — Market Data Retrieval

COUNTY		DISTRICTS	SCHOOLS	ELEM ENROLL[1]	MIDDLE/JHS ENROLL[2]	SENIOR ENROLL[3]	TOTAL ENROLL[4]	% OF STATE	SCHOOLS BY GRADE SPAN							
									K-5[5]	K-6	K-8	5-8[6]	7-9[7]	7-12[8]	K-12[9]	OTHER[10]
WASHINGTON	PUBLIC	7	24	3,712	1,234	3,218	8,476		6	6	1	2	0	6	0	3
	NONPUBLIC	0	5	471	0	63	534		0	0	2	0	0	0	3	0
	TOTAL	7	29	4,183	1,234	3,281	9,010	0.5	6	6	3	2	0	6	3	3
WAYNE	PUBLIC	11	42	7,118	2,956	5,749	16,548		10	5	3	6	2	13	1	2
	NONPUBLIC	0	5	679	0	77	756		0	0	4	0	0	0	1	0
	TOTAL	11	47	7,797	2,956	5,826	17,304	0.9	10	5	7	6	2	13	2	2
WILLIAMS	PUBLIC	7	10	3,358	430	1,859	5,926		1	2	0	0	0	2	5	0
	NONPUBLIC	0	3	264	0	21	285		0	0	1	0	0	0	1	0
	TOTAL	7	13	3,622	430	1,880	6,211	0.3	1	3	1	0	0	2	6	0
WOOD	PUBLIC	10	35	8,614	3,422	5,342	19,843		13	3	0	6	1	9	0	3
	NONPUBLIC	0	6	1,024	0	45	1,069		0	2	3	0	0	0	1	0
	TOTAL	10	41	9,638	3,422	5,387	20,912	1.1	13	5	3	6	1	9	1	3
WYANDOT	PUBLIC	3	8	1,803	542	1,031	3,410		3	0	0	1	0	1	2	1
	NONPUBLIC	0	2	301	0	0	301		0	1	1	0	0	0	0	0
	TOTAL	3	10	2,104	542	1,031	3,711	0.2	3	1	1	1	0	1	2	1
STATE TOTAL	PUBLIC*	657	3,570	793,314	295,905	528,240	1,779,448		1,200	368	198	428	113	724	106	197
	NONPUBLIC	0	713	137,871	0	53,130	191,036		32	51	366	4	3	78	154	25
	TOTAL	657	4,283	931,185	295,905	581,370	1,970,484		1,232	419	564	432	116	802	260	222

[1] **Elem Enroll** is the school by school total of enrollments in K-4, K-5, K-6, K-8 schools, elementary and middle/JHS students in K-12 schools and students in special ed schools. Public enrollments include public and county-operated schools.

[2] **Middle/JHS Enroll** is the school by school total of enrollments in 5-8 and 7-9 public schools. Public enrollments include public and county-operated schools. Private middle/JHS enrollments are included in Senior Enroll.

[3] **Senior Enroll** is the school by school total of enrollments in 7-12 and 9-12 schools, the secondary students in K-12 schools and students in vocational ed schools. Public enrollments include public and county-operated schools. For private schools, Senior Enroll includes middle/JHS enrollment plus senior enrollment.

[4] **Public Total Enroll** columns are not the sum of school building enrollments. They are projected district-wide Fall enrollments provided to MDR by each school district office, plus county-operated school enrollments.

[5] **K-5** includes pre-kindergarten, kindergarten, K-3, K-4, K-5 schools.

[6] **5-8** includes schools with low grades of 4, 5, 6 and high grades of 7, 8, 9 (e.g., 4-8, 5-8, 6-8, 6-9).

[7] **7-9** includes schools with low grades of 7, 8 and high grades of 7, 8, 9 (e.g., 7-7, 7-8, 7-9, 8-9).

[8] **7-12** includes 7-12, 8-12, 9-12, 10-12, etc.

[9] **K-12** includes schools with both elementary and secondary grades.

[10] **Other** includes special ed, vocational ed and adult schools.

*****Public State Totals** for all columns can exceed the sum of the counties because state totals include state-operated schools and their enrollments.

OH–B8 800-333-8802 School Year 2019-2020

DISTRICT BUYING POWER INDEX

COUNTIES RANKED BY PERCENTAGE OF STATE SPENDING

COUNTY / DISTRICT	PID	COUNTY % OF STATE	DISTRICT % OF COUNTY	DISTRICT % OF STATE	NUMBER OF SCHOOLS	ENROLL	EXP	POV
CUYAHOGA		10.41						
Cleveland Metro School Dist	00791041		40.84	4.25	112	38,949	HIGH	HIGH
Cleveland Hts-Univ Hts City SD	00792825		5.14	0.54	11	5,200	HIGH	MED-HIGH
Parma City School Dist	00794081		5.06	0.53	15	10,712	LOW	MED-LOW
Shaker Heights City Sch Dist	00794500		4.32	0.45	9	5,180	HIGH	MED-LOW
Lakewood City School Dist	00793477		4.05	0.42	12	4,000	MED	MED-HIGH
South Euclid-Lyndhurst City SD	00794691		3.42	0.36	6	3,500	HIGH	MED-LOW
Bedford City School Dist	00790530		2.95	0.31	6	3,292	HIGH	MED-HIGH
Solon City School Dist	00794639		2.60	0.27	7	4,547	MED	MED-LOW
Westlake City School Dist	00794990		2.23	0.23	4	3,500	MED	MED-LOW
Bay Village City School Dist	00790401		2.00	0.21	4	2,442	MED	LOW
Euclid City School Dist	00793128		1.91	0.20	7	5,100	LOW	HIGH
Maple Heights City School Dist	00793623		1.86	0.19	5	3,800	LOW	HIGH
Chagrin Falls Exempted Vlg SD	00790994		1.70	0.18	4	2,000	HIGH	LOW
Olmsted Falls City School Dist	00793972		1.70	0.18	5	3,628	LOW	MED-LOW
Warrensville Heights City SD	00794926		1.70	0.18	5	1,700	HIGH	HIGH
Mayfield City School Dist	00793714		1.64	0.17	6	4,000	LOW	MED-LOW
North Royalton City Sch Dist	00793922		1.63	0.17	5	4,060	LOW	MED-LOW
East Cleveland City Sch Dist	00793037		1.55	0.16	6	2,300	MED	HIGH
Garfield Heights City SD	00793350		1.46	0.15	6	3,721	LOW	MED-HIGH
Berea City School Dist	00790633		1.45	0.15	7	5,817	LOW	MED-LOW
North Olmsted City School Dist	00793817		1.17	0.12	8	3,900	LOW	MED-HIGH
Beachwood City School Dist	00790475		1.15	0.12	5	1,612	MED	MED-LOW
Independence Local School Dist	00793439		1.13	0.12	3	1,075	HIGH	MED-LOW
Rocky River City School Dist	00794421		1.08	0.11	5	2,610	LOW	MED-LOW
Brecksville Broadview Hts CSD	00790889		0.94	0.10	5	3,850	LOW	LOW
Polaris Joint Voc School Dist	01484825		0.92	0.10	1	1,000	HIGH	
Orange City School Dist	00794031		0.90	0.09	4	2,000	LOW	MED-LOW
Fairview Park City Sch Dist	00793283		0.69	0.07	4	1,702	LOW	MED-LOW
Cuyahoga Heights Local SD	00793001		0.62	0.06	3	900	MED	MED-LOW
Cuyahoga Vly Career Ctr Voc SD	00795279		0.62	0.06	1	1,000	MED	
Brooklyn City School Dist	00790956		0.62	0.06	2	1,300	LOW	MED-HIGH
Strongsville City School Dist	00794823		0.52	0.05	8	5,553	LOW	MED-LOW
Richmond Heights Local SD	00794380		0.40	0.04	2	850	LOW	MED-HIGH
FRANKLIN		8.43						
Columbus City School Dist	00799603		21.06	1.78	113	52,000	LOW	HIGH
South-Western City School Dist	00801816		13.91	1.17	33	22,790	LOW	MED-HIGH
Westerville City School Dist	00802250		11.76	0.99	24	15,000	MED	MED-LOW
Worthington School Dist	00802509		7.85	0.66	20	12,500	MED	MED-LOW
Dublin City School Dist	00802200		7.24	0.61	20	16,200	LOW	MED-LOW
Hilliard City School Dist	00801713		5.83	0.49	25	16,600	LOW	MED-LOW
Upper Arlington City Sch Dist	00802092		5.66	0.48	8	6,000	MED	LOW
Groveport Madison Local SD	00801488		5.03	0.42	11	7,200	MED	MED-HIGH
Canal Winchester Local SD	00799574		4.90	0.41	4	3,600	HIGH	MED-HIGH
Gahanna-Jefferson Public SD	00801397		3.94	0.33	11	7,543	LOW	MED-LOW
Bexley City School Dist	00799524		3.42	0.29	5	2,463	HIGH	LOW
Reynoldsburg City School Dist	00801634		3.22	0.27	16	7,572	LOW	MED-LOW
Whitehall City School Dist	00802420		2.62	0.22	6	3,200	MED	HIGH
New Albany-Plain Local SD	00801593		1.52	0.13	5	5,100	LOW	MED-LOW
Hamilton Local School Dist	00801347		1.31	0.11	4	3,200	LOW	MED-HIGH
Grandview Heights City SD	00801294		0.62	0.05	4	1,075	LOW	LOW
Eastland-Ffld Career Tech VSD	00802688		0.11	0.01	3	1,500	LOW	
HAMILTON		6.02						
Cincinnati City School Dist	00805290		19.66	1.18	61	35,000	LOW	HIGH
Great Oaks Career Campuses	00810439		10.09	0.61	4	3,000	HIGH	
Forest Hills School Dist	00806476		8.25	0.50	9	7,450	MED	MED-LOW
Northwest Local School Dist	00807121		7.30	0.44	11	9,000	LOW	MED-HIGH
Sycamore Cmty School Dist	00807767		6.88	0.41	7	5,481	MED	MED-LOW
Princeton City School Dist	00807432		5.98	0.36	10	6,500	MED	MED-HIGH
Winton Woods City School Dist	00806579		4.97	0.30	7	3,500	MED	MED-HIGH
Loveland City School Dist	00806804		4.68	0.28	6	4,700	MED	MED-LOW
Mt Healthy City School Dist	00806983		4.06	0.24	3	3,300	MED	HIGH
Oak Hills Local School Dist	00807341		3.81	0.23	9	8,700	LOW	MED-LOW
Norwood City School Dist	00807262		3.25	0.20	5	2,000	HIGH	MED-HIGH
Indian Hill Exempted Vlg SD	00806696		3.25	0.20	4	2,030	HIGH	LOW
Madeira City School Dist	00806878		2.32	0.14	3	1,400	HIGH	LOW
Mariemont City School Dist	00806921		2.31	0.14	4	1,700	MED	MED-LOW
Wyoming City School Dist	00807901		2.03	0.12	5	1,950	MED	MED-LOW
Three Rivers Local School Dist	00807834		1.98	0.12	2	2,200	LOW	MED-LOW
Southwest Local School Dist	00807638		1.95	0.12	6	4,044	LOW	MED-HIGH
Finneytown Local School Dist	00806414		1.61	0.10	3	1,400	MED	MED-LOW
Deer Park Cmty School Dist	00806361		1.58	0.10	2	1,261	MED	MED-HIGH

DISTRICT BUYING POWER INDEX

Market Data Retrieval

DISTRICT BUYING POWER INDEX
COUNTIES RANKED BY PERCENTAGE OF STATE SPENDING

COUNTY / DISTRICT	PID	COUNTY % OF STATE	DISTRICT % OF COUNTY	DISTRICT % OF STATES	NUMBER OF SCHOOLS	ENROLL	EXP	POV
Reading Cmty City School Dist	00807573		1.43	0.09	4	1,535	LOW	MED-HIGH
St Bernard-Elmwood Place Schs	00807717		1.15	0.07	3	1,000	MED	MED-HIGH
North College Hill City SD	00807078		0.85	0.05	3	1,650	LOW	HIGH
Lockland School Dist	00806763		0.60	0.04	3	550	LOW	HIGH
MONTGOMERY		4.62						
Dayton Public School Dist	00824064		33.46	1.55	25	13,792	HIGH	HIGH
Centerville City School Dist	00823955		11.95	0.55	13	8,200	MED	MED-LOW
Miami Valley Career Tech VSD	00825977		8.01	0.37	2	2,100	HIGH	
Kettering City School Dist	00824832		7.51	0.35	12	7,400	LOW	MED-LOW
Huber Heights City School Dist	00825721		6.70	0.31	8	6,100	LOW	MED-HIGH
Miamisburg City School Dist	00825240		4.67	0.22	10	5,500	LOW	MED-LOW
Trotwood-Madison City SD	00825161		4.45	0.21	5	2,300	MED	HIGH
Mad River Local School Dist	00825056		4.38	0.20	8	3,800	LOW	MED-HIGH
West Carrollton City Sch Dist	00825848		4.23	0.20	6	3,700	LOW	MED-HIGH
Oakwood City School Dist	00825549		3.83	0.18	5	1,988	MED	MED-LOW
Northmont City School Dist	00825379		3.23	0.15	8	5,800	LOW	MED-LOW
New Lebanon Local School Dist	00825331		2.19	0.10	3	1,100	HIGH	MED-HIGH
Northridge Local School Dist	00825484		1.59	0.07	4	1,500	LOW	HIGH
Vandalia Butler City Sch Dist	00825630		1.39	0.06	5	3,225	LOW	MED-LOW
Valley View Local School Dist	00825587		0.87	0.04	4	1,900	LOW	MED-LOW
Jefferson Twp Local Sch Dist	00824777		0.79	0.04	2	345	HIGH	MED-HIGH
Brookville Local School Dist	00823905		0.76	0.04	3	1,500	LOW	MED-LOW
SUMMIT		4.15						
Akron Public Schools	00833833		48.64	2.02	45	21,343	HIGH	HIGH
Hudson City School Dist	00835099		8.80	0.36	6	4,600	MED	LOW
Nordonia Hills City Sch Dist	00835180		7.39	0.31	6	3,585	MED	MED-LOW
Stow-Munroe Falls City SD	00835506		6.70	0.28	10	5,158	LOW	MED-LOW
Copley-Fairlawn City Sch Dist	00834681		6.24	0.26	5	2,886	HIGH	MED-LOW
Barberton City School Dist	00834502		5.19	0.22	5	3,813	MED	MED-HIGH
Revere Local School Dist	00835348		2.81	0.12	4	2,700	LOW	LOW
Tallmadge City School Dist	00835594		2.56	0.11	4	2,412	LOW	MED-LOW
Cuyahoga Falls City Sch Dist	00834825		2.42	0.10	10	4,500	LOW	MED-LOW
Twinsburg City School Dist	00835661		2.32	0.10	5	4,200	LOW	MED-LOW
Woodridge Local School Dist	00834643		2.22	0.09	3	2,000	LOW	MED-LOW
Springfield Local School Dist	00835403		1.44	0.06	4	2,222	LOW	MED-LOW
Norton City School Dist	00835269		1.35	0.06	4	2,500	LOW	MED-LOW
Manchester Local School Dist	00834978		1.10	0.05	3	1,400	LOW	MED-LOW
Coventry Local School Dist	00834758		0.83	0.03	3	1,900	LOW	MED-LOW
STARK		3.85						
Canton City School Dist	00832396		20.06	0.77	27	9,500	MED	HIGH
Plain Local School Dist	00833510		11.12	0.43	9	6,000	MED	MED-HIGH
Perry Local School Dist	00833417		8.31	0.32	8	4,500	MED	MED-LOW
Massillon City School Dist	00833039		7.11	0.27	7	3,900	MED	MED-HIGH
Alliance City School Dist	00832190		6.99	0.27	6	3,100	HIGH	HIGH
Jackson Local School Dist	00832798		6.74	0.26	6	5,817	LOW	MED-LOW
Canton Local School Dist	00832308		5.01	0.19	3	2,000	HIGH	MED-HIGH
Northwest Local School Dist	00833326		4.61	0.18	4	1,783	HIGH	MED-LOW
Lake Local School Dist	00832853		4.45	0.17	3	3,300	LOW	MED-LOW
Sandy Valley Local School Dist	00833649		3.63	0.14	3	1,500	HIGH	MED-HIGH
Marlington Local School Dist	00832970		3.55	0.14	5	2,300	MED	MED-LOW
Louisville City School Dist	00832906		2.90	0.11	4	2,797	LOW	MED-LOW
Fairless Local School Dist	00832712		2.73	0.11	3	1,501	MED	MED-HIGH
Green Local School Dist	00835025		2.69	0.10	5	4,253	LOW	MED-LOW
Minerva Local School Dist	00833170		2.57	0.10	3	1,900	LOW	MED-HIGH
Portage Lakes Joint Voc SD	01601554		2.20	0.08	1	650	HIGH	
Tuslaw Local School Dist	00833699		1.55	0.06	3	1,390	LOW	MED-LOW
Stark Co Area Voc Sch Dist	01601530		1.40	0.05	1	700	MED	
North Canton City School Dist	00833247		1.32	0.05	7	4,437	LOW	MED-LOW
Osnaburg Local School Dist	00833388		1.07	0.04	3	850	LOW	MED-LOW
BUTLER		3.22						
Lakota Local School Dist	00786644		27.85	0.90	23	16,500	LOW	LOW
Fairfield City School Dist	00786357		16.23	0.52	11	10,000	LOW	MED-LOW
Butler Tech Career Dev Schs	01483053		14.06	0.45	1	900	HIGH	
Hamilton City School Dist	00786424		13.25	0.43	13	10,300	LOW	MED-HIGH
Middletown City School Dist	00786761		10.93	0.35	10	6,561	LOW	MED-HIGH
Ross Local School Dist	00787064		4.20	0.14	4	2,500	LOW	MED-LOW
Edgewood City School Dist	00786280		4.18	0.13	5	3,800	LOW	MED-LOW
Talawanda School Dist	00787117		3.54	0.11	5	3,100	LOW	MED-LOW
Monroe Local School Dist	04913801		3.02	0.10	4	2,900	LOW	MED-LOW
Madison Local School Dist	00786711		1.54	0.05	2	1,600	LOW	MED-LOW
New Miami Local School Dist	00787026		1.19	0.04	2	620	LOW	MED-HIGH

Ohio School Directory — DISTRICT BUYING POWER INDEX

DISTRICT BUYING POWER INDEX
COUNTIES RANKED BY PERCENTAGE OF STATE SPENDING

COUNTY / DISTRICT	PID	COUNTY % OF STATE	DISTRICT % OF COUNTY	DISTRICT % OF STATES	NUMBER OF SCHOOLS	ENROLL	EXP	POV
LUCAS		3.00						
Toledo Public Schools	00817310		38.16	1.14	52	24,000	LOW	HIGH
Washington Local School Dist	00818089		18.37	0.55	13	7,042	MED	MED-HIGH
Sylvania City School Dist	00817205		14.04	0.42	12	7,704	LOW	MED-LOW
Maumee City School Dist	00816940		10.50	0.31	5	2,222	HIGH	MED-LOW
Oregon City School Dist	00817023		7.20	0.22	8	3,800	LOW	MED-LOW
Ottawa Hills Local Sch Dist	00817114		4.57	0.14	2	1,000	HIGH	MED-LOW
Anthony Wayne Local Sch Dist	00816873		4.03	0.12	6	4,400	LOW	MED-LOW
Springfield Local School Dist	00817140		3.13	0.09	6	4,000	LOW	MED-LOW
LORAIN		2.58						
Lorain City School Dist	00816263		21.38	0.55	14	6,500	MED	HIGH
Elyria City School Dist	00815908		10.46	0.27	13	7,010	LOW	MED-HIGH
Lorain Co Joint Voc Sch Dist	00816847		9.17	0.24	1	1,500	HIGH	
Avon Local School Dist	00815685		8.82	0.23	5	4,650	LOW	LOW
Avon Lake City School Dist	00815726		8.27	0.21	7	3,819	MED	LOW
Amherst Exempted Village SD	00815611		7.63	0.20	4	3,800	LOW	MED-LOW
North Ridgeville City Sch Dist	00816562		7.52	0.19	5	4,600	LOW	MED-LOW
Midview Local School Dist	00816483		5.18	0.13	5	3,000	LOW	MED-LOW
Sheffield-Sheffield Lake CSD	00816689		4.07	0.10	5	1,747	LOW	MED-LOW
Keystone Local School Dist	00816213		3.36	0.09	3	1,500	LOW	MED-LOW
Firelands Local School Dist	00816146		3.22	0.08	4	1,626	LOW	MED-LOW
Clearview Local School Dist	00815805		3.11	0.08	3	1,644	LOW	HIGH
Columbia Local School Dist	00815855		2.80	0.07	3	900	MED	MED-LOW
Wellington Exempted Village SD	00816782		2.64	0.07	3	1,304	MED	MED-LOW
Oberlin City School Dist	00816627		2.39	0.06	4	1,200	MED	MED-HIGH
WARREN		2.15						
Mason City School Dist	00838467		21.63	0.46	5	10,396	LOW	LOW
Little Miami Local School Dist	00838405		14.44	0.31	6	5,020	MED	LOW
Springboro Cmty School Dist	00838156		13.86	0.30	6	6,093	LOW	LOW
Kings Local School Dist	00838194		13.02	0.28	7	4,650	MED	LOW
Franklin City School Dist	00838247		10.82	0.23	8	2,750	MED	MED-LOW
Wayne Local School Dist	00838510		9.79	0.21	3	1,473	HIGH	LOW
Lebanon City School Dist	00838340		9.09	0.20	5	6,000	LOW	LOW
Warren Co Voc School Dist	01537824		3.83	0.08	1	775	HIGH	
Carlisle Local School Dist	00838106		3.52	0.08	4	1,593	LOW	
CLARK		1.90						
Springfield City School Dist	00787935		60.99	1.16	16	7,583	HIGH	HIGH
Northeastern Local School Dist	00787791		10.87	0.21	7	3,300	MED	MED-LOW
Tecumseh Local School Dist	00787686		7.13	0.14	5	3,130	LOW	MED-HIGH
Clark-Shawnee Local Sch Dist	00788226		5.36	0.10	5	2,057	LOW	MED-LOW
Northwestern Local School Dist	00787868		4.69	0.09	2	1,643	LOW	MED-LOW
Springfield-Clark Co JVSD	00788290		4.02	0.08	1	700	HIGH	
Southeastern Local School Dist	00787909		3.53	0.07	2	778	HIGH	MED-LOW
Greenon Local School Dist	00787612		3.41	0.06	3	1,486	LOW	MED-LOW
WOOD		1.69						
Perrysburg Exempted Village SD	00840408		26.89	0.45	7	5,400	MED	LOW
Penta Co JT Voc School Dist	00840513		19.98	0.34	1	1,500	HIGH	
Bowling Green City Sch Dist	00839942		15.67	0.26	6	3,450	MED	MED-LOW
Eastwood Local School Dist	00840044		10.74	0.18	3	1,500	HIGH	MED-LOW
Elmwood Local School Dist	00840111		5.73	0.10	3	1,275	MED	MED-LOW
Lake Local School Dist	00840173		5.72	0.10	3	1,679	LOW	MED-LOW
Otsego Local School Dist	00840331		5.56	0.09	3	1,650	MED	MED-LOW
Rossford Exempted Village SD	00840458		4.67	0.08	3	1,650	LOW	MED-LOW
Northwood Local School Dist	00840288		2.68	0.05	2	950	LOW	MED-LOW
North Baltimore Local Sch Dist	00840238		2.37	0.04	2	700	MED	MED-LOW
MAHONING		1.67						
Youngstown City School Dist	00820446		21.32	0.36	15	5,275	MED	HIGH
Mahoning Co Joint Voc Sch Dist	00820898		10.94	0.18	2	778	HIGH	
Boardman Local School Dist	00819796		9.93	0.17	6	4,000	LOW	MED-HIGH
Austintown Local School Dist	00819708		9.51	0.16	4	4,567	LOW	MED-LOW
West Branch Local School Dist	00820331		8.89	0.15	5	2,100	MED	MED-HIGH
Poland Local School Dist	00820056		8.25	0.14	3	1,888	MED	MED-LOW
Struthers City School Dist	00820252		6.03	0.10	3	1,785	LOW	MED-HIGH
Springfield Local School Dist	00820202		4.63	0.08	3	942	MED	MED-LOW
Canfield Local School Dist	00819928		4.62	0.08	4	2,600	LOW	MED-LOW
South Range Local School Dist	00820161		3.70	0.06	3	1,247	LOW	MED-LOW
Jackson-Milton Local Sch Dist	00819978		3.36	0.05	2	700	HIGH	MED-HIGH
Campbell City School Dist	00819875		3.05	0.05	2	1,071	LOW	HIGH
Sebring Local School Dist	00820123		2.66	0.04	2	600	MED	MED-HIGH
Western Reserve Local Sch Dist	00820408		1.82	0.03	1	850	LOW	MED-LOW
Lowellville Local School Dist	00820020		1.30	0.02	1	499	LOW	MED-LOW

School Year 2019-2020

DISTRICT BUYING POWER INDEX

Market Data Retrieval

DISTRICT BUYING POWER INDEX
COUNTIES RANKED BY PERCENTAGE OF STATE SPENDING

COUNTY / DISTRICT	PID	COUNTY % OF STATE	DISTRICT % OF COUNTY	DISTRICT % OF STATES	NUMBER OF SCHOOLS	ENROLL	EXP	POV
LICKING		1.62						
Newark City School Dist	00814930		29.84	0.48	13	6,500	MED	MED-HIGH
Licking Heights Local Sch Dist	00814825		10.94	0.18	5	4,700	LOW	MED-LOW
Granville Exempted Village SD	00814605		8.58	0.14	4	2,500	LOW	LOW
Johnstown-Monroe Local SD	00814708		7.91	0.13	3	1,600	MED	LOW
Lakewood Local School Dist	00814758		7.76	0.13	4	1,900	MED	MED-LOW
North Fork Local School Dist	00815142		7.73	0.12	4	1,800	MED	MED-LOW
Southwest Licking Local SD	00815271		7.72	0.12	6	4,300	LOW	MED-LOW
Licking Valley Local Sch Dist	00814863		6.86	0.11	3	2,000	LOW	MED-LOW
Licking Co Joint Voc Sch Dist	00815324		6.68	0.11	1	750	HIGH	
Heath City School Dist	00814655		3.79	0.06	4	1,730	LOW	MED-LOW
Northridge Local School Dist	00815219		2.20	0.04	4	1,300	LOW	MED-LOW
TRUMBULL		1.61						
Warren City School Dist	00836782		19.19	0.31	5	4,300	MED	HIGH
Lakeview Local School Dist	00836392		11.59	0.19	3	1,732	HIGH	MED-LOW
Champion Local School Dist	00835946		9.24	0.15	2	1,525	HIGH	MED-LOW
Girard City School Dist	00836079		7.49	0.12	4	1,699	MED	MED-HIGH
Niles City School Dist	00836653		7.06	0.11	4	2,209	LOW	MED-HIGH
Liberty Local School Dist	00836433		6.18	0.10	3	1,244	HIGH	MED-HIGH
Newton Falls Exempted Vlg SD	00836603		4.91	0.08	4	1,100	MED	MED-HIGH
Howland Local School Dist	00836146		4.37	0.07	6	2,685	LOW	MED-LOW
Maplewood Local School Dist	00836524		4.00	0.06	2	750	HIGH	MED-LOW
Mathews Local School Dist	00836029		3.48	0.06	3	675	MED	MED-HIGH
Hubbard Exempted Village SD	00836237		3.31	0.05	3	1,932	LOW	MED-LOW
Weathersfield Local Sch Dist	00837011		3.13	0.05	2	992	LOW	MED-HIGH
McDonald Local School Dist	00836574		2.87	0.05	2	768	MED	MED-HIGH
Bristol Local School Dist	00835855		2.67	0.04	2	550	MED	MED-LOW
Joseph Badger Local Sch Dist	00836287		2.63	0.04	3	750	LOW	MED-LOW
Labrae Local School Dist	00836330		2.06	0.03	4	1,078	LOW	MED-HIGH
Lordstown Local School Dist	00836483		1.70	0.03	2	500	LOW	MED-HIGH
Brookfield Local School Dist	00835881		1.62	0.03	3	900	LOW	MED-HIGH
Southington Local School Dist	00836756		1.30	0.02	1	500	LOW	MED-LOW
Bloomfield-Mespo Local SD	00835817		1.22	0.02	2	314	MED	MED-LOW
FAIRFIELD		1.59						
Lancaster City School Dist	00799031		42.75	0.68	9	6,300	HIGH	MED-HIGH
Pickerington Local School Dist	00799225		28.05	0.45	15	10,600	LOW	MED-LOW
Amanda-Clearcreek Local SD	00798855		7.30	0.12	4	1,445	MED	MED-LOW
Bloom-Carroll Local Sch Dist	00798922		7.24	0.12	4	2,000	LOW	LOW
Liberty Union-Thurstn Sch Dist	00799184		6.01	0.10	3	1,350	MED	MED-LOW
Fairfield Union Local Sch Dist	00798972		3.89	0.06	4	2,000	LOW	MED-LOW
Berne Union Local School Dist	00798893		2.52	0.04	2	950	LOW	MED-LOW
Walnut Twp Local School Dist	00799275		2.24	0.04	2	490	MED	MED-LOW
CLERMONT		1.45						
Milford Exempted Village SD	00788537		29.36	0.43	10	6,600	MED	MED-LOW
Clermont Northeastern Local SD	00788393		15.14	0.22	3	1,350	HIGH	MED-LOW
Goshen Local School Dist	00788484		14.29	0.21	4	2,800	MED	MED-LOW
West Clermont Local Sch Dist	00788680		13.04	0.19	10	9,500	LOW	MED-LOW
New Richmond Exempted Vlg SD	00788616		12.09	0.18	4	2,400	MED	MED-LOW
U S Grant Career School Dist	01537707		4.98	0.07	1	400	HIGH	
Williamsburg Local School Dist	00788800		4.52	0.07	2	994	MED	MED-HIGH
Bethel-Tate Local School Dist	00788343		3.36	0.05	4	1,600	LOW	MED-LOW
Felicity-Franklin Local SD	00788458		2.28	0.03	3	800	LOW	MED-LOW
Batavia Local School Dist	00788317		0.94	0.01	3	2,289	LOW	MED-HIGH
DELAWARE		1.44						
Olentangy Local School Dist	00798300		63.51	0.92	25	22,125	LOW	LOW
Delaware City School Dist	00798221		14.49	0.21	7	5,459	LOW	MED-LOW
Big Walnut Local School Dist	00798104		11.73	0.17	7	4,000	LOW	LOW
Delaware Joint Voc Sch Dist	00798348		6.15	0.09	2	1,000	HIGH	
Buckeye Valley Local Sch Dist	00798166		4.13	0.06	4	2,202	LOW	MED-LOW
MEDINA		1.44						
Medina City School Dist	00822389		23.31	0.34	11	7,100	LOW	LOW
Wadsworth City School Dist	00822444		22.93	0.33	8	4,800	MED	MED-LOW
Brunswick City School Dist	00822119		14.47	0.21	11	7,123	LOW	MED-LOW
Medina Co Joint Voc Sch Dist	00822535		12.85	0.19	1	1,100	HIGH	
Highland Local School Dist	00822339		11.87	0.17	5	3,233	LOW	LOW
Cloverleaf Local School Dist	00822250		5.89	0.09	3	2,264	LOW	MED-LOW
Black River Local School Dist	00822066		5.30	0.08	2	631	HIGH	MED-LOW
Buckeye Local School Dist	00822195		3.39	0.05	4	2,300	LOW	MED-LOW
LAKE		1.37						
Mentor Exempted Village SD	00813352		28.93	0.40	11	7,415	LOW	MED-LOW
Willoughby-Eastlake City SD	00813845		14.17	0.19	13	8,090	LOW	MED-LOW

School Year 2019-2020

Ohio School Directory

DISTRICT BUYING POWER INDEX

DISTRICT BUYING POWER INDEX
COUNTIES RANKED BY PERCENTAGE OF STATE SPENDING

COUNTY / DISTRICT	PID	COUNTY % OF STATE	DISTRICT % OF COUNTY	DISTRICT % OF STATES	NUMBER OF SCHOOLS	ENROLL	EXP	POV
Madison Local School Dist	00813285		11.47	0.16	5	3,120	LOW	MED-LOW
Riverside Local School Dist	00813522		11.01	0.15	6	3,987	LOW	MED-LOW
Painesville City Local SD	00813649		9.39	0.13	6	3,000	LOW	MED-HIGH
Perry Local School Dist	00813730		8.69	0.12	3	1,700	MED	MED-LOW
Auburn Vocational School Dist	00814100		6.96	0.10	1	745	HIGH	
Kirtland Local School Dist	00813235		4.29	0.06	3	1,155	LOW	LOW
Wickliffe City School Dist	00813780		3.09	0.04	3	1,290	LOW	MED-LOW
Fairport Harbor Exempt Vlg SD	00813209		2.01	0.03	2	720	LOW	MED-HIGH
GREENE		1.26						
Beavercreek City School Dist	00804466		20.83	0.26	11	7,200	LOW	LOW
Xenia Community School Dist	00804818		19.05	0.24	8	4,600	LOW	MED-HIGH
Bellbrook-Sugarcreek Schools	00804765		18.98	0.24	5	2,875	MED	LOW
Greene Co Voc School Dist	00804985		12.14	0.15	1	685	HIGH	
Fairborn City School Dist	00804595		11.42	0.14	4	4,300	LOW	MED-HIGH
Greeneview Local School Dist	00804715		8.15	0.10	3	1,400	MED	MED-LOW
Cedar Cliff Local School Dist	00804569		6.10	0.08	2	650	HIGH	MED-LOW
Yellow Springs Exempted Vlg SD	00804935		3.33	0.04	2	696	LOW	MED-LOW
MIAMI		1.25						
Troy City School Dist	00823591		26.86	0.34	9	4,400	MED	MED-LOW
Piqua City School Dist	00823412		20.62	0.26	5	3,500	MED	MED-HIGH
Tipp City Exempted Village SD	00823539		12.97	0.16	5	2,605	MED	LOW
Upper Valley JT Voc Sch Dist	01417523		9.69	0.12	1	780	HIGH	
Covington Exempted Village SD	00823228		7.97	0.10	2	850	HIGH	MED-LOW
Miami East Local School Dist	00823266		6.21	0.08	3	1,300	MED	MED-LOW
Newton Local School Dist	00823383		5.94	0.07	1	600	HIGH	MED-LOW
Bethel Local School Dist	00823163		5.52	0.07	2	1,400	LOW	MED-LOW
Milton-Union Exempted Vlg SD	00823333		2.98	0.04	3	1,500	LOW	MED-LOW
Bradford Exempted Village SD	00823199		1.25	0.02	2	487	LOW	MED-LOW
TUSCARAWAS		1.18						
New Philadelphia City Sch Dist	00837334		26.92	0.32	8	3,800	HIGH	MED-HIGH
Buckeye Joint Voc School Dist	00837580		18.60	0.22	1	975	HIGH	
Claymont City School Dist	00837061		15.32	0.18	6	2,000	MED	MED-HIGH
Indian Valley Local Sch Dist	00837267		9.33	0.11	5	1,900	MED	MED-HIGH
Dover City School Dist	00837140		7.59	0.09	5	2,712	LOW	MED-LOW
Tuscarawas Valley Local SD	00837528		7.02	0.08	4	1,380	MED	MED-LOW
Garaway Local School Dist	00837205		6.70	0.08	5	1,300	MED	MED-LOW
Newcomerstown Exempted Vlg SD	00837437		5.97	0.07	4	1,100	MED	MED-HIGH
Strasburg Franklin Local SD	00837499		2.54	0.03	2	534	LOW	MED-LOW
ALLEN		1.09						
Lima City School Dist	00783769		39.42	0.43	9	4,000	HIGH	HIGH
Elida Local School Dist	00783721		11.67	0.13	3	2,500	LOW	MED-HIGH
Apollo Joint Voc School Dist	01537678		10.66	0.12	1	600	HIGH	
Allen East Local School Dist	00783549		7.06	0.08	3	1,200	MED	MED-LOW
Perry Local School Dist	00783953		6.33	0.07	2	753	MED	MED-HIGH
Bluffton Exempted Village Sch	00783630		5.26	0.06	3	1,220	LOW	MED-LOW
Shawnee Local School Dist	00783989		5.10	0.06	4	2,500	LOW	MED-LOW
Bath Local School Dist	00783587		5.01	0.05	3	1,900	LOW	MED-LOW
Spencerville Local School Dist	00784036		4.97	0.05	3	965	LOW	MED-LOW
Delphos City School Dist	00783678		4.52	0.05	3	1,050	LOW	MED-LOW
PORTAGE		1.09						
Kent City School Dist	00828412		22.79	0.25	6	3,400	MED	MED-HIGH
Streetsboro City School Dist	00828668		15.58	0.17	4	2,200	MED	MED-LOW
Ravenna School Dist	00828503		8.70	0.09	7	2,200	MED	MED-HIGH
Crestwood Local School Dist	00828230		7.91	0.09	4	1,600	LOW	MED-LOW
Field Local School Dist	00828319		6.97	0.08	4	1,900	LOW	MED-LOW
Aurora City School Dist	00828163		6.81	0.07	5	3,000	LOW	LOW
Maplewood JT Voc School Dist	00828802		6.17	0.07	1	700	HIGH	
Windham Exempted Vlg Sch Dist	00828761		5.25	0.06	3	600	MED	MED-HIGH
Mogadore Local School Dist	00835154		5.07	0.06	2	875	MED	MED-LOW
Southeast Local School Dist	00828632		4.65	0.05	4	1,484	LOW	MED-LOW
Rootstown Local School Dist	00828591		4.32	0.05	3	1,200	LOW	MED-LOW
James A Garfield Local SD	00828371		3.82	0.04	3	1,379	LOW	MED-LOW
Waterloo Local School Dist	00828723		1.97	0.02	3	1,100	LOW	MED-LOW
HANCOCK		1.07						
Findlay City School Dist	00809832		54.95	0.59	15	6,000	HIGH	MED-LOW
Riverdale Local School Dist	00810348		9.08	0.10	3	1,030	HIGH	MED-LOW
McComb Local School Dist	00810049		7.87	0.08	3	700	HIGH	MED-LOW
Liberty-Benton Local Sch Dist	00810013		7.21	0.08	3	1,242	LOW	MED-LOW
Van Buren Local School Dist	00810087		5.63	0.06	3	1,080	LOW	LOW
Cory-Rawson Local School Dist	00809791		5.21	0.06	2	550	HIGH	MED-LOW
Arcadia Local School Dist	00809739		4.87	0.05	1	575	HIGH	MED-LOW

School Year 2019-2020

DISTRICT BUYING POWER INDEX

Market Data Retrieval

DISTRICT BUYING POWER INDEX
COUNTIES RANKED BY PERCENTAGE OF STATE SPENDING

COUNTY / DISTRICT	PID	COUNTY % OF STATE	DISTRICT % OF COUNTY	DISTRICT % OF STATES	NUMBER OF SCHOOLS	ENROLL	EXP	POV
Arlington Local School Dist	00809765		3.85	0.04	1	570	MED	LOW
Vanlue Local School Dist	00810116		1.32	0.01	1	180	MED	MED-LOW
WAYNE		1.07						
Wooster City School Dist	00839485		23.70	0.25	7	3,650	MED	MED-HIGH
Northwestern Local School Dist	00839198		12.43	0.13	3	1,320	HIGH	MED-LOW
Wayne Co Joint Voc School Dist	00839617		11.68	0.12	1	879	HIGH	
Orrville City School Dist	00839241		10.38	0.11	3	1,600	MED	MED-LOW
Chippewa Local School Dist	00839007		8.27	0.09	3	1,290	MED	MED-LOW
Green Local School Dist	00839095		7.69	0.08	3	1,056	MED	MED-LOW
Rittman Exempted Village SD	00839306		7.14	0.08	4	999	MED	MED-HIGH
Dalton Local School Dist	00839045		7.06	0.08	2	875	HIGH	MED-HIGH
Triway Local School Dist	00839423		6.11	0.07	4	1,637	LOW	MED-HIGH
Southeast Local School Dist	00839356		3.17	0.03	6	1,400	LOW	MED-HIGH
Norwayne Local School Dist	00839148		2.36	0.03	3	1,400	LOW	MED-LOW
RICHLAND		1.05						
Mansfield City Schools	00829674		17.06	0.18	8	3,350	LOW	HIGH
Ontario Local School Dist	00829997		14.32	0.15	3	2,158	MED	MED-LOW
Madison Local School Dist	00829571		12.61	0.13	5	2,956	LOW	MED-HIGH
Lexington Local School Dist	00829480		11.07	0.12	5	2,510	LOW	MED-LOW
Clear Fork Vly Local Sch Dist	00829404		10.37	0.11	4	1,692	MED	MED-LOW
Pioneer Joint Voc School Dist	00830051		9.22	0.10	1	1,250	MED	
Crestview Local School Dist	00829442		8.96	0.09	3	1,100	HIGH	MED-HIGH
Shelby City School Dist	00829923		7.64	0.08	5	1,918	LOW	MED-LOW
Lucas Local School Dist	00829545		5.75	0.06	3	565	HIGH	MED-LOW
Plymouth-Shiloh Local Sch Dist	00829882		3.00	0.03	3	681	LOW	MED-HIGH
COLUMBIANA		1.04						
East Liverpool City Sch Dist	00789232		16.24	0.17	4	2,050	MED	HIGH
Salem City School Dist	00789531		12.69	0.13	5	2,100	MED	MED-HIGH
Crestview Local School Dist	00789397		10.33	0.11	3	1,245	MED	MED-HIGH
Columbiana Co Voc Sch Dist	01601487		10.22	0.11	1	450	HIGH	
Columbiana Exempted Village SD	00789191		9.65	0.10	3	1,077	HIGH	MED-LOW
Wellsville Local Sch Dist	00789713		9.32	0.10	3	850	HIGH	HIGH
Southern Local School Dist	00789610		7.70	0.08	2	920	HIGH	MED-HIGH
United Local School Dist	00789684		7.68	0.08	2	1,300	MED	MED-HIGH
Beaver Local School Dist	00789127		7.43	0.08	3	1,800	LOW	MED-HIGH
Leetonia Exempted Village SD	00789438		4.15	0.04	1	780	LOW	MED-HIGH
Lisbon Exempted Village SD	00789490		2.54	0.03	2	850	LOW	MED-HIGH
East Palestine City Sch Dist	00789311		2.05	0.02	3	1,087	LOW	MED-HIGH
ERIE		0.91						
Ehove Joint Voc School Dist	00798829		25.01	0.23	1	850	HIGH	
Margaretta Local School Dist	00798506		21.84	0.20	3	2,602	HIGH	MED-LOW
Sandusky City School Dist	00798611		15.14	0.14	7	3,250	LOW	HIGH
Edison Local Schools District	00798374		11.39	0.10	3	1,650	MED	MED-LOW
Perkins Local School Dist	00798556		10.02	0.09	4	1,950	LOW	MED-LOW
Huron City School Dist	00798427		9.50	0.09	4	1,324	MED	MED-LOW
Vermilion Local School Dist	00798752		7.03	0.06	3	1,900	LOW	MED-LOW
Kelleys Island Local Sch Dist	00798477		0.07	0.00	1	5	HIGH	
LAWRENCE		0.88						
Ironton City School Dist	00814277		21.95	0.19	3	1,400	HIGH	MED-HIGH
Lawrence Co Joint Voc Sch Dist	01548108		16.60	0.15	1	475	HIGH	
Rock Hill Local School Dist	00814370		13.14	0.12	3	1,450	MED	HIGH
Fairland Local School Dist	00814239		12.89	0.11	4	1,569	MED	MED-HIGH
South Point Local School Dist	00814447		11.66	0.10	4	1,500	MED	MED-HIGH
Dawson-Bryant Local Sch Dist	00814174		10.99	0.10	3	1,200	HIGH	MED-HIGH
Chesapeake Union Exempt Vlg SD	00814136		6.81	0.06	3	1,400	LOW	MED-HIGH
Symmes Valley Local Sch Dist	00814526		5.98	0.05	2	743	MED	MED-HIGH
JEFFERSON		0.79						
Steubenville City School Dist	00812504		34.13	0.27	6	2,600	HIGH	HIGH
Indian Creek Local Sch Dist	00812396		18.61	0.15	4	2,300	MED	MED-HIGH
Edison Local School Dist	00812279		18.27	0.14	3	2,000	MED	MED-HIGH
Jefferson Co JT Voc Sch Dist	01417444		13.31	0.10	1	350	HIGH	
Buckeye Local School Dist	00812102		9.36	0.07	5	1,700	LOW	MED-HIGH
Toronto City School Dist	00812607		6.32	0.05	2	891	LOW	MED-HIGH
FULTON		0.75						
Archbold Area Local Sch Dist	00803503		18.17	0.14	3	1,212	HIGH	MED-LOW
Evergreen Local School Dist	00803553		16.15	0.12	3	1,300	HIGH	MED-LOW
Four-Co Joint Voc School Dist	00810881		15.71	0.12	1	1,000	HIGH	
Wauseon Exempted Village SD	00803802		14.22	0.11	4	1,770	MED	MED-LOW
Pike-Delta-York Local Sch Dist	00803682		13.81	0.10	3	1,100	MED	MED-LOW
Swanton Local School Dist	00803747		13.44	0.10	3	1,300	MED	MED-LOW

Ohio School Directory

DISTRICT BUYING POWER INDEX

DISTRICT BUYING POWER INDEX
COUNTIES RANKED BY PERCENTAGE OF STATE SPENDING

COUNTY / DISTRICT	PID	COUNTY % OF STATE	DISTRICT % OF COUNTY	DISTRICT % OF STATES	NUMBER OF SCHOOLS	ENROLL	EXP	POV
Fayette Local Sch Dist	00803618		5.82	0.04	1	370	HIGH	MED-LOW
Pettisville Local School Dist	00803656		2.67	0.02	2	525	LOW	LOW
SCIOTO		0.74						
Scioto Co Joint Vocational SD	00831392		17.39	0.13	1	540	HIGH	
Washington-Nile Local Sch Dist	00831304		12.73	0.09	3	1,449	MED	MED-HIGH
Wheelersburg Local School Dist	00831366		10.94	0.08	3	1,600	LOW	MED-HIGH
Northwest Local School Dist	00831067		9.93	0.07	3	1,373	LOW	MED-HIGH
Portsmouth City School Dist	00831122		9.29	0.07	3	1,700	LOW	HIGH
Green Local School Dist	00830958		8.39	0.06	2	600	HIGH	MED-HIGH
Clay Local School Dist	00830910		7.43	0.05	1	714	MED	MED-HIGH
Minford Local School Dist	00830984		6.98	0.05	3	1,401	LOW	MED-HIGH
Valley Local School Dist	00831251		6.96	0.05	3	1,020	LOW	MED-HIGH
New Boston Local School Dist	00831029		5.17	0.04	3	500	MED	HIGH
Bloom-Vernon Local Sch Dist	00830867		4.79	0.04	2	900	LOW	MED-HIGH
MUSKINGUM		0.72						
Zanesville City School Dist	00826658		27.16	0.19	6	3,307	LOW	MED-HIGH
Tri-Valley Local School Dist	00826440		20.91	0.15	6	3,100	LOW	MED-HIGH
Mideast Career & Tech Ctrs	00826842		16.01	0.11	3	1,100	HIGH	
Maysville Local School Dist	00826373		13.51	0.10	3	2,200	LOW	MED-HIGH
East Muskingum Local Sch Dist	00826309		8.99	0.06	6	2,200	LOW	MED-LOW
Franklin Local School Dist	00826505		7.69	0.06	5	2,000	LOW	MED-HIGH
West Muskingum Local Sch Dist	00826581		5.73	0.04	3	1,400	LOW	MED-LOW
MARION		0.71						
Marion City School Dist	00821713		26.73	0.19	9	4,200	LOW	HIGH
River Valley Local School Dist	00821983		22.27	0.16	4	2,260	MED	MED-LOW
Tri-Rivers Joint Voc Sch Dist	01417482		17.37	0.12	1	550	HIGH	
Pleasant Local School Dist	00821892		13.39	0.10	4	1,320	MED	MED-HIGH
Elgin Local School Dist	00821658		12.77	0.09	3	1,200	HIGH	MED-LOW
Ridgedale Local School Dist	00821933		7.46	0.05	2	642	MED	MED-LOW
ROSS		0.64						
Chillicothe City School Dist	00830128		21.48	0.14	5	2,800	LOW	MED-HIGH
Union Scioto Local Sch Dist	00830374		17.96	0.11	3	2,175	LOW	MED-HIGH
Southeastern Local Sch Dist	00830312		16.03	0.10	3	1,040	HIGH	MED-HIGH
Adena Local School Dist	00830087		13.04	0.08	3	1,200	MED	MED-HIGH
Huntington Local School Dist	00830245		11.67	0.07	3	1,120	MED	MED-HIGH
Zane Trace Local School Dist	00830427		8.04	0.05	3	1,301	LOW	MED-LOW
Paint Valley Local School Dist	00830271		7.43	0.05	3	890	LOW	MED-HIGH
Pickaway-Ross Co JT Voc SD	00830465		4.35	0.03	1	800	LOW	
BELMONT		0.63						
Union Local School Dist	00785937		21.83	0.14	3	1,521	HIGH	MED-LOW
Barnesville Exempted Vlg SD	00785561		17.24	0.11	3	1,480	MED	MED-LOW
St Clairsville-Richland CSD	00785884		13.87	0.09	3	1,700	LOW	MED-LOW
Bridgeport School Dist	00785690		12.76	0.08	3	820	HIGH	MED-HIGH
Belmont-Harrison Voc Sch Dist	00786008		10.80	0.07	2	408	HIGH	
Martins Ferry City School Dist	00785743		10.44	0.07	3	1,500	LOW	MED-HIGH
Bellaire Local School Dist	00785597		10.43	0.07	3	1,159	LOW	MED-HIGH
Shadyside Local School Dist	00785834		2.62	0.02	3	800	LOW	MED-LOW
HURON		0.62						
Norwalk City School Dist	00811615		24.93	0.15	6	2,750	LOW	MED-HIGH
Bellevue City School Dist	00811457		24.51	0.15	3	2,000	MED	MED-LOW
Willard City School Dist	00811794		17.90	0.11	2	1,520	MED	MED-HIGH
Monroeville Local School Dist	00811548		11.79	0.07	2	593	HIGH	MED-LOW
Western Reserve Local Sch Dist	00811744		7.83	0.05	3	994	LOW	MED-LOW
New London Local School Dist	00811574		6.57	0.04	4	900	LOW	MED-HIGH
South Central Local Sch Dist	00811691		6.47	0.04	3	750	LOW	MED-HIGH
HIGHLAND		0.61						
Greenfield Exempted Village SD	00810984		43.65	0.26	5	2,250	HIGH	MED-HIGH
Hillsboro City School Dist	00811043		28.22	0.17	3	2,300	MED	MED-HIGH
Fairfield Local Sch Dist	00810958		10.74	0.07	3	950	MED	MED-LOW
Lynchburg-Clay Local Sch Dist	00811093		9.05	0.05	3	1,150	LOW	MED-LOW
Bright Local School Dist	00810910		8.35	0.05	2	700	MED	MED-HIGH
SANDUSKY		0.61						
Vanguard-Sentinel JT Voc SD	00830831		45.86	0.28	2	2,300	HIGH	
Clyde-Green Spgs Exmpt Vlg SD	00830491		20.23	0.12	4	2,300	LOW	MED-LOW
Fremont City School Dist	00830556		18.11	0.11	9	3,843	MED	MED-HIGH
Lakota Local School Dist	00830702		8.75	0.05	3	1,140	LOW	MED-LOW
Gibsonburg Exempted Village SD	00830661		7.05	0.04	3	950	LOW	MED-LOW
MERCER		0.57						
Celina City School Dist	00822793		29.49	0.17	5	2,300	MED	MED-LOW

School Year 2019-2020   800-333-8802

DISTRICT BUYING POWER INDEX

Market Data Retrieval

DISTRICT BUYING POWER INDEX
COUNTIES RANKED BY PERCENTAGE OF STATE SPENDING

COUNTY / DISTRICT	PID	COUNTY % OF STATE	DISTRICT % OF COUNTY	DISTRICT % OF STATES	NUMBER OF SCHOOLS	ENROLL	EXP	POV
Coldwater Exempted Village SD	00822858		19.88	0.11	3	1,375	MED	MED-LOW
Ft Recovery Local School Dist	00823046		16.25	0.09	2	920	HIGH	MED-LOW
Parkway Local School Dist	00823008		14.33	0.08	3	1,000	MED	MED-LOW
St Henry Cons Local Sch Dist	00823101		11.82	0.07	3	950	MED	LOW
Marion Local School Dist	00822913		8.22	0.05	2	860	LOW	LOW
LOGAN		0.55						
Ohio Hi-Point Joint Voc SD	00815594		41.90	0.23	1	500	HIGH	
Benjamin Logan Local Sch Dist	00815439		20.17	0.11	3	1,750	MED	MED-LOW
Bellefontaine City School Dist	00815362		19.80	0.11	4	2,600	LOW	MED-HIGH
Riverside Local School Dist	00815556		9.79	0.05	2	633	MED	MED-LOW
Indian Lake Local School Dist	00815506		8.34	0.05	3	1,516	LOW	MED-HIGH
SENECA		0.55						
Fostoria City School Dist	00831457		35.68	0.20	2	1,845	HIGH	MED-HIGH
Tiffin City School Dist	00831706		19.54	0.11	6	2,800	LOW	MED-LOW
Hopewell-Loudon Local SD	00831548		19.51	0.11	1	821	HIGH	MED-LOW
Seneca East Local School Dist	00831641		10.23	0.06	1	880	MED	MED-LOW
New Riegel Local School Dist	00831574		7.56	0.04	1	500	MED	MED-LOW
Old Fort Local School Dist	00831615		7.47	0.04	2	750	MED	MED-LOW
DARKE		0.53						
Greenville City School Dist	00797576		34.61	0.18	3	2,507	MED	MED-LOW
Versailles Exempted Village SD	00797758		16.26	0.09	3	1,305	MED	LOW
Ansonia Local School Dist	00797461		13.83	0.07	2	700	HIGH	MED-LOW
Mississinawa Valley Sch Dist	00797667		12.50	0.07	2	700	HIGH	MED-HIGH
Franklin-Monroe Local Sch Dist	00797540		11.86	0.06	2	625	HIGH	MED-HIGH
Arcanum Butler Local Sch Dist	00797502		7.70	0.04	4	1,125	LOW	MED-LOW
Tri-Village Local Sch Dist	00797708		3.24	0.02	1	827	LOW	MED-LOW
SHELBY		0.52						
Sidney City School Dist	00832061		35.99	0.19	6	3,350	LOW	MED-LOW
Anna Local School Dist	00831811		13.36	0.07	2	1,200	MED	LOW
Ft Loramie Local School Dist	00831940		11.75	0.06	2	793	MED	LOW
Hardin-Houston Local Sch Dist	00831976		10.97	0.06	1	860	MED	MED-LOW
Botkins Local School Dist	00831861		8.77	0.05	1	644	MED	LOW
Jackson Center Local Sch Dist	00832009		7.05	0.04	1	600	MED	MED-LOW
Russia Local School Dist	00832035		6.66	0.03	1	430	MED	LOW
Fairlawn Local School Dist	00831902		5.45	0.03	2	650	LOW	MED-LOW
ADAMS		0.51						
Adams Co Ohio Valley Sch Dist	00783343		68.84	0.35	7	3,800	HIGH	MED-HIGH
Eastern Local School Dist	00786046		24.82	0.13	4	1,350	HIGH	MED-HIGH
Manchester Local School Dist	05339375		6.34	0.03	2	856	LOW	MED-HIGH
ASHTABULA		0.51						
Ashtabula Area City Sch Dist	00784385		20.31	0.10	8	3,600	LOW	HIGH
Geneva Area City School Dist	00784696		19.86	0.10	5	2,415	LOW	MED-HIGH
Ashtabula Co Tech & Career SD	00784933		16.21	0.08	1	694	HIGH	
Buckeye Local School Dist	00784529		15.22	0.08	4	1,800	LOW	MED-HIGH
Pymatuning Valley Local SD	00784880		10.24	0.05	3	1,200	LOW	HIGH
Jefferson Area Local SD	00784828		8.39	0.04	4	1,651	LOW	MED-HIGH
Grand Valley Local School Dist	00784763		4.98	0.03	3	1,075	LOW	MED-HIGH
Conneaut Area City Sch Dist	00784608		4.78	0.02	4	1,604	LOW	MED-HIGH
CRAWFORD		0.50						
Galion City School Dist	00790255		45.18	0.23	4	1,817	HIGH	MED-HIGH
Wynford Local School Dist	00790334		15.49	0.08	2	1,200	MED	MED-HIGH
Bucyrus City School Dist	00790059		15.06	0.08	2	1,300	MED	MED-HIGH
Buckeye Central Local Sch Dist	00790011		11.66	0.06	3	650	HIGH	MED-LOW
Crestline Exempted Village SD	00790205		6.79	0.03	1	570	LOW	MED-HIGH
Colonel Crawford Local SD	00790140		5.82	0.03	3	920	LOW	MED-LOW
PIKE		0.50						
Pike Co Area JT Voc Sch Dist	00828137		40.99	0.20	1	500	HIGH	
Waverly City School Dist	00828034		20.49	0.10	4	1,825	LOW	MED-HIGH
Western Local School Dist	00828084		13.83	0.07	2	790	HIGH	HIGH
Scioto Valley Local Sch Dist	00827999		13.17	0.07	2	1,300	LOW	MED-HIGH
Eastern Local School Dist	00827951		11.52	0.06	3	901	MED	MED-HIGH
ASHLAND		0.49						
Ashland City School Dist	00784103		39.99	0.20	5	3,800	MED	MED-LOW
Loudonville-Perrysville SD	00784256		22.79	0.11	3	1,100	HIGH	MED-LOW
Mapleton Local School Dist	00784309		15.31	0.07	3	890	MED	MED-HIGH
Ashland Co-West Holmes JVSD	00784359		13.91	0.07	1	450	HIGH	
Hillsdale Local School Dist	00784218		7.99	0.04	3	850	LOW	MED-LOW

Ohio School Directory

DISTRICT BUYING POWER INDEX

COUNTIES RANKED BY PERCENTAGE OF STATE SPENDING

COUNTY / DISTRICT	PID	COUNTY % OF STATE	DISTRICT % OF COUNTY	DISTRICT % OF STATES	NUMBER OF SCHOOLS	ENROLL	EXP	POV
PICKAWAY		0.49						
Teays Valley Local School Dist	00827822		40.84	0.20	7	4,350	LOW	MED-LOW
Westfall Local School Dist	00827884		20.08	0.10	3	1,432	MED	MED-LOW
Circleville City School Dist	00827664		19.66	0.10	3	2,174	LOW	MED-HIGH
Logan Elm Local School Dist	00827755		19.42	0.10	6	1,880	LOW	MED-LOW
WASHINGTON		0.48						
Warren Local School Dist	00838857		34.84	0.17	4	2,022	MED	MED-LOW
Marietta City School Dist	00838730		16.43	0.08	6	2,580	LOW	MED-HIGH
Frontier Local School Dist	00838687		13.51	0.06	3	625	HIGH	MED-HIGH
Washington Co JT Voc Sch Dist	00838962		13.49	0.06	1	487	HIGH	
Ft Frye Local School Dist	00838625		10.05	0.05	4	1,031	LOW	MED-LOW
Belpre City School Dist	00838572		7.99	0.04	2	1,000	LOW	MED-HIGH
Wolf Creek Local School Dist	00838924		3.69	0.02	2	606	LOW	MED-LOW
KNOX		0.45						
Mt Vernon City School Dist	00813053		45.79	0.20	8	4,000	LOW	MED-LOW
Centerburg Local School Dist	00812918		18.65	0.08	2	1,088	MED	MED-LOW
Knox Co Voc School Dist	00813170		15.66	0.07	1	640	HIGH	
East Knox Local School Dist	00812970		7.53	0.03	2	1,100	LOW	MED-LOW
Fredericktown Local Sch Dist	00813015		6.67	0.03	3	1,197	LOW	MED-LOW
Danville Local School Dist	00812944		5.70	0.03	2	615	LOW	MED-HIGH
PUTNAM		0.45						
Ottawa-Glandorf Local Sch Dist	00829284		26.73	0.12	4	1,400	MED	MED-LOW
Pandora Gilboa Local Sch Dist	00829351		12.26	0.06	3	524	HIGH	LOW
Columbus Grove Local Sch Dist	00829088		11.48	0.05	2	879	MED	MED-LOW
Ottoville Local School Dist	00829325		10.12	0.05	2	430	HIGH	LOW
Continental Local School Dist	00829129		9.46	0.04	2	480	HIGH	MED-LOW
Kalida Local School Dist	00829181		8.67	0.04	2	605	MED	LOW
Jennings Local School Dist	00829155		8.37	0.04	1	400	HIGH	LOW
Leipsic Local School Dist	00829210		8.34	0.04	2	650	MED	MED-LOW
Miller City-New Cleveland SD	00829246		4.59	0.02	3	485	LOW	LOW
BROWN		0.44						
Western Brown Local Sch Dist	00786216		46.66	0.21	4	3,400	MED	MED-HIGH
Southern Hills Joint Voc SD	00786266		20.10	0.09	1	380	HIGH	
Ripley-Union-Lewis-Huntngtn SD	00786175		15.51	0.07	3	850	MED	MED-HIGH
Georgetown Exempted Village SD	00786137		13.49	0.06	2	1,100	MED	MED-HIGH
Fayetteville Perry Local SD	00786101		4.23	0.02	3	855	LOW	MED-LOW
FAYETTE		0.44						
Miami Trace Local School Dist	00799328		54.35	0.24	3	2,582	HIGH	MED-HIGH
Washington Court House City SD	00799457		45.65	0.20	4	2,200	HIGH	MED-HIGH
MADISON		0.43						
London City School Dist	00819564		30.97	0.13	3	2,103	MED	MED-LOW
Jonathan Alder Local Sch Dist	00819514		28.67	0.12	5	2,270	LOW	MED-LOW
Tolles Career & Tech Sch Dist	01417468		16.74	0.07	1	640	HIGH	
Madison Plains Local Sch Dist	00819629		13.50	0.06	4	1,173	LOW	MED-LOW
Jefferson Local School Dist	00819461		10.13	0.04	3	1,200	LOW	MED-LOW
PERRY		0.43						
Crooksville Exempted Vlg SD	00827418		41.33	0.18	3	1,100	HIGH	MED-HIGH
New Lexington School Dist	00827470		32.87	0.14	4	1,980	MED	MED-HIGH
Northern Local School Dist	00827535		20.23	0.09	5	2,251	LOW	MED-LOW
Southern Local School Dist	00827597		5.56	0.02	2	664	LOW	MED-HIGH
WILLIAMS		0.43						
Bryan City School Dist	00839643		25.62	0.11	2	2,200	LOW	MED-LOW
Millcreek-West Unity Local SD	00839784		18.69	0.08	1	520	HIGH	MED-LOW
North Central Local Sch Dist	00839863		17.14	0.07	1	600	HIGH	MED-LOW
Montpelier Exempted Village SD	00839825		15.43	0.07	1	1,100	MED	MED-LOW
Stryker Local School Dist	00839904		11.00	0.05	2	407	HIGH	MED-LOW
Edon Northwest Local Sch Dist	00839746		6.53	0.03	1	500	LOW	MED-LOW
Edgerton Local School Dist	00839708		5.59	0.02	2	599	LOW	MED-HIGH
GEAUGA		0.42						
Chardon Local School Dist	00804167		33.69	0.14	4	2,772	LOW	LOW
Kenston Local School Dist	00804234		23.94	0.10	4	2,858	LOW	LOW
West Geauga Local School Dist	00804387		16.85	0.07	4	1,874	LOW	LOW
Berkshire Local School Dist	00804052		11.05	0.05	3	1,200	LOW	MED-LOW
Cardinal Local School Dist	00804105		8.26	0.03	3	1,000	LOW	MED-LOW
Newbury Local School Dist	00804337		6.21	0.03	2	270	MED	MED-LOW
ATHENS		0.41						
Athens City School Dist	00785028		29.64	0.12	6	2,483	LOW	MED-HIGH
Nelsonville-York City Sch Dist	00785157		18.38	0.07	3	1,206	MED	MED-HIGH

DISTRICT BUYING POWER INDEX

Market Data Retrieval

DISTRICT BUYING POWER INDEX
COUNTIES RANKED BY PERCENTAGE OF STATE SPENDING

COUNTY / DISTRICT	PID	COUNTY % OF STATE	DISTRICT % OF COUNTY	DISTRICT % OF STATES	NUMBER OF SCHOOLS	ENROLL	EXP	POV
Alexander Local School Dist	00784971		16.13	0.07	2	1,495	LOW	MED-HIGH
Trimble Local School Dist	00785224		14.22	0.06	3	900	MED	HIGH
Tri-Co Joint Voc Sch Dist	00785262		11.83	0.05	1	450	HIGH	
Federal Hocking Local Sch Dist	00785107		9.80	0.04	3	1,000	LOW	MED-HIGH
AUGLAIZE		0.41						
Wapakoneta City School Dist	00785444		45.39	0.19	4	3,081	MED	MED-LOW
St Mary's City School Dist	00785365		18.86	0.08	4	1,996	LOW	MED-LOW
Minster Local School Dist	00785286		14.40	0.06	2	849	MED	LOW
New Bremen Local School Dist	00785315		8.35	0.03	2	760	LOW	LOW
Waynesfield-Goshen Local SD	00785523		7.09	0.03	2	500	MED	MED-LOW
New Knoxville Local Sch Dist	00785341		5.91	0.02	1	392	MED	MED-LOW
PREBLE		0.40						
Preble-Shawnee Local Sch Dist	00828955		25.58	0.10	3	1,430	MED	MED-LOW
Eaton Cmty School Dist	00828905		23.57	0.09	4	1,943	LOW	MED-LOW
Twin Valley Cmty Local SD	00829002		22.45	0.09	2	837	HIGH	MED-LOW
Tri-Co North School Dist	02199487		16.67	0.07	3	786	MED	MED-LOW
National Trail Local Sch Dist	00828838		11.73	0.05	3	1,100	LOW	MED-HIGH
CLINTON		0.39						
Wilmington City School Dist	00789024		45.38	0.18	5	3,000	MED	MED-HIGH
Clinton-Massie Local Sch Dist	00788939		26.11	0.10	3	1,800	LOW	MED-LOW
Blanchester Local School Dist	00788862		15.47	0.06	4	1,650	LOW	MED-LOW
East Clinton Local School Dist	00788989		13.04	0.05	4	1,300	LOW	MED-HIGH
OTTAWA		0.39						
Port Clinton City School Dist	00827171		25.89	0.10	4	1,700	LOW	MED-HIGH
Genoa Area Local School Dist	00827078		25.48	0.10	3	1,323	MED	MED-LOW
Danbury Local School Dist	00827042		17.69	0.07	1	543	HIGH	MED-LOW
Woodmore Local School Dist	00830776		15.43	0.06	2	974	MED	MED-LOW
Benton-Carroll-Salem Local SD	00826983		13.06	0.05	3	1,500	LOW	MED-LOW
Put-In-Bay Local School Dist	00827248		2.45	0.01	1	72	HIGH	LOW
VAN WERT		0.39						
Crestview Local School Dist	00837815		29.62	0.11	1	820	HIGH	MED-LOW
Van Wert City School Dist	00837932		28.52	0.11	4	2,084	LOW	MED-LOW
Vantage Career Center Sch Dist	01537800		26.89	0.10	1	480	HIGH	
Lincolnview Local School Dist	00837853		14.96	0.06	3	900	MED	MED-LOW
DEFIANCE		0.37						
Defiance City School Dist	00797916		46.65	0.17	3	2,400	MED	MED-LOW
Northeastern Local School Dist	00798025		22.59	0.08	4	1,082	MED	MED-LOW
Central Local School Dist	00797851		10.69	0.04	3	1,050	LOW	MED-LOW
Hicksville Exempted Village SD	00797992		10.27	0.04	2	1,000	LOW	MED-LOW
Ayersville Local School Dist	00797813		9.80	0.04	3	700	LOW	MED-LOW
GALLIA		0.35						
Gallia Co Local School Dist	00803917		46.54	0.16	8	2,200	MED	MED-HIGH
Gallia-Jackson-Vinton JVSD	00804038		34.57	0.12	1	500	HIGH	
Gallipolis City School Dist	00803852		18.89	0.07	5	2,052	LOW	MED-HIGH
HENRY		0.33						
Liberty Center Local Sch Dist	00810714		32.87	0.11	3	1,174	HIGH	MED-LOW
Napoleon Area City School Dist	00810740		31.33	0.10	3	1,700	MED	MED-LOW
Patrick Henry Local Sch Dist	00810817		26.32	0.09	3	855	HIGH	MED-LOW
Holgate Local School Dist	00810685		9.48	0.03	1	470	MED	MED-LOW
JACKSON		0.33						
Jackson City School Dist	00811897		44.81	0.15	5	2,450	MED	MED-HIGH
Oak Hill Union Local Sch Dist	00811988		33.53	0.11	2	1,220	HIGH	MED-HIGH
Wellston City School Dist	00812059		21.66	0.07	4	1,450	LOW	MED-HIGH
PAULDING		0.32						
Paulding Exempted Village SD	00827315		43.96	0.14	4	1,475	HIGH	MED-LOW
Wayne Trace Local School Dist	00827365		32.90	0.11	3	1,000	HIGH	MED-LOW
Antwerp Local School Dist	00827286		23.14	0.07	1	800	HIGH	MED-LOW
COSHOCTON		0.31						
Coshocton City School Dist	00789787		38.03	0.12	2	1,600	MED	MED-HIGH
Ridgewood Local School Dist	00789866		32.31	0.10	3	1,275	MED	MED-HIGH
River View Local School Dist	00789921		17.90	0.05	5	2,100	LOW	MED-HIGH
Coshocton Co Joint Voc SD	01831589		11.76	0.04	1	246	HIGH	
UNION		0.30						
Marysville Exempted Village SD	00837657		60.79	0.18	10	5,100	LOW	LOW
North Union Local School Dist	00837712		26.59	0.08	3	1,540	LOW	MED-LOW
Fairbanks Local School Dist	00837607		12.62	0.04	3	1,072	LOW	LOW

Ohio School Directory

DISTRICT BUYING POWER INDEX

COUNTIES RANKED BY PERCENTAGE OF STATE SPENDING

COUNTY / DISTRICT	PID	COUNTY % OF STATE	DISTRICT % OF COUNTY	DISTRICT % OF STATES	NUMBER OF SCHOOLS	ENROLL	EXP	POV
GUERNSEY		0.29						
East Guernsey Local Sch Dist	00805240		38.72	0.11	3	1,200	HIGH	MED-HIGH
Cambridge City School Dist	00805018		35.62	0.10	4	1,954	LOW	MED-HIGH
Rolling Hills Local Sch Dist	00805159		25.67	0.08	6	1,650	LOW	MED-HIGH
CHAMPAIGN		0.28						
Triad Local School Dist	00787442		31.76	0.09	3	830	HIGH	MED-LOW
Urbana City School Dist	00787492		25.57	0.07	3	2,000	LOW	MED-HIGH
Graham Local School Dist	00787351		22.95	0.06	3	1,836	LOW	MED-LOW
Mechanicsburg Exempted Vlg SD	00787416		14.88	0.04	2	900	LOW	MED-LOW
West Liberty-Salem Local SD	00787569		4.85	0.01	1	1,250	LOW	MED-LOW
HARDIN		0.28						
Kenton City School Dist	00810221		57.14	0.16	3	1,848	MED	MED-HIGH
Hardin Northern Local Sch Dist	00810192		13.44	0.04	2	405	HIGH	MED-LOW
ADA Exempted Village Sch Dist	00810166		11.33	0.03	1	890	LOW	MED-HIGH
Ridgemont Local School Dist	00810312		9.49	0.03	2	511	LOW	MED-LOW
Upper Scioto Valley Local SD	00810398		8.59	0.02	1	450	LOW	MED-HIGH
MONROE		0.24						
Switzerland of Ohio Local SD	00823711		100.00	0.24	9	2,300	HIGH	MED-HIGH
MORROW		0.23						
Mt Gilead Exempted Village SD	00826191		38.54	0.09	3	1,200	MED	MED-LOW
Highland Local School Dist	00826141		24.21	0.06	3	1,850	LOW	MED-LOW
Cardington-Lincoln Local SD	00826103		19.72	0.05	4	1,200	LOW	MED-LOW
Northmor Local School Dist	00826256		17.53	0.04	1	1,042	LOW	MED-HIGH
WYANDOT		0.22						
Upper Sandusky Exempted Vlg SD	00840642		38.08	0.08	5	1,600	LOW	MED-LOW
Carey Exempted Village SD	00840551		32.79	0.07	1	850	HIGH	MED-LOW
Mohawk Local School Dist	00840599		29.13	0.06	1	930	MED	MED-LOW
HOCKING		0.19						
Logan-Hocking Local Sch Dist	00811146		100.00	0.19	7	3,945	LOW	MED-HIGH
MEIGS		0.18						
Meigs Local School Dist	00822602		65.27	0.12	4	1,700	MED	HIGH
Southern Local School Dist	00822705		17.66	0.03	2	728	LOW	MED-HIGH
Eastern Local School Dist	00822559		17.07	0.03	3	820	LOW	MED-HIGH
CARROLL		0.17						
Carrollton Exempted Village SD	00787272		75.44	0.13	2	2,150	MED	MED-HIGH
Brown Local School Dist	00787246		24.56	0.04	3	630	MED	MED-HIGH
MORGAN		0.17						
Morgan Local School Dist	00826012		100.00	0.17	5	1,763	HIGH	MED-HIGH
HOLMES		0.12						
West Holmes Local School Dist	00811378		58.01	0.07	6	2,100	LOW	MED-HIGH
East Holmes Local School Dist	00811275		41.99	0.05	8	1,615	LOW	MED-LOW
NOBLE		0.12						
Noble Local School Dist	00826921		56.18	0.07	2	900	MED	MED-LOW
Caldwell Exempted Village SD	00826878		43.82	0.05	2	800	MED	MED-HIGH
HARRISON		0.11						
Harrison Hills City Sch Dist	00810544		64.55	0.07	3	1,600	LOW	MED-HIGH
Conotton Valley Union Local SD	00810491		35.45	0.04	2	402	HIGH	MED-LOW
VINTON		0.11						
Vinton Co Local School Dist	00838039		100.00	0.11	5	2,100	LOW	MED-HIGH

Ohio School Directory

NEW PUBLIC SCHOOLS AND KEY PERSONNEL

NEW SCHOOLS/NEW PRINCIPALS

SCHOOL	PRINCIPAL	GRADES	ENROLLMENT	COUNTY	PAGE
Clifton Area Neighborhd Sch	Zoller, James	PK-2	120	Hamilton	87
James N Gamble Montessori ES	Ridley, Melissa	PK-6	270	Hamilton	88

NEW PRINCIPALS

SCHOOL	PRINCIPAL	GRADES	ENROLLMENT	COUNTY	PAGE
Peebles Elem Sch	McFarland, Amanda	PK-6	586	Adams	6
West Union High Sch	Ruckel, Brian	7-12	540	Adams	6
Jefferson Middle Sch	Fruchey, Brian	6-8	229	Allen	8
Shawnee High Sch	Verroco, Mark	9-12	664	Allen	9
Ashland Co-W Holmes Career Ctr	Brindley, Rick	Voc	450	Ashland	11
Hillsdale High Sch	Baker, Davis	9-12	219	Ashland	11
Rock Creek Elem Sch	Candela, Steve	K-6	293	Ashtabula	13
East-West Elem Sch	Sycks, Jeanna	K-6	575	Athens	14
Belmont Career Center	Caldwell, Ryan	Voc	300	Belmont	18
Harrison Career Center	Bossell, Larry	Voc	108	Belmont	18
Fayetteville Elem Sch	Fiscus, Aric	K-5	378	Brown	19
Ripley-Union-Lewis-Huntngtn ES	Marshall, Emily	PK-4	273	Brown	20
Southern Hills Career Tech Ctr	Burrows, Christopher	Voc	380	Brown	20
Edgewood Middle Sch	Dallio, Jim	6-8	870	Butler	21
Elda Elem Sch	Hull, Adam	K-4	549	Butler	24
Endeavor Elem Sch	Brock, Theresa	3-6	717	Butler	22
Fairwood Elem Sch	Cremeans, Heather	PK-6	757	Butler	22
Hamilton HS-Freshman Campus	Weisbrod, Jessica	9-9	710	Butler	22
Madison Junior Senior High Sch	Huber, Andrew	7-12	646	Butler	23
Monroe Primary Sch	Niehaus, Gayle, Dr	PK-1	471	Butler	23
New Miami Middle High Sch	Brakhage, Kara	6-12	372	Butler	24
Shawnee Early Childhood Sch	Thomas, Kevin	K-2	567	Butler	22
Malvern Middle Sch	Babiczuk, Timothy	6-8	153	Carroll	25
Fulton Elem Sch	Howard, Deborah	K-6	351	Clark	28
Northwestern Jr Sr High Sch	Swafford, Lori	7-12	712	Clark	28
Possum Elem Sch	Jude, Joseph	K-6	460	Clark	27
Reid Sch	Phelps, Kyle	K-6	484	Clark	27
Snowhill Elem Sch	Berlean, Kellie	K-6	470	Clark	28
Amelia Elem Sch	Short, Shane	PK-5	777	Clermont	31
Charles L Seipelt Elem Sch	Carraher, Melissa	K-6	502	Clermont	31
Holly Hill Elem Sch	Parker, Erin	PK-5	392	Clermont	31
Milford Junior High Sch	Misty, Goetz	7-8	1,100	Clermont	31
Monroe Elem Sch	Kunz, Jamie	PK-5	620	Clermont	31
Pattison Elem Sch	Selm, Tiffany	K-6	534	Clermont	31
Summerside Elem Sch	Courtney, Lisa	PK-5	450	Clermont	31
Blanchester High Sch	McCarty, Pandy	9-12	254	Clinton	32
Blanchester Middle Sch	Briggs, Ryan	6-8	376	Clinton	32
Roy E Holmes Elem Sch	Tanner, Marilee	K-2	564	Clinton	33
Sabina Elem Sch	Willian, Matthew	PK-5	362	Clinton	33
Crestview High Sch	Nappi, Laura	9-12	380	Columbiana	34
Southern Local Jr Sr HS	Kiger, J	7-12	399	Columbiana	36
Conesville Elem Sch	Renner, Jarred	PK-6	323	Coshocton	37
Ridgewood Middle Sch	Raach, Bryan	4-7	377	Coshocton	37
Crestline Sch	Fourman, Kevin	PK-12	570	Crawford	38
Wynford Elem Sch	Ratliff, Nelle	PK-6	651	Crawford	39
Wynford High Sch	Miller, Julie	7-12	476	Crawford	39
Beachwood High Sch	Chase, Paul	9-12	645	Cuyahoga	40
Beachwood Middle Sch	Srithai, Tony	6-8	305	Cuyahoga	40
Bedford High Sch	Thompson, Christopher	9-12	1,052	Cuyahoga	41
Berea-Midpark High Sch	Smithberger, Mark, Dr	9-12	1,800	Cuyahoga	41
Bessie Kinsner Elem Sch	Diedrick, Steven	K-5	548	Cuyahoga	51
Brooklyn Sch	Cicco, Cristin	PK-7	710	Cuyahoga	41
Chagrin Falls Middle Sch	Discenza, Laila	7-8	301	Cuyahoga	42
Cleveland Sch of Arch & Design	Brown, Odell	9-12	320	Cuyahoga	43
Columbus Intermediate Sch	Golden, Virginia	4-6	376	Cuyahoga	41
Design Lab Early College HS	Scarcella, Christopher	9-12	265	Cuyahoga	43
Dike School of the Arts	Evans, Alisha	PK-8	359	Cuyahoga	43
Falls-Lennox Primary Sch	Williams, Lisa	1-3	702	Cuyahoga	48
Garfield Elem Sch	Bosley, Jacob	PK-8	554	Cuyahoga	43
Gates Mills Elem Sch	Ravida, Laurel	K-5	129	Cuyahoga	47
Independence Primary Sch	Ebert, TJ	PK-4	406	Cuyahoga	47
JFK-Pact Academy	Feagins, Marie	9-12	268	Cuyahoga	44
Lomond Elem Sch	Clark, George	PK-4	374	Cuyahoga	50
Luis Munoz Marin Elem Sch	Roman, Samuel	PK-8	527	Cuyahoga	44
Maple Heights High Sch	Parnes, Zelina	9-12	1,082	Cuyahoga	47

NEW PUBLIC SCHOOLS AND KEY PERSONNEL

Market Data Retrieval

School	Contact	Grades	Enrollment	County	
Milkovich Middle Sch	Bennett, Matthew	6-8	857	Cuyahoga	47
Monticello Middle Sch	Johnston, Jeffrey, Dr	6-8	600	Cuyahoga	42
Near West Intergenerationl Sch	Maimone, April	K-8	248	Cuyahoga	44
Olmsted Falls High Sch	Spagnola, Leo	9-12	1,265	Cuyahoga	48
Promise Academy	Adams, Lisa	9-12	231	Cuyahoga	44
Roosevelt Elem Sch	Aber, Allison	PK-5	290	Cuyahoga	47
Roxboro Middle Sch	Coleman, Rachel	6-8	582	Cuyahoga	42
Shaker Heights High Sch	Juli, Eric	9-12	1,640	Cuyahoga	50
Shaker Hts HS-the IC	Spurrier, Ann, Dr	9-12	80	Cuyahoga	50
Strongsville High Sch	Mueller, Joseph	9-12	1,963	Cuyahoga	51
Strongsville Middle Sch	Marino, Adam	6-8	1,279	Cuyahoga	51
Sunbeam Sch	Humphrey, Jessica	PK-8	448	Cuyahoga	45
Warner Girls Leadership Acad	Wilkins, Kristel	PK-8	458	Cuyahoga	45
Waverly Sch	Fountain, Sommer	PK-8	260	Cuyahoga	45
Whitney M Young Gifted Campus	Wheeler, Ivy	5-12	175	Cuyahoga	45
Ayersville Middle Sch	Jones, Kirk	5-8	236	Defiance	57
Defiance Middle Sch	Carr, Matthew	6-8	605	Defiance	57
Alum Creek Elem Sch	Brandy, Worth	PK-5	568	Delaware	59
Gen Rosecrans Elem Sch	Thoma, Kate	K-4	503	Delaware	58
Glen Oak Elem Sch	Peters, Stephen	PK-5	653	Delaware	59
Laura Woodward Elem Sch	Barr, Eric	PK-5	629	Delaware	58
Mills Elem Sch	Prieto, Marie	PK-6	360	Erie	61
Amanda-Clearcreek Elem Sch	Wills, Elizabeth	3-5	340	Fairfield	62
Amanda-Clearcreek Middle Sch	Cochran, Aimee	6-8	352	Fairfield	62
Amanda-Clearcreek Primary Sch	Marshall, Brooke	K-2	321	Fairfield	63
Rushville Middle Sch	Haughn, Tricia	5-8	595	Fairfield	63
Ann Simpson Davis Middle Sch	Perez, Ann, Dr	6-8	1,010	Franklin	69
Chapelfield Elem Sch	Bates, Thomas	K-5	436	Franklin	70
Dublin Jerome High Sch	Aurin, Michael	9-12	1,761	Franklin	69
East Franklin Elem Sch	DeCastro, Matthew	K-4	220	Franklin	73
Emerald Campus	Venne, Kristy	Voc	600	Franklin	70
Emerson Elementary	Poynter, Chris	1-5	228	Franklin	74
Fairmoor Elem Sch	Stockard, Maria	PK-5	366	Franklin	68
Finland Elem Sch	McDaniel, Brittney	K-4	454	Franklin	73
Galloway Ridge Interm Sch	Budimirovic, Brittany	5-6	767	Franklin	73
Goshen Lane Elem Sch	Graves, Daniel	K-5	539	Franklin	70
Groveport Madison MS Central	Brown, John	6-8	454	Franklin	71
Hamilton Intermediate Sch	Altiers, Kelly	4-6	747	Franklin	71
Hanby Elementary	McCaulla, Megan	1-5	253	Franklin	75
Hawthorne Elem Sch	Clinkscale, Ernest	K-5	733	Franklin	75
Hoffman Trails Elem Sch	Salyer, Katie	K-5	579	Franklin	72
Innovative Learning Hub	Vroom, Craig	Voc	500	Franklin	72
Kilbourne Middle Sch	Garris, Greg	6-8	490	Franklin	75
Linden Park Ecec	Childs, Rhonda	PK-PK	400	Franklin	68
Longfellow Elem Sch	Poynter, Chris	K-K	80	Franklin	75
Mary Emma Bailey Elem Sch	Ritter, Shawn	PK-5	631	Franklin	70
Norwich Elem Sch	Heitzman, Michael	K-5	535	Franklin	72
Phoenix Middle Sch	Flynn, Sean	7-8	166	Franklin	76
Pointview Elem Sch	Bennett, David	K-5	327	Franklin	75
Scottish Corners Elem Sch	Windham, Lauren	PK-5	652	Franklin	70
Summit Road STEM Elem Sch	Turner, Latasha	K-4	501	Franklin	73
Waggoner Rd Junior High Sch	Black, Twana, Dr	7-8	585	Franklin	73
Washington Elem Sch	Campana, Monica	K-5	399	Franklin	72
Whittier Elem Sch	Hoffman, Andrew	K-5	344	Franklin	75
Winchester Trail Elem Sch	Lallathin, Max	3-5	1,012	Franklin	66
Woodward Park Middle Sch	Bailey, Paul	6-8	928	Franklin	69
Worthington Academy	Flynn, Sean	9-12	30	Franklin	76
Washington Elem Sch	Cochrane, Kimberly	PK-5	476	Gallia	81
Cardinal High Sch	Perkins, Markiel	9-12	314	Geauga	81
Greeneview Middle Sch	Callewaert, Wendy	5-8	413	Greene	84
Xenia High Sch	Torrence, David	9-12	1,038	Greene	85
Brent Elem Sch	Baker, Meredith	K-2	188	Hamilton	89
Carson Sch	Thomas, Terrez	PK-6	650	Hamilton	87
Deer Park Jr Sr High Sch	Hartley, Shane	7-12	522	Hamilton	89
Fairview-Clifton German Sch	Sippel, Stephen	K-6	723	Hamilton	87
Gilbert A Dater High Sch	Salazar, Ana	7-12	1,271	Hamilton	87
James N Gamble Montessori HS	Porter, Taylor	7-12	480	Hamilton	88
Mariemont Junior High Sch	Polca, Rob	7-8	280	Hamilton	91
Monfort Heights Elem Sch	Randall, Kaitlyn	K-5	632	Hamilton	91
North College Hill High Sch	Sies, Timothy	9-12	393	Hamilton	91
Pleasant Run Middle Sch	Watkins, Brad	6-8	777	Hamilton	91
Princeton High Sch	Bollmer, Ron	9-12	1,558	Hamilton	92
Taylor Middle High Sch	Smiley, Mark	6-12	998	Hamilton	94
Winton Woods Elem Sch	Homan, Nelson	3-4	582	Hamilton	94
Cory-Rawson High Sch	Gaietto, Jodi	7-12	232	Hancock	97
Glenwood Middle Sch	Miller, Krista	6-8	556	Hancock	98

Ohio School Directory

NEW PUBLIC SCHOOLS AND KEY PERSONNEL

School	Contact	Grades	Enrollment	County	Page
Jacobs Primary Sch	Wohlgamuth, Kelly	K-3	259	Hancock	98
Liberty-Benton Middle Sch	Leatherman, Kyle	6-8	361	Hancock	98
Holgate Sch	Hughes, Brian	K-12	470	Henry	101
Liberty Center Elem Sch	Postl, Allison	K-4	353	Henry	101
Fairfield Local Middle Sch	Hackett, Stephen	5-8	307	Highland	102
Greenfield Middle Sch	Sexton, Ron	6-8	448	Highland	103
Rainsboro Elem Sch	Lyons, Maggie	PK-5	185	Highland	103
Chieftain Elem Sch	Rice, Andy	PK-4	387	Hocking	104
Logan High Sch	Hacker, Eli	9-12	1,105	Hocking	104
Union Furnace Elem Sch	Roberts-Schein, Yancy	PK-4	215	Hocking	104
New London Middle Sch	Yetter, Eric	6-8	181	Huron	106
Buckeye Local High Sch	Parsons, Lucas	9-12	419	Jefferson	108
Fredericktown High Sch	Garee, Brent	9-12	319	Knox	111
McKinley Elem Sch	Fischer, Doreen	PK-5	308	Lake	112
Melridge Elem Sch	Walker, Michelle	PK-5	303	Lake	114
North Elem Sch	Mayer, William	K-5	621	Lake	113
Parkside Elem Sch	Walker, Michelle	K-5	500	Lake	114
Wickliffe High Sch	Metsker, Shyla	9-12	432	Lake	114
Wickliffe Middle Sch	Rodman, Lori	5-8	415	Lake	114
Ironton Elem Sch	Rowe, Joe	PK-5	643	Lawrence	116
Ironton High Sch	Hairston, Jeff	9-12	369	Lawrence	116
Northridge High Sch	Bernowski, Amanda	9-12	365	Licking	119
Northridge Middle Sch	Grieger, Justin	6-8	288	Licking	120
Eastwood Elem Sch	Baker, Meisha	PK-2	241	Lorain	125
Langston Middle Sch	Hicks, Sheila	6-8	216	Lorain	125
Midview West Elem Sch	Hall, Beth	PK-4	540	Lorain	125
Palm Elem Sch	Winter, Carol, Dr	PK-5	293	Lorain	124
Stevan Dohanos Elem Sch	Deshuk, Marie	PK-5	315	Lorain	124
Vincent Elem Sch	Ryan, Lisa	K-4	611	Lorain	123
Anthony Wayne Jr High Sch	Contat, Brad	7-8	761	Lucas	127
Fallen Timbers Middle Sch	Bocian, James, Dr	5-6	659	Lucas	127
Highland Elem Sch	Swaggerty, Steve	K-5	702	Lucas	129
Holloway Elem Sch	Brown, Robb	K-5	408	Lucas	128
Monac Elem Sch	Wray, Carrie	K-6	506	Lucas	130
Northview High Sch	Pugh, Mark	9-12	1,348	Lucas	129
Jonathan Alder High Sch	Hayes, Clint	9-12	652	Madison	132
Jonathan Alder Junior High Sch	Malany, Ryan	7-8	387	Madison	132
Fitch High Sch	Kelty, Timothy	9-12	1,353	Mahoning	134
Robinwood Lane Elem Sch	Johnson, Billie	K-3	332	Mahoning	134
Youngstown Virtual Academy	Gurski, Rick	9-12	401	Mahoning	137
Elgin Elem Sch	Holsinger, Matt	PK-5	507	Marion	138
Pleasant High Sch	Ringer, Steven	9-12	367	Marion	138
Pleasant Middle Sch	Malcom, Michael	6-8	285	Marion	138
Buckeye High Sch	Flood, Dan	9-12	689	Medina	140
Buckeye Intermediate Sch	Davisson, Kelli	4-6	623	Medina	140
Buckeye Junior High Sch	Conley, Shannon	7-8	396	Medina	140
Edwards Middle Sch	Perry, Andrew	6-8	463	Medina	140
Willetts Middle Sch	Simon, Linda	6-8	654	Medina	140
Eastern Middle Sch	Bush, Shawn	5-8	340	Meigs	142
Fort Recovery Elem Mid Sch	Thobe, Kelli	PK-8	720	Mercer	144
Bethel Middle High Sch	Swope, Barret	6-12	741	Miami	145
Bethel Middle High Sch	Caudill, Duane	6-12	741	Miami	145
Covington High Sch	Meyer, Josh	9-12	228	Miami	145
Nevin Coppock Elem Sch	Gingerich, Galen	K-1	368	Miami	146
Beavertown Elem Sch	Friz, Carmella	PK-5	373	Montgomery	150
Brantwood Elem Sch	Monnin, Misha	K-4	428	Montgomery	151
C F Holliday Elem Sch	Glover, Dorian	1-5	550	Montgomery	153
Dunbar Early College HS	Henry, Sean	9-12	606	Montgomery	149
Edwin Smith Elem Sch	Elliott, Chrissy	PK-6	481	Montgomery	152
Harold Schnell Elem Sch	Dudley, Pamela	1-5	442	Montgomery	153
J E Prass Elem Sch	Paxson, Jennifer	K-5	425	Montgomery	150
John F Kennedy Elem Sch	Enix, Monica	PK-5	606	Montgomery	150
Ruskin Elem Sch	Ertsgaard, Bryan	PK-6	557	Montgomery	149
Stivers School for Arts	Griffith, Gerry	7-12	869	Montgomery	149
W O Cline Elem Sch	Barker, Katy	2-5	385	Montgomery	149
Morgan Junior High Sch	Bragg, Jeff	7-8	272	Morgan	155
Morgan South Elem Sch	Fox, Joel	PK-6	292	Morgan	155
Highland High Sch	Carpenter, Chad	9-12	550	Morrow	155
Northmor Sch	Gwirtz, Brendan	K-12	1,042	Morrow	156
Frazeysburg Elem Sch	Norris, Rebecca	K-6	307	Muskingum	157
Pike Elem Sch	Atkins, Leigh	K-2	118	Muskingum	156
West Muskingum High Sch	Smith, Kevin	9-12	385	Muskingum	157
Junction City Elem Sch	Cannon, Maggie	PK-5	360	Perry	161
Craddock Elem Sch	Menta, Kim	1-2	400	Portage	165
Crestwood Middle Sch	Kosek, Edward	6-8	391	Portage	165
Windham High Sch	Christopher, Justin	9-12	145	Portage	167

NEW PUBLIC SCHOOLS AND KEY PERSONNEL

Market Data Retrieval

School	Contact	Grades	Enrollment	County	Page
Eaton Middle Sch	Camp, Brian	6-8	479	Preble	168
Hollingsworth East Elem Sch	Woodin, Teresa	K-2	424	Preble	168
National Trail High Sch	Eyler, Michael	9-12	309	Preble	168
Twin Valley Middle High Sch	Flatter, Derek	7-12	288	Preble	169
Crestview Elem Sch	Gilbert, Chris	K-3	276	Richland	171
Crestview Middle Sch	Lemon, Chad	4-8	443	Richland	171
Lucas High Sch	Metcalf, Jim, Dr	8-12	199	Richland	172
Mansfield Middle Sch	Folson, Milton, Dr	7-8	467	Richland	172
Woodland Elem Sch	Brennan, Michael	K-3	184	Richland	173
Emerson Elem Sch	Klingshirn, Stephanie	K-4	340	Shelby	183
Hardin-Houston Local Sch	Judy, Jeff	K-12	860	Shelby	183
Northwood Elem Sch	Moore, Michael	K-5	453	Shelby	183
Sidney High Sch	Morrison, Denny	9-12	967	Shelby	183
Arts Academy at Summit	Bowling, Jeanie	K-8	295	Stark	184
Clearmount Elem Sch	Kandel, Gary	K-2	385	Stark	187
Dukes Digital Academy	Bush, Gary	6-12	401	Stark	186
East Canton High Sch	Hinton, Gary	9-12	286	Stark	188
Frazer Elem Sch	Downing, Jill	K-4	345	Stark	188
Marlington High Sch	Spondyl, Yianni	9-12	734	Stark	186
Middlebranch Elem Sch	Easterling, J	K-4	533	Stark	188
Tuslaw Middle Sch	Dinko, Richard	5-8	413	Stark	189
Barberton Preschool	Boulder, Rachel	PK-PK	401	Summit	192
Cuyahoga Falls High Sch	Vargyas, Kevin	9-12	1,496	Summit	192
Innes Cmty Learning Ctr	Kurzen, David	6-8	729	Summit	191
Lincoln Elem Sch	Vargyas, Kevin	K-5	492	Summit	192
Champion High Sch	Herrholtz, Tracy	9-12	389	Trumbull	197
Champion K-8 Elementery Sch	Nannicola, Alexandra	K-8	930	Trumbull	197
Champion K-8 Elementery Sch	Campbell, Heather	K-8	930	Trumbull	197
Jefferson PK-8 Sch	Boyer, Carrie	PK-8	748	Trumbull	200
Jefferson PK-8 Sch	Israel, Gary	PK-8	748	Trumbull	200
Lincoln PK-8 Sch	Burns, Dani	PK-8	1,194	Trumbull	200
Lincoln PK-8 Sch	Guthrie, Josh	PK-8	1,194	Trumbull	200
Tuscarawas Vly Interm Sch	Clements, Andrea	2-4	299	Tuscarawas	203
Vinton Co High Sch	Milliken, Jj	9-12	572	Vinton	206
Carlisle High Sch	Slamer, Dave	9-12	445	Warren	207
Franklin Junior High Sch	Burchfield, Tammy	7-8	487	Warren	207
Harlan-Butlerville Prim Sch	Miles, Jamie	1-2	272	Warren	208
Kings Junior High Sch	Dunn, Eric	7-8	650	Warren	207
Mason Intermediate Sch	Messer, Eric	5-6	1,648	Warren	208
Pennyroyal Elem Sch	Ward, Jeremy	1-6	264	Warren	207
Springboro Intermediate Sch	Coulter, Brooke	6-6	494	Warren	208
Belpre Elem Sch	Keeling, Lauren	K-6	555	Washington	209
Belpre High Sch	Pepper, Samuel	7-12	405	Washington	209
Washington Elem Sch	McIntire, Alicia	K-5	320	Washington	210
Dalton Local Elem Middle Sch	Watkins, Steven	K-8	620	Wayne	212
Edgerton Elem Sch	Grieser, Brett	K-6	293	Williams	214
Crim Elem Sch	Kellough, Zeb	K-5	484	Wood	216
Carey Exempted Village Sch	Elchert, Tammy, Dr	PK-12	850	Wyandot	219

NEW SUPERINTENDENTS

DISTRICT	SUPERINTENDENT	GRADES	ENROLLMENT	COUNTY	PAGE
Delphos City School Dist	Westrick, Douglas	K-12	1,050	Allen	8
Pymatuning Valley Local SD	Edison, Chris	PK-12	1,200	Ashtabula	13
Federal Hocking Local Sch Dist	Hanning, David	PK-12	1,000	Athens	14
Bridgeport School Dist	Ripley, Brent	PK-12	820	Belmont	18
Fayetteville Perry Local SD	Carlier, Tim	PK-12	855	Brown	19
Georgetown Exempted Village SD	Winterod, Brad	PK-12	1,100	Brown	19
Middletown City School Dist	Styles, Marlon	K-12	6,561	Butler	23
Graham Local School Dist	Curtis, Matt	PK-12	1,836	Champaign	25
New Richmond Exempted Vlg SD	Miller, Tracey	PK-12	2,400	Clermont	31
Salem City School Dist	Kirkland, Sean	K-12	2,100	Columbiana	35
Bucyrus City School Dist	Chrispin, Matthew	PK-12	1,300	Crawford	38
Crestline Exempted Village SD	Henderson, Matthew	PK-12	570	Crawford	38
Berea City School Dist	Wheeler, Tracy	PK-12	5,817	Cuyahoga	41
Cleveland Hts-Univ Hts City SD	Kirby, Elizabeth, Dr	PK-12	5,200	Cuyahoga	42
East Cleveland City Sch Dist	Pettiegrew, Henry, Dr	PK-12	2,300	Cuyahoga	45
Garfield Heights City SD	Hanke, Chris	PK-12	3,721	Cuyahoga	46
Shaker Heights City Sch Dist	Glasner, David, Dr	PK-12	5,180	Cuyahoga	50
Defiance City School Dist	Morton, Robert	K-12	2,400	Defiance	57
Liberty Union-Thurstn Sch Dist	Johnson, Mike	K-12	1,350	Fairfield	64
Fayette Local Sch Dist	Belcher, Angie	PK-12	370	Fulton	79
Wauseon Exempted Village SD	Armstrong, Troy	K-12	1,770	Fulton	79
Cardinal Local School Dist	Kermavner, Bill	K-12	1,000	Geauga	81
Lockland School Dist	Longworth, Bob	PK-12	550	Hamilton	90

Ohio School Directory

NEW PUBLIC SCHOOLS AND KEY PERSONNEL

District	Superintendent	Grades	Enrollment	County	Code
Wyoming City School Dist	Weber, Tim	K-12	1,950	Hamilton	94
Cory-Rawson Local School Dist	Huffman, Heath	PK-12	550	Hancock	97
Upper Scioto Valley Local SD	Hurley, Craig	K-12	450	Hardin	100
Greenfield Exempted Village SD	Gray, Quincey	PK-12	2,250	Highland	103
Sylvania City School Dist	Spurgeon, Jane	K-12	7,704	Lucas	128
Washington Local School Dist	Anstadt, Kadee	K-12	7,042	Lucas	130
Austintown Local School Dist	Cappozzello, David	K-12	4,567	Mahoning	133
Ft Recovery Local School Dist	Brownlae, Larry	PK-12	920	Mercer	144
Bethel Local School Dist	Firks, Justin	K-12	1,400	Miami	145
Switzerland of Ohio Local SD	Caldwell, Bob	PK-12	2,300	Monroe	147
Huber Heights City School Dist	Basora, Mario	PK-12	6,100	Montgomery	150
Jefferson Twp Local Sch Dist	Mitchell, C	PK-12	345	Montgomery	150
Trotwood-Madison City SD	Howard, Marlon	PK-12	2,300	Montgomery	152
Windham Exempted Vlg Sch Dist	Curtis, Aireane	PK-12	600	Portage	167
Twin Valley Cmty Local SD	Cottingim, Scott	K-12	837	Preble	169
Madison Local School Dist	Thomas, John	PK-12	2,956	Richland	172
Mansfield City Schools	Jefferson, Stan	PK-12	3,350	Richland	172
Hardin-Houston Local Sch Dist	Maier, Ryan	K-12	860	Shelby	182
Canton City School Dist	Graham, Jeffery, Dr	PK-12	9,500	Stark	184
Northwest Local School Dist	Lambes, Dennis	K-12	1,783	Stark	187
Brookfield Local School Dist	Gibson, Toby	K-12	900	Trumbull	197
Champion Local School Dist	Grabowski, John	PK-12	1,525	Trumbull	197
Girard City School Dist	O'Hara, Bryan	K-12	1,699	Trumbull	197
Lakeview Local School Dist	Taylor, Jo	K-12	1,732	Trumbull	198
Fairbanks Local School Dist	Schirg, Adham	PK-12	1,072	Union	204
Belpre City School Dist	Greenley, Jeffery	K-12	1,000	Washington	209
Mohawk Local School Dist	Burke, Mark	PK-12	930	Wyandot	219

Ohio School Directory

OHIO

Ohio Department of Education PID: 00783331 877/644-6338
25 S Front St, Columbus 43215 Fax 614/387-0964

Schools: 236

Paolo DeMaria 1	Dr David Bowlin 5
Dr John Richard 8,15,69,79,294	Jeremy Marks 11
Dan Minnich 16,71	Leah Amstutz 27
Dr Wendy Grove 34	David Brauer 57,271
Donna Villareal 57	Dr Kim Monachino 58,81
Laura Kohler 67	Pamela King 68
Dr Heather Boughton 69,70,294	Shaun Yoder 69,298
Buddy Harris 285	

STATE-OPERATED SCHOOLS

State Schs..Principal	Grd	Prgm	Enr/#Cls	SN	
A Plus Arts Acad-Fair Campus 1395 Fair Ave, Columbus 43205 Randy Printup	K-6	T	360 10		614/725-1305 Fax 614/725-2305
A Plus Arts Acad-Maybury 2633 Maybury Rd, Columbus 43232 Renene Craft	K-6		240 9		614/626-2250 Fax 614/626-2258
A Plus Arts Acad-Napoleon 270 S Napoleon Ave, Columbus 43213 J Rishell	7-8		100		614/338-0767 Fax 614/338-0787
A Plus Children's Academy 114 Obetz Rd, Columbus 43207 Cathy Blankenship	K-6	T	130		614/491-8502
Academy for Urban Scholars 3405 Market St, Youngstown 44507 Sabrina Jones	9-12	T	210	98%	330/744-9070 Fax 330/746-9636
Academy for Urban Scholars HS 1808 E Broad St, Columbus 43203 Roger Fox	9-12	T	331	95%	614/545-9890 Fax 614/545-9889
Academy of Arts & Science 201 W Erie Ave Uppr, Lorain 44052 James Sinclair	K-2	T	266		440/244-0156 Fax 440/244-3935
Achieve Career Prep Academy [200] 3891 Martha Ave, Toledo 43612 Julieta Flowers	8-12	T	158 13		419/243-8559 Fax 419/243-8583
Akron Preparatory Sch [238] 1200 E Market St # 3360, Akron 44316 Ashley Miles	K-8		224		330/247-6232 Fax 330/299-7173
Beacon Academy 1379 Garfield Ave SW, Canton 44706 Karla Robinson	K-8		183		330/941-5848
Bennett Venture Academy [203] 5130 Bennett Rd, Toledo 43612 Nicolette Whitson	K-8	T	688 25		419/269-2247 Fax 419/269-2257
Bio-Med Science Academy 4209 State Route 44, Rootstown 44272 Stephanie Lammlein	9-9		100	13%	330/325-6186 Fax 330/325-5982
Blue Ash Elem Charter Sch 10149 Kenwood Rd, Cincinnati 45242 Mary Schlok	PK-K		50		513/891-1723 Fax 513/898-8984
Bridge Gate Cmty Sch 4060 Sullivant Ave, Columbus 43228 Deshannon Butler	7-12		47		614/501-3820
Bridges Cmty Academy 190 Saint Francis Ave Unit Ofc, Tiffin 44883 Catherine Smith	K-12	T	145 10	75%	419/455-9295 Fax 419/455-9296
Broadway Academy [238] 3398 E 55th St, Cleveland 44127 Sheree Dillians	K-5	T	176 10		216/271-7747 Fax 216/271-6438
Brookwood Academy 2685 E Livingston Ave, Columbus 43209 Ellen Wristen	Spec	T	97	96%	614/231-1199
Buckeye Preparatory Academy [238] 1414 Gault St, Columbus 43205 David Mounts	K-7	T	184		614/300-3685 Fax 614/252-7083
Canton Harbor High Sch 1731 Grace Ave NE, Canton 44705 Steven Nichols	10-12	T	132 5		330/452-8414 Fax 330/452-8452
Capital High Sch 640 Harrisburg Pike, Columbus 43223 Monica Scott	9-12	T	150		614/228-2854 Fax 614/228-4679
Castle High Sch 3950 Prospect Ave E, Cleveland 44115 Jaeda Dancy	9-12	AGT	192		216/583-5210 Fax 216/443-9017
Central Academy of Ohio [195] 2727 Kenwood Blvd, Toledo 43606 Jamie Johnson	K-6	T	122		419/205-9800 Fax 419/754-2608
Central High Sch 840 W State St, Columbus 43222 Thomas Rogan	8-12		401		614/362-7530
Cesar Chavez College Prep Sch [243] 2400 Mock Rd, Columbus 43219 Dr Linda Gibson	K-5	T	337		614/294-3020 Fax 614/299-3680
Chapelside Cleveland Academy [238] 3845 E 131st St, Cleveland 44120 Anna Turner	K-6	T	259 19		216/283-6589 Fax 216/283-3087
Cincinnati College Prep Acad 1425 Linn St, Cincinnati 45214 Lee Vincent \ Keith Hickman	K-12	T	650 31		513/684-0777 Fax 513/684-8888
Citizens Leadership Acad East [239] 12523 Woodside Ave, Cleveland 44108 Ricardo Franklin	6-7		150		216/352-5900
Citizens Leadership Academy [239] 9711 Lamont Ave, Cleveland 44106 Sydney Gruhin	6-8		251		216/229-8185 Fax 216/229-8516
City Day Community Sch 320 S Main St, Dayton 45402 Paula Leone	K-8	T	160 12	85%	937/223-8130 Fax 937/223-8136
Clark Preparatory Academy 637 South Center St, Springfield 45506 Stefanie Page	K-7	T	88		937/504-1175
Cleveland Arts & Soc Sci Acad [238] 10701 Shaker Blvd, Cleveland 44104 A Cory McDaniel	K-8	T	300		216/229-3000 Fax 216/229-3182
Cleveland Preparatory Academy [238] 4850 Pearl Rd, Cleveland 44109 Markiel Perkins	K-12		128		216/741-2991
Cliff Park High Sch 821 N Limestone St, Springfield 45503 Jeff Waechter	9-12	T	185		937/342-3006
Colonial Preparatory Academy 2199 5th St SW, Akron 44314 Leeanna Simmons	K-8	T	221		330/752-2792 Fax 330/745-9748
Columbus Arts & Tech Academy [238] 2255 Kimberly Pkwy E, Columbus 43232 Derrick Shelton	K-12	T	586 22		614/577-0900 Fax 614/866-0300
Columbus Bilingual Acad-North [238] 2100 Morse Rd, Columbus 43229 Courtney Williams	K-7	T	298		614/547-4500 Fax 614/547-4501
Columbus Collegiate Acad-Dana [249] 300 Dana Ave, Columbus 43223 Jenna Cook	6-8	T	249		614/545-9570
Columbus Collegiate Acad-Main [249] 1469 E Main St, Columbus 43205 Melissa Barrett	6-8	T	237		614/299-5284 Fax 614/299-5303
Columbus Humanities Arts & Tech [238] 1333 Morse Rd, Columbus 43229 Erin Johnson	K-8	T	573 17	89%	614/261-1200 Fax 614/261-1201
Columbus Prep & Fitness Acad [247] 1258 Demorest Rd, Columbus 43204 Jeff Luelleman	K-8	T	437 6	86%	614/318-0606 Fax 614/491-8669
Columbus Preparatory Academy [238] 3330 Chippewa St, Columbus 43204 Erin Johnson	K-11	T	745 30	45%	614/275-3600 Fax 614/275-3601

OH–1

School	Grades		Enroll	Phone
© Cornerstone Academy [238] 6015 E Walnut St, Westerville 43081 Luis Leon	K-8	T	670 6	53% 614/775-0615 Fax 614/775-0633
Ⓐ Coshocton Opportunity Sch © 1205 Cambridge Rd, Coshocton 43812 Tom Hilgenberg	10-12		15	740/622-3600 Fax 740/622-6860
© Dayton Leadership Academy 1416 W Riverview Ave, Dayton 45402 Tess Asinjo	K-8	T	448 55	937/567-9426 Fax 937/567-9446
© Dayton Liberty Academy 1416 W Riverview Ave, Dayton 45402 Tess Mitchnr-Asinjo	K-8		658	937/567-9426 Fax 937/567-9446
Dayton Regional STEM Sch 1724 Woodman Dr, Dayton 45420 Andrew Sears \ Jessica Short	6-12		500	20% 937/256-3777 Fax 937/256-7655
© Dayton Smart Bilingual Academy 601 S Keowee St, Dayton 45410 Cindy Koth	K-6		100	937/222-2812 Fax 937/222-2594
© Deca Prep 200 Homewood Ave, Dayton 45405 Aileen Ernst	K-6	T	550	78% 937/610-0110
© Discovery Academy 2740 W Central Ave, Toledo 43606 Noah Campbell	K-6	T	340	419/214-3266 Fax 419/214-3269
© E Prep & Village Prep-Willard [239] 9401 Willard Ave, Cleveland 44102 Jasmine Williams	K-8		300	93% 216/586-3892 Fax 216/651-1959
© E Prep & Vlg Prep Cliffs Sch [239] 1415 E 36th St, Cleveland 44114 Dr Randy Yates	K-8		747	216/456-2070 Fax 216/361-9717
© E Prep Cliffs Middle Campus 1417 E 36th St, Cleveland 44114 Dr Randy Yates	K-8		700	216/456-2070 Fax 216/361-9717
© E Prep Woodland Hills Sch [239] 9201 Crane Ave, Cleveland 44105 Lynesha Richardson	5-8	T	287	216/298-1164 Fax 216/341-0106
© East Academy [238] 15720 Kipling Ave, Cleveland 44110 Nehemiah Thomas	K-8		318 16	216/383-1214 Fax 216/383-1422
© East Bridge Acad of Excellence 2323 Lake Club Dr, Columbus 43232 Jul'Yanna Collier	K-8		38	614/501-3822
© Eastland Performance Academy [247] 2220 S Hamilton Rd, Columbus 43232 Joan Pammer \ Norbert Tate	K-8		359	614/318-0602 Fax 614/577-1933
© Eastland Preparatory Academy [238] 2741 S Hamilton Rd, Columbus 43232 Shannon Jones	K-8		275	614/547-4493 Fax 614/547-4494
© Eastside Arts Academy [242] 6700 Lansing Ave, Cleveland 44105 Katherine Rybak	K-6	T	135	216/441-9830 Fax 216/441-9834
© Educational Acad-Boys & Girls [243] 35 Midland Ave, Columbus 43223 Jameica Shoultz	K-5		95	614/351-1774 Fax 614/351-1968
© Euclid Preparatory Sch [238] 23001 Euclid Ave, Euclid 44117 Darlene Montague	K-8		257	216/750-2070 Fax 216/675-6176
© Flex High Sch 115 S Gift St, Columbus 43215 Jason Morton	9-12		238	614/610-9749
© Focus Lrng Acad-E Columbus [244] 4480 Refugee Rd, Columbus 43232 Jason Morton	9-12	T	168 6	72% 614/269-0150 Fax 614/269-0151
© Focus Lrng Acad-W Columbus [244] 190 Southwood Ave, Columbus 43207 Kerry Hill	9-12	T	264 7	90% 614/545-2000 Fax 614/545-1995
© Focus North High Sch [244] 4807 Evanswood Dr Ste 100, Columbus 43229 Kelly Straight	9-12	T	177	89% 614/310-0430 Fax 614/310-0469
© Foundation Academy [238] 1050 Wyandotte Ave, Mansfield 44906 Mitzi Kimani	K-8	T	404	419/526-9540 Fax 419/526-9542
© Foxfire Schools 2805 Pinkerton Ln, Zanesville 43701 Jason Lee	9-12	AT	229 12	740/453-4509 Fax 740/455-4084
© Franklinton Preparatory Acad 40 Chicago Ave, Columbus 43222 Martin Griffith	9-12	T	194	614/636-3721
© Frederick Douglass High Sch 3167 Fulton Rd Ste 209, Cleveland 44109 Amy Harrington	9-12		140	216/273-3033
© Garfield Academy 1379 Garfield Ave SW, Canton 44706 Brian Hairston	K-8		217 13	330/454-3128 Fax 330/454-3145
© Gateway Academy of Ohio 2323 Lake Club Dr, Columbus 43232 Juliana Collier	K-8	T	51	614/856-1149 Fax 614/856-7966
Ⓐ Geo Voinovich Reclamation Acad [135] © 3167 Fulton Rd Ste 200, Cleveland 44109 Ralph Tucker	9-12	T	77	216/273-3033
© Global Ambassadors Language CS 13442 Lorain Ave, Cleveland 44111 Dr Michael Salwiesz	K-12		401	90% 216/315-7942
© Global Impact STEM Academy 700 S Limestone St, Springfield 45505 Joshua Jennings	6-12		401	33% 937/328-6600 Fax 937/328-6655
© Goal Digital Academy 890 W 4th St Ste 400, Mansfield 44906 Cheri Nolting	K-12	T	250	419/521-9008 Fax 419/529-2976
© Greater Ohio Virtual Sch 1879 Deerfield Rd, Lebanon 45036 Brian Barot	7-12	T	700	513/695-2977 Fax 513/695-2588
© Greater Summit County ELC 1651 Massillon Rd, Akron 44312 Danny Reiman	K-4		145	234/718-2626 Fax 234/718-2628
© Green Inspiration Academy 4265 Northfield Rd, Cleveland 44128 Leon Rallings	K-8	T	256	94% 216/378-9573 Fax 216/378-9437
© Hardin Cmty Sch 400 Decatur St, Kenton 43326 Wade Melton	6-12	T	43	84% 419/673-3210
© Harvard Ave Performance Acad [247] 12000 Harvard Ave, Cleveland 44105 Lachelle Dixon-Harris	K-8	T	336	216/283-5100
Ⓐ Hillcrest Academy © 246 Bonham Rd, Cincinnati 45215 Larry Ballew	7-12		100 14	513/552-1200 Fax 513/772-0159
© Hope Academy Northwest [238] © 1441 W 116th St, Cleveland 44102 Nicole Dykstra	K-8	T	221 16	216/226-6800 Fax 216/226-6805
© Hope Academy-Brown St Campus 1035 Clay St, Akron 44301 Margaret Sternefeld	K-8		310 10	330/785-0180 Fax 330/785-0681
© Hope Academy-Northcoast [238] 4310 E 71st St, Cleveland 44105 Dr Martin Ngom	K-8	T	310	216/429-0232 Fax 216/429-0249
© Hope Academy-West 12913 Bennington Ave, Cleveland 44135 Michael Jaissle	K-8		220	216/251-5450 Fax 216/251-6410
© Horizon Sci Acad-Cincinnati [153] 1055 Laidlaw Ave, Cincinnati 45237 Ufak Orhan	K-8	T	237 10	99% 513/242-0099 Fax 513/242-2467

1	Superintendent	8	Curric/Instruct K-12	19	Chief Financial Officer	29	Family/Consumer Science
2	Bus/Finance/Purchasing	9	Curric/Instruct Elem	20	Art K-12	30	Adult Education
3	Buildings And Grounds	10	Curric/Instruct Sec	21	Art Elem	31	Career/Sch-to-Work K-12
4	Food Service	11	Federal Program	22	Art Sec	32	Career/Sch-to-Work Elem
5	Transportation	12	Title I	23	Music K-12	33	Career/Sch-to-Work Sec
6	Athletic	13	Title V	24	Music Elem	34	Early Childhood Ed
7	Health Services	14	Asst Superintendent	25	Music Sec	35	Health/Phys Education
		15	Instructional Media Svcs	26	Business Education	36	Guidance Services K-12
		16	Chief Operations Officer	27	Career & Tech Ed	37	Guidance Services Elem
		17	Chief Academic Officer	28	Technology Education	38	Guidance Services Sec

39	Social Studies K-12	49	English/Lang Arts Elem	59	Special Education Elem	69	Academic Assessment
40	Social Studies Elem	50	English/Lang Arts Sec	60	Special Education Sec	70	Research/Development
41	Social Studies Sec	51	Reading K-12	61	Foreign/World Lang K-12	71	Public Information
42	Science K-12	52	Reading Elem	62	Foreign/World Lang Elem	72	Summer School
43	Science Elem	53	Reading Sec	63	Foreign/World Lang Sec	73	Instructional Tech
44	Science Sec	54	Remedial Reading K-12	64	Religious Education K-12	74	Inservice Training
45	Math K-12	55	Remedial Reading Elem	65	Religious Education Elem	75	Marketing/Distributive
46	Math Elem	56	Remedial Reading Sec	66	Religious Education Sec	76	Info Systems
47	Math Sec	57	Bilingual/ELL	67	School Board President	77	Psychological Assess
48	English/Lang Arts K-12	58	Special Education K-12	68	Teacher Personnel	78	Affirmative Action

Ohio School Directory

School	Grades	Type	Enrollment	%	Phone
Horizon Sci Acad-Cleveland HS [153] 6000 S Marginal Rd, Cleveland 44103 Mehmet Gurbuz	9-12	T	427 46	76%	216/432-3660 Fax 216/432-3670
Horizon Sci Acad-Columbus ES [153] 2835 Morse Rd, Columbus 43231 Jessica Shoaf	2-5	T	500		614/475-4585 Fax 614/475-4587
Horizon Sci Acad-Columbus MS [153] 2350 Morse Rd, Columbus 43229 Hasan Akkaya	6-8	T	513 19	94%	614/428-6564 Fax 614/428-6574
Horizon Sci Acad-Columbus Prim [153] 2899 Morse Rd, Columbus 43231 Crystal Seeley	K-1		463		614/532-3311 Fax 614/532-3310
Horizon Sci Acad-Dayton Downtn [153] 121 S Monmouth St, Dayton 45403 Mustafa Ada	K-8	T	215		937/281-1980 Fax 937/281-1979
Horizon Sci Acad-Dayton ES [153] 4751 Sue Ann Blvd, Dayton 45415 Kellie Berlean	K-5	T	173 16		937/277-1177 Fax 937/277-3090
Horizon Sci Acad-Dayton HS [153] 250 Shoup Mill Rd, Dayton 45415 Akan Bagcioglu	6-12	T	337 14	92%	937/281-1480
Horizon Sci Acad-Sprngfld [153] 630 S Reynolds Rd, Toledo 43615 Erin Schreiner	K-8	T	372		419/535-0524 Fax 419/535-0525
Horizon Sci Acad-Youngstwn [153] 3403 Southern Blvd, Youngstown 44507 Ferhat Kapki	K-8	T	405		330/782-3003 Fax 330/782-3356
Horizon Sci Academy-Lorain [153] 760 Tower Blvd, Lorain 44052 Fatih Sumer	K-12	T	678	88%	440/282-4277 Fax 440/282-4278
Horizon Sci Academy-Toledo [153] 2600 W Sylvania Ave Ste 109, Toledo 43613 Aydin Kara	K-12	T	533		419/474-3350 Fax 419/474-3351
Ilead Spring Meadows 1615 Timber Wolf Dr, Holland 43528 Sarah Hawley	K-8		213	63%	419/491-7423
Imac Academy 215 N Trimble Rd, Mansfield 44906 David Shirley	9-12		38 4		419/525-0105 Fax 419/525-0106
Imagine Academy at Sullivant [245] 3435 Sullivant Ave, Columbus 43204 Jamie Lama	K-6	T	335		614/308-5991 Fax 614/368-5622
Imagine Akron Kinder Academy [245] 1585 Frederick Blvd, Akron 44320 Walter Thompson	K-K	T	52		330/379-1034 Fax 330/379-0489
Imagine Bella Acad Excellence [245] 19114 Bella Dr, Cleveland 44119 Arun Dutt	K-6	T	298		216/481-1500 Fax 216/481-4515
Imagine Clay Ave Cmty ES [245] 1030 Clay Ave, Toledo 43608 Sarah Bennett \ Jodi Johns	K-4	T	405		419/727-9900 Fax 419/727-9902
Imagine Columbus Primary Acad [245] 4656 Heaton Rd, Columbus 43229 Selethia Benn	K-5	T	235		614/433-7510 Fax 614/433-7515
Imagine Groveport Cmty ES [245] 4485 S Hamilton Rd, Groveport 43125 Dair Foster	K-8	T	500		614/574-4100 Fax 614/574-4107
Imagine Groveport Prep Sch [245] 4085 Venture Pl, Groveport 43125 Jo Lowther	5-8		500		614/574-0037 Fax 614/574-4107
Imagine Harrisburg PK Cmty Sch [245] 680 Harrisburg Pike, Columbus 43223 Dreama Carroll	K-6	T	221		614/223-1510 Fax 614/223-1584
Imagine Hill Ave Environ Sch [245] 6145 Hill Ave, Toledo 43615 Daphne Williams	K-5	T	126		419/867-8167 Fax 419/867-8091
Imagine Klepinger Rd Cmty Sch [245] 3650 Klepinger Rd, Dayton 45416 Melissa McManaway	3-8	T	430		937/610-1710 Fax 937/610-0052
Imagine Madison Ave Sch-Arts [245] 1511 Madison Ave, Toledo 43604 Lindsey Day	K-5	T	526		419/259-4000 Fax 419/243-1513
Imagine Woodbury Academy [245] 100 E Woodbury Dr, Dayton 45415 Melissa McManaway	K-2	T	185		937/610-1710 Fax 937/985-9504
Indian River Sch 2775 Indian River Rd SW, Massillon 44646	7-12	V	150 25	97%	330/837-4211 Fax 330/832-6318
Invictus High Sch 3122 Euclid Ave, Cleveland 44115 Dean Manke	9-12	T	423	40%	216/539-7200 Fax 216/361-3090
King Academy Cmty Sch 224 W Liberty St, Cincinnati 45202 Andrea Martinez	K-8	T	120 7		513/421-7519 Fax 513/421-5768
KIPP Columbus Sch [246] 2900 Inspire Dr, Columbus 43224 Danielle Thompson \ Ashley Ferguson \ Alexandros Thanos	PK-12	T	1,400		614/263-6137 Fax 614/263-6207
L Hollingworth School for Tag 653 Miami St, Toledo 43605 Terrence Franklin	K-8	T	342		419/705-3411 Fax 419/720-4923
Lake Erie International HS 11650 Detroit Ave, Cleveland 44102 Larry Burt	9-12	T	248		216/539-7229 Fax 216/651-6174
Lake Erie Preparatory Sch [238] 14405 Saint Clair Ave, Cleveland 44110 Denecia Dillard	K-8		238		216/453-4556 Fax 216/649-0774
Lakeshore Intergenerationl Sch 18025 Marcella Rd, Cleveland 44119 Robin Bartley	K-6	T	217		216/586-3872 Fax 216/486-3724
Liberty High Sch 140 N Keowee St Ste E, Dayton 45402 Sean Fadden	9-12		181		937/701-7945
Life Skills Center of Dayton 1721 N Main St, Dayton 45405 Lanicka Masey	9-12	AT	139 6		937/274-2841 Fax 937/274-2873
Life Skills Center of Elyria 2015 W River Rd N, Elyria 44035 Crystal Garmon	9-12	TV	128 4		440/324-1755 Fax 440/324-1723
Life Skills Center of Toledo 1830 Adams St, Toledo 43604 Vanice S'Williams	9-12	T	154 4		419/241-5504 Fax 419/241-9176
Life Skills Ctr of Cincinnati 2612 Gilbert Ave, Cincinnati 45206 Karen Luehrman	9-12	TV	98 4		513/475-0222 Fax 513/475-0444
Life Skills Ctr of N Columbus 1900 E Dublin Granville Rd, Columbus 43229 Dr Sharon Watkins	9-12	T	115 4		614/891-9041 Fax 614/891-8571
Life Skills HS of Columbus SE 2400 S Hamilton Rd, Columbus 43232 Unique Seifullah	9-12	T	127		614/863-9175 Fax 614/863-9185
Life Skills HS of N Akron 1458 Brittain Rd, Akron 44310 Tanunya Scruggs	9-12	V	104 6		330/510-5827 Fax 330/633-7005
Lighthouse Community Sch 6100 Desmond St, Cincinnati 45227 Daniel Trujillo	7-12	T	41 6		513/561-7888 Fax 513/561-7818
Lincoln Park Academy [238] 3185 W 41st St, Cleveland 44109 Alissa Clugh	K-8		291 7		216/263-7008 Fax 216/263-7007
Lincoln Preparatory Academy 4215 Robert Ave, Cleveland 44109 Alissa Clugh \ Lisa Lyons	K-8	T	207		216/772-1336

79 Student Personnel
80 Driver Ed/Safety
81 Gifted/Talented
82 Video Services
83 Substance Abuse Prev
84 Erate
85 AIDS Education
88 Alternative/At Risk
89 Multi-Cultural Curriculum
90 Social Work

91 Safety/Security
92 Magnet School
93 Parental Involvement
95 Tech Prep Program
97 Chief Infomation Officer
98 Chief Technology Officer
270 Character Education
271 Migrant Education
273 Teacher Mentor
274 Before/After Sch

275 Response To Intervention
277 Remedial Math K-12
280 Literacy Coach
285 STEM
286 Digital Learning
288 Common Core Standards
294 Accountability
295 Network System
296 Title II Programs
297 Webmaster

298 Grant Writer/Ptnrships
750 Chief Innovation Officer
751 Chief of Staff
752 Social Emotional Learning

Other School Types
Ⓐ = Alternative School
Ⓒ = Charter School
Ⓜ = Magnet School
Ⓨ = Year-Round School

School Programs
A = Alternative Program
G = Adult Classes
M = Magnet Program
T = Title I Schoolwide
V = Career & Tech Ed Programs

New Schools are shaded
New Superintendents and Principals are bold
Personnel with email addresses are underscored

Social Media
 = Facebook
 = Twitter

OH-3

School	Grades	Type	Enroll	%	Phone
© Lorain Bilingual Academy [238] 309 W 7th St, Lorain 44052 Raul Saez	K-6		111		440/434-6320
© Lorain Preparatory Academy [238] 4119 Leavitt Rd, Lorain 44053 James Sinclair	K-8	T	531 7		440/282-3127 Fax 440/282-3179
Ⓐ Luther E Ball High Sch 4321 Green Rd, Cleveland 44128 Dan Hamstein	8-12	V	200 22	97%	216/464-8200 Fax 216/682-0220
© Madisonville Smart Elem Sch 4324 Homer Ave, Cincinnati 45227 G Henderson	K-6	T	127		513/241-1101 Fax 513/241-0167 f t
© Main Preparatory Academy 1035 Clay St, Akron 44301 Nikita Tidwell	K-5		145		234/738-1925 Fax 330/812-3059
Ⓐ Marshall High Sch © 4720 Roosevelt Blvd, Middletown 45044 Chuck Hall	9-12	T	269	80%	513/318-7078 Fax 513/425-6951
© Mason Run High Sch 923 S James Rd, Columbus 43227 Aaron Butler	9-12		148		614/362-7540
Ⓐ Mercer Co Alternative Sch 441 E Market St, Celina 45822 Stephen Laux	9-12		10 1		419/586-6722 Fax 419/586-3377
Metro Early Clg Mid High Sch 1929 Kenny Rd, Columbus 43210 Krista Miller	6-12		530	28%	614/259-6639 Fax 614/259-7176
Metro Institute of Technology 303 S Grant Ave, Columbus 43215 Caroline Davis	9-12	T	215	63%	614/797-4797
© Miami Valley Academies 5656 Springboro Pike, Dayton 45449 Marvis Meeks	K-8	T	117	95%	937/294-4522 Fax 937/294-4545
© Middlebury Academy Charter Sch 88 Kent St, Akron 44305 Leeanna Simmons	K-8	T	269		330/752-2766 Fax 330/940-1339
© Middletown Prep & Fitness Acad [247] 816 2nd Ave, Middletown 45044 Caitlin Stevens	K-8	T	280 17		513/424-6110 Fax 513/424-6121
© Midnimo Cross Cultural CMS [243] 1557 Loretta Ave, Columbus 43211 Amy Shrock	6-8	T	119		614/261-7480 Fax 614/261-7481
© Monroe Preparatory Academy [238] 328 E Monroe St, Sandusky 44870 Dr Erik Thorson	K-5		117		567/998-7522
© Montgomery Preparatory Academy [238] 2745 S Smithville Rd, Dayton 45420 Emory Wyckoff	K-8		212		937/991-2900 Fax 937/991-2899
© Mound St Health Careers Acad 354 Mound St, Dayton 45402 James Grimsle	9-12	T	170 6		937/223-3041 Fax 937/223-5867
© Mound St Info & Tech Academy 354 Mound St, Dayton 45402 Ron Cothran	9-12		51 5		937/223-3041 Fax 937/223-5867 f t
© Mound St Tech Trade Military 354 Mound St, Dayton 45402 James Grimsley	9-12	T	33 5	95%	937/223-3041 Fax 937/223-5867 f t
© Mount Auburn Preparatory Acad [238] 244 Southern Ave, Cincinnati 45219 Angela Klinedinst	K-11		329		513/975-3391 Fax 513/975-3399
© New Day Academy 32114 Vine St, Willowick 44095 Terrance Walton	K-12		200 12		440/516-0866 Fax 440/854-6022
© Newbridge Math Reading Academy 3850 Sullivant Ave, Columbus 43228 Andrew Carr	K-5	T	160		614/279-6000 Fax 614/279-6001
© Noble Academy Cleveland [153] 1200 E 200th St, Euclid 44117 Hakan Bagcioglu	K-8	T	442 15	76%	216/486-8866 Fax 216/486-2846
© Noble Academy-Columbus [153] 1329 Bethel Rd, Columbus 43220 Kadir Parlar	K-8	T	338	86%	614/326-0687 Fax 614/326-0691
© Northeast Ohio College Prep [238] 2357 Tremont Ave, Cleveland 44113 Veda Giles-Weeks	9-12	T	451		216/965-0580 Fax 216/574-2203
© Northland Prep & Fitness Acad [247] 1875 Morse Rd, Columbus 43229 Lynn Hursey	K-8	T	208 15		614/318-0600 Fax 614/262-9111
© Ohdela Academy 121 S Main St Ste 310, Akron 44308 Jaime Campbell	K-12		1,900		330/253-8680 f t
© Ohio College Preparatory Sch [238] 21100 Southgate Park Blvd, Maple Heights 44137 Robert Williams	K-8	T	300		216/453-4550 Fax 216/586-2660
© Ohio Connections Academy [181] 130 E Wilson Bridge Rd Ste 25, Worthington 43085 Katie Brecheisen	K-12		4,902		216/361-9460 Fax 614/840-9437
© Ohio Construction Academy 1725 Jetway Blvd, Columbus 43219 Jennifer Johnston	Voc		250		614/532-1863
Ohio School for the Deaf 500 Morse Rd, Columbus 43214 Joshua Doudt \ Jason Franklin	Spec		165 60		614/728-4030 Fax 614/995-3448
Ohio State Sch for the Blind 5220 N High St, Columbus 43214 Danny Ransey	Spec	AV	119 30		614/752-1152 Fax 614/752-1713
© Ohio Virtual Academy 1690 Woodlands Dr Ste 200, Maumee 43537 Amy Helm-Borchers \ Laura Houser \ Marie Mueller	K-12	T	14,264		419/482-0948 Fax 419/482-0955
Ⓐ Old Brook High Sch © 4877 Pearl Rd, Cleveland 44109 Jamila Smith	8-12	T	401	77%	216/721-0845
© Old Brooklyn Cmty Elem Sch [242] 4430 State Rd, Cleveland 44109 Cherie Kaiser	K-4	T	333	45%	216/661-7888 Fax 216/661-5975
© Old Brooklyn Cmty Middle Sch [242] 4430 State Rd, Cleveland 44109 Cherie Kaiser	5-8	T	273	38%	216/351-0280 Fax 216/661-5975
© Pearl Academy 4850 Pearl Rd, Cleveland 44109 Michael Jaissle	K-8		227		216/741-2991 Fax 216/741-3204
© Phoenix Cmty Learning Center 3595 Washington Ave, Cincinnati 45229 Melissa Brown \ Dr Elaine Wilson	K-12	T	499 18	93%	513/351-5801 Fax 513/351-5809
© Reach Academy [200] 2014 Consaul St, Toledo 43605 Dawn Milner	K-5	T	179 12		419/691-4876 Fax 419/691-5184
© Regent High Sch 5806 Broadway Ave, Cleveland 44127 Jason Windon	9-12	T	215		216/512-0076 Fax 216/441-0208
© Renaissance Academy 1555 Elaine Rd, Columbus 43227	K-8	T	127		614/235-1900 Fax 614/866-8494
© Richard Allen Academy-Hamilton 1206 Shuler Ave, Hamilton 45011 Yolanda Cooper	K-6	T	168 20		513/795-6549 Fax 513/805-7723
© Richard Allen Prep-Dayton 627 Salem Ave, Dayton 45406 Mrs Daugherty	K-3		240 16		937/723-7721 Fax 937/723-7738
© Richard Allen Prep-Downtown 184 Salem Ave, Dayton 45406 Gabrielle Billingsley	4-8		319 20		937/951-2800 Fax 937/951-2936

1	Superintendent	8	Curric/Instruct K-12	19	Chief Financial Officer	29	Family/Consumer Science	39	Social Studies K-12	49	English/Lang Arts Elem	59	Special Education Elem	69	Academic Assessment
2	Bus/Finance/Purchasing	9	Curric/Instruct Elem	20	Art K-12	30	Adult Education	40	Social Studies Elem	50	English/Lang Arts Sec	60	Special Education Sec	70	Research/Development
3	Buildings And Grounds	10	Curric/Instruct Sec	21	Art Elem	31	Career/Sch-to-Work K-12	41	Social Studies Sec	51	Reading K-12	61	Foreign/World Lang K-12	71	Public Information
4	Food Service	11	Federal Program	22	Art Sec	32	Career/Sch-to-Work Elem	42	Science K-12	52	Reading Elem	62	Foreign/World Lang Elem	72	Summer School
5	Transportation	12	Title I	23	Music K-12	33	Career/Sch-to-Work Sec	43	Science Elem	53	Reading Sec	63	Foreign/World Lang Sec	73	Instructional Tech
6	Athletic	13	Title V	24	Music Elem	34	Early Childhood Ed	44	Science Sec	54	Remedial Reading K-12	64	Religious Education K-12	74	Inservice Training
7	Health Services	15	Asst Superintendent	25	Music Sec	35	Health/Phys Education	45	Math K-12	55	Remedial Reading Elem	65	Religious Education Elem	75	Marketing/Distributive
		16	Instructional Media Svcs	26	Business Education	36	Guidance Services K-12	46	Math Elem	56	Remedial Reading Sec	66	Religious Education Sec	76	Info Systems
		17	Chief Operations Officer	27	Career & Tech Ed	37	Guidance Services Elem	47	Math Sec	57	Bilingual/ELL	67	School Board President	77	Psychological Assess
		18	Chief Academic Officer	28	Technology Education	38	Guidance Services Sec	48	English/Lang Arts K-12	58	Special Education K-12	68	Teacher Personnel	78	Affirmative Action

Ohio School Directory

School	Grades	Type	Enroll	%	Phone
Richland Sch of Academic Arts 1456 Park Ave W, Mansfield 44906 Sandra Sutherland	K-8	T	318	64%	419/522-7273
River Gate High Sch 458 Franklin St SE, Warren 44483 Jason Cooper	9-12	T	180	98%	330/647-6500 Fax 330/392-0046
Riverside Academy [238] 3280 River Rd, Cincinnati 45204 Keyonna Hutchins	K-8	T	236 11		513/921-7777 Fax 513/921-7704
Sciotoville Cmty East High Sch 224 Marshall St, Portsmouth 45662 James Mahlmister	6-12	TV	266 22		740/776-6777 Fax 740/776-6812
Sciotoville Elem Academy 5523 3rd St, Portsmouth 45662 Foresta Shope	K-4	T	131 6		740/776-2920 Fax 740/776-2916
South Columbus Prep Acad [238] 3220 Groveport Rd, Columbus 43207 Kyle Glispie	K-8		120		614/986-0116
South Side Academy 1400 Oak Hill Ave, Youngstown 44507 Stephanie Groscost	K-8	T	155		330/774-5562
Southwest Ohio Prep Sch 5555 Little Flower Ave, Cincinnati 45239 Simone Bess	K-8		214		513/975-4946 Fax 513/975-4947
Springfield Prep-Fitness Acad [247] 1615 Selma Rd, Springfield 45505 Darren Fansler	K-8	T	154 11		937/323-6250 Fax 937/323-6252
Stambaugh Charter Academy [203] 2420 Donald Ave, Youngstown 44509 Wendy Thomas	K-8	T	425 37		330/792-4806 Fax 330/787-0278
Stark High Sch 1379 Garfield Ave SW, Canton 44706 Carly Hart	9-12		144		234/214-4140
Steam Acad Warrensvlle Heights [238] 4700 Richmond Rd Ste 3000, Cleveland 44128 Dr Kimberly Taylor	K-8	T	220		216/595-2866 Fax 216/595-3180
Steam Academy of Akron [118] 1350 Virginia Ave, Akron 44306 Nova O'Callaghan	K-7	T	161		330/773-1100
Steam Academy of Warren [238] 261 Elm Rd NE, Warren 44483 Jon Natko	K-6	T	176		330/394-3200 Fax 330/394-3600
Stepstone Academy 3328 Carnegie Ave, Cleveland 44115 Kelly Krupa	K-3	T	180		440/260-6400 Fax 216/202-1013
Summit Acad Cmty Sch-Columbus [248] 2521 Fairwood Ave Ste 100, Columbus 43207 Cheryl Elliott	Spec		113 7		614/237-5497 Fax 614/237-6519
Summit Acad Sec Sch-Middletown [248] 7 S Marshall Rd, Middletown 45044 Kelli Frisby	Spec	T	48 9	55%	513/420-9767 Fax 513/727-1520
Summit Acad Trans HS-Columbus [248] 2521 Fairwood Ave Ste 300, Columbus 43207 Trina Moore	Spec		60 7		614/880-0714 Fax 614/880-0732
Summit Academy Alt Lrng-Canton [248] 1620 Market Ave S, Canton 44707 Robert Housel	Spec	T	131 7		330/458-0393 Fax 330/458-0518
Summit Academy Alt Lrng-Warren [248] 1461 Moncrest Dr NW, Warren 44485 Erin Bradley	8-12		101		330/399-1692 Fax 330/399-1768
Summit Academy Elem Sch-Akron [248] 2503 Leland Ave, Akron 44312 Dawn Presley	K-5	T	146 7		330/253-7441 Fax 330/253-7457
Summit Academy Mid Sch-Akron [248] 464 S Hawkins Ave Ste 100, Akron 44320 Crystal Yingling	6-8	T	80 7		330/252-1510 Fax 330/784-8347
Summit Academy Sec Sch-Akron [248] 464 S Hawkins Ave, Akron 44320 Ralph Grant	Spec	T	71 11		330/434-2343 Fax 330/434-5295
Summit Academy Trans HS-Cinn [248] 5800 Salvia Ave, Cincinnati 45224 Stephen Geresy	Spec	T	100 6	95%	513/541-4000 Fax 513/541-4075
Summit Academy Trans HS-Dayton [248] 251 Erdiel Dr, Dayton 45415 Gary Miller	Spec	T	84		937/813-8592
Summit Academy Youngstown 144 N Schenley Ave, Youngstown 44509 Michael Majzun	Spec		85		330/743-9235 Fax 330/259-0424
Summit Academy-Toledo 301 Collingwood Blvd Ste 1, Toledo 43604 Brent Cummings	Spec		83 8		419/243-1815 Fax 419/392-9810
Summit Academy-Youngstown [248] 144 N Schenley Ave, Youngstown 44509 Micheal Majzun	K-7	T	213		330/259-0421 Fax 330/259-0424
T Squared Honors Academy 18450 S Miles Rd, Warrensvl HTS 44128 Dr India Ford	7-12		120		216/510-5458 Fax 216/510-5457
Tcp World Academy 6000 Ridge Ave, Cincinnati 45213 Karen French	K-6	T	510 16	73%	513/531-9500 Fax 513/531-2406
The Steel Academy 1570 Creighton Ave, Akron 44310 Troy Powell	Spec	T	115	76%	330/633-1383 Fax 330/294-1719
The Tomorrow Center 3700 County Road 168, Cardington 43315 Jamie Byrne	6-12	T	128		419/718-4242 Fax 419/718-4246
Toledo Prep & Fitness Academy [247] 3001 Hill Ave, Toledo 43607 Valerie Sandy	K-8	T	193		419/535-3700 Fax 419/535-3701
Toledo School for the Arts 333 14th St Fl 4, Toledo 43604 Letha Ferguson	6-12	TV	692 45	26%	419/246-8732 Fax 419/244-3979
Toledo Smart Elem Sch 1850 Airport Hwy, Toledo 43609 Jessica Molina Kuhlman	K-5	T	200		419/214-3290 Fax 419/214-3294
Towpath Trail High Sch 275 W Market St, Akron 44303 Christina Fraser	9-12	GTV	300 4	82%	234/542-0102 Fax 330/374-3961
Treca Digital Academy 107 N Main St Ste 100, Marion 43302 Adam Clark	K-12	T	2,441		740/389-4798 Fax 740/389-6695
Trotwood Prep & Fitness Acad [247] 3100 Shiloh Springs Rd, Trotwood 45426 Jeff Neely	K-8	T	323 19		937/854-4100 Fax 937/837-9759
United Preparatory Acad-East [249] 1469 E Main St, Columbus 43205 Valerie Kunze	K-1		98		614/586-1228
United Preparatory Acad-State [249] 617 W State St, Columbus 43215 Benjamin Pacht	K-5	T	289		614/453-8993 Fax 614/375-1337
Univ of Cleveland Prep Sch [238] 1906 E 40th St, Cleveland 44103 Kelly Walland	K-8	T	283		216/361-9720 Fax 216/431-3375
University Academy [238] 107 S Arlington St, Akron 44306 Willie Banks	K-8	T	234 9		330/535-7728 Fax 330/535-7864
Village Prep Sch-Woodland [239] 9201 Crane Ave, Cleveland 44105 Chris O'Brien	K-4	T	420		216/298-1164 Fax 216/341-0106
West Central Learning Academy 522 W North St, Lima 45801	7-12	T	35		419/227-9252 Fax 419/227-2511

---

79 Student Personnel	91 Safety/Security	275 Response To Intervention	298 Grant Writer/Ptnrships	**School Programs**
80 Driver Ed/Safety	92 Magnet School	277 Remedial Math K-12	750 Chief Innovation Officer	A = Alternative Program
81 Gifted/Talented	93 Parental Involvement	280 Literacy Coach	751 Chief of Staff	G = Adult Classes
82 Video Services	95 Tech Prep Program	285 STEM	752 Social Emotional Learning	M = Magnet Program
83 Substance Abuse Prev	97 Chief Infomation Officer	286 Digital Learning		T = Title I Schoolwide
84 Erate	98 Chief Technology Officer	288 Common Core Standards	**Other School Types**	V = Career & Tech Ed Programs
85 AIDS Education	270 Character Education	294 Accountability	Ⓐ = Alternative School	
88 Alternative/At Risk	271 Migrant Education	295 Network System	Ⓒ = Charter School	**Social Media**
89 Multi-Cultural Curriculum	273 Teacher Mentor	296 Title II Programs	Ⓜ = Magnet School	= Facebook
90 Social Work	274 Before/After Sch	297 Webmaster	Ⓨ = Year-Round School	= Twitter

New Schools are shaded
New Superintendents and Principals are bold
Personnel with email addresses are underscored

OH—5

Adams County

School	Grade	Prgm	Enr/#Cls		Phone
© West Park Academy [238] 12913 Bennington Ave, Cleveland 44135 Michael Jaissle	K-8		215		216/251-5450
© West Preparatory Academy 13111 Crossburn Ave, Cleveland 44135 James West	K-8	T	110		216/772-1340 Fax 216/898-5894
© Westside Academy 4330 Clime Rd N, Columbus 43228 Heather O'Bannon	K-6	T	226		614/272-9392 Fax 614/272-8940
© Westside Cmty Sch of the Arts [242] 3727 Bosworth Rd, Cleveland 44111 Deborah Rotolo	K-8	T	335		216/688-1900 Fax 216/688-1902
© Westwood Preparatory Academy 1183 Essex Ave, Columbus 43201 Christopher Antjas	K-12	A	401		330/510-5400 Fax 614/295-5047
© Whitehall Prep & Fitness Acad [247] 3474 E Livingston Ave, Columbus 43227 Matt Dolan	K-8	T	302		614/324-4585 Fax 614/238-3184
© Wildwood Environmental Acad K5 [200] 1546 Dartford Rd, Maumee 43537 Elizabeth Lewin	K-5	T	368 7	23%	419/868-9885 Fax 419/868-9981
© Wings Academy 10615 Lamontier Ave, Cleveland 44104 Anthony Williams	K-8		250 6		216/812-0244 Fax 216/812-0234
© Wings Academy K-8 10615 Lamontier Ave, Cleveland 44104 Anthony Williams	K-8		226		216/812-0244
© Wings Academy Lower Sch 10615 Lamontier Ave, Cleveland 44104 Anthony Williams	K-8		105		216/812-0244 Fax 216/812-0234
© Winton Preparatory Academy [238] 4750 Winton Rd, Cincinnati 45232 Dr Duane Crowe	K-8	T	410		513/276-4166 Fax 513/541-2317
© Wright Preparatory Academy [238] 1500 Superior Ave NE, Canton 44705 Ken Debos	K-8		134	97%	234/207-5455
© Young Scholars Prep Sch 1533 Cleveland Ave, Columbus 43211 Rene Nunmarker	K-5		70		614/653-2116
© Youngstown Acad of Excellence [238] 1408 Rigby St, Youngstown 44506 Jennifer Hutton	K-8	T	172 12		330/746-3970 Fax 330/746-3965
© Youngstown Community Sch 50 Essex St, Youngstown 44502 Gregory Dobrowolski	K-6	T	339 19		330/746-2240 Fax 330/746-6618
© Youthbuild Columbus Cmty Sch 1183 Essex Ave, Columbus 43201 Nkenge Jacobs	10-12	AT	79 8		614/291-0805 Fax 614/291-0890
© Zenith Academy East 2261 S Hamilton Rd, Columbus 43232 H Birch	K-8	T	280		614/577-0997 Fax 614/577-0995
© Zenith Academy North 4606 Heaton Rd, Columbus 43229 Bridget Egan	K-12	T	600 23		614/589-8497 Fax 614/468-0322
© Zenith Academy West 3385 South Blvd, Columbus 43204 H Birch	K-8	T	401		614/272-6300 Fax 614/272-6301

ADAMS COUNTY

ADAMS COUNTY SCHOOLS

County Schs..Principal	Grd	Prgm	Enr/#Cls	SN	
Oliver Sch 3964 Wheat Ridge Rd, West Union 45693 R Scott Amen	Spec	G	28 1		937/544-2574 Fax 937/544-2223

ADAMS PUBLIC SCHOOLS

• **Adams Co Ohio Valley Sch Dist** PID: 00783343   937/544-5586
141 Lloyd Rd, West Union 45693   Fax 937/347-5897

Schools: 7 \ *Teachers:* 220 \ *Students:* 3,800 \ *Special Ed Students:* 646 \ *LEP Students:* 3 \ *College-Bound:* 37% \ *Ethnic:* Hispanic 1%, Caucasian 99% \ *Exp:* $308 (High) \ *Poverty:* 25% \ *Title I:* $1,742,232 \ *Special Education:* $840,000 \ *Open-Close:* 08/21 - 05/22 \ *DTBP:* $196 (High)

Richard Seas 1		Steve Wolfe 2,3,91	
Krystia Hess 4		Melissa Baker 5	
Lisa Toole 9,37,72,273,288*		Tad Mitchell 10,33,270*	
Robin Lucas 11,83,88,298		Marketta Lawhorn 16,73,76,84,95	
Jennifer Grimes 27		Tracy Spiers 58*	
Charlie Bess 67		Greg Grooms 68,78,79	
Janice Day 81		Karl Boerger 275*	
Eddie Butcher 295*			

Public Schs..Principal	Grd	Prgm	Enr/#Cls	SN	
North Adams Elem Sch 2295 Moores Rd, Seaman 45679 Deirdre Mills	PK-6	T	706 40	52%	937/386-2516 Fax 937/347-3486
North Adams Jr Sr High Sch 96 Green Devil Dr, Seaman 45679 Linda Naylor	7-12	T	533 33	46%	937/386-2528 Fax 937/347-3495
Ohio Valley Career Tech Ctr 175 Lloyd Rd, West Union 45693 Tad Mitchell	11-12	AT	249 39	64%	937/544-2336 Fax 937/347-3468
Peebles Elem Sch 700 Peebles Indian Rd, Peebles 45660 **Amanda McFarland**	PK-6	T	586 35	62%	937/587-2611 Fax 937/347-3499
Peebles High Sch 144 Peebles Indian Rd, Peebles 45660 Steve Appelman	7-12	T	392 35	55%	937/587-2681 Fax 937/347-3503
West Union Elem Sch 555 Lloyd Rd, West Union 45693 Ben King	PK-6	T	722 43	74%	937/544-2951 Fax 937/347-3508
West Union High Sch 97 Dragon Lair Dr, West Union 45693 **Brian Ruckel**	7-12	T	540 50	61%	937/544-5553 Fax 937/347-3509

1 Superintendent	8 Curric/Instruct K-12	19 Chief Financial Officer	29 Family/Consumer Science	39 Social Studies K-12	49 English/Lang Arts Elem	59 Special Education Elem	69 Academic Assessment
2 Bus/Finance/Purchasing	9 Curric/Instruct Elem	20 Art K-12	30 Adult Education	40 Social Studies Elem	50 English/Lang Arts Sec	60 Special Education Sec	70 Research/Development
3 Buildings And Grounds	10 Curric/Instruct Sec	21 Art Elem	31 Career/Sch-to-Work K-12	41 Social Studies Sec	51 Reading K-12	61 Foreign/World Lang K-12	71 Public Information
4 Food Service	11 Federal Program	22 Art Sec	32 Career/Sch-to-Work Elem	42 Science K-12	52 Reading Elem	62 Foreign/World Lang Elem	72 Summer School
5 Transportation	12 Title I	23 Music K-12	33 Career/Sch-to-Work Sec	43 Science Elem	53 Reading Sec	63 Foreign/World Lang Sec	73 Instructional Tech
6 Athletic	13 Title V	24 Music Elem	34 Early Childhood Ed	44 Science Sec	54 Remedial Reading K-12	64 Religious Education K-12	74 Inservice Training
7 Health Services	15 Asst Superintendent	25 Music Sec	35 Health/Phys Education	45 Math K-12	55 Remedial Reading Elem	65 Religious Education Elem	75 Marketing/Distributive
	16 Instructional Media Svcs	26 Business Education	36 Guidance Services K-12	46 Math Elem	56 Remedial Reading Sec	66 Religious Education Sec	76 Info Systems
	17 Chief Operations Officer	27 Career & Tech Ed	37 Guidance Services Elem	47 Math Sec	57 Bilingual/ELL	67 School Board President	77 Psychological Assess
	18 Chief Academic Officer	28 Technology Education	38 Guidance Services Sec	48 English/Lang Arts K-12	58 Special Education K-12	68 Teacher Personnel	78 Affirmative Action

Ohio School Directory

Allen County

● **Eastern Local School Dist** PID: 00786046   937/695-9030
11479 US Highway 62, Winchester 45697   Fax 937/695-9046

Schools: 4 \ **Teachers:** 71 \ **Students:** 1,350 \ **Special Ed Students:** 205 \ **College-Bound:** 70% \ **Ethnic:** African American 1%, Hispanic 1%, Caucasian 99% \ **Exp:** $335 (High) \ **Poverty:** 17% \ **Title I:** $378,366 \ **Special Education:** $255,000 \ **Open-Close:** 08/15 - 05/22 \ **DTBP:** $193 (High)

Michele Filon	1	Kevin Kendall		2
Jimmy Simpson	3,5	Jared Jodfrey		6
Tracy Kramer	7,85	Katrina Wagoner		9*
Dawn Wallace	11,34,58,61,69,81,298	Alana Humphrey		36,69,83*
Lowell Richey	67	Jerry Sawyers		73,76,84,286,295

Public Schs..Principal	Grd	Prgm	Enr/#Cls	SN	
Eastern Local High Sch 11557 US Highway 62, Winchester 45697 Bill Garrett	9-12	T	371 30	42%	937/695-0959 Fax 937/695-0303
Eastern Middle Sch 11519 US Highway 62, Winchester 45697 Jordan Michael	6-8	T	307 18	49%	937/695-1249 Fax 937/695-1299
Russellville Elem Sch 239 W Main St, Russellville 45168 Katrina Wagoner	K-5	T	279 26	55%	937/377-4771 Fax 937/377-9110
Sardinia Elem Sch 7742 Tricounty Hwy, Sardinia 45171 Josh Michael	PK-5	T	315 19	63%	937/446-2250 Fax 937/446-3518

● **Manchester Local School Dist** PID: 05339375   937/549-4777
130 Wayne Frye Dr, Manchester 45144   Fax 937/549-4744

Schools: 2 \ **Teachers:** 53 \ **Students:** 856 \ **Special Ed Students:** 179 \ **College-Bound:** 75% \ **Ethnic:** Caucasian 99% \ **Exp:** $125 (Low) \ **Poverty:** 22% \ **Title I:** $326,817 \ **Special Education:** $182,000 \ **Open-Close:** 08/21 - 05/22 \ **DTBP:** $136 (High)

Brian Rau	1,11,73	Eva Elliott		2
Cheri McClanahan	5	Cheri McClanahan		6*
Rick Foster	67	Leigha Wilkins		69
Garrett Stevenson	76,286,295			

Public Schs..Principal	Grd	Prgm	Enr/#Cls	SN	
Manchester Elem Sch 130 Wayne Frye Dr, Manchester 45144 Nick Roberts	PK-6	T	478 24	66%	937/549-4777 Fax 937/549-1289
Manchester Local High Sch 130 Wayne Frye Dr, Manchester 45144 Dana Pollock	7-12	T	378 37	57%	937/549-4777 Fax 937/549-2872

ADAMS PRIVATE SCHOOLS

Private Schs..Principal	Grd	Prgm	Enr/#Cls	SN	
Adams County Christian Sch 187 Willow Dr, West Union 45693 Kennith Clark	K-12		114 12		937/544-5502

ALLEN COUNTY

ALLEN COUNTY SCHOOLS

● **Allen Co Ed Service Center** PID: 00784098   419/222-1836
1920 Slabtown Rd, Lima 45801   Fax 419/224-0718

Craig Kupfereerg	1	Karla Wireman		2
Joe Dietrich	5	Mindy Schulz		10
Kim Nellis	58	Sharon Bowers		81

County Schs..Principal	Grd	Prgm	Enr/#Cls	SN	
Allen Co Pre-School Unit 1920 Slabtown Rd, Lima 45801 Amy Recker	Spec		150 3		419/227-0600 Fax 419/224-1010
Ⓐ Auglaize Co Educational Acad 1130 E Albert St, Lima 45804 Ann Harvey	K-12		100		419/738-4572 Fax 419/738-4591
Ⓒ Heir Force Cmty Sch 150 W Grand Ave, Lima 45801 Darwin Lofton	K-8	T	245		419/228-9241 Fax 419/228-1555 f
Marimor Sch 2550 Ada Rd, Lima 45801 Barb Blass	Spec	V	28 11		419/221-1262 Fax 419/225-5184

ALLEN PUBLIC SCHOOLS

● **Allen East Local School Dist** PID: 00783549   419/648-3333
9105 Harding Hwy, Harrod 45850   Fax 419/648-5282

Schools: 3 \ **Teachers:** 53 \ **Students:** 1,200 \ **Special Ed Students:** 120 \ **LEP Students:** 6 \ **College-Bound:** 48% \ **Ethnic:** African American 1%, Hispanic 2%, Caucasian 96% \ **Exp:** $229 (Med) \ **Poverty:** 9% \ **Title I:** $114,925 \ **Special Education:** $199,000 \ **Open-Close:** 08/28 - 05/29 \ **DTBP:** $206 (High)

Mel Rentschler	1	Andrea Snyder		2,11,19
Perry Heise	3,5	Vera Vernell		4*
Jacqualine Smith	6,33,38,69,83,88	David Pryer		7
Heather Patterson	12*	Keith Baumgartner		58*
Brad Richardson	67	Eric Miller		73,84,295
Casey Bright	286			

Public Schs..Principal	Grd	Prgm	Enr/#Cls	SN	
Ⓨ Allen East Elem Sch 9105 Harding Hwy, Harrod 45850 Heather Patterson	PK-5	M	547 68		419/648-3333
Ⓨ Allen East High Sch 9105 Harding Hwy, Harrod 45850 Keith Baumgartner	9-12	M	340 30	99%	419/648-3333
Allen East Middle Sch 9105 Harding Hwy, Harrod 45850 Jarrod Wehri	6-8		253		419/648-3333

79	Student Personnel	91	Safety/Security	275	Response To Intervention	298	Grant Writer/Ptnrships	
80	Driver Ed/Safety	92	Magnet School	277	Remedial Math K-12	750	Chief Innovation Officer	
81	Gifted/Talented	93	Parental Involvement	280	Literacy Coach	751	Chief of Staff	
82	Video Services	95	Tech Prep Program	285	STEM	752	Social Emotional Learning	
83	Substance Abuse Prev	97	Chief Infomation Officer	286	Digital Learning			
84	Erate	98	Chief Technology Officer	288	Common Core Standards		**Other School Types**	
85	AIDS Education	270	Character Education	294	Accountability		Ⓐ = Alternative School	
88	Alternative/At Risk	271	Migrant Education	295	Network System		Ⓒ = Charter School	
89	Multi-Cultural Curriculum	273	Teacher Mentor	296	Title II Programs		Ⓜ = Magnet School	
90	Social Work	274	Before/After Sch	297	Webmaster		Ⓨ = Year-Round School	

School Programs
A = Alternative Program
G = Adult Classes
M = Magnet Program
T = Title I Schoolwide
V = Career & Tech Ed Programs

Social Media
f = Facebook
t = Twitter

New Schools are shaded
New Superintendents and Principals are bold
Personnel with email addresses are underscored

OH-7

Allen County

Market Data Retrieval

- **Apollo Joint Voc School Dist** PID: 01537678
  3325 Shawnee Rd, Lima 45806
  419/998-2911
  Fax 419/998-2929

  Schools: 1 \ *Teachers:* 53 \ *Students:* 600 \ *Exp:* $666 (High) \
  Open-Close: 08/26 - 05/27 \ *DTBP:* $260 (High)

Keith Horner	1,11	Maria Rellinger	2,19,84
Barbara Cook	7*	Lila Whyman	16*
Tasha Sheipline	30*	Marnie Lowden	33,88*
Jamie Buell	38,60,79*	Ned Stackshloney	67
Dick Schroyer	73*	Bruce Johnson	286*

Public Schs..Principal	Grd	Prgm	Enr/#Cls SN	
Apollo Career High Sch 3325 Shawnee Rd, Lima 45806 Doug Bodey	Voc	AG	600	419/998-2908

- **Bath Local School Dist** PID: 00783587
  2650 Bible Rd, Lima 45801
  419/221-0807
  Fax 419/221-0983

  Schools: 3 \ *Teachers:* 96 \ *Students:* 1,900 \ *Special Ed Students:* 185
  \ *LEP Students:* 17 \ *College-Bound:* 49% \ *Ethnic:* Asian 2%, African
  American 5%, Hispanic 3%, Caucasian 89% \ *Exp:* $98 (Low) \ *Poverty:* 12%
  \ *Title I:* $309,866 \ *Special Education:* $331,000 \ *Open-Close:* 08/26 -
  05/28 \ *DTBP:* $110 (High)

Rich Dackin	1	Annette Morman	2
Greg Cogley	3,91*	Mariah Ross	4
Keanna McNamara	5	Cameron Staley	6*
Todd Fleharty	6*	Chris Renner	11,296*
Sue Plikerd	16*	Stephanie Miller	38*
Chris Clark	59*	Robert Birkemeier	67
Shawn Sommers	77*	Diane Armentrout	84
Tim Gough	286*		

Public Schs..Principal	Grd	Prgm	Enr/#Cls SN	
Bath Elem Sch 2450 Bible Rd, Lima 45801 Chris Renner	K-5	T	835 47	54% 419/221-1837 Fax 419/221-3937
Bath High Sch 2850 Bible Rd, Lima 45801 Brian Jesko	9-12	V	443 25	39% 419/221-0366 Fax 419/221-0766
Bath Middle Sch 2700 Bible Rd, Lima 45801 Brad Clark	6-8	T	455 40	49% 419/221-1839 Fax 419/221-2431

- **Bluffton Exempted Village Sch** PID: 00783630
  102 S Jackson St, Bluffton 45817
  419/358-5901
  Fax 419/358-4871

  Schools: 3 \ *Teachers:* 67 \ *Students:* 1,220 \ *Special Ed Students:* 99
  \ *LEP Students:* 12 \ *College-Bound:* 56% \ *Ethnic:* Asian 1%, African
  American 1%, Hispanic 2%, Caucasian 96% \ *Exp:* $171 (Low) \ *Poverty:* 7%
  \ *Title I:* $96,268 \ *Special Education:* $191,000 \ *Open-Close:* 08/26 -
  05/27 \ *DTBP:* $230 (High)

Greg Denecker	1	Paula Parish	2
Alex Hannah	6*	Tim Closson	11*
Marty Herr	16,73,286*	Elizabeth Smith	38,69*
Wes Klinger	67	Marden Herr	84

Public Schs..Principal	Grd	Prgm	Enr/#Cls SN	
Bluffton Elem Sch 102 S Jackson St, Bluffton 45817 Tim Closson	K-5		592 23	419/358-7951
Bluffton High Sch 106 W College Ave, Bluffton 45817 Mike Minnig	9-12	V	301 20	20% 419/358-7941 Fax 419/358-6586
Bluffton Middle Sch 116 S Jackson St, Bluffton 45817 Kyle Leatherman	6-8		279 17	69% 419/358-7961

- **Delphos City School Dist** PID: 00783678
  234 N Jefferson St, Delphos 45833
  419/692-2509
  Fax 419/692-2653

  Schools: 3 \ *Teachers:* 62 \ *Students:* 1,050 \ *Special Ed Students:* 179
  \ *LEP Students:* 14 \ *College-Bound:* 51% \ *Ethnic:* African American
  1%, Hispanic 4%, Caucasian 95% \ *Exp:* $153 (Low) \ *Poverty:* 10% \
  Title I: $203,995 \ *Special Education:* $261,000 \ *Open-Close:* 08/21 -
  05/21 \ *DTBP:* $233 (High)

Douglas Westrick	1	Brad Rostorfer	2,11
Barb Duval	8,273*	Kathy Buettner	9,58*
Jacqueline Rex	16,82	Erica Pimpas	67
Kendra Kerner	69	Rick Suever	73
Stacey Ricker	83,85*	Kay Wilhelm	286

Public Schs..Principal	Grd	Prgm	Enr/#Cls SN	
Franklin Elem Sch 310 E 4th St, Delphos 45833 Bob Hohlbein	K-5	T	375 36	61% 419/692-8766 Fax 419/692-2766
Jefferson Middle Sch 227 N Jefferson St, Delphos 45833 Brian Fruchey	6-8	T	229 15	51% 419/695-2523 Fax 419/692-2302
Jefferson Senior High Sch 901 Wildcat Ln, Delphos 45833 Chad Brinkman	9-12	V	303 25	37% 419/695-1786 Fax 419/692-2287

- **Elida Local School Dist** PID: 00783721
  4380 Sunnydale St, Elida 45807
  419/331-4155
  Fax 419/331-1656

  Schools: 3 \ *Teachers:* 131 \ *Students:* 2,500 \ *Special Ed Students:* 291
  \ *LEP Students:* 21 \ *College-Bound:* 47% \ *Ethnic:* Asian 1%,
  African American 14%, Hispanic 7%, Caucasian 78% \ *Exp:* $182 (Low)
  \ *Poverty:* 17% \ *Title I:* $721,262 \ *Special Education:* $445,000 \
  Open-Close: 08/27 - 05/27 \ *DTBP:* $172 (High) \

Joel Mengerink	1	Joel Parker	2
Sara Newland	4	Gregg Roth	5
Dave Evans	6*	Julie Simmons	8,11,57,273,288,294,296,298
Gwen Johns	58	Brenda Stocker	67
Craig Kerns	73,76,295*	Sam Boyer	80
Sharon Lawley	84	Kathleen Pipps	93
Dustin Dobie	286*		

Public Schs..Principal	Grd	Prgm	Enr/#Cls SN	
Elida Elem Sch 300 Pioneer Rd, Elida 45807 Michelle Allison	K-4	T	857 37	59% 419/331-7901 Fax 419/331-2706
Elida High Sch 401 E North St, Elida 45807 Darren Sharp	9-12	T	659 50	42% 419/331-4115 Fax 419/339-3523
Elida Middle Sch 4500 Sunnydale St, Elida 45807 Doug Drury	5-8	T	790 40	50% 419/331-2505 Fax 419/331-6822

1	Superintendent	8	Curric/Instruct K-12	19	Chief Financial Officer	29	Family/Consumer Science	39	Social Studies K-12	49	English/Lang Arts Elem	59	Special Education Elem	69	Academic Assessment
2	Bus/Finance/Purchasing	9	Curric/Instruct Elem	20	Art K-12	30	Adult Education	40	Social Studies Elem	50	English/Lang Arts Sec	60	Special Education Sec	70	Research/Development
3	Buildings And Grounds	10	Curric/Instruct Sec	21	Art Elem	31	Career/Sch-to-Work K-12	41	Social Studies Sec	51	Reading K-12	61	Foreign/World Lang K-12	71	Public Information
4	Food Service	11	Federal Program	22	Art Sec	32	Career/Sch-to-Work Elem	42	Science K-12	52	Reading Elem	62	Foreign/World Lang Elem	72	Summer School
5	Transportation	12	Title I	23	Music K-12	33	Career/Sch-to-Work Sec	43	Science Elem	53	Reading Sec	63	Foreign/World Lang Sec	73	Instructional Tech
6	Athletic	13	Title V	24	Music Elem	34	Early Childhood Ed	44	Science Sec	54	Remedial Reading K-12	64	Religious Education K-12	74	Inservice Training
7	Health Services	15	Asst Superintendent	25	Music Sec	35	Health/Phys Education	45	Math K-12	55	Remedial Reading Elem	65	Religious Education Elem	75	Marketing/Distributive
		16	Instructional Media Svcs	26	Business Education	36	Guidance Services K-12	46	Math Elem	56	Remedial Reading Sec	66	Religious Education Sec	76	Info Systems
		17	Chief Operations Officer	27	Career & Tech Ed	37	Guidance Services Elem	47	Math Sec	57	Bilingual/ELL	67	School Board President	77	Psychological Assess
		18	Chief Academic Officer	28	Technology Education	38	Guidance Services Sec	48	English/Lang Arts K-12	58	Special Education K-12	68	Teacher Personnel	78	Affirmative Action

Ohio School Directory   Allen County

● **Lima City School Dist** PID: 00783769   419/996-3400
  755 Saint Johns Ave, Lima 45804   Fax 419/996-3401

Schools: 9 \ **Teachers:** 262 \ **Students:** 4,000 \ **Special Ed Students:** 815 \ **LEP Students:** 12 \ **College-Bound:** 29% \ **Ethnic:** African American 49%, Hispanic 6%, Caucasian 44% \ **Exp:** $368 (High) \ **Poverty:** 36% \ **Title I:** $3,466,325 \ **Special Education:** $1,392,000 \ **Open-Close:** 08/14 - 05/22 \ **DTBP:** $225 (High) \ [f]

Jill Ackerman 1,11,57,83	Shelly Reiff 2
Randy Crossley 3,5	Carrie Woodruff 4
John Zell 6	Kate Morman 7*
Jacqueline Blosser 12*	Kristin Lee 20,23,92
Ball Laura 30	Brian Wischmeyer 58*
Alicia Anderson 67	Pete Badertscher 73*
Beth Jokinen 76	Nathan Garlock 91

Public Schs..Principal	Grd	Prgm	Enr/#Cls	SN
Freedom Elem Sch 575 Calumet Ave, Lima 45804 Chandra Nuveman	PK-4	T	227 25	419/996-3380 Fax 419/996-3381
Heritage Elem Sch 816 College Ave, Lima 45805 Stacy Barker	PK-4	T	453 23	419/996-3390 Fax 419/996-3391
Independence Elem Sch 615 Tremont Ave, Lima 45801 Matthew Quatman	PK-4	T	343 20	419/996-3330 Fax 419/996-3331
Ⓜ Liberty Arts Magnet Sch 338 W Kibby St, Lima 45804 Angela Haffner	K-8	T	413 19	419/996-3320 Fax 419/996-3321
Lima North Middle Sch 1135 N West St, Lima 45801 Julie Stewart	5-6	T	383 30	419/996-3100 Fax 419/996-3101
Ⓐ Lima Senior High Sch 1 Spartan Way, Lima 45801 Fran Mort	9-12	GTV	1,043 75	419/996-3030 Fax 419/996-3001
Lima West Middle Sch 503 N Cable Rd, Lima 45805 Thomas Winkler	7-8	T	405 30	419/996-3150 Fax 419/996-3151
Ⓜ South Science Tech Magnet Sch 755 Saint Johns Ave, Lima 45804 Chad Fallis	PK-8	T	163 16	419/996-3190 Fax 419/996-3191
Unity Elem Sch 925 E 3rd St, Lima 45804 Tricia Winkler	PK-4	T	219 18	419/996-3300 Fax 419/996-3301

● **Perry Local School Dist** PID: 00783953   419/221-2770
  2770 E Breese Rd, Lima 45806   Fax 419/224-6215

Schools: 2 \ **Teachers:** 44 \ **Students:** 753 \ **Special Ed Students:** 78 \ **College-Bound:** 50% \ **Ethnic:** African American 30%, Hispanic 2%, Caucasian 68% \ **Exp:** $297 (Med) \ **Poverty:** 22% \ **Title I:** $199,871 \ **Special Education:** $170,000 \ **Open-Close:** 08/26 - 05/28 \ **DTBP:** $241 (High)

Alison VanGorder 1	Esther Ruhe 2
Barb Heronn 4*	Gina Shively 6,7*
Jesse Kill 8,57,83,271	Kelly Schooler 9,11,59,88*
Heather Smith 16,288*	Linda Hoersten 33,36,69*
Mary Iiames 37*	Ann Schroeder 58
Marc Sidner 67	Steve Mittendorf 73

Public Schs..Principal	Grd	Prgm	Enr/#Cls	SN
Perry Elem Sch 2770 E Breese Rd, Lima 45806 Kelly Schooler	K-6	T	416 30	85% 419/221-2771 Fax 419/224-6312
Perry High Sch 2770 E Breese Rd, Lima 45806 Nicholas Weingart	7-12	T	337 26	82% 419/221-2773

● **Shawnee Local School Dist** PID: 00783989   419/998-8031
  3255 Zurmehly Rd, Lima 45806   Fax 419/998-8050

Schools: 4 \ **Teachers:** 133 \ **Students:** 2,500 \ **Special Ed Students:** 222 \ **LEP Students:** 8 \ **College-Bound:** 62% \ **Ethnic:** Asian 2%, African American 6%, Hispanic 3%, Caucasian 89% \ **Exp:** $78 (Low) \ **Poverty:** 8% \ **Title I:** $291,095 \ **Special Education:** $566,000 \ **Open-Close:** 08/22 - 05/29 \ **DTBP:** $197 (High)

James Kanable 1	Christina Cross 2,91
Jamie Spyker 3	Sally Allen 4*
Mike Bosch 5	Amber Straub 8,69,74,88
Jennie Hefner 11,57,58,83,296,298	Mike Carpenter 67
Jeff Heistan 73*	

Public Schs..Principal	Grd	Prgm	Enr/#Cls	SN
Elmwood Primary Sch 4295 Shawnee Rd, Lima 45806 Leigh Daily	K-2		507 23	31% 419/998-8090 Fax 419/998-8110
Maplewood Intermediate Sch 1670 Wonderlick Rd, Lima 45805 Larry Foos	3-4		382 16	31% 419/998-8076 Fax 419/998-8085
Shawnee High Sch 3333 Zurmehly Rd, Lima 45806 **Mark Verroco**	9-12		664 48	27% 419/998-8000 Fax 419/998-8026
Shawnee Middle Sch 3235 Zurmehly Rd, Lima 45806 Judy Gephart	5-8		813 48	28% 419/998-8057 Fax 419/222-6572

● **Spencerville Local School Dist** PID: 00784036   419/647-4111
  600 School St, Spencerville 45887   Fax 419/647-5124

Schools: 3 \ **Teachers:** 56 \ **Students:** 965 \ **Special Ed Students:** 144 \ **College-Bound:** 46% \ **Ethnic:** African American 1%, Hispanic 2%, Caucasian 97% \ **Exp:** $195 (Low) \ **Poverty:** 14% \ **Title I:** $168,123 \ **Special Education:** $168,000 \ **Open-Close:** 08/27 - 05/29 \ **DTBP:** $180 (High)

Dennis Fuge 1	Brenda Core 2
Zach Stemen 3*	Debb Kill 4
Scott Gephart 5*	John Zerbe 6*
Diane Binkley 12,52,55*	Georgia McMichael 16*
Jane Baumgartner 31,38,69,85*	John Goecke 67
Amy Shoppell 73*	

Public Schs..Principal	Grd	Prgm	Enr/#Cls	SN
Spencerville Elem Sch 2500 Wisher Dr, Spencerville 45887 Susan Wagner	K-4	T	352 21	99% 419/647-4113
Spencerville High Sch 2500 Wisher Dr, Spencerville 45887 Scott Gephart	9-12	V	263 15	419/647-4111
Spencerville Middle Sch 2500 Wisher Dr, Spencerville 45887 Scott Gephart	5-8		325 25	419/647-4112

79 Student Personnel	91 Safety/Security	275 Response To Intervention	298 Grant Writer/Ptnrships	**School Programs**	**Social Media**	
80 Driver Ed/Safety	92 Magnet School	277 Remedial Math K-12	750 Chief Innovation Officer	A = Alternative Program		
81 Gifted/Talented	93 Parental Involvement	280 Literacy Coach	751 Chief of Staff	G = Adult Classes	[f] = Facebook	
82 Video Services	95 Tech Prep Program	285 STEM	752 Social Emotional Learning	M = Magnet Program		
83 Substance Abuse Prev	97 Chief Infomation Officer	286 Digital Learning		T = Title I Schoolwide	[t] = Twitter	
84 Erate	98 Chief Technology Officer	288 Common Core Standards	**Other School Types**	V = Career & Tech Ed Programs		
85 AIDS Education	270 Character Education	294 Accountability	Ⓐ = Alternative School			
88 Alternative/At Risk	271 Migrant Education	295 Network System	Ⓒ = Charter School	**New Schools are shaded**		
89 Multi-Cultural Curriculum	273 Teacher Mentor	296 Title II Programs	Ⓜ = Magnet School	**New Superintendents and Principals are bold**		
90 Social Work	274 Before/After Sch	297 Webmaster	Ⓨ = Year-Round School	Personnel with email addresses are underscored		**OH—9**

Ashland County

ALLEN CATHOLIC SCHOOLS

- **Diocese of Toledo Ed Office** PID: 00818297
  Listing includes only schools located in this county. See District Index for location of Diocesan Offices.

Catholic Schs..Principal	Grd	Prgm	Enr/#Cls SN	
Lima Central Catholic High Sch 720 S Cable Rd, Lima 45805 Stephanie Willams	9-12		280 45	419/222-4276 Fax 419/222-6933
St Charles Borremo Sch 2175 W Elm St, Lima 45805 Megan Scheid	PK-8		450 24	419/222-2536 Fax 419/222-8720
St Gerard Sch 1311 N Main St, Lima 45801 Natalie Schoonover	PK-8		200 16	419/222-0431 Fax 419/224-6580
St John Elem Sch 110 N Pierce St, Delphos 45833 Nathan Stant	K-6		321 24	419/692-8561 Fax 419/692-4501
St John's High Sch 515 E 2nd St, Delphos 45833 Adam Lee	7-12		282 25	419/692-5371 Fax 419/879-6874
St Rose Catholic Sch 523 N West St, Lima 45801 Donna Judy	PK-8		110 9	419/223-6361 Fax 419/222-2032

ALLEN PRIVATE SCHOOLS

Private Schs..Principal	Grd	Prgm	Enr/#Cls SN	
Bible Believers Christian Sch 3500 Spencerville Rd, Lima 45805 Rapp Crook	K-12		39 11	419/999-5517 Fax 419/224-1982
Golden Bridge Academy 319 W Market St, Lima 45801 Karen Beard	PK-7		150 4	419/222-6858 Fax 419/222-6836
Liberty Christian Sch 801 Bellefontaine Ave, Lima 45801 Cheryl Lawrence-Jones	PK-12		11 5	419/229-6266
Lima Christian Academy 3180 W Elm St, Lima 45805 Keith Hamblen	K-12		10 3	419/999-2219 Fax 419/991-5780
Temple Christian Sch 982 Brower Rd, Lima 45801 Erin Marshall	PK-12		211 17	419/227-1644 Fax 419/227-6635

ALLEN REGIONAL CENTERS

- **Northwest Ohio Computer Co-op** PID: 04499453   419/228-7417
  4277 East Rd, Lima 45807   Fax 419/222-5635

Ray Burden 1

ASHLAND COUNTY

ASHLAND COUNTY SCHOOLS

County Schs..Principal	Grd	Prgm	Enr/#Cls	SN	
Ⓐ Ashland Co Cmty Academy 716 Union St, Ashland 44805 Allen Wilson	7-12	T	81 4	74%	419/903-0295 Fax 419/903-0341
Dale Roy Sch 1256 Center St, Ashland 44805 Eric Billing	Spec	GV	85 9		419/289-7518 Fax 419/281-2820
Tri County Pre-School 1256 Center St, Ashland 44805 Michelle Linton	Spec		230 5		419/281-4239 Fax 419/281-2517

ASHLAND PUBLIC SCHOOLS

- **Ashland City School Dist** PID: 00784103   419/289-1117
  1407 Claremont Ave, Ashland 44805   Fax 419/289-9534

Schools: 5 \ *Teachers:* 172 \ *Students:* 3,800 \ *Special Ed Students:* 440 \ *LEP Students:* 25 \ *College-Bound:* 58% \ *Ethnic:* Asian 1%, African American 1%, Hispanic 2%, Caucasian 97% \ *Exp:* $207 (Med) \ *Poverty:* 15% \ *Title I:* $949,898 \ *Special Education:* $640,000 \ *Open-Close:* 08/26 - 05/29 \ *DTBP:* $198 (High)

Dr Doug Marrah 1   Robert Knabe 2
Randy Heller 3,91   Kristie Ward 4
Doug Shipper 5   Jason Goings 6*
Katie Ramsey 7   Linda McKibben 8,11,54,57,273,296,298
Tammy Webb 58,79,275   Cheryl Benway 67
Phillip McNaull 73   Michelle Fisher 76
Kimberly Bracken .... 81*   Kaye Pomesky 288

Public Schs..Principal	Grd	Prgm	Enr/#Cls	SN	
Ashland High Sch 1440 King Rd, Ashland 44805 Mike Riley	9-12	V	950 70		419/289-7968 Fax 419/289-8218
Ashland Middle Sch 1520 King Rd, Ashland 44805 Matt White	6-8	TV	750 40	39%	419/289-7966 Fax 419/289-2303
Edison Elem Sch 1202 Masters Ave, Ashland 44805 Krist Manley	K-3	T	468 23	53%	419/289-7965 Fax 419/281-3947
Reagan Elem Sch 850 Jackson Dr, Ashland 44805 Nicole Brodie	PK-3	T	610	37%	419/289-7967 Fax 419/289-4571
Taft Intermediate Sch 825 Smith Rd, Ashland 44805 Stephen McDonnell	4-5	T	500 23	46%	419/289-7969 Fax 419/281-4516

- **Ashland Co-West Holmes JVSD** PID: 00784359   419/289-3313
  1783 State Route 60, Ashland 44805   Fax 419/289-3729

Schools: 1 \ *Teachers:* 32 \ *Students:* 450 \ *College-Bound:* 28% \ *Exp:* $583 (High) \ *Open-Close:* 08/19 - 05/28 \ *DTBP:* $188 (High)

Rodney Cheyney 1   Julie Smith 2

1	Superintendent	8	Curric/Instruct K-12	19	Chief Financial Officer	29	Family/Consumer Science	39	Social Studies K-12	49	English/Lang Arts Elem	59	Special Education Elem	69	Academic Assessment
2	Bus/Finance/Purchasing	9	Curric/Instruct Elem	20	Art K-12	30	Adult Education	40	Social Studies Elem	50	English/Lang Arts Sec	60	Special Education Sec	70	Research/Development
3	Buildings And Grounds	10	Curric/Instruct Sec	21	Art Elem	31	Career/Sch-to-Work K-12	41	Social Studies Sec	51	Reading K-12	61	Foreign/World Lang K-12	71	Public Information
4	Food Service	11	Federal Program	22	Art Sec	32	Career/Sch-to-Work Elem	42	Science K-12	52	Reading Elem	62	Foreign/World Lang Elem	72	Summer School
5	Transportation	12	Title I	23	Music K-12	33	Career/Sch-to-Work Sec	43	Science Elem	53	Reading Sec	63	Foreign/World Lang Sec	73	Instructional Tech
6	Athletic	13	Title V	24	Music Elem	34	Early Childhood Ed	44	Science Sec	54	Remedial Reading K-12	64	Religious Education K-12	74	Inservice Training
7	Health Services	14	Asst Superintendent	25	Music Sec	35	Health/Phys Education	45	Math K-12	55	Remedial Reading Elem	65	Religious Education Elem	75	Marketing/Distributive
		15	Instructional Media Svcs	26	Business Education	36	Guidance Services K-12	46	Math Elem	56	Remedial Reading Sec	66	Religious Education Sec	76	Info Systems
		16	Chief Operations Officer	27	Career & Tech Ed	37	Guidance Services Elem	47	Math Sec	57	Bilingual/ELL	67	School Board President	77	Psychological Assess
		17	Chief Academic Officer	28	Technology Education	38	Guidance Services Sec	48	English/Lang Arts K-12	58	Special Education K-12	68	Teacher Personnel	78	Affirmative Action

Ohio School Directory / Ashtabula County

Joseph Bowman 3*	Michael Parry 11
Melisa Carr 30	Jason Chio 67
John Davis 69*	Andy Huffman 73*

Public Schs..Principal	Grd	Prgm	Enr/#Cls	SN	
Ashland Co-W Holmes Career Ctr 1783 State Route 60, Ashland 44805 **Rick Brindley**	Voc	G	450 32		419/289-3313

• **Hillsdale Local School Dist** PID: 00784218   419/368-8231
485 Township Road 1902, Jeromesville 44840   Fax 419/368-7504

Schools: 3 \ *Teachers:* 49 \ *Students:* 850 \ *Special Ed Students:* 89 \ *College-Bound:* 66% \ *Ethnic:* Hispanic 1%, Caucasian 99% \ *Exp:* $166 (Low) \ *Poverty:* 10% \ *Title I:* $151,278 \ *Special Education:* $150,000 \ *Open-Close:* 08/21 - 05/28 \ *DTBP:* $244 (High) \ 🇫 🇹

Steven Dickerson 1,84	Rick Blahnik 2
Scott Hinkle 3*	Ora Flickinger 4,5
Jodi Long 6*	Alyson Baker 8
Tom Williams 12*	Kelly Hohler 36*
Deanna Gilmore 58*	Villa King 67
David Moore 73	

Public Schs..Principal	Grd	Prgm	Enr/#Cls	SN	
Hillsdale Elem Sch W Main St, Hayesville 44838 Tom Williams	K-4		285 17	38%	419/368-4364 Fax 419/368-3701
Hillsdale High Sch 485 Township Road 1902, Jeromesville 44840 **Davis Baker**	9-12	V	219 30	33%	419/368-6841
Hillsdale Middle Sch 144 N High St, Jeromesville 44840 Tim Keib	5-8		276 30	45%	419/368-4911 Fax 419/368-3613

• **Loudonville-Perrysville SD** PID: 00784256   419/994-3912
210 E Main St, Loudonville 44842   Fax 419/994-5528

Schools: 3 \ *Teachers:* 70 \ *Students:* 1,100 \ *Special Ed Students:* 215 \ *LEP Students:* 3 \ *College-Bound:* 49% \ *Ethnic:* African American 4%, Hispanic 1%, Caucasian 94% \ *Exp:* $366 (High) \ *Poverty:* 14% \ *Title I:* $275,484 \ *Special Education:* $226,000 \ *Open-Close:* 08/27 - 06/03 \ *DTBP:* $189 (High)

Cathrine Puster 1	Christine Anger 2,11
Shane McCaskey 3,91*	Terri Blanchard 4*
Kenny Carroll 5	Kevin Malwich 6,35,286
Annette Gorrell 12,34,296*	Beth Ring 37*
David Lance 38,83,85*	Dianna McMillen 54,58,275
Roy Templeman 67	Leslie Kamenik 73,295*
Rhonda Curtis 77*	

Public Schs..Principal	Grd	Prgm	Enr/#Cls	SN	
Budd Elem Sch 210 E Main St, Loudonville 44842 Kelly Seboe	4-6	T	222 15	46%	419/994-3327 Fax 419/994-7003
Loudonville High Sch 421 Campus Ave, Loudonville 44842 Chrissie Butts	7-12	V	481 32	42%	419/994-4101 Fax 419/994-3485
McMullen Elem Sch 224 E Bustle St, Loudonville 44842 Annette Gorrell	K-3	T	298 15	46%	419/994-3913 Fax 419/994-5116

• **Mapleton Local School Dist** PID: 00784309   419/945-2188
635 County Road 801, Ashland 44805   Fax 419/945-8133

Schools: 3 \ *Teachers:* 49 \ *Students:* 890 \ *Special Ed Students:* 104 \ *LEP Students:* 3 \ *College-Bound:* 46% \ *Ethnic:* Hispanic 1%, Caucasian 99% \ *Exp:* $277 (Med) \ *Poverty:* 17% \ *Title I:* $292,321 \ *Special Education:* $186,000 \ *Open-Close:* 08/22 - 06/01 \ *DTBP:* $186 (High)

Scott Smith 1	Katy Wiley 2
Scott Loescher 3	Tammy Reynolds 5
Morgan Lengacher 58*	Tom Donley 67
Matt Triplett 73,295	Shelby Ortiz 288

Public Schs..Principal	Grd	Prgm	Enr/#Cls	SN	
Mapleton Elem Sch 2 Mountie Dr, Ashland 44805 Michelle Roblin	PK-5	T	398 7	39%	419/945-2188 Fax 419/945-8119
Mapleton High Sch 1 Mountie Dr, Ashland 44805 Corey Kline	9-12	V	266	64%	419/945-2188 Fax 419/945-8166
Mapleton Middle Sch 635 County Road 801, Ashland 44805 Corey Kline	6-8	TV	226 22		419/945-2188 Fax 419/945-8166

ASHLAND CATHOLIC SCHOOLS

• **Diocese of Cleveland Ed Office** PID: 00795308
Listing includes only schools located in this county. See District Index for location of Diocesan Offices.

Catholic Schs..Principal	Grd	Prgm	Enr/#Cls	SN	
St Edward Elem Sch 433 Cottage St, Ashland 44805 Sue Ellen Valentine	K-8		126 9		419/289-7456 Fax 419/289-9474 🇫

ASHLAND PRIVATE SCHOOLS

Private Schs..Principal	Grd	Prgm	Enr/#Cls	SN	
Ashland Christian Sch 1144 W Main St, Ashland 44805 Chris Clark	PK-8		185 20		419/289-6617 Fax 419/281-1425
Scenic Ridge Christian Sch 2053 State Route 89, Jeromesville 44840 Joe Lehman	1-8		24 3		419/368-0307 Fax 419/368-8393

ASHTABULA COUNTY

ASHTABULA COUNTY SCHOOLS

• **Ashtabula Co Ed Service Center** PID: 00784957   440/576-9023
2630 W 13th St Ste A, Ashtabula 44004   Fax 440/576-3065

John Rubesich 1	Mary Gillespie 2
William Mullane 9	Teresa Parker 58
Denise Hunt 81	

79	Student Personnel	91	Safety/Security	275	Response To Intervention	298	Grant Writer/Ptnrships
80	Driver Ed/Safety	92	Magnet School	277	Remedial Math K-12	750	Chief Innovation Officer
81	Gifted/Talented	93	Parental Involvement	280	Literacy Coach	751	Chief of Staff
82	Video Services	95	Tech Prep Program	285	STEM	752	Social Emotional Learning
83	Substance Abuse Prev	97	Chief Information Officer	286	Digital Learning		
84	Erate	98	Chief Technology Officer	288	Common Core Standards		Other School Types
85	AIDS Education	270	Character Education	294	Accountability	Ⓐ	= Alternative School
88	Alternative/At Risk	271	Migrant Education	295	Network System	Ⓒ	= Charter School
89	Multi-Cultural Curriculum	273	Teacher Mentor	296	Title II Programs	Ⓜ	= Magnet School
90	Social Work	274	Before/After Sch	297	Webmaster	Ⓨ	= Year-Round School

School Programs
A = Alternative Program
G = Adult Classes
M = Magnet Program
T = Title I Schoolwide
V = Career & Tech Ed Programs

Social Media
🇫 = Facebook
🇹 = Twitter

New Schools are shaded
New Superintendents and Principals are bold
Personnel with email addresses are underscored

Ashtabula County

Market Data Retrieval

County Schs..Principal	Grd	Prgm	Enr/#Cls SN	
Ashtabula Co Educ Svc Ctr 4200 State Road Ashtabula, Ashtabula 44004 John Rubesich	Spec		50 7	440/576-4085 Fax 440/576-3065
Happy Hearts Sch 2505 S Ridge Rd E, Ashtabula 44004 Patrick Guliano	Spec		100 12	440/224-2177 Fax 440/224-3696

ASHTABULA PUBLIC SCHOOLS

• **Ashtabula Area City Sch Dist** PID: 00784385   440/992-1200
6610 Sanborn Rd, Ashtabula 44004   Fax 440/992-1209

Schools: 8 \ *Teachers:* 174 \ *Students:* 3,600 \ *Special Ed Students:* 948 \ *LEP Students:* 208 \ *College-Bound:* 75% \ *Ethnic:* African American 9%, Hispanic 17%, Caucasian 74% \ *Exp:* $94 (Low) \ *Poverty:* 33% \ *Title I:* $2,595,176 \ *Special Education:* $924,000 \ *Open-Close:* 08/19 - 05/28 \ *DTBP:* $200 (High)

Mark Potts 1
Pamela Peck 4*
Jason Baxter 6
Rebecca Evanston 34
Mark Astroino 2,3,17,19,73,91
Michael Gatll 5
Cynthia Thomassetti 8,11,58,69,74,79,81
William Neni 67

Public Schs..Principal	Grd	Prgm	Enr/#Cls SN	
Aacs Early Lrng Center 2304 Wade Ave, Ashtabula 44004 Lisa Newson	PK-PK	T	177 9	440/992-1280 Fax 440/964-0485
Erie Intermediate Sch 2306 Wade Ave, Ashtabula 44004 Michele Boiarski	5-6	T	530 20	440/992-1260 Fax 440/992-1262
Huron Primary Sch 2300 Wade Ave, Ashtabula 44004 Valarie Harper	1-1	T	225 12	440/992-1230 Fax 440/992-1232
Lakeside High Sch 6600 Sanborn Rd, Ashtabula 44004 Robert Klinar	9-12	ATV	945 75	440/993-2522 Fax 440/993-2480
Lakeside Junior High Sch 6620 Sanborn Rd, Ashtabula 44004 Scott Anservitz	7-8	T	497 40	440/993-2618 Fax 440/993-2647
Michigan Primary Sch 2304 Wade Ave, Ashtabula 44004 Janie Carey	K-K	T	410 16	440/992-1250 Fax 440/992-1252
Ontario Primary Sch 2302 Wade Ave, Ashtabula 44004 Lisa Newsome	2-2	T	256 11	440/992-1240 Fax 440/992-1242
Superior Intermediate Sch 2308 Wade Ave, Ashtabula 44004 Cristine Rutz	3-4	T	550 15	440/992-1270 Fax 440/992-1272

• **Ashtabula Co Tech & Career SD** PID: 00784933   440/576-6015
1565 State Route 167, Jefferson 44047   Fax 440/576-6502

Schools: 1 \ *Teachers:* 51 \ *Students:* 694 \ *College-Bound:* 37% \ *Exp:* $408 (High) \ *Open-Close:* 08/19 - 05/28 \ *DTBP:* $163 (High)

Dr Jerome Brockway 1,11
Jon Whipple 27*
Allyson Clark 60*
Nicholas Leavitt 295
Keith Biber 2
Ken Porter 31*
Barbara Klingensmith 67

Public Schs..Principal	Grd	Prgm	Enr/#Cls SN	
Ashtabula Co Tech & Career Ctr 1565 State Route 167, Jefferson 44047 Paul Brockett	Voc	G	694 100	440/576-6015

• **Buckeye Local School Dist** PID: 00784529   440/998-4411
3436 Edgewood Dr, Ashtabula 44004   Fax 440/992-8369

Schools: 4 \ *Teachers:* 95 \ *Students:* 1,800 \ *Special Ed Students:* 235 \ *LEP Students:* 3 \ *College-Bound:* 45% \ *Ethnic:* African American 1%, Hispanic 5%, Caucasian 93% \ *Exp:* $152 (Low) \ *Poverty:* 16% \ *Title I:* $418,750 \ *Open-Close:* 08/26 - 06/03 \ *DTBP:* $213 (High)

Patrick Colucci 1
Lisa Loomis 4
Steven Kray 6*
Teresa Parker 58*
John Radwancky 73,295*
Jamie Davis 2
Karl Brunell 5,8
Rocco Adduci 8,11,72*
Mary Wisnyai 67

Public Schs..Principal	Grd	Prgm	Enr/#Cls SN	
Edgewood High Sch 2428 Blake Rd, Ashtabula 44004 Michael Notar	9-12	T	511 40	54% 440/997-5301 Fax 440/998-6143
Kingsville Elem Sch 5875 State Route 193, Kingsville 44048 William Billington	K-5	T	398 20	51% 440/224-0281 Fax 440/224-2452
Ridgeview Elem Sch 3456 Liberty St, Ashtabula 44004 Danyel Ryan	K-5	T	398 19	66% 440/997-7321 Fax 440/998-2842
Wallace H Braden Middle Sch 3436 Edgewood Dr, Ashtabula 44004 Dan Sapanaro	6-8	T	430 24	51% 440/998-0550 Fax 440/998-2793

• **Conneaut Area City Sch Dist** PID: 00784608   440/593-7200
230 Gateway Ave Ste B, Conneaut 44030   Fax 440/593-6253

Schools: 4 \ *Teachers:* 99 \ *Students:* 1,604 \ *Special Ed Students:* 292 \ *LEP Students:* 5 \ *College-Bound:* 33% \ *Ethnic:* Asian 1%, African American 1%, Hispanic 3%, Caucasian 95% \ *Exp:* $46 (Low) \ *Poverty:* 26% \ *Title I:* $921,300 \ *Special Education:* $437,000 \ *Open-Close:* 08/26 - 06/03 \ *DTBP:* $185 (High)

Lori Riley 1,288
Pam Anderson 4*
Joel Taylor 6*
Kris Mucci 8,12,296
Katie Newcomb 29*
Aimee Cool 69,77
Jaclynne Miranda 2
Kelly Thompson 5
Wenonah Chonich 7*
Sarah Baumgardner 11,34,57,58,271,286
Joan Norton 67
Brian Chase 73

Public Schs..Principal	Grd	Prgm	Enr/#Cls SN	
Conneaut High Sch 381 Mill St, Conneaut 44030 Dr Timothy Neal	9-12	ATV	398 40	61% 440/593-7210 Fax 440/593-6899
Conneaut Middle Sch 230 Gateway Ave, Conneaut 44030 Jim Kennedy	6-8	AT	357 45	56% 440/593-7240 Fax 440/593-6289
Gateway Elem Sch 229 Gateway Ave, Conneaut 44030 Dawn Zappitelli	3-5	AT	390 21	66% 440/593-7280 Fax 440/599-2703
Lakeshore Primary Sch 755 Chestnut St, Conneaut 44030 Wendy Tisch	PK-2	T	433 21	63% 440/593-7250 Fax 440/599-7149

1 Superintendent	8 Curric/Instruct K-12	19 Chief Financial Officer	29 Family/Consumer Science	39 Social Studies K-12	49 English/Lang Arts Elem	59 Special Education Elem	69 Academic Assessment
2 Bus/Finance/Purchasing	9 Curric/Instruct Elem	20 Art K-12	30 Adult Education	40 Social Studies Elem	50 English/Lang Arts Sec	60 Special Education Sec	70 Research/Development
3 Buildings And Grounds	10 Curric/Instruct Sec	21 Art Elem	31 Career/Sch-to-Work K-12	41 Social Studies Sec	51 Reading K-12	61 Foreign/World Lang K-12	71 Public Information
4 Food Service	11 Federal Program	22 Art Sec	32 Career/Sch-to-Work Elem	42 Science K-12	52 Reading Elem	62 Foreign/World Lang Elem	72 Summer School
5 Transportation	12 Title I	23 Music K-12	33 Career/Sch-to-Work Sec	43 Science Elem	53 Reading Sec	63 Foreign/World Lang Sec	73 Instructional Tech
6 Athletic	13 Title V	24 Music Elem	34 Early Childhood Ed	44 Science Sec	54 Remedial Reading K-12	64 Religious Education K-12	74 Inservice Training
7 Health Services	15 Asst Superintendent	25 Music Sec	35 Health/Phys Education	45 Math K-12	55 Remedial Reading Elem	65 Religious Education Elem	75 Marketing/Distributive
	16 Instructional Media Svcs	26 Business Education	36 Guidance Services K-12	46 Math Elem	56 Remedial Reading Sec	66 Religious Education Sec	76 Info Systems
	17 Chief Operations Officer	27 Career & Tech Ed	37 Guidance Services Elem	47 Math Sec	57 Bilingual/ELL	67 School Board President	77 Psychological Assess
	18 Chief Academic Officer	28 Technology Education	38 Guidance Services Sec	48 English/Lang Arts K-12	58 Special Education K-12	68 Teacher Personnel	78 Affirmative Action

Ohio School Directory

Ashtabula County

• Geneva Area City School Dist   PID: 00784696
135 S Eagle St, Geneva 44041
440/466-4831
Fax 440/466-0908

Schools: 5 \ **Teachers:** 119 \ **Students:** 2,415 \ **Special Ed Students:** 358 \ **LEP Students:** 45 \ **College-Bound:** 54% \ **Ethnic:** African American 1%, Hispanic 6%, Caucasian 92% \ **Exp:** $144 (Low) \ **Poverty:** 20% \ **Title I:** $768,451 \ **Special Education:** $529,000 \ **Open-Close:** 08/26 - 06/04 \ **DTBP:** $202 (High)

Eric Kujala 1	Kevin Lillie 2
Tom Currence 3,5	Laura Jones 4
Charlotte Leonard 5	Jeniffer Crossley 6
Cindy Drought 7*	Brett Horvath 8,11,16,34,88,270,285,288
Amy Burzanko 31,34*	Amanda Gibson 57*
John Kubec 58,69,77	Richard Arndt 67
Amy Richmond 68	Gerald Burgard 73*
Anthony Markijohn 91*	

Public Schs..Principal	Grd	Prgm	Enr/#Cls	SN	
Austinburg Elem Sch 3030 State Route 307, Austinburg 44010 Amy Burzanko	PK-5	T	267 14	38%	440/466-4831 Fax 440/275-0789
Cork Elem Sch 341 State Route 534 S, Geneva 44041 Melissa Doherty	K-5	T	275 11	55%	440/466-4831 Fax 440/466-0433
Geneva High Sch 1301 S Ridge Rd E, Geneva 44041 Doug Wetherholt	9-12	TV	729 80	57%	440/466-4831 Fax 440/466-8547
Geneva Middle Sch 839 Sherman St, Geneva 44041 Alex Anderson	6-8	T	584 27	64%	440/466-4831 Fax 440/466-0217
Geneva Platt R Spencer ES 755 Austin Rd, Geneva 44041 Julie Gustin	K-5	T	459 16		440/415-9325 Fax 440/466-0206

• Grand Valley Local School Dist   PID: 00784763
111 W Grand Valley Ave, Orwell 44076
440/805-4545
Fax 440/437-1025

Schools: 3 \ **Teachers:** 71 \ **Students:** 1,075 \ **Special Ed Students:** 194 \ **College-Bound:** 50% \ **Ethnic:** African American 1%, Hispanic 2%, Caucasian 97% \ **Exp:** $78 (Low) \ **Poverty:** 18% \ **Title I:** $481,297 \ **Open-Close:** 08/20 - 05/29 \ **DTBP:** $174 (High)

Dr William Nye 1	Lisa Moodt 2
Terry Hejduk 3,6	Jeanette Bower 4
Ellen Winer 11,296,298	Lowell Moodt 27*
Debra Fredrick 29*	Lisa McClain 38*
Glen Blabolil 58*	Tim Keeney 67
Brad Dawson 73*	Doug Sarbach 73,84,295
Kassi Brand 76,79*	

Public Schs..Principal	Grd	Prgm	Enr/#Cls	SN	
Grand Valley Elem Sch 111 W Grand Valley Ave Ste B, Orwell 44076 Ellen Winer	PK-4	T	450 23	68%	440/805-4545 Fax 440/437-2050 f t
Grand Valley High Sch 111 W Grand Valley Ave Ste C, Orwell 44076 Doug Hitchcock	9-12	TV	352 25	50%	440/805-4545 Fax 440/437-6254
Grand Valley Middle Sch 111 W Grand Valley Ave Ste D, Orwell 44076 Roberta Cozad	5-8	T	338 30	36%	440/805-4545 Fax 440/437-6156

• Jefferson Area Local SD   PID: 00784828
121 S Poplar St, Jefferson 44047
440/576-9180
Fax 440/576-9876

Schools: 4 \ **Teachers:** 84 \ **Students:** 1,651 \ **Special Ed Students:** 259 \ **LEP Students:** 4 \ **Ethnic:** Hispanic 2%, Caucasian 97% \ **Exp:** $89 (Low) \ **Poverty:** 21% \ **Title I:** $600,009 \ **Open-Close:** 08/19 - 05/26 \ **DTBP:** $162 (High)

John Montanaro 1	Brian Stevens 2
Joe Brady 3,91*	Lisa Loomis 4*
Seanna Butler 5	Steve Locy 6*
Amy Beckwith 7,85*	William Mullane 8,11,57,83,286,288,296,298
Terry Furman 16*	Ginger Blabolil 58*
Phil Pawlowski 67	Mark Pickard 73*

Public Schs..Principal	Grd	Prgm	Enr/#Cls	SN	
Jefferson Area Jr High Sch 207 W Mulberry St Ste B, Jefferson 44047 Richard Hoyson	7-8	T	283	46%	440/576-4731 Fax 440/576-3082
Jefferson Area Sr High Sch 207 W Mulberry St Ste A, Jefferson 44047 Jeremy Huber	9-12	T	458 65	39%	440/576-4736 Fax 440/576-7344 t
Jefferson Elem Sch 204 W Mulberry St, Jefferson 44047 Steve Candela	K-6	T	617 50	51%	440/576-2646 Fax 440/576-0179
Rock Creek Elem Sch 3134 N Main St, Rock Creek 44084 Steve Candela	K-6	T	293 21	45%	440/563-3820 Fax 440/563-5609

• Pymatuning Valley Local SD   PID: 00784880
5571 US Route 6, Andover 44003
440/293-6488
Fax 440/293-7654

Schools: 3 \ **Teachers:** 63 \ **Students:** 1,200 \ **Special Ed Students:** 179 \ **LEP Students:** 4 \ **College-Bound:** 37% \ **Ethnic:** Hispanic 2%, Caucasian 98% \ **Exp:** $148 (Low) \ **Poverty:** 30% \ **Title I:** $834,842 \ **Open-Close:** 08/14 - 05/21 \ **DTBP:** $161 (High)

Chris Edison 1,11	Tom Brockway 2
William Dick 3,5,91*	Jeffrey Richards 4
Billie Williams 8,58,298*	Andrea Wonderling 27*
Curt Harvey 67	Cory Watts 73,295*
Dan Jackson 79*	Robert Wlyudyga 285

Public Schs..Principal	Grd	Prgm	Enr/#Cls	SN	
Pymatuning Valley High Sch 5571 US Route 6, Andover 44003 Dan Jackson	9-12	TV	308 50	72%	440/293-6263 Fax 440/293-7214
Pymatuning Valley Middle Sch 5445 US Route 6, Andover 44003 Hendrick Wolfert	5-8	T	376 35	65%	440/293-6981 Fax 440/293-7237
Pymatuning Valley Primary Sch 191 W Main St, Andover 44003 Lori Slekar	PK-4	T	476 22	71%	440/293-6206 Fax 440/293-5152

ASHTABULA CATHOLIC SCHOOLS

• Diocese of Youngstown Ed Off   PID: 00820915
Listing includes only schools located in this county. See District Index for location of Diocesan Offices.

Athens County

Catholic Schs..Principal | Grd | Prgm | Enr/#Cls SN

St John Sch — PK-12 — 250 — 440/997-5531
7911 Depot Rd, Ashtabula 44004 — 8 — Fax 440/998-1661
Scott Plescia

ASHTABULA PRIVATE SCHOOLS

Private Schs..Principal	Grd	Prgm	Enr/#Cls	SN
Grand River Academy 3042 College St, Austinburg 44010 Tim Oditt	9-12		100 20	440/275-2811 Fax 440/275-1825
Southridge Christian Academy 924 Center Rd, Conneaut 44030 Stuart Watson	PK-12		75 5	440/593-4657 Fax 440/593-4761

ATHENS COUNTY

ATHENS COUNTY SCHOOLS

- **Athens Meigs Ed Service Center** PID: 02089105 — 740/797-0064
  21 Birge Dr, Chauncey 45719 — Fax 740/797-0070

Heather Wolfe 1,73   Bryan Swann 2
Angie Gibbs 34   Lisa Bonner 58

County Schs..Principal	Grd	Prgm	Enr/#Cls	SN
Athens Meigs ESC 21 Birge Dr, Chauncey 45719 Rick Edwards	Spec		120	740/593-8001
Beacon Sch 801 W Union St, Athens 45701 Rebecca Maetin	Spec	G	50 6	740/594-3539 Fax 740/593-3189

ATHENS PUBLIC SCHOOLS

- **Alexander Local School Dist** PID: 00784971 — 740/698-8831
  6091 Ayers Rd, Albany 45710 — Fax 740/698-2038

Schools: 2 \ **Teachers:** 98 \ **Students:** 1,495 \ **Special Ed Students:** 286 \ **LEP Students:** 3 \ **College-Bound:** 60% \ **Ethnic:** Caucasian 99% \ **Exp:** $148 (Low) \ **Poverty:** 22% \ **Title I:** $578,893 \ **Special Education:** $374,000 \ **Open-Close:** 08/22 - 05/28 \ **DTBP:** $179 (High)

Lindy Douglas 1   Aaron Schirm 2
Bryan McCollum 3   Dan Phillips 5
Teresa Stalder 7   Sandy Clonch 8,11,69,286,288,296
Erin Roush 34,58,77   John Hutchison 67
Mark Rice 84,295

Public Schs..Principal	Grd	Prgm	Enr/#Cls	SN
Alexander Elem Sch 6105 School Rd, Albany 45710 Melissa Guffey	PK-5	T	720 26	740/698-8831 Fax 740/698-2137
Alexander Jr Sr High Sch 6125 School Rd, Albany 45710 Frank Doudna	6-12	T	775 45	100% 740/698-8831 Fax 740/698-3614

- **Athens City School Dist** PID: 00785028 — 740/797-4544
  25 S Plains Rd, The Plains 45780 — Fax 740/797-2486

Schools: 6 \ **Teachers:** 173 \ **Students:** 2,483 \ **Special Ed Students:** 414 \ **LEP Students:** 83 \ **College-Bound:** 68% \ **Ethnic:** Asian 4%, African American 2%, Hispanic 3%, Caucasian 91% \ **Exp:** $147 (Low) \ **Poverty:** 25% \ **Title I:** $995,401 \ **Special Education:** $495,000 \ **Open-Close:** 08/22 - 05/28 \ **DTBP:** $210 (High)

Dr Thomas Gibbs 1   Matt Bunting 2
Marvin Lawrence 3   Tamra Dicken 4
Sharon Ervin 5   Richard Guimond 6
Heidi Shaw 7,35,85   Tom Parsons 8,11,36,74,286,288,294,298
Tammy Hawk 16,73,95,297   Susan Powell 38
Nate Young 58   Kim Goldsberry 67
Steve Gunderson 73,84,295   Jeanna Sycks 78*
Amy Bentley 81   Chad Springer 83

Public Schs..Principal	Grd	Prgm	Enr/#Cls	SN
Acs Early Learning Center 21 Birge Dr, Chauncey 45719 Brandi Engle	PK-PK		37	740/797-4589 Fax 740/797-8119
Athens High Sch 1 High School Rd, The Plains 45780 David Hanning	9-12	AV	758	34% 740/797-4521 Fax 740/797-1421
Athens Middle Sch 51 W State St 55, Athens 45701 Kara Bolin	7-8	T	388 45	36% 740/593-7107 Fax 740/594-6506
East-West Elem Sch 41 Central Ave, Athens 45701 Jeanna Sycks	K-6		575 16	37% 740/593-6866 Fax 740/594-3178
Morrison Elem Sch 793 W Union St, Athens 45701 Penny McDowell	K-6		395 24	33% 740/593-5445 Fax 740/594-5362
The Plains Elem Sch 90 Connett Rd, The Plains 45780 Heather Skinner	K-6	T	421 22	80% 740/797-4572 Fax 740/797-4432

- **Federal Hocking Local Sch Dist** PID: 00785107 — 740/662-6691
  8461 State Route 144, Stewart 45778

Schools: 3 \ **Teachers:** 63 \ **Students:** 1,000 \ **Special Ed Students:** 220 \ **College-Bound:** 50% \ **Ethnic:** African American 2%, Hispanic 1%, Caucasian 97% \ **Exp:** $135 (Low) \ **Poverty:** 26% \ **Title I:** $528,429 \ **Special Education:** $246,000 \ **Open-Close:** 08/21 - 05/27 \ **DTBP:** $158 (High) \

David Hanning 1   Bruce Steenrod 2
Pat Tabler ....3,5,91*   Jamie Linscott 4*
Kirby Seeger ....6*   Jennifer Spero 8,11,296,298
Mary Mitchell ....9*   Amy Buchman 38,69,286
Jonathan Amlin 58   Dan Torrence 67
Jason Richard ....73,76*   Sonja Coble 73*
Damien Bawn 295

Public Schs..Principal	Grd	Prgm	Enr/#Cls	SN
Amesville Elem Sch State Route 329 N, Amesville 45711 Cathe Blower	PK-6	T	300 16	740/448-2501 Fax 740/448-3500
Coolville Elem Sch 26461 Main St, Coolville 45723 Mary Mitchell	PK-6	T	268 29	740/667-3121 Fax 740/667-6183
Federal Hocking Mid High Sch 8461 State Route 144, Stewart 45778 Cliff Bonner	7-12	AV	434 40	740/662-6691 Fax 740/662-3805

---

1 Superintendent	8 Curric/Instruct K-12	19 Chief Financial Officer	29 Family/Consumer Science	39 Social Studies K-12	49 English/Lang Arts Elem	59 Special Education Elem	69 Academic Assessment
2 Bus/Finance/Purchasing	9 Curric/Instruct Elem	20 Art K-12	30 Adult Education	40 Social Studies Elem	50 English/Lang Arts Sec	60 Special Education Sec	70 Research/Development
3 Buildings And Grounds	10 Curric/Instruct Sec	21 Art Elem	31 Career/Sch-to-Work K-12	41 Social Studies Sec	51 Reading K-12	61 Foreign/World Lang K-12	71 Public Information
4 Food Service	11 Federal Program	22 Art Sec	32 Career/Sch-to-Work Elem	42 Science K-12	52 Reading Elem	62 Foreign/World Lang Elem	72 Summer School
5 Transportation	12 Title I	23 Music K-12	33 Career/Sch-to-Work Sec	43 Science Elem	53 Reading Sec	63 Foreign/World Lang Sec	73 Instructional Tech
6 Athletic	13 Title V	24 Music Elem	34 Early Childhood Ed	44 Science Sec	54 Remedial Reading K-12	64 Religious Education K-12	74 Inservice Training
7 Health Services	14 Instructional Media Svcs	25 Music Sec	35 Health/Phys Education	45 Math K-12	55 Remedial Reading Elem	65 Religious Education Elem	75 Marketing/Distributive
	15 Asst Superintendent	26 Business Education	36 Guidance Services K-12	46 Math Elem	56 Remedial Reading Sec	66 Religious Education Sec	76 Info Systems
	16 Chief Operations Officer	27 Career & Tech Ed	37 Guidance Services Elem	47 Math Sec	57 Bilingual/ELL	67 School Board President	77 Psychological Assess
	17 Chief Academic Officer	28 Technology Education	38 Guidance Services Sec	48 English/Lang Arts K-12	58 Special Education K-12	68 Teacher Personnel	78 Affirmative Action

Ohio School Directory | Auglaize County

• **Nelsonville-York City Sch Dist** PID: 00785157   740/753-4441
2 Buckeye Dr, Nelsonville 45764   Fax 740/753-1968

Schools: 3 \ **Teachers:** 80 \ **Students:** 1,206 \ **Special Ed Students:** 263 \ **LEP Students:** 3 \ **College-Bound:** 54% \ **Ethnic:** African American 1%, Hispanic 1%, Caucasian 98% \ **Exp:** $212 (Med) \ **Poverty:** 28% \ **Title I:** $612,648 \ **Special Education:** $274,000 \ **Open-Close:** 08/19 - 05/26 \ **DTBP:** $176 (High)

Rick Edwards 1
Paul Huston 3,91
Elden Dexter 5
Autumn Carlson 7,83,85
Tina McWilliams 11,34,54,58,83,296,298*
Jay Saner 73,295
Sandi Hurd 2,294
Patrick Janiszewski 4
Rusty Richards 6
Amy Riccardi 8,69,273,286
Micah Covert 67
Ginger Stotts 76

Public Schs..Principal	Grd	Prgm	Enr/#Cls	SN	
Nelsonville-York Elem Sch 4 Buckeye Dr, Nelsonville 45764 Becky Steenrod	PK-6	T	706 43	70%	740/753-5145 Fax 740/753-6207
Nelsonville-York High Sch 1 Buckeye Dr, Nelsonville 45764 Elise Stephan	9-12	T	327 30	96%	740/753-1964 Fax 740/753-1420
Nelsonville-York Jr High Sch 3 Buckeye Dr, Nelsonville 45764 Tom Taggart	7-8	T	173 18		740/753-1254 Fax 740/753-9450

• **Tri-Co Joint Voc Sch Dist** PID: 00785262   740/753-3511
15676 State Route 691, Nelsonville 45764   Fax 740/753-5127

Schools: 1 \ **Teachers:** 38 \ **Students:** 450 \ **College-Bound:** 50% \ **Exp:** $389 (High) \ **Open-Close:** 08/20 - 05/22 \ **DTBP:** $118 (High)

Connie Altier 1,11
Kelly Leffler 3,30*
Jana Chapman 16,82*
Steve Wheeler 69*
Kim Jarvis 273*
Laura Dukes 2
Connie Stage 4*
Bruce Nottke 67
Mindy Ingram 76

Public Schs..Principal	Grd	Prgm	Enr/#Cls	SN	
Tri-Co Career Center 15676 State Route 691, Nelsonville 45764 Tom McGreevy	Voc	G	450 50		740/753-3511 Fax 740/753-5376

• **Trimble Local School Dist** PID: 00785224   740/767-4444
1 Tomcat Dr, Glouster 45732   Fax 740/767-4901

Schools: 3 \ **Teachers:** 59 \ **Students:** 900 \ **Special Ed Students:** 189 \ **College-Bound:** 48% \ **Ethnic:** African American 1%, Caucasian 99% \ **Exp:** $242 (Med) \ **Poverty:** 31% \ **Title I:** $500,689 \ **Special Education:** $174,000 \ **Open-Close:** 08/14 - 05/27 \ **DTBP:** $185 (High)

John Hurd 1
Billie Limo 4*
Austin Downs 6
Matt Curtis 8*
Michael Kunzler 16,73,273,295*
Dave Owen 67
Jared Bunting 2,11
Bob Lowery 5
Dr Diane Hobson 8,288*
Jaime Taylor 9,12,273
Thadius Fields 58
Valerie Ives 81*

Public Schs..Principal	Grd	Prgm	Enr/#Cls	SN	
Trimble Elem Sch 18500 Jacksonville Rd, Glouster 45732 Jamie Taylor	PK-5	T	350 30		740/767-2810 Fax 740/767-9523
Trimble High Sch 1 Tomcat Dr, Glouster 45732 Matt Curtis	9-12	T	213 35		740/767-3434
Trimble Middle Sch 18500 Jacksonville Rd, Glouster 45732 Jamie Taylor	6-8	T	200 25		740/767-2810 Fax 740/767-9523

ATHENS REGIONAL CENTERS

• **SE Ohio Voluntary Ed Co-op** PID: 04499611   740/594-7663
221 Columbus Rd, Athens 45701   Fax 740/592-6251

Jimmy Battrell 1
Jeremy Jones 295
Jessica James 2

• **State Support Team-Region 16** PID: 02228325   740/797-0150
21 Birge Dr, Chauncey 45719   Fax 740/797-0154

Heather Wolfe 1
Angie Gibbs 34

AUGLAIZE COUNTY

AUGLAIZE COUNTY SCHOOLS

• **Auglaize Co Ed Service Center** PID: 00785559   419/738-3422
1045 Dearbaugh Ave Ste 2, Wapakoneta 45895   Fax 419/738-1267

Shawn Brown 1
Vaughn Ray 8
Lisa Tobin 8
Amy Becher 58

AUGLAIZE PUBLIC SCHOOLS

• **Minster Local School Dist** PID: 00785286   419/628-3397
50 E 7th St, Minster 45865   Fax 419/628-2482

Schools: 2 \ **Teachers:** 51 \ **Students:** 849 \ **Special Ed Students:** 108 \ **LEP Students:** 3 \ **College-Bound:** 81% \ **Ethnic:** Asian 1%, African American 1%, Hispanic 2%, Caucasian 97% \ **Exp:** $243 (Med) \ **Poverty:** 4% \ **Title I:** $29,129 \ **Special Education:** $141,000 \ **Open-Close:** 09/03 - 05/28 \ **DTBP:** $174 (High)

Brenda Boeke 1,11
Mike Timmerman 3*
Josh Clune 5,6*
Austin Kaylor 10
Kurt Forsthoesfel 67
Laura Klosterman 2
Donna Borges 4*
Leanne Keller 9*
Melissa Vtrup 38,83*
Doug Axe 73*

Public Schs..Principal	Grd	Prgm	Enr/#Cls	SN	
Minster Elem Sch 50 E 7th St, Minster 45865 Leanne Keller	K-6		427 15	13%	419/628-4174
Minster Jr/Sr High Sch 100 E 7th St, Minster 45865 Jason Spencer	7-12	V	410 21	7%	419/628-2324 Fax 419/628-2495

---

79 Student Personnel	91 Safety/Security	275 Response To Intervention	298 Grant Writer/Ptnrships	**School Programs**	**Social Media**
80 Driver Ed/Safety	92 Magnet School	277 Remedial Math K-12	750 Chief Innovation Officer	A = Alternative Program	
81 Gifted/Talented	93 Parental Involvement	280 Literacy Coach	751 Chief of Staff	G = Adult Classes	❡ = Facebook
82 Video Services	95 Tech Prep Program	285 STEM	752 Social Emotional Learning	M = Magnet Program	
83 Substance Abuse Prev	97 Chief Infomation Officer	286 Digital Learning		T = Title I Schoolwide	❡ = Twitter
84 Erate	98 Chief Technology Officer	288 Common Core Standards	**Other School Types**	V = Career & Tech Ed Programs	
85 AIDS Education	270 Character Education	294 Accountability	Ⓐ = Alternative School		
88 Alternative/At Risk	271 Migrant Education	295 Network System	Ⓒ = Charter School	New Schools are shaded	
89 Multi-Cultural Curriculum	273 Teacher Mentor	296 Title II Programs	Ⓜ = Magnet School	New Superintendents and Principals are bold	
90 Social Work	274 Before/After Sch	297 Webmaster	Ⓨ = Year-Round School	Personnel with email addresses are underscored	

OH—15

Auglaize County

New Bremen Local School Dist PID: 00785315
901 E Monroe St, New Bremen 45869
419/629-8606
Fax 419/629-0115

Schools: 2 \ **Teachers:** 56 \ **Students:** 760 \ **Special Ed Students:** 79 \ **LEP Students:** 7 \ **College-Bound:** 71% \ **Ethnic:** Asian 1%, African American 1%, Hispanic 2%, Caucasian 97% \ **Exp:** $154 (Low) \ **Poverty:** 3% \ **Title I:** $32,147 \ **Special Education:** $147,000 \ **Open-Close:** 08/14 - 05/11 \ **DTBP:** $175 (High) \

Jason Schrader 1,11,57	Jill Ahlers 2
Jeremy Krieg 3,91	Mary Williams 4*
Rob Sniegowski 5	Chad Wells 6*
Diane Kramer 9,12,51,54,85*	Marcus Overman 10,31,83
Shelley This 16,82*	Lauren Link 37*
Tricia Wendel 38,69,88*	Shelly Busse 67
Brian Puthoff 73,295	Mike Heuker 285*

Public Schs..Principal	Grd	Prgm	Enr/#Cls	SN	
New Bremen Elem Sch 202 S Walnut St 210, New Bremen 45869 Diane Kramer	K-8		514 40	7%	419/629-3244 Fax 419/629-8113
New Bremen High Sch 901 E Monroe St, New Bremen 45869 Marcus Overman	9-12	V	238 26	7%	419/629-8606

New Knoxville Local Sch Dist PID: 00785341
345 S Main St, New Knoxville 45871
419/753-2431
Fax 419/753-2333

Schools: 1 \ **Teachers:** 31 \ **Students:** 392 \ **Special Ed Students:** 33 \ **LEP Students:** 3 \ **College-Bound:** 72% \ **Exp:** $206 (Med) \ **Poverty:** 6% \ **Title I:** $26,359 \ **Special Education:** $69,000 \ **Open-Close:** 08/20 - 05/21 \ **DTBP:** $190 (High)

Kimberly Waterman 1,11	Amy Reineke 2
Scott Schroer 3*	Sherry Zwiep 4*
Kay Webb 6*	Marna Katterheinrich 12*
Jennifer Heitkamp 36*	Dawn Houser 54,59*
Jenny Ruhenkamp 60*	Shawn Eggbert 67
Nick Wirwille 73*	Leslie Krieg 76

Public Schs..Principal	Grd	Prgm	Enr/#Cls	SN
New Knoxville Sch 345 S Main St, New Knoxville 45871 Kimberly Waterman \ Jenny Fledderjohann	K-12		392 50	419/753-2431

St Mary's City School Dist PID: 00785365
2250 State Route 66, Saint Marys 45885
419/394-4312
Fax 419/394-5638

Schools: 4 \ **Teachers:** 123 \ **Students:** 1,996 \ **Special Ed Students:** 325 \ **LEP Students:** 4 \ **College-Bound:** 47% \ **Ethnic:** African American 1%, Hispanic 2%, Caucasian 97% \ **Exp:** $128 (Low) \ **Poverty:** 11% \ **Title I:** $323,184 \ **Special Education:** $472,000 \ **Open-Close:** 08/20 - 05/21 \ **DTBP:** $177 (High)

Bill Ruane 1	Greg Adams 3*
Nicole Rasmussen 4*	Dan Grothause 5,91
Tim Hollman 6*	Diana Halco 7,85
Kim Overman 8,12,81*	Cary Roehm 58*
Brian Little 67	Kyle Menchhofer 73,295
Sara Dieringer 77*	Nathan Overley 295

Public Schs..Principal	Grd	Prgm	Enr/#Cls	SN	
St Marys Intermediate Sch 1301 W High St, Saint Marys 45885 Lisa Elson	3-5	T	437 23	40%	419/394-2016 Fax 419/394-1881

Market Data Retrieval

St Marys Memorial High Sch 2250 State Route 66, Saint Marys 45885 John Burke	9-12		783 52	419/394-4011 Fax 419/394-1932
St Marys Middle Sch 2250 State Route 66, Saint Marys 45885 Mary Miller	6-8	T	465 25	82% 419/394-2112 Fax 419/394-3022
St Marys Primary Sch 650 Armstrong St, Saint Marys 45885 Sue Sherman	K-2	T	398 35	46% 419/394-2616 Fax 419/394-1149

Wapakoneta City School Dist PID: 00785444
1102 Gardenia Dr, Wapakoneta 45895
419/739-2900
Fax 419/739-2918

Schools: 4 \ **Teachers:** 143 \ **Students:** 3,081 \ **Special Ed Students:** 453 \ **LEP Students:** 14 \ **College-Bound:** 53% \ **Ethnic:** Asian 1%, Hispanic 2%, Caucasian 97% \ **Exp:** $208 (Med) \ **Poverty:** 12% \ **Title I:** $444,664 \ **Special Education:** $598,000 \ **Open-Close:** 08/20 - 05/21 \ **DTBP:** $195 (High)

Aaron Rex 1	Mike Watt 2,3,5,16,27,91
Todd Gerstner 3	Lori McKean 4*
David Tangeman 5	Brad Rex 6*
Jeanne Van Horn 7*	Erin Recks 11,288
Cheri Brandt 12*	Elise Minick 13,34,77*
Dede Pulley 16*	Kim Metz 36*
Carrie Knoch 54,69,273,274,280*	Scott Minnig 57*
Kassie Hill 58	Ronald Mertz 67
Nick Shrider 73,76,295	Nikki Sutton 93*

Public Schs..Principal	Grd	Prgm	Enr/#Cls	SN	
Cridersville Elem Sch 501 Reichelderfer Rd, Cridersville 45806 Jason Wolke	PK-4	T	310 14	60%	419/645-3000 Fax 419/645-3003
Wapakoneta Elem Sch 900 N Blackhoof St, Wapakoneta 45895 Mark Selvaggio	PK-4	T	916 39	40%	419/739-5000 Fax 419/739-5051
Wapakoneta High Sch 1 Redskin Trl, Wapakoneta 45895 Scott Minnig	8-12	A	1,100 70	48%	419/739-5200 Fax 419/739-5306
Wapakoneta Middle Sch 400 W Harrison St, Wapakoneta 45895 Will Snyder	5-7	T	755 32	47%	419/739-5100 Fax 419/739-5165

Waynesfield-Goshen Local SD PID: 00785523
500 N Westminster St, Waynesfield 45896
419/568-9100
Fax 419/568-8024

Schools: 2 \ **Teachers:** 38 \ **Students:** 500 \ **Special Ed Students:** 57 \ **College-Bound:** 51% \ **Ethnic:** African American 1%, Hispanic 1%, Caucasian 98% \ **Exp:** $201 (Med) \ **Poverty:** 10% \ **Title I:** $72,201 \ **Special Education:** $101,000 \ **Open-Close:** 08/15 - 05/21 \ **DTBP:** $181 (High) \

Chris Pfister 1	Tonia Hovest 2,11
Tim Buffenbarger 3*	Brett Purcell 6*
Tim Pence 12,58,69*	Chelsea Junkins 31*
Abby Dellinger 37*	Kyley Jordan 57*
Tom Brookhart 67	Brian Shaw 73*

Public Schs..Principal	Grd	Prgm	Enr/#Cls	SN	
Waynesfield-Goshen Elem Sch 500 N Westminster St, Waynesfield 45896 Tim Pence	PK-5	TV	261 43		419/568-9100 Fax 419/568-9120
Waynesfield-Goshen Mid/Hi Sch 500 N Westminster St, Waynesfield 45896 Brian Hogan	6-12	V	226	58%	419/568-9100

1	Superintendent	8	Curric/Instruct K-12	19	Chief Financial Officer	29	Family/Consumer Science	39 Social Studies K-12	49 English/Lang Arts Elem	59 Special Education Elem	69 Academic Assessment
2	Bus/Finance/Purchasing	9	Curric/Instruct Elem	20	Art K-12	30	Adult Education	40 Social Studies Elem	50 English/Lang Arts Sec	60 Special Education Sec	70 Research/Development
3	Buildings And Grounds	10	Curric/Instruct Sec	21	Art Elem	31	Career/Sch-to-Work K-12	41 Social Studies Sec	51 Reading K-12	61 Foreign/World Lang K-12	71 Public Information
4	Food Service	11	Federal Program	22	Art Sec	32	Career/Sch-to-Work Elem	42 Science K-12	52 Reading Elem	62 Foreign/World Lang Elem	72 Summer School
5	Transportation	12	Title I	23	Music K-12	33	Career/Sch-to-Work Sec	43 Science Elem	53 Reading Sec	63 Foreign/World Lang Sec	73 Instructional Tech
6	Athletic	13	Title V	24	Music Elem	34	Early Childhood Ed	44 Science Sec	54 Remedial Reading K-12	64 Religious Education K-12	74 Inservice Training
7	Health Services	15	Asst Superintendent	25	Music Sec	35	Health/Phys Education	45 Math K-12	55 Remedial Reading Elem	65 Religious Education Elem	75 Marketing/Distributive
		16	Instructional Media Svcs	26	Business Education	36	Guidance Services K-12	46 Math Elem	56 Remedial Reading Sec	66 Religious Education Sec	76 Info Systems
		17	Chief Operations Officer	27	Career & Tech Ed	37	Guidance Services Elem	47 Math Sec	57 Bilingual/ELL	67 School Board President	77 Psychological Assess
		18	Chief Academic Officer	28	Technology Education	38	Guidance Services Sec	48 English/Lang Arts K-12	58 Special Education K-12	68 Teacher Personnel	78 Affirmative Action

Ohio School Directory — Belmont County

AUGLAIZE CATHOLIC SCHOOLS

• **Archdiocese Cincinnati Ed Off** PID: 00808096
Listing includes only schools located in this county. See District Index for location of Diocesan Offices.

Catholic Schs..Principal	Grd	Prgm	Enr/#Cls	SN	
Holy Rosary Sch	PK-8		158		419/394-5291
128 S Pine St, Saint Marys 45885			10		Fax 419/394-0184
Lora Krugh					f

AUGLAIZE PRIVATE SCHOOLS

Private Schs..Principal	Grd	Prgm	Enr/#Cls	SN	
Grand Lake Christian Sch	PK-12		61		419/300-9001
1001 Holly St Ste A, Saint Marys 45885			9		Fax 419/300-9011
Michael Miller					

AUGLAIZE REGIONAL CENTERS

• **State Support Team-Region 6** PID: 02228349 419/738-9224
1045 Dearbaugh Ave Ste 1, Wapakoneta 45895 Fax 419/738-9199

Rebecca Rees 1   Cherie Smith 36,58,77

BELMONT COUNTY

BELMONT COUNTY SCHOOLS

• **East Central Ohio ESC-St Clair** PID: 02089117 740/695-9773
67400 Betty Lee Way, St Clairsvle 43950 Fax 866/422-3216

Randy Lucas 1   Matt King 2
Lori Robson 8,298   Melanie Cronebach 58
Nicholas Brown 73   Lisa Stupak 81
Edward Chanoski 88

County Schs..Principal	Grd	Prgm	Enr/#Cls	SN	
Ⓐ Belmont Co Alt Program	K-12		30		740/695-9773
68353 Bannock Rd, St Clairsvle 43950			3		
Leslie Kosanovic					

BELMONT PUBLIC SCHOOLS

• **Barnesville Exempted Vlg SD** PID: 00785561 740/425-3615
210 W Church St, Barnesville 43713 Fax 740/425-5000

Schools: 3 \ **Teachers:** 84 \ **Students:** 1,480 \ **Special Ed Students:** 156 \ **LEP Students:** 3 \ **College-Bound:** 56% \ **Ethnic:** Hispanic 1%, Caucasian 99% \ **Exp:** $269 (Med) \ **Poverty:** 15% \ **Title I:** $258,430 \ **Special Education:** $267,000 \ **Open-Close:** 08/19 - 05/22 \ **DTBP:** $177 (High)

Angela Hanahs 1   Cheryl Pritts 2
John Blotler 3,5   Mark Cook 4
Mark Cook .... 6*   Micah Fuchs 8,11,58,69,288,296,298*
Melissa McMillen 12   Lisa Gallagher 16*
Natasha Shilling .... 38*   Robert Miller 67
Andrew Daugherty .... 73,76,286*   Vicki Klatt 77*

Public Schs..Principal	Grd	Prgm	Enr/#Cls	SN	
Barnesville Elem Sch	PK-4	T	622	40%	740/425-3639
210 W Church St, Barnesville 43713			21		Fax 740/425-1136
Clinton Abbott					
Barnesville High Sch	9-12	TV	355	32%	740/425-3617
910 Shamrock Dr, Barnesville 43713			25		Fax 740/425-9254
Ron Clark					
Barnesville Middle Sch	5-8	T	427	39%	740/425-3116
970 Shamrock Dr, Barnesville 43713			25		Fax 740/425-9204
Casey Mayo					

• **Bellaire Local School Dist** PID: 00785597 740/676-1826
340 34th St, Bellaire 43906 Fax 740/671-6002

Schools: 3 \ **Teachers:** 51 \ **Students:** 1,159 \ **Special Ed Students:** 242 \ **College-Bound:** 39% \ **Ethnic:** African American 4%, Hispanic 1%, Caucasian 95% \ **Exp:** $195 (Low) \ **Poverty:** 22% \ **Title I:** $482,777 \ **Special Education:** $244,000 \ **Open-Close:** 08/22 - 05/25 \ **DTBP:** $188 (High)

Darren Jenkins 1   Cathy Moore 2
Jim Hill 3,4,5,91   Molly Feller 6*
Shay Young 8   Darrin Jenkins 11*
Rebecca Zwack .... 57*   John LaRoche 67
Susan Klempa .... 72*   Terry Savage 77
Wendy Ware .... 79*   Jennifer Kaczor 81*
Ben Doyle 285

Public Schs..Principal	Grd	Prgm	Enr/#Cls	SN	
Bellaire Elem Sch	PK-4	T	463	73%	740/676-1272
53299 Pike St, Bellaire 43906			37		Fax 740/671-6010
Ben Doyle					
Bellaire High Sch	9-12	T	331	48%	740/676-3652
349 35th St, Bellaire 43906			32		Fax 740/671-6024
Derrick McAfee					
Bellaire Middle Sch	5-8	T	365	60%	740/676-1635
54555 Bellaire-Neffs Rd, Bellaire 43906			30		Fax 740/676-3014
Derrick McAfee					

• **Belmont-Harrison Voc Sch Dist** PID: 00786008 740/695-9130
68090 Hammond Rd, St Clairsvle 43950 Fax 740/695-5340

Schools: 2 \ **Teachers:** 48 \ **Students:** 408 \ **College-Bound:** 75% \ **Exp:** $604 (High) \ **Open-Close:** 08/22 - 05/22 \ **DTBP:** $214 (High)

---

79 Student Personnel	91 Safety/Security	275 Response To Intervention	298 Grant Writer/Ptnrships	**School Programs**	**Social Media**
80 Driver Ed/Safety	92 Magnet School	277 Remedial Math K-12	750 Chief Innovation Officer	A = Alternative Program	f = Facebook
81 Gifted/Talented	93 Parental Involvement	280 Literacy Coach	751 Chief of Staff	G = Adult Classes	t = Twitter
82 Video Services	95 Tech Prep Program	285 STEM	752 Social Emotional Learning	M = Magnet Program	
83 Substance Abuse Prev	97 Chief Information Officer	286 Digital Learning		T = Title I Schoolwide	
84 Erate	98 Chief Technology Officer	288 Common Core Standards	**Other School Types**	V = Career & Tech Ed Programs	
85 AIDS Education	270 Character Education	294 Accountability	Ⓐ = Alternative Program		
88 Alternative/At Risk	271 Migrant Education	295 Network System	Ⓒ = Charter School	New Schools are shaded	
89 Multi-Cultural Curriculum	273 Teacher Mentor	296 Title II Programs	Ⓜ = Magnet School	New Superintendents and Principals are bold	
90 Social Work	274 Before/After Sch	297 Webmaster	Ⓨ = Year-Round School	Personnel with email addresses are underscored	

OH-17

Belmont County

Market Data Retrieval

Richard Schoene 1
Heather Hanson 10,68*
Roger Stewart 67
Mark Lucas 2
Paula Norman 60,69*
Jack Fisher 275*

Public Schs..Principal	Grd	Prgm	Enr/#Cls	SN	
Belmont Career Center 68090 Hammond Rd, St Clairsvle 43950 **Ryan Caldwell**	Voc	A	300 35		740/695-9130
Harrison Career Center 82500 Jewett Rd, Cadiz 43907 **Larry Bossell**	Voc	A	108 12		740/942-2148 Fax 740/695-4866

● **Bridgeport School Dist** PID: 00785690 740/635-1713
55781 National Rd, Bridgeport 43912 Fax 740/635-6003

Schools: 3 \ *Teachers:* 49 \ *Students:* 820 \ *Special Ed Students:* 114 \ *College-Bound:* 47% \ *Ethnic:* African American 5%, Hispanic 2%, Caucasian 94% \ *Exp:* $356 (High) \ *Poverty:* 25% \ *Title I:* $415,159 \ *Special Education:* $197,000 \ *Open-Close:* 08/22 - 05/22 \ *DTBP:* $220 (High)

Brent Ripley 1
Anthony Eden 3,5
Leslie Kosanovic 8,288
Raymond Wukeson 21*
Sarah Donley 57*
Don Cash 67
Jean Hartman 77*
Sharon Liston 273*
Dana Garrison 2,4,11,296,298
Greg Harkness 6
Lisa Clark 11,16,73,280,285,286*
Vicki Falcone 31,38,69*
Beverly Prati 58*
Frank Ferrel 76,295*
Holly Garven 83,85,88

Public Schs..Principal	Grd	Prgm	Enr/#Cls	SN	
Bridgeport Elem Sch 55707 Industrial Dr, Bridgeport 43912 **Kamaron Sabinski**	PK-4	T	370 10		740/635-0853 Fax 740/635-6009
Bridgeport High Sch 55707 Industrial Dr, Bridgeport 43912 **Tom Daley**	9-12	ATV	191 20	99%	740/635-0853 Fax 740/635-6008
Bridgeport Middle Sch 55707 Industrial Dr, Bridgeport 43912 **Anne Haverty**	5-8	T	215		740/635-0853 Fax 740/635-6008

● **Martins Ferry City School Dist** PID: 00785743 740/633-1732
5001 Ayers Lime Stone Rd, Martins Ferry 43935 Fax 740/633-5666

Schools: 3 \ *Teachers:* 39 \ *Students:* 1,500 \ *Special Ed Students:* 284 \ *College-Bound:* 50% \ *Ethnic:* African American 6%, Hispanic 2%, Caucasian 91% \ *Exp:* $156 (Low) \ *Poverty:* 21% \ *Title I:* $508,100 \ *Special Education:* $364,000 \ *Open-Close:* 08/20 - 05/21 \ *DTBP:* $212 (High)

Jim Fogle 1
Todd Yoder 3
Randell Reasdeck 5
Sue Ferrelli 8,11,57,69,288*
Jodi Jackfert 58,77
Bruce Hotlosz 73,285*
Karen Blake 2
Rhonda Yoder 4
Kim Appolloni 6,16,76,79*
John Bennett 16,38,45,83,88*
Nick Stankovich 67
Barb McKeegan 81*

Public Schs..Principal	Grd	Prgm	Enr/#Cls	SN	
Ayers Elem Sch 5002 Ayers Lime Stone Rd, Martins Ferry 43935 **Nickolas Stankovich**	PK-4	T	594 11	61%	740/633-3754 Fax 740/633-5918
Martins Ferry High Sch 5000 Ayers Lime Stone Rd, Martins Ferry 43935 **Joe Mamone**	9-12	ATV	416 40	99%	740/633-0684 Fax 740/635-6103
Martins Ferry Middle Sch 5000 Ayers Lime Stone Rd, Martins Ferry 43935 **Mike Delatore**	5-8	T	470 20		740/633-9741 Fax 740/635-6107

● **Shadyside Local School Dist** PID: 00785834 740/676-3235
3890 Lincoln Ave, Shadyside 43947 Fax 740/676-6616

Schools: 3 \ *Teachers:* 47 \ *Students:* 800 \ *Special Ed Students:* 98 \ *College-Bound:* 58% \ *Ethnic:* Hispanic 2%, Caucasian 98% \ *Exp:* $67 (Low) \ *Poverty:* 11% \ *Title I:* $104,254 \ *Special Education:* $174,000 \ *Open-Close:* 08/21 - 05/26 \ *DTBP:* $233 (High)

John Haswell 1
Robert Crozier 3,5
Leslie Kosanovic 8
Mark Figalkowski 67
Melissa Visnic 2
Cynthia Caldwell 4,273*
Kevin Roseberry 11*
John Grinch 73*

Public Schs..Principal	Grd	Prgm	Enr/#Cls	SN	
Jefferson Avenue Elem Sch 4895 Jefferson Ave, Shadyside 43947 **Cynthia Caldwell**	PK-2		207 17	37%	740/676-9669 Fax 740/671-5002
Leona Middle Sch 3795 Leona Ave, Shadyside 43947 **Kevin Roseberry**	3-6	T	236 13	66%	740/676-9220 Fax 740/671-5003
Shadyside High Sch 3890 Lincoln Ave, Shadyside 43947 **John Poilek**	7-12	V	363 35		740/676-3235

● **St Clairsville-Richland CSD** PID: 00785884 740/695-1624
108 Woodrow Ave, St Clairsvle 43950 Fax 740/695-1627

Schools: 3 \ *Teachers:* 93 \ *Students:* 1,700 \ *Special Ed Students:* 176 \ *LEP Students:* 5 \ *College-Bound:* 72% \ *Ethnic:* Asian 1%, African American 1%, Hispanic 1%, Caucasian 96% \ *Exp:* $172 (Low) \ *Poverty:* 6% \ *Title I:* $175,344 \ *Special Education:* $330,000 \ *Open-Close:* 08/20 - 05/22 \ *DTBP:* $236 (High)

Walt Skaggs 1
Lowell Perkins 4
Karry Sheperd 7,83,85
Diane Thompson 11,58,296,298
Jim Yates 73,84,95,295
Tammy Weisal 294
Amy Porter 2,19
Luke Nelson 6
Christina Sirbaugh 8
Michael Jacob 67
Corey Heilman 77*

Public Schs..Principal	Grd	Prgm	Enr/#Cls	SN	
St Clairsville Elem Sch 120 Norris St, St Clairsvle 43950 **Amber Shepherd-Smith**	PK-4	T	659 35	32%	740/695-0884 Fax 740/695-2753
St Clairsville High Sch 102 Woodrow Ave, St Clairsvle 43950 **Justin Sleutz**	9-12	AV	571 30		740/695-1584 Fax 740/695-2513
St Clairsville Middle Sch 104 Woodrow Ave, St Clairsvle 43950 **Michael McKeever**	5-8		490 40	63%	740/695-1591 Fax 740/695-2317

● **Union Local School Dist** PID: 00785937 740/782-1208
66779 Belmont Morristown Rd, Belmont 43718 Fax 740/782-1212

Schools: 3 \ *Teachers:* 107 \ *Students:* 1,521 \ *Special Ed Students:* 214 \ *College-Bound:* 53% \ *Ethnic:* Caucasian 100% \ *Exp:* $326 (High) \ *Poverty:* 10% \ *Title I:* $192,205 \ *Special Education:* $372,000 \ *Open-Close:* 08/21 - 05/22 \ *DTBP:* $170 (High)

Ben Porter 1,11
Rod Roby 3,4,5
Tracey Childress 7*
Dana Kendziorski 12*
Rhonda Eberhart 36,83,85,88*
Kelsey Wise 69,77*
Mike Menges 91*
Janet Hissrich 2
Nick Nardo 6*
Jayme Yonak 8,58
Jeffrey Bazzarri 16,73,95,295*
Daniel Lukus 67
Jeff Bizzarri 84
Ronald Bober 273*

1	Superintendent	8	Curric/Instruct K-12	19	Chief Financial Officer	29	Family/Consumer Science	39	Social Studies K-12	49	English/Lang Arts Elem	59	Special Education Elem	69	Academic Assessment
2	Bus/Finance/Purchasing	9	Curric/Instruct Elem	20	Art K-12	30	Adult Education	40	Social Studies Elem	50	English/Lang Arts Sec	60	Special Education Sec	70	Research/Development
3	Buildings And Grounds	10	Curric/Instruct Sec	21	Art Elem	31	Career/Sch-to-Work K-12	41	Social Studies Sec	51	Reading K-12	61	Foreign/World Lang K-12	71	Public Information
4	Food Service	11	Federal Program	22	Art Sec	32	Career/Sch-to-Work Elem	42	Science K-12	52	Reading Elem	62	Foreign/World Lang Elem	72	Summer School
5	Transportation	12	Title I	23	Music K-12	33	Career/Sch-to-Work Sec	43	Science Elem	53	Reading Sec	63	Foreign/World Lang Sec	73	Instructional Tech
6	Athletic	13	Title V	24	Music Elem	34	Early Childhood Ed	44	Science Sec	54	Remedial Reading K-12	64	Religious Education K-12	74	Inservice Training
7	Health Services	14	Asst Superintendent	25	Music Sec	35	Health/Phys Education	45	Math K-12	55	Remedial Reading Elem	65	Religious Education Elem	75	Marketing/Distributive
		15	Instructional Media Svcs	26	Business Education	36	Guidance Services K-12	46	Math Elem	56	Remedial Reading Sec	66	Religious Education Sec	76	Info Systems
		17	Chief Operations Officer	27	Career & Tech Ed	37	Guidance Services Elem	47	Math Sec	57	Bilingual/ELL	67	School Board President	77	Psychological Assess
		18	Chief Academic Officer	28	Technology Education	38	Guidance Services Sec	48	English/Lang Arts K-12	58	Special Education K-12	68	Teacher Personnel	78	Affirmative Action

Ohio School Directory

Helen Puperi 298

Public Schs..Principal	Grd	Prgm	Enr/#Cls	SN	
Union Local Elem Sch 66699 Belmont Morristown Rd, Belmont 43718 Dana Kendziorski \ Zach Powell	PK-5	T	723 34	44%	740/782-1384 Fax 740/782-0181
Union Local High Sch 66779 Belmont Morristown Rd, Belmont 43718 Joel Davia	9-12	V	380 50	45%	740/782-1181 Fax 740/782-1346
Union Local Middle Sch 66859 Belmont Morristown Rd, Belmont 43718 Rick Barnhouse	6-8	T	347 30	41%	740/782-1388 Fax 740/782-1474

BELMONT CATHOLIC SCHOOLS

• **Diocese of Steubenville Ed Off** PID: 00812671
Listing includes only schools located in this county. See District Index for location of Diocesan Offices.

Catholic Schs..Principal	Grd	Prgm	Enr/#Cls	SN	
St John Central Academy 3625 Guernsey St, Bellaire 43906 Selena Brooks	PK-12		150 24		740/676-4932 Fax 740/676-4934
St Mary Central Sch 24 N 4th St, Martins Ferry 43935 Theresa Young	PK-8		129 12		740/633-5424 Fax 740/633-5462
St Mary Central Sch 226 W Main St, St Clairsvle 43950 Nannette Kennedy	PK-8		160 12		740/695-3189 Fax 740/695-3851

BELMONT PRIVATE SCHOOLS

Private Schs..Principal	Grd	Prgm	Enr/#Cls	SN	
Barnesville Ind Elem Sch 998 Shamrock Dr, Barnesville 43713 Clinton Abbott	K-8		37 4		740/425-3420
East Richland Christian Sch 67888 Friends Church Rd, St Clairsvle 43950 Adam Mitchell	PK-12		198 12		740/695-2281 Fax 740/296-5219
Fox Run Sch 67670 Traco Dr, St Clairsvle 43950 Ed Chanoski	K-12		65 14		740/695-2131 Fax 740/695-7158
Martins Ferry Christian Sch 710 S Zane Hwy, Martins Ferry 43935 Becky Hill	K-7		80 6		740/633-0199 Fax 740/633-0974
Olney Friends Sch 61830 Sandy Ridge Rd, Barnesville 43713 Christian Acemah	9-12	V	46 10		740/425-3655 Fax 740/425-3202

Brown County

BROWN COUNTY

BROWN COUNTY SCHOOLS

• **Brown Co Ed Service Center** PID: 00786254   937/378-6118
9231 Hamer Rd, Georgetown 45121   Fax 937/378-4286

James Frazier 1,11	Blinda Boothby 2
Susan McFarland 34	Michael Roades 58
Dale Knechtly 73	Dayne Michael 74
Jackie Miller 74	Cindy Call 81
Evelyn Yockey 298	

County Schs..Principal	Grd	Prgm	Enr/#Cls	SN	
Educational Svc Ctr Pre-School 9231 Hamer Rd # B, Georgetown 45121 Susan McFarland	PK-PK		250 13		937/378-6118 Fax 937/378-4286

BROWN PUBLIC SCHOOLS

• **Fayetteville Perry Local SD** PID: 00786101   513/875-2423
551 S Apple St, Fayetteville 45118   Fax 513/875-2703

Schools: 3 \ **Teachers:** 50 \ **Students:** 855 \ **Special Ed Students:** 94 \ **LEP Students:** 3 \ **College-Bound:** 43% \ **Ethnic:** Hispanic 2%, Caucasian 98% \ **Exp:** $77 (Low) \ **Poverty:** 13% \ **Title I:** $146,472 \ **Special Education:** $165,000 \ **Open-Close:** 08/14 - 05/21 \ **DTBP:** $178 (High)

Tim Carlier 1	Lisa Tussey 2
John Gauche 3,5*	Cindy Phillips 4*
Tracy Johnson 7*	Paula Wiederhold 11,58,296,298*
Craig Smucker 67	Bill Siegler 73,76,295
Sharon Sheets 74,288	

Public Schs..Principal	Grd	Prgm	Enr/#Cls	SN	
Fayetteville Elem Sch 601 S Apple St, Fayetteville 45118 **Aric Fiscus**	K-5	T	378 23	55%	513/875-2083 Fax 513/875-4511
Fayetteville High Sch 501 S Apple St, Fayetteville 45118 Tim Carlier	9-12	V	243		513/875-3520 Fax 513/875-4512
Fayetteville Middle Sch 521 S Apple St, Fayetteville 45118 Ryan Briggs	6-8	T	185 14	91%	513/875-2829 Fax 513/875-4523

• **Georgetown Exempted Village SD** PID: 00786137   937/378-3730
1043 Mount Orab Pike, Georgetown 45121   Fax 937/378-2219

Schools: 2 \ **Teachers:** 59 \ **Students:** 1,100 \ **Special Ed Students:** 129 \ **College-Bound:** 42% \ **Ethnic:** African American 1%, Hispanic 1%, Caucasian 98% \ **Exp:** $203 (Med) \ **Poverty:** 26% \ **Title I:** $428,593 \ **Special Education:** $202,000 \ **Open-Close:** 08/14 - 05/15 \ **DTBP:** $222 (High)

Brad Winterod 1	Eric Toole 2
Micheal Dotson 3	Krista Cahall 4
Cory Copus 6	Nina Miller 11,288,296*
Gar Seigla 16,73*	Matthew Carpenter 16*

Butler County   Market Data Retrieva

Bethany Fitzpatrick	36*	Susan Noll	57*
Melissa Oconnor	58*	Raymond Virost	67
Carrie Kratzer	68	Maria Hill	752

Public Schs..Principal	Grd	Prgm	Enr/#Cls	SN	
Georgetown Elem Sch 935 Mount Orab Pike, Georgetown 45121 Nina Miller	PK-6	T	585 24	57%	937/378-6235 Fax 937/378-3489
Georgetown Jr Sr High Sch 987 Mount Orab Pike, Georgetown 45121 Jerry Underwood	7-12	TV	492 41	52%	937/378-6730 Fax 937/378-2442

• **Ripley-Union-Lewis-Huntngtn SD** PID: 00786175   937/392-4396
  502 S 2nd St, Ripley 45167   Fax 937/392-7003

Schools: 3 \ *Teachers:* 56 \ *Students:* 850 \ *Special Ed Students:* 164 \ *College-Bound:* 37% \ *Ethnic:* African American 2%, Hispanic 2%, Caucasian 95% \ *Exp:* $286 (Med) \ *Poverty:* 20% \ *Title I:* $342,446 \ *Special Education:* $213,000 \ *Open-Close:* 08/14 - 05/22 \ *DTBP:* $180 (High)

Jamie Wilkins	1	Jeff Rowley	2
Dick Zurbuch	3,91	Michele Rau	4*
Bill Frazier	5	Chris Young	6
Elaine Manning	7,35,85*	Russ Curtis	8,73,295*
Kara Williams	11,54,58,69,77,275	Jasmine Osman	36*
Linda Douglas	57*	Jeff Cluxton	67
Ken Stucky	78		

Public Schs..Principal	Grd	Prgm	Enr/#Cls	SN	
Ripley-Union-Lewis-Huntngtn ES 502 S 2nd St, Ripley 45167 **Emily Marshall**	PK-4	T	273 37	74%	937/392-1141 Fax 937/392-7027
Ripley-Union-Lewis-Huntngtn HS 1317 S 2nd St, Ripley 45167 Chris Young	9-12	ATV	259 30	64%	937/392-4384 Fax 937/392-7017
Ripley-Union-Lewis-Huntngtn MS 2300 Rains Eitel Rd, Aberdeen 45101 Jerod Michael	5-8	T	244 35	65%	937/795-8001 Fax 937/795-8035

• **Southern Hills Joint Voc SD** PID: 00786266   937/378-6131
  9193 Hamer Rd, Georgetown 45121   Fax 937/378-4577

Schools: 1 \ *Teachers:* 27 \ *Students:* 380 \ *College-Bound:* 60% \ *Exp:* $762 (High) \ *Open-Close:* 08/14 - 05/20 \ *DTBP:* $205 (High)

Kevin Kratzer	1	Carey Barnes	2
Paula Moore	4*	Jackie Hanson	7,85
Vickie Carrington	30*	Patricia Whittaker	33*
Angela Gray	38*	Chandra Bridges	60,83*
Richie Pride	67	Dale Knechely	73,76,295*
Guy Hopkins	88,288*		

Public Schs..Principal	Grd	Prgm	Enr/#Cls	SN	
Southern Hills Career Tech Ctr 9193 Hamer Rd, Georgetown 45121 **Christopher Burrows**	Voc	G	380 60		937/378-6131 Fax 937/378-4863

• **Western Brown Local Sch Dist** PID: 00786216   937/444-2044
  524 W Main St, Mount Orab 45154   Fax 937/444-4303

Schools: 4 \ *Teachers:* 148 \ *Students:* 3,400 \ *Special Ed Students:* 444 \ *College-Bound:* 40% \ *Ethnic:* Hispanic 1%, Caucasian 99% \ *Exp:* $237 (Med) \ *Poverty:* 19% \ *Title I:* $894,424 \ *Special Education:* $595,000 \ *Open-Close:* 08/14 - 05/20 \ *DTBP:* $191 (High) \

Raegan White	1	Dennis Dunlap	2
David Tatman	3	Stella Schneider	4
Kelly Day	5	Timothy Cook	6*
Jina Bohl	8,11,15,288,296,298	Gregg McKenzie	16*
Jennifer Bohrer	34,58	Joann Hildebrandt	67
Mike Drake	73,76*		

Public Schs..Principal	Grd	Prgm	Enr/#Cls	SN	
Hamersville Elem Sch 1950 State Route 125, Hamersville 45130 Mindy Pride	K-8	T	643 45	53%	937/379-1144 Fax 937/379-1676
Mt Orab Elem Sch 474 W Main St, Mount Orab 45154 Marty Paeltz	K-4	T	770 38	61%	937/444-2528 Fax 937/444-4183
Mt Orab Middle Sch 472 W Main St, Mount Orab 45154 Sabrina Armstrong	5-8	T	652 42	49%	937/444-2529 Fax 937/444-4268
Western Brown High Sch 476 W Main St, Mount Orab 45154 Heather Cooper	9-12	T	882 50	49%	937/444-2544 Fax 937/444-4355

BROWN CATHOLIC SCHOOLS

• **Archdiocese Cincinnati Ed Off** PID: 00808096
  Listing includes only schools located in this county. See District Index for location of Diocesan Offices.

Catholic Schs..Principal	Grd	Prgm	Enr/#Cls	SN	
St Michael Sch 300 Market St, Ripley 45167 Andy Arn	PK-8		103 6		937/392-4202 Fax 937/392-4248

BUTLER COUNTY

BUTLER COUNTY SCHOOLS

• **Butler Co Ed Service Center** PID: 00787234   513/887-3710
  400 N Erie Hwy Ste A, Hamilton 45011   Fax 513/887-3709

Chris Brown	1	Ken Ulm	2
Georgine Bowman	8	Laura Theiss	15,68
Suzanne Prescott	34	Wendy Folino	58,77
Adam Markham	71	Matt Worthen	73
Deanna Carson	88		

County Schs..Principal	Grd	Prgm	Enr/#Cls	SN	
© Summit Acad Alt Lrng-Middleton [248] 4700 Central Ave, Middletown 45044 Megan Bockleman	K-6	T	98		513/422-8540 Fax 513/423-6352

---

1 Superintendent	8 Curric/Instruct K-12	19 Chief Financial Officer	29 Family/Consumer Science	39 Social Studies K-12	49 English/Lang Arts Elem	59 Special Education Elem	69 Academic Assessment
2 Bus/Finance/Purchasing	9 Curric/Instruct Elem	20 Art K-12	30 Adult Education	40 Social Studies Elem	50 English/Lang Arts Sec	60 Special Education Sec	70 Research/Development
3 Buildings And Grounds	10 Curric/Instruct Sec	21 Art Elem	31 Career/Sch-to-Work K-12	41 Social Studies Sec	51 Reading K-12	61 Foreign/World Lang K-12	71 Public Information
4 Food Service	11 Federal Program	22 Art Sec	32 Career/Sch-to-Work Elem	42 Science K-12	52 Reading Elem	62 Foreign/World Lang Elem	72 Summer School
5 Transportation	12 Title I	23 Music K-12	33 Career/Sch-to-Work Sec	43 Science Elem	53 Reading Sec	63 Foreign/World Lang Sec	73 Instructional Tech
6 Athletic	13 Title V	24 Music Elem	34 Early Childhood Ed	44 Science Sec	54 Remedial Reading K-12	64 Religious Education K-12	74 Inservice Training
7 Health Services	15 Asst Superintendent	25 Music Sec	35 Health/Phys Education	45 Math K-12	55 Remedial Reading Elem	65 Religious Education Elem	75 Marketing/Distributive
	16 Instructional Media Svcs	26 Business Education	36 Guidance Services K-12	46 Math Elem	56 Remedial Reading Sec	66 Religious Education Sec	76 Info Systems
	17 Chief Operations Officer	27 Career & Tech Ed	37 Guidance Services Elem	47 Math Sec	57 Bilingual/ELL	67 School Board President	77 Psychological Assess
	18 Chief Academic Officer	28 Technology Education	38 Guidance Services Sec	48 English/Lang Arts K-12	58 Special Education K-12	68 Teacher Personnel	78 Affirmative Action

Ohio School Directory — Butler County

BUTLER PUBLIC SCHOOLS

Butler Tech Career Dev Schs PID: 01483053
3603 Hamilton Middletown Rd, Hamilton 45011
513/868-6300
Fax 513/868-9348

Schools: 1 \ **Teachers:** 193 \ **Students:** 900 \ **LEP Students:** 70 \ **College-Bound:** 25% \ **Exp:** $2,206 (High) \ **Open-Close:** 08/13 - 05/29 \ **DTBP:** $233 (High)

Jon Graft	1	Paul Carpenter	2,19
David Plotts	3,5,73,295*	David Helms	10
Kathy DiBlasi	10,285	Sharon Winstead	11,30
Marni Durham	15,68	Angela Stitzel	16,82*
Jeff Travers	30	Mike Berding	67
Lori Thesken	68	Pam Kariofiles	69
Kip Hamilton	286	Tony Huff	296

Public Schs..Principal	Grd	Prgm	Enr/#Cls	SN	
Butler Tech Career Center 3603 Hamilton Middletown Rd, Hamilton 45011 Cheryl Brackman	Voc	AG	900 65		513/868-6300 Fax 513/868-1701

Edgewood City School Dist PID: 00786280
3440 Busenbark Rd, Trenton 45067
513/867-3400
Fax 513/894-5100

Schools: 5 \ **Teachers:** 178 \ **Students:** 3,800 \ **Special Ed Students:** 528 \ **LEP Students:** 14 \ **College-Bound:** 53% \ **Ethnic:** African American 2%, Hispanic 2%, Caucasian 96% \ **Exp:** $119 (Low) \ **Poverty:** 8% \ **Title I:** $412,575 \ **Special Education:** $564,000 \ **Open-Close:** 08/15 - 05/21 \ **DTBP:** $190 (High) \ [f]

Russ Fussnecker	1	Randy Stiver	2
John Thomas	3,5,91	David Jewell	4*
Shane Swartz	5	Greg Brown	6
Beth Birchwell	7,72,85*	Scott Fussnecker	8
Kate Little	58*	Gary Gabbard	67
Alesia Beckett	68	Rhonda Bohannon	68
Pat Wiita	69,77*	Pam Pratt	71
Chris Andrews	73*		

Public Schs..Principal	Grd	Prgm	Enr/#Cls	SN	
Babeck Early Childhood Ctr 100 Maple Ave, Trenton 45067 Jeffrey Banks	PK-1	T	500 22	45%	513/867-3430 Fax 513/988-5561
Edgewood Elem Sch 3440 Busenbark Rd, Trenton 45067 Jenny Halsey	2-5	T	852 41	45%	513/867-3440 Fax 513/988-7571
Edgewood High Sch 3045 Busenbark Rd, Trenton 45067 Doug Geygan	9-12	V	1,127 45	34%	513/867-6300 Fax 513/867-6341
Edgewood Middle Sch 5005 Trenton Oxford Rd, Trenton 45067 **Jim Dallio**	6-8	TV	870 60	39%	513/867-3450 Fax 513/867-7428 [f]
Seven Mile Elem Sch 200 W Ritter St, Seven Mile 45062 Lori Harrison	K-5		375 19	30%	513/867-3420 Fax 513/726-6239

Fairfield City School Dist PID: 00786357
4641 Bach Ln, Fairfield 45014
513/829-6300
Fax 513/829-0148

Schools: 11 \ **Teachers:** 490 \ **Students:** 10,000 \ **Special Ed Students:** 1,329 \ **LEP Students:** 790 \ **College-Bound:** 75% \ **Ethnic:** Asian 4%, African American 19%, Hispanic 10%, Caucasian 66% \ **Exp:** $179 (Low) \ **Poverty:** 9% \ **Title I:** $1,424,821 \ **Special Education:** $1,614,000 \ **Open-Close:** 08/21 - 05/28 \ **DTBP:** $209 (High) \ [f][t]

Billy Smith	1	Joe Penny	2
Jamie Bertke	3	Bill Westerbeck	5
Aaron Blankenship	6	Mandy Aug	8
Jennie Thompson	9	Kathryn Pospisil	10
Roger Martin	15	Kathy Gilbert	34,58
Dawn Hildreth	57	Michael Berding	67
Katie Myers	68	Gina Fletcher	71
Dan Jeffers	73	Cheryl Geisler	76
Deanna Samuels	274		

Public Schs..Principal	Grd	Prgm	Enr/#Cls	SN	
Fairfield Academy 211-A Donald Dr, Fairfield 45014 Kyle Jamison	9-12		120		513/858-7600
Fairfield Central Elem Sch 5054 Dixie Hwy, Fairfield 45014 Karrie Gallo	K-5	T	723 28	59%	513/829-7979 Fax 513/829-7830
Fairfield Compass Elem Sch 8801 Holden Blvd, Fairfield 45014 Kim Wotring	K-5		800		513/858-8700 Fax 513/858-8699
Fairfield Creekside Mid Sch 1111 Nilles Rd, Fairfield 45014 Kari Franchini	6-8		1,161	38%	513/829-4433 Fax 513/829-6480 [f][t]
Fairfield Crossroads Mid Sch 255 Donald Dr, Fairfield 45014 David Maine	6-8		1,200 85		513/829-4504 Fax 513/829-7447 [f][t]
Fairfield East Elem Sch 6711 Morris Rd, Hamilton 45011 Paige Gillespie	PK-5	T	660 30	40%	513/737-5000 Fax 513/737-5225 [f][t]
Fairfield Freshman High Sch 8790 N Gilmore Rd, Fairfield 45014 Michael Berkemeier	9-9		800 38	36%	513/829-8300 Fax 513/829-4733 [f][t]
Fairfield North Elem Sch 6116 Morris Rd, Hamilton 45011 Dennis Hayes	K-5		702 28	20%	513/868-0070 Fax 513/868-3621 [f][t]
Fairfield Senior High Sch 8800 Holden Blvd, Fairfield 45014 William Rice	10-12		2,500 100	32%	513/942-2999 Fax 513/942-3288
Fairfield South Elem Sch 5460 Bibury Rd, Fairfield 45014 Jason Hussel	K-5	T	767 33	35%	513/829-3078 Fax 513/829-8350
Fairfield West Elem Sch 4700 River Rd, Fairfield 45014 Missy Muller	PK-5	T	830 41	38%	513/868-3021 Fax 513/868-3624 [f][t]

Hamilton City School Dist PID: 00786424
533 Dayton St, Hamilton 45011
513/887-5000
Fax 513/887-5014

Schools: 13 \ **Teachers:** 498 \ **Students:** 10,300 \ **Special Ed Students:** 1,715 \ **LEP Students:** 674 \ **College-Bound:** 36% \ **Ethnic:** African American 13%, Hispanic 15%, Caucasian 71% \ **Exp:** $150 (Low) \ **Poverty:** 21% \ **Title I:** $4,261,248 \ **Special Education:** $2,097,000 \ **Open-Close:** 08/12 - 05/21 \ **DTBP:** $226 (High) \ [t]

Mike Holbrook	1	Jeffrey Kilby	2,11,91,274,296,298
Robert Hancock	2	Thomas Schulte	3

Legend

Code		Code		Code		Code	
79	Student Personnel	91	Safety/Security	275	Response To Intervention	298	Grant Writer/Ptnrships
80	Driver Ed/Safety	92	Magnet School	277	Remedial Math K-12	750	Chief Innovation Officer
81	Gifted/Talented	93	Parental Involvement	280	Literacy Coach	751	Chief of Staff
82	Video Services	95	Tech Prep Program	285	STEM	752	Social Emotional Learning
83	Substance Abuse Prev	97	Chief Infomation Officer	286	Digital Learning		
84	Erate	98	Chief Technology Officer	288	Common Core Standards		
85	AIDS Education	270	Accountability	294	Alternative School		
88	Alternative/At Risk	271	Migrant Education	295	Network System		
89	Multi-Cultural Curriculum	273	Teacher Mentor	296	Title II Programs		
90	Social Work	274	Before/After Sch	297	Webmaster		

School Programs
A = Alternative Program
G = Adult Classes
M = Magnet Program
T = Title I Schoolwide
V = Career & Tech Ed Programs

Other School Types
Ⓐ = Alternative School
Ⓒ = Charter School
Ⓜ = Magnet School
Ⓨ = Year-Round School

Social Media
[f] = Facebook
[t] = Twitter

New Schools are shaded
New Superintendents and Principals are bold
Personnel with email addresses are underscored

OH—21

Butler County

Market Data Retrieval

Name	Page
Cinde Gorbandt	4*
Todd Grimm	6*
Kristan Hinson	12,52,280
Tari McKee	20,23*
Andre Gendreau	34,58,77,88,275
Steve Connaughton	48,51*
Steven Isgro	67
Tricia Smith	73,286,295*
Michael Wright	79*
Becky Goosey	5
Andrea Blevins	9
Dr Chad Konkle	15,68,74,78
Richard Pate	27,31*
Sherri Morrison	45,277*
Corbin Moore	57,69,81,288
Joni Copas	71
Susan Bachmann	76
Lori Pierson	273*
Rob Kramer	68,74,273
Todd Wesley	73,98,295
Krista Heidenreich	286
Dan Hudson	69
Shawn Smith	76

Public Schs..Principal	Grd	Prgm	Enr/#Cls	SN	
Bridgeport Elem Sch 2171 Bridgeport Dr, Hamilton 45013 Vicki Kowalk	PK-6	T	735 14	69%	513/868-5580 Fax 513/868-5585
Brookwood Elem Sch 1325 Stahlheber Rd, Rossville 45013 Jessica Weisbrod	K-6	T	706 21	62%	513/868-5590 Fax 513/868-5595
Crawford Woods Elem Sch 2200 Hensley Ave, Hamilton 45011 Aaron Hopkins	K-6	T	685 21	90%	513/868-5600 Fax 513/868-5605
Fairwood Elem Sch 281 N Fair Ave, Hamilton 45011 **Heather Cremeans**	PK-6	T	757 15	81%	513/868-5610 Fax 513/868-5615
Garfield Middle Sch 250 N Fair Ave, Hamilton 45011 Brandon Stanfill	7-8	T	850	75%	513/887-5035 Fax 513/887-4700
Hamilton High Sch 1165 Eaton Ave, Hamilton 45013 John Wilhelm	10-12	T	2,100 65	60%	513/868-7700 Fax 513/887-4810
Hamilton HS-Freshman Campus 2260 NW Washington Blvd, Hamilton 45013 **Jessica Weisbrod**	9-9	AT	710	68%	513/896-3400 Fax 513/896-3402
Highland Elem Sch 1125 Main St, Hamilton 45013 Jeffrey Smallwood	K-6	T	688 31	68%	513/868-5620 Fax 513/868-5625
Linden Elem Sch 801 Hoadley Ave, Hamilton 45015 Alice Rose	PK-6	T	725 14	70%	513/868-5630 Fax 513/868-5639
Ridgeway Elem Sch 267 Wasserman Rd, Hamilton 45013 Kathy Wagonfield	PK-6	T	870 12	52%	513/868-5640 Fax 513/868-5645
Riverview Elem Sch 250 Knightsbridge Dr, Hamilton 45011 Joshua Margerum	PK-6	T	720 25	98%	513/887-5650 Fax 513/868-5655
ⓐ The Miami Sch 140 Ross Ave, Hamilton 45013 Michael Wright	9-12		100		513/887-5197 Fax 513/318-1451
Wilson Middle Sch 714 Eaton Ave, Hamilton 45013 Jonathan Szary	7-8	T	626 45	67%	513/887-5170 Fax 513/887-5186

- **Lakota Local School Dist** PID: 00786644 — 513/874-5505
  5572 Princeton Rd, Liberty Twp 45011 — Fax 513/644-1167

Schools: 23 \ **Teachers:** 689 \ **Students:** 16,500 \
Special Ed Students: 1,740 \ **LEP Students:** 1,079 \ **College-Bound:** 75% \
\ **Ethnic:** Asian 7%, African American 12%, Hispanic 7%, Caucasian 74% \ **Exp:** $191 (Low) \ **Poverty:** 5% \ **Title I:** $1,701,747 \
Special Education: $3,079,000 \ **Open-Close:** 08/15 - 05/21 \ **DTBP:** $207 (High)

Name	Page
Matthew Miller	1
Jenni Logan	2,19
Craig Hatfield	4
Kim McGowan	11
Lauren Boettcher	16,71
Julie Schaffer	67
Chris Passarge	2,3,17,91
Tim Penton	2
Keith Koehne	8
Robb Vogelmann	15
Andrea Longworth	58
Jenifer Lodovico	68

Public Schs..Principal	Grd	Prgm	Enr/#Cls	SN	
Adena Elem Sch 9316 Minuteman Way, West Chester 45069 John Mattingly	3-6		599 35	17%	513/777-0100 Fax 513/777-3475
ⓐ Career Readiness Academy 5030 Tylersville Rd, West Chester 45069 Nicole Isaacs	9-12		100		513/682-4117 Fax 513/682-4219
Cherokee Elem Sch 5345 Kyles Station Rd, Liberty Twp 45011 Valerie Montgomery	3-6		658 68	23%	513/755-8200 Fax 513/755-8067
Creekside Early Childhood Sch 5070 Tylersville Rd, West Chester 45069 Linda Pavlinac	K-2		710 27	19%	513/874-0175 Fax 513/682-4213
Endeavor Elem Sch 4400 Smith Rd, West Chester 45069 **Theresa Brock**	3-6		717	27%	513/759-8300 Fax 513/759-8301
Freedom Elem Sch 6035 Beckett Ridge Blvd, West Chester 45069 Lance Green	3-6		602 31	29%	513/777-9787 Fax 513/777-6014
Heritage Early Childhood Sch 5052 Hamilton Mason Rd, Liberty Twp 45011 Missy Alexander	K-2		571 30	20%	513/863-7060 Fax 513/887-5483
Hopewell Early Childhood Sch 8300 Cox Rd, West Chester 45069 Christina French	K-2		739 33	27%	513/777-6128 Fax 513/777-3805
Hopewell Junior High Sch 8200 Cox Rd, West Chester 45069 Jeff Rouff	7-8		515 60	22%	513/777-2258 Fax 513/777-1908
Independence Elem Sch 7480 Princeton Rd, Liberty TWP 45044 Dr Greg Finke	3-6		557 50	18%	513/755-8300 Fax 513/755-6941
Lakota East Freshman Campus 7630 Bethany Rd, Liberty TWP 45044 Suzanna Davis	9-9		620		513/588-7700 Fax 513/759-2024
Lakota East High Sch 6840 Lakota Ln, Liberty TWP 45044 Susan Davis	10-12	V	2,500 93	15%	513/755-7211 Fax 513/759-8633
Lakota West Freshman Campus 5050 Tylersville Rd, West Chester 45069 Gary Card	9-9		670 40		513/874-8390 Fax 513/682-4230
Lakota West High Sch 8940 Union Centre Blvd, West Chester 45069 Gary Card	10-12		1,700 140	17%	513/874-5699 Fax 513/682-4133
Liberty Early Childhood Sch 6040 Princeton Rd, Liberty Twp 45011 Carrie Montgomery	K-2		426 25	22%	513/777-6194 Fax 513/759-2672
Liberty Junior High Sch 7055 Dutchland Pkwy, Liberty TWP 45044 Eric Bauman	7-8	V	770 45	15%	513/777-4420 Fax 513/777-7950
Plains Junior High Sch 5500 Princeton Rd, Liberty Twp 45011 Kim Wade	7-8		732 235	13%	513/644-1130 Fax 513/644-1135
Ridge Junior High Sch 6199 Beckett Ridge Blvd, West Chester 45069 Ben Brown	7-8		600 41	29%	513/777-0552 Fax 513/777-0919
Shawnee Early Childhood Sch 9394 Sterling Dr, Cincinnati 45241 **Kevin Thomas**	K-2		567 34	32%	513/779-3014 Fax 513/779-3494
Union Elem Sch 7672 Lesourdsville-West, West Chester 45069 Kyle Lichey	3-6		608 26	29%	513/777-2201 Fax 513/777-2603

#		#		#		#		#		#		#	
1	Superintendent	8	Curric/Instruct K-12	19	Chief Financial Officer	29	Family/Consumer Science	39	Social Studies K-12	49	English/Lang Arts Elem	59	Special Education Elem	69	Academic Assessment
2	Bus/Finance/Purchasing	9	Curric/Instruct Elem	20	Art K-12	30	Adult Education	40	Social Studies Elem	50	English/Lang Arts Sec	60	Special Education Sec	70	Research/Development
3	Buildings And Grounds	10	Curric/Instruct Sec	21	Art Elem	31	Career/Sch-to-Work K-12	41	Social Studies Sec	51	Reading K-12	61	Foreign/World Lang K-12	71	Public Information
4	Food Service	11	Federal Program	22	Art Sec	32	Career/Sch-to-Work Elem	42	Science K-12	52	Reading Elem	62	Foreign/World Lang Elem	72	Summer School
5	Transportation	12	Title I	23	Music K-12	33	Career/Sch-to-Work Sec	43	Science Elem	53	Reading Sec	63	Foreign/World Lang Sec	73	Instructional Tech
6	Athletic	13	Title V	24	Music Elem	34	Early Childhood Ed	44	Science Sec	54	Remedial Reading K-12	64	Religious Education K-12	74	Inservice Training
7	Health Services	15	Asst Superintendent	25	Music Sec	35	Health/Phys Education	45	Math K-12	55	Remedial Reading Elem	65	Religious Education Elem	75	Marketing/Distributive
		16	Instructional Media Svcs	26	Business Education	36	Guidance Services K-12	46	Math Elem	56	Remedial Reading Sec	66	Religious Education Sec	76	Info Systems
		17	Chief Operations Officer	27	Career & Tech Ed	37	Guidance Services Elem	47	Math Sec	57	Bilingual/ELL	67	School Board President	77	Psychological Assess
		18	Chief Academic Officer	28	Technology Education	38	Guidance Services Sec	48	English/Lang Arts K-12	58	Special Education K-12	68	Teacher Personnel	78	Affirmative Action

Ohio School Directory — Butler County

School	Grd	Prgm	Enr/#Cls	SN	Phone
Van Gorden Elem Sch 6475 Lsrdsvl-W Chestr Rd, Liberty Twp 45011 Gail Allshouse	3-6		551 37	4%	513/644-1150 Fax 513/644-1160
Woodland Elem Sch 6923 Dutchland Pkwy, Liberty TWP 45044 John Wise	3-6		641 31	35%	513/779-7775 Fax 513/779-7389
Wyandot Early Childhood Sch 7667 Summerlin Blvd, Liberty TWP 45044 Elizabeth Gruber	K-2		593	15%	513/759-8100 Fax 513/759-8105

● **Madison Local School Dist** PID: 00786711   513/420-4750
1324 Middletown Eaton Rd, Middletown 45042   Fax 513/420-4781

Schools: 2 \ **Teachers:** 80 \ **Students:** 1,600 \ **Special Ed Students:** 191 \ **Ethnic:** African American 1%, Hispanic 2%, Caucasian 97% \ **Exp:** $113 (Low) \ **Poverty:** 9% \ **Title I:** $201,754 \ **Special Education:** $263,000 \ **Open-Close:** 08/15 - 05/21 \ **DTBP:** $109 (High) \ f

Lisa Tuttlehuff 1   Rich Natiello 2,298
Matt Morrison 3,6   Kathy Middleton 5
Christina Anspach 7,83,85   Gen Wilcox 8,11,69,72,285,288
Jason Jackson 12   Carrie Hunter 58,77*
David French 67   Joy Shaw 73*
Debbie Morrison 77*

Public Schs..Principal	Grd	Prgm	Enr/#Cls	SN	
Madison Elem Sch 5795 W Alexandria Rd, Middletown 45042 Jason Jackson	PK-6	T	822 20	43%	513/420-4755 Fax 513/420-4915 f
Madison Junior Senior High Sch 5797 W Alexandria Rd, Middletown 45042 Andrew Huber	7-12		646 60	48%	513/420-4760 Fax 513/420-4914

● **Middletown City School Dist** PID: 00786761   513/423-0781
1 Donham Plz 4th Fl, Middletown 45042   Fax 513/420-4579

Schools: 10 \ **Teachers:** 356 \ **Students:** 6,561 \ **Special Ed Students:** 1,194 \ **LEP Students:** 361 \ **College-Bound:** 39% \ **Ethnic:** African American 19%, Hispanic 13%, Caucasian 67% \ **Exp:** $185 (Low) \ **Poverty:** 24% \ **Title I:** $3,974,557 \ **Special Education:** $1,837,000 \ **Open-Close:** 08/13 - 05/20 \ **DTBP:** $229 (High) \ f t

Marlon Styles 1   Randy Bertram 2
Tom Weiser 2,73,76,95,294   Cindy Dezarn 4
Sharon Earnhart 5   JD Foust 6
Fran Morrison ... 11,57,69,285,286,288,296,298   Debbie Sander 58
Chris Urso 67   Liz Beadle 71

Public Schs..Principal	Grd	Prgm	Enr/#Cls	SN	
Amanda Elem Sch 1300 Oxford State Rd, Middletown 45044 Beth Hendricks	PK-5	T	454 30		513/420-4542 Fax 513/420-4632 f t
Central Academy 4601 Sophie Ave, Middletown 45042 Misha Monnin	K-6	T	341 13		513/420-4537 Fax 513/420-4589 f
Creekview Elem Sch 4800 Timber Trail Dr, Middletown 45044 Michelle Peterson	PK-5	T	514 23		513/420-4544 Fax 513/420-4587
Highview 6th Grade Center 106 S Highview Rd, Middletown 45044 Jennifer Dennis	6-6	T	475 40		513/420-4566 Fax 513/420-4647 f t
Mayfield Elem Sch 3325 Burbank Ave, Middletown 45044 Heather Keal	K-5		488 18		513/420-4549 Fax 513/420-4551
Middletown High Sch 601 N Breiel Blvd, Middletown 45042 Carmela Cotter	9-12	ATV	1,520		513/420-4500 Fax 513/420-4648
Middletown Middle Sch 551 N Breiel Blvd, Middletown 45042 Michael Valenti	7-8	T	965		513/420-4528 Fax 513/420-4527
Miller Ridge Elem Sch 4704 Miller Rd, Middletown 45042 Kee Edwards	K-5	T	455 21		513/420-4559 Fax 513/420-4560 f t
Rosa Parks Elem Sch 1210 S Verity Pkwy, Middletown 45044 Tracy Neeley	K-5	T	571 20		513/420-4552 Fax 513/420-4553 f t
Wildwood Elem Sch 3300 Wildwood Rd, Middletown 45042 Keri Hensley	K-5	T	558 21		513/420-4564 Fax 513/420-4627

● **Monroe Local School Dist** PID: 04913801   513/539-2536
500 Yankee Rd, Monroe 45050   Fax 513/539-2648

Schools: 4 \ **Teachers:** 131 \ **Students:** 2,900 \ **Special Ed Students:** 280 \ **LEP Students:** 151 \ **College-Bound:** 61% \ **Ethnic:** Asian 3%, African American 4%, Hispanic 8%, Caucasian 85% \ **Exp:** $119 (Low) \ **Poverty:** 7% \ **Title I:** $218,894 \ **Special Education:** $464,000 \ **Open-Close:** 08/15 - 05/21 \ **DTBP:** $166 (High) \ t

Cathy Demers 1   Holly Cakall 2,19
Jessie Catanzaro 2   Jody Long 11,51,69,296*
Teri Rollins 11,57,58   Leslie Stone 67
Tony Thornton 73,76,84

Public Schs..Principal	Grd	Prgm	Enr/#Cls	SN	
Monroe Elem Sch 230 Yankee Rd, Monroe 45050 Nancy Stratton	2-6		1,117 55	30%	513/539-8101 Fax 513/539-8151 f
Monroe High Sch 220 Yankee Rd, Monroe 45050 Tom Prohaska	9-12	V	762 60	24%	513/539-8471 Fax 513/539-8474
Monroe Jr High Sch 220 Yankee Rd, Monroe 45050 Joe Ward	7-8		439		513/539-8471 Fax 513/539-8474
Monroe Primary Sch 225 MacReady Ave, Monroe 45050 Dr Gayle Niehaus	PK-1		471	27%	513/360-0700 Fax 513/360-0720

● **New Miami Local School Dist** PID: 00787026   513/863-0833
600 Seven Mile Ave, Hamilton 45011   Fax 513/863-0497

Schools: 2 \ **Teachers:** 45 \ **Students:** 620 \ **Special Ed Students:** 112 \ **LEP Students:** 3 \ **College-Bound:** 28% \ **Ethnic:** African American 3%, Hispanic 3%, Caucasian 95% \ **Exp:** $165 (Low) \ **Poverty:** 18% \ **Title I:** $287,528 \ **Special Education:** $333,000 \ **Open-Close:** 08/21 - 05/28 \ **DTBP:** $254 (High)

Rhonda Parker 1,11   Robin Bonar 2
Nick Pegram 3,91   Karen Trousdell 4*
Robert Spencer 5   Eric Hayes 6*
Tonja Fangman .... 7,83,85*   Kim Davidson 8
Doug Yeazel .... 16,73,82*   Julie Barber 38*
Katie Klei 58   Randy Cook 67

Public Schs..Principal	Grd	Prgm	Enr/#Cls	SN	
New Miami Elem Sch 600 Seven Mile Ave, Hamilton 45011 Tabatha Class	PK-5	T	359 35		513/896-7153 Fax 513/896-9313

Legend:
89 Student Personnel / 91 Safety/Security / 92 Magnet School / 93 Parental Involvement / 95 Tech Prep Program / 97 Chief Information Officer / 98 Chief Technology Officer / 270 Character Education / 271 Migrant Education / 273 Teacher Mentor / 274 Before/After Sch / 275 Response To Intervention / 277 Remedial Math K-12 / 280 Literacy Coach / 285 STEM / 286 Digital Learning / 288 Common Core Standards / 294 Accountability / 295 Network System / 296 Title II Programs / 297 Webmaster / 298 Grant Writer/Ptnrships / 750 Chief Innovation Officer / 751 Chief of Staff / 752 Social Emotional Learning

School Programs: A = Alternative Program / G = Adult Classes / M = Magnet Program / T = Title I Schoolwide / V = Career & Tech Ed Programs

Other School Types: A = Alternative School / C = Charter School / M = Magnet School / Y = Year-Round School

Social Media: f = Facebook / t = Twitter

New Schools are shaded
New Superintendents and Principals are bold
Personnel with email addresses are underscored

OH—23

Butler County

Market Data Retrieval

New Miami Middle High Sch	6-12	372	513/863-4917
600 Seven Mile Ave, Hamilton 45011			Fax 513/896-3956
Kara Brakhage			

• **Ross Local School Dist** PID: 00787064   513/863-1253
3371 Hamilton Cleves Rd, Hamilton 45013   Fax 513/863-6250

Schools: 4 \ **Teachers:** 141 \ **Students:** 2,500 \ **Special Ed Students:** 318 \ **LEP Students:** 3 \ **College-Bound:** 65% \ **Ethnic:** Hispanic 1%, Caucasian 99% \ **Exp:** $162 (Low) \ **Poverty:** 6% \ **Title I:** $242,462 \ **Special Education:** $509,000 \ **Open-Close:** 08/21 - 05/28 \ **DTBP:** $55 (Low)

Scott Gates 1,83	John Kinsel 2	
Devin Huff 3	Debbie Christophel 4*	
Peggy Lehmann 5	Jake Richards 6*	
Shelli Turco 7,85*	Becky Tomkins 8,11,31,271,296	
Jayne Neufarth 16*	Bradley Webb 34,58,88,270	
Keith Klinefelter 67	Andy Klaber 73,295*	
Melinda Kelly 81		

Public Schs..Principal	Grd	Prgm	Enr/#Cls	SN
Elda Elem Sch	K-4		549	22% 513/738-1972
3980 Hamilton Cleves Rd, Hamilton 45013			26	Fax 513/738-0163
Adam Hull				
Morgan Elem Sch	PK-4		542	18% 513/738-1986
3427 Chapel Rd, Hamilton 45013			21	Fax 513/380-0347
Tom Perry				
Ross High Sch	9-12	V	815	19% 513/863-1252
3601 Hamilton Cleves Rd, Hamilton 45013			60	Fax 513/863-8340
Brian Martin				
Ross Middle Sch	5-8		925	25% 513/863-1251
3425 Hamilton Cleves Rd, Hamilton 45013			35	Fax 513/863-0066
Chris Saylor				

• **Talawanda School Dist** PID: 00787117   513/273-3100
131 W Chestnut St, Oxford 45056   Fax 513/273-3113

Schools: 5 \ **Teachers:** 173 \ **Students:** 3,100 \ **Special Ed Students:** 316 \ **LEP Students:** 65 \ **College-Bound:** 56% \ **Ethnic:** Asian 2%, African American 2%, Hispanic 2%, Caucasian 94% \ **Exp:** $130 (Low) \ **Poverty:** 8% \ **Title I:** $375,902 \ **Special Education:** $548,000 \ **Open-Close:** 08/14 - 05/21 \ **DTBP:** $83 (Med) \

Ed Theroux 1	Mike Davis 2,11,19
Bill Hubbard 3,91	Dennis Malone 4,68
Marylynn Bierman 4	Mike Sokol 5
Wes Cole 6*	Amy Macechko 7,83*
Lindsey Greg 8,12,57,76,285,286,288	Teresa Peter 31,38*
Stephanie Norris 34,58*	Mark Butterfield 67
Christopher Thompson 69	Matthew Rand 73,76,84
Holli Morrish 79,298	Jessica Moore 81
Kathy James 280	

Public Schs..Principal	Grd	Prgm	Enr/#Cls	SN
Bogan Elem Sch	K-5		417	34% 513/273-3400
5200 Hamilton Richmond Rd, Oxford 45056				Fax 513/273-3405
Jeff Winslow				
Kramer Elem Sch	K-5		561	37% 513/273-3500
400 W Sycamore St, Oxford 45056			23	Fax 513/273-3505
Jason Merz				
Marshall Elem Sch	K-5		367	41% 513/273-3600
3260 Oxford Millville Rd, Oxford 45056			24	Fax 513/273-3606
Chad Hinton				
Talawanda High Sch	9-12	AV	950	29% 513/273-3200
5301 University Park Blvd, Oxford 45056			72	Fax 513/273-3203
Tom York				
Talawanda Middle Sch	6-8		702	32% 513/273-3300
4030 Oxford Reily Rd, Oxford 45056			63	Fax 513/273-3303
Mike Malone				

BUTLER CATHOLIC SCHOOLS

• **Archdiocese Cincinnati Ed Off** PID: 00808096
Listing includes only schools located in this county. See District Index for location of Diocesan Offices.

Catholic Schs..Principal	Grd	Prgm	Enr/#Cls	SN
John XXIII Catholic Elem Sch	PK-8		459	513/424-1196
3806 Manchester Rd, Middletown 45042			31	Fax 513/420-8480
Dawn Pickerill				
Mother Teresa Cath ES	K-8		530	513/779-6585
7197 Mother Teresa Ln, Middletown 45044			20	Fax 513/779-6468
Aideen Briggs				
Queen of Peace Elem Sch	PK-8		208	513/863-8705
2550 Millville Ave, Hamilton 45013			14	Fax 513/863-4310
T Conners				
Sacred Heart of Jesus Sch	K-8		446	513/858-4215
400 Nilles Rd, Fairfield 45014			23	Fax 513/858-4218
Joseph Nagle				
St Ann Catholic Sch	PK-8		138	513/863-0604
3064 Pleasant Ave, Hamilton 45015			9	Fax 513/863-2017
Gwenda Laney				
St Joseph Consolidated Sch	K-8		200	513/863-8758
925 S 2nd St, Hamilton 45011			10	Fax 513/863-5772
Bill Hicks				
St Peter In Chains Sch	K-8		185	513/863-0685
451 Ridgelawn Ave, Hamilton 45013			14	Fax 513/863-1859
Michael Collins				
Stephen T Badin High Sch	9-12		612	513/863-3993
571 Hamilton New London Rd, Hamilton 45013				Fax 513/785-2844
Brian Pendergast				

BUTLER PRIVATE SCHOOLS

Private Schs..Principal	Grd	Prgm	Enr/#Cls	SN
Cincinnati Christian Elem Sch	PK-6		276	513/874-8500
7350 Dixie Hwy, Fairfield 45014			20	Fax 513/874-9718
Donna Hempelmann				
Cincinnati Christian High Sch	7-12		400	513/892-8500
7474 Morris Rd, Hamilton 45011			20	Fax 513/892-0516
Kim Stone				
GATE	Spec		200	513/420-4617
1 Donham Plz, Middletown 45042				
Debbie Houser				
Hamilton Christian Sch	K-12		135	513/863-3107
40 Wrenwood Dr, Hamilton 45013			10	Fax 513/863-3991
Aaron Miller				
Immanuel Lutheran Sch	PK-8		120	513/895-9212
1285 Main St, Hamilton 45013			7	Fax 513/863-2502
Lukas Bickel				
Int'l Academy of Cincinnati	PK-8		170	513/755-0169
8094 Plantation Dr, West Chester 45069			17	Fax 513/755-0179
Marie Marawi				
McGuffey Montessori Sch	PK-8		72	513/523-7742
5128 Westgate Dr, Oxford 45056			9	Fax 513/523-4220
Nancy Hawthorne				

1 Superintendent	8 Curric/Instruct K-12	19 Chief Financial Officer	29 Family/Consumer Science	39 Social Studies K-12	49 English/Lang Arts Elem	59 Special Education Elem	69 Academic Assessment
2 Bus/Finance/Purchasing	9 Curric/Instruct Elem	20 Art K-12	30 Adult Education	40 Social Studies Elem	50 English/Lang Arts Sec	60 Special Education Sec	70 Research/Development
3 Buildings And Grounds	10 Curric/Instruct Sec	21 Art Elem	31 Career/Sch-to-Work K-12	41 Social Studies Sec	51 Reading K-12	61 Foreign/World Lang K-12	71 Public Information
4 Food Service	11 Federal Program	22 Art Sec	32 Career/Sch-to-Work Elem	42 Science K-12	52 Reading Elem	62 Foreign/World Lang Elem	72 Summer School
5 Transportation	12 Title I	23 Music K-12	33 Career/Sch-to-Work Sec	43 Science Elem	53 Reading Sec	63 Foreign/World Lang Sec	73 Instructional Tech
6 Athletic	13 Title V	24 Music Elem	34 Early Childhood Ed	44 Science Sec	54 Remedial Reading K-12	64 Religious Education K-12	74 Inservice Training
7 Health Services	14 Asst Superintendent	25 Music Sec	35 Health/Phys Education	45 Math K-12	55 Remedial Reading Elem	65 Religious Education Elem	75 Marketing/Distributive
	15 Instructional Media Svcs	26 Business Education	36 Guidance Services K-12	46 Math Elem	56 Remedial Reading Sec	66 Religious Education Sec	76 Info Systems
	16 Chief Operations Officer	27 Career & Tech Ed	37 Guidance Services Elem	47 Math Sec	57 Bilingual/ELL	67 School Board President	77 Psychological Assess
	17 Chief Academic Officer	28 Technology Education	38 Guidance Services Sec	48 English/Lang Arts K-12	58 Special Education K-12	68 Teacher Personnel	78 Affirmative Action

Ohio School Directory

Champaign County

Ohio Christian Academy PK-12 25 513/594-4334
4419 Nelson Rd, Middletown 45042
Carol Brengelman

BUTLER REGIONAL CENTERS

• **Southwest Ohio OCA** PID: 04499623 513/867-1028
3611 Hamilton Middletown Rd, Hamilton 45011 Fax 513/867-0754

Donna Davis	1	Donna Norris	15
Brad Pursell	73	Marc Hopkins	76
Michael Mulcahey	295		

CARROLL COUNTY

CARROLL COUNTY SCHOOLS

County Schs..Principal	Grd	Prgm	Enr/#Cls	SN	
Carroll Hills Sch	Spec		85		330/627-7651
2167 Kensington Rd NE, Carrollton 44615			6		Fax 330/627-6606
Ryan Buck					

CARROLL PUBLIC SCHOOLS

• **Brown Local School Dist** PID: 00787246 330/863-1355
3242 Coral Rd NW, Malvern 44644 Fax 330/863-1172

Schools: 3 \ *Teachers:* 40 \ *Students:* 630 \ *Special Ed Students:* 122 \ *College-Bound:* 48% \ *Ethnic:* African American 1%, Hispanic 2%, Caucasian 97% \ *Exp:* $232 (Med) \ *Poverty:* 18% \ *Title I:* $193,833 \ *Special Education:* $140,000 \ *Open-Close:* 08/21 - 06/02 \ *DTBP:* $241 (High) \ 🅴

Scott Bowling	1	James Carman	2,11
Doug Wackerly	3	Lavern Davenport	4*
Rodney Wise	5	Dave Tucci	6*
Dawn Kaufman	8,58,270*	Cathy Maffett	16,82*
Jim Levering	16,73,76,295	Tami Hulit	67
Kim Brahler	68	Jeremy Taylor	69

Public Schs..Principal	Grd	Prgm	Enr/#Cls	SN	
Malvern Elem Sch	K-5	T	304		330/863-1355
3242 Coral Rd NW, Malvern 44644			20		Fax 330/863-1366
Ashley Weber					
Malvern High Sch	9-12	TV	153	98%	330/863-1355
3242 Coral Rd NW, Malvern 44644			18		Fax 330/863-1366
Timothy Babiczuk					
Malvern Middle Sch	6-8		153		330/863-1355
3242 Coral Rd NW, Malvern 44644					
Timothy Babiczuk					

• **Carrollton Exempted Village SD** PID: 00787272 330/627-2181
1020 Scio Rd SW, Carrollton 44615 Fax 330/627-2182

Schools: 2 \ *Teachers:* 116 \ *Students:* 2,150 \ *Special Ed Students:* 420 \ *LEP Students:* 11 \ *College-Bound:* 50% \ *Ethnic:* Hispanic 2%, Caucasian 97% \ *Exp:* $230 (Med) \ *Poverty:* 16% \ *Title I:* $598,159 \ *Special Education:* $701,000 \ *Open-Close:* 08/20 - 05/20 \ *DTBP:* $217 (High)

David Quattrochi	1,11,83	Roxanne Mazur	2,296
Barbara Burns	4	Wayne Baughman	5
Jason Eddy	6*	Jane Evans	7,85*
Ed Robinson	8,57,88,285,288	Stephanie Glacier	8
Laura Logan	27*	Renae Gross	31,38*
Tricia Green	58,275	Rose Seck	67
Matt White	73	Christopher Barto	273

Public Schs..Principal	Grd	Prgm	Enr/#Cls	SN	
Carrollton Elem Sch	PK-5	T	890	47%	330/627-4592
252 3rd St NE, Carrollton 44615			26		Fax 330/627-8433
Tim Albrecht					
Carrollton Middle High Sch	6-12	ATV	1,250	36%	330/627-2134
205 Scio Rd SW, Carrollton 44615			36		Fax 330/627-8446
Dave Davis					

CARROLL PRIVATE SCHOOLS

Private Schs..Principal	Grd	Prgm	Enr/#Cls	SN	
Carroll Co Christian Academy	K-12		60		330/627-5124
1211 Lincoln Ave NW, Carrollton 44615			9		Fax 330/627-5602
Dave Powell					

CHAMPAIGN COUNTY

CHAMPAIGN COUNTY SCHOOLS

• **Madison-Champaign Ed Svc Ctr** PID: 00787600 937/484-1557
1512 US Hwy S 68 Ste J100, Urbana 43078 Fax 937/484-1571

Dr Daniel Kaffenbarger	1	Matthew Ketcham	2
Donna Stelzer	15	Sheila Roberts	79
Michele Roberts	81	Steve Allen	298

CHAMPAIGN PUBLIC SCHOOLS

• **Graham Local School Dist** PID: 00787351 937/663-4123
7790 US Highway 36, Saint Paris 43072 Fax 937/663-4670

Schools: 3 \ *Teachers:* 115 \ *Students:* 1,836 \ *Special Ed Students:* 286 \ *College-Bound:* 50% \ *Ethnic:* Asian 1%, African American 1%, Hispanic 2%, Caucasian 97% \ *Exp:* $117 (Low) \ *Poverty:* 11% \ *Title I:* $279,634 \ *Special Education:* $427,000 \ *Open-Close:* 08/21 - 06/01 \ *DTBP:* $174 (High) \ 🅴

Matt Curtis	1	Judy Geers	2,84
Don Burley	3,4,5,73,76	Jay Lewis	6

OH–25

Champaign County

Joe Jude 9
Emily Smith 12,34,58,69,88
Carrie Draper 73
Adam Mowery 10
Ryan Pine 67
Karla Green 85

Public Schs..Principal	Grd	Prgm	Enr/#Cls	SN	
Graham Elem Sch 9464 US Highway 36, Saint Paris 43072 Chad Miller	PK-5	T	829 45	38%	937/663-4449 Fax 937/663-0257
Graham High Sch 7800 US Highway 36, Saint Paris 43072 Ryan Rismiller	9-12	V	563	28%	937/663-4127 Fax 937/663-0396
Graham Middle Sch 9644 US Highway 36, Saint Paris 43072 Chad Lensman	6-8		444 45	31%	937/663-5339 Fax 937/663-4674

• **Mechanicsburg Exempted Vlg SD** PID: 00787416   937/834-2453
  60 High St, Mechanicsburg 43044   Fax 937/834-3954

Schools: 2 \ *Teachers:* 51 \ *Students:* 900 \ *Special Ed Students:* 121 \ *College-Bound:* 68% \ *Ethnic:* African American 1%, Hispanic 2%, Caucasian 97% \ *Exp:* $165 (Low) \ *Poverty:* 10% \ *Title I:* $106,582 \ *Special Education:* $156,000 \ *Open-Close:* 08/21 - 05/29 \ *DTBP:* $189 (High)

Danielle Prohaska 1
David Eades 3
Cindy Pullman 7
Kristyn Campbell 16,82
Ce Greene 58*
Pam Wenning-Earp 73,95,286
Scott Maruniak 2,19
Matt Mayberry 5
Mary Huffman 8,11,280,285,294*
Carol Carpenter 37,88*
Scott DeLong 67

Public Schs..Principal	Grd	Prgm	Enr/#Cls	SN	
Dohron Wilson Elem Sch 60 High St, Mechanicsburg 43044 Christy Garver	K-5		373 21		937/834-2453 Fax 937/834-2080
Mechanicsburg Jr Sr High Sch 60 High St, Mechanicsburg 43044 Marlo Schipfer \ Paul Hershberger	6-12	V	472 60	99%	937/834-2453 Fax 937/834-7103

• **Triad Local School Dist** PID: 00787442   937/826-4961
  7920 Brush Lake Rd, N Lewisburg 43060   Fax 937/826-3281

Schools: 3 \ *Teachers:* 56 \ *Students:* 830 \ *Special Ed Students:* 132 \ *College-Bound:* 53% \ *Ethnic:* Hispanic 2%, Caucasian 97% \ *Exp:* $356 (High) \ *Poverty:* 13% \ *Title I:* $154,716 \ *Special Education:* $164,000 \ *Open-Close:* 08/20 - 05/27 \ *DTBP:* $180 (High)

Vickie Hoffman 1
Neil Laughbaum 3,5
Gary Davis 6*
Lee Claypool 9,11
Ryan Thompson 16,73,295*
Michele Peters 58,88,275*
Jessica Dunlavy 294
Connie Cohn 2
Shirley Weaver 4*
Morgan Fagnani 8,69,285,296,298
Meredith Ford 12*
Kacy Moore 38*
Chris Millice 67

Public Schs..Principal	Grd	Prgm	Enr/#Cls	SN	
Triad Elem Sch 7920 Brush Lake Rd, N Lewisburg 43060 Lee Claypool	K-4	T	296 19	49%	937/826-3102 Fax 937/826-0111
Triad High Sch 8099 Brush Lake Rd, N Lewisburg 43060 Kyle Huffman	9-12		272 20	33%	937/826-3771 Fax 937/826-2002
Triad Middle Sch 7941 Brush Lake Rd, N Lewisburg 43060 Doug Lowery	5-8		262 20	35%	937/826-3071 Fax 937/826-1000

• **Urbana City School Dist** PID: 00787492   937/653-1402
  711 Wood St, Urbana 43078   Fax 937/652-3845

Schools: 3 \ *Teachers:* 114 \ *Students:* 2,000 \ *Special Ed Students:* 438 \ *LEP Students:* 5 \ *College-Bound:* 55% \ *Ethnic:* Asian 1%, African American 4%, Hispanic 3%, Caucasian 93% \ *Exp:* $121 (Low) \ *Poverty:* 19% \ *Title I:* $617,390 \ *Special Education:* $476,000 \ *Open-Close:* 08/22 - 05/28 \ *DTBP:* $182 (High)

Charles Thiel 1
Nathan Bails 3
Daniel Shay 6
Joanne Petty 12*
Katie Miller 36,83*
Gina Lingrell 37*
Darrell Thomas 67
Kelli Marsh 286*
Bob Huelsman 2
Mike Puhalla 5
Dr Julie Willoughby 8
Kendell Burcham 16*
Valerie Leonard 36,83*
Lucas Pozenel 58,77
Kurt Hanson 73*

Public Schs..Principal	Grd	Prgm	Enr/#Cls	SN	
Urbana Elem Sch 1673 S US Highway 68, Urbana 43078 Jill Weimer	PK-5	T	981 20	58%	937/653-1453
Urbana High Sch 500 Washington Ave A, Urbana 43078 Kristin Mays	9-12	TV	534 50	59%	937/653-1412 Fax 937/653-1476
Urbana Junior High Sch 1673 S US Highway 68, Urbana 43078 Jason Shultz	6-8	TV	486 30		937/653-1439 Fax 937/653-1487

• **West Liberty-Salem Local SD** PID: 00787569   937/465-1075
  7208 US Highway 68 N, West Liberty 43357   Fax 937/465-1095

Schools: 1 \ *Teachers:* 80 \ *Students:* 1,250 \ *Special Ed Students:* 124 \ *College-Bound:* 72% \ *Exp:* $39 (Low) \ *Poverty:* 8% \ *Title I:* $130,204 \ *Special Education:* $215,000 \ *Open-Close:* 09/03 - 05/28 \ *DTBP:* $203 (High)

Kraig Hissong 1
Kathy Smith 4*
Jennifer Douthwaite 7*
Rebekah Troyer 11*
Kim Hollar 35,83,85,88*
Chuck Buck 67
Andy McGill 91*
Chelsea Baldwin 2
Linda Harr 5
Stacy Dunn 8,69,294*
Molly Smith 31,36*
Julie Hartsel 58,275*
Rich Johnson 73*

Public Schs..Principal	Grd	Prgm	Enr/#Cls	SN	
West Liberty-Salem Sch 7208 US Highway 68 N, West Liberty 43357 Greg Johnson \ Aaron Hollar	K-12	V	1,250 70		937/465-1075

CHAMPAIGN PRIVATE SCHOOLS

Private Schs..Principal	Grd	Prgm	Enr/#Cls	SN	
Victory Christian Sch 960 Childrens Home Rd, Urbana 43078 Josh Hunter	K-12		82 7		937/652-1133 Fax 937/652-0062

---

1 Superintendent	8 Curric/Instruct K-12	19 Chief Financial Officer	29 Family/Consumer Science	39 Social Studies K-12	49 English/Lang Arts Elem	59 Special Education Elem	69 Academic Assessment
2 Bus/Finance/Purchasing	9 Curric/Instruct Elem	20 Art K-12	30 Adult Education	40 Social Studies Elem	50 English/Lang Arts Sec	60 Special Education Sec	70 Research/Development
3 Buildings And Grounds	10 Curric/Instruct Sec	21 Art Elem	31 Career/Sch-to-Work K-12	41 Social Studies Sec	51 Reading K-12	61 Foreign/World Lang K-12	71 Public Information
4 Food Service	11 Federal Program	22 Art Sec	32 Career/Sch-to-Work Elem	42 Science K-12	52 Reading Elem	62 Foreign/World Lang Elem	72 Summer School
5 Transportation	12 Title I	23 Music K-12	33 Career/Sch-to-Work Sec	43 Science Elem	53 Reading Sec	63 Foreign/World Lang Sec	73 Instructional Tech
6 Athletic	13 Title V	24 Music Elem	34 Early Childhood Ed	44 Science Sec	54 Remedial Reading K-12	64 Religious Education	74 Inservice Training
7 Health Services	14 Instructional Media Svcs	25 Music Sec	35 Health/Phys Education	45 Math K-12	55 Remedial Reading Elem	65 Religious Education Elem	75 Marketing/Distributive
	15 Asst Superintendent	26 Business Education	36 Guidance Services K-12	46 Math Elem	56 Remedial Reading Sec	66 Religious Education Sec	76 Info Systems
	16 Chief Operations Officer	27 Career & Tech Ed	37 Guidance Services Elem	47 Math Sec	57 Bilingual/ELL	67 School Board President	77 Psychological Assess
	18 Chief Academic Officer	28 Technology Education	38 Guidance Services Sec	48 English/Lang Arts K-12	58 Special Education K-12	68 Teacher Personnel	78 Affirmative Action

Ohio School Directory

Clark County

CLARK COUNTY SCHOOLS

Clark Co Ed Service Center PID: 00788288 937/325-7671
25 W Pleasant St Ste 1, Springfield 45506 Fax 937/717-0518

Daniel Bennett .... 1 Pamela Mustovich 2
Eileen Tener .... 58 Dale Steinlage 67

CLARK PUBLIC SCHOOLS

Clark-Shawnee Local Sch Dist PID: 00788226 937/328-5378
3680 Selma Rd, Springfield 45502 Fax 937/328-5379

Schools: 5 \ **Teachers:** 111 \ **Students:** 2,057 \ **Special Ed Students:** 242 \ **LEP Students:** 11 \ **College-Bound:** 66% \ **Ethnic:** Asian 1%, African American 3%, Hispanic 2%, Caucasian 93% \ **Exp:** $178 (Low) \ **Poverty:** 15% \ **Title I:** $416,927 \ **Special Education:** $344,000 \ **Open-Close:** 08/21 - 05/27 \ **DTBP:** $209 (High)

Brian Kuhn .... 1 Cindy Claar 2
Dennis Williams .... 3 Jacob Mattern 5
Steve Tincher .... 6* Brian Masser 11,15,72
Joyce Aills .... 16* Eric Lennartz 27,73*
Rosie Matthies .... 45* Melissa Jewell 58
Michelle Garrett 67

Public Schs..Principal	Grd	Prgm	Enr/#Cls	SN
Possum Elem Sch 2589 S Yellow Springs St, Springfield 45506 Joseph Jude	K-6	T	460 35	73% 937/328-5383 Fax 937/328-5390
Reid Sch 3640 E High St, Springfield 45505 **Kyle Phelps**	K-6	T	484 25	67% 937/328-5380 Fax 937/328-5392
Rockway Elem Sch 3500 W National Rd, Springfield 45504 Amanda Shaffer	PK-6		207 15	39% 937/328-5385 Fax 937/328-5399
Shawnee High Sch 1675 E Possum Rd, Springfield 45502 Nathan Dockter	9-12		450 50	53% 937/325-9296 Fax 937/328-5389
Shawnee Middle Sch 1675 E Possum Rd, Springfield 45502 Amanda Ike	7-8		285	937/328-5378 Fax 937/521-1095

Greenon Local School Dist PID: 00787612 937/864-1202
120 S Xenia Dr, Enon 45323 Fax 937/864-2470

Schools: 3 \ **Teachers:** 85 \ **Students:** 1,486 \ **Special Ed Students:** 264 \ **LEP Students:** 7 \ **College-Bound:** 60% \ **Ethnic:** Asian 1%, African American 1%, Hispanic 3%, Caucasian 95% \ **Exp:** $137 (Low) \ **Poverty:** 11% \ **Title I:** $270,629 \ **Special Education:** $327,000 \ **Open-Close:** 08/21 - 05/28 \ **DTBP:** $241 (High) \ f t

Brad Silvus .... 1 Brad McKee 2,11*
John Gummel .... 4* Elmer Beard 5*
Carolyn Agresta .... 7* Lauren Spencer 38*
Dennis Henry .... 67 Corey Oconner 73
Darren Kanapki 275

Public Schs..Principal	Grd	Prgm	Enr/#Cls	SN
Enon Primary Sch 120 S Xenia Dr, Enon 45323 Darrin Knapke	K-1	T	236 20	937/864-7361 Fax 937/864-6014
Greenon Jr Sr High Sch 3950 S Tecumseh Rd, Springfield 45502 Tim Hale	7-12	TV	619 50	96% 937/340-6372 Fax 937/340-6371
Indian Valley Intermediate Sch 510 S Xenia Dr, Enon 45323 Darrin Knapke	2-6	T	631 23	13% 937/864-7348 Fax 937/864-6009 f t

Northeastern Local School Dist PID: 00787791 937/325-7615
1414 Bowman Rd, Springfield 45502 Fax 937/328-6592

Schools: 7 \ **Teachers:** 174 \ **Students:** 3,300 \ **Special Ed Students:** 323 \ **LEP Students:** 11 \ **College-Bound:** 50% \ **Ethnic:** Asian 1%, African American 2%, Hispanic 2%, Caucasian 94% \ **Exp:** $208 (Med) \ **Poverty:** 8% \ **Title I:** $340,374 \ **Special Education:** $589,000 \ **Open-Close:** 08/21 - 05/28 \ **DTBP:** $198 (High)

Dr John Kronour .... 1 Dale Miller 2,11
Randy Phares .... 3,5,91 Terri Parks 4
Chuck Ripperman .... 6* Kris Spriggs 6*
Shawn Blazer .... 8,15,69,288 Jim Templeton 23*
David Wilson .... 25* Jane Warren 36*
Steve Linson .... 57,58,83,88,275,280,294,298 Jill Parker 67
John Schmid .... 73,76,286,295 Lennie Linson 81

Public Schs..Principal	Grd	Prgm	Enr/#Cls	SN
Kenton Ridge High Sch 4444 Middle Urbana Rd, Springfield 45503 John Hill	9-12		554 40	20% 937/390-1274 Fax 937/390-0013
Northeastern High Sch 1480 Bowman Rd, Springfield 45502 Todd Justice	9-12	V	334 43	26% 937/328-6575 Fax 937/346-0856
Northridge Elem Sch 4445 Ridgewood Rd E, Springfield 45503 Samuel Shaffer	K-5		428 30	54% 937/342-4627 Fax 937/342-1359
Northridge Middle Sch 4445 Ridgewood Rd E, Springfield 45503 Gary Miller	6-8		452 25	937/399-2852 Fax 937/342-4631
Rolling Hills Elem Sch 2613 Moorefield Rd, Springfield 45502 Drew Snyder	PK-5		542 24	25% 937/399-2250 Fax 937/399-3454 f t
South Vienna Elem Sch 140 W Main St, South Vienna 45369 Denise Jones	PK-5		515 45	53% 937/346-0840 Fax 937/346-0842
South Vienna Middle Sch 140 W Main St, South Vienna 45369 Zach Dobbelaere	6-8		297 15	937/346-0880 Fax 937/568-4778

Northwestern Local School Dist PID: 00787868 937/964-1318
5610 Troy Rd, Springfield 45502 Fax 937/964-6019

Schools: 2 \ **Teachers:** 95 \ **Students:** 1,643 \ **Special Ed Students:** 244 \ **Ethnic:** African American 1%, Hispanic 3%, Caucasian 96% \ **Exp:** $169 (Low) \ **Poverty:** 12% \ **Title I:** $288,816 \ **Special Education:** $325,000 \ **Open-Close:** 08/21 - 05/28 \ **DTBP:** $174 (High)

Jessie Steiner .... 1 Julie Gibson 2
Christopher Howell .... 3 Sue Geis 4
Johanna Brents .... 5 Jeffrey Hobby 6
Sharon Fonders .... 8,57 Sharon Saunders 11
Amy Fraker .... 38,69,83,88* Rachel Poynter 38
Chrissy Miller .... 58 Andy Gundolf 67
Kevin Graham .... 73 Lori Ballentine 81*

---

79 Student Personnel	91 Safety/Security	275 Response To Intervention	298 Grant Writer/Ptnrships	**School Programs**	**Social Media**
80 Driver Ed/Safety	92 Magnet School	277 Remedial Math K-12	750 Chief Innovation Officer	A = Alternative Program	f = Facebook
81 Gifted/Talented	93 Parental Involvement	280 Literacy Coach	751 Chief of Staff	G = Adult Classes	t = Twitter
82 Video Services	95 Tech Prep Program	285 STEM	752 Social Emotional Learning	M = Magnet Program	
83 Substance Abuse Prev	97 Chief Infomation Officer	286 Digital Learning		T = Title I Schoolwide	
84 Erate	98 Chief Technology Officer	288 Common Core Standards	**Other School Types**	V = Career & Tech Ed Programs	
85 AIDS Education	270 Character Education	294 Accountability	Ⓐ = Alternative School		
88 Alternative/At Risk	271 Migrant Education	295 Network System	Ⓒ = Charter School	New Schools are shaded	
89 Multi-Cultural Curriculum	273 Teacher Mentor	296 Title II Programs	Ⓜ = Magnet School	New Superintendents and Principals are bold	
90 Social Work	274 Before/After Sch	297 Webmaster	Ⓨ = Year-Round School	Personnel with email addresses are underscored	

OH–27

Clark County

Market Data Retrieval

Public Schs..Principal	Grd	Prgm	Enr/#Cls	SN
Northwestern Elem Sch 5610 Troy Rd, Springfield 45502 Luke Everhart	PK-6	T	931 35	37% 937/964-3240 Fax 937/964-3244
Northwestern Jr Sr High Sch 5780 Troy Rd, Springfield 45502 Lori Swafford	7-12	V	712 40	30% 937/964-1324 Fax 937/964-6006

- **Southeastern Local School Dist** PID: 00787909 216/462-8388
  226 Clifton Rd, S Charleston 45368 Fax 216/207-9654

Schools: 2 \ *Teachers:* 25 \ *Students:* 778 \ *Special Ed Students:* 134 \ *College-Bound:* 65% \ *Ethnic:* African American 1%, Hispanic 1%, Caucasian 98% \ *Exp:* $451 (High) \ *Poverty:* 13% \ *Title I:* $146,724 \ *Special Education:* $130,000 \ *Open-Close:* 08/29 - 05/28 \ *DTBP:* $180 (High)

David Shea 1,11	Ben Kitchen 2
Chuck McNier 5	Bren Dean 16,82
Scott Lamb 16,73*	Tony Entler 67

Public Schs..Principal	Grd	Prgm	Enr/#Cls	SN
Miami View Elem Sch 230 Clifton Rd, S Charleston 45368 David Shea	PK-6		419 29	30% 937/462-8364 Fax 937/462-7914
Southeastern Jr Sr High Sch 195 E Jamestown St, S Charleston 45368 P J Bertemes	7-12	V	183 30	937/462-8308 Fax 937/462-8394

- **Springfield City School Dist** PID: 00787935 937/505-2800
  1500 W Jefferson St, Springfield 45506 Fax 937/505-2978

Schools: 16 \ *Teachers:* 485 \ *Students:* 7,583 \ *Special Ed Students:* 1,555 \ *LEP Students:* 247 \ *Ethnic:* Asian 1%, African American 26%, Hispanic 8%, Caucasian 65% \ *Exp:* $501 (High) \ *Poverty:* 31% \ *Title I:* $4,970,628 \ *Special Education:* $1,858,000 \ *Open-Close:* 08/21 - 05/27 \ *DTBP:* $229 (High)

Dr Robert Hill 1	Nicole Cottrell 2
John Parrish 3	Jerri Arthur 4
Tammie Weaver 5	Michael Dellapina 6
Emily Jablonka 8,74	Kristen Kettlehake 8,74
Cristina Sanches 9	Paul Schneider 11,57,271,296
Stacy Parr 16,73,76,295	Kelly Wiggins 30
Jen Bogenrife 58	Lourdes Narvaez 61
Ed Leventhal 67	Lydia Gaddis 68,74,78,83,273,275
Crystal Aker 69,294	Cherie Moore 71
Dave Lyle 91	Karri Kiss 274
Sean Kiriakis 286	

Public Schs..Principal	Grd	Prgm	Enr/#Cls	SN
Clark Pre-School 1500 W Jefferson St, Springfield 45506 Debra Accurso	PK-PK		417	937/505-4170 Fax 937/325-9358
Fulton Elem Sch 631 S Yellow Springs St, Springfield 45506 Deborah Howard	K-6	T	351 25	937/505-4150 Fax 937/322-5246
Hayward Middle Sch 1700 Clifton Ave, Springfield 45505 Edna Chapman	7-8	T	314 31	937/505-4190 Fax 937/323-9812
Horace Mann Elem Sch 521 Mount Joy St, Springfield 45505 Kevin Schalnat	K-6	T	428 24	937/505-4280 Fax 937/323-7646
Kenwood Elem Sch 1421 Nagley St, Springfield 45505 Allyson Thurman	K-6	T	423 20	937/505-4220 Fax 937/324-9721
Lagonda Elem Sch 800 E McCreight Ave, Springfield 45503 Cathie Scott	K-6	T	406 18	937/505-4240 Fax 937/342-8954
Lincoln Elem Sch 1500 Tibbetts Ave, Springfield 45505 Mike Wilson	K-6	T	388 22	937/505-4260 Fax 937/324-8684
On Course 601 Selma Rd, Springfield 45505 Monica Fee	9-12		53	937/505-4120 Fax 937/323-8784
Perrin Woods Elem Sch 431 W John St, Springfield 45506 Nena Dorsey	K-6	T	381 26	937/505-4310 Fax 937/322-7576
Roosevelt Middle Sch 721 E Home Rd, Springfield 45503 Monte Brigham	7-8	T	385 40	937/505-4370 Fax 937/342-0280
Schaefer Middle Sch 147 S Fostoria Ave, Springfield 45505 Kimberly Watkins	7-8	T	275 31	937/505-4390 Fax 937/325-8974
Simon Kenton Elem Sch 731 E Home Rd, Springfield 45503 Amy Paul	K-6	T	454 21	937/505-4210 Fax 937/342-8528
Snowhill Elem Sch 531 W Harding Rd, Springfield 45504 Kellie Berlean	K-6	T	470 22	937/505-4410 Fax 937/399-2585
Snyder Park Elem Sch 1600 Maiden Ln, Springfield 45504 Walter Sledge	K-6	T	424 26	937/505-4430 Fax 937/324-2246
Springfield High Sch 701 E Home Rd, Springfield 45503 Patrick Smith	9-12	TV	1,715	937/505-4320 Fax 937/342-4110
Warder Park Wayne Elem Sch 2820 Hillside Ave, Springfield 45503 Scott Blackburn	K-6	T	461 31	937/505-4450 Fax 937/323-7924

- **Springfield-Clark Co JVSD** PID: 00788290 937/325-7368
  1901 Selma Rd, Springfield 45505 Fax 937/325-7452

Schools: 1 \ *Teachers:* 54 \ *Students:* 700 \ *LEP Students:* 3 \ *Exp:* $374 (High) \ *Open-Close:* 08/16 - 05/22 \ *DTBP:* $107 (High)

Michelle Patrick 1	Steve Clark 2
Nathan Lasso 10	Chris James 27
Jamie Callan 67	Jeff Thoman 76

Public Schs..Principal	Grd	Prgm	Enr/#Cls	SN
Springfield-Clark Career Tech 1901 Selma Rd, Springfield 45505 Jason Chilman	Voc		700 70	937/325-7368 Fax 937/325-3990

- **Tecumseh Local School Dist** PID: 00787686 937/845-3576
  9760 W National Rd, New Carlisle 45344 Fax 937/845-4453

Schools: 5 \ *Teachers:* 163 \ *Students:* 3,130 \ *Special Ed Students:* 435 \ *LEP Students:* 247 \ *College-Bound:* 49% \ *Ethnic:* African American 1%, Hispanic 14%, Caucasian 84% \ *Exp:* $149 (Low) \ *Poverty:* 19% \ *Title I:* $833,325 \ *Special Education:* $631,000 \ *Open-Close:* 08/21 - 06/04 \ *DTBP:* $191 (High)

Paula Crew 1	Denise Robinson 2,3,17
Roger Diller 3	Stacy Reynolds 4*
Karen Lokai 5	Craig Eier 6*
Beth Moore 8,91,285	Ivan Gehret 8,11,15,16,18,69
Susan Wile 58,76,83,275,296	Corinne Scott 67
Veronica Cassidy 73,295,297*	Pam Ulrich 274*
Tammy McBroom 274*	Deanna Gehret 298*

Ohio School Directory — Clermont County

Public Schs..Principal	Grd	Prgm	Enr/#Cls	SN	
Donnelsville Elem Sch 150 E Main St, Donnelsville 45319 Jay Burkholder	2-3	T	427 16	68%	937/845-4540 Fax 937/845-4504
New Carlisle Elem Sch 1203 Kennison Ave, New Carlisle 45344 Kathryn Randenburg	4-5	T	465 21	69%	937/845-4480 Fax 937/845-5029
Park Layne Elem Sch 12355 Dille Rd, New Carlisle 45344 Karyl Strader	K-1	T	434 19	65%	937/845-4470 Fax 937/849-6750
Tecumseh High Sch 9830 W National Rd, New Carlisle 45344 Aaron Oakes	9-12	TV	912 70	61%	937/845-4500 Fax 937/845-4547
Tecumseh Middle Sch 10000 W National Rd, New Carlisle 45344 Brian Dixon	6-8	T	653 25	64%	937/845-4465 Fax 937/845-4484

CLARK CATHOLIC SCHOOLS

• **Archdiocese Cincinnati Ed Off** PID: 00808096
Listing includes only schools located in this county. See District Index for location of Diocesan Offices.

Catholic Schs..Principal	Grd	Prgm	Enr/#Cls	SN	
Catholic Central ES-Limestone 1817 N Limestone St, Springfield 45503 Shannon DeWeese	PK-PK		45 20		937/399-5451 Fax 937/342-0042 f t
Catholic Central Jr Sr HS 1200 E High St, Springfield 45505 Shannon DeWeese \ Patrick Rizer	7-12		367 26		937/325-9204 Fax 937/328-7426 f t
Catholic Central Sch 1200 E High St, Springfield 45505 Shannon DeWeese	K-12		491 9		937/324-4551 Fax 937/328-7426 f t

CLARK PRIVATE SCHOOLS

Private Schs..Principal	Grd	Prgm	Enr/#Cls	SN	
Emmanuel Christian Academy 2177 Emmanuel Way, Springfield 45502 Danny Moore	K-12		480 34		937/390-3777 Fax 937/390-0966 f
Nightingale Montessori Sch 1106 E High St, Springfield 45505 Maria Taylor	PK-12		105 6		937/324-0336 Fax 937/398-0086
Ridgewood Sch 2420 Saint Paris Pike, Springfield 45504 Aliya Ranginwala	K-8		144 12		937/399-8900 Fax 937/399-8173 f t
Risen Christ Lutheran Sch 41 E Possum Rd, Springfield 45502 Rebecca Reid	PK-6		80		937/323-3688 Fax 937/323-3746
Springfield Christian Sch 311 W High St, Springfield 45506 Judy Loy	PK-8		140 12		937/325-3113 Fax 937/325-9302

CLERMONT COUNTY

CLERMONT COUNTY SCHOOLS

• **Clermont Co Ed Service Center** PID: 00788850   513/735-8300
2400 Clermont Center Dr, Batavia 45103   Fax 513/735-8371

Jeff Weir 1   Al Fleckinger 2
Dr Dawn Betts 15,36,68   Chris Curtin 58
Duane Yockey 73

County Schs..Principal	Grd	Prgm	Enr/#Cls	SN	
Clermont Co Hearing Hndcp Unit 3520 State Route 132, Amelia 45102 Beth Koenig	Spec		20 3		513/943-8980 Fax 513/735-8370
Clermont Educ Collaborative-N 1039 Business 28, Milford 45150 Tamara Ratley	Spec		37		513/735-8302 Fax 513/735-8373
Clermont Educ Collaborative-S 549 W Main St Ste B, Williamsburg 45176 Sarah Bose	Spec		100		513/724-8555 Fax 513/724-0708
Thomas A Wildey Sch 2040 US Highway 50, Batavia 45103 Jay Williams	Spec		50 8		513/732-7015 Fax 513/732-4950

CLERMONT PUBLIC SCHOOLS

• **Batavia Local School Dist** PID: 00788317   513/732-2343
800 Bauer Ave, Batavia 45103   Fax 513/732-3221

Schools: 3 \ **Teachers:** 125 \ **Students:** 2,289 \ **Special Ed Students:** 358 \ **LEP Students:** 21 \ **College-Bound:** 55% \ **Ethnic:** Asian 1%, African American 3%, Hispanic 3%, Caucasian 92% \ **Exp:** $21 (Low) \ **Poverty:** 18% \ **Title I:** $556,729 \ **Special Education:** $376,000 \ **Open-Close:** 08/14 - 05/21 \ **DTBP:** $234 (High) \ f t

Keith Millard 1,11   Michael Ashmore 2
Adrian Thompkins 4   Shawn Young 5
Matt Blandin 6   Cindy Jacobs 57,58,81*
Michael Enriquez 67

Public Schs..Principal	Grd	Prgm	Enr/#Cls	SN	
Batavia Elem Sch 3 Bulldog Pl, Batavia 45103 Renee Munro	PK-5	T	1,240 43	49%	513/732-0780 Fax 513/732-1863
Batavia High Sch 1 Bulldog Pl, Batavia 45103 Tim Derickson	9-12	ATV	518 22	38%	513/732-2341 Fax 513/732-9740
Batavia Middle Sch 800 Bauer Ave, Batavia 45103 Stephen Brokamp	6-8	T	531 47	46%	513/732-9534 Fax 513/732-3696

---

79 Student Personnel
80 Driver Ed/Safety
81 Gifted/Talented
82 Video Services
83 Substance Abuse Prev
84 Erate
85 AIDS Education
88 Alternative/At Risk
89 Multi-Cultural Curriculum
90 Social Work

91 Safety/Security
92 Magnet School
93 Parental Involvement
95 Tech Prep Program
97 Chief Information Officer
98 Chief Technology Officer
270 Character Education
271 Migrant Education
273 Teacher Mentor
274 Before/After Sch

275 Response To Intervention
277 Remedial Math K-12
280 Literacy Coach
285 STEM
286 Digital Learning
288 Common Core Standards
294 Accountability
295 Network System
296 Title II Programs
297 Webmaster

298 Grant Writer/Ptnrships
750 Chief Innovation Officer
751 Chief of Staff
752 Social Emotional Learning

Other School Types
Ⓐ = Alternative School
Ⓒ = Charter School
Ⓜ = Magnet School
Ⓨ = Year-Round School

School Programs
A = Alternative Program
G = Adult Classes
M = Magnet Program
T = Title I Schoolwide
V = Career & Tech Ed Programs

New Schools are shaded
New Superintendents and Principals are bold
Personnel with email addresses are underscored

Social Media
f = Facebook
t = Twitter

Clermont County

Bethel-Tate Local School Dist PID: 00788343
675 W Plane St, Bethel 45106
513/734-2271
Fax 513/734-4792

Schools: 4 \ **Teachers:** 91 \ **Students:** 1,600 \ **Special Ed Students:** 267 \ **College-Bound:** 57% \ **Ethnic:** African American 1%, Hispanic 2%, Caucasian 97% \ **Exp:** $93 (Low) \ **Poverty:** 12% \ **Title I:** $293,679 \ **Special Education:** $275,000 \ **Open-Close:** 08/14 - 05/20 \ **DTBP:** $242 (High)

Melissa Kircher 1
John Burns 3,73,295,297
Kim Fontaine 5
Matt Wagner 11,52*
Caitlin Spiller 36,69,81*
Mary Tucker 58,298
Christine Davis 83*
Karen Royer 2,19,84
Darlene Parks 4
Matt Folkerth 6
Greg Chandler 12,69*
Rea Reynolds 38*
David Brannock 67

Public Schs..Principal	Grd	Prgm	Enr/#Cls	SN		
Bethel-Tate High Sch 3420 State Route 125, Bethel 45106 George Sturgeon	9-12	T	460 35	28%	513/734-2271 Fax 513/734-1355	
Bethel-Tate Middle Sch 649 W Plane St, Bethel 45106 Christine Davis	6-8	T	370	39%	513/734-2271 Fax 513/734-0888	
Ebon C Hill Intermediate Sch 150 Fossyl Dr, Bethel 45106 Matt Wagner	3-5	T	375 20	43%	513/734-2271 Fax 513/734-3013	
William Bick Primary Sch 101 Fossyl Dr, Bethel 45106 Kay Nau	K-2	T	296 30	42%	513/734-2271 Fax 513/734-0444	

Clermont Northeastern Local SD PID: 00788393
2792 US Highway 50, Batavia 45103
513/625-1211
Fax 513/625-8060

Schools: 3 \ **Teachers:** 80 \ **Students:** 1,350 \ **Special Ed Students:** 262 \ **College-Bound:** 43% \ **Ethnic:** African American 1%, Hispanic 1%, Caucasian 98% \ **Exp:** $542 (High) \ **Poverty:** 12% \ **Title I:** $344,884 \ **Special Education:** $190,000 \ **Open-Close:** 08/19 - 05/21 \ **DTBP:** $240 (High)

Michael Brandt 1
Rick McEvoy 3
Lori Diekmann 7,85*
Trina Farrell 12*
Dave Pennington 67
Al Porter 2
Terri Hoerth 4
Glenda Greene 11,58
Karen Amster 16*
Andy Seals 295*

Public Schs..Principal	Grd	Prgm	Enr/#Cls	SN		
Clermont Northeastern Elem Sch 5347 Hutchinson Rd, Batavia 45103 Tonya Schmidt	K-5	T	646 29	45%	513/625-1211 Fax 513/732-0285	
Clermont Northeastern High Sch 5327 Hutchinson Rd, Batavia 45103 Tj Glassmeyer	9-12	V	405 28	30%	513/625-1211 Fax 513/625-3328	
Clermont Northeastern Mid Sch 2792 US Highway 50, Batavia 45103 Laura Nazzarine	6-8	T	329	43%	513/625-1211 Fax 513/625-3325	

Felicity-Franklin Local SD PID: 00788458
105 Market St, Felicity 45120
513/876-2113
Fax 513/876-2519

Schools: 3 \ **Teachers:** 50 \ **Students:** 800 \ **Special Ed Students:** 171 \ **College-Bound:** 31% \ **Ethnic:** African American 1%, Hispanic 1%, Caucasian 98% \ **Exp:** $135 (Low) \ **Poverty:** 14% \ **Title I:** $211,024 \ **Special Education:** $200,000 \ **Open-Close:** 08/20 - 05/22 \ **DTBP:** $178 (High) \ f

David Gibson 1,11
Michelle Utter 4*
Ryan Talbe 6
Brad Ellis 58
Charlie Marshall 73,98,295,297
Jennifer Guy 296
Christina Laubach 2
Tammy Tatman 5
Kristin Baird 31,36,69,83,88*
Yovona Backer 67
Beth Francis 285

Public Schs..Principal	Grd	Prgm	Enr/#Cls	SN		
Felicity-Franklin Elem Sch 105 Market St, Felicity 45120 Jennifer Keller	PK-4	T	269 18	62%	513/876-2112 Fax 513/876-2051	
Felicity-Franklin High Sch 105 Market St, Felicity 45120 Bob Walker	9-12	TV	211 24	55%	513/876-2560 Fax 513/876-2111	
Felicity-Franklin Middle Sch 105 Market St, Felicity 45120 Joe Pfeffer	5-8	T	276 16	55%	513/876-2662 Fax 513/876-2848	

Goshen Local School Dist PID: 00788484
6694 Goshen Rd, Goshen 45122
513/722-2222
Fax 513/722-3767

Schools: 4 \ **Teachers:** 144 \ **Students:** 2,800 \ **Special Ed Students:** 455 \ **LEP Students:** 17 \ **College-Bound:** 38% \ **Ethnic:** African American 1%, Hispanic 3%, Caucasian 96% \ **Exp:** $252 (Med) \ **Poverty:** 13% \ **Title I:** $535,878 \ **Special Education:** $483,000 \ **Open-Close:** 08/15 - 05/27 \ **DTBP:** $70 (Low)

Darrell Edwards 1
Chuck Smith 3
Bryan Howard 5
Karen Garrett 7
Brian Bailey 15,36,57,69,79,83,88,285
Nancy Spears 58
Mark Slagle 73,76,295*
Todd Shinkle 2
Linda Ramsey 4
Scott Wake 6*
Theresa Scherzinger ...8,11,69,288,296,298
Emily Slagle 16,82*
John Benthien 67
Megan Ginther 280*

Public Schs..Principal	Grd	Prgm	Enr/#Cls	SN		
Goshen High Sch 6707 Goshen Rd, Goshen 45122 Stephanie Walker	9-12	TV	803 45	60%	513/722-2227 Fax 513/722-2247	
Goshen Middle Sch 6692 Goshen Rd, Goshen 45122 Wendy Flynn	6-8	T	664 33	60%	513/722-2226 Fax 513/722-2246	
Marr Cook Elem Sch 6696 Goshen Rd, Goshen 45122 Troy Smith	PK-2	T	707 30	49%	513/722-2224 Fax 513/722-2244	
Spaulding Elem Sch 6755 Linton Rd, Goshen 45122 Tom Turner	3-5	T	673	61%	513/722-2225 Fax 513/722-2245	

Milford Exempted Village SD PID: 00788537
1099 State Route 131, Milford 45150
513/831-1314
Fax 513/965-6159

Schools: 10 \ **Teachers:** 325 \ **Students:** 6,600 \ **Special Ed Students:** 853 \ **LEP Students:** 94 \ **College-Bound:** 72% \ **Ethnic:** Asian 2%, African American 2%, Hispanic 3%, Caucasian 93% \ **Exp:** $218 (Med) \ **Poverty:** 6% \ **Title I:** $608,548 \ **Special Education:** $1,069,000 \ **Open-Close:** 08/19 - 05/28 \ **DTBP:** $185 (High) \ f t

Nancy House 1
Edward Beverly 3
Jud Phillips 5
Dr Jill Hollandsworth 8,11,15,16,288,294,296,298*
Lynn Miller 12
George Lucas 67
Stacy Smith 73,286
Jeff Johnson 2
Geraldine Levy 4
Aaron Zupka 6
.... Paul Daniels 10
Jennie Berkley 58
John Spieser 68

---

1 Superintendent	19 Chief Financial Officer	39 Social Studies K-12	59 Special Education Elem	69 Academic Assessment
2 Bus/Finance/Purchasing	20 Art K-12	40 Social Studies Elem	60 Special Education Sec	70 Research/Development
3 Buildings And Grounds	21 Art Elem	41 Social Studies Sec	61 Foreign/World Lang K-12	71 Public Information
4 Food Service	22 Art Sec	42 Science K-12	62 Foreign/World Lang Elem	72 Summer School
5 Transportation	23 Music K-12	43 Science Elem	63 Foreign/World Lang Sec	73 Instructional Tech
6 Athletic	24 Music Elem	44 Science Sec	64 Religious Education K-12	74 Inservice Training
7 Health Services	25 Music Sec	45 Math K-12	65 Religious Education Elem	75 Marketing/Distributive
8 Curric/Instruct K-12	26 Business Education	46 Math Elem	66 Religious Education Sec	76 Info Systems
9 Curric/Instruct Elem	27 Career & Tech Ed	47 Math Sec	67 School Board President	77 Psychological Assess
10 Curric/Instruct Sec	28 Technology Education	48 English/Lang Arts K-12	68 Teacher Personnel	78 Affirmative Action
11 Federal Program	29 Family/Consumer Science	49 English/Lang Arts Elem		
12 Title I	30 Adult Education	50 English/Lang Arts Sec		
13 Title V	31 Career/Sch-to-Work K-12	51 Reading K-12		
14 Instructional Media Svcs	32 Career/Sch-to-Work Elem	52 Reading Elem		
15 Asst Superintendent	33 Career/Sch-to-Work Sec	53 Reading Sec		
16 Chief Operations Officer	34 Early Childhood Ed	54 Remedial Reading K-12		
17 Chief Academic Officer	35 Health/Phys Education	55 Remedial Reading Elem		
18 Chief Academic Officer	36 Guidance Services K-12	56 Remedial Reading Sec		
	37 Guidance Services Elem	57 Bilingual/ELL		
	38 Guidance Services Sec	58 Special Education K-12		

Ohio School Directory — Clermont County

Public Schs..Principal	Grd	Prgm	Enr/#Cls	SN	
Boyd E Smith Elem Sch 1052 Jer Les Dr, Milford 45150 Doug Savage	K-6		526 23	16%	513/575-1643 Fax 513/575-2835
Charles L Seipelt Elem Sch 900 State Route 131, Milford 45150 Melissa Carraher	K-6	T	502 21	32%	513/831-9460 Fax 513/248-5443
McCormick Elem Sch 751 Loveland Miamiville Rd, Loveland 45140 Tom Willson	K-6		614 26	22%	513/575-0190 Fax 513/575-4019
Meadowview Elem Sch 5556 Mount Zion Rd, Milford 45150 Kelli Ellison	K-6		684 25	23%	513/831-9170 Fax 513/831-9340
Milford High Sch 1 Eagles Way, Milford 45150 Josh Kauffman	9-12	V	1,933	23%	513/831-2990 Fax 513/831-9714
Milford Junior High Sch 5735 Pleasant Hill Rd, Milford 45150 Goetz Misty	7-8		1,100 56	24%	513/831-1900 Fax 513/248-3451
Milford Preschool 1039 Business 28, Milford 45150 Jennie Berkley	PK-PK		171	12%	513/728-7400 Fax 513/831-8764
Mulberry Elem Sch 5950 Buckwheat Rd, Milford 45150 Sarah Greb	K-6		596 26	36%	513/722-3588 Fax 513/722-4584
Pattison Elem Sch 5330 S Milford Rd, Milford 45150 Tiffany Selm	K-6		534 29	18%	513/831-6570 Fax 513/831-9693
Success Academy 1 Eagles Way, Milford 45150 Mary Lou Assell	9-12		120		513/576-8943

New Richmond Exempted Vlg SD   PID: 00788616
212 Market St 3rd Fl, New Richmond 45157
513/553-2616   Fax 513/553-6431

Schools: 4 \ **Teachers:** 143 \ **Students:** 2,400 \ **Special Ed Students:** 386 \ **LEP Students:** 7 \ **College-Bound:** 57% \ **Ethnic:** African American 1%, Hispanic 2%, Caucasian 97% \ **Exp:** $251 (Med) \ **Poverty:** 13% \ **Title I:** $432,731 \ **Special Education:** $548,000 \ **Open-Close:** 08/15 - 05/21 \ **DTBP:** $174 (High)

Tracey Miller 1
Andrew Mays 5
John Frye 8,11,58,69,74,271,288,296
Tim Dufau 67
Cindy Banfield 83*
Julia Toth 2
Doug Foote 6*
Matt Prichard 16,73,295,297
Cindy Groman 77*

Public Schs..Principal	Grd	Prgm	Enr/#Cls	SN	
Locust Corner Elem Sch 3431 Locust Corner Rd, Cincinnati 45245 Joe Roach	PK-5		620 32	32%	513/752-1432 Fax 513/752-0611
Monroe Elem Sch 2117 Laurel Lindale Rd, New Richmond 45157 Jamie Kunz	PK-5	T	620 25	41%	513/553-3183 Fax 513/553-6033
New Richmond High Sch 1131 Bethel New Richmond Rd, New Richmond 45157 Mark Bailey	9-12	V	646 60	37%	513/553-3191 Fax 513/553-2531
New Richmond Middle Sch 1135 Bethel New Richmond Rd, New Richmond 45157 Court Lilly	6-8		513 20	48%	513/553-3161 Fax 513/553-6412

U S Grant Career School Dist   PID: 01537707
718 W Plane St, Bethel 45106
513/734-6222   Fax 513/734-4758

Schools: 1 \ **Teachers:** 42 \ **Students:** 400 \ **College-Bound:** 60% \ **Exp:** $688 (High) \ **Open-Close:** 08/16 - 05/22 \ **DTBP:** $274 (High)

Michael Parry 1
Kurt Wood 3*
Lisa Tuttle-Huff 11
Susan Hakel 60*
Matthew Schumann 73,84*
Patricia Patten 2
Shel Rammel 10,69*
Barry Doulton 27,75,288*
Kim Hayden 67
Doug Flamm 91*

Public Schs..Principal	Grd	Prgm	Enr/#Cls	SN	
U S Grant Career Center 718 W Plane St, Bethel 45106 Barry Doulton	Voc	G	400 30		513/734-6222

West Clermont Local Sch Dist   PID: 00788680
4350 Aicholtz Rd Ste 220, Cincinnati 45245
513/943-5000   Fax 513/752-6158

Schools: 10 \ **Teachers:** 445 \ **Students:** 9,500 \ **Special Ed Students:** 1,172 \ **LEP Students:** 144 \ **College-Bound:** 50% \ **Ethnic:** Asian 2%, African American 4%, Hispanic 3%, Caucasian 93% \ **Exp:** $72 (Low) \ **Poverty:** 11% \ **Title I:** $1,594,794 \ **Special Education:** $1,739,000 \ **Open-Close:** 08/28 - 06/04 \ **DTBP:** $186 (High)

Natasha Adams 1
Lance Perry 3,5
James Collins 6*
Ellie Preston 12,36,69,79,88,288,298
Jeff Riel 16
Tina Sanborn 67
Kelly Sininger 2
Tiffany McCleese 4
Amy Storer 11,57,294*
Michale Overbey 15
Larry Parece 16,73,84,91,95,270,295

Public Schs..Principal	Grd	Prgm	Enr/#Cls	SN	
Amelia Elem Sch 5 E Main St, Amelia 45102 Shane Short	PK-5	T	777 36	38%	513/943-3800 Fax 513/943-3642
Clough Pike Elem Sch 808 Clough Pike, Cincinnati 45245 Kevin Thacker	PK-5		601 50	23%	513/943-6700 Fax 513/752-7347
Holly Hill Elem Sch 3520 State Route 132, Amelia 45102 Erin Parker	PK-5	T	392 22	65%	513/943-8900 Fax 513/797-5604
Merwin Elem Sch 1040 Gaskins Rd, Cincinnati 45245 Cheryl Turner	PK-5		513 32	35%	513/947-7800 Fax 513/752-5629
Summerside Elem Sch 4639 Vermona Dr, Cincinnati 45245 Lisa Courtney	PK-5	T	450 23	49%	513/947-7900 Fax 513/528-3520
West Clermont High Sch 4101 Bach Buxton Rd, Batavia 45103 Randy Gebhardt	9-12		2,301		513/947-7600 Fax 513/947-3460
West Clermont Middle Sch 1351 Clough Pike, Batavia 45103 Lori Crowe	6-8		1,934 45		513/947-7400
West Clermont Virtual Academy 4101 Bach Buxton Rd, Batavia 45103 Brian Wallace	9-12		145		513/943-5075
Willowville Elem Sch 4529 Schoolhouse Rd, Batavia 45103 Michelle Kennedy	K-5		448 24	31%	513/943-6800 Fax 513/752-9181
Withamsville-Tobasco Elem Sch 3950 Britton Blvd, Cincinnati 45245 Sue Litman-Hall	PK-5	T	520 21	48%	513/943-6900 Fax 513/752-6571

79 Student Personnel	91 Safety/Security	275 Response To Intervention	298 Grant Writer/Ptnrships	School Programs	Social Media
80 Driver Ed/Safety	92 Magnet School	277 Remedial Math K-12	750 Chief Innovation Officer	A = Alternative Program	= Facebook
81 Gifted/Talented	93 Parental Involvement	280 Literacy Coach	751 Chief of Staff	G = Adult Classes	= Twitter
82 Video Services	95 Tech Prep Program	285 STEM	752 Social Emotional Learning	M = Magnet Program	
83 Substance Abuse Prev	97 Chief Infomation Officer	286 Digital Learning		T = Title I Schoolwide	
84 Erate	98 Chief Technology Officer	288 Common Core Standards	Other School Types	V = Career & Tech Ed Programs	
85 AIDS Education	270 Character Education	294 Accountability	Ⓐ = Alternative School		
88 Alternative/At Risk	271 Migrant Education	295 Network System	Ⓒ = Charter School	New Schools are shaded	
89 Multi-Cultural Curriculum	273 Teacher Mentor	296 Title II Programs	Ⓜ = Magnet School	New Superintendents and Principals are bold	
90 Social Work	274 Before/After Sch	297 Webmaster	Ⓨ = Year-Round School	Personnel with email addresses are underscored	

OH–31

Clinton County

Market Data Retrieval

- **Williamsburg Local School Dist** PID: 00788800 — 513/724-2211
  549 W Main St Ste A, Williamsburg 45176 — Fax 513/724-1504

Schools: 2 \ *Teachers:* 52 \ *Students:* 994 \ *Special Ed Students:* 129 \ *LEP Students:* 3 \ *College-Bound:* 53% \ *Ethnic:* African American 1%, Hispanic 1%, Caucasian 97% \ *Exp:* $231 (Med) \ *Poverty:* 20% \ *Title I:* $345,219 \ *Special Education:* $188,000 \ *Open-Close:* 08/15 - 05/20 \ *DTBP:* $174 (High)

Matthew Earley	1,83	Joanne Carraher	2
Randy Jermer	3	Shelley O'Connell	4
Rick Healey	6*	Lynnett Lonaker	16*
Morgan Capucini	31,36,69*	Greg Wells	67
Stephanie Hoeppner	73,295*	Leslie Zurmehly	79

Public Schs..Principal	Grd	Prgm	Enr/#Cls	SN
Williamsburg Elem Sch 839 Spring St, Williamsburg 45176 Kevin Dunn	PK-5	T	465 22	46% 513/724-2241 Fax 513/724-3902
Williamsburg Middle High Sch 500 S 5th St, Williamsburg 45176 Jason Tackett \ Heather Powell	6-12		529 25	32% 513/724-2211 Fax 513/724-6577

CLERMONT CATHOLIC SCHOOLS

- **Archdiocese Cincinnati Ed Off** PID: 00808096
  Listing includes only schools located in this county. See District Index for location of Diocesan Offices.

Catholic Schs..Principal	Grd	Prgm	Enr/#Cls	SN
SS Andrew-Elizabeth Seton Sch 5900 Buckwheat Rd, Milford 45150 Nick Grieco	PK-8		305 20	513/575-0093 Fax 513/575-1078
St Bernadette Sch 1453 Locust Lake Rd, Amelia 45102 Lizanne Ingram	PK-8		250 15	513/753-4744 Fax 513/753-9018
St Columban Sch 896 Oakland Rd, Loveland 45140 Jo Rhoten	PK-8		535 28	513/683-7903 Fax 513/683-7904
St Louis Sch 250 N Broadway, Owensville 45160 Elizabeth Leu	PK-8		131 10	513/732-0636 Fax 513/732-1748
St Margaret of York Sch 9495 Columbia Rd, Loveland 45140 Kristen Penley	K-8		686 27	513/697-3100 Fax 513/683-8949
St Thomas More Sch 788 Ohio Pike, Cincinnati 45245 Candace Hurley	PK-8		252 16	513/753-2540 Fax 513/753-2554

CLERMONT PRIVATE SCHOOLS

Private Schs..Principal	Grd	Prgm	Enr/#Cls	SN
Children's Mtng House Mont Sch 927 Obannonville Rd, Loveland 45140 Diane Gersten	PK-6		120 6	513/683-4757 Fax 513/697-4191
Cozaddale Baptist Academy 10632 Eltzroth Rd, Goshen 45122 Travis Burk	K-12		60 6	513/722-2064 Fax 513/722-0096
Milford Christian Academy 1365 Woodville Pike, Milford 45150 Mike Goodson	PK-12		245 13	513/575-1708 Fax 513/575-0121

St Mark's Lutheran Sch — PK-8 — 158 — 513/575-3354
5849 Buckwheat Rd, Milford 45150 — Fax 513/575-2472
Tim Kollmorgen

CLERMONT REGIONAL CENTERS

- **Hamilton-Clermont Co-op OCA** PID: 04499477 — 513/931-7120
  1007 Cottonwood Dr, Loveland 45140 — Fax 513/931-7202

Thomas Collins	1	Kelley Underwood	73
Tim Thompson	295		

CLINTON COUNTY

CLINTON COUNTY SCHOOLS

- **Southern Ohio Ed Serv Ctr** PID: 00789115 — 937/382-6921
  3321 Airborne Rd, Wilmington 45177 — Fax 937/383-3171

Beth Justice	1	Rachel Meyer	2
Kimberly Adams	8	Amy Luttrel	58
Rogina Conroy	68	Kimberly Douglas	79,275
Curt Bradshaw	81		

CLINTON PUBLIC SCHOOLS

- **Blanchester Local School Dist** PID: 00788862 — 937/783-3523
  951 Cherry St, Blanchester 45107 — Fax 937/783-2990

Schools: 4 \ *Teachers:* 97 \ *Students:* 1,650 \ *Special Ed Students:* 261 \ *LEP Students:* 3 \ *College-Bound:* 42% \ *Ethnic:* African American 1%, Hispanic 1%, Caucasian 98% \ *Exp:* $122 (Low) \ *Poverty:* 14% \ *Title I:* $295,922 \ *Special Education:* $281,000 \ *Open-Close:* 08/15 - 05/20 \ *DTBP:* $172 (High)

Dean Lynch	1	Charlotte Kratzer	2
Darlene Kassner	2	Dave Fangmeyer	3
Vanessa Swinderman	4	Barb Prater	5
Brian Pennix	6*	Linda Miller	7
Raechel Purdon	8,11,69,72,273,288	Brendan Hatfield	16,73,295
Kristin Unversaw	58,298	Kyle Wilson	67
Brice Dickinson	76		

Public Schs..Principal	Grd	Prgm	Enr/#Cls	SN
Blanchester High Sch 953 Cherry St, Blanchester 45107 **Pandy McCarty**	9-12	V	254 35	41% 937/783-2461 Fax 937/783-5666
Blanchester Intermediate Sch 951 Cherry St, Blanchester 45107 Marci Goodrich	4-5	T	254 12	937/783-2040 Fax 937/783-1284
Blanchester Middle Sch 955 Cherry St, Blanchester 45107 **Ryan Briggs**	6-8	T	376 27	80% 937/783-3642 Fax 937/783-3477
Putman Elem Sch 327 E Baldwin St, Blanchester 45107 Michael Snider	PK-3	T	455 24	46% 937/783-2681 Fax 937/783-2229

---

1 Superintendent	8 Curric/Instruct K-12	19 Chief Financial Officer	29 Family/Consumer Science	39 Social Studies K-12	49 English/Lang Arts Elem	59 Special Education Elem	69 Academic Assessment
2 Bus/Finance/Purchasing	9 Curric/Instruct Elem	20 Art K-12	30 Adult Education	40 Social Studies Elem	50 English/Lang Arts Sec	60 Special Education Sec	70 Research/Development
3 Buildings And Grounds	10 Curric/Instruct Sec	21 Art Elem	31 Career/Sch-to-Work K-12	41 Social Studies Sec	51 Reading K-12	61 Foreign/World Lang K-12	71 Public Information
4 Food Service	11 Federal Program	22 Art Sec	32 Career/Sch-to-Work Elem	42 Science K-12	52 Reading Elem	62 Foreign/World Lang Elem	72 Summer School
5 Transportation	12 Title I	23 Music K-12	33 Career/Sch-to-Work Sec	43 Science Elem	53 Reading Sec	63 Foreign/World Lang Sec	73 Instructional Tech
6 Athletic	13 Title V	24 Music Elem	34 Early Childhood Ed	44 Science Sec	54 Remedial Reading K-12	64 Religious Education K-12	74 Inservice Training
7 Health Services	14 Instructional Media Svcs	25 Music Sec	35 Health/Phys Education	45 Math K-12	55 Remedial Reading Elem	65 Religious Education Elem	75 Marketing/Distributive
	15 Asst Superintendent	26 Business Education	36 Guidance Services K-12	46 Math Elem	56 Remedial Reading Sec	66 Religious Education Sec	76 Info Systems
	16 Instructional Media Svcs	27 Career & Tech Ed	37 Guidance Services Elem	47 Math Sec	57 Bilingual/ELL	67 School Board President	77 Psychological Assess
	17 Chief Operations Officer	28 Technology Education	38 Guidance Services Sec	48 English/Lang Arts K-12	58 Special Education K-12	68 Teacher Personnel	78 Affirmative Action
	18 Chief Academic Officer						

Ohio School Directory — Columbiana County

• **Clinton-Massie Local Sch Dist** PID: 00788939 937/289-2471
2556 Lebanon Rd, Clarksville 45113 Fax 937/289-3313

Schools: 3 \ **Teachers:** 96 \ **Students:** 1,800 \ **Special Ed Students:** 196 \ **College-Bound:** 57% \ **Ethnic:** Asian 1%, Hispanic 1%, Caucasian 98% \ **Exp:** $183 (Low) \ **Poverty:** 9% \ **Title I:** $217,748 \ **Special Education:** $318,000 \ **Open-Close:** 08/14 - 05/21 \ **DTBP:** $172 (High)

Matt Baker 1	Carrie Bir 2
Tracy Mathews 2,4*	Stephen Ford 3,5
Cindy Running 6	Cindy Stenger 7,280*
Sharri Ford 16,82*	Donna Potts 27,31,38,83,270*
Rachel Cornett 36	Jennifer Horner 37*
Betsy Muterspaw 58	Jeremy Lamb 67
David Moss 73,76,295*	Rachael Sams 90,752

Public Schs..Principal	Grd	Prgm	Enr/#Cls	SN
Clinton-Massie Elem Sch 2380 Lebanon Rd, Clarksville 45113 Jennifer Updike	PK-5		762	19% 937/289-2515 Fax 937/289-3608
Clinton-Massie High Sch 2556 Lebanon Rd, Clarksville 45113 Barrett Swope	9-12	V	539	19% 937/289-2109 Fax 937/289-7019
Clinton-Massie Middle Sch 2556 Lebanon Rd, Clarksville 45113 Joseph Hollon	6-8		420	29% 937/289-2932 Fax 937/289-8100

• **East Clinton Local School Dist** PID: 00788989 937/584-2461
97 Astro Way, Sabina 45169 Fax 937/584-2817

Schools: 4 \ **Teachers:** 72 \ **Students:** 1,300 \ **Special Ed Students:** 249 \ **College-Bound:** 45% \ **Ethnic:** Hispanic 2%, Caucasian 98% \ **Exp:** $134 (Low) \ **Poverty:** 21% \ **Title I:** $448,087 \ **Special Education:** $271,000 \ **Open-Close:** 08/14 - 05/20 \ **DTBP:** $176 (High)

Eric MaGee 1,83	John Stanley 2
Jim McDowell 3	Anne Woodruff 4
Jim Marsh 6*	Lisa Stephens 7
Terri Barton 8,11,73,285,288,296*	Pam Early 16,82,271*
Steven Sodini 58	Linda Compton 67
Curt Bradshaw 81	Cheryl Roberts 88*

Public Schs..Principal	Grd	Prgm	Enr/#Cls	SN
East Clinton High Sch 174 Larrick Rd, Sabina 45169 Kerri Matheny	9-12	T	329 33	48% 937/584-2474 Fax 937/584-7451
East Clinton Middle Sch 174 Larrick Rd, Sabina 45169 Robbin Luck	6-8	T	304 15	52% 937/584-9267 Fax 937/584-7452
New Vienna Elem Sch 301 E Church St, New Vienna 45159 Jason Jones	PK-5	T	257 16	55% 937/987-2448 Fax 937/584-7453
Sabina Elem Sch 246 W Washington St, Sabina 45169 **Matthew Willan**	PK-5	T	362 20	49% 937/584-5421 Fax 937/584-7454

• **Wilmington City School Dist** PID: 00789024 937/382-1641
341 S Nelson Ave, Wilmington 45177 Fax 937/382-1645

Schools: 5 \ **Teachers:** 142 \ **Students:** 3,000 \ **Special Ed Students:** 402 \ **LEP Students:** 28 \ **College-Bound:** 53% \ **Ethnic:** Asian 1%, African American 4%, Hispanic 5%, Caucasian 90% \ **Exp:** $209 (Med) \ **Poverty:** 18% \ **Title I:** $858,727 \ **Special Education:** $575,000 \ **Open-Close:** 08/14 - 05/20 \ **DTBP:** $195 (High)

Melinda Stewart 1	Curt Bone 2
Kim DeWeese 2	Jim Schutte 3,91
Jodie Havert 4*	Jason Leeth 5
Troy Diels 6*	Nicole Quallen 8,11,57,286,288,296,298
Steven Reed 16*	Natalie Harmeling 31,58,81,83,93
Brooke McCoy 37	Justin Goodman 37*
Tyler Williams 38*	Michael Flanigan 67
Don Stutton 73,295*	

Public Schs..Principal	Grd	Prgm	Enr/#Cls	SN
Denver Place Elem Sch 291 Lorish Ave, Wilmington 45177 Karen Long	3-4	T	443 25	51% 937/382-2380 Fax 937/383-2711 t
East End Elem Sch 769 Rombach Ave, Wilmington 45177 Jennifer Martin	5-5	T	266 14	56% 937/382-2443 Fax 937/382-2872 f
Roy E Holmes Elem Sch 1350 W Truesdell St, Wilmington 45177 **Marilee Tanner**	K-2	T	564 35	65% 937/382-2750 Fax 937/382-2881 f
Wilmington High Sch 300 Richardson Pl, Wilmington 45177 Matthew Unger	9-12	T	828 70	48% 937/382-7716 Fax 937/382-1139
Wilmington Middle Sch 275 Thorne Ave, Wilmington 45177 Bert Martini	6-8	T	700 55	52% 937/382-7556 Fax 937/382-3295

CLINTON PRIVATE SCHOOLS

Private Schs..Principal	Grd	Prgm	Enr/#Cls	SN
Wilmington Christian Academy 642 Davids Dr, Wilmington 45177 Susan Simpson	K-12		35	937/383-1319 Fax 937/366-6188

COLUMBIANA COUNTY

COLUMBIANA COUNTY SCHOOLS

• **Columbiana Co Ed Service Ctr** PID: 02089131 330/424-9591
38720 Saltwell Rd, Lisbon 44432 Fax 330/424-9481

Anna Marie Vaughn 1	Cynthia Lengyel 2
Angela Arbogast 5	Marie Williams 8
Katrina Moore 27	Cheryl McGrath 58,88
Joe Warchol 73,295	Kitty Kromer 275

County Schs..Principal	Grd	Prgm	Enr/#Cls	SN
ⓒ Buckeye Online Sch-Success [240] 119 E 5th St, E Liverpool 43920 Madeline Baker \ Andrea Dobbins	K-12	T	652	330/385-1987 Fax 330/385-4535
Columbiana Co Ed Center 38720 Saltwell Rd, Lisbon 44432 Cheryl McGrath	Spec		65 22	330/424-9591
Columbiana Co Hi Unit 38720 Saltwell Rd, Lisbon 44432 Anna Marie Vaughn	Spec		23 2	330/424-9591
Columbiana Co Orthopedic Unit 38720 Saltwell Rd, Lisbon 44432 Anna Marie Vaughn	Spec		10 1	330/424-9591 Fax 330/424-4481

Columbiana County

Columbiana Co Pre-School Unit 38720 Saltwell Rd, Lisbon 44432 Anna Marie Vaughn	Spec	68	330/424-9591
Columbiana Ed Service Center 38720 Saltwell Rd, Lisbon 44432 Anna Marie Vaughn	Spec	500	330/424-9591
Robert Bycroft Sch 35947 State Route 172, Lisbon 44432 Andrew Garbor	Spec	50 11	330/424-7787 Fax 330/424-6656
© Utica Shale Academy of Ohio 38095 State Route 39, Salineville 43945 Eric Sampson	9-12	59	330/420-5353

COLUMBIANA PUBLIC SCHOOLS

● **Beaver Local School Dist** PID: 00789127 330/385-6831
46090 Bell School Rd, E Liverpool 43920 Fax 330/386-8711

Schools: 3 \ *Teachers:* 101 \ *Students:* 1,800 \ *Special Ed Students:* 293 \ *LEP Students:* 3 \ *College-Bound:* 57% \ *Ethnic:* Hispanic 1%, Caucasian 98% \ *Exp:* $143 (Low) \ *Poverty:* 16% \ *Title I:* $446,679 \ *Special Education:* $162,000 \ *Open-Close:* 08/26 - 05/29 \ *DTBP:* $195 (High)

Eric Lowe 1		Stacy Williams 2,19		
Matt Bastian 3		Josh Croxall 5		
Mike McKenzie 6		Theresa Ash 7		
Andy Reeves 11,58		Mike Agnew 36*		
Jerry Barnett 67		Nate Aldrich 73,84		
Robin Curran 273		Molly Young 280*		

Public Schs..Principal	Grd	Prgm	Enr/#Cls	SN	
Beaver Local Elem Sch 46090 Bell School Rd, E Liverpool 43920 Brianne Hall	K-4	T	668 17	46%	330/386-8700 Fax 330/386-8720
Beaver Local High Sch 46090 Bell School Rd, E Liverpool 43920 Thomas Cunningham	9-12	TV	527 36	89%	330/386-8700 Fax 330/386-8720
Beaver Local Middle Sch 46090 Bell School Rd, E Liverpool 43920 Jake Walgate	5-8	T	561 75		330/386-8700 Fax 330/386-8720

● **Columbiana Co Voc Sch Dist** PID: 01601487 330/424-9561
9364 State Route 45, Lisbon 44432 Fax 330/424-9719

Schools: 1 \ *Teachers:* 22 \ *Students:* 450 \ *College-Bound:* 68% \ *Exp:* $811 (High) \ *Open-Close:* 08/19 - 05/21 \ *DTBP:* $165 (High) \

Willard Adkins 1	Katherine Mihalich 2	
Dave Starcher 3*	Kelly Darney 16,30*	
Sue Allison 38*	Curt Kaiser 60,88*	
Mr Lammert 67	Phil James 73,295*,297*	
Jamie Stacy 273*		

Public Schs..Principal	Grd	Prgm	Enr/#Cls	SN	
Columbiana Co Career Tech Ctr 9364 State Route 45, Lisbon 44432 Jordan Williams	Voc	G	450		330/424-9561

● **Columbiana Exempted Village SD** PID: 00789191 330/482-5352
700 Columbiana Waterford Rd, Columbiana 44408 Fax 330/482-5361

Schools: 3 \ *Teachers:* 58 \ *Students:* 1,077 \ *Special Ed Students:* 157 \ *College-Bound:* 65% \ *Ethnic:* Asian 1%, Hispanic 2%, Caucasian 97% \ *Exp:* $319 (High) \ *Poverty:* 13% \ *Title I:* $174,381 \ *Special Education:* $225,000 \ *Open-Close:* 08/20 - 05/22 \ *DTBP:* $174 (High) \

Donald Mook 1	Kathy Davies 2
James Robert 3	Tina Minamyer 4
Leslie Best 5	Erin Heasley 6*
Leslie Costal 7*	Kimberly Sharshan 9,11,51,54,273*
David Buzzard 10,288*	Ron Stallsmith 16,82*
Cathi Rob-Carney 37,83,270*	Amanda Cleghorn 38,88
Marci Freedy 57,58,275*	Mark Hutson 67
Audra Hatch 81	Dan Becker 91
Jason Martin 286,295,297*	

Public Schs..Principal	Grd	Prgm	Enr/#Cls	SN	
Columbiana High Sch 700 Columbiana Waterford Rd, Columbiana 44408 David Buzzard	9-12		308 30	33%	330/482-3818 Fax 330/482-5360
Columbiana Middle Sch 720 Columbiana Waterford Rd, Columbiana 44408 Jason Martin	5-8	T	340 25	34%	330/482-5354 Fax 330/482-6332
Joshua Dixon Elem Sch 333 N Middle St, Columbiana 44408 Kimberly Sharshan	PK-4	T	414 17	29%	330/482-5355 Fax 330/482-5358

● **Crestview Local School Dist** PID: 00789397 330/482-5526
44100 Crestview Rd Ste A, Columbiana 44408 Fax 330/482-5367

Schools: 3 \ *Teachers:* 72 \ *Students:* 1,245 \ *Special Ed Students:* 130 \ *College-Bound:* 40% \ *Ethnic:* Hispanic 1%, Caucasian 99% \ *Exp:* $292 (Med) \ *Poverty:* 20% \ *Title I:* $282,528 \ *Open-Close:* 08/21 - 05/20 \ *DTBP:* $174 (High)

Matthew Manley 1,11	Charlene Mercure 2,84
Jay Radman 3	Richard Burbick 5
Paul Cusick 6*	Richard Gates 12
Dr Edward Miller 67	Kayla Sidell 69*
Daryl Miller 73,88,295*	Cindy Schmidt 76

Public Schs..Principal	Grd	Prgm	Enr/#Cls	SN	
Crestview Elem Sch 3407 Middleton Rd, Columbiana 44408 Marian Dangerfield	K-4	T	485 20	45%	330/482-5370 Fax 330/482-5373
Crestview High Sch 44100 Crestview Rd Ste B, Columbiana 44408 Laura Nappi	9-12		380 21	40%	330/482-4744 Fax 330/482-5369
Crestview Middle Sch 44100 Crestview Rd Ste C, Columbiana 44408 Allison Lemaster	5-8		357 22	42%	330/482-4648 Fax 330/482-5374

● **East Liverpool City Sch Dist** PID: 00789232 330/385-7132
810 W 8th St, E Liverpool 43920 Fax 330/386-8763

Schools: 4 \ *Teachers:* 141 \ *Students:* 2,050 \ *Special Ed Students:* 379 \ *LEP Students:* 3 \ *College-Bound:* 54% \ *Ethnic:* African American 5%, Hispanic 2%, Caucasian 93% \ *Exp:* $282 (Med) \ *Poverty:* 30% \ *Title I:* $1,449,561 \ *Special Education:* $592,000 \ *Open-Close:* 08/26 - 05/29 \ *DTBP:* $177 (High)

Randy Taylor 1,288	Kathy Jo Laughlin 2
Sam Halstead 3,91	Margie Wright 4

Ohio School Directory — Columbiana County

Tammy Reed 5
John Dawson 7*
Sarah Porter 67
Greg Voorhees 6*
Jennifer Enochs 58
Chris Cardelein 73,84

Public Schs..Principal	Grd	Prgm	Enr/#Cls SN	
East Liverpool Jr Sr High Sch 100 Maine Blvd, E Liverpool 43920 Jonathan Ludwig	7-12	T	824 80	330/386-8750 Fax 330/386-8753
La Croft Elem Sch 2460 Boring Ln, E Liverpool 43920 Jacob Walgate	K-4	T	434 26	330/386-8774 Fax 330/382-1867
North Elem Sch 90 Maine Blvd, E Liverpool 43920 Jack Cunningham	K-4	T	438 35	330/386-8772 Fax 330/386-4228
Westgate Middle Sch 810 W 8th St, E Liverpool 43920 Bryian Burson	5-6	T	380 35	330/386-8765

East Palestine City Sch Dist PID: 00789311
200 W North Ave, E Palestine 44413
330/426-4191
Fax 330/426-9592

Schools: 3 \ **Teachers:** 39 \ **Students:** 1,087 \ **Special Ed Students:** 185 \ **LEP Students:** 6 \ **College-Bound:** 47% \ **Ethnic:** African American 1%, Hispanic 2%, Caucasian 97% \ **Exp:** $66 (Low) \ **Poverty:** 21% \ **Title I:** $426,101 \ **Open-Close:** 08/26 - 05/28 \ **DTBP:** $174 (High) \ f

Chris Neifer 1
Barry Weigle 3,5
Duane Pavkovich 6
James Young 16*
Sue Weigle 67
Rick Ellis 2,84
Jennifer Schiraldi 4
Carol Vollnogle 11,58,298*
Samantha Kerns 37,83*

Public Schs..Principal	Grd	Prgm	Enr/#Cls SN	
East Palestine Elem Sch 195 W Grant St, E Palestine 44413 Kim Russo	PK-4	T	443 24	56% 330/426-3638 Fax 330/426-5109
East Palestine High Sch 360 W Grant St, E Palestine 44413 James Rook	9-12	T	342 30	47% 330/426-9401 Fax 330/426-5105 f t
East Palestine Middle Sch 320 W Grant St, E Palestine 44413 James Rook	5-8	T	302 16	59% 330/426-9451 Fax 330/426-5118

Leetonia Exempted Village SD PID: 00789438
450 Walnut St, Leetonia 44431
330/427-6594
Fax 330/427-1136

Schools: 1 \ **Teachers:** 44 \ **Students:** 780 \ **Special Ed Students:** 132 \ **College-Bound:** 38% \ **Ethnic:** Hispanic 2%, Caucasian 97% \ **Exp:** $189 (Low) \ **Poverty:** 22% \ **Title I:** $252,335 \ **Special Education:** $151,000 \ **Open-Close:** 08/21 - 05/28

Rob Mehno 1,11,288
Becky Jones 16*
Richard Hendricks 67
Tiffany Davis 280*
Jennifer Coldsnow 2,84
Mary Rice 36,286
Ryan Clapsadle 73,295*

Public Schs..Principal	Grd	Prgm	Enr/#Cls SN	
Leetonia Sch 450 Walnut St, Leetonia 44431 Troy Radinsky \ Jackie Dunnigan	K-12	T	780 60	330/427-2444 Fax 330/427-6904

Lisbon Exempted Village SD PID: 00789490
317 N Market St, Lisbon 44432
330/424-7714
Fax 330/424-0135

Schools: 2 \ **Teachers:** 56 \ **Students:** 850 \ **Special Ed Students:** 146 \ **College-Bound:** 31% \ **Ethnic:** African American 1%, Hispanic 1%, Caucasian 99% \ **Exp:** $101 (Low) \ **Poverty:** 24% \ **Title I:** $332,597 \ **Special Education:** $199,000 \ **Open-Close:** 08/19 - 05/29 \ **DTBP:** $200 (High)

Joseph Siefke 1
Ed Duko 3
Angie Arbogast 5
Kyle Bing 6*
Colleen Van Leeuwen 16*
Eugene Gallo 67
Vickie Provitt 2
Melissa Adams 4
Doug Patterson 5
Daniel Kemats 11*
Dave Brookes 58*
Adam Fill 73

Public Schs..Principal	Grd	Prgm	Enr/#Cls SN	
David Anderson Jr Sr High Sch 260 W Pine St, Lisbon 44432 Keith Edenfield	6-12	T	417 35	52% 330/424-3215 Fax 330/424-1004
McKinley Elem Sch 441 E Chestnut St, Lisbon 44432 Daniel Kemats	PK-5	T	447 28	61% 330/424-9869 Fax 330/424-9860

Salem City School Dist PID: 00789531
1226 E State St, Salem 44460
330/332-0316
Fax 330/332-8936

Schools: 5 \ **Teachers:** 119 \ **Students:** 2,100 \ **Special Ed Students:** 306 \ **LEP Students:** 111 \ **College-Bound:** 54% \ **Ethnic:** Hispanic 6%, Caucasian 93% \ **Exp:** $215 (Med) \ **Poverty:** 21% \ **Title I:** $844,508 \ **Special Education:** $187,000 \ **Open-Close:** 08/21 - 05/28 \ f t

Sean Kirkland 1
Jason Austin 3
Jeff Mertig 5
Jamie Karnets 8,11
Luann Haddad 67
Michael Douglas 2
Michele Fisher 4
Matt Freeman 6
Kristy Erb 58,81
Aaron Vogh 295

Public Schs..Principal	Grd	Prgm	Enr/#Cls SN	
Buckeye Elem Sch 1200 Buckeye Ave, Salem 44460 John Lundin	K-2	T	447 23	64% 330/332-8917 Fax 330/332-2137
Reilly Elem Sch 491 Reilly Ave, Salem 44460 Cindy Viscounte	3-4	T	317 24	61% 330/332-8921 Fax 330/332-2138
Salem High Sch 1200 E 6th St, Salem 44460 Sean Kirkland	9-12	TV	659 50	70% 330/332-8905 Fax 330/332-8943
Salem Junior High Sch 1200 E 6th St, Salem 44460 Sean Kirkland	7-8	T	337 30	330/332-8914 Fax 330/332-8923
Southeast Elem Sch 2200 Merle Rd, Salem 44460 Lisa DeRose	5-6	T	317 12	45% 330/332-8925 Fax 330/332-8953

Southern Local School Dist PID: 00789610
38095 State Route 39, Salineville 43945
330/679-2343
Fax 330/679-0193

Schools: 2 \ **Teachers:** 69 \ **Students:** 920 \ **Special Ed Students:** 140 \ **Ethnic:** African American 1%, Hispanic 2%, Caucasian 97% \ **Exp:** $316 (High) \ **Poverty:** 19% \ **Title I:** $270,079 \ **Special Education:** $75,000 \ **Open-Close:** 08/22 - 05/28 \ **DTBP:** $176 (High)

Thomas Cunningham 1
James Rigby 3,91
Robert Marra 5
Greg Savvato 2
Kerry Morrissey 4
Robert Shansky 6*

Code	Description	Code	Description	Code	Description	Code	Description
79	Student Personnel	91	Safety/Security	275	Response To Intervention	298	Grant Writer/Ptnrships
80	Driver Ed/Safety	92	Magnet School	277	Remedial Math K-12	750	Chief Innovation Officer
81	Gifted/Talented	93	Parental Involvement	280	Literacy Coach	751	Chief of Staff
82	Video Services	95	Tech Prep Program	285	STEM	752	Social Emotional Learning
83	Substance Abuse Prev	97	Chief Information Officer	286	Digital Learning		
84	Erate	98	Chief Technology Officer	288	Common Core Standards		
85	AIDS Education	270	Character Education	294	Accountability		
88	Alternative/At Risk	271	Migrant Education	295	Network System		
89	Multi-Cultural Curriculum	273	Teacher Mentor	296	Title II Programs		
90	Social Work	274	Before/After Sch	297	Webmaster		

School Programs
A = Alternative Program
G = Adult Classes
M = Magnet Program
T = Title I Schoolwide
V = Career & Tech Ed Programs

Other School Types
Ⓐ = Alternative School
Ⓒ = Charter School
Ⓜ = Magnet School
Ⓨ = Year-Round School

Social Media
f = Facebook
t = Twitter

New Schools are shaded
New Superintendents and Principals are bold
Personnel with email addresses are underscored

OH–35

Coshocton County

Market Data Retrieval

Heidi McIntosh 7*	Laura Krulik 11,58,298*	
Kristy Sambon 12	Josh Manist 16	
Marjorie Hiller 16,73,82*	Larry Rudloff 37,83,88*	
Karla Calderone 57,61*	Jay Cole 67	

Public Schs..Principal	Grd	Prgm	Enr/#Cls SN	
Southern Elem Sch 38095 State Route 39, Salineville 43945 Kristy Sampson	PK-6	T	457 21	330/679-2305 Fax 330/679-3004
Southern Local Jr Sr HS 38095 State Route 39, Salineville 43945 J Kiger	7-12	T	399 25	99% 330/679-2305 Fax 330/679-3004

- **United Local School Dist** PID: 00789684 330/223-1521
  8143 State Route 9, Hanoverton 44423 Fax 330/223-2363

> *Schools:* 2 \ *Teachers:* 74 \ *Students:* 1,300 \ *Special Ed Students:* 147 \ *College-Bound:* 56% \ *Ethnic:* African American 1%, Hispanic 1%, Caucasian 99% \ *Exp:* $226 (Med) \ *Poverty:* 16% \ *Title I:* $273,734 \ *Open-Close:* 08/22 - 05/29 \ *DTBP:* $172 (High)

Lance Hostetler 1	Melissa Baker 2	
Tom Clemens 3*	Kaitlyn Klein 4	
Mike Greenawalt 5	Dj Ogilvie 6	
Andy Trotter 9*	William Young 10*	
Mary-Alice Sigler 11,58,88,273,275,296*	Denise Ward 16,82*	
Kerri O'Donnell 37*	Samantha Muniz 38,69,294*	
Mike Ellyson 67	Dennis Klaustermeyer 73,295*	
Frank Baker 83*		

Public Schs..Principal	Grd	Prgm	Enr/#Cls SN	
United Local Elem Sch 8143 State Route 9, Hanoverton 44423 Andy Trotter	K-6	T	594 45	330/223-8001 Fax 330/223-1216
United Local High Sch 8143 State Route 9, Hanoverton 44423 William Young	7-12	TV	548 60	88% 330/223-7102

- **Wellsville Local Sch Dist** PID: 00789713 330/532-2643
  929 Center St, Wellsville 43968 Fax 330/532-6204

> *Schools:* 3 \ *Teachers:* 58 \ *Students:* 850 \ *Special Ed Students:* 163 \ *College-Bound:* 32% \ *Ethnic:* African American 3%, Hispanic 1%, Caucasian 96% \ *Exp:* $391 (High) \ *Poverty:* 31% \ *Title I:* $416,138 \ *Special Education:* $224,000 \ *Open-Close:* 08/28 - 06/05 \ *DTBP:* $182 (High)

Richard Bereschik 1	Robert Barrett 2,4,84	
Joseph Traina 3*	Don Elliott 6*	
Lisa Ferguson 11,296*	Melody Allison 36*	
Gary Althiser 67	Bill Ricciardulli 73*	

Public Schs..Principal	Grd	Prgm	Enr/#Cls SN	
Daw Elem Sch 929 Center St, Wellsville 43968 Richard Prescott	4-7	T	250 30	330/532-1372
Garfield Elem Sch 1600 Lincoln Ave, Wellsville 43968 Lisa Ferguson	PK-3	T	237 15	330/532-3301 Fax 330/532-1108
Wellsville Jr Sr High Sch 1 Bengal Blvd, Wellsville 43968 Linda Rolley	8-12	ATV	280 20	65% 330/532-1188 Fax 330/532-9004

COLUMBIANA CATHOLIC SCHOOLS

- **Diocese of Youngstown Ed Off** PID: 00820915
  Listing includes only schools located in this county. See District Index for location of Diocesan Offices.

Catholic Schs..Principal	Grd	Prgm	Enr/#Cls SN	
St Paul Sch 925 E State St, Salem 44460 David Pancurak	PK-6		115 8	330/337-3451 Fax 330/337-3607

COLUMBIANA PRIVATE SCHOOLS

Private Schs..Principal	Grd	Prgm	Enr/#Cls SN	
Columbiana Co Opportunity Ctr 260 W Lincoln Way, Lisbon 44432 Sarah Underwood	8-12		47	330/424-4047 Fax 330/424-4050
East Liverpool Christian Sch 46682 Florence St, E Liverpool 43920 Peggy Bouscher	PK-12		137 13	330/385-5588 Fax 330/385-1267
Heartland Christian Sch 28 Pittsburgh St, Columbiana 44408 Betsy Lariccia	PK-12		310 20	330/482-2331 Fax 330/482-2413
Salem Wesleyan Academy 1095 Newgarden Ave, Salem 44460 Dan Forrider	K-12		80 7	330/332-4819

COSHOCTON COUNTY

COSHOCTON COUNTY SCHOOLS

County Schs..Principal	Grd	Prgm	Enr/#Cls SN	
Hopewell Sch 23720 Airport Rd, Coshocton 43812 Shannon Shontz	Spec		75 6	740/622-2032 Fax 740/622-0832

COSHOCTON PUBLIC SCHOOLS

- **Coshocton City School Dist** PID: 00789787 740/622-1901
  1207 Cambridge Rd, Coshocton 43812 Fax 740/623-5803

> *Schools:* 2 \ *Teachers:* 102 \ *Students:* 1,600 \ *Special Ed Students:* 349 \ *Ethnic:* Asian 1%, African American 3%, Hispanic 1%, Caucasian 95% \ *Exp:* $264 (Med) \ *Poverty:* 28% \ *Title I:* $820,875 \ *Special Education:* $532,000 \ *Open-Close:* 08/21 - 05/22 \ *DTBP:* $182 (High)

Dr David Hire 1	Felicia Drummey 2	
Todd Johnson 3,58*	Jennifer Andrews 4,5	
Tim Fortney 6*	Kaitlyn Ashbrook 8,11,69,74,273,288,296	
Dr Jere Butcher 67	Jason Olinger 73,84	

---

1 Superintendent	8 Curric/Instruct K-12	19 Chief Financial Officer	29 Family/Consumer Science	39 Social Studies K-12	49 English/Lang Arts Elem	59 Special Education Elem	69 Academic Assessment
2 Bus/Finance/Purchasing	9 Curric/Instruct Elem	20 Art K-12	30 Adult Education	40 Social Studies Elem	50 English/Lang Arts Sec	60 Special Education Sec	70 Research/Development
3 Buildings And Grounds	10 Curric/Instruct Sec	21 Art Elem	31 Career/Sch-to-Work K-12	41 Social Studies Sec	51 Reading K-12	61 Foreign/World Lang K-12	71 Public Information
4 Food Service	11 Federal Program	22 Art Sec	32 Career/Sch-to-Work Elem	42 Science K-12	52 Reading Elem	62 Foreign/World Lang Elem	72 Summer School
5 Transportation	12 Title I	23 Music K-12	33 Career/Sch-to-Work Sec	43 Science Elem	53 Reading Sec	63 Foreign/World Lang Sec	73 Instructional Tech
6 Athletic	13 Title V	24 Music Elem	34 Early Childhood Ed	44 Science Sec	54 Remedial Reading K-12	64 Religious Education K-12	74 Inservice Training
7 Health Services	15 Asst Superintendent	25 Music Sec	35 Health/Phys Education	45 Math K-12	55 Remedial Reading Elem	65 Religious Education Elem	75 Marketing/Distributive
	16 Instructional Media Svcs	26 Business Education	36 Guidance Services K-12	46 Math Elem	56 Remedial Reading Sec	66 Religious Education Sec	76 Info Systems
	17 Chief Operations Officer	27 Career & Tech Ed	37 Guidance Services Elem	47 Math Sec	57 Bilingual/ELL	67 School Board President	77 Psychological Assess
	18 Chief Academic Officer	28 Technology Education	38 Guidance Services Sec	48 English/Lang Arts K-12	58 Special Education K-12	68 Teacher Personnel	78 Affirmative Action

Ohio School Directory — Crawford County

Public Schs..Principal	Grd	Prgm	Enr/#Cls	SN
Coshocton Elem Sch 1203 Cambridge Rd, Coshocton 43812 Dave Skelton	PK-6	T	903 27	740/622-5514 Fax 740/295-7715
Coshocton High Sch 1205 Cambridge Rd, Coshocton 43812 Grant Fauver	7-12	TV	649 100	740/622-9433 Fax 740/295-7717

Coshocton Co Joint Voc SD   PID: 01831589
23640 Airport Rd, Coshocton 43812
740/622-0211
Fax 740/623-4651

Schools: 1 \ **Teachers:** 1 \ **Students:** 246 \ **College-Bound:** 46% \ **Exp:** $466 (High) \ **Open-Close:** 08/14 - 05/18 \ **DTBP:** $151 (High)

Rick Raach 1   Eddie Dovenbarger 10,31,69,88*
Jason Prater .... 60* H Tad Johnson 67

Public Schs..Principal	Grd	Prgm	Enr/#Cls	SN
Coshocton Co Career Center 23640 Airport Rd, Coshocton 43812 Eddie Dovenbarger	Voc		246 30	740/622-0211 [f] [t]

Ridgewood Local School Dist   PID: 00789866
301 S Oak St, W Lafayette 43845
740/545-6354
Fax 740/545-6336

Schools: 3 \ **Teachers:** 66 \ **Students:** 1,275 \ **Special Ed Students:** 157 \ **College-Bound:** 47% \ **Ethnic:** Hispanic 1%, Caucasian 98% \ **Exp:** $279 (Med) \ **Poverty:** 19% \ **Title I:** $388,315 \ **Special Education:** $327,000 \ **Open-Close:** 08/20 - 05/20 \ **DTBP:** $187 (High)

Mike Masloski 1   Jay Tingle 2
Doug Patterson 3,5   Michelle Stoffer 4
Matt Colvin .... 6*   Barbara Bond 7,85*
Shirley Smith .... 16,73,76*   Sue Davis 27*
Stacy Ionno .... 38* Peggy Ball 58
Cathy McCrea 67   Andi Dobbins 81*

Public Schs..Principal	Grd	Prgm	Enr/#Cls	SN
Ridgewood Elem Sch 225 W Union Ave, W Lafayette 43845 Lori Cabot	PK-3	T	424 19	740/545-5312 Fax 740/545-7015
Ridgewood High Sch 602 Johnson St, W Lafayette 43845 Todd Stoffer	8-12	T	470 25	55% 740/545-6345 Fax 740/545-5311
Ridgewood Middle Sch 517 S Oak St, W Lafayette 43845 Bryan Raach	4-7	AT	377 40	61% 740/545-6335 Fax 740/545-5300

River View Local School Dist   PID: 00789921
26496 State Route 60, Warsaw 43844
740/824-3521
Fax 740/824-3760

Schools: 5 \ **Teachers:** 121 \ **Students:** 2,100 \ **Special Ed Students:** 317 \ **College-Bound:** 53% \ **Ethnic:** African American 2%, Hispanic 2%, Caucasian 96% \ **Exp:** $89 (Low) \ **Poverty:** 20% \ **Title I:** $734,577 \ **Special Education:** $396,000 \ **Open-Close:** 08/22 - 05/27 \ **DTBP:** $176 (High)

Dalton Summers 1   Lee Jane Williamson 2
Roger Boatman .... 3,91*   Jovi Metz 4
Joel Moore 5   Rod Lindsey 6*
Kayla Davis .... 7,85 Christie Ireland 8,72,273,274,286,288*
Tracey Herron .... 11,296* Janell Davis 16*
Keith Watson .... 23* Rose Olinger 33,36,69*
Sheri Fortune .... 34,58,78,81* Jeff Vickers 58
Daniel Hothem 67   Jeff Eick 73,76

Public Schs..Principal	Grd	Prgm	Enr/#Cls	SN
Conesville Elem Sch 199 State St, Conesville 43811 Jarred Renner	PK-6	T	323 15	60% 740/829-2334 Fax 740/829-2856
Keene Elem Sch 27052 County Road 1, Coshocton 43812 Beth Hamersley	K-6	T	244 14	56% 740/622-5884 Fax 740/622-5458
River View High Sch 26496 State Route 60, Warsaw 43844 Charles Rinkes	9-12	V	572 46	44% 740/824-3522 Fax 740/824-4746
River View Junior High Sch 26496 State Route 60, Warsaw 43844 Jerry Olinger	7-8	T	309 20	52% 740/824-3523 Fax 740/824-5241
Warsaw Elem Sch 501 Blissfield Rd, Warsaw 43844 Tracey Herron	PK-6	T	325 25	60% 740/824-3727 Fax 740/824-4267

COSHOCTON CATHOLIC SCHOOLS

- **Diocese of Columbus Ed Office**   PID: 00802717
  Listing includes only schools located in this county. See District Index for location of Diocesan Offices.

Catholic Schs..Principal	Grd	Prgm	Enr/#Cls	SN
Sacred Heart Sch 39 Burt Ave, Coshocton 43812 Mary Kobel	PK-6		53 7	740/622-3728 Fax 740/622-9151

COSHOCTON PRIVATE SCHOOLS

Private Schs..Principal	Grd	Prgm	Enr/#Cls	SN
Coshocton Christian Sch 23891 Airport Rd, Coshocton 43812 Gary Bennett	PK-12		60 6	740/622-5052 Fax 740/622-9244

CRAWFORD COUNTY

CRAWFORD COUNTY SCHOOLS

County Schs..Principal	Grd	Prgm	Enr/#Cls	SN
Fairway Sch 1650 E Southern Ave, Bucyrus 44820 Kathy Wells	Spec		75 6	419/562-3321 Fax 419/562-3176

---

79 Student Personnel	91 Safety/Security	275 Response To Intervention	298 Grant Writer/Ptnrships	**School Programs**	**Social Media**		
80 Driver Ed/Safety	92 Magnet School	277 Remedial Math K-12	750 Chief Innovation Officer	A = Alternative Program	[f] = Facebook		
81 Gifted/Talented	93 Parental Involvement	280 Literacy Coach	751 Chief of Staff	G = Adult Classes			
82 Video Services	95 Tech Prep Program	285 STEM	752 Social Emotional Learning	M = Magnet Program	[t] = Twitter		
83 Substance Abuse Prev	97 Chief Infomation Officer	286 Digital Learning		T = Title I Schoolwide			
84 Erate	98 Chief Technology Officer	288 Common Core Standards	**Other School Types**	V = Career & Tech Ed Programs			
85 AIDS Education	270 Character Education	294 Accountability	Ⓐ = Alternative School				
88 Alternative/At Risk	271 Migrant Education	295 Network System	Ⓒ = Charter School	**New Schools are shaded**			
89 Multi-Cultural Curriculum	273 Teacher Mentor	296 Title II Programs	Ⓜ = Magnet School	**New Superintendents and Principals are bold**			
90 Social Work	274 Before/After Sch	297 Webmaster	Ⓨ = Year-Round School	Personnel with email addresses are underscored			

OH–37

Crawford County

CRAWFORD PUBLIC SCHOOLS

● **Buckeye Central Local Sch Dist** PID: 00790011   419/492-2864
938 S Kibler St, New Washingtn 44854   Fax 419/492-2039

Schools: 3 \ *Teachers:* 46 \ *Students:* 650 \ *Special Ed Students:* 132 \ *LEP Students:* 3 \ *College-Bound:* 64% \ *Ethnic:* African American 1%, Hispanic 3%, Caucasian 96% \ *Exp:* $320 (High) \ *Poverty:* 11% \ *Title I:* $147,153 \ *Special Education:* $133,000 \ *Open-Close:* 08/20 - 05/21 \ *DTBP:* $172 (High)

Mark Robinson	1	Nancy Ackerman	2,11,296
Jarrod Clady	3*	Judy Auck	4*
Deb Briggs	5	Phil Loy	6*
Mike Martin	10*	Christine Close	38,79*
Lisa McGinnis	58*	Melissa McDougal	67
Rachel Stubbelbine	69	Tammy Studer	73*

Public Schs..Principal	Grd	Prgm	Enr/#Cls	SN
Buckeye Central Elem Sch 938 S Kibler St, New Washingtn 44854 Matt Millinger	K-4	T	230 7	419/492-1022
Buckeye Central High Sch 938 S Kibler St, New Washingtn 44854 Mike Martin	9-12		163 35	419/492-2266
Buckeye Central Middle Sch 938 S Kibler St, New Washingtn 44854 Deborah Daniel	5-8	T	191 7	419/492-1035

● **Bucyrus City School Dist** PID: 00790059   419/562-4045
170 Plymouth St, Bucyrus 44820   Fax 419/562-3990

Schools: 2 \ *Teachers:* 81 \ *Students:* 1,300 \ *Special Ed Students:* 352 \ *LEP Students:* 9 \ *College-Bound:* 41% \ *Ethnic:* Asian 1%, African American 1%, Hispanic 2%, Caucasian 96% \ *Exp:* $205 (Med) \ *Poverty:* 29% \ *Title I:* $773,460 \ *Open-Close:* 08/21 - 05/27 \ *DTBP:* $176 (High)

Matthew Chrispin	1,11	Ryan Cook	2,19
Jacob Grau	3	Martin Schuster	5*
Dr Paul Johnson	67		

Public Schs..Principal	Grd	Prgm	Enr/#Cls	SN
Bucyrus Elem Sch 245 Woodlawn Ave, Bucyrus 44820 Timothy Souder	PK-5	T	619 12	73% 419/562-6089 Fax 419/562-2367
Bucyrus Secondary Sch 900 W Perry St, Bucyrus 44820 Dr Mark Burke	6-12	TV	609 40	61% 419/562-7721 Fax 419/562-7819

● **Colonel Crawford Local SD** PID: 00790140   419/562-6755
2303 State Route 602, N Robinson 44856   Fax 419/562-3304

Schools: 3 \ *Teachers:* 56 \ *Students:* 920 \ *Special Ed Students:* 124 \ *College-Bound:* 71% \ *Ethnic:* Asian 1%, African American 1%, Hispanic 1%, Caucasian 97% \ *Exp:* $106 (Low) \ *Poverty:* 11% \ *Title I:* $111,166 \ *Special Education:* $174,000 \ *Open-Close:* 08/20 - 05/21 \ *DTBP:* $217 (High)

Todd Martin	1	Vickie Stump	2,11
Mike Hensley	3	Kerri Wiohite	4
David Sheldon	6	April Bond	12*
Greg Flannigan	16,73*	Karissa Fankhauser	16*

Brad McKibben	67	Lori Carman	69,93*
Mary Lyons	273*		

Public Schs..Principal	Grd	Prgm	Enr/#Cls	SN
Colonel Crawford High Sch 2303 State Route 602, N Robinson 44856 Jacob Bruner	9-12	V	266 25	419/562-4666
Hannah Crawford Elem Sch 5444 Crestline Rd, Crestline 44827 Cindy Voss	PK-5		468 19	31% 419/562-5753 Fax 419/562-2983
William Crawford Interm Sch 5444 Crestline Rd, Crestline 44827 April Bond	6-8		220 15	33% 419/562-7529

● **Crestline Exempted Village SD** PID: 00790205   419/683-3647
401 Heiser Ct, Crestline 44827   Fax 419/683-4984

Schools: 1 \ *Teachers:* 40 \ *Students:* 570 \ *Special Ed Students:* 130 \ *LEP Students:* 3 \ *College-Bound:* 30% \ *Ethnic:* African American 3%, Caucasian 96% \ *Exp:* $189 (Low) \ *Poverty:* 29% \ *Title I:* $451,415 \ *Special Education:* $199,000 \ *Open-Close:* 08/20 - 06/02 \ *DTBP:* $174 (High)

Matthew Henderson	1	Alena Nemick	2
Ben Hocker	3	Kerri Wilhite	4*
Bev Payne	5	Ashley Rebillot	58
Jeff Wilheigh	67		

Public Schs..Principal	Grd	Prgm	Enr/#Cls	SN
Crestline Sch 435 Oldfield Rd, Crestline 44827 Julie Theodore \ Kevin Fourman	PK-12		570 23	419/683-3647 Fax 419/683-0330

● **Galion City School Dist** PID: 00790255   419/468-3432
470 Portland Way N, Galion 44833   Fax 419/468-4333

Schools: 4 \ *Teachers:* 80 \ *Students:* 1,817 \ *Special Ed Students:* 329 \ *LEP Students:* 3 \ *College-Bound:* 44% \ *Ethnic:* African American 1%, Hispanic 2%, Caucasian 97% \ *Exp:* $446 (High) \ *Poverty:* 24% \ *Title I:* $759,718 \ *Special Education:* $361,000 \ *Open-Close:* 08/21 - 05/26 \ *DTBP:* $183 (High)

Jim Grubbs	1	Charlene Parkinson	2
Laurie Penington	4*	Kyle Baughn	6*
Jennifer Allerding	8,288	Paul Wheeler	11,57,296,298*
Cindy Parrott	58,752	Grant Garverick	67
Veronica Rinehart	73*	Steve Hammond	76,295*

Public Schs..Principal	Grd	Prgm	Enr/#Cls	SN
Galion High Sch 472 Portland Way N, Galion 44833 Ron Williams	9-12	T	406 50	69% 419/468-6500 Fax 419/469-5562
Galion Intermediate Sch 476 Portland Way N, Galion 44833 Alex Sharick	3-5	T	418	67% 419/468-3676 Fax 567/202-0530
Galion Middle Sch 474 Portland Way N, Galion 44833 Paul Wheeler	6-8	T	431 32	62% 419/468-3134 Fax 567/393-4159
Galion Primary Sch 478 Portland Way N, Galion 44833 Melisa Watters	PK-2	T	473	62% 419/478-4010 Fax 419/710-4845

---

1 Superintendent	8 Curric/Instruct K-12	19 Chief Financial Officer	29 Family/Consumer Science	39 Social Studies K-12	49 English/Lang Arts Elem	59 Special Education Elem	69 Academic Assessment
2 Bus/Finance/Purchasing	9 Curric/Instruct Elem	20 Art K-12	30 Adult Education	40 Social Studies Elem	50 English/Lang Arts Sec	60 Special Education Sec	70 Research/Development
3 Buildings And Grounds	10 Curric/Instruct Sec	21 Art Elem	31 Career/Sch-to-Work K-12	41 Social Studies Sec	51 Reading K-12	61 Foreign/World Lang K-12	71 Public Information
4 Food Service	11 Federal Program	22 Art Sec	32 Career/Sch-to-Work Elem	42 Science K-12	52 Reading Elem	62 Foreign/World Lang Elem	72 Summer School
5 Transportation	12 Title I	23 Music K-12	33 Career/Sch-to-Work Sec	43 Science Elem	53 Reading Sec	63 Foreign/World Lang Sec	73 Instructional Tech
6 Athletic	13 Title V	24 Music Elem	34 Early Childhood Ed	44 Science Sec	54 Remedial Reading K-12	64 Religious Education K-12	74 Inservice Training
7 Health Services	14 Instructional Media Svcs	25 Music Sec	35 Health/Phys Education	45 Math K-12	55 Remedial Reading Elem	65 Religious Education Elem	75 Marketing/Distribute
	15 Asst Superintendent	26 Business Education	36 Guidance Services K-12	46 Math Elem	56 Remedial Reading Sec	66 Religious Education Sec	76 Info Systems
	16 Instructional Media Svcs	27 Career & Tech Ed	37 Guidance Services Elem	47 Math Sec	57 Bilingual/ELL	67 School Board President	77 Psychological Assess
	17 Chief Operations Officer	28 Technology Education	38 Guidance Services Sec	48 English/Lang Arts K-12	58 Special Education K-12	68 Teacher Personnel	78 Affirmative Action
	18 Chief Academic Officer						

Ohio School Directory

Cuyahoga County

• **Wynford Local School Dist** PID: 00790334   419/562-7828
3288 Holmes Center Rd, Bucyrus 44820   Fax 419/562-7825

Schools: 2 \ *Teachers:* 66 \ *Students:* 1,200 \ *Special Ed Students:* 162 \ *College-Bound:* 70% \ *Ethnic:* Asian 1%, Hispanic 1%, Caucasian 98% \ *Exp:* $237 (Med) \ *Poverty:* 20% \ *Title I:* $297,207 \ *Special Education:* $233,000 \ *Open-Close:* 08/21 - 05/22 \ *DTBP:* $165 (High)

Fred Fox 1
Brian Shupp 5
Nelle Ratliff 9*
Tessa Martin 27*
Elizabeth Heinlen 36*
Brenda Adams 58
Aj Reichard 273*
Leesa Smith 2,11
Brent Konkoe 6
Todd Enders 16,82*
Crystal Jennings 29*
Krista Richmond 51*
Steve Crall 67

Public Schs..Principal	Grd	Prgm	Enr/#Cls	SN	
Wynford Elem Sch 3300 Holmes Center Rd, Bucyrus 44820 **Nelle Ratliff**	PK-6	T	651 30	39%	419/562-4619 Fax 419/563-2905
Wynford High Sch 3288 Holmes Center Rd, Bucyrus 44820 **Julie Miller**	7-12	T	476 35	63%	419/562-7828 Fax 419/563-2905

CRAWFORD CATHOLIC SCHOOLS

• **Diocese of Toledo Ed Office** PID: 00818297
Listing includes only schools located in this county. See District Index for location of Diocesan Offices.

Catholic Schs..Principal	Grd	Prgm	Enr/#Cls	SN	
St Bernard Elem Sch 320 W Mansfield St, New Washingtn 44854 Mary Obringer	K-8		30 8		419/492-2693
St Joseph Catholic Sch 138 N Liberty St, Galion 44833 Janice Stupka	PK-8		86 10		419/468-5436
St Joseph Catholic Sch 333 N Thoman St, Crestline 44827 Dan Salvati	K-8		82 5		419/683-1284 Fax 419/683-8957

CRAWFORD PRIVATE SCHOOLS

Private Schs..Principal	Grd	Prgm	Enr/#Cls	SN	
Wayside Christian Sch 2345 Kerstetter Rd, Bucyrus 44820 Donald Helman	PK-12		65 6		419/562-5930 Fax 419/562-2066

CUYAHOGA COUNTY

CUYAHOGA COUNTY SCHOOLS

• **Cuyahoga Co Ed Service Center** PID: 00795293   216/524-3000
6393 Oak Tree Blvd Ste 300, Independence 44131   Fax 216/524-3683

Dr Robert Mengerink 1,11
Dr Christine Krol 67
Paula Kucinic 74
Bruce Basalla 2
Steve Rogaski 68,79
Jennifer Dodd 298

County Schs..Principal	Grd	Prgm	Enr/#Cls	SN	
© Albert Einstein Acad-Westlake 3600 Crocker Rd, Westlake 44145 Alexis Hall	4-12		250		440/471-4982 Fax 440/617-6809
© Apex Academy [203] 16005 Terrace Rd, E Cleveland 44112 Jennifer Littlefield	K-8	T	512 27		216/451-1725 Fax 216/274-9364
© Citizens Academy [239] 10118 Hampden Ave, Cleveland 44108 Kimberly Peterlin	K-5	T	414 18		216/791-4195 Fax 216/791-3013
© Citizens Academy East [239] 12523 Woodside Ave, Cleveland 44108 Jennifer Taylor	K-5	T	808		216/367-9392 Fax 216/761-7398
© Citizens Academy Southeast [239] 15700 Lotus Dr, Cleveland 44128 Charlie Coddington	K-5	T	404		216/586-3887 Fax 216/561-1121
© Cleveland College Prep [238] 4906 Fleet Ave, Cleveland 44105 Phillip Penn	K-8	T	283		216/341-1347 Fax 216/341-4466
© East Preparatory Academy 4129 Superior Ave, Cleveland 44103 Joy Beasley	K-8	T	195		216/539-0595
© Global Village Academy 5720 State Rd Ste 1, Parma 44134 Anna Holowatyj	K-7	T	142	68%	216/767-5956 Fax 216/767-5653
Green Road Developmental Ctr 4329 Green Rd, Highland Hls 44128 Tyrone McCann	Spec	V	90 18		216/931-7340 Fax 216/464-7342
Greenview Day Treatment Center 14201 Southington Rd, Shaker HTS 44120 D Kyle Rose	Spec		84		216/751-8453 Fax 216/751-3780
© Horizon Sci Acad-Cleveland MS 6100 S Marginal Rd, Cleveland 44103 Bill Aslan	K-8		352		216/432-9940 Fax 216/432-9941
© Horizon Sci Academy-Denison [153] 1700 Denison Ave, Cleveland 44109 Daniel Akben	K-8	T	330 24		216/739-9911 Fax 216/739-9913
© Intergenerational Sch 11327 Shaker Blvd Ste 200, Cleveland 44104 Sylvia Kruger	K-8	T	242 14	69%	216/721-0120 Fax 216/721-0126
© Madison Cmty Elem Sch [242] 2015 W 95th St, Cleveland 44102 Brittney Lester	K-8	T	256 16		216/651-5212 Fax 216/651-9040
© Menlo Park Academy 2149 W 53rd St, Cleveland 44102 Stacy Stuhldreher	K-8		502 17		440/925-6365 Fax 440/925-0698
© Parma Cmty Elem Sch [242] 7667 Day Dr, Parma 44129 Linda Geyer	K-3		352 16		440/888-5490 Fax 440/888-5890

---

79 Student Personnel
80 Driver Ed/Safety
81 Gifted/Talented
82 Video Services
83 Substance Abuse Prev
84 Erate
85 AIDS Education
88 Alternative/At Risk
89 Multi-Cultural Curriculum
90 Social Work

91 Safety/Security
92 Magnet School
93 Parental Involvement
95 Tech Prep Program
97 Chief Information Officer
98 Chief Technology Officer
270 Character Education
271 Migrant Education
273 Teacher Mentor
274 Before/After Sch

275 Response To Intervention
277 Remedial Math K-12
280 Literacy Coach
285 STEM
286 Digital Learning
288 Common Core Standards
294 Accountability
295 Network System
296 Title II Programs
297 Webmaster

298 Grant Writer/Ptnrships
750 Chief Innovation Officer
751 Chief of Staff
752 Social Emotional Learning

Other School Types
Ⓐ = Alternative School
Ⓒ = Charter School
Ⓜ = Magnet School
Ⓨ = Year-Round School

School Programs
A = Alternative Program
G = Adult Classes
M = Magnet Program
T = Title I Schoolwide
V = Career & Tech Ed Programs

New Schools are shaded
New Superintendents and Principals are bold
Personnel with email addresses are underscored

Social Media
= Facebook
= Twitter

Cuyahoga County

© Parma Cmty High Sch [242] 5983 W 54th St, Parma 44129 Linda Geyer	9-12		410		440/887-0319 Fax 440/845-2834
© Parma Cmty Pearl Rd Elem Sch [242] 6125 Pearl Rd, Cleveland 44130 Linda Geyer	K-3		99		440/345-5960 Fax 440/882-6169
© Parma Community Middle Sch [242] 5983 W 54th St, Parma 44129 Leah Walden	7-8		400		440/845-2587 Fax 440/845-2834
Parma Developmental Center 6149 W 130th St, Parma 44130 Allan Wilks	Spec		44 5		216/362-6450 Fax 216/362-4919
© Pinnacle Academy [203] 860 E 222nd St, Euclid 44123 Charlena Hunt	K-8	T	732	95%	216/731-0127 Fax 216/731-0688
© Puritas Cmty Elememtary Sch [242] 15204 Puritas Ave, Cleveland 44135 Meg Colwell	K-4	T	211	79%	216/688-0680 Fax 216/688-0609
© Puritas Cmty Middle Sch [242] 15204 Puritas Ave, Cleveland 44135 Deborah Piazza	5-8	T	176	74%	216/251-1596 Fax 216/251-3540
© Stockyard Cmty Elem Sch [242] 3200 W 65th St, Cleveland 44102 Gary Vojtush	K-6	T	260 17		216/651-5143 Fax 216/651-9515
© Stockyard Cmty Middle Sch [242] 3200 W 65th St, Cleveland 44102 Gary Vojtush	7-8		67		216/961-5052 Fax 216/961-9227
© Summit Academy Cmty Sch-Parma [248] 5868 Stumph Rd, Parma 44130 Diane Robinson	Spec	T	190 12		440/888-5407 Fax 440/888-5417
© Washington Park Cmty Sch 4000 Washington Park Blvd, Newburgh HTS 44105 Robert Horrocks	K-8	T	207 14	92%	216/271-6055 Fax 216/271-6099
© Westpark Cmty Elem Sch [242] 16210 Lorain Ave, Cleveland 44111 Sheila Delzani	K-4	T	322 7	57%	216/688-0271 Fax 216/688-0273
© Westpark Cmty Middle Sch [242] 16210 Lorain Ave, Cleveland 44111 Sheila Delzani	5-8	T	231	52%	216/251-7200 Fax 216/251-0355
William Patrick Day EC Center 2421 Community College Ave, Cleveland 44115 Celeste Bajorek	Spec		250 10		216/736-2920 Fax 216/736-3393

CUYAHOGA PUBLIC SCHOOLS

• **Bay Village City School Dist** PID: 00790401 440/617-7300
   377 Dover Center Rd, Bay Village 44140   Fax 440/617-7301

Schools: 4 \ *Teachers:* 160 \ *Students:* 2,442 \ *Special Ed Students:* 334 \ *LEP Students:* 9 \ *College-Bound:* 87% \ *Ethnic:* Asian 1%, African American 1%, Hispanic 3%, Caucasian 95% \ *Exp:* $294 (Med) \ *Poverty:* 4% \ *Title I:* $89,013 \ *Special Education:* $498,000 \ *Open-Close:* 08/15 - 05/29 \ *DTBP:* $150 (High) \

Jodi Hausmann 1
Jodi Higgins 4*
Char Shryock 8,11,16,69,73,273,288*
Richard Toth 16,82*
Francine Yoder 57*
Holly Schaffer 68
Brian Reynolds 76*
Daryl Stumph 2,3,15,298
Thomas Knick 5
Martha Patton 15,58
Ken Schroeder 36*
Beth Lally 67
Karen Derby-Lovell 71
Richard Bogielski 77

Public Schs..Principal	Grd	Prgm	Enr/#Cls	SN	
Bay High Sch 29230 Wolf Rd, Bay Village 44140 Jason Martin	9-12		804 60	10%	440/617-7400 Fax 440/617-7401
Bay Middle Sch 27725 Wolf Rd, Bay Village 44140 Sean McAndrews	5-8		767 42	8%	440/617-7600 Fax 440/617-7601
Normandy Elem Sch 26920 Normandy Rd, Bay Village 44140 Daniel Sebring	K-2		532 25	6%	440/617-7350 Fax 440/617-7351
Westerly Elem Sch 30301 Wolf Rd, Bay Village 44140 Josie Sanfilippo	3-4		339 17	9%	440/617-7550 Fax 440/617-7551

• **Beachwood City School Dist** PID: 00790475 216/464-2600
   24601 Fairmount Blvd, Beachwood 44122   Fax 216/292-2340

Schools: 5 \ *Teachers:* 121 \ *Students:* 1,612 \ *Special Ed Students:* 209 \ *LEP Students:* 94 \ *College-Bound:* 85% \ *Ethnic:* Asian 18%, African American 22%, Hispanic 2%, Native American: 1%, Caucasian 58% \ *Exp:* $260 (Med) \ *Poverty:* 6% \ *Title I:* $116,896 \ *Special Education:* $343,000 \ *Open-Close:* 08/14 - 06/02 \ *DTBP:* $248 (High) \

Dr Robert Hardis 1
Brian Koss 3,91
Ryan Peters 6
Linda Logaobo 8
Dr Brian Weiss 67
Vytas Saldunas 295
Michele Mills 2,19
Lisa Brockwell 5
Lauren Broderick 7,11,57,58,69,88,275,296
Dr Ken Veon 15,28,76
Cj Piro 91

Public Schs..Principal	Grd	Prgm	Enr/#Cls	SN	
Beachwood High Sch 25100 Fairmount Blvd, Beachwood 44122 **Paul Chase**	9-12	AV	645 40	9%	216/831-2080 Fax 216/292-4169
Beachwood Middle Sch 2860 Richmond Rd, Beachwood 44122 **Tony Srithai**	6-8	A	305 20	9%	216/831-0355 Fax 216/831-1891
Bryden Elem Sch 25501 Bryden Rd, Beachwood 44122 Sherry Miller	K-2		276 25	6%	216/831-3933 Fax 216/292-2375
Fairmount Early Childhood Ctr 24601 Fairmount Blvd, Beachwood 44122 Sherry Miller	PK-PK		83 5		216/464-2600 Fax 216/292-4174
Hilltop Elem Sch 24524 Hilltop Dr, Beachwood 44122 Rebecca Holthaus	3-5		303 14	10%	216/831-7144 Fax 216/292-4236

• **Bedford City School Dist** PID: 00790530 440/439-1500
   475 Northfield Rd, Bedford 44146   Fax 440/439-4850

Schools: 6 \ *Teachers:* 212 \ *Students:* 3,292 \ *Special Ed Students:* 607 \ *LEP Students:* 82 \ *College-Bound:* 60% \ *Ethnic:* African American 87%, Hispanic 4%, Caucasian 9% \ *Exp:* $301 (High) \ *Poverty:* 22% \ *Title I:* $1,523,261 \ *Special Education:* $715,000 \ *Open-Close:* 08/19 - 06/02 \ *DTBP:* $202 (High) \

Andrea Celico 1
Jerry Zgrabik 2
Patrick Carney 5
Felice Willis 10,69,288
Diane Schentur 58
Rasheeda Hoston 58
James Meyer 76
Darlene Redic 90
Janet Pavlic 2
John Sommers 3
Mark Zofka 6
Cassandra Johnson 15
Rasheeda Smialek 58
Tim Tench 67
Kenneth Elder 79,752

1	Superintendent	8	Curric/Instruct K-12	19	Chief Financial Officer	29	Family/Consumer Science	39	Social Studies K-12	49	English/Lang Arts Elem	59	Special Education Elem	69	Academic Assessment
2	Bus/Finance/Purchasing	9	Curric/Instruct Elem	20	Art K-12	30	Adult Education	40	Social Studies Elem	50	English/Lang Arts Sec	60	Special Education Sec	70	Research/Development
3	Buildings And Grounds	10	Curric/Instruct Sec	21	Art Elem	31	Career/Sch-to-Work K-12	41	Social Studies Sec	51	Reading K-12	61	Foreign/World Lang K-12	71	Public Information
4	Food Service	11	Federal Program	22	Art Sec	32	Career/Sch-to-Work Elem	42	Science K-12	52	Reading Elem	62	Foreign/World Lang Elem	72	Summer School
5	Transportation	12	Title I	23	Music K-12	33	Career/Sch-to-Work Sec	43	Science Elem	53	Reading Sec	63	Foreign/World Lang Sec	73	Instructional Training
6	Athletic	13	Title V	24	Music Elem	34	Early Childhood Ed	44	Science Sec	54	Remedial Reading K-12	64	Religious Education K-12	74	Inservice Training
7	Health Services	14	Instructional Media Svcs	25	Music Sec	35	Health/Phys Education	45	Math K-12	55	Remedial Reading Elem	65	Religious Education Elem	75	Marketing/Distributive
		15	Asst Superintendent	26	Business Education	36	Guidance Services K-12	46	Math Elem	56	Remedial Reading Sec	66	Religious Education Sec	76	Info Systems
		16	Chief Operations Officer	27	Career & Tech Ed	37	Guidance Services Elem	47	Math Sec	57	Bilingual/ELL	67	School Board President	77	Psychological Assess
		18	Chief Academic Officer	28	Technology Education	38	Guidance Services Sec	48	English/Lang Arts K-12	58	Special Education K-12	68	Teacher Personnel	78	Affirmative Action

Ohio School Directory — Cuyahoga County

Public Schs..Principal	Grd	Prgm	Enr/#Cls	SN	
Bedford High Sch 481 Northfield Rd, Bedford 44146 Christopher Thompson	9-12	ATV	1,052 100	65%	440/439-4848 Fax 440/439-4627
Carylwood Intermediate Sch 1387 Caryl Dr, Bedford 44146 Mary Ratkosky	4-6	T	338 22	66%	440/439-4509 Fax 440/439-0365
Central Primary Sch 799 Washington St, Bedford 44146 Monique Winston	K-3	T	479 24	77%	440/439-4225 Fax 440/439-4361
Columbus Intermediate Sch 23600 Columbus Rd, Bedford HTS 44146 Virginia Golden	4-6	T	376 25	80%	440/786-3322 Fax 440/439-0495
Glendale Primary Sch 400 W Glendale St, Bedford 44146 Nora Beach	PK-3	T	482 17	61%	440/439-4227 Fax 440/439-3487
Heskett Middle Sch 5771 Perkins Rd, Bedford HTS 44146 Virginia Golden	7-8	T	517 40	71%	440/439-4450 Fax 440/786-3572

● **Berea City School Dist** PID: 00790633 216/898-8300
390 Fair St, Berea 44017 Fax 216/898-8551

Schools: 7 \ *Teachers:* 358 \ *Students:* 5,817 \ *Special Ed Students:* 990 \ *LEP Students:* 192 \ *College-Bound:* 64% \ *Ethnic:* Asian 5%, African American 5%, Hispanic 6%, Caucasian 83% \ *Exp:* $89 (Low) \ *Poverty:* 12% \ *Title I:* $1,513,913 \ *Special Education:* $1,462,000 \ *Open-Close:* 08/22 - 06/04 \ *DTBP:* $187 (High)

Tracy Wheeler 1
Rob Verhest 3,91
Corrina Mollica 5
Rebecca Elder 7
Michale Draves 15
Tamara Klammer 58
Mike Slivochka 68
Kevin Jaynes 73,84
David Klag 295
Jeff Grosse 2
Briana Cates 4
Adam Howard 6*
Karen Frimmel 8,11,54,61,69,81
Lori Bobincheck 58,79
Ana Chapman 67
Cristina Carosielli 70,71
Elaine Galbincea 274

Public Schs..Principal	Grd	Prgm	Enr/#Cls	SN	
Berea-Midpark High Sch 165 E Bagley Rd, Berea 44017 Dr Mark Smithberger	9-12	AV	1,800 70	29%	216/898-8900 Fax 216/898-8558
Berea-Midpark Middle Sch 7000 Paula Dr, Middlebrg HTS 44130 Paul Kish	5-8		1,809	24%	216/676-8400 Fax 216/676-2070
Big Creek Elem Sch 7247 Big Creek Pkwy, Middlebrg HTS 44130 Katherine Rolland	PK-4		624 37	23%	216/898-8303 Fax 216/898-8562
Brook Park Memorial Elem Sch 16900 Holland Rd, Brookpark 44142 Mike Kostyack	PK-4	T	584	36%	216/433-1350 Fax 216/676-2073
Brookview Elem Sch 14105 Snow Rd, Brookpark 44142 Tracy Schneid	PK-4	T	414 22	41%	216/676-4334 Fax 216/676-2074
Grindstone Elem Sch 191 Race St, Berea 44017 Teri Grimm	PK-4		701 13	28%	216/898-8305 Fax 216/898-8563
J & G Snow Sch 202 E Bagley Rd, Berea 44017 Joe Kornick	Spec		78 10		440/260-8251

● **Brecksville Broadview Hts CSD** PID: 00790889 440/740-4000
6638 Mill Rd, Brecksville 44141 Fax 440/740-4004

Schools: 5 \ *Teachers:* 190 \ *Students:* 3,850 \ *Special Ed Students:* 409 \ *LEP Students:* 135 \ *College-Bound:* 85% \ *Ethnic:* Asian 6%, African American 3%, Hispanic 3%, Caucasian 88% \ *Exp:* $87 (Low) \ *Poverty:* 5% \ *Title I:* $324,330 \ *Special Education:* $677,000 \ *Open-Close:* 08/21 - 06/03 \ *DTBP:* $205 (High)

Joelle Magyar 1
John Scott 2,19
Heidi Means 5
David Martin 8,69,288,298*
Gina Symsek 12*
Kathleen Mack 67
John Schinker 73,76,286*
John Schinker 84
Chris Coad 2
Cindy Fihoner 4*
Mark Maslona 6*
Gina Symsek 11,36,58,79
Todd Wasil 16*
Brian Wycuff 68
Kelly Lazar 83,88*

Public Schs..Principal	Grd	Prgm	Enr/#Cls	SN	
Brecksville Broadview Hts HS 6380 Mill Rd, Broadview HTS 44147 Steven Ast	9-12		1,345	9%	440/740-4700 Fax 440/740-4704
Brecksville Broadview Hts MS 6376 Mill Rd, Broadview HTS 44147 Todd Rings	4-8		898 50	11%	440/740-4400 Fax 440/740-4405
Chippewa Elem Sch 8611 Wiese Rd, Brecksville 44141 Beverly Chambers	K-3		312 17	6%	440/740-4200 Fax 440/740-4204
Highland Drive Elem Sch 9457 Highland Dr, Brecksville 44141 Eva O'Mara	K-3		300 13	16%	440/740-4300 Fax 440/740-4304
Hilton Elem Sch 6812 Mill Rd, Brecksville 44141 David Martin	PK-3		376 14	13%	440/740-4600 Fax 440/740-4604

● **Brooklyn City School Dist** PID: 00790956 216/485-8100
9200 Biddulph Rd, Brooklyn 44144 Fax 216/485-8118

Schools: 2 \ *Teachers:* 65 \ *Students:* 1,300 \ *Special Ed Students:* 228 \ *LEP Students:* 90 \ *College-Bound:* 60% \ *Ethnic:* Asian 5%, African American 7%, Hispanic 22%, Caucasian 65% \ *Exp:* $170 (Low) \ *Poverty:* 25% \ *Title I:* $556,912 \ *Special Education:* $305,000 \ *Open-Close:* 08/26 - 06/04 \ *DTBP:* $228 (High)

Mark Gleichauf 1
James Verba 6*
Paula Jones 12,58,79
Rocky Neale 67
Taylor Smith 73*
Sandra Neale 2,3
Michele Kalish 8,11,15,74,273,288
Wendy Smith 16*
Gary Plucinsky 69,83*

Public Schs..Principal	Grd	Prgm	Enr/#Cls	SN	
Brooklyn High Sch 9200 Biddulph Rd, Brooklyn 44144 William Wingler	8-12	T	564 20	63%	216/485-8162 Fax 216/485-8124
Brooklyn Sch 9200 Biddulph Rd, Brooklyn 44144 Cristin Cicco	PK-7	T	710 24	78%	216/485-8176 Fax 216/485-8120

---

79 Student Personnel
80 Driver Ed/Safety
81 Gifted/Talented
82 Video Services
83 Substance Abuse Prev
84 Erate
85 AIDS Education
88 Alternative/At Risk
89 Multi-Cultural Curriculum
90 Social Work

91 Safety/Security
92 Magnet School
93 Parental Involvement
95 Tech Prep Program
97 Chief Information Officer
98 Chief Technology Officer
270 Character Education
271 Migrant Education
273 Teacher Mentor
274 Before/After Sch

275 Response To Intervention
277 Remedial Math K-12
280 Literacy Coach
285 STEM
286 Digital Learning
288 Common Core Standards
294 Accountability
295 Network System
296 Title II Programs
297 Webmaster

298 Grant Writer/Ptnrships
750 Chief Innovation Officer
751 Chief of Staff
752 Social Emotional Learning

Other School Types
Ⓐ = Alternative School
Ⓒ = Charter School
Ⓜ = Magnet School
Ⓨ = Year-Round School

School Programs
A = Alternative Program
G = Adult Classes
M = Magnet Program
T = Title I Schoolwide
V = Career & Tech Ed Programs

New Schools are shaded
New Superintendents and Principals are bold
Personnel with email addresses are underscored

Social Media
 = Facebook
 = Twitter

Cuyahoga County

Market Data Retrieval

● **Chagrin Falls Exempted Vlg SD** PID: 00790994   440/247-5500
400 E Washington St, Chagrin Falls 44022   Fax 440/247-5883

Schools: 4 \ *Teachers:* 121 \ *Students:* 2,000 \ *Special Ed Students:* 222 \ *LEP Students:* 29 \ *College-Bound:* 90% \ *Ethnic:* Asian 1%, African American 2%, Hispanic 3%, Caucasian 94% \ *Exp:* $304 (High) \ *Poverty:* 4% \ *Title I:* $60,016 \ *Special Education:* $347,000 \ *Open-Close:* 08/20 - 06/01 \ *DTBP:* $235 (High) \ f t

Robert Hunt 1	Ashley Brundo 2
Christopher Woofter 3,68,273,298	James Nace 3
Marti Jacobson 4	Michael Morgan 5
Charles Barch 6	Rebecca Quinn 8,288
Lisa Shannon 11,57,58,69,88,275,294,296	Angie Jameson 16,82*
Kathryn Garvey 67	Charlene Paparizos 71
Lauren Jones 72	Mike Daugherty 73,286,295

Public Schs..Principal	Grd	Prgm	Enr/#Cls	SN	
Chagrin Falls High Sch 400 E Washington St, Chagrin Falls 44022 Monica Asher	9-12		757	6%	440/247-2583 Fax 440/247-2071
Chagrin Falls Intermediate Sch 77 E Washington St, Chagrin Falls 44022 Sarah Read	4-6		362 19	5%	440/893-7691 Fax 440/893-7694
Chagrin Falls Middle Sch 342 E Washington St, Chagrin Falls 44022 **Laila Discenza**	7-8		301 20	6%	440/893-7695 Fax 440/247-4855
Gurney Elem Sch 1155 Bell Rd, Chagrin Falls 44022 Dr Rachel Jones	PK-3		489 15	4%	440/893-4030 Fax 440/338-4272 t

● **Cleveland Hts-Univ Hts City SD** PID: 00792825   216/371-7171
2155 Miramar Blvd, University Ht 44118   Fax 216/397-3698

Schools: 11 \ *Teachers:* 393 \ *Students:* 5,200 \ *Special Ed Students:* 1,074 \ *LEP Students:* 123 \ *College-Bound:* 57% \ *Ethnic:* Asian 2%, African American 73%, Hispanic 3%, Caucasian 21% \ *Exp:* $362 (High) \ *Poverty:* 20% \ *Title I:* $2,751,467 \ *Special Education:* $1,481,000 \ *Open-Close:* 08/19 - 05/29 \ *DTBP:* $191 (High) \ f t

Dr Elizabeth Kirby 1	George Petkac 2
Scott Gainer 2,19	Anjali Rosendale 4
Tanera Winters 4	Scott Smith 5
Joe D'Amato 6	Robert Swaggard 8
Susan Pardee 11,298	Elizabeth Rae 12
Felisha Gould 15,57,74,288	Dr Paul Lombardo 15,68,78
Bradley Callender 27	Karen Liddell-Anders 36,58,79
Erin Hanna 58,273	Jodi Sourini 67
Allison Byrd 70	Scott Wortman 71,297
Christina Bauer 73,286*	Deborah Moore 79
Lindsay Baar 79	Brian Williams 88
Karen Heinsbergen 280	

Public Schs..Principal	Grd	Prgm	Enr/#Cls	SN	
Boulevard Elem Sch 1749 Lee Rd, Cleveland HTS 44118 Dr Michael Jenkins	K-5	T	267 23		216/371-7140 Fax 216/397-5955
Canterbury Elem Sch 2530 Canterbury Rd, Cleveland HTS 44118 Dr Erica Wigton	K-5	T	415 18		216/371-7470 Fax 216/397-5956
Cleveland Heights High Sch 13263 Cedar Rd, Cleveland HTS 44118 Byron Hopkins	9-12	V	1,767		216/371-7101
ⓐ Delisle Options Center 14780 Superior Rd, Cleveland 44118 Dr Brian Williams	9-12		100		216/320-2390 Fax 216/320-2391
Fairfax Elem Sch 3150 Fairfax Rd, Cleveland HTS 44118 Quatrice James	K-5	T	344 30		216/371-7480 Fax 216/397-5958
Gearity Professional Dev Sch 2323 Wrenford Rd, University Ht 44118 Katrina Hicks	PK-5	T	365 20		216/371-6515 Fax 216/397-5959
Monticello Middle Sch 3665 Monticello Blvd, Cleveland HTS 44121 Dr Jeffrey Johnston	6-8		600		216/397-5967
Noble Elem Sch 1293 Ardoon St, Cleveland HTS 44121 Patrick Carpenter	PK-5	T	354 20		216/371-6535 Fax 216/397-5960 f t
Oxford Elem Sch 939 Quilliams Rd, Cleveland HTS 44121 Teresa Taylor-Ware	PK-5	T	276 18		216/371-6525 Fax 216/397-5961 f t
Roxboro Elem Sch 2405 Roxboro Rd, Cleveland HTS 44106 Shelley Pulling	K-5	T	323 30		216/371-7115 Fax 216/397-5962
Roxboro Middle Sch 2400 Roxboro Rd, Cleveland HTS 44106 Rachel Coleman	6-8		582		216/371-7440 Fax 216/397-3857

● **Cleveland Metro School Dist** PID: 00791041   216/838-0000
1111 Superior Ave E Ste 1800, Cleveland 44114   Fax 216/436-5144

Schools: 112 \ *Teachers:* 2,843 \ *Students:* 38,949 \ *Special Ed Students:* 8,487 \ *LEP Students:* 3,447 \ *College-Bound:* 77% \ *Ethnic:* Asian 1%, African American 67%, Hispanic 16%, Caucasian 16% \ *Exp:* $373 (High) \ *Poverty:* 42% \ *Title I:* $54,776,742 \ *Special Education:* $17,677,000 \ *Open-Close:* 07/24 - 06/16 \ *DTBP:* $289 (High) \ f t

Eric Gordon 1	Angela Foraker 2
Derek Richey 2,19	Larry Johnston 2
Patrick Zohn 3,17	Chris Burkhardt 4
Eric Taylor 5	Desiree Powell 7,35
Elizabeth Nelson-Creel 8,45	Dr Michelle Pierre-Farid 8,18
Nicole Vitale 8,34	Tracy Hill 12,93
Shawn Braxton 16,73	Jeffery Allen 20,23
Anthony Battaglia 27,30,31	Lavora Gadison 39
Dr Terri Wade-Lyles 43,285*	Kirsten Mahovlich 44,285
Jose Gonzalez 57,89*	Jessica Baldwin 58,275
Anne Bingham 67	Lori Ward 68
Christine Fowler-Mack 69	Matt Linick 70
Dr Roseann Canfora 71	Curtis Timmons 73,76,84,97,295
Dr Jacquinette Brown 74	Susanne Farkas 76
Mary Ellen Carras 81*	Lester Fultz 91
Chris Broughton 294	Michael Goodill 297
Karen Thompson 751	

Public Schs..Principal	Grd	Prgm	Enr/#Cls	SN	
Adlai Stevenson Elem Sch 18300 Woda Ave, Cleveland 44122 Christopher Wyland	PK-8	T	450 20		216/838-5300 Fax 216/921-1212
Alfred Benesch Academy 5393 Quincy Ave, Cleveland 44104 Erin Murphy	K-8	TV	271 60		216/838-1300 Fax 216/391-0173
Almira Academy 3375 W 99th St, Cleveland 44102 James Greene	PK-8	T	500 24		216/838-6150 Fax 216/634-2206
Andrew J Rickoff Elem Sch 3500 E 147th St, Cleveland 44120 Shelby Schutt	PK-8	T	490 26		216/838-4150 Fax 216/767-2101
Anton Grdina Sch 2955 E 71st St, Cleveland 44104 Latosha Glass	PK-8	T	398 34		216/838-1150 Fax 216/341-6895

1	Superintendent	8	Curric/Instruct K-12	19	Chief Financial Officer	29	Family/Consumer Science	39	Social Studies K-12	49	English/Lang Arts Elem	59	Special Education Elem	69	Academic Assessment
2	Bus/Finance/Purchasing	9	Curric/Instruct Elem	20	Art K-12	30	Adult Education	40	Social Studies Elem	50	English/Lang Arts Sec	60	Special Education Sec	70	Research/Development
3	Buildings And Grounds	10	Curric/Instruct Sec	21	Art Elem	31	Career/Sch-to-Work K-12	41	Social Studies Sec	51	Reading K-12	61	Foreign/World Lang K-12	71	Public Information
4	Food Service	11	Federal Program	22	Art Sec	32	Career/Sch-to-Work Elem	42	Science K-12	52	Reading Elem	62	Foreign/World Lang Elem	72	Summer School
5	Transportation	12	Title I	23	Music K-12	33	Career/Sch-to-Work Sec	43	Science Elem	53	Reading Sec	63	Foreign/World Lang Sec	73	Instructional Tech
6	Athletic	13	Title V	24	Music Elem	34	Early Childhood Ed	44	Science Sec	54	Remedial Reading K-12	64	Religious Education K-12	74	Inservice Training
7	Health Services	14	Instructional Media Svcs	25	Music Sec	35	Health/Phys Education	45	Math K-12	55	Remedial Reading Elem	65	Religious Education Elem	75	Marketing/Distributive
		15	Asst Superintendent	26	Business Education	36	Guidance Services K-12	46	Math Elem	56	Remedial Reading Sec	66	Religious Education Sec	76	Info Systems
		16	Chief Operations Officer	27	Career & Tech Ed	37	Guidance Services Elem	47	Math Sec	57	Bilingual/ELL	67	School Board President	77	Psychological Assess
		17	Chief Academic Officer	28	Technology Education	38	Guidance Services Sec	48	English/Lang Arts K-12	58	Special Education K-12	68	Teacher Personnel	78	Affirmative Action

OH—42

Ohio School Directory — Cuyahoga County

School	Grades		Enroll	Phone
Artemus Ward Sch 4315 W 140th St, Cleveland 44135 Christopher Myslenski	PK-8	T	510 22	216/838-6200 Fax 216/476-4467
Bard HS Early Clg East Campus 3817 Martin Luther King Jr Dr, Cleveland 44105 Lea Dotson	10-10		40	216/838-4100
Bard HS Early College 13501 Terminal Ave, Cleveland 44135 Dr Dumaine Williams	9-12	T	420	216/838-9700
Ⓜ Benjamin Franklin Elem Sch 1905 Spring Rd, Cleveland 44109 Rachel Snider	PK-8	T	626 36	216/838-3150 Fax 216/778-6575
Bolton Elem Sch 9803 Quebec Ave, Cleveland 44106 Juliet King	PK-8	T	300 25	216/838-1200 Fax 216/795-2948
Buhrer Dual Language Elem Sch 1600 Buhrer Ave, Cleveland 44109 Michelle Sanchez	PK-8	T	399 40	216/838-8350 Fax 216/621-8461
Campus International Sch North 2160 Payne Ave, Cleveland 44114 Julie Beers	K-8	T	745	216/838-8000
Campus International Sch South 3100 Chester Ave Fl 1, Cleveland 44114 Ameer Kim El-Mallawany	9-11		180	216/838-8100
Case Elem Sch 4050 Superior Ave, Cleveland 44103 Janet McDowell	PK-8	T	255 25	216/838-1350 Fax 216/431-4375
Charles A Mooney Sch 3213 Montclair Ave, Cleveland 44109 Michelle Person	PK-8	TV	453 80	216/838-3200 Fax 216/351-6488
Charles Dickens at Corlett 13013 Corlett Ave, Cleveland 44105 Jocelyn Smith	PK-8	T	360 20	216/838-4200 Fax 216/295-4523
Charles W Eliot Elem Sch 15700 Lotus Dr, Cleveland 44128 Ivy Wheeler	PK-8	TV	300 35	216/838-5350 Fax 216/295-3570
Clara E Westropp Elem Sch 19101 Puritas Ave, Cleveland 44135 Krystle George	PK-8	T	366 32	216/267-3706 Fax 216/267-5940
Clark Elem Sch 5550 Clark Ave, Cleveland 44102 Amanda Rodriguez	PK-8	T	609 26	216/838-7300 Fax 216/634-2217
Cleveland Early College HS 2075 Stokes Blvd, Cleveland 44106 Chaundria Smith	9-12	T	315 10	216/838-8250 Fax 216/229-0087
Cleveland HS for Digital Arts 1440 Lakeside Ave E, Cleveland 44114 Jasmine Maze	9-12	T	315	216/838-9650
Cleveland Sch of Arch & Design 2075 Stokes Blvd, Cleveland 44106 **Odell Brown**	9-12	T	320	216/838-8200 Fax 216/229-0072
Cleveland Sch of Science & Med 2075 Stokes Blvd, Cleveland 44106 Michelle Perez	9-12	T	413	216/838-8300 Fax 216/335-7475
Ⓜ Cleveland School of the Arts 2064 Stearns Rd, Cleveland 44106 John Lepelley	9-12	T	500	216/838-9000 Fax 216/421-7689
Daniel E Morgan Elem Sch 8912 Morris Ct, Cleveland 44106 Dessie Sanders	PK-8	T	229 26	216/838-1400 Fax 216/983-8301
Davis Aerospace & Maritime HS 1440 Lakeside Ave E, Cleveland 44114 Tim Jones	9-10		120	216/838-2500
Denison Elem Sch 3799 W 33rd St, Cleveland 44109 Sonja Clark	PK-8	T	294 29	216/838-3250 Fax 216/778-6578
Design Lab Early College HS 1740 E 32nd St, Cleveland 44114 Christopher Scarcella	9-12	T	265	216/838-8150 Fax 216/592-6879
Ⓜ Dike School of the Arts 2501 E 61st St, Cleveland 44104 **Alisha Evans**	PK-8	T	359 18	216/838-9150 Fax 216/361-2018
Douglas MacArthur Girls Ldrshp 4401 Valleyside Rd, Cleveland 44135 Victoria King	PK-8	T	321	216/838-8400 Fax 216/433-7466
Ⓐ Downtown Educational Ctr 9300 Quincy Ave, Cleveland 44106 Wayne Marok	6-12		106	216/443-4902 Fax 216/443-4903
East Clark Elem Sch 885 E 146th St, Cleveland 44110 Charlene Hilliard	PK-8	T	236 25	216/838-0650 Fax 216/851-3361
East Technical High Sch 2439 E 55th St, Cleveland 44104 Temujin Taylor	9-12	T	337	216/838-1000
Euclid Park Sch 17914 Euclid Ave, Cleveland 44112 Jennifer Woody	PK-8	T	383	216/838-0700 Fax 216/383-5111
Facing History New Tech Sch 3213 Montclair Ave 3rd Fl, Cleveland 44109 Marc Engoglia	9-12	T	337	216/838-8600 Fax 216/838-8610
Franklin D Roosevelt Academy 800 Linn Dr, Cleveland 44108 Sherie Turner	PK-8	T	470 15	216/838-2200 Fax 216/268-6954
Fullerton Elem Sch 5920 Fullerton Ave, Cleveland 44105 Kevin Payton	K-8	T	202 17	216/838-4400 Fax 216/441-8049
Garfield Elem Sch 3800 W 140th St, Cleveland 44111 **Jacob Bosley**	PK-8	T	554	216/838-6300 Fax 216/476-4223
Ⓜ Garrett Morgan Sch 4016 Woodbine Ave, Cleveland 44113 Quenton Davis	9-12		257	216/838-8450 Fax 216/634-2113
George W Carver-STEM Sch 2200 E 55th St, Cleveland 44103 Susan Harvey	PK-8	T	408 25	216/838-1450 Fax 216/391-5041
Ginn Academy 655 E 162nd St, Cleveland 44110 Damon Holmes	9-12	T	362	216/838-4466 Fax 216/531-2874
Glenville High Sch 650 E 113th St, Cleveland 44108 Jacqueline Bell	9-12	T	325	216/838-2000 Fax 216/541-7666
Ⓜ H B Booker Wraparound Sch 2121 W 67th St, Cleveland 44102 Nicholas Scheibelhood	PK-8	T	370	216/838-6350 Fax 216/634-2225
Hannah Gibbons STEM Sch 1401 Larchmont Rd, Cleveland 44110 Gregory Adkins	PK-8	T	275 9	216/838-0750 Fax 216/383-4556
Harvey Rice Wraparound 2730 E 116th St, Cleveland 44120 Jason Tidmore	PK-8	T	463 19	216/838-1500 Fax 216/472-5348
High Tech Academy 2900 Community College Ave, Cleveland 44115 Stacy Hutchinson	Voc		230	216/987-3549
Int'l Newcomers Acad-Jefferson 3145 W 46th St, Cleveland 44102 Marisol Burgos	PK-12	T	522	216/838-7150 Fax 216/404-5490
Iowa Maple Elem Sch 12510 Maple Ave, Cleveland 44108 Natalie Smith-Benson	PK-8		245 26	216/838-0800
James F Rhodes High Sch 5100 Biddulph Ave, Cleveland 44144 Brian Evans	9-12	TV	600 95	216/838-3000 Fax 216/777-5372

79 Student Personnel	91 Safety/Security	275 Response To Intervention	298 Grant Writer/Ptnrships
80 Driver Ed/Safety	92 Magnet School	277 Remedial Math K-12	750 Chief Innovation Officer
81 Gifted/Talented	93 Parental Involvement	280 Literacy Coach	751 Chief of Staff
82 Video Services	95 Tech Prep Program	285 STEM	752 Social Emotional Learning
83 Substance Abuse Prev	97 Chief Infomation Officer	286 Digital Learning	
84 Erate	98 Chief Technology Officer	288 Common Core Standards	Other School Types
85 AIDS Education	270 Character Education	294 Accountability	Ⓐ = Alternative School
88 Alternative/At Risk	271 Migrant Education	295 Network System	Ⓒ = Charter School
89 Multi-Cultural Curriculum	273 Teacher Mentor	296 Title II Programs	Ⓜ = Magnet School
90 Social Work	274 Before/After Sch	297 Webmaster	Ⓨ = Year-Round School

School Programs
A = Alternative Program
G = Adult Classes
M = Magnet Program
T = Title I Schoolwide
V = Career & Tech Ed Programs

Social Media
▪ = Facebook
▪ = Twitter

New Schools are shaded
New Superintendents and Principals are bold
Personnel with email addresses are underscored

OH–43

Cuyahoga County

School	Grades		Enroll	Phone
Ⓜ Jane Addams Bus Career Center 2373 E 30th St, Cleveland 44115 Diane Grondin	9-12	GTV	250 20	216/838-9250 Fax 216/621-3910
JFK E3Agle Academy 17100 Harvard Ave, Cleveland 44128 Andre Rudolph	10-12	T	260	216/838-5150
JFK-Pact Academy 17100 Harvard Ave, Cleveland 44128 **Marie Feagins**	9-12	T	268	216/838-5200 Fax 216/518-3872
John Adams Clg & Career Acad 3817 Martin Luther King Jr Dr, Cleveland 44105 Kristen Kelly	9-10		215	216/838-4050
John Adams High Sch 3817 Martin Luther King Jr Dr, Cleveland 44105 Terrance Menefee	11-12	T	332	216/838-4000 Fax 216/295-4645
John Marshall-Civic & Business 3952 W 140th St, Cleveland 44111 Sara Kidner	9-12	T	400	216/838-6050
John Marshall-Engineering 3952 W 140th St, Cleveland 44111 Timothy Primus	9-12	T	343	216/838-6102
John Marshall-Info Tech 3952 W 140th St, Cleveland 44111 Chelsey Kohn	9-12	T	375	216/838-6850
Joseph M Gallagher Elem Sch 6601 Franklin Blvd, Cleveland 44102 Thomas Kubiak	PK-8	T	738 77	216/838-6400 Fax 216/634-2353
Kenneth Clement Boys Academy 14311 Woodworth Rd, Cleveland 44112 Derrick Holifield	PK-8	T	165	216/838-8800 Fax 216/486-5202
Lincoln-West High Sch 3202 W 30th St, Cleveland 44109 Iteisha Bankston	12-12	T	120	216/838-7000 Fax 216/634-2403
Lincoln-West HS Global Studies 3202 W 30th St, Cleveland 44109 Dr Irene Javier	9-12		270	216/838-7050
Lincoln-West Sch Sci & Health 3202 W 30th St, Cleveland 44109 Michelle Hughes	9-12		219	216/838-7100
Louis Agassiz Elem Sch 3595 Bosworth Rd, Cleveland 44111 Angela Boie	PK-8	T	283 23	216/838-6450 Fax 216/251-4735
Louisa May Alcott Elem Sch 10308 Baltic Rd, Cleveland 44102 Eileen Stull	K-5	T	222 12	216/838-6500 Fax 216/281-4459
Luis Munoz Marin Elem Sch 1701 Castle Ave, Cleveland 44113 **Samuel Roman**	PK-8	TV	527 52	216/838-3300 Fax 216/685-5177
Marion C Seltzer Elem Sch 1468 W 98th St, Cleveland 44102 Caitlin Kilbane	PK-8	T	460 33	216/838-6550 Fax 216/634-8733
Marion Sterling Elem Sch 3033 Central Ave, Cleveland 44115 Kelly Gibbs	PK-8	T	325 20	216/838-1550 Fax 216/694-4746
Martin L King Career Campus 1651 E 71st St, Cleveland 44103 Latonia Davis	Voc	GT	35 24	216/838-9350
Mary B Martin STEM Academy 8200 Brookline Ave, Cleveland 44103 Gary McPherson	PK-8	T	272 23	216/838-1600 Fax 216/229-2052
Mary M Bethune Elem Sch 11815 Moulton Ave, Cleveland 44106 Melanie Nakonachny	PK-8	T	305 21	216/838-2250 Fax 216/231-0110
Max S Hayes High Sch 2211 W 65th St, Cleveland 44102 Christopher Scarcella	9-12	GT	602 40	216/838-9400 Fax 216/634-2175
MC2 STEM HS-Cleveland State 2124 Chester Ave, Cleveland 44115 Jeffrey McClellan	11-12		133	216/838-8500 Fax 216/592-6879
Ⓜ MC2 STEM HS-GE Lighting 1975 Noble Rd Bldg 336, E Cleveland 44112 Ms Mack	10-10		133	216/838-8520 Fax 216/744-1530
MC2 STEM HS-Grt Lakes Sci Ctr 601 Erieside Ave, Cleveland 44114 Feowyn MacKinnon	9-9	T	133	216/838-8550 Fax 216/858-1264
Ⓨ Memorial Year-Round Sch 410 E 152nd St, Cleveland 44110 Maria Dinkins	PK-8	MT	400 11	216/838-0850
Michael R White STEM Sch 1000 E 92nd St, Cleveland 44108 Ariel Hayes	K-8	T	158 23	216/838-2300 Fax 216/451-4692
Miles Elem Sch 11918 Miles Ave, Cleveland 44105 Roy James	PK-8	T	439 15	216/838-5250 Fax 216/838-6196
Miles Park Elem Sch 4090 E 93rd St, Cleveland 44105 Tamika Ivory	PK-8	T	476 30	216/838-4450 Fax 216/641-2819
Mound-STEM Sch 5935 Ackley Rd, Cleveland 44105 Velma McNeil	PK-8	T	420 16	216/838-1650 Fax 216/441-8092
Nathan Hale Elem Sch 3588 Martin Luther King Jr Dr, Cleveland 44105 Joelle McIntosh	PK-8	GT	493 40	216/838-4250 Fax 216/441-8034
© Near West Intergenerationl Sch 3805 Terrett Ave, Cleveland 44113 **April Maimone**	K-8	T	248	216/961-4308
New Tech Collinwood 15210 Saint Clair Ave, Cleveland 44110 Mary Miller	9-12	TV	288	216/838-0500 Fax 216/268-6057
New Tech High School-East 2439 E 55th St, Cleveland 44104 Christy Nickerson	9-12	T	133	216/838-8650 Fax 216/361-3282
New Tech High School-West 11801 Worthington Ave, Cleveland 44111 Shaunamichele Leonard	9-12	T	280	216/838-8700 Fax 216/281-1050
Ⓜ Newton D Baker School of Arts 3690 W 159th St, Cleveland 44111 Wendy Rose-Geiling	PK-8	T	530 30	216/838-6650 Fax 216/777-5414
Oliver Hazard Perry Academy 18400 Schenely Ave, Cleveland 44119 Brittani Irvin	PK-8	T	275 26	216/838-0090 Fax 216/383-5164
Orchard STEM Sch 4200 Bailey Ave, Cleveland 44113 Kathryn Francis	PK-8	T	465 28	216/838-7350 Fax 216/634-2135
Patrick Henry Sch 11901 Durant Ave, Cleveland 44108 Brittany Anderson	PK-8	TV	288 23	216/838-2350 Fax 216/268-6163
Paul L Dunbar Elem Sch 2159 W 29th St, Cleveland 44113 Sofia Piperis	PK-8	T	375 20	216/838-7400 Fax 216/634-2779
Ⓐ Promise Academy © 1701 E 13th St, Cleveland 44114 **Lisa Adams**	9-12	T	231	216/443-0500 Fax 216/443-0506
Rhodes College & Career Acad 5100 Biddulph Ave, Cleveland 44144 Alyssa Starinski	9-11		275	216/838-3050
Rhodes Sch Environmental Study 5100 Biddulph Ave, Cleveland 44144 Tara Drouhard	9-11		250	216/838-3100
Riverside Sch 14601 Montrose Ave, Cleveland 44111 Jessica Gamble	PK-8	T	514 26	216/838-6700 Fax 216/688-3603

1 Superintendent	8 Curric/Instruct K-12	19 Chief Financial Officer	29 Family/Consumer Science	39 Social Studies K-12	49 English/Lang Arts Elem	59 Special Education Elem	69 Academic Assessment
2 Bus/Finance/Purchasing	9 Curric/Instruct Elem	20 Art K-12	30 Adult Education	40 Social Studies Elem	50 English/Lang Arts Sec	60 Special Education Sec	70 Research/Development
3 Buildings And Grounds	10 Curric/Instruct Sec	21 Art Elem	31 Career/Sch-to-Work K-12	41 Social Studies Sec	51 Reading K-12	61 Foreign/World Lang K-12	71 Public Information
4 Food Service	11 Federal Program	22 Art Sec	32 Career/Sch-to-Work Elem	42 Science K-12	52 Reading Elem	62 Foreign/World Lang Elem	72 Summer School
5 Transportation	12 Title I	23 Music K-12	33 Career/Sch-to-Work Sec	43 Science Elem	53 Reading Sec	63 Foreign/World Lang Sec	73 Instructional Tech
6 Athletic	13 Title V	24 Music Elem	34 Early Childhood Ed	44 Science Sec	54 Remedial Reading K-12	64 Religious Education K-12	74 Inservice Training
7 Health Services	14 Asst Superintendent	25 Music Sec	35 Health/Phys Education	45 Math K-12	55 Remedial Reading Elem	65 Religious Education Elem	75 Marketing/Distributive
	15 Instructional Media Svcs	26 Business Education	36 Guidance Services K-12	46 Math Elem	56 Remedial Reading Sec	66 Religious Education Sec	76 Info Systems
	16 Chief Operations Officer	27 Career & Tech Ed	37 Guidance Services Elem	47 Math Sec	57 Bilingual/ELL	67 School Board President	77 Psychological Assess
	17 Chief Academic Officer	28 Technology Education	38 Guidance Services Sec	48 English/Lang Arts K-12	58 Special Education K-12	68 Teacher Personnel	78 Affirmative Action

Ohio School Directory　　　　　　　　　　　　　　　　　　　　　　　　　　　　　Cuyahoga County

School	Grd	Prgm	Enr/#Cls		Phone
Robert H Jamison Sch 4092 E 146th St, Cleveland 44128 Sharon Cooper	PK-8	T	390 35		216/838-5400 Fax 216/295-3512
Robinson G Jones Elem Sch 4550 W 150th St, Cleveland 44135 Melissa Watts	PK-8	T	493 23		216/838-6750 Fax 216/433-7249
School of One 3575 W 130th St, Cleveland 44111 Maryum Sims	7-12	T	257		216/838-8850
Scranton Elem Sch 1991 Barber Ave, Cleveland 44113 Troy Beadling	PK-8	T	508 27		216/838-7450 Fax 216/363-5038
Stonebrook Montessori Sch 975 East Blvd, Cleveland 44108 Jaqueline Miller	PK-6		194	70%	216/644-3012
Sunbeam Sch 11731 Mount Overlook Ave, Cleveland 44120 Jessica Humphrey	PK-8	T	448 21		216/838-1700 Fax 216/229-5308
Tremont Montessori Sch 2409 W 10th St, Cleveland 44113 Natalie Celeste	PK-8	T	472 40		216/838-9850 Fax 216/261-2082
Valley View Boys Ldrshp Acad 17200 Valleyview Ave, Cleveland 44135 Terrance Mitchell	PK-8	T	218		216/838-8900 Fax 216/889-4093
Wade Park Elem Sch 7600 Wade Park Ave, Cleveland 44103 Dr Lee Buddy	PK-8	T	456		216/838-1750 Fax 216/432-4989
Walton Elem Sch 3409 Walton Ave, Cleveland 44113 Gretchen Liggens	PK-8	T	282 35		216/838-7500 Fax 216/634-8790
Warner Girls Leadership Acad 8315 Jeffries Ave, Cleveland 44105 Kristel Wilkins	PK-8	T	458		216/838-8950 Fax 216/206-4621
Washington Park Env Stud Acad 3875 Washington Park Blvd, Cleveland 44105 Tiffany James	9-12	T	278		216/838-9200 Fax 216/441-8030
Waverly Sch 1422 W 74th St, Cleveland 44102 Sommer Fountain	PK-8	T	260 28		216/838-7550
Whitney M Young Gifted Campus 17900 Harvard Ave, Cleveland 44128 Ivy Wheeler	5-12	T	175 25		216/838-5500 Fax 216/295-3547
Wilbur Wright Sch 11005 Parkhurst Dr, Cleveland 44111 Virmeal Finley	PK-8	T	550 75		216/838-6800 Fax 216/476-4206
William Cullen Bryant Sch 3121 Oak Park Ave, Cleveland 44109 Amy Mobley	PK-8	T	448 22		216/838-3350 Fax 216/749-8139
William Rainey Harper Sch 5515 Ira Ave, Cleveland 44144 Ajayi Monell	PK-3		170		216/838-3400
Willow Sch 5004 Glazier Ave, Cleveland 44127 Lisa Locklear	PK-8	T	232 16		216/838-1800 Fax 216/429-3294
Willson Elem Sch 1126 Ansel Rd, Cleveland 44108 Dawn Hayden	PK-8	T	350		216/838-1850 Fax 216/920-1284

● **Cuyahoga Heights Local SD** PID: 00793001　　　216/429-5700
4820 E 71st St, Cleveland 44125　　　　　　　　　　Fax 216/341-3737

Schools: 3 \ *Teachers:* 58 \ *Students:* 900 \ *Special Ed Students:* 71 \
College-Bound: 77% \ *Ethnic:* Asian 2%, African American 1%, Hispanic 3%, Caucasian 93% \ *Exp:* $289 (Med) \ *Poverty:* 8% \ *Title I:* $82,515 \
Open-Close: 08/20 - 06/04 \ *DTBP:* $229 (High)

Tom Evans ....1　　Matt Mucchio 2,11
Neil Peterson ....3*　　Pam Meade 4*
Ryan Kelber ....6　　Dr Ted Caleris 8,15,84,273,288,296,752
Karen Bergen ....16　　Carolyn Douglas 36,275*
Nancy Wanyerka ....56*　　George Burich 58*
Lyndie Schuckert ....67　　David Wallis 73*

Public Schs..Principal	Grd	Prgm	Enr/#Cls	SN
Cuyahoga Heights Elem Sch 4880 E 71st St, Cleveland 44125 Joy Houchen	PK-5		344 20	24% 216/429-5880 Fax 216/429-5883
Cuyahoga Heights High Sch 4820 E 71st St, Cleveland 44125 Patrick Coleman	9-12		249 26	36% 216/429-5707 Fax 216/429-5706
Cuyahoga Heights Middle Sch 4840 E 71st St, Cleveland 44125 Patrick Coleman	6-8		214 15	216/429-5757 Fax 216/429-5735

● **Cuyahoga Vly Career Ctr Voc SD** PID: 00795279　　440/526-5200
8001 Brecksville Rd, Brecksville 44141　　　　　　　Fax 440/746-8298

Schools: 1 \ *Teachers:* 40 \ *Students:* 1,000 \ *Exp:* $222 (Med) \
Open-Close: 08/21 - 06/03 \ *DTBP:* $175 (High) \

David Mangas ....1　　Richard Berdine 2
Dr Celena Roebuck ....11　　Connie Mangan 16*
Mary Trew ....30　　Amy Jaramillo 38,83,85*
Erol Sommer ....60*　　James Gilbride 67
Kyle Livengood ....73*　　Alan Kilgore 76
Todd Nicodemus 88*

Public Schs..Principal	Grd	Prgm	Enr/#Cls	SN
Cuyahoga Valley Career Center 8001 Brecksville Rd, Brecksville 44141 David Mangas	Voc	AG	1,000 40	440/526-5200 Fax 440/838-8944

● **East Cleveland City Sch Dist** PID: 00793037　　　216/268-6600
1843 Stanwood Rd, E Cleveland 44112　　　　　　Fax 216/268-6676

Schools: 6 \ *Teachers:* 160 \ *Students:* 2,300 \ *Special Ed Students:* 434
\ *College-Bound:* 35% \ *Ethnic:* African American 100%, \ *Exp:* $245
(Med) \ *Poverty:* 48% \ *Title I:* $3,384,342 \ *Special Education:* $580,000 \
Open-Close: 08/22 - 06/05 \ *DTBP:* $191 (High)

Dr Henry Pettiegrew ....1　　Allen Wolf 2,4
David Martin ....3　　Dennis Bunkley 7,36,58,79,90
Paula Elder ....8,69,296　　Anndrat Fitzgerald 11,298
Courtney Jones ....58　　Dr Una Keenon 67
Kevin Harrell ....68　　Donshon Wilson 73

Public Schs..Principal	Grd	Prgm	Enr/#Cls	SN
Caledonia Elem Sch 914 Caledonia Ave, E Cleveland 44112 Charles McCants	K-6	T	223 25	216/268-6690 Fax 216/268-6463
Chambers Elem Sch 14305 Shaw Ave, E Cleveland 44112 Crystal Cash	K-6	T	272 30	216/268-6640 Fax 216/268-6272
Heritage Middle Sch 14410 Terrace Rd, E Cleveland 44112 Danielle Simmons	7-8	T	221	216/268-6610 Fax 216/268-6617
Mayfair Elem Sch 13916 Mayfair Ave, E Cleveland 44112 Sabrina Ingram	K-6	T	182 20	216/268-6651 Fax 216/268-6496
Shaw High Sch 15320 Euclid Ave, E Cleveland 44112 Lori Crum	9-12	A	731 90	216/268-6887 Fax 216/268-6433

79　Student Personnel　　　　91　Safety/Security　　　　275　Response To Intervention　　298　Grant Writer/Ptnrships　　School Programs　　　　Social Media
80　Driver Ed/Safety　　　　　92　Magnet School　　　　　277　Remedial Math K-12　　　　750　Chief Innovation Officer　　A = Alternative Program
81　Gifted/Talented　　　　　93　Parental Involvement　　280　Literacy Coach　　　　　　751　Chief of Staff　　　　　　　G = Adult Classes　　　　　　= Facebook
82　Video Services　　　　　 95　Tech Prep Program　　　285　STEM　　　　　　　　　　　752　Social Emotional Learning　 M = Magnet Program
83　Substance Abuse Prev　　97　Chief Infomation Officer　286　Digital Learning　　　　　　　　　　　　　　　　　　　　　T = Title I Schoolwide　　　　= Twitter
84　Erate　　　　　　　　　　98　Chief Technology Officer　288　Common Core Standards　 Other School Types　　　　 V = Career & Tech Ed Programs
85　AIDS Education　　　　 270　Character Education　　 294　Accountability　　　　　　　Ⓐ = Alternative School
88　Alternative/At Risk　　　271　Migrant Education　　　　295　Network System　　　　　　Ⓒ = Charter School　　　　　New Schools are shaded
89　Multi-Cultural Curriculum　273　Teacher Mentor　　　　　296　Title II Programs　　　　　　Ⓜ = Magnet School　　　　　New Superintendents and Principals are bold
90　Social Work　　　　　　274　Before/After Sch　　　　 297　Webmaster　　　　　　　　Ⓨ = Year-Round School　　　Personnel with email addresses are underscored

OH–45

Cuyahoga County

Market Data Retrieval

Superior Elem Sch   PK-6   T   305   216/268-6670
1865 Garfield Rd, E Cleveland 44112   30   Fax 216/268-6497
Shawna Lesure

- **Euclid City School Dist** PID: 00793128   216/261-2900
  651 E 222nd St, Euclid 44123   Fax 216/261-3120

Schools: 7 \ *Teachers:* 346 \ *Students:* 5,100 \ *Special Ed Students:* 821 \ *College-Bound:* 41% \ *Ethnic:* African American 89%, Hispanic 1%, Caucasian 9% \ *Exp:* $127 (Low) \ *Poverty:* 30% \ *Title I:* $3,904,728 \ *Special Education:* $1,104,000 \ *Open-Close:* 08/15 - 05/28 \ *DTBP:* $208 (High) \ f t

Dr Marvin Jones 1	Matthew Brown 2
Patrick Higley 2,91	Glenn Hummell 3
Tara Frdley 4	Florence Masella 9,77
Ken Ferlito 11,54	Christopher Papouras 15
Donna Sudar 67	Veonta Weathers 68
Karen Brown 70	James Yane 73
Elaine Thirion 76	Sherrell Benton 79,92
Tajuana Hunnicutt 79	Kevin Kelly 91

Public Schs..Principal	Grd	Prgm	Enr/#Cls	SN
Arbor Elem Sch 20400 Arbor Ave, Euclid 44123 Lawanda Johnson	K-5	T	552	82% 216/797-6200 Fax 216/383-1912
Bluestone Elem Sch 1455 E 260th St, Euclid 44132 Lynnette Stevens	K-5	T	518	84% 216/797-6300 Fax 216/289-6619
Central Middle Sch 20701 Euclid Ave, Euclid 44117 Michael Mennel	6-7	T	775	77% 216/797-5300 Fax 216/797-5333
ⓜ Chardon Hills Magnet Sch 1750 E 234th St, Euclid 44117 Chris Papouras	K-5	T	472	68% 216/797-6400 Fax 216/692-9239
Euclid Child Dev Center 22800 Fox Ave, Euclid 44123 Rasheeda Hoston	PK-PK	T	244 9	56% 216/322-2700 Fax 216/732-2705
Euclid City High Sch 711 E 22nd St, Euclid 44123 Janis Svoboda	8-12	AGTV	2,118	64% 216/797-7800 Fax 216/797-7900
Shoreview Elem Sch 490 E 260th St, Euclid 44132 Mary Thomas	K-5	T	499	83% 216/797-6500 Fax 216/797-1252

- **Fairview Park City Sch Dist** PID: 00793283   440/331-5500
  21620 Mastick Rd, Fairview Park 44126   Fax 440/356-3545

Schools: 4 \ *Teachers:* 102 \ *Students:* 1,702 \ *Special Ed Students:* 247 \ *LEP Students:* 43 \ *College-Bound:* 68% \ *Ethnic:* Asian 2%, African American 4%, Hispanic 6%, Caucasian 88% \ *Exp:* $138 (Low) \ *Poverty:* 10% \ *Title I:* $280,780 \ *Special Education:* $436,000 \ *Open-Close:* 09/05 - 06/11 \ *DTBP:* $229 (High) \ f t

Dr William Wagner 1	Kim Sperling 2
Michael Matthews 3,5,68,74	Joe Dianetti 6
Melanie Wightman 8,285,288	Janice Price 11,36,57,58,69,77,271,296
Matt Dunlap 16,73,295*	Joe Shucofsky 67
Amanda Lloyd 71	

Public Schs..Principal	Grd	Prgm	Enr/#Cls	SN
Fairview High Sch 4507 W 213th St, Fairview Park 44126 Christopher Vicha	9-12		519 35	28% 440/356-3500 Fax 440/356-3529
Gilles-Sweet Elem Sch 4320 W 220th St, Fairview Park 44126 Barbara Brady	1-5		637 17	31% 440/356-3525 Fax 440/356-3701 f t
Lewis F Mayer Middle Sch 21200 Campus Dr, Fairview Park 44126 Chris Vicha	6-8		396 15	31% 440/356-3510 Fax 440/895-2191
Parkview Early Education Ctr 21620 Mastick Rd # B, Fairview Park 44126 Trish Moran	PK-K		150	440/356-3515 Fax 440/356-3544

- **Garfield Heights City SD** PID: 00793350   216/475-8100
  5640 Briarcliff Dr, Garfield HTS 44125   Fax 216/475-1824

Schools: 6 \ *Teachers:* 211 \ *Students:* 3,721 \ *Special Ed Students:* 698 \ *LEP Students:* 24 \ *College-Bound:* 41% \ *Ethnic:* Asian 1%, African American 74%, Hispanic 3%, Caucasian 21% \ *Exp:* $148 (Low) \ *Poverty:* 29% \ *Title I:* $2,182,567 \ *Special Education:* $857,000 \ *Open-Close:* 08/22 - 05/29 \ *DTBP:* $194 (High) \ f t

Chris Hanke 1	Allen Sluka 2
Kathy Hanus 2	David Palmer 3
Carrie Bergholz 5	Dale Krzynowek 6*
Leanne Reisland 8	Shari Bailey 16,73,295,297
Dr Gordon DuPree 57,79,91	Brooke Pillets 58
Gary Wolske 67	Judy Saxon 74
Kathy Baylog 81	Jim Kosuda 295

Public Schs..Principal	Grd	Prgm	Enr/#Cls	SN
Elmwood Elem Sch 5275 Turney Rd, Garfield HTS 44125 Gwen Abraham	K-5	T	415 18	96% 216/475-8110 Fax 216/475-8371
Garfield Heights High Sch 4900 Turney Rd, Cleveland 44125 Tammy Hager	9-12	ATV	1,203 60	62% 216/662-2800 Fax 216/271-6183
ⓐ Garfield Heights Learning Ctr 12000 Maple Leaf Dr, Cleveland 44125 Lemon Bradford	8-12		125	216/475-8105 Fax 216/475-8146
Garfield Heights Middle Sch 12000 Maple Leaf Dr, Garfield HTS 44125 Chris Sauer	6-8	T	1,000 38	72% 216/475-8105 Fax 216/465-8146
Maple Leaf Elem Sch 5764 Turney Rd, Garfield HTS 44125 Jean Rizi	K-5	T	505 22	83% 216/662-3800 Fax 216/662-9949 f t
William Foster Elem Sch 12801 Bangor Ave, Garfield HTS 44125 Brynn Morris	PK-5	T	671 25	78% 216/475-8123 Fax 216/475-8080

- **Independence Local School Dist** PID: 00793439   216/642-5850
  7733 Stone Rd, Independence 44131   Fax 216/642-3482

Schools: 3 \ *Teachers:* 78 \ *Students:* 1,075 \ *Special Ed Students:* 111 \ *LEP Students:* 7 \ *College-Bound:* 82% \ *Ethnic:* Asian 1%, African American 1%, Hispanic 1%, Caucasian 97% \ *Exp:* $372 (High) \ *Poverty:* 6% \ *Title I:* $92,829 \ *Open-Close:* 08/28 - 06/09 \ *DTBP:* $233 (High) \ f

Ben Hegedish 1	Eric Koehler 2
Annie McGhee 6,83,88	Mike Pennington ...8,11,31,35,69,73,273,295
Laura Janosek 16*	Mary Dolejs 36*
Sandra McCullough 58,275	Lynne Laski 67
Charlene Paparizos 71	

Public Schs..Principal	Grd	Prgm	Enr/#Cls	SN
Independence High Sch 6001 Archwood Rd, Independence 44131 William McGuinness	9-12		336 28	12% 216/642-5860 Fax 216/642-5881

1	Superintendent	8	Curric/Instruct K-12	19	Chief Financial Officer	29	Family/Consumer Science	39	Social Studies K-12	49	English/Lang Arts Elem	59	Special Education Elem	69	Academic Assessment
2	Bus/Finance/Purchasing	9	Curric/Instruct Elem	20	Art K-12	30	Adult Education	40	Social Studies Elem	50	English/Lang Arts Sec	60	Special Education Sec	70	Research/Development
3	Buildings And Grounds	10	Curric/Instruct Sec	21	Art Elem	31	Career/Sch-to-Work K-12	41	Social Studies Sec	51	Reading K-12	61	Foreign/World Lang K-12	71	Public Information
4	Food Service	11	Federal Program	22	Art Sec	32	Career/Sch-to-Work Elem	42	Science K-12	52	Reading Elem	62	Foreign/World Lang Elem	72	Summer School
5	Transportation	12	Title I	23	Music K-12	33	Career/Sch-to-Work Sec	43	Science Elem	53	Reading Sec	63	Foreign/World Lang Sec	73	Instructional Tech
6	Athletic	13	Title V	24	Music Elem	34	Early Childhood Ed	44	Science Sec	54	Remedial Reading K-12	64	Religious Education K-12	74	Inservice Training
7	Health Services	14	Instructional Media Svcs	25	Music Sec	35	Health/Phys Education	45	Math K-12	55	Remedial Reading Elem	65	Religious Education Elem	75	Marketing/Distributive
		15	Asst Superintendent	26	Business Education	36	Guidance Services K-12	46	Math Elem	56	Remedial Reading Sec	66	Religious Education Sec	76	Info Systems
		16	Chief Operations Officer	27	Career & Tech Ed	37	Guidance Services Elem	47	Math Sec	57	Bilingual/ELL	67	School Board President	77	Psychological Assess
		18	Chief Academic Officer	28	Technology Education	38	Guidance Services Sec	48	English/Lang Arts K-12	58	Special Education K-12	68	Teacher Personnel	78	Affirmative Action

Ohio School Directory — Cuyahoga County

Independence Middle Sch 5-8 333 10% 216/642-5865
6111 Archwood Rd, Independence 44131   25   Fax 216/642-1247
Jamie Vanek

Independence Primary Sch PK-4 406 10% 216/642-5870
7600 Hillside Rd, Independence 44131   38   Fax 216/642-5851
Tj Ebert

● Lakewood City School Dist   PID: 00793477   216/529-4000
1470 Warren Rd, Lakewood 44107   Fax 216/529-4273

Schools: 12 \ **Teachers:** 315 \ **Students:** 4,000 \ **Special Ed Students:** 703 \ **LEP Students:** 428 \ **College-Bound:** 68% \ **Ethnic:** Asian 6%, African American 9%, Hispanic 7%, Caucasian 77% \ **Exp:** $283 (Med) \ **Poverty:** 17% \ **Title I:** $1,629,934 \ **Special Education:** $1,342,000 \ **Open-Close:** 08/20 - 06/02 \ **DTBP:** $194 (High) \ [f]

Dr Michael Barnes 1
Christopher Donahoe 3,5
Sean Jackson 6
Dr Christine Palumbo 8,12,288
William Dimacio 27
Tess Yurick 30
Jeff Schlade 68
Elizabeth Rogel 79
Paul Kidd 79
Terrilynn Bornino-Elwell 88*
Kent Zeman 2,19
Nancy Early 4
Lisa Bruening 7,11,35,36,77,79,83,296
Maggie Niedzwicki 15
Teresa Yurik 30
Linda Beebe 67
Christine Gordillo 71
Gordana Dimacchia 79
Carissa Spitzer 81

Public Schs..Principal	Grd	Prgm	Enr/#Cls	SN	
Emerson Elem Sch 13439 Clifton Blvd, Lakewood 44107 Denice Leddy	PK-5	T	432 14	44%	216/529-4254 Fax 216/227-5752 [f]
Ⓐ Franklin School of Opportunity 13465 Franklin Blvd, Lakewood 44107 Terrilynn Bornino-Elwell	7-12		90 8		216/529-4037 Fax 216/227-5975 [f][t]
Garfield Middle Sch 13114 Detroit Ave, Lakewood 44107 Robin Beavers	6-8	T	530	54%	216/529-4241 Fax 216/529-4146 [f][t]
Grant Elem Sch 1470 Victoria Ave, Lakewood 44107 Kaitlyn Turner	PK-5	T	325 17	32%	216/529-4217 Fax 216/227-5535
Harding Middle Sch 16601 Madison Ave, Lakewood 44107 Joe Niemantsverdri	6-8	T	581 35	31%	216/529-4261 Fax 216/529-4708 [f][t]
Harrison Elem Sch 2080 Quail St, Lakewood 44107 Sabrina Crawford	PK-5	T	364 11	77%	216/529-4230 Fax 216/227-5556
Hayes Elem Sch 16401 Delaware Ave, Lakewood 44107 Sandra Powers	PK-5	T	355 21	37%	216/529-4228 Fax 216/227-5575 [f][t]
Horace Mann Elem Sch 1215 W Clifton Blvd, Lakewood 44107 Merritt Waters	PK-5	T	302 10	44%	216/529-4257 Fax 216/227-5828 [f][t]
Lakewood High Sch 14100 Franklin Blvd, Lakewood 44107 Mark Walter	9-12	AGTV	1,453	40%	216/529-4028 Fax 216/529-4459 [f][t]
Lincoln Elem Sch 15615 Clifton Blvd, Lakewood 44107 Sandra Kozlaka	PK-5	T	281 19	31%	216/529-4232 Fax 216/227-5722
Roosevelt Elem Sch 14237 Athens Ave, Lakewood 44107 Allison Aber	PK-5	T	290 10	44%	216/529-4224 Fax 216/227-5739
West Shore Career & Tech Sch 14100 Franklin Blvd, Lakewood 44107 William DiMascio	Voc		800		216/529-4163 Fax 216/529-5172 [f][t]

● Maple Heights City School Dist   PID: 00793623   216/587-6100
5740 Lawn Ave, Maple Heights 44137   Fax 216/518-2674

Schools: 5 \ **Teachers:** 192 \ **Students:** 3,800 \ **Special Ed Students:** 550 \ **College-Bound:** 40% \ **Ethnic:** African American 95%, Hispanic 2%, Caucasian 2% \ **Exp:** $179 (Low) \ **Poverty:** 35% \ **Title I:** $2,599,257 \ **Special Education:** $863,000 \ **Open-Close:** 08/21 - 06/03 \ **DTBP:** $177 (High)

Dr Charles Keenan 1
Virgil Calloway 3
Nicholas Kaliszewski 6*
Frank Major 11,68,79*
Dr Meghan Shelby 57,58,77,83
Richard Richey 91*
Muata Niamke 2,4
Charinita McDonald 5
Susan Jaroscak 8,11,69,275,285,288,296,298
Michael May 11,68,79
Pam Crews 67

Public Schs..Principal	Grd	Prgm	Enr/#Cls	SN	
Abraham Lincoln Elem Sch 6009 Dunham Rd, Maple Heights 44137 Dawn Besteder	PK-1	T	559 23		216/438-6030 Fax 216/587-4376
Barack Obama Sch 5800 Glenwood Ave, Maple Heights 44137 Dr Octavia Reid	4-5	T	585 29		216/438-6020 Fax 216/587-4269
J F Kennedy Sch 5933 Dunham Rd, Maple Heights 44137 Valencia Thomas	2-3	T	533 26		216/438-6010 Fax 216/587-4187
Maple Heights High Sch 1 Mustang Way, Maple Heights 44137 Zelina Pames	9-12	AV	1,082 70		216/438-6400 Fax 216/587-3259
Milkovich Middle Sch 19800 Stafford Ave, Maple Heights 44137 Matthew Bennett	6-8	T	857 45		216/438-6000 Fax 216/587-4523

● Mayfield City School Dist   PID: 00793714   440/995-6800
1101 Som Center Rd, Mayfield HTS 44124   Fax 440/995-7205

Schools: 6 \ **Teachers:** 515 \ **Students:** 4,000 \ **Special Ed Students:** 519 \ **LEP Students:** 171 \ **College-Bound:** 74% \ **Ethnic:** Asian 8%, African American 19%, Hispanic 3%, Caucasian 69% \ **Exp:** $143 (Low) \ **Poverty:** 7% \ **Title I:** $394,238 \ **Special Education:** $860,000 \ **Open-Close:** 08/15 - 05/28 \ **DTBP:** $203 (High)

Dr Keith Kelly 1
Steve Nedlik 2
Robin Smeal 4*
Keith Lessler 6
Victoria Loncar 8,12,273
Sue Groszek 67
Andrew Fetchik 2,68,79
Ken Taylor 3
Megan Kaiser 5*
Denise Cirino 7,36,57,58,69,81,88,275
John Duplay 16,73,286*
Laurie Uhlir 71

Public Schs..Principal	Grd	Prgm	Enr/#Cls	SN	
Gates Mills Elem Sch 7639 Colvin Rd, Gates Mills 44040 Laurel Ravida	K-5		129 6	23%	440/995-7500 Fax 440/995-7505
Lander Elem Sch 1714 Lander Rd, Mayfield HTS 44124 Felecia Evans	K-5		502 25	33%	440/995-7350 Fax 440/995-7355
Mayfield Center Elem Sch 6625 Wilson Mills Rd, Mayfield VLG 44143 Katharine Rateno	K-5		455 26	17%	440/995-7400 Fax 440/995-7405
Mayfield High Sch 6116 Wilson Mills Rd, Mayfield VLG 44143 Jeffrey Legan	9-12	V	1,700 100	20%	440/995-6900 Fax 440/995-6805
Mayfield Middle Sch 1123 Som Center Rd, Mayfield HTS 44124 Paul Destino	6-8		904 28	16%	440/995-7800 Fax 440/449-1413 [f][t]

---

79 Student Personnel	91 Safety/Security	275 Response To Intervention	298 Grant Writer/Ptnrships	**School Programs**	**Social Media**
80 Driver Ed/Safety	92 Magnet School	277 Remedial Math K-12	750 Chief Innovation Officer	A = Alternative Program	[f] = Facebook
81 Gifted/Talented	93 Parental Involvement	280 Literacy Coach	751 Chief of Staff	G = Adult Classes	[t] = Twitter
82 Video Services	95 Tech Prep Program	285 STEM	752 Social Emotional Learning	M = Magnet Program	
83 Substance Abuse Prev	97 Chief Information Officer	286 Digital Learning		T = Title I Schoolwide	
84 Erate	98 Chief Technology Officer	288 Common Core Standards	**Other School Types**	V = Career & Tech Ed Programs	
85 AIDS Education	270 Character Education	294 Accountability	Ⓐ = Alternative School		
86 Alternative/At Risk	271 Migrant Education	295 Network System	Ⓒ = Charter School	**New Schools are shaded**	
89 Multi-Cultural Curriculum	273 Teacher Mentor	296 Title II Programs	Ⓜ = Magnet School	**New Superintendents and Principals are bold**	
90 Social Work	274 Before/After Sch	297 Webmaster	Ⓨ = Year-Round School	Personnel with email addresses are underscored	

OH—47

Cuyahoga County

Millridge Elem Sch   PK-5   603   21% **440/995-7250**
962 Millridge Rd, Highland Hgts 44143   24   Fax 440/995-7255
Craig Caroff

- **North Olmsted City School Dist**   PID: 00793817   **440/588-5300**
  26669 Butternut Ridge Rd, North Olmsted 44070   Fax 440/588-5370

Schools: 8 \ *Teachers:* 216 \ *Students:* 3,900 \ *Special Ed Students:* 504 \ *LEP Students:* 291 \ *College-Bound:* 70% \ *Ethnic:* Asian 2%, African American 4%, Hispanic 8%, Caucasian 86% \ *Exp:* $108 (Low) \ *Poverty:* 17% \ *Title I:* $1,086,330 \ *Special Education:* $720,000 \ *Open-Close:* 08/26 - 06/03 \ *DTBP:* $195 (High)

Dr Michael Zalar 1	Robert Matson 2,11
Patty Kinch 4	David Leigh 5
Michael McDade 5,73	Michael Ptacek 6*
Scott Moore 8	Priscilla Wiles 16*
Brigid Reese 31*	Terry Groden 67
Leah Blaze 73	Amy Younglas 76
Chris Caleris 79	Dr Heather Keenan 81

Public Schs..Principal	Grd	Prgm	Enr/#Cls	SN	
Birch Primary Sch 24100 Palm Dr, North Olmsted 44070 Frank Samerigo	K-2	T	358 28	47%	**440/779-3570** Fax 440/779-3521
Chestnut Intermediate Sch 30395 Lorain Rd, North Olmsted 44070 Brent Monnin	3-5		266 12	37%	**440/779-3641** Fax 440/779-3645
Forest Primary Sch 28963 Tudor Dr, North Olmsted 44070 Denise Ressler	PK-2	T	331 11	37%	**440/779-3527** Fax 440/779-3529
Maple Intermediate Sch 24101 Maple Ridge Rd, North Olmsted 44070 Jim Alexandrou	3-5	T	249 35	51%	**440/779-3533** Fax 440/779-3617
North Olmsted High Sch 27301 Butternut Ridge Rd, North Olmsted 44070 Zach Weagley	9-12	V	1,239 80	33%	**440/779-8825** Fax 440/777-2216
North Olmsted Middle Sch 27401 Butternut Ridge Rd, North Olmsted 44070 Bryan Busold	6-8	T	852 60	41%	**440/588-5700** Fax 440/588-5724
Pine Intermediate Sch 4267 Dover Center Rd, North Olmsted 44070 Terese D'Amico	3-5		279	46%	**440/779-3536** Fax 440/779-3618
Spruce Primary Sch 28590 Windsor Dr, North Olmsted 44070 Mary McDade	PK-2	T	213 9	28%	**440/779-3541** Fax 440/779-3542

- **North Royalton City Sch Dist**   PID: 00793922   **440/237-8800**
  6579 Royalton Rd, N Royalton 44133   Fax 440/582-7336

Schools: 5 \ *Teachers:* 223 \ *Students:* 4,060 \ *Special Ed Students:* 456 \ *LEP Students:* 159 \ *College-Bound:* 81% \ *Ethnic:* Asian 6%, African American 2%, Hispanic 3%, Caucasian 89% \ *Exp:* $140 (Low) \ *Poverty:* 7% \ *Title I:* $436,642 \ *Special Education:* $787,000 \ *Open-Close:* 08/19 - 05/29 \ *DTBP:* $191 (High)

Greg Gurka 1	Laura Petroff 2
Brian Clark 3	Mary Ellen Figgi 4
Greg Hovan 5	Carolyn Baetjer 7*
Melissa Vojta 8,69,288,294	James Presot 15
Julie Bogden 36,58,81,83*	Cristina Zukowski 58
Dr John Kelly 67	Patrick Farrell 68
Charlene Paparizos 71	John Nickell 73,76*
Tricia Pozsgai 73,286	Beth Burdick 81

Public Schs..Principal	Grd	Prgm	Enr/#Cls	SN	
Albion Elem Sch 9360 Albion Rd, N Royalton 44133 Vince Ketterer	K-4		468 25	15%	**440/582-9060** Fax 440/230-5100
North Royalton High Sch 14713 Ridge Rd, N Royalton 44133 Sean Osborne	9-12	V	1,461 60	14%	**440/582-7801** Fax 440/582-7337
North Royalton Middle Sch 14709 Ridge Rd, N Royalton 44133 Jeff Cicerchi	5-8		1,253 80	15%	**440/582-9120** Fax 440/582-7229
Royalview Elem Sch 13220 Ridge Rd, N Royalton 44133 Kirk Pavelich	PK-4		486 20	17%	**440/582-9080** Fax 440/582-7254
Valley Vista Elem Sch 4049 Wallings Rd, N Royalton 44133 Jeffrey Hill	K-4		392 19	15%	**440/582-9101** Fax 440/582-7239

- **Olmsted Falls City School Dist**   PID: 00793972   **440/427-6000**
  26937 Bagley Rd, Olmsted Falls 44138   Fax 440/427-6010

Schools: 5 \ *Teachers:* 188 \ *Students:* 3,628 \ *Special Ed Students:* 456 \ *LEP Students:* 36 \ *College-Bound:* 75% \ *Ethnic:* Asian 2%, African American 2%, Hispanic 2%, Caucasian 94% \ *Exp:* $165 (Low) \ *Poverty:* 6% \ *Title I:* $299,117 \ *Special Education:* $714,000 \ *Open-Close:* 08/28 - 06/09 \ *DTBP:* $195 (High)

Dr James Lloyd 1	Timothy Atkinson 2,3,5,91
Denise Tabar 4*	Heath Krakowiak 5
Rob Coxton 6*	Kelli Cogan 8,15,69,74,273,288
Shannon Goss 11,54,58,77,79,81,92,296	Maridi Gurtsak 36*
Lisa Palmison 38*	Holly Neumann 67
James Tatman 68	Kim Petrina 71
Joseph Magrey 73,95,295*	Tim Wulfhoop 294

Public Schs..Principal	Grd	Prgm	Enr/#Cls	SN	
Falls-Lennox Primary Sch 26450 Bagley Rd, Olmsted Falls 44138 Lisa Williams	1-3		702 40	18%	**440/427-6400** Fax 440/427-6410
Olmsted Falls Early Chldhd Ctr 7105 Fitch Rd, Olmsted Falls 44138 Melinda Falconi	PK-K		297	10%	**440/427-6360** Fax 440/427-6370
Olmsted Falls High Sch 26939 Bagley Rd, Olmsted Falls 44138 Leo Spagnola	9-12	V	1,265 50	13%	**440/427-6100** Fax 440/427-6110
Olmsted Falls Intermediate Sch 27043 Bagley Rd, Olmsted Falls 44138 Donald Svec	4-5		510 20	19%	**440/427-6500** Fax 440/427-6510
Olmsted Falls Middle Sch 27045 Bagley Rd, Olmsted Falls 44138 Mark Kurz	6-8		854	15%	**440/427-6200** Fax 440/427-6210

- **Orange City School Dist**   PID: 00794031   **216/831-8600**
  32000 Chagrin Blvd, Pepper Pike 44124   Fax 216/831-8029

Schools: 4 \ *Teachers:* 140 \ *Students:* 2,000 \ *Special Ed Students:* 319 \ *LEP Students:* 44 \ *College-Bound:* 88% \ *Ethnic:* Asian 7%, African American 20%, Hispanic 2%, Caucasian 71% \ *Exp:* $146 (Low) \ *Poverty:* 8% \ *Title I:* $241,815 \ *Special Education:* $416,000 \ *Open-Close:* 08/19 - 06/04 \ *DTBP:* $251 (High) \ 🅕 🅣

Dr Lynn Campbell 1	Ted Roseberry 2,91
Todd Puster 2,19	Gina Battaglia 3
Cindy Alekna 4*	Larry Lerch 5
Karen Moore 11,288	Jill Karsok 30
Maria Hill 34	Kershini Naidu 58
Beth Wilson-Fish 67	Lou DeVincentis 71

---

1 Superintendent	8 Curric/Instruct K-12	19 Chief Financial Officer	29 Family/Consumer Science	39 Social Studies K-12	49 English/Lang Arts Elem	59 Special Education Elem	69 Academic Assessment
2 Bus/Finance/Purchasing	9 Curric/Instruct Elem	20 Art K-12	30 Adult Education	40 Social Studies Elem	50 English/Lang Arts Sec	60 Special Education Sec	70 Research/Development
3 Buildings And Grounds	10 Curric/Instruct Sec	21 Art Elem	31 Career/Sch-to-Work Elem	41 Social Studies Sec	51 Reading K-12	61 Foreign/World Lang K-12	71 Public Information
4 Food Service	11 Federal Program	22 Art Sec	32 Career/Sch-to-Work Elem	42 Science K-12	52 Reading Elem	62 Foreign/World Lang Elem	72 Summer School
5 Transportation	12 Title I	23 Music K-12	33 Career/Sch-to-Work Sec	43 Science Elem	53 Reading Sec	63 Foreign/World Lang Sec	73 Instructional Tech
6 Athletic	13 Title V	24 Music Elem	34 Early Childhood Ed	44 Science Sec	54 Remedial Reading K-12	64 Religious Education K-12	74 Inservice Training
7 Health Services	15 Asst Superintendent	25 Music Sec	35 Health/Phys Education	45 Math K-12	55 Remedial Reading Elem	65 Religious Education Elem	75 Marketing/Distributive
	16 Instructional Media Svcs	26 Business Education	36 Guidance Services K-12	46 Math Elem	56 Remedial Reading Sec	66 Religious Education Sec	76 Info Systems
	17 Chief Operations Officer	27 Career & Tech Ed	37 Guidance Services Elem	47 Math Sec	57 Bilingual/ELL	67 School Board President	77 Psychological Assess
	18 Chief Academic Officer	28 Technology Education	38 Guidance Services Sec	48 English/Lang Arts K-12	58 Special Education K-12	68 Teacher Personnel	78 Affirmative Action

Ohio School Directory — Cuyahoga County

Jeannette Irish-Glass .... 73,76,295,297 Judy Robinson 79

Public Schs..Principal	Grd	Prgm	Enr/#Cls	SN	
Ballard Brady Middle Sch Gail Allison Dr, Pepper Pike 44124 Brian Frank	6-8		448 42	14%	216/831-8600 Fax 216/839-1335 f t
Moreland Hills Elem Sch 32000 Chagrin Blvd, Pepper Pike 44124 Renee Tuttle	K-5		852	12%	216/831-8600 Fax 216/831-4298
Orange High Sch 32000 Chagrin Blvd, Pepper Pike 44124 Paul Lucas	9-12	V	693 50	15%	216/831-8600 Fax 216/831-2595 f t
Orange Inclusive Pre-School 32000 Chagrin Blvd, Pepper Pike 44124 Christine Goudy	PK-PK		44		216/831-8600 Fax 216/831-0963

● Parma City School Dist PID: 00794081
5311 Longwood Ave, Parma 44134
440/842-5300
Fax 440/885-8304

Schools: 15 \ *Teachers:* 593 \ *Students:* 10,712 \ *Special Ed Students:* 1,722 \ *LEP Students:* 249 \ *College-Bound:* 62% \ *Ethnic:* Asian 2%, African American 5%, Hispanic 10%, Caucasian 83% \ *Exp:* $172 (Low) \ *Poverty:* 15% \ *Title I:* $3,724,708 \ *Special Education:* $2,501,000 \ *Open-Close:* 08/21 - 05/25 \ *DTBP:* $216 (High) \ f

Charles Smialek 1	Sean Nuccio 2,19	
James Leigh 3,5	William Greene 3,17	
Robert Gorman 4	Michelle Kocar 9	
Jeff Cook 10,18	Ava Yeager 11	
Kristen Plageman 27,30	L'Taundra Everhart 58	
John Schweitzer 67	Patrick Hoy 68	
Debora Vanek 69,76,288	Pam Edmonds 79	
Drew Stevens 84,95	Rick Vanek 91	
Rosemarie Gross 274	Cheryl Meriwether 298	

Public Schs..Principal	Grd	Prgm	Enr/#Cls	SN	
Dentzler Elem Sch 3600 Dentzler Rd, Parma 44134 Renee Dzurnak	K-4	T	399 20	57%	440/885-2430 Fax 440/885-3704
Green Valley Elem Sch 2401 W Pleasant Valley Rd, Parma 44134 Jacqueline Marconi	K-4	T	335 16	32%	440/885-2433 Fax 440/885-3705 f
Greenbriar Middle Sch 11810 Huffman Rd, Parma 44130 Jill Schissler	5-7	GTV	857 55	55%	440/885-2370 Fax 440/885-8353
Hillside Middle Sch 1 Educational Park Dr, Seven Hills 44131 Michelle Cook	5-7	GTV	594 39	47%	440/885-2373 Fax 216/236-6056
John Muir Elem Sch 5531 W 24th St, Parma 44134 Karl Schneider	K-4	T	392 42	60%	440/885-2424 Fax 216/954-4251
Normandy High Sch 2500 W Pleasant Valley Rd, Parma 44134 Rachel Urban	8-12	GV	1,294 80	36%	440/885-2400 Fax 440/885-2402 f
Parma Park Elem Sch 6800 Commonwealth Blvd, Parma Heights 44130 Wendy Jewell	K-4	T	304 19	56%	440/885-2390 Fax 440/885-3707
Parma Senior High Sch 6285 W 54th St, Parma 44129 Leo Spagnola	8-12	GTV	1,520 94	58%	440/885-2300 Fax 440/888-0358
Pleasant Valley Elem Sch 9906 W Pleasant Valley Rd, Parma 44130 Stephanie Boka	K-4	T	803 30	45%	440/885-2380 Fax 440/885-8664 f
Pleasantview First Step Sch 7700 Malibu Dr, Parma 44130 Shelia Ullman	PK-PK		204 10		440/885-8665 Fax 440/842-9832
Renwood Elem Sch 8020 Deerfield Dr, Parma 44129 Lashonda Abdussatar	K-4	T	301 13	63%	440/885-2338 Fax 440/481-3494
Ridge-Brook Elem Sch 7915 Manhattan Ave, Parma 44129 Stephen Perry	K-4	T	319 16	69%	440/885-2350 Fax 440/885-3716
Shiloh Middle Sch 2303 Grantwood Dr, Parma 44134 Andrew Suttell	5-7	TV	680 64	63%	440/885-8485 Fax 440/885-8486
Thoreau Park Elem Sch 5401 W 54th St, Parma 44129 Theodore Bickley	K-4	T	374 26	68%	440/885-2351 Fax 216/954-4225
Valley Forge High Sch 9999 Independence Blvd, Parma Heights 44130 Janine Andrzejewski	8-12	GTV	1,455	50%	440/885-2330 Fax 440/885-8412 f

● Polaris Joint Voc School Dist PID: 01484825
7285 Old Oak Blvd, Middlebrg HTS 44130
440/891-7600
Fax 440/243-3952

Schools: 1 \ *Teachers:* 48 \ *Students:* 1,000 \ *Exp:* $329 (High) \ *Open-Close:* 08/21 - 06/01 \ *DTBP:* $230 (High) \ f t

Bob Timmons 1,11	Mike Robinson 2
Chris McCully 15*	Gerald Lanning 27,69,75*
Diane Xander 29,60,79,81*	Karen Rayk 30,57*
Richard Micho 67	Doug Miller 71*
Frank Olle 73,295	

Public Schs..Principal	Grd	Prgm	Enr/#Cls	SN	
Polaris Career Ctr High Sch 7285 Old Oak Blvd, Middlebrg HTS 44130 Gerald Lanning	Voc	G	1,000 30		440/891-7600

● Richmond Heights Local SD PID: 00794380
447 Richmond Rd, Richmond HTS 44143
216/692-0086
Fax 216/692-2820

Schools: 2 \ *Teachers:* 55 \ *Students:* 850 \ *Special Ed Students:* 141 \ *LEP Students:* 22 \ *College-Bound:* 48% \ *Ethnic:* Asian 3%, African American 91%, Hispanic 1%, Caucasian 5% \ *Exp:* $180 (Low) \ *Poverty:* 20% \ *Title I:* $364,109 \ *Special Education:* $147,000 \ *Open-Close:* 08/14 - 05/28 \ *DTBP:* $267 (High)

Dr Renee Willis 1	Cooper Martin 2,19
Don Ferritto 3	Phil Stevens 3,5,91*
Ann Demell 4*	Quentin Rogers 6*
Maraday Chhay 57*	Lakisha Davies 58
Nneka Slade Jackson 67	Joy Howard 73
Kelly Askew 298	

Public Schs..Principal	Grd	Prgm	Enr/#Cls	SN	
Richmond Heights Elem Sch 447 Richmond Rd, Richmond HTS 44143 Elizabeth Boyd	PK-6	T	449 23	75%	216/692-0099 Fax 216/692-8499
Richmond Heights Secondary Sch 447 Richmond Rd, Richmond HTS 44143 Marnisha Brown	7-12	T	342 25	67%	216/692-0094 Fax 216/692-8495

---

79 Student Personnel	91 Safety/Security	275 Response To Intervention	298 Grant Writer/Ptnrships	**School Programs**	**Social Media**
80 Driver Ed/Safety	92 Magnet School	277 Remedial Math K-12	750 Chief Innovation Officer	A = Alternative Program	f = Facebook
81 Gifted/Talented	93 Parental Involvement	280 Literacy Coach	751 Chief of Staff	G = Adult Classes	t = Twitter
82 Video Services	95 Tech Prep Program	285 STEM	752 Social Emotional Learning	M = Magnet Program	
83 Substance Abuse Prev	97 Chief Information Officer	286 Digital Learning		T = Title I Schoolwide	
84 Erate	98 Chief Technology Officer	288 Common Core Standards	**Other School Types**	V = Career & Tech Ed Programs	
85 AIDS Education	270 Accountability	294 Accountability	Ⓐ = Alternative School		
88 Alternative/At Risk	271 Migrant Education	295 Network System	Ⓒ = Charter School	New Schools are shaded	
89 Multi-Cultural Curriculum	273 Teacher Mentor	296 Title II Programs	Ⓜ = Magnet School	New Superintendents and Principals are bold	
90 Social Work	274 Before/After Sch	297 Webmaster	Ⓨ = Year-Round School	Personnel with email addresses are underscored	

Cuyahoga County

Rocky River City School Dist PID: 00794421 440/356-6000
1101 Morewood Pkwy, Rocky River 44116   Fax 440/356-6014

Schools: 5 \ **Teachers:** 157 \ **Students:** 2,610 \ **Special Ed Students:** 288 \ **LEP Students:** 82 \ **College-Bound:** 87% \ **Ethnic:** Asian 2%, African American 2%, Hispanic 4%, Caucasian 92% \ **Exp:** $146 (Low) \ **Poverty:** 7% \ **Title I:** $256,713 \ **Special Education:** $719,000 \ **Open-Close:** 08/21 - 06/04 \ **DTBP:** $193 (High) \

Dr Michael Shoaf 1	Greg Markus 2
Adam Sywanyk 3*	Tina Wasserbauer 4
Erin Peacock 5*	Mark Wagner 6*
Elizabeth Anderson 8,11,15,73,81,273,288,296	Jennifer Norman 11,27,34,57,58,69,83,88
Julie Morriss 36*	Ruth Beach 67
Sam Gifford 68,298	Dr Bryan Drost 71,73,76,91,286,295
Stacy Kozar Kocsis 77*	

Public Schs..Principal	Grd	Prgm	Enr/#Cls	SN	
Beach Sch 1101 Morewood Pkwy, Rocky River 44116 Tara Marley	PK-PK		76		440/356-6000 Fax 440/356-6008
Goldwood Primary Sch 21600 Center Ridge Rd, Rocky River 44116 Dr Carol Rosiak	K-2		532		440/356-6720 Fax 440/356-6044
Kensington Intermediate Sch 20140 Lake Rd, Rocky River 44116 Todd Murphy	3-5		577 24		440/356-6770 Fax 440/356-6050
Rocky River High Sch 20951 Detroit Rd, Rocky River 44116 Rob Winton	9-12		871 46	11%	440/356-6800 Fax 440/331-2189
Rocky River Middle Sch 1631 Lakeview Ave, Rocky River 44116 Megan Rose	6-8		669 40	13%	440/356-6870 Fax 440/356-6881

Shaker Heights City Sch Dist PID: 00794500 216/295-1400
15600 Parkland Dr, Shaker HTS 44120   Fax 216/295-4344

Schools: 9 \ **Teachers:** 345 \ **Students:** 5,180 \ **Special Ed Students:** 763 \ **LEP Students:** 130 \ **College-Bound:** 75% \ **Ethnic:** Asian 4%, African American 49%, Hispanic 3%, Caucasian 44% \ **Exp:** $311 (High) \ **Poverty:** 11% \ **Title I:** $815,407 \ **Special Education:** $997,000 \ **Open-Close:** 08/21 - 06/03 \ **DTBP:** $227 (High) \

Dr David Glasner 1	David Boyer 3
Mark Jacobs 4	Erin Spevak 5
Mickey Crantz 8,11,15,57	John Rizzo 16,73
Jeff Grosse 17	Dr Marla Robinson 18
Jeffrey Isaacs 67	Dr Erin Herbruck 68,74
Scott Stephens 71	Chris Rateno 76,294
Elizabeth Kimmel 79	Vic Ferrell 91
Keith Langford 93	

Public Schs..Principal	Grd	Prgm	Enr/#Cls	SN	
Boulevard Elem Sch 14900 Drexmore Rd, Shaker HTS 44120 Neal Robinson	K-4		326 18	38%	216/295-4020 Fax 216/295-4019
Fernway Elem Sch 17420 Fernway Rd, Shaker HTS 44120 Christopher Hayward	K-4		292 15	27%	216/295-4040 Fax 216/295-4036
Lomond Elem Sch 17917 Lomond Blvd, Shaker HTS 44122 George Clark	PK-4	T	374 24	51%	216/295-4050 Fax 216/295-4016
Mercer Elem Sch 23325 Wimbledon Rd, Shaker HTS 44122 J Lindsay Florence	PK-4		352 20	25%	216/295-4070 Fax 216/295-4017
Onaway Elem Sch 3115 Woodbury Rd, Shaker HTS 44120 Eric Forman	PK-4		395 24	29%	216/295-4080 Fax 216/295-4018
Shaker Heights High Sch 15911 Aldersyde Dr, Shaker HTS 44120 Eric Juli	9-12	AV	1,640	35%	216/295-4200 Fax 216/295-4277
Shaker Heights Middle Sch 20600 Shaker Blvd, Shaker HTS 44122 Miata Hunter	7-8	TV	775 57	33%	216/295-4100 Fax 216/295-4129
Shaker Hts HS-the IC 3450 Lee Rd, Shaker HTS 44120 Dr Ann Spurrier	9-12	AV	80		216/295-6272 Fax 216/991-2015
Woodbury Elem Sch 15400 S Woodland Rd, Shaker HTS 44120 H Danny Young	5-6		763 35	36%	216/295-4150 Fax 216/295-4032

Solon City School Dist PID: 00794639 440/248-1600
33800 Inwood Dr, Solon 44139   Fax 440/248-7665

Schools: 7 \ **Teachers:** 259 \ **Students:** 4,547 \ **Special Ed Students:** 464 \ **LEP Students:** 227 \ **College-Bound:** 84% \ **Ethnic:** Asian 20%, African American 16%, Hispanic 3%, Caucasian 62% \ **Exp:** $202 (Med) \ **Poverty:** 7% \ **Title I:** $429,766 \ **Special Education:** $850,000 \ **Open-Close:** 08/21 - 06/04 \ **DTBP:** $193 (High) \

Joseph Regano 1	Fred Bolden 2,15,68
Lyn Huchinson 4	Lisa Shirkey 5
Jim Mquaide 6	Tebra Page 7,36,57,58,77,79,92,294
Debbie Siegel 8,11,83,88,285,288,296,298	Tamara Strom 16,71
Mary Simecek 27,31*	Kirk Miller 28,73,76,84,95,286,295
John Heckman 67	Joseph Ferencie 82*
Jeff Pedicino 91*	Anne Dellamorte 93
Brynt Sines 297*	

Public Schs..Principal	Grd	Prgm	Enr/#Cls	SN	
Dorothy E Lewis Elem Sch 32345 Cannon Rd, Solon 44139 Mike Acomb	K-4		518 17	11%	440/349-6225 Fax 440/349-8012
Grace L Roxbury Elem Sch 6795 Solon Blvd, Solon 44139 Mariann Moeschberger	K-4		507 19	10%	440/349-6220 Fax 440/349-8048
Orchard Middle Sch 6800 Som Center Rd, Solon 44139 Cariann Mineard	5-6		640 33	10%	440/349-7252 Fax 440/349-8054
Parkside Elem Sch 6845 Som Center Rd, Solon 44139 Amanda Sullen	K-4		463 21	11%	440/349-2175 Fax 440/349-8055
Solon High Sch 33600 Inwood Dr, Solon 44139 Erin Short	9-12		1,601 90	9%	440/349-6230 Fax 440/349-8041
Solon Middle Sch 6835 Som Center Rd, Solon 44139 Scott Hatteberg	7-8		730 60	10%	440/349-3848 Fax 440/349-8034
Solon Pre-Chool 33425 Arthur Rd, Solon 44139 Terry Brownlow	PK-PK		74	8%	440/349-6210 Fax 440/349-8018

South Euclid-Lyndhurst City SD PID: 00794691 216/691-2000
5044 Mayfield Rd, Lyndhurst 44124   Fax 216/691-2033

Schools: 6 \ **Teachers:** 205 \ **Students:** 3,500 \ **Special Ed Students:** 587 \ **LEP Students:** 57 \ **College-Bound:** 52% \ **Ethnic:** Asian 2%, African American 74%, Hispanic 3%, Caucasian 21% \ **Exp:** $349 (High) \ **Poverty:** 14% \ **Title I:** $1,105,520 \ **Special Education:** $955,000 \ **Open-Close:** 08/15 - 05/28 \ **DTBP:** $201 (High) \

---

1 Superintendent	8 Curric/Instruct K-12	19 Chief Financial Officer	29 Family/Consumer Science	39 Social Studies K-12	49 English/Lang Arts Elem	59 Special Education Elem	69 Academic Assessment
2 Bus/Finance/Purchasing	9 Curric/Instruct Elem	20 Art K-12	30 Adult Education	40 Social Studies Elem	50 English/Lang Arts Sec	60 Special Education Sec	70 Research/Development
3 Buildings And Grounds	10 Curric/Instruct Sec	21 Art Elem	31 Career/Sch-to-Work K-12	41 Social Studies Sec	51 Reading K-12	61 Foreign/World Lang K-12	71 Public Information
4 Food Service	11 Federal Program	22 Art Sec	32 Career/Sch-to-Work Elem	42 Science K-12	52 Reading Elem	62 Foreign/World Lang Elem	72 Summer School
5 Transportation	12 Title I	23 Music K-12	33 Career/Sch-to-Work Sec	43 Science Elem	53 Reading Sec	63 Foreign/World Lang Sec	73 Instructional Tech
6 Athletic	13 Title V	24 Music Elem	34 Early Childhood Ed	44 Science Sec	54 Remedial Reading K-12	64 Religious Education K-12	74 Inservice Training
7 Health Services	15 Asst Superintendent	25 Music Sec	35 Health/Phys Education	45 Math K-12	55 Remedial Reading Elem	65 Religious Education Elem	75 Marketing/Distributive
	16 Instructional Media Svcs	26 Business Education	36 Guidance Services K-12	46 Math Elem	56 Remedial Reading Sec	66 Religious Education Sec	76 Info Systems
	17 Chief Operations Officer	27 Career & Tech Ed	37 Guidance Services Elem	47 Math Sec	57 Bilingual/ELL	67 School Board President	77 Psychological Assess
	18 Chief Academic Officer	28 Technology Education	38 Guidance Services Sec	48 English/Lang Arts K-12	58 Special Education K-12	68 Teacher Personnel	78 Affirmative Action

Ohio School Directory — Cuyahoga County

Linda Reid 1	Dana Stearns 3,4,5,73,91
Kevin Needham 4*	Lee Heitman 5
Mike Murphy 6,35,85*	Melissa Thompson 7,79,90
Karen Valenza 8	Dr Veronica Motley 8,12,15,16,72,73,74,81
Ben Moles 34,57,58,69,77	Stephanie Rhine 67
William Miller 68,78	Ron Johnson 69
Joe Allessandro 73*	

Public Schs..Principal	Grd	Prgm	Enr/#Cls	SN	
Adrian Elem Sch 1071 Homestead Rd, Cleveland 44121 Kenneth Lasky	K-3	T	273 14	62%	216/691-2170 Fax 216/691-2295
Brush High Sch 4875 Glenlyn Rd, Lyndhurst 44124 Karl Williamson	9-12	AV	1,132 100	41%	216/691-2065 Fax 216/691-2064
Greenview Upper Elem Sch 1825 S Green Rd, South Euclid 44121 Kelly Murphy	4-6	T	703 36	56%	216/691-2245 Fax 216/691-3482
Memorial Junior High Sch 1250 Professor Rd, Cleveland 44124 Dominick Kaple	7-8	T	508 50	53%	216/691-2141 Fax 216/691-2159 f t
Rowland Elem Sch 4300 Bayard Rd, South Euclid 44121 Maleeka Bussey	PK-3	T	441 21	53%	216/691-2200 Fax 216/691-2206
Sunview Elem Sch 5520 Meadow Wood Blvd, Lyndhurst 44124 Arika Taylor	K-3		304 18	31%	216/691-2225 Fax 216/691-2226 f t

● **Strongsville City School Dist** PID: 00794823   440/572-7010
18199 Cook Ave, Strongsville 44136   Fax 440/572-7041

Schools: 8 \ *Teachers:* 248 \ *Students:* 5,553 \ *Special Ed Students:* 622 \ *LEP Students:* 224 \ *College-Bound:* 79% \ *Ethnic:* Asian 6%, African American 3%, Hispanic 4%, Caucasian 87% \ *Exp:* $33 (Low) \ *Poverty:* 6% \ *Title I:* $573,021 \ *Special Education:* $1,159,000 \ *Open-Close:* 08/19 - 05/29 \ *DTBP:* $189 (High)

Dr Cameron Ryba 1	Stephen Breckner 2,3,4,5,76,91,286
Michael Nowosielski 4	Lori Senic 5
Denny Ziegler 6*	Perry Ziegler 6
Crystal Tackaberry 7*	Erin Green 8,11,57,69,81,288,296,298
Jennifer Pelko 15,68,74,78,273	David Binkley 16,73
David Binkley 16,73*	Andy Trujillo 58,79
Carl Naso 67	Elizabeth Burdick 81
James Hamelic 84	

Public Schs..Principal	Grd	Prgm	Enr/#Cls	SN	
Bessie Kinsner Elem Sch 19091 Waterford Pkwy, Strongsville 44149 **Steven Diedrick**	K-5		548 26	17%	440/572-7120 Fax 440/572-7125
Edith Whitney Elem Sch 13548 Whitney Rd, Strongsville 44136 Glen Stacho	K-5		413 21	33%	440/572-7180 Fax 440/572-7185
Edna Surrarrer Elem Sch 9306 Priem Rd, Strongsville 44136 Dr Sally Raso	K-5		349 14	14%	440/572-7170 Fax 440/572-7175
Helen Muraski Elem Sch 20270 Royalton Rd, Strongsville 44149 Justina Peters	K-5		490 20	25%	440/572-7160 Fax 440/572-7165
Howard Chapman Elem Sch 13883 Drake Rd, Strongsville 44136 Amy Moore	PK-5		355 20	23%	440/572-7140 Fax 440/572-7146 f t
Strongsville Early Learning PS 19543 Lunn Rd, Strongsville 44149 Megan Surso	PK-PK		102		440/572-7046 Fax 440/846-3227
Strongsville High Sch 20025 Lunn Rd, Strongsville 44149 **Joseph Mueller**	9-12	A	1,963 100	17%	440/572-7100 Fax 440/572-7107 f t
Strongsville Middle Sch 13200 Pearl Rd, Strongsville 44136 Adam Marino	6-8		1,279 20	20%	440/572-7090 Fax 440/572-7094

● **Warrensville Heights City SD** PID: 00794926   216/295-7710
4500 Warrensville Center Rd, Warrensvl HTS 44128   Fax 216/921-5902

Schools: 5 \ *Teachers:* 101 \ *Students:* 1,700 \ *Special Ed Students:* 330 \ *LEP Students:* 7 \ *College-Bound:* 44% \ *Ethnic:* African American 98%, Hispanic 1%, Caucasian 1% \ *Exp:* $356 (High) \ *Poverty:* 35% \ *Title I:* $1,618,076 \ *Special Education:* $360,000 \ *Open-Close:* 08/14 - 05/20 \ *DTBP:* $296 (High) \ f t

Donald Jolly 1	Dr Michael Rock 2
Robert Hayles 3	Jackie Thompson 4*
Matt Heinl 4	Elaine Callahan 5
Dr Tamea Caver 8,15,288	Ruth Ray 10
Arneice Basit 11,294,298	Jamie Lindsey 58
Traci Mitchell 67	Kenya Hunt 68
Bailey Morres 69	Kayla Pallas 71
Constance Rudolph 79	Thaddeus Hete 91
Dawnyell Smiley 93	Salina Miller 93
Mike Kromer 295	

Public Schs..Principal	Grd	Prgm	Enr/#Cls	SN	
Eastwood Elem Sch 4050 Eastwood Ln, Warrensvl HTS 44122 Andrea Bishop	4-5	T	223 15		216/336-6546 Fax 216/921-6463
John Dewey Elem Sch 23401 Emery Rd, Warrensvl HTS 44128 Takiba Thompson	PK-1	T	250 35		216/755-8743 Fax 216/921-5905
Warrensville Heights High Sch 4270 Northfield Rd, Warrensvl HTS 44128 Richard Reynolds	9-12	TV	537 36		216/336-6651 Fax 216/752-8116 f t
Warrensville Heights Mid Sch 4285 Warrensville Center Rd, Warrensvl HTS 44128 Lisa Braxton	6-8	T	356 45		216/336-6575 Fax 216/921-5813 f t
Westwood Elem Sch 19000 Garden Blvd, Cleveland 44128 Rafiq Vaughn	2-3		240		216/865-4934

● **Westlake City School Dist** PID: 00794990   440/871-7300
24525 Hilliard Blvd, Westlake 44145   Fax 440/871-6034

Schools: 4 \ *Teachers:* 219 \ *Students:* 3,500 \ *Special Ed Students:* 552 \ *LEP Students:* 250 \ *College-Bound:* 89% \ *Ethnic:* Asian 6%, African American 2%, Hispanic 6%, Caucasian 86% \ *Exp:* $204 (Med) \ *Poverty:* 8% \ *Title I:* $465,293 \ *Special Education:* $783,000 \ *Open-Close:* 08/29 - 06/11 \ *DTBP:* $191 (High) \ f t

Scott Goggin 1	Todd Hopkins 2,11,19,298
Dave Kocevar 3,4,84,91	Gavin Berwald 5
Tony Cipollone 6	Alex Flemming 8,12,74,273,296
Kathi Maxwell 15	Jacy Nichols 16,82*
Pete Zagray 16,73	Stephanie Morgan 36,58,69,79,81
Barb Leszynski 67	Brady Sheets 68,79
Kim Bonvissuto 71	Kathryn McGinty 83*
Lynda Appel 297	

Public Schs..Principal	Grd	Prgm	Enr/#Cls	SN	
Dover Intermediate Sch 2240 Dover Center Rd, Westlake 44145 Nicholas Miller	5-6		508 24	23%	440/835-5494 Fax 440/250-1060

79 Student Personnel	91 Safety/Security	275 Response To Intervention	298 Grant Writer/Ptnrships	**School Programs**	**Social Media**
80 Driver Ed/Safety	92 Magnet School	277 Remedial Math K-12	750 Chief Innovation Officer	A = Alternative Program	
81 Gifted/Talented	93 Parental Involvement	280 Literacy Coach	751 Chief of Staff	G = Adult Classes	f = Facebook
82 Video Services	95 Tech Prep Program	285 STEM	752 Social Emotional Learning	M = Magnet Program	
83 Substance Abuse Prev	97 Chief Information Officer	286 Digital Learning		T = Title I Schoolwide	t = Twitter
84 Erate	98 Chief Technology Officer	288 Common Core Standards	**Other School Types**	V = Career & Tech Ed Programs	
85 AIDS Education	270 Character Education	294 Accountability	Ⓐ = Alternative School		
88 Alternative/At Risk	271 Migrant Education	295 Network System	Ⓒ = Charter School	New Schools are shaded	
89 Multi-Cultural Curriculum	273 Teacher Mentor	296 Title II Programs	Ⓜ = Magnet School	New Superintendents and Principals are bold	
90 Social Work	274 Before/After Sch	297 Webmaster	Ⓨ = Year-Round School	Personnel with email addresses are underscored	

OH—51

Cuyahoga County

Lee Burneson Middle Sch — 7-8 — 573 / 32 — 20% — 440/835-6340 — Fax 440/808-8964
2260 Dover Center Rd, Westlake 44145
Amanda Musselman

West Lake Elem Sch — PK-4 — 1,231 / 18 — 22% — 440/250-1200 — Fax 440/250-1202
27555 Center Ridge Rd, Westlake 44145
Jim Sanifilippo

Westlake High Sch — 9-12 — 1,150 / 55 — 19% — 440/835-6352 — Fax 440/835-5572
27830 Hilliard Blvd, Westlake 44145
Paul Wilson

CUYAHOGA CATHOLIC SCHOOLS

• **Diocese of Cleveland Ed Office** PID: 00795308 216/696-6525 Fax 216/579-9655
1404 E 9th St, Cleveland 44114

Schools: 106 \ *Students:* 40,303

Listing includes only schools located in this county. See District Index for location of Diocesan Offices.

Frank O'Linn 1
Ed Morel 4
Monica Dietz 9,15
Tracey Arnone 9
Tom McBride 73
Dennis Beckstrom 2
Jenny Miroglotta 8
Susan Biggs 9,15
Pamela Ouzts 11
Denise Smithberger 74

Catholic Schs..Principal	Grd	Prgm	Enr/#Cls SN	Phone/Fax
Academy of St Adalbert 56 Adelbert St, Berea 44017 George Mitchell	PK-8		150 / 10	440/234-5529 Fax 440/234-2881
Academy of St Bartholomew 14875 Bagley Rd, Middlebrg HTS 44130 Elizabeth Palascak	PK-8		457 / 18	440/845-6660 Fax 440/845-6672
Archbishop Lyke-St Henry ES 18230 Harvard Ave, Cleveland 44128 Margarete Smith	K-8		200	216/991-9644 Fax 216/991-9470
Assumption Academy 9183 Broadview Rd, Broadview HTS 44147 Richard Kaliszewski	PK-8		150 / 20	440/526-4877 Fax 440/526-3752
Beaumont Sch 3301 N Park Blvd, Cleveland HTS 44118 Nicholas Beyer	9-12		335 / 35	216/321-2954 Fax 216/321-3947
Benedictine High Sch 2900 Martin Luther King Jr Dr, Cleveland 44104 Ryan Ryzner	9-12		352 / 35	216/421-2080 Fax 216/421-0107
Cleveland Central Catholic HS 6550 Baxter Ave, Cleveland 44105 Sr Allison Gusdanovic	9-12		560 / 30	216/441-4700 Fax 216/441-8353
Communion of Saints Sch 2160 Stillman Rd, Cleveland HTS 44118 Gerry Whiteley	K-8		268 / 13	216/932-4177 Fax 216/932-7439
Gesu Catholic Sch 2450 Miramar Blvd, University Ht 44118 Lucy Iemmolo	PK-8		741 / 27	216/932-0620 Fax 216/932-8326
Gilmour Academy 34001 Cedar Rd, Gates Mills 44040 Kathleen Kenny	PK-12		715 / 53	440/442-1104 Fax 440/473-8157
Holy Family Catholic Sch 7367 York Rd, Parma 44130 Thomas Brownfield	K-8		235 / 19	440/842-7785 Fax 440/842-3634
Holy Family Learning Center 14808 Lake Ave, Lakewood 44107 Jennifer Berardinelli	PK-PK		150 / 8	216/521-4352 Fax 216/521-0515
Holy Name Elem Sch 8328 Broadway Ave Rear, Cleveland 44105 Lorenzo Jones	K-8		177 / 15	216/341-0084 Fax 216/341-1122
Holy Name High Sch 6000 Queens Hwy, Parma Heights 44130 Shelbrey Blanc	9-12		605 / 44	440/886-0300 Fax 440/886-1267
Incarnate Word Academy 6620 Pearl Rd, Parma Heights 44130 Janette Cicerchi	PK-8		425 / 18	440/842-6818 Fax 440/888-1377
Julie Billiart Sch 4982 Clubside Rd, Cleveland 44124 Jodi Johnston	Spec		129 / 9	216/381-1191 Fax 216/381-2216
Lakewood Catholic Academy 14808 Lake Ave, Lakewood 44107 Brenna Warrell	PK-8		614 / 30	216/521-0559 Fax 216/521-0515
Magnificat High Sch 20770 Hilliard Blvd, Rocky River 44116 Kari Strathern	9-12		797 / 45	440/331-1572 Fax 440/331-7257
Mary Queen of Peace Sch 4419 Pearl Rd, Cleveland 44109 Jessica Robertson	PK-8		310 / 15	216/741-3685 Fax 216/741-5534
Metro Catholic Sch 1910 W 54th St, Cleveland 44102 Kari Strathern	PK-8		600 / 27	216/281-4044 Fax 216/634-2853
Our Lady Mt Carmel Sch 1355 W 70th St, Cleveland 44102 Shelley Schenek	PK-8		280 / 11	216/281-7146 Fax 216/281-7001
Our Lady of Angels Sch 3644 Rocky River Dr, Cleveland 44111 Kathy Krupar	PK-8		410 / 18	216/251-6841 Fax 216/251-7831
Our Lady of the Lake 175 E 200th St, Euclid 44119 Jennifer Millett	PK-8		334 / 18	216/481-6824 Fax 216/481-9841
Padua Franciscan High Sch 6740 State Rd, Parma 44134 David Stec	9-12		792	440/845-2444 Fax 440/845-5710
SS Agatha & Aloysius Sch 640 Lakeview Rd, Cleveland 44108 K Frank Jones	PK-8		194 / 9	216/451-2050 Fax 216/541-1601
SS Joseph & John Sch 12580 Pearl Rd, Strongsville 44136 Joseph Akosi	K-8		700 / 29	440/238-4877 Fax 440/238-8745
SS Robert & William Sch 351 E 260th St, Euclid 44132 Meg Cosgriff	PK-8		475 / 19	216/731-3066 Fax 216/731-0300
St Adalbert-Cleveland Sch 2345 E 83rd St, Cleveland 44104 James Smith	PK-8		234 / 10	216/881-6250 Fax 216/881-9030
St Albert the Great Sch 6667 Wallings Rd, N Royalton 44133 Edward Vittardi	K-8		787 / 34	440/237-1032 Fax 440/237-3308
St Angela Merici Sch 20830 Lorain Rd, Fairview Park 44126 Elizabeth Andrachik \ Lisa Whelan	K-8		454 / 40	440/333-2126 Fax 440/333-8480
St Anthony Padua Elem Sch 6800 State Rd, Parma 44134 Patrick Klimkewicz	K-8		229 / 12	440/845-3444 Fax 440/884-4548
St Benedict Catholic Sch 13633 Rockside Rd, Garfield HTS 44125 Lisa Oriti	K-8		391 / 18	216/662-9380 Fax 216/662-3137
St Bernadette Sch 2300 Clague Rd, Westlake 44145 Maureen Goodwin	K-8		365 / 20	440/734-7717 Fax 440/734-9198
St Brendan Sch 4242 Brendan Ln, North Olmsted 44070 Julie Onacila	PK-8		161 / 10	440/777-8433 Fax 440/779-7997

1 Superintendent	8 Curric/Instruct K-12	19 Chief Financial Officer
2 Bus/Finance/Purchasing	9 Curric/Instruct Elem	20 Art K-12
3 Buildings And Grounds	10 Curric/Instruct Sec	21 Art Elem
4 Food Service	11 Federal Program	22 Art Sec
5 Transportation	12 Title I	23 Music K-12
6 Athletic	13 Title V	24 Music Elem
7 Health Services	14 Asst Superintendent	25 Music Sec
	15 Instructional Media Svcs	26 Business Education
	16 Chief Operations Officer	27 Career & Tech Ed
	17 Chief Operations Officer	28 Technology Education
	18 Chief Academic Officer	

29 Family/Consumer Science	39 Social Studies K-12	49 English/Lang Arts Elem	59 Special Education Elem	69 Academic Assessment
30 Adult Education	40 Social Studies Elem	50 English/Lang Arts Sec	60 Special Education Sec	70 Research/Development
31 Career/Sch-to-Work K-12	41 Social Studies Sec	51 Reading K-12	61 Foreign/World Lang K-12	71 Public Information
32 Career/Sch-to-Work Elem	42 Science K-12	52 Reading Elem	62 Foreign/World Lang Elem	72 Summer School
33 Career/Sch-to-Work Sec	43 Science Elem	53 Reading Sec	63 Foreign/World Lang Sec	73 Instructional Tech
34 Early Childhood Ed	44 Science Sec	54 Remedial Reading K-12	64 Religious Education K-12	74 Inservice Training
35 Health/Phys Education	45 Math K-12	55 Remedial Reading Elem	65 Religious Education Elem	75 Marketing/Distributive
36 Guidance Services K-12	46 Math Elem	56 Remedial Reading Sec	66 Religious Education Sec	76 Info Systems
37 Guidance Services Elem	47 Math Sec	57 Bilingual/ELL	67 School Board President	77 Psychological Assess
38 Guidance Services Sec	48 English/Lang Arts K-12	58 Special Education K-12	68 Teacher Personnel	78 Affirmative Action

Ohio School Directory — Cuyahoga County

School	Grades	Prgm	Enr/#Cls	Phone
St Bridget of Kildare Sch 5620 Hauserman Rd, Parma 44130 Matt Falk	PK-8	G	200 10	440/886-1468 Fax 440/886-5121 [f][t]
St Charles Borromeo Sch 7107 Wilber Ave, Parma 44129 Eileen Updegrove	PK-8		375 24	440/886-5546 Fax 440/886-1163
St Christopher Sch 1610 Lakeview Ave, Rocky River 44116 Scott Raiff	K-8		310 19	440/331-3075 Fax 440/331-0674
St Columbkille Sch 6740 Broadview Rd, Parma 44134 Renee Cerny	PK-8		600 16	216/524-4816 Fax 216/524-4153 [f][t]
St Dominic Sch 3455 Norwood Rd, Beachwood 44122 Mrs Covington	K-8		200 15	216/561-4400 Fax 216/561-1573 [t]
St Edward High Sch 13500 Detroit Ave, Lakewood 44107 Kc McKenna	9-12		900 45	216/221-3776 Fax 216/221-4609 [t]
St Francis of Assisi Sch 6850 Mayfield Rd, Gates Mills 44040 Susan Herman	PK-8		458 21	440/442-7450 Fax 440/446-1132 [f][t]
St Francis School-Cleveland 7206 Myron Ave, Cleveland 44103 Scott Embacher	K-8		215 9	216/361-4858 Fax 216/361-1673 [f]
St Ignatius High Sch 1911 W 30th St, Cleveland 44113 Dan Bradesca	9-12		1,532 56	216/651-0222 Fax 216/651-6313 [f][t]
St Ignatius of Antioch ES 10205 Lorain Ave, Cleveland 44111 Marge Ricksecker	K-8		270 18	216/671-0535 Fax 216/671-0536
St Jerome Elem Sch 15100 Lake Shore Blvd, Cleveland 44110 Susan Coan	K-8		175 9	216/486-3587 Fax 216/486-4288
St Joan of Arc Sch 498 E Washington St, Chagrin Falls 44022 Shelley DiBacco	K-8		177 12	440/247-6530 Fax 440/247-2045
St Joseph Academy 3470 Rocky River Dr, Cleveland 44111 Jeff Sutliff	9-12		700 40	216/251-6788 Fax 216/251-5809 [f][t]
St Leo the Great Sch 4900 Broadview Rd, Cleveland 44109 Denise Burns	PK-8		257 11	216/661-2120
St Mark Sch 15724 Montrose Ave, Cleveland 44111 Karen Cocita	PK-8		409	216/521-4115 Fax 216/221-8664
St Mary Byzantine Sch 4600 State Rd, Cleveland 44109 Rita Basalla	PK-8		165 9	216/749-7980
St Mary Catholic Sch 265 Baker St, Berea 44017 Andrew Carner	PK-8		305 20	440/243-4555 Fax 440/243-6214
St Mary of the Falls Sch 8262 Columbia Rd, Olmsted Falls 44138 Annemarie Rajnicek	PK-8		270 13	440/235-4580 Fax 440/235-6833
St Michael Sch 6906 Chestnut Rd, Independence 44131 Margaret Campisi	PK-8		360 26	216/524-6405 Fax 216/524-7538
St Paschal Baylon Sch 5360 Wilson Mills Rd, Highland Hgts 44143 Diane Raguz	K-8		429 23	440/442-6766 Fax 440/442-1729
St Raphael Sch 525 Dover Center Rd, Bay Village 44140 Ken Mitskavich	K-8		690 26	440/871-6760 Fax 440/871-1358
St Rita Sch 33200 Baldwin Rd, Solon 44139 Deborah Grgic	PK-8		300 20	440/248-1350 Fax 440/248-9442
St Rocco Sch 3205 Fulton Rd, Cleveland 44109 Renee Cerny	K-8		150 9	216/961-8557 Fax 216/961-1845
St Stanislaus Elem Sch 6615 Forman Ave, Cleveland 44105 Deborah Martin	K-8		200 15	216/883-3307 Fax 216/883-0514
St Thomas Aquinas Sch 9101 Superior Ave, Cleveland 44106 Katy Rankin	K-8		200 10	216/421-4668 Fax 216/721-8444
St Thomas More Sch 4180 N Amber Dr, Brooklyn 44144 Jennifer Francis	PK-8		260 12	216/749-1660 Fax 216/398-4265
Trinity High Sch 12425 Granger Rd, Garfield HTS 44125 Linda Bacho	9-12		361 25	216/581-1644 Fax 216/581-9348 [f][t]
Villa Angela-St Joseph HS 18491 Lake Shore Blvd, Cleveland 44119 Dave Csank	9-12		500 42	216/481-8414 Fax 216/486-1035 [f][t]

CUYAHOGA PRIVATE SCHOOLS

Private Schs..Principal	Grd	Prgm	Enr/#Cls	SN
AL Ihsan Islamic Sch 4600 Rocky River Dr, Cleveland 44135 Maysa Jadallah	K-6		60 6	216/676-5006 Fax 216/676-2777
AL Ihsan Sch 6055 W 130th St, Parma 44130 Maysa Jadallah	PK-6		70	440/799-4875 Fax 440/799-4876
Bethany Lutheran Sch 6041 Ridge Rd, Parma 44129 William Moses	PK-8		250 18	440/884-1010 Fax 440/884-9834 [f]
Bethel Christian Academy 12901 W Pleasant Valley Rd, Parma 44130 Jeremy Burnett	PK-8		140 10	440/842-8575 Fax 440/842-3226
Birchwood School of Hawken 4400 W 140th St, Cleveland 44135 Charles Debelak	PK-8		205 19	216/251-2321 Fax 216/251-2787 [f][t]
Bridge Academy 3389 Fulton Rd, Cleveland 44109 Daniel McElwain	5-8		30	216/965-8426
ⒶCas-Gerson Sch 10427 Detroit Ave, Cleveland 44102 Donald Copehaver	6-12		50 7	216/694-7200 Fax 216/521-2604
ⒶCas-Jones Campus 3518 W 25th St, Cleveland 44109 Dakota Williams	6-12		28	216/741-2241
Chaviva High Sch 3300 Mayfield Rd, Cleveland 44118 Rochie Berkowitz	9-12		15	216/303-9574
ⒶCleveland Christian Home Ctr 11401 Lorain Ave, Cleveland 44111 Dakota Williams	K-12		54	216/416-4277
Corpus Christi Academy 5655 Mayfield Rd, Cleveland 44124 Ken Mitskavich	PK-8		204	440/449-4242
Education Alternative 5445 Smith Rd, Brookpark 44142 Gerry Swartz	K-12		42	216/332-9360 Fax 216/332-9375
Fuchs Mizrachi Sch 26600 Shaker Blvd, Beachwood 44122 Malkie Ginsburg \ Jeremy Bruce	PK-12	G	450 11	216/932-0220 Fax 216/932-0345
Gross Schechter Day Sch 27601 Fairmount Blvd, Pepper Pike 44124 Randy Boroff	PK-8	G	275 20	216/763-1400 Fax 216/763-1106

79 Student Personnel	91 Safety/Security	275 Response To Intervention	298 Grant Writer/Ptnrships	School Programs	Social Media
80 Driver Ed/Safety	92 Magnet School	277 Remedial Math K-12	750 Chief Innovation Officer	A = Alternative Program	[f] = Facebook
81 Gifted/Talented	93 Parental Involvement	280 Literacy Coach	751 Chief of Staff	G = Adult Classes	[t] = Twitter
82 Video Services	95 Tech Prep Program	285 STEM	752 Social Emotional Learning	M = Magnet Program	
83 Substance Abuse Prev	97 Chief Information Officer	286 Digital Learning		T = Title I Schoolwide	
84 Erate	98 Chief Technology Officer	288 Common Core Standards	Other School Types	V = Career & Tech Ed Programs	
85 AIDS Education	270 Accountability	294 Accountability	Ⓐ = Alternative School		
86 Character Education	271 Migrant Education	295 Network System	Ⓒ = Charter School	New Schools are shaded	
88 Alternative/At Risk	273 Teacher Mentor	296 Title II Programs	Ⓜ = Magnet School	New Superintendents and Principals are bold	
89 Multi-Cultural Curriculum	274 Before/After Sch	297 Webmaster	Ⓨ = Year-Round School	Personnel with email addresses are underscored	
90 Social Work					

OH—53

Cuyahoga County

School	Grades	Enrollment	Phone
Hathaway Brown Sch 19600 N Park Blvd, Shaker HTS 44122 Becky Kline	PK-12	835	216/932-4214 Fax 216/371-1501
Hawken Lower-Middle Sch 5000 Clubside Rd, Cleveland 44124 Scott Looney	PK-8	434 18	440/423-2031 Fax 440/423-2123
Hawken Sch 12465 County Line Road, Gates Mills 44040 Scott Looney	9-12	424	440/423-4446 Fax 440/423-2960
Hebrew Academy of Cleveland 1860 S Taylor Rd, Cleveland HTS 44118 Simcha Dessler	PK-12	800	216/321-5838 Fax 216/321-3636
Heritage Christian Sch 4403 Tiedeman Rd Frnt, Brooklyn 44144 Luke Brown	K-12	207 20	216/476-7976 Fax 216/476-9140
Holy Cross Lutheran Sch 4260 Rocky River Dr, Cleveland 44135 Nancy Clark	PK-8	56 6	216/941-2770 Fax 216/941-3035
Joseph & Florence Mandel Sch 26500 Shaker Blvd, Beachwood 44122 Halle Dubin \ Kim Favor	PK-8	450 25	216/464-4055 Fax 216/464-3229
Lakewood Lutheran Elem Sch 14560 Madison Ave, Lakewood 44107 Carolyn Potantus	K-8	15 3	216/221-6941 Fax 216/226-4082
Laurel Sch 1 Lyman Cir, Shaker HTS 44122 Ann Klotz	PK-12	600	216/464-1441 Fax 216/464-8993
Lawrence Lower Sch 1551 E Wallings Rd, Broadview HTS 44147 Douglas Hamilton	Spec	123 15	440/526-0003 Fax 440/526-0595
Le Chaperon Rouge Elem Sch 27390 Center Ridge Rd, Westlake 44145 Grace Birney	K-5	17 3	440/899-9477 Fax 440/835-8126
Lillian & Betty Ratner Sch 27575 Shaker Blvd, Pepper Pike 44124 Michael Griffith	PK-8	200 12	216/464-0033 Fax 216/464-0031
Luther Memorial Sch 4464 Pearl Rd, Cleveland 44109 Nicole Levy	PK-8	165 4	216/749-5300
Lutheran High School East 3565 Mayfield Rd, Cleveland 44118 Andrew Prusinski	9-12 V	225 14	216/382-6100 Fax 216/382-6119
Lutheran High School West 3850 Linden Rd, Rocky River 44116 Mike Waugh	9-12	450 30	440/333-1660 Fax 440/333-1729
Messiah Lutheran Elem Sch 4401 W 215th St, Fairview Park 44126 Helen Casselberry	PK-8	130 11	440/331-6553 Fax 440/331-1604
Monarch Sch of Bellefaire Jcb 22001 Fairmount Blvd, Shaker HTS 44118 Debra Mandell	Spec	156	216/320-8945
Montessori Childrens Sch 28370 Bassett Rd, Westlake 44145 Barbara Kincaid	PK-3	160 7	440/871-8773 Fax 440/871-1799
Montessori HS-Univ Circle 11025 Magnolia Dr, Cleveland 44106 Gregg Good	9-12	125	216/421-3033 Fax 216/421-1874
Padre Pio Academy 12920 Madison Ave, Lakewood 44107 Patrick Andrews	K-12	80 5	216/226-4854
Parma Heights Chrn Academy 8971 W Ridgewood Dr, Parma Heights 44130 Dave Griffey	K-6	150 12	440/845-8668 Fax 440/886-5748
Ramah Junior Academy 4770 Lee Rd, Cleveland 44128 Juanita Walker	PK-8	80 5	216/581-2626 Fax 216/581-4128
Royal Redeemer Lutheran Sch 11680 Royalton Rd, N Royalton 44133 Heidi Malone	PK-8	465 15	440/237-7988 Fax 440/237-7713
Ruffing Mont Rocky River Sch 1285 Orchard Park Dr, Rocky River 44116 John McNamara	PK-8	300 10	440/333-2250 Fax 440/333-2540
Ruffing Montessori Ingalls Sch 3380 Fairmount Blvd, Cleveland HTS 44118 Kathie Freer	PK-8	290 10	216/321-7571 Fax 216/321-7568
South Suburban Montessori Sch 4450 Oakes Rd Bldg 6, Brecksville 44141 Amy Macki-Barr	PK-8	133 6	440/526-1966 Fax 440/526-6026
St John Lutheran Sch 1027 E 176th St, Cleveland 44119 David Peck	K-8	144 9	216/531-8204
St John Lutheran Sch 4386 Mayfield Rd, South Euclid 44121 Tammy Szoyka	PK-8	50 8	216/381-8595 Fax 216/381-1564
St Martin De Porres High Sch 6202 Saint Clair Ave, Cleveland 44103 John Fay	9-12	431 24	216/881-1689 Fax 216/881-8303
St Paul Lutheran Sch 27981 Detroit Rd, Westlake 44145 Jeremy Louden	PK-8	280 17	440/835-3051 Fax 440/835-8216
The Lyceum 1556 S Green Rd, Cleveland 44121 Luke Macik	9-12	401	216/707-1121
University High Sch 2785 Som Center Rd, Chagrin Falls 44022 Patrick Gallagher	9-12	400 20	216/831-2200 Fax 216/292-7808
University Sch-Shaker Campus 20701 Brantley Rd, Shaker HTS 44122 Patrick Gallagher	K-8	454 60	216/321-8260 Fax 216/321-4074
Westside Christian Academy 23096 Center Ridge Rd, Westlake 44145 Timothy Piazza \ Kristen Zuccola	PK-12	129 10	440/331-1300 Fax 440/331-1301
Yavne High Sch 2475 S Green Rd, Beachwood 44122 Lisa Weinberg	7-12	200 17	216/691-5838 Fax 216/691-1448
Yeshiva Derech Ha Torah 1700 S Taylor Rd, Cleveland 44118 Esther Greenberger \ Shoshana Munk	PK-12	253 22	216/321-1547 Fax 216/321-7505
Yeshiva Derech Ha Torah 1508 Warrensville Center Rd, Cleveland 44121 Yitreack Margaret	K-8	300 14	216/382-6248 Fax 216/382-4585

CUYAHOGA REGIONAL CENTERS

• **Connect Information Tech Ctr** PID: 04499415 216/520-6900
5700 W Canal Rd, Valley View 44125 Fax 216/520-6969

John Mitchell 1
Keith Delury 16,73,76
Gary White 68
Matt Zenubi 79
Julia Rozsnyai 2
Bob Mangerink 67
Steven Foster 76
Jon Axe 295

• **North Coast Ed Media Center** PID: 02100840 216/901-4233
5811 Canal Rd Ste 235, Valley View 44125 Fax 216/901-4249

Roni Staimpel 1

• **State Support Team 3** PID: 02228208 216/524-3000
6393 Oak Tree Blvd, Independence 44131 Fax 216/446-3829

Michele Gaski 1   Dr Lynn Hruschak 8,74

1 Superintendent	8 Curric/Instruct K-12	19 Chief Financial Officer	29 Family/Consumer Science	39 Social Studies K-12	49 English/Lang Arts Elem	59 Special Education Elem	69 Academic Assessment
2 Bus/Finance/Purchasing	9 Curric/Instruct Elem	20 Art K-12	30 Adult Education	40 Social Studies Elem	50 English/Lang Arts Sec	60 Special Education Sec	70 Research/Development
3 Buildings And Grounds	10 Curric/Instruct Sec	21 Art Elem	31 Career/Sch-to-Work K-12	41 Social Studies Sec	51 Reading K-12	61 Foreign/World Lang K-12	71 Public Information
4 Food Service	11 Federal Program	22 Art Sec	32 Career/Sch-to-Work Elem	42 Science K-12	52 Reading Elem	62 Foreign/World Lang Elem	72 Summer School
5 Transportation	12 Title I	23 Music K-12	33 Career/Sch-to-Work Sec	43 Science Elem	53 Reading Sec	63 Foreign/World Lang Sec	73 Instructional Tech
6 Athletic	13 Title V	24 Music Elem	34 Early Childhood Ed	44 Science Sec	54 Remedial Reading K-12	64 Religious Education K-12	74 Inservice Training
7 Health Services	15 Asst Superintendent	25 Music Sec	35 Health/Phys Education	45 Math K-12	55 Remedial Reading Elem	65 Religious Education Elem	75 Marketing/Distributive
	16 Instructional Media Svcs	26 Business Education	36 Guidance Services K-12	46 Math Elem	56 Remedial Reading Sec	66 Religious Education Sec	76 Info Systems
	17 Chief Operations Officer	27 Career & Tech Ed	37 Guidance Services Elem	47 Math Sec	57 Bilingual/ELL	67 School Board President	77 Psychological Assess
	18 Chief Academic Officer	28 Technology Education	38 Guidance Services Sec	48 English/Lang Arts K-12	58 Special Education K-12	68 Teacher Personnel	78 Affirmative Action

Ohio School Directory — Darke County

Susan Schraff 15,58,93   Linda Thayer 27

DARKE COUNTY

DARKE COUNTY SCHOOLS

Darke Co Ed Service Center PID: 00797801   937/548-4915
5279 Education Dr, Greenville 45331   Fax 937/548-8920

Mike Gray 1	Emiko Augsburger 2
April Hoying 8	Lisa Giuffre 59,77
Jodi Rinehart 60,77	Mike Corcoran 73,295

County Schs..Principal	Grd	Prgm	Enr/#Cls	SN
Anthony Wayne Early Chldhd Ctr	Spec		160	937/548-8323
4932 Children's Home Rd, Greenville 45331			7	Fax 937/548-8947
Roxann Bickel				

DARKE PUBLIC SCHOOLS

Ansonia Local School Dist PID: 00797461   937/337-4000
600 E Canal St, Ansonia 45303   Fax 937/337-9520

Schools: 2 \ **Teachers:** 50 \ **Students:** 700 \ **Special Ed Students:** 75 \ **LEP Students:** 3 \ **College-Bound:** 56% \ **Ethnic:** Hispanic 2%, Caucasian 98% \ **Exp:** $328 (High) \ **Poverty:** 10% \ **Title I:** $126,136 \ **Open-Close:** 08/27 - 05/29 \ **DTBP:** $164 (High)

James Atchley 1	Nick Hamilton 2
Rob Grillot 3*	Paula Moody 4
Jerry Barga 5	Matt Macy 6*
Ashlee Forman 9,11,51,54,88*	Jim Robson 10*
Cathy Swabb 16,82	Matt Sutter 31,36,57,69,83,270,273*
Nicholas Eifert 35,85*	Rhonda Williams 67
Shawn Peters 73*	

Public Schs..Principal	Grd	Prgm	Enr/#Cls	SN
Ansonia Elem Sch	PK-6		477	52% 937/337-5141
600 E Canal St, Ansonia 45303			25	
Ashlee Forman				
Ansonia Jr Sr High Sch	7-12	TV	313	937/337-4000
600 E Canal St, Ansonia 45303			24	
Jim Robson				

Arcanum Butler Local Sch Dist PID: 00797502   937/692-5174
2011 Trojan Ave, Arcanum 45304   Fax 937/692-5959

Schools: 4 \ **Teachers:** 59 \ **Students:** 1,125 \ **Special Ed Students:** 109 \ **College-Bound:** 52% \ **Ethnic:** Caucasian 99% \ **Exp:** $128 (Low) \ **Poverty:** 9% \ **Title I:** $130,869 \ **Open-Close:** 08/27 - 05/29 \ **DTBP:** $174 (High) \ f

John Stephens 1	Brenda Hale 2
Jeffrey Brown 3	Jordan Greve 4
Kevin Stanley 5	Jason Schondelmyer 6*
Joni Pechie 11,69,72*	Ashley Matheson 38*
Katherine Bourelle 38	Ed Everman 67
Roberta Zimmer 73	David Baker 84

Public Schs..Principal	Grd	Prgm	Enr/#Cls	SN
Arcanum Early Learning Center	PK-PK		78	937/692-5092
310 N Main St, Arcanum 45304				
Joni Pechie				
Arcanum Elem Sch	PK-4		473	937/692-5174
2011 Trojan Ave, Arcanum 45304			23	Fax 937/692-8865
Joni Pechie				
Arcanum High Sch	9-12		311	84% 937/692-5174
2011 Trojan Ave, Arcanum 45304			22	Fax 937/692-8865
Jason Stephan				
Butler Middle Sch	5-8		351	937/692-5174
2011 Trojan Ave, Arcanum 45304			20	Fax 937/692-8865
Jason Vince				

Franklin-Monroe Local Sch Dist PID: 00797540   937/947-1212
8639 Oakes Rd, Arcanum 45304   Fax 937/947-1372

Schools: 2 \ **Teachers:** 38 \ **Students:** 625 \ **Special Ed Students:** 51 \ **LEP Students:** 3 \ **College-Bound:** 56% \ **Ethnic:** Asian 1%, Hispanic 1%, Caucasian 98% \ **Exp:** $343 (High) \ **Poverty:** 7% \ **Title I:** $61,886 \ **Open-Close:** 08/26 - 05/29 \ **DTBP:** $174 (High)

Jeremy Pequignot 1	Greg Hinds 2,11
Clay Spencer 3*	Angela Weaver 4*
Merriha Knop Buchanan 5	Tyler Rhodus 6,27
Sara Fox 12,55*	Ami Coomer 16*
Laura Ayres 31,36,69,83*	Pj Burgett 38*
Scott Myers 67	Tim Sargent 73*

Public Schs..Principal	Grd	Prgm	Enr/#Cls	SN
Franklin-Monroe Elem Sch	K-6		340	937/947-1327
8591 Oakes Rd, Arcanum 45304			21	Fax 937/947-1206
Megan Linder				t
Franklin-Monroe Jr Sr High Sch	7-12		268	36% 937/947-1328
8591 Oakes Rd, Arcanum 45304			23	Fax 937/947-1371
Pj Burgett				

Greenville City School Dist PID: 00797576   937/548-3185
215 W 4th St, Greenville 45331   Fax 937/548-6943

Schools: 3 \ **Teachers:** 145 \ **Students:** 2,507 \ **Special Ed Students:** 409 \ **LEP Students:** 28 \ **College-Bound:** 41% \ **Ethnic:** Asian 1%, African American 1%, Hispanic 2%, Caucasian 95% \ **Exp:** $248 (Med) \ **Poverty:** 14% \ **Title I:** $651,142 \ **Special Education:** $351,000 \ **Open-Close:** 08/26 - 05/27 \ **DTBP:** $202 (High)

Douglas Fries 1	Andrea Townsend 2,27,58
Jenna Jurosic 2	Kurtis Combs 3
Tonya Wright 4*	Andrew Grasty 5
Dusty Yingst 6	Kathy Jetter 7*
Jim Hooper 8	Shawna Wise 16,73,82,295
Amy Schoen 34*	Tiffany Fine 37*
Becky Curtis 38*	Brad Gettinger 67
Carl Brown 69*	Laura Bemus 81

Public Schs..Principal	Grd	Prgm	Enr/#Cls	SN
Greenville Elem Sch	PK-4	T	879	61% 937/548-3185
1111 N Ohio St, Greenville 45331			40	
Jody Harter				
Greenville Middle Sch	5-8	T	768	937/548-3185
1111 N Ohio St, Greenville 45331			29	
Chris Mortensen				
Greenville Senior High Sch	9-12	AGTV	860	40% 937/548-4188
100 Greenwave Way, Greenville 45331				Fax 937/548-3082
Stan Hughes				

79	Student Personnel	91	Safety/Security	275	Response To Intervention	298	Grant Writer/Ptnrships
80	Driver Ed/Safety	92	Magnet School	277	Remedial Math K-12	750	Chief Innovation Officer
81	Gifted/Talented	93	Parental Involvement	280	Literacy Coach	751	Chief of Staff
82	Video Services	95	Tech Prep Program	285	STEM	752	Social Emotional Learning
83	Substance Abuse Prev	97	Chief Infomation Officer	286	Digital Learning		
84	Erate	98	Chief Technology Officer	288	Common Core Standards		
85	AIDS Education	270	Accountability	294	Accountability		
88	Alternative/At Risk	271	Migrant Education	295	Network System		
89	Multi-Cultural Curriculum	273	Teacher Mentor	296	Title II Programs		
90	Social Work	274	Before/After Sch	297	Webmaster		

School Programs
A = Alternative Program
G = Adult Classes
M = Magnet Program
T = Title I Schoolwide
V = Career & Tech Ed Programs

Other School Types
Ⓐ = Alternative School
Ⓒ = Charter School
Ⓜ = Magnet School
Ⓨ = Year-Round School

Social Media
f = Facebook
t = Twitter

New Schools are shaded
New Superintendents and Principals are bold
Personnel with email addresses are underscored

Defiance County

Market Data Retrieval

- **Mississinawa Valley Sch Dist** PID: 00797667   937/968-5656
  1469 State Road 47 E, Union City 45390   Fax 937/968-6731

  Schools: 2 \ *Teachers:* 44 \ *Students:* 700 \ *Special Ed Students:* 92 \ *LEP Students:* 9 \ *College-Bound:* 40% \ *Ethnic:* Hispanic 9%, Caucasian 91% \ *Exp:* $350 (High) \ *Poverty:* 16% \ *Title I:* $174,705 \ *Open-Close:* 08/28 - 06/02 \ *DTBP:* $174 (High)

Doug Dunham	1,11		Nicholas Hamilton	2
Tony Neargarder	3*		Katie Walters	4
Stephanie Klingshirn	12*		Shawn Peters	16,73*
Terry Niekamp	35*		Gayle Breymier	67

Public Schs..Principal	Grd	Prgm	Enr/#Cls	SN
Mississinawa Valley Elem Sch 10480 Staudt Rd, Union City 45390 Stephanie Kemp	PK-6	T	382 30	89% 937/968-4464 Fax 937/968-3434
Mississinawa Valley Jr Sr HS 10480 Staudt Rd, Union City 45390 Jeffery Winchester	7-12	T	269 25	937/968-4464 Fax 937/968-3434

- **Tri-Village Local Sch Dist** PID: 00797708   937/996-6261
  315 S Main St, New Madison 45346   Fax 937/996-5537

  Schools: 1 \ *Teachers:* 49 \ *Students:* 827 \ *Special Ed Students:* 78 \ *LEP Students:* 3 \ *College-Bound:* 42% \ *Ethnic:* Hispanic 1%, Native American: 1%, Caucasian 98% \ *Exp:* $72 (Low) \ *Poverty:* 12% \ *Title I:* $135,707 \ *Open-Close:* 08/27 - 05/29 \ *DTBP:* $197 (High)

Josh Sagester	1		Kim Chowning	2
Chris Pearson	3,73,91		Sheryll Hedger	4,7*
Jerry Hollinger	5		Bradley Gray	6*
Annette Black	8,34,38,57,69,83,88*		Shane Mead	12,296*
Angie Thomas	60*		Tom Schley	67
John Lay	76,295*		Christine Gutierrez	285*

Public Schs..Principal	Grd	Prgm	Enr/#Cls	SN
Tri-Village Sch 315 S Main St, New Madison 45346 Shane Mead \ Lee Morris	K-12	V	827 40	39% 937/996-6261 Fax 937/996-0307

- **Versailles Exempted Village SD** PID: 00797758   937/526-4773
  459 S Center St, Versailles 45380   Fax 937/526-5745

  Schools: 3 \ *Teachers:* 72 \ *Students:* 1,305 \ *Special Ed Students:* 80 \ *LEP Students:* 3 \ *College-Bound:* 72% \ *Ethnic:* Caucasian 100% \ *Exp:* $224 (Med) \ *Poverty:* 5% \ *Title I:* $84,807 \ *Special Education:* $227,000 \ *Open-Close:* 08/27 - 05/28

Aaron Moran	1		Ken Moorman	3*
Janet Mendenhall	4*		Scott Droerman	6*
Brian Shappie	7*		Jon Hemmelgorn	8,11*
Mary Frey	16*		Michelle Hartings	37*
Hollie Ahrens	38,83*		Julie Golen	57*
Joni Robinson	58*		Hope Batty	67
Brenda Braun	69,270,288*		Michael Goubeaux	73,286,295*
Amy Hoying	83*			

Public Schs..Principal	Grd	Prgm	Enr/#Cls	SN
Versailles Elem Sch 280 Marker Rd, Versailles 45380 Brenda Braun	K-4		491 21	42% 937/526-4681 Fax 937/526-3480
Versailles High Sch 280 Marker Rd, Versailles 45380 Roger McEldowney	9-12	V	403 50	937/526-4427 Fax 937/526-4356
Versailles Middle Sch 280 Marker Rd, Versailles 45380 Jon Hemmelgorn	5-8		411 9	937/526-4426 Fax 937/526-3480

DARKE CATHOLIC SCHOOLS

- **Archdiocese Cincinnati Ed Off** PID: 00808096
  Listing includes only schools located in this county. See District Index for location of Diocesan Offices.

Catholic Schs..Principal	Grd	Prgm	Enr/#Cls	SN
St Mary Sch 238 W 3rd St, Greenville 45331 Vernon Rosenbeck	PK-8		81 9	937/548-2345 Fax 937/548-0878

DARKE PRIVATE SCHOOLS

Private Schs..Principal	Grd	Prgm	Enr/#Cls	SN
Church of God Academy 5065 S State Route 49, Greenville 45331 Ray Tinsman	PK-12		99	937/316-7777
Decolores Mnt Jr High Farm Sch 6104 Arcanum Bearsmill Rd, Greenville 45331 Dr Nancy Dean	7-8		20	937/316-6104
Decolores Montessori Sch 312 Central Ave, Greenville 45331 Nancy Dean	PK-9		148	937/547-1334

DEFIANCE COUNTY

DEFIANCE COUNTY SCHOOLS

County Schs..Principal	Grd	Prgm	Enr/#Cls	SN
Good Samaritan Sch 195 Island Park Ave, Defiance 43512 Tara Shumaker	Spec		60 10	419/782-6621 Fax 419/784-5199

DEFIANCE PUBLIC SCHOOLS

- **Ayersville Local School Dist** PID: 00797813   419/395-1111
  28046 Watson Rd, Defiance 43512   Fax 419/395-9990

  Schools: 3 \ *Teachers:* 48 \ *Students:* 700 \ *Special Ed Students:* 68 \ *College-Bound:* 60% \ *Ethnic:* Asian 1%, African American 1%, Hispanic 11%, Caucasian 87% \ *Exp:* $168 (Low) \ *Poverty:* 8% \ *Title I:* $58,740 \ *Special Education:* $110,000 \ *Open-Close:* 08/27 - 05/28 \ *DTBP:* $192 (High) \

Don Diglia	1		Abby Sharp	2,298
Steve Brown	3,5		Brad Bailey	4*
Rob Luderman	6		Beth Hench	11,93*
Alexis Zippay	16*		Augusta Niese	38*
Troy Merillat	58		Jessica Myers	67

---

1 Superintendent	8 Curric/Instruct K-12	19 Chief Financial Officer	29 Family/Consumer Science	39 Social Studies K-12	49 English/Lang Arts Elem	59 Special Education Elem	69 Academic Assessment
2 Bus/Finance/Purchasing	9 Curric/Instruct Elem	20 Art K-12	30 Adult Education	40 Social Studies Elem	50 English/Lang Arts Sec	60 Special Education Sec	70 Research/Development
3 Buildings And Grounds	10 Curric/Instruct Sec	21 Art Elem	31 Career/Sch-to-Work K-12	41 Social Studies Sec	51 Reading K-12	61 Foreign/World Lang K-12	71 Public Information
4 Food Service	11 Federal Program	22 Art Sec	32 Career/Sch-to-Work Elem	42 Science K-12	52 Reading Elem	62 Foreign/World Lang Elem	72 Summer School
5 Transportation	12 Title I	23 Music K-12	33 Career/Sch-to-Work Sec	43 Science Elem	53 Reading Sec	63 Foreign/World Lang Sec	73 Instructional Tech
6 Athletic	13 Title V	24 Music Elem	34 Early Childhood Ed	44 Science Sec	54 Remedial Reading K-12	64 Religious Education K-12	74 Inservice Training
7 Health Services	14 Instructional Media Svcs	25 Music Sec	35 Health/Phys Education	45 Math K-12	55 Remedial Reading Elem	65 Religious Education Elem	75 Marketing/Distributive
	15 Asst Superintendent	26 Business Education	36 Guidance Services K-12	46 Math Elem	56 Remedial Reading Sec	66 Religious Education Sec	76 Info Systems
	16 Chief Operations Officer	27 Career & Tech Ed	37 Guidance Services Elem	47 Math Sec	57 Bilingual/ELL	67 School Board President	77 Psychological Assess
	17 Chief Academic Officer	28 Technology Education	38 Guidance Services Sec	48 English/Lang Arts K-12	58 Special Education K-12	68 Teacher Personnel	78 Affirmative Action

Ohio School Directory — Defiance County

Phil Liebrecht 73*

Public Schs..Principal	Grd	Prgm	Enr/#Cls SN	
Ayersville Elem Sch 28046 Watson Rd, Defiance 43512 Beth Hench	K-4		292 26	419/395-1111 Fax 419/395-2566
Ayersville High Sch 28046 Watson Rd, Defiance 43512 Jeremy Kuhlman	9-12	V	236	58% 419/395-1111
Ayersville Middle Sch 28046 Watson Rd, Defiance 43512 Kirk Jones	5-8		236	419/395-1111

• **Central Local School Dist** PID: 00797851   419/658-2808
6289 US Highway 127, Sherwood 43556   Fax 419/658-4010

Schools: 3 \ **Teachers:** 63 \ **Students:** 1,050 \ **Special Ed Students:** 175 \ **LEP Students:** 13 \ **College-Bound:** 40% \ **Ethnic:** Hispanic 6%, Caucasian 93% \ **Exp:** $135 (Low) \ **Poverty:** 8% \ **Title I:** $138,056 \ **Special Education:** $224,000 \ **Open-Close:** 08/27 - 05/22 \ **DTBP:** $175 (High)

Steve Arnold 1,83   Kerry Samples 2,19
Phil Hetrik 3,5   Laura Brady 4
Paul Yunker 6   Sherrie Brown 9,11,285,296,298*
Suzanne Geis .... 11*   Sally Miller 16
Adam Singer .... 28,73,286,295*   Lori Polter 33,38,69*
Lindsey Froelich 37   Scott Shinler 67
Nancy Mills 81   Tracy Robinson 273*

Public Schs..Principal	Grd	Prgm	Enr/#Cls SN	
Fairview Elem Sch 14060 Blosser Rd, Sherwood 43556 Sherrie Brown	K-5	T	419 30	46% 419/658-2511 Fax 419/658-2302
Fairview High Sch 6289 US Highway 127, Sherwood 43556 Tim Breyman	9-12	V	291 13	78% 419/658-2378 Fax 419/658-4011 t
Fairview Middle Sch 6289 US Highway 127, Sherwood 43556 Suzanne Geis	6-8	T	245 22	419/658-2331 Fax 419/658-4011 t

• **Defiance City School Dist** PID: 00797916   419/782-0070
801 S Clinton St, Defiance 43512   Fax 419/782-4395

Schools: 3 \ **Teachers:** 155 \ **Students:** 2,400 \ **Special Ed Students:** 393 \ **LEP Students:** 7 \ **College-Bound:** 49% \ **Ethnic:** African American 6%, Hispanic 25%, Caucasian 68% \ **Exp:** $240 (Med) \ **Poverty:** 15% \ **Title I:** $564,458 \ **Special Education:** $569,000 \ **Open-Close:** 08/21 - 05/28 \ **DTBP:** $195 (High)

Robert Morton 1   Cheryl Swisher 2
John Mayes 3,91   Deanna Hull 4*
Mark Widenhammer 5   Jerry Buti 6*
Todd Fruth 7,57,58,83,85,88,271,274   Sheri Styer 8,11,27,31,54,69,296,298
Jeanie Mansfield .... 16*   Renee Wank 37*
Wesley Moats 67   Andrew Eckhart 73

Public Schs..Principal	Grd	Prgm	Enr/#Cls SN	
Defiance Elem Sch 400 Carter Rd, Defiance 43512 Deanne Held \ Jane Myers	K-5	T	1,111 22	62% 419/785-2260 Fax 419/785-2261
Defiance High Sch 1755 Palmer Dr, Defiance 43512 Bob Morton	9-12	TV	721 50	50% 419/784-2777 Fax 419/784-2957
Defiance Middle Sch 1755 Palmer Dr, Defiance 43512 Matthew Carr	6-8	AT	605 50	52% 419/782-0050 Fax 419/782-0060

• **Hicksville Exempted Village SD** PID: 00797992   419/542-7665
958 E High St, Hicksville 43526   Fax 419/542-8534

Schools: 2 \ **Teachers:** 70 \ **Students:** 1,000 \ **Special Ed Students:** 181 \ **LEP Students:** 3 \ **College-Bound:** 46% \ **Ethnic:** Asian 1%, Hispanic 7%, Caucasian 91% \ **Exp:** $140 (Low) \ **Poverty:** 13% \ **Title I:** $166,220 \ **Special Education:** $184,000 \ **Open-Close:** 08/26 - 05/29 \ **DTBP:** $174 (High) \ f

Keith Countryman 1   Micheal Ruen 2
Eric Bassett 3   Paul Overmyer 6*
Travis Lichty .... 9,12*   Christie Hoffman 16,82*
Jeffrey Shaffer .... 16,73*   Mike Blue 38,69,83*
Jay Geiger .... 57*   Minda Jones 67
Sharon Sweet .... 85*   Sandi Brown 273*

Public Schs..Principal	Grd	Prgm	Enr/#Cls SN	
Hicksville Elem Sch 958 E High St, Hicksville 43526 Travis Lichty	K-6	TV	519 35	419/542-7475 Fax 419/542-8711
Hicksville Jr Sr High Sch 958 E High St, Hicksville 43526 Jeffrey Slattery	7-12	T	387 35	93% 419/542-7636 Fax 419/542-5284

• **Northeastern Local School Dist** PID: 00798025   419/497-3461
5921 Domersville Rd, Defiance 43512   Fax 419/497-3401

Schools: 4 \ **Teachers:** 70 \ **Students:** 1,082 \ **Special Ed Students:** 148 \ **College-Bound:** 60% \ **Ethnic:** Asian 1%, African American 1%, Hispanic 8%, Caucasian 90% \ **Exp:** $257 (Med) \ **Poverty:** 13% \ **Title I:** $165,030 \ **Open-Close:** 08/27 - 05/29 \ **DTBP:** $174 (High)

James Roach 1,11   Susan Garmyn 2
Jackie Hoschak .... 4*   Craig Rutter 6
Nichole Wells .... 9*   Eric Spiller 12*
Eric Tipton .... 27,31,88*   Tammy Harr 31*
Tricia Rinkel .... 38*   Ken Keller 67
Lisa Maxwell .... 72*   Brenda Arps 73*

Public Schs..Principal	Grd	Prgm	Enr/#Cls SN	
Noble Elem Sch 10553 Haller St, Defiance 43512 Denise Wright	K-1		182 13	28% 419/782-7941 Fax 419/784-3788
Tinora Elem Sch 5751 Domersville Rd, Defiance 43512 Nichole Wells	2-6		411 20	26% 419/497-1022 Fax 419/497-1024
Tinora High Sch 5921 Domersville Rd, Defiance 43512 Eric Tipton	9-12	GV	313 28	32% 419/497-2621
Tinora Junior High Sch 5921 Domersville Rd, Defiance 43512 Lisa Maxwell	7-8		176 16	419/497-2361 Fax 419/494-3401

DEFIANCE CATHOLIC SCHOOLS

• **Diocese of Toledo Ed Office** PID: 00818297
Listing includes only schools located in this county. See District Index for location of Diocesan Offices.

---

79 Student Personnel	91 Safety/Security	275 Response To Intervention	298 Grant Writer/Ptnrships	**School Programs**	**Social Media**
80 Driver Ed/Safety	92 Magnet School	277 Remedial Math K-12	750 Chief Innovation Officer	A = Alternative Program	
81 Gifted/Talented	93 Parental Involvement	280 Literacy Coach	751 Chief of Staff	G = Adult Classes	f = Facebook
82 Video Services	95 Tech Prep Program	285 STEM	752 Social Emotional Learning	M = Magnet Program	
83 Substance Abuse Prev	97 Chief Infomation Officer	286 Digital Learning		T = Title I Schoolwide	t = Twitter
84 Erate	98 Chief Technology Officer	288 Common Core Standards	**Other School Types**	V = Career & Tech Ed Programs	
85 AIDS Education	270 Character Education	294 Accountability	Ⓐ = Alternative School		
88 Alternative/At Risk	271 Migrant Education	295 Network System	Ⓒ = Charter School	New Schools are shaded	
89 Multi-Cultural Curriculum	273 Teacher Mentor	296 Title II Programs	Ⓜ = Magnet School	New Superintendents and Principals are bold	
90 Social Work	274 Before/After Sch	297 Webmaster	Ⓨ = Year-Round School	Personnel with email addresses are underscored	

OH—57

Delaware County

Market Data Retrieval

Catholic Schs..Principal	Grd	Prgm	Enr/#Cls	SN
Holy Cross Cath Sch-Defiance 1745 S Clinton St, Defiance 43512 Rose Reinhart	PK-8		125 6	419/784-2021

DEFIANCE PRIVATE SCHOOLS

Private Schs..Principal	Grd	Prgm	Enr/#Cls	SN
St John Lutheran Sch 655 Wayne Ave, Defiance 43512 Shellie Kosmerchock	PK-8		150 10	419/782-6166

DELAWARE COUNTY

DELAWARE PUBLIC SCHOOLS

● **Big Walnut Local School Dist** PID: 00798104   740/965-3010
110 Tippett Ct, Sunbury 43074   Fax 740/965-4688

Schools: 7 \ *Teachers:* 182 \ *Students:* 4,000 \ *Special Ed Students:* 361 \ *LEP Students:* 20 \ *College-Bound:* 71% \ *Ethnic:* Asian 1%, African American 1%, Hispanic 2%, Caucasian 96% \ *Exp:* $155 (Low) \ *Poverty:* 5% \ *Title I:* $249,837 \ *Special Education:* $627,000 \ *Open-Close:* 08/14 - 05/22 \ *DTBP:* $199 (High) \

Angie Hamberg 1,11		Jeremy Buskirk 2	
Ron McClure 3,4,5		Linda Klamfoth 4	
Brain Shelton 6		Brian Shelton 6*	
Jen Wilson 8		Jen Young 8*	
Mark Cooper 15		Tammy Jordan 36,72,88,270*	
Laura Lawrence 58		Brad Schneider 67	
Wayne Thompson 73,286		Erin Curtis 79	
Katie Yeager 81*			

Public Schs..Principal	Grd	Prgm	Enr/#Cls	SN	
Big Walnut Elem Sch 940 S Old 3C Rd, Sunbury 43074 Andrea Clark	PK-4		407 21	13%	740/965-3902 Fax 740/965-3168
Big Walnut High Sch 555 S Old 3C Rd, Sunbury 43074 Andy Jados	9-12	V	1,030 50	12%	740/965-3766 Fax 740/965-1954
Big Walnut Intermediate Sch 105 Baughman St, Sunbury 43074 Gary Hankins	5-6		580	16%	740/965-7800 Fax 740/965-7801
Big Walnut Middle Sch 777 Cheshire Rd, Sunbury 43074 Josh Frame	7-8		569 30	15%	740/965-3006 Fax 740/965-6471
Gen Rosecrans Elem Sch 301 S Miller Dr, Sunbury 43074 Kate Thoma	K-4		503 15	9%	740/965-8900 Fax 740/965-8993
Harrison Street Elem Sch 70 Harrison St, Sunbury 43074 Kim Castiglione	PK-4		299	26%	740/965-7850 Fax 740/965-7851
Hylen Souders Elem Sch 4121 Miller Paul Rd, Galena 43021 Matt Cox	PK-4		365 18	20%	740/965-3200 Fax 740/965-3986

● **Buckeye Valley Local Sch Dist** PID: 00798166   740/369-8735
679 Coover Rd, Delaware 43015   Fax 740/363-7654

Schools: 4 \ *Teachers:* 114 \ *Students:* 2,202 \ *Special Ed Students:* 264 \ *LEP Students:* 9 \ *College-Bound:* 64% \ *Ethnic:* Asian 1%, African American 1%, Hispanic 3%, Caucasian 95% \ *Exp:* $92 (Low) \ *Poverty:* 6% \ *Title I:* $262,444 \ *Special Education:* $540,000 \ *Open-Close:* 08/15 - 05/27 \ *DTBP:* $235 (High)

Andrew Miller 1		Kelly Ziegler 2	
Jeremy Frolick 3,4,5		Stacy Peterson 4	
Michael Yinger 6*		Barbara Kirk-Chappa 7	
Kristine Michael 8,12,79,288		Karen Kehoe 11,34,57,58,79,275*	
Cassie Holewinski 16,73,82,286,295*		Jessica Combs 36*	
Justin Osborn 67		Holley Napier 274	

Public Schs..Principal	Grd	Prgm	Enr/#Cls	SN	
Buckeye Valley East Elem Sch 522 E High St, Ashley 43003 Katie Karacson	PK-4	T	337 15	34%	740/747-2266 Fax 740/747-3510
Buckeye Valley High Sch 901 Coover Rd, Delaware 43015 James Albanese	9-12	V	714 50	18%	740/363-1349 Fax 740/363-9380
Buckeye Valley Middle Sch 683 Coover Rd, Delaware 43015 Brian Baker	5-8		663 30	21%	740/363-6626 Fax 740/363-4483
Buckeye Valley West Elem Sch 4340 State Route 257 S, Ostrander 43061 Barry Lyons	PK-4		488 19	11%	740/666-2731 Fax 740/666-2221

● **Delaware City School Dist** PID: 00798221   740/833-1100
74 W William St, Delaware 43015   Fax 740/833-1799

Schools: 7 \ *Teachers:* 290 \ *Students:* 5,459 \ *Special Ed Students:* 833 \ *LEP Students:* 95 \ *College-Bound:* 64% \ *Ethnic:* Asian 1%, African American 5%, Hispanic 6%, Caucasian 88% \ *Exp:* $128 (Low) \ *Poverty:* 10% \ *Title I:* $807,116 \ *Special Education:* $1,155,000 \ *Open-Close:* 08/14 - 05/27 \ *DTBP:* $177 (High) \

Paul Craft 1		Melissa Swearlingen 2,19	
Jason Sherman 3,5,91		Sally Rathje 4	
Steve Glesenkamp 6*		Heidi Kegley 8,15,69	
Joseph Uher 9		Angie Macwhinney 58	
Jayna McDaniel-Brown 67		Jerry Stewart 68,79	
Jennifer Ruhe 71		Stan McDonald 73*	
Pam Steurer 274			

Public Schs..Principal	Grd	Prgm	Enr/#Cls	SN	
ⓨ David Smith Elem Sch 355 N Liberty St, Delaware 43015 Rochelle Thompson	PK-5	M	448 18	31%	740/833-1350 Fax 740/833-1399
ⓨ Dempsey Middle Sch 599 Pennsylvania Ave, Delaware 43015 Daniel Bartha	6-8	M	1,303 45	32%	740/833-1800 Fax 740/833-1899
ⓨ Ervin Carlisle Elem Sch 746 W Central Ave, Delaware 43015 Paula Vertikoff	K-5	M	576 22	24%	740/833-1450 Fax 740/833-1499
ⓨ James Conger Elem Sch 10 Channing St, Delaware 43015 Josh Page	K-5	MT	407 18	41%	740/833-1300 Fax 740/833-1349
ⓨ Laura Woodward Elem Sch 200 S Washington St, Delaware 43015 Eric Barr	PK-5	MT	629 22	49%	740/833-1600 Fax 740/833-1649
ⓨ Robert F Schultz Elem Sch 499 Applegate Ln, Delaware 43015 Travis Woodworth	K-5	M	691 20	29%	740/833-1400 Fax 740/833-1449

1	Superintendent	8	Curric/Instruct K-12	19	Chief Financial Officer	29	Family/Consumer Science	
2	Bus/Finance/Purchasing	9	Curric/Instruct Elem	20	Art K-12	30	Adult Education	
3	Buildings And Grounds	10	Curric/Instruct Sec	21	Art Elem	31	Career/Sch-to-Work K-12	
4	Food Service	11	Federal Program	22	Art Sec	32	Career/Sch-to-Work Elem	
5	Transportation	12	Title I	23	Music K-12	33	Career/Sch-to-Work Sec	
6	Athletic	13	Title V	24	Music Elem	34	Early Childhood Ed	
7	Health Services	14	Asst Superintendent	25	Music Sec	35	Health/Phys Education	
		15	Instructional Media Svcs	26	Business Education	36	Guidance Services K-12	
		16	Chief Operations Officer	27	Career & Tech Ed	37	Guidance Services Elem	
		17	Chief Academic Officer	28	Technology Education	38	Guidance Services Sec	
39	Social Studies K-12	49	English/Lang Arts Elem	59	Special Education Elem	69	Academic Assessment	
40	Social Studies Elem	50	English/Lang Arts Sec	60	Special Education Sec	70	Research/Development	
41	Social Studies Sec	51	Reading K-12	61	Foreign/World Lang K-12	71	Public Information	
42	Science K-12	52	Reading Elem	62	Foreign/World Lang Elem	72	Summer School	
43	Science Elem	53	Reading Sec	63	Foreign/World Lang Sec	73	Instructional Tech	
44	Science Sec	54	Remedial Reading K-12	64	Religious Education K-12	74	Inservice Training	
45	Math K-12	55	Remedial Reading Elem	65	Religious Education Elem	75	Marketing/Distributive	
46	Math Elem	56	Remedial Reading Sec	66	Religious Education Sec	76	Info Systems	
47	Math Sec	57	Bilingual/ELL	67	School Board President	77	Psychological Assess	
48	English/Lang Arts K-12	58	Special Education K-12	68	Teacher Personnel	78	Affirmative Action	

Ohio School Directory — Delaware County

Rutherford B Hayes High Sch | 9-12 | 1,611 | 29% | 740/833-1010
289 Euclid Ave, Delaware 43015 | | | | Fax 740/833-1099
Rick Stranges

● **Delaware Joint Voc Sch Dist** PID: 00798348 — 740/363-1993
4565 Columbus Pike, Delaware 43015 — Fax 740/548-0710

Schools: 2 \ **Teachers:** 50 \ **Students:** 1,000 \ **LEP Students:** 3 \ **Exp:** $304 (High) \ **Open-Close:** 08/13 - 05/21 \ **DTBP:** $237 (High) \ 🇫 🇹

Marybeth Freeman 1	Christopher Bell 2
Jack Higgins 3*	Ryan Eldridge 10,69*
Tammy Hall 11,288,298	Tom Marchetti 30*
Kathy Tornes 38,83,88*	David Gilliam 60,79*
Julie Wagner-Feasel 67	Alicia Mowry 71
Rory Gaydos 73,76,295*	Wayne Strunk 73,76,295*
Kristina Lucas 273*	

Public Schs..Principal	Grd	Prgm	Enr/#Cls	SN	
Delaware Area Career Ctr-North 1610 State Route 521, Delaware 43015 Tom Marchetti	Voc	G	600 30		740/363-1993 Fax 740/362-6461
Delaware Area Career Ctr-South 4565 Columbus Pike, Delaware 43015 Kristina Lucas	Voc	G	500 28		740/548-0708

● **Olentangy Local School Dist** PID: 00798300 — 740/657-4050
7840 Graphics Way, Lewis Center 43035 — Fax 740/657-4009

Schools: 25 \ **Teachers:** 1,032 \ **Students:** 22,125 \ **Special Ed Students:** 2,324 \ **LEP Students:** 450 \ **College-Bound:** 84% \ **Ethnic:** Asian 12%, African American 4%, Hispanic 3%, Caucasian 80% \ **Exp:** $149 (Low) \ **Poverty:** 2% \ **Title I:** $337,171 \ **Special Education:** $2,362,000 \ **Open-Close:** 08/15 - 05/21 \ **DTBP:** $198 (High) \ 🇫 🇹

Mark Raiff 1	Jeffrey Gordon 2
Randy Wright 3,5,15,68,91	Todd Meyer 3,17,68
Bethany Lanko 4	Lori Carter Evans 5
Jack Fette 8,18,69,288	Peggy McMurry 8
Marty Arganbright 11,58,77,79	Tonya Riedel 34*
Mindy Patrick 67	Devon Immelt 71
Krista Davis 71	Robert Sexton 73

Public Schs..Principal	Grd	Prgm	Enr/#Cls	SN	
Alum Creek Elem Sch 2515 Parklawn Dr, Lewis Center 43035 **Worth Brandy**	PK-5		568 31	2%	740/657-4600 Fax 740/657-4649
Arrowhead Elem Sch 2385 Hollenback Rd, Lewis Center 43035 Bridget McMillen	PK-5		684 31	17%	740/657-4650 Fax 740/657-4699
Berkshire Middle Sch 2869 S 3 Bs and K Rd, Galena 43021 Carla Baker	6-8		1,066	5%	740/657-5200 Fax 740/657-5299
Berlin High Sch 3140 Berlin Station Rd, Delaware 43015 Todd Spinner	9-12		905		740/657-5901
Chesire Elem Sch 2681 Gregory Rd, Delaware 43015 Anthony Elkins	PK-5		632	2%	740/657-5750 Fax 740/657-5799
Freedom Trail Elem Sch 6743 Bale Kenyon Rd, Lewis Center 43035 Steve Sargent	K-5		639	4%	740/657-5700 Fax 740/657-5749
Glen Oak Elem Sch 7300 Blue Holly Dr, Lewis Center 43035 Stephen Peters	PK-5		653	14%	740/657-5500 Fax 740/657-5549
Heritage Elem Sch 679 Lewis Center Rd, Lewis Center 43035 Susan Staum	PK-5		612	7%	740/657-5000 Fax 740/657-5049
Hyatts Middle Sch 6885 Sawmill Pkwy, Powell 43065 Derrick Gilliam	6-8		944 48	3%	740/657-5400 Fax 740/657-5499
Indian Springs Elem Sch 3828 Home Rd, Powell 43065 Chris Heuser	PK-5		665 29	1%	740/657-4950 Fax 740/657-4999
Johnnycake Corners Elem Sch 6783 Falling Meadows Dr, Galena 43021 Peter Stern	PK-5		688 24	2%	740/657-5650 Fax 740/657-5699
Liberty High Sch 3584 Home Rd, Powell 43065 Michael Starner	9-12		2,148	3%	740/657-4200 Fax 740/657-4299 🇫 🇹
Liberty Middle Sch 7940 Liberty Rd N, Powell 43065 Nichole Crothers	6-8		1,035	2%	740/657-4400 Fax 740/657-4499
Liberty Tree Elem Sch 6877 Sawmill Pkwy, Powell 43065 Terri Caton	PK-5		628 38	2%	740/657-5600 Fax 740/657-5649
Oak Creek Elem Sch 1256 Westwood Dr, Lewis Center 43035 Julie Lather	PK-5		664 40	13%	740/657-4700 Fax 740/657-4749
Olentangy High Sch 675 Lewis Center Rd, Lewis Center 43035 Robert Griffiths	9-12		1,445	6%	740/657-4100 Fax 740/657-4199
Olentangy Meadows Elem Sch 8950 Emerald Hill Dr, Lewis Center 43035 Kristin Baker	K-5		705	14%	740/657-5550 Fax 740/657-5599
Olentangy Spec Needs Pre-Sch 814 Sawmill Pkwy, Powell 43065 Tonya Riedel	Spec		200 19		740/657-4350 Fax 740/657-4399
Orange High Sch 2840 E Orange Rd, Lewis Center 43035 Trond Smith	9-12		2,020	11%	740/657-5100 Fax 740/657-5199
Orange Middle Sch 2680 E Orange Rd, Lewis Center 43035 Scott Cunningham	6-8		1,067	15%	740/657-5300 Fax 740/657-5399
Scioto Ridge Elem Sch 8715 Big Bear Ave, Powell 43065 Melany Ondrus	PK-5		621 30	7%	740/657-4800 Fax 740/657-4849
Shanahan Middle Sch 814 Shanahan Rd, Lewis Center 43035 Josh McDainels	6-8		971 20	6%	740/657-4300 Fax 740/657-4398 🇫 🇹
Tyler Run Elem Sch 580 Salisbury Dr, Powell 43065 Jennifer Mazza	PK-5		677 30	1%	740/657-4900 Fax 740/657-4949
Walnut Creek Elem Sch 5600 Grand Oak Blvd, Galena 43021 Michelle Seitz	PK-5		640 31	3%	740/657-4750 Fax 740/657-4799
Wyandot Run Elem Sch 2800 Carriage Rd, Powell 43065 Mo Ross	PK-5		695 50	3%	740/657-4850 Fax 740/657-4899

DELAWARE CATHOLIC SCHOOLS

● **Diocese of Columbus Ed Office** PID: 00802717
Listing includes only schools located in this county. See District Index for location of Diocesan Offices.

---

79 Student Personnel	91 Safety/Security	275 Response To Intervention	298 Grant Writer/Ptnrships	**School Programs**	**Social Media**		
80 Driver Ed/Safety	92 Magnet School	277 Remedial Math K-12	750 Chief Innovation Officer	A = Alternative Program			
81 Gifted/Talented	93 Parental Involvement	280 Literacy Coach	751 Chief of Staff	G = Adult Classes	🇫 = Facebook		
82 Video Services	95 Tech Prep Program	285 STEM	752 Social Emotional Learning	M = Magnet Program			
83 Substance Abuse Prev	97 Chief Information Officer	286 Digital Learning		T = Title I Schoolwide	🇹 = Twitter		
84 Erate	98 Chief Technology Officer	288 Common Core Standards	**Other School Types**	V = Career & Tech Ed Programs			
85 AIDS Education	270 Character Education	294 Accountability	Ⓐ = Alternative School				
88 Alternative/At Risk	271 Migrant Education	295 Network System	Ⓒ = Charter School	New Schools are shaded			
89 Multi-Cultural Curriculum	273 Teacher Mentor	296 Title II Programs	Ⓜ = Magnet School	New Superintendents and Principals are bold			
90 Social Work	274 Before/After Sch	297 Webmaster	Ⓨ = Year-Round School	Personnel with email addresses are underscored			

Erie County

Market Data Retrieval

Catholic Schs..Principal	Grd	Prgm	Enr/#Cls SN	
St Mary Sch 66 E William St, Delaware 43015 Gina Stull	PK-8		373 20	740/362-8961 Fax 740/362-3733
St Paul Sch 61 Moss Rd, Westerville 43082 Dr Kathleen Norris	K-8		866 26	614/882-2710 Fax 614/882-5998

DELAWARE PRIVATE SCHOOLS

Private Schs..Principal	Grd	Prgm	Enr/#Cls SN	
All Children of the World Acad 6841 Freeman Rd, Westerville 43082 Nancy Dumford	PK-K		220 8	614/890-8985 Fax 614/890-3825
Christian Life Church Academy 425 N Spring Rd, Westerville 43082 Jason Elliott	K-12		13	614/794-2529 Fax 614/794-9166
Delaware Christian Sch 45 Belle Ave, Delaware 43015 Tom Carroll	K-12		300 16	740/363-8425 Fax 740/369-8378
Genoa Christian Academy 7562 Lewis Center Rd, Westerville 43082 Shelly Miller \ Craig Bartley	PK-12		208 20	740/965-5433 Fax 740/965-8214
Grace Community Sch 715 W William St, Delaware 43015 Phil Mears	K-7		63	740/363-5800
Polaris Christian Academy 2150 E Powell Rd, Lewis Center 43035 Judy Hoban	K-8		140 9	614/431-6888 Fax 614/431-0137
Primrose Sch of Lewis Center 8273 Owenfield Dr, Powell 43065 Sheri Schmidt	PK-K		165 1	740/548-5808 Fax 740/548-5833
Village Academy 284 S Liberty St, Powell 43065 Tres Marangoni	PK-12		325	614/841-0050 Fax 614/841-0501

ERIE COUNTY

ERIE COUNTY SCHOOLS

• **North Point Ed Svc Ctr** PID: 00798843   419/627-3900
4918 Milan Rd, Sandusky 44870   Fax 419/627-3999

Douglas Crooks 1,11
Andrea Smith 8,15
Karen Ruf 34,58
Matt Bauer 2
John Ruf 15
Dwayne Arnold 81

ERIE PUBLIC SCHOOLS

• **Edison Local Schools District** PID: 00798374   419/499-3000
140 S Main St, Milan 44846   Fax 419/499-4859

Schools: 3 \ *Teachers:* 89 \ *Students:* 1,650 \ *Special Ed Students:* 196 \ *LEP Students:* 15 \ *College-Bound:* 78% \ *Ethnic:* African American 1%, Hispanic 5%, Caucasian 93% \ *Exp:* $225 (Med) \ *Poverty:* 15% \ *Title I:* $332,675 \ *Special Education:* $268,000 \ *Open-Close:* 08/21 - 05/29 \ *DTBP:* $189 (High)

Thomas Roth 1
Shelly Geason 4
Rita Harpring 5
Dean Stanfield 8,11,16,69,74,83,288,298
Stephanie Bradley 11,57,58
Elisa Brown 38*
Jason La Civita 73*
Jeff Goodwin 88*
Anne Arnold 2
Joe Ryan 5
Rebecca Emery 7
Stanfield Dean 8
Elysa Brown 31,36*
John Betts 67
Rob Laconis 76,295,297*

Public Schs..Principal	Grd	Prgm	Enr/#Cls SN	
Edison Elem Sch 140 S Main St, Milan 44846 Davy Hermes	PK-3	T	514 30	47% 419/499-4625
Edison High Sch 2603 State Route 113 E, Milan 44846 Jeff Goodwin	9-12	V	398 25	28% 419/499-4652 Fax 419/499-2035
Edison Middle Sch 20 Center St, Berlin HTS 44814 Cory Smith	4-8	T	564 17	41% 419/588-2079 Fax 419/588-3212

• **Ehove Joint Voc School Dist** PID: 00798829   419/499-4663
316 Mason Rd W, Milan 44846   Fax 419/499-4076

Schools: 1 \ *Teachers:* 54 \ *Students:* 850 \ *College-Bound:* 40% \ *Exp:* $917 (High) \ *Open-Close:* 08/20 - 05/27 \ *DTBP:* $164 (High)

Sharon Mastroianni 1,11
David Jenkins 3,73,76,84,295
Katy Reed-Brown 16,82*
Matthew Ehrhardt 60,83,88*
Sharon MacNicol 273*
Tim Coffman 2,19
Terri Jones 12,30
Laura Dowdell 30
Paul Lockwood 67

Public Schs..Principal	Grd	Prgm	Enr/#Cls SN	
Ehove Career Center 316 Mason Rd W, Milan 44846 Erika Beckman	Voc	AG	850	419/499-4663

• **Huron City School Dist** PID: 00798427   419/433-1234
712 Cleveland Rd E, Huron 44839   Fax 419/433-7095

Schools: 4 \ *Teachers:* 76 \ *Students:* 1,324 \ *Special Ed Students:* 186 \ *LEP Students:* 5 \ *College-Bound:* 63% \ *Ethnic:* Asian 1%, African American 1%, Hispanic 4%, Caucasian 93% \ *Exp:* $219 (Med) \ *Poverty:* 12% \ *Title I:* $245,613 \ *Special Education:* $259,000 \ *Open-Close:* 08/28 - 06/09 \ *DTBP:* $236 (High)

Dennis Muratori 1
Sue Whitaker 4*
Julie McDonald 8,11,31,273,296,298
Jodi Mast 67
Dawn Jacobs 2,84
Janis Wallace 7,83,85*
Holly Charville 12,58,88*

---

1 Superintendent	8 Curric/Instruct K-12	19 Chief Financial Officer	29 Family/Consumer Science	39 Social Studies K-12
2 Bus/Finance/Purchasing	9 Curric/Instruct Elem	20 Art K-12	30 Adult Education	40 Social Studies Elem
3 Buildings And Grounds	10 Curric/Instruct Sec	21 Art Elem	31 Career/Sch-to-Work K-12	41 Social Studies Sec
4 Food Service	11 Federal Program	22 Art Sec	32 Career/Sch-to-Work Elem	42 Science K-12
5 Transportation	12 Title I	23 Music K-12	33 Career/Sch-to-Work Sec	43 Science Elem
6 Athletic	13 Title V	24 Music Elem	34 Early Childhood Ed	44 Science Sec
7 Health Services	14 Asst Superintendent	25 Music Sec	35 Health/Phys Education	45 Math K-12
	15 Instructional Media Svcs	26 Business Education	36 Guidance Services K-12	46 Math Elem
	16 Chief Operations Officer	27 Career & Tech Ed	37 Guidance Services Elem	47 Math Sec
	17 Chief Academic Officer	28 Technology Education	38 Guidance Services Sec	48 English/Lang Arts K-12
49 English/Lang Arts Elem	59 Special Education Elem	69 Academic Assessment		
50 English/Lang Arts Sec	60 Special Education Sec	70 Research/Development		
51 Reading K-12	61 Foreign/World Lang K-12	71 Public Information		
52 Reading Elem	62 Foreign/World Lang Elem	72 Summer School		
53 Reading Sec	63 Foreign/World Lang Sec	73 Instructional Tech		
54 Remedial Reading K-12	64 Religious Education K-12	74 Inservice Training		
55 Remedial Reading Elem	65 Religious Education Elem	75 Marketing/Distributive		
56 Remedial Reading Sec	66 Religious Education Sec	76 Info Systems		
57 Bilingual/ELL	67 School Board President	77 Psychological Assess		
58 Special Education K-12	68 Teacher Personnel	78 Affirmative Action		

Ohio School Directory — Erie County

Public Schs..Principal	Grd	Prgm	Enr/#Cls	SN	
Huron High Sch 710 Cleveland Rd W, Huron 44839 Tim Lamb	9-12		463 35	22%	419/433-1234 Fax 419/433-2339
McCormick Junior High Sch 325 Ohio St, Huron 44839 Chad Carter	7-8		195 21	26%	419/433-1234 Fax 419/433-8427
Shawnee Elem Sch 712 Cleveland Rd E, Huron 44839 Brian Kucbel	PK-2	T	294	33%	419/433-1234 Fax 419/616-0054
Woodlands Intermediate Sch 1810 Maple Ave, Huron 44839 Mark Doughty	3-6		372 36	34%	419/433-1234 Fax 419/433-9619

• Kelleys Island Local Sch Dist PID: 00798477
528 Division St, Kelleys Is 43438
419/746-2730 Fax 419/746-2271

Schools: 1 \ **Students:** 5 \ **College-Bound:** 100% \ **Ethnic:** Caucasian 100% \ **Exp:** $767 (High) \ **Open-Close:** 08/27 - 06/05 \ **DTBP:** $174 (High)

Phil Thiede 1,11,84
Jane Ehnsperger 7
Betty Schwiefert 2
Dr Pete LeGere 67

Public Schs..Principal	Grd	Prgm	Enr/#Cls	SN	
Kelleys Island Local Sch 528 Division St, Kelleys Is 43438 Phil Thiede	PK-12		5 5		419/746-2730

• Margaretta Local School Dist PID: 00798506
305 S Washington St, Castalia 44824
419/684-5322 Fax 419/684-9003

Schools: 3 \ **Teachers:** 63 \ **Students:** 2,602 \ **Special Ed Students:** 166 \ **College-Bound:** 48% \ **Ethnic:** African American 3%, Hispanic 6%, Caucasian 91% \ **Exp:** $307 (High) \ **Poverty:** 10% \ **Title I:** $165,512 \ **Special Education:** $213,000 \ **Open-Close:** 08/27 - 06/05 \ **DTBP:** $254 (High) \ [f]

Dennis Mock 1,83
Sarah Ransom 4
Drew Grahl 6*
Kathleen Hall 58,77,275*
Mark Freeh 73*
Diane Keegan 2,3
Courtney Dresser 5
Heather Lott 36*
Andrew Warner 67

Public Schs..Principal	Grd	Prgm	Enr/#Cls	SN	
Margaretta Elem Sch 5906 Bogart Rd W, Castalia 44824 Keven Wise	PK-5	T	557 28	35%	419/684-5357 Fax 419/684-6049
Margaretta High Sch 209 Lowell St, Castalia 44824 Rod Smith	6-12		586 48	31%	419/684-5351 Fax 419/684-5632
Ⓐ Townsend Cmty Sch © 207 Lowell St, Castalia 44824 Ryan Bohn	9-12	T	1,459		419/684-5402 Fax 419/684-5537

• Perkins Local School Dist PID: 00798556
3714 Campbell St Ste B, Sandusky 44870
419/625-0484 Fax 419/621-2052

Schools: 4 \ **Teachers:** 119 \ **Students:** 1,950 \ **Special Ed Students:** 196 \ **LEP Students:** 14 \ **College-Bound:** 71% \ **Ethnic:** Asian 2%, African American 5%, Hispanic 7%, Caucasian 86% \ **Exp:** $136 (Low) \ **Poverty:** 8% \ **Title I:** $209,726 \ **Special Education:** $560,000 \ **Open-Close:** 08/28 - 06/04 \ **DTBP:** $107 (High) \ [f] [t]

Todd Boggs 1
Dan Bowman 2
Greg Linkenbach 3
Randy Conaway 5
Rena McClelan 8,69,280
Alice James 37*
Dr Bradley Mitchel 67
Brittany Remaklus 79
Karen Wells 4
Matthew Smith 6*
Margaret Warnicke 36,83*
Chris Guss 58*
Annette Senish 76

Public Schs..Principal	Grd	Prgm	Enr/#Cls	SN	
Briar Middle Sch 3700 South Ave, Sandusky 44870 Scott Matheny	6-8		445 29	34%	419/625-0132 Fax 419/625-0523
Furry Elem Sch 310 Douglas Dr, Sandusky 44870 Jenn Long	PK-2		459 22	35%	419/625-4352 Fax 419/625-6211 [f] [t]
Meadowlawn Intermediate Sch 1313 E Strub Rd, Sandusky 44870 Jeremy Hiser	3-5	T	423 23	34%	419/625-0214 Fax 419/625-6459 [f] [t]
Perkins High Sch 3714 Campbell St, Sandusky 44870 Jeffrey Harbal	9-12		573 25	26%	419/625-1252 Fax 419/621-2057 [f] [t]

• Sandusky City School Dist PID: 00798611
407 Decatur St, Sandusky 44870
419/626-6940 Fax 419/621-2784

Schools: 7 \ **Teachers:** 208 \ **Students:** 3,250 \ **Special Ed Students:** 577 \ **LEP Students:** 19 \ **College-Bound:** 40% \ **Ethnic:** African American 45%, Hispanic 6%, Caucasian 49% \ **Exp:** $134 (Low) \ **Poverty:** 30% \ **Title I:** $2,001,373 \ **Special Education:** $916,000 \ **Open-Close:** 08/29 - 06/04 \ **DTBP:** $188 (High)

Dr Eugene Sanders 1
Kevin Toms 3,91
Kraft Bradley 4
Shawn Coakley 6*
Megan Peugeot 8,57,58,88
Dr Stephen Sturgill 15,68,79,294,751
Brigitte Churchwell 67
Eric Eckenrode 73,98
Rebecca Muratori 274*
Gina Deppert 2,19
Brad Kraft 4
Ted Peters 5
Julie McDonald 8,11,81,288,296*
Dr Vilicia Cade 12
Elizabeth Herman-Wells 16*
Claire Grantier 73,295
Jamie Biecheler 79
Sherry Smith 286

Public Schs..Principal	Grd	Prgm	Enr/#Cls	SN	
Hancock Elem Sch 2314 Hancock St, Sandusky 44870 Kathy Pace-Sanders	PK-6	T	417 15		419/984-1210 Fax 419/621-2854
Mills Elem Sch 1918 Mills St, Sandusky 44870 Marie Prieto	PK-6	T	360 15		419/984-1230 Fax 419/621-2855
Ontario Elem Sch 924 Ontario St, Sandusky 44870 Cosetta Adkins	K-6	T	360 17		419/984-1250 Fax 419/621-2852
Osborne Elem Sch 920 W Osborne St, Sandusky 44870 Rebecca Muratori	K-6	T	379 20		419/984-1270 Fax 419/626-9435
Sandusky High Sch 2130A Hayes Ave, Sandusky 44870 Eric Talbot	9-12	T	898 85		419/984-1068 Fax 419/621-2751
Sandusky Middle Sch 2130 Hayes Ave, Sandusky 44870 Timothy Kozak	7-8	T	487 30		419/984-1182 Fax 419/621-2849
Venice Heights Elem Sch 4501 Venice Heights Blvd, Sandusky 44870 Donna Brown	K-6	T	289 19		419/984-1290 Fax 419/621-2850

---

79 Student Personnel
80 Driver Ed/Safety
81 Gifted/Talented
82 Video Services
83 Substance Abuse Prev
84 Erate
85 AIDS Education
88 Alternative/At Risk
89 Multi-Cultural Curriculum
90 Social Work

91 Safety/Security
92 Magnet School
93 Parental Involvement
95 Tech Prep Program
97 Chief Infomation Officer
98 Chief Technology Officer
270 Character Education
271 Migrant Education
273 Teacher Mentor
274 Before/After Sch

275 Response To Intervention
277 Remedial Math K-12
280 Literacy Coach
285 STEM
286 Digital Learning
288 Common Core Standards
294 Accountability
295 Network System
296 Title II Programs
297 Webmaster

298 Grant Writer/Ptnrships
750 Chief Innovation Officer
751 Chief of Staff
752 Social Emotional Learning

Other School Types
Ⓐ = Alternative School
© = Charter School
Ⓜ = Magnet School
Ⓨ = Year-Round School

School Programs
A = Alternative Program
G = Adult Classes
M = Magnet Program
T = Title I Schoolwide
V = Career & Tech Ed Programs

Social Media
[f] = Facebook
[t] = Twitter

New Schools are shaded
New Superintendents and Principals are bold
Personnel with email addresses are underscored

Fairfield County

Market Data Retrieval

- **Vermilion Local School Dist** PID: 00798752   440/204-1700
  1250 Sanford St Ste A, Vermilion 44089   Fax 440/204-1771

Schools: 3 \ **Teachers:** 90 \ **Students:** 1,900 \ **Special Ed Students:** 329 \ **LEP Students:** 4 \ **College-Bound:** 57% \ **Ethnic:** Asian 1%, Hispanic 5%, Caucasian 94% \ **Exp:** $119 (Low) \ **Poverty:** 13% \ **Title I:** $372,178 \ **Special Education:** $528,000 \ **Open-Close:** 08/29 - 06/09 \ **DTBP:** $241 (High) \ f

Name	#	Name	#
Phill Pempin	1	Justin Klingshirn	2
James Williamson	3	Denise Zielske	4
David Johnson	5	Andrew Stillman	6
Jim Balotta	8,11,57,69,91,273,285,288	Laura Wheeler	31,36,83*
Karen Blackburn	58*	Michael Stark	67
Shawn Bergman	73,295		

Public Schs..Principal	Grd	Prgm	Enr/#Cls	SN	
Sailorway Middle Sch 5355 Sailorway Dr, Vermilion 44089 Beth Bartlome	4-7	T	541 45	39%	440/204-1702 Fax 440/204-1756 f t
Vermilion Elem Sch 1285 Douglas St, Vermilion 44089 Bonnie Meyer	PK-3	T	547 23	45%	440/204-1703 Fax 440/204-1747
Vermilion High Sch 1250 Sanford St, Vermilion 44089 Lisa Deliz	8-12		737 56	37%	440/204-1701 Fax 440/204-1781

ERIE CATHOLIC SCHOOLS

- **Diocese of Toledo Ed Office** PID: 00818297
  Listing includes only schools located in this county. See District Index for location of Diocesan Offices.

Catholic Schs..Principal	Grd	Prgm	Enr/#Cls	SN
Sandusky Central Catholic Sch 410 W Jefferson St, Sandusky 44870 Ryan Wikel	PK-12	V	647 37	419/626-1892 Fax 419/621-2252
St Mary Catholic Sch 5450 Ohio St, Vermilion 44089 Barb Bialko	PK-6		130 8	440/967-7911 Fax 440/967-8287
St Peter Catholic Sch 429 Huron St, Huron 44839 Anne Asher	PK-8		175 11	419/433-4640 Fax 419/433-2118

ERIE PRIVATE SCHOOLS

Private Schs..Principal	Grd	Prgm	Enr/#Cls	SN
Firelands Christian Academy 3809 Maple Ave, Castalia 44824 Rusty Yost	K-10		48 5	419/684-8642 Fax 419/684-5378
Firelands Montessori Academy 329 Ohio St, Huron 44839 Heather Gray	PK-8		87 6	419/433-6181 Fax 419/433-8199

ERIE REGIONAL CENTERS

- **Noeca-Northern Ohio Ed CA** PID: 04499582   419/627-1439
  219 Howard Dr, Sandusky 44870   Fax 419/627-5608

Name	#	Name	#
Laurie Hille	1	Nancy Clark	2
Amanda Fackler	16	Diane Young	79
George Yakoobian	295		

FAIRFIELD COUNTY

FAIRFIELD COUNTY SCHOOLS

- **Fairfield Co Ed Service Center** PID: 02089155   740/653-3193
  955 Liberty Dr, Lancaster 43130   Fax 740/653-4053

Name	#	Name	#
Dr Marie Ward	1	Laura Cassell	2
Paul Alford	8	Sarah Patterson	58
Lou Stemen	67	Matt Connell	73
James Young	81		

County Schs..Principal	Grd	Prgm	Enr/#Cls	SN
Fairfield Co Early Chldhd Ctr 1592 Granville Pike, Lancaster 43130 Jodi Blais	Spec		58 8	740/652-7225 Fax 740/681-5731
Forest Rose Sch 1592 Granville Pike, Lancaster 43130 Cathy Hunter	Spec		53 8	740/652-7225 Fax 740/681-5731

FAIRFIELD PUBLIC SCHOOLS

- **Amanda-Clearcreek Local SD** PID: 00798855   740/969-7250
  328 E Main St, Amanda 43102   Fax 740/969-7620

Schools: 4 \ **Teachers:** 94 \ **Students:** 1,445 \ **Special Ed Students:** 188 \ **LEP Students:** 3 \ **College-Bound:** 45% \ **Ethnic:** Hispanic 1%, Caucasian 98% \ **Exp:** $273 (Med) \ **Poverty:** 9% \ **Title I:** $242,621 \ **Special Education:** $303,000 \ **Open-Close:** 08/13 - 05/21 \ **DTBP:** $173 (High) \ t

Name	#	Name	#
Jb Dick	1	Jill Bradford	2
Connie Shaffer	4*	Jordyn Lee	5
Emily Leist	7*	Paul Alford	8,58
Becky Wagner	11*	Liah Davis	37*
Brandon Kern	67	Karen Shull	73*
Nathan Downour	295*		

Public Schs..Principal	Grd	Prgm	Enr/#Cls	SN
Amanda-Clearcreek Elem Sch 328 E Main St, Amanda 43102 **Elizabeth Wills**	3-5	T	340 19	740/969-7253 Fax 740/969-4764
Amanda-Clearcreek High Sch 328 E Main St, Amanda 43102 Scott Hinton	9-12	V	432 30	88% 740/969-7251 Fax 740/969-4764
Amanda-Clearcreek Middle Sch 328 E Main St, Amanda 43102 Aimee Cochran	6-8	T	352 25	740/969-7252 Fax 740/969-4764

#		#		#		#		#		#	
1	Superintendent	8	Curric/Instruct K-12	19	Chief Financial Officer	29	Family/Consumer Science	39	Social Studies K-12	49	English/Lang Arts Elem	59	Special Education Elem	69	Academic Assessment
2	Bus/Finance/Purchasing	9	Curric/Instruct Elem	20	Art K-12	30	Adult Education	40	Social Studies Elem	50	English/Lang Arts Sec	60	Special Education Sec	70	Research/Development
3	Buildings And Grounds	10	Curric/Instruct Sec	21	Art Elem	31	Career/Sch-to-Work K-12	41	Social Studies Sec	51	Reading K-12	61	Foreign/World Lang K-12	71	Public Information
4	Food Service	11	Federal Program	22	Art Sec	32	Career/Sch-to-Work Elem	42	Science K-12	52	Reading Elem	62	Foreign/World Lang Elem	72	Summer School
5	Transportation	12	Title I	23	Music K-12	33	Career/Sch-to-Work Sec	43	Science Elem	53	Reading Sec	63	Foreign/World Lang Sec	73	Instructional Program
6	Athletic	13	Title V	24	Music Elem	34	Early Childhood Ed	44	Science Sec	54	Remedial Reading K-12	64	Religious Education K-12	74	Inservice Training
7	Health Services	15	Asst Superintendent	25	Music Sec	35	Health/Phys Education	45	Math K-12	55	Remedial Reading Elem	65	Religious Education Elem	75	Marketing/Distributive
		16	Instructional Media Svcs	26	Business Education	36	Guidance Services K-12	46	Math Elem	56	Remedial Reading Sec	66	Religious Education Sec	76	Info Systems
		17	Chief Operations Officer	27	Career & Tech Ed	37	Guidance Services Elem	47	Math Sec	57	Bilingual/ELL	67	School Board President	77	Psychological Assess
		18	Chief Academic Officer	28	Technology Education	38	Guidance Services Sec	48	English/Lang Arts K-12	58	Special Education K-12	68	Teacher Personnel	78	Affirmative Action

Ohio School Directory

Fairfield County

Amanda-Clearcreek Primary Sch	K-2	T	321	51%	740/969-7254
414 N School St, Amanda 43102					Fax 740/969-3086
Brooke Marshall					

• **Berne Union Local School Dist** PID: 00798893   740/746-8341
506 N Main St, Sugar Grove 43155   Fax 740/746-9824

Schools: 2 \ **Teachers:** 55 \ **Students:** 950 \ **Special Ed Students:** 142 \ **College-Bound:** 53% \ **Ethnic:** African American 1%, Hispanic 1%, Caucasian 98% \ **Exp:** $159 (Low) \ **Poverty:** 14% \ **Title I:** $192,731 \ **Special Education:** $152,000 \ **Open-Close:** 08/20 - 06/03 \ **DTBP:** $187 (High)

Richard Spindler	1,11	Kirk Grandy	2
James Snoke	3,5	Sherry Folds	4*
Paul Alford	8,273	Jennifer Lehman	58
Rex Coleman	67	David McMannis	73,76,295*
Nicole Jones	77	Melissa Drewery	298

Public Schs..Principal	Grd	Prgm	Enr/#Cls	SN	
Berne Union Elem Sch	PK-6	T	456		740/746-9668
506 N Main St, Sugar Grove 43155			22		
Steven Templin					
Berne Union High Sch	7-12	TV	373	99%	740/746-9956
506 N Main St, Sugar Grove 43155			27		Fax 740/746-0291
John Parker					

• **Bloom-Carroll Local Sch Dist** PID: 00798922   614/837-6560
5240 Plum Rd, Carroll 43112   Fax 740/756-4221

Schools: 4 \ **Teachers:** 91 \ **Students:** 2,000 \ **Special Ed Students:** 197 \ **LEP Students:** 4 \ **College-Bound:** 61% \ **Ethnic:** Asian 1%, African American 1%, Hispanic 1%, Caucasian 97% \ **Exp:** $196 (Low) \ **Poverty:** 5% \ **Title I:** $121,480 \ **Special Education:** $216,000 \ **Open-Close:** 08/22 - 05/28 \ **DTBP:** $167 (High) \ 🇫 🇹

Shawn Haughn	1	Travis Bigam	2,11,84,298
John Pugh	3	Marilyn Enyart	4
Carmen Pfelman	5	Chad Little	6*
Jodi Raneger	8,11,51,54,57,286,288,296	Mary Ford	16,82*
Amy Moore	27,30*	Richard Gaulke	36,69*
Cynthia Freeman	58,88	Joe Abbott	67
Mark Thomas	73,76,295*		

Public Schs..Principal	Grd	Prgm	Enr/#Cls	SN	
Bloom-Carroll High Sch	9-12		561	17%	740/756-4317
5240 Plum Rd, Carroll 43112			35		Fax 740/756-9525
Nathan Conrad					
Bloom-Carroll Intermediate Sch	3-4		332	19%	614/837-4044
200 S Market Street, Lithopolis 43136			18		Fax 740/756-9525
Stephen Rozeski					
Bloom-Carroll Middle Sch	5-8		669	18%	614/837-6205
71 S Beaver St, Carroll 43112			20		Fax 740/756-7466
Chad Young					🇫 🇹
Bloom-Carroll Primary	K-2		482	19%	740/756-4326
69 S Beaver St, Carroll 43112			18		Fax 740/756-7551
Vicky Pease					

• **Fairfield Union Local Sch Dist** PID: 00798972   740/536-7384
6417 Cincinnati-Zainsville Rd, Lancaster 43130   Fax 740/536-9132

Schools: 4 \ **Teachers:** 100 \ **Students:** 2,000 \ **Special Ed Students:** 262 \ **LEP Students:** 3 \ **Ethnic:** African American 1%, Hispanic 1%, Caucasian 98% \ **Exp:** $111 (Low) \ **Poverty:** 10% \ **Title I:** $265,882 \ **Special Education:** $322,000 \ **Open-Close:** 08/15 - 05/21 \ **DTBP:** $192 (High)

Chad Bellville	1	Kevin Miller	2
Scott Philabaum	3,8,11,15,16,69,73,297	Sally McCandlish	4*
Barbara Gaskins	5	Andy Clark	6
Carole Osborne	7,85*	Eydie Schilling	11,296,298
Elsie Sullivan	16,82*	Cathy Poston	36,83*
Brian Funk	37,273*	Tiffany Wade	58
Ben Myers	67	Andy Doss	295*

Public Schs..Principal	Grd	Prgm	Enr/#Cls	SN	
Bremen Elem Sch	K-4	T	360	45%	740/569-4135
210 Strayer Ave, Bremen 43107			16		Fax 740/569-9605
Dawn Rice					
Fairfield Union High Sch	9-12	V	576	33%	740/536-7306
6675 Cincinnati-Zainsvl Rd NE, Lancaster 43130			37		Fax 740/536-7911
Matt McPhail					
Pleasantville Elem Sch	K-4	T	373	40%	740/468-2181
300 W Columbus St, Pleasantville 43148			16		Fax 740/468-3539
Michael Myers					
Rushville Middle Sch	5-8	T	595	35%	740/536-7249
6409 Cincinnati-Zainsville Rd, Lancaster 43130			15		Fax 740/536-7211
Tricia Haughn					

• **Lancaster City School Dist** PID: 00799031   740/687-7300
345 E Mulberry St, Lancaster 43130   Fax 740/687-7303

Schools: 9 \ **Teachers:** 327 \ **Students:** 6,300 \ **Special Ed Students:** 993 \ **LEP Students:** 20 \ **College-Bound:** 48% \ **Ethnic:** African American 3%, Hispanic 2%, Caucasian 95% \ **Exp:** $382 (High) \ **Poverty:** 17% \ **Title I:** $1,793,910 \ **Special Education:** $1,251,000 \ **Open-Close:** 08/21 - 06/02 \ **DTBP:** $188 (High) \ 🇫

Steve Wigton	1	Jerry Rainey	2,73
Casey Rainier	3	Kara Smith	4
Kip Slater	5	Pam Bosser	6
Sarah Thimmes	7	Jenny O'Hare	8,11,16,69,275
Kevin Snyder	10	Ben Factor	23*
Donna McCance	58	Dianne Garlinger	67
Nathan Hale	68	Sarah Westbrooks	69
Jackie McCurdy	76	Ashley Jones	81

Public Schs..Principal	Grd	Prgm	Enr/#Cls	SN	
General Sherman Jr High Sch	6-8	T	697	54%	740/687-7344
1930 Election House Rd NW, Lancaster 43130			20		Fax 740/687-3443
Charles Page					
Gorsuch West Elem Sch	K-5	T	560	74%	740/687-7332
440 Trace Dr, Lancaster 43130			20		Fax 740/687-7202
Terri Garrett					
Lancaster City Pre-School	PK-PK		87		740/687-7340
1450 Marietta Rd, Ashville 43103					Fax 740/687-7208
Brenda Zeiders					
Lancaster Senior High Sch	9-12	TV	1,821	45%	740/681-7500
1312 Granville Pike, Lancaster 43130			50		Fax 740/681-7505
Scott Burre					
Medill Elem Sch	K-5	T	680		740/687-7352
1160 Sheridan Dr, Lancaster 43130			24		Fax 740/687-7205
Jennifer Woods					🇫

79 Student Personnel	91 Safety/Security	275 Response To Intervention	298 Grant Writer/Ptnrships	**School Programs**	**Social Media**
80 Driver Ed/Safety	92 Magnet School	277 Remedial Math K-12	750 Chief Innovation Officer	A = Alternative Program	🇫 = Facebook
81 Gifted/Talented	93 Parental Involvement	280 Literacy Coach	751 Chief of Staff	G = Adult Classes	
82 Video Services	95 Tech Prep Program	285 STEM	752 Social Emotional Learning	M = Magnet Program	🇹 = Twitter
83 Substance Abuse Prev	97 Chief Infomation Officer	286 Digital Learning		T = Title I Schoolwide	
84 Erate	98 Chief Technology Officer	288 Common Core Standards	**Other School Types**	V = Career & Tech Ed Programs	
85 AIDS Education	270 Character Education	294 Accountability	Ⓐ = Alternative School		
88 Alternative/At Risk	271 Migrant Education	295 Network System	Ⓒ = Charter School	New Schools are shaded	
89 Multi-Cultural Curriculum	273 Teacher Mentor	296 Title II Programs	Ⓜ = Magnet School	New Superintendents and Principals are bold	
90 Social Work	274 Before/After Sch	297 Webmaster	Ⓨ = Year-Round School	Personnel with email addresses are underscored	

OH—63

Fairfield County

Mt Pleasant Elem Sch 712 N Broad St, Lancaster 43130 Shannon Burke	K-5	T	544 18	24%	740/687-7338 Fax 740/687-7207
Tallmadge Elem Sch 694 Talmadge Ave, Lancaster 43130 Jacob Campbell	K-5	T	578 24	73%	740/687-7336 Fax 740/687-7204
Tarhe Trails Elem Sch 2141 Greencrest Way, Lancaster 43130 Dustin Knight	K-5	T	604 19	42%	740/687-7330 Fax 740/687-7201
Thomas Ewing Jr High Sch 2024 Sheridan Dr, Lancaster 43130 Steve Poston	6-8	T	725 35	52%	740/687-7347 Fax 740/687-3446

• **Liberty Union-Thurstn Sch Dist** PID: 00799184   740/862-4171
1108 S Main St, Baltimore 43105   Fax 740/862-2015

Schools: 3 \ *Teachers:* 80 \ *Students:* 1,350 \ *Special Ed Students:* 197 \ *LEP Students:* 3 \ *College-Bound:* 72% \ *Ethnic:* Asian 1%, Hispanic 1%, Caucasian 98% \ *Exp:* $260 (Med) \ *Poverty:* 13% \ *Title I:* $241,514 \ *Open-Close:* 08/14 - 05/21 \ *DTBP:* $217 (High)

Mike Johnson	...1		April Bolyard	...2,11	
Joe Peardon	...3		Jan Friedrich	...4*	
Adam Leith	...5		Janet McKlaskey	...6	
Jeff Dupler	...7*		Jenifer Blackstone	...8,57,288,296	
Angela Kaper	...12*		Debbie Howdyshell	...16*	
Thomas Duplinsky	...38*		Sara Hayes	...58	
Caryl Caito	...67		Linda Rainey	...69*	
John LaBelle	...73,295*				

Public Schs..Principal	Grd	Prgm	Enr/#Cls		SN
Liberty Union Elem Sch 1000 S Main St, Baltimore 43105 Linda Rainey	K-4		439 24	42%	740/862-4143 Fax 740/862-0253
Liberty Union High Sch 500 W Washington St, Baltimore 43105 Matt Gallatin	9-12	V	393 45	30%	740/862-4107 Fax 740/862-4100
Liberty Union Middle Sch 994 S Main St, Baltimore 43105 Tim Turner	5-8		390 21	31%	740/862-4126 Fax 740/862-0239

• **Pickerington Local School Dist** PID: 00799225   614/833-2110
90 N East St, Pickerington 43147   Fax 614/833-2143

Schools: 15 \ *Teachers:* 521 \ *Students:* 10,600 \ *Special Ed Students:* 1,460 \ *LEP Students:* 487 \ *College-Bound:* 75% \ *Ethnic:* Asian 4%, African American 25%, Hispanic 6%, Caucasian 66% \ *Exp:* $150 (Low) \ *Poverty:* 7% \ *Title I:* $977,088 \ *Special Education:* $1,585,000 \ *Open-Close:* 08/15 - 05/22 \ *DTBP:* $205 (High)

Dr Chris Briggs	...1		Vince Utterback	...2	
Anna Ziebel	...3		Judy Riley	...4*	
Greg Kelley	...5		Sharon Schmitz	...7,85	
Sharon Caccimelio	...8*		Bob Blackburn	...15,79,83,91	
Zack Howard	...15,68		Erik Barbon	...57*	
Kristina Hulse	...58,296		Michelle Waterhouse	...67	
Debra Porter-Sawyer	...68		Crystal Davis	...71	
Brian Seymour	...73*		Ron Denton	...76	
Todd Stanley	...81				

Public Schs..Principal	Grd	Prgm	Enr/#Cls		SN
Diley Middle Sch 750 Preston Trails Dr, Pickerington 43147 Heather Hedgepeth	5-6		630 17	18%	614/830-2900 Fax 614/830-2910
Fairfield Elem Sch 13000 Coventry Ave, Pickerington 43147 Ruth Stickel	K-4	T	495 22	36%	614/834-7600 Fax 614/834-7610
Harmon Middle Sch 12410 Harmon Rd, Pickerington 43147 Jared Moore	5-6	T	548 26	40%	614/835-2000 Fax 614/835-2010
Heritage Elem Sch 100 N East St, Pickerington 43147 Chad Rice	K-4		342	27%	614/833-6385 Fax 614/883-6415
Lakeview Junior High Sch 12445 Ault Rd, Pickerington 43147 Pamela Bertke	7-8		776 50	27%	614/830-2200 Fax 614/834-3267
Ⓐ Pickerington Alternative Sch 7800 Refugee Rd, Pickerington 43147 Tom Phillips	9-12		92		614/830-2797 Fax 614/830-2768
Pickerington Elem Sch 775 Long Rd, Pickerington 43147 Melissa Moriarty	PK-4		446 28	27%	614/548-1400 Fax 614/548-1410
Pickerington High Sch Central 300 Opportunity Way, Pickerington 43147 Stacy Tennenbaum	9-12		1,768 34	26%	614/548-1800 Fax 614/548-1810
Pickerington High School North 7800 Refugee Rd, Pickerington 43147 Mark Ulbrich	9-12		1,644	20%	614/830-2700 Fax 614/833-3660
Ridgeview STEM Junior High Sch 130 Hill Rd S, Pickerington 43147 Eric Koch	7-8		918 46	25%	614/548-1700 Fax 614/548-1710
Sycamore Creek Elem Sch 500 Sycamore Creek St, Pickerington 43147 Nikki Arnold	PK-4		654	12%	614/834-6200 Fax 614/834-6210
Toll Gate Elem Sch 12183 Tollgate Rd, Pickerington 43147 Kristi Motsch	K-4		699	12%	614/834-6300 Fax 614/834-6310
Toll Gate Middle Sch 12089 Tollgate Rd, Pickerington 43147 Kara Jackson	5-6		489	22%	614/834-6400 Fax 614/834-6410
Tussing Elem Sch 7117 Tussing Rd, Reynoldsburg 43068 Matthew Dansby	PK-4	T	615 50	46%	614/834-2600 Fax 614/834-2610
Violet Elem Sch 8855 Education Dr, Pickerington 43147 Dorethia Copas	PK-4		539 27	18%	614/548-1500 Fax 614/548-1510

• **Walnut Twp Local School Dist** PID: 00799275   740/467-2802
11850 Lancaster St, Millersport 43046   Fax 740/467-3494

Schools: 2 \ *Teachers:* 34 \ *Students:* 490 \ *Special Ed Students:* 89 \ *College-Bound:* 49% \ *Ethnic:* African American 3%, Hispanic 1%, Caucasian 97% \ *Exp:* $225 (Med) \ *Poverty:* 13% \ *Title I:* $115,715 \ *Special Education:* $106,000 \ *Open-Close:* 08/19 - 05/29 \ *DTBP:* $280 (High)

Randy Cotner	...1		Christy Moore	...2,294	
William Yates	...3,5*		Karen Reedy	...4*	
Jill Wiles	...7,83,85*		Kim Yenni	...9,11*	
John Phipps	...36,69		Karen Keller	...67	
Joe Brownfield	...73*				

Public Schs..Principal	Grd	Prgm	Enr/#Cls		SN
Millersport Elem Sch 11850 Lancaster St, Millersport 43046 Kim Yenni	K-6	T	271 15	57%	740/467-2216
Millersport Jr Sr High Sch 11850 Lancaster St, Millersport 43046 Jeffrey Stought	7-12	T	216 23	51%	740/467-2929

1 Superintendent	8 Curric/Instruct K-12	19 Chief Financial Officer	29 Family/Consumer Science	39 Social Studies K-12	49 English/Lang Arts Elem	59 Special Education Elem	69 Academic Assessment
2 Bus/Finance/Purchasing	9 Curric/Instruct Elem	20 Art K-12	30 Adult Education	40 Social Studies Elem	50 English/Lang Arts Sec	60 Special Education Sec	70 Research/Development
3 Buildings And Grounds	10 Curric/Instruct Sec	21 Art Elem	31 Career/Sch-to-Work K-12	41 Social Studies Sec	51 Reading K-12	61 Foreign/World Lang K-12	71 Public Information
4 Food Service	11 Federal Program	22 Art Sec	32 Career/Sch-to-Work Elem	42 Science K-12	52 Reading Elem	62 Foreign/World Lang Elem	72 Summer School
5 Transportation	12 Title I	23 Music K-12	33 Career/Sch-to-Work Sec	43 Science Elem	53 Reading Sec	63 Foreign/World Lang Sec	73 Instructional Tech
6 Athletic	13 Title V	24 Music Elem	34 Early Childhood Ed	44 Science Sec	54 Remedial Reading K-12	64 Religious Education K-12	74 Inservice Training
7 Health Services	15 Asst Superintendent	25 Music Sec	35 Health/Phys Education	45 Math K-12	55 Remedial Reading Elem	65 Religious Education Elem	75 Marketing/Distributive
	16 Instructional Media Svcs	26 Business Education	36 Guidance Services K-12	46 Math Elem	56 Remedial Reading Sec	66 Religious Education Sec	76 Info Systems
	17 Chief Operations Officer	27 Career & Tech Ed	37 Guidance Services Elem	47 Math Sec	57 Bilingual/ELL	67 School Board President	77 Psychological Assess
	18 Chief Academic Officer	28 Technology Education	38 Guidance Services Sec	48 English/Lang Arts K-12	58 Special Education K-12	68 Teacher Personnel	78 Affirmative Action

Ohio School Directory — Franklin County

FAIRFIELD CATHOLIC SCHOOLS

• **Diocese of Columbus Ed Office** PID: 00802717
Listing includes only schools located in this county. See District Index for location of Diocesan Offices.

Catholic Schs..Principal	Grd	Prgm	Enr/#Cls	SN	
St Bernadette Sch 1325 Wheeling Rd NE, Lancaster 43130 Pamela Eltringham	PK-5		150 7		740/654-3137 Fax 740/654-1602
St Mary Sch 309 E Chestnut St, Lancaster 43130 Erin Schornack	K-8		426 18		740/654-1632 Fax 614/654-0877
William V Fisher Catholic HS 1803 Granville Pike, Lancaster 43130 Jim Globokar	9-12		180 16		740/654-1231 Fax 740/654-1233

FAIRFIELD PRIVATE SCHOOLS

Private Schs..Principal	Grd	Prgm	Enr/#Cls	SN	
Fairfield Christian Academy 1965 N Columbus St, Lancaster 43130 Laura Putinski \ Craig Carpenter	PK-12		700		740/654-2889 Fax 740/654-7689
Lancaster SDA Elem Sch 2640 Lancaster-Thornvill, Lancaster 43130 Tom Hughes	1-8		8 2		740/687-1741 Fax 740/687-4746

FAYETTE COUNTY

FAYETTE COUNTY SCHOOLS

County Schs..Principal	Grd	Prgm	Enr/#Cls	SN	
Fayette Progressive Sch 1351 Leesburg Ave Ste 200, Wshngtn Ct Hs 43160 Jamie Roe	Spec		80 4		740/335-1391 Fax 740/333-3546

FAYETTE PUBLIC SCHOOLS

• **Miami Trace Local School Dist** PID: 00799328   740/335-3010
3818 State Route 41 NW, Wshngtn Ct Hs 43160   Fax 740/335-1959

Schools: 3 \ **Teachers:** 137 \ **Students:** 2,582 \ **Special Ed Students:** 364 \ **LEP Students:** 17 \ **College-Bound:** 50% \ **Ethnic:** African American 1%, Hispanic 3%, Caucasian 96% \ **Exp:** $320 (High) \ **Poverty:** 19% \ **Title I:** $771,149 \ **Special Education:** $506,000 \ **Open-Close:** 08/14 - 05/15 \ **DTBP:** $177 (High)

David Lewis 1
Debbie Black 2,19,71
Joni Daniels-Blouse 5
Amy Boston 9,11,280,296*
Amy O'Dierno 59
Mike Henry 67
Pam Thornburg 93*
Bill Franke 2,3,4,5,79,91
Gary Campbell 4
Aaron Hammond 6
Kim Pittser 15,273,285,286,288,294
Justin Lanman 60*
Amy Gustin 73,295*

Public Schs..Principal	Grd	Prgm	Enr/#Cls	SN	
Miami Trace Elem Sch 3836 State Route 41 NW, Wshngtn Ct Hs 43160 Ryan Davis	PK-5	T	1,230 6	56%	740/333-2400 Fax 740/333-2300
Miami Trace High Sch 300 Bloomingburg New Holand Rd, Wshngtn Ct Hs 43160 Rob Enochs	9-12	AV	714 40	37%	740/333-4700 Fax 740/636-2010
Miami Trace Middle Sch 3800 State Route 41 NW, Wshngtn Ct Hs 43160 Jason Binegar	6-8	AT	608 20	49%	740/333-4900 Fax 740/333-4901

• **Washington Court House City SD** PID: 00799457   740/335-6620
306 Highland Ave, Wshngtn Ct Hs 43160   Fax 740/335-1245

Schools: 4 \ **Teachers:** 133 \ **Students:** 2,200 \ **Special Ed Students:** 457 \ **LEP Students:** 17 \ **Ethnic:** Asian 1%, African American 3%, Hispanic 4%, Caucasian 91% \ **Exp:** $330 (High) \ **Poverty:** 23% \ **Title I:** $856,135 \ **Special Education:** $474,000 \ **Open-Close:** 08/14 - 05/21 \ **DTBP:** $169 (High) \

Tom Bailey 1,11
Mike Skaggs 3
Regina Williams 5
Stacy Forby 8,13,16,69,74*
Beth Keller 16*
Shannon Caplinger 34,58
Trevor Patton 71
Becky Mullins 2
Stephanie Lanning 4
Mark Biehl 6
Dianna Wayne 9*
Steve Powers 16,73,286
Ken Upthegrove 67
Nancy McDermott 81

Public Schs..Principal	Grd	Prgm	Enr/#Cls	SN	
Belle Aire Intermediate Sch 1120 High St, Wshngtn Ct Hs 43160 Jeff Conroy	3-5	T	512 22	66%	740/335-1810 Fax 740/335-6432
Cherry Hill Primary Sch 720 W Oakland Ave, Wshngtn Ct Hs 43160 Craig Maddux	PK-2	T	577 25	59%	740/335-3370 Fax 740/335-2897
Washington High Sch 400 S Elm St, Wshngtn Ct Hs 43160 Tracy Rose	9-12	T	566 40	53%	740/636-4221 Fax 740/636-4261
Washington Middle Sch 500 S Elm St, Wshngtn Ct Hs 43160 Eric Wayne	6-8	T	529 43	60%	740/335-0291 Fax 740/333-3606

FRANKLIN COUNTY

FRANKLIN COUNTY SCHOOLS

• **Educational Serv Ctr-Ctl Ohio** PID: 00802705   614/445-3750
2080 Citygate Dr, Columbus 43219   Fax 614/445-3767

Tom Goodney 1
Tom Reed 8,74,294
Lynn Brannon 58,79,88
Janet Gillig 79,81
Alan Hutchinson 2
Michael Trego 15
Lewis Stemen 68

County Schs..Principal	Grd	Prgm	Enr/#Cls	SN	
© Arts & College Prep Academy 4401 Hilton Corporate Dr, Columbus 43232 Richard Albeit \ Amanda Waluzak	7-12	T	400 15	53%	614/986-9974 Fax 614/986-9976
© Cesar Chavez North Sch 2400 Mock Rd, Columbus 43219 Dr Linda Gibson	K-5		60 18		614/294-3020 Fax 614/299-3680

---

79 Student Personnel
80 Driver Ed/Safety
81 Gifted/Talented
82 Video Services
83 Substance Abuse Prev
84 Erate
85 AIDS Education
88 Alternative/At Risk
89 Multi-Cultural Curriculum
90 Social Work

91 Safety/Security
92 Magnet School
93 Parental Involvement
95 Tech Prep Program
97 Chief Information Officer
98 Chief Technology Officer
270 Character Education
271 Migrant Education
273 Teacher Mentor
274 Before/After Sch

275 Response To Intervention
277 Remedial Math K-12
280 Literacy Coach
285 STEM
286 Digital Learning
288 Common Core Standards
294 Accountability
295 Network System
296 Title II Programs
297 Webmaster

298 Grant Writer/Ptnrships
750 Chief Innovation Officer
751 Chief of Staff
752 Social Emotional Learning

Other School Types
Ⓐ = Alternative School
Ⓒ = Charter School
Ⓜ = Magnet School
Ⓨ = Year-Round School

School Programs
A = Alternative Program
G = Adult Classes
M = Magnet Program
T = Title I Schoolwide
V = Career & Tech Ed Programs

Social Media
 = Facebook
 = Twitter

New Schools are shaded
New Superintendents and Principals are bold
Personnel with email addresses are underscored

Franklin County

© Charles Sch at Ohio Dominican 9-12 T 360 66% 614/258-8588
1270 Brentnell Ave, Columbus 43219   16   Fax 614/258-8584
Greg Brown

© Columbus Performance Academy [247] K-8 T 204   614/318-0720
274 E 1st Ave Ste 200, Columbus 43201   Fax 614/375-1995
Roni Jamison

© Early College Academy 11-12 T 169 60% 614/298-4742
345 E 5th Ave, Columbus 43201   Fax 614/298-9107
Jonathan Stevens

© Graham Elem and Middle Sch K-8   453   614/253-4000
140 E 16th Ave, Columbus 43201   Fax 614/253-4002
Greg Brown

© Graham Sch 9-12   247   614/262-1111
3950 Indianola Ave, Columbus 43214   27 Fax 614/262-5878
Greg Brown

© Horizon Science Acad-Columbus [153] 9-12 T 499 86% 614/846-7616
1070 Morse Rd, Columbus 43229
Mr Sechen

© Imagine Great Western Academy [245] K-8 T 763   614/276-1028
310 N Wilson Rd, Columbus 43204   30   Fax 614/276-1049
Kathryn Kountz

© International Academy Columbus K-8 T 268   614/794-0644
2439 Fuji Dr, Columbus 43229   Fax 614/794-0697
Mouhamed Tarazi

© Millennium Community Sch K-8 T 528 92% 614/255-5585
3500 Refugee Rd, Columbus 43232   Fax 614/255-5580
Tijuana Russell

North East Center Spec AV 90   614/476-0530
500 N Hamilton Rd, Gahanna 43230   14 Fax 614/342-5095
Jack Karner

© Oakstone Cmty Sch K-12   210   614/458-1085
5747 Cleveland Ave, Columbus 43231
Heather Kronewetter

© Road to Success Academy [135] 9-12 T 66   614/252-4656
1555 Bryden Rd, Columbus 43205
Alicia Henry

© South Scioto Perform Academy [247] K-8 T 230   614/445-7684
2200 Winslow Dr, Columbus 43207   6 Fax 614/445-7688
Donnell Drake

West Central Sch Spec V 100   614/276-8231
1481 W Town St, Columbus 43223   17 Fax 614/342-5260
Dr Mary Ellis Turner

FRANKLIN PUBLIC SCHOOLS

• **Bexley City School Dist** PID: 00799524 614/231-7611
348 S Cassingham Rd, Bexley 43209 Fax 614/231-8448

Schools: 5 \ *Teachers:* 139 \ *Students:* 2,463 \ *Special Ed Students:* 262 \ *LEP Students:* 15 \ *College-Bound:* 81% \ *Ethnic:* Asian 3%, African American 6%, Hispanic 3%, Caucasian 89% \ *Exp:* $449 (High) \ *Poverty:* 5% \ *Title I:* $186,805 \ *Special Education:* $512,000 \ *Open-Close:* 08/13 - 05/29 \ *DTBP:* $233 (High)

Dr Kimberly Pietsch Miller ....1 John Eikenberry 2,84
Brett Santantonio ....3 Dr Harley Williams 3,17,273
Julianna Carvi ....4 Art Banks 5
Eli Goldberger ....6 Jill Abraham 8,11,16,69,288,296,298
Stephanie Krosnosky ....38* Samantha McMasters 57,58
John Barno ....67 Tyler Trill 71
Brad Pettit ....73 Leisan Smith 83,85,88,752

Public Schs..Principal	Grd	Prgm	Enr/#Cls	SN
Bexley High Sch 326 S Cassingham Rd, Columbus 43209 Kristin Robbins	9-12		753	18% 614/231-4591 Fax 614/338-2087
Bexley Middle Sch 300 S Cassingham Rd, Bexley 43209 Jason Caudill	6-8		576 30	614/237-4277 Fax 614/338-2090
Cassingham Elem Sch 250 S Cassingham Rd, Bexley 43209 Jeannine Hetzler	K-5		434 17	614/237-4266 Fax 614/382-2092
Maryland Ave Elem Sch 2754 Maryland Ave, Bexley 43209 Susan Drake	PK-5		313 25	11% 614/237-3280 Fax 614/338-2080
Montrose Elem Sch 2555 E Main St, Bexley 43209 Quint Gage	PK-5		382 19	12% 614/237-4226 Fax 614/338-2088

• **Canal Winchester Local SD** PID: 00799574 614/837-4533
100 Washington St, Canal Wnchstr 43110 Fax 614/833-2165

Schools: 4 \ *Teachers:* 219 \ *Students:* 3,600 \ *Special Ed Students:* 471 \ *LEP Students:* 97 \ *College-Bound:* 62% \ *Ethnic:* Asian 2%, African American 23%, Hispanic 5%, Caucasian 70% \ *Exp:* $373 (High) \ *Poverty:* 18% \ *Title I:* $1,179,721 \ *Special Education:* $550,000 \ *Open-Close:* 08/28 - 06/02 \ *DTBP:* $188 (High)

James Sotlar ....1 Nick Roberts 2
Mike Bruning ....5 Pat Durbin 6*
Cyndi Toledo ....8,69,273 Jodell Klamfoth 12*
Kiya Hunt ....15 Shari Boggs 16,82*
Tammy Phelps ....38* Mirka Visnjic 57*
Brooke Hippler ....58,88 Brian Niceswanger 67
William Whitlatch ....69 John-Paul Hoffman 73*
Danielle Bartos 81

Public Schs..Principal	Grd	Prgm	Enr/#Cls	SN
Canal Winchester High Sch 300 Washington St, Canal Wnchstr 43110 Kirk Henderson	9-12	V	1,160 45	28% 614/833-2157 Fax 614/833-2163
Canal Winchester Middle Sch 7155 Parkview Dr, Canal Wnchstr 43110 Kelly Zywczyk	6-8	T	927 56	32% 614/833-2151 Fax 614/833-2173
Indian Trail Elem Sch 6767 Gender Rd, Canal Wnchstr 43110 Eric Riddle	K-2	T	765 30	30% 614/833-2154 Fax 614/833-2167
Winchester Trail Elem Sch 6865 Gender Rd, Canal Wnchstr 43110 Max Lallathin	3-5	T	1,012 22	34% 614/833-2150 Fax 614/833-2161

• **Columbus City School Dist** PID: 00799603 614/365-5000
270 E State St, Columbus 43215 Fax 614/365-5689

Schools: 113 \ *Teachers:* 3,369 \ *Students:* 52,000 \ *Special Ed Students:* 8,554 \ *LEP Students:* 7,019 \ *College-Bound:* 41% \ *Ethnic:* Asian 4%, African American 57%, Hispanic 12%, Caucasian 26% \ *Exp:* $119 (Low) \ *Poverty:* 35% \ *Title I:* $56,404,067 \ *Special Education:* $13,602,000 \ *Open-Close:* 08/22 - 05/28 \ *DTBP:* $266 (High)

Dr Talisa Dixon ....1 Scott Gooding 2
Stanley Bahorek ....2,19 Dejuan Hood 3
Maurice Oldham ....3,17 Gary Bright 5
Kate King ....7 Alesia Gillison 8,18
Andrea Richardson ....11,296 Leslie Kelly 16,285
Botty Hill ....20,23 Pegeen Cleary 27,30,31,95*
Ann Lockett ....34 Donald Cain 35*

Ohio School Directory

Franklin County

Michael Sain 57
Gary Baker 67
Scott Wortman 71
Chris Ward 91
Angela Nelson 274*

Katherine Leffler 58,79
Mira Wright 68
Dr Colleen Boyle 81*
Christopher Ward 91*
Dr Machelle Kline 294

Public Schs..Principal	Grd	Prgm	Enr/#Cls	SN
ACES 2323 Lexington Ave, Columbus 43211 Edward O'Reilly	Adult	V	700 12	614/365-6000 Fax 614/365-6458
Alpine Elem Sch 1590 Alpine Dr, Columbus 43229 Rhonda Peeples	K-3	T	345 27	614/365-5359 Fax 614/365-5358
Arts Impact Middle Sch 680 Jack Gibbs Blvd, Columbus 43215 Erica Dodson	6-8	ATV	527 30	614/365-5558 Fax 614/365-5561
Avalon Elem Sch 5220 Avalon Ave, Columbus 43229 Lenelle Taylor	K-3	T	450 24	614/365-5361 Fax 614/365-8221
Avondale Elem Sch 141 Hawkes Ave, Columbus 43222 April Knight	PK-5	T	280 14	614/365-6511 Fax 614/365-8205
Beatty Park Elem Sch 519 Trevitt St Unit B, Columbus 43203 Jessica Waddell	Spec	T	73 12	614/365-6074 Fax 614/365-6076
Beechcroft High Sch 6100 Beechcroft Rd, Columbus 43229 Samuel Johnson	9-12	ATV	623 48	614/365-5364 Fax 614/365-6963
Ⓐ Berwick Alternative Elem Sch 2655 Scottwood Rd, Columbus 43209 Kyla Mitchell	PK-8	T	759 14	614/365-6140 Fax 614/365-6142
Binns Elem Sch 1080 Binns Blvd, Columbus 43204 Joel Grant	K-5	T	389 18	614/365-5911 Fax 614/365-5910
Briggs High Sch 2555 Briggs Rd, Columbus 43223 Dr Tonya Milligan	9-12	TV	968 42	614/365-5915 Fax 614/365-6964
Broadleigh Elem Sch 3039 Maryland Ave, Columbus 43209 Jennifer Vargo	PK-5	T	322 23	614/365-6144 Fax 614/365-6143
Buckeye Middle Sch 2950 Parsons Ave, Columbus 43207 Stephanie McCoy	6-8	TV	427 45	614/365-5417 Fax 614/365-5895
Burroughs Elem Sch 551 S Richardson Ave, Columbus 43204 Laura Schnebelen	PK-5	T	455 11	614/365-5923 Fax 614/365-5924
Cassady Elem Sch 2500 N Cassady Ave, Columbus 43219 Natosha Schaffer	PK-5	T	361 13	614/365-5456 Fax 614/365-8700
Cedarwood Elem Sch 775 Bartfield Dr, Columbus 43207 Latasha Turner	PK-5	T	388 19	614/365-5421 Fax 614/365-5420
Centennial High Sch 1441 Bethel Rd, Columbus 43220 Stephanie Porta	9-12	AV	742 38	614/365-5491 Fax 614/365-6967 f t
Champion Middle Sch 284 N 22nd St, Columbus 43203 Stephanie Bland	6-8	TV	414 50	614/365-6082 Fax 614/365-6080
Clinton Elem Sch 10 Clinton Heights Ave, Columbus 43202 Patricia Price	K-5		491 17	614/365-6532 Fax 614/365-6530
Colerain Sch 499 E Weisheimer Rd, Columbus 43214 Candace Nespeca	Spec	T	199 18	614/365-6001 Fax 614/365-6706
Columbus Africentric EC 9-12 3223 Allegheny Ave, Columbus 43209 Tonya Walker	9-12		320	614/365-8675 Fax 614/365-8908
Columbus Africentric EC K8 Sch 3223 Allegheny Ave, Columbus 43209 Tyree Pollard \ Sherri Edwards	K-8		950 40	614/365-8675 Fax 614/365-6520
Ⓐ Columbus Alternative High Sch 2632 McGuffey Rd, Columbus 43211 Darryl Sanders	9-12	V	810 60	614/365-6006 Fax 614/365-6300 f
Columbus City Prep Sch-Boys 3450 Medway Ave, Columbus 43213 Dion Drakeford	6-8	T	168	614/365-6166 Fax 614/365-6164
Columbus City Prep Sch-Girls 1390 Bryden Rd, Columbus 43205 Stephanie Patton	6-8	T	283	614/365-6113 Fax 614/365-6112
Columbus Downtown High Sch 364 S 4th St, Columbus 43215 Cheryl Watson	Voc	G	32 20	614/365-2283 Fax 614/365-2287
Columbus Gifted Academy 100 W 4th Ave, Columbus 43201 Amanda Reidenbaugh	3-8		500	614/365-6961
Columbus Global Academy 4077 Karl Rd, Columbus 43224 Derick Vickroy	6-12	A	630	614/365-8472 Fax 614/365-6909
Columbus N International Sch 4077 Karl Rd, Columbus 43224 Kenton Lee	7-12	T	503	614/365-4054 Fax 614/365-4089
Columbus Scioto 2951 S High St, Columbus 43207 Michelle Milner	Spec	T	126 8	614/365-6085 Fax 614/365-5839
Columbus Span Immersion Acad 3940 Karl Rd, Columbus 43224 Kathryn Myers	PK-6	T	405 15	614/365-8129 Fax 614/365-8130
Como Elem Sch 2989 Reis Ave, Columbus 43224 Summer Anthony	PK-5	T	356 21	614/365-6013 Fax 614/365-6011
Cranbrook Elem Sch 908 Bricker Blvd, Columbus 43221 Stanley Embry	K-5	T	288 17	614/365-5497 Fax 614/365-5496
Devonshire Elem Sch 6286 Ambleside Dr, Columbus 43229 Anastasia Brown	PK-5	T	522 20	614/365-5335 Fax 614/365-8094
Dominion Middle Sch 330 E Dominion Blvd, Columbus 43214 Dorothy Flanagan	6-8	TV	685 35	614/365-6020 Fax 614/365-6018
Duxberry Park Elem Sch 1779 E Maynard Ave, Columbus 43219 Vera Babbs	PK-5	T	252 13	614/365-6023 Fax 614/365-6022
Eakin Elem Sch 3774 Eakin Rd, Columbus 43228 Theresa Eraybar	PK-5	T	281 14	614/365-5928 Fax 614/365-5930
East Columbus Elem Sch 3100 E 7th Ave, Columbus 43219 Jaime Spreen	PK-5	T	378 15	614/365-6147 Fax 614/365-6146
East High Sch 1500 E Broad St, Columbus 43205 Charles Richardson	9-12	ATV	525 60	614/365-6096 Fax 614/365-6966
East Linden Elem Sch 2505 Brentnell Ave, Columbus 43211 Cheryl Jones	PK-5	T	316 12	614/365-5459 Fax 614/365-5458
Eastgate Elem Sch 1925 Stratford Way, Columbus 43219 India Wilson	PK-5	T	280 12	614/365-6132 Fax 614/365-6131
Easthaven Elem Sch 2360 Garnet Pl, Columbus 43232 Vern Miller	PK-5	T	440 12	614/365-6149 Fax 614/365-6721
Ⓐ Eastmoor Academy 417 S Weyant Ave, Columbus 43213 Brian Morton	9-12	V	755 55	614/365-6158 Fax 614/365-6960

79 Student Personnel
80 Driver Ed/Safety
81 Gifted/Talented
82 Video Services
83 Substance Abuse Prev
84 Erate
85 AIDS Education
88 Alternative/At Risk
89 Multi-Cultural Curriculum
90 Social Work

91 Safety/Security
92 Magnet School
93 Parental Involvement
95 Tech Prep Program
97 Chief Information Officer
98 Chief Technology Officer
270 Character Education
271 Migrant Education
273 Teacher Mentor
274 Before/After Sch

275 Response To Intervention
277 Remedial Math K-12
280 Literacy Coach
285 STEM
286 Digital Learning
288 Common Core Standards
294 Accountability
295 Network System
296 Title II Programs
297 Webmaster

298 Grant Writer/Ptnrships
750 Chief Innovation Officer
751 Chief of Staff
752 Social Emotional Learning

Other School Types
Ⓐ = Alternative School
Ⓒ = Charter School
Ⓜ = Magnet School
Ⓨ = Year-Round School

School Programs
A = Alternative Program
G = Adult Classes
M = Magnet Program
T = Title I Schoolwide
V = Career & Tech Ed Programs

New Schools are shaded
New Superintendents and Principals are bold
Personnel with email addresses are underscored

Social Media
f = Facebook
t = Twitter

OH-67

Franklin County

School	Grades		Enrollment	Phone
Ecole Kenwood FR Immersion ES 3770 Shattuck Ave, Columbus 43220 Emily Corbin	PK-6	AT	376 25	614/365-5502 Fax 614/365-5504
Fairmoor Elem Sch 3281 Mayfair Park Pl, Columbus 43213 **Maria Stockard**	PK-5	T	366 20	614/365-6169 Fax 614/365-6171
Fairwood Elem Sch 726 Fairwood Ave, Columbus 43205 DeWayne Davis	PK-6	T	299 20	614/365-6111 Fax 614/365-6110
Forest Park Elem Sch 5535 Sandalwood Blvd, Columbus 43229 Rhonna McKibbin	K-5	T	396 23	614/365-5337 Fax 614/365-8219
Gables Elem Sch 1680 Becket Ave, Columbus 43235 Gene Smith	K-5	T	421 13	614/365-5499 Fax 614/365-6451
Georgian Heights Elem Sch 784 Georgian Dr, Columbus 43228 Nakita Smoot	PK-5	T	516 20	614/365-5931 Fax 614/365-6885
Hamilton STEM Academy 2047 Hamilton Ave, Columbus 43211 Christopher Brady	PK-6	T	451 19	614/365-5568 Fax 614/365-5570
Hayes Art & Academic HS 546 Jack Gibbs Blvd, Columbus 43215 Dr Milton Ruffin	9-12	AGV	697	614/365-6681 Fax 614/365-5620
Highland Elem Sch 40 S Highland Ave, Columbus 43223 Dr Elizabeth McNally	PK-5	T	302 30	614/365-5935 Fax 614/365-8726
Hilltonia Middle Sch 2345 W Mound St, Columbus 43204 Joyce Albright	6-8	TV	510 40	614/365-5937 Fax 614/365-8015
Ⓐ Hubbard Mastery Sch 104 W Hubbard Ave, Columbus 43215 Robert Losee	PK-6	T	345 13	614/365-5564 Fax 614/365-5562
Huy Elem Sch 1545 Huy Rd, Columbus 43224 Denyse Woods	PK-5	T	456 15	614/365-5977 Fax 614/365-5941
Independence High Sch 5175 East Refugee Rd, Columbus 43232 Ernest West	9-12	ATV	742 40	614/365-5372 Fax 614/365-8286
Indian Springs Elem Sch 50 E Henderson Rd, Columbus 43214 Megan Noble	K-5	T	443 16	614/365-6032 Fax 614/365-6031
Ⓐ Indianola K-8 Sch 251 E Weber Rd, Columbus 43202 Brandy Koeth	K-8		701 15	614/365-5579 Fax 614/365-8324
Innis Elem Sch 3399 Kohr Blvd, Columbus 43224 Amber Hatcher	K-5	T	343 24	614/365-5462 Fax 614/365-5461
Johnson Park Middle Sch 1130 S Waverly St, Columbus 43227 David Walker	6-8	ATV	403 32	614/365-6501 Fax 614/365-8698
Leawood Elem Sch 1677 S Hamilton Rd, Columbus 43227 Maria Malik	PK-5	T	288 18	614/365-6504 Fax 614/365-6506
Liberty Elem Sch 2901 Whitlow Rd, Columbus 43232 Shalonda Likely	PK-5	T	521 20	614/365-6482 Fax 614/365-5698
Lincoln Park Elem Sch 579 E Markison Ave, Columbus 43207 Karla Case	PK-6	T	355 13	614/365-5524 Fax 614/365-5523
Lindbergh Elem Sch 2541 Lindbergh Dr, Columbus 43223 Annette Tooman	PK-5	T	298 17	614/365-6727 Fax 614/365-5598
Linden Park Ecec 1400 Myrtle Ave, Columbus 43211 **Rhonda Childs**	PK-PK		400	614/365-7963
Linden STEM Academy 2626 Cleveland Ave, Columbus 43211 Adrean Winfrey	PK-6	T	398 21	614/365-6537 Fax 614/365-6536
Linden-McKinley STEM Academy 1320 Duxberry Ave, Columbus 43211 Duane Bland	7-12	ATV	643 50	614/365-5583 Fax 614/365-6968
Livingston Elem Sch 825 E Livingston Ave, Columbus 43205 Stacy Macarthy	PK-6	T	419 13	614/365-5527 Fax 614/365-5526
Maize Elem Sch 4360 Maize Rd, Columbus 43224 Tiffany Genton	PK-5	T	288 20	614/365-6040 Fax 614/365-6039
Marion-Franklin High Sch 1265 Koebel Rd, Columbus 43207 Lucas Cech	9-12	TV	469 100	614/365-5342 Fax 614/365-6625
Medina Middle Sch 1425 Huy Rd, Columbus 43224 Charmaine Tinker	6-8	T	442 47	614/365-6050 Fax 614/365-8136
Mifflin High Sch 3245 Oak Spring St, Columbus 43219 Kimberly Mills	9-12	ATV	779	614/365-5466 Fax 614/365-6628
Mifflin Middle Sch 3000 Agler Rd, Columbus 43219 Tracey Colson	6-8	T	431 50	614/365-5474 Fax 614/365-5477
Moler Elem Sch 1201 Moler Rd, Columbus 43207 Jameica Shoultz	PK-6	T	397 14	614/365-5529 Fax 614/365-5531
North Linden Elem Sch 1718 E Cooke Rd, Columbus 43224 Sarah Foster	K-5	T	463 15	614/365-6055 Fax 614/365-6054
Northgate Intermediate Sch 6655 Sharon Woods Blvd, Columbus 43229 Andre Jones	4-5	T	311	614/365-8815
Northland High Sch 1919 Northcliff Dr, Columbus 43229 Jason Johnson	9-12	ATV	1,029	614/365-5342 Fax 614/365-6479
Northtowne Elem Sch 4767 Northtowne Blvd, Columbus 43229 Jason Brasno	PK-5	T	300 11	614/365-5488 Fax 614/365-5487
Oakland Park Elem Sch 3392 Atwood Ter, Columbus 43224 Mark Caudill	PK-5	T	336 15	614/365-6058 Fax 614/365-6057
Oakmont Elem Sch 5666 Oakmont Dr, Columbus 43232 Shawyna McFadden	K-5	T	342 16	614/365-5385 Fax 614/365-5384
Ohio Avenue Elem Sch 505 S Ohio Ave, Columbus 43205 Kyle Miller	PK-5	T	316 19	614/365-6130 Fax 614/365-6128
Olde Orchard Elem Sch 800 McNaughten Rd, Columbus 43213 Joan Bucy	K-5	T	529 23	614/365-5388 Fax 614/365-5387
Parkmoor Elem Sch 1711 Penworth Dr, Columbus 43229 Charmaine Campbell	PK-5	T	319 11	614/365-5349 Fax 614/365-5348
Parsons Elem Sch 3231 Lee Ellen Pl, Columbus 43207 Shannon Clemons	PK-5	T	464 12	614/365-5099 Fax 614/365-5115
Ridgeview Middle Sch 4241 Rudy Rd, Columbus 43214 Natalie James	6-8	TV	561 30	614/365-5506 Fax 614/365-5505
Salem Elem Sch 1040 Garvey Rd, Columbus 43229 Nikki Myers	K-5	T	314 22	614/365-5351 Fax 614/365-5353
Scottwood Elem Sch 3392 Scottwood Rd, Columbus 43227 Kerri Myers	PK-5	T	480 15	614/365-6507 Fax 614/365-6509

---

1. Superintendent
2. Bus/Finance/Purchasing
3. Buildings And Grounds
4. Food Service
5. Transportation
6. Athletic
7. Health Services
8. Curric/Instruct K-12
9. Curric/Instruct Elem
10. Curric/Instruct Sec
11. Federal Program
12. Title I
13. Title V
14. Asst Superintendent
15. Instructional Media Svcs
16. Chief Operations Officer
17. Chief Academic Officer
18. Chief Financial Officer
19. Art K-12
20. Art Elem
21. Art Sec
22. Music K-12
23. Music Elem
24. Music Sec
25. Business Education
26. Career & Tech Ed
27. Technology Education
28. Family/Consumer Science
29. Adult Education
30. Career/Sch-to-Work K-12
31. Career/Sch-to-Work Elem
32. Career/Sch-to-Work Sec
33. Early Childhood Ed
34. Health/Phys Education
35. Guidance Services K-12
36. Guidance Services Elem
37. Guidance Services Sec
38. Social Studies K-12
39. Social Studies Elem
40. Social Studies Sec
41. Science K-12
42. Science Elem
43. Science Sec
44. Math K-12
45. Math Elem
46. Math Sec
47. English/Lang Arts K-12
48. English/Lang Arts Elem
49. English/Lang Arts Sec
50. Reading K-12
51. Reading Elem
52. Reading Sec
53. Remedial Reading K-12
54. Remedial Reading Elem
55. Remedial Reading Sec
56. Bilingual/ELL
57. Special Education K-12
58. Special Education Elem
59. Special Education Sec
60. Foreign/World Lang K-12
61. Foreign/World Lang Elem
62. Foreign/World Lang Sec
63. Religious Education K-12
64. Religious Education Elem
65. Religious Education Sec
66. School Board President
67. Teacher Personnel
68. Academic Assessment
69. Research/Development
70. Public Information
71. Summer School
72. Instructional Tech
73. Inservice Training
74. Marketing/Distributive
75. Info Systems
76. Psychological Assess
77. Affirmative Action

Ohio School Directory

Franklin County

School	Grades	Prgm	Enr/#Cls	Phone
Shady Lane Elem Sch 1444 Shady Lane Rd, Columbus 43227 Kevin Hainer	PK-5	T	428 12	614/365-5391 Fax 614/365-5390
Sherwood Middle Sch 1400 Shady Lane Rd, Columbus 43227 Kevin Freeman	6-8	TV	528	614/365-5393 Fax 614/365-8351
Siebert Elem Sch 385 Reinhard Ave, Columbus 43206 Debra Wilkerson	PK-6	T	353 13	614/365-6613 Fax 614/365-6612
South High Sch 1160 Ann St, Columbus 43206 Edmund Baker	7-12	ATV	977 50	614/365-5541 Fax 614/365-5538
South Mifflin STEM Academy 2365 Middlehurst Dr, Columbus 43219 Pamela Horton	PK-6	T	311 21	614/365-6135 Fax 614/365-6134
Southwood Elem Sch 1500 S 4th St, Columbus 43207 Danita Turner	PK-6	T	311 21	614/365-5553 Fax 614/365-8071
Starling STEM PK-8 Sch 145 S Central Ave, Columbus 43222 Angela Moore-Tyler	PK-8	TV	591 32	614/365-5945 Fax 614/365-5942
Stewart Alternative Elem Sch 40 Stewart Ave, Columbus 43206 James Eslinger	PK-6	T	330 12	614/365-5556 Fax 614/365-6704
Sullivant Elem Sch 791 Griggs Ave, Columbus 43223 Lisa Stamos	PK-5	T	301 15	614/365-6524 Fax 614/365-6522
Trevitt Elem Sch 519 Trevitt St Unit A, Columbus 43203 Patrese Mason	PK-5	T	209 7	614/365-6137 Fax 614/365-6139
Valley Forge Elem Sch 1321 Urban Dr, Columbus 43229 Andrew Smith	PK-5	T	347 22	614/365-5648 Fax 614/365-5779
Valleyview Elem Sch 2989 Valleyview Dr, Columbus 43204 Pamela Artrip	PK-5	T	267 16	614/365-6312 Fax 614/365-6768
Walnut Ridge High Sch 4841 E Livingston Ave, Columbus 43227 Carl Chamberlain	9-12	ATV	735 65	614/365-5400 Fax 614/365-5662
Watkins Elem Sch 1520 Watkins Rd, Columbus 43207 Thomas Revou	PK-5	T	342 16	614/365-6411 Fax 614/365-6415
Wedgewood Middle Sch 3800 Briggs Rd, Columbus 43228 Diane Campbell	6-8	TV	549 26	614/365-5947 Fax 614/365-5950
Weinland Park Elem Sch 211 E 7th Ave, Columbus 43201 Porsha Robinson-Ervin	PK-5	MT	377 20	614/365-5321 Fax 614/365-5431
West Broad Elem Sch 2744 W Broad St, Columbus 43204 Christina Ifill	PK-5	T	485 26	614/365-5964 Fax 614/365-5966
West High Sch 179 S Powell Ave, Columbus 43204 Gregory Costello	9-12	ATV	914	614/365-5956 Fax 614/365-6970
West Mound Elem Sch 2051 W Mound St, Columbus 43223 Ebone Johnson	PK-5	T	429 21	614/365-5968 Fax 614/365-6937
Westgate Elem Sch 3080 Wicklow Rd, Columbus 43204 Angela Martin	PK-5	T	331 24	614/365-5971 Fax 614/365-5149
Westmoor Middle Sch 3001 Valleyview Dr, Columbus 43204 Paul Bailey	6-8	TV	501 24	614/365-5974 Fax 614/365-6705
Whetstone High Sch 4405 Scenic Dr, Columbus 43214 Janet Routzong	9-12	AV	957 70	614/365-6060 Fax 614/365-6971
Windsor-STEM Academy 1219 E 12th Ave, Columbus 43211 Lee DuMond	PK-6	T	397 18	614/365-5906 Fax 614/365-6939
Winterset Elem Sch 4776 Winterset Dr, Columbus 43220 Audra Pearson	PK-5	T	273 16	614/365-5510 Fax 614/365-5509
Ⓨ Woodcrest Elem Sch 5321 E Livingston Ave, Columbus 43232 Brianne Pannell	PK-5	MT	359 17	614/365-6747 Fax 614/365-6751
Woodward Park Middle Sch 5151 Karl Rd, Columbus 43229 Paul Bailey	6-8	TV	928 40	614/365-5354 Fax 614/365-5357
Yorktown Middle Sch 5600 E Livingston Ave, Columbus 43232 Shannon Tucker	6-8	ATV	381 45	614/365-5408 Fax 614/365-5411

● **Dublin City School Dist** PID: 00802200 614/764-5913
5175 Emerald Pkwy, Dublin 43017 Fax 614/761-5856

Schools: 20 \ *Teachers:* 814 \ *Students:* 16,200 \
Special Ed Students: 1,700 \ *LEP Students:* 1,711 \ *College-Bound:* 83%
\ *Ethnic:* Asian 22%, African American 5%, Hispanic 7%, Caucasian 67% \ *Exp:* $138 (Low) \ *Poverty:* 7% \ *Title I:* $1,528,463 \
Special Education: $2,089,000 \ *Open-Close:* 08/14 - 05/22 \ *DTBP:* $199 (High) \ 🅣

Todd Hoadley	1	Brian Kern	2
Brion Deitsch	2,3	Chris McDowell	2,10
Brian Hunt	4*	Amy Salay	5
John Bernans	6	Nick Magistrale	6*
Amanda Spring	7	Mark Avery	7,13,34,58,83
Jill Reinhart	8	Kim Miller	8,11,16,27,35,36,298
Dr Tracey Deagle	8,15,68	Jill Abraham	9
Tyler Wolfe	9	Craig Heath	10
Donneta Oremus	27	Vanessa Ohlinger	34
Lori Marple	45	Erica Stone	57
Scott Melody	67	Gale Marsh	68
Richard Bailey	68,70*	Jessica Kroetz	69
Doug Baker	71	Lindie Schweitzer	73,286
Scott Gill	76	Chris Ondrus	79
Jara Packer	79	Lenore Cereghini	79
Michael Leopold	79	Shawn Heimlich	79
Tom McDonnell	79	Marge Mulcahy	81
Tracey Miller	91	Andrew Hatton	285

Public Schs..Principal	Grd	Prgm	Enr/#Cls	SN	
Albert Chapman Elem Sch 8450 Sawmill Rd, Powell 43065 Scott Zeoli	PK-5		720 25	21%	614/761-5864 Fax 614/761-5867
Ann Simpson Davis Middle Sch 2400 Sutter Pkwy, Dublin 43016 **Dr Ann Perez**	6-8		1,010	32%	614/761-5820 Fax 614/761-5893
Daniel Wright Elem Sch 2335 West Case Rd, Columbus 43235 Lucas Bauer	PK-5	T	741 41	44%	614/538-0464 Fax 614/538-0469
Deer Run Elem Sch 8815 Avery Rd, Dublin 43017 Susann Wittig	K-5		422 20	1%	614/764-5932 Fax 614/718-8759
Dr Henry Karrer Middle Sch 7245 Tullymore Dr, Dublin 43016 Brooke Menduni	6-8		866 50	4%	614/873-0459 Fax 614/873-1492
Dublin Coffman High Sch 6780 Coffman Rd, Dublin 43017 Mike Ulring	9-12	GV	1,915 90	12%	614/764-5900 Fax 614/764-5925
Dublin Jerome High Sch 8300 Hyland Croy Rd, Dublin 43016 **Michael Aurin**	9-12		1,761	1%	614/873-7377 Fax 614/873-7340

79 Student Personnel	91 Safety/Security	275 Response To Intervention	298 Grant Writer/Ptnrships	School Programs	Social Media
60 Driver Ed/Safety	92 Magnet School	277 Remedial Math K-12	750 Chief Innovation Officer	A = Alternative Program	
61 Gifted/Talented	93 Parental Involvement	280 Literacy Coach	751 Chief of Staff	G = Adult Classes	▮ = Facebook
82 Video Services	95 Tech Prep Program	285 STEM	752 Social Emotional Learning	M = Magnet Program	
83 Substance Abuse Prev	97 Chief Information Officer	286 Digital Learning		T = Title I Schoolwide	🅣 = Twitter
64 Erate	98 Chief Technology Officer	288 Common Core Standards	Other School Types	V = Career & Tech Ed Programs	
85 AIDS Education	270 Character Education	294 Accountability	Ⓐ = Alternative School		
88 Alternative/At Risk	271 Migrant Education	295 Network System	Ⓒ = Charter School	New Schools are shaded	
89 Multi-Cultural Curriculum	273 Teacher Mentor	296 Title II Programs	Ⓜ = Magnet School	New Superintendents and Principals are bold	
90 Social Work	274 Before/After Sch	297 Webmaster	Ⓨ = Year-Round School	Personnel with email addresses are underscored	

OH-69

Franklin County

School	Grade	Prgm	Enr/#Cls	SN	Phone
Dublin Scioto High Sch 4000 Hard Rd, Dublin 43016 Robert Scott	9-12		1,325	30%	614/717-2464 Fax 614/717-2484
Eli Pinney Elem Sch 9989 Concord Rd, Dublin 43017 William Ehrsam	PK-5		747 28	2%	614/798-3570 Fax 614/718-8961
Emerald Campus 5175 Emerald Pkwy, Dublin 43017 Kristy Venne	Voc	A	600		614/764-5857
Glacier Ridge Elem Sch 7175 Glacier Ridge Blvd, Dublin 43017 Peter Kurty	K-5		739	2%	614/733-0012 Fax 614/718-8791
Griffith Thomas Elem Sch 4671 Tuttle Rd, Dublin 43017 Jenny Davis	K-5		811 44	17%	614/764-5970 Fax 614/718-8879
Indian Run Elem Sch 80 W Bridge St, Dublin 43017 Jennifer Schwanke	K-5		692 25	15%	614/764-5928 Fax 614/764-5998
John Sells Middle Sch 150 W Bridge St, Dublin 43017 Matt Sachtleben	6-8		920 45	20%	614/764-5919 Fax 614/764-5923
Mary Emma Bailey Elem Sch 4900 Brandonway Dr, Dublin 43017 Shawn Ritter	PK-5		631 29	2%	614/717-6611 Fax 614/717-6610
Olde Sawmill Elem Sch 2485 Olde Sawmill Blvd, Dublin 43016 Martha Barley	PK-5		458 9	20%	614/764-5936 Fax 614/764-5988
Riverside Elem Sch 3260 Riverside Green Dr, Dublin 43017 Staci Lutz	K-5	T	373 25	36%	614/764-5940 Fax 614/764-5987
Scottish Corners Elem Sch 5950 Sells Mill Dr, Dublin 43017 Lauren Windham	PK-5		652 27	4%	614/764-5963 Fax 614/761-5814
Willard Grizzell Middle Sch 8705 Avery Rd, Dublin 43017 Corinne Evans	6-8		921 50	2%	614/798-3569 Fax 614/761-6514
Wyandot Elem Sch 5620 Dublinshire Dr, Dublin 43017 Renae Schwartz	K-5		612 25	1%	614/761-5840 Fax 614/718-8929

- **Eastland-Ffld Career Tech VSD** PID: 00802688   614/836-4530
  4300 Amalgamated Pl 150, Groveport 43125   Fax 614/836-0203

Schools: 3 \ **Teachers:** 82 \ **Students:** 1,500 \ **LEP Students:** 3 \ **Exp:** $21 (Low) \ **Open-Close:** 08/14 - 05/29 \ **DTBP:** $218 (High) \

Bonnie Hopkins 1
Kathryn Anderson 16,82
Angela Ward 30*
Bill McGowan 67
Michele Gille 76
Dawn Lemley 2
Renee Cook 16,82*
Teresa Durkin 38,60,79,85
Don Nuss 73
Phil Miller 83,88*

Public Schs..Principal	Grd	Prgm	Enr/#Cls	SN	
Adult Work Force Dev Center 4300 Amalgamated Pl, Groveport 43125 Angela Ward	Adult	V	125 5		614/836-4541
Eastland Career Center 4465 S Hamilton Rd, Groveport 43125 Nelson Karshner	Voc	AG	1,000 50		614/836-5725 Fax 614/836-4525
Fairfield Career Center 3985 Coonpath Rd, Carroll 43112 Derek Roeth	Voc	AG	400 40		614/837-9443 Fax 740/756-4680

- **Gahanna-Jefferson Public SD** PID: 00801397   614/471-7065
  160 S Hamilton Rd, Gahanna 43230   Fax 614/478-5568

Schools: 11 \ **Teachers:** 414 \ **Students:** 7,543 \
Special Ed Students: 1,163 \ **LEP Students:** 400 \ **College-Bound:** 68% \ **Ethnic:** Asian 4%, African American 23%, Hispanic 7%, Caucasian 66% \ **Exp:** $156 (Low) \ **Poverty:** 10% \ **Title I:** $1,366,782 \
Special Education: $1,723,000 \ **Open-Close:** 08/14 - 05/27 \ **DTBP:** $187 (High) \

Steve Barrett 1
Allan Fordham 3,91
Don Williams 5
Jill Elliott 15
Sharon Suriano 35,42,45
Corinne Fields 58
Beryl Piccolantonio 67
Judy Hengstebeck 71
Stephanie Collins 76
Scott Lofton 2
Linda Green 4
Tia Holliman 8
Melissa Smith 34
Erin Schmidt 39,48,74
Sue Wieging 58
Stephanie Loucka 68
Jeff Collett 73

Public Schs..Principal	Grd	Prgm	Enr/#Cls	SN	
Blacklick Elem Sch 6540 Havens Corners Rd, Blacklick 43004 Kristen Groves	K-5		545 30	8%	614/759-5100 Fax 614/759-5110
Chapelfield Elem Sch 280 Chapelfield Rd, Gahanna 43230 Thomas Bates	K-5		436 16	24%	614/478-5575 Fax 614/337-3755
Gahanna Middle School-East 730 Clotts Rd, Gahanna 43230 Brad Barboza	6-8		517 30	14%	614/478-5550 Fax 614/478-5544
Gahanna Middle School-South 349 Shady Spring Dr, Gahanna 43230 Robin Murdock	6-8		615 32	23%	614/337-3730 Fax 614/337-3734
Gahanna Middle School-West 350 N Stygler Rd, Gahanna 43230 Aaron Winner	6-8	T	639 35	40%	614/478-5570 Fax 614/337-3771
Goshen Lane Elem Sch 370 Goshen Ln, Gahanna 43230 Daniel Graves	K-5	T	539 20	50%	614/478-5580 Fax 614/337-3757
High Point Elem Sch 700 Venetian Way, Gahanna 43230 Kathleen Erhard	K-5		525 24	7%	614/478-5545 Fax 614/337-3762
Jefferson Elem Sch 136 Carpenter Rd, Gahanna 43230 Roben Frentzel	K-5		549 23	20%	614/478-5560 Fax 614/337-3766
Lincoln Elem Sch 515 Havens Corners Rd, Gahanna 43230 Claire Giardino	K-5		414 27	23%	614/478-5555 Fax 614/337-3750
Lincoln High Sch 140 S Hamilton Rd, Gahanna 43230 Jessica Slocum	9-12		2,240	24%	614/478-5500 Fax 614/337-3769
Royal Manor Elem Sch 299 Empire Dr, Gahanna 43230 Alissa Lopez	K-5	T	490 18	48%	614/478-5585 Fax 614/337-2160

- **Grandview Heights City SD** PID: 00801294   614/485-4015
  1587 W 3rd Ave, Columbus 43212   Fax 614/481-3648

Schools: 4 \ **Teachers:** 76 \ **Students:** 1,075 \ **Special Ed Students:** 102 \ **LEP Students:** 11 \ **College-Bound:** 88% \ **Ethnic:** Asian 1%, African American 1%, Hispanic 3%, Caucasian 95% \ **Exp:** $164 (Low) \ **Poverty:** 4% \ **Title I:** $45,810 \ **Special Education:** $243,000 \ **Open-Close:** 08/14 - 05/21 \ **DTBP:** $247 (High)

Andrew Culp 1
Brett Bradley 3,91
Beth Collier 2,296
Kyle Mahan 4

1 Superintendent	8 Curric/Instruct K-12	19 Chief Financial Officer	29 Family/Consumer Science	39 Social Studies K-12	49 English/Lang Arts Elem	59 Special Education Elem	69 Academic Assessment
2 Bus/Finance/Purchasing	9 Curric/Instruct Elem	20 Art K-12	30 Adult Education	40 Social Studies Elem	50 English/Lang Arts Sec	60 Special Education Sec	70 Research/Development
3 Buildings And Grounds	10 Curric/Instruct Sec	21 Art Elem	31 Career/Sch-to-Work K-12	41 Social Studies Sec	51 Reading K-12	61 Foreign/World Lang K-12	71 Public Information
4 Food Service	11 Federal Program	22 Art Sec	32 Career/Sch-to-Work Elem	42 Science K-12	52 Reading Elem	62 Foreign/World Lang Elem	72 Summer School
5 Transportation	12 Title I	23 Music K-12	33 Career/Sch-to-Work Sec	43 Science Elem	53 Reading Sec	63 Foreign/World Lang Sec	73 Instructional Tech
6 Athletic	13 Title V	24 Music Elem	34 Early Childhood Ed	44 Science Sec	54 Remedial Reading K-12	64 Religious Education K-12	74 Inservice Training
7 Health Services	15 Asst Superintendent	25 Music Sec	35 Health/Phys Education	45 Math K-12	55 Remedial Reading Elem	65 Religious Education Elem	75 Marketing/Distributive
	16 Instructional Media Svcs	26 Business Education	36 Guidance Services K-12	46 Math Elem	56 Remedial Reading Sec	66 Religious Education Sec	76 Info Systems
	17 Chief Operations Officer	27 Career & Tech Ed	37 Guidance Services Elem	47 Math Sec	57 Bilingual/ELL	67 School Board President	77 Psychological Assess
	18 Chief Academic Officer	28 Technology Education	38 Guidance Services Sec	48 English/Lang Arts K-12	58 Special Education K-12	68 Teacher Personnel	78 Affirmative Action

Ohio School Directory

Franklin County

Brad Bertani 6*	Madeline Partlow 7,11,57,58,69,88,271,298	
Mary Mauro 7*	Jamie Lusher 8,18,68,74,273,288	
Chris Deis 16,73,76,98,295,297	Kristi Jump 16,82*	
Bryan Stork 38,83,275	Jesse Trurett 67	
Colleen Adkinson 274*	Mark Alter 286	

Public Schs..Principal	Grd	Prgm	Enr/#Cls	SN	
Grandview Heights High Sch 1587 W 3rd Ave, Columbus 43212 Robert Brown	9-12	V	317 40	10%	614/485-4000 Fax 614/485-1067 t
Larry Larson Middle Sch 1240 Oakland Ave, Columbus 43212 Tracie Lees	6-8		240		614/485-4100 Fax 614/481-3628
Robert L Stevenson Elem Sch 1065 Oxley Rd, Columbus 43212 Angela Ullum	PK-3		349 18	7%	614/485-4200 Fax 614/429-6083
Thomas A Edison Interm Sch 1240 Oakland Ave, Columbus 43212 Tracie Lees	4-5		159 15	21%	614/485-4100 Fax 614/481-3628

• **Groveport Madison Local SD** PID: 00801488   614/492-2520
4400 Marketing Pl Ste B, Groveport 43125   Fax 614/492-2532

Schools: 11 \ **Teachers:** 305 \ **Students:** 7,200 \ **Special Ed Students:** 975 \ **LEP Students:** 252 \ **College-Bound:** 42% \ **Ethnic:** Asian 2%, African American 43%, Hispanic 7%, Caucasian 48% \ **Exp:** $223 (Med) \ **Poverty:** 23% \ **Title I:** $3,232,471 \ **Special Education:** $1,239,000 \ **Open-Close:** 08/22 - 06/02 \ **DTBP:** $194 (High) \ f t

Garilee Ogden 1	John Walsh 2	
Jaime Groob 3,91	Lou Emick 4*	
Antawn Sidberry 5	Steve Petros 6	
Scott Nelson 8,11,69,273,288,294,298	Susan Martin 11,296	
Mitzi Boyd 58*	Maggie Riley 59	
Nancy Christensen 60	Brian Shoemaker 67	
Matt Cygnor 68	Jeff Warner 71	
Peter Dotson 73,76,98	Shea Reed 79,91	
Lynnea Johnson 81	Jeannie Grubb 274*	

Public Schs..Principal	Grd	Prgm	Enr/#Cls	SN	
Asbury Elem Sch 5127 Harbor Blvd, Columbus 43232 Staci Peters	PK-5	T	433 16	74%	614/833-2000 Fax 614/833-2004 f t
Ⓐ Cruiser Academy Ⓒ 4400 Marketing Pl Ste A, Groveport 43125 William Young	9-12		110	47%	614/237-8756 Fax 614/237-9308
Dunloe Elem Sch 3200 Dunloe Rd, Columbus 43232 Natalie Lewellen	K-5	T	435 15	86%	614/833-2008 Fax 614/833-2007 f t
Glendening Elem Sch 4200 Glendenning Dr, Groveport 43125 Curt Brogan	K-5	T	477 21	75%	614/836-4972 Fax 614/836-4974 f
Groveport Elem Sch 715 Main St, Groveport 43125 April Bray	PK-5	T	419 20		614/836-4975 Fax 614/836-4680
Groveport Madison High Sch 4475 S Hamilton Rd, Groveport 43125 Jaivir Singh	9-12	AT	1,689 56	60%	614/836-4964 Fax 614/836-4998
Groveport Madison MS Central 751 Main St, Groveport 43125 **John Brown**	6-8	TV	454 30	99%	614/836-4957 Fax 614/836-4999
Groveport Madison MS South 4400 Glendenning Dr, Groveport 43125 Darren Fillman	6-8	T	447 25	80%	614/836-4953 Fax 614/836-4956
Groveport Madison MS-North 5474 Sedalia Dr, Columbus 43232 Jeffrey Jones	6-8	T	505 23	73%	614/837-5508 Fax 614/833-2033

Madison Elem Sch 4600 Madison School Dr, Columbus 43232 Tricia Faulkner	K-5	T	382 24	81%	614/833-2011 Fax 614/836-4683 f t
Sedalia Elem Sch 5400 Sedalia Dr, Columbus 43232 Kenneth Pease	PK-5	T	670 19	78%	614/833-2014 Fax 614/833-2429

• **Hamilton Local School Dist** PID: 00801347   614/491-8044
775 Rathmell Rd, Columbus 43207   Fax 614/491-8323

Schools: 4 \ **Teachers:** 160 \ **Students:** 3,200 \ **Special Ed Students:** 319 \ **LEP Students:** 18 \ **College-Bound:** 49% \ **Ethnic:** Asian 1%, African American 11%, Hispanic 5%, Caucasian 82% \ **Exp:** $125 (Low) \ **Poverty:** 16% \ **Title I:** $797,778 \ **Special Education:** $540,000 \ **Open-Close:** 08/14 - 05/21 \ **DTBP:** $203 (High) \ t

Mark Tyler 1	Adam Collier 2	
J Michael Meade 3,4,5,91	Tamara May 5	
Ryan Fitzgerald 6	Kathy Brickey 7,83,85*	
Carole Morbitzer ... 8,11,57,68,69,288,296,298	Karen Schutte 16,82*	
Lisa Mautz 16,73,84	Jamie Angelini 34,58	
David Schutte 67	Jane Strahm 273	
Michael Morbitzer 296,298		

Public Schs..Principal	Grd	Prgm	Enr/#Cls	SN	
Hamilton Elem Sch 745 Rathmell Rd, Columbus 43207 Josh Conley	K-3	T	938 47	58%	614/491-8044 Fax 614/492-1499
Hamilton Intermediate Sch 765 Rathmell Rd, Columbus 43207 Kelly Altiers	4-6	T	747 35	62%	614/491-8044 Fax 614/492-1059
Hamilton Middle Sch 755 Rathmell Rd, Columbus 43207 Jeff Endres	7-8	T	435 50	63%	614/491-8044 Fax 614/491-0260
Hamilton Twp High Sch 1105 Rathmell Rd, Columbus 43207 Robert Lanthorn	9-12	T	816 30	57%	614/491-8044 Fax 614/492-1495

• **Hilliard City School Dist** PID: 00801713   614/921-7000
2140 Atlas St, Columbus 43228   Fax 614/921-7001

Schools: 25 \ **Teachers:** 873 \ **Students:** 16,600 \ **Special Ed Students:** 2,045 \ **LEP Students:** 1,287 \ **College-Bound:** 73% \ **Ethnic:** Asian 7%, African American 7%, Hispanic 8%, Caucasian 77% \ **Exp:** $102 (Low) \ **Poverty:** 8% \ **Title I:** $1,963,759 \ **Special Education:** $2,706,000 \ **Open-Close:** 08/21 - 05/29 \ **DTBP:** $203 (High) \ f t

Dr John Marschhausen 1	Anita Dalluge 2	
Brian Wilson 2,19	Cliff Hetzel 2	
Dave Huston 3	Mike McDonough 3,15,91	
Kyle Mahone 4	Andi Cunningham 5	
Chris Ludban 6*	Nate Boobek 6,35*	
Debbie Cochran 7,36,58,77,79,85,88	John Bandow 10	
Vicky Clark 15	Brian Hart 34	
Paul Lambert 67	Roy Walker 68,78	
Stacie Raterman 71	Carrie Higginbotham 72,280*	
Mark Pohlman 73	Rich Boettner 73,95,98,295	
Cori Kindl 74,273	Chris Lewis 76	
Kelly Wigg 274		

Public Schs..Principal	Grd	Prgm	Enr/#Cls	SN	
Alton Darby Elem Sch 2730 Alton Darby Creek Rd, Hilliard 43026 Samantha Chatman	K-5		525 22	21%	614/921-5000 Fax 614/921-5001

---

79 Student Personnel	91 Safety/Security	275 Response To Intervention	298 Grant Writer/Ptnrships	**School Programs**	**Social Media**
80 Driver Ed/Safety	92 Magnet School	277 Remedial Math K-12	750 Chief Innovation Officer	A = Alternative Program	
81 Gifted/Talented	93 Parental Involvement	280 Literacy Coach	751 Chief of Staff	G = Adult Classes	f = Facebook
82 Video Services	95 Tech Prep Program	285 STEM	752 Social Emotional Learning	M = Magnet Program	
83 Substance Abuse Prev	97 Chief Infomation Officer	286 Digital Learning		T = Title I Schoolwide	t = Twitter
84 Erate	98 Chief Technology Officer	288 Common Core Standards	**Other School Types**	V = Career & Tech Ed Programs	
85 AIDS Education	270 Character Education	294 Accountability	Ⓐ = Alternative School		
88 Alternative/At Risk	271 Migrant Education	295 Network System	Ⓒ = Charter School	New Schools are shaded	
89 Multi-Cultural Curriculum	273 Teacher Mentor	296 Title II Programs	Ⓜ = Magnet School	**New Superintendents and Principals are bold**	
90 Social Work	274 Before/After Sch	297 Webmaster	Ⓨ = Year-Round School	Personnel with email addresses are underscored	

OH-71

Franklin County

School	Grd	Prgm	Enr/#Cls	SN	Phone
Avery Elem Sch 4388 Avery Rd, Hilliard 43026 Kevin Landon	K-5		402 21	25%	614/921-5100 Fax 614/921-5101
Beacon Elem Sch 3600 Lacon Rd, Hilliard 43026 Matthew Sparks	K-5		491 28	41%	614/921-5200 Fax 614/921-5201
Britton Elem Sch 4501 Britton Pkwy, Hilliard 43026 Stephanie Borlaza	K-5		448 22	34%	614/921-5300 Fax 614/921-5301
Brown Elem Sch 2494 Walker Rd, Hilliard 43026 Kate Miller	K-5		555 20	32%	614/921-5400 Fax 614/921-5401
Darby Creek Elem Sch 6305 Pinefield Dr, Hilliard 43026 Cindy Teske	K-5		415 21	9%	614/921-5500 Fax 614/921-5501
Hilliard Bradley High Sch 2800 Walker Rd, Hilliard 43026 Mindy Mordarski	9-12		1,661	23%	614/921-7400 Fax 614/921-7401
Hilliard City Pre-School 2874 Alton Darby Creek Rd R, Hilliard 43026 Brian Hart	PK-K		344		614/921-5050 Fax 614/921-5051
Hilliard Crossing Elem Sch 3340 Hilliard Rome Rd, Hilliard 43026 Kayla Pinnick	K-5		506 33	27%	614/921-5600 Fax 614/921-5601
Hilliard Darby High Sch 4200 Leppert Rd, Hilliard 43026 Joyce Brickley	9-12	V	1,591 72	21%	614/921-7300 Fax 614/921-7301
Hilliard Davidson High Sch 5100 Davidson Rd, Hilliard 43026 Aaron Cookson	9-12	V	1,857 80	19%	614/921-7200 Fax 614/921-7201
Hilliard Heritage Middle Sch 5670 Scioto Darby Rd, Hilliard 43026 Matthew Trombitas	7-8	V	774	21%	614/921-7500 Fax 614/921-7521
Hilliard Horizon Elem Sch 6000 Renner Rd, Columbus 43228 Hilary Sloat	K-5	T	606 25	48%	614/921-5800 Fax 614/921-5801
Hilliard Memorial Middle Sch 2900 Walker Rd, Hilliard 43026 Barry Bay	7-8	V	863 38	25%	614/921-7600 Fax 614/921-7601
Hilliard Station 6th Grade Sch 5600 Scioto Darby Rd, Hilliard 43026 Lauren Schmidt	6-6		783 40	21%	614/921-6800 Fax 614/921-6801
Hilliard Tharp 6th Grade Sch 4681 Leap Rd, Hilliard 43026 Jessica Rardon	6-6		544 26	29%	614/921-6900 Fax 614/921-6901
Hilliard Weaver Middle Sch 4600 Avery Rd, Hilliard 43026 Chad Schulte	7-8	V	920 42	25%	614/921-7500 Fax 614/921-7701
Hoffman Trails Elem Sch 4301 Hoffman Farms Dr, Hilliard 43026 **Katie Salyer**	K-5		579 26	10%	614/921-5700 Fax 614/921-5701
Innovative Learning Hub 3859 Main St, Hilliard 43026 **Craig Vroom**	Voc		500		614/921-4850
J W Reason Elem Sch 4790 Cemetery Rd, Hilliard 43026 Jacki Prati	K-5	T	483 18	52%	614/921-5900 Fax 614/921-5901
ⓐ McVey Innovative Learning Ctr 5323 Cemetery Rd, Hilliard 43026 Brent Wise	7-12		150		614/921-4800
Norwich Elem Sch 4454 Davidson Rd, Hilliard 43026 **Michael Heitzman**	K-5		535 24	15%	614/921-6000 Fax 614/921-6001
Ridgewood Elem Sch 4237 Dublin Rd, Hilliard 43026 Kevin Buchman	K-5		579 24	17%	614/921-6100 Fax 614/921-6101
Scioto Darby Elem Sch 5380 Scioto Darby Rd, Hilliard 43026 Tamar Campbell-Sauer	K-5		455 24	16%	614/921-6300 Fax 614/921-6301
Washington Elem Sch 5675 Eiterman Rd, Dublin 43016 **Monica Campana**	K-5		399 30	17%	614/921-6200 Fax 614/921-6201

• **New Albany-Plain Local SD** PID: 00801593 614/855-2040
55 N High St, New Albany 43054 Fax 614/855-2043

Schools: 5 \ *Teachers:* 256 \ *Students:* 5,100 \ *Special Ed Students:* 581 \ *LEP Students:* 209 \ *College-Bound:* 87% \ *Ethnic:* Asian 14%, African American 9%, Hispanic 4%, Caucasian 74% \ *Exp:* $89 (Low) \ *Poverty:* 6% \ *Title I:* $373,610 \ *Special Education:* $588,000 \ *Open-Close:* 08/15 - 05/28 \ *DTBP:* $191 (High)

Michael Sawyers	1	Monica Gerhart	2	
Rebecca Jenkins	2,19	Dwight Shrigley	3	
Carol Hamilton	4	Linda Honaker	5	
Richard Wildenhaus	6*	Dr Shirley Hamilton	8	
Scott Emery	9	Lori Lofton	15,68	
Darren Falk	23*	Sheila Saunders	58,296	
John McClelland	67	Jessica Marnais	69,294	
Elizabeth Steel	71	Patrick Gallaway	71	
Michael Voss	73	Crystal Spires	76	
Jon Hood	79,91			

Public Schs..Principal	Grd	Prgm	Enr/#Cls	SN	Phone
New Albany Early Learning Ctr 5101 Swickard Woods Blvd, New Albany 43054 Michelle Unger	PK-K		464 24	5%	614/413-8700 Fax 614/413-8701
New Albany High Sch 7600 Fodor Rd, New Albany 43054 Ken Kraemer	9-12		1,596 58	14%	614/413-8300 Fax 614/413-8301
New Albany Interm Sch 177 N High St, New Albany 43054 Jennifer Denny	4-6		1,110		614/413-3000 Fax 614/741-3001
New Albany Middle Sch 6600 E Dublin Granville Rd, New Albany 43054 Donna LeBeau	7-8		793		614/413-8500 Fax 614/413-8501
New Albany Primary Sch 87 N High St, New Albany 43054 Teresa Smith	1-3		1,067 52	8%	614/413-8600 Fax 614/413-8601

• **Reynoldsburg City School Dist** PID: 00801634 614/501-1020
7244 E Main St, Reynoldsburg 43068 Fax 614/501-1050

Schools: 16 \ *Teachers:* 294 \ *Students:* 7,572 \ *Special Ed Students:* 791 \ *LEP Students:* 681 \ *College-Bound:* 64% \ *Ethnic:* Asian 5%, African American 45%, Hispanic 8%, Caucasian 41% \ *Exp:* $104 (Low) \ *Poverty:* 15% \ *Title I:* $1,812,473 \ *Special Education:* $979,000 \ *Open-Close:* 08/19 - 05/28 \ *DTBP:* $191 (High)

Melvin Brown	1	Chris Reed	2,3,4,5,76,295,298
Wendy Novotni	4	Theresa Ritchie	5
Jacob Perkins	6	Jocelyn Cosgrave	8,18
Sharon Smith	12	Kimberly Halley	15
Shawn Strohl	34,57,58,81,90	Joe Begeny	67
Dr Tanya Davis	68	Valerie Wunder	71,297,298
Ben Jones	73,84	James Young	81
Nick Keisel	91		

Public Schs..Principal	Grd	Prgm	Enr/#Cls	SN	Phone
Bell Academy 6699 E Livingston Ave, Reynoldsburg 43068 Carla Brown	9-12		430	81%	614/501-4000 Fax 614/501-4003

1	Superintendent	8	Curric/Instruct K-12	19	Chief Financial Officer	29	Family/Consumer Science	39	Social Studies K-12	49	English/Lang Arts Elem	59	Special Education Elem	69	Academic Assessment
2	Bus/Finance/Purchasing	9	Curric/Instruct Elem	20	Art K-12	30	Adult Education	40	Social Studies Elem	50	English/Lang Arts Sec	60	Special Education Sec	70	Research/Development
3	Buildings And Grounds	10	Curric/Instruct Sec	21	Art Elem	31	Career/Sch-to-Work K-12	41	Social Studies Sec	51	Reading K-12	61	Foreign/World Lang K-12	71	Public Information
4	Food Service	11	Federal Program	22	Art Sec	32	Career/Sch-to-Work Elem	42	Science K-12	52	Reading Elem	62	Foreign/World Lang Elem	72	Summer School
5	Transportation	12	Title I	23	Music K-12	33	Career/Sch-to-Work Sec	43	Science Elem	53	Reading Sec	63	Foreign/World Lang Sec	73	Instructional Tech
6	Athletic	13	Title V	24	Music Elem	34	Early Childhood Ed	44	Science Sec	54	Remedial Reading K-12	64	Religious Education K-12	74	Inservice Training
7	Health Services	14	Asst Superintendent	25	Music Sec	35	Health/Phys Education	45	Math K-12	55	Remedial Reading Elem	65	Religious Education Elem	75	Marketing/Distributive
		15	Instructional Media Svcs	26	Business Education	36	Guidance Services K-12	46	Math Elem	56	Remedial Reading Sec	66	Religious Education Sec	76	Info Systems
		16	Chief Operations Officer	27	Career & Tech Ed	37	Guidance Services Elem	47	Math Sec	57	Bilingual/ELL	67	School Board President	77	Psychological Assess
		17	Chief Academic Officer	28	Technology Education	38	Guidance Services Sec	48	English/Lang Arts K-12	58	Special Education K-12	68	Teacher Personnel	78	Affirmative Action

Ohio School Directory

Franklin County

Encore Academy	9-12	TV	571		614/501-2300
8579 Summit Rd, Reynoldsburg 43068					Fax 614/501-2299
Dr Tonya Bailey					
Everest High Sch	9-12		66		614/501-1033
1555 Graham Rd, Reynoldsburg 43068					
Mark Fuller					
French Run Elem Sch	K-4	T	499	57%	614/367-1950
1200 Epworth Ave, Reynoldsburg 43068			28		Fax 614/367-1958
Terra Baker					
Hanna J Ashton Middle Sch	5-8	T	571	77%	614/367-1530
1482 Jackson St, Reynoldsburg 43068			25		Fax 614/367-1549
Jamie Wilson					
Herbert Mills Elem Sch	PK-4	T	451	56%	614/367-2160
6826 Retton Rd, Reynoldsburg 43068			15		Fax 614/367-2168
Mary Weeks					
Patriot Preparatory Academy	K-12	T	601	67%	614/864-5332
4938 Beatrice Dr, Columbus 43227					Fax 614/864-5381
Brenda Williams					
Reynolds HS-HS2 STEM Academy	9-12	T	555		614/501-4030
6699 E Livingston Ave, Reynoldsburg 43068					Fax 614/501-2260
Dawn McCloud					
Reynoldsburg HS-E STEM Academy	9-12		633		614/501-2310
8579 Summit Rd, Reynoldsburg 43068					Fax 614/501-2250
Scott Bennett					
Rose Hill Elem Sch	PK-4	T	410	57%	614/367-2380
760 Rosehill Rd, Reynoldsburg 43068			18		Fax 614/367-2386
Derrick Shelton					
Slate Ridge Elem Sch	PK-4	T	591	55%	614/501-5500
10466 Taylor Rd SW, Reynoldsburg 43068			22		Fax 614/501-5520
Micca Conley					
STEM Middle at Baldwin Rd JHS	5-8	T	712	43%	614/367-1600
2300 Baldwin Pl, Reynoldsburg 43068			45		Fax 614/367-1625
Toby Fischer					
Summit Road STEM Elem Sch	K-4		501	28%	614/501-5530
8591 Summit Rd, Reynoldsburg 43068					Fax 614/501-5699
Latasha Turner					
Taylor Road Elem Sch	PK-4		464	35%	614/367-2930
8200 Taylor Rd SW, Reynoldsburg 43068			22		Fax 614/367-2933
Jamie Johnson					
Waggoner Rd Junior High Sch	7-8	T	585	44%	614/501-5700
360 Waggoner Rd, Reynoldsburg 43068					Fax 614/501-5720
Dr Twana Black					
Waggoner Road Middle Sch	5-6	T	540	55%	614/501-5600
340 Waggoner Rd, Reynoldsburg 43068					Fax 614/501-5622
Dawn McCloud					

South-Western City School Dist PID: 00801816   614/801-3000
3805 Marlane Dr, Grove City 43123   Fax 614/871-2781

Schools: 33 \ **Teachers:** 1,169 \ **Students:** 22,790 \
Special Ed Students: 3,274 \ **LEP Students:** 3,234 \ **College-Bound:** 52%
\ **Ethnic:** Asian 3%, African American 15%, Hispanic 16%, Caucasian 66% \ **Exp:** $191 (Low) \ **Poverty:** 20% \ **Title I:** $9,745,480 \
Special Education: $3,843,000 \ **Open-Close:** 08/21 - 05/28 \ **DTBP:** $73 (Low) \

Dr Bill Wise 1	Monte Detterman 2,4,5
Lisa Hamrick 4	Tim Cox 5
Dr Erik Shuey 6,10	Amber Hufford 7,79,83
Brad Faust 8,12,13,15,275	Brian Bowser 9,34
Melvina Torbert 11,296,298	Carl Metzger 15,68
Margaret Towery 16,20,23,39,48,61	Hugh Garside 19
Amy Schakat 27,31	April Weese 35,42,45
Ed Kennedy 57,89	Nicole Tyo 58
Mindy Garverick 67	Dr Cheryl Spain 69,81
Sandra Nekoloff 71	Rob Moore 73,286,295
Maria Boyarko 74,273	Bryan Mulvany 76,294

Public Schs..Principal	Grd	Prgm	Enr/#Cls	SN	
Alton Hall Elem Sch	K-4	T	539	63%	614/801-8000
982 Alton Rd, Galloway 43119			26		Fax 614/851-5879
Stefanie Hatfield					
Bolton Crossing Elem Sch	K-4		513	61%	614/801-8275
2695 Holt Rd, Grove City 43123					Fax 614/878-4037
Michele Harkins					
Brookpark Middle Sch	7-8	TV	556	53%	614/801-3500
2803 Southwest Blvd, Grove City 43123			34		Fax 614/871-6512
Holly Carr					
Buckeye Ranch Sch	Spec	V	85		614/539-6456
5665 Hoover Rd, Grove City 43123			12		Fax 614/539-6460
Ron Wheeler					
Buckeye Woods Elem Sch	K-4		737	15%	614/801-8025
2525 Holton Rd, Grove City 43123			22		Fax 614/871-1131
Jenniffer Kauffeld					
Central Crossing High Sch	9-12	TV	1,693	42%	614/801-6500
4500 Big Run South Rd, Grove City 43123					Fax 614/875-1249
Dr Jill Burke					
Darby Woods Elem Sch	K-4	T	702	71%	614/801-8075
255 Westwoods Blvd, Galloway 43119			29		Fax 614/853-1047
Brian Novar					
Darbydale Elem Sch	K-4	T	381	50%	614/801-8050
7000 State Route 665, Darbydale 43123			10		Fax 614/877-9553
Jim Micciulla					
East Franklin Elem Sch	K-4		220		614/801-8100
1955 Richmond Rd, Columbus 43223					Fax 614/274-1267
Matthew DeCastro					
Finland Elem Sch	K-4	T	454	86%	614/801-8125
1835 Finland Ave, Columbus 43223			15		Fax 614/279-3241
Brittney McDaniel					
Finland Middle Sch	7-8	TV	693	78%	614/801-3600
1825 Finland Ave, Columbus 43223			45		Fax 614/278-6334
Lori Balough					
Franklin Heights High Sch	9-12	TV	1,336	68%	614/801-3200
1001 Demorest Rd, Columbus 43204			90		Fax 614/272-2290
Timothy Donahue					
Franklin Woods Interm Sch	5-6	TV	727	84%	614/801-8600
1831 Finland Ave, Columbus 43223			32		Fax 614/351-8651
Andy Stotz					
Galloway Ridge Interm Sch	5-6	TV	767	73%	614/801-8850
122 Galloway Rd, Galloway 43119			30		Fax 614/851-2494
Brittany Budimirovic					
Grove City High Sch	9-12	AV	1,889	22%	614/801-3300
4665 Hoover Rd, Grove City 43123					Fax 614/871-6563
Bryan O'Shea					
Hayes Intermediate Sch	5-6		482	15%	614/801-6200
4436 Haughn Rd, Grove City 43123			20		Fax 614/271-2836
Michael Nesler					
Highland Park Elem Sch	K-4	T	482	65%	614/801-8200
2600 Cameron St, Grove City 43123			19		Fax 614/817-0585
Stephanie Baker					
Holt Crossing Intermediate Sch	5-6	TV	749	71%	614/801-8700
2706 Holt Rd, Grove City 43123			36		Fax 614/871-4055
Tyler Winner					
J C Sommer Elem Sch	K-4	T	643	29%	614/801-8350
3055 Kingston Ave, Grove City 43123			25		Fax 614/875-0089
Elaine McLaughlin					
Jackson Middle Sch	7-8	V	661	21%	614/801-3800
2271 Holton Rd, Grove City 43123					Fax 614/871-0516
Daniel Boland					
James A Harmon Elem Sch	K-4	T	544	76%	614/801-8150
1861 Gantz Rd, Grove City 43123			24		Fax 614/272-1249
Michael Wang					
Monterey Elem Sch	K-4	T	473	40%	614/801-8250
3811 Hoover Rd, Grove City 43123			23		Fax 614/871-3805
Margaret Moretti					

79 Student Personnel	91 Safety/Security	275 Response To Intervention	298 Grant Writer/Ptnrships
40 Driver Ed/Safety	92 Magnet School	277 Remedial Math K-12	750 Chief Innovation Officer
41 Gifted/Talented	93 Parental Involvement	280 Literacy Coach	751 Chief of Staff
42 Video Services	95 Tech Prep Program	285 STEM	752 Social Emotional Learning
43 Substance Abuse Prev	97 Chief Information Officer	286 Digital Learning	
44 Erate	98 Chief Technology Officer	288 Common Core Standards	**Other School Types**
45 AIDS Education	270 Character Education	294 Accountability	Ⓐ = Alternative School
48 Alternative/At Risk	271 Migrant Education	295 Network System	Ⓒ = Charter School
49 Multi-Cultural Curriculum	273 Teacher Mentor	296 Title II Programs	Ⓜ = Magnet School
40 Social Work	274 Before/After Sch	297 Webmaster	Ⓨ = Year-Round School

School Programs
A = Alternative Program
G = Adult Classes
M = Magnet Program
T = Title I Schoolwide
V = Career & Tech Ed Programs

Social Media
= Facebook
= Twitter

New Schools are shaded
New Superintendents and Principals are bold
Personnel with email addresses are underscored

OH—73

Franklin County

Market Data Retrieval

School	Grd	Prgm	Enr/#Cls	SN	Phone
Norton Middle Sch 215 Norton Rd, Columbus 43228 Tresa Davis	7-8	TV	602 28	75%	614/801-3700 Fax 614/870-5528
Park Street Intermediate Sch 3205 Park St, Grove City 43123 Clint Rardon	5-6	T	767 29	49%	614/801-8800 Fax 614/871-4209
Pleasant View Middle Sch 7255 Kropp Rd, Grove City 43123 Brett Harmon	7-8	TV	871 34	68%	614/801-3900 Fax 614/801-3923
Prairie Lincoln Elem Sch 4900 Amesbury Way, Columbus 43228 Julie Kenney	K-4	T	596 26	75%	614/801-8300 Fax 614/878-8028
Prairie Norton Elem Sch 105 Norton Rd, Columbus 43228 Mike Gosztyla	K-4	T	551 19	80%	614/801-8450 Fax 614/851-0298
Richard Avenue Elem Sch 3646 Richard Ave, Grove City 43123 Cathy Moore	K-4	T	439 20	57%	614/801-8325 Fax 614/871-0712
South Western Preschool 4324 Haughn Rd, Grove City 43123 Dawn Brewer	Spec		418		614/801-8448 Fax 614/871-9568
South-Western Career Academy 4750 Big Run South Rd, Grove City 43123 James Marion	Voc	AGT	466 30		614/801-3400 Fax 614/801-6138
Stiles Elem Sch 4700 Stiles Ave, Columbus 43228 Naim Sanders	K-4	T	567 24	89%	614/801-8375 Fax 614/853-0798
West Franklin Elem Sch 3501 Briggs Rd, Columbus 43204 Dr Dawn Lauridsen	K-4	T	582 25	87%	614/801-8400 Fax 614/351-4911
Westland High Sch 146 Galloway Rd, Galloway 43119 Dr James Miller	9-12	ATV	1,825 85	64%	614/851-7000 Fax 614/870-5531

• **Upper Arlington City Sch Dist** PID: 00802092   614/487-5000
1950 N Mallway Dr, Upper Arlngtn 43221   Fax 614/487-5012

Schools: 8 \ **Teachers:** 388 \ **Students:** 6,000 \ **Special Ed Students:** 868 \ **LEP Students:** 94 \ **College-Bound:** 90% \ **Ethnic:** Asian 7%, African American 1%, Hispanic 3%, Caucasian 89% \ **Exp:** $272 (Med) \ **Poverty:** 3% \ **Title I:** $250,138 \ **Special Education:** $1,146,000 \ **Open-Close:** 08/15 - 05/29 \ **DTBP:** $190 (High)

Paul Imhoff 1	Andrew Geistfeld 2
Christopher Potts 3,17,91	Phil De Roche 3
Irene Hunt 4	Don Williams 5
Anthony Pusateri 6*	Michelle Banks 7,8,57
Keith Pomeroy 8,18,36,74,288,298	Dr Kevin Gorman 11,58,77,88,275,296
Kathleen Jenney 15,68	Jeff Stevenson 16*
Judy Deal 16	Jeanne Gogolski 27,31
Kathy Lawton 34	Stacey Royer 67
Tammy Yockey 69,286,294	Karen Truett 71
Denise Lutz 73,295	M Denise Lutz 73,98
Stephanie Collins 76	Andrew Hatton 83*
Erin Miguel-Keith 273	Ann Sidesinger 274*

Public Schs..Principal	Grd	Prgm	Enr/#Cls	SN	Phone
Barrington Elem Sch 1780 Barrington Rd, Upper Arlngtn 43221 Carla Wilson	K-5		739 35		614/487-5180 Fax 614/487-5189
Greensview Elem Sch 4301 Greensview Dr, Upper Arlngtn 43220 Jason Wulf	K-5		490 20		614/487-5050 Fax 614/487-5190
Hastings Middle Sch 1850 Hastings Ln, Upper Arlngtn 43220 Robb Gonda	6-8		675 60		614/487-5100 Fax 614/487-5116
Jones Middle Sch 2100 Arlington Ave, Upper Arlngtn 43221 Jason Fine	6-8		737 64		614/487-5080 Fax 614/487-5307
Tremont Elem Sch 2900 Tremont Rd, Upper Arlngtn 43221 Jim Buffer	K-5		668 28	8%	614/487-5170 Fax 614/487-5746
Upper Arlington High Sch 1650 Ridgeview Rd, Upper Arlngtn 43221 Andrew Theado	9-12		1,871 100		614/487-5200 Fax 614/487-5238
© Wickliffe Elem Sch 2405 Wickliffe Rd, Upper Arlngtn 43221 Chris Collaros	K-5		485 22		614/487-5150 Fax 614/487-5161
Windermere Elem Sch 4101 Windermere Rd, Upper Arlngtn 43220 Julie Nolan	K-5		466 20	5%	614/487-5060 Fax 614/487-5378

• **Westerville City School Dist** PID: 00802250   614/797-5700
936 Eastwind Dr Ste 200, Westerville 43081   Fax 614/797-5701

Schools: 24 \ **Teachers:** 761 \ **Students:** 15,000 \ **Special Ed Students:** 2,037 \ **LEP Students:** 1,589 \ **College-Bound:** 73% \ **Ethnic:** Asian 4%, African American 26%, Hispanic 7%, Caucasian 62% \ **Exp:** $222 (Med) \ **Poverty:** 11% \ **Title I:** $2,974,600 \ **Special Education:** $2,574,000 \ **Open-Close:** 08/13 - 05/21 \ **DTBP:** $199 (High) \

Dr John Kellogg 1	Bob Lynde 2,5
Nicole Marshall 2,19	Jeff Lerose 3
Scott Dorne 3	Scott Reeves 6,10,31,69
Deborah Meissner 7,91	Jennifer Knapp 8,285
Barbara Wallace 9,34,92	Cheryl Relsford 9,16,752
Juliet Peoples 11,296,298	Mark Hershiser 15
Anne Baldwin 27,38,95	Tami Santa 37,752
Dr Lucy Radar-Brown 57*	Guerdie Glass 59
Gerrie Cotter 67	Dr Paul Hopkins 68
Steven Mazzi 68	Greg Viebranz 71
Dr Scott Ebrecht 72	Greg Lewis 76,84
Caley Baker 81	Dr Scott Ebbrecht 83,88*
Matt Davis 297	

Public Schs..Principal	Grd	Prgm	Enr/#Cls	SN	Phone
Ⓐ Academic Enrichment Center 336 S Otterbein Ave, Westerville 43081 Dr Scott Ebbrecht	9-12		120		614/797-7450 Fax 614/797-7451
Alcott Elem Sch 7117 Mount Royal Ave, Westerville 43082 Earl Rahm	K-5		553 26	13%	614/797-7350 Fax 614/797-7351
Annehurst Elem Sch 925 W Main St, Westerville 43081 Tabatha Wilburn	K-5	T	409 17	40%	614/797-7000 Fax 614/797-7001
Blendon Middle Sch 223 S Otterbein Ave, Westerville 43081 Kendall Harris	6-8	V	717 25	35%	614/797-6400 Fax 614/797-6401
Cherrington Elem Sch 522 Cherrington Rd, Westerville 43081 Andrew Heck	K-5	T	450 18	38%	614/797-7050 Fax 614/797-7051
Ⓜ Emerson Elementary 44 N Vine St, Westerville 43081 Chris Poynter	1-5		228 10	14%	614/797-7080 Fax 614/797-7081
Fouse Elem Sch 5800 S Old 3C Hwy, Westerville 43082 Robert Stranges	K-5		641	24%	614/797-7400 Fax 614/797-7401
Genoa Middle Sch 5948 S Old 3C Hwy, Westerville 43082 Scott Gaddis	6-8		890	16%	614/797-6500 Fax 614/797-6501

1 Superintendent	8 Curric/Instruct K-12	19 Chief Financial Officer	29 Family/Consumer Science	39 Social Studies K-12	49 English/Lang Arts Elem	59 Special Education Elem	69 Academic Assessment
2 Bus/Finance/Purchasing	9 Curric/Instruct Elem	20 Art K-12	30 Adult Education	40 Social Studies Elem	50 English/Lang Arts Sec	60 Special Education Sec	70 Research/Development
3 Buildings And Grounds	10 Curric/Instruct Sec	21 Art Elem	31 Career/Sch-to-Work K-12	41 Social Studies Sec	51 Reading K-12	61 Foreign/World Lang K-12	71 Public Information
4 Food Service	11 Federal Program	22 Art Sec	32 Career/Sch-to-Work Elem	42 Science K-12	52 Reading Elem	62 Foreign/World Lang Elem	72 Summer School
5 Transportation	12 Title I	23 Music K-12	33 Career/Sch-to-Work Sec	43 Science Elem	53 Reading Sec	63 Foreign/World Lang Sec	73 Instructional Tech
6 Athletic	13 Title V	24 Music Elem	34 Early Childhood Ed	44 Science Sec	54 Remedial Reading K-12	64 Religious Education K-12	74 Inservice Training
7 Health Services	15 Asst Superintendent	25 Music Sec	35 Health/Phys Education	45 Math K-12	55 Remedial Reading Elem	65 Religious Education Elem	75 Marketing/Distributive
	16 Instructional Media Svcs	26 Business Education	36 Guidance Services K-12	46 Math Elem	56 Remedial Reading Sec	66 Religious Education Sec	76 Info Systems
	17 Chief Operations Officer	27 Career & Tech Ed	37 Guidance Services Elem	47 Math Sec	57 Bilingual/ELL	67 School Board President	77 Psychological Assess
	18 Chief Academic Officer	28 Technology Education	38 Guidance Services Sec	48 English/Lang Arts K-12	58 Special Education K-12	68 Teacher Personnel	78 Affirmative Action

Ohio School Directory

Franklin County

Public Schs..Principal	Grd	Prgm	Enr/#Cls		SN
Hanby Elementary 56 S State St, Westerville 43081 **Megan McCaulla**	1-5		253 14	33%	614/797-7100 Fax 614/797-7101
Hawthorne Elem Sch 5001 Farview Rd, Columbus 43231 **Ernest Clinkscale**	K-5	T	733 32	59%	614/797-7130 Fax 614/797-7131
Heritage Middle Sch 390 N Spring Rd, Westerville 43082 **Dru Tomlin**	6-8	TV	959 55	50%	614/797-6600 Fax 614/797-6601 f t
Huber Ridge Elem Sch 5757 Buenos Aires Blvd, Westerville 43081 **Tyson Hilkert**	K-5	T	554 24	57%	614/797-7150 Fax 614/797-7151
Longfellow Elem Sch 120 Hiawatha Ave, Westerville 43081 **Chris Poynter**	K-K		80		614/797-7180 Fax 614/797-7181
Mark Twain Elem Sch 799 E Walnut St, Westerville 43081 **Vicki Moss**	K-5		595 19	39%	614/797-7200 Fax 614/797-7201
McVay Elem Sch 270 S Hempstead Rd, Westerville 43081 **Jim Swain**	K-5	T	528 27	33%	614/797-7230 Fax 614/797-7231
Pointview Elem Sch 720 Pointview Dr, Westerville 43081 **David Bennett**	K-5	T	327 14	70%	614/797-7250 Fax 614/797-7251
Preschool Early Learning Ctr 936 Eastwind Dr, Westerville 43081 **Suzanne Kile**	PK-PK		240		614/797-7450 Fax 614/797-7451
Robert Frost Elem Sch 270 N Spring Rd, Westerville 43082 **Sarah Berka**	K-5		442 19	27%	614/797-7280 Fax 614/797-7281
Walnut Springs Middle Sch 888 E Walnut St, Westerville 43081 **Becca Yanni**	6-8	TV	938	43%	614/797-6700 Fax 614/797-6701
Westerville Central High Sch 7118 Mount Royal Ave, Westerville 43082 **Thomas Lanier**	9-12	G	1,846 100	26%	614/797-6800 Fax 614/797-6801
Westerville North High Sch 950 County Line Rd, Westerville 43081 **Kurt Yancey**	9-12	GV	1,540 86	32%	614/797-6200 Fax 614/797-6201
Westerville South High Sch 303 S Otterbein Ave, Westerville 43081 **Michael Hinze**	9-12	GV	1,523	38%	614/797-6000 Fax 614/797-6001
Whittier Elem Sch 130 E Walnut St, Westerville 43081 **Andrew Hoffman**	K-5		344 16	19%	614/797-7300 Fax 614/797-7301
Wilder Elem Sch 6375 Goldfinch Dr, Westerville 43081 **Dr Victoria Hazlett**	K-5	T	494 22	37%	614/797-7330 Fax 614/797-7331

● **Whitehall City School Dist** PID: 00802420   614/417-5000
625 S Yearling Rd, Whitehall 43213   Fax 614/417-5025

Schools: 6 \ **Teachers:** 190 \ **Students:** 3,200 \ **Special Ed Students:** 503
\ **LEP Students:** 524 \ **College-Bound:** 39% \ **Ethnic:** Asian 1%,
African American 46%, Hispanic 23%, Caucasian 30% \ **Exp:** $252 (Med)
\ **Poverty:** 30% \ **Title I:** $1,800,444 \ **Special Education:** $651,000 \
Open-Close: 08/21 - 06/02 \ **DTBP:** $184 (High)

Brian Hamler 1   Steve McAfee 2
Dave Hausmann 3,5,16,73,76,82,91,295   Patty Schick 4
Bill Hewitt .... 6,35*   Wendy Siegel 7*
Mark Trace 15,68,79   Rita Valenzuela 37*
Yvonne Osbourne .... 37*   Anna Shultz 58
Anna Telerski 58   Michael Adkins 67
y Debevoise 71   Kristin Barker 296

Public Schs..Principal	Grd	Prgm	Enr/#Cls		SN
Beechwood Elem Sch 455 Beechwood Rd, Whitehall 43213 **Ashley Gates**	2-5	T	570 21	78%	614/417-5300 Fax 614/417-5304 f t
C Ray Williams Early Chldhd 4738 Kae Ave, Columbus 43213 **Shirley Drakes**	PK-K		320 5	98%	614/417-5680 Fax 614/559-0085
Etna Road Elem Sch 4531 Etna Rd, Whitehall 43213 **Jessica Moore**	2-5	T	550 19	64%	614/417-5400 Fax 614/417-5410 f t
Kae Avenue Elem Sch 4738 Kae Ave, Whitehall 43213 **Kelly Golsby**	PK-1	T	530 22	64%	614/417-5600 Fax 614/417-5607 f t
Rosemore Middle Sch 4800 Langley Ave, Whitehall 43213 **Rochelle Rankin**	6-8	T	733 45	68%	614/417-5200 Fax 614/417-5212
Whitehall Yearling High Sch 675 S Yearling Rd, Whitehall 43213 **Paul Smathers**	9-12	T	850 40	57%	614/417-5100 Fax 614/417-5133

● **Worthington School Dist** PID: 00802509   614/450-6000
200 E Wilson Bridge Rd Ste 200, Worthington 43085   Fax 614/883-3010

Schools: 20 \ **Teachers:** 604 \ **Students:** 12,500 \
Special Ed Students: 1,424 \ **LEP Students:** 640 \ **College-Bound:** 75%
\ **Ethnic:** Asian 6%, African American 10%, Hispanic 9%, Caucasian
75% \ **Exp:** $208 (Med) \ **Poverty:** 7% \ **Title I:** $1,033,746 \
Special Education: $1,717,000 \ **Open-Close:** 08/14 - 05/20 \ **DTBP:** $189
(High) \ f t

Dr Trent Bowers 1   Jeffrey McCuen 2
Timothy Gehring 3   Brian Hunt 4
Jeffrey Eble 4,5,7,91   George Sontag 5
Jeffrey Todd .... 6*   Angie Adrean 8,11,18,88,285,288,294,296
Patrick Callaghan 9   Dr Neil Gupta 10
Jeffrey Maddox 11,36,68,79,83,270,296   Randy Banks 15,79,273
Brian Geniusz 42   Ben Rule 57
Kimberly Brown 58,79   Jennifer Best 67
Victoria Gnezda 71   Kelly Wegley 72
Keith Schlarb 73,76   Susanne Palmer 81
Trisha Merenda 280

Public Schs..Principal	Grd	Prgm	Enr/#Cls		SN
Bluffsview Elem Sch 7111 Linworth Rd, Columbus 43235 **Cindy Fox**	K-6		537	16%	614/450-5100 Fax 614/883-2710
Brookside Elem Sch 6700 McVey Blvd, Columbus 43235 **Jenny Wielinski**	K-6	T	334 33	42%	614/450-5300 Fax 614/883-2760 f t
Colonial Hills Elem Sch 5800 Greenwich St, Worthington 43085 **Sherri Berridge**	K-6	T	453 16	39%	614/450-5400 Fax 614/883-2810 f t
Evening Street Elem Sch 885 Evening St, Worthington 43085 **Mary Rykowski**	K-5		518 20	3%	614/450-4400 Fax 614/883-2860 f t
Granby Elem Sch 1490 Hard Rd, Columbus 43235 **Patti Schlagel**	K-6		476 20	29%	614/450-4500 Fax 614/883-2910
Kilbourne Middle Sch 50 E Dublin Granville Rd, Worthington 43085 **Greg Garris**	6-8		490 30	22%	614/450-4200 Fax 614/883-3510
Liberty Elem Sch 8081 Saddle Run, Powell 43065 **Craig Belair**	K-6		475 35	34%	614/450-5200 Fax 614/883-2960 f t
ⓐ Linworth Alternative High Sch 2075 W Dublin Granville Rd, Worthington 43085 **Chris Hasebrook**	9-12		180 8		614/450-6900 Fax 614/883-3710

9 Student Personnel	91 Safety/Security	275 Response To Intervention	298 Grant Writer/Ptnrships	**School Programs**	**Social Media**
10 Driver Ed/Safety	92 Magnet School	277 Remedial Math K-12	750 Chief Innovation Officer	A = Alternative Program	
1 Gifted/Talented	93 Parental Involvement	280 Literacy Coach	751 Chief of Staff	G = Adult Classes	f = Facebook
2 Video Services	95 Tech Prep Program	285 STEM	752 Social Emotional Learning	M = Magnet Program	
3 Substance Abuse Prev	97 Chief Information Officer	286 Digital Learning		T = Title I Schoolwide	t = Twitter
4 Erate	98 Chief Technology Officer	288 Common Core Standards	**Other School Types**	V = Career & Tech Ed Programs	
5 AIDS Education	270 Character Education	294 Accountability	ⓐ = Alternative School		
6 Alternative/At Risk	271 Migrant Education	295 Network System	ⓒ = Charter School	New Schools are shaded	
9 Multi-Cultural Curriculum	273 Teacher Mentor	296 Title II Programs	ⓜ = Magnet School	New Superintendents and Principals are bold	
10 Social Work	274 Before/After Sch	297 Webmaster	ⓨ = Year-Round School	Personnel with email addresses are underscored	

OH—75

Franklin County

School	Grd	Prgm	Enr/#Cls	SN	Phone
McCord Middle Sch 1500 Hard Rd, Columbus 43235 Michael Kuri	7-8	V	548 20	22%	614/450-4000 Fax 614/883-3560
Ⓐ Phoenix Middle Sch 2341 Snouffer Rd, Worthington 43085 Sean Flynn	7-8	V	166 35		614/450-4100 Fax 614/883-3610
Slate Hill Elem Sch 7625 Alta View Blvd, Worthington 43085 Elizabeth Audette	K-6	T	494 22	58%	614/450-5000 Fax 614/883-3210
Sutter Park Pre-School 1850 Sutter Pkwy, Powell 43065 Patricia Hosking	PK-PK		293 30		614/450-4900 Fax 614/883-3260
Thomas Worthington High Sch 300 W Granville Rd, Worthington 43085 Peter Scully	9-12	V	1,735 90	27%	614/450-6200 Fax 614/883-2260
Wilson Hill Elem Sch 6500 Northland Rd, Worthington 43085 Dan Girard	K-6		472 23	31%	614/450-4800 Fax 614/883-3310
Ⓐ Worthington Academy 200 E Wilson Bridge Rd, Worthington 43085 Sean Flynn	9-12		30		614/450-6000
Worthington Estates Elem Sch 6760 Rieber St, Worthington 43085 Rob Messenheimer	K-6		654 22	24%	614/450-4600 Fax 614/883-3360
Worthington Hills Elem Sch 1221 Candlewood Dr, Columbus 43235 Alexandra Seiling	K-6		550 21	5%	614/450-4700 Fax 614/883-3410
Worthington Kilbourne High Sch 1499 Hard Rd, Columbus 43235 Aric Thomas	9-12		1,240 74	20%	614/450-6400 Fax 614/883-2560
Worthington Park Elem Sch 500 Park Rd, Westerville 43081 Jen Young	K-6		446 30	26%	614/450-5500 Fax 614/883-3460
Worthingway Middle Sch 6625 Guyer St, Worthington 43085 Nathan Kellenberger	7-8		425 35	37%	614/450-4300 Fax 614/883-3660

FRANKLIN CATHOLIC SCHOOLS

• **Diocese of Columbus Ed Office** PID: 00802717   614/221-5829
197 E Gay St Ste 1, Columbus 43215   Fax 614/241-2563

Schools: 53 \ **Students:** 15,418

Listing includes only schools located in this county. See District Index for location of Diocesan Offices.

Adam Dufault 1		Daphne Irby 9	
Susan Streitenberger 10		Kitty Quinn 34,83	
Dr Barbara Romanello 64		Jeanne Gissel 68,71	

Catholic Schs..Principal	Grd	Prgm	Enr/#Cls	SN	Phone
All Saints Academy 2855 E Livingston Ave, Columbus 43209 Laura Miller	PK-8		329 14		614/231-3391 Fax 614/338-2170
Bishop Hartley High Sch 1285 Zettler Rd, Columbus 43227 Mike Winters	9-12		352		614/237-5421 Fax 614/237-3809
Bishop Ready High Sch 707 Salisbury Rd, Columbus 43204 Matthew Brickner	9-12	G	400 25		614/276-5263 Fax 614/276-5116
Bishop Watterson High Sch 99 E Cooke Rd, Columbus 43214 Chris Campbell	9-12		975 50		614/268-8671 Fax 614/268-0551
Holy Spirit Sch 4382 Duchene Ln, Columbus 43213 Amy Chessler	K-8		260 12		614/861-0475 Fax 614/861-8608
Immaculate Conception Sch 366 E North Broadway St, Columbus 43214 Colleen Kent	K-8		400 223		614/267-6579 Fax 614/267-2549
Our Lady of Bethlehem Sch 4567 Olentangy River Rd, Columbus 43214 Barbara Casson	PK-K		100 4		614/459-8285 Fax 614/451-3706
Our Lady of Peace Sch 40 E Dominion Blvd, Columbus 43214 Jim Silcott	K-8		220 10		614/267-4535 Fax 614/267-2333
Our Lady-Perpetual Help Sch 3752 Broadway, Grove City 43123 Julie Freeman	PK-8		315 17		614/875-6779
St Agatha Sch 1880 Northam Rd, Columbus 43221 Luna Alsharaiha	K-8		250 20		614/488-9000 Fax 614/488-5783
St Andrew Sch 4081 Reed Rd, Columbus 43220 Joel Wichtman	K-8		450 23		614/451-1626 Fax 614/451-0272
St Anthony Sch 1300 Urban Dr, Columbus 43229 Christina Iaconis	K-8		207 9		614/888-4268 Fax 614/888-4435
St Brendan Sch 4475 Dublin Rd, Hilliard 43026 Will Gruber	K-8		488 17		614/876-6132 Fax 614/529-8929
St Brigid of Kildare Elem Sch 7175 Avery Rd, Dublin 43017 Kathleen O'Reilly	PK-8		569 20		614/718-5825 Fax 614/718-5831
St Catharine Sch 2865 Fair Ave, Columbus 43209 Janet Weisner	PK-8		271 14		614/235-1396 Fax 614/235-9708
St Cecilia Sch 440 Norton Rd, Columbus 43228 Laurie Smith	PK-8	G	226 10		614/878-3555 Fax 614/878-6852
St Charles Preparatory Sch 2010 E Broad St, Columbus 43209 James Lower	9-12		626 30		614/252-6714 Fax 614/251-6800
St Francis DeSales High Sch 4212 Karl Rd, Columbus 43224 Dan Garrick	9-12		828 35		614/267-7808 Fax 614/265-3375
St James the Less Sch 1628 Oakland Park Ave, Columbus 43224 Samary Cecchetti	K-8		496 17		614/268-3311 Fax 614/268-1808
St Joseph Montessori Sch 933 Hamlet St, Columbus 43201 Brenda Huth	PK-8		227 9		614/291-8601 Fax 614/291-7411
St Mary Magdalene Sch 2940 Parkside Rd, Columbus 43204 Mark Watts	PK-8		250 10		614/279-9935 Fax 614/279-9575
St Mary Sch 700 S 3rd St, Columbus 43206 Kayla Walton	PK-8		340 9		614/444-8994 Fax 614/449-2853
St Matthew Sch 795 Havens Corners Rd, Gahanna 43230 Susan Maloy	PK-8		606 19		614/471-4930 Fax 614/471-1673
St Matthias Sch 1566 Ferris Rd, Columbus 43224 Dan Kinley	K-8		275 9		614/268-3030 Fax 614/268-4681
St Michael Sch 64 E Selby Blvd, Worthington 43085 Sr John Paul	K-8		400 22		614/885-3149 Fax 614/885-1249
St Pius X Sch 1061 Waggoner Rd, Reynoldsburg 43068 Darren Smith	K-8		550 18		614/866-6050 Fax 614/866-6187

1	Superintendent	8	Curric/Instruct K-12	19	Chief Financial Officer	29	Family/Consumer Science
2	Bus/Finance/Purchasing	9	Curric/Instruct Elem	20	Art K-12	30	Adult Education
3	Buildings And Grounds	10	Curric/Instruct Sec	21	Art Elem	31	Career/Sch-to-Work K-12
4	Food Service	11	Federal Program	22	Art Sec	32	Career/Sch-to-Work Elem
5	Transportation	12	Title I	23	Music K-12	33	Career/Sch-to-Work Sec
6	Athletic	13	Title V	24	Music Elem	34	Early Childhood Ed
7	Health Services	14	Instructional Media Svcs	25	Music Sec	35	Health/Phys Education
		15	Asst Superintendent	26	Business Education	36	Guidance Services K-12
		16	Chief Operations Officer	27	Career & Tech Ed	37	Guidance Services Elem
		18	Chief Academic Officer	28	Technology Education	38	Guidance Services Sec

39	Social Studies K-12	49	English/Lang Arts Elem	59	Special Education Elem	69	Academic Assessment
40	Social Studies Elem	50	English/Lang Arts Sec	60	Special Education Sec	70	Research/Development
41	Social Studies Sec	51	Reading K-12	61	Foreign/World Lang K-12	71	Public Information
42	Science K-12	52	Reading Elem	62	Foreign/World Lang Elem	72	Summer School
43	Science Elem	53	Reading Sec	63	Foreign/World Lang Sec	73	Instructional Tech
44	Science Sec	54	Remedial Reading K-12	64	Religious Education K-12	74	Inservice Training
45	Math K-12	55	Remedial Reading Elem	65	Religious Education Elem	75	Marketing/Distributive
46	Math Elem	56	Remedial Reading Sec	66	Religious Education Sec	76	Info Systems
47	Math Sec	57	Bilingual/ELL	67	School Board President	77	Psychological Assess
48	English/Lang Arts K-12	58	Special Education K-12	68	Teacher Personnel	78	Affirmative Action

Ohio School Directory — Franklin County

St Timothy Sch	K-8	250	614/451-1405
1070 Thomas Ln, Columbus 43220		9	Fax 614/451-3108
George Mosholder			
Trinity Cath Elem Sch	PK-8	183	614/488-7650
1440 Grandview Ave, Columbus 43212		9	Fax 614/488-7885
Kimber Moehrman			

FRANKLIN PRIVATE SCHOOLS

Private Schs..Principal	Grd	Prgm	Enr/#Cls	SN
Beautiful Savior Luth Sch	PK-8		66	614/875-1147
2213 White Rd, Grove City 43123			5	Fax 614/875-9637
David Knittel				
Brice Christian Academy	K-8		200	614/866-6789
3160 Brice Rd, Brice 43109			13	Fax 614/861-4217
Margaret McCoy				
Bridgeway Academy		Spec	401	614/262-7520
2500 Medary Ave, Columbus 43202				f
Erin Nealy				
Calumet Christian Sch	PK-8		300	614/261-8136
2774 Calumet St, Columbus 43202			12	Fax 614/261-9086
Jim Fulford				
Central College Christian Acad	K-8		185	614/882-2347
975 S Sunbury Rd, Westerville 43081			9	Fax 614/794-8146
Howard Baum				
Childhood League Center		Spec	170	614/253-6933
674 Cleveland Ave, Columbus 43215			6	Fax 614/253-6935
Jennifer Haddow				
Children's Academy	PK-K		98	614/491-3270
100 Obetz Rd, Columbus 43207			2	Fax 614/492-0035
Ronald Sams				
Clintonville Academy	PK-8		125	614/267-4799
3916 Indianola Ave, Columbus 43214			10	Fax 614/267-1723
Sally Lindsay				
Columbus Academy	PK-12		930	614/475-2311
4300 Cherry Bottom Rd, Gahanna 43230			130	Fax 614/475-0396
Mark Hansen \ Shaka Arnold \ Cory Izokaitis				f t
Columbus Adventist Academy	K-8		153	614/471-2083
3650 B Sunbury Rd, Columbus 43219				Fax 614/471-5035
Brenda Arthurs				
Columbus Jewish Day Sch	PK-6		100	614/939-5311
150 E Dublin Granville Rd, New Albany 43054			12	Fax 614/939-5312
Rachel Arcus-Goldberg				f
Columbus Mont Educational Ctr	PK-6		225	614/231-3790
979 S James Rd, Columbus 43227			12	Fax 614/231-3780
Jamie Gottesman				
Columbus School for Girls	PK-12		617	614/252-0781
65 S Drexel Ave, Columbus 43209				Fax 614/252-0571
Jennifer Ciccarelli				f t
Columbus Torah Academy	K-12		215	614/864-0299
181 Noe Bixby Rd, Columbus 43213			30	Fax 614/864-2119
Nicole Miller \ Lou Staffilino				f t
Cristo Rey Columbus High Sch	9-12		100	614/223-9261
400 E Town St, Columbus 43215				
Cathy Thomas				
Cypress Christian Sch	K-8		341	614/870-1181
375 Alton Darby Creek Rd, Galloway 43119			18	Fax 614/878-5866
Michael Jameson				
Eastwood SDA Junior Academy	K-8		59	614/794-6350
6350 S Sunbury Rd, Westerville 43081			4	Fax 614/794-6352
Warren Johnson				
Gahanna Christian Academy	PK-12		525	614/471-9270
817 N Hamilton Rd, Columbus 43230			30	Fax 614/471-9201
Anitra Simmons				
Gloria S Friend Christian Acad	K-6		50	614/221-1518
428 E Main St, Columbus 43215			7	Fax 614/221-8470
Nadia Reed				
Grace Christian Sch	K-8		380	614/861-0724
7510 E Broad St, Blacklick 43004			21	Fax 614/863-8509
Cindy Phillips				f t
Grove City Christian Sch	K-12		687	614/875-3000
4750 Hoover Rd, Grove City 43123			45	Fax 614/875-8933
David Muschott \ Debbie Edwards \ Jim McMillan				f t
Harvest Preparatory Sch	PK-12		500	614/382-1111
4595 Gender Rd, Canal Wnchstr 43110			35	Fax 614/837-9591
Lisa Mahoney \ Andrew Mills				
High Street Christian Academy	PK-12		65	614/888-5121
7399 N High St, Columbus 43235				Fax 614/888-0173
Tom Biernacki				
Highland Community Lrng Ctr		Spec	32	614/210-0830
5120 Godown Rd, Columbus 43220				
Joshua Harning				
Madison Christian Sch	PK-12		523	614/497-3456
3565 Bixby Rd, Groveport 43125			36	Fax 614/497-3057
Christina Jones \ Sue White				
Mansion Day Sch	PK-5		70	614/258-4449
72 Woodland Ave, Columbus 43203			9	Fax 614/258-7001
Dee James				
Marburn Academy		Spec	180	614/433-0822
9555 Johnstown Rd, New Albany 43054				Fax 614/433-0812
Jamie Williamson				
Mater Dei Academy	K-8		11	614/231-1984
3695 Elm St, Columbus 43213			5	Fax 614/231-2196
Collene Moss				
Northside Christian Sch	PK-12		180	614/882-1493
2655 W Schrock Rd, Westerville 43081			20	Fax 614/882-5011
Jessie Stout				f t
Oakstone Academy	PK-4		200	614/890-7854
2655 Oakstone Dr, Columbus 43231				Fax 614/890-2304
Nikki Kerns				
Oakstone Academy Mid High Sch		Spec	600	614/865-0400
939 S State St, Westerville 43081				
Eddie Nabura				
Rosemont Center		Spec	30	614/471-2626
2440 Dawnlight Ave, Columbus 43211			9	Fax 614/478-3234
Amy Gamber				
Shepherd Christian Sch	K-5		130	614/471-0859
425 S Hamilton Rd, Columbus 43230				
Michael Fluhart				
Sonshine Christian Academy	PK-8		350	614/498-0082
1965 Gladstone Ave, Columbus 43211			23	
Carol Parron				
St Paul's Lutheran Sch	K-8		70	614/444-4216
322 Stewart Ave, Columbus 43206			4	
Charles Galecki				f
St Vincent Family Center		Spec	63	614/252-0731
1490 E Main St, Columbus 43205			12	
Susan Lewis Kaylor				
Sunrise Academy	K-8		420	614/527-0465
5657 Scioto Darby Rd, Hilliard 43026			15	Fax 614/527-4265
Mona Salti				f
Tree of Life Christian Sch	PK-5		170	614/299-4906
2141 Indianola Ave, Columbus 43201			7	Fax 614/299-3047
Colleen Hoffman				
Tree of Life Christian Sch	6-12	V	348	614/263-2688
935 Northridge Rd, Columbus 43224			30	Fax 614/263-6450
Lynn Tolley \ Brent Davis				
Tree of Life Christian Sch	PK-5		134	614/792-2671
2900 Martin Rd, Dublin 43017			8	Fax 614/588-0236
Lydia Seevers				f t

79 Student Personnel
80 Driver Ed/Safety
81 Gifted/Talented
82 Video Services
83 Substance Abuse Prev
84 Erate
85 AIDS Education
88 Alternative/At Risk
89 Multi-Cultural Curriculum
90 Social Work
91 Safety/Security
92 Magnet School
93 Parental Involvement
95 Tech Prep Program
97 Chief Information Officer
98 Chief Technology Officer
270 Character Education
271 Migrant Education
273 Teacher Mentor
274 Before/After Sch
275 Response To Intervention
277 Remedial Math K-12
280 Literacy Coach
285 STEM
286 Digital Learning
288 Common Core Standards
294 Accountability
295 Network System
296 Title II Programs
297 Webmaster
298 Grant Writer/Ptnrships
750 Chief Innovation Officer
751 Chief of Staff
752 Social Emotional Learning

Other School Types
Ⓐ = Alternative School
Ⓒ = Charter School
Ⓜ = Magnet School
Ⓨ = Year-Round School

School Programs
A = Alternative Program
G = Adult Classes
M = Magnet Program
T = Title I Schoolwide
V = Career & Tech Ed Programs

Social Media
f = Facebook
t = Twitter

New Schools are shaded
New Superintendents and Principals are bold
Personnel with email addresses are underscored

Fulton County

Market Data Retrieval

Veritas Academy 6200 Linworth Rd, Worthington 43085 Charles Zaffini	5-12	76	614/885-2810
Wellington Sch 3650 Reed Rd, Columbus 43220 Rachel Althof	PK-12	610 48	614/457-7883 Fax 614/442-3286
Worthington Adventist Academy 870 Griswold St, Worthington 43085 Valerie Green	K-8	36 4	614/885-9525 Fax 614/885-9501
Worthington Christian High Sch 6670 Worthington Galena Rd, Columbus 43085 Dr Scott Inboden	9-12	320 20	614/431-8210 Fax 614/431-8213
Worthington Christian Mid Sch 8225 Worthington Galena Rd, Westerville 43081 Tammy Evans	6-8	231	614/431-8230 Fax 614/431-8216
Worthington Chrstn Westview ES 50 Westview Ave, Columbus 43214 Jim Parrish	K-5	364 14	614/431-8240 Fax 614/438-5581

FRANKLIN REGIONAL CENTERS

- **Meta Solutions** PID: 04499544 614/473-8300
  2100 Citygate Dr, Columbus 43219 Fax 614/473-8324

  Jamie Grube 1   Jeff Culwell 2
  Lisa Wendt 16   Jimmy Battrell 71,97
  Robert Brown 76

- **State Support Team 11** PID: 02228193 614/753-4690
  2080 Citygate Dr, Columbus 43219 Fax 614/753-4699

  Rhonda Dickson 1   Gregory Mathews 15
  Helene Stacho 34

FULTON COUNTY

FULTON COUNTY SCHOOLS

- **North West Ohio Ed Service Ctr** PID: 00803840 567/444-4807
  205 Nolan Pkwy, Archbold 43502 Fax 567/444-4802

  Kerri Gearhart 1   Homer Hendricks 2
  Jim Hacker ....2*   Kris Dobbelaere 8,74
  Jill Gilliland 58

County Schs..Principal	Grd	Prgm	Enr/#Cls	SN
Fulton Co Bd-Dev Disabilities 1210 N Ottokee St, Wauseon 43567 Beth Friess	Spec	G	20	419/337-4575 Fax 419/335-3082

FULTON PUBLIC SCHOOLS

- **Archbold Area Local Sch Dist** PID: 00803503 419/445-5579
  600 Lafayette St, Archbold 43502 Fax 419/445-8536

  Schools: 3 \ **Teachers:** 73 \ **Students:** 1,212 \ **Special Ed Students:** 138 \ **LEP Students:** 24 \ **College-Bound:** 58% \ **Ethnic:** Asian 1%, African American 1%, Hispanic 19%, Caucasian 79% \ **Exp:** $384 (High) \ **Poverty:** 9% \ **Title I:** $137,525 \ **Special Education:** $217,000 \ **Open-Close:** 08/21 - 05/29 \ **DTBP:** $237 (High)

  Dr Jayson Selgo 1   Chris Ziegler 2,19*
  Sandy Babcock ....4*   Linda Schmidt 5
  Allan Gladieux 6   Michele Bagrowski 8,273*
  Tess Pinter ....16,82*   Jeremy Hurst 67
  Shawn Grime ....69,88*   Lorinda Brader 73*
  Royal Short 83*

Public Schs..Principal	Grd	Prgm	Enr/#Cls	SN
Archbold Elem Sch 500 Lafayette St, Archbold 43502 Dorothy Lambert	K-4		469 30	32% 419/446-2727 Fax 419/446-4627
Archbold High Sch 600 Lafayette St, Archbold 43502 Royal Short	9-12		365 30	22% 419/445-5579
Archbold Middle Sch 306 Stryker St, Archbold 43502 Matthew Shields	5-8		378	25% 419/446-2726 Fax 419/445-8402

- **Evergreen Local School Dist** PID: 00803553 419/644-3521
  14544 County Road 6, Metamora 43540 Fax 419/644-6070

  Schools: 3 \ **Teachers:** 82 \ **Students:** 1,300 \ **Special Ed Students:** 202 \ **LEP Students:** 4 \ **College-Bound:** 50% \ **Ethnic:** Hispanic 7%, Caucasian 93% \ **Exp:** $343 (High) \ **Poverty:** 7% \ **Title I:** $123,773 \ **Special Education:** $251,000 \ **Open-Close:** 08/14 - 05/21 \ **DTBP:** $174 (High)

  Eric Smola 1   Denise Leu 2
  Brent Miller ....3,91*   Adrian Myer 4,31,38,79,83,88
  Carrie Brown 5   Eric Simon 6
  Karen King ....7,35*   Jane Draheim 9,11,51,273,280,285,296*
  Dan Curtis 10   Dan Curtis 10*
  Tina Jones ....16,82*   Susan Hanifan 27*
  Amanda Brehm ....37,69*   Natalie Lambert 57*
  Kristy Schmidlin ....58,275*   Nora Kiefer 67
  Angela Infante 73,76,84,286,295

Public Schs..Principal	Grd	Prgm	Enr/#Cls	SN
Evergreen Elem Sch 14544 County Road 6, Metamora 43540 Jane Draheim	PK-5		532 28	38% 419/644-9221 Fax 419/644-9226
Evergreen High Sch 14544 County Road 6, Metamora 43540 Dan Curtis	9-12	V	379 30	30% 419/644-2951 Fax 419/644-6735
Evergreen Middle Sch 14544 County Road 6, Metamora 43540 Joe Zabowski	6-8		271 25	33% 419/644-2331 Fax 419/644-1376

---

1 Superintendent	8 Curric/Instruct K-12	19 Chief Financial Officer	29 Family/Consumer Science	39 Social Studies K-12	49 English/Lang Arts Elem	59 Special Education Elem	69 Academic Assessment
2 Bus/Finance/Purchasing	9 Curric/Instruct Elem	20 Art K-12	30 Adult Education	40 Social Studies Elem	50 English/Lang Arts Sec	60 Special Education Sec	70 Research/Development
3 Buildings And Grounds	10 Curric/Instruct Sec	21 Art Elem	31 Career/Sch-to-Work K-12	41 Social Studies Sec	51 Reading K-12	61 Foreign/World Lang K-12	71 Public Information
4 Food Service	11 Federal Program	22 Art Sec	32 Career/Sch-to-Work Elem	42 Science K-12	52 Reading Elem	62 Foreign/World Lang Elem	72 Summer School
5 Transportation	12 Title I	23 Music K-12	33 Career/Sch-to-Work Sec	43 Science Elem	53 Reading Sec	63 Foreign/World Lang Sec	73 Instructional Tech
6 Athletic	13 Title V	24 Music Elem	34 Early Childhood Ed	44 Science Sec	54 Remedial Reading K-12	64 Religious Education K-12	74 Inservice Training
7 Health Services	14 Asst Superintendent	25 Music Sec	35 Health/Phys Education	45 Math K-12	55 Remedial Reading Elem	65 Religious Education Elem	75 Marketing/Distributive
	15 Instructional Media Svcs	26 Business Education	36 Guidance Services K-12	46 Math Elem	56 Remedial Reading Sec	66 Religious Education Sec	76 Info Systems
	16 Chief Operations Officer	27 Career & Tech Ed	37 Guidance Services Elem	47 Math Sec	57 Bilingual/ELL	67 School Board President	77 Psychological Assess
	18 Chief Academic Officer	28 Technology Education	38 Guidance Services Sec	48 English/Lang Arts K-12	58 Special Education K-12	68 Teacher Personnel	78 Affirmative Action

Ohio School Directory — Fulton County

Fayette Local Sch Dist PID: 00803618
400 E Gamble Rd, Fayette 43521
419/237-2573
Fax 419/237-3125

Schools: 1 \ **Teachers:** 31 \ **Students:** 370 \ **Special Ed Students:** 61 \ **LEP Students:** 11 \ **College-Bound:** 65% \ **Ethnic:** Asian 1%, Hispanic 18%, Caucasian 81% \ **Exp:** $358 (High) \ **Poverty:** 13% \ **Title I:** $78,444 \ **Special Education:** $83,000 \ **Open-Close:** 08/15 - 05/27 \ **DTBP:** $161 (High)

Angie Belcher 1,11	Kelly Bentley 2,84
Amy Gorsuch 4	Sally Kovar 8*
Carol Burkholder 12	Amy Hibbard 16*
Janna Ballmer 36,69*	Allie Reucher 58*
Kirk Keiser 67	Becky Short 73*
Alexander Reucher 79	

Public Schs..Principal	Grd	Prgm	Enr/#Cls	SN	
Fayette Sch	PK-12	A	370	98%	419/237-2114
400 E Gamble Rd, Fayette 43521			45		Fax 419/237-4306
Jon Molter \ Allie Reucher					

Four-Co Joint Voc School Dist PID: 00810881
22900 State Route 34, Archbold 43502
419/267-3331
Fax 419/267-2345

Schools: 1 \ **Teachers:** 83 \ **Students:** 1,000 \ **Exp:** $402 (High) \ **Open-Close:** 08/14 - 05/21 \ **DTBP:** $233 (High)

Tim Meister 1	Connie Nicely 2
Rick Bachman 3,27,34,75,288*	Marsha Heilman
Rick Hupe 11,28,73,79*	Krissy Cheslock 16,33,38,60,83,88*
Doug Beck 30*	Brian Baker 67
Pam Kuhn 69*	Rob Williams 76,82*
Linda Mahnke 85*	

Public Schs..Principal	Grd	Prgm	Enr/#Cls	SN	
Four Co Career Center	Voc	AG	1,000		419/267-3331
22900 State Route 34, Archbold 43502			200		
Rick Bachman					

Pettisville Local School Dist PID: 00803656
232 Summit St, Pettisville 43553
419/446-2705
Fax 419/445-2992

Schools: 2 \ **Teachers:** 35 \ **Students:** 525 \ **Special Ed Students:** 41 \ **College-Bound:** 79% \ **Ethnic:** Asian 2%, African American 1%, Hispanic 12%, Caucasian 85% \ **Exp:** $137 (Low) \ **Poverty:** 5% \ **Title I:** $25,213 \ **Special Education:** $79,000 \ **Open-Close:** 08/21 - 06/03 \ **DTBP:** $170 (High)

Dr Stephen Switzer 1	Chris Lee 2
Ron Burkholder 3*	Sandy Blackwood 4*
Deb Graber 5	Brian Leppelmeier 6*
Michael Lane 8,69*	Jason Waldvogel 9*
Shelly Schramm 16*	Mandy Wyman 36,83,88*
Dan Bruner 67	Mike Zimmerman 73*

Public Schs..Principal	Grd	Prgm	Enr/#Cls	SN	
Pettisville Elem Sch	K-6		287		419/446-2705
232 Summit St, Pettisville 43553			12		
Jason Waldvogel					
Pettisville Jr Sr High Sch	7-12	V	238	47%	419/446-2705
232 Summit St, Pettisville 43553					
Michael Lane					

Pike-Delta-York Local Sch Dist PID: 00803682
504 Fernwood St, Delta 43515
419/822-3391
Fax 419/822-4478

Schools: 3 \ **Teachers:** 82 \ **Students:** 1,100 \ **Special Ed Students:** 225 \ **LEP Students:** 20 \ **College-Bound:** 59% \ **Ethnic:** African American 1%, Hispanic 6%, Caucasian 93% \ **Exp:** $288 (Med) \ **Poverty:** 11% \ **Title I:** $173,052 \ **Special Education:** $266,000 \ **Open-Close:** 08/19 - 05/28 \ **DTBP:** $238 (High)

Ted Haselman 1	Matt Feasel 2,19
Jim Wolpert 3,5	Brenda McCollough 4*
Andrew Hange 6	Andrea Johnson 8,11,288
Katie Butlar 37*	Amy Kramer 58,275
Mike Ford 67	Derek Friess 73,76,295*

Public Schs..Principal	Grd	Prgm	Enr/#Cls	SN	
Delta Elem Sch	K-4	T	452	42%	419/822-5630
1099 Panther Pride Dr, Delta 43515					Fax 419/822-2828
Ellen Bernal					
Delta Middle Sch	5-8	T	402	41%	419/822-9118
1101 Panther Pride Dr, Delta 43515			23		Fax 419/822-8490
Doug Ford					
Pike-Delta-York High Sch	9-12		331	36%	419/822-8247
605 Taylor St, Delta 43515			20		Fax 419/822-2826
Kristie Reighard					

Swanton Local School Dist PID: 00803747
108 N Main St, Swanton 43558
419/826-7085
Fax 419/825-1197

Schools: 3 \ **Teachers:** 71 \ **Students:** 1,300 \ **Special Ed Students:** 189 \ **LEP Students:** 5 \ **College-Bound:** 59% \ **Ethnic:** African American 2%, Hispanic 6%, Caucasian 91% \ **Exp:** $286 (Med) \ **Poverty:** 10% \ **Title I:** $191,389 \ **Open-Close:** 08/20 - 05/29 \ **DTBP:** $233 (High)

Chris Lake 1	Joyce Kinsman 2,11,84,296
Glen Dominique 3	Christian Martinez 4
Jeff Bella 5	Wade Haselman 6*
Sharon Marvin 8,12,58	Steve Bremer 67
Anthony Menna 69	Julie LaPoint 73*
Brandon Schroth 76,295	Kim Floyd 273*
Matthew Smith 294*	

Public Schs..Principal	Grd	Prgm	Enr/#Cls	SN	
Swanton Elem Sch	K-4	T	431	66%	419/826-8991
111 Crestwood Dr, Swanton 43558			15		Fax 419/826-8646
Kristi Molter					
Swanton High Sch	9-12	T	379	36%	419/826-3045
601 N Main St, Swanton 43558			35		Fax 419/826-1611
Jason Longbrake					
Swanton Middle Sch	5-8	T	402	42%	419/826-4016
101 Elton Pkwy, Swanton 43558			15		Fax 419/826-5176
Matt Smith					

Wauseon Exempted Village SD PID: 00803802
930 E Oak St, Wauseon 43567
419/335-6616
Fax 419/335-3978

Schools: 4 \ **Teachers:** 99 \ **Students:** 1,770 \ **Special Ed Students:** 237 \ **LEP Students:** 55 \ **College-Bound:** 48% \ **Ethnic:** Asian 1%, African American 1%, Hispanic 21%, Caucasian 77% \ **Exp:** $202 (Med) \ **Poverty:** 9% \ **Title I:** $235,546 \ **Special Education:** $328,000 \ **Open-Close:** 08/19 - 05/28 \ **DTBP:** $244 (High)

Troy Armstrong 1	Dave Fleming 2
Jim Figy 3	Brittani Gerken 4
Pamela Waugh 5	Matt Hutchinson 6*
Michelle Leatherman 8,11*	Jennifer Grime 58*

79	Student Personnel	91	Safety/Security	275	Response To Intervention	298	Grant Writer/Ptnrships	**School Programs**
30	Driver Ed/Safety	92	Magnet School	277	Remedial Math K-12	750	Chief Innovation Officer	A = Alternative Program
31	Gifted/Talented	93	Parental Involvement	280	Literacy Coach	751	Chief of Staff	G = Adult Classes
32	Video Services	95	Tech Prep Program	285	STEM	752	Social Emotional Learning	M = Magnet Program
33	Substance Abuse Prev	97	Chief Information Officer	286	Digital Learning			T = Title I Schoolwide
34	Erate	98	Chief Technology Officer	288	Common Core Standards	**Other School Types**		V = Career & Tech Ed Programs
35	AIDS Education	270	Character Education	294	Accountability	Ⓐ = Alternative School		
38	Alternative/At Risk	271	Migrant Education	295	Network System	Ⓒ = Charter School		**Social Media**
39	Multi-Cultural Curriculum	273	Teacher Mentor	296	Title II Programs	Ⓜ = Magnet School		= Facebook
90	Social Work	274	Before/After Sch	297	Webmaster	Ⓨ = Year-Round School		= Twitter

New Schools are shaded
New Superintendents and Principals are bold
Personnel with email addresses are underscored

Gallia County

Market Data Retrieval

Sandra Griggs 67
Curt Crew 73*
Kim Hinton 81*
Joe Friess 72*
Timothy McQuade 77

Public Schs..Principal	Grd	Prgm	Enr/#Cls	SN	
Wauseon Elem Sch 950 E Oak St, Wauseon 43567 Theresa Vietmeier	3-5	T	425 24		419/335-6581 Fax 419/335-0045
ⓒ Wauseon High Sch 840 Parkview St, Wauseon 43567 Keith Leatherman	9-12	AV	535 50	34%	419/335-5756 Fax 419/335-4228
Wauseon Middle Sch 940 E Oak St, Wauseon 43567 Joe Friess	6-8		432 35	82%	419/335-2701 Fax 419/335-0089
Wauseon Primary Sch 940 E Leggett St, Wauseon 43567 Blake Young	PK-2	T	378	39%	419/335-4000 Fax 419/335-4003

FULTON CATHOLIC SCHOOLS

• **Diocese of Toledo Ed Office** PID: 00818297
Listing includes only schools located in this county. See District Index for location of Diocesan Offices.

Catholic Schs..Principal	Grd	Prgm	Enr/#Cls	SN	
Holy Trinity Sch 2639 US Highway 20, Swanton 43558 Brandon Kulka	PK-8		131 11		419/644-3971 Fax 419/644-9372
St Richard Sch 333 Brookside Dr, Swanton 43558 Sr Jean Walczak	PK-8		70 10		419/826-5041 Fax 419/826-7256

FULTON REGIONAL CENTERS

• **Northwest Ohio Computer Assoc** PID: 04499594   419/267-5565
209 Nolan Pkwy, Archbold 43502   Fax 419/267-5248

Dr Tod Hug 1   Joe Prchlik 16,73

GALLIA COUNTY

GALLIA COUNTY SCHOOLS

• **Gallia-Vinton Ed Svc Center** PID: 00804040   740/245-0593
60 Ridge Ave, Rio Grande 45674   Fax 740/245-0596

Dr Denise Shockley 1   Lily Blevins 2
Mary Thacker 8,11   Wendy Halley 58,74
Mark Carlisle 73

GALLIA PUBLIC SCHOOLS

• **Gallia Co Local School Dist** PID: 00803917   740/379-9085
4836 State Route 325, Patriot 45658   Fax 740/379-9135

Schools: 8 \ **Teachers:** 148 \ **Students:** 2,200 \ **Special Ed Students:** 354 \ **College-Bound:** 54% \ **Ethnic:** African American 3%, Hispanic 1%, Caucasian 96% \ **Exp:** $256 (Med) \ **Poverty:** 23% \ **Title I:** $966,992 \ **Open-Close:** 08/21 - 05/22 \ **DTBP:** $174 (High)

Jude Meyers 1
Todd Boothe 3,73,295
Larry Carter 5*
Sandra Plantz 11,81,273
Beth James 67
Scott West 286
Lilly Blevins 2
Lora DeLaney 4
Rochelle Halley 8,16,51,68,74
Wendy Halley 58,88,275
Leslie Henry 69

Public Schs..Principal	Grd	Prgm	Enr/#Cls	SN	
Addaville Elem Sch 1333 Brick School Rd, Gallipolis 45631 Brandon Mitchem	PK-5	T	328 20		740/367-7283 Fax 740/367-5004
Hannan Trace Elem Sch 9345 State Route 218, Crown City 45623 Edie Bostic	K-6	T	240 40		740/256-6468 Fax 740/256-1803
River Valley High Sch 8785 State Route 160, Bidwell 45614 Timothy Edwards	9-12	V	443 40		740/446-2926 Fax 740/446-7382
River Valley Middle Sch 8779 State Route 160, Bidwell 45614 Ed Moore	6-8	T	375 25		740/446-8399 Fax 740/441-3038
South Gallia High Sch 55 Rebel Dr, Crown City 45623 Scott West	9-12	V	147 16		740/256-1054 Fax 740/256-6399
South Gallia Middle Sch 55 Rebel Dr, Crown City 45623 Bray Shamblin	6-8	T	134 15		740/256-1054 Fax 740/256-6399
Southwestern Elem Sch 4834 State Route 325, Patriot 45658 Larry Carter	PK-5	T	148 20		740/379-2532 Fax 740/379-2000
Vinton Elem Sch 123 Keystone Rd, Vinton 45686 Leslie Henry	PK-5	T	378 28		740/388-8261 Fax 740/388-4000

• **Gallia-Jackson-Vinton JVSD** PID: 00804038   740/245-5334
351 Buckeyehills Rd, Rio Grande 45674   Fax 740/245-9465

Schools: 1 \ **Teachers:** 49 \ **Students:** 500 \ **Exp:** $848 (High) \ **Open-Close:** 08/22 - 05/25 \ **DTBP:** $177 (High)

Jaime Nash 1,11,83
James Collins 3*
Leesa Lewis 10,33,60,69,79*
Jeffery Thacker 67
Stephanie Rife 2
Timothy Updike 5*
Donald Armstrong 27,30,73,88*

Public Schs..Principal	Grd	Prgm	Enr/#Cls	SN	
Buckeye Hills Career Center 351 Buckeye Hills Road, Rio Grande 45674 Timothy Updike	Voc	G	500		740/245-5334

1	Superintendent	8	Curric/Instruct K-12	19	Chief Financial Officer	29	Family/Consumer Science	39	Social Studies K-12	49	English/Lang Arts Elem	59	Special Education Elem	69	Academic Assessment
2	Bus/Finance/Purchasing	9	Curric/Instruct Elem	20	Art K-12	30	Adult Education	40	Social Studies Elem	50	English/Lang Arts Sec	60	Special Education Sec	70	Research/Development
3	Buildings And Grounds	10	Curric/Instruct Sec	21	Art Elem	31	Career/Sch-to-Work K-12	41	Social Studies Sec	51	Reading K-12	61	Foreign/World Lang K-12	71	Public Information
4	Food Service	11	Federal Program	22	Art Sec	32	Career/Sch-to-Work Elem	42	Science K-12	52	Reading Elem	62	Foreign/World Lang Elem	72	Summer School
5	Transportation	12	Title I	23	Music K-12	33	Career/Sch-to-Work Sec	43	Science Elem	53	Reading Sec	63	Foreign/World Lang Sec	73	Instructional Tech
6	Athletic	13	Title V	24	Music Elem	34	Early Childhood Ed	44	Science Sec	54	Remedial Reading K-12	64	Religious Education K-12	74	Inservice Training
7	Health Services	14	Instructional Media Svcs	25	Music Sec	35	Health/Phys Education	45	Math K-12	55	Remedial Reading Elem	65	Religious Education Elem	75	Marketing/Distributive
		15	Asst Superintendent	26	Business Education	36	Guidance Services K-12	46	Math Elem	56	Remedial Reading Sec	66	Religious Education Sec	76	Info Systems
		16	Instructional Media Svcs	27	Career & Tech Ed	37	Guidance Services Elem	47	Math Sec	57	Bilingual/ELL	67	School Board President	77	Psychological Assess
		17	Chief Operations Officer	28	Technology Education	38	Guidance Services Sec	48	English/Lang Arts K-12	58	Special Education K-12	68	Teacher Personnel	78	Affirmative Action

Ohio School Directory

Geauga County

● **Gallipolis City School Dist** PID: 00803852 740/446-3211
61 State, Gallipolis 45631 Fax 740/446-6433

Schools: 5 \ **Teachers:** 124 \ **Students:** 2,052 \ **Special Ed Students:** 487 \ **LEP Students:** 3 \ **College-Bound:** 59% \ **Ethnic:** Asian 1%, African American 4%, Hispanic 1%, Caucasian 94% \ **Exp:** $113 (Low) \ **Poverty:** 25% \ **Title I:** $908,117 \ **Special Education:** $554,000 \ **Open-Close:** 08/22 - 05/27 \ **DTBP:** $160 (High)

Craig Wright 1	Beth Vollborn 2
Thomas Call 4*	Troy Johnson 5,91
Adam Clark 6*	Jan Koronich 7*
Jeremy Hout 8,12,74,273,288	Susan Eachus 11,34,58,88,296
Amanda Bailey 16	Morgan Saunders 67
Lauren Ott 69,77	Shaun Northup 73*
Dustin Dickson 295*	

Public Schs..Principal	Grd	Prgm	Enr/#Cls	SN	
Gallia Academy High Sch 2855 Centenary Rd, Gallipolis 45631 Josh Donley	9-12	T	534	41%	740/446-3212 Fax 740/446-3436
Gallia Academy Middle Sch 340 4th Ave, Gallipolis 45631 Lisa Blakeman	6-8	AT	424	54%	740/446-3214 Fax 740/446-2493
Green Elem Sch 113 Centenary Church Rd, Gallipolis 45631 Corey Luce	PK-5	T	305 20	47%	740/446-3236 Fax 740/446-0482
Rio Grande Elem Sch 439 Blake Dr, Rio Grande 45674 Julie Bays	PK-5	T	313 15	52%	740/245-5333 Fax 740/245-9235
Washington Elem Sch 450 4th Ave, Gallipolis 45631 Kimberly Cochrane	PK-5	T	476 29	76%	740/446-3213 Fax 740/446-0355

GALLIA PRIVATE SCHOOLS

Private Schs..Principal	Grd	Prgm	Enr/#Cls	SN	
Ohio Valley Christian Sch 1100 4th Ave, Gallipolis 45631 Patrick O'Donnell	PK-12		120 16		740/446-0374 Fax 740/446-3961

GEAUGA COUNTY

GEAUGA COUNTY SCHOOLS

● **Geauga Co Ed Service Center** PID: 00804454 440/279-1700
470 Center St Bldg 2, Chardon 44024 Fax 440/286-7106

Jennifer Felker 1,11	Sue Sotkovsky 2
Debra Iammarino 27,31	

GEAUGA PUBLIC SCHOOLS

● **Berkshire Local School Dist** PID: 00804052 440/834-3380
14259 Claridon Troy Rd, Burton 44021 Fax 440/834-2058

Schools: 3 \ **Teachers:** 70 \ **Students:** 1,200 \ **Special Ed Students:** 192 \ **LEP Students:** 3 \ **College-Bound:** 55% \ **Ethnic:** Asian 1%, African American 1%, Hispanic 1%, Caucasian 97% \ **Exp:** $127 (Low) \ **Poverty:** 7% \ **Title I:** $205,142 \ **Special Education:** $276,000 \ **Open-Close:** 08/21 - 06/01 \ **DTBP:** $174 (High) \ f t

John Stoddard 1	Beth McCaffrey 2
Jim Badanjek 3	Jenny Harrison 4*
Julie Sollars 4*	Suzanne Steinhoff 5
Brian Hiscox 6*	Kathy Pinkava 7,85*
Dawn Fleming 8,11,58,81,296	Jim Boyd 67
Bonnie Makowski 294	

Public Schs..Principal	Grd	Prgm	Enr/#Cls	SN	
Berkshire Jr Sr High Sch 14510 N Cheshire St, Burton 44021 Michael King	7-12		602 25	24%	440/834-3380 Fax 440/834-0440
Burton Elem Sch 13724 Carlton St, Burton 44021 Mandy Randles	K-6		481 16	28%	440/834-3380 Fax 440/834-8361
Ledgemont Elem Sch 16200 Burrows Rd, Thompson 44086 Kelly Rinehart	K-6		196 35	37%	440/298-3341 Fax 440/298-3342

● **Cardinal Local School Dist** PID: 00804105 440/632-0261
15982 E High St, Middlefield 44062 Fax 440/632-5886

Schools: 3 \ **Teachers:** 68 \ **Students:** 1,000 \ **Special Ed Students:** 192 \ **LEP Students:** 20 \ **College-Bound:** 52% \ **Ethnic:** Hispanic 1%, Caucasian 98% \ **Exp:** $99 (Low) \ **Poverty:** 11% \ **Title I:** $528,157 \ **Special Education:** $306,000 \ **Open-Close:** 08/14 - 05/27 \ **DTBP:** $229 (High)

Bill Kermavner 1	Merry Lou Knuckles 2
Janis Benton 4	Diane Baumgartner 5
Alysha Makowski 7	Dr Jennifer Sabol 8*
Michele Nizen 11	Anne Dalby 37*
Jill Deramo 38*	Ken Klima 67
Joe DiMattia 85*	Melissa Cardinal 280
Shaun Spence 285	

Public Schs..Principal	Grd	Prgm	Enr/#Cls	SN	
A J Jordak Elem Sch 16000 E High St, Middlefield 44062 Michelle Nizen	K-4	T	300 22	85%	440/632-0261 Fax 440/632-5192
Cardinal High Sch 14785 Thompson Ave, Middlefield 44062 **Markiel Perkins**	9-12		314 30	36%	440/632-0264 Fax 440/632-1734
Cardinal Middle Sch 16175 Almeda Dr, Middlefield 44062 Andy Cardinal	5-8		273 18	43%	440/632-0261 Fax 440/632-0294

Geauga County

Market Data Retrieval

• **Chardon Local School Dist** PID: 00804167 440/285-4052
428 North St, Chardon 44024 Fax 440/285-7229

Schools: 4 \ *Teachers:* 148 \ *Students:* 2,772 \ *Special Ed Students:* 369 \ *LEP Students:* 35 \ *College-Bound:* 75% \ *Ethnic:* Asian 1%, African American 1%, Hispanic 4%, Caucasian 95% \ *Exp:* $156 (Low) \ *Poverty:* 5% \ *Title I:* $263,234 \ *Special Education:* $253,000 \ *Open-Close:* 08/14 - 05/22 \ *DTBP:* $189 (High) \

Name	Codes
Dr Michael Hanlon	1,11
Doug Snyder	6*
Kelly Moran	8,12*
Victoria Eby	16,82*
Linda Elegante	57,58,81
Bill Nells	73,84
Steven Kofol	2,3,15,91,271
Jane Hoffman	7
Ed Klein	15
Nikki Hetrick	36
Madelon Horvath	67
Kelly Misch	76

Public Schs..Principal	Grd	Prgm	Enr/#Cls	SN		
Chardon High Sch 151 Chardon Ave, Chardon 44024 Douglas Murray	8-12	GV	1,250 38	16%	440/285-4057 Fax 440/285-9463	
Chardon Middle Sch 424 North St, Chardon 44024 Timothy Velotta	4-7	V	845 30	15%	440/285-4062 Fax 440/286-0461	
Munson Elem Sch 12687 Bass Lake Rd, Chardon 44024 Mathew Prezioso	K-3		348 12	15%	440/286-5901 Fax 440/286-3460	
Park Elem Sch 111 Goodrich Ct, Chardon 44024 Rhonda Garrett	K-3		371 14	21%	440/285-4067 Fax 440/286-0484	

• **Kenston Local School Dist** PID: 00804234 440/543-9677
17419 Snyder Rd, Chagrin Falls 44023 Fax 440/543-8634

Schools: 4 \ *Teachers:* 183 \ *Students:* 2,858 \ *Special Ed Students:* 302 \ *LEP Students:* 15 \ *College-Bound:* 84% \ *Ethnic:* Asian 2%, African American 4%, Hispanic 2%, Caucasian 92% \ *Exp:* $127 (Low) \ *Poverty:* 3% \ *Title I:* $87,665 \ *Special Education:* $194,000 \ *Open-Close:* 08/15 - 05/28 \ *DTBP:* $195 (High)

Name	Codes
Nancy Santilli	1
Marc Lobosco	3
Melody Coniglio	5
Kathleen Poe	8,11,27,69,83,288,296,298
Bev Buettner	16
Melissa Miller	58
Beth Krause	67
Katy McGrath	71
John Molnar	76,84
Paul Pestello	2
Andrew Mendez	4
Reed Guarnieri	6
Jeremy McDevitt	15
Santina Lucarelli	38*
Rita Pressman	58
Caren Vicich	68
Erin Lewis	73*
Alicia Paulsey	88

Public Schs..Principal	Grd	Prgm	Enr/#Cls	SN		
Kenston High Sch 9500 Bainbridge Rd, Chagrin Falls 44023 Thomas Gabram	9-12	V	943 50		440/543-9821 Fax 440/543-9021	
Kenston Intermediate Sch 17419 Snyder Rd Ste 1, Chagrin Falls 44023 Adam Fender	4-5		381	12%	440/543-9722 Fax 440/543-3159	
Kenston Middle Sch 17425 Snyder Rd, Chagrin Falls 44023 Pat Brockway	6-8		607 40	10%	440/543-8241 Fax 440/543-4851	
Timmons Elem Sch 9595 Washington St, Chagrin Falls 44023 Dave Rogaliner	PK-3		724 30	10%	440/543-9380 Fax 440/543-9163	

• **Newbury Local School Dist** PID: 00804337 440/564-5501
14775 Auburn Rd, Newbury 44065 Fax 440/564-9460

Schools: 2 \ *Teachers:* 35 \ *Students:* 270 \ *Special Ed Students:* 106 \ *LEP Students:* 3 \ *College-Bound:* 55% \ *Ethnic:* African American 4%, Hispanic 4%, Caucasian 91% \ *Exp:* $241 (Med) \ *Poverty:* 7% \ *Title I:* $72,201 \ *Special Education:* $90,000 \ *Open-Close:* 08/21 - 06/03 \ *DTBP:* $172 (High) \

Name	Codes
Dr Jacqueline Hoynes	1,11
Roger Riera	3,91
Anthony Forfia	6*
Maggie Zock	67
Sarah Palm	2
Debbie Parr	4
Ruth Cavanagh	7
Robert Cireddu	73

Public Schs..Principal	Grd	Prgm	Enr/#Cls	SN		
Newbury Elem Sch 14775 Auburn Rd, Newbury 44065 Cyndi Tomassetti	K-5		143 20		440/564-2282 Fax 440/564-9690	
Newbury Jr Sr High Sch 14775 Auburn Rd, Newbury 44065 Michael Chaffee	6-12		204 30	60%	440/564-2281 Fax 440/564-9788	

• **West Geauga Local School Dist** PID: 00804387 440/729-5900
8615 Cedar Rd, Chesterland 44026 Fax 440/729-5939

Schools: 4 \ *Teachers:* 98 \ *Students:* 1,874 \ *Special Ed Students:* 263 \ *LEP Students:* 8 \ *College-Bound:* 78% \ *Ethnic:* Asian 1%, African American 1%, Hispanic 1%, Caucasian 97% \ *Exp:* $130 (Low) \ *Poverty:* 3% \ *Title I:* $64,063 \ *Special Education:* $498,000 \ *Open-Close:* 08/20 - 06/04 \ *DTBP:* $179 (High)

Name	Codes
Richard Markwardt	1
Sean Whelan	2*
Cheryl Fowler	5
Nancy Benincasa	8,48,51,54,69,74,273,298
Edward Chandler	16,73,295
Ben Kotowski	67
Karen Penler	2,11,19
Michelle Pipic	4
Ben Stehura	6
Amy Daves	11,31,34,58,88,271,275
Sarah Widman	36*
Jim Kish	72*

Public Schs..Principal	Grd	Prgm	Enr/#Cls	SN		
Robert C Lindsey Elem Sch 11844 Caves Rd, Chesterland 44026 Kim Menta	K-5		354 30	15%	440/729-5980 Fax 440/729-5989	
West Geauga High Sch 13401 Chillicothe Rd, Chesterland 44026 Jay Bishop	9-12	V	680 65	8%	440/729-5950 Fax 440/729-5959	
West Geauga Middle Sch 8611 Cedar Rd, Chesterland 44026 Jim Kish	6-8		435 57	12%	440/729-5940 Fax 440/729-5949	
Westwood Elem Sch 13738 Caves Rd, Novelty 44072 Deborah Nanney	K-5		375 19	10%	440/729-5990 Fax 440/729-5924	

GEAUGA CATHOLIC SCHOOLS

• **Diocese of Cleveland Ed Office** PID: 00795308
Listing includes only schools located in this county. See District Index for location of Diocesan Offices.

Catholic Schs..Principal	Grd	Prgm	Enr/#Cls	SN		
Notre Dame Cathedral Latin Sch 13000 Auburn Rd, Chardon 44024 Joseph Waler	9-12		695 40		440/286-6226 Fax 440/286-7199	

1	Superintendent	8	Curric/Instruct K-12	19	Chief Financial Officer	29	Family/Consumer Science	39	Social Studies K-12
2	Bus/Finance/Purchasing	9	Curric/Instruct Elem	20	Art K-12	30	Adult Education	40	Social Studies Elem
3	Buildings And Grounds	10	Curric/Instruct Sec	21	Art Elem	31	Career/Sch-to-Work K-12	41	Social Studies Sec
4	Food Service	11	Federal Program	22	Art Sec	32	Career/Sch-to-Work Elem	42	Science K-12
5	Transportation	12	Title I	23	Music K-12	33	Career/Sch-to-Work Sec	43	Science Elem
6	Athletic	13	Title V	24	Music Elem	34	Early Childhood Ed	44	Science Sec
7	Health Services	14	Instructional Media Svcs	25	Music Sec	35	Health/Phys Education	45	Math K-12
		15	Asst Superintendent	26	Business Education	36	Guidance Services K-12	46	Math Elem
		16	Chief Operations Officer	27	Career & Tech Ed	37	Guidance Services Elem	47	Math Sec
		17	Chief Academic Officer	28	Technology Education	38	Guidance Services Sec	48	English/Lang Arts K-12
49	English/Lang Arts Elem	59	Special Education Elem	69	Academic Assessment				
50	English/Lang Arts Sec	60	Special Education Sec	70	Research/Development				
51	Reading K-12	61	Foreign/World Lang K-12	71	Public Information				
52	Reading Elem	62	Foreign/World Lang Elem	72	Summer School				
53	Reading Sec	63	Foreign/World Lang Sec	73	Instructional Tech				
54	Remedial Reading K-12	64	Religious Education K-12	74	Inservice Training				
55	Remedial Reading Elem	65	Religious Education Elem	75	Marketing/Distributive				
56	Remedial Reading Sec	66	Religious Education Sec	76	Info Systems				
57	Bilingual/ELL	67	School Board President	77	Psychological Assess				
58	Special Education K-12	68	Teacher Personnel	78	Affirmative Action				

Ohio School Directory

Greene County

Notre Dame Elem Sch	PK-8	520	440/279-1127
13000 Auburn Rd, Chardon 44024		25	Fax 440/286-1235
Barbara Doering			[f]
St Anselm Sch	PK-8	259	440/729-7806
13013 Chillicothe Rd, Chesterland 44026		15	Fax 440/729-3524
Susan Pohly			
St Helen Sch	PK-8	228	440/564-7125
12060 Kinsman Rd, Newbury 44065		9	Fax 440/564-7969
Patrick Gannon			[f][t]
St Mary Sch	K-8	330	440/286-3590
401 North St, Chardon 44024		25	Fax 440/285-2818
Friederike Wintersteller			

GEAUGA PRIVATE SCHOOLS

Private Schs..Principal	Grd	Prgm	Enr/#Cls	SN	
Hershey Montessori Sch	7-9		50		440/636-6290
11530 Madison Rd, Huntsburg 44046			9		Fax 440/636-5665
Paula Leigh Doyle					

GREENE COUNTY

GREENE COUNTY SCHOOLS

● **Greene Co Ed Service Center** PID: 00805006 937/767-1303
360 E Enon Rd, Yellow Spgs 45387 Fax 937/767-1025

Dr Terry Strieter ....1 Robert Arledge 2
Kathy Harper ....8,11,15,34 Cassiee Darr 58
Paul Osborne 73

County Schs..Principal	Grd	Prgm	Enr/#Cls	SN	
Four Oaks Early Intervention	Spec		345		937/562-6779
245 N Valley Rd, Xenia 45385			4		Fax 937/562-7539
Mary Ann Campbell					
● Summit Academy Alt Lrng-Xenia [248]	Spec		184	62%	937/372-5210
1694 Pawnee Dr, Xenia 45385			6		Fax 937/372-5250
Cassy Stidham					

GREENE PUBLIC SCHOOLS

● **Beavercreek City School Dist** PID: 00804466 937/426-1522
3040 Kemp Rd, Beavercreek 45431 Fax 937/429-7517

Schools: 11 \ **Teachers:** 419 \ **Students:** 7,200 \ **Special Ed Students:** 1,151 \ **LEP Students:** 297 \ **College-Bound:** 75% \ **Ethnic:** Asian 7%, African American 3%, Hispanic 3%, Caucasian 86% \ **Exp:** $125 (Low) \ **Poverty:** 4% \ **Title I:** $283,224 \ **Special Education:** $1,332,000 \ **Open-Close:** 08/14 - 05/22 \ **DTBP:** $183 (High)

Paul Otten ....1 Penny Rucker 2
Greg Thompson ....3,5,71,91 John Csillag 3
Joshua Ashley ....4 Lindy Shumaker 5
Brad Pompos ....6* Jason Enix 8,15
Bobby Fiori ....11,58,79 Mike Shuman 16,73
Elisabeth Sizemore ......26,39,45,81 Mary Fenwick 51,54*
Jo Anne Rigano ....67 Deron Schwieterman 68,74,78
Kylea Kimmerly ....76 Chuck Zoller 295

Public Schs..Principal	Grd	Prgm	Enr/#Cls	SN	
Beavercreek High Sch	10-12	AGV	1,790	11%	937/429-7547
2660 Dayton Xenia Rd, Beavercreek 45434			125		Fax 937/429-7546
George Caras					
Beavercreek Preschool Center	PK-PK		192		937/458-2360
3038 Kemp Rd, Beavercreek 45431					Fax 937/458-2361
Bobbie Fiori					
Fairbrook Elem Sch	K-5		556	14%	937/429-7616
260 N Fairfield Rd, Dayton 45430			24		Fax 937/429-7687
Joell Mangan					
Ferguson Hall Freshman Sch	9-9	V	592		937/429-7533
2680 Dayton Xenia Rd, Beavercreek 45434					Fax 937/458-2396
Jaimie Sweet					
Herman K Ankeney Middle Sch	6-8		712	14%	937/429-7567
4085 Shakertown Rd, Dayton 45430			40		Fax 937/429-7685
Dale Wren					
Jacob Coy Middle Sch	6-8		1,020	12%	937/429-7577
1786 Dayton Xenia Rd, Xenia 45385			51		Fax 937/429-7686
Andrea Ferguson					
Main Elem Sch	K-5		596	23%	937/429-7588
2942 Dayton Xenia Rd, Dayton 45434			34		Fax 937/429-7688
Sharma Nachlinger					
Parkwood Elem Sch	PK-5		509	25%	937/429-7604
1791 Wilene Dr, Beavercreek 45432			25		Fax 937/429-7684
Sue Bamford					
Shaw Elem Sch	K-5		655	13%	937/429-7610
3560 Kemp Rd, Beavercreek 45431			28		Fax 937/429-7690
Susan Peveler					
Trebein Elem Sch	K-5		816	4%	937/458-2300
1728 Dayton Xenia Rd, Xenia 45385					Fax 937/458-2395
Lisa Walk					
Valley Elem Sch	K-5		497	12%	937/429-7597
3601 Jonathon Dr, Beavercreek 45434			22		Fax 937/429-7691
Dan Schwieterman					

● **Bellbrook-Sugarcreek Schools** PID: 00804765 937/848-5001
3757 Upper Bellbrook Rd, Bellbrook 45305 Fax 937/848-5018

Schools: 5 \ **Teachers:** 136 \ **Students:** 2,875 \ **Special Ed Students:** 284 \ **LEP Students:** 43 \ **College-Bound:** 85% \ **Ethnic:** Asian 2%, African American 4%, Hispanic 4%, Caucasian 90% \ **Exp:** $299 (Med) \ **Poverty:** 4% \ **Title I:** $202,739 \ **Special Education:** $442,000 \ **Open-Close:** 08/14 - 05/21 \ **DTBP:** $213 (High)

Dr Doug Cozad ....1 Jeff Lewis 2
Kevin Liming ....2 Tom Fryman 3
Jennifer Hoehn ....4* Beverly Wetzel 5
Charlie O'Dell ....6,72* Jenny Kaffenberger 7*
Betsy Chadd ....8,11,88,273,288,294 Betsy Chadd 12*
Joshua Boles ....16,73,286,295 Debra Sanderman 31,38,69,83*
Michael Garison ....57* Tonya Wilson 58
Elizabeth Betz ....67 Sheila Woody 68
Craig Spriggs 295

Public Schs..Principal	Grd	Prgm	Enr/#Cls	SN	
Bell Creek Intermediate Sch	3-5		610	20%	937/848-3777
3777 Upper Bellbrook Rd, Bellbrook 45305			17		Fax 937/848-5078
Jill Adams					
Bellbrook High Sch	9-12	V	853		937/848-3737
3737 Upper Bellbrook Rd, Bellbrook 45305			40		Fax 937/848-5016
Christopher Baker					
Bellbrook Middle Sch	6-8	V	650	22%	937/848-2141
3600 Feedwire Rd, Bellbrook 45305			50		Fax 937/848-2152
Jenness Sigman					

79 Student Personnel	91 Safety/Security	275 Response To Intervention	298 Grant Writer/Ptnrships	**School Programs**	**Social Media**
80 Driver Ed/Safety	92 Magnet School	277 Remedial Math K-12	750 Chief Innovation Officer	A = Alternative Program	[f] = Facebook
81 Gifted/Talented	93 Parental Involvement	280 Literacy Coach	751 Chief of Staff	G = Adult Classes	[t] = Twitter
82 Video Services	95 Tech Prep Program	285 STEM	752 Social Emotional Learning	M = Magnet Program	
83 Substance Abuse Prev	97 Chief Information Officer	286 Digital Learning		T = Title I Schoolwide	
84 Erate	98 Chief Technology Officer	288 Common Core Standards	**Other School Types**	V = Career & Tech Ed Programs	
85 AIDS Education	270 Character Education	294 Accountability	Ⓐ = Alternative School		
88 Alternative/At Risk	271 Migrant Education	295 Network System	Ⓒ = Charter School	New Schools are shaded	
89 Multi-Cultural Curriculum	273 Teacher Mentor	296 Title II Programs	Ⓜ = Magnet School	New Superintendents and Principals are bold	
90 Social Work	274 Before/After Sch	297 Webmaster	Ⓨ = Year-Round School	Personnel with email addresses are underscored	

OH-83

Greene County

Market Data Retrieval

St Pierre Education Center PK-PK 120 937/848-5001
3757 Upper Bellbrook Rd, Bellbrook 45305
Dr Keith St Pierre

Stephen Bell Elem Sch K-2 568 22% 937/848-7831
4122 N Linda Dr, Bellbrook 45305   19   Fax 937/848-5007
Ginger Keeton

- **Cedar Cliff Local School Dist** PID: 00804569 937/766-6000
  248 N Main St, Cedarville 45314 Fax 937/766-5211

Schools: 2 \ **Teachers:** 36 \ **Students:** 650 \ **Special Ed Students:** 71 \ **College-Bound:** 80% \ **Ethnic:** Asian 2%, African American 2%, Hispanic 4%, Caucasian 93% \ **Exp:** $438 (High) \ **Poverty:** 7% \ **Title I:** $64,178 \ **Special Education:** $101,000 \ **Open-Close:** 08/21 - 05/29 \ **DTBP:** $237 (High)

Chad Mason	1	Joy Kitzmiller	2
Chris Williams	3	Terry Satchell	4*
Tom Morgan	5	Glen Satchell	6
Ted Williams	8*	Mark Gainer	11,298*
Karen Mossing	13,16,82	Rachell Tingelstad	31*
Angela Curlette	36,69,274*	Maryann Fenwick	54,57,58
Charlene Campbell	67	Chris Sidell	73,76,84
Jane Butler	81*		

Public Schs..Principal	Grd	Prgm	Enr/#Cls	SN
Cedarville Elem Sch 194 Walnut St, Cedarville 45314 Mark Gainer	K-5		278 17	937/766-3811 Fax 937/766-4717
Cedarville Middle High Sch 194 Walnut St, Cedarville 45314 Chad Haemmerle	6-12		341 22	35% 937/766-1871

- **Fairborn City School Dist** PID: 00804595 937/878-3961
  306 E Whittier Ave, Fairborn 45324 Fax 937/879-8180

Schools: 4 \ **Teachers:** 250 \ **Students:** 4,300 \ **Special Ed Students:** 685 \ **LEP Students:** 124 \ **College-Bound:** 60% \ **Ethnic:** Asian 2%, African American 10%, Hispanic 4%, Caucasian 84% \ **Exp:** $107 (Low) \ **Poverty:** 19% \ **Title I:** $1,467,886 \ **Special Education:** $976,000 \ **Open-Close:** 08/20 - 05/28 \ **DTBP:** $195 (High) \ 🅕 🅣

Gene Lolli	1	Jeffery Dysinger	3
Kathleen Housman	4*	Brenda Huff	5
Gary Walker	7,36,68,69,79,88	Dr Sue Brackenhoff	8,11,280,285,286,288,294,296
Krista Guy	16	Mutsimi Vargas	57
Jill Anon	58,275	Andrew Wilson	67
Pam Gayheart	71,298	Emly Giesler	73,76,295
Michele Berning	77*	Sarah Fulton	81*
Gretchen Wudke	88		

Public Schs..Principal	Grd	Prgm	Enr/#Cls	SN
Baker Middle Sch 200 Lincoln Dr, Fairborn 45324 Bradley Holt	6-8	T	934 42	71% 937/878-4681 Fax 937/879-8193
Fairborn High Sch 900 E Dayton Yellow Springs Rd, Fairborn 45324 Amy Gayheart	9-12	TV	1,037 64	49% 937/879-3611 Fax 937/879-8190
Fairborn Intermediate Sch 25 Dellwood Dr, Fairborn 45324 Betsy Wyatt	4-5	T	652 27	937/878-3969 Fax 937/879-8191
Fairborn Primary Sch 4 W Dayton Yellow Springs Rd, Fairborn 45324 Vicki Hudepohl	PK-3	T	1,567 74	937/878-8668 Fax 937/879-8196

- **Greene Co Voc School Dist** PID: 00804985 937/372-6941
  2960 W Enon Rd, Xenia 45385 Fax 937/372-8283

Schools: 1 \ **Teachers:** 56 \ **Students:** 685 \ **College-Bound:** 55% \ **Exp:** $751 (High) \ **Open-Close:** 08/14 - 05/21 \ **DTBP:** $241 (High)

David Deskins	1,11	Eva Anderson	2
Pamela Downing	10,288*	Cathy Mullen	16*
Ron Bolender	27,71,75*	Mary Frantz	67
Brian Hall	73,84*		

Public Schs..Principal	Grd	Prgm	Enr/#Cls	SN
Greene Co Career Center 2960 W Enon Rd, Xenia 45385 Matt Lindley	Voc	G	685 35	937/372-6941 Fax 937/372-3125

- **Greeneview Local School Dist** PID: 00804715 937/675-2728
  4800 Cottonville Rd, Jamestown 45335 Fax 937/675-6807

Schools: 3 \ **Teachers:** 78 \ **Students:** 1,400 \ **Special Ed Students:** 211 \ **LEP Students:** 4 \ **College-Bound:** 67% \ **Ethnic:** African American 1%, Hispanic 2%, Caucasian 98% \ **Exp:** $268 (Med) \ **Poverty:** 10% \ **Title I:** $200,202 \ **Special Education:** $254,000 \ **Open-Close:** 08/14 - 05/21 \ **DTBP:** $246 (High)

Isaac Seevers	1	Jacob McGraph	2,11
James Rhinehart	4	Tommy Morgan	5
Mark Rinehart	6*	Nancy Warnock	7,88*
Beverly Walkden	8,69,273,288*	Bill Hayes	12*
Brooke Rich	16*	Kim Reffitt	27*
Kathy Harper	34	Jeff Zipes	38*
Jacob George	58*	Suzanne Arthur	67
Thomas Davis	73	Thomas Mandrick	77

Public Schs..Principal	Grd	Prgm	Enr/#Cls	SN
Greeneview Elem Sch 53 N Limestone St, Jamestown 45335 Bill Hayes	K-4		542 23	38% 937/675-6867 Fax 937/675-2438
Greeneview High Sch 4710 Cottonville Rd, Jamestown 45335 Neal Kasner	9-12		375 25	25% 937/675-9711 Fax 937/675-6805
Greeneview Middle Sch 4990 Cottonville Rd, Jamestown 45335 Wendy Callewaert	5-8		413 20	33% 937/675-9391 Fax 937/675-6866

- **Xenia Community School Dist** PID: 00804818 937/376-2961
  819 Colorado Dr, Xenia 45385 Fax 937/372-4701

Schools: 8 \ **Teachers:** 224 \ **Students:** 4,600 \ **Special Ed Students:** 745 \ **LEP Students:** 20 \ **College-Bound:** 54% \ **Ethnic:** Asian 1%, African American 14%, Hispanic 2%, Caucasian 84% \ **Exp:** $183 (Low) \ **Poverty:** 18% \ **Title I:** $1,501,359 \ **Special Education:** $927,000 \ **Open-Close:** 08/15 - 05/28 \ **DTBP:** $192 (High)

Dr Gabriel Lofton	1	Bryan Shirey	2,3,73
Nathan Kopp	6	Sabrina Woodruff	8,11,69,288
Kay Gerspacher	16*	Dianna Alliod	58,275*
Jennifer Jones	58	Robert Billaplain	67
Mike Earley	68,79		

Public Schs..Principal	Grd	Prgm	Enr/#Cls	SN
Arrowood Elem Sch 1588 Pawnee Dr, Xenia 45385 Travis Yost	K-5	T	491 18	937/372-9251 Fax 937/374-4402

1	Superintendent	**8**	Curric/Instruct K-12	**19**	Chief Financial Officer	**29**	Family/Consumer Science	**39**	Social Studies K-12	**49**	English/Lang Arts Elem	**59**	Special Education Elem	**69**	Academic Assessment
2	Bus/Finance/Purchasing	**9**	Curric/Instruct Elem	**20**	Art K-12	**30**	Adult Education	**40**	Social Studies Elem	**50**	English/Lang Arts Sec	**60**	Special Education Sec	**70**	Research/Development
3	Buildings And Grounds	**10**	Curric/Instruct Sec	**21**	Art Elem	**31**	Career/Sch-to-Work K-12	**41**	Social Studies Sec	**51**	Reading K-12	**61**	Foreign/World Lang K-12	**71**	Public Information
4	Food Service	**11**	Federal Program	**22**	Art Sec	**32**	Career/Sch-to-Work Elem	**42**	Science K-12	**52**	Reading Elem	**62**	Foreign/World Lang Elem	**72**	Summer School
5	Transportation	**12**	Title I	**23**	Music K-12	**33**	Career/Sch-to-Work Sec	**43**	Science Elem	**53**	Reading Sec	**63**	Foreign/World Lang Sec	**73**	Instructional Tech
6	Athletic	**13**	Title V	**24**	Music Elem	**34**	Early Childhood Ed	**44**	Science Sec	**54**	Remedial Reading K-12	**64**	Religious Education K-12	**74**	Inservice Training
7	Health Services	**14**	Asst Superintendent	**25**	Music Sec	**35**	Health/Phys Education	**45**	Math K-12	**55**	Remedial Reading Elem	**65**	Religious Education Elem	**75**	Marketing/Distributive
		15	Instructional Media Svcs	**26**	Business Education	**36**	Guidance Services K-12	**46**	Math Elem	**56**	Remedial Reading Sec	**66**	Religious Education Sec	**76**	Info Systems
		16	Chief Operations Officer	**27**	Career & Tech Ed	**37**	Guidance Services Elem	**47**	Math Sec	**57**	Bilingual/ELL	**67**	School Board President	**77**	Psychological Assess
		17	Chief Academic Officer	**28**	Technology Education	**38**	Guidance Services Sec	**48**	English/Lang Arts K-12	**58**	Special Education K-12	**68**	Teacher Personnel	**78**	Affirmative Action

Ohio School Directory

Guernsey County

Cox Elem Sch 506 Dayton Ave, Xenia 45385 Lisa Peterson	K-5	T	306 39		937/372-9201 Fax 937/374-4723
McKinley Elem Sch 829 Colorado Dr, Xenia 45385 Garry Hawes	K-5	T	355 20	55%	937/372-1251 Fax 937/374-4406
Shawnee Elem Sch 92 E Ankeney Mill Rd, Xenia 45385 Scott Poole	K-5	T	444 13		937/372-6461 Fax 937/374-4230
Tecumseh Elem Sch 1058 Old Springfield Pike, Xenia 45385 Cathryn Rice	K-5	T	303 16	50%	937/372-3321 Fax 937/374-4398
Warner Middle Sch 600 Buckskin Trl, Xenia 45385 Ted Holop	6-8	T	910 50	59%	937/376-9488 Fax 937/562-9962
Xenia High Sch 303 Kinsey Rd, Xenia 45385 **David Torrence**	9-12	TV	1,038 75	47%	937/372-6983 Fax 937/374-4219
Xenia Preschool 425 Edison Blvd, Xenia 45385 Jean Brady	PK-PK		250		937/562-9706 Fax 937/374-4235

● **Yellow Springs Exempted Vlg SD** PID: 00804935   937/767-7381
201 S Walnut St, Yellow Spgs 45387   Fax 937/767-6604

Schools: 2 \ *Teachers:* 47 \ *Students:* 696 \
Special Ed Students: 78 \ *LEP Students:* 3 \ *College-Bound:* 70% \
Ethnic: Asian 2%, African American 10%, Hispanic 8%, Native American: 1%, Caucasian 80% \ *Exp:* $196 (Low) \ *Poverty:* 9% \ *Title I:* $83,831 \
Special Education: $140,000 \ *Open-Close:* 08/22 - 05/29 \ *DTBP:* $177 (High)

Mario Basora 1		Tammy Emrick 2,11,296	
Craig Carter 3		Sharon Horne 5	
Nathan Baker 6*		Matt Housh 9*	
Jack Hatert 10,83,88*		Kristin McNeely 12*	
Eli Hurwitz 16*		Dave Smith 31,69*	
Donna Frist 58		Steve Conn 67	
Tom Young 73,295		Dawn Boyer 298	

Public Schs..Principal	Grd	Prgm	Enr/#Cls SN		
Mills Lawn Elem Sch 200 S Walnut St, Yellow Spgs 45387 Matt Housh	K-6	AT	362 17	31%	937/767-7217 Fax 937/767-6602
Yellow Springs High Sch 420 E Enon Rd, Yellow Spgs 45387 Tim Krier	7-12	A	334 36	30%	937/767-7224 Fax 937/767-6154

GREENE CATHOLIC SCHOOLS

● **Archdiocese Cincinnati Ed Off** PID: 00808096
Listing includes only schools located in this county. See District Index for location of Diocesan Offices.

Catholic Schs..Principal	Grd	Prgm	Enr/#Cls SN	
Carroll High Sch 4524 Linden Ave, Dayton 45432 Matt Sableski	9-12		790 45	937/253-8188 Fax 937/424-9636
St Brigid Sch 312 Fairground Rd, Xenia 45385 Terry Adkins	K-8	G	191 10	937/372-3222 Fax 937/374-3622

St Helen Sch 5086 Burkhardt Rd, Riverside 45431 Chrissy Buschur	PK-8		428 16	937/256-1761 Fax 937/254-4614
St Luke Sch 1442 N Fairfield Rd, Beavercreek 45432 Leslie Vondrell	K-8		445 17	937/426-8551 Fax 937/426-6435

GREENE PRIVATE SCHOOLS

Private Schs..Principal	Grd	Prgm	Enr/#Cls SN	
Bethlehem Lutheran Sch 1240 S Maple Ave, Fairborn 45324 Beth Landon	PK-8		80	937/878-7050 Fax 937/878-8794
East Dayton Christian Sch 999 Spinning Rd, Dayton 45431 Stacie Auvil	PK-12		395 35	937/252-5400 Fax 937/258-4099
Legacy Christian Academy 1101 Wesley Ave, Xenia 45385 Tim Combs	PK-12		401	937/352-1640 Fax 937/352-1641
The Antioch Sch 1160 Corry St, Yellow Spgs 45387 M Richlen	PK-6		73 5	937/767-7642

GREENE REGIONAL CENTERS

● **Miami Valley Educational CA** PID: 04499556   937/767-1468
330 E Enon Rd, Yellow Spgs 45387   Fax 937/767-1793

Thor Sage 1		Liz Dunn 2	
Brian Hoehner 3		Linda Sidell 16	
Mike Wheeler 73,76,295			

● **State Support Team-Region 10** PID: 02228258   937/236-9965
4801 Springfield St, Dayton 45431   Fax 937/233-0161

Betsy Apolito 1		Kristina Ropos 27	
Jennifer Beam 71			

GUERNSEY COUNTY

GUERNSEY COUNTY SCHOOLS

● **Ohio Valley Ed Service Center** PID: 00805288   740/439-3558
128 E 8th St, Cambridge 43725   Fax 740/439-0012

Andy Brooks 1		Megan Atkinson 2	
Aaron Sikora 73,76		Penny Boggs 81	
Tammy Hanger 93			

County Schs..Principal	Grd	Prgm	Enr/#Cls SN	
Bright Beginnings Pre-School 128 E 8th St, Cambridge 43725 Ann Bowen	Spec		450 11	740/435-0320 Fax 740/432-5048
Golden Rule Sch 60770 Southgate Rd, Byesville 43723	Spec		3 2	740/439-4451 Fax 740/439-7114

79 Student Personnel	91 Safety/Security	275 Response To Intervention	298 Grant Writer/Ptnrships	School Programs	Social Media
30 Driver Ed/Safety	92 Magnet School	277 Remedial Math K-12	750 Chief Innovation Officer	A = Alternative Program	
31 Gifted/Talented	93 Parental Involvement	280 Literacy Coach	751 Chief of Staff	G = Adult Classes	⦿ = Facebook
32 Video Services	95 Tech Prep Program	285 STEM	752 Social Emotional Learning	M = Magnet Program	
33 Substance Abuse Prev	97 Chief Infomation Officer	286 Digital Learning		T = Title I Schoolwide	⦿ = Twitter
34 Erate	98 Chief Technology Officer	288 Common Core Standards	Other School Types	V = Career & Tech Ed Programs	
35 AIDS Education	270 Character Education	294 Accountability	Ⓐ = Alternative School		
38 Alternative/At Risk	271 Migrant Education	295 Network System	Ⓒ = Charter School	New Schools are shaded	
39 Multi-Cultural Curriculum	273 Teacher Mentor	296 Title II Programs	Ⓜ = Magnet School	New Superintendents and Principals are bold	
90 Social Work	274 Before/After Sch	297 Webmaster	Ⓨ = Year-Round School	Personnel with email addresses are underscored	

OH—85

Guernsey County

Market Data Retrieval

GUERNSEY PUBLIC SCHOOLS

- **Cambridge City School Dist** PID: 00805018 — 740/439-5021
  518 S 8th St, Cambridge 43725 — Fax 740/439-3796

Schools: 4 \ **Teachers:** 121 \ **Students:** 1,954 \ **Special Ed Students:** 433 \ **LEP Students:** 3 \ **College-Bound:** 36% \ **Ethnic:** African American 2%, Hispanic 1%, Caucasian 96% \ **Exp:** $171 (Low) \ **Poverty:** 28% \ **Title I:** $1,082,526 \ **Special Education:** $501,000 \ **Open-Close:** 08/19 - 05/20 \ **DTBP:** $207 (High)

Dan Coffman 1
Jamie Heyhurst 3
Dan Daugherty 5
Rose Daymut 8,11,69,72,288,296,298
Rodney Gray 36*
Erica Miller 37*
Amy Froelich 67
Perry Waltz 77
Dave Caldwell 2
Heath Urbaniak 4
Dave Gray 6
Carmen Feldner 34,58
Trudy Pedal 36*
Kristin Trimmer 38*
Steve Fraunfelter 73*

Public Schs..Principal	Grd	Prgm	Enr/#Cls	SN	
Cambridge High Sch 1401 Deerpath Dr, Cambridge 43725 Peg Wilcox	9-12	T	503 50	64%	740/435-1100 Fax 740/435-1101
Cambridge Interm Sch 1451 Deerpath Dr, Cambridge 43725 Laurie Goggin	3-5	T	445 22	65%	740/435-1180 Fax 740/435-1181
Cambridge Middle Sch 1400 Deerpath Dr, Cambridge 43725 Duane Poland	6-8	T	452 55	58%	740/435-1140 Fax 740/435-1141
Cambridge Primary Sch 1115 Clairmont Ave, Cambridge 43725 Leslie Leppla	PK-2	T	554 19	78%	740/439-7547 Fax 740/439-7590

- **East Guernsey Local Sch Dist** PID: 00805240 — 740/489-5190
  65591 Wintergreen Rd, Lore City 43755

Schools: 3 \ **Teachers:** 57 \ **Students:** 1,200 \ **Special Ed Students:** 158 \ **College-Bound:** 58% \ **Ethnic:** Hispanic 1%, Caucasian 99% \ **Exp:** $326 (High) \ **Poverty:** 18% \ **Title I:** $355,479 \ **Special Education:** $248,000 \ **Open-Close:** 08/16 - 05/22 \ **DTBP:** $186 (High)

Adam Pittis 1
Julia Cunninghamn 5
Chase Rosser 8,11,69,74,288*
Cindy Johnson 58,88
Matt Hardy 73*
Matt Reed 2
Aaron Bates 6
Stephanie Forshey 36*
Denny Patterson 67

Public Schs..Principal	Grd	Prgm	Enr/#Cls	SN	
Buckeye Trail Elem Sch 65553 Wintergreen Rd, Lore City 43755 Trisha DeLaney	PK-5	T	511 40		740/489-5100
Buckeye Trail High Sch 65555 Wintergreen Rd, Lore City 43755 William Hartmeyer	9-12	T	250 20	56%	740/489-5005 Fax 740/489-9839
Buckeye Trail Middle Sch 65553 Wintergreen Rd, Lore City 43755 Bill Hartmeyer	6-8	T	261	95%	740/489-5005 Fax 740/489-9839

- **Rolling Hills Local Sch Dist** PID: 00805159 — 740/432-6952
  60851 Southgate Rd, Cambridge 43725 — Fax 740/432-6523

Schools: 6 \ **Teachers:** 110 \ **Students:** 1,650 \ **Special Ed Students:** 282 \ **LEP Students:** 3 \ **College-Bound:** 49% \ **Ethnic:** Hispanic 1%, Caucasian 98% \ **Exp:** $173 (Low) \ **Poverty:** 24% \ **Title I:** $731,790 \ **Special Education:** $347,000 \ **Open-Close:** 08/16 - 05/22 \ **DTBP:** $174 (High)

Kandi Raach 2,19
Liz Meredith 280,298
James Buckey 73,98
Natalie Warren 285

Public Schs..Principal	Grd	Prgm	Enr/#Cls	SN	
Brook Intermediate Sch 58601 Marietta Rd, Byesville 43723 Shelley Sowers	3-5	T	346 20	60%	740/685-2526 Fax 740/685-5230
Byesville Elem Sch 212 Main St, Byesville 43723 Gail Thomas	K-2	T	175 13		740/685-2523 Fax 740/685-5410
Ⓐ Foxfire East Academy Ⓒ 60901 Beech Grove Ln, Cambridge 43725 Paul Arick	9-12	T	70		740/432-5457
Meadowbrook High Sch 58615 Marietta Rd, Byesville 43723 Devvon Dettra	9-12	ATV	473 40	49%	740/685-2566 Fax 740/685-2797
Meadowbrook Middle Sch 58607 Marietta Rd, Byesville 43723 Scott Baughman	6-8	T	383 32	56%	740/685-2561 Fax 740/685-2628
Secrest Elem Sch 58860 Wintergreen Rd, Senecaville 43780 Jude Black	K-2	T	152 12	64%	740/685-2504

GUERNSEY CATHOLIC SCHOOLS

- **Diocese of Steubenville Ed Off** PID: 00812671
  Listing includes only schools located in this county. See District Index for location of Diocesan Offices.

Catholic Schs..Principal	Grd	Prgm	Enr/#Cls	SN	
St Benedict Sch 220 N 7th St, Cambridge 43725 Sue Sanders	PK-8		110 11		740/432-6751 Fax 740/432-4511

GUERNSEY REGIONAL CENTERS

- **State Support Team-Region 12** PID: 02228210 — 740/439-9383
  60788 Southgate Rd, Byesville 43723 — Fax 740/439-9310

Lisa Baker 1
Kayley Andrews 93
Gail Gallwitz 34

1	Superintendent	8	Curric/Instruct K-12	19	Chief Financial Officer	29	Family/Consumer Science	39	Social Studies K-12	49	English/Lang Arts Elem	59	Special Education Elem	69	Academic Assessment
2	Bus/Finance/Purchasing	9	Curric/Instruct Elem	20	Art K-12	30	Adult Education	40	Social Studies Elem	50	English/Lang Arts Sec	60	Special Education Sec	70	Research/Development
3	Buildings And Grounds	10	Curric/Instruct Sec	21	Art Elem	31	Career/Sch-to-Work K-12	41	Social Studies Sec	51	Reading K-12	61	Foreign/World Lang K-12	71	Public Information
4	Food Service	11	Federal Program	22	Art Sec	32	Career/Sch-to-Work Elem	42	Science K-12	52	Reading Elem	62	Foreign/World Lang Elem	72	Summer School
5	Transportation	12	Title I	23	Music K-12	33	Career/Sch-to-Work Sec	43	Science Elem	53	Reading Sec	63	Foreign/World Lang Sec	73	Instructional Tech
6	Athletic	13	Title V	24	Music Elem	34	Early Childhood Ed	44	Science Sec	54	Remedial Reading K-12	64	Religious Education K-12	74	Inservice Training
7	Health Services	14	Instructional Media Svcs	25	Music Sec	35	Health/Phys Education	45	Math K-12	55	Remedial Reading Elem	65	Religious Education Elem	75	Marketing/Distributive
		15	Asst Superintendent	26	Business Education	36	Guidance Services K-12	46	Math Elem	56	Remedial Reading Sec	66	Religious Education Sec	76	Info Systems
		16	Chief Operations Officer	27	Career & Tech Ed	37	Guidance Services Elem	47	Math Sec	57	Bilingual/ELL	67	School Board President	77	Psychological Assess
		17	Chief Academic Officer	28	Technology Education	38	Guidance Services Sec	48	English/Lang Arts K-12	58	Special Education K-12	68	Teacher Personnel	78	Affirmative Action

Ohio School Directory — Hamilton County

HAMILTON COUNTY

HAMILTON COUNTY SCHOOLS

Hamilton Co Ed Service Center PID: 00808084 — 513/674-4200
11083 Hamilton Ave, Cincinnati 45231 — Fax 513/742-8339

David Distel 1	Donald Rabe 2	
Vikki Clemons 11	Kathy Tirey 34	
Greg Hester 68	Bill Sears 73,295	
Karen Austin 81		

County Schs..Principal	Grd	Prgm	Enr/#Cls		SN
Ⓒ Alliance Academy of Cincinnati [203] 1712 Duck Creek Rd, Cincinnati 45207 Elizabeth King	K-8	T	599 17		513/751-5555 Fax 513/672-9467
Bobbie B Fairfax Sch 4999 Kingsley Dr, Cincinnati 45227 Kim Martindell	Spec		70 12		513/271-2313 Fax 513/272-4324
Ⓒ Dohn Cmty High Sch 608 E McMillan St, Cincinnati 45206 Ramone Davenport	9-12	TV	660 8		513/281-6100 Fax 513/281-6103 f t
Ⓒ Hamilton Co Math & Sci Academy 2675 Civic Center Dr, Cincinnati 45231 Dwan Moore	K-8	T	624	69%	513/728-8620 Fax 513/728-8623 f
Learning Ctr at North Norwood 5017 Marion Ave, Cincinnati 45212 Melissa Hitzman	Spec		60 9		513/396-5941 Fax 513/396-5942
Margaret Rost Sch 5858 Bridgetown Rd, Cincinnati 45248 Duerk Zinn	Spec		45 15		513/574-2372 Fax 513/598-2963
Ⓒ Mt Healthy Prep & Fitness Acad [247] 7601 Harrison Ave, Cincinnati 45231 Bobbie Lanham	K-8	T	269		513/587-6280 Fax 513/521-4509 f t
Ⓒ Orion Academy [203] 1798 Queen City Ave, Cincinnati 45214 Kendall Dorsey	K-8	T	552 23		513/251-6000 Fax 513/206-9829
Ⓒ Summit Acad Sch-Cincinnati [248] 1660 Sternblock Ln, Cincinnati 45237 Dale Leever	Spec	T	136 10		513/321-0561 Fax 513/321-0795 f

HAMILTON PUBLIC SCHOOLS

Cincinnati City School Dist PID: 00805290 — 513/363-0000
2651 Burnet Ave, Cincinnati 45219 — Fax 513/363-0055

Schools: 61 \ *Teachers:* 1,729 \ *Students:* 35,000 \
Special Ed Students: 6,751 \ *LEP Students:* 2,205 \ *College-Bound:* 48% \
Ethnic: Asian 2%, African American 67%, Hispanic 6%, Caucasian 26% \ *Exp:* $115 (Low) \ *Poverty:* 38% \ *Title I:* $37,867,679 \
Special Education: $10,861,000 \ *Open-Close:* 08/19 - 05/21 \ *DTBP:* $251 (High) \ t

Laura Mitchell 1	Jennifer Wagner 2,19
Sarah Trimble-Oliver 2,73,76,98,286,295*	Trina Levins 2
Bill Moehring 3,91	Jessica Shelly 4
John Davis 5	Josh Hardin 6
Cynthia Eghbalnia 7,83,85	Tya Grengbondai 11,298
Susan Bunte 15,58	Tianay Amat-Outlaw 15*
Michael Turner 27	Roberta Thomas 30
Vera Brooks 34	David Traubert 39
Jennifer Williams 42	Emily Campbell 45
Eneida Uehlin 57	Carolyn Jones 67
Paul McDole 68	Connie Solano 69,294
Sarah Trimble-Oliver 73,98	Betsy Singh 81*
Patricia Neal-Miller 93*	Terry Davis 298

Public Schs..Principal	Grd	Prgm	Enr/#Cls		SN
Ⓜ Acad Multilingual Immer Stud 1908 Seymour Ave, Cincinnati 45237 Janice Pitts	PK-8	T	491 60		513/363-1800 Fax 513/363-1820
Ⓜ Academy of World Languages 2030 Fairfax Ave, Cincinnati 45207 Jacquelyn Rowedder	PK-8	T	507 59		513/363-7800 Fax 513/363-7820
Aiken High Sch 5641 Belmont Ave, Cincinnati 45224 Lisa Votaw	7-12	GTV	858 30		513/363-6700 Fax 513/363-6720
Bond Hill Academy 1510 California Ave, Cincinnati 45237 Renee Crawford	PK-6	T	326 20		513/363-7900 Fax 513/363-7920
Ⓜ Cans Sch 2120 Vine St, Cincinnati 45202 Jaren Sinney	PK-K		200		513/363-6500 Fax 513/363-6520
Carson Sch 4323 Glenway Ave, Cincinnati 45205 Terrez Thomas	PK-6	T	650 31		513/363-9800 Fax 513/363-9820
Ⓜ Chase Sch 4151 Turrill St, Cincinnati 45223 Sherwin Ealy	PK-6	T	370 35		513/363-1300 Fax 513/363-1320
Ⓜ Cheviot Elem Sch 4040 Harrison Ave, Cincinnati 45211 Tammy Solomon Gray	PK-6	T	578 24		513/363-1400 Fax 513/363-1420
Ⓐ Cincinnati Digital Academy 425 Ezzard Charles Dr, Cincinnati 45203 Eric Rozier	K-12		285		513/363-2040 Fax 513/363-2099
Clark Montessori Sch 3030 Erie Ave, Cincinnati 45208 Dean Blase	7-12		674 30	33%	513/363-7100 Fax 513/363-7120
Clifton Area Neighborhd Sch 3711 Clifton Ave, Cincinnati 45220 James Zoller	PK-2		120		513/363-2200
Ⓜ College Hill Fundamental Acad 1625 Cedar Ave, Cincinnati 45224 Lauren Shockley	PK-6	T	437 26		513/363-1600 Fax 513/363-1620
Covedale Elem Sch 5130 Sidney Rd, Cincinnati 45238 Michele Kipp	K-6	T	541 22		513/363-1700 Fax 513/363-1720
Ⓜ Dater Montessori Sch 2840 Boudinot Ave, Cincinnati 45238 Anthony Greco	PK-6		797		513/363-0900 Fax 513/363-0920
Ethel M Taylor Academy 1930 Fricke Rd, Cincinnati 45225 Pia Spaulding	PK-6	T	323 13		513/363-3600 Fax 513/363-3620
Evanston Academy 1835 Fairfax Ave, Cincinnati 45207 Stacey Hill-Simmons	PK-6	T	294 25		513/363-2700 Fax 513/363-2720
Ⓜ Fairview-Clifton German Sch 3689 Clifton Ave, Cincinnati 45220 Stephen Sippel	K-6		723 37	25%	513/363-2100 Fax 513/363-2120
Ⓨ Frederick Douglass Elem Sch 2627 Park Ave, Cincinnati 45206 Jeffery Hall	PK-6	MT	279 23		513/363-1900 Fax 513/363-1920
Gilbert A Dater High Sch 2146 Ferguson Rd, Cincinnati 45238 Ana Salazar	7-12	TV	1,271 46		513/363-7200 Fax 513/363-7220

79 Student Personnel	91 Safety/Security	275 Response To Intervention	298 Grant Writer/Ptnrships	**School Programs**
80 Driver Ed/Safety	92 Magnet School	277 Remedial Math K-12	750 Chief Innovation Officer	A = Alternative Program
81 Gifted/Talented	93 Parental Involvement	280 Literacy Coach	751 Chief of Staff	G = Adult Classes
82 Video Services	95 Tech Prep Program	285 STEM	752 Social Emotional Learning	M = Magnet Program
83 Substance Abuse Prev	97 Chief Information Officer	286 Digital Learning		T = Title I Schoolwide
84 Erate	98 Chief Technology Officer	288 Common Core Standards	**Other School Types**	V = Career & Tech Ed Programs
85 AIDS Education	270 Character Education	294 Accountability	Ⓐ = Alternative School	
88 Alternative/At Risk	271 Migrant Education	295 Network System	Ⓒ = Charter School	**Social Media**
89 Multi-Cultural Curriculum	273 Teacher Mentor	296 Title II Programs	Ⓜ = Magnet School	f = Facebook
90 Social Work	274 Before/After Sch	297 Webmaster	Ⓨ = Year-Round School	t = Twitter

New Schools are shaded
New Superintendents and Principals are bold
Personnel with email addresses are underscored

OH–87

Hamilton County

School	Grades		Enroll		Phone
Hartwell Sch 8320 Vine St, Cincinnati 45216 Antwan Lewis	PK-8	T	560 27		513/363-2300 Fax 513/363-2320
Hays-Porter Elem Sch 1030 Cutter St, Cincinnati 45203 Nedria McClain	PK-6	T	306 30		513/363-1000 Fax 513/363-1020
Hughes STEM High Sch 2515 Clifton Ave, Cincinnati 45219 Kathy Wright	7-12	T	949		513/363-7400 Fax 513/363-7520
Hyde Park Sch 3401 Edwards Rd, Cincinnati 45208 Jill Sunderman	K-6		545	17%	513/363-2800 Fax 513/363-2820
James N Gamble Montessori ES 2700 Felicity Pl, Cincinnati 45211 Melissa Ridley	PK-6		270		513/363-9600 Fax 513/363-9620
James N Gamble Montessori HS 3036 Werk Rd, Cincinnati 45211 Taylor Porter	7-12	T	480		513/363-2600 Fax 513/363-2620
John P Parker Elem Sch 5051 Anderson Pl, Cincinnati 45227 Kimberly Mack	PK-6	T	440 32		513/363-2900 Fax 513/363-2920
Kilgour Elem Sch 1339 Herschel Ave, Cincinnati 45208 Angela Cook-Frazier	K-6		635 27	16%	513/363-3000 Fax 513/363-3020
Ⓜ Leap Academy 2001 Baltimore Ave, Cincinnati 45225 Priya Sonty	PK-4		264		513/363-1200 Fax 513/363-1220
Midway Elem Sch 3156 Glenmore Ave, Cincinnati 45211 Martha Hasselbusch	PK-8	T	615 23		513/363-3500 Fax 513/363-3520
Mt Airy Elem Sch 5730 Colerain Ave, Cincinnati 45239 Angel Roddy	PK-6	T	650 37		513/363-3700 Fax 513/363-3720
Mt Washington Sch 1730 Mears Ave, Cincinnati 45230 Debra Klein	PK-6	T	365 24		513/363-3800 Fax 513/363-3820
Ⓜ North Avondale Montessori Sch 615 Clinton Springs Ave, Cincinnati 45229 Roger Lewis	PK-6		599 33		513/363-3900 Fax 513/363-3920
Oyler Sch 2121 Hatmaker St, Cincinnati 45204 Amy Randolph	PK-12	T	685 50		513/363-4100 Fax 513/363-4120
Ⓜ Parker Woods Montessori Sch 4370 Beech Hill Ave, Cincinnati 45223 Whitney Simmons	PK-6	T	587 20		513/363-6200 Fax 513/363-6220
Pleasant Hill Academy 1350 W North Bend Rd, Cincinnati 45224 Shauna McDowell	PK-6	T	602 35		513/363-4300 Fax 513/363-4320
Pleasant Ridge Montessori Sch 5945 Montgomery Rd, Cincinnati 45213 Melissa Ridley	PK-6	T	642 20		513/363-4400 Fax 513/363-4420
Rees E Price Academy 1228 Considine Ave, Cincinnati 45204 Jennifer Myree	PK-6	T	593 40		513/363-6000 Fax 513/363-6020
Rising Stars Academy 2120 Vine St, Cincinnati 45202 Jeren Finney	PK-PK		200		513/363-6500 Fax 513/363-6520
Riverview East Academy 3555 Kellogg Ave, Cincinnati 45226 Charlene Myers	K-12	T	612 40		513/363-3400 Fax 513/363-3420
Robert A Taft Info Tech HS 420 Ezzard Charles Dr, Cincinnati 45214 Michael Turner	7-12	GTV	637 62		513/363-8200 Fax 513/363-8220
Ⓜ Roberts Paideia Academy 1702 Grand Ave, Cincinnati 45214 Alpacino Beauchamp	PK-8	T	765 40		513/363-4600 Fax 513/363-4620
Rockdale Academy 335 Rockdale Ave, Cincinnati 45229 Belinda Tubbs-Wallace	PK-6	T	347 33		513/363-4700 Fax 513/363-4720
Roll Hill Sch 2411 Baltimore Ave, Cincinnati 45225 Vicki Graves-Hill	PK-6	T	502 31		513/363-4000 Fax 513/363-4020
Roselawn Condon Sch 1594 Summit Rd, Cincinnati 45237 Harry Voll	PK-8	T	414 40		513/363-4800 Fax 513/363-4820
Rothenberg Preparatory Academy 241 E Clifton Ave, Cincinnati 45202 Amber Simpson	PK-6	T	366 25		513/363-5700 Fax 513/363-5720
Ⓜ Sands Montessori Sch 6421 Corbly Rd, Cincinnati 45230 Sarah Lord	PK-6		695 30	23%	513/363-5000 Fax 513/363-5020
Sayler Park Sch 6700 Home City Ave, Cincinnati 45233 Jamie Sowders	PK-8	T	320 20		513/363-5100 Fax 513/363-5120
Ⓜ Sch for Creative Perform Arts 108 W Central Pkwy, Cincinnati 45202 Michael Owens	K-12	TV	1,335 75	49%	513/363-8000 Fax 513/363-8020
Shroder High Sch 5030 Duck Creek Rd, Cincinnati 45227 Larry Williams	7-12	TV	804 65		513/363-6900 Fax 513/363-6920
Ⓜ Silverton Paideia Academy 7451 Montgomery Rd, Cincinnati 45236 Kristin Grote	PK-6	T	364 21		513/363-5400 Fax 513/363-5420
South Avondale Elem Sch 636 Prospect Pl, Cincinnati 45229 Michael Alisson	PK-6	T	402 35		513/363-5500 Fax 513/363-5520
Ⓜ Spencer Ctr-Gifted 2825 Alms Pl, Cincinnati 45206 Nina Ginocchio	3-12		325		513/363-5800 Fax 513/363-5820
Virtual High Sch 425 Ezzard Charles Dr Ste 4, Cincinnati 45203 Eric Rozier	K-12	GT	654 5		513/363-2060 Fax 513/363-2093
Walnut Hills High Sch 3250 Victory Pkwy, Cincinnati 45207 John Chambers	7-12	GV	2,990 50	17%	513/363-8400 Fax 513/363-8420
Western Hills Univ High Sch 2144 Ferguson Rd, Cincinnati 45238 Carlos Blair	7-12	TV	1,053 40		513/363-8900 Fax 513/363-8920
Westwood Sch 2981 Montana Ave, Cincinnati 45211 Christopher Grant	PK-8	T	529 19		513/363-5900 Fax 513/363-5920
William H Taft Elem Sch 270 Southern Ave, Cincinnati 45219 Dr Jonathan Brown	PK-6	AT	297 15		513/363-5600 Fax 513/363-5620
Winton Hills Academy 5300 Winneste Ave, Cincinnati 45232 Benjamin Fulton	PK-6	T	365 25		513/363-6300 Fax 513/363-6320
Withrow University High Sch 2488 Madison Rd, Cincinnati 45208 Jerron Gray	9-12	TV	1,300 28		513/363-9200 Fax 513/363-9220
Ⓜ Woodford Paideia Sch 3716 Woodford Rd, Cincinnati 45213 Ross Turpeau	PK-6	T	344 27		513/363-6400 Fax 513/363-6420
Woodward Career Tech High Sch 7005 Reading Rd, Cincinnati 45237 Shauna Murphy	7-12	TV	960 25		513/363-9300 Fax 513/363-9320

1 Superintendent	8 Curric/Instruct K-12	19 Chief Financial Officer	29 Family/Consumer Science	39 Social Studies K-12	49 English/Lang Arts Elem	59 Special Education Elem	69 Academic Assessment
2 Bus/Finance/Purchasing	9 Curric/Instruct Elem	20 Art K-12	30 Adult Education	40 Social Studies Elem	50 English/Lang Arts Sec	60 Special Education Sec	70 Research/Development
3 Buildings And Grounds	10 Curric/Instruct Sec	21 Art Elem	31 Career/Sch-to-Work K-12	41 Social Studies Sec	51 Reading K-12	61 Foreign/World Lang K-12	71 Public Information
4 Food Service	11 Federal Program	22 Art Sec	32 Career/Sch-to-Work Elem	42 Science K-12	52 Reading Elem	62 Foreign/World Lang Elem	72 Summer School
5 Transportation	12 Title I	23 Music K-12	33 Career/Sch-to-Work Sec	43 Science Elem	53 Reading Sec	63 Foreign/World Lang Sec	73 Instructional Tech
6 Athletic	13 Title V	24 Music Elem	34 Early Childhood Ed	44 Science Sec	54 Remedial Reading K-12	64 Religious Education K-12	74 Inservice Training
7 Health Services	15 Asst Superintendent	25 Music Sec	35 Health/Phys Education	45 Math K-12	55 Remedial Reading Elem	65 Religious Education Elem	75 Marketing/Distributive
	16 Instructional Media Svcs	26 Business Education	36 Guidance Services K-12	46 Math Elem	56 Remedial Reading Sec	66 Religious Education Sec	76 Info Systems
	17 Chief Operations Officer	27 Career & Tech Ed	37 Guidance Services Elem	47 Math Sec	57 Bilingual/ELL	67 School Board President	77 Psychological Assess
	18 Chief Academic Officer	28 Technology Education	38 Guidance Services Sec	48 English/Lang Arts K-12	58 Special Education K-12	68 Teacher Personnel	78 Affirmative Action

Ohio School Directory — Hamilton County

Deer Park Cmty School Dist PID: 00806361   513/891-0222
8688 Donna Ln, Cincinnati 45236   Fax 513/891-2930

Schools: 2 \ **Teachers:** 68 \ **Students:** 1,261 \ **Special Ed Students:** 207 \ **LEP Students:** 35 \ **College-Bound:** 48% \ **Ethnic:** Asian 4%, African American 8%, Hispanic 6%, Caucasian 82% \ **Exp:** $259 (Med) \ **Poverty:** 16% \ **Title I:** $351,907 \ **Special Education:** $342,000 \ **Open-Close:** 08/13 - 05/21 \ **DTBP:** $237 (High)

Jack Phillips	1	Melissa Harner	2
Dave Conover	3	Mary Lynne Bierman	4
Greg Huster	6*	Dave Bergan	8,11,15,57,58,71,288,298*
Corrie Madden	38*	Peggy Bosse	67
Kelly Synder	69,77,85	Steve Hoock	69
Patricia Hadden	79	Chris Beerman	88*

Public Schs..Principal	Grd	Prgm	Enr/#Cls	SN	
Amity Elem Sch 4320 E Galbraith Rd, Cincinnati 45236 Mark Smiley	K-6	T	688 12	49%	513/891-5995 Fax 513/891-3508
Deer Park Jr Sr High Sch 8351 Plainfield Rd, Cincinnati 45236 Shane Hartley	7-12	T	522 40	45%	513/891-0010 Fax 513/891-3845

Finneytown Local School Dist PID: 00806414   513/728-3700
8916 Fontainebleau Ter, Cincinnati 45231   Fax 513/931-0986

Schools: 3 \ **Teachers:** 79 \ **Students:** 1,400 \ **Special Ed Students:** 277 \ **LEP Students:** 74 \ **College-Bound:** 59% \ **Ethnic:** Asian 6%, African American 48%, Hispanic 4%, Caucasian 42% \ **Exp:** $224 (Med) \ **Poverty:** 15% \ **Title I:** $440,216 \ **Special Education:** $569,000 \ **Open-Close:** 08/21 - 05/29 \ **DTBP:** $237 (High)

Terri Noe	1,11	Doug Lantz	2
Karen Smith	5	Gerald Warmack	6
Troy Edie	8	Patty D'Arcy	58
Tony Gast	67	Missy Knight	71
Laurie Banks	79		

Public Schs..Principal	Grd	Prgm	Enr/#Cls	SN	
Brent Elem Sch 8791 Brent Dr, Cincinnati 45231 **Meredith Baker**	K-2	T	188 15	58%	513/728-3720 Fax 513/728-7243
Finneytown Secondary Sch 8916 Fontainebleau Ter, Cincinnati 45231 Jennifer Dinan	6-12	TV	826 50	48%	513/931-0712 Fax 513/728-7230
Whitaker Elem Sch 7400 Winton Rd, Cincinnati 45224 Grant Anderson	2-5	T	410 21		513/728-3737 Fax 513/728-3725

Forest Hills School Dist PID: 00806476   513/231-3600
7946 Beechmont Ave, Cincinnati 45255   Fax 513/231-3830

Schools: 9 \ **Teachers:** 390 \ **Students:** 7,450 \ **Special Ed Students:** 659 \ **LEP Students:** 103 \ **College-Bound:** 80% \ **Ethnic:** Asian 3%, African American 2%, Hispanic 3%, Caucasian 92% \ **Exp:** $225 (Med) \ **Poverty:** 7% \ **Title I:** $869,301 \ **Special Education:** $1,598,000 \ **Open-Close:** 08/15 - 05/22 \ **DTBP:** $308 (High)

Scot Prebles	1	Alana Cropper	2,294
John Eckert	3,91	Larry Corley	3
Tia Straus	4	Jonathan Daniels	5
Richard Porter	5	Chris Newton	6
Betsy Ryan	7,12,35,36,60,83,270,752	Greg Sears	8,69
Robert Buck	9,11,51,54,92,296*	Brian Lynn	10,27,31,61,271,273*
Mike Broadwater	15	Anita Eshleman	57,69,88
Melissa Buckalew	59*	Randy Smith	67
Tamela Carnahan	68,78,79	Breanna Gilroy	71
Stephen Meece	73,76	Kyle Mack	286*
Brian Robinson	288		

Public Schs..Principal	Grd	Prgm	Enr/#Cls	SN	
Anderson High Sch 7560 Forest Rd, Cincinnati 45255 Robert Fellows	9-12		1,246 145	11%	513/232-2772 Fax 513/232-2295
Ayer Elem Sch 8471 Forest Rd, Cincinnati 45255 Todd Hartman	K-6		625	13%	513/474-3811 Fax 513/474-7228
Maddux Elem Sch 943 Rosetree Ln, Cincinnati 45230 Stephen Troehler	K-6		545 35	17%	513/231-0780 Fax 513/231-5308
Mercer Elem Sch 2600 Bartels Rd, Cincinnati 45244 Jodi Davidson	PK-6		714 38	18%	513/232-7000 Fax 513/232-3156
Nagel Middle Sch 1500 Nagel Rd, Cincinnati 45255 Anita Eshleman	7-8		1,156 100	11%	513/474-5407 Fax 513/474-5584
Sherwood Elem Sch 7080 Grantham Way, Cincinnati 45230 Daniel Hamilton	PK-6		630 25	9%	513/231-7565 Fax 513/231-3666
Summit Elem Sch 8400 Northport Dr, Cincinnati 45255 Michele Sulfsted	PK-6		620 25	9%	513/474-2270 Fax 513/474-1525
Turpin High Sch 2650 Bartels Rd, Cincinnati 45244 David Spencer	9-12	A	1,114 67	8%	513/232-7770 Fax 513/232-9047
Wilson Elem Sch 2465 Little Dry Run Rd, Cincinnati 45244 Erin Storer	K-6		709 28	4%	513/231-3240 Fax 513/231-3202 t

Great Oaks Career Campuses PID: 00810439   513/771-8840
110 Great Oaks Dr, Cincinnati 45241   Fax 513/771-6575

Schools: 4 \ **Teachers:** 250 \ **Students:** 3,000 \ **LEP Students:** 14 \ **College-Bound:** 44% \ **Exp:** $744 (High) \ **Open-Close:** 08/15 - 05/22 \ **DTBP:** $192 (High) \ f

Harry Snyder	1	Ben VanHorn	2,11
Jeff Johnson	3,4,5,73,95	Philip Brewer	5
Al Gille	7	Daniel Rush	10*
Nancy Mulvey	10,30,72,285,288*	Dan Cox	12,27*
Steve Jacobs	28,76	Tina Reichert	60,88
David Yockey	67	Karla Berger	68,273
Laura Gale	69	Jonathan Weidlich	71
Julie Woodward	71*		

Public Schs..Principal	Grd	Prgm	Enr/#Cls	SN	
Diamond Oaks Career Dev Campus 6375 Harrison Ave, Cincinnati 45247 Daniel Rush	Voc	G	605		513/574-1300 Fax 513/574-3953 f
Laurel Oaks Career Dev Campus 300 Oak Dr, Wilmington 45177 Mike Thomas	Voc	AG	530		937/382-1411 Fax 937/383-2095
Live Oaks Career Dev Campus 5956 Buckwheat Rd, Milford 45150 Dan Cox	Voc	AG	600 40		513/575-1900 Fax 513/575-0805 f
Scarlet Oaks Career Dev Campus 3254 E Kemper Rd, Cincinnati 45241 Julie Woodward	Voc	AG	1,265		513/771-8810 Fax 513/771-4928

---

79 Student Personnel	91 Safety/Security	275 Response To Intervention	298 Grant Writer/Ptnrships	**School Programs**	**Social Media**		
40 Driver Ed/Safety	92 Magnet School	277 Remedial Math K-12	750 Chief Innovation Officer	A = Alternative Program			
81 Gifted/Talented	93 Parental Involvement	280 Literacy Coach	751 Chief of Staff	G = Adult Classes	f = Facebook		
82 Video Services	95 Tech Prep Program	285 STEM	752 Social Emotional Learning	M = Magnet Program			
83 Substance Abuse Prev	97 Chief Information Officer	286 Digital Learning		T = Title I Schoolwide	t = Twitter		
84 Erate	98 Chief Technology Officer	288 Common Core Standards	**Other School Types**	V = Career & Tech Ed Programs			
85 AIDS Education	270 Character Education	294 Accountability	Ⓐ = Alternative School				
87 Alternative/At Risk	271 Migrant Education	295 Network System	Ⓒ = Charter School	New Schools are shaded			
89 Multi-Cultural Curriculum	273 Teacher Mentor	296 Title II Programs	Ⓜ = Magnet School	New Superintendents and Principals are bold			
90 Social Work	274 Before/After Sch	297 Webmaster	Ⓨ = Year-Round School	Personnel with email addresses are underscored			

Hamilton County

Market Data Retrieval

• **Indian Hill Exempted Vlg SD** PID: 00806696   513/272-4500
6855 Drake Rd, Cincinnati 45243   Fax 513/272-4512

Schools: 4 \ *Teachers:* 154 \ *Students:* 2,030 \ *Special Ed Students:* 167 \ *LEP Students:* 44 \ *College-Bound:* 88% \ *Ethnic:* Asian 10%, African American 3%, Hispanic 4%, Caucasian 83% \ *Exp:* $333 (High) \ *Poverty:* 5% \ *Title I:* $174,198 \ *Special Education:* $515,000 \ *Open-Close:* 08/15 - 05/28 \ *DTBP:* $229 (High)

Name	Ref
Dr Mark Miles	1
Ken Stegman	3
Jeff Zidron	6*
Erica Leppert	12,13,58,79,296,298
Victoria Mendoza	16*
Nancy Aichholz	67
Mark Richardson	73,286*
Mick Davis	2
Barb Leonard	5
Dr Melissa Stewart	8,11,15,34,69,288
Dr Mark Ault	15
Susan Schonauer	27*
Andrea Brady	71,75,91
Kathy Yeager	83,85,88*

Public Schs..Principal	Grd	Prgm	Enr/#Cls	SN	
Indian Hill Elem Sch 6100 Drake Rd, Cincinnati 45243 Whitney Buell	3-5		464 24	7%	513/272-4703 Fax 513/272-4708
Indian Hill High Sch 6865 Drake Rd, Cincinnati 45243 Jeff Damadeo	9-12	V	633 50		513/272-4550 Fax 513/272-4557
Indian Hill Middle Sch 6845 Drake Rd, Cincinnati 45243 Jennifer Ulland	6-8		512 42		513/272-4642 Fax 513/272-4690
Indian Hill Primary Sch 6207 Drake Rd, Cincinnati 45243 Jim Nichols	K-2		421 24	7%	513/272-4754 Fax 513/272-4759

• **Lockland School Dist** PID: 00806763   513/563-5000
210 N Cooper Ave, Lockland 45215   Fax 513/563-9611

Schools: 3 \ *Teachers:* 32 \ *Students:* 550 \ *Special Ed Students:* 83 \ *LEP Students:* 70 \ *College-Bound:* 37% \ *Ethnic:* African American 49%, Hispanic 8%, Caucasian 43% \ *Exp:* $177 (Low) \ *Poverty:* 39% \ *Title I:* $533,146 \ *Special Education:* $131,000 \ *Open-Close:* 08/14 - 05/21 \ *DTBP:* $261 (High) \

Name	Ref
Bob Longworth	1
Chad Welage	3*
Justin Gibson	12,58*
Kate Lavik	77,275*
Doug Ackermann	2
Jennifer Arlinghaus	4
Terry Gibson	67
Jen Schierloh	83,85*

Public Schs..Principal	Grd	Prgm	Enr/#Cls	SN	
Lockland Elem Sch 210 N Cooper Ave, Lockland 45215 Anthony Comer	K-6	T	290 28	99%	513/563-5000
Lockland High Sch 249 W Forrer St, Lockland 45215 Anthony Comer	9-12	AT	170 20		513/563-5000 Fax 513/563-9017
Lockland Middle Sch 249 W Forrer St, Lockland 45215 Bob Longworth	7-8	T	90		513/563-5000 Fax 513/733-0800

• **Loveland City School Dist** PID: 00806804   513/683-5600
757 S Lebanon Rd, Loveland 45140   Fax 513/683-5697

Schools: 6 \ *Teachers:* 226 \ *Students:* 4,700 \ *Special Ed Students:* 583 \ *LEP Students:* 45 \ *College-Bound:* 75% \ *Ethnic:* Asian 2%, African American 2%, Hispanic 3%, Caucasian 93% \ *Exp:* $205 (Med) \ *Poverty:* 6% \ *Title I:* $487,168 \ *Special Education:* $772,000 \ *Open-Close:* 08/20 - 05/28 \ *DTBP:* $191 (High) \

Name	Ref
Dr Amy Crouse	1,11,83
Lindsey Masse	2
Chris Tracy	4
Eric Dool	11,58
Jane Ernst	16,82*
Peggy Johnson	36*
Susanne Quigley	71,75,97
John Ames	2,73,91,295
Bill Cole	3
Brian Conatser	6
Robin Wiley	15,68,79
Judy Learny	35*
Art Jarvais	67
David Knapp	76,286

Public Schs..Principal	Grd	Prgm	Enr/#Cls	SN	
Loveland Early Childhood Ctr 6740 Loveland Miamiville Rd, Loveland 45140 Jesse Kohls	PK-1		484 17	10%	513/683-4200 Fax 513/677-7960
Loveland Elem Sch 600 Loveland Madeira Rd, Loveland 45140 Jennifer Forren	3-4		670 28	17%	513/683-4333 Fax 513/677-7932
Loveland High Sch 1 Tiger Trl, Loveland 45140 Peggy Johnson	9-12	AV	1,446 85	12%	513/683-1920 Fax 513/677-7952
Loveland Intermediate Sch 757 S Lebanon Rd, Loveland 45140 Garth Carlier	5-6		715 28	13%	513/697-3024 Fax 513/677-7978
Loveland Middle Sch 801 S Lebanon Rd, Loveland 45140 Charles Ogdan	7-8	A	738 44	15%	513/683-3100 Fax 513/677-7986
Loveland Primary Sch 550 Loveland Madeira Rd, Loveland 45140 Kevin Fancher	1-2		539 24	20%	513/683-3101 Fax 513/677-7922

• **Madeira City School Dist** PID: 00806878   513/985-6070
7465 Loannes Dr, Cincinnati 45243   Fax 513/985-6072

Schools: 3 \ *Teachers:* 85 \ *Students:* 1,400 \ *Special Ed Students:* 166 \ *LEP Students:* 15 \ *College-Bound:* 86% \ *Ethnic:* Asian 3%, African American 1%, Hispanic 4%, Caucasian 91% \ *Exp:* $322 (High) \ *Poverty:* 4% \ *Title I:* $55,970 \ *Special Education:* $269,000 \ *Open-Close:* 08/14 - 05/21 \ *DTBP:* $251 (High) \

Name	Ref
Kenji Matsudo	1
Druien Downs	3*
Joe Kimling	6,35,80,91*
Melissa Broome	16*
Jessica Stevens	58
Diane Nichols	71
Emily Hauser	2
Kathy Moses	5
Dave Bergan	8,11,69,79,83,88,288
Mary Ann McPherson	34*
Richard Palmer	67
Matt Jones	73,295

Public Schs..Principal	Grd	Prgm	Enr/#Cls	SN	
Madeira Elem Sch 7840 Thomas Dr, Cincinnati 45243 Chris Flanagan	PK-4		628 28	8%	513/985-6080 Fax 513/985-6082
Madeira High Sch 7465 Loannes Dr, Cincinnati 45243 Dave Kennedy	9-12		402 45	8%	513/891-8222 Fax 513/985-6089
Madeira Middle Sch 6612 Miami Ave, Cincinnati 45243 Tom Olson	5-8		485 15	11%	513/561-5555 Fax 513/272-4145

• **Mariemont City School Dist** PID: 00806921   513/272-7500
2 Warrior Way, Cincinnati 45227   Fax 513/527-3436

Schools: 4 \ *Teachers:* 101 \ *Students:* 1,700 \ *Special Ed Students:* 173 \ *LEP Students:* 6 \ *College-Bound:* 80% \ *Ethnic:* Asian 2%, African American 1%, Hispanic 2%, Caucasian 95% \ *Exp:* $290 (Med) \ *Poverty:* 10% \ *Title I:* $224,624 \ *Special Education:* $313,000 \ *Open-Close:* 08/28 - 06/04 \ *DTBP:* $233 (High) \

Name	Ref
Steven Estepp	1
Lance Hollander	3
Tom Golinar	2,11,19
Tom Nerl	6*

Ohio School Directory — Hamilton County

Shannon Kromer 8,288
Amanda Leszczuk 31*
Alexander Lange 71
Tricia Beaufort 11,57,79,83
Kelli Neville 67
Brent Wise 73,295

Public Schs..Principal	Grd	Prgm	Enr/#Cls	SN	
Mariemont Elem Sch 6750 Wooster Pike, Cincinnati 45227 Ericka Simmons	K-6		563 28	11%	513/272-7400 Fax 513/527-3411
Mariemont High Sch 1 Warrior Way, Cincinnati 45227 Dr James Renner	9-12	G	500 40	10%	513/272-7600 Fax 513/527-5991
Mariemont Junior High Sch 3847 Southern Ave, Cincinnati 45227 Rob Polca	7-8		280 30	12%	513/272-7300 Fax 513/527-3432
Terrace Park Elem Sch 723 Elm Ave, Terrace Park 45174 Tami Croll	K-6		300 21	6%	513/272-7700 Fax 513/831-1249

● **Mt Healthy City School Dist** PID: 00806983   513/729-0077
7615 Harrison Ave, Cincinnati 45231   Fax 513/729-2819

Schools: 3 \ **Teachers:** 140 \ **Students:** 3,300 \ **Special Ed Students:** 605 \ **LEP Students:** 102 \ **College-Bound:** 44% \ **Ethnic:** Asian 2%, African American 78%, Hispanic 4%, Caucasian 16% \ **Exp:** $249 (Med) \ **Poverty:** 32% \ **Title I:** $2,782,451 \ **Special Education:** $729,000 \ **Open-Close:** 08/15 - 05/28 \ **DTBP:** $190 (High)

Dr Reva Cosby 1
Rebecca Brooks 2
Dr Apollos Harris 7,58,79,88
Jana Wolfe 9
Karen O'Connell 11,31,69,298
Karen Green 68
Elizabeth Wessel 79*
Jennifer Wethington 2
Fredrika Richardson 4
Michelle Hughes 8,288
Yzvetta Macon 10
Lori Jones 67
Lawanda Engleman 76

Public Schs..Principal	Grd	Prgm	Enr/#Cls	SN	
Mt Healthy Jr Sr High Sch 8101 Hamilton Ave, Cincinnati 45231 Robert Buchheim	7-12	ATV	800 85		513/729-0130 Fax 513/728-4695
North Elem Sch 2170 Struble Rd, Cincinnati 45231 Jamal Maxsam	PK-6	T	797 15		513/742-6004 Fax 513/742-3460
South Elem Sch 1743 Adams Rd, Cincinnati 45231 Yzvetta Macon	PK-6	T	867 21		513/728-4683 Fax 513/521-0796

● **North College Hill City SD** PID: 00807078   513/931-8181
1731 Goodman Ave, Cincinnati 45239   Fax 513/728-4774

Schools: 3 \ **Teachers:** 79 \ **Students:** 1,650 \ **Special Ed Students:** 303 \ **LEP Students:** 22 \ **College-Bound:** 50% \ **Ethnic:** Asian 1%, African American 86%, Hispanic 2%, Caucasian 11% \ **Exp:** $106 (Low) \ **Poverty:** 34% \ **Title I:** $1,299,271 \ **Special Education:** $353,000 \ **Open-Close:** 08/08 - 05/21 \ **DTBP:** $221 (High)

Eugene Blalock 1
Tom Mara 3
Carol Anderson 6
Michelle Garton 12
Connie Prairie 58
Joe Vlachos 73,76
Nicholas Martin 2
Dottie Petry 4
Courtney Colins 8,11,273
Bonnie Donofrio 27,69*
Barbara Graves 67

Public Schs..Principal	Grd	Prgm	Enr/#Cls	SN	
North College Hill Elem Sch 6955 Grace Ave, Cincinnati 45239 Tiffany Williams	PK-4	T	640 30	82%	513/728-4787 Fax 513/728-4788
North College Hill High Sch 1620 W Galbraith Rd, Cincinnati 45239 Timothy Sies	9-12	ATV	393 45	99%	513/728-4783 Fax 513/728-4784
North College Hill Mid Sch 1624 W Galbraith Rd, Cincinnati 45239 Tim Sies	5-8	T	577		513/728-4785 Fax 513/728-4786

● **Northwest Local School Dist** PID: 00807121   513/923-1000
3240 Banning Rd, Cincinnati 45239   Fax 513/923-3644

Schools: 11 \ **Teachers:** 459 \ **Students:** 9,000 \ **Special Ed Students:** 1,524 \ **LEP Students:** 398 \ **Ethnic:** Asian 4%, African American 30%, Hispanic 5%, Caucasian 61% \ **Exp:** $167 (Low) \ **Poverty:** 17% \ **Title I:** $3,857,275 \ **Special Education:** $1,862,000 \ **Open-Close:** 08/15 - 05/21 \ **DTBP:** $197 (High)

Todd Bowling 1
Christopher McKee 2
Bonnie Telinda 4
Matt Fischer 6,71,73,74,295
Brenda Miller 8,69,270,294
Heidi Stickney 8,58
Leslie Silbernagel 8,42
Eric Lorta 16,297
Stephanie Kessling 57,68,273
Chevonne Neal 58
Mary Barnaclo 58
Brian Hafer 76
Vicky Coleman 93
Amy Wells 2,8,18,19
Chuck Bostic 3,91
Lisa Robison 4
Keva Brice 7,83,85*
Darrell Yater 8,15
Jenny Blust 8,11,34,35,36,77,286,288
Chris Rabold 16*
Heather Kidd 45
Amy Bertram 58
Lindsey Giesting 58
Pam Detzel 67
Dustin Gehring 79,88

Public Schs..Principal	Grd	Prgm	Enr/#Cls	SN	
Colerain Elem Sch 4850 Poole Rd, Cincinnati 45251 Collin Climer	K-5	T	610 35	48%	513/385-8740 Fax 513/385-8770
Colerain High Sch 8801 Cheviot Rd, Cincinnati 45251 Jack Fisher	9-12	AV	1,809 80	40%	513/385-6424 Fax 513/741-5032
Colerain Middle Sch 4700 Poole Rd, Cincinnati 45251 Libby Styles	6-8	T	641 45	53%	513/385-8490 Fax 513/385-6685
Houston Early Learning Center 3308 Compton Rd, Cincinnati 45251 Aimee Murray	PK-PK		231 23	42%	513/385-8000 Fax 513/385-8090
Monfort Heights Elem Sch 3711 W Fork Rd, Cincinnati 45247 Kaitlyn Randall	K-5	T	632 36	36%	513/389-1570 Fax 513/389-1572
Northwest High Sch 10761 Pippin Rd, Cincinnati 45231 Susan Smith	9-12	ATV	884 55	57%	513/851-7300 Fax 513/742-6376
Pleasant Run Elem Sch 11780 Pippin Rd, Cincinnati 45231 Casey Scherz	K-5	T	917 40	68%	513/825-7070 Fax 513/825-1076
Pleasant Run Middle Sch 11770 Pippin Rd, Cincinnati 45231 **Brad Watkins**	6-8	T	777 100	64%	513/851-2400 Fax 513/851-7071
Struble Elem Sch 2760 Jonrose Ave, Cincinnati 45239 Karen Grayson	K-5	T	945 19	62%	513/522-2700 Fax 513/522-2711
Taylor Elem Sch 3173 Springdale Rd, Cincinnati 45251 Trey Rischmann	K-5	T	909 25	66%	513/825-3000 Fax 513/825-2983
White Oak Middle Sch 3130 Jessup Rd, Cincinnati 45239 Kevin Gale	6-8	T	774 34	55%	513/741-4300 Fax 513/741-0717

---

79 Student Personnel
80 Driver of/Safety
81 Gifted/Talented
82 Video Services
83 Substance Abuse Prev
84 Erate
85 AIDS Education
88 Alternative/At Risk
89 Multi-Cultural Curriculum
90 Social Work

91 Safety/Security
92 Magnet School
93 Parental Involvement
95 Tech Prep Program
97 Chief Infomation Officer
98 Chief Technology Officer
270 Character Education
271 Migrant Education
273 Teacher Mentor
274 Before/After Sch

275 Response To Intervention
277 Remedial Math K-12
280 Literacy Coach
285 STEM
286 Digital Learning
288 Common Core Standards
294 Accountability
295 Network System
296 Title II Programs
297 Webmaster

298 Grant Writer/Ptnrships
750 Chief Innovation Officer
751 Chief of Staff
752 Social Emotional Learning

Other School Types
Ⓐ = Alternative School
Ⓒ = Charter School
Ⓜ = Magnet School
Ⓨ = Year-Round School

School Programs
A = Alternative Program
G = Adult Classes
M = Magnet Program
T = Title I Schoolwide
V = Career & Tech Ed Programs

Social Media
[f] = Facebook
[t] = Twitter

New Schools are shaded
New Superintendents and Principals are bold
Personnel with email addresses are underscored

Hamilton County

Norwood City School Dist PID: 00807262
2132 Williams Ave, Norwood 45212
513/924-2500
Fax 513/396-6420

Schools: 5 \ **Teachers:** 133 \ **Students:** 2,000 \ **Special Ed Students:** 330 \ **LEP Students:** 95 \ **College-Bound:** 43% \ **Ethnic:** African American 14%, Hispanic 12%, Caucasian 74% \ **Exp:** $518 (High) \ **Poverty:** 29% \ **Title I:** $1,340,390 \ **Special Education:** $381,000 \ **Open-Close:** 08/21 - 05/22 \ **DTBP:** $261 (High)

Dr Kathy Sabo 1
Julie Kamphaus 2
John Peter 3
Rodger Kipp 4*
Alex Heinz 6
Kathy Strasser 7*
Kristina Chesson .. 8,11,57,73,88,288,296,298
Shannon Eshman 58,271
Valerie Orza 67
Randall Grandstaff 295*

Public Schs..Principal	Grd	Prgm	Enr/#Cls	SN	
Norwood High Sch 2020 Sherman Ave, Norwood 45212 Brad Winterod	9-12	AT	496 35	56%	513/924-2800 Fax 513/396-5559
Norwood Middle Sch 2060 Sherman Ave, Norwood 45212 Joe Miller	7-8	T	291 40	66%	513/924-2700 Fax 513/396-5537
Norwood View Elem Sch 5328 Carthage Ave, Norwood 45212 Lin Yates	K-6	T	380 28	68%	513/924-2610 Fax 513/396-5527
Sharpsburg Elem Sch 4400 Smith Rd, Norwood 45212 Joe Westendorf	PK-6	T	283 16	71%	513/924-2600 Fax 513/396-5528
Williams Avenue Elem Sch 2132 Williams Ave, Norwood 45212 Mark Gabbard	PK-6	T	307 19	53%	513/924-2520 Fax 513/396-5593

Oak Hills Local School Dist PID: 00807341
6325 Rapid Run Rd, Cincinnati 45233
513/574-3200
Fax 513/598-2947

Schools: 9 \ **Teachers:** 370 \ **Students:** 8,700 \ **Special Ed Students:** 1,328 \ **LEP Students:** 92 \ **College-Bound:** 60% \ **Ethnic:** Asian 1%, African American 4%, Hispanic 2%, Caucasian 93% \ **Exp:** $98 (Low) \ **Poverty:** 9% \ **Title I:** $1,478,715 \ **Special Education:** $1,583,000 \ **Open-Close:** 08/13 - 05/21 \ **DTBP:** $191 (High)

Jeff Brandt 1
Steve Bain 2
John Beckemeyer 3,7
Kelly Weldele 4
Tracy Spragu-Marcum 5
Ben Hageman 6
Ben Hageman 6*
Dr Tim Cybulski 8,11,15,57,58,69,88,298
Corey Kessler 9,294
Bridgette Smiley 10,16,30,73,286,295
Christen Long 16,73,286,295
Candice Lessing 34
Jeannie Schoonerover 67
Dan Beckenhaupt 68
Emily Buckley 71
Karen Zahneis 76
Rachel Searcy 79,93,275
Bart West 91
Travis Hunt 270

Public Schs..Principal	Grd	Prgm	Enr/#Cls	SN	
Bridgetown Middle Sch 3900 Race Rd, Cincinnati 45211 Adam Taylor	6-8		665 33		513/574-3511 Fax 513/574-6689
C O Harrison Elem Sch 585 Neeb Rd, Cincinnati 45233 Brian Conners	K-5		895 36	37%	513/922-1485 Fax 513/922-3330
Delhi Middle Sch 5280 Foley Rd, Cincinnati 45238 Scott Toon	6-8	T	547 39	42%	513/922-8400 Fax 513/922-8472
Delshire Elem Sch 4402 Glenhaven Rd, Cincinnati 45238 Tara Willig	PK-5	T	538 22	55%	513/471-1766 Fax 513/471-1767
John Foster Dulles Elem Sch 6481 Bridgetown Rd, Cincinnati 45248 Elizabeth Riesenberger	PK-5		840 38	19%	513/574-3443 Fax 513/574-3182
Oak Hills High Sch 3200 Ebenezer Rd, Cincinnati 45248 Travis Hunt	9-12	A	2,232 120		513/922-2300 Fax 513/922-4900
Oakdale Elem Sch 3850 Virginia Ct, Cincinnati 45248 Emily Winkle	K-5		771 29	31%	513/574-1100 Fax 513/574-5116
Rapid Run Middle Sch 6345 Rapid Run Rd, Cincinnati 45233 Geoff Harold	6-8		682		513/467-0300 Fax 513/467-0333
Springmyer Elem Sch 4179 Ebenezer Rd, Cincinnati 45248 Mark Winters	K-5		463 20	20%	513/574-1205 Fax 513/574-1206

Princeton City School Dist PID: 00807432
3900 Cottingham Dr, Cincinnati 45241
513/864-1000
Fax 513/864-1896

Schools: 10 \ **Teachers:** 305 \ **Students:** 6,500 \ **Special Ed Students:** 882 \ **LEP Students:** 1,263 \ **College-Bound:** 50% \ **Ethnic:** Asian 4%, African American 43%, Hispanic 26%, Caucasian 27% \ **Exp:** $215 (Med) \ **Poverty:** 21% \ **Title I:** $2,161,592 \ **Special Education:** $1,104,000 \ **Open-Close:** 08/15 - 05/29 \ **DTBP:** $191 (High)

Tom Burton 1
Christine Poetter 2
Jean Sparks 4*
Joe Rogers 6*
Dr Mari Phillips 58
Theresa Warren 58
Mary Cleveland 67
Dr Donis Toler 68
Chris Lockhart 73,286
Debra Burch 76
Valerie Hawkins 78
Ali Moore 91
Tricia Roddy 298

Public Schs..Principal	Grd	Prgm	Enr/#Cls	SN	
Evendale Elem Sch 3940 Glendale Milford Rd, Cincinnati 45241 Joycelyn Senter	PK-5	T	256 18	39%	513/864-1200 Fax 513/864-1291
Glendale Elem Sch 930 Congress Ave, Cincinnati 45246 Tracy Jennings	K-5	T	274 15	78%	513/864-1300 Fax 513/864-1391
Heritage Hill Elem Sch 11961 Chesterdale Rd, Cincinnati 45246 Shari Hoskins	K-5	T	502 60	99%	513/864-1400 Fax 513/864-1491
Lincoln Heights Elem Sch 1113 Adams St, Cincinnati 45215 Dawn Bailey	K-5	T	290 38	99%	513/864-2400 Fax 513/864-2491
Princeton Cmty Middle Sch 200 Viking Way, Cincinnati 45246 David Mackzum	6-8		1,443	67%	513/864-2000 Fax 513/552-8511
Princeton High Sch 100 Viking Way, Cincinnati 45246 **Ron Bollmer**	9-12	AGTV	1,558	55%	513/864-1500 Fax 513/552-8224
Sharonville Elem Sch 11150 Maple St, Cincinnati 45241 Kasi Jordan	K-5	T	447 20	68%	513/864-2600 Fax 513/864-2691
Springdale Elem Sch 350 W Kemper Rd, Cincinnati 45246 Lisa Tenbarge	PK-5	T	440 26	55%	513/864-2700 Fax 513/864-2791
Stewart Elem Sch 11850 Conrey Rd, Cincinnati 45249 Ronald Fausnaugh	PK-5	T	509 23	76%	513/864-2800 Fax 513/864-2891
Woodlawn Elem Sch 31 Riddle Rd, Cincinnati 45215 Sherry Thompson	PK-5	T	184 10	79%	513/864-2900 Fax 513/864-2991

1	Superintendent	8	Curric/Instruct K-12	19	Chief Financial Officer	29	Family/Consumer Science	39	Social Studies K-12	49	English/Lang Arts Elem	59	Special Education Elem	69	Academic Assessment
2	Bus/Finance/Purchasing	9	Curric/Instruct Elem	20	Art K-12	30	Adult Education	40	Social Studies Elem	50	English/Lang Arts Sec	60	Special Education Sec	70	Research/Development
3	Buildings And Grounds	10	Curric/Instruct Sec	21	Art Elem	31	Career/Sch-to-Work K-12	41	Social Studies Sec	51	Reading K-12	61	Foreign/World Lang K-12	71	Public Information
4	Food Service	11	Federal Program	22	Art Sec	32	Career/Sch-to-Work Elem	42	Science K-12	52	Reading Elem	62	Foreign/World Lang Elem	72	Summer School
5	Transportation	12	Title I	23	Music K-12	33	Career/Sch-to-Work Sec	43	Science Elem	53	Reading Sec	63	Foreign/World Lang Sec	73	Instructional Tech
6	Athletic	13	Title V	24	Music Elem	34	Early Childhood Ed	44	Science Sec	54	Remedial Reading K-12	64	Religious Education K-12	74	Inservice Training
7	Health Services	15	Asst Superintendent	25	Music Sec	35	Health/Phys Education	45	Math K-12	55	Remedial Reading Elem	65	Religious Education Elem	75	Marketing/Distributive
		16	Instructional Media Svcs	26	Business Education	36	Guidance Services K-12	46	Math Elem	56	Remedial Reading Sec	66	Religious Education Sec	76	Info Systems
		17	Chief Operations Officer	27	Career & Tech Ed	37	Guidance Services Elem	47	Math Sec	57	Bilingual/ELL	67	School Board President	77	Psychological Assess
		18	Chief Academic Officer	28	Technology Education	38	Guidance Services Sec	48	English/Lang Arts K-12	58	Special Education K-12	68	Teacher Personnel	78	Affirmative Action

Ohio School Directory

Hamilton County

- **Reading Cmty City School Dist** PID: 00807573   513/554-1800
  1301 Bonnell St, Reading 45215   Fax 513/483-6754

Schools: 4 \ **Teachers:** 100 \ **Students:** 1,535 \ **Special Ed Students:** 275 \ **LEP Students:** 33 \ **College-Bound:** 45% \ **Ethnic:** Asian 1%, African American 9%, Hispanic 3%, Caucasian 87% \ **Exp:** $174 (Low) \ **Poverty:** 21% \ **Title I:** $500,415 \ **Special Education:** $434,000 \ **Open-Close:** 09/03 - 06/04 \ **DTBP:** $230 (High)

Chuck LaFata	1,11,57,288	Cary Furniss	2
Marylynn Bearman	4*	Jon Payne	6*
Heidi Sandlin	7*	Susan Fraley	12*
Kolene Willman	16,82*	Kevin Kaiser	67
Pete Baird	73	Carletta Jacobs	273*

Public Schs..Principal	Grd	Prgm	Enr/#Cls	SN	
Central Elem Sch 416 W Vine St, Reading 45215 Susan Fraley	K-5	T	333 14		513/554-1001 Fax 513/483-6792
Hilltop Elem Sch 2236 Bolser Dr, Reading 45215 Daniel Kist	PK-5		446 23	37%	513/733-4322 Fax 513/483-6772
Reading High Sch 810 E Columbia Ave, Reading 45215 Dennis Ramsey	9-12	AT	373 30	49%	513/733-4422 Fax 513/483-6792 f
Reading Middle Sch 230 Halker Ave, Reading 45215 Damon Davis	6-8	T	383	57%	513/842-5151 Fax 513/842-5146

- **Southwest Local School Dist** PID: 00807638   513/367-4139
  230 S Elm St, Harrison 45030   Fax 513/367-2287

Schools: 6 \ **Teachers:** 163 \ **Students:** 4,044 \ **Special Ed Students:** 589 \ **LEP Students:** 6 \ **College-Bound:** 75% \ **Ethnic:** African American 1%, Hispanic 3%, Caucasian 96% \ **Exp:** $107 (Low) \ **Poverty:** 16% \ **Title I:** $1,032,990 \ **Special Education:** $807,000 \ **Open-Close:** 08/20 - 05/27 \ **DTBP:** $189 (High)

John Hamstra	1	Thomas Lowe	2
Mike Morris	3*	Bonnie Berkemeyer	4,5
Corinne Hayes	8,15,69,74,275	Lara Meyers	11,57,58,79,296
Jeffrey Biddle	67	Mitzi Smith	68
Ginny Hizer	71	Roger McGregor	76
Sandy Knose	79		

Public Schs..Principal	Grd	Prgm	Enr/#Cls	SN	
Crosby Elem Sch 8382 New Haven Rd, Harrison 45030 Kiersten Rogers	K-5		494 13	26%	513/738-1717 Fax 513/738-1718
Harrison Elem Sch 600 E Broadway St, Harrison 45030 Ron Mangus	K-5	T	578 49	47%	513/367-4161 Fax 513/367-1856
Miamitown Elem Sch 6578 State Rt 128, Miamitown 45041 Dave Kelly	K-5	T	405 16		513/353-1416 Fax 513/353-9026
Whitewater Valley Elem Sch 10800 Campbell Rd, Harrison 45030 Mia Neckel	K-5		483 23	28%	513/367-5577 Fax 513/367-5594
William Henry Harrison HS 9860 West Rd, Harrison 45030 Matthew Lindley	9-12	AV	983	36%	513/367-4169 Fax 513/367-7251
William Henry Harrison Jr HS 9830 West Rd, Harrison 45030 Christian Tracy	6-8		1,006 45	36%	513/367-4831 Fax 513/367-0370

- **St Bernard-Elmwood Place Schs** PID: 00807717   513/482-7121
  105 Washington Ave, Saint Bernard 45217   Fax 513/641-0066

Schools: 3 \ **Teachers:** 63 \ **Students:** 1,000 \ **Special Ed Students:** 213 \ **LEP Students:** 29 \ **College-Bound:** 36% \ **Ethnic:** Asian 1%, African American 39%, Hispanic 4%, Caucasian 56% \ **Exp:** $252 (Med) \ **Poverty:** 25% \ **Title I:** $451,564 \ **Special Education:** $366,000 \ **Open-Close:** 08/15 - 05/28 \ **DTBP:** $233 (High)

Dr Mimi Webb	1	Emily Hauser	2
Paul Finkes	3	Linda Radtke	67
Bruce Helwagen	73,295*	Pam Carroll	76
Brenda Schildmeyer	273*		

Public Schs..Principal	Grd	Prgm	Enr/#Cls	SN	
Elmwood Place Elem Sch 400 Maple St, Elmwood Place 45216 Sherry Peters	PK-6	T	264 16	92%	513/482-7115 Fax 513/641-5502
St Bernard Elem Sch 4515 Tower Ave, Saint Bernard 45217 Karen Clemons	K-6	T	260 12	75%	513/482-7110 Fax 513/641-0278
St Bernard-Elmwood Place HS 4615 Tower Ave, Saint Bernard 45217 Robert Reynolds	7-12	T	381 30	78%	513/482-7100 Fax 513/641-4878

- **Sycamore Cmty School Dist** PID: 00807767   513/686-1700
  5959 Hagewa Dr, Cincinnati 45242   Fax 513/791-4873

Schools: 7 \ **Teachers:** 330 \ **Students:** 5,481 \ **Special Ed Students:** 607 \ **LEP Students:** 412 \ **College-Bound:** 77% \ **Ethnic:** Asian 17%, African American 8%, Hispanic 6%, Caucasian 68% \ **Exp:** $264 (Med) \ **Poverty:** 6% \ **Title I:** $484,776 \ **Special Education:** $1,120,000 \ **Open-Close:** 08/14 - 05/21 \ **DTBP:** $193 (High) \ f

Frank Forsthoefel	1	Beth Weber	2,76
Chad Lewis	2	David Foster	3,91
Kelsey Warren	4	Michael Miller	
Mark Harden	6	Stacey Spencer	7,11,58,83,88,285
Kelly Wegener	8,12	Karen Naber	12,15,280,288,296,298
Brad Williams	26	Bill Fritz	28,73,84,286
Edward Clark	35*	Ann Delehanty-Koen	38*
Callie Hoffman	45*	Melissa Wolfe-Izworski	48,273*
Emily William	57	Paul Balelt	67
Brian Wallace	68	Mallory Bonbright	71
Belitta Croley	90*		

Public Schs..Principal	Grd	Prgm	Enr/#Cls	SN	
Blue Ash Elem Sch 9541 Plainfield Rd, Cincinnati 45236 Leslie Combs	K-4		515 24	21%	513/686-1710 Fax 513/792-0305
Edwin H Greene Interm Sch 5200 Aldine Dr, Cincinnati 45242 Matt Tudor	5-6		867 50		513/686-1750 Fax 513/792-6172
Maple Dale Elem Sch 6100 Hagewa Dr, Cincinnati 45242 Ann Reinke	PK-4		656	12%	513/686-1720 Fax 513/792-6112
Montgomery Elem Sch 9609 Montgomery Rd, Cincinnati 45242 Linda Overbeck	K-4		481 25	12%	513/686-1730 Fax 513/792-6131
Sycamore High Sch 7400 Cornell Rd, Cincinnati 45242 Doug Mader	9-12	V	1,640 100	14%	513/686-1770 Fax 513/489-7425
Sycamore Junior High Sch 5757 Cooper Rd, Cincinnati 45242 Traci Rea	7-8		811 70	13%	513/686-1760 Fax 513/891-3162

Hamilton County

Symmes Elem Sch	K-4		502	27%	513/686-1740
11820 Enyart Rd, Loveland 45140			27		Fax 513/677-7861
Anne VanKirk					

• **Three Rivers Local School Dist** PID: 00807834   513/941-6400
401 N Miami Ave, Cleves 45002   Fax 513/941-1102

Schools: 2 \ *Teachers:* 99 \ *Students:* 2,200 \ *Special Ed Students:* 369 \ *LEP Students:* 8 \ *College-Bound:* 61% \ *Ethnic:* Asian 1%, African American 1%, Hispanic 2%, Caucasian 96% \ *Exp:* $193 (Low) \ *Poverty:* 11% \ *Title I:* $452,687 \ *Special Education:* $412,000 \ *Open-Close:* 08/13 - 05/22 \ *DTBP:* $239 (High) \ f

Craig Hockenberry 1	Alice Gundler 2	
Jeff Langdon 3,68	Marlinda Updegrove 4	
Tim Wagner 5	Larry Herges 6	
Amanda Witterstaeter 7,35,85	Gretchen Bloomstrom 8,69	
Mandy Aug 11,18,57,73,271,288,296	Megan Rivet 34,58*	
Chris Oser 67	Lisa Whiteley 71	

Public Schs..Principal	Grd	Prgm	Enr/#Cls	SN	
Taylor Middle High Sch	6-12	V	998	38%	513/467-3200
56 Cooper Ave, Cleves 45002			20		Fax 513/467-0053
Mark Smiley					
Three Rivers Elem Sch	PK-5	T	1,166	41%	513/467-3210
56 Cooper Ave, Cleves 45002			15		Fax 513/467-0053
Adam Biedenbach					

• **Winton Woods City School Dist** PID: 00806579   513/619-2300
825 Waycross Rd Ste A, Cincinnati 45240   Fax 513/619-2309

Schools: 7 \ *Teachers:* 208 \ *Students:* 3,500 \ *Special Ed Students:* 567 \ *LEP Students:* 653 \ *College-Bound:* 51% \ *Ethnic:* Asian 6%, African American 63%, Hispanic 19%, Caucasian 12% \ *Exp:* $273 (Med) \ *Poverty:* 23% \ *Title I:* $1,847,198 \ *Special Education:* $908,000 \ *Open-Close:* 08/19 - 05/21 \ *DTBP:* $182 (High) \ f t

Anthony Smith 1	Steve Denny 2,11,91,288,294,296,298
James Tate 3	Mark Docter 4
Kristi Hooper 5	David Lumpkin 6*
Tonya Bray 7,11,58,79	Dr Terri Holden 8
Michelle Sisk 16,82*	Gary Giblin 57*
Viola Johnson 67	Courtney Wilson 68,79
Corina Denny 71	Rhonda Hobbs 73,76,286,295
Dwight Campbell 83	Brenda Hodges 88
Matt Jones 295	

Public Schs..Principal	Grd	Prgm	Enr/#Cls	SN	
Winton Woods Elem Sch	3-4	T	582	79%	513/619-2490
1501 Kingsbury Dr, Cincinnati 45240			30		Fax 513/619-2497
Nelson Homan					
Winton Woods HS-Global Studies	9-12		1,100		513/619-2420
1231 W Kemper Rd, Cincinnati 45240					Fax 513/619-2417
Eric Martin					
Winton Woods HS-New Tech Acad	9-12	ATV	1,116	65%	513/619-2420
1231 W Kemper Rd, Cincinnati 45240			212		Fax 513/619-2417
Eric Martin					f t
Winton Woods Interm Sch	5-6	T	582	77%	513/619-2450
825 Waycross Rd, Cincinnati 45240			22		Fax 513/619-2451
Jeremy Day					f t
Winton Woods Middle Sch	7-8	AT	522	78%	513/619-2440
147 Farragut Rd, Cincinnati 45218			60		Fax 513/619-2452
Doug Sanker					
Winton Woods Primary Sch-North	PK-2	T	535	69%	513/619-2390
73 Junefield Ave, Cincinnati 45218			16		Fax 513/619-2398
Kevin Jones					f t
Winton Woods Primary Sch-South	K-2	T	450	78%	513/619-2470
825 Lakeridge Dr, Cincinnati 45231			24		Fax 513/619-2479
Danielle Wallace					

• **Wyoming City School Dist** PID: 00807901   513/206-7000
420 Springfield Pike, Wyoming 45215   Fax 513/672-3355

Schools: 5 \ *Teachers:* 119 \ *Students:* 1,950 \ *Special Ed Students:* 177 \ *LEP Students:* 22 \ *College-Bound:* 86% \ *Ethnic:* Asian 3%, African American 11%, Hispanic 2%, Caucasian 83% \ *Exp:* $214 (Med) \ *Poverty:* 7% \ *Title I:* $177,636 \ *Special Education:* $327,000 \ *Open-Close:* 08/13 - 05/29 \ *DTBP:* $234 (High)

Tim Weber 1	Rhonda Johnson 2,5,19
Thomas Wright 3	Gerry Levy 4*
Jan Wilking 6	Dr Tracy Quattrone 7,13,54,57,58,79,81,88
Ashley Whitely 8,12,15,68,69,83,288*	Ladora Hill 9,34*
Susan House 37*	Mary Beth Corbin 38*
Jeanie Zoller 67	Cleighton Weiland 69,77
Zach McCormick 73,98,286	

Public Schs..Principal	Grd	Prgm	Enr/#Cls	SN	
Elm Primary Sch	K-4		226	8%	513/206-7315
134 Elm Ave, Wyoming 45215			10		Fax 513/206-7337
Ladora Hill					
Hilltop Primary Sch	K-4		286	3%	513/206-7270
425 Oliver Rd, Wyoming 45215			16		Fax 513/206-7305
Ladora Hill					
Vermont Primary Sch	K-4		208	11%	513/206-7345
33 Vermont Ave, Wyoming 45215			9		Fax 513/206-7370
Ladora Hill					
Wyoming High Sch	9-12	V	656	5%	513/206-7050
106 Pendery Ave, Wyoming 45215			38		Fax 513/206-7132
Karen Bare					
Wyoming Middle Sch	5-8		623	6%	513/206-7170
17 Wyoming Ave, Wyoming 45215			40		Fax 513/206-7245
Jennifer Klein					

HAMILTON CATHOLIC SCHOOLS

• **Archdiocese Cincinnati Ed Off** PID: 00808096   513/421-3131
100 E 8th St, Cincinnati 45202   Fax 513/421-6271

Schools: 107 \ *Students:* 42,000

Listing includes only schools located in this county. See District Index for location of Diocesan Offices.

Susan Gibbons 1	Vince Woodall 2
Dr Carole Roberts 8,69	Mary Ann Bernier 11
Cyndi Hardesty 15,45	Kathy Kane 15,68,273
Mayra Wilson 271	

Catholic Schs..Principal	Grd	Prgm	Enr/#Cls	SN	
All Saints Sch	K-8		498		513/792-4732
8939 Montgomery Rd, Cincinnati 45236			20		Fax 513/792-7990
Kevan Hartman					f
Annunciation Sch	PK-8	G	156		513/221-1230
3545 Clifton Ave, Cincinnati 45220			9		Fax 513/281-8009
Anthony Ertel					f t
Archbishop McNicholas HS	9-12		650		513/231-3500
6536 Beechmont Ave, Cincinnati 45230					Fax 513/231-1351
David Mueller					f t

1	Superintendent	8	Curric/Instruct K-12	19	Chief Financial Officer	29	Family/Consumer Science	39	Social Studies K-8	49	English/Lang Arts Elem	59	Special Education Elem	69	Academic Assessment
2	Bus/Finance/Purchasing	9	Curric/Instruct Elem	20	Art K-12	30	Adult Education	40	Social Studies Elem	50	English/Lang Arts Sec	60	Special Education Sec	70	Research/Development
3	Buildings And Grounds	10	Curric/Instruct Sec	21	Art Elem	31	Career/Sch-to-Work K-12	41	Social Studies Sec	51	Reading K-12	61	Foreign/World Lang K-12	71	Public Information
4	Food Service	11	Federal Program	22	Art Sec	32	Career/Sch-to-Work Elem	42	Science K-12	52	Reading Elem	62	Foreign/World Lang Elem	72	Summer School
5	Transportation	12	Title I	23	Music K-12	33	Career/Sch-to-Work Sec	43	Science Elem	53	Reading Sec	63	Foreign/World Lang Sec	73	Instructional Tech
6	Athletic	13	Title V	24	Music Elem	34	Early Childhood Ed	44	Science Sec	54	Remedial Reading K-12	64	Religious Education K-12	74	Inservice Training
7	Health Services	15	Asst Superintendent	25	Music Sec	35	Health/Phys Education	45	Math K-12	55	Remedial Reading Elem	65	Religious Education Elem	75	Marketing/Distributive
		16	Instructional Media Svcs	26	Business Education	36	Guidance Services K-12	46	Math Elem	56	Remedial Reading Sec	66	Religious Education Sec	76	Info Systems
		17	Chief Operations Officer	27	Career & Tech Ed	37	Guidance Services Elem	47	Math Sec	57	Bilingual/ELL	67	School Board President	77	Psychological Assess
		18	Chief Academic Officer	28	Technology Education	38	Guidance Services Sec	48	English/Lang Arts K-12	58	Special Education K-12	68	Teacher Personnel	78	Affirmative Action

Ohio School Directory — Hamilton County

School	Grades	Enroll	Phone
Archbishop Moeller High Sch 9001 Montgomery Rd, Cincinnati 45242 Carl Kremer	9-12	890 42	513/791-1680 Fax 513/792-3343
Cardinal Pacelli Sch 927 Ellison Ave, Cincinnati 45226 Terri Cento	PK-8	378 20	513/321-1048 Fax 513/533-6113 [f][t]
Corryville Catholic Elem Sch 108 Calhoun St, Cincinnati 45219 Lauren Clements	PK-8	200 13	513/281-4856 Fax 513/281-6497
Elder High Sch 3900 Vincent Ave, Cincinnati 45205 Kurt Ruffing	9-12	915 60	513/921-3744 Fax 513/921-8123 [f][t]
Good Shepherd Montessori Sch 4460 Berwick St, Cincinnati 45227 Anne Vega	PK-8	218 8	513/271-4171 Fax 513/271-4680
Guardian Angels Sch 6539 Beechmont Ave, Cincinnati 45230 Corey Stoops	PK-8	450 29	513/624-3141 Fax 513/624-3150
Holy Family Catholic Sch 3001 Price Ave, Cincinnati 45205 Katie Puthoff	PK-8	217 9	513/921-8483 Fax 513/921-2460
Immaculate Heart of Mary Sch 7800 Beechmont Ave, Cincinnati 45255 Krista DeVine	PK-8	660 27	513/388-4086 Fax 513/388-3026
John Paul II Catholic Sch 9375 Winton Rd, Cincinnati 45231 Leanora Roach	K-8	502 30	513/521-0860 Fax 513/728-3101
La Salle High Sch 3091 North Bend Rd, Cincinnati 45239 Aaron Marshall	9-12	625 38	513/741-3000 Fax 513/741-2666 [f][t]
Mercy McAuley High Sch 6000 Oakwood Ave, Cincinnati 45224 Connie Kampschmidt	9-12	735 46	513/681-1800 [f]
Mercy Montessori Center Sch 2335 Grandview Ave, Cincinnati 45206 Patty Normile	PK-8	293 18	513/475-6700 Fax 513/475-6755
Mt Notre Dame High Sch 711 E Columbia Ave, Cincinnati 45215 Karen Day	9-12	787 36	513/821-3044 Fax 513/821-6068
Nativity of Our Lord Sch 5936 Ridge Ave, Cincinnati 45213 Chris Shisler	K-8	400 18	513/458-6767 Fax 513/458-6769
Our Lady of Grace Sch 2940 W Galbraith Rd, Cincinnati 45239 Mandy Kirk	K-8	405 25	513/931-3070 Fax 513/931-3707
Our Lady of Lourdes Sch 5835 Glenway Ave, Cincinnati 45238 Heather Bessler	K-8	300 18	513/347-2660 Fax 513/347-2663
Our Lady of Victory Sch 808 Neeb Rd, Cincinnati 45233 Amy Borgman	PK-8	430 30	513/347-2072 Fax 513/347-2073
Our Lady of Visitation Sch 3180 South Rd, Cincinnati 45248 Holly Aug	K-8	760 38	513/347-2222 Fax 513/347-2225
Purcell Marian High Sch 2935 Hackberry St, Cincinnati 45206 Andy Farfsing	9-12 V	404 30	513/751-1230 Fax 513/751-1395 [f]
Resurrection of Our Lord Sch 1740 Iliff Ave, Cincinnati 45205 Patti Lowe	K-8	193 9	513/471-6600 Fax 513/471-2610
Roger Bacon High Sch 4320 Vine St, Cincinnati 45217 Steve Schad	9-12	594 38	513/641-1300 Fax 513/641-0498 [f][t]
Seton High Sch 3901 Glenway Ave, Cincinnati 45205 Karen White	9-12	530 48	513/471-2600 [f]
St Aloysius Gonzaga Sch 4390 Bridgetown Rd, Cincinnati 45211 Sandra Staud	PK-8	250 9	513/574-4035 Fax 513/574-5421 [f]
St Antoninus Sch 5425 Julmar Dr, Cincinnati 45238 Shelly Kahny	K-8	459 23	513/922-2500 Fax 513/922-5519 [f]
St Bernard Taylor Creek Sch 7115 Springdale Rd, Cincinnati 45247 Courtney Brown	K-8	207 9	513/353-4224 Fax 513/353-3958
St Boniface Sch 4305 Pitts Ave, Cincinnati 45223 Sr Miriam Kaeser	K-8	200 10	513/541-5122 Fax 513/541-3939
St Catharine Sch 3324 Wunder Ave, Cincinnati 45211 Jerry Metz	K-8	196 11	513/481-7683 Fax 513/481-9438
St Cecilia Sch 4115 Taylor Ave, Cincinnati 45209 Mike Goedde	PK-8	205 15	513/533-6060 Fax 513/533-6068 [f]
St Clement Sch 4534 Vine St, Cincinnati 45217 Jeff Eiser	PK-8	173 15	513/641-2137 Fax 513/242-6036
St Dominic Sch 371 Pedretti Ave, Cincinnati 45238 Bill Cavanaugh	K-8	531 27	513/251-1276 Fax 513/251-6428
St Francis DeSales Sch 1602 Madison Rd, Cincinnati 45206 Joanne Browarsky	PK-8	250 9	513/961-1953 Fax 513/961-2900
St Francis Seraph Sch 14 E Liberty St, Cincinnati 45202 Halsey Mabry	K-8	134	513/721-7778 Fax 513/721-5445 [f]
St Gabriel Consolidated Sch 18 W Sharon Rd, Cincinnati 45246 Stacie Wendt	K-8	418 18	513/771-5220 Fax 513/771-5133 [f]
St Gertrude Sch 6543 Miami Ave, Cincinnati 45243 Sr Maria Christi	K-8	320 19	513/561-8020 Fax 513/561-7184 [f]
St Ignatius Sch 5222 N Bend Rd, Cincinnati 45247 Kevin Vance	K-8	1,047 39	513/389-3242 Fax 513/389-3255
St James the Greater Sch 6111 Cheviot Rd, Cincinnati 45247 Jeff Fulmer	K-8	556 35	513/741-5333 Fax 513/741-5312 [f]
St John Baptist Sch 508 Park Ave, Harrison 45030 Nicole Herman	PK-8	301 16	513/367-6826 Fax 513/367-6864 [f]
St John the Baptist Sch 5375 Dry Ridge Rd, Cincinnati 45252 Daniel Minelli	PK-8	450 30	513/385-7970 Fax 513/699-6964
St Joseph Sch 745 Ezzard Charles Dr, Cincinnati 45203 Barry Williams	K-8 G	186 13	513/381-2126 Fax 513/381-6513
St Jude Sch 5940 Bridgetown Rd, Cincinnati 45248 Lou Eichhold	PK-8	515 23	513/598-2100 Fax 513/598-2118 [f]
St Lawrence Sch 1020 Carson Ave, Cincinnati 45205 Richard Klus	PK-8	250 17	513/921-4996 Fax 513/921-5108 [f]
St Martin of Tours Sch 3729 Harding Ave, Cincinnati 45211 Jason Fightmaster	K-8	272 9	513/661-7609 Fax 513/661-8102
St Mary Sch 2845 Erie Ave, Cincinnati 45208 Marianne Rosemond	K-8	463 24	513/321-0703 Fax 513/533-6388 [f]
St Michael Sch 11136 Oak St, Sharonville 45241 Carolyn Murphy	K-8	400 18	513/554-3555 Fax 513/554-3551

79 Student Personnel
80 Driver Ed/Safety
81 Gifted/Talented
82 Video Services
83 Substance Abuse Prev
84 Erate
85 AIDS Education
88 Alternative/At Risk
89 Multi-Cultural Curriculum
90 Social Work

91 Safety/Security
92 Magnet School
93 Parental Involvement
95 Tech Prep Program
97 Chief Information Officer
98 Chief Technology Officer
270 Character Education
271 Migrant Education
273 Teacher Mentor
274 Before/After Sch

275 Response To Intervention
277 Remedial Math K-12
280 Literacy Coach
285 STEM
286 Digital Learning
288 Common Core Standards
294 Accountability
295 Network System
296 Title II Programs
297 Webmaster

298 Grant Writer/Ptnrships
750 Chief Innovation Officer
751 Chief of Staff
752 Social Emotional Learning

Other School Types
Ⓐ = Alternative School
Ⓒ = Charter School
Ⓜ = Magnet School
Ⓨ = Year-Round School

School Programs
A = Alternative Program
G = Adult Classes
M = Magnet Program
T = Title I Schoolwide
V = Career & Tech Ed Programs

Social Media
[f] = Facebook
[t] = Twitter

New Schools are shaded
New Superintendents and Principals are bold
Personnel with email addresses are underscored

Hamilton County

School	Grd	Enr/#Cls	Phone
St Nicholas Academy 170 Siebenthaler Ave, Cincinnati 45215 Aideen Briggs	PK-8	167 18	513/686-2727 Fax 513/686-2729
St Rita School for the Deaf 1720 Glendale Milford Rd, Cincinnati 45215 Megan Havens \ Natalie Marsh	Spec	125 25	513/771-7600 Fax 513/326-8264
St Teresa of Avila Sch 1194 Rulison Ave, Cincinnati 45238 J Ostertag	K-8	225 22	513/471-4530 Fax 513/471-1254
St Ursula Academy 1339 E McMillan St, Cincinnati 45206 Mari Thomas	9-12	710 40	513/961-3410 Fax 513/961-3856
St Ursula Villa Sch 3660 Vineyard Pl, Cincinnati 45226 Polly Duplace	PK-8	300 22	513/871-7218 Fax 513/871-0082
St Veronica Sch 4475 Mount Carmel Tobasco Rd, Cincinnati 45244 Sharon Bresler	K-8	480 22	513/528-0442
St Vincent Ferrer Sch 7754 Montgomery Rd, Cincinnati 45236 Kimberly Roy	PK-8	150 9	513/791-6320 Fax 513/791-3332
St Vivian Sch 885 Denier Pl, Cincinnati 45224 Jane Brack	PK-8	260 18	513/522-6858 Fax 513/728-4336
St William Sch 4125 Saint Williams Ave, Cincinnati 45205 Jennifer O'Brien	PK-8	242 14	513/471-2989 Fax 513/471-8226
St Xavier High Sch 600 W North Bend Rd, Cincinnati 45224 Terrence Tyrrell	9-12	1,557	513/761-7600 Fax 513/761-3811
Summit Country Day Sch 2161 Grandin Rd, Cincinnati 45208 Mike Johnson \ John Thornburg	PK-12	957	513/871-4700 Fax 513/871-6558
Ursuline Academy 5535 Pfeiffer Rd, Cincinnati 45242 Thomas Barhorst	9-12	660 50	513/791-5791 Fax 513/791-5802

HAMILTON PRIVATE SCHOOLS

Private Schs..Principal	Grd	Prgm	Enr/#Cls SN	Phone
Aldersgate Christian Academy 1810 Young St, Cincinnati 45202 Tim Makcen	K-12		137 11	513/763-6655 Fax 513/763-6643
Beautiful Savior Luth Sch 11981 Pippin Rd, Cincinnati 45231 Daniel Markgraf	PK-8		113 5	513/825-2290 Fax 513/825-2172
Bethany Sch 555 Albion Ave, Cincinnati 45246 David Gould	K-8		250 18	513/771-7462 Fax 513/771-2292
Central Baptist Academy 7645 Winton Rd, Cincinnati 45224 Angela Helton	K-8		102 9	513/521-5481 Fax 513/728-3682
Chca-Edyth B Lindner Elem Sch 11312 Snider Rd, Cincinnati 45249 Steve Sideris	PK-4		500	513/247-0900 Fax 513/247-0125
Chca-Founders Campus Upper Sch 11300 Snider Rd, Cincinnati 45249 Nancy Buckman	5-8		375	513/247-0900 Fax 513/247-9362
Chca-Martha S Lindner High Sch 11525 Snider Rd, Cincinnati 45249 Dean Nicholas	9-12		425 25	513/247-0900 Fax 513/247-0982
Chca-Otto Armleder Mem Ed Ctr 140 W 9th St, Cincinnati 45202 Cammie Montgomery	PK-6		139	513/721-2422 Fax 513/721-3300
Children's Home Sch 5050 Madison Rd, Cincinnati 45227 Jasmin Madison	Spec		100 10	513/272-2800 Fax 513/272-2807
Cincinnati Country Day Sch 6905 Given Rd, Cincinnati 45243 Anthony Jaccaci	PK-12		870	513/561-7298 Fax 513/527-7600
Cincinnati Hebrew Day Sch 2222 Losantiville Ave, Cincinnati 45237 Yuval Kernerman	PK-8		200 15	513/351-7777 Fax 513/351-7794
Cincinnati Junior Academy 3898 Clifton Ave, Cincinnati 45220 Kimberly Hollie	K-8		67 4	513/751-1255 Fax 513/751-1224
Cincinnati Waldorf Sch 6743 Chestnut St, Cincinnati 45227 Christine Masur	PK-12		350 13	513/541-0220 Fax 513/541-3586
DePaul Cristo Rey High Sch 1133 Clifton Hills Ave, Cincinnati 45220 Paul Ebert	9-12		89	513/861-0600
Eden Grove Academy 6277 Collegevue Pl, Cincinnati 45224 Chad Harville	PK-8		128 10	513/542-0643 Fax 513/681-3450
Immaculate Conception Academy 4510 Floral Ave, Norwood 45212 William Jenkins	K-12		166	513/731-0154 Fax 513/731-8864
Linden Grove Sch 4122 Myrtle Ave, Cincinnati 45236 Kristin Tennyson	Spec		40 12	513/984-2215 Fax 513/984-2272
Miami Valley Christian Academy 6830 School St, Cincinnati 45244 Jody Hilsher	PK-12		350	513/272-6822 Fax 513/272-3711
New School Montessori 3 Burton Woods Ln, Cincinnati 45229 Jeff Groh	PK-6		145 7	513/281-7999 Fax 513/281-7996
Rockwern Academy 8401 Montgomery Rd, Cincinnati 45236 Dr David Finell	PK-8		140 30	513/984-3770 Fax 513/984-3787
Schilling Sch-Gifted Children 8100 Cornell Rd, Cincinnati 45249 Sandra Schilling	K-12		45 11	513/489-8940 Fax 513/489-8941
Seven Hills Sch-Doherty Campus 2726 Johnstone Pl, Cincinnati 45206 Chris Garten	PK-5		200 40	513/272-5180 Fax 513/728-2352
Springer School and Center 2121 Madison Rd, Cincinnati 45208 Eldrich Carr	Spec		192 16	513/871-6081 Fax 513/871-6428
SS Peter & Paul Academy 231 Clark Rd, Cincinnati 45215 Glenda Donnelly	K-8		120	513/761-7772 Fax 513/761-0652
St Aloysius Educational Center 4721 Reading Rd, Cincinnati 45237 Linda Hart	Spec		80	513/242-7600 Fax 513/242-2845
St Edmund Campion Academy 6000 Murray Ave, Cincinnati 45227 Dr Arthur Kunath	1-12		40	513/871-0331
The Seven Hills Sch 5400 Red Bank Rd, Cincinnati 45227 Tracy Murch \ Bill Waskowitz \ Matt Bolton	PK-12		1,017	513/728-2400 Fax 513/728-2409
Winton Place Baptist Academy 4600 N Edgewood Ave, Cincinnati 45232 Shawn Duncan	PK-12		19 5	513/681-9480
Xavier Univ Montessori Lab Sch 1024 Dana Ave, Cincinnati 45229 Rosemary Quaranta	PK-8	G	130 2	513/745-3424 Fax 513/745-4378

1	Superintendent	8	Curric/Instruct K-12	19	Chief Financial Officer	29	Family/Consumer Science	39	Social Studies K-12	49	English/Lang Arts Elem	59	Special Education Elem	69	Academic Assessment
2	Bus/Finance/Purchasing	9	Curric/Instruct Elem	20	Art K-12	30	Adult Education	40	Social Studies Elem	50	English/Lang Arts Sec	60	Special Education Sec	70	Research/Development
3	Buildings And Grounds	10	Curric/Instruct Sec	21	Art Elem	31	Career/Sch-to-Work K-12	41	Social Studies Sec	51	Reading K-12	61	Foreign/World Lang K-12	71	Public Information
4	Food Service	11	Federal Program	22	Art Sec	32	Career/Sch-to-Work Elem	42	Science K-12	52	Reading Elem	62	Foreign/World Lang Elem	72	Summer School
5	Transportation	12	Title I	23	Music K-12	33	Career/Sch-to-Work Sec	43	Science Elem	53	Reading Sec	63	Foreign/World Lang Sec	73	Instructional Tech
6	Athletic	13	Title V	24	Music Elem	34	Early Childhood Ed	44	Science Sec	54	Remedial Reading K-12	64	Religious Education K-12	74	Inservice Training
7	Health Services	15	Asst Superintendent	25	Music Sec	35	Health/Phys Education	45	Math K-12	55	Remedial Reading Elem	65	Religious Education Elem	75	Marketing/Distributive
		16	Instructional Media Svcs	26	Business Education	36	Guidance Services K-12	46	Math Elem	56	Remedial Reading Sec	66	Religious Education Sec	76	Info Systems
		17	Chief Operations Officer	27	Career & Tech Ed	37	Guidance Services Elem	47	Math Sec	57	Bilingual/ELL	67	School Board President	77	Psychological Assess
		18	Chief Academic Officer	28	Technology Education	38	Guidance Services Sec	48	English/Lang Arts Elem	58	Special Education K-12	68	Teacher Personnel	78	Affirmative Action

Ohio School Directory

Hancock County

HAMILTON REGIONAL CENTERS

Hamilton County ESC PID: 04499673
11083 Hamilton Ave, Cincinnati 45231
513/674-4200
Fax 513/742-8339

Dave Distel 1
Greg Ferris 3
Chad Hilliker 15
Connie Reyes-Rao 57
Greg Hester 68
Arline Pique 73
Don Rabe 2
Karen Austin 8,74
Kathy Tirey 34
Sally Demmler 58,275
Rob Kovacs 71

State Support Team-Region 13 PID: 02228337
11083 Hamilton Ave, Cincinnati 45231
513/674-4200
Fax 513/742-8875

Tracy Atchison 1
Vikki Miller 34

HANCOCK COUNTY

HANCOCK COUNTY SCHOOLS

Hancock Co Ed Service Center PID: 00810154
7746 County Road 140 Unit A, Findlay 45840
419/422-7525
Fax 419/422-8766

Larry Busdeker 1,11
Tim Bodnarik 8,74
Donna Losiewicz 34
Greg Spiess 2
Dana Helfrich 16,73
Marlene North 58

County Schs..Principal	Grd	Prgm	Enr/#Cls	SN	
Blanchard Valley Sch 1700 E Sandusky St, Findlay 45840 Tanya Pike	Spec	AGV	72 10		419/422-8173 Fax 419/425-7055 🇫 🇹
Hancock Co MH Unit 7746 County Road 140, Findlay 45840 Larry Busdeker	Spec		25 1		419/422-7525 Fax 419/422-8766
Hancock Co SBH Unit 7746 County Road 140, Findlay 45840 Marlene North	Spec		150 1		419/422-7525 Fax 419/422-8766

HANCOCK PUBLIC SCHOOLS

Arcadia Local School Dist PID: 00809739
19033 State Route 12, Arcadia 44804
419/894-6431
Fax 419/894-6970

Schools: 1 \ *Teachers:* 38 \ *Students:* 575 \ *Special Ed Students:* 56 \ *College-Bound:* 60% \ *Ethnic:* Asian 2%, Hispanic 8%, Native American 1%, Caucasian 89% \ *Exp:* $301 (High) \ *Poverty:* 8% \ *Title I:* $55,010 \ *Special Education:* $110,000 \ *Open-Close:* 09/03 - 05/29

Bruce Kidder 1,11
Craig Recker 3*
Angie Stoner 12*
Pat Ramsey 38,69,83,85,88,270*
Ryan George 67
Tim Saltzman 91*
Angie Spridgeon 2
Bret Voges 5
Angie Trusty 16
Marlene North 58
Gregg McKee 73,95,286*

Public Schs..Principal	Grd	Prgm	Enr/#Cls	SN	
Arcadia Sch 19033 State Route 12, Arcadia 44804 Bill Dobbins \ Dave Golden	K-12	V	575 30	98%	419/894-6431

Arlington Local School Dist PID: 00809765
336 S Main St, Arlington 45814
419/365-5121
Fax 419/365-1282

Schools: 1 \ *Teachers:* 44 \ *Students:* 570 \ *Special Ed Students:* 102 \ *College-Bound:* 69% \ *Ethnic:* Hispanic 1%, Caucasian 99% \ *Exp:* $248 (Med) \ *Poverty:* 5% \ *Title I:* $44,819 \ *Special Education:* $107,000 \ *Open-Close:* 09/03 - 05/22 \ *DTBP:* $189 (High)

Kevin Haught 1,11,83,288
Tim Huston 3*
Dick Leonard 6*
Marybeth Hutcheson 31,38,79,88*
Clint Dillon 84,295*
Roy Swartz 2
Dawn Gault 4*
Scott Marcum 11,58*
Craig Durliat 67

Public Schs..Principal	Grd	Prgm	Enr/#Cls	SN	
Arlington Local Sch 336 S Main St, Arlington 45814 Scott Marcum \ Nate Sorg	K-12	V	570 48	42%	419/365-5121

Cory-Rawson Local School Dist PID: 00809791
3930 County Road 26, Rawson 45881
419/963-3415
Fax 419/963-4400

Schools: 2 \ *Teachers:* 44 \ *Students:* 550 \ *Special Ed Students:* 119 \ *College-Bound:* 39% \ *Ethnic:* Asian 1%, African American 2%, Hispanic 2%, Caucasian 95% \ *Exp:* $345 (High) \ *Poverty:* 8% \ *Title I:* $69,909 \ *Special Education:* $126,000 \ *Open-Close:* 09/03 - 05/29 \ *DTBP:* $172 (High)

Heath Huffman 1
Wayne Young 3,91*
Ben Smith 5
Melissa McFarland 8,11,36*
Michael Lampton 35,83,85*
Tina Bils 57*
Michael Quinlan 73,76,295*
Sheila Hausknecht 2
Kirsten Gast 4*
Caleb Scott 6
Beth Vorst 16,37*
Tracy Stockwell 54*
Deb Core 67
Liz Bock 88*

Public Schs..Principal	Grd	Prgm	Enr/#Cls	SN	
Cory-Rawson Elem Sch 3930 County Road 26, Rawson 45881 Ben Thiel	K-6		294 12		419/963-3415 Fax 419/963-7017
Cory-Rawson High Sch 3930 County Road 26, Rawson 45881 Jodi Gaietto	7-12		232 22	95%	419/963-2611 Fax 419/963-7017

Findlay City School Dist PID: 00809832
2019 Broad Ave, Findlay 45840
419/427-5487
Fax 419/425-8203

Schools: 15 \ *Teachers:* 346 \ *Students:* 6,000 \ *Special Ed Students:* 1,040 \ *LEP Students:* 114 \ *College-Bound:* 64% \ *Ethnic:* Asian 3%, African American 4%, Hispanic 9%, Caucasian 84% \ *Exp:* $336 (High) \ *Poverty:* 14% \ *Title I:* $1,251,158 \ *Special Education:* $1,237,000 \ *Open-Close:* 08/28 - 05/21 \ *DTBP:* $130 (High) \ 🇫

Edward Kurt 1,11
Dennis McPheron 3,91
John Dell 5
Rich Steiner 7,10,38,57,69,79,90,298
Stephanie Roth 9,34,35,85,270,273,280,288
Troy Roth 15,68,70,71,74,78
Pam Hamlin 34*
Michael Barnhart 2
Teresa Welty 4*
Nate Weihrauch 6*
Janice Panuto 8,18,83,88
Krista Miller 12,54,296*
Martin White 16,73,76,84,295
Kathy Young 58*

---

79 Student Personnel
80 Driver Ed/Safety
81 Gifted/Talented
82 Video Services
83 Substance Abuse Prev
84 Erate
85 AIDS Education
88 Alternative/At Risk
89 Multi-Cultural Curriculum
90 Social Work

91 Safety/Security
92 Magnet School
93 Parental Involvement
95 Tech Prep Program
97 Chief Information Officer
98 Chief Technology Officer
270 Character Education
271 Migrant Education
273 Teacher Mentor
274 Before/After Sch

275 Response To Intervention
277 Remedial Math K-12
280 Literacy Coach
285 STEM
286 Digital Learning
288 Common Core Standards
294 Accountability
295 Network System
296 Title II Programs
297 Webmaster

298 Grant Writer/Ptnrships
750 Chief Innovation Officer
751 Chief of Staff
752 Social Emotional Learning

Other School Types
Ⓐ = Alternative School
Ⓒ = Charter School
Ⓜ = Magnet School
Ⓨ = Year-Round School

School Programs
A = Alternative Program
G = Adult Classes
M = Magnet Program
T = Title I Schoolwide
V = Career & Tech Ed Programs

Social Media
🇫 = Facebook
🇹 = Twitter

New Schools are shaded
New Superintendents and Principals are bold
Personnel with email addresses are underscored

OH–97

Hancock County — Market Data Retrieval

Name	Page
Chris Aldrich	67
Amanda Byers	77*
Tiffani Murray	274*
Sara Sublett	69,90*
Judy Withrow	81,285
Rosemary Rooker	286*

Public Schs..Principal	Grd	Prgm	Enr/#Cls	SN	Phone	Fax
Bigelow Hill Intermediate Sch 300 Hillcrest Ave, Findlay 45840 Jennifer Theis	4-5	T	254 15	64%	419/425-8317	Fax 419/427-5456
Chamberlin Hill Interm Sch 600 W Yates Ave, Findlay 45840 Lyndsey Stephenson	3-5	T	323 12	36%	419/425-8328	Fax 419/427-5457
Donnell Middle Sch 301 Baldwin Ave, Findlay 45840 Don Williams	6-8	T	560	33%	419/425-8370	Fax 419/429-3764
© Findlay Digital Academy 1219 W Main Cross St Ste 101, Findlay 45840 Larry Grove	9-12	T	163		419/425-3598	Fax 419/425-3588
Findlay High Sch 1200 Broad Ave, Findlay 45840 Ryan Imke	9-12	V	1,858 70	27%	419/425-8289	Fax 419/427-5448
Findlay Learning Center 1100 Broad Ave, Findlay 45840 Victoria Swartz	K-12	T	75	60%	419/429-8938	Fax 419/427-5483
Glenwood Middle Sch 1715 N Main St, Findlay 45840 **Krista Miller**	6-8	T	556 30	43%	419/425-8373	Fax 419/429-3763
Jacobs Primary Sch 600 Jacobs Ave, Findlay 45840 **Kelly Wohlgamuth**	K-3	T	259 15	77%	419/425-8299	Fax 419/427-5458
Jefferson Primary Sch 204 Fairlawn Pl, Findlay 45840 Kim Plesec	K-2	T	322 12		419/425-8298	Fax 419/427-5459
Lincoln Elem Sch 200 W Lincoln St, Findlay 45840 Michael Scoles	K-5	T	319 36	59%	419/425-8310	Fax 419/427-5460
Millstream Career Center 1150 Broad Ave, Findlay 45840 Chris Renn	Voc		150		419/425-8277	Fax 419/420-3309
Northview Primary Sch 133 Lexington Ave, Findlay 45840 Eric Payne	K-3	T	322 17	45%	419/425-8290	Fax 419/427-5462
Washington Preschool 1100 Broad Ave, Findlay 45840 Kathy Young	PK-PK	T	224	38%	419/425-8231	
Whittier Primary Sch 733 Wyandot St, Findlay 45840 Kelly Stahl	K-2	T	315 16	29%	419/425-8358	Fax 419/427-5464
Wilson Vance Intermediate Sch 610 Bristol Dr, Findlay 45840 Matthew Best	3-5	T	318 17	25%	419/425-8332	Fax 419/427-5465

● **Liberty-Benton Local Sch Dist** PID: 00810013 419/422-8526
9190 County Road 9, Findlay 45840   Fax 419/422-5108

Schools: 3 \ *Teachers:* 83 \ *Students:* 1,242 \ *Special Ed Students:* 150 \ *LEP Students:* 3 \ *College-Bound:* 69% \ *Ethnic:* Asian 2%, African American 1%, Hispanic 6%, Caucasian 91% \ *Exp:* $183 (Low) \ *Poverty:* 6% \ *Title I:* $97,414 \ *Special Education:* $215,000 \ *Open-Close:* 09/03 - 05/29 \ *DTBP:* $162 (High)

Name	Page	Name	Page
Mark Kowalski	1	Lisa Dobbins	2
Ken Bertke	3	Scott Garlock	6*
Brian Burkett	9,57*	Ken Hortsman	11*
Alida Hause	16*	Tracie Herr	35,36,69,83,88*
A Granger	67	Alvin Trusty	73,295*
Brenda Frankart	270,273*		

Public Schs..Principal	Grd	Prgm	Enr/#Cls	SN	Phone	Fax
Liberty-Benton Elem Sch 9150 State Rte 12, Findlay 45840 Brian Burkett	K-5		661 26	23%	419/422-9161	Fax 419/420-9237
Liberty-Benton High Sch 9190 County Road 9, Findlay 45840 Brenda Frankart	9-12	AV	430 27	14%	419/424-5351	Fax 419/424-5352
Liberty-Benton Middle Sch 9050 W State Route 12, Findlay 45840 Kyle Leatherman	6-8		361 31	22%	419/422-9166	Fax 419/424-5350

● **McComb Local School Dist** PID: 00810049 419/293-3979
328 S Todd St, Mc Comb 45858   Fax 419/293-2412

Schools: 3 \ *Teachers:* 49 \ *Students:* 700 \ *Special Ed Students:* 92 \ *LEP Students:* 24 \ *College-Bound:* 49% \ *Ethnic:* Asian 1%, African American 1%, Hispanic 12%, Caucasian 86% \ *Exp:* $410 (High) \ *Poverty:* 9% \ *Title I:* $101,368 \ *Special Education:* $142,000 \ *Open-Close:* 09/03 - 05/29 \ *DTBP:* $172 (High)

Name	Page	Name	Page
Tony Fenstermaker	1,11	Linda Clymer	2,296,298
Luke Ewing	3,5*	Steve Rider	4*
Shawn Woolf	6*	Roberta Nichols	16,82*
Heather Bell	37	Lisa Mansfield	67
Connie Cawley	73,295*	Toni Hassan	285*

Public Schs..Principal	Grd	Prgm	Enr/#Cls	SN	Phone	Fax
McComb Elem Sch 328 S Todd St, Mc Comb 45858 Dr Joyce Jackson	PK-6	T	356 21	74%	419/293-3286	Fax 419/293-3107
McComb High Sch 328 S Todd St, Mc Comb 45858 Jeremy Herr	9-12	V	226 20		419/293-3853	Fax 419/293-3107
McComb Middle Sch 328 S Todd St, Mc Comb 45858 Jeremy Herr	7-8		107 12		419/293-3853	Fax 419/293-3107

● **Riverdale Local School Dist** PID: 00810348 419/694-4994
20613 State Route 37, Mt Blanchard 45867   Fax 419/694-6465

Schools: 3 \ *Teachers:* 72 \ *Students:* 1,030 \ *Special Ed Students:* 177 \ *LEP Students:* 3 \ *College-Bound:* 49% \ *Ethnic:* African American 1%, Hispanic 2%, Caucasian 97% \ *Exp:* $336 (High) \ *Poverty:* 13% \ *Title I:* $187,414 \ *Special Education:* $184,000 \ *Open-Close:* 08/21 - 05/22 \ *DTBP:* $176 (High)

Name	Page	Name	Page
Jeffrey Young	1,11	Jodie Ribley	2
Duane Brodman	3	Mike Rickle	3
Dave Hankins	5*	Craig Taylor	6*
Julie Greer	9,11*	Dan Evans	10*
Tessa Swavel	37,83*	Nicole Williams	38
Michelle Courtad	67	John Demotte	73*
Deb Metzger	76,295		

Public Schs..Principal	Grd	Prgm	Enr/#Cls	SN	Phone	Fax
Riverdale Elem Sch 20613 State Route 37, Mt Blanchard 45867 Julie Greer	K-5		471 21		419/694-2211	Fax 419/694-8005
Riverdale Local High Sch 20613 State Route 37, Mt Blanchard 45867 Dan Evans	9-12	V	306 16	99%	419/694-2211	Fax 419/694-5008
Riverdale Middle Sch 20613 State Route 37, Mt Blanchard 45867 Dan Evans	6-8		246 25		419/694-2211	Fax 419/694-5008

Code	Description	Code	Description	Code	Description	Code	Description	Code	Description	Code	Description	Code	Description
1	Superintendent	8	Curric/Instruct K-12	19	Chief Financial Officer	29	Family/Consumer Science	39	Social Studies K-12	49	English/Lang Arts Elem	59	Special Education Elem	69	Academic Assessment
2	Bus/Finance/Purchasing	9	Curric/Instruct Elem	20	Art K-12	30	Adult Education	40	Social Studies Elem	50	English/Lang Arts Sec	60	Special Education Sec	70	Research/Development
3	Buildings And Grounds	10	Curric/Instruct Sec	21	Art Elem	31	Career/Sch-to-Work K-12	41	Social Studies Sec	51	Reading K-12	61	Foreign/World Lang K-12	71	Public Information
4	Food Service	11	Federal Program	22	Art Sec	32	Career/Sch-to-Work Elem	42	Science K-12	52	Reading Elem	62	Foreign/World Lang Elem	72	Summer School
5	Transportation	12	Title I	23	Music K-12	33	Career/Sch-to-Work Sec	43	Science Elem	53	Reading Sec	63	Foreign/World Lang Sec	73	Instructional Tech
6	Athletic	13	Title V	24	Music Elem	34	Early Childhood Ed	44	Science Sec	54	Remedial Reading K-12	64	Religious Education K-12	74	Inservice Training
7	Health Services	14	Asst Superintendent	25	Music Sec	35	Health/Phys Education	45	Math K-12	55	Remedial Reading Elem	65	Religious Education Elem	75	Marketing/Distributive
		15	Instructional Media Svcs	26	Business Education	36	Guidance Services K-12	46	Math Elem	56	Remedial Reading Sec	66	Religious Education Sec	76	Info Systems
		16	Chief Operations Officer	27	Career & Tech Ed	37	Guidance Services Elem	47	Math Sec	57	Bilingual/ELL	67	School Board President	77	Psychological Assess
		17	Chief Academic Officer	28	Technology Education	38	Guidance Services Sec	48	English/Lang Arts K-12	58	Special Education K-12	68	Teacher Personnel	78	Affirmative Action

Ohio School Directory — Hardin County

● Van Buren Local School Dist PID: 00810087   419/299-3578
217 S Main St, Van Buren 45889

Schools: 3 \ **Teachers:** 69 \ **Students:** 1,080 \ **Special Ed Students:** 98 \ **LEP Students:** 16 \ **College-Bound:** 72% \ **Ethnic:** Asian 2%, Hispanic 3%, Caucasian 94% \ **Exp:** $191 (Low) \ **Poverty:** 5% \ **Title I:** $63,032 \ **Special Education:** $171,000 \ **Open-Close:** 09/03 - 05/28 \ **DTBP:** $164 (High)

Tim Myers 1	Alex Binger 2	
Jon Kelley 3,5*	Brianna Reinhard 4	
Justin Slauterbeck 6*	Cassie Schaffer 8,11,69,88,286,288	
Michael Newcomer 9,11,52,55,296*	Kevin Shoup 11,273*	
Chelsea Burden 16,82*	Martin Zender 38*	
Anne Bryan 57*	Jim Griffith 67	
Chris Kniss 73*	Robert Smith 73,76,295	

Public Schs..Principal	Grd	Prgm	Enr/#Cls	SN	
Van Buren Elem Sch 301 S Main St, Van Buren 45889 Michael Newcomer	K-5	V	453 24	18%	419/299-3416 Fax 419/299-3566
Van Buren High Sch 217 S Main St, Van Buren 45889 Kevin Shoup	9-12	V	348 20	26%	419/299-3384 Fax 419/299-3340
Van Buren Middle Sch 217 S Main St, Van Buren 45889 Jay Clark	6-8		272 15		419/299-3384 Fax 419/299-3340

● Vanlue Local School Dist PID: 00810116   419/387-7724
301 S East St, Vanlue 45890   Fax 419/387-7722

Schools: 1 \ **Teachers:** 20 \ **Students:** 180 \ **Special Ed Students:** 41 \ **College-Bound:** 71% \ **Ethnic:** African American 2%, Hispanic 3%, Caucasian 95% \ **Exp:** $211 (Med) \ **Poverty:** 8% \ **Title I:** $27,505 \ **Special Education:** $59,000 \ **Open-Close:** 09/02 - 05/27 \ **DTBP:** $181 (High) \ ▪

Traci Conley 1	Tracy Hiller 2,11
Cj Couch 3,5*	Kari King 4*
Jeremy Kloepfer 6	Robyn Hudley 8*
Heather Nielson 12,54*	Samuel McCoy 16,73,76,295
Nikki Smith 36,69*	Andrea Bower 59*
Jonathon Thomas 67	Lindy Devooght 82*

Public Schs..Principal	Grd	Prgm	Enr/#Cls	SN	
Vanlue Local Sch 301 S East St, Vanlue 45890 Robyn Hudley	K-12		180 30	67%	419/387-7724

HANCOCK CATHOLIC SCHOOLS

● Diocese of Toledo Ed Office PID: 00818297
Listing includes only schools located in this county. See District Index for location of Diocesan Offices.

Catholic Schs..Principal	Grd	Prgm	Enr/#Cls	SN	
St Michael Sch 723 Sutton Pl, Findlay 45840 Amy Holzwart	PK-8		498 22		419/423-2738 Fax 419/423-2720

HANCOCK PRIVATE SCHOOLS

Private Schs..Principal	Grd	Prgm	Enr/#Cls	SN	
Heritage Christian Sch 2000 Broad Ave, Findlay 45840 Will Long	PK-12		80 20		419/424-9511 ▪
Trinity Lutheran Sch 105 Allen St, Jenera 45841 Mr Strong	PK-8		63 5		419/326-4685

HARDIN COUNTY

HARDIN COUNTY SCHOOLS

County Schs..Principal	Grd	Prgm	Enr/#Cls	SN	
Little River Pre-School 510 S Courtright St, Mc Guffey 45859 Lori Berger	Spec		30 8		419/757-3231 Fax 419/747-0135
Simon Kenton Sch 705 N Ida St, Kenton 43326 Kara Brown	Spec	G	115 4		419/674-4158 Fax 419/675-3274
Victory Garden Pre-School 560 Taylor St W, Mount Victory 43340 Jill Stover	Spec		40 1		937/354-2141 Fax 937/354-5099

HARDIN PUBLIC SCHOOLS

● ADA Exempted Village Sch Dist PID: 00810166   419/634-6421
725 W North Ave, Ada 45810   Fax 419/634-0311

Schools: 1 \ **Teachers:** 54 \ **Students:** 890 \ **Special Ed Students:** 109 \ **LEP Students:** 11 \ **College-Bound:** 53% \ **Ethnic:** Asian 1%, African American 2%, Hispanic 2%, Caucasian 95% \ **Exp:** $129 (Low) \ **Poverty:** 16% \ **Title I:** $208,681 \ **Special Education:** $147,000 \ **Open-Close:** 08/21 - 05/28 \ **DTBP:** $164 (High)

Meri Skilliter 1	Kim Light 2
Mike Lenhart 3,5*	Ann Hersey 4*
Eric Perkins 6	Marlene Vermillion 7*
Robin VanBuskirk 8,11,288*	Debbie Poling 12*
Ben Thaxton 13,73,84,295*	Chanda Smith 16,82*
Sheila Hughes 58	Dr Amy Mullins 67
Erinn Prater 69,83,88,270*	Barth Montel 286

Public Schs..Principal	Grd	Prgm	Enr/#Cls	SN	
ADA Sch 725 W North Ave, Ada 45810 Ben Thaxton \ Dan Lee	K-12	V	890 45	74%	419/634-6421

Harrison County

Market Data Retrieval

- **Hardin Northern Local Sch Dist** PID: 00810192   419/759-2331
  11589 State Route 81, Dola 45835   Fax 419/759-2581

Schools: 2 \ *Teachers:* 35 \ *Students:* 405 \ *Special Ed Students:* 76 \ *College-Bound:* 52% \ *Ethnic:* Hispanic 1%, Caucasian 98% \ *Exp:* $321 (High) \ *Poverty:* 14% \ *Title I:* $90,930 \ *Special Education:* $82,000 \ *Open-Close:* 08/15 - 05/22 \ *DTBP:* $176 (High)

Dr Jeff Price	1	Wes Potter		2,11
Brian Webb	3*	Andy Ayers		4*
Teressa Combs	5,71	Carla Stevenson		7*
John Andrew Wilson	8,57,69	Clare Poling		12*
Darlene Wilson	16*	Andrew Cano		58*
Michelle Obenour	67	Andy Emerine		73,295*
Brett Halsey	288*			

Public Schs..Principal	Grd	Prgm	Enr/#Cls	SN	
Hardin Northern Elem Sch 11589 State Route 81, Dola 45835 Brett Halsey	PK-6	T	225 14		419/759-3158
Hardin Northern High Sch 11589 State Route 81, Dola 45835 Andrew Cano	7-12		180 21	90%	419/759-3515 Fax 419/715-2591

- **Kenton City School Dist** PID: 00810221   419/673-0775
  222 W Carrol St, Kenton 43326   Fax 419/673-3180

Schools: 3 \ *Teachers:* 120 \ *Students:* 1,848 \ *Special Ed Students:* 342 \ *College-Bound:* 42% \ *Ethnic:* African American 1%, Hispanic 4%, Caucasian 95% \ *Exp:* $295 (Med) \ *Poverty:* 23% \ *Title I:* $704,555 \ *Special Education:* $340,000 \ *Open-Close:* 08/15 - 05/25 \ *DTBP:* $169 (High) \

Jennifer Penczarski	1	Tracy Hiller		2,11,91,296
Doug Comstock	3	Regina Camstock		4*
Bryan Clawson	5	Joseph Day		6*
Jodi Cole	8,16,82,288*	Heather Hoppe		58*
Mark Push	67	Ryan Collins		73*
Amy Kohl	83*	Amy Cole		83*
Robin Bame	286*			

Public Schs..Principal	Grd	Prgm	Enr/#Cls	SN	
Kenton Elem Sch 631 Silver St, Kenton 43326 Angela Butterman	PK-6	T	1,070 12	63%	419/673-7248 Fax 419/675-0681
Kenton High Sch 200 Harding Ave, Kenton 43326 Chad Thrush	9-12	T	511 50	46%	419/673-1286 Fax 419/675-5200
Kenton Middle Sch 300 Oriental St, Kenton 43326 Kirk Cameron	7-8	T	267 26	51%	419/673-1237 Fax 419/673-1626

- **Ridgemont Local School Dist** PID: 00810312   937/354-2141
  560 Taylor St W, Mount Victory 43340   Fax 937/354-2194

Schools: 2 \ *Teachers:* 44 \ *Students:* 511 \ *Special Ed Students:* 67 \ *LEP Students:* 3 \ *College-Bound:* 43% \ *Ethnic:* African American 2%, Hispanic 2%, Native American: 1%, Caucasian 95% \ *Exp:* $185 (Low) \ *Poverty:* 13% \ *Title I:* $123,543 \ *Special Education:* $111,000 \ *Open-Close:* 08/15 - 05/22 \ *DTBP:* $183 (High)

Sally Henrick	1,11,57,83	Melissa Pollom		2
J Mac Geissinger	3,5*	Bev Wasserbeck		4*
Ernin Holycross	5	Stephanie Jolliss		27
Kim Hawk	31*	Greg Johnson		35*
Eric Hill	67	Tom Mustain		73,295*

Pam Robinson 273*

Public Schs..Principal	Grd	Prgm	Enr/#Cls	SN	
Ridgemont Jr Sr High Sch 162 E Hale St, Ridgeway 43345 Jill Stover	7-12	V	236 25		937/363-2701 Fax 937/363-2066
Ridgemont Local Sch 560 Taylor St W, Mount Victory 43340 Jill Stover	K-12	T	275 20		937/354-2141 Fax 937/354-5099

- **Upper Scioto Valley Local SD** PID: 00810398   419/757-3231
  510 S Courtright St, Mc Guffey 45859   Fax 419/757-0135

Schools: 1 \ *Teachers:* 35 \ *Students:* 450 \ *Special Ed Students:* 109 \ *LEP Students:* 5 \ *College-Bound:* 40% \ *Ethnic:* African American 1%, Hispanic 1%, Caucasian 98% \ *Exp:* $183 (Low) \ *Poverty:* 20% \ *Title I:* $215,039 \ *Special Education:* $141,000 \ *Open-Close:* 08/14 - 05/21 \ *DTBP:* $187 (High) \

Craig Hurley	1	Stacy Gratz		2
Logan Rolsten	3,5	Tiffany Daring		4*
Craig Hurley	8,12,58,270,273,288*	Michelle Underwood		16,31,36,69*
Marylynn Schumm	57	Barry Campbell		67
Drew Snow	73,295*			

Public Schs..Principal	Grd	Prgm	Enr/#Cls	SN	
Upper Scioto Valley Sch 510 S Courtright St, Mc Guffey 45859 Craig Hurley	K-12	T	450 60	98%	419/757-3231 Fax 419/757-0134

HARRISON COUNTY

HARRISON COUNTY SCHOOLS

County Schs..Principal	Grd	Prgm	Enr/#Cls	SN	
Harrison Co Developmental Pgrm 82480 Cadiz Jewett Rd, Cadiz 43907	Spec	G	33 4		740/942-2158 Fax 740/942-9066
© Lakeland Academy Community Sch 101 E Main St, Freeport 43973 Mindy Pittis	K-12		31		740/658-1042 Fax 740/658-1062

HARRISON PUBLIC SCHOOLS

- **Conotton Valley Union Local SD** PID: 00810491   740/269-2000
  21 Mound St, Sherrodsville 44675   Fax 740/269-7901

Schools: 2 \ *Teachers:* 26 \ *Students:* 402 \ *Special Ed Students:* 94 \ *LEP Students:* 3 \ *College-Bound:* 50% \ *Ethnic:* Hispanic 2%, Caucasian 98% \ *Exp:* $310 (High) \ *Poverty:* 14% \ *Title I:* $120,436 \ *Special Education:* $111,000 \ *Open-Close:* 08/27 - 05/22 \ *DTBP:* $177 (High)

Todd Herman	1,83	Denise Ketchum		2,294
Randy Robinson	3,4,5*	Dave DiDonato		6*
Stephanie Garrott	8,11*	Kelly Edwards		36,79*
Jenna Dress	58*	Lauren Hanstine		58*
Chris Bower	67	Keith Imes		73,295*
Jackie Burkhart	76	Michele Higgenbotham		79

1 Superintendent	8 Curric/Instruct K-12	19 Chief Financial Officer	29 Family/Consumer Science	39 Social Studies K-12	49 English/Lang Arts Elem	59 Special Education Elem	69 Academic Assessment
2 Bus/Finance/Purchasing	9 Curric/Instruct Elem	20 Art K-12	30 Adult Education	40 Social Studies Elem	50 English/Lang Arts Sec	60 Special Education Sec	70 Research/Development
3 Buildings And Grounds	10 Curric/Instruct Sec	21 Art Elem	31 Career/Sch-to-Work K-12	41 Social Studies Sec	51 Reading K-12	61 Foreign/World Lang K-12	71 Public Information
4 Food Service	11 Federal Program	22 Art Sec	32 Career/Sch-to-Work Elem	42 Science K-12	52 Reading Elem	62 Foreign/World Lang Elem	72 Summer School
5 Transportation	12 Title I	23 Music K-12	33 Career/Sch-to-Work Sec	43 Science Elem	53 Reading Sec	63 Foreign/World Lang Sec	73 Instructional Tech
6 Athletic	13 Title V	24 Music Elem	34 Early Childhood Ed	44 Science Sec	54 Remedial Reading K-12	64 Religious Education K-12	74 Inservice Training
7 Health Services	15 Asst Superintendent	25 Music Sec	35 Health/Phys Education	45 Math K-12	55 Remedial Reading Elem	65 Religious Education Elem	75 Marketing/Distributive
	16 Instructional Media Svcs	26 Business Education	36 Guidance Services K-12	46 Math Elem	56 Remedial Reading Sec	66 Religious Education Sec	76 Info Systems
	17 Chief Operations Officer	27 Career & Tech Ed	37 Guidance Services Elem	47 Math Sec	57 Bilingual/ELL	67 School Board President	77 Psychological Assess
	18 Chief Academic Officer	28 Technology Education	38 Guidance Services Sec	48 English/Lang Arts K-12	58 Special Education K-12	68 Teacher Personnel	78 Affirmative Action

Ohio School Directory

Henry County

Keith Imes 84
Matt Grezlik 91*

Public Schs..Principal	Grd	Prgm	Enr/#Cls	SN	
Conotton Valley Elem Sch 7205 Cumberland Rd SW, Bowerston 44695 Mike Wright	PK-5		200 11		740/269-2141 Fax 740/269-4405
Conotton Valley High Sch 7205 Cumberland Rd SW, Bowerston 44695 Danielle Caldwell	6-12	AT	210 22	44%	740/269-2711 Fax 740/269-4405

● **Harrison Hills City Sch Dist** PID: 00810544 740/942-7800
100 Huskies Way, Cadiz 43907 Fax 740/942-7812

Schools: 3 \ **Teachers:** 77 \ **Students:** 1,600 \ **Special Ed Students:** 292 \ **College-Bound:** 50% \ **Ethnic:** African American 2%, Caucasian 98% \ **Exp:** $168 (Low) \ **Poverty:** 19% \ **Title I:** $579,732 \ **Special Education:** $428,000 \ **Open-Close:** 08/26 - 05/27 \ **DTBP:** $174 (High) \

Dana Snider 1
Michael Saffell 3,4,5,91
Duran Morgan 8,11,58,88,275,288,294
Keith Eddy 73,76,84,295
Ken Parker 83*
Roxane Harding 2,298
Raymond Hibbs 6*
Deborah Kenny 67
Jenny Gibson 79
Rob Richards 286*

Public Schs..Principal	Grd	Prgm	Enr/#Cls	SN	
Harrison Centrl Jr Sr High Sch 100 Huskies Way, Cadiz 43907 Ken Parker	7-12	TV	619 81	47%	740/942-7700 Fax 740/942-7705
Harrison East Elem Sch 410 Normal St, Hopedale 43976 Jennifer Birney	PK-6	T	551 29	58%	740/942-7550 Fax 740/942-7554
Harrison North Elem Sch 322 W Main St, Scio 43988 Mike Saffell	PK-6	T	309 20	66%	740/942-7500 Fax 740/942-7505

HARRISON PRIVATE SCHOOLS

Private Schs..Principal	Grd	Prgm	Enr/#Cls	SN	
Antrim Mennonite Sch 20360 Cadiz Rd, Freeport 43973 Titus Lapp	K-12		66		740/489-5161

HENRY COUNTY

HENRY PUBLIC SCHOOLS

● **Holgate Local School Dist** PID: 00810685 419/264-5141
801 Joe E Brown Ave, Holgate 43527 Fax 419/264-1965

Schools: 1 \ **Teachers:** 36 \ **Students:** 470 \ **Special Ed Students:** 45 \ **College-Bound:** 52% \ **Ethnic:** Hispanic 9%, Caucasian 91% \ **Exp:** $245 (Med) \ **Poverty:** 9% \ **Title I:** $44,696 \ **Special Education:** $93,000 \ **Open-Close:** 08/21 - 05/21 \ **DTBP:** $110 (High)

Kelly Meyers 1
Lori Clady 4*
Diane Nicholason 7*
Kent Seeman 2
Richard Finley 6*
Beth Peck 8,31,36,69,83*

Laura Young 9*
Greg Thomas 67
Susan Hall 274*
Brian Hughes 10,11*
Julie Schroeder 273*
C J Richardson 295*

Public Schs..Principal	Grd	Prgm	Enr/#Cls	SN	
Holgate Sch 801 Joe E Brown Ave, Holgate 43527 **Brian Hughes** \ Laura Young	K-12		470 30	64%	419/264-5141

● **Liberty Center Local Sch Dist** PID: 00810714 419/533-5011
100 Tiger Trl, Liberty CTR 43532 Fax 419/533-5036

Schools: 3 \ **Teachers:** 69 \ **Students:** 1,174 \ **Special Ed Students:** 155 \ **LEP Students:** 5 \ **College-Bound:** 63% \ **Ethnic:** Asian 1%, Hispanic 8%, Caucasian 91% \ **Exp:** $356 (High) \ **Poverty:** 6% \ **Title I:** $118,042 \ **Open-Close:** 08/21 - 05/20 \ **DTBP:** $171 (High)

Richard Peters 1
Clarence Weirauch 3
Sheri Stacey 5
Brandon Readshaw 27*
Jan Dishop 51,54*
Neil Carter 67
Amanda Voss 77
Brett Green 286*
Janell Buenger 2,19
Donna Eickholt 4*
Kaleb Puhlman 6*
Pam Righi 37*
Kimberly Kamelesky 58
Trevor Hug 73,76*
Stacey Bowers 285
Nick Mariano 298*

Public Schs..Principal	Grd	Prgm	Enr/#Cls	SN	
Liberty Center Elem Sch 100 Tiger Trl, Liberty CTR 43532 Allison Postl	K-4	A	353 30		419/533-2604 Fax 419/533-1205
Liberty Center High Sch 100 Tiger Trl, Liberty CTR 43532 Larry Black	9-12		346 30	99%	419/533-6641 Fax 419/533-1021
Liberty Center Middle Sch 100 Tiger Trl, Liberty CTR 43532 Nick Mariano	5-8	V	332		419/533-0020

● **Napoleon Area City School Dist** PID: 00810740 419/599-7015
701 Briarheath Ave Ste 108, Napoleon 43545 Fax 419/599-7035

Schools: 3 \ **Teachers:** 106 \ **Students:** 1,700 \ **Special Ed Students:** 350 \ **LEP Students:** 31 \ **College-Bound:** 56% \ **Ethnic:** Asian 1%, African American 1%, Hispanic 11%, Caucasian 87% \ **Exp:** $235 (Med) \ **Poverty:** 11% \ **Title I:** $341,283 \ **Open-Close:** 08/22 - 05/22 \ **DTBP:** $185 (High)

Dr Steve Fogo 1,11
Cory Niekamp 3
Jeff Nicely 5
Wendy Nashu 8,69,288,296
Jared Rex 73,84,286,295
Mike Bostleman 2
Jennifer Conner 4
Andy Ham 6
Ty Otto 67
Brett Ziegler 88*

Public Schs..Principal	Grd	Prgm	Enr/#Cls	SN	
Napoleon Elem Sch 3-6 725 Westmoreland Ave, Napoleon 43545 Adam Niese	3-6	T	518 15	48%	419/592-6991 Fax 419/599-7638
Napoleon Elem Sch PK-2 725 Westmoreland Ave, Napoleon 43545 Matt Dietrich	PK-2		518 11		419/592-6991 Fax 419/599-7638
Napoleon Jr Sr High Sch 701 Briarheath Ave Ste 23, Napoleon 43545 Ryan Wilde	7-12		876 40	36%	419/599-1050 Fax 419/599-8537

Highland County

Market Data Retrieval

- **Patrick Henry Local Sch Dist** PID: 00810817
  6900 State Route 18, Hamler 43524
  419/274-5451
  Fax 877/275-8939

Schools: 3 \ **Teachers:** 73 \ **Students:** 855 \ **Special Ed Students:** 136 \ **LEP Students:** 3 \ **College-Bound:** 40% \ **Ethnic:** Asian 1%, Hispanic 10%, Caucasian 89% \ **Exp:** $309 (High) \ **Poverty:** 10% \ **Title I:** $136,407 \ **Special Education:** $206,000 \ **Open-Close:** 08/21 - 05/22 \ **DTBP:** $171 (High)

Joshua Biederstedt 1	Breanna Snyder 2,11,19
Mike Meyer 3,5	Katie Yarnell 4*
Ben George 6*	Michael Knueven 67
Dustin Ruffell 73,295*	Allison Ludeman 79

Public Schs..Principal	Grd	Prgm	Enr/#Cls	SN	
Patrick Henry Elem Sch E076 County Road 7, Hamler 43524 Bryan Hieber	K-4	T	330 15		419/274-3015
Patrick Henry High Sch 6900 State Route 18, Hamler 43524 Josh Biederstedt	9-12	T	249 40	99%	419/274-3015
Patrick Henry Middle Sch E050 County Road 7, Hamler 43524 Kyle Lacy	5-8	T	270 20		419/274-3015 Fax 419/274-1890

HENRY CATHOLIC SCHOOLS

- **Diocese of Toledo Ed Office** PID: 00818297
  Listing includes only schools located in this county. See District Index for location of Diocesan Offices.

Catholic Schs..Principal	Grd	Prgm	Enr/#Cls	SN	
St Augustine Sch 722 Monroe St, Napoleon 43545 James George	PK-8		60 8		419/592-3641

HENRY PRIVATE SCHOOLS

Private Schs..Principal	Grd	Prgm	Enr/#Cls	SN	
St John Lutheran Sch 16035 County Road U, Napoleon 43545 Charles Kramer	PK-8		86 6		419/598-8702 Fax 419/598-8518
St Paul Lutheran Sch 1075 Glenwood Ave, Napoleon 43545 Julie Bourgeois	PK-8		242 11		419/592-5536

HIGHLAND COUNTY

HIGHLAND COUNTY SCHOOLS

County Schs..Principal	Grd	Prgm	Enr/#Cls	SN	
Highland Co Pre-School Unit 8919 US Highway 50, Hillsboro 45133 Suzie Janasov	Spec		24 3		937/393-4237 Fax 937/393-5871
Hills & Dales Training Center 8919 US Highway 50, Hillsboro 45133 Chelsey Feeling	Spec		30 2		937/393-4237 Fax 937/393-5871

HIGHLAND PUBLIC SCHOOLS

- **Bright Local School Dist** PID: 00810910
  44 N High St, Mowrystown 45155
  937/442-3114
  Fax 937/442-6655

Schools: 2 \ **Teachers:** 42 \ **Students:** 700 \ **Special Ed Students:** 119 \ **College-Bound:** 34% \ **Ethnic:** African American 1%, Hispanic 1%, Native American: 1%, Caucasian 97% \ **Exp:** $250 (Med) \ **Poverty:** 23% \ **Title I:** $302,203 \ **Special Education:** $181,000 \ **Open-Close:** 08/16 - 05/21 \ **DTBP:** $186 (High)

Ted Downing 1,11,83	Lana Fairchild 2
Daniel Knoblauch 3*	Debbie Roberson 4
Lynn Decker 5*	John Combs 6*
Tami Ellis 10*	Travis Bogart 16,73*
Alison Oliver 36,69*	Lisa Beresford 58*
Angie Wright 67	Luke Stevenson 73,295*
Cathy Forsythe 76	

Public Schs..Principal	Grd	Prgm	Enr/#Cls	SN	
Bright Elem Sch 6100 Fair Ridge Rd, Hillsboro 45133 Michael Bick	PK-6	T	418 25	72%	937/927-7010 Fax 937/927-7015
Whiteoak Jr Sr High Sch 44 N High St, Mowrystown 45155 Brian Ruckel	7-12	TV	318 23	88%	937/442-2241 Fax 937/442-2111

- **Fairfield Local Sch Dist** PID: 00810958
  11611 State Route 771, Leesburg 45135
  937/780-2221
  Fax 937/780-6900

Schools: 3 \ **Teachers:** 53 \ **Students:** 950 \ **Special Ed Students:** 115 \ **College-Bound:** 63% \ **Ethnic:** Hispanic 1%, Caucasian 98% \ **Exp:** $249 (Med) \ **Poverty:** 15% \ **Title I:** $208,129 \ **Special Education:** $171,000 \ **Open-Close:** 08/15 - 05/21 \ **DTBP:** $171 (High)

Tim Dettwiller 1	Michael Morrow 2
Wyatt Sowders 3,5	Tony Williams 6
Kesia McCoy 8	Mindy Hamilton 11,58,288
Debborah Mangus 36,83	Rindy Matthews 67
Tim Crowder 73*	

Public Schs..Principal	Grd	Prgm	Enr/#Cls	SN	
Fairfield Local Elem Sch 11611 State Route 771, Leesburg 45135 Kathryn Streber	K-4	T	340 17	88%	937/780-2988 Fax 937/780-2841
Fairfield Local High Sch 11611 State Route 771, Leesburg 45135 Stephen Hackett	9-12	V	261 17		937/780-2966 Fax 937/780-2841
Fairfield Local Middle Sch 11611 State Route 771, Leesburg 45135 Stephen Hackett	5-8		307 13		937/780-2977 Fax 937/780-2841

1 Superintendent	8 Curric/Instruct K-12	19 Chief Financial Officer	29 Family/Consumer Science	39 Social Studies K-12	49 English/Lang Arts Elem	59 Special Education Elem	69 Academic Assessment
2 Bus/Finance/Purchasing	9 Curric/Instruct Elem	20 Art K-12	30 Adult Education	40 Social Studies Elem	50 English/Lang Arts Sec	60 Special Education Sec	70 Research/Development
3 Buildings And Grounds	10 Curric/Instruct Sec	21 Art Elem	31 Career/Sch-to-Work K-12	41 Social Studies Sec	51 Reading K-12	61 Foreign/World Lang K-12	71 Public Information
4 Food Service	11 Federal Program	22 Art Sec	32 Career/Sch-to-Work Elem	42 Science K-12	52 Reading Elem	62 Foreign/World Lang Elem	72 Summer School
5 Transportation	12 Title I	23 Music K-12	33 Career/Sch-to-Work Sec	43 Science Elem	53 Reading Sec	63 Foreign/World Lang Sec	73 Instructional Tech
6 Athletic	13 Title V	24 Music Elem	34 Early Childhood Ed	44 Science Sec	54 Remedial Reading K-12	64 Religious Education K-12	74 Inservice Training
7 Health Services	15 Asst Superintendent	25 Music Sec	35 Health/Phys Education	45 Math K-12	55 Remedial Reading Elem	65 Religious Education Elem	75 Marketing/Distributive
	16 Instructional Media Svcs	26 Business Education	36 Guidance Services K-12	46 Math Elem	56 Remedial Reading Sec	66 Religious Education Sec	76 Info Systems
	17 Chief Operations Officer	27 Career & Tech Ed	37 Guidance Services Elem	47 Math Sec	57 Bilingual/ELL	67 School Board President	77 Psychological Assess
	18 Chief Academic Officer	28 Technology Education	38 Guidance Services Sec	48 English/Lang Arts K-12	58 Special Education K-12	68 Teacher Personnel	78 Affirmative Action

Ohio School Directory   Highland County

● **Greenfield Exempted Village SD** PID: 00810984   937/981-2152
200 N 5th St, Greenfield 45123   Fax 937/981-4395

Schools: 5 \ **Teachers:** 110 \ **Students:** 2,250 \ **Special Ed Students:** 250 \ **College-Bound:** 30% \ **Ethnic:** African American 1%, Hispanic 1%, Caucasian 98% \ **Exp:** $412 (High) \ **Poverty:** 26% \ **Title I:** $914,831 \ **Special Education:** $720,000 \ **Open-Close:** 08/20 - 05/28 \ **DTBP:** $178 (High)

Quincey Gray 1	Joe Pat Smith 2
Jeff Pence 3,91	Dorothy Balzer 4*
Bradley George 5	Trevor Arnett 6
Katie Pryor 7*	Alisa Barrett 8*
Robert Schumm 8,69,72,81,288*	Jan Wilson 11,296*
Heather Dratwa ... 12,58,83,88,273,274	Jason Potts 27,31,75*
Melissa Murdock 37*	Dan Raike 38*
Eric Zint 67	Jesse Mitchell 73,76*
Matt Shelton 275*	

Public Schs..Principal	Grd	Prgm	Enr/#Cls	SN	
Buckskin Elem Sch 4297 Broadway St, South Salem 45681 Mike Shumate	K-5	T	201 15	60%	937/981-2673 Fax 937/981-1924
Greenfield Elem Sch 200 N 5th St, Greenfield 45123 Robert Schumm	PK-5	T	541 19	44%	937/981-3241 Fax 937/981-2521
Greenfield Middle Sch 200 N 5th St, Greenfield 45123 Ron Sexton	6-8	T	448 35	60%	937/981-2197 Fax 937/981-0417
McClain High Sch 200 N 5th St, Greenfield 45123 Jason Potts	9-12	ATV	544 36	46%	937/981-7731 Fax 937/981-4792
Rainsboro Elem Sch 12916 Barrett Mill Rd, Bainbridge 45612 Maggie Lyons	PK-5	T	185 13	54%	937/365-1271 Fax 937/365-2006

● **Hillsboro City School Dist** PID: 00811043   937/393-3475
39 Willetsville Pike, Hillsboro 45133   Fax 937/393-5841

Schools: 3 \ **Teachers:** 150 \ **Students:** 2,300 \ **Special Ed Students:** 379 \ **LEP Students:** 3 \ **College-Bound:** 53% \ **Ethnic:** African American 2%, Hispanic 2%, Caucasian 95% \ **Exp:** $249 (Med) \ **Poverty:** 25% \ **Title I:** $1,073,945 \ **Special Education:** $499,000 \ **Open-Close:** 08/14 - 05/19 \ **DTBP:** $191 (High)

Tim Davis 1	Ben Teeters 2
Dean Armstrong 3	Jessica Walker 4*
Ron Ward 5	Dave Dietrick 6*
Katie Greer 7*	Alicia Sellins 8,288*
Michelle Beumer 8	Diane Michael 11,57,68,69,74,88,296,298
Pam Sebastian 58	Bill Myers 67
Eric Hennison 73,98*	

Public Schs..Principal	Grd	Prgm	Enr/#Cls	SN	
Hillsboro Elem Sch 500 US Highway 62, Hillsboro 45133 Pam Hollon	PK-5	T	1,062 60	99%	937/393-3132 Fax 937/393-2418
Hillsboro High Sch 550 US Highway 62, Hillsboro 45133 Jason Snively	9-12	AT	700 40	97%	937/393-3485 Fax 937/393-5842
Hillsboro Middle Sch 550 US Highway 62, Hillsboro 45133 Kim Beam	6-8	T	579 42		937/393-9877 Fax 937/393-5842

● **Lynchburg-Clay Local Sch Dist** PID: 00811093   937/364-2338
301 E Pearl St, Lynchburg 45142   Fax 937/364-2339

Schools: 3 \ **Teachers:** 74 \ **Students:** 1,150 \ **Special Ed Students:** 201 \ **College-Bound:** 50% \ **Ethnic:** Hispanic 1%, Caucasian 99% \ **Exp:** $162 (Low) \ **Poverty:** 14% \ **Title I:** $279,364 \ **Special Education:** $188,000 \ **Open-Close:** 08/14 - 05/20 \ **DTBP:** $170 (High)

Brett Justice 1	Brad Barber 2,4
Richard Hawk 2,84	Barry Custis 3
Ryan Collins 5*	Mark Faust 6*
Angie Godby 8*	Dr Casey Smith 11,31,83,88,296,298*
Jo Heather Arnett 16,73*	Michelle Truman 35*
Whitney Lewis 36	Deborah Gilbert 37,69,77*
Holly Fouch 57*	Jim Walls 58*
Gary West 67	

Public Schs..Principal	Grd	Prgm	Enr/#Cls	SN	
ⓨ Lynchburg-Clay Elem Sch 6760 State Route 134, Lynchburg 45142 Angela Godby	PK-5	MT	538 33	46%	937/364-9119 Fax 937/364-8119
ⓨ Lynchburg-Clay High Sch 6762 State Route 134, Lynchburg 45142 Linda Hatten	9-12	AMV	326 40	39%	937/364-2250 Fax 937/364-6133
ⓨ Lynchburg-Clay Middle Sch 8250 State Route 134, Lynchburg 45142 Dr Casey Smith	6-8	MT	266 25	42%	937/364-2811 Fax 937/364-2159

HIGHLAND CATHOLIC SCHOOLS

● **Archdiocese Cincinnati Ed Off** PID: 00808096
Listing includes only schools located in this county. See District Index for location of Diocesan Offices.

Catholic Schs..Principal	Grd	Prgm	Enr/#Cls	SN	
St Mary Sch 212 S High St, Hillsboro 45133 Amanda Hunter	PK-4		55 4		937/840-9932

HIGHLAND PRIVATE SCHOOLS

Private Schs..Principal	Grd	Prgm	Enr/#Cls	SN	
Southern Ohio Christian Sch 13122 Stafford Rd, Leesburg 45135 Matt Stoll	K-8		30		937/780-5470

HIGHLAND REGIONAL CENTERS

● **State Support Team-Region 14** PID: 02228234   937/393-1904
5350 W New Market Rd, Hillsboro 45133   Fax 937/393-0496

Jeff Royalty 1

---

79 Student Personnel	91 Safety/Security	275 Response To Intervention	298 Grant Writer/Ptnrships	**School Programs**	**Social Media**
80 Driver Ed/Safety	92 Magnet School	277 Remedial Math K-12	750 Chief Innovation Officer	A = Alternative Program	
81 Gifted/Talented	93 Parental Involvement	280 Literacy Coach	751 Chief of Staff	G = Adult Classes	= Facebook
82 Video Services	95 Tech Prep Program	285 STEM	752 Social Emotional Learning	M = Magnet Program	
83 Substance Abuse Prev	97 Chief Infomation Officer	286 Digital Learning		T = Title I Schoolwide	= Twitter
84 Erate	98 Chief Technology Officer	288 Common Core Standards	**Other School Types**	V = Career & Tech Ed Programs	
85 AIDS Education	270 Accountability	294 Accountability	Ⓐ = Alternative School		
68 Alternative/At Risk	271 Migrant Education	295 Network System	Ⓒ = Charter School	New Schools are shaded	
69 Multi-Cultural Curriculum	273 Teacher Mentor	296 Title II Programs	Ⓜ = Magnet School	New Superintendents and Principals are bold	
90 Social Work	274 Before/After Sch	297 Webmaster	Ⓨ = Year-Round School	Personnel with email addresses are underscored	

Hocking County

HOCKING COUNTY

HOCKING PUBLIC SCHOOLS

- **Logan-Hocking Local Sch Dist** PID: 00811146   740/385-8517
  2019 E Front St, Logan 43138   Fax 740/385-3683

  Schools: 7 \ *Teachers:* 220 \ *Students:* 3,945 \ *Special Ed Students:* 682 \ *College-Bound:* 52% \ *Ethnic:* African American 1%, Hispanic 1%, Caucasian 98% \ *Exp:* $163 (Low) \ *Poverty:* 19% \ *Title I:* $1,096,289 \ *Special Education:* $774,000 \ *Open-Close:* 08/14 - 05/21 \ *DTBP:* $190 (High) \

Monty Bainter 1		Paul Shaw 2	
Cory Blair 3,17*		E Harris 3,91	
Cassie McGowan 4*		Dennis Morgan 5	
Theresa Schultheiss 6*		Kathy Kennard 7*	
Trina Barrell 8,11,273,286		Christy Bosch 11,15,74,83	
Kristi Walders 34		Carrie Cooke-Porter 58,77,79,88	
Lance Bell 67		Leigh Ann Leach 69	
Josh Straus 73*			

Public Schs..Principal	Grd	Prgm	Enr/#Cls	SN	
Central Elem Sch 445 N Market St, Logan 43138 Lisa Van Horn	PK-4	T	436 7	64%	740/380-4664 Fax 740/422-9957
Chieftain Elem Sch 28296 Chieftain Dr, Logan 43138 Andy Rice	PK-4	T	387 16	64%	740/385-1171 Fax 740/652-6007
Green Elem Sch 13495 Maysville Williams Rd, Logan 43138 Rebecca Osburn	PK-4	T	292 17	65%	740/385-7789 Fax 740/277-1040
Hocking Hills Elem Sch 19197 State Route 664 S, Logan 43138 Andy Rice	PK-4	T	152 14	83%	740/385-7071 Fax 740/652-3589
Logan High Sch 14470 S Rte 328, Logan 43138 Eli Hacker	9-12	AGTV	1,105 60	69%	740/385-2069 Fax 740/385-9564
Logan-Hocking Middle Sch 1 Middleschool Dr, Logan 43138 Chad Grow	5-8	TV	1,174 50	65%	740/385-8764 Fax 740/385-9547
Union Furnace Elem Sch 36140 Lime Bank Rd, Union Furnace 43158 Yancy Roberts-Schein	PK-4	T	215 10	69%	740/380-6881 Fax 740/652-3757

HOCKING CATHOLIC SCHOOLS

- **Diocese of Columbus Ed Office** PID: 00802717
  Listing includes only schools located in this county. See District Index for location of Diocesan Offices.

Catholic Schs..Principal	Grd	Prgm	Enr/#Cls	SN	
St John Sch 321 N Market St, Logan 43138 Andrew Potter	PK-6		74 5		740/385-2767 Fax 740/385-9727

HOCKING PRIVATE SCHOOLS

Private Schs..Principal	Grd	Prgm	Enr/#Cls	SN	
Logan Christian Sch 650 Walhonding Ave, Logan 43138 Thomas Gates	PK-4		50 5		740/385-5360

HOLMES COUNTY

HOLMES COUNTY SCHOOLS

County Schs..Principal	Grd	Prgm	Enr/#Cls	SN	
Holmes Co Training Center 8001 Township Road 574, Holmesville 44633 Roda Mast	Spec		91 7		330/674-8045 Fax 330/674-5182
Tri-County Pre-School Unit 8001 Township Road 574, Holmesville 44633 Kimberly Riley	Spec		250 2		330/674-0246 Fax 330/674-0326

HOLMES PUBLIC SCHOOLS

- **East Holmes Local School Dist** PID: 00811275   330/893-2610
  6108 County Road 77, Millersburg 44654   Fax 330/893-2838

  Schools: 8 \ *Teachers:* 103 \ *Students:* 1,615 \ *Special Ed Students:* 213 \ *LEP Students:* 558 \ *College-Bound:* 55% \ *Ethnic:* African American 1%, Hispanic 1%, Caucasian 98% \ *Exp:* $106 (Low) \ *Poverty:* 11% \ *Title I:* $830,875 \ *Special Education:* $355,000 \ *Open-Close:* 08/20 - 05/28 \ *DTBP:* $40 (Low) \

Erik Beun 1		Marsha Clark 2	
Lewis Yoder 3		Melissa Biltz 4	
Kevin Duff 5		Art Yoder 6*	
Jon Wilson 8,11,57,83,288,296,298		Lori Pringle 16,82*	
Deb Hershberger 37*		Noah Boyd 38*	
Karrie Kalzo 58,79,275		James Gertz 67	
Joseph Rodriguez 77		Toby Yoder 280	

Public Schs..Principal	Grd	Prgm	Enr/#Cls	SN	
Berlin Elem Sch 4978 W Main Street, Berlin 44610 Darren Bolchlinger	K-6	T	319 21	28%	330/893-2817 Fax 330/893-3503
Chestnut Ridge Elem Sch 5088 Township Road 401, Berlin 44610 James Luneborg	K-8	T	235 10	41%	330/893-2413 Fax 330/893-2827
Flatridge Elem Sch 2609 County Road 600, Charm 44617 Casey Travis	K-4	T	104 7	34%	330/893-3156
Hiland Jr Sr High Sch 4400 State Route 39, Berlin 44610 Cj Spreng	7-12		441 25	18%	330/893-2626 Fax 330/893-3570
Mt Hope Elem Sch 8242 State Route 241, Mount Hope 44660 James Luneborg	K-8	T	64 9	49%	330/674-0418 Fax 330/647-4647
Walnut Creek Elem Sch 4840 Olde Pump Street, Walnut Creek 44687 Darrell Haven	K-6		147 10	26%	330/893-2213 Fax 330/893-2964

1 Superintendent	19 Chief Financial Officer	39 Social Studies K-12	59 Special Education Elem
2 Bus/Finance/Purchasing	20 Art K-12	40 Social Studies Elem	60 Special Education Sec
3 Buildings And Grounds	21 Art Elem	41 Social Studies Sec	61 Foreign/World Lang K-12
4 Food Service	22 Art Sec	42 Science K-12	62 Foreign/World Lang Elem
5 Transportation	23 Music K-12	43 Science Elem	63 Foreign/World Lang Sec
6 Athletic	24 Music Elem	44 Science Sec	64 Religious Education K-12
7 Health Services	25 Music Sec	45 Math K-12	65 Religious Education Elem
8 Curric/Instruct K-12	26 Business Education	46 Math Elem	66 Religious Education Sec
9 Curric/Instruct Elem	27 Career & Tech Ed	47 Math Sec	67 School Board President
10 Curric/Instruct Sec	28 Technology Education	48 English/Lang Arts K-12	68 Teacher Personnel
11 Federal Program	29 Family/Consumer Science	49 English/Lang Arts Elem	69 Academic Assessment
12 Title I	30 Adult Education	50 English/Lang Arts Sec	70 Research/Development
13 Title V	31 Career/Sch-to-Work K-12	51 Reading K-12	71 Public Information
14 Early Childhood Ed	32 Career/Sch-to-Work Elem	52 Reading Elem	72 Summer School
15 Asst Superintendent	33 Career/Sch-to-Work Sec	53 Reading Sec	73 Instructional Tech
16 Instructional Media Svcs	34 Early Childhood Ed	54 Remedial Reading K-12	74 Inservice Training
17 Chief Operations Officer	35 Health/Phys Education	55 Remedial Reading Elem	75 Marketing/Distributive
18 Chief Academic Officer	36 Guidance Services K-12	56 Remedial Reading Sec	76 Info Systems
	37 Guidance Services Elem	57 Bilingual/ELL	77 Psychological Assess
	38 Guidance Services Sec	58 Special Education K-12	78 Affirmative Action

Ohio School Directory — Huron County

Winesburg Elem Sch	K-6	T	175	28%	330/359-5059
2165 State Route 62, Winesburg 44690			9		Fax 330/359-5759
Darrell Haven					
Wise Elem Sch	5-8	T	84	24%	330/893-2505
4579 County Road 120, Charm 44617			5		Fax 330/893-3041
Casey Travis					

West Holmes Local School Dist PID: 00811378
28 W Jackson St, Millersburg 44654
330/674-3546
Fax 330/674-6833

Schools: 6 \ **Teachers:** 120 \ **Students:** 2,100 \ **Special Ed Students:** 430 \ **LEP Students:** 10 \ **College-Bound:** 39% \ **Ethnic:** Hispanic 2%, Caucasian 97% \ **Exp:** $97 (Low) \ **Poverty:** 16% \ **Title I:** $834,188 \ **Special Education:** $526,000 \ **Open-Close:** 08/21 - 05/28 \ **DTBP:** $194 (High)

Bill Sterling 1	Jamie Zeigler 2
Mitch Neece 3,91	Dawn Martin 4
Coreena Johnson 5	Adam Brately 6*
Brian Baughman ... 8,11,16,57,69,280,296,298	Alison Rogers 38,83*
Dawne O'Donnell 38*	Julie Snyder 58*
Bradley Welsh 67	Dave Rhoades 73,295*
Rob Moser 73,295	

Public Schs..Principal	Grd	Prgm	Enr/#Cls	SN	
Killbuck Elem Sch	K-5	T	193	48%	330/276-2891
299 School St, Killbuck 44637			14		Fax 330/276-1382
Carrie Maltarich					
Lakeville Elem Sch	3-5	T	124	47%	419/827-2006
14059 State Route 226, Lakeville 44638			7		Fax 419/827-2352
Rick Mullins					
Millersburg Elem Sch	K-5	T	383	45%	330/674-5681
430 E Jackson St, Millersburg 44654			21		Fax 330/674-2506
Renee Woods					
Nashville Elem Sch	K-2	T	134	48%	330/378-2111
13495 State Route 39, Big Prairie 44611			12		Fax 330/378-2323
Brian Zimmerly					
West Holmes High Sch	9-12	T	686	34%	330/674-6085
10909 State Route 39, Millersburg 44654			50		Fax 330/674-0818
Aaron Kaufman					
West Holmes Middle Sch	6-8	T	514	37%	330/674-4761
10901 State Route 39, Millersburg 44654			40		Fax 330/674-2311
Jeff Woods					

HURON COUNTY

HURON COUNTY SCHOOLS

County Schs..Principal	Grd	Prgm	Enr/#Cls	SN	
Christie Lane Sch	Spec		18		419/668-8840
120 Shady Lane Dr, Norwalk 44857			3		Fax 419/663-2321
Kari Smith					

HURON PUBLIC SCHOOLS

• Bellevue City School Dist PID: 00811457
125 North St, Bellevue 44811
419/484-5000
Fax 419/483-0723

Schools: 3 \ **Teachers:** 105 \ **Students:** 2,000 \ **Special Ed Students:** 290 \ **College-Bound:** 51% \ **Ethnic:** Hispanic 6%, Caucasian 94% \ **Exp:** $270 (Med) \ **Poverty:** 12% \ **Title I:** $365,818 \ **Special Education:** $440,000 \ **Open-Close:** 08/21 - 05/29 \ **DTBP:** $173 (High)

Kim Schubert 1	Tammy Flicker 2
Adam Gerhardstein 3	Jackie Hess 4
Jaqueline Hess 4	Kathy Hillman 5
Brian Schubert 6*	Kim Swartz 8,11,285
Robin Hasselbach 31	Luana Copps 34*
Jacquie Montgomery 57,58,79*	John Redd 67
Mike Wobser 73,84,295,297	Jacquline Montgomery 79

Public Schs..Principal	Grd	Prgm	Enr/#Cls	SN	
Bellevue Elem Sch	PK-5	T	887	40%	419/484-5050
1150 Castalia St, Bellevue 44811			19		Fax 419/484-5105
Kyle Hintze					
Bellevue Middle Sch	6-8	T	427	40%	419/484-5060
1035 Castalia St, Bellevue 44811			25		Fax 419/484-5096
John Bollinger					
Bellevue Senior High Sch	9-12	V	598	29%	419/484-5070
200 Oakland Ave, Bellevue 44811			50		Fax 419/484-5107
Nate Artino					

• Monroeville Local School Dist PID: 00811548
101 West St, Monroeville 44847
419/465-2610
Fax 419/465-4263

Schools: 2 \ **Teachers:** 46 \ **Students:** 593 \ **Special Ed Students:** 106 \ **College-Bound:** 47% \ **Ethnic:** Hispanic 3%, Caucasian 97% \ **Exp:** $417 (High) \ **Poverty:** 14% \ **Title I:** $130,649 \ **Special Education:** $117,000 \ **Open-Close:** 08/21 - 05/29 \ **DTBP:** $184 (High) \ facebook twitter

Ralph Moore 1,11,83	Stephanie Hanna 2
Jeremy Loose 3	Don Beck 5
Benjamin Paul 6*	Teri Smith 12,55*
Kari Pisano 16,82*	Jennifer Meyer 58*
Nancy Brown 67	Adam Gerber 73,295*

Public Schs..Principal	Grd	Prgm	Enr/#Cls	SN	
Monroeville Elem Sch	PK-6		310		419/465-2533
101 West St, Monroeville 44847			16		
William Butler					facebook twitter
Monroeville High Sch	7-12		283	56%	419/465-2531
101 West St, Monroeville 44847			22		Fax 419/465-4580
James Kaczor					

• New London Local School Dist PID: 00811574
2 Wildcat Dr, New London 44851
419/929-8433
Fax 419/929-4108

Schools: 4 \ **Teachers:** 53 \ **Students:** 900 \ **Special Ed Students:** 157 \ **College-Bound:** 48% \ **Ethnic:** African American 3%, Caucasian 97% \ **Exp:** $146 (Low) \ **Poverty:** 20% \ **Title I:** $299,684 \ **Special Education:** $202,000 \ **Open-Close:** 08/26 - 05/28 \ **DTBP:** $179 (High)

Brad Romano 1,11	Jim Hudson 2,84
Mike Snyder 3*	Samantha Matthews 4*
Dan Bailey 5	Tom Howell 6,69*
Amanda Accavallo 12,34*	Diana Schwinn 16*

79	Student Personnel	91	Safety/Security	275	Response To Intervention	298	Grant Writer/Ptnrships	
80	Driver Ed/Safety	92	Magnet School	277	Remedial Math K-12	750	Chief Innovation Officer	
81	Gifted/Talented	93	Parental Involvement	280	Literacy Coach	751	Chief of Staff	
82	Video Services	95	Tech Prep Program	285	STEM	752	Social Emotional Learning	
83	Substance Abuse Prev	97	Chief Infomation Officer	286	Digital Learning			
84	Erate	98	Chief Technology Officer	288	Common Core Standards			
85	AIDS Education	270	Character Education	294	Accountability			
86	Alternative/At Risk	271	Migrant Education	295	Network System			
89	Multi-Cultural Curriculum	273	Teacher Mentor	296	Title II Programs			
90	Social Work	274	Before/After Sch	297	Webmaster			

School Programs
A = Alternative Program
G = Adult Classes
M = Magnet Program
T = Title I Schoolwide
V = Career & Tech Ed Programs

Other School Types
Ⓐ = Alternative School
Ⓒ = Charter School
Ⓜ = Magnet School
Ⓨ = Year-Round School

Social Media
facebook = Facebook
twitter = Twitter

New Schools are shaded
New Superintendents and Principals are bold
Personnel with email addresses are underscored

OH–105

Huron County

Market Data Retrieval

Melissa Vorhies 58,79
Kori Falk 71*
William Given 67

Public Schs..Principal	Grd	Prgm	Enr/#Cls	SN	
Digital Academy 3 Wildcat Dr, New London 44851 Cosetta Adkins	9-12		15		419/929-8191
New London Elem Sch 1 Wildcat Dr, New London 44851 Amanda Accavallo	PK-5		446		419/929-1586
New London High Sch 1 Wildcat Dr, New London 44851 Eric Yetter	9-12	V	245		419/929-1586 Fax 419/929-9513
New London Middle Sch 2 Wildcat Dr, New London 44851 Eric Yetter	6-8		181		419/929-1586

• Norwalk City School Dist PID: 00811615
134 Benedict Ave, Norwalk 44857
419/668-2779
Fax 419/663-3302

Schools: 6 \ *Teachers:* 141 \ *Students:* 2,750 \ *Special Ed Students:* 399 \ *LEP Students:* 115 \ *College-Bound:* 55% \ *Ethnic:* African American 1%, Hispanic 14%, Caucasian 85% \ *Exp:* $179 (Low) \ *Poverty:* 19% \ *Title I:* $878,485 \ *Special Education:* $705,000 \ *Open-Close:* 08/22 - 06/02 \ *DTBP:* $193 (High) \

George Fisk 1
Kelly Ross 3,4*
Josh Schlotterer 6*
Kim Majoy 29*
Michelle Sandor 36,69*
Lisa Wick 67
Adam Kreischer 273*
Joyce DuPont 2
Kelly Ross 5
Corey Ream 8,11,83,275,285,288,296,298
Jennifer King 31,34,58,77,88*
Elena Perez 57
Amie Swope 73,76*

Public Schs..Principal	Grd	Prgm	Enr/#Cls	SN	
League Elem Sch 16 E League St, Norwalk 44857 Adam Kreischer	4-4	T	194 13	68%	419/668-2450 Fax 419/668-6794
Main Street Sch 80 E Main St, Norwalk 44857 Dan Bauman	5-6	T	466 30	62%	419/660-1957 Fax 419/668-0354
Maplehurst Elem Sch 195 Saint Marys St, Norwalk 44857 Ken Moore	PK-1	T	477 22	63%	419/668-6035 Fax 419/668-5895
Norwalk High Sch 350 Shady Lane Dr, Norwalk 44857 Brad Cooley	9-12	T	722 45	57%	419/660-6500 Fax 419/668-4719
Norwalk Middle Sch 64 Christie Ave, Norwalk 44857 Gary Swartz	7-8	T	448 28	54%	419/668-8370 Fax 419/668-6622
Pleasant Elem Sch 16 S Pleasant St, Norwalk 44857 V Janice Smith	2-3	T	386 17	67%	419/668-4134 Fax 419/668-4964

• South Central Local Sch Dist PID: 00811691
3305 Greenwich Angling Rd, Greenwich 44837
419/752-3815
Fax 419/752-0182

Schools: 3 \ *Teachers:* 50 \ *Students:* 750 \ *Special Ed Students:* 113 \ *LEP Students:* 5 \ *College-Bound:* 55% \ *Ethnic:* Hispanic 3%, Caucasian 97% \ *Exp:* $182 (Low) \ *Poverty:* 19% \ *Title I:* $267,333 \ *Special Education:* $155,000 \ *Open-Close:* 08/21 - 05/28 \ *DTBP:* $176 (High)

Benjamin Chaffee 1,11,83
Jeff Deeble 3,5
Mary McKee 8,36,57,69
Chris Worick 2
Darren Hunt 6*
Tyler Lauber 58

Thomas Lucha 67
Sue Sparks 73,84,295

Public Schs..Principal	Grd	Prgm	Enr/#Cls	SN	
South Central Elem Sch 3291 Greenwich Angling Rd, Greenwich 44837 Nathaniel Richards	PK-4	V	300 24		419/752-5021 Fax 419/752-8705
South Central High Sch 3305 Greenwich Angling Rd, Greenwich 44837 Thomas Hellickson	9-12	V	177 19	37%	419/752-3354 Fax 419/752-6927
South Central Middle Sch 3291 Greenwich Angling Rd, Greenwich 44837 Alicia McKee	5-8		189		419/752-0011

• Western Reserve Local Sch Dist PID: 00811744
3765 State Route 20, Collins 44826
419/660-8508
Fax 419/660-8429

Schools: 3 \ *Teachers:* 55 \ *Students:* 994 \ *Special Ed Students:* 167 \ *LEP Students:* 3 \ *Ethnic:* Hispanic 1%, Caucasian 98% \ *Exp:* $117 (Low) \ *Poverty:* 15% \ *Title I:* $242,552 \ *Special Education:* $260,000 \ *Open-Close:* 08/22 - 06/03 \ *DTBP:* $162 (High)

Rodge Wilson 1
Ryan Falknor 6
Mark Starkey 27*
Jami White 67
Gayle Kovach 273*
Brett Robson 2
Alison Bell 16,82*
Elizabeth French 38*
Micheal McGill 73,295*

Public Schs..Principal	Grd	Prgm	Enr/#Cls	SN	
Western Reserve Elem Sch 3851 State Route 20, Collins 44826 Melanie Conaway	PK-5	T	481 38	48%	419/660-9824 Fax 419/660-8566
Western Reserve High Sch 3841 State Route 20, Collins 44826 Lisa Border	9-12		251 60	65%	419/668-8470 Fax 419/663-5916
Western Reserve Middle Sch 3841 State Route 20, Collins 44826 Lisa Border	6-8	T	262 26		419/668-8470 Fax 419/663-5916

• Willard City School Dist PID: 00811794
110 S Myrtle Ave, Willard 44890
419/935-1541
Fax 419/935-8491

Schools: 2 \ *Teachers:* 96 \ *Students:* 1,520 \ *Special Ed Students:* 224 \ *LEP Students:* 284 \ *College-Bound:* 43% \ *Ethnic:* Hispanic 30%, Caucasian 69% \ *Exp:* $248 (Med) \ *Poverty:* 25% \ *Title I:* $706,913 \ *Special Education:* $446,000 \ *Open-Close:* 08/20 - 05/29 \ *DTBP:* $174 (High)

Jeff Ritz 1
Michael Lillo 3,5
Joe Crawford 6*
Jenni Smith 8,280,285,288
Juanita Megger 31,58,83,88,271
Chris Rothhaar 67
Cynthia Shoup 2
Shannon King 4
Ricky Branham 7*
Tracey Stephens 11,69,72,296*
Steve Vipperm Vipperman 36*
Mark White 73

Public Schs..Principal	Grd	Prgm	Enr/#Cls	SN	
Willard Elem Sch 1 Flashes Ave, Willard 44890 Tracey Stephens	PK-5	T	712 30	63%	419/935-5341
Willard Middle High Sch 1 Flashes Ave, Willard 44890 Mike Eicher \ Chris Schaaf	6-12	ATV	782 50	50%	419/935-0181 Fax 419/933-6701

1	Superintendent	8	Curric/Instruct K-12	19	Chief Financial Officer	29	Family/Consumer Science	39	Social Studies K-12	49	English/Lang Arts Elem	59	Special Education Elem	69	Academic Assessment
2	Bus/Finance/Purchasing	9	Curric/Instruct Elem	20	Art K-12	30	Adult Education	40	Social Studies Elem	50	English/Lang Arts Sec	60	Special Education Sec	70	Research/Development
3	Buildings And Grounds	10	Curric/Instruct Sec	21	Art Elem	31	Career/Sch-to-Work K-12	41	Social Studies Sec	51	Reading K-12	61	Foreign/World Lang K-12	71	Public Information
4	Food Service	11	Federal Program	22	Art Sec	32	Career/Sch-to-Work Elem	42	Science K-12	52	Reading Elem	62	Foreign/World Lang Elem	72	Summer School
5	Transportation	12	Title I	23	Music K-12	33	Career/Sch-to-Work Sec	43	Science Elem	53	Reading Sec	63	Foreign/World Lang Sec	73	Instructional Tech
6	Athletic	13	Title V	24	Music Elem	34	Early Childhood Ed	44	Science Sec	54	Remedial Reading K-12	64	Religious Education K-12	74	Inservice Training
7	Health Services	14	Asst Superintendent	25	Music Sec	35	Health/Phys Education	45	Math K-12	55	Remedial Reading Elem	65	Religious Education Elem	75	Marketing/Distributive
		15	Instructional Media Svcs	26	Business Education	36	Guidance Services K-12	46	Math Elem	56	Remedial Reading Sec	66	Religious Education Sec	76	Info Systems
		16	Chief Operations Officer	27	Career & Tech Ed	37	Guidance Services Elem	47	Math Sec	57	Bilingual/ELL	67	School Board President	77	Psychological Assess
		18	Chief Academic Officer	28	Technology Education	38	Guidance Services Sec	48	English/Lang Arts K-12	58	Special Education K-12	68	Teacher Personnel	78	Affirmative Action

Ohio School Directory — Jackson County

HURON CATHOLIC SCHOOLS

• **Diocese of Toledo Ed Office** PID: 00818297
Listing includes only schools located in this county. See District Index for location of Diocesan Offices.

Catholic Schs..Principal	Grd	Prgm	Enr/#Cls	SN	
Immaculate Conception Sch 304 E Main St, Bellevue 44811 Pamela Griebel	K-8		180 9		419/483-6066
Norwalk Cath JHS-St Paul HS 93 E Main St, Norwalk 44857 Jim Tokarsky	7-12		295 30		419/668-3005 Fax 419/668-6417 f t
Norwalk Catholic ECC 77 State St, Norwalk 44857 Angie Smith	PK-K		222 15		419/668-8480 Fax 419/668-3269
Norwalk Catholic Elem Sch 31 Milan Ave, Norwalk 44857 Melissa Englert	1-6		301 14		419/668-6091 Fax 419/668-5584
St Francis Xavier Sch 25 W Perry St, Willard 44890 Donna McDowell	K-6		125 8		419/935-4744 Fax 419/933-6000
St Joseph Sch 79 Chapel St, Monroeville 44847 David McDowell	PK-8		90 12		419/465-2625 Fax 419/465-2170

HURON PRIVATE SCHOOLS

Private Schs..Principal	Grd	Prgm	Enr/#Cls	SN	
Celeryville Christian Sch 4200 Broadway Rd, Willard 44890 Jacob Bush	PK-8		65 9		419/935-3633 Fax 419/933-6030
Clarksfield SDA Sch State Route 60 & 18, Wakeman 44889 Leona Bange	1-8		11 2		419/929-7833
Trinity Christian Academy 250 Benedict Ave, Norwalk 44857 Molly Rychener	K-9		40		419/668-2011 Fax 419/499-3208 f

JACKSON COUNTY

JACKSON COUNTY SCHOOLS

County Schs..Principal	Grd	Prgm	Enr/#Cls	SN	
Hope Haven Sch 822 Sellars Dr, Jackson 45640 Heather Micheal	Spec	G	80 4		740/286-6491 Fax 740/286-6657

JACKSON PUBLIC SCHOOLS

• **Jackson City School Dist** PID: 00811897   740/286-6442
450 Vaughn St, Jackson 45640   Fax 740/286-6445

Schools: 5 \ *Teachers:* 156 \ *Students:* 2,450 \ *Special Ed Students:* 337 \ *College-Bound:* 57% \ *Ethnic:* African American 1%, Hispanic 1%, Caucasian 98% \ *Exp:* $205 (Med) \ *Poverty:* 25% \ *Title I:* $1,030,826 \ *Special Education:* $539,000 \ *Open-Close:* 08/19 - 05/22 \ *DTBP:* $195 (High)

Phil Howard 1   Joseph Hemsley 2,4,5,15,27,69,88
Rachelle Rachel 2   Jerry Mullins 3,91
Charles Stevens 6   Lori Moore 7,83*
Deborah Crabtree 11,93,286,288,296,298   Scott Lowe 11,36,57,58,81
Steve Marion 16,73,84,295   Joe Finch 38*
Kim Harless 67   Melissa Hughes 68

Public Schs..Principal	Grd	Prgm	Enr/#Cls	SN	
Jackson High Sch 500 Vaughn St, Jackson 45640 Thad Haines	9-12	TV	616 45	48%	740/286-7575 Fax 740/286-8197
Jackson Middle Sch 21 Tropic St, Jackson 45640 Mark Broermann	6-8	T	544 45	57%	740/286-7586 Fax 740/286-8637
Northview Elem Sch 11507 Chillicothe Pike, Jackson 45640 Melissa Ball	PK-5	T	378 30	69%	740/286-2390 Fax 740/286-7845
Southview Elem Sch 13842 State Route 93, Jackson 45640 Phillip Kuhn	PK-5	T	418 25	50%	740/286-1831 Fax 740/286-7834
Westview Elem Sch 16349 Beaver Pike, Jackson 45640 Karen Ochsenbein	PK-5	T	397 19	54%	740/286-2790 Fax 740/286-7831

• **Oak Hill Union Local Sch Dist** PID: 00811988   740/682-7595
205 Western Ave, Oak Hill 45656   Fax 740/682-6998

Schools: 2 \ *Teachers:* 70 \ *Students:* 1,220 \ *Special Ed Students:* 217 \ *College-Bound:* 39% \ *Ethnic:* Caucasian 99% \ *Exp:* $318 (High) \ *Poverty:* 22% \ *Title I:* $455,830 \ *Special Education:* $279,000 \ *Open-Close:* 08/20 - 05/21 \ *DTBP:* $169 (High)

Michael McCoy 1   Rhonda Harrison 2,11,19,84
Tim Swann 3   Rebecca Terry 4
Steve Carpenter ....5*   Norm Persin 6*
Adam Michael ....8,11,31,83,288,296*   David Loomis 57*
Beth Michael ....58*   Aaron Michael 67
Karen Speese ....69*   Ron Johnson 73*
Scott Hughes 91*

Public Schs..Principal	Grd	Prgm	Enr/#Cls	SN	
Oak Hill Elem Sch 401 Evans St, Oak Hill 45656 Adam Michael	PK-5	ATV	583 31	79%	740/682-7096 Fax 740/682-7065
Oak Hill Middle High Sch 5063 State Route 93, Oak Hill 45656 Steve Carpenter \ Randy Layton	6-12	ATV	611 35	76%	740/682-7055 Fax 740/682-6075

Jefferson County

Market Data Retrieval

- **Wellston City School Dist** PID: 00812059   740/384-2152
  1 E Broadway St, Wellston 45692   Fax 740/384-3948

> **Schools:** 4 \ **Teachers:** 87 \ **Students:** 1,450 \ **Special Ed Students:** 291 \ **College-Bound:** 40% \ **Ethnic:** African American 1%, Caucasian 99% \ **Exp:** $184 (Low) \ **Poverty:** 27% \ **Title I:** $692,294 \ **Special Education:** $425,000 \ **Open-Close:** 08/21 - 05/28 \ **DTBP:** $175 (High)

Karen Boch 1,11	Tami Downard 2
Paul Sims 3	Tina King 4
Jeff Hendershott 5,6	Kelly Waugh 7,83,88*
Beth Duffy 8,288	Michelle Kight 11,69,72,74,273,294*
Ashley Sturgill 31	Christine Hedderick 33,38*
Leah Massie 58,79,275	Terry Gill 67
Joey Rapp 73,295*	

Public Schs..Principal	Grd	Prgm	Enr/#Cls	SN	
Bundy Elem Sch 527 Missouri Ave, Wellston 45692 Dana Eberts	PK-2	T	322 24		740/384-6245 Fax 740/384-4683
Wellston High Sch 200 Golden Rocket Dr, Wellston 45692 Megan Sowers	9-12	T	368 35	55%	740/384-2162 Fax 740/384-9581
Wellston Intermediate Sch 225 Golden Rocket Dr, Wellston 45692 Michelle Lanning	3-5	T	311 22		740/384-2060 Fax 740/384-9801
Wellston Middle Sch 227 Golden Rocket Dr, Wellston 45692 Brandi Cupp	6-8	T	337 40		740/384-2251 Fax 740/384-9801

JACKSON CATHOLIC SCHOOLS

- **Diocese of Columbus Ed Office** PID: 00802717
  Listing includes only schools located in this county. See District Index for location of Diocesan Offices.

Catholic Schs..Principal	Grd	Prgm	Enr/#Cls	SN	
SS Peter & Paul Cath Sch 229 S New York Ave, Wellston 45692 Kristyl Fulton	PK-8		105 6		740/384-6354 Fax 740/384-2945

JACKSON PRIVATE SCHOOLS

Private Schs..Principal	Grd	Prgm	Enr/#Cls	SN	
Christian Life Academy 10595 Chillicothe Pike, Jackson 45640 Melissa Boggs	PK-12		145 8		740/286-1234 Fax 740/286-0234

JEFFERSON COUNTY

JEFFERSON COUNTY SCHOOLS

- **Jefferson Co Ed Service Center** PID: 00812669   740/283-3347
  2023 Sunset Blvd, Steubenville 43952   Fax 740/283-2709

Dr Chuck Kokiko 1	Donald Donahue 2
Ron Sismondo 8,74	Jeff Oblak 58
Mark Masloski 73	Linda Lenzi 81

County Schs..Principal	Grd	Prgm	Enr/#Cls	SN	
@ Jefferson Co Alt Sch 1400 Adams St, Steubenville 43952 Fred Abdalla	K-12		52 2		740/283-8557 Fax 740/283-8694
School of Bright Promise 256 John Scott Hwy, Steubenville 43952 Jamie Bodo	Spec	V	67 10		740/264-7176 Fax 740/264-0399

JEFFERSON PUBLIC SCHOOLS

- **Buckeye Local School Dist** PID: 00812102   740/769-7395
  6899 State Route 150, Dillonvale 43917   Fax 740/769-2361

> **Schools:** 5 \ **Teachers:** 161 \ **Students:** 1,700 \ **Special Ed Students:** 294 \ **College-Bound:** 68% \ **Ethnic:** African American 1%, Caucasian 98% \ **Exp:** $140 (Low) \ **Poverty:** 17% \ **Title I:** $494,477 \ **Special Education:** $430,000 \ **Open-Close:** 08/21 - 05/27 \ **DTBP:** $186 (High)

Kimberley Leonard 1	Merri Matthews 2
Tony Panapucci 3	Scott Celestin 5,91
Sam Jones 6*	Mary-Kay Mayle 7*
William Luther 8,11,16,27,74,88,273,275*	Krista Kinyo 38*
Krista Blackwell 58	Brooke Stingle 67
Vince Pastre 73,295*	Robin Rozenk 84

Public Schs..Principal	Grd	Prgm	Enr/#Cls	SN	
Buckeye Local High Sch 10692 State Route 150, Rayland 43943 Lucas Parsons	9-12	TV	419 50	69%	740/859-2196 Fax 740/859-2857
Buckeye Local Jr High Sch 10692 State Route 150, Rayland 43943 Jason Kovalski	7-8	T	241 26	65%	740/859-2196 Fax 740/859-6874
North Elem Sch 1004 3rd St, Brilliant 43913 Susan Nolan	PK-6	T	312 20	66%	740/598-4589 Fax 740/598-3909
South Elem Sch 100 Walden Ave, Tiltonsville 43963 Julie Packer	PK-6	T	342 21	66%	740/859-2800 Fax 740/859-4004
West Elem Sch 243 N Mill St, Adena 43901 Lucas Parsons	PK-6	T	261 10	62%	740/546-3331 Fax 740/546-3815

1 Superintendent	8 Curric/Instruct K-12	19 Chief Financial Officer	29 Family/Consumer Science	39 Social Studies K-12	49 English/Lang Arts Elem	59 Special Education Elem	69 Academic Assessment
2 Bus/Finance/Purchasing	9 Curric/Instruct Elem	20 Art K-12	30 Adult Education	40 Social Studies Elem	50 English/Lang Arts Sec	60 Special Education Sec	70 Research/Development
3 Buildings And Grounds	10 Curric/Instruct Sec	21 Art Elem	31 Career/Sch-to-Work K-12	41 Social Studies Sec	51 Reading K-12	61 Foreign/World Lang K-12	71 Public Information
4 Food Service	11 Federal Program	22 Art Sec	32 Career/Sch-to-Work Elem	42 Science K-12	52 Reading Elem	62 Foreign/World Lang Elem	72 Summer School
5 Transportation	12 Title I	23 Music K-12	33 Career/Sch-to-Work Sec	43 Science Elem	53 Reading Sec	63 Foreign/World Lang Sec	73 Instructional Tech
6 Athletic	13 Title V	24 Music Elem	34 Early Childhood Ed	44 Science Sec	54 Remedial Reading K-12	64 Religious Education K-12	74 Inservice Training
7 Health Services	15 Asst Superintendent	25 Music Sec	35 Health/Phys Education	45 Math K-12	55 Remedial Reading Elem	65 Religious Education Elem	75 Marketing/Distributive
	16 Instructional Media Svcs	26 Business Education	36 Guidance Services K-12	46 Math Elem	56 Remedial Reading Sec	66 Religious Education Sec	76 Info Systems
	17 Chief Operations Officer	27 Career & Tech Ed	37 Guidance Services Elem	47 Math Sec	57 Bilingual/ELL	67 School Board President	77 Psychological Assess
	18 Chief Academic Officer	28 Technology Education	38 Guidance Services Sec	48 English/Lang Arts K-12	58 Special Education K-12	68 Teacher Personnel	78 Affirmative Action

Ohio School Directory | Jefferson County

Edison Local School Dist PID: 00812279
14890 State Route 213, Hammondsville 43930
330/532-4590
Fax 330/532-2860

Schools: 3 \ *Teachers:* 81 \ *Students:* 2,000 \ *Special Ed Students:* 291 \ *College-Bound:* 54% \ *Ethnic:* Hispanic 1%, Caucasian 99% \ *Exp:* $242 (Med) \ *Poverty:* 20% \ *Title I:* $625,292 \ *Special Education:* $444,000 \ *Open-Close:* 08/21 - 05/22 \ *DTBP:* $183 (High)

Bill Beattie 1,11
Joe Debold 3,5
Jo Stagani 6*
Leah Eff 38*
Rachael Granatir 73,84
Lisa Bruzzese 2
Fatima Smuck 4,58
Julie Kireta 8,12,288
Aaron Richardson 67

Public Schs..Principal	Grd	Prgm	Enr/#Cls	SN
Edison Jr Sr High Sch 9890 State Route 152, Richmond 43944 Matt Morrison	7-12	TV	1,139 45	740/765-4313 Fax 740/765-4961
John E Gregg Elem Sch 212 County Road 75A, Bergholz 43908 Tammy Burchfield	PK-6	T	402 29	62% 740/768-2100 Fax 740/768-2616
Stanton Elem Sch 14890 State Route 213, Hammondsville 43930 Julie Kireta	PK-6	T	428 26	62% 740/282-5501 Fax 330/532-1106

Indian Creek Local Sch Dist PID: 00812396
587 Bantam Ridge Rd, Wintersville 43953
740/264-3502
Fax 740/266-2915

Schools: 4 \ *Teachers:* 124 \ *Students:* 2,300 \ *Special Ed Students:* 342 \ *College-Bound:* 54% \ *Ethnic:* African American 4%, Hispanic 2%, Caucasian 94% \ *Exp:* $237 (Med) \ *Poverty:* 19% \ *Title I:* $688,455 \ *Special Education:* $434,000 \ *Open-Close:* 08/21 - 05/22 \ *DTBP:* $218 (High)

Dr Thomas Chappelear 1
Brenda Staffilino 5
John Belt 15
Jim Maul 38*
Zach Murray 73,295
Denise Todoroff 2
Joseph Dunlevy 6*
Steve Eft 37
Dr Ted Starkey 67
Nicole McDonald 288

Public Schs..Principal	Grd	Prgm	Enr/#Cls	SN
Hills Elem Sch 2281 Wilson Ave, Mingo Jct 43938 Michelle Minto	PK-4	T	384 25	72% 740/283-2479 Fax 740/283-2286
Indian Creek High Sch 200 Park Dr, Wintersville 43953 Louie Retton	9-12	GT	548 36	54% 740/264-1163 Fax 740/266-2929 f
Indian Creek Middle Sch 2379 Wilson Ave, Mingo Jct 43938 Dr Holly Minch-Hick	5-8	T	652 24	52% 740/282-0834 Fax 740/282-3092
Wintersville Elem Sch 100 Park Dr, Wintersville 43953 Lorrie Jarrett	PK-4	T	427 24	62% 740/264-1691 Fax 740/264-8879 f

Jefferson Co JT Voc Sch Dist PID: 01417444
1509 County Road 22A, Bloomingdale 43910
740/264-5545
Fax 740/264-3144

Schools: 1 \ *Teachers:* 30 \ *Students:* 350 \ *College-Bound:* 41% \ *Exp:* $1,197 (High) \ *Open-Close:* 08/21 - 05/26 \ *DTBP:* $263 (High)

Dr Todd Phillipson 1,11
Jeff Copeland 30
Robert George 67
Karen Spoonemore 2
Jill McVicker 60*
Ron Peach 73*

Public Schs..Principal	Grd	Prgm	Enr/#Cls	SN
Jefferson Co Joint Voc Sch 1509 County Road 22A, Bloomingdale 43910 Dan Hartman	Voc	AG	350 33	740/264-5545

Steubenville City School Dist PID: 00812504
1400 Adams St, Steubenville 43952
740/283-3767
Fax 740/283-8930

Schools: 6 \ *Teachers:* 127 \ *Students:* 2,600 \ *Special Ed Students:* 321 \ *LEP Students:* 3 \ *College-Bound:* 64% \ *Ethnic:* African American 28%, Hispanic 2%, Caucasian 69% \ *Exp:* $383 (High) \ *Poverty:* 35% \ *Title I:* $1,418,840 \ *Special Education:* $510,000 \ *Open-Close:* 08/20 - 05/28 \ *DTBP:* $107 (High)

Melinda Young 1,11
Glen Wood 3,5
Lynn Meyer 6*
Dr Shana D'Aurora 11,31,78,89*
Kayla DiMarzio 42
Sarah Elliott 58,69,77,90*
Jacqueline Reeves 72,81*
Shanna Wydra 285,298
Kala Whitlatch 2,71,294
Rich Mesera 4
Amy Neely 7*
Jennifer Agresta ...36,83,85,88,270,275*
Greg Bowers 45*
Greg Gresta 67
Brian Daurora 73,84,91,286

Public Schs..Principal	Grd	Prgm	Enr/#Cls	SN
Garfield East Elem Sch 936 N 5th St, Steubenville 43952 Shawn Crosier	PK-4	T	393 18	740/282-5112 Fax 740/283-8935
Harding Middle Sch 2002 Sunset Blvd, Steubenville 43952 Bryan Mills	5-8		744 35	740/282-3481 Fax 740/283-8949
STEM Academy 1400 Adams St, Steubenville 43952 Dr Shana D'Aurora	PK-4		75	740/284-5613
Steubenville High Sch 420 N 4th St, Steubenville 43952 Ted Gorman	9-12	V	640 30	740/282-9741 Fax 740/283-8959
Wells Academy 420 N 4th St, Steubenville 43952 Shawn Crosier	PK-4	T	306 18	740/282-1651 Fax 740/283-8937
West Pugleise Elem Sch 435 N John Scott Connectr, Steubenville 43952 Lynnett Gorman	PK-4	T	467 19	740/346-0903 Fax 740/264-2190

Toronto City School Dist PID: 00812607
1307 Dennis Way, Toronto 43964
740/537-2456
Fax 740/537-1102

Schools: 2 \ *Teachers:* 51 \ *Students:* 891 \ *Special Ed Students:* 103 \ *College-Bound:* 51% \ *Ethnic:* Asian 1%, African American 2%, Hispanic 1%, Caucasian 96% \ *Exp:* $182 (Low) \ *Poverty:* 26% \ *Title I:* $296,478 \ *Special Education:* $164,000 \ *Open-Close:* 08/21 - 05/28 \ *DTBP:* $225 (High)

Maureen Taggert 1
Mark Blascoe 3
Chelsey Fletcher 6*
Christopher Dopp 8*
David Lucci 16*
Carol Murray 38,69,88*
Michelle Blazek 273*
Colleen Wickham 2
Laura Erwin 4
Katy Long 7*
Cindy Heinerman 8,11,58,83,85,288,296
Robert Suffoletta 16,73,295*
Jay Foster 67

Public Schs..Principal	Grd	Prgm	Enr/#Cls	SN
J T Karaffa Elem Sch 1307 Dennis Way, Toronto 43964 Kenneth Emery	PK-5	T	499 23	58% 740/537-2471 Fax 740/537-5144

OH-109

Knox County

Toronto High Sch — 6-12 TV 392 55% 740/537-2442
1305 Dennis Way, Toronto 43964 — 28
Betsy Jones

JEFFERSON CATHOLIC SCHOOLS

- **Diocese of Steubenville Ed Off** PID: 00812671   740/282-3631
  422 Washington St, Steubenville 43952   Fax 740/282-3327

Schools: 12 \ **Students:** 1,900

Listing includes only schools located in this county. See District Index for location of Diocesan Offices.

Paul Ward 1,11   James Dunfee 2

Catholic Schs..Principal	Grd	Prgm	Enr/#Cls	SN	
Bishop Mussio Ctl Elem Sch	PK-6		393		740/264-2550
100 Etta Ave, Steubenville 43952			10		Fax 740/266-2843
T Danaher					
Bishop Mussio Ctl Jr High Sch	7-8		108		740/346-0028
320 Westview Ave Ste 2, Steubenville 43952			16		Fax 740/346-0070
Theresa Danaher					
Catholic Central High Sch	9-12		263		740/264-5538
320 Westview Ave, Steubenville 43952			26		Fax 740/264-5443
T Costello					ⓕ

JEFFERSON PRIVATE SCHOOLS

Private Schs..Principal	Grd	Prgm	Enr/#Cls	SN	
Jefferson Co Christian Sch	PK-12		180		740/535-1337
125 Fernwood Rd Ste 1, Wintersville 43953			20		
Sherri Ware					

JEFFERSON REGIONAL CENTERS

- **Ohio Mid-Eastern RESA** PID: 04499609   740/283-2050
  2230 Sunset Blvd Ste 2, Steubenville 43952   Fax 740/283-1500

Angela Underwood 1   Missy Valkosky 2
Wendy Barr 2   Adam Truex 15
Dave Savastone 16   John Harwell 67
Missy Sutherland 73,98   Ryan Brown 73,76

KNOX COUNTY

KNOX COUNTY SCHOOLS

- **Knox Co Ed Service Center** PID: 02089193   740/393-6767
  308 Martinsburg Rd, Mount Vernon 43050   Fax 740/393-6812

Dr Timm Mackley 1   Brittany Keller 2
Kathy Lumpkins 34   Ben Snedeker 58
Richard McLarnan 67   Jared Tarbert 73
Don Garvic 81

County Schs..Principal	Grd	Prgm	Enr/#Cls	SN	
Knox County Head Start	Spec		200		740/397-9304
11700 Upper Gilchrist Rd Ste B, Mount Vernon 43050			3		Fax 740/397-9329
Lindsay Lamp					

KNOX PUBLIC SCHOOLS

- **Centerburg Local School Dist** PID: 00812918   740/625-6346
  119 S Preston St, Centerburg 43011   Fax 740/625-9939

Schools: 2 \ **Teachers:** 63 \ **Students:** 1,088 \ **Special Ed Students:** 122 \ **College-Bound:** 63% \ **Ethnic:** Asian 1%, Hispanic 1%, Caucasian 98% \ **Exp:** $262 (Med) \ **Poverty:** 10% \ **Title I:** $179,321 \ **Special Education:** $221,000 \ **Open-Close:** 08/15 - 05/21 \ **DTBP:** $178 (High)

Mike Hebenthal 1   Lori Houck 2
Randy Bradford 3,5   Autumn Pauley 4
Rich Porter 6   Willaim Humphrey 8
Connie Hatley 11,58,83,88,275,296   Christine Lees 16*
Stephen Parpart .... 31,36,69*   Sally Simpson 54*
Tracey Myers 67   Joanna Bryant 73,295*
Lori Lybarger 90*

Public Schs..Principal	Grd	Prgm	Enr/#Cls	SN	
Centerburg Elem Sch	K-5		514	29%	740/625-6488
207 S Preston St, Centerburg 43011			25		Fax 740/625-5894
John Morgan					
Centerburg High Sch	6-12	V	574	33%	740/625-6055
3782 Columbus Rd, Centerburg 43011			60		Fax 740/625-5799
William Humphrey \ Ryan Gallwitz					

- **Danville Local School Dist** PID: 00812944   740/599-6116
  405 S Market St, Danville 43014   Fax 740/599-5417

Schools: 2 \ **Teachers:** 48 \ **Students:** 615 \ **Special Ed Students:** 97 \ **LEP Students:** 6 \ **College-Bound:** 48% \ **Ethnic:** Asian 1%, Hispanic 2%, Native American: 1%, Caucasian 97% \ **Exp:** $141 (Low) \ **Poverty:** 19% \ **Title I:** $232,196 \ **Special Education:** $140,000 \ **Open-Close:** 08/15 - 05/21 \ **DTBP:** $173 (High)

Jason Snively 1   Tonya Mickley 2
Kevin Byers .... 3,91*   Elaine Didinger 4*
Philip Blubaugh 5   Matt Moore 6*
Kay Crawford .... 16*   Matthew Proper 58,69
David Dusthimer 67   Kevin Langdon 73

Public Schs..Principal	Grd	Prgm	Enr/#Cls	SN	
Danville Elem Middle Sch	K-8		455		740/599-6116
205 Rambo St, Danville 43014			35		Fax 740/599-5904
Tara Bond \ Matt Proper					
Danville High Sch	9-12	V	160		740/599-6116
10 Rambo St, Danville 43014			18		Fax 740/599-5418
Ed Honabarger					

1	Superintendent	8	Curric/Instruct K-12	19	Chief Financial Officer	29	Family/Consumer Science	39	Social Studies K-12	49	English/Lang Arts Elem	59	Special Education Elem	69	Academic Assessment
2	Bus/Finance/Purchasing	9	Curric/Instruct Elem	20	Art K-12	30	Adult Education	40	Social Studies Elem	50	English/Lang Arts Sec	60	Special Education Sec	70	Research/Development
3	Buildings And Grounds	10	Curric/Instruct Sec	21	Art Elem	31	Career/Sch-to-Work K-12	41	Social Studies Sec	51	Reading K-12	61	Foreign/World Lang K-12	71	Public Information
4	Food Service	11	Federal Program	22	Art Sec	32	Career/Sch-to-Work Elem	42	Science K-12	52	Reading Elem	62	Foreign/World Lang Elem	72	Summer School
5	Transportation	12	Title I	23	Music K-12	33	Career/Sch-to-Work Sec	43	Science Elem	53	Reading Sec	63	Foreign/World Lang Sec	73	Instructional Tech
6	Athletic	13	Title V	24	Music Elem	34	Early Childhood Ed	44	Science Sec	54	Remedial Reading K-12	64	Religious Education K-12	74	Inservice Training
7	Health Services	14	Asst Superintendent	25	Music Sec	35	Health/Phys Education	45	Math K-12	55	Remedial Reading Elem	65	Religious Education Elem	75	Marketing/Distributive
		15	Instructional Media Svcs	26	Business Education	36	Guidance Services K-12	46	Math Elem	56	Remedial Reading Sec	66	Religious Education Sec	76	Info Systems
		16	Chief Operations Officer	27	Career & Tech Ed	37	Guidance Services Elem	47	Math Sec	57	Bilingual/ELL	67	School Board President	77	Psychological Assess
		18	Chief Academic Officer	28	Technology Education	38	Guidance Services Sec	48	English/Lang Arts K-12	58	Special Education K-12	68	Teacher Personnel	78	Affirmative Action

Ohio School Directory   Knox County

• East Knox Local School Dist PID: 00812970   740/599-7000
23201 Coshocton Rd, Howard 43028   Fax 740/599-5863

Schools: 2 \ **Teachers:** 54 \ **Students:** 1,100 \ **Special Ed Students:** 172 \ **LEP Students:** 3 \ **College-Bound:** 40% \ **Ethnic:** African American 1%, Hispanic 1%, Caucasian 98% \ **Exp:** $127 (Low) \ **Poverty:** 13% \ **Title I:** $317,590 \ **Special Education:** $239,000 \ **Open-Close:** 08/14 - 05/21 \ **DTBP:** $170 (High) \ f

Steve Larcomb 1,11
Crystal Gallwitz 4
Denise Campbell 7*
Corby Frere 58*
Jessi Busenburg 2
Angela Wells 5
Stephanie Whitesel 36*
Dustin Buckingham 67

Public Schs..Principal	Grd	Prgm	Enr/#Cls	SN	
East Knox Elem Sch 23081 Coshocton Rd, Howard 43028 Cody Reese	K-6	T	472 32	50%	740/599-7000 Fax 740/599-6397
East Knox Junior Senior HS 23227 Coshocton Rd, Howard 43028 Alan Keesee	7-12	T	415 28	46%	740/599-7000 Fax 740/599-2922

• Fredericktown Local Sch Dist PID: 00813015   740/694-2956
117 Columbus Rd, Fredericktown 43019   Fax 740/694-0956

Schools: 3 \ **Teachers:** 55 \ **Students:** 1,197 \ **Special Ed Students:** 223 \ **College-Bound:** 55% \ **Ethnic:** Hispanic 2%, Native American: 1%, Caucasian 98% \ **Exp:** $84 (Low) \ **Poverty:** 14% \ **Title I:** $275,329 \ **Special Education:** $261,000 \ **Open-Close:** 08/16 - 05/15 \ **DTBP:** $176 (High)

Matthew Chrispin 1
Neil Kirkpatrick 3
Cale Grubb 5
Jennifer Kline 11,58,275,288*
Mary Elder 16,82*
Leeanne Jurkowitz 38*
Brenton Wolfe 73
Heather Darnold 2
Teresa Thompson 4*
Deirdre Barns 7,83,85
Miguel Thompson 11,78*
Molly Compton 37,69*
Charles Streby 67
Sharon Streby 274*

Public Schs..Principal	Grd	Prgm	Enr/#Cls	SN	
Fredericktown Elem Sch 111 Stadium Dr, Fredericktown 43019 Miguel Thompson	K-5	T	553 17	84%	740/694-2781 Fax 740/694-1294
Fredericktown High Sch 111 Stadium Dr, Fredericktown 43019 Brent Garee	9-12	V	319 27		740/694-2726 Fax 740/694-1294
Fredericktown Middle Sch 111 Stadium Dr, Fredericktown 43019 Matthew Caputo	6-8		325 25		740/694-2726 Fax 740/694-1294

• Knox Co Voc School Dist PID: 00813170   740/397-5820
306 Martinsburg Rd, Mount Vernon 43050   Fax 740/397-7040

Schools: 1 \ **Teachers:** 67 \ **Students:** 640 \ **College-Bound:** 98% \ **Exp:** $384 (High) \ **Open-Close:** 08/14 - 05/21 \ **DTBP:** $179 (High)

Katherine Greenich 1
Jordan Kandel 3*
John Feltman 38*
Richard McLarnan 67
Jeff LaVin 288*
Tracy Elliott 2,11
Jane Marlow 30*
Elaine Robinson 60*
Paul Napier 73,286*

Public Schs..Principal	Grd	Prgm	Enr/#Cls	SN	
Knox County Career Center 306 Martinsburg Rd, Mount Vernon 43050 Derek Fisher	Voc	G	640 47		740/397-5820

• Mt Vernon City School Dist PID: 00813053   740/397-7422
300 Newark Rd, Mount Vernon 43050   Fax 740/393-5949

Schools: 8 \ **Teachers:** 222 \ **Students:** 4,000 \ **Special Ed Students:** 682 \ **LEP Students:** 42 \ **College-Bound:** 51% \ **Ethnic:** Asian 1%, African American 1%, Hispanic 4%, Caucasian 94% \ **Exp:** $180 (Low) \ **Poverty:** 15% \ **Title I:** $1,008,727 \ **Special Education:** $1,036,000 \ **Open-Close:** 08/21 - 05/28 \ **DTBP:** $86 (Med)

Bill Seder 1
Rick Shaffer 3
Todd Conant 5
Kathy Kasler 10
Pam Rose 58
Bonny Buffington 79
Judy Forney 2
Mark Kime 4
Dr Eric Brown 9
Laura Rochte 16*
Dr Margie Bennett 67
Donald Garvic 81

Public Schs..Principal	Grd	Prgm	Enr/#Cls	SN	
Columbia Elem Sch 150 Columbus Rd, Mount Vernon 43050 Andrew Thompson	PK-5	T	246 12	54%	740/393-5975 Fax 740/393-5976
Dan Emmett Elem Sch 108 Mansfield Ave, Mount Vernon 43050 Margy Arck	PK-5	T	297 21		740/393-5950 Fax 740/393-5953
East Elem Sch 714 E Vine St, Mount Vernon 43050 Karly Watterson	PK-5	T	245 11	51%	740/393-5985 Fax 740/393-5987
Mt Vernon High Sch 300 Martinsburg Rd, Mount Vernon 43050 Scott Will	9-12	T	1,053 80	41%	740/393-5900 Fax 740/397-6018
Mt Vernon Middle Sch 298 Martinsburg Rd, Mount Vernon 43050 Darin Prince	6-8	T	867 75	43%	740/392-6867 Fax 740/392-3369
Pleasant St Elem Sch 305 E Pleasant St, Mount Vernon 43050 Teresa Weaver	PK-5	T	353 22		740/393-5990 Fax 740/393-3175
Twin Oak Elem Sch 8888 Martinsburg Rd, Mount Vernon 43050 Suzanne Miller	PK-5	T	375 14	53%	740/393-5970 Fax 740/397-2598
Wiggin St Elem Sch 207 Wiggin St, Gambier 43022 Matthew Dill	PK-5		243 11	22%	740/427-4262 Fax 740/427-3926

KNOX CATHOLIC SCHOOLS

• Diocese of Columbus Ed Office PID: 00802717
Listing includes only schools located in this county. See District Index for location of Diocesan Offices.

Catholic Schs..Principal	Grd	Prgm	Enr/#Cls	SN	
St Vincent De Paul Sch 206 E Chestnut St, Mount Vernon 43050 Justine Maag	PK-8		204 12		740/393-3611 Fax 740/393-0236

KNOX PRIVATE SCHOOLS

Private Schs..Principal	Grd	Prgm	Enr/#Cls	SN	
Christian Star Academy 7 E Sugar St, Mount Vernon 43050 Suzanne Feasel	K-12		9 2		740/393-0251 Fax 740/393-0067

---

79 Student Personnel
80 Driver Ed/Safety
81 Gifted/Talented
82 Video Services
83 Substance Abuse Prev
84 Erate
85 AIDS Education
88 Alternative/At Risk
89 Multi-Cultural Curriculum
90 Social Work

91 Safety/Security
92 Magnet School
93 Parental Involvement
95 Tech Prep Program
97 Chief Infomation Officer
98 Chief Technology Officer
270 Character Education
271 Migrant Education
273 Teacher Mentor
274 Before/After Sch

275 Response To Intervention
277 Remedial Math K-12
280 Literacy Coach
285 STEM
286 Digital Learning
288 Common Core Standards
294 Accountability
295 Network System
296 Title II Programs
297 Webmaster

298 Grant Writer/Ptnrships
750 Chief Innovation Officer
751 Chief of Staff
752 Social Emotional Learning

Other School Types
Ⓐ = Alternative School
Ⓒ = Charter School
Ⓜ = Magnet School
Ⓨ = Year-Round School

School Programs
A = Alternative Program
G = Adult Classes
M = Magnet Program
T = Title I Schoolwide
V = Career & Tech Ed Programs

New Schools are shaded
New Superintendents and Principals are bold
Personnel with email addresses are underscored

Social Media
f = Facebook
t = Twitter

OH–111

Lake County

Market Data Retrieval

Mount Vernon SDA Elem Sch 221 Sychar Rd, Mount Vernon 43050 Kimberly Myers	K-8	25 3	740/393-7060

LAKE COUNTY

LAKE COUNTY SCHOOLS

• **State Support Team-Region 4** PID: 00814124   440/350-2563
8221 Auburn Rd, Concord Twp 44077

Merrie Darrah 1

County Schs..Principal	Grd	Prgm	Enr/#Cls SN	
Broadmoor Sch 8090 Broadmoor Rd, Mentor 44060 Sheryl Kline	Spec		120 20	440/602-1000 Fax 440/602-1003
Crossroads Day Treatment Ctr 8445 Munson Rd, Mentor 44060 Dana Bickel	Spec		100 3	440/255-1700 Fax 440/205-2417
Lake Academy 503 Vegas Dr, Eastlake 44095 Steve Straussdaugh	Spec		55	440/942-7401 Fax 440/942-1790
ⓒ Summit Acad Cmty Sch-Painsvlle [248] 268 N State St, Painesville 44077 Frank Cheraso	Spec	T	90	440/358-0877 Fax 440/358-0397

LAKE PUBLIC SCHOOLS

• **Auburn Vocational School Dist** PID: 00814100   440/357-7542
8140 Auburn Rd, Painesville 44077   Fax 440/357-0310

Schools: 1 \ **Teachers:** 26 \ **Students:** 745 \ **College-Bound:** 75% \
Exp: $466 (High) \ **Open-Close:** 08/14 - 05/29 \ **DTBP:** $233 (High) \ f

Dr Brian Bontempo 1   Sherry Williamson 2,19
Sherry Williamson .... 2,11*   Joe Atwell 3*
Shelby Kaminski 13   Jeff Slavkovsky 15*
Andrea Tracy .... 30*   Erik Walters 67
Bob Cireddu .... 73*   Justin Slazkovski 91
Kelley Gollinar 294

Public Schs..Principal	Grd	Prgm	Enr/#Cls SN	
Auburn Career Center 8140 Auburn Rd, Painesville 44077 Dee Stark	Voc	AG	675	440/357-7542 f

• **Fairport Harbor Exempt Vlg SD** PID: 00813209   440/354-5400
329 Vine St, Fairport Hbr 44077   Fax 440/357-1478

Schools: 2 \ **Teachers:** 33 \ **Students:** 720 \ **Special Ed Students:** 45
\ **LEP Students:** 6 \ **College-Bound:** 52% \ **Ethnic:** African American
1%, Hispanic 11%, Caucasian 87% \ **Exp:** $134 (Low) \ **Poverty:** 16% \
Title I: $123,402 \ **Special Education:** $157,000 \ **Open-Close:** 08/21 -
06/02 \ **DTBP:** $241 (High)

Dominic Paolo 1   Jennifer Polak 8,11,58*
Michelle Jurick .... 36,69*   Mary Javins 67

Bob Ceredue 73*

Public Schs..Principal	Grd	Prgm	Enr/#Cls SN	
Harding Middle High Sch 329 Vine St, Fairport Hbr 44077 Katie Rumbarger	6-12		409 24	43% 440/354-3592 Fax 440/354-5426
McKinley Elem Sch 602 Plum St, Fairport Hbr 44077 Doreen Fischer	PK-5	T	308 12	49% 440/354-4982 Fax 440/350-2566

• **Kirtland Local School Dist** PID: 00813235   440/256-3360
9252 Chillicothe Rd, Kirtland 44094   Fax 440/256-3831

Schools: 3 \ **Teachers:** 65 \ **Students:** 1,155 \ **Special Ed Students:** 142
\ **LEP Students:** 3 \ **College-Bound:** 86% \ **Ethnic:** Asian 1%, Hispanic
1%, Caucasian 98% \ **Exp:** $168 (Low) \ **Poverty:** 5% \ **Title I:** $92,829 \
Special Education: $178,000 \ **Open-Close:** 08/21 - 06/02 \ **DTBP:** $222
(High)

William Wade 1   Lewis Galante 2
Sheila Dikowicz 5   Matthew Paul 6*
Kimberly Crawford 7   Becky Malinas 11,285,288
Ed Bradac .... 16*   Timothy Cosgrove 67
John Renwick 73,295*

Public Schs..Principal	Grd	Prgm	Enr/#Cls SN	
Kirtland Elem Sch 9140 Chillicothe Rd, Kirtland 44094 Chad Vanarnhem	PK-5		488 25	440/256-3344 Fax 440/256-1045
Kirtland High Sch 9150 Chillicothe Rd, Kirtland 44094 Scott Amstutz	9-12		423 24	440/256-3366 Fax 440/256-1042
Kirtland Middle Sch 9152 Chillicothe Rd, Kirtland 44094 Scott Amstutz	6-8		282 16	440/256-3358 Fax 440/256-3928

• **Madison Local School Dist** PID: 00813285   440/428-2166
1956 Red Bird Rd, Madison 44057   Fax 440/428-9379

Schools: 5 \ **Teachers:** 141 \ **Students:** 3,120 \ **Special Ed Students:** 325
\ **LEP Students:** 46 \ **Ethnic:** Asian 1%, African American 1%, Hispanic 6%,
Caucasian 93% \ **Exp:** $170 (Low) \ **Poverty:** 12% \ **Title I:** $493,959 \
Special Education: $556,000 \ **Open-Close:** 08/14 - 05/26 \ **DTBP:** $197
(High)

Angela Smith 1,11,288   Mike Vaccariello 2
Patrick Smith 3,92   Kelly Minnick 4
Kim Boggs 5   John Dragas 6*
Jenette Blake .... 7,85*   David Bull 15
Joseph Neasel 16   Katherine Kaminski 36*
Patricia Leibhardt 54,57,58,271,275   Shawn Douglas 67
Bob Cireddu 73,286,295

Public Schs..Principal	Grd	Prgm	Enr/#Cls SN	
Madison High Sch 3100 Burns Rd, Madison 44057 William Fisher	9-12	T	984	41% 440/428-2161 Fax 440/428-2165
Madison Middle Sch 6079 Middle Ridge Rd, Madison 44057 Tom Brady	6-8	T	697 45	43% 440/428-1196 Fax 440/428-9389
Madison Pre-K 1956 Red Bird Rd, Madison 44057 Jovette Hiltunen	PK-PK		167 7	440/428-5111 Fax 440/428-9311
Madison South Elem Sch 92 E Main St, Madison 44057 Shannon Kriegmont	K-5	T	646 25	38% 440/428-5121 Fax 440/526-2911

1	Superintendent	8	Curric/Instruct K-12	19	Chief Financial Officer	29	Family/Consumer Science	39	Social Studies K-12	49	English/Lang Arts Elem	59	Special Education Elem	69	Academic Assessment
2	Bus/Finance/Purchasing	9	Curric/Instruct Elem	20	Art K-12	30	Adult Education	40	Social Studies Elem	50	English/Lang Arts Sec	60	Special Education Sec	70	Research/Development
3	Buildings And Grounds	10	Curric/Instruct Sec	21	Art Elem	31	Career/Sch-to-Work K-12	41	Social Studies Sec	51	Reading K-12	61	Foreign/World Lang K-12	71	Public Information
4	Food Service	11	Federal Program	22	Art Sec	32	Career/Sch-to-Work Elem	42	Science K-12	52	Reading Elem	62	Foreign/World Lang Elem	72	Summer School
5	Transportation	12	Title I	23	Music K-12	33	Career/Sch-to-Work Sec	43	Science Elem	53	Reading Sec	63	Foreign/World Lang Sec	73	Instructional Tech
6	Athletic	13	Title V	24	Music Elem	34	Early Childhood Ed	44	Science Sec	54	Remedial Reading K-12	64	Religious Education K-12	74	Inservice Training
7	Health Services	14	Asst Superintendent	25	Music Sec	35	Health/Phys Education	45	Math K-12	55	Remedial Reading Elem	65	Religious Education Elem	75	Marketing/Distributive
		15	Instructional Media Svcs	26	Business Education	36	Guidance Services K-12	46	Math Elem	56	Remedial Reading Sec	66	Religious Education Sec	76	Info Systems
		16	Chief Operations Officer	27	Career & Tech Ed	37	Guidance Services Elem	47	Math Sec	57	Bilingual/ELL	67	School Board President	77	Psychological Assess
		17	Chief Academic Officer	28	Technology Education	38	Guidance Services Sec	48	English/Lang Arts K-12	58	Special Education K-12	68	Teacher Personnel	78	Affirmative Action

Ohio School Directory — Lake County

North Elem Sch	K-5	T	621	53%	440/428-2151
1941 Red Bird Rd, Madison 44057			33		Fax 440/428-9384
William Mayer					

● Mentor Exempted Village SD PID: 00813352
6451 Center St, Mentor 44060
440/255-4444
Fax 440/255-4622

Schools: 11 \ **Teachers:** 411 \ **Students:** 7,415 \ **Special Ed Students:** 944 \ **LEP Students:** 147 \ **College-Bound:** 72% \ **Ethnic:** Asian 2%, African American 3%, Hispanic 2%, Caucasian 92% \ **Exp:** $181 (Low) \ **Poverty:** 7% \ **Title I:** $801,588 \ **Special Education:** $1,629,000 \ **Open-Close:** 08/19 - 05/28 \ **DTBP:** $228 (High)

William Porter 1
Rick Kolar 3
Jeffery Cassella 6
Alice Marthe 12,51*
Jason Crowe 26,27,31*
Kerry Bowser 58
Kathy Burnett 68
Daniel Wilson 2,19
Kim O'Keefe 5
Barb Bonnes 8,81,286,288,296
Tim Hamman 15
Ann Heramb 36*
Tom Tuttle 67
Jeremy Woodworth 73,84,295

Public Schs..Principal	Grd	Prgm	Enr/#Cls	SN	
Bellflower Elem Sch	K-5		502	20%	440/255-4212
6655 Reynolds Rd, Mentor 44060			23		Fax 440/255-1602
Heather Hardy					
Cares Center	Spec		70		440/257-5951
5028 Forest Rd, Mentor 44060					Fax 440/257-8766
Christy LaPaglia					
Fairfax Elem Sch	K-5		378	28%	440/255-7223
6465 Curtiss Ct, Mentor 44060			21		Fax 440/974-5294
Melanie Pearn					
Hopkins Elem Sch	K-5		492	18%	440/255-6179
7565 Hopkins Rd, Mentor 44060			26		Fax 440/974-5419
Christine Miley					
Lake Elem Sch	K-5	T	341	48%	440/257-5953
7625 Pinehurst Dr, Mentor 44060			18		Fax 440/257-8773
Laurie Hoynes					
Memorial Middle Sch	6-8		903	20%	440/974-2250
8979 Mentor Ave, Mentor 44060			45		Fax 440/974-2259
Ericka Blackburn					
Mentor High Sch	9-12	AV	2,600	23%	440/974-5300
6477 Center St, Mentor 44060					Fax 440/974-5216
Jason Crowe					
Orchard Hollow Elem Sch	K-5		441	20%	440/257-5955
8700 Hendricks Rd, Mentor 44060			30		Fax 440/257-8779
Karen Trunk					
Ridge Elem Sch	PK-5	T	777	31%	440/255-5400
7860 Johnnycake Ridge Rd, Mentor 44060			16		
Pam Hutto					
Shore Middle Sch	6-8	AV	864	31%	440/257-8750
5670 Hopkins Rd, Mentor 44060			50		Fax 440/257-8761
Mike Sears					
Sterling Morton Elem Sch	K-5	T	307	42%	440/257-5954
9292 Jordan Dr, Mentor 44060			21		Fax 440/257-8799
Jacki Sturm					

● Painesville City Local SD PID: 00813649
58 Jefferson St, Painesville 44077
440/392-5060
Fax 440/392-5089

Schools: 6 \ **Teachers:** 164 \ **Students:** 3,000 \ **Special Ed Students:** 534 \ **LEP Students:** 911 \ **College-Bound:** 38% \ **Ethnic:** African American 19%, Hispanic 56%, Caucasian 25% \ **Exp:** $165 (Low) \ **Poverty:** 29% \ **Title I:** $1,385,491 \ **Special Education:** $576,000 \ **Open-Close:** 08/15 - 05/26 \ **DTBP:** $175 (High) \ **f**

Dr Joshua Englehart 1,73
Sherri Samac 2,294

Kelly Minnick 4
Christine Young 7,34,58,69
Heidi Fyffeyocum 9,11,76,88,273,286,296,298
Heidi Fyffe 11
David Schade 16,295,297*
Wendy Camper 42,45*
Kathleen Powers-Dolney 67
Marwin Walling 6
Wendy Camper 8,280,285,288
Erin Cirino 10
Michael Choksi 15
Raquel Griesmer 31,83*
Ruth Haines 57,271
Lisa Elliott 77*

Public Schs..Principal	Grd	Prgm	Enr/#Cls	SN	
Chestnut Elem Sch	K-5	T	438		440/392-5350
341 Chestnut St, Painesville 44077			26		Fax 440/392-5359
Jamie Smith					
Elm Street Elem Sch	K-5	T	442		440/392-5520
585 Elm St, Painesville 44077			30		Fax 440/392-5529
Cynthia Urbic					
Heritage Middle Sch	6-8	T	636		440/392-5250
135 Cedarbrook Dr, Painesville 44077			42		Fax 440/392-5259
Melissa DeAngelis					
Maple Elem Sch	K-5	T	435		440/392-5440
560 W Jackson St, Painesville 44077			14		Fax 440/392-5449
Zachary Cousins					
Red Raiders Pre-School	PK-PK		112		440/392-5612
350 Cedarbrook Dr, Painesville 44077					
Karen Capretta					
T W Harvey High Sch	9-12		820		440/392-5110
200 W Walnut Ave, Painesville 44077			46		Fax 440/392-5149
Van McWreath					

● Perry Local School Dist PID: 00813730
4325 Manchester Rd, Perry 44081
440/259-9200
Fax 440/259-3607

Schools: 3 \ **Teachers:** 94 \ **Students:** 1,700 \ **Special Ed Students:** 174 \ **LEP Students:** 80 \ **College-Bound:** 92% \ **Ethnic:** African American 2%, Hispanic 10%, Caucasian 87% \ **Exp:** $241 (Med) \ **Poverty:** 9% \ **Title I:** $193,681 \ **Special Education:** $317,000 \ **Open-Close:** 08/13 - 05/28 \ **DTBP:** $251 (High)

Dr Jack Thompson 1
James Smith 3
Sheila Dikowicz 5
Dr Betty Jo Malchesky 8,15,288,296
Lisa Shields 58
Robin Naughton 71,97
Sandy Yankie 85*
Lew Galante 2,19
Vickie Peters 4
Tj Rockwell 6
Carol Needham 38*
Mark Welch 67
Darci Leskovec 73,76
Christy Patriarca 280

Public Schs..Principal	Grd	Prgm	Enr/#Cls	SN	
Perry Elem Sch	K-4		538	26%	440/599-9600
1 Learning Ln, Perry 44081			30		Fax 440/259-9649
Arianna Neading					**f t**
Perry High Sch	9-12		610	22%	440/599-9300
1 Success Blvd, Perry 44081			40		Fax 440/259-9290
Todd Porcello					**f t**
Perry Middle Sch	5-8		485	31%	440/599-9500
2 Learning Ln, Perry 44081			45		Fax 440/259-5149
Robert Knisely					

● Riverside Local School Dist PID: 00813522
585 Riverside Dr, Painesville 44077
440/352-0668
Fax 440/639-1959

Schools: 6 \ **Teachers:** 220 \ **Students:** 3,987 \ **Special Ed Students:** 547 \ **LEP Students:** 153 \ **College-Bound:** 84% \ **Ethnic:** Asian 1%, African American 3%, Hispanic 7%, Caucasian 88% \ **Exp:** $124 (Low) \ **Poverty:** 8% \ **Title I:** $599,380 \ **Special Education:** $628,000 \ **Open-Close:** 09/03 - 06/05 \ **DTBP:** $196 (High)

Jim Kalis 1
Gary Platko 2,7,19,84

---

79 Student Personnel	91 Safety/Security	275 Response To Intervention	298 Grant Writer/Ptnrships	**School Programs**	**Social Media**	
80 Driver Ed/Safety	92 Magnet School	277 Remedial Math K-12	750 Chief Innovation Officer	A = Alternative Program	**f** = Facebook	
81 Gifted/Talented	93 Parental Involvement	280 Literacy Coach	751 Chief of Staff	G = Adult Classes		
82 Video Services	95 Tech Prep Program	285 STEM	752 Social Emotional Learning	M = Magnet Program	**t** = Twitter	
83 Substance Abuse Prev	97 Chief Information Officer	286 Digital Learning		T = Title I Schoolwide		
84 Erate	98 Chief Technology Officer	288 Common Core Standards	**Other School Types**	V = Career & Tech Ed Programs		
85 AIDS Education	270 Character Education	294 Accountability	Ⓐ = Alternative School			
88 Alternative/At Risk	271 Migrant Education	295 Network System	Ⓒ = Charter School	New Schools are shaded		
89 Multi-Cultural Curriculum	273 Teacher Mentor	296 Title II Programs	Ⓜ = Magnet School	New Superintendents and Principals are bold		
90 Social Work	274 Before/After Sch	297 Webmaster	Ⓨ = Year-Round School	Personnel with email addresses are underscored		

OH-113

Lake County

Market Data Retrieval

Name	Ref
Dan Wayner	3,91
James Haffa	5
Melissa Mlakar	8*
Cheryl Lanning	13,58
Scott Bailis	27,31,36*
Jennifer Harden	67
Jared Donda	76
Michelle Gifford	4
Dave Bors	6*
Charles Schlick	11,15,36,57,69,79,271,294
Lisa Wade	16,82*
Heather Kilfoyle	57
Nicholas Carrabine	71
Julie Belako	274
Nikki Stotler	8
Donna Solano	11
Alison Ciferno	12
Margaret Warner	67
Alison Ciferno	11,81,92,296*
Eileen Bowers	11,58,79,271*
Charles Murphy	15
Patrick McKinney	73,286

Public Schs..Principal	Grd	Prgm	Enr/#Cls	SN
Buckeye Elem Sch 175 Buckeye Rd, Painesville 44077 Cassandre Smolen	K-5		328 15	29% 440/352-2191 Fax 440/352-1087
Henry F Lamuth Middle Sch 6700 Auburn Rd, Painesville 44077 Nick Orlando	6-7		682 35	31% 440/354-4394 Fax 440/354-8218
Melridge Elem Sch 6689 Melridge Dr, Painesville 44077 Michelle Walker	PK-5		303 18	19% 440/352-3854 Fax 440/352-2076
Parkside Elem Sch 12428 Concord Hambden Rd, Painesville 44077 Michelle Walker	K-5	T	500 12	46% 440/352-8822
Riverside Campus 585 Riverside Dr, Painesville 44077 Peter Hliatzos	8-12	AV	1,806 53	22% 440/352-3341 Fax 440/352-1257
Riverview Elem Sch 845 Madison Ave, Painesville 44077 Traci Shantery	K-5		500 20	23% 440/352-0688

- **Wickliffe City School Dist** PID: 00813780   440/943-6900
  2221 Rockefeller Rd, Wickliffe 44092   Fax 440/943-7738

Schools: 3 \ *Teachers:* 86 \ *Students:* 1,290 \ *Special Ed Students:* 221 \ *LEP Students:* 6 \ *College-Bound:* 61% \ *Ethnic:* Asian 1%, African American 9%, Hispanic 3%, Caucasian 88% \ *Exp:* $105 (Low) \ *Poverty:* 13% \ *Title I:* $278,488 \ *Special Education:* $393,000 \ *Open-Close:* 08/19 - 05/28 \ *DTBP:* $236 (High)

Name	Ref
Joseph Spiccia	1
Leonard Forinash	3
Harrison McCall	6
Katie Thomas	12*
Daniel Thomeier	67
Julie Ramos	285
Susan Haffey	2,73
Paulette Grennan	5
Marylou Ezzo	8,11,16,58*
Leah Porcello	36*
David Dewey	81

Public Schs..Principal	Grd	Prgm	Enr/#Cls	SN
Wickliffe Elem Sch 1821 Lincoln Rd, Wickliffe 44092 Kelly Bearer	K-4	T	443 24	37% 440/943-0320 Fax 440/943-7781
Wickliffe High Sch 2255 Rockefeller Rd, Wickliffe 44092 Shyla Metsker	9-12	V	432 40	30% 440/944-0800 Fax 440/943-7705
Wickliffe Middle Sch 29240 Euclid Ave, Wickliffe 44092 Lori Rodman	5-8	T	415 22	31% 440/943-3220 Fax 440/943-7755

- **Willoughby-Eastlake City SD** PID: 00813845   440/946-5000
  35353 Curtin Blvd, Eastlake 44095   Fax 440/946-4671

Schools: 13 \ *Teachers:* 461 \ *Students:* 8,090 \ *Special Ed Students:* 1,360 \ *LEP Students:* 102 \ *College-Bound:* 60% \ *Ethnic:* Asian 2%, African American 10%, Hispanic 1%, Caucasian 86% \ *Exp:* $78 (Low) \ *Poverty:* 11% \ *Title I:* $1,223,065 \ *Special Education:* $1,437,000 \ *Open-Close:* 08/15 - 05/21 \

Name	Ref
Steve Thompson	1
Gina Kfuvern	8,79
Bill Parkinson	2
Gina Keuvern	8,57,69,285

Public Schs..Principal	Grd	Prgm	Enr/#Cls	SN
Eastlake Middle Sch 35972 Lake Shore Blvd, Eastlake 44095 Dr Colleen Blaurock	6-8	T	381	41% 440/942-5696 Fax 440/918-8973
Edison Elem Sch 5288 Karen Isle Dr, Willoughby 44094 Jatina Threat	K-5		677 24	31% 440/942-2099 Fax 440/975-3707
Grant Elem Sch 2838 Lost Nation Rd, Willoughby 44094 Michael Samber	K-5	T	614 20	39% 440/942-5944 Fax 440/918-8980
Jefferson Elem Sch 35980 Lake Shore Blvd, Eastlake 44095 Lisa George	K-5	T	471 19	39% 440/942-7244 Fax 440/954-3550
Longfellow Elem Sch 35200 Stevens Blvd, Eastlake 44095 Allison Aber	K-5	T	459 24	63% 440/975-3720 Fax 440/269-3022
North High Sch 34041 Stevens Blvd, Eastlake 44095 Eric Frei	9-12		1,301 70	35% 440/975-3666 Fax 440/975-3671
Northern Career Institute 34343 Euclid Ave, Willoughby 44094 Deanna Elsing	11-12	V	156 8	440/946-7085
Royalview Elem Sch 31500 Royalview Dr, Willowick 44095 Kimberly Cantwell	K-5	T	801 46	40% 440/944-3130 Fax 440/943-9965
South High Sch 5000 Shankland Rd, Willoughby 44094 Robin Hopkins	9-12		1,180	26% 440/975-3648 Fax 440/975-3645
W-E School of Innovation 32500 Chardon Rd, Willoughby 44094 Brian Patrick	3-8		450	14% 440/942-1525 Fax 440/347-0273
Willoughby Middle Sch 36901 Ridge Rd, Willoughby 44094 Lawrence Keller	6-8		691	33% 440/975-3600 Fax 440/975-3618
Willoughby-Eastlake Preschool 34050 Glen Dr, Eastlake 44095 Dr Ruth Ann Plate	PK-PK		179	440/283-2220 Fax 440/269-3099
Willowick Middle Sch 31500 Royalview Dr, Willowick 44095 Brett McCann	6-8	T	556 60	42% 440/943-2950 Fax 440/943-9964

LAKE CATHOLIC SCHOOLS

- **Diocese of Cleveland Ed Office** PID: 00795308
  Listing includes only schools located in this county. See District Index for location of Diocesan Offices.

Catholic Schs..Principal	Grd	Prgm	Enr/#Cls	SN
All Saints-St John Vianney Sch 28702 Euclid Ave, Wickliffe 44092 Terri Armelli	PK-8		288 17	440/943-1395 Fax 440/943-4468
Lake Catholic High Sch 6733 Reynolds Rd, Mentor 44060 Rick Koenig	9-12		830 25	440/578-1020 Fax 440/974-9087
Mater Dei Academy 29840 Euclid Ave, Wickliffe 44092 Joanie Klemens	PK-8		420 11	440/585-0800

1 Superintendent	8 Curric/Instruct K-12	19 Chief Financial Officer	29 Family/Consumer Science	39 Social Studies K-12	49 English/Lang Arts Elem	59 Special Education Elem	69 Academic Assessment
2 Bus/Finance/Purchasing	9 Curric/Instruct Elem	20 Art K-12	30 Adult Education	40 Social Studies Elem	50 English/Lang Arts Sec	60 Special Education Sec	70 Research/Development
3 Buildings And Grounds	10 Curric/Instruct Sec	21 Art Elem	31 Career/Sch-to-Work K-12	41 Social Studies Sec	51 Reading K-12	61 Foreign/World Lang K-12	71 Public Information
4 Food Service	11 Federal Program	22 Art Sec	32 Career/Sch-to-Work Elem	42 Science K-12	52 Reading Elem	62 Foreign/World Lang Elem	72 Summer School
5 Transportation	12 Title I	23 Music K-12	33 Career/Sch-to-Work Sec	43 Science Elem	53 Reading Sec	63 Foreign/World Lang Sec	73 Instructional Tech
6 Athletic	13 Title V	24 Music Elem	34 Early Childhood Ed	44 Science Sec	54 Remedial Reading K-12	64 Religious Education K-12	74 Inservice Training
7 Health Services	15 Asst Superintendent	25 Music Sec	35 Health/Phys Education	45 Math K-12	55 Remedial Reading Elem	65 Religious Education Elem	75 Marketing/Distributive
	16 Instructional Media Svcs	26 Business Education	36 Guidance Services K-12	46 Math Elem	56 Remedial Reading Sec	66 Religious Education Sec	76 Info Systems
	17 Chief Operations Officer	27 Career & Tech Ed	37 Guidance Services Elem	47 Math Sec	57 Bilingual/ELL	67 School Board President	77 Psychological Assess
	18 Chief Academic Officer	28 Technology Education	38 Guidance Services Sec	48 English/Lang Arts K-12	58 Special Education K-12	68 Teacher Personnel	78 Affirmative Action

Ohio School Directory   Lawrence County

St Gabriel Sch	K-8	726	440/352-6169
9935 Johnnycake Ridge Rd, Mentor 44060		28	Fax 440/639-0143
Ann Ulrich			
St Mary of the Assumption Sch	PK-8	452	440/255-9781
8540 Mentor Ave, Mentor 44060		20	Fax 440/974-8107
Mary Benns			

LAKE PRIVATE SCHOOLS

Private Schs..Principal	Grd	Prgm	Enr/#Cls SN	
Andrews Osborne Academy	PK-12		340	440/942-3600
38588 Mentor Ave, Willoughby 44094			40	Fax 440/942-3660
Larry Goodman				
Cornerstone Christian Academy	K-12		400	440/943-9260
2846 Som Center Rd, Willoughby 44094				
Bernadette Bileci \ Sandi Ortiz				
Hershey Montessori Sch	PK-9		250	440/357-0918
10229 Prouty Rd, Painesville 44077			9	Fax 440/357-9096
Paula Leigh-Doyle				
Mentor Christian Sch	PK-12	V	135	440/257-3172
8600 Lake Shore Blvd, Mentor 44060			16	Fax 440/257-9309
Frank Davis				
Our Shepherd Lutheran Sch	K-8		150	440/357-7776
508 Mentor Ave, Painesville 44077			9	Fax 440/358-1149
Barb Riley				
RE-Education Aspire Access	Spec		401	440/257-3131
6176 Reynolds Rd, Mentor 44060				Fax 440/257-3132
Wendy Bergant				
Willo-Hill Christian Sch	PK-6		95	440/951-5391
4200 State Route 306, Willoughby 44094			8	Fax 440/951-5434
Mark Tedeschi				

LAKE REGIONAL CENTERS

- **Lgca-Lake Geauga Ohio OCA** PID: 04499489   440/357-9383
  8221 Auburn Rd, Painesville 44077   Fax 440/357-8713

James Turk 1   Kirk Atwell 3
Jeremy Hunter 8   Brian Ruffner 73,76

LAWRENCE COUNTY

LAWRENCE COUNTY SCHOOLS

- **Lawrence Co Ed Service Center** PID: 00814590   740/532-4223
  304 N 2nd St, Ironton 45638   Fax 740/532-7226

Jeff Saunders 1   Brenda Hill 2
Becky Bowling 8   Beverly Tillis 8
Johnna Lunsford 58   Julie Mayo 58
Dave Rumley 88

County Schs..Principal	Grd	Prgm	Enr/#Cls SN	
© Lawrence Co Academy	7-12		79	740/867-6641
11627 State Route 243, Chesapeake 45619				
Bob Wilds				

Open Door Sch	Spec	V	70	740/532-1234
421 Lorain St, Ironton 45638			8	Fax 740/532-2001
Kendra Heim				

LAWRENCE PUBLIC SCHOOLS

- **Chesapeake Union Exempt Vlg SD** PID: 00814136   740/867-3135
  10183 County Road 1, Chesapeake 45619   Fax 740/867-3136

Schools: 3 \ **Teachers:** 68 \ **Students:** 1,400 \ **Special Ed Students:** 201 \ **College-Bound:** 53% \ **Ethnic:** African American 1%, Hispanic 1%, Caucasian 98% \ **Exp:** $144 (Low) \ **Poverty:** 21% \ **Title I:** $393,682 \ **Special Education:** $341,000 \ **Open-Close:** 08/14 - 05/22 \ **DTBP:** $233 (High)

Jerry McConnell 1   Sue Ann Dial 2,11
Ben Burk 3   Dee Lovejoy 4*
Ryan Davis .... 6* Jamie Shield 8,11,58,77,286,288
Arthur Suiter 67   Andrew Smith 73,84

Public Schs..Principal	Grd	Prgm	Enr/#Cls SN	
Chesapeake Elem Sch	PK-4	T	522	64% 740/867-3448
11359 County Road 1, Chesapeake 45619			30	Fax 740/867-1110
Trisha Harris				
Chesapeake High Sch	9-12	T	359	61% 740/867-5958
10181 County Road 1, Chesapeake 45619			30	Fax 740/867-1130
Chris Smith				
Chesapeake Middle Sch	5-8	T	449	63% 740/867-3972
10335 County Road 1, Chesapeake 45619			40	Fax 740/867-1120
Ty Johnson				

- **Dawson-Bryant Local Sch Dist** PID: 00814174   740/532-6451
  701 High St, Coal Grove 45638   Fax 740/533-6019

Schools: 3 \ **Teachers:** 67 \ **Students:** 1,200 \ **Special Ed Students:** 219 \ **LEP Students:** 3 \ **College-Bound:** 42% \ **Ethnic:** African American 1%, Caucasian 99% \ **Exp:** $300 (High) \ **Poverty:** 20% \ **Title I:** $311,435 \ **Special Education:** $196,000 \ **Open-Close:** 08/15 - 05/22 \ **DTBP:** $236 (High) \

Steve Easterling 1   Audra Deere 2*
Chad Scott 3   Sharon Brammer 4*
Tim Sparks 5   Brian Mulkey 6,274*
Ellen Adkins .... 8,11,58,69,83,88,288* Brady Harrison 67
Rodney McFarland 73*

Public Schs..Principal	Grd	Prgm	Enr/#Cls SN	
Dawson-Bryant Elem Sch	PK-5	T	548	740/532-6898
4503 State Route 243, Ironton 45638			40	Fax 740/534-5582
Angela LaFon				
Dawson-Bryant High Sch	9-12	AT	279	740/532-6345
1 Hornet Ln, Coal Grove 45638			35	Fax 740/533-6013
Dean Mader				
Dawson-Bryant Middle Sch	6-8	AT	271	740/533-6008
1 Hornet Ln, Coal Grove 45638			30	Fax 740/533-6002
Rick Roach				

Lawrence County

Market Data Retrieval

- **Fairland Local School Dist** PID: 00814239   740/886-3100
  228 Private Drive 10010, Proctorville 45669   Fax 740/886-7253

Schools: 4 \ *Teachers:* 82 \ *Students:* 1,569 \ *Special Ed Students:* 220 \ *College-Bound:* 44% \ *Ethnic:* African American 1%, Hispanic 1%, Caucasian 98% \ *Exp:* $248 (Med) \ *Poverty:* 18% \ *Title I:* $410,785 \ *Special Education:* $341,000 \ *Open-Close:* 08/14 - 05/22 \ *DTBP:* $229 (High)

Roni Hayes 1,11,73,84   Loretta Wirzfeld 2
Gary Sowards 67

Public Schs..Principal	Grd	Prgm	Enr/#Cls	SN	
Fairland East Elem Sch 10732 County Road 107, Proctorville 45669 Abbie Pannell	PK-2	T	412 20	49%	740/886-3120 Fax 740/886-7630
Fairland High Sch 812 County Road 411, Proctorville 45669 Chad Belville	9-12	AV	379 35	41%	740/886-3250 Fax 740/886-6738
Fairland Middle Sch 7875 County Road 107, Proctorville 45669 Aaron Lewis	6-8	AT	408 25	41%	740/886-3200 Fax 740/886-5125
Fairland West Elem Sch 110 Township Road 1125, Proctorville 45669 Teresa Johnson	3-5	T	370 32	50%	740/886-3150 Fax 740/886-5259

- **Ironton City School Dist** PID: 00814277   740/532-4133
  105 S 5th St, Ironton 45638   Fax 740/532-2314

Schools: 3 \ *Teachers:* 78 \ *Students:* 1,400 \ *Special Ed Students:* 253 \ *LEP Students:* 3 \ *College-Bound:* 56% \ *Ethnic:* African American 4%, Hispanic 1%, Caucasian 94% \ *Exp:* $483 (High) \ *Poverty:* 28% \ *Title I:* $709,430 \ *Special Education:* $391,000 \ *Open-Close:* 08/14 - 05/22 \ *DTBP:* $231 (High)

Joseph Geletka 1   Patty Wade 2,19
David Webb 3   Mark LaFon 4,59*
Dave Lawless .... 5*   Heather Lambert 7,85
William Dressel 8,11,15,83,273   Kathryn Price 16,297*
Sarah Wellman 36,58,69,77   Marissa Fields 38*
Tim Johnson 67   Joel Utsinger 73*

Public Schs..Principal	Grd	Prgm	Enr/#Cls	SN	
ⓐ Ironton Elem Sch 302 Delaware St, Ironton 45638 **Joe Rowe**	PK-5	T	643 9		740/532-2209 Fax 740/532-3077
ⓐ Ironton High Sch 1701 S 7th St, Ironton 45638 **Jeff Hairston**	9-12	V	369 31		740/532-3911 Fax 740/533-6027
ⓐ Ironton Middle Sch 302 Delaware St, Ironton 45638 **Toben Schreck**	6-8		340 7		740/532-3347 Fax 740/532-3077

- **Lawrence Co Joint Voc Sch Dist** PID: 01548108   740/867-6641
  11627 State Route 243, Chesapeake 45619   Fax 740/867-2009

Schools: 1 \ *Teachers:* 57 \ *Students:* 475 \ *Exp:* $911 (High) \ *Open-Close:* 08/16 - 05/25 \ *DTBP:* $246 (High)

Stephen Dodgion 1   Richard Sketel 2,11,85
Andrea Zaph .... 10,29,74,273*   Jim Howard 27,88,274*
Chris Leese .... 28,73,295*   Robert Pleasant 67
Jaime Chafin .... 69,294*   Sondra Andrews 298*

Public Schs..Principal	Grd	Prgm	Enr/#Cls	SN	
Collins Career Center 11627 State Route 243, Chesapeake 45619 Jim Howard	Voc	G	475 44		740/867-6641 Fax 740/867-1371

- **Rock Hill Local School Dist** PID: 00814370   740/532-7030
  2325 County Road 26 Unit A, Ironton 45638   Fax 740/532-7043

Schools: 3 \ *Teachers:* 91 \ *Students:* 1,450 \ *Special Ed Students:* 220 \ *College-Bound:* 45% \ *Ethnic:* African American 1%, Hispanic 1%, Caucasian 99% \ *Exp:* $276 (Med) \ *Poverty:* 31% \ *Title I:* $1,090,558 \ *Special Education:* $446,000 \ *Open-Close:* 08/14 - 05/22 \ *DTBP:* $236 (High)

David Hopper 1   Thomas Robinson 2
Bill Barker 5   Barry Litteral 6*
Kathy Bowling 8,15,76   Eric Floyd 11,15,69,288
Jane Whitworth .... 16*   Bridget Malone 38*
Laura Kelley 58   Mark Harper 67
Lloyd Bailey 73,297*

Public Schs..Principal	Grd	Prgm	Enr/#Cls	SN	
Rock Hill Elem Sch 2676 County Road 26, Ironton 45638 Fred Evans	PK-5	T	744 55		740/532-7016 Fax 740/532-7020
Rock Hill High Sch 2415 County Road 26, Ironton 45638 David Hopper	9-12	V	349 30		740/532-7012 Fax 740/532-7015
Rock Hill Middle Sch 2171 County Road 26, Ironton 45638 Jason Owens	6-8		325 35		740/532-7026 Fax 740/532-7028

- **South Point Local School Dist** PID: 00814447   740/377-4315
  302 High St, South Point 45680   Fax 740/377-9735

Schools: 4 \ *Teachers:* 85 \ *Students:* 1,500 \ *Special Ed Students:* 219 \ *LEP Students:* 3 \ *College-Bound:* 46% \ *Ethnic:* African American 6%, Hispanic 1%, Caucasian 92% \ *Exp:* $228 (Med) \ *Poverty:* 28% \ *Title I:* $894,317 \ *Special Education:* $388,000 \ *Open-Close:* 08/14 - 05/22 \ *DTBP:* $228 (High)

Mark Christian 1   Terri Baker 2
Joanna Rice 4   Carla Rowe 5
Dave Adams .... 6*   T J Howard 12,15,288
Natalie Adams 67   Nick Clay 73

Public Schs..Principal	Grd	Prgm	Enr/#Cls	SN	
Burlington Elem Sch 8781 County Road 1, South Point 45680 Michael Clay	PK-5	T	422 25		740/894-4230 Fax 740/894-4201
South Point Elem Sch 201 Park Ave, South Point 45680 Chris Mathes	PK-5	T	386 27		740/377-2756 Fax 740/377-3229
South Point High Sch 983 County Road 60, South Point 45680 Ben Coleman	9-12	A	393 35		740/377-4323 Fax 740/377-3228
South Point Middle Sch 983 County Road 60, South Point 45680 Mylissa Bentley	6-8		349		740/377-4343 Fax 740/377-3228

1 Superintendent	8 Curric/Instruct K-12	19 Chief Financial Officer	29 Family/Consumer Science	39 Social Studies K-12	49 English/Lang Arts Elem	59 Special Education Elem	69 Academic Assessment
2 Bus/Finance/Purchasing	9 Curric/Instruct Elem	20 Art K-12	30 Adult Education	40 Social Studies Elem	50 English/Lang Arts Sec	60 Special Education Sec	70 Research/Development
3 Buildings And Grounds	10 Curric/Instruct Sec	21 Art Elem	31 Career/Sch-to-Work K-12	41 Social Studies Sec	51 Reading K-12	61 Foreign/World Lang K-12	71 Public Information
4 Food Service	11 Federal Program	22 Art Sec	32 Career/Sch-to-Work Elem	42 Science K-12	52 Reading Elem	62 Foreign/World Lang Elem	72 Summer School
5 Transportation	12 Title I	23 Music K-12	33 Career/Sch-to-Work Sec	43 Science Elem	53 Reading Sec	63 Foreign/World Lang Sec	73 Instructional Tech
6 Athletic	13 Title V	24 Music Elem	34 Early Childhood Ed	44 Science Sec	54 Remedial Reading K-12	64 Religious Education K-12	74 Inservice Training
7 Health Services	15 Asst Superintendent	25 Music Sec	35 Health/Phys Education	45 Math K-12	55 Remedial Reading Elem	65 Religious Education Elem	75 Marketing/Distributive
	16 Instructional Media Svcs	26 Business Education	36 Guidance Services K-12	46 Math Elem	56 Remedial Reading Sec	66 Religious Education Sec	76 Info Systems
	17 Chief Operations Officer	27 Career & Tech Ed	37 Guidance Services Elem	47 Math Sec	57 Bilingual/ELL	67 School Board President	77 Psychological Assess
	18 Chief Academic Officer	28 Technology Education	38 Guidance Services Sec	48 English/Lang Arts K-12	58 Special Education K-12	68 Teacher Personnel	78 Affirmative Action

Ohio School Directory   Licking County

- **Symmes Valley Local Sch Dist** PID: 00814526   740/643-2451
  14778 State Route 141, Willow Wood 45696   Fax 740/643-1219

Schools: 2 \ **Teachers:** 54 \ **Students:** 743 \ **Special Ed Students:** 133 \ **College-Bound:** 46% \ **Ethnic:** Caucasian 100% \ **Exp:** $244 (Med) \ **Poverty:** 18% \ **Title I:** $218,238 \ **Special Education:** $204,000 \ **Open-Close:** 08/16 - 05/25 \ **DTBP:** $51 (Low)

Darrell Humphreys 1,11,57,83	Jack Webb 2	
Joe Cook 5	Brandon Walker 6*	
Kim Wells 10,69,288,298*	Jeff Pauley 16,73,295*	
Leslie Edens 16,82*	Sarah Wright 27*	
Crystal Bloomfield 38*	Nathan Hieronimus 67	

Public Schs..Principal	Grd	Prgm	Enr/#Cls	SN	
Symmes Valley Elem Sch 14860 State Route 141, Willow Wood 45696 Eric Holmes	PK-8	T	532 47		740/643-0023 Fax 740/643-0033
Symmes Valley High Sch 14778 State Route 141, Willow Wood 45696 Greg Bowman	9-12	V	211 21		740/643-2371 Fax 740/643-1606

LAWRENCE CATHOLIC SCHOOLS

- **Diocese of Steubenville Ed Off** PID: 00812671
  Listing includes only schools located in this county. See District Index for location of Diocesan Offices.

Catholic Schs..Principal	Grd	Prgm	Enr/#Cls	SN	
St Joseph High Sch 912 S 6th St, Ironton 45638 Chris Monte	7-12		99 10		740/532-0485 Fax 740/532-3699
St Lawrence Elem Sch 315 S 6th St, Ironton 45638 Chris Monte	PK-6		130 16		740/532-5052 Fax 740/532-5082

LAWRENCE PRIVATE SCHOOLS

Private Schs..Principal	Grd	Prgm	Enr/#Cls	SN	
Sugar Creek Christian Academy 4824 State Route 141, Ironton 45638 Michael Long	K-12		90		740/533-2215 f

LICKING COUNTY

LICKING COUNTY SCHOOLS

- **Licking Co Ed Service Center** PID: 02089208   740/349-6084
  621 Mount Vernon Rd, Newark 43055   Fax 740/349-6107

Dale Lewellen 1	Julio Valdares 2	
Jason Hankinson 8,68	Deborah Peger 34	
Kareen Robbins 58	Forest Yocum 67	
Glenn Welker 73,295	Holly Hartman 81	

County Schs..Principal	Grd	Prgm	Enr/#Cls	SN	
Flying Colors Pub Sch Pre-Sch 119 Union St, Newark 43055 Davelyn Ross	Spec		200 12		740/349-1629 Fax 740/349-1644

LICKING PUBLIC SCHOOLS

- **Granville Exempted Village SD** PID: 00814605   740/587-8101
  130 N Granger St, Granville 43023   Fax 888/683-7730

Schools: 4 \ **Teachers:** 131 \ **Students:** 2,500 \ **Special Ed Students:** 316 \ **LEP Students:** 30 \ **College-Bound:** 87% \ **Ethnic:** Asian 2%, African American 1%, Hispanic 2%, Caucasian 96% \ **Exp:** $193 (Low) \ **Poverty:** 3% \ **Title I:** $79,835 \ **Special Education:** $351,000 \ **Open-Close:** 08/21 - 05/28 \ **DTBP:** $193 (High) \ f t

Jeffery Brown 1	Michael Sobul 2,11	
Tonya Sherburne 2,3,68	Frank Fahner 3	
Jonathan Harbaugh 4*	Kim Clary 5	
Kevin Jarrett 6*	Gina Burdick 7*	
Ryan Bernath 8,15,273,288	Ruth Kozman 12*	
Sally Gummere 16,82*	Gwenn Spence 58,79*	
Russell Ginise 67	Cari Butler 71	
Glen Welker 73,295	Jeanna Giovannelli 81*	

Public Schs..Principal	Grd	Prgm	Enr/#Cls	SN	
Granville Elem Sch 310 N Granger St, Granville 43023 Travis Morris	K-3		712 40	5%	740/587-8102 Fax 740/587-2374 f t
Granville High Sch 248 New Burg St, Granville 43023 Matthew Durst	9-12		815 55	8%	740/587-8105 t
Granville Intermediate Sch 2025 Burg St, Granville 43023 Gayle Burris	4-6		578 19	6%	740/587-8103 f t
Granville Middle Sch 210 New Burg St, Granville 43023 Lisa Ormond	7-8		395 30		740/587-8104 t

- **Heath City School Dist** PID: 00814655   740/238-7110
  107 Lancaster Dr, Heath 43056   Fax 740/238-7053

Schools: 4 \ **Teachers:** 87 \ **Students:** 1,730 \ **Special Ed Students:** 210 \ **LEP Students:** 7 \ **College-Bound:** 54% \ **Ethnic:** Asian 1%, African American 2%, Hispanic 2%, Caucasian 94% \ **Exp:** $123 (Low) \ **Poverty:** 10% \ **Title I:** $314,502 \ **Special Education:** $192,000 \ **Open-Close:** 08/22 - 05/29 \ **DTBP:** $233 (High)

Dr Trevor Thomas 1	Karl Zarins 2	
Mike Whittington 3,5	Karen Guse 4	
Esther Villinger 7	Kelly Holbrook 8,11,15,57,69	
Tara Clark 36*	Jennifer McComas 58,77	
Debbie Kelley 67	Michelle Berry 73*	

Public Schs..Principal	Grd	Prgm	Enr/#Cls	SN	
Garfield Elem Sch 680 S 30th St, Heath 43056 Jeff Hempleman	K-2	T	394 18	48%	740/238-7120 Fax 740/238-7060
Heath High Sch 300 Licking View Dr, Heath 43056 Kat Feilds	9-12		485 30	41%	740/238-7150 Fax 740/238-7079
Heath Middle Sch 310 Licking View Dr, Heath 43056 Holly Myers	6-8	T	421 23	42%	740/238-7140 Fax 740/238-7072

79 Student Personnel	91 Safety/Security	275 Response To Intervention	298 Grant Writer/Ptnrships
30 Driver Ed/Safety	92 Magnet School	277 Remedial Math K-12	750 Chief Innovation Officer
31 Gifted/Talented	93 Parental Involvement	280 Literacy Coach	751 Chief of Staff
32 Video Services	95 Tech Prep Program	285 STEM	752 Social Emotional Learning
33 Substance Abuse Prev	97 Chief Information Officer	286 Digital Learning	
34 Erate	98 Chief Technology Officer	288 Common Core Standards	**Other School Types**
35 AIDS Education	270 Character Education	294 Accountability	Ⓐ = Alternative School
38 Alternative/At Risk	271 Migrant Education	295 Network System	Ⓒ = Charter School
39 Multi-Cultural Curriculum	273 Teacher Mentor	296 Title II Programs	Ⓜ = Magnet School
90 Social Work	274 Before/After Sch	297 Webmaster	Ⓨ = Year-Round School

School Programs
A = Alternative Program
G = Adult Classes
M = Magnet Program
T = Title I Schoolwide
V = Career & Tech Ed Programs

Social Media
f = Facebook
t = Twitter

New Schools are shaded
New Superintendents and Principals are bold
Personnel with email addresses are underscored

OH-117

Licking County — Market Data Retrieval

Stevenson Elem Sch	3-5	T	385	48%	740/238-7130
152 Cynthia St, Heath 43056			25		Fax 740/238-7066
Andra Kisner					

• Johnstown-Monroe Local SD   PID: 00814708
441 S Main St, Johnstown 43031   740/967-6846   Fax 740/967-1106

Schools: 3 \ **Teachers:** 88 \ **Students:** 1,600 \ **Special Ed Students:** 158 \ **LEP Students:** 23 \ **College-Bound:** 63% \ **Ethnic:** Asian 1%, Hispanic 4%, Caucasian 94% \ **Exp:** $274 (Med) \ **Poverty:** 5% \ **Title I:** $136,627 \ **Special Education:** $269,000 \ **Open-Close:** 08/21 - 05/28 \ **DTBP:** $244 (High)

Dale Dickson 1		Zach Niblick 2		
Michael Cartwright 4		Kristi Chumney 6*		
Christie Eyerman 12,58,273		Tim Swauyck 67		
Angela Newlon 73		Marissa Ballard 286*		

Public Schs..Principal	Grd	Prgm	Enr/#Cls	SN	
Johnstown Elem Sch	K-5	A	778		740/967-5461
200 Leafy Dell Rd, Johnstown 43031			15		Fax 740/966-5566
Janet Smith					
Johnstown-Monroe High Sch	9-12	AV	499	19%	740/967-2721
401 S Oregon St, Johnstown 43031			25		Fax 740/967-1140
Derick Busenburg					
Willis C Adams Middle Sch	6-8	AV	392	25%	740/967-8766
80 W Maple St, Johnstown 43031			25		Fax 740/967-0051
Kris Almendinger					

• Lakewood Local School Dist   PID: 00814758
525 E Main St, Hebron 43025   740/928-5878   Fax 740/928-3152

Schools: 4 \ **Teachers:** 130 \ **Students:** 1,900 \ **Special Ed Students:** 304 \ **LEP Students:** 4 \ **College-Bound:** 46% \ **Ethnic:** African American 1%, Hispanic 3%, Caucasian 96% \ **Exp:** $229 (Med) \ **Poverty:** 9% \ **Title I:** $362,400 \ **Special Education:** $358,000 \ **Open-Close:** 08/20 - 05/28 \ **DTBP:** $175 (High)

Mary Kay Andrews 1	Glenna Plaisted 2,19
Kyle Matthews 3	Jennifer Stove 4
Rodney Stufflebean 5	Scott Harris 6*
Amy Morrison 7*	Patti Pickering 8,11,69,79,288,294,296,298
Mark Severance 12,57,58,81	Dee Martindale 13*
Elisabeth Rauch 16,82,273*	Michael Mohler 31,88*
Tara Houdeshell 67	Mike Huntshield 73,76
Deanna Martindale 285	

Public Schs..Principal	Grd	Prgm	Enr/#Cls	SN	
Hebron Elem Sch	K-2	T	410	50%	740/928-7126
709 Deacon St, Hebron 43025			24		Fax 740/928-7510
Nicole Henry					
Jackson Intermediate Sch	3-5	T	470	50%	740/928-1915
9370 Lancer Rd, Hebron 43025			13		Fax 740/928-3756
Carol Field					
Lakewood High Sch	9-12	TV	548	33%	740/928-4526
9331 Lancer Rd, Hebron 43025			79		Fax 740/928-3731
Kevin Krier					
Lakewood Middle Sch	6-8	T	428	46%	740/928-8340
5222 National Rd SE, Hebron 43025			24		Fax 740/928-5627
Jessica Fry					

• Licking Co Joint Voc Sch Dist   PID: 00815324
150 Price Rd, Newark 43055   740/364-2832   Fax 740/364-2815

Schools: 1 \ **Teachers:** 48 \ **Students:** 750 \ **Exp:** $592 (High) \ **Open-Close:** 08/15 - 05/22 \ **DTBP:** $190 (High)

Dr Joyce Malainy 1,11	Benjamin Streby 2
Thomas Gamertsfelder 3,5,10*	Michelle Snow 10
Rocky Ringhiser 28,73,76,295*	Lauren Massie 30
Elissa Johnston 33,294*	Michelle McNeely 38,83,88*
Shirley Migliore 60*	Tina Hummel 60*
Bev Niccum 67	

Public Schs..Principal	Grd	Prgm	Enr/#Cls	SN	
Career Tech Ed Ctr Licking Co	Voc	G	750		740/364-2832
150 Price Rd, Newark 43055			40		Fax 740/364-2691
Thomas Gamertsfelder					

• Licking Heights Local Sch Dist   PID: 00814825
6539 Summit Rd SW, Pataskala 43062   740/927-6926   Fax 740/927-9043

Schools: 5 \ **Teachers:** 216 \ **Students:** 4,700 \ **Special Ed Students:** 517 \ **LEP Students:** 331 \ **College-Bound:** 72% \ **Ethnic:** Asian 3%, African American 30%, Hispanic 5%, Caucasian 63% \ **Exp:** $144 (Low) \ **Poverty:** 11% \ **Title I:** $616,571 \ **Special Education:** $427,000 \ **Open-Close:** 08/14 - 05/22 \ **DTBP:** $196 (High)

Dr Philip Wagner 1	Todd Griffith 2
Ginger Parsons 4*	Darlene Mortine 5
Rita Pendexter 6	Jennifer Price 7,83,88,275*
Mitch Tom 11,57,58,79,296*	Dr Bill Sternberg 15
Beth Chatfield 38*	Brian Bagley 67
Kim Henderson 68	Darian Kovach 73,76
Angel King 280*	

Public Schs..Principal	Grd	Prgm	Enr/#Cls	SN	
Licking Heights Central MS	6-8		1,010	41%	740/927-3365
6565 Summit Rd SW, Pataskala 43062					Fax 740/927-5845
Anna Annett					
Licking Heights High Sch	9-12	V	1,181	40%	740/927-9046
4000 Mink St SW, Pataskala 43062			19		Fax 740/927-3197
Tiffane Warren					
Licking Heights North Elem Sch	5-5		350	39%	740/927-3268
6507 Summit Rd SW, Pataskala 43062					Fax 740/927-5736
Anna Annett					
Licking Heights South Elem Sch	K-4	T	900	46%	740/964-1674
6623 Summit Rd SW, Pataskala 43062			31		Fax 740/964-1625
Kurt Scheiderer					
Licking Heights West Elem Sch	K-4	T	933	36%	614/864-9089
1490 Climbing Fig Dr, Blacklick 43004			29		Fax 614/501-4672
Belinda Hohman					

• Licking Valley Local Sch Dist   PID: 00814863
1379 Licking Valley Rd, Newark 43055   740/763-3525   Fax 740/763-0471

Schools: 3 \ **Teachers:** 109 \ **Students:** 2,000 \ **Special Ed Students:** 182 \ **College-Bound:** 56% \ **Ethnic:** African American 1%, Caucasian 99% \ **Exp:** $189 (Low) \ **Poverty:** 9% \ **Title I:** $317,479 \ **Special Education:** $360,000 \ **Open-Close:** 08/21 - 05/28 \ **DTBP:** $240 (High)

Dr David Hile 1,11	Jolynn Torbert 2,19
Jack Shinn 3,91	Jan Jennings 4*
Kate Paterson 4*	Mickie Archer 5
Mark McCullough 6*	Ashley Knowlton 8,12,13,58,69,275,285,296
Mike Kelly 16,71,84	Tracy Boehmer 16*

1	Superintendent	8	Curric/Instruct K-12	19	Chief Financial Officer	29	Family/Consumer Sci	39	Social Studies K-12
2	Bus/Finance/Purchasing	9	Curric/Instruct Elem	20	Art K-12	30	Adult Education	40	Social Studies Elem
3	Buildings And Grounds	10	Curric/Instruct Sec	21	Art Elem	31	Career/Sch-to-Work K-12	41	Social Studies Sec
4	Food Service	11	Federal Program	22	Art Sec	32	Career/Sch-to-Work Elem	42	Science K-12
5	Transportation	12	Title I	23	Music K-12	33	Career/Sch-to-Work Sec	43	Science Elem
6	Athletic	13	Title V	24	Music Elem	34	Early Childhood Ed	44	Science Sec
7	Health Services	15	Asst Superintendent	25	Music Sec	35	Health/Phys Education	45	Math K-12
		16	Instructional Media Svcs	26	Business Education	36	Guidance Services K-12	46	Math Elem
		17	Chief Operations Officer	27	Career & Tech Ed	37	Guidance Services Elem	47	Math Sec
		18	Chief Academic Officer	28	Technology Education	38	Guidance Services Sec	48	English/Lang Arts K-12

49	English/Lang Arts Elem	59	Special Education Elem	69	Academic Assessment
50	English/Lang Arts Sec	60	Special Education Sec	70	Research/Development
51	Reading K-12	61	Foreign/World Lang K-12	71	Public Information
52	Reading Elem	62	Foreign/World Lang Elem	72	Summer School
53	Reading Sec	63	Foreign/World Lang Sec	73	Instructional Tech
54	Remedial Reading K-12	64	Religious Education K-12	74	Inservice Training
55	Remedial Reading Elem	65	Religious Education Elem	75	Marketing/Distributive
56	Remedial Reading Sec	66	Religious Education Sec	76	Info Systems
57	Bilingual/ELL	67	School Board President	77	Psychological Assess
58	Special Education K-12	68	Teacher Personnel	78	Affirmative Action

Ohio School Directory

Licking County

Courtney Lichtenauer 38,83*	Lisa Bennet 38				
Mary Kay Martin 67	Travis Baughman 73,286,295				
Denise Mullett 88*					

Public Schs..Principal	Grd	Prgm	Enr/#Cls	SN	
Licking Valley Elem Sch 1510 Licking Valley Rd, Newark 43055 Todd Carmer \ Sherry Crum	K-5	T	963 40	42%	740/763-2865 Fax 740/763-3653
Licking Valley High Sch 100 Hainsview Dr, Newark 43055 Wes Weaver	9-12	V	568 48	31%	740/763-3721 Fax 740/763-0847
Licking Valley Middle Sch 1379 Licking Valley Rd, Newark 43055 Scott Beery	6-8	V	494 42	40%	740/763-3396 Fax 740/763-2612

● **Newark City School Dist** PID: 00814930   740/670-7000
621 Mount Vernon Rd, Newark 43055   Fax 740/670-7009

Schools: 13 \ *Teachers:* 336 \ *Students:* 6,500 \
Special Ed Students: 1,323 \ *LEP Students:* 36 \ *College-Bound:* 45%
\ *Ethnic:* Asian 1%, African American 4%, Hispanic 2%, Caucasian
93% \ *Exp:* $258 (Med) \ *Poverty:* 20% \ *Title I:* $3,263,762 \
Special Education: $1,100,000 \ *Open-Close:* 08/22 - 05/29 \ *DTBP:* $205
(High)

Douglas Ute 1	Mark Shively 2,3,78,91		
Todd Gallup 4*	Teresa Saward 5		
Jeff Quackenbush 6*	Maura Horgan 8,57,74,286,288		
Tara Boyer 11,69,74,294,296,298	Melinda Vaughn 58,275		
Jennifer McMahon 59	Nicole Garrison 60		
Warren Weber 67	Barbara Quackenbush 68		
Seth Roy 71	Amy Norman 73,295*		
Stephanie Debevoise 81	Laura Sluss 273		
Denise Rowe 280*			

Public Schs..Principal	Grd	Prgm	Enr/#Cls	SN	
Ben Franklin Elem Sch 533 Beacon Rd, Newark 43055 Dena Cable-Miller	PK-5	T	384 17	72%	740/670-7340 Fax 740/670-7349
Carson Elem Sch 549 E Main St, Newark 43055 Julie Elwell	K-5	T	443 15	79%	740/670-7300 Fax 740/670-7309
Cherry Valley Elem Sch 1040 W Main St, Newark 43055 Chet Coleman	PK-5	T	451 17	57%	740/670-7330 Fax 740/670-7339
Heritage Middle Sch 600 Arlington Ave, Newark 43055 Nolan Sadler	6-8	T	532 35	69%	740/670-7110 Fax 740/670-7119 f t
Hillview Elem Sch 1927 Horns Hill Rd, Newark 43055 Nicholas Myers	PK-5	T	458 15	61%	740/670-7310 Fax 740/670-7319
John Clem Elem Sch 475 Jefferson Rd, Newark 43055 Lynda Nabors	PK-5	T	467 20	62%	740/670-7130 Fax 740/670-7139 f
Legend Elem Sch 1075 Evans Blvd, Newark 43055 Ellen Cooper	PK-5	T	532 23	44%	740/670-7100 Fax 740/670-7109
Liberty Middle Sch 1055 Evans Blvd, Newark 43055 Brent Fickes	6-8	T	509 40	47%	740/670-7320 Fax 740/670-7329
McGuffey Elem Sch 130 Green Wave Dr, Newark 43055 Cynthia Baker	K-5	T	473 17	73%	740/670-7140 Fax 740/670-7149
ⒸNewark Digital Academy 255 Woods Ave, Newark 43055 John Lutz	5-12	T	425		740/328-2022 Fax 740/328-2270
Newark High Sch 314 Granville St, Newark 43055 Thomas Bowman	9-12	T	1,479 90	53%	740/670-7400 Fax 740/670-7409 f t
ⒸPar Excellence Academy 1350 Granville Rd, Newark 43055 Gisele James	K-6	T	252 7		740/344-7279 Fax 740/344-7272
Wilson Middle Sch 805 W Church St, Newark 43055 John Davis	6-8	T	410 25	64%	740/670-7120 Fax 740/670-7129

● **North Fork Local School Dist** PID: 00815142   740/892-3666
312 Maple Ave, Utica 43080   Fax 740/892-2937

Schools: 4 \ *Teachers:* 97 \ *Students:* 1,800 \ *Special Ed Students:* 259
\ *LEP Students:* 5 \ *College-Bound:* 44% \ *Ethnic:* African American
1%, Hispanic 1%, Caucasian 98% \ *Exp:* $238 (Med) \ *Poverty:* 11% \
Title I: $322,720 \ *Special Education:* $311,000 \ *Open-Close:* 08/21 -
05/28 \ *DTBP:* $174 (High)

Scott Hartley 1	Kelly Breehl 2,19,76
Adam Reynolds 3,91*	Mike Maxwell 4,5
Brian Radabaugh 6*	Jayme Blackstone 8,58,79,288*
Michele Gorius 11,35,83,85*	Kristina Grigsby 31*
Katherine Robinson 36	Farrah Cooperider 67
Ann Wright 68	Stephanie Kimpel 69*
Larry Smith 73,286,295*	Holly Hartman 81

Public Schs..Principal	Grd	Prgm	Enr/#Cls	SN	
Newton Elem Sch 6645 Mount Vernon Rd, Newark 43055 Michele Gorius	K-5	T	365 19	39%	740/745-5982 Fax 740/745-5524
Utica Elem Sch 367 Church St, Utica 43080 Brett Ballinger	K-5	T	420 21	46%	740/892-2551 Fax 740/892-2138
Utica Junior High Sch 260 N Jefferson St, Utica 43080 Marcia Rutherford	6-8	T	366 25	99%	740/892-2691 Fax 740/892-2203
Utica Senior High Sch 260 N Jefferson St, Utica 43080 Mark Bowman	9-12	GTV	443 26		740/892-2855 Fax 740/892-2090

● **Northridge Local School Dist** PID: 00815219   740/967-6631
6097 Johnstown Utica Rd, Johnstown 43031   Fax 740/967-5022

Schools: 4 \ *Teachers:* 69 \ *Students:* 1,300 \ *Special Ed Students:* 134
\ *LEP Students:* 16 \ *College-Bound:* 73% \ *Ethnic:* Hispanic 2%,
Caucasian 98% \ *Exp:* $95 (Low) \ *Poverty:* 7% \ *Title I:* $143,652 \
Special Education: $219,000 \ *Open-Close:* 08/20 - 05/28 \ *DTBP:* $264
(High)

Scott Schmidt 1	Britt Lewis 2,19
David Liggett 3*	Carley Lewis 4
Mike George 6	Jaime Scott 8
Jan Kelly 16,82,273*	Chad Scott 35,85*
Jenny Rauchenstein 38*	Michell McJecee 57,275
Doug Hart 67	Jack Kruse 73
Cathy McCormick 271	

Public Schs..Principal	Grd	Prgm	Enr/#Cls	SN	
Northridge High Sch 6066 Johnstown Utica Rd, Johnstown 43031 **Amanda Bernowski**	9-12	V	365 28	24%	740/967-6651 Fax 740/967-6958
Northridge Intermediate Sch 6066 Johnstown Utica Rd, Johnstown 43031 John Rathburn	4-5	T	170	38%	740/967-1401 Fax 740/967-2140

---

79 Student Personnel	91 Safety/Security	275 Response To Intervention	298 Grant Writer/Ptnrships
80 Driver Ed/Safety	92 Magnet School	277 Remedial Math K-12	750 Chief Innovation Officer
81 Gifted/Talented	93 Parental Involvement	280 Literacy Coach	751 Chief of Staff
82 Video Services	95 Tech Prep Program	285 STEM	752 Social Emotional Learning
83 Substance Abuse Prev	97 Chief Information Officer	286 Digital Learning	
84 Erate	98 Chief Technology Officer	288 Common Core Standards	**Other School Types**
85 AIDS Education	270 Character Education	294 Accountability	Ⓐ = Alternative School
88 Alternative/At Risk	271 Migrant Education	295 Network System	Ⓒ = Charter School
89 Multi-Cultural Curriculum	273 Teacher Mentor	296 Title II Programs	Ⓜ = Magnet School
90 Social Work	274 Before/After Sch	297 Webmaster	Ⓨ = Year-Round School

School Programs
A = Alternative Program
G = Adult Classes
M = Magnet Program
T = Title I Schoolwide
V = Career & Tech Ed Programs

Social Media
f = Facebook
t = Twitter

New Schools are shaded
New Superintendents and Principals are bold
Personnel with email addresses are underscored

OH—119

Logan County

Market Data Retrieval

Northridge Middle Sch 6-8 288 36% 740/967-6671
6066 Johnstown Utica Rd, Johnstown 43031   21   Fax 740/967-7083
Justin Grieger

Northridge Primary Sch K-3 316 32% 740/924-2691
124 College St, Alexandria 43001 20 Fax 740/924-6013
Jill Beaver

• **Southwest Licking Local SD** PID: 00815271 740/927-3941
927 South St Unit A, Pataskala 43062 Fax 740/927-4648

Schools: 6 \ *Teachers:* 210 \ *Students:* 4,300 \ *Special Ed Students:* 582 \ *LEP Students:* 35 \ *College-Bound:* 56% \ *Ethnic:* Asian 1%, African American 3%, Hispanic 3%, Caucasian 93% \ *Exp:* $102 (Low) \ *Poverty:* 6% \ *Title I:* $467,264 \ *Special Education:* $679,000 \ *Open-Close:* 08/20 - 05/28 \ *DTBP:* $199 (High)

Robert Jennell 1	Milinda Sturm 2
Richard Jones 2,84	Cindy Pickering 4
Todd Liston 5	Lisa Morelli-Nutter 6*
Tirzah Hammond 7,85*	Kasey Perkins 8,12,16,69,73,288,295,296
Paula Brunton 11,31,57,58,79,88,271,275	Adreana Carter 34
Kandee Engle 67	Tanya Moore 71*
Erin Miller 83*	Paula Ball 298

Public Schs..Principal	Grd	Prgm	Enr/#Cls	SN	
Etna Elem Sch 8500 Columbia Rd SW, Pataskala 43062 Alissa Hurstman	4-5		660 46	28%	740/927-5906 Fax 740/964-0129
Kirkersville Elem Sch 215 N 5th St, Kirkersville 43033 Brad Wehrman	K-2		619 20	30%	740/927-7281 Fax 740/964-1103
Pataskala Elem Sch 395 S High St, Pataskala 43062 Jospeh Pratt	2-3		640	29%	740/927-3861 Fax 740/927-7259
Southwest Licking ELC 927 South St Unit B, Pataskala 43062 Adrienne Carter	PK-PK		116		740/927-5437
Watkins Memorial High Sch 8868 Watkins Rd SW, Pataskala 43062 Michael Tanchevski	9-12	V	1,228 70	26%	740/927-3846 Fax 740/964-0088
Watkins Middle Sch 8808 Watkins Rd SW, Pataskala 43062 Ryan Brown	6-8		957 50	23%	740/927-5767 Fax 740/927-2337

LICKING CATHOLIC SCHOOLS

• **Diocese of Columbus Ed Office** PID: 00802717
Listing includes only schools located in this county. See District Index for location of Diocesan Offices.

Catholic Schs..Principal	Grd	Prgm	Enr/#Cls	SN	
Blessed Sacrament Sch 394 E Main St, Newark 43055 Joshua Caton	PK-8		175 9		740/345-4125 Fax 740/345-6168
Newark Catholic High Sch 1 Green Wave Dr, Newark 43055 Beth Hill	9-12		215 24		740/344-3594 Fax 740/344-0421
St Francis DeSales Elem Sch 38 Granville St, Newark 43055 Sally Mummey	PK-8		275 22		740/345-4049 Fax 740/345-9768

LICKING PRIVATE SCHOOLS

Private Schs..Principal	Grd	Prgm	Enr/#Cls	SN	
Granville Christian Academy 1820 Newark Granville Rd, Granville 43023 Jayme Diener	K-12		300 20		740/587-4423 Fax 740/587-4776
Kairos Academy 50 S 2nd St Ste 3, Newark 43055 Lea Anderson	Spec		40		740/345-1995 Fax 740/345-5577
Liberty Christian Academy 10447 Refugee Rd SW, Pataskala 43062 Amanda Cecil \ Melanie Gilliland \ Kimberly Kussmaul	PK-12		321		740/964-2211 Fax 740/964-2311
Licking County Christian Acad 81 Licking View Dr, Heath 43056 Craig Westerlund	PK-12		61 18		740/522-3600 Fax 740/522-3619
Newark SDA Sch 701 Linnville Rd, Heath 43056	K-12		17 1		740/323-4222
Welsh Hills Sch 2610 Newark Granville Rd, Granville 43023 Michele Lerner	PK-10		20 5		740/522-2020 Fax 740/522-1500

LICKING REGIONAL CENTERS

• **Laca-Licking Area Cmop Assoc** PID: 04499427 740/345-3400
150 S Quentin Rd, Newark 43055 Fax 740/345-3427

Chad Carson 1	Trish Baker 16
Annie Epperson 58	Jerry Edy 73
Joseph Alexander 76,295	

LOGAN COUNTY

LOGAN COUNTY SCHOOLS

• **Midwest Reg Ed Service Center** PID: 00810489 937/599-5195
121 S Opera St, Bellefontaine 43311 Fax 937/599-1959

Scott Howell ....1 Keith Thomas 2

County Schs..Principal	Grd	Prgm	Enr/#Cls	SN	
Mac-A-Cheek Learning Center 401 E Pine Ave, Bellefontaine 43311 Christine Jeffers	Spec		72 7		937/292-7956 Fax 937/592-0120

LOGAN PUBLIC SCHOOLS

• **Bellefontaine City School Dist** PID: 00815362 937/593-9060
820 Ludlow Rd, Bellefontaine 43311 Fax 937/599-1346

Schools: 4 \ *Teachers:* 170 \ *Students:* 2,600 \ *Special Ed Students:* 451 \ *LEP Students:* 11 \ *College-Bound:* 42% \ *Ethnic:* Asian 1%, African American 4%, Hispanic 3%, Caucasian 93% \ *Exp:* $160 (Low) \ *Poverty:* 19% \ *Title I:* $782,738 \ *Special Education:* $554,000 \ *Open-Close:* 08/14 - 05/21 \ *DTBP:* $199 (High)

1 Superintendent	8 Curric/Instruct K-12	19 Chief Financial Officer	29 Family/Consumer Science	39 Social Studies K-12	49 English/Lang Arts Elem	59 Special Education Elem	69 Academic Assessment
2 Bus/Finance/Purchasing	9 Curric/Instruct Elem	20 Art K-12	30 Adult Education	40 Social Studies Elem	50 English/Lang Arts Sec	60 Special Education Sec	70 Research/Development
3 Buildings And Grounds	10 Curric/Instruct Sec	21 Art Elem	31 Career/Sch-to-Work K-12	41 Social Studies Sec	51 Reading K-12	61 Foreign/World Lang K-12	71 Public Information
4 Food Service	11 Federal Program	22 Art Sec	32 Career/Sch-to-Work Elem	42 Science K-12	52 Reading Elem	62 Foreign/World Lang Elem	72 Summer School
5 Transportation	12 Title I	23 Music K-12	33 Career/Sch-to-Work Sec	43 Science Elem	53 Reading Sec	63 Foreign/World Lang Sec	73 Instructional Tech
6 Athletic	13 Title V	24 Music Elem	34 Early Childhood Ed	44 Science Sec	54 Remedial Reading K-12	64 Religious Education K-12	74 Inservice Training
7 Health Services	14 Asst Superintendent	25 Music Sec	35 Health/Phys Education	45 Math K-12	55 Remedial Reading Elem	65 Religious Education Elem	75 Marketing/Distributive
	15 Instructional Media Svcs	26 Business Education	36 Guidance Services K-12	46 Math Elem	56 Remedial Reading Sec	66 Religious Education Sec	76 Info Systems
	16 Chief Operations Officer	27 Career & Tech Ed	37 Guidance Services Elem	47 Math Sec	57 Bilingual/ELL	67 School Board President	77 Psychological Assess
	17 Chief Academic Officer	28 Technology Education	38 Guidance Services Sec	48 English/Lang Arts K-12	58 Special Education K-12	68 Teacher Personnel	78 Affirmative Action

Ohio School Directory

Logan County

Bradley Hall 1
Max Earick 3*
Tammie Garman 5
Katie Busskin 7,85*
Eric Hamm 36*
Joan Haushalter 67
Angela Horvath 81*
Roger Ely 2,5,91
Winnie Jacks 4
Matt Comstock 6*
Shanel Henry 8,11,288,296,298*
Kyle Daring 57,58*
Marie Borba 76,295*

Public Schs..Principal	Grd	Prgm	Enr/#Cls	SN
Bellefontaine Elem Sch 1001 Ludlow Rd, Bellefontaine 43311 Pat Martz	K-2	T	539 20	57% 937/599-4431 Fax 937/599-3262
Bellefontaine High Sch 555 E Lake Ave, Bellefontaine 43311 Dr Pamela Noeth	9-12	T	687 60	38% 937/593-0545 Fax 937/593-0575
Bellefontaine Intermediate Sch 509 N Park St, Bellefontaine 43311 Krista Adelsberger	3-5	T	562 17	57% 937/592-5646 Fax 937/599-3327
Bellefontaine Middle Sch 1201 Ludlow Rd, Bellefontaine 43311 Lynda Holycross	6-8	T	560 50	48% 937/593-9010 Fax 937/593-9030

● Benjamin Logan Local Sch Dist PID: 00815439
4740 County Road 26, Bellefontaine 43311
937/593-9211
Fax 937/599-4059

Schools: 3 \ **Teachers:** 105 \ **Students:** 1,750 \ **Special Ed Students:** 222 \ **LEP Students:** 3 \ **College-Bound:** 47% \ **Ethnic:** Hispanic 2%, Caucasian 98% \ **Exp:** $227 (Med) \ **Poverty:** 8% \ **Title I:** $199,411 \ **Special Education:** $246,000 \ **Open-Close:** 08/14 - 05/21 \ **DTBP:** $181 (High)

David Harmon 1
Matt Pennington 3
Brenda Fahle 5
Amanda Siefring 7
Colleen Bodin 9,69*
Scott LeVan 58,275
Nic George 73
Mandie Frandt 2
Jann McBrien 4
Scott Reule 6*
Sally Stolly 8,11,16,83,298
Brian Hunt 11,274
Susan Allen 67
Andy Higgins 77*

Public Schs..Principal	Grd	Prgm	Enr/#Cls	SN
Benjamin Logan Elem Sch 4560 County Road 26, Bellefontaine 43311 Colleen Bodin	K-4		626 35	32% 937/592-4838 Fax 937/599-4063
Benjamin Logan High Sch 6609 State Route 47 E, Bellefontaine 43311 Mark Butler	9-12	V	489 35	23% 937/592-1666 Fax 937/599-4061
Benjamin Logan Middle Sch 4626 County Road 26, Bellefontaine 43311 Scott Frederick	5-8		589 29	26% 937/599-2386 Fax 937/599-4062

● Indian Lake Local School Dist PID: 00815506
6210 State Route 235 N, Lewistown 43333
937/686-8601
Fax 937/686-8421

Schools: 3 \ **Teachers:** 105 \ **Students:** 1,516 \ **Special Ed Students:** 225 \ **College-Bound:** 39% \ **Ethnic:** African American 1%, Hispanic 3%, Caucasian 96% \ **Exp:** $106 (Low) \ **Poverty:** 18% \ **Title I:** $453,544 \ **Special Education:** $422,000 \ **Open-Close:** 08/21 - 05/20 \ **DTBP:** $177 (High)

Robert Underwood 1,11
Dustin Plikerd 3
Susan Young 4*
Jeff Courter 6
Suzy Mallory 37*
Meaghan Tidwell 58*
Ron Borgerding 73*
Coleen Reprogle 2
Matt Hurley 3
Patrick Smith 5
Kelli Tebbe 8,296
Lakeisha Steierhoff 38*
Gabe Wickline 67

Public Schs..Principal	Grd	Prgm	Enr/#Cls	SN
Indian Lake Elem Sch 8770 County Road 91, Lewistown 43333 Molly Hall	K-4	T	553 14	50% 937/686-7323 Fax 937/686-0049
Indian Lake High Sch 6210 State Route 235 N, Lewistown 43333 Kyle Wagner	9-12		393	43% 937/686-8851 Fax 937/686-0024
Indian Lake Middle Sch 8920 County Road 91, Lewistown 43333 Erin Miller	5-8	T	523 40	45% 937/686-8833 Fax 937/686-8993

● Ohio Hi-Point Joint Voc SD PID: 00815594
2280 State Route 540, Bellefontaine 43311
937/599-3010
Fax 937/599-2318

Schools: 1 \ **Teachers:** 72 \ **Students:** 500 \ **College-Bound:** 60% \ **Exp:** $1,578 (High) \ **Open-Close:** 08/15 - 05/22 \ **DTBP:** $170 (High)

Rick Smith 1,11
Robert Walker 3*
Amy McCarthy 7,91*
John Case 73*
Eric Adelsberger 2
Don Jaunzemis 4*
Anne Reames 67

Public Schs..Principal	Grd	Prgm	Enr/#Cls	SN
Ohio Hi-Point Career Center 2280 State Route 540, Bellefontaine 43311 Tonya Ramey	Voc	AG	500 20	937/599-3010 Fax 937/592-9733

● Riverside Local School Dist PID: 00815556
2096 County Road 24 S, De Graff 43318
937/585-5981
Fax 937/585-4599

Schools: 2 \ **Teachers:** 47 \ **Students:** 633 \ **Special Ed Students:** 103 \ **College-Bound:** 41% \ **Ethnic:** Hispanic 2%, Caucasian 97% \ **Exp:** $267 (Med) \ **Poverty:** 11% \ **Title I:** $155,562 \ **Special Education:** $167,000 \ **Open-Close:** 08/14 - 05/21 \ **DTBP:** $173 (High)

Scott Mann 1,11
Jason Bell 3,4,5
Mason Bryan 8,13,285,288*
Debbie Gonterman 36,83,88*
Dr Bradley Adams 67
Ronnie Fitzpatrick 2,298
Rodney Yoder 6*
Lori Roberts 16*
Pam Gibson 58*
Brandi Thompson 73

Public Schs..Principal	Grd	Prgm	Enr/#Cls	SN
Riverside Elem Sch 2096 County Road 24 S, De Graff 43318 Mason Bryan	PK-6	T	323 23	94% 937/585-5981
Riverside Jr Sr High Sch 2096 County Road 24 S, De Graff 43318 Kelly Kauffman	7-12	TV	329 27	937/585-5981

LOGAN PRIVATE SCHOOLS

Private Schs..Principal	Grd	Prgm	Enr/#Cls	SN
Calvary Christian Sch 1140 Rush Ave, Bellefontaine 43311 Paul Green	PK-12		273 10	937/599-6847 Fax 937/599-4879

Lorain County

LORAIN COUNTY

LORAIN COUNTY SCHOOLS

• **Ed Service Center Lorain Co** PID: 00816823   440/324-5777
1885 Lake Ave, Elyria 44035   Fax 440/324-7355

Franco Gallo	....	1
Moira Erwine	....	8,74,275
Elizabeth Fleming Krall	....	34
Dave Miller	....	73,76,295
Jill Orseno	....	2
Jody Weidrick	....	11
Jamie Maassen	....	58
Julie Blankenship	....	275*

County Schs..Principal	Grd	Prgm	Enr/#Cls	SN	
ⓒ Elyria Cmty Elem Middle Sch [242] 300 Abbe Rd N, Elyria 44035 Thomas Flood	K-8		491 14		440/366-5225 Fax 440/366-6280
ⓒ Lorain Cmty Elem Sch [242] 1110 W 4th St, Lorain 44052 Adam Peters	K-4	T	188 10		440/204-2130 Fax 440/204-2134
ⓒ Lorain Cmty Middle Sch [242] 1110 W 4th St, Lorain 44052 Adam Peters	5-8	T	138		440/242-2023 Fax 440/204-2134
Murray Ridge Sch 9750 Murray Ridge Rd, Elyria 44035 Dann Swift	Spec		130 22		440/329-3760 Fax 440/322-5849
ⓐ Pathways to Success 15233 State Route 58, Oberlin 44074 Graham Henderson	6-9		50		440/775-0276
ⓒ Summit Acad Alt Lrng-Lorain 2140 E 36th St, Lorain 44055 Albert Charpentier	Spec	AT	138		440/277-4110 Fax 440/277-4112
ⓒ Summit Academy Sch-Lorain [248] 346 Illinois Ave, Lorain 44052 Michael Willinston	6-12	T	110 4		440/288-0448 Fax 440/288-0997

LORAIN PUBLIC SCHOOLS

• **Amherst Exempted Village SD** PID: 00815611   440/988-4406
185 Forest St, Amherst 44001   Fax 440/988-4413

Schools: 4 \ *Teachers:* 190 \ *Students:* 3,800 \ *Special Ed Students:* 522 \ *LEP Students:* 10 \ *College-Bound:* 72% \ *Ethnic:* Asian 1%, African American 3%, Hispanic 13%, Caucasian 83% \ *Exp:* $186 (Low) \ *Poverty:* 7% \ *Title I:* $351,835 \ *Special Education:* $826,000 \ *Open-Close:* 08/21 - 05/28 \ *DTBP:* $192 (High) \

Steven Sayers	....	1
Chuck Grimmept	....	3
Cathy Gale	....	5
Michael Molnar	....	8,11,15,286,288,294,296
Rhonda Neuoff	....	57
Beth Schwartz	....	69,274*
Amanda Sears	....	285
Amelia Gioffredo	....	2
Deanne Pastva	....	4
Casey Wolf	....	6*
Sarah Walker	....	11,34,58
Rex Engle	....	67
Doug Cogdell	....	73,295

Public Schs..Principal	Grd	Prgm	Enr/#Cls	SN	
Amherst Junior High Sch 548 Milan Ave, Amherst 44001 Andrew Gibson	6-8		774	21%	440/988-0324 Fax 440/988-0328
Powers Elem Sch 401 Washington St, Amherst 44001 Beth Schwartz	PK-2		796 30	26%	440/988-8670 Fax 440/988-8674
Steele High Sch 450 Washington St, Amherst 44001 Joseph Tellier	9-12	V	1,305 67	16%	440/988-4433 Fax 440/988-5087
Walter G Nord Middle Sch 501 Lincoln St, Amherst 44001 Jill Jiovanazzo	3-6		743 25	20%	440/988-4441 Fax 440/988-2371

• **Avon Lake City School Dist** PID: 00815726   440/933-6210
175 Avon Belden Rd, Avon Lake 44012   Fax 440/933-6711

Schools: 7 \ *Teachers:* 203 \ *Students:* 3,819 \ *Special Ed Students:* 404 \ *LEP Students:* 22 \ *College-Bound:* 84% \ *Ethnic:* Asian 2%, African American 1%, Hispanic 2%, Caucasian 95% \ *Exp:* $208 (Med) \ *Poverty:* 4% \ *Title I:* $118,684 \ *Special Education:* $618,000 \ *Open-Close:* 08/21 - 06/03 \ *DTBP:* $187 (High)

Robert Scott	....	1
Thomas Barone	....	2,3
Sue Cole	....	5
Becky Busch	....	7
James Stobe	....	67
Vishtasp Nuggud	....	285*
Autumn Reed	....	2,11,19,288,296
Bruce Kauffman	....	3,91
Brent Schremp	....	6*
Dr Daniel Murdock	....	31,57,58,69,88
Scott Wuensch	....	73,84,98

Public Schs..Principal	Grd	Prgm	Enr/#Cls	SN	
Avon Lake High Sch 175 Avon Belden Rd, Avon Lake 44012 Joseph Mueller	9-12	AV	1,249 100	11%	440/933-6290 Fax 440/930-2798
Eastview Elem Sch 230 Lear Rd, Avon Lake 44012 James Franko	K-4		431 18	6%	440/933-6283 Fax 440/930-7012
Erieview Elem Sch 32630 Electric Blvd, Avon Lake 44012 David Schindler	K-4		278 13	7%	440/933-6282 Fax 440/933-6381
Learwood Middle Sch 340 Lear Rd, Avon Lake 44012 Vishtasp Nuggud	7-8		616 38	12%	440/933-8142 Fax 440/933-8406
Redwood Elem Sch 32967 Redwood Blvd, Avon Lake 44012 Tj Ebert	PK-4		408 28	17%	440/933-5145 Fax 440/933-6230
Troy Intermediate Sch 237 Belmar Blvd, Avon Lake 44012 Andrew Peltz	5-6		604 21	13%	440/933-2701 Fax 440/930-8297
Westview Elem Sch 155 Moore Rd, Avon Lake 44012 Nick Moore	K-4		211 14	16%	440/933-8131 Fax 440/933-7025

• **Avon Local School Dist** PID: 00815685   440/937-4680
36600 Detroit Rd, Avon 44011   Fax 440/937-4688

Schools: 5 \ *Teachers:* 197 \ *Students:* 4,650 \ *Special Ed Students:* 502 \ *LEP Students:* 92 \ *College-Bound:* 87% \ *Ethnic:* Asian 4%, African American 3%, Hispanic 7%, Caucasian 87% \ *Exp:* $180 (Low) \ *Poverty:* 4% \ *Title I:* $138,915 \ *Special Education:* $663,000 \ *Open-Close:* 08/22 - 06/03 \ *DTBP:* $182 (High)

Michael Laub	....	1
Greg Manik	....	3
Jim Blodgett	....	5
Benjamin Hodge	....	8,11,15,57,288,296
Jason Call	....	11,36,58,77
John Weigman	....	67
Larry Fish	....	73
Amanda Shultzaberger	....	274*
Katie Henes	....	2
Nancy Kowalczyk	....	4*
Erich Frombach	....	6
Valerie Kaminski	....	8
Kelly Gonzalez	....	16*
Sherry Pietch	....	69*
Dr Craig Koehler	....	83,88

---

1 Superintendent	8 Curric/Instruct K-12	19 Chief Financial Officer	29 Family/Consumer Science	39 Social Studies K-12	49 English/Lang Arts Elem	59 Special Education Elem	69 Academic Assessment
2 Bus/Finance/Purchasing	9 Curric/Instruct Elem	20 Art K-12	30 Adult Education	40 Social Studies Elem	50 English/Lang Arts Sec	60 Special Education Sec	70 Research/Development
3 Buildings And Grounds	10 Curric/Instruct Sec	21 Art Elem	31 Career/Sch-to-Work K-12	41 Social Studies Sec	51 Reading K-12	61 Foreign/World Lang K-12	71 Public Information
4 Food Service	11 Federal Program	22 Art Sec	32 Career/Sch-to-Work Elem	42 Science K-12	52 Reading Elem	62 Foreign/World Lang Elem	72 Summer School
5 Transportation	12 Title I	23 Music K-12	33 Career/Sch-to-Work Sec	43 Science Elem	53 Reading Sec	63 Foreign/World Lang Sec	73 Instructional Tech
6 Athletic	13 Title V	24 Music Elem	34 Early Childhood Ed	44 Science Sec	54 Remedial Reading K-12	64 Religious Education K-12	74 Inservice Training
7 Health Services	14 Instructional Media Svcs	25 Music Sec	35 Health/Phys Education	45 Math K-12	55 Remedial Reading Elem	65 Religious Education Elem	75 Marketing/Distributive
	15 Asst Superintendent	26 Business Education	36 Guidance Services K-12	46 Math Elem	56 Remedial Reading Sec	66 Religious Education Sec	76 Info Systems
	16 Instructional Media Svcs	27 Career & Tech Ed	37 Guidance Services Elem	47 Math Sec	57 Bilingual/ELL	67 School Board President	77 Psychological Assess
	17 Chief Operations Officer	28 Technology Education	38 Guidance Services Sec	48 English/Lang Arts K-12	58 Special Education K-12	68 Teacher Personnel	78 Affirmative Action
	18 Chief Academic Officer						

Ohio School Directory — Lorain County

Public Schs..Principal	Grd	Prgm	Enr/#Cls	SN	
Avon Early Learning Center
3075 Stoney Ridge Rd, Avon 44011
Colleen Mudore	K-K		254
13	12%	440/934-5124
Fax 440/934-2147
Avon Heritage Elem Sch
35575 Detroit Rd, Avon 44011
Jen Fitch	3-5		984
23		440/937-9660
Fax 440/937-9620
Avon High Sch
37545 Detroit Rd, Avon 44011
Kristina Buller	9-12		1,359
40	10%	440/934-6171
Fax 440/934-5450
Avon Middle Sch
3445 Long Rd, Avon 44011
Dr Craig Koehler	6-8		1,102
30	11%	440/934-3800
Fax 440/934-3803
East Elem Sch
3100 Nagel Rd, Avon 44011
Erin Holzhauer	1-2		632
20	10%	440/937-6015
Fax 440/937-5525

Clearview Local School Dist PID: 00815805
4700 Broadway, Lorain 44052
440/233-5412 Fax 440/233-6034

Schools: 3 \ **Teachers:** 79 \ **Students:** 1,644 \ **Special Ed Students:** 140 \ **LEP Students:** 25 \ **College-Bound:** 59% \ **Ethnic:** African American 13%, Hispanic 38%, Caucasian 48% \ **Exp:** $170 (Low) \ **Poverty:** 30% \ **Title I:** $532,487 \ **Special Education:** $312,000 \ **Open-Close:** 08/21 - 06/02 \ **DTBP:** $25 (Low) \ f t

Jerome Davis 1
Mark Smarsh 3
Giles Brown 5
Susan Loper 7*
Lynne Stark 12,72,274
Tammy Sanfelippo 57*
Heidi Adkins 67
Deborah Molnar 273*
Maryann Nowak 2,11,19,298
Cheryl Gillies 4
Mike Collier 6*
Dr Paul Kish 8,270,296
Danielle Long 16,82
Doreen Morell 58,271
Alicia Howard 69*
Hillary Rios 297*

Public Schs..Principal	Grd	Prgm	Enr/#Cls	SN	
Clearview High Sch
4700 Broadway, Lorain 44052
Noeleen Rothacker	9-12	T	503
50		440/233-6313
Fax 440/233-6311
Durling Middle Sch
100 N Ridge Rd W, Lorain 44053
Laura Manning	5-8	T	530
12		440/233-6869
Fax 440/233-6042 f t
Vincent Elem Sch
2303 N Ridge Rd E, Lorain 44055
Lisa Ryan	K-4	T	611
28		440/233-7113
Fax 440/233-7114 f t

Columbia Local School Dist PID: 00815855
25796 Royalton Rd, Columbia Sta 44028
440/236-5008 Fax 440/236-8817

Schools: 3 \ **Teachers:** 61 \ **Students:** 900 \ **Special Ed Students:** 99 \ **College-Bound:** 60% \ **Ethnic:** Hispanic 4%, Caucasian 96% \ **Exp:** $298 (Med) \ **Poverty:** 10% \ **Title I:** $128,357 \ **Special Education:** $165,000 \ **Open-Close:** 09/03 - 06/03 \ **DTBP:** $272 (High)

Graig Bansek 1,84
Bernard Gault 3
Jeff Jump 6*
Lynley Roncone 13,69,77
Judy Skoczen 58
Jessica Bowman 81*
Pat Eddy 2,11
Alan Cantrell 5
Carrie Atkinson 8,12,73,76,285,286,288,298
Suzie Neff 38*
Wayne Brassell 67

Public Schs..Principal	Grd	Prgm	Enr/#Cls	SN	
Columbia High Sch
14168 W River Rd, Columbia Sta 44028
Sean Lynch	9-12	V	270
22	32%	440/236-5001
Fax 440/236-3081 t
Columbia Middle Sch
13646 W River Rd, Columbia Sta 44028
Robert Magyar	5-8		270
16	61%	440/236-5741
Fax 440/236-9274
Copopa Elem Sch
13644 W River Rd, Columbia Sta 44028
Troy Bunner	K-4		291
30		440/236-5020
Fax 440/236-1220

Elyria City School Dist PID: 00815908
42101 Griswold Rd, Elyria 44035
440/284-8000 Fax 440/284-0678

Schools: 13 \ **Teachers:** 370 \ **Students:** 7,010 \ **Special Ed Students:** 1,133 \ **LEP Students:** 134 \ **College-Bound:** 55% \ **Ethnic:** African American 25%, Hispanic 12%, Caucasian 62% \ **Exp:** $131 (Low) \ **Poverty:** 25% \ **Title I:** $3,275,885 \ **Special Education:** $1,501,000 \ **Open-Close:** 08/28 - 06/03 \ **DTBP:** $221 (High) \ f

Ann Schloss 1
Kyle Suerth 4
Heather Beck 6*
Ramona Mendak 8,81
Denise Blatt 58
Jaimie Barnier 68,74,273
Brian Kokai 73
Jacob Karmony 2,3,5,91
Nicole McDaniel 5
Amy Keir 8
Carrie Pope 58
Greg Elek 67
Amy Higgins 71

Public Schs..Principal	Grd	Prgm	Enr/#Cls	SN	
Crestwood Elem Sch
42331 Griswold Rd, Elyria 44035
Steve Grossman	K-5	T	441
20	77%	440/284-8002
Fax 440/284-8131
Early College High Sch
1005 Abbe Rd N, Elyria 44035
Shane Newark	9-12		300
8		440/365-5222
Fax 440/366-4710
Eastern Heights Middle Sch
528 Garford Ave, Elyria 44035
Kimberly Bennetto	6-8	TV	421
45	60%	440/284-8015
Fax 440/323-0827
Ely Elem Sch
312 Gulf Rd, Elyria 44035
Dr Jack Dibee	K-5		408
23	68%	440/284-8005
Fax 440/284-8148
Elyria Early Childhood Village
42101 Griswold Rd, Elyria 44035
Robyn Fisher	PK-K	T	341
14	46%	440/284-8000
Fax 440/284-8162
Elyria High Sch
601 Middle Ave, Elyria 44035
Timothy Brown	9-12	TV	1,813
60%	440/284-8300
Fax 440/323-2543 f
Franklin Elem Sch
446 11th St, Elyria 44035
Lisa Licht	PK-5	T	453
22	93%	440/284-8007
Fax 440/284-8371
McKinley Elem Sch
620 E River St, Elyria 44035
Virginia Fitch	K-5	T	345
19	57%	440/284-8009
Fax 440/284-8382
Northwood Middle Sch
700 Gulf Rd, Elyria 44035
Michael Basinski	6-8	TV	425
40	60%	440/284-8016
Fax 440/284-1546
Oakwood Elem Sch
925 Spruce St, Elyria 44035
Joy Jones	1-5	T	268
23	87%	440/284-8010
Fax 440/284-8181
Prospect Elem Sch
1410 Prospect St, Elyria 44035
Jessica Barwacz	K-5	T	356
21	56%	440/284-8011
Fax 440/284-3885
Westwood Middle Sch
42180 Adelbert St, Elyria 44035
Theresa Lengel	6-8	TV	425
30	69%	440/284-8017
Fax 440/284-1055
Windsor Elem Sch
264 Windsor Dr, Elyria 44035
Miranda Rosco	K-5	T	397
20	52%	440/284-8014

---

79 Student Personnel
80 Driver Ed/Safety
81 Gifted/Talented
82 Video Services
83 Substance Abuse Prev
84 Erate
85 AIDS Education
88 Alternative/At Risk
89 Multi-Cultural Curriculum
90 Social Work

91 Safety/Security
92 Magnet School
93 Parental Involvement
95 Tech Prep Program
97 Chief Infomation Officer
98 Chief Technology Officer
270 Character Education
271 Migrant Education
273 Teacher Mentor
274 Before/After Sch

275 Response To Intervention
277 Remedial Math K-12
280 Literacy Coach
285 STEM
286 Digital Learning
288 Common Core Standards
294 Accountability
295 Network System
296 Title II Programs
297 Webmaster

298 Grant Writer/Ptnrships
750 Chief of Innovation Officer
751 Chief of Staff
752 Social Emotional Learning

Other School Types
Ⓐ = Alternative School
Ⓒ = Charter School
Ⓜ = Magnet School
Ⓨ = Year-Round School

School Programs
A = Alternative Program
G = Adult Classes
M = Magnet Program
T = Title I Schoolwide
V = Career & Tech Ed Programs

Social Media
f = Facebook
t = Twitter

New Schools are shaded
New Superintendents and Principals are bold
Personnel with email addresses are underscored

OH—123

Lorain County

Market Data Retrieval

- **Firelands Local School Dist** PID: 00816146
  112 N Lake St, South Amherst 44001
  440/965-5821
  Fax 440/986-5702

Schools: 4 \ *Teachers:* 95 \ *Students:* 1,626 \ *Special Ed Students:* 200 \ *College-Bound:* 68% \ *Ethnic:* African American 1%, Hispanic 4%, Caucasian 96% \ *Exp:* $175 (Low) \ *Poverty:* 11% \ *Title I:* $244,107 \ *Special Education:* $318,000 \ *Open-Close:* 08/27 - 05/29 \ *DTBP:* $234 (High)

Mike Von Gunten 1	Keri Angney 2
Charles Galloway 3,91	Judy Baumann 4
Milt Sayler 5	Ty Stillman 6
Laureen Roemer 8,16,73	Dr Edward Roshaun 58*
Mike O'Keefe 67	Jennifer Butchko 71

Public Schs..Principal	Grd	Prgm	Enr/#Cls	SN	
ⓐ Firelands Digital Academy 10648 Vermilion Rd, Oberlin 44074 Kenny Searight	9-12		10		440/965-4255
Firelands Elem Sch 10779 Vermilion Rd, Oberlin 44074 Sun Choe	K-5		724 17	34%	440/965-5381 Fax 440/965-8849
Firelands High Sch 10643 Vermilion Rd, Oberlin 44074 Robert Maver	9-12		494 35	33%	440/965-4255 Fax 440/965-5296
South Amherst Middle Sch 152 W Main St, South Amherst 44001 Cara Gomez	6-8		408 35	33%	440/986-7021 Fax 440/986-7022

- **Keystone Local School Dist** PID: 00816213
  531 Opportunity Way, Lagrange 44050
  440/355-2424
  Fax 440/355-4465

Schools: 3 \ *Teachers:* 77 \ *Students:* 1,500 \ *Special Ed Students:* 185 \ *College-Bound:* 65% \ *Ethnic:* Asian 1%, Hispanic 3%, Caucasian 95% \ *Exp:* $197 (Low) \ *Poverty:* 9% \ *Title I:* $189,097 \ *Special Education:* $216,000 \ *Open-Close:* 08/26 - 05/21 \ *DTBP:* $176 (High) \ 🅵 🆃

Daniel White 1	Michael Resar 2
Albert Trego 3	Jody White 4*
Jonathan Dailey 6	Dana Corrani 7,85
Dave Kish 8,11*	Lynn Gagnon 16*
James Kohler 27,31*	Joe Phillips 28,73*
Jaqueline Vance 57,58	Dennis Walter 67
Toni Filut 69,81*	Phillip Tuttle 273*
Jacquelynn Daymut 285*	

Public Schs..Principal	Grd	Prgm	Enr/#Cls	SN	
Keystone Elem Sch 531 Opportunity Way, Lagrange 44050 Jacob Alferio	K-5		671 28		440/355-2300 Fax 440/355-4240 🅵 🆃
Keystone High Sch 580 Opportunity Way, Lagrange 44050 James Kohler	9-12	V	449 35	25%	440/355-2400 Fax 440/355-6017 🅵 🆃
Keystone Middle Sch 501 Opportunity Way, Lagrange 44050 Antonietta Filut	6-8		350 35	26%	440/355-2200 Fax 440/355-6678

- **Lorain City School Dist** PID: 00816263
  2601 Pole Ave, Lorain 44052
  440/233-2271
  Fax 440/282-9151

Schools: 14 \ *Teachers:* 434 \ *Students:* 6,500 \ *Special Ed Students:* 1,432 \ *LEP Students:* 579 \ *College-Bound:* 41% \ *Ethnic:* African American 29%, Hispanic 44%, Caucasian 26% \ *Exp:* $282 (Med) \ *Poverty:* 36% \ *Title I:* $6,622,358 \ *Special Education:* $1,537,000 \ *Open-Close:* 08/21 - 05/20 \ *DTBP:* $191 (High) \ 🅵 🆃

David Hardy 1	Josh Hill 2
Kevin Haupt 3	Frank Horvatich 4
Shonteea Ford 5	Bryan Koury 6,35
Diane Agosto 11	Rachel Tansey 11,36,274,298
Lakim Brown 15,751	Mickey Becerra 15
Joseph Bock 16,82*	Ruben Figueroa 27
Susanne Silva 57*	Dorinda Hall 58*
Mark Ballard 67	Jacqueline Younker 68
Eric Bomar 71	Brett Kluiber 73,295
Willie Ohle 76	Doreen Morell 79
Jrayene Nimene 83*	Nikole Davis 88
Jamie Montague 91	Eddie Holman 295

Public Schs..Principal	Grd	Prgm	Enr/#Cls	SN	
Admiral King Elem Sch 720 Washington Ave, Lorain 44052 Jay Keefer	PK-5	T	309 21		440/830-4120 Fax 440/245-4251
Frank Jacinto Elem Sch 2515 Marshall Ave, Lorain 44052 Paula Baldwin	PK-5	T	307 16		440/830-4130 Fax 440/960-5810
Garfield Elem Sch 200 W 31st St, Lorain 44055 Michelle Spotts-Hayes	PK-5	T	255 14		440/830-4140 Fax 440/246-1121
General Johnny Wilson Mid Sch 2700 Washington Ave, Lorain 44052 Bryan Hilko	6-8	TV	450 36		440/830-4240 Fax 440/246-1016 🅵 🆃
Hawthorne Elem Sch 610 W 20th St, Lorain 44052 Stephanie Johnson	PK-5	T	280 20		440/830-4150 Fax 440/246-1083 🅵 🆃
Helen Steiner Rice Elem Sch 4500 Tacoma Ave, Lorain 44055 Brandon Easton	PK-5	T	281 26		440/830-4160 Fax 440/240-1221
Larkmoor Elem Sch 1201 Nebraska Ave, Lorain 44052 Chantelle Lewis	PK-5	T	396 22		440/830-4170 Fax 440/288-5017 🅵 🆃
Longfellow Middle Sch 305 Louisiana Ave, Lorain 44052 Ray Basstock	6-8	T	370 50		440/830-4220 Fax 440/288-1149 🅵 🆃
Lorain High Sch 2600 Ashland Ave, Lorain 44052 Robin Hopkins	9-12	TV	1,994 70		440/233-2200 Fax 440/277-1163
Palm Elem Sch 2319 E 34th St, Lorain 44055 **Dr Carol Winter**	PK-5	T	293 18		440/830-4180 Fax 440/277-1225
Southview Middle Sch 2321 Fairless Dr, Lorain 44055 Rae Bastock	6-8	TV	439		440/830-4280 Fax 440/277-5566
Stevan Dohanos Elem Sch 1625 E 32nd St, Lorain 44055 **Marie Deshuk**	PK-5	T	315 27		440/830-4190 Fax 440/277-1014 🅵 🆃
Toni Morrison Elem Sch 1830 W 40th St, Lorain 44053 Megan Young	PK-5	T	327		440/830-4200 Fax 440/960-7015
Washington Elem Sch 1025 W 23rd St, Lorain 44052 John Monteleone	PK-5	T	302 20		440/830-4210 Fax 440/246-4920

1	Superintendent	8	Curric/Instruct K-12	19	Chief Financial Officer	29	Family/Consumer Science	39	Social Studies K-12	49	English/Lang Arts Elem	59	Special Education Elem	69	Academic Assessment
2	Bus/Finance/Purchasing	9	Curric/Instruct Elem	20	Art K-12	30	Adult Education	40	Social Studies Elem	50	English/Lang Arts Sec	60	Special Education Sec	70	Research/Development
3	Buildings And Grounds	10	Curric/Instruct Sec	21	Art Elem	31	Career/Sch-to-Work K-12	41	Social Studies Sec	51	Reading K-12	61	Foreign/World Lang K-12	71	Public Information
4	Food Service	11	Federal Program	22	Art Sec	32	Career/Sch-to-Work Elem	42	Science K-12	52	Reading Elem	62	Foreign/World Lang Elem	72	Summer School
5	Transportation	12	Title I	23	Music K-12	33	Career/Sch-to-Work Sec	43	Science Elem	53	Reading Sec	63	Foreign/World Lang Sec	73	Instructional Tech
6	Athletic	13	Title V	24	Music Elem	34	Early Childhood Ed	44	Science Sec	54	Remedial Reading K-12	64	Religious Education K-12	74	Inservice Training
7	Health Services	15	Asst Superintendent	25	Music Sec	35	Health/Phys Education	45	Math K-12	55	Remedial Reading Elem	65	Religious Education Elem	75	Marketing/Distributive
		16	Instructional Media Svcs	26	Business Education	36	Guidance Services K-12	46	Math Elem	56	Remedial Reading Sec	66	Religious Education Sec	76	Info Systems
		17	Chief Operations Officer	27	Career & Tech Ed	37	Guidance Services Elem	47	Math Sec	57	Bilingual/ELL	67	School Board President	77	Psychological Assess
		18	Chief Academic Officer	28	Technology Education	38	Guidance Services Sec	48	English/Lang Arts K-12	58	Special Education K-12	68	Teacher Personnel	78	Affirmative Action

Ohio School Directory — Lorain County

● **Lorain Co Joint Voc Sch Dist** PID: 00816847 440/774-1051
15181 State Route 58, Oberlin 44074   Fax 440/774-2144

Schools: 1 \ *Teachers:* 78 \ *Students:* 1,500 \ *LEP Students:* 6 \ *Exp:* $540 (High) \ *Open-Close:* 08/27 - 05/14 \ *DTBP:* $233 (High) \ 🅕 🅣

Dr Glenn Faircloth 1,11	Cory Thompson 2	
Duane Auble 3*	Amanda Mayle 7,83,85*	
Jerry Pavlik 15	Kristian Smith 30	
Denise Scarpucci 58,88*	Deborah Melda 67	
Courtney Griffiths 69*	Betty Halliburton 71	

Public Schs..Principal	Grd	Prgm	Enr/#Cls	SN	
Lorain Co Joint Voc Sch 15181 State Route 58, Oberlin 44074 Jill Petitti	Voc	AG	1,500 90		440/774-1051 Fax 440/774-6421 🅕 🅣

● **Midview Local School Dist** PID: 00816483 440/748-5353
13050 Durkee Rd, Grafton 44044   Fax 440/748-5395

Schools: 5 \ *Teachers:* 169 \ *Students:* 3,000 \ *Special Ed Students:* 395 \ *LEP Students:* 5 \ *College-Bound:* 64% \ *Ethnic:* Asian 1%, African American 3%, Hispanic 5%, Caucasian 92% \ *Exp:* $130 (Low) \ *Poverty:* 9% \ *Title I:* $398,823 \ *Special Education:* $581,000 \ *Open-Close:* 09/03 - 06/05 \ *DTBP:* $190 (High) \ 🅣

Dr Bruce Willingham 1	Rob Showalter 2
Ron Ignaczak 3	Sharon Henry 4
Chad Tucker 5	Daniel May 6
Leslie Rowe 16*	Sharon Novak 58,77,79
Tom Tomasheski 67	

Public Schs..Principal	Grd	Prgm	Enr/#Cls	SN	
Midview East Intermediate Sch 13060 Durkee Rd, Grafton 44044 Shane Sullivan	5-6		427 31	36%	440/748-1851 Fax 440/748-7016 🅣
Midview High Sch 38199 Capel Rd, Grafton 44044 Tom Faska	9-12	V	948 100	29%	440/748-2124 Fax 440/748-5277
Midview Middle Sch 12865 Grafton Rd, Grafton 44044 John Brown	7-8	TV	459 40	38%	440/748-2122 Fax 440/748-0411 🅣
Midview North Elem Sch 13070 Durkee Rd, Grafton 44044 Carla Molnar	K-2	T	559 20	42%	440/748-6869 Fax 440/748-7056 🅣
Midview West Elem Sch 13080 Durkee Rd, Grafton 44044 **Beth Hall**	PK-4	T	540 21	46%	440/748-2305 Fax 440/748-4032 🅣

● **North Ridgeville City Sch Dist** PID: 00816562 440/327-4444
34620 Bainbridge Rd, N Ridgeville 44039   Fax 440/230-8363

Schools: 5 \ *Teachers:* 212 \ *Students:* 4,600 \ *Special Ed Students:* 541 \ *LEP Students:* 26 \ *College-Bound:* 66% \ *Ethnic:* Asian 1%, African American 2%, Hispanic 5%, Caucasian 91% \ *Exp:* $154 (Low) \ *Poverty:* 6% \ *Title I:* $365,587 \ *Special Education:* $748,000 \ *Open-Close:* 08/21 - 06/03 \ *DTBP:* $181 (High) \ 🅕 🅣

Roxann Ramsey 1	Micheal Verlingo 2,84
Matt Yunker 3,5,91*	Kyle Suerth 4
Tammy Butler 5	Don Sparks 6
Rhonda Carson 7	David Pritt 8,11,69,74,76,288,296,298
David Pritt 8,11,69,76,288,296,298*	Hayley Bryson 23
Kelly McCarthy 67	Sam Ameen 71
Paul Hieronymus 73,76,295	Julie D'Alberti 79
Petie Bianca 79*	Lynn Pritt 273*

Melissa Durkin 285*

Public Schs..Principal	Grd	Prgm	Enr/#Cls	SN	
Early Childhood Learning Cmty 5490 Mills Creek Ln, N Ridgeville 44039 Andrea Vance	PK-K		466 7	11%	440/353-1100 Fax 440/327-1824
Liberty Sch 5700 Jaycox Rd, N Ridgeville 44039 Mitchell Heffron	1-2		639 23	22%	440/327-6767 Fax 440/353-3683 🅕 🅣
North Ridgeville Academic Ctr 34620 Bainbridge Rd, N Ridgeville 44039 Greg Plantner \ Amy Peck	5-8	V	1,520 35		440/353-1180 Fax 440/353-1144
North Ridgeville High Sch 34600 Bainbridge Rd, N Ridgeville 44039 Tom Szendrey	9-12	V	1,204 60	26%	440/327-1992 Fax 440/327-1413
Ranger High-Tech Academy 5580 Lear Nagle Rd, N Ridgeville 44039 Melissa Durkin	2-8		218		440/353-1178 Fax 440/353-1172

● **Oberlin City School Dist** PID: 00816627 440/774-1458
153 N Main St, Oberlin 44074   Fax 440/774-4492

Schools: 4 \ *Teachers:* 74 \ *Students:* 1,200 \ *Special Ed Students:* 150 \ *LEP Students:* 14 \ *College-Bound:* 77% \ *Ethnic:* Asian 2%, African American 26%, Hispanic 11%, Caucasian 60% \ *Exp:* $218 (Med) \ *Poverty:* 16% \ *Title I:* $286,255 \ *Special Education:* $258,000 \ *Open-Close:* 08/26 - 06/02 \ *DTBP:* $233 (High)

Dr David Hall 1	Angela Dotson 2
John Carter 6	William Baylis 8,11,57,74,273,285,298*
Susan Alig 58,79	Anne Schaum 67
Steve Neilson 73,295*	Steve Nielsen 295

Public Schs..Principal	Grd	Prgm	Enr/#Cls	SN	
Eastwood Elem Sch 198 E College St, Oberlin 44074 **Meisha Baker**	PK-2	T	241 14	46%	440/775-3473 Fax 440/774-7209
Langston Middle Sch 150 N Pleasant St, Oberlin 44074 **Sheila Hicks**	6-8	AT	216 26	58%	440/775-7961 Fax 440/776-4520
Oberlin High Sch 281 N Pleasant St, Oberlin 44074 Michael Scott	9-12	AT	290 30	63%	440/774-1295 Fax 440/774-5099
Prospect Elem Sch 36 S Prospect St, Oberlin 44074 Jim Eibel	3-5	T	216 9	73%	440/774-4421 Fax 440/775-2609

● **Sheffield-Sheffield Lake CSD** PID: 00816689 440/949-6181
1824 Harris Rd, Sheffield VLG 44054   Fax 440/949-4204

Schools: 5 \ *Teachers:* 94 \ *Students:* 1,747 \ *Special Ed Students:* 258 \ *LEP Students:* 6 \ *College-Bound:* 68% \ *Ethnic:* Asian 2%, African American 2%, Hispanic 10%, Native American: 1%, Caucasian 86% \ *Exp:* $197 (Low) \ *Poverty:* 14% \ *Title I:* $358,305 \ *Special Education:* $507,000 \ *Open-Close:* 08/29 - 06/05 \ *DTBP:* $179 (High)

Michael Cook 1	Michael Pissini 2,19
Steve Parker 3,4,91	Kevin Shupe 5
Richard Kerschbaum 6*	Sharon Young 7
Krista Kotechi 8,11,69,74,298*	Gretchen Loper 9*
Lisa Rutger 16,82*	Catherina McNichols 38,83
Mariah Hall 58,77,88,275	Sheila Lopez 67
Jessica Schremp 273*	

				School Programs	Social Media
79 Student Personnel	91 Safety/Security	275 Response To Intervention	298 Grant Writer/Ptnrships	A = Alternative Program	
80 Driver Ed/Safety	92 Magnet School	277 Remedial Math K-12	750 Chief Innovation Officer	G = Adult Classes	🅕 = Facebook
81 Gifted/Talented	93 Parental Involvement	280 Literacy Coach	751 Chief of Staff	M = Magnet Program	
82 Video Services	95 Tech Prep Program	285 STEM	752 Social Emotional Learning	T = Title I Schoolwide	🅣 = Twitter
83 Substance Abuse Prev	97 Chief Information Officer	286 Digital Learning		V = Career & Tech Ed Programs	
84 Erate	98 Chief Technology Officer	288 Common Core Standards	Other School Types		
85 AIDS Education	270 Character Education	294 Accountability	Ⓐ = Alternative School		
88 Alternative/At Risk	271 Migrant Education	295 Network System	Ⓒ = Charter School	New Schools are shaded	
89 Multi-Cultural Curriculum	273 Teacher Mentor	296 Title II Programs	Ⓜ = Magnet School	New Superintendents and Principals are bold	
90 Social Work	274 Before/After Sch	297 Webmaster	Ⓨ = Year-Round School	Personnel with email addresses are underscored	

OH-125

Lorain County

Market Data Retrieval

Public Schs..Principal	Grd	Prgm	Enr/#Cls	SN	
Brookside High Sch 1662 Harris Rd, Sheffield VLG 44054 Joy Morgan	9-12	V	477 45	51%	440/949-4220 Fax 440/949-2257
Brookside Intermediate Sch 1812 Harris Rd, Sheffield VLG 44054 Daniel Rahm	3-6	T	505 12	48%	440/949-4237 Fax 440/949-4279
Brookside Middle Sch 1662 Harris Rd, Sheffield VLG 44054 Emily Adkins	7-8	TV	273 40	48%	440/949-4228 Fax 440/949-2632
Forestlawn Elem Sch 3975 Forestlawn Ave, Sheffield Lk 44054 Gretchen Loper	2-2	T	127 6	52%	440/949-4238 Fax 440/949-4265
Knollwood Elem Sch 4975 Oster Rd, Sheffield Lk 44054 Gretchen Loper	PK-1	T	271 20	38%	440/949-4234 Fax 440/949-4259

- **Wellington Exempted Village SD** PID: 00816782   440/647-4286
  305 Union St, Wellington 44090   Fax 440/647-4806

Schools: 3 \ *Teachers:* 61 \ *Students:* 1,304 \ *Special Ed Students:* 183 \ *LEP Students:* 3 \ *College-Bound:* 58% \ *Ethnic:* African American 1%, Hispanic 3%, Caucasian 95% \ *Exp:* $209 (Med) \ *Poverty:* 11% \ *Title I:* $190,243 \ *Special Education:* $220,000 \ *Open-Close:* 08/29 - 06/08 \ *DTBP:* $252 (High) \

Edward Weber 1	Tina Gabler 2,11
Carrie Beegle 4,295	John Bowman 6
Patrick Gallion 31*	Nancy Nimmo 57,58
Dan Rosecrans 67	Jim Perchinske 73
Mark Millar 81	Kellsey Horton 83,88
Katie Custar 273*	

Public Schs..Principal	Grd	Prgm	Enr/#Cls	SN	
McCormick Middle Sch 627 N Main St, Wellington 44090 Nathan Baxendale	4-8	T	435 45	43%	440/647-2342 Fax 440/647-7310
Wellington High Sch 629 N Main St, Wellington 44090 Tina Drake	9-12	V	279 25	41%	440/647-3734 Fax 440/647-0512
Westwood Elem Sch 305 Union St, Wellington 44090 Erica Ward	K-3	T	294 21	59%	440/647-3636 Fax 440/647-1089

LORAIN CATHOLIC SCHOOLS

- **Diocese of Cleveland Ed Office** PID: 00795308
  Listing includes only schools located in this county. See District Index for location of Diocesan Offices.

Catholic Schs..Principal	Grd	Prgm	Enr/#Cls	SN	
Elyria Catholic High Sch 725 Gulf Rd, Elyria 44035 Suzanne Lester	9-12	V	399 28		440/365-1821 Fax 440/365-7536
Holy Trinity Sch 2610 Nagel Rd, Avon 44011 Kim Kuchta	PK-8		500 18		440/937-6420 Fax 440/937-1029
St Anthony of Padua Sch 1339 E Erie Ave, Lorain 44052 Lucia Heddleson	PK-8		260 10		440/288-2155 Fax 440/288-2159
St Joseph Parish Sch 32946 Electric Blvd, Avon Lake 44012 John Stipek	K-8		280 16		440/933-6233 Fax 440/933-2463
St Joseph Sch 175 Saint Joseph Dr, Amherst 44001 Amy Makruski	PK-8		233 13		440/988-4244 Fax 440/988-5249
St Jude Sch 594 Poplar St, Elyria 44035 Molly Hibler	PK-8		496 16		440/366-1681 Fax 440/366-5238
St Mary School-Avon 2680 Stoney Ridge Rd, Avon 44011 Colleen Schager	PK-8		190 1		440/934-6246 Fax 440/934-6250
St Mary School-Elyria 237 4th St, Elyria 44035 Sharon Urig	PK-8		427 11		440/322-2808 Fax 440/322-1423
St Peter Sch 35749 Center Ridge Rd, N Ridgeville 44039 Roger Brooks	K-8		274 13		440/327-3212 Fax 440/327-6843
St Peter School-Lorain 3601 Oberlin Ave, Lorain 44053 Rebecca Brown	PK-8		516 25		440/282-9909 Fax 440/282-9490

LORAIN PRIVATE SCHOOLS

Private Schs..Principal	Grd	Prgm	Enr/#Cls	SN	
Christian Community Sch 35716 Royalton Rd, Grafton 44044 Rachel Willis	K-12		120		440/748-6224 Fax 440/748-1007
Education Alternatives 333 Naples Dr, Elyria 44035 Carrie Cercone	K-12		65		440/324-1168 Fax 440/365-3762
First Baptist Christian Sch 11400 Lagrange Rd, Elyria 44035 Jennifer Kime	PK-12		115 13		440/458-5185 Fax 440/458-8717
Lake Ridge Academy 37501 Center Ridge Rd, N Ridgeville 44039 Mitch White	K-12		416		440/327-1175 Fax 440/327-3641
Open Door Christian Sch 8287 W Ridge Rd, Elyria 44035 Angie Lowe \ Ben Williams	PK-12		505 26		440/322-6386 Fax 440/284-6033

LORAIN REGIONAL CENTERS

- **Connect Information Tech Ctr** PID: 04499491   440/324-3185
  1885 Lake Ave, Elyria 44035   Fax 440/324-6140

John Mitchell 1	Julia Rozsnyai 2
Keith Delury 15,16,73	Steven Foster 76
Matt Zenobi 79	

- **State Support Team-Region 2** PID: 02228296   440/324-5777
  1885 Lake Ave, Elyria 44035   Fax 440/324-7355

Tracy Lichtenfels 1,11	Stacey Vince 34

Ohio School Directory

Lucas County

LUCAS COUNTY

LUCAS COUNTY SCHOOLS

Ed Service Ctr Lake Erie West PID: 00818285   419/245-4150
2275 Collingwood Blvd, Toledo 43620   Fax 419/245-4186

Sandra Frisch	1,11	Richard Cox	2
Susan Short	8,69	Brenda Gift	58,81
Mary Himmelein	68	Jason Garcia	73,295
Thomas Naveaux	77,79	Joyce Clemens	298

County Schs..Principal	Grd	Prgm	Enr/#Cls	SN	
Ⓒ Academy of Educ Excellence 728 Parkside Blvd, Toledo 43607 Dr Israel Koppisch	K-6		140		419/382-2280
Ⓒ Aurora Academy [238] 824 6th St, Toledo 43605 Kristy Sprague	K-6	AT	155 15		419/693-6841 Fax 419/693-4799
Ⓒ Autism Academy of Learning 110 Arco Dr Ste 1, Toledo 43607 James Jones	Spec	AGT	56 9		419/865-7487 Fax 419/865-8360
Ⓒ Autism Model Sch 3020 Tremainsville Rd, Toledo 43613 Jeana Kirkendall	Spec	T	111 18		419/897-4400 Fax 419/897-4403
ⒶGlass City Academy Ⓒ 1000 Monroe St Ste 1, Toledo 43604 Stuart Jesse	11-12		229		419/720-6311 Fax 419/720-6315 🅕🅣
Ⓒ Hope Learning Academy Toledo 4234 Monroe St, Toledo 43606 Joella Simmons	K-8	T	27		419/297-6313
Lucas Co Pre-School Unit 2275 Collingwood Blvd, Toledo 43620 Page Panneff	Spec		225 13		419/245-4150 Fax 419/725-2063
Ⓒ Maritime Academy of Toledo 803 Water St, Toledo 43604 Aaron Lusk	5-12	T	302 15	76%	419/244-9999 Fax 419/244-9898
Ⓒ Rise & Shine Academy 3248 Warsaw St, Toledo 43608 Tashlai Burney	K-6	T	111		419/244-9900
Ⓒ Star Academy of Toledo [238] 5025 Glendale Ave, Toledo 43614 Amy Printy	K-8	T	152		419/720-6330 Fax 419/720-7372 🅕🅣
Ⓒ Summit Academy Elem Sch-Toledo 5115 Glendale Ave, Toledo 43614 Brent Cummings	Spec		100 12		419/476-0784 Fax 419/476-0763
The Alternate Learning Center 3939 Wrenwood Rd, Toledo 43623 Marc Opsincs	Spec		93 12		419/473-3442 Fax 419/473-3445
Ⓒ Winterfield Venture Academy [203] 305 Wenz Rd, Toledo 43615 Nate Preston	K-8	T	581		419/531-3285 Fax 419/531-3637

LUCAS PUBLIC SCHOOLS

● Anthony Wayne Local Sch Dist PID: 00816873   419/877-5377
9565 Bucher Rd, Whitehouse 43571   Fax 419/877-9352

> **Schools:** 6 \ **Teachers:** 198 \ **Students:** 4,400 \ **Special Ed Students:** 506 \ **LEP Students:** 25 \ **College-Bound:** 77% \ **Ethnic:** Asian 2%, African American 1%, Hispanic 1%, Caucasian 96% \ **Exp:** $94 (Low) \ **Poverty:** 6% \ **Title I:** $405,699 \ **Special Education:** $722,000 \ **Open-Close:** 08/21 - 05/29 \ **DTBP:** $195 (High) \ 🅕

Dr Jim Fritz	1	Kerri Johnson	2
Matt Dick	3,91	Tammy Tapley	5
John Snyder	6*	Kevin Herman	15,69
Jennifer Karl-Thompson	59	Angela Gardner	60
Doug Zimmerman	67	Chris Hamady	73
Jim Conner	285,288,298		

Public Schs..Principal	Grd	Prgm	Enr/#Cls	SN	
Anthony Wayne High Sch 5967 Finzel Rd, Whitehouse 43571 Kevin Pfefferle	9-12		1,336 75	10%	419/877-0466 Fax 419/877-5028
Anthony Wayne Jr High Sch 6035 Finzel Rd, Whitehouse 43571 **Brad Contat**	7-8		761 50	11%	419/877-5342 Fax 419/877-1203 🅕
Fallen Timbers Middle Sch 6119 Finzel Rd, Whitehouse 43571 Dr James Bocian	5-6		659 27	11%	419/877-0601 Fax 419/877-4907
Monclova Primary Sch 8035 Monclova Rd, Monclova 43542 Betsey Murry	K-4		548 20	7%	419/865-9408 Fax 419/865-1397
Waterville Primary Sch 457 Sycamore Ln, Waterville 43566 Jamie Hollinger	K-4		503 26	13%	419/878-2436 Fax 419/878-4312
Whitehouse Primary Sch 6510 N Texas St, Whitehouse 43571 Brad Rhodes	K-4		464 32	19%	419/877-0543 Fax 419/877-4905

● Maumee City School Dist PID: 00816940   419/893-3200
716 Askin St, Maumee 43537   Fax 419/891-5387

> **Schools:** 5 \ **Teachers:** 139 \ **Students:** 2,222 \ **Special Ed Students:** 354 \ **LEP Students:** 24 \ **College-Bound:** 68% \ **Ethnic:** Asian 2%, African American 8%, Hispanic 8%, Caucasian 82% \ **Exp:** $449 (High) \ **Poverty:** 14% \ **Title I:** $516,438 \ **Special Education:** $539,000 \ **Open-Close:** 08/14 - 05/22 \ **DTBP:** $177 (High)

Dr Todd Cramer	1	Paul Brotzki	2
Larry Burda	3,91	Mary Bottoni	4,5
Tricia Samuel	7,79	Michelle Shafer	8,69,288
Nancy Sayre	11,296	Steven Lee	15,68
Karen Brebberman	16*	Donna Massingill	36*
Mike Wiley	67	Jason Dugan	73,286,295*
Donald Adamski	83		

Public Schs..Principal	Grd	Prgm	Enr/#Cls	SN	
Fairfield Elem Sch 1313 Eastfield Dr, Maumee 43537 Michele Loboschefski	K-3		279 18	34%	419/893-9821 Fax 419/891-5377
Ft Miami Elem Sch 2501 River Rd, Maumee 43537 Joel Hefner	K-3	T	332 13	45%	419/893-2201 Fax 419/891-5380
Gateway Middle Sch 900 Gibbs St, Maumee 43537 Angela Wojcik	6-8		548	35%	419/893-3386 Fax 419/893-2263

79	Student Personnel	91	Safety/Security	275	Response To Intervention	298	Grant Writer/Ptnrships
80	Driver Ed/Safety	92	Magnet School	277	Remedial Math K-12	750	Chief Innovation Officer
81	Gifted/Talented	93	Parental Involvement	280	Literacy Coach	751	Chief of Staff
82	Video Services	95	Tech Prep Program	285	STEM	752	Social Emotional Learning
83	Substance Abuse Prev	97	Chief Infomation Officer	286	Digital Learning		
84	Erate	98	Chief Technology Officer	288	Common Core Standards		
85	AIDS Education	270	Character Education	294	Accountability		
88	Alternative/At Risk	271	Migrant Education	295	Network System		
89	Multi-Cultural Curriculum	273	Teacher Mentor	296	Title II Programs		
90	Social Work	274	Before/After Sch	297	Webmaster		

School Programs
A = Alternative Program
G = Adult Classes
M = Magnet Program
T = Title I Schoolwide
V = Career & Tech Ed Programs

Other School Types
Ⓐ = Alternative School
Ⓒ = Charter School
Ⓜ = Magnet School
Ⓨ = Year-Round School

Social Media
🅕 = Facebook
🅣 = Twitter

New Schools are shaded
New Superintendents and Principals are bold
Personnel with email addresses are underscored

Lucas County

Maumee High Sch 9-12 657 30% 419/893-8778
1147 Saco St, Maumee 43537   60   Fax 419/893-5621
Matt Dick

Wayne Trail Elem Sch 4-5 378 41% 419/893-2851
1147 7th St, Maumee 43537   16   Fax 419/891-5378
Nick Neiderhouse

● Oregon City School Dist PID: 00817023   419/693-0661
5721 Seaman Rd, Oregon 43616   Fax 419/698-6016

Schools: 8 \ *Teachers:* 226 \ *Students:* 3,800 \ *Special Ed Students:* 451 \ *LEP Students:* 13 \ *College-Bound:* 53% \ *Ethnic:* Asian 1%, African American 2%, Hispanic 14%, Caucasian 82% \ *Exp:* $194 (Low) \ *Poverty:* 12% \ *Title I:* $571,875 \ *Special Education:* $575,000 \ *Open-Close:* 08/14 - 05/22 \ *DTBP:* $196 (High)

Hal Gregory 1,11,57,83
Vicki Laurell 4
Mark Beach 6
Jennifer Conkle 8,286,288
Dee Hepperly 58,77
Dawn Schiavone 73,76,295*
Dean Sandwisch 2,3,84,91
Terry Dellinger 5
Cherie Sexton 7
Rebecca Bihn 27,31*
Carol Molnar 67

Public Schs..Principal	Grd	Prgm	Enr/#Cls	SN	
Clay High Sch
5665 Seaman Rd, Oregon 43616
Jim Jurski	9-12	AGTV	1,178
150	45%	419/693-0665
Fax 419/698-6066
Coy Elem Sch
3604 Pickle Rd, Oregon 43616
Amy Molnar	K-4	AT	369
30	51%	419/693-0624
Fax 419/698-6018
Eisenhower Intermediate Sch
331 S North Curtice Rd, Oregon 43616
Tim Holcombe	5-6	ATV	584
38		419/836-8498
Fax 419/836-2005
Fassett Junior High Sch
3025 Starr Ave, Oregon 43616
Paul Gibbs	7-8	ATV	591
30	51%	419/693-0455
Fax 419/698-6048
Jerusalem Elem Sch
535 S Yondota Rd, Curtice 43412
Jeff Straka	K-4	AT	389
16	44%	419/836-6111
Fax 419/836-1501
© Oregon Eagle Learning Center
2665 Navarre Ave Ste C, Oregon 43616
Doug Dippman	9-12		81		419/720-2003
Fax 419/720-2007
Starr Elem Sch
3230 Starr Ave, Oregon 43616
Tricia Soltesz	K-4	AT	455
36	53%	419/693-0589
Fax 419/698-6019
ⓐ Wynn Center
5224 Bayshore Rd, Oregon 43616
Lori Beverage	PK-12		25		419/698-8003

● Ottawa Hills Local Sch Dist PID: 00817114   419/536-6371
3600 Indian Rd, Toledo 43606   Fax 419/534-5380

Schools: 2 \ *Teachers:* 65 \ *Students:* 1,000 \ *Special Ed Students:* 42 \ *LEP Students:* 3 \ *College-Bound:* 87% \ *Ethnic:* Asian 11%, African American 1%, Hispanic 5%, Caucasian 83% \ *Exp:* $496 (High) \ *Poverty:* 7% \ *Title I:* $82,515 \ *Special Education:* $215,000 \ *Open-Close:* 08/20 - 05/28 \ *DTBP:* $224 (High)

Dr Adam Finseke 1
Donnie Stevens 3
Bill Miller 8,12,57,288,298*
Rebecca McLean 16*
Shane Patacca 73,76*
Bradley Browne 2
Tammy Talmage 6
Jill Michaelson 11,58,88
Corey Hupp 67

Public Schs..Principal	Grd	Prgm	Enr/#Cls	SN	
Ottawa Hills Elem Sch
3602 Indian Rd, Toledo 43606
Kori Kawczynski	K-6		488
25		419/536-8329
Fax 419/536-6932
Ottawa Hills Jr Sr High Sch
2532 Evergreen Rd, Ottawa Hills 43606
Benjamin McMurray	7-12		485
39		419/534-5376
Fax 419/534-5384

● Springfield Local School Dist PID: 00817140   419/867-5600
6900 Hall St, Holland 43528   Fax 419/867-5700

Schools: 6 \ *Teachers:* 190 \ *Students:* 4,000 \ *Special Ed Students:* 589 \ *LEP Students:* 36 \ *College-Bound:* 89% \ *Ethnic:* Asian 3%, African American 19%, Hispanic 8%, Caucasian 70% \ *Exp:* $76 (Low) \ *Poverty:* 14% \ *Title I:* $910,606 \ *Special Education:* $649,000 \ *Open-Close:* 08/16 - 05/27 \ *DTBP:* $192 (High)

Matt Geha 1,11
Dustin Hamilton 3,91
Dana Falkenberg 8,15,69,288
Paulette Baz 11
Ellen Barnhizer 16*
Kristina White 71
Bill Geha 83*
Ryan Lockwood 2
Mr Renwand 6*
Taryn Miley 9
Cheri Copelandshaw 16*
Rachel Kramer 58
Cory Cantu 73,84,286

Public Schs..Principal	Grd	Prgm	Enr/#Cls	SN	
Crissey Elem Sch
9220 Geiser Rd, Holland 43528
Oatis Amick	K-5	T	342
22	51%	419/867-5677
Fax 419/867-5739
Dorr Street Elem Sch
1205 King Rd, Toledo 43617
Cheri Copeland-Shull	PK-5	T	404
19	53%	419/867-5666
Fax 419/867-5734
Holland Elem Sch
7001 Madison Ave, Holland 43528
Hilary Steinmiller	K-5	T	449
40		419/867-5655
Fax 419/867-5738
Holloway Elem Sch
6611 Pilliod Rd, Holland 43528
Robb Brown	K-5	T	408
20	51%	419/867-5703
Fax 419/867-5707
Springfield High Sch
1470 S McCord Rd, Holland 43528
Rhonda Kimmons	9-12	TV	1,038
80	59%	419/867-5633
Fax 419/867-5618
Springfield Middle Sch
7001 Madison Ave, Holland 43528
Jeffrey Pendry	6-8	T	883
76	83%	419/867-5644
Fax 419/867-5732

● Sylvania City School Dist PID: 00817205   419/824-8500
4747 N Holland Sylvania Rd, Sylvania 43560   Fax 419/824-8503

Schools: 12 \ *Teachers:* 390 \ *Students:* 7,704 \ *Special Ed Students:* 926 \ *LEP Students:* 205 \ *College-Bound:* 78% \ *Ethnic:* Asian 5%, African American 5%, Hispanic 4%, Caucasian 86% \ *Exp:* $182 (Low) \ *Poverty:* 8% \ *Title I:* $1,015,781 \ *Special Education:* $1,273,000 \ *Open-Close:* 08/19 - 05/28 \ *DTBP:* $191 (High) \ 🅕 🅣

Jane Spurgeon 1
Alan Bacho 3
Joe Beck 5
James Huss 6*
Alex Clarckson 8,13,27,31,288
Kieth Limes 15,68
Najwa Badawi 30
Rose Gaiffe 58
Amy Addington 71
Bill Geha 83,88,275
Lisa Shanks 2,19
Joe Sharny 4
Chris Irwin 6*
Bob Verhelst 7,57,79,91
Tim Zeroff 8,15
Sheryl O'Shea 16,73,286,295
Julie Sanford 31,69,95,285
James Nofbaum 67
Kathy Pollock 81

1	Superintendent	8	Curric/Instruct K-12	19	Chief Financial Officer	29	Family/Consumer Science	39	Social Studies K-12	49	English/Lang Arts Elem	59	Special Education Elem	69	Academic Assessment
2	Bus/Finance/Purchasing	9	Curric/Instruct Elem	20	Art K-12	30	Adult Education	40	Social Studies Elem	50	English/Lang Arts Sec	60	Special Education Sec	70	Research/Development
3	Buildings And Grounds	10	Curric/Instruct Sec	21	Art Elem	31	Career/Sch-to-Work K-12	41	Social Studies Sec	51	Reading K-12	61	Foreign/World Lang K-12	71	Public Information
4	Food Service	11	Federal Program	22	Art Sec	32	Career/Sch-to-Work Elem	42	Science K-12	52	Reading Elem	62	Foreign/World Lang Elem	72	Summer School
5	Transportation	12	Title I	23	Music K-12	33	Career/Sch-to-Work Sec	43	Science Elem	53	Reading Sec	63	Foreign/World Lang Sec	73	Instructional Tech
6	Athletic	13	Title V	24	Music Elem	34	Early Childhood Ed	44	Science Sec	54	Remedial Reading K-12	64	Religious Education K-12	74	Inservice Training
7	Health Services	15	Asst Superintendent	25	Music Sec	35	Health/Phys Education	45	Math K-12	55	Remedial Reading Elem	65	Religious Education Elem	75	Marketing/Distributive
		16	Instructional Media Svcs	26	Business Education	36	Guidance Services K-12	46	Math Elem	56	Remedial Reading Sec	66	Religious Education Sec	76	Info Systems
		17	Chief Operations Officer	27	Career & Tech Ed	37	Guidance Services Elem	47	Math Sec	57	Bilingual/ELL	67	School Board President	77	Psychological Assess
		18	Chief Academic Officer	28	Technology Education	38	Guidance Services Sec	48	English/Lang Arts K-12	58	Special Education K-12	68	Teacher Personnel	78	Affirmative Action

Lucas County

Public Schs..Principal	Grd	Prgm	Enr/#Cls	SN	
Arbor Hills Junior High Sch 5334 Whiteford Rd, Sylvania 43560 Mellisa McDonald	6-8	V	554 40	31%	419/824-8640 Fax 419/824-8659
Central Trail Elem Sch 4321 Mitchaw Rd, Sylvania 43560 Amanda Ogren	K-5		609 25	12%	419/824-8610 Fax 419/824-8606
Highland Elem Sch 7720 Erie St, Sylvania 43560 **Steve Swaggerty**	K-5		702 27	6%	419/824-8611 Fax 419/824-8635
Hill View Elem Sch 5424 Whiteford Rd, Sylvania 43560 Chad Kolebuck	K-5	T	419 17	45%	419/824-8612 Fax 419/824-8639
Maplewood Elem Sch 6769 Maplewood Ave, Sylvania 43560 John Duwve	PK-5		480 17	18%	419/824-8613 Fax 419/824-8649
McCord Junior High Sch 4304 N McCord Rd, Sylvania 43560 Josh Tyburski	6-8	V	654 40	13%	419/824-8650 Fax 419/824-8619
Northview High Sch 5403 Silica Dr, Sylvania 43560 **Mark Pugh**	9-12	V	1,348 110	18%	419/824-8570 Fax 419/824-8698 f t
Southview High Sch 7225 Sylvania Ave, Sylvania 43560 Kasey Vens	9-12	V	1,044 90	22%	419/824-8580 Fax 419/824-8678 f
Stranahan Elem Sch 3840 N Holland Sylvania Rd, Toledo 43615 Jeremy Bauer	K-5	T	560 25	28%	419/824-8614 Fax 419/824-8665
Sylvan Elem Sch 4830 Wickford Dr E, Sylvania 43560 Juliane Gault	K-5		391 22	31%	419/824-8615 Fax 419/824-8679
Timberstone Junior High Sch 9000 Sylvania Ave, Sylvania 43560 Mike Bader	6-8	V	615 60	13%	419/824-8680 Fax 419/824-8690
Whiteford Elem Sch 4708 Whiteford Rd, Toledo 43623 Andrew Duncan	PK-5		387 20	31%	419/824-8616 Fax 419/824-8697

Toledo Public Schools PID: 00817310
1609 N Summit St, Toledo 43604

419/671-0001
Fax 419/671-0087

Schools: 52 \ **Teachers:** 1,418 \ **Students:** 24,000 \
Special Ed Students: 4,475 \ **LEP Students:** 371 \ **College-Bound:** 34%
\ **Ethnic:** Asian 1%, African American 48%, Hispanic 11%, Caucasian 40% \ **Exp:** $169 (Low) \ **Poverty:** 34% \ **Title I:** $25,098,069 \
Special Education: $5,779,000 \ **Open-Close:** 08/16 - 05/27 \ **DTBP:** $246 (High)

Dr Romules Durant 1
Rey Deboas 4
Jennifer Deyarman 8
Robert Mendenhall 8
Trent Leedy 12
Thomas Dimetren 27
Karla Spangler 31,58,77
Jose Luna 57,271
Dr Su Breymaier 69
Chad Henderly 76
Christopher Evans 295
James Gant 2,3,5,15,73,91,296
Ann Cipriani 7,83,85
Jim Gault 8,11,69,70,88,274,288,294
Joseph Corfman 11
Patricia Mazur 16,71
Larry Warniment 30
Dr Amy Allen 34,58
Linda Bringman 68
Tirrell Brenneman 74
Benjamin Donato 295

Public Schs..Principal	Grd	Prgm	Enr/#Cls	SN	
Arlington Elem Sch 707 Woodsdale Ave, Toledo 43609 Melisa Viers	K-8	T	359 20		419/671-2550 Fax 419/671-2595
Beverly Elem Sch 3548 S Detroit Ave, Toledo 43614 Matt Rowely	K-8		615 22	34%	419/671-2600 Fax 419/671-2645
Birmingham Elem Sch 2222 Bakewell St, Toledo 43605 Stacey Scharf	PK-8	T	373 20		419/671-7700 Fax 419/671-7745
Bowsher High Sch 2200 Arlington Ave, Toledo 43614 Teri Sherwood	9-12	GTV	1,296 85	50%	419/671-2000 Fax 419/671-2060
Burroughs Elem Sch 2420 South Ave, Toledo 43609 Barbara Fischer	K-8	T	355 19		419/671-2350 Fax 419/671-2395
Byrnedale Elem Sch 3635 Glendale Ave, Toledo 43614 Thomas Drescher	PK-8	TV	470 50		419/671-2200 Fax 419/671-2261
Chase Stemm Academy 600 Bassett St, Toledo 43611 Jack Hunter	K-8	T	317 18		419/671-6650 Fax 419/671-6695
Crossgates Pre-School 3901 Shadylawn Dr, Toledo 43614 Lynn Pearson	PK-PK		365		419/671-2750 Fax 419/677-2751
DeVeaux Elem Sch 2620 W Sylvania Ave, Toledo 43613 Shaun Mitchell	K-8	T	594 70		419/671-3200 Fax 419/671-3260
East Broadway Elem Sch 1755 E Broadway St, Toledo 43605 Craig Otterson	K-8	TV	482		419/671-7200 Fax 419/671-7260
Edgewater Elem Sch 5549 Edgewater Dr, Toledo 43611 Elizabeth Bethany	K-8	T	160 13		419/671-6750 Fax 419/671-6795
Ella P Stewart Acad for Girls 707 Avondale Ave, Toledo 43604 Teresa Quinn	PK-6	T	220 14		419/671-5350 Fax 419/671-5395
Elmhurst Elem Sch 4530 Elmhurst Rd, Toledo 43613 Lynn Moran	K-8		476 15	37%	419/671-3550 Fax 419/671-3595
Garfield Elem Sch 1103 N Ravine Pkwy, Toledo 43605 Janice Richardson	K-8		406 25		419/671-7550 Fax 419/671-7595
Glendale-Feilbach Elem Sch 2317 Cass Rd, Toledo 43614 Susan Chorba	K-8	T	415 35		419/671-2650 Fax 419/617-2695
Glenwood Elem Sch 2860 Glenwood Ave, Toledo 43610 Michael Carr	PK-8	T	356		419/671-4600 Fax 419/671-4645
Grove Patterson Academy 3020 Marvin Ave, Toledo 43606 Herneika Johnson	K-8		387 25	38%	419/671-3350 Fax 419/671-3395
Harvard Elem Sch 1949 Glendale Ave, Toledo 43614 John Jordan	PK-8	T	367 22		419/671-2700 Fax 419/671-2745
Hawkins Elem Sch 5550 W Bancroft St, Toledo 43615 Jeff Hanthorn	K-8	T	411 24		419/671-1550 Fax 419/671-1595
Jones Leadership Academy 430 Nebraska Ave, Toledo 43604 Ward Barnett	7-12	T	200		419/671-5400 Fax 419/671-5460
Keyser Elem Sch 3900 Hill Ave, Toledo 43607 Natasha Allen	PK-8	T	300 28		419/671-1450 Fax 419/671-1495
Larchmont Elem Sch 1515 Slater St, Toledo 43612 Kari Sharp	K-8	T	454 16		419/671-3650 Fax 419/671-3695
Leverette Elem Sch 445 E Manhattan Blvd, Toledo 43608 Kimberly Sams	PK-8	TV	449 44		419/671-6200 Fax 419/671-6260
Longfellow Elem Sch 1955 W Laskey Rd, Toledo 43613 Yolanda Johnson	K-8	T	676 28		419/671-3800 Fax 419/671-3845

79 Student Personnel
80 Driver Ed/Safety
81 Gifted/Talented
82 Video Services
83 Substance Abuse Prev
84 Erate
85 AIDS Education
88 Alternative/At Risk
89 Multi-Cultural Curriculum
90 Social Work
91 Safety/Security
92 Magnet School
93 Parental Involvement
95 Tech Prep Program
97 Chief Information Officer
98 Chief Technology Officer
270 Character Education
271 Migrant Education
273 Teacher Mentor
274 Before/After Sch
275 Response To Intervention
277 Remedial Math K-12
280 Literacy Coach
285 STEM
286 Digital Learning
288 Common Core Standards
294 Accountability
295 Network System
296 Title II Programs
297 Webmaster
298 Grant Writer/Ptnrships
750 Chief Innovation Officer
751 Chief of Staff
752 Social Emotional Learning

Other School Types
Ⓐ = Alternative School
Ⓒ = Charter School
Ⓜ = Magnet School
Ⓨ = Year-Round School

School Programs
A = Alternative Program
G = Adult Classes
M = Magnet Program
T = Title I Schoolwide
V = Career & Tech Ed Programs

Social Media
f = Facebook
t = Twitter

New Schools are shaded
New Superintendents and Principals are bold
Personnel with email addresses are underscored

Lucas County

Market Data Retrieval

School	Grades	Prgm	Enr/#Cls		Phone
M Luther King Academy for Boys 1300 Forest Ave, Toledo 43607 Willie Ward	PK-6	T	200	10	419/671-4550 Fax 419/671-4595
Marshall Elem Sch 415 Colburn St, Toledo 43609 Douglas Bell	K-8	T	362	29	419/671-5700 Fax 419/671-5745
McKinley Stemm Academy 3344 Westland Ave, Toledo 43613 Christina Ramsey	K-8	T	245	26	419/671-3750 Fax 419/671-3795
McTigue Elem Sch 5555 Nebraska Ave, Toledo 43615 Tiffany Turner	PK-8	TV	511	40	419/671-1200 Fax 419/671-1260
Navarre Elem Sch 800 Kingston Ave, Toledo 43605 Katherine Taylor	PK-8	T	454	25	419/671-7600 Fax 419/671-7645
Oakdale Elem Sch 1620 E Broadway St, Toledo 43605 Robert Yenrick	PK-8	T	434	17	419/671-7350 Fax 419/671-7395
Old Orchard Elem Sch 2402 Cheltenham Rd, Toledo 43606 Valerie Dreier	PK-8	T	339	16	419/671-3700 Fax 419/671-3745
Old West End Academy 3131 Cambridge St, Toledo 43610 Kathy Gregory	K-8	T	282	16	419/671-4700 Fax 419/671-4745
Ottawa River Elem Sch 4747 290th St, Toledo 43611 Tamra Bacon	PK-8	T	455	15	419/671-6350 Fax 419/671-6395
Pickett Academy 1144 Blum St, Toledo 43607 Martha Jude	PK-8	T	240	30	419/671-5600 Fax 419/671-5645
Raymer Elem Sch 550 Raymer Blvd, Toledo 43605 Barbara Ferguson	PK-8	T	396	38	419/671-7650 Fax 419/671-7695
Reynolds Elem Sch 5000 Norwich Rd, Toledo 43615 Monica Clarke-Eagle	K-8	T	380	27	419/671-1500 Fax 419/671-1545
Riverside Elem Sch 500 Chicago St, Toledo 43611 Nathan Mollenhauer	K-8	T	386	40	419/671-6700 Fax 419/671-6745
Robinson Achievement 1075 Horace St, Toledo 43606 Kate Snyder	Spec		60		419/671-4200
Robinson Elem Sch 1075 Horace St, Toledo 43606 James Jones	K-8	TV	332	40	419/671-4200 Fax 419/671-4260
Rogers High Sch 222 McTigue Dr, Toledo 43615 Trudie Neely	9-12	TV	725		419/671-1000 Fax 419/671-1060
Rosa Parks Elem Sch 3350 Cherry St, Toledo 43608 Angela Richburg	PK-8	T	335	30	419/671-4350 Fax 419/671-4395
Scott High Sch 2400 Collingwood Blvd, Toledo 43620 Dr Carnel Smith	9-12	GTV	623		419/617-4000 Fax 419/671-4052
Sherman Elem Sch 817 Sherman St, Toledo 43608 Kelli Williams	PK-8	T	240	42	419/671-6550 Fax 419/671-6595
Spring Elem Sch 730 Spring St, Toledo 43608 Victoria Dipman	PK-8	T	294		419/671-6600 Fax 419/671-6645
Start High Sch 2010 Tremainsville Rd, Toledo 43613 Edward Perozek	9-12	GTV	1,532	95	57% 419/671-3000 Fax 419/671-3060
Toledo Early College High Sch 320 W Scott Park Dr, Toledo 43607 Karen Berman	7-12		500		30% 419/530-3003 Fax 419/530-3040
Toledo Technology Academy 3301 Upton Ave, Toledo 43613 Gary Thompson	Voc	T	335	15	41% 419/671-3900 Fax 419/479-3192
Waite High Sch 301 Morrison Dr, Toledo 43605 Todd Deem	9-12	AGTV	1,040	80	419/671-7000 Fax 419/671-7060
Walbridge Elem Sch 1245 Walbridge Ave, Toledo 43609 Monica Peace	K-8	T	264	15	419/671-5650 Fax 419/671-5695
Westfield Achievement 617 Western Ave, Toledo 43609 Kate Snyder	Spec		120		419/725-5008
Whittier Elem Sch 4221 Walker Ave, Toledo 43612 Eric Remley	PK-8	T	540	29	419/671-3600 Fax 419/671-3645
Woodward High Sch 701 E Central Ave, Toledo 43608 Jack Renz	9-12	GTV	748		419/671-6000 Fax 419/671-6050

● **Washington Local School Dist** PID: 00818089   419/473-8220
3505 W Lincolnshire Blvd, Toledo 43606   Fax 419/473-8247

Schools: 13 \ *Teachers:* 399 \ *Students:* 7,042 \ *Special Ed Students:* 983 \ *LEP Students:* 67 \ *Ethnic:* Asian 1%, African American 10%, Hispanic 12%, Caucasian 77% \ *Exp:* $277 (Med) \ *Poverty:* 20% \ *Title I:* $2,267,274 \ *Special Education:* $1,504,000 \ *Open-Close:* 08/21 - 06/03 \ *DTBP:* $223 (High) \

Kadee Anstadt 1	Jefferey Fouke 2,19
Jay Merritt 3	Deb Warren 4*
Rebecca Fuller 5	Thomas Snook 6,35*
Neil Rochotte 7,11,36,58,69,77,81,83	Katie Spenthoff 8
Mark Sholl 11,296	Brian Davis 15
Elizabeth Ziegler 16,82*	Mark Hughes 67
Laura Berryman 68*	Frank Farley 76
Kim Kovin 81	

Public Schs..Principal	Grd	Prgm	Enr/#Cls	SN	
Greenwood Elem Sch 760 Northlawn Dr, Toledo 43612 William Colon	K-6	T	528	20	69% 419/473-8263 Fax 419/473-8264
Hiawatha Elem Sch 3020 Photos Dr, Toledo 43613 Albert Bernhardt	K-6	T	354	20	57% 419/473-8268 Fax 419/473-8269
Jackman Elem Sch 2010 Northover Rd, Toledo 43613 Amy Franco	K-6	T	387	23	66% 419/473-8274 Fax 419/473-8275
Jefferson Junior High Sch 5530 Whitmer Dr, Toledo 43613 Lisa Morse-Grnt	7-7	ATV	551	40	60% 419/473-8482 Fax 419/473-8393
Ⓐ Malcolm-Bain Center 5601 Clegg Dr, Toledo 43613 Christie Martin	11-12	V	62		419/473-8331
McGregor Elem Sch 3535 McGregor Ln, Toledo 43623 Jerry Bell	K-6	T	472	20	45% 419/473-8279 Fax 419/473-8280
Meadowvale Elem Sch 2755 Edgebrook Dr, Toledo 43613 Christene Williams	K-6	T	556	25	55% 419/473-8284 Fax 419/473-8285
Monac Elem Sch 3845 Clawson Ave, Toledo 43623 **Carrie Wray**	K-6	T	506	22	52% 419/473-8289 Fax 419/473-8290
Shoreland Elem Sch 5650 Suder Ave, Toledo 43611 Kim Dedo	K-6	T	661	22	56% 419/473-8294 Fax 419/473-8295

---

1 Superintendent	8 Curric/Instruct K-12	19 Chief Financial Officer	29 Family/Consumer Science	39 Social Studies K-12	49 English/Lang Arts Elem	59 Special Education Elem	69 Academic Assessment
2 Bus/Finance/Purchasing	9 Curric/Instruct Elem	20 Art K-12	30 Adult Education	40 Social Studies Elem	50 English/Lang Arts Sec	60 Special Education Sec	70 Research/Development
3 Buildings And Grounds	10 Curric/Instruct Sec	21 Art Elem	31 Career/Sch-to-Work K-12	41 Social Studies Sec	51 Reading K-12	61 Foreign/World Lang K-12	71 Public Information
4 Food Service	11 Federal Program	22 Art Sec	32 Career/Sch-to-Work Elem	42 Science K-12	52 Reading Elem	62 Foreign/World Lang Elem	72 Summer School
5 Transportation	12 Title I	23 Music K-12	33 Career/Sch-to-Work Sec	43 Science Elem	53 Reading Sec	63 Foreign/World Lang Sec	73 Instructional Tech
6 Athletic	13 Title V	24 Music Elem	34 Early Childhood Ed	44 Science Sec	54 Remedial Reading K-12	64 Religious Education K-12	74 Inservice Training
7 Health Services	15 Asst Superintendent	25 Music Sec	35 Health/Phys Education	45 Math K-12	55 Remedial Reading Elem	65 Religious Education Elem	75 Marketing/Distributive
	16 Instructional Media Svcs	26 Business Education	36 Guidance Services K-12	46 Math Elem	56 Remedial Reading Sec	66 Religious Education Sec	76 Info Systems
	17 Chief Operations Officer	27 Career & Tech Ed	37 Guidance Services Elem	47 Math Sec	57 Bilingual/ELL	67 School Board President	77 Psychological Assess
	18 Chief Academic Officer	28 Technology Education	38 Guidance Services Sec	48 English/Lang Arts K-12	58 Special Education K-12	68 Teacher Personnel	78 Affirmative Action

Ohio School Directory

Lucas County

Washington Junior High Sch 5700 Whitmer Dr, Toledo 43613 Jennifer Bronikowski	8-8	ATV	564 50	54%	419/473-8449 Fax 419/473-8340
Wernert Elem Sch 5050 Douglas Rd, Toledo 43613 Scott Scharf	K-6	T	360 18	68%	419/473-8218 Fax 419/473-8219
Whitmer Career & Tech Center 5719 Clegg Dr, Toledo 43613 Debra Heban	Voc	G	450 80		419/473-8339 Fax 419/473-8309
Whitmer High Sch 5601 Clegg Dr, Toledo 43613 Kristine Martin	9-12	AGTV	2,117	46%	419/473-8490 Fax 419/473-8461

LUCAS CATHOLIC SCHOOLS

Diocese of Toledo Ed Office PID: 00818297 419/244-6711
1933 Spielbusch Ave, Toledo 43604 Fax 419/255-8269

Schools: 68 \ **Students:** 15,000

Listing includes only schools located in this county. See District Index for location of Diocesan Offices.

Dr Vincent Schmidt .... 1 Timothy Mahoney 8
Peggy Riehl .... 9 Tony Mass 10
David McCutchen .... 64 Vicki Fitts 73

Catholic Schs..Principal	Grd	Prgm	Enr/#Cls	SN	
Blessed Sacrament Sch 4255 Bellevue Rd, Toledo 43613 Greg Sattler	K-8		215 15		419/472-1121 Fax 419/472-1679 f t
Cardinal Stritch Cath HS-Acad 3225 Pickle Rd, Oregon 43616 Melissa Empie	PK-12		524 31		419/693-0465 Fax 419/697-2816 f
Central Catholic High Sch 2550 Cherry St, Toledo 43608 Kevin Parkins	9-12	G	696 50		419/255-2280 Fax 419/259-2848 f t
Christ the King Sch 4100 Harvest Ln, Toledo 43623 Joseph Carroll	PK-8		514 24		419/475-0909 Fax 419/475-4050
Gesu Sch 2045 Parkside Blvd, Toledo 43607 Manuel Gonzales	K-8		375 23		419/536-5634 Fax 419/531-8932 f
Lial Sch 5700 Davis Rd, Whitehouse 43571 Sr Patricia McClain	PK-8		191 8		419/877-5167 Fax 419/877-9385
Notre Dame Academy 3535 W Sylvania Ave, Toledo 43623 Sarah Cullum	7-12		640 50		419/475-9359 Fax 419/724-2640 f t
Our Lady-Perpetual Help Sch 2255 Central Grv, Toledo 43614 Kari Bonnell	PK-8		269 14		419/382-5696 Fax 419/382-7360 f t
Queen of Apostles Sch 235 Courtland Ave, Toledo 43609 Sr Joselyn Weeman	K-8		164 9		419/241-7829 Fax 419/241-4180
Regina Coeli Sch 600 Regina Pkwy, Toledo 43612 Dr Debra Bloomquist	K-8		190 16		419/476-0920 Fax 419/476-6792
Rosary Cathedral Sch 2535 Collingwood Blvd, Toledo 43610 Sr Lynda Snyder	K-8		193 12		419/243-4396 Fax 419/243-6049
St Benedict Catholic Sch 5522 Dorr St, Toledo 43615 Martha Hartman	PK-8		225 9		419/536-1194 Fax 419/531-5140
St Catherine of Siena ECC 115 Corbin Rd, Toledo 43612 Chris Kummer	PK-PK		140		419/478-9900 Fax 419/478-9434
St Francis DeSales High Sch 2323 W Bancroft St, Toledo 43607 John Hall	9-12		588 27		419/531-1618 Fax 419/531-9740
St Joan of Arc Sch 5950 Heatherdowns Blvd, Toledo 43614 Jennifer Guzman	PK-8		424 20		419/866-6177 Fax 419/866-4107 f
St John's Jesuit High Sch 5901 Airport Hwy, Toledo 43615 Christopher Knight	6-12		770 40		419/865-5743 Fax 419/861-5002
St Joseph Sch 5411 Main St, Sylvania 43560 Robert Edwards	K-8		789 27		419/882-6670 Fax 419/885-1990 f t
St Joseph Sch 112 W Broadway St, Maumee 43537 Dave Nichols	PK-8		307 17		419/893-3304 Fax 419/891-6969
St Patrick-Heatherdowns Sch 4201 Heatherdowns Blvd, Toledo 43614 Tina Abel	PK-8		500 30		419/381-1775 Fax 419/389-1161 f
St Pius X Sch 2950 Ilger Ave, Toledo 43606 Susan Richardson	PK-8		180 10		419/535-7688 Fax 419/535-7829
St Ursula Academy 4025 Indian Rd, Toledo 43606 Nichole Flores	6-12		565 42		419/531-1693 Fax 419/534-5777 t

LUCAS PRIVATE SCHOOLS

Private Schs..Principal	Grd	Prgm	Enr/#Cls	SN	
Apostolic Christian Academy 5701 W Sylvania Ave, Toledo 43623 Mike Cavin	K-12		90 8		419/885-5334 Fax 419/885-3857
Emmanuel Christian Sch 4607 W Laskey Rd, Toledo 43623 Ron Farrington \ David Regnier	K-12	G	400 25		419/885-3558 Fax 419/885-0139 f
Maumee Valley Country Day Sch 1715 S Reynolds Rd, Toledo 43614 James Lassman \ Erik Graham \ Molly Macek	PK-12		535 40		419/381-1313 Fax 419/381-1314 f t
Monclova Christian Academy 7819 Monclova Rd, Monclova 43542 Neil Black	K-12		180		419/866-7630 Fax 419/868-1062
Sunbridge Sch 2105 N McCord Rd, Toledo 43615 Diana Bergman	K-6		327		419/725-5437 Fax 419/754-2073
Toledo Christian Sch 2303 Brookford Dr, Toledo 43614 Joy McWhinnie \ Jeff Wilbarger	PK-12	V	636 50		419/389-8700 Fax 419/389-8703 f
Toledo Islamic Academy 5225 Alexis Rd, Sylvania 43560 Nabila Gomaa	PK-12		200 24		419/882-3339 Fax 419/882-3334
Toledo Junior Academy 4909 W Sylvania Ave, Toledo 43623 Annette Bradley-Martes	K-8		51 4		419/841-0082 Fax 419/843-5494
Trinity Lutheran Sch 4560 Glendale Ave, Toledo 43614 Jim Landskroener	PK-8		225 13		419/385-2301 Fax 419/385-2636
West Side Montessori 7115 W Bancroft St, Toledo 43615 Lynn Fisher	PK-8		394 13		419/866-1931 f
Westside Montessori Middle Sch 7115 W Bancroft St, Toledo 43615 Lynn Fisher	PK-8		300		419/843-5703 Fax 419/886-4310

79 Student Personnel	91 Safety/Security	275 Response To Intervention	298 Grant Writer/Ptnrships	**School Programs**	**Social Media**
80 Driver Ed/Safety	92 Magnet School	277 Remedial Math K-12	750 Chief Innovation Officer	A = Alternative Program	
81 Gifted/Talented	93 Parental Involvement	280 Literacy Coach	751 Chief of Staff	G = Adult Classes	f = Facebook
82 Video Services	95 Tech Prep Program	285 STEM	752 Social Emotional Learning	M = Magnet Program	
83 Substance Abuse Prev	97 Chief Infomation Officer	286 Digital Learning		T = Title I Schoolwide	t = Twitter
84 Erate	98 Chief Technology Officer	288 Common Core Standards	**Other School Types**	V = Career & Tech Ed Programs	
85 AIDS Education	270 Character Education	294 Accountability	Ⓐ = Alternative School		
88 Alternative/At Risk	271 Migrant Education	295 Network System	Ⓒ = Charter School	New Schools are shaded	
89 Multi-Cultural Curriculum	273 Teacher Mentor	296 Title II Programs	Ⓜ = Magnet School	New Superintendents and Principals are bold	
90 Social Work	274 Before/After Sch	297 Webmaster	Ⓨ = Year-Round School	Personnel with email addresses are underscored	

OH–131

Madison County

Market Data Retrieval

Zion Lutheran Sch	K-8	35	419/531-1507
630 Cuthbert Rd, Toledo 43607		2	
Luke Scherschel			

LUCAS REGIONAL CENTERS

- **State Support Team-Region 1** PID: 02228301 — 419/720-8999
  2275 Collingwood Blvd C, Toledo 43620 — Fax 419/720-8998

  Lynn McKahan 1   Heather Gaskins 34

MADISON COUNTY

MADISON COUNTY SCHOOLS

County Schs..Principal	Grd	Prgm	Enr/#Cls	SN	
Fairhaven Sch	Spec	G	60		740/852-7052
510 Elm St, London 43140			5		Fax 740/852-7053
Mike Mast					

MADISON PUBLIC SCHOOLS

- **Jefferson Local School Dist** PID: 00819461 — 614/879-7654
  906 W Main St, W Jefferson 43162 — Fax 614/879-5376

Schools: 3 \ **Teachers:** 68 \ **Students:** 1,200 \ **Special Ed Students:** 210 \ **LEP Students:** 10 \ **Ethnic:** African American 1%, Hispanic 2%, Caucasian 97% \ **Exp:** $114 (Low) \ **Poverty:** 11% \ **Title I:** $162,738 \ **Special Education:** $249,000 \ **Open-Close:** 08/21 - 05/29 \ **DTBP:** $226 (High)

Bill Mullett 1	Jill Smith 2
Robert Hiss 3,5	Christine Elkins 4*
Mitch Daulton 6*	Melissa Ferguson 7*
Andrea Buescher 9*	Joan Scofield 10,11,57,74,81,88,275,288*
Kristin Kearns 16*	Joe Palazzo 38*
Jennifer Merb 58,285	David Harper 67
Curt Dennis 73,76,286*	Deborah Omen 273*
Doris Picken 274*	

Public Schs..Principal	Grd	Prgm	Enr/#Cls	SN	
Norwood Elem Sch	K-5	T	518	46%	614/879-7642
899 Norwood Dr, W Jefferson 43162			30		Fax 614/879-5377
Sue Barte					
West Jefferson High Sch	9-12		331	65%	614/879-7681
1 Roughrider Dr, W Jefferson 43162			20		Fax 614/879-5381
Michael Bute					
West Jefferson Middle Sch	6-8	T	305		614/879-8345
2 Roughrider Dr, W Jefferson 43162			25		Fax 614/879-5399
Deborah Omen					

- **Jonathan Alder Local Sch Dist** PID: 00819514 — 614/873-5621
  9200 US Highway 42 S, Plain City 43064 — Fax 614/873-8462

Schools: 5 \ **Teachers:** 112 \ **Students:** 2,270 \ **Special Ed Students:** 265 \ **LEP Students:** 39 \ **College-Bound:** 64% \ **Ethnic:** Hispanic 4%, Caucasian 96% \ **Exp:** $191 (Low) \ **Poverty:** 7% \ **Title I:** $224,624 \ **Special Education:** $453,000 \ **Open-Close:** 08/21 - 05/29 \ **DTBP:** $182 (High)

Gary Chapman 1	Aaron Johnson 2
Mark Syx 3*	Rebecca Rings 4
Rachel Miller 5	Tom Vargo 6*
Andrea Spencer 7,85*	Dr Misty Swanger ..8,11,285,288,294,296,298
Nicole Schrock 16,28,73,286*	Jolynn Wheatley 31,83*
Beth Woods 37	Kati Lupia 37*
Jen Korn 57,58,88	Steve Votaw 67
Bret Longberry 76,295	Sheila Core 77
Mark Fenik 91	Taylor Bojc 280

Public Schs..Principal	Grd	Prgm	Enr/#Cls	SN	
Canaan Middle Sch	5-6		348	27%	614/733-3975
7055 US Highway 42 S, Plain City 43064			35		Fax 614/733-3972
Matthew Keller					
Jonathan Alder High Sch	9-12	A	652	16%	614/873-4642
9200 US Highway 42 S, Plain City 43064			19		Fax 614/873-4252
Clint Hayes					
Jonathan Alder Junior High Sch	7-8		387	28%	614/873-4635
6440 Kilbury Huber Rd, Plain City 43064			18		Fax 614/873-0845
Ryan Malany					
Monroe Elem Sch	PK-4	T	228	55%	614/873-8503
5000 State Route 38 NW, London 43140			14		Fax 614/873-0685
Micki Hughes					
Plain City Elem Sch	PK-4		610	22%	614/873-4608
580 S Chillicothe St, Plain City 43064			24		Fax 614/873-2559
Kelly Hicks					

- **London City School Dist** PID: 00819564 — 740/852-5700
  380 Elm St 2nd Fl, London 43140 — Fax 740/845-3282

Schools: 3 \ **Teachers:** 113 \ **Students:** 2,103 \ **Special Ed Students:** 386 \ **LEP Students:** 28 \ **College-Bound:** 52% \ **Ethnic:** Asian 1%, African American 4%, Hispanic 2%, Caucasian 93% \ **Exp:** $214 (Med) \ **Poverty:** 12% \ **Title I:** $394,445 \ **Special Education:** $332,000 \ **Open-Close:** 08/14 - 05/21 \ **DTBP:** $219 (High) \ 🅵 🆃

Dr Lou Kramer 1	Trevor Gummere 2
James Helmecamp 3	Teresa Murray 4*
Kimberly Adams 5	Jim Wolverton 6*
Kylie Pritchard 8,11,275,288	Kim Davis 16*
Linda Alexander 30	Betsy Dennis 31*
Denise Congleton 57*	Cheryl Stauffer 58,81*
Darryl Brown 67	Dillan Shumaker 73

Public Schs..Principal	Grd	Prgm	Enr/#Cls	SN	
London Elem Sch	PK-5	T	1,032	49%	740/845-3272
380 Elm St, London 43140			20		Fax 740/845-3283
John Riley					
London High Sch	9-12	V	588	36%	740/852-5705
336 Elm St, London 43140			45		Fax 740/845-3284 🆃
Michael Browning					
London Middle Sch	6-8	T	483	48%	740/852-5701
270 Keny Blvd, London 43140			40		Fax 740/845-1279
Michael Belmont					

1 Superintendent	8 Curric/Instruct K-12	19 Chief Financial Officer	29 Family/Consumer Science	39 Social Studies K-12	49 English/Lang Arts Elem	59 Special Education Elem	69 Academic Assessment
2 Bus/Finance/Purchasing	9 Curric/Instruct Elem	20 Art K-12	30 Adult Education	40 Social Studies Elem	50 English/Lang Arts Sec	60 Special Education Sec	70 Research/Development
3 Buildings And Grounds	10 Curric/Instruct Sec	21 Art Elem	31 Career/Sch-to-Work K-12	41 Social Studies Sec	51 Reading K-12	61 Foreign/World Lang K-12	71 Public Information
4 Food Service	11 Federal Program	22 Art Sec	32 Career/Sch-to-Work Elem	42 Science K-12	52 Reading Elem	62 Foreign/World Lang Elem	72 Summer School
5 Transportation	12 Title I	23 Music K-12	33 Career/Sch-to-Work Sec	43 Science Elem	53 Reading Sec	63 Foreign/World Lang Sec	73 Instructional Tech
6 Athletic	13 Title V	24 Music Elem	34 Early Childhood Ed	44 Science Sec	54 Remedial Reading K-12	64 Religious Education K-12	74 Inservice Training
7 Health Services	14 Asst Superintendent	25 Music Sec	35 Health/Phys Education	45 Math K-12	55 Remedial Reading Elem	65 Religious Education Elem	75 Marketing/Distributive
	15 Instructional Media Svcs	26 Business Education	36 Guidance Services K-12	46 Math Elem	56 Remedial Reading Sec	66 Religious Education Sec	76 Info Systems
	16 Chief Operations Officer	27 Career & Tech Ed	37 Guidance Services Elem	47 Math Sec	57 Bilingual/ELL	67 School Board President	77 Psychological Assess
	18 Chief Academic Officer	28 Technology Education	38 Guidance Services Sec	48 English/Lang Arts K-12	58 Special Education K-12	68 Teacher Personnel	78 Affirmative Action

Ohio School Directory   Mahoning County

Madison Plains Local Sch Dist PID: 00819629   740/852-0290
55 Linson Rd, London 43140   Fax 740/852-5895

Schools: 4 \ **Teachers:** 74 \ **Students:** 1,173 \ **Special Ed Students:** 165 \ **LEP Students:** 3 \ **College-Bound:** 47% \ **Ethnic:** African American 1%, Hispanic 2%, Caucasian 97% \ **Exp:** $166 (Low) \ **Poverty:** 11% \ **Title I:** $205,814 \ **Special Education:** $212,000 \ **Open-Close:** 08/19 - 05/21 \ **DTBP:** $263 (High) \ t

Chad Eisler	1	Todd Mustain		2,19
Joe Penney	3,4,16,73,76,82	Kim Rogers		5
Matt Mason	6	Karen Grigsby		8,12,273,288*
Kimberly LeGault	11,58,88,275*	Mark Mason		67
Vicki Blosser	68	Sara Hyatt		77*

Public Schs..Principal	Grd	Prgm	Enr/#Cls	SN
Madison Plains Elem Sch 47 Linson Rd, London 43140 Brad Miller	K-3		368 16	740/490-0610 Fax 740/490-0612
Madison Plains High Sch 800 Linson Rd, London 43140 Michelle Teis	9-12	AV	316 40	56% 740/852-0364 Fax 740/852-3046
Madison Plains Interm Sch 9940 State Route 38 SW, London 43140 Kimberly LeGault	4-6	T	302 18	740/490-0610 Fax 740/490-0612
Madison Plains Junior HS 803 Linson Rd, London 43140 Michelle Teis	7-8		187	740/852-1707 Fax 740/852-6351

Tolles Career & Tech Sch Dist PID: 01417468   614/873-4666
7877 US Highway 42 S, Plain City 43064   Fax 614/873-6909

Schools: 1 \ **Teachers:** 54 \ **Students:** 640 \ **LEP Students:** 13 \ **Exp:** $399 (High) \ **Open-Close:** 08/15 - 05/29 \ **DTBP:** $166 (High)

Emmy Beeson	1	Ervin Baldwin		3,5*
Julie Mason	4*	Connie Strebe		10,38,83,294*
Christina Van Dyke	16*	Connie Strebe		27,69
Cindy Zellar	30	Tom Bichel		67
Jackie Kuffel	69*	Lee Wirick		73*

Public Schs..Principal	Grd	Prgm	Enr/#Cls	SN
Tolles Career & Tech Center 7877 US Highway 42 S, Plain City 43064 Jackie Kuffel	Voc	AG	640 106	614/873-4666

MADISON CATHOLIC SCHOOLS

Diocese of Columbus Ed Office PID: 00802717
Listing includes only schools located in this county. See District Index for location of Diocesan Offices.

Catholic Schs..Principal	Grd	Prgm	Enr/#Cls	SN
St Patrick Sch 226 Elm St, London 43140 Dr Jacob Froning	PK-8		136 9	740/852-0161 Fax 740/852-0602

MADISON PRIVATE SCHOOLS

Private Schs..Principal	Grd	Prgm	Enr/#Cls	SN
Shekinah Christian Sch 10040 Lafayette Plain City Rd, Plain City 43064 Brice Kauffman	K-12		120 8	614/873-3130 Fax 614/873-3699

MAHONING COUNTY

MAHONING COUNTY SCHOOLS

Mahoning Co Ed Service Center PID: 00820886   330/533-8755
7320 N Palmyra Rd, Canfield 44406   Fax 330/533-8777

Dr Ronald Iarussi	1	Blaise Karlovic		2
Cheryl McArthur	2,68	Kim Davis		8
Douglas Hiscox	15	Andrew Velchek		16,73,295
Linda Yosay	34,58	Richard Scarsella		67
Jennifer Merritt	88			

County Schs..Principal	Grd	Prgm	Enr/#Cls	SN
Leonard Kirtz Sch 4801 Woodridge Dr, Austintown 44515 Jeff Novack	Spec	G	72 9	330/797-2847 Fax 330/797-2861
Ⓐ Mahoning Co High Sch Ⓒ 940 Bryn Mawr Ave, Youngstown 44505 Jennifer Whittemore	9-12	T	73	330/965-2860 Fax 330/965-2861
Ⓒ Mahoning Unlimited Classroom 4211 Evelyn Rd, Youngstown 44511 Sean Sich	4-12	T	142	330/533-8755 Fax 330/729-9349
Ⓒ Summit Acad Sec Sch-Youngstown [248] 2800 Shady Run Rd, Youngstown 44502 Ashely Martin	Spec	T	120	234/228-8235 Fax 234/228-8239

MAHONING PUBLIC SCHOOLS

Austintown Local School Dist PID: 00819708   330/797-3900
700 S Raccoon Rd, Youngstown 44515   Fax 330/792-8625

Schools: 4 \ **Teachers:** 293 \ **Students:** 4,567 \ **Special Ed Students:** 713 \ **LEP Students:** 25 \ **College-Bound:** 58% \ **Ethnic:** Asian 1%, African American 13%, Hispanic 6%, Caucasian 80% \ **Exp:** $118 (Low) \ **Poverty:** 15% \ **Title I:** $1,025,079 \ **Special Education:** $956,000 \ **Open-Close:** 08/27 - 06/05 \ **DTBP:** $193 (High)

David Cappozzello	1	Andrea Apisa		2,68,79
Matthew Bostian	3,91*	Alexis Weber		4
Angie Mraz	5	Paula Lipke		5
James Penk	6	Liz Grdic		7
Janet Polish	9	Dr William Young		10
Blaise Karlovic	11	William Klein		23*
Wesley O'Connor	25*	Christine Kinnick		26*
Maribeth McGlynn	36,69*	Sandra Thorndike		58
Don Sherwood	67	Thomas Ventresco		73,295*
Cindy Douglas	76	Roy Piedermann		76

79	Student Personnel	91	Safety/Security	275	Response To Intervention	298	Grant Writer/Ptnrships	
80	Driver Ed/Safety	92	Magnet School	277	Remedial Math K-12	750	Chief Innovation Officer	
81	Gifted/Talented	93	Parental Involvement	280	Literacy Coach	751	Chief of Staff	
82	Video Services	95	Tech Prep Program	285	STEM	752	Social Emotional Learning	
83	Substance Abuse Prev	97	Chief Infomation Officer	286	Digital Learning			
84	Erate	98	Chief Technology Officer	288	Common Core Standards			
85	AIDS Education	270	Accountability	294	Alternative Education			
88	Alternative/At Risk	271	Migrant Education	295	Network System			
89	Multi-Cultural Curriculum	273	Teacher Mentor	296	Title II Programs			
90	Social Work	274	Before/After Sch	297	Webmaster			

School Programs
A = Alternative Program
G = Adult Classes
M = Magnet Program
T = Title I Schoolwide
V = Career & Tech Ed Programs

Other School Types
Ⓐ = Alternative School
Ⓒ = Charter School
Ⓜ = Magnet School
Ⓨ = Year-Round School

Social Media
f = Facebook
t = Twitter

New Schools are shaded
New Superintendents and Principals are bold
Personnel with email addresses are underscored

OH–133

Mahoning County — Market Data Retrieval

Public Schs..Principal	Grd	Prgm	Enr/#Cls	SN	
Austintown Elem Sch 245 Idaho Rd, Youngstown 44515 Tim Kelty	K-2	T	1,025 17	61%	330/797-3901 Fax 330/792-7124
Austintown Intermediate Sch 225 Idaho Rd, Youngstown 44515 Angel Owens	3-5	T	1,001 19	59%	330/797-3901 Fax 330/792-5750
Austintown Middle Sch 800 S Raccoon Rd, Youngstown 44515 Ben Baldner	6-8	ATV	1,072 60	53%	330/797-3900 Fax 330/792-9130
Fitch High Sch 4560 Falcon Dr, Youngstown 44515 Timothy Kelty	9-12	ATV	1,353 102	55%	330/797-3900 Fax 330/797-3944

● **Boardman Local School Dist** PID: 00819796 330/726-3404
7410 Market St, Boardman 44512 Fax 330/726-3432

Schools: 6 \ *Teachers:* 255 \ *Students:* 4,000 \ *Special Ed Students:* 686 \ *LEP Students:* 78 \ *College-Bound:* 70% \ *Ethnic:* Asian 3%, African American 9%, Hispanic 7%, Caucasian 81% \ *Exp:* $135 (Low) \ *Poverty:* 16% \ *Title I:* $1,099,906 \ *Special Education:* $855,000 \ *Open-Close:* 08/26 - 06/05 \ *DTBP:* $215 (High)

Timothy Saxton 1
Natalie Winkle 4
Dennise Gorski 6*
Lorraine Colon 7
Christopher Rhodes 16,73,76,82,286*
Julie Sturgis 39
Katie Fallo 58
Edward Adams 285,298
Matt McKenzie 3
Ryan Dunn 5
Marco Marinucci 6
Jared Cardillo 8,11,51,54,81,273,288,296
Anna Bott 27,36,69,77,83
Larry Davis 42
Jeffrey Barone 67

Public Schs..Principal	Grd	Prgm	Enr/#Cls	SN	
Boardman Center Middle Sch 7410 Market St, Boardman 44512 Randall Ebie	4-6		675 36		330/726-3400 Fax 330/726-3431
Boardman High Sch 7777 Glenwood Ave, Boardman 44512 Cynthia Fernback	9-12	GV	1,275 50	36%	330/758-7511 Fax 330/758-7515
Glenwood Junior High Sch 7635 Glenwood Ave, Boardman 44512 Bart Smith	7-8	T	684 40	42%	330/726-3414 Fax 330/758-8067
Robinwood Lane Elem Sch 835 Indianola Rd, Boardman 44512 Billie Johnson	K-3	T	332 18	45%	330/782-3164 Fax 330/782-2405
Stadium Drive Elem Sch 111 Stadium Dr, Boardman 44512 Michael Zoccali	K-3	T	353 20	30%	330/726-3428 Fax 330/726-0496
West Boulevard Elem Sch 6125 West Blvd, Boardman 44512 Al Cervello	K-3	T	380 20	44%	330/726-3427 Fax 330/726-0397

● **Campbell City School Dist** PID: 00819875 330/799-8777
280 6th St, Campbell 44405 Fax 330/799-0875

Schools: 2 \ *Teachers:* 72 \ *Students:* 1,071 \ *Special Ed Students:* 189 \ *LEP Students:* 56 \ *College-Bound:* 38% \ *Ethnic:* African American 32%, Hispanic 32%, Caucasian 35% \ *Exp:* $163 (Low) \ *Poverty:* 39% \ *Title I:* $955,159 \ *Special Education:* $288,000 \ *Open-Close:* 08/20 - 05/28 \ *DTBP:* $225 (High)

Matthew Bowen 1
Curtis Brown 3,91
Michael Bobic 5
Jane Buckingham 8,11,58,69,72*
Richard Gozur 31*
Nora Montanez 2
Caitlyn Ruggiero 4
Ronald Aulet 6*
Lynette Romito 16*
Marilyn McCallister 38*
Tony Kelly 67
Catherine Scali 77*
Patsy Bakos 298*
Eric Gonzalez 73*
Patsy Bakos 84

Public Schs..Principal	Grd	Prgm	Enr/#Cls	SN	
Campbell K-7 Sch 2002 Community Cir, Campbell 44405 Jame Klingensmith	PK-7	T	689 30	75%	330/799-5211 Fax 330/799-8272
Memorial High Sch 280 6th St, Campbell 44405 Bradly Yeager	8-12	TV	382 40	71%	330/799-1515 Fax 330/799-6390

● **Canfield Local School Dist** PID: 00819928 330/533-3303
100 Wadsworth St, Canfield 44406 Fax 330/533-6827

Schools: 4 \ *Teachers:* 144 \ *Students:* 2,600 \ *Special Ed Students:* 320 \ *LEP Students:* 11 \ *College-Bound:* 85% \ *Ethnic:* Asian 3%, African American 1%, Hispanic 3%, Caucasian 93% \ *Exp:* $101 (Low) \ *Poverty:* 6% \ *Title I:* $223,478 \ *Special Education:* $486,000 \ *Open-Close:* 08/26 - 06/04 \ *DTBP:* $197 (High)

Alex Geordan 1
Don Adams 3,91*
Richard Hammond 5
Regina Reynolds 7*
Joe Maroni 9*
Dr Rebecca Heikkinen 36,83,270*
Candy Reed 69*
Lynette Brownlee 76*
Patricia Prince 2
Terri Hutchinson 4*
Michael Cochran 6
John Tullio 8
John Vitto 11,58,81,88,298
David Wilkeson 67
George Malich 73*
Carol Young 280

Public Schs..Principal	Grd	Prgm	Enr/#Cls	SN	
C H Campbell Elem Sch 300 Moreland Dr, Canfield 44406 Travis Lavery	K-4		433 25	15%	330/533-5959 Fax 330/702-7061
Canfield High Sch 100 Cardinal Dr, Canfield 44406 Mike Moldovan	9-12	AV	875 70	11%	330/533-5507 Fax 330/533-1919
Canfield Village Middle Sch 42 Wadsworth St, Canfield 44406 Judd Rubin	5-8		800 36	12%	330/533-4019 Fax 330/702-7064
Hilltop Elem Sch 400 Hilltop Blvd, Canfield 44406 Joe Maroni	K-4		449 22	15%	330/533-9806 Fax 330/702-7051

● **Jackson-Milton Local Sch Dist** PID: 00819978 330/538-3232
13910 Mahoning Ave, North Jackson 44451 Fax 330/538-6297

Schools: 2 \ *Teachers:* 47 \ *Students:* 700 \ *Special Ed Students:* 106 \ *LEP Students:* 5 \ *College-Bound:* 62% \ *Ethnic:* African American 1%, Hispanic 1%, Caucasian 98% \ *Exp:* $679 (High) \ *Poverty:* 19% \ *Title I:* $223,427 \ *Special Education:* $156,000 \ *Open-Close:* 09/04 - 06/10 \ *DTBP:* $174 (High)

Kirk Baker 1
Dave Snowden 3
Darlene Pellin 5
Sarah Barnes 27,29*
Ryan Rotuna 73,84
John Zinger 2
Dave Snowden 3*
Kim Fisk 12,58*
Mitch Mascioli 67

Public Schs..Principal	Grd	Prgm	Enr/#Cls	SN	
Jackson-Milton Elem Sch 14110 Mahoning Ave, North Jackson 44451 Kim Fisk	K-6	T	455 22	42%	330/538-2257 Fax 330/538-2259
Jackson-Milton Middle High Sch 13910 Mahoning Ave, North Jackson 44451 David Vega	7-12		290 42	58%	330/538-3308 Fax 330/538-0821

1 Superintendent	8 Curric/Instruct K-12	19 Chief Financial Officer	29 Family/Consumer Services	39 Social Studies K-12	49 English/Lang Arts Elem	59 Special Education Elem	69 Academic Assessment
2 Bus/Finance/Purchasing	9 Curric/Instruct Elem	20 Art K-12	30 Adult Education	40 Social Studies Elem	50 English/Lang Arts Sec	60 Special Education Sec	70 Research/Development
3 Buildings And Grounds	10 Curric/Instruct Sec	21 Art Elem	31 Career/Sch-to-Work K-12	41 Social Studies Sec	51 Reading K-12	61 Foreign/World Lang K-12	71 Public Information
4 Food Service	11 Federal Program	22 Art Sec	32 Career/Sch-to-Work Elem	42 Science K-12	52 Reading Elem	62 Foreign/World Lang Elem	72 Summer School
5 Transportation	12 Title I	23 Music K-12	33 Career/Sch-to-Work Sec	43 Science Elem	53 Reading Sec	63 Foreign/World Lang Sec	73 Instructional Tech
6 Athletic	13 Title V	24 Music Elem	34 Early Childhood Ed	44 Science Sec	54 Remedial Reading K-12	64 Religious Education K-12	74 Inservice Training
7 Health Services	15 Asst Superintendent	25 Music Sec	35 Health/Phys Education	45 Math K-12	55 Remedial Reading Elem	65 Religious Education Elem	75 Marketing/Distributive
	16 Instructional Media Svcs	26 Business Education	36 Guidance Services K-12	46 Math Elem	56 Remedial Reading Sec	66 Religious Education Sec	76 Info Systems
	17 Chief Operations Officer	27 Career & Tech Ed	37 Guidance Services Elem	47 Math Sec	57 Bilingual/ELL	67 School Board President	77 Psychological Assess
	18 Chief Academic Officer	28 Technology Education	38 Guidance Services Sec	48 English/Lang Arts K-12	58 Special Education K-12	68 Teacher Personnel	78 Affirmative Action

Ohio School Directory — Mahoning County

Lowellville Local School Dist   PID: 00820020
52 Rocket Pl, Lowellville 44436
330/536-8426
Fax 330/536-8221

Schools: 1 \ **Teachers:** 36 \ **Students:** 499 \ **Special Ed Students:** 48 \ **College-Bound:** 70% \ **Ethnic:** African American 2%, Hispanic 8%, Caucasian 90% \ **Exp:** $142 (Low) \ **Poverty:** 14% \ **Title I:** $62,431 \ **Special Education:** $93,000 \ **Open-Close:** 08/28 - 05/29

Dr Eugene Thomas 1,83
Dennis Hines 11,73,296*
Mr Ramunno 67
Maureen Lloyd 2
Marsha Kanensky 16*

Public Schs..Principal	Grd	Prgm	Enr/#Cls	SN	
Lowellville K-12 Sch 52 Rocket Pl, Lowellville 44436 Dennis Hines	K-12	TV	499 38	87%	330/536-8426

Mahoning Co Joint Voc Sch Dist   PID: 00820898
7300 N Palmyra Rd, Canfield 44406
330/729-4000
Fax 330/729-4050

Schools: 2 \ **Teachers:** 44 \ **Students:** 778 \ **Ethnic:** African American 11%, Hispanic 5%, Caucasian 84% \ **Exp:** $966 (High) \ **Open-Close:** 08/21 - 06/02 \ **DTBP:** $188 (High)

John Zehentbauer 1,11
Mara Banfield 10,38,60,79,88,288
Matt Campbell 26*
Kim Chaney 30
Blaise Karlovic 2,19
Chris Stewart 16,73*
Mara Banfield 27*
Kathi Menabb-Welsh 67

Public Schs..Principal	Grd	Prgm	Enr/#Cls	SN	
Mahoning Co Career Tech Ctr 7300 N Palmyra Rd, Canfield 44406 Mara Banfield	Voc	G	750		330/729-4000 f t
Valley STEM and ME2 Academy 7300 N Palmyra Rd, Canfield 44406 Mara Banfield	9-10		100		330/729-4000

Poland Local School Dist   PID: 00820056
3199 Dobbins Rd, Poland 44514
330/757-7000
Fax 330/757-2390

Schools: 3 \ **Teachers:** 102 \ **Students:** 1,888 \ **Special Ed Students:** 228 \ **LEP Students:** 20 \ **College-Bound:** 76% \ **Ethnic:** Asian 2%, African American 1%, Hispanic 3%, Caucasian 94% \ **Exp:** $247 (Med) \ **Poverty:** 6% \ **Title I:** $182,221 \ **Special Education:** $414,000 \ **Open-Close:** 08/22 - 06/02 \ **DTBP:** $232 (High)

David Janofa 1
Howard Hallas 3
Brian Banfield 6
Jonathan Pera 16,76,295
Elizabeth Calderon 31,38,69
Janet Muntean 2,19
Megan Roemer 4
Mark Zura 11,36,57,58,73,88
Ruth Riley 16*
Jim Lovonni 67

Public Schs..Principal	Grd	Prgm	Enr/#Cls	SN	
Poland MS-McKinley Elem Sch 7 Elm St, Poland 44514 David Purins	3-8	V	822 30	16%	330/757-7003 Fax 330/757-7007
Poland Seminary High Sch 3199 Dobbins Rd, Poland 44514 Kevin Snyder	9-12	AGV	596 42	11%	330/757-7018 Fax 330/757-2305
Union Elem Sch 30 Riverside Dr, Poland 44514 Michael Masucci	K-2		362 15	17%	330/757-7014

Sebring Local School Dist   PID: 00820123
510 N 14th St, Sebring 44672
330/938-6165
Fax 330/938-4701

Schools: 2 \ **Teachers:** 31 \ **Students:** 600 \ **Special Ed Students:** 112 \ **LEP Students:** 3 \ **College-Bound:** 44% \ **Ethnic:** African American 1%, Hispanic 3%, Caucasian 95% \ **Exp:** $254 (Med) \ **Poverty:** 23% \ **Title I:** $202,004 \ **Special Education:** $151,000 \ **Open-Close:** 08/19 - 05/20 \ **DTBP:** $229 (High)

Toni Viscounte 1,11,57
Sue Hughes 4*
Mary Jackson 36*
Debra Green 67
Vickie Tibbs 83,85*
Dawn Meeks 2,84
Brian Clark 6*
Robert Clumen 58
Kevin Howell 73*

Public Schs..Principal	Grd	Prgm	Enr/#Cls	SN	
B L Miller Elem Sch 506 W Virginia Ave, Sebring 44672 Heather Whipkey	K-6	T	201 25		330/938-2025 Fax 330/938-2686
Sebring McKinley Jr/Sr High 225 E Indiana Ave, Sebring 44672 Joe Krumpak	7-12	T	250 25		330/938-2963 Fax 330/938-4702

South Range Local School Dist   PID: 00820161
11300 Columbiana Canfield Rd, Canfield 44406
330/549-5226
Fax 330/549-4740

Schools: 3 \ **Teachers:** 72 \ **Students:** 1,247 \ **Special Ed Students:** 148 \ **College-Bound:** 75% \ **Ethnic:** Asian 1%, Hispanic 1%, Caucasian 98% \ **Exp:** $167 (Low) \ **Poverty:** 9% \ **Title I:** $134,087 \ **Special Education:** $214,000 \ **Open-Close:** 08/19 - 06/02 \ **DTBP:** $244 (High)

Dennis Dunham 1
Dean Pagnotta 3,73,84,295
James Terry 5
Connie Stewart 7*
Rossana Pluchinsky 16*
Ericka Burkey 36,69*
Lindsay Samblanet 76
Sam Landry 83*
Brock Miller 273*
James Phillips 2,19
Katleen Pizzola 4
Don Feren 6*
Shari Lewis 8,11,58,275,286,288,296,298
Lawrence Barth 33
Corey Yoakam 67
Michael Sobota 82*
Brian Hartman 91

Public Schs..Principal	Grd	Prgm	Enr/#Cls	SN	
South Range Elem Sch 11300 Columbiana Canfield Rd, Canfield 44406 Steven Matos	K-4		458 16	25%	330/549-5578 Fax 330/549-3430
South Range High Sch 11300 Columbiana Canfield Rd, Canfield 44406 Steve Rohan	9-12	V	393 27	18%	330/549-2163 Fax 330/549-4083
South Range Middle Sch 11300 Columbiana Canfield Rd, Canfield 44406 Dan Szolek	5-8		396 29	24%	330/549-4071 Fax 330/549-4073

Springfield Local School Dist   PID: 00820202
11335 Youngstown Pittsburgh Rd, New Middletwn 44442
330/542-2929
Fax 330/542-9453

Schools: 3 \ **Teachers:** 43 \ **Students:** 942 \ **Special Ed Students:** 130 \ **LEP Students:** 3 \ **College-Bound:** 60% \ **Ethnic:** Hispanic 4%, Caucasian 96% \ **Exp:** $263 (Med) \ **Poverty:** 12% \ **Title I:** $184,804 \ **Special Education:** $168,000 \ **Open-Close:** 09/05 - 06/05 \ **DTBP:** $166 (High)

Thomas Yazvac 1,11
Dana Mirone 3*
Debbie Brothers 5
Anthony Albanese 9,34*
Edward Sobnosky 2
Joyce Dicks 4*
Mark Carden 6
Anthony DeFelice 10*

79	Student Personnel	91	Safety/Security	275	Response To Intervention	298	Grant Writer/Ptnrships
30	Driver Ed/Safety	92	Magnet School	277	Remedial Math K-12	750	Chief Innovation Officer
31	Gifted/Talented	93	Parental Involvement	280	Literacy Coach	751	Chief of Staff
32	Video Services	95	Tech Prep Program	285	STEM	752	Social Emotional Learning
33	Substance Abuse Prev	97	Chief Infomation Officer	286	Digital Learning		
34	Erate	98	Chief Technology Officer	288	Common Core Standards		**Other School Types**
35	AIDS Education	270	Character Education	294	Accountability	Ⓐ	= Alternative School
38	Alternative/At Risk	271	Migrant Education	295	Network System	Ⓒ	= Charter School
39	Multi-Cultural Curriculum	273	Teacher Mentor	296	Title II Programs	Ⓜ	= Magnet School
90	Social Work	274	Before/After Sch	297	Webmaster	Ⓨ	= Year-Round School

School Programs
A = Alternative Program
G = Adult Classes
M = Magnet Program
T = Title I Schoolwide
V = Career & Tech Ed Programs

Social Media
f = Facebook
t = Twitter

New Schools are shaded
New Superintendents and Principals are bold
Personnel with email addresses are underscored

OH-135

Mahoning County — Market Data Retrieval

Laura McBride ....58,81*   Matt Gentile 67
Dave Whorten 73*

Public Schs..Principal	Grd	Prgm	Enr/#Cls	SN	
Springfield Elem Sch 11419 Youngstown Pittsburgh Rd, New Middletwn 44442 Anthony Albanese	K-4	T	355 21	41%	330/542-3722 Fax 330/542-2488
Springfield High Sch 11335 Youngstown Pittsburgh Rd, New Middletwn 44442 Anthony DeFelice	9-12		289 32	67%	330/542-3626 Fax 330/542-3274
Springfield Local Interm Sch 11333 Youngstown Pittsburgh Rd, New Middletwn 44442 David Malone	5-8	T	298 42		330/542-3626 Fax 330/542-2159

● **Struthers City School Dist** PID: 00820252   330/750-1061
99 Euclid Ave, Struthers 44471   Fax 330/750-5516

Schools: 3 \ *Teachers:* 92 \ *Students:* 1,785 \ *Special Ed Students:* 258 \ *LEP Students:* 9 \ *College-Bound:* 56% \ *Ethnic:* African American 7%, Hispanic 7%, Caucasian 86% \ *Exp:* $185 (Low) \ *Poverty:* 26% \ *Title I:* $731,101 \ *Special Education:* $368,000 \ *Open-Close:* 08/26 - 06/02 \ *DTBP:* $221 (High)

Peter Pirone 1,83   Brian Bella 2,5,294
Dru Clyde .... 4*   Nancy Knight 6*
Amanda McNinch .... 11,58,69,77,296*   Ron Shives 67
Kevin Stoklosa .... 73,295* Kate Sanna 81*
Robert Zanni .... 82*   Sandy Horvath 280*

Public Schs..Principal	Grd	Prgm	Enr/#Cls	SN	
Struthers Elem Sch 520 9th St, Struthers 44471 Joan Jones	PK-4	T	695 40	69%	330/750-1065 Fax 330/750-1489
Struthers High Sch 111 Euclid Ave, Struthers 44471 Roger Day	9-12	TV	492 60	63%	330/750-1062 Fax 330/755-4525
Struthers Middle Sch 800 5th St, Struthers 44471 Robert Gelonese	5-8	T	598 50	68%	330/750-1064 Fax 330/755-4749

● **West Branch Local School Dist** PID: 00820331   330/938-9324
14277 S Main St, Beloit 44609   Fax 330/938-6815

Schools: 5 \ *Teachers:* 122 \ *Students:* 2,100 \ *Special Ed Students:* 243 \ *LEP Students:* 10 \ *College-Bound:* 52% \ *Ethnic:* Hispanic 1%, Caucasian 98% \ *Exp:* $243 (Med) \ *Poverty:* 17% \ *Title I:* $514,602 \ *Special Education:* $233,000 \ *Open-Close:* 09/05 - 06/04 \ *DTBP:* $203 (High)

Timothy Saxton 1   Larry Stuckey 3
Lorie Weingart 4   Sherri Malloy 5
Elli Geiger .... 6*   David Drawl 11
Maryjane Egli 12,34,36,57,58,83,88,296   Leigh Martin 16,82
Lori McLaughlin 67   Jim Graham 73,76*
Abbie Millard 273*

Public Schs..Principal	Grd	Prgm	Enr/#Cls	SN	
Damascus Elem Sch 14405 Pricetown Rd, Salem 44460 Fritz Schlueter	K-4		394	33%	330/938-4500 Fax 330/938-4501
Knox Elem Sch 2900 Knox School Rd, Alliance 44601 Robert Graham	K-4	T	339 12	53%	330/938-1122 Fax 330/938-1121
ⓐ Warrior Academy 14277 S Main St, Beloit 44609 Curtis Ahrens	6-12		25		330/938-2183
West Branch High Sch 14277 S Main St, Beloit 44609 Brian Coffee	9-12	V	594 50	37%	330/938-2183 Fax 330/938-4444
West Branch Middle Sch 14409 Beloit Snodes Rd, Beloit 44609 Steve Fowler	5-8	TV	680	42%	330/938-4300 Fax 330/938-4301

● **Western Reserve Local Sch Dist** PID: 00820408   330/547-4100
13850 W Akron Canfield Rd, Berlin Center 44401   Fax 330/547-9302

Schools: 1 \ *Teachers:* 45 \ *Students:* 850 \ *Special Ed Students:* 77 \ *College-Bound:* 62% \ *Ethnic:* Caucasian 99% \ *Exp:* $155 (Low) \ *Poverty:* 8% \ *Title I:* $60,740 \ *Special Education:* $134,000 \ *Open-Close:* 09/04 - 06/10 \ *DTBP:* $192 (High)

Doug McGlynn 1   Cathy Romack 2,298
Nora Jamison .... 7*   Danielle Matos 37*
Greg Malito .... 38,69,83*   Kathy Shook 58*
Mark Halls 67   Kathy Yaist 273*

Public Schs..Principal	Grd	Prgm	Enr/#Cls	SN	
Western Reserve Local Sch 13850 W Akron Canfield Rd, Berlin Center 44401 Deb Farelli \ Mike Sauner \ Dallas Saunders	K-12		850 60	94%	330/547-4100

● **Youngstown City School Dist** PID: 00820446   330/744-6900
474 Bennington Ave, Youngstown 44505   Fax 330/743-1157

Schools: 15 \ *Teachers:* 360 \ *Students:* 5,275 \ *Special Ed Students:* 1,179 \ *LEP Students:* 298 \ *College-Bound:* 34% \ *Ethnic:* African American 67%, Hispanic 18%, Caucasian 15% \ *Exp:* $244 (Med) \ *Poverty:* 47% \ *Title I:* $10,258,924 \ *Special Education:* $2,780,000 \ *Open-Close:* 08/12 - 05/22 \ *DTBP:* $246 (High) \ 🄵 🅃

Joseph Meranto 1   Anthony Deniro 2
Susan Paris 4   Colleen Murphy-Penk 5
Rick Shepas 6,35   Christine Sawicki 8,18
Ava Yeager 11,296   A J Ginetti 19
Tracy Vivo 20   Linda Yosay 58,79
Brenda Kimble 67   Thomas Hill 68
Timothy Filipovich .... 69,294 Denise Dick 71
John LaPlante 73,76,97,98   Michele McCaughtry 81
William Morvay 91   Linda Hoey 93

Public Schs..Principal	Grd	Prgm	Enr/#Cls	SN	
ⓜ Chaney High Sch 731 S Hazelwood Ave, Youngstown 44509 Bob Klinar	9-12	T	642		330/744-8822 Fax 330/793-8002 🄵 🄶
Choffin Career & Technical Ctr 200 E Wood St, Youngstown 44503 Mike Saville	Voc	G	300 42		330/744-8700 Fax 330/744-8705
East High Sch 474 Bennington Ave, Youngstown 44505 Sonya Gordon	9-12	TV	475 65		330/740-4005 Fax 330/742-6464
Harding Elem Sch 1903 Cordova Ave, Youngstown 44504 Robert Kearns	PK-8	T	354 20		330/744-7517 Fax 330/744-8589
Kirkmere Elem Sch 2851 Kirk Rd, Youngstown 44511 Misha Scott	PK-8		400 21		330/744-7725 Fax 330/792-6691
Martin Luther King Elem Sch 2724 Mariner Ave, Youngstown 44505 Artemus Scissum	PK-8		336 30		330/744-7823 Fax 330/480-1907
Paul C Bunn Elem Sch 1825 Sequoya Dr, Youngstown 44514 William Baun	PK-8	T	323 20		330/744-8963 Fax 330/788-6934

1	Superintendent	8	Curric/Instruct K-12	19	Chief Financial Officer	29	Family/Consumer Science	39	Social Studies K-12	49	English/Lang Arts Elem	59	Special Education Elem	69	Academic Assessment
2	Bus/Finance/Purchasing	9	Curric/Instruct Elem	20	Art K-12	30	Adult Education	40	Social Studies Elem	50	English/Lang Arts Sec	60	Special Education Sec	70	Research/Development
3	Buildings And Grounds	10	Curric/Instruct Sec	21	Art Elem	31	Career/Sch-to-Work K-12	41	Social Studies Sec	51	Reading K-12	61	Foreign/World Lang K-12	71	Public Information
4	Food Service	11	Federal Program	22	Art Sec	32	Career/Sch-to-Work Elem	42	Science K-12	52	Reading Elem	62	Foreign/World Lang Elem	72	Summer School
5	Transportation	12	Title I	23	Music K-12	33	Career/Sch-to-Work Sec	43	Science Elem	53	Reading Sec	63	Foreign/World Lang Sec	73	Instructional Tech
6	Athletic	13	Title V	24	Music Elem	34	Early Childhood Ed	44	Science Sec	54	Remedial Reading K-12	64	Religious Education K-12	74	Inservice Training
7	Health Services	14	Asst Superintendent	25	Music Sec	35	Health/Phys Education	45	Math K-12	55	Remedial Reading Elem	65	Religious Education Elem	75	Marketing/Distributive
		15	Instructional Media Svcs	26	Business Education	36	Guidance Services K-12	46	Math Elem	56	Remedial Reading Sec	66	Religious Education Sec	76	Info Systems
		16	Chief Operations Officer	27	Career & Tech Ed	37	Guidance Services Elem	47	Math Sec	57	Bilingual/ELL	67	School Board President	77	Psychological Assess
		17	Chief Academic Officer	28	Technology Education	38	Guidance Services Sec	48	English/Lang Arts K-12	58	Special Education K-12	68	Teacher Personnel	78	Affirmative Action

Ohio School Directory

Marion County

	Grd	Prgm	Enr/#Cls	
Rayen Early College Interm Sch 731 S Hazelwood Ave, Youngstown 44509 Deborah DiFrancesco	5-8	T	360	330/744-7602 Fax 330/793-9675
Taft Elem Sch 730 E Avondale Ave, Youngstown 44502 John McMahan	PK-8	T	317 19	330/744-7973 Fax 330/788-6809
Volney Rogers Elem Sch 2400 S Schenley Ave, Youngstown 44511 Misha Scott	PK-8		295	330/744-8845 Fax 330/792-6866
William Holmes McGuffey ES 310 S Schenley Ave, Youngstown 44509 Cathy Dorbish	PK-8	T	702 38	330/744-7999 Fax 330/792-8051
Williamson Elem Sch 58 Williamson Ave, Youngstown 44507 Michelle Payich	PK-8	T	252 21	330/744-7155 Fax 330/480-1902
Wilson Elem Sch 2725 Gibson St, Youngstown 44502 Jennifer Walker	PK-8		285 30	330/744-8002 Fax 330/788-1326
Youngstown Early College HS 20 W Wood St, Youngstown 44503 Monica Jones	9-12	T	263	330/744-7923 Fax 330/480-5875
Youngstown Virtual Academy 200 E Wood St, Youngstown 44503 **Rick Gurski**	9-12		401	330/744-8700

MAHONING CATHOLIC SCHOOLS

• **Diocese of Youngstown Ed Off** PID: 00820915   330/744-8451
144 W Wood St, Youngstown 44503   Fax 330/744-5099

Schools: 27 \ **Students:** 6,100

Listing includes only schools located in this county. See District Index for location of Diocesan Offices.

Mary Fiala 1   Patrick Kelly 2
Randall Rair 6,11,15   Lori Crofford 73

Catholic Schs..Principal	Grd	Prgm	Enr/#Cls	SN
Cardinal Mooney High Sch 2545 Erie St, Youngstown 44507 Mark Vollmer	9-12	V	470 45	330/788-5007 Fax 330/788-4511 f t
Holy Family Sch 2731 Center Rd, Poland 44514 Kathleen Stoops	PK-8		255 16	330/757-3713 Fax 330/757-7648
St Charles Sch 7325 Westview Dr, Boardman 44512 Mary Welsh	K-8		449 20	330/758-6689 Fax 330/758-7404
St Christine Sch 3125 S Schenley Ave, Youngstown 44511 Mr Carpenter	K-8		350 18	330/792-4544 Fax 330/792-6888 f
St Joseph the Provider Sch 1145 Turin St, Youngstown 44510 Cheryl Jablonski	K-8		173 9	330/259-0353 Fax 330/259-0364
St Nicholas Sch 762 5th St, Struthers 44471 Elizabeth McCullough	K-8		150 11	330/755-2128 Fax 330/755-2129
Ursuline High Sch 750 Wick Ave, Youngstown 44505 Matthew Sammartino	9-12		450 35	330/744-4563 Fax 330/744-3358

MAHONING PRIVATE SCHOOLS

Private Schs..Principal	Grd	Prgm	Enr/#Cls	SN
Akiva Academy 505 Gypsy Ln, Youngstown 44504 Kathleen Mioni	K-8		150 8	330/747-0452 Fax 330/747-2226
Montessori Sch-Mahoning Valley 2008 Lynn Ave, Youngstown 44514 Amy-Anne Kibler	PK-8		82 6	330/788-4622 Fax 330/788-1754
Rich Center for Autism 1 University Plz, Youngstown 44555 Melanie Carsolo	Spec		70	330/941-1927 Fax 330/941-4670
Valley Christian Sch 4401 Southern Blvd, Youngstown 44512 Michael Pecchia	PK-12		650 27	330/788-8088 Fax 330/788-2875

MAHONING REGIONAL CENTERS

• **Access** PID: 04499465   330/702-7860
7320 N Palmyra Rd Ste 127, Canfield 44406

Lisa Smith 1   Brian Stidham 2
Tom Davies 16,295   Toni Viscounte 67
Patrick Rager 76   Diane Fabino 79

• **State Support Team-Region 5** PID: 02228284   330/533-8755
7320 N Palmyra Rd, Canfield 44406   Fax 330/533-8777

Michele Moore 1   Dr Andrew Tommelleo 27
Tina DeVito 34   Terry Grimm 73

MARION COUNTY

MARION COUNTY SCHOOLS

• **North Central Ohio Ed Svc Ctr** PID: 02089210   740/387-6625
333 E Center St, Marion 43302   Fax 740/383-4804

Dr James Lahoski 1,11   Dawn Jacobs 2
Brenda Luhring 15   Mike McCreary 15
Heather Justen 34   Cynthia Moore 58
Kathy Mohr 73,74

County Schs..Principal	Grd	Prgm	Enr/#Cls	SN
Marie English ECC 2387 Harding Hwy E, Marion 43302 Kattie Harmon	Spec		240 5	740/387-1035 Fax 740/375-0596

			School Programs	**Social Media**
79 Student Personnel	91 Safety/Security	275 Response To Intervention	298 Grant Writer/Ptnrships	A = Alternative Program
80 Driver Ed/Safety	92 Magnet School	277 Remedial Math K-12	750 Chief Innovation Officer	G = Adult Classes	f = Facebook
81 Gifted/Talented	93 Parental Involvement	280 Literacy Coach	751 Chief of Staff	M = Magnet Program	t = Twitter
82 Video Services	95 Tech Prep Program	285 STEM	752 Social Emotional Learning	T = Title I Schoolwide	
83 Substance Abuse Prev	97 Chief Information Officer	286 Digital Learning		V = Career & Tech Ed Programs	
84 Erate	98 Chief Technology Officer	288 Common Core Standards	**Other School Types**		
85 AIDS Education	270 Character Education	294 Accountability	Ⓐ = Alternative School		
86 Alternative/At Risk	271 Migrant Education	295 Network System	Ⓒ = Charter School	New Schools are shaded	
89 Multi-Cultural Curriculum	273 Teacher Mentor	296 Title II Programs	Ⓜ = Magnet School	New Superintendents and Principals are bold	
90 Social Work	274 Before/After Sch	297 Webmaster	Ⓨ = Year-Round School	Personnel with email addresses are underscored	

OH—137

Marion County Market Data Retrieval

MARION PUBLIC SCHOOLS

- **Elgin Local School Dist** PID: 00821658
1239 Keener Rd S, Marion 43302
740/382-1101
Fax 740/382-1672

Schools: 3 \ *Teachers:* 60 \ *Students:* 1,200 \ *Special Ed Students:* 137 \ *LEP Students:* 13 \ *College-Bound:* 47% \ *Ethnic:* Hispanic 4%, Caucasian 96% \ *Exp:* $316 (High) \ *Poverty:* 12% \ *Title I:* $213,278 \ *Special Education:* $229,000 \ *Open-Close:* 08/19 - 05/25 \ *DTBP:* $16 (Low)

Name	Ref
Bruce Gast	1
Dan Gilliam	3
Shannon Downing	5
Morgan Burrma	11,296
Kathy Quires	16,58,82
Kim Reynolds	2
Teresa Vermillion	4*
Jason Hix	6*
Cynthia Gilbert	16,73*
Jennifer Conroy	67

Public Schs..Principal	Grd	Prgm	Enr/#Cls	SN	Phone
Elgin Elem Sch 1250 Keener Rd S, Marion 43302 **Matt Holsinger**	PK-5	T	507	55%	740/223-4301 Fax 740/223-4311
Elgin High Sch 1150 Keener Rd S, Marion 43302 Chad Cunningham	9-12	T	285 25	43%	740/223-4300 Fax 740/223-4310
Elgin Middle Sch 1200 Keener Rd S, Marion 43302 Michael Malcom	6-8	T	237 20	51%	740/223-4300 Fax 740/233-4310

- **Marion City School Dist** PID: 00821713
420 Presidential Dr Ste B, Marion 43302
740/387-3300
Fax 740/223-4400

Schools: 9 \ *Teachers:* 271 \ *Students:* 4,200 \ *Special Ed Students:* 841 \ *LEP Students:* 78 \ *College-Bound:* 47% \ *Ethnic:* African American 7%, Hispanic 7%, Caucasian 86% \ *Exp:* $152 (Low) \ *Poverty:* 30% \ *Title I:* $2,527,765 \ *Special Education:* $1,020,000 \ *Open-Close:* 08/19 - 05/22 \ *DTBP:* $64 (Low) \

Name	Ref
Dr Ronald Iarussi	1
Brian Mitchell	3
Jason Heilman	5
Sean Kearns	6*
Ben Porter	8,288*
Marsha Pitts	11,54,69,83,88,296
Angie Osborne	81,298
Veronica Reinhart	2
Edwina Brewer	4
Mike Lindsey	6*
Kelley Barber	7,57,58
Jennifer Lawson	8,15,16,74,280
Ted McKinniss	67
Greg Menzie	294

Public Schs..Principal	Grd	Prgm	Enr/#Cls	SN	Phone
Benjamin Harrison Elem Sch 625 Brightwood Dr, Marion 43302 Leah Filliater	PK-5	T	500 25		740/223-4999 Fax 740/223-4990
Garfield Elem Sch 1170 Brookside Rd, Marion 43302 Marianne Bailey	PK-5	T	420 20		740/223-4444 Fax 740/223-4485
George Washington Elem Sch 400 Pennsylvania Ave, Marion 43302 Scott Curtis	PK-5	T	436 22		740/223-3883 Fax 740/223-3726
Grant Middle Sch 420 Presidential Dr, Marion 43302 Kirk Ballinger	6-8	T	897 23		740/223-4900 Fax 740/223-4820
Harding High Sch 1500 Harding Hwy E, Marion 43302 Jennifer Musbach	9-12	AGTV	1,096 95		740/223-4700 Fax 740/223-4705
Hayes Elem Sch 750 Silver St, Marion 43302 Rick Glenn	PK-5	T	277 16		740/223-4950 Fax 740/223-4960
McKinley Elem Sch 925 Chatfield Rd, Marion 43302 Matt Holsinger	PK-5	T	422 27		740/223-4600 Fax 740/223-4574
Ⓐ Rushmore Academy Ⓒ 2222 Marion Mount Gilead Rd, Marion 43302 Steve Vanderhoff	9-12	T	332		740/387-2043 Fax 740/387-2169
Taft Elem Sch 1000 Robinson St, Marion 43302 Adam Mowery	PK-5	T	453 23		740/223-4500 Fax 740/223-4499

- **Pleasant Local School Dist** PID: 00821892
1107 Owens Rd W, Marion 43302
740/389-4479
Fax 740/389-6985

Schools: 4 \ *Teachers:* 92 \ *Students:* 1,320 \ *Special Ed Students:* 86 \ *LEP Students:* 18 \ *College-Bound:* 72% \ *Ethnic:* Asian 1%, African American 1%, Hispanic 2%, Caucasian 96% \ *Exp:* $236 (Med) \ *Poverty:* 16% \ *Title I:* $269,513 \ *Special Education:* $207,000 \ *Open-Close:* 08/21 - 05/29 \ *DTBP:* $169 (High) \

Name	Ref
Jennifer Adams	1
Joshua Nease	3
Tom Haley	5
Jeff Rainey	16*
Dr Shelly Dawson	60,79*
Jolene Carter	2
Lori Kramp	4*
Eric Holman	6
Chris Webb	38,69,83,85*
Pam Freshour	67

Public Schs..Principal	Grd	Prgm	Enr/#Cls	SN	Phone
Ⓒ Pleasant Cmty Digital Academy 1105 Owens Rd W, Marion 43302 Dr Shelly Dason	K-12	T	100		740/389-4815 Fax 740/389-5063
Pleasant Elem Sch 1105 Owens Rd W, Marion 43302 Dr Shelly Dawson	K-5		664 32	50%	740/389-4815 Fax 740/389-5063
Pleasant High Sch 1101 Owens Rd W, Marion 43302 **Steven Ringer**	9-12		367 30	23%	740/389-2389 Fax 740/389-3904
Pleasant Middle Sch 3507 Smeltzer Rd, Marion 43302 **Michael Malcom**	6-8		285 22	35%	740/389-5167 Fax 740/389-5111

- **Ridgedale Local School Dist** PID: 00821933
3103 Hillman Ford Rd, Morral 43337
740/382-6065
Fax 740/383-6538

Schools: 2 \ *Teachers:* 49 \ *Students:* 642 \ *Special Ed Students:* 70 \ *College-Bound:* 54% \ *Ethnic:* Hispanic 3%, Caucasian 97% \ *Exp:* $274 (Med) \ *Poverty:* 14% \ *Title I:* $134,051 \ *Special Education:* $110,000 \ *Open-Close:* 08/20 - 06/22 \ *DTBP:* $38 (Low)

Name	Ref
Robert Britton	1
Robin Townsend	5
Brian Sparling	8*
Brian Sloan	16,73,76,82,84,295
Patrick Ballinger	67,288
Megan Mitchell	4
Jessica Parthemore	6,83,88,275
Sam Staton	9,11*
Chris Looney	57*
Cherie Leach	85*

Public Schs..Principal	Grd	Prgm	Enr/#Cls	SN	Phone
Ridgedale Elem Sch 3105 Hillman Ford Rd, Morral 43337 Sam Staton	K-5	T	314 18	56%	740/383-2020
Ridgedale Jr Sr High Sch 3165 Hillman Ford Rd, Morral 43337 Greg Rossman	6-12	T	328 43		740/383-2167 Fax 740/387-8525

1 Superintendent	8 Curric/Instruct K-12	19 Chief Financial Officer	29 Family/Consumer Science	39 Social Studies K-12	49 English/Lang Arts Elem	59 Special Education Elem	69 Academic Assessment
2 Bus/Finance/Purchasing	9 Curric/Instruct Elem	20 Art K-12	30 Adult Education	40 Social Studies Elem	50 English/Lang Arts Sec	60 Special Education Sec	70 Research/Development
3 Buildings And Grounds	10 Curric/Instruct Sec	21 Art Elem	31 Career/Sch-to-Work K-12	41 Social Studies Sec	51 Reading K-12	61 Foreign/World Lang K-12	71 Public Information
4 Food Service	11 Federal Program	22 Art Sec	32 Career/Sch-to-Work Elem	42 Science K-12	52 Reading Elem	62 Foreign/World Lang Elem	72 Summer School
5 Transportation	12 Title I	23 Music K-12	33 Career/Sch-to-Work Sec	43 Science Elem	53 Reading Sec	63 Foreign/World Lang Sec	73 Instructional Tech
6 Athletic	13 Title V	24 Music Elem	34 Early Childhood Ed	44 Science Sec	54 Remedial Reading K-12	64 Religious Education K-12	74 Inservice Training
7 Health Services	15 Asst Superintendent	25 Music Sec	35 Health/Phys Education	45 Math K-12	55 Remedial Reading Elem	65 Religious Education Elem	75 Marketing/Distributive
	16 Instructional Media Svcs	26 Business Education	36 Guidance Services K-12	46 Math Elem	56 Remedial Reading Sec	66 Religious Education Sec	76 Info Systems
	17 Chief Operations Officer	27 Career & Tech Ed	37 Guidance Services Elem	47 Math Sec	57 Bilingual/ELL	67 School Board President	77 Psychological Assess
	18 Chief Academic Officer	28 Technology Education	38 Guidance Services Sec	48 English/Lang Arts K-12	58 Special Education K-12	68 Teacher Personnel	78 Affirmative Action

Ohio School Directory — Medina County

River Valley Local School Dist PID: 00821983
197 Brocklesby Rd, Caledonia 43314
740/725-5400
Fax 740/725-5499

Schools: 4 \ **Teachers:** 97 \ **Students:** 2,260 \ **Special Ed Students:** 188 \ **LEP Students:** 6 \ **College-Bound:** 63% \ **Ethnic:** Asian 1%, African American 2%, Hispanic 2%, Caucasian 95% \ **Exp:** $282 (Med) \ **Poverty:** 11% \ **Title I:** $265,738 \ **Special Education:** $342,000 \ **Open-Close:** 08/19 - 05/28 \ **DTBP:** $71 (Low) \ f t

Cathryn Zimmer 2
Brent Herdman 4*
Barry Dutt 10,83,88*
Heather Kantzer 58
Ginger McDaniels 274*
Scott Hoffman 3,5
Nancy Talley 8
Sandy Richards 12*
Brian Stover 67

Public Schs..Principal	Grd	Prgm	Enr/#Cls	SN	
Heritage Elem Sch 720 Columbus Sandusky Rd S, Marion 43302 Melanie Comstock	K-5		510 23	32%	740/725-5500 Fax 740/725-5599
Liberty Elem Sch 1932 Whetstone River Rd N, Caledonia 43314 Sandy Richards	PK-5	T	426 21	57%	740/725-5600 Fax 419/845-2699
River Valley High Sch 4280 Marion Mount Gilead Rd, Caledonia 43314 David Coleman	9-12		537 36	35%	740/725-5800 Fax 740/725-5899
River Valley Middle Sch 4334 Marion Mount Gilead Rd, Caledonia 43314 Don Gliebe	6-8	T	481 25	38%	740/725-5700 Fax 740/725-5799

Tri-Rivers Joint Voc Sch Dist PID: 01417482
2222 Marion Mount Gilead Rd, Marion 43302
740/389-4681
Fax 740/389-2963

Schools: 1 \ **Teachers:** 38 \ **Students:** 550 \ **Exp:** $852 (High) \ **Open-Close:** 08/14 - 05/21 \ **DTBP:** $195 (High) \ f t

Charles Speelman 1
Emeline Kelly 7
Mike Wellin 16,73*
Jodi Gaietto 38,88*
Ellen Messenger 71
Steve Earnest 2,19
Larry Hickman 10,11,27,60*
Richard George 30*
Jim McFarland 67
Carol Bebout 270*

Public Schs..Principal	Grd	Prgm	Enr/#Cls	SN
Tri-Rivers Career Center HS 2222 Marion Mount Gilead Rd, Marion 43302 Carol Bebout	Voc	AG	550 70	740/389-4681

MARION CATHOLIC SCHOOLS

Diocese of Columbus Ed Office PID: 00802717
Listing includes only schools located in this county. See District Index for location of Diocesan Offices.

Catholic Schs..Principal	Grd	Prgm	Enr/#Cls	SN
St Mary Sch 274 N Prospect St, Marion 43302 Jack Mental	K-8		108 7	740/382-1607 Fax 740/382-6577

MARION PRIVATE SCHOOLS

Private Schs..Principal	Grd	Prgm	Enr/#Cls	SN
Heritage Christian Sch 193 Marion Williamsport Rd E, Marion 43302 John Burroughs	PK-12		35 4	740/382-6248 Fax 740/387-1015

MARION REGIONAL CENTERS

Meta Solutions PID: 04499506
100 Executive Dr, Marion 43302
740/389-4798
Fax 740/389-4517

Dr Wade Lucas 1
Brittany Rutter 68
David Varda 2
Tim Snyder 73

MEDINA COUNTY

MEDINA COUNTY SCHOOLS

Ed Svc Center of Medina Co PID: 02089222
124 W Washington St Ste 1B, Medina 44256
330/723-6393
Fax 330/723-0573

William Koran 1,11
April Johnson 5
John Hovorka 16,73,295
Kent Patterson 67
Tom Magier 88
Anthony Hatmaker 2
Jacinda Yonker 8,74,81
Rachel Krauss 58
Kimberly Tomashefski 68

County Schs..Principal	Grd	Prgm	Enr/#Cls	SN
Windfall Sch 4691 Windfall Rd, Medina 44256 Dr Kaye Stanley-Bryson	Spec	GV	60 9	330/725-7751 Fax 330/722-4854

MEDINA PUBLIC SCHOOLS

Black River Local School Dist PID: 00822066
257A County Road 40, Sullivan 44880
419/736-3300
Fax 419/736-3308

Schools: 2 \ **Teachers:** 70 \ **Students:** 631 \ **Special Ed Students:** 180 \ **LEP Students:** 4 \ **College-Bound:** 45% \ **Ethnic:** African American 1%, Hispanic 2%, Caucasian 97% \ **Exp:** $641 (High) \ **Poverty:** 11% \ **Title I:** $281,252 \ **Special Education:** $275,000 \ **Open-Close:** 08/27 - 05/29 \ **DTBP:** $192 (High)

Chris Clark 1
Joe Kmitt 3
Bruce Berry 5
Jill Beiser 8,11,288
Angelique Kuba 58*
Scott Meredith 73
Connie Hange 2,84
Bonnie Cooper 4*
Ted Gordon 6
Linda Coad 38,58
Chuck Stiver 67

Public Schs..Principal	Grd	Prgm	Enr/#Cls	SN
Black River Education Center 257 County Road 40, Sullivan 44880 Becky Luth \ Kathy Aviles	K-8	T	303 22	419/736-2161 Fax 419/736-3309

---

79 Student Personnel	91 Safety/Security	275 Response To Intervention	298 Grant Writer/Ptnrships	**School Programs**	**Social Media**		
60 Driver Ed/Safety	92 Magnet School	277 Remedial Math K-12	750 Chief Innovation Officer	A = Alternative Program			
61 Gifted/Talented	93 Parental Involvement	280 Literacy Coach	751 Chief of Staff	G = Adult Classes	f = Facebook		
32 Video Services	95 Tech Prep Program	285 STEM	752 Social Emotional Learning	M = Magnet Program			
83 Substance Abuse Prev	97 Chief Infomation Officer	286 Digital Learning		T = Title I Schoolwide	t = Twitter		
64 Erate	98 Chief Technology Officer	288 Common Core Standards	**Other School Types**	V = Career & Tech Ed Programs			
85 AIDS Accountability	270 Character Education	294 Accountability	Ⓐ = Alternative School				
68 Alternative/At Risk	271 Migrant Education	295 Network System	Ⓒ = Charter School	New Schools are shaded			
69 Multi-Cultural Curriculum	273 Teacher Mentor	296 Title II Programs	Ⓜ = Magnet School	New Superintendents and Principals are bold			
90 Social Work	274 Before/After Sch	297 Webmaster	Ⓨ = Year-Round School	Personnel with email addresses are underscored			

Medina County

Market Data Retrieval

Black River High Sch — 9-12 V 339 38% 419/736-3303
233 County Road 40, Sullivan 44880 — 28 — Fax 419/736-3302
Tracey Lambdin

• Brunswick City School Dist PID: 00822119
3643 Center Rd, Brunswick 44212
330/225-7731
Fax 330/273-0507

Schools: 11 \ **Teachers:** 389 \ **Students:** 7,123 \ **Special Ed Students:** 797 \ **LEP Students:** 71 \ **College-Bound:** 72% \ **Ethnic:** Asian 1%, African American 2%, Hispanic 3%, Caucasian 94% \ **Exp:** $98 (Low) \ **Poverty:** 6% \ **Title I:** $655,536 \ **Special Education:** $1,297,000 \ **Open-Close:** 08/13 - 05/21 \ **DTBP:** $182 (High)

Michael Mayell 1	Salvatore Grida 2
Robert Kelly 3,91	Karen Becker 4*
Jim Hedrick 5	John Justice 6
Donna Amato 8,11,270,288,298	Patrick Geschke 8
Tracy Wheeler 15,68,81	Carol Yost 57
Leann Alferio 58	Grant Relic 67
Michael Draves 68*	Amy Rutledge 71
Kathleen Verhest 73,76	Roger West 73
Taya Neuman 79	Debbie Marshall 83

Public Schs..Principal	Grd	Prgm	Enr/#Cls	SN	
Applewood Elem Sch 3891 Applewood Dr, Brunswick 44212 Amren Fowler	K-5	T	485 21	29%	330/273-0481 Fax 330/273-0508
Brunswick High Sch 3581 Center Rd, Brunswick 44212 Keith Merrill	9-12	V	2,213 103	20%	330/273-0496 Fax 330/225-5393
C R Towslee Elem Sch 3555 Center Rd, Brunswick 44212 Claire Trujillo	K-5	T	410 35	33%	330/273-0487 Fax 330/273-0516
Crestview Elem Sch 300 W 130th St, Brunswick 44212 Jamie Schulke	K-5		440 20	11%	330/273-0482 Fax 330/273-0446
Edwards Middle Sch 1497 Pearl Rd, Brunswick 44212 Andrew Perry	6-8		463 38		330/273-0488 Fax 330/273-0544
Hickory Ridge Elem Sch 4628 Hickory Ridge Ave, Brunswick 44212 Marisa Bavaro	K-5		436 19	15%	330/273-0483 Fax 330/273-0510
Huntington Elem Sch 1931 Huntington Cir, Brunswick 44212 Kesh Boodheshwar	K-5		351 26	27%	330/273-0484 Fax 330/273-0388
Memorial Elem Sch 3845 Magnolia Dr, Brunswick 44212 Katie Mann	K-5	T	402 26	28%	330/273-0486 Fax 330/273-0513
Visintainer Middle Sch 1459 Pearl Rd, Brunswick 44212 Brian Sharosky	6-8		543 40	22%	330/273-0402 Fax 330/273-0400
Walter Kidder Elem Sch 3650 Grafton Rd, Brunswick 44212 Bonnie Kubec	PK-5		518 18	14%	330/273-0485 Fax 330/273-0511
Willetts Middle Sch 1045 Hadcock Rd, Brunswick 44212 **Linda Simon**	6-8		654 40		330/273-0489 Fax 330/273-0564

• Buckeye Local School Dist PID: 00822195
3044 Columbia Rd, Medina 44256
330/722-8257
Fax 330/722-5793

Schools: 4 \ **Teachers:** 118 \ **Students:** 2,300 \ **Special Ed Students:** 245 \ **LEP Students:** 5 \ **College-Bound:** 72% \ **Ethnic:** Asian 1%, African American 1%, Hispanic 2%, Caucasian 96% \ **Exp:** $73 (Low) \ **Poverty:** 7% \ **Title I:** $208,580 \ **Special Education:** $428,000 \ **Open-Close:** 08/21 - 05/28 \ **DTBP:** $208 (High)

Kent Morgan 1	Jennifer Knapp 2,68
Glen Reisner 3	Gale Luther 4
Greg Pollock 5	Tom Harrington 6*
Dr Christina Collins 8,16,74,81	Gayle Telford 11,83,88,275*
Karl Walker 16,73*	Vicki Ludwig 37*
Linda Depew 38	Brendan Zepp 58
Barbara Gunkleman 67	

Public Schs..Principal	Grd	Prgm	Enr/#Cls	SN	
Buckeye High Sch 3084 Columbia Rd, Medina 44256 **Dan Flood**	9-12		689 41	25%	330/722-8257 Fax 330/723-5606
Buckeye Intermediate Sch 3140 Columbia Rd, Medina 44256 **Kelli Davisson**	4-6		623 23	23%	330/722-8257 Fax 330/725-0164
Buckeye Junior High Sch 3024 Columbia Rd, Medina 44256 **Shannon Conley**	7-8		396 27	21%	330/722-8257 Fax 330/725-2413
Buckeye Primary Sch 3180 Columbia Rd, Medina 44256 Dawn Kochanek	K-3		610 20	27%	330/722-8257 Fax 330/723-0651

• Cloverleaf Local School Dist PID: 00822250
8525 Friendsville Rd, Lodi 44254
330/948-2500
Fax 330/948-1034

Schools: 3 \ **Teachers:** 128 \ **Students:** 2,264 \ **Special Ed Students:** 311 \ **College-Bound:** 58% \ **Ethnic:** Asian 1%, African American 1%, Hispanic 2%, Caucasian 97% \ **Exp:** $124 (Low) \ **Poverty:** 8% \ **Title I:** $317,454 \ **Special Education:** $569,000 \ **Open-Close:** 08/20 - 05/28 \ **DTBP:** $188 (High)

Daryl Kubilus 1	James Hudson 2,84
Ken Flecher 3,91	Kenneth Fletcher 3
Carrie Beegle 4	John Ewart 5
Craig Walkup 6	Robert Hevener 8,11,72,74,93,273,296*
Cheri Weigand 16*	Laura Hutson 30
Jason Myers 67	John Gladden 71
Deb Bican 83*	

Public Schs..Principal	Grd	Prgm	Enr/#Cls	SN	
Cloverleaf Elem Sch 8337 Friendsville Rd, Seville 44273 Karen Martin	PK-5		1,064 33	38%	330/302-0103 Fax 330/721-3901
Cloverleaf High Sch 8525 Friendsville Rd, Lodi 44254 Ronald Tisher	9-12	AV	665 36	33%	330/948-2500 Fax 330/721-3559
Cloverleaf Middle Sch 7500 Buffham Rd, Seville 44273 Brian Madigan	6-8		535 45	31%	330/302-0207 Fax 330/302-0520

1 Superintendent	8 Curric/Instruct K-12	19 Chief Financial Officer	29 Family/Consumer Science	39 Social Studies K-12	49 English/Lang Arts Elem	59 Special Education Elem	69 Academic Assessment
2 Bus/Finance/Purchasing	9 Curric/Instruct Elem	20 Art K-12	30 Adult Education	40 Social Studies Elem	50 English/Lang Arts Sec	60 Special Education Sec	70 Research/Development
3 Buildings And Grounds	10 Curric/Instruct Sec	21 Art Elem	31 Career/Sch-to-Work K-12	41 Social Studies Sec	51 Reading K-12	61 Foreign/World Lang K-12	71 Public Information
4 Food Service	11 Federal Program	22 Art Sec	32 Career/Sch-to-Work Elem	42 Science K-12	52 Reading Elem	62 Foreign/World Lang Elem	72 Summer School
5 Transportation	12 Title I	23 Music K-12	33 Career/Sch-to-Work Sec	43 Science Elem	53 Reading Sec	63 Foreign/World Lang Sec	73 Instructional Tech
6 Athletic	13 Title IV	24 Music Elem	34 Early Childhood Ed	44 Science Sec	54 Remedial Reading K-12	64 Religious Education K-12	74 Inservice Training
7 Health Services	14 Asst Superintendent	25 Music Sec	35 Health/Phys Education	45 Math K-12	55 Remedial Reading Elem	65 Religious Education Elem	75 Marketing/Distributive
	15 Instructional Media Svcs	26 Business Education	36 Guidance Services K-12	46 Math Elem	56 Remedial Reading Sec	66 Religious Education Sec	76 Info Systems
	16 Chief Operations Officer	27 Career & Tech Ed	37 Guidance Services Elem	47 Math Sec	57 Bilingual/ELL	67 School Board President	77 Psychological Assess
	18 Chief Academic Officer	28 Technology Education	38 Guidance Services Sec	48 English/Lang Arts K-12	58 Special Education K-12	68 Teacher Personnel	78 Affirmative Action

Ohio School Directory

Medina County

● **Highland Local School Dist** PID: 00822339
3880 Ridge Rd, Medina 44256
330/239-1901
Fax 330/239-2456

Schools: 5 \ **Teachers:** 159 \ **Students:** 3,233 \ **Special Ed Students:** 384 \ **LEP Students:** 14 \ **College-Bound:** 99% \ **Ethnic:** Asian 2%, African American 1%, Hispanic 1%, Caucasian 97% \ **Exp:** $185 (Low) \ **Poverty:** 4% \ **Title I:** $112,615 \ **Special Education:** $469,000 \ **Open-Close:** 08/21 - 05/29 \ **DTBP:** $191 (High) \

Catherine Aukerman 1
Tod Davis 3
Debbie Parker 5
Laurie Boedicker 8,11,57,69,88,288
Dr Norman Christopher 67
Amy Cruse 81
Sue Kahlik 274*
Neil Barnes 2
Evelyn Makarek 4*
Dr John Deuber 6*
Deborah Yorko 34,58
Roger Saffle 73*
Mary Kosman 274*

Public Schs..Principal	Grd	Prgm	Enr/#Cls	SN	
Granger Elem Sch 3940 Ridge Rd, Medina 44256 Leann Gausnan	PK-5		498 25	9%	330/239-1901 Fax 330/239-7379
Highland High Sch 4150 Ridge Rd, Medina 44256 Carrie Knapp	9-12		1,039 55	6%	330/239-1901 Fax 330/239-7385
Highland Middle Sch 3880 Ridge Rd, Medina 44256 Rob Henry	6-8		781 38	7%	330/239-1901 Fax 330/239-7388
Hinckley Elem Sch 1586 Center Rd, Hinckley 44233 James Carpenter	K-5		369	11%	330/239-1901 Fax 330/239-7390
Sharon Elem Sch 6335 Ridge Rd, Sharon Center 44274 Kathryn Kowza	K-5		546 18	8%	330/239-1901 Fax 330/239-7391

● **Medina City School Dist** PID: 00822389
739 Weymouth Rd, Medina 44256
330/725-8831
Fax 380/636-3808

Schools: 11 \ **Teachers:** 341 \ **Students:** 7,100 \ **Special Ed Students:** 925 \ **LEP Students:** 62 \ **College-Bound:** 73% \ **Ethnic:** Asian 1%, African American 3%, Hispanic 3%, Caucasian 93% \ **Exp:** $148 (Low) \ **Poverty:** 5% \ **Title I:** $559,268 \ **Special Education:** $1,635,000 \ **Open-Close:** 08/19 - 05/28 \ **DTBP:** $186 (High) \

Aaron Sable 1
Jon Burkhart 2
Robert Travis 5
Missy Pipa 7
Tina Cassidy 8*
Ron Ross 67
Amy Busby 71
Shayna Samosky 81*
David Chambers 2
Angie Sellars 4
Todd Hodkey 6*
Dr Kristine Quallich 8,15,58,73,74,81
Mine Pazitka 34,57,58,79
Jim Shields 68
Ryan O'Cull 73,295

Public Schs..Principal	Grd	Prgm	Enr/#Cls	SN	
A I Root Middle Sch 333 W Sturbridge Dr, Medina 44256 Bryan Farson	6-8		842 45	13%	330/636-3500 Fax 330/764-1471
Claggett Middle Sch 420 E Union St, Medina 44256 Paul Worsencroft	6-8		786 45	23%	330/636-3600 Fax 330/725-9349
Eliza Northrop Elem Sch 950 E Reagan Pkwy, Medina 44256 Kimberly Hallock	PK-5		562	28%	330/636-4600 Fax 330/636-3807
Ella Canavan Elem Sch 825 Lawrence St, Medina 44256 Brian Condit	K-5		402 26	24%	330/636-4000 Fax 330/636-3829
Evolve Academy 222 S Broadway St, Medina 44256 Peg Hufnagel	Spec	T	12		330/636-4213 Fax 330/636-4215
Garfield Elem Sch 234 S Broadway St, Medina 44256 Karen McGinty	K-5	T	251 29	69%	330/636-4200 Fax 330/725-9396
H G Blake Elem Sch 4704 Lexington Ridge Dr, Medina 44256 Eldora Lavdas	K-5		482 35	15%	330/636-3900 Fax 330/764-3569
Heritage Elem Sch 833 Guilford Blvd, Medina 44256 Shannon Federinko	K-5		356 30	22%	330/636-4400 Fax 330/725-9394
Medina High Sch 777 E Union St, Medina 44256 Jeff Harrison	9-12	V	2,116 65	16%	330/636-3200 Fax 330/636-3802
Ralph Waite Elem Sch 4765 Cobblestone Park Dr, Medina 44256 Cindy Grice	K-5		503	6%	330/636-4500 Fax 330/722-8010
Sidney Fenn Elem Sch 320 N Spring Grove St, Medina 44256 Craig Komar	K-5		384 21	26%	330/636-4100 Fax 330/636-3826

● **Medina Co Joint Voc Sch Dist** PID: 00822535
1101 W Liberty St, Medina 44256
330/725-8461
Fax 330/725-5870

Schools: 1 \ **Teachers:** 60 \ **Students:** 1,100 \ **College-Bound:** 92% \ **Exp:** $707 (High) \ **Open-Close:** 08/19 - 05/28 \ **DTBP:** $233 (High)

Steven Chrisman 1
Jon List 3*
Margaret Reeves 11
Tresa Goodwin 26,273*
Mari Englehart 73*
Aaron Butts 2
Melonie Queberg 7*
Margaret Reeves 11,30,38,79*
Robert Skidmore 67
Liz Swartz 83,88*

Public Schs..Principal	Grd	Prgm	Enr/#Cls	SN	
Medina Co Career Center 1101 W Liberty St, Medina 44256 Tresa Goodwin	Voc	G	1,100		330/725-8461

● **Wadsworth City School Dist** PID: 00822444
524 Broad St, Wadsworth 44281
330/336-3571
Fax 330/335-1313

Schools: 8 \ **Teachers:** 232 \ **Students:** 4,800 \ **Special Ed Students:** 572 \ **LEP Students:** 11 \ **College-Bound:** 70% \ **Ethnic:** Asian 1%, African American 1%, Hispanic 2%, Caucasian 96% \ **Exp:** $227 (Med) \ **Poverty:** 6% \ **Title I:** $380,486 \ **Special Education:** $739,000 \ **Open-Close:** 08/21 - 05/28 \ **DTBP:** $191 (High)

Dr Andrew Hill 1
Kelly Gnap 4*
Brad Musgrave 6
Dr Michelle Evans 8,11,69,73,270,285
Roger Wright 27,31,75
Linda Kramer 67
Erin Simpson 280*
Douglas Beeman 2
Deborah Miller 5*
Lynn Decker 7*
Gabe Tudor 15
Joyce Walker 58,79
Kristen Rodkey 76

Public Schs..Principal	Grd	Prgm	Enr/#Cls	SN	
Central Intermediate Sch 151 Main St, Wadsworth 44281 Joanne Gahan	5-6		726 29	21%	330/335-1480 Fax 330/335-1484
Franklin Elem Sch 200 Takacs Dr, Wadsworth 44281 Roger Havens	K-4		232 12	27%	330/335-1470 Fax 330/335-1468
Isham Memorial Elem Sch 325 Sunset Blvd, Wadsworth 44281 Nance Watts	K-4		361 21	25%	330/335-1440 Fax 330/335-1330

79 Student Personnel	91 Safety/Security	275 Response To Intervention	298 Grant Writer/Ptnrships	School Programs	Social Media
80 Driver Ed/Safety	92 Magnet School	277 Remedial Math K-12	750 Chief Innovation Officer	A = Alternative Program	
81 Gifted/Talented	93 Parental Involvement	280 Literacy Coach	751 Chief of Staff	G = Adult Classes	= Facebook
82 Video Services	95 Tech Prep Program	285 STEM	752 Social Emotional Learning	M = Magnet Program	
83 Substance Abuse Prev	97 Chief Information Officer	286 Digital Learning		T = Title I Schoolwide	= Twitter
84 Erate	98 Chief Technology Officer	288 Common Core Standards	Other School Types	V = Career & Tech Ed Programs	
85 AIDS Education	270 Character Education	294 Accountability	Ⓐ = Alternative School		
88 Alternative/At Risk	271 Migrant Education	295 Network System	Ⓒ = Charter School	New Schools are shaded	
89 Multi-Cultural Curriculum	273 Teacher Mentor	296 Title II Programs	Ⓜ = Magnet School	New Superintendents and Principals are bold	
90 Social Work	274 Before/After Sch	297 Webmaster	Ⓨ = Year-Round School	Personnel with email addresses are underscored	

OH-141

Meigs County

School	Grade	Prgm	Enr/#Cls	SN	Phone
Lincoln Elem Sch 280 N Lyman St, Wadsworth 44281 Steve Brady	K-4	T	234 12	35%	330/335-1460 Fax 330/335-1462
Overlook Elem Sch 650 Broad St, Wadsworth 44281 Erin Simpson	PK-4		446 9	20%	330/335-1420 Fax 330/335-1425
Valley View Elem Sch 625 Orchard St, Wadsworth 44281 Christopher Roberts	K-4		369 16	21%	330/335-1430 Fax 330/335-1428
Wadsworth High Sch 625 Broad St, Wadsworth 44281 Steven Moore	9-12	AGV	1,601 69	18%	330/335-1400 Fax 330/335-1376
Wadsworth Middle Sch 150 Silvercreek Rd, Wadsworth 44281 Eric Jackson	7-8		756 50	20%	330/335-1410 Fax 330/336-3820

MEDINA CATHOLIC SCHOOLS

• **Diocese of Cleveland Ed Office** PID: 00795308
Listing includes only schools located in this county. See District Index for location of Diocesan Offices.

Catholic Schs..Principal	Grd	Prgm	Enr/#Cls	SN	Phone
Sacred Heart Parish Sch 110 Humbolt Ave, Wadsworth 44281 Bill Adams	PK-8		282 15		330/334-6272 Fax 330/334-3236
St Ambrose Sch 923 Pearl Rd, Brunswick 44212 Lisa Cinadr	PK-8		477 18		330/225-2116 Fax 330/225-5425
St Francis Xavier Sch 612 E Washington St, Medina 44256 Danene Beal	PK-8		20 21		330/725-3345 Fax 330/721-8626

MEDINA PRIVATE SCHOOLS

Private Schs..Principal	Grd	Prgm	Enr/#Cls	SN	Phone
Medina Christian Academy 3646 Medina Rd, Medina 44256 Joe Timco \ Tammy Hall	PK-12		150 20		330/725-3227 Fax 330/725-7762 f t

MEDINA REGIONAL CENTERS

• **Medina Co Sch Educl Svcs Ctr** PID: 02100943 330/723-4114
124 W Washington St Ste 1B, Medina 44256 Fax 330/723-0573

William Koran 1   Rachel Krauss 58,275
Denise Valerio .... 73 Kim Tomashefski 74

MEIGS COUNTY

MEIGS COUNTY SCHOOLS

County Schs..Principal	Grd	Prgm	Enr/#Cls	SN	Phone
Carlton Sch 1310 Carlton St, Syracuse 45779 Kay Davis	Spec	G	45 5		740/992-6683 Fax 740/992-6438

MEIGS PUBLIC SCHOOLS

• **Eastern Local School Dist** PID: 00822559   740/667-6079
50008 State Route 681, Reedsville 45772   Fax 740/667-3978

Schools: 3 \ *Teachers:* 53 \ *Students:* 820 \ *Special Ed Students:* 103 \ *Ethnic:* Hispanic 2%, Caucasian 98% \ *Exp:* $122 (Low) \ *Poverty:* 24% \ *Title I:* $310,678 \ *Special Education:* $152,000 \ *Open-Close:* 08/23 - 05/22 \ *DTBP:* $185 (High)

Steve Ohlinger 1   Lisa Ritchie 2,19
Randy Boston .... 3,5 Brian Collins 4
Josh Folger 6   Rachel Martin 8,11,57,58,286,288*
Steve Scarberry .... 16* Sheryl Roush 38,69*
Floyd Ridenour 67

Public Schs..Principal	Grd	Prgm	Enr/#Cls	SN	Phone
Eastern Elem Sch 38850 State Route 7, Reedsville 45772 Robin Burrow	K-4	T	330 34	56%	740/985-3304 Fax 740/985-4318
Eastern High Sch 38900 State Route 7, Reedsville 45772 Shawn Bush	9-12	T	269 20	42%	740/985-3329 Fax 740/985-3778
Eastern Middle Sch 38850 State Route 7, Reedsville 45772 Shawn Bush	5-8		340		740/985-3304

• **Meigs Local School Dist** PID: 00822602   740/992-2153
41765 Pomeroy Pike, Pomeroy 45769   Fax 740/992-7814

Schools: 4 \ *Teachers:* 107 \ *Students:* 1,700 \ *Special Ed Students:* 304 \ *College-Bound:* 43% \ *Ethnic:* African American 1%, Hispanic 1%, Caucasian 98% \ *Exp:* $239 (Med) \ *Poverty:* 31% \ *Title I:* $1,085,253 \ *Special Education:* $398,000 \ *Open-Close:* 08/22 - 05/25 \ *DTBP:* $176 (High) \ f t

Scot Gheen 1   Roy Johnson 2
William Ellis .... 3,91 Chrissy Musser 4*
Dean Harris 5   Kristy Powell 7*
Michael Barnett .... 11,83,288,298* Douglas Dunn 16*
Douglas Dunn 16   Travis Abbott 27,75*
Abby Harris .... 38* Karla Brown 58
Ryan Mahr .... 67 Matt Simpson 73,295
Billi Arnott .... 76 Billi Barnott 76*
Jennifer Henson 273*

Public Schs..Principal	Grd	Prgm	Enr/#Cls	SN	Phone
Meigs High Sch 42091 Charles Chancey Dr, Pomeroy 45769 Travis Abbott	9-12		559 60		740/992-2158 Fax 740/992-5839

#		#		#		#		#		#		#	
1	Superintendent	8	Curric/Instruct K-12	19	Chief Financial Officer	29	Family/Consumer Science	39	Social Studies K-12	49	English/Lang Arts Elem	59	Special Education Elem	69	Academic Assessment
2	Bus/Finance/Purchasing	9	Curric/Instruct Elem	20	Art K-12	30	Adult Education	40	Social Studies Elem	50	English/Lang Arts Sec	60	Special Education Sec	70	Research/Development
3	Buildings And Grounds	10	Curric/Instruct Sec	21	Art Elem	31	Career/Sch-to-Work K-12	41	Social Studies Sec	51	Reading K-12	61	Foreign/World Lang K-12	71	Public Information
4	Food Service	11	Federal Program	22	Art Sec	32	Career/Sch-to-Work Elem	42	Science K-12	52	Reading Elem	62	Foreign/World Lang Elem	72	Summer School
5	Transportation	12	Title I	23	Music K-12	33	Career/Sch-to-Work Sec	43	Science Elem	53	Reading Sec	63	Foreign/World Lang Sec	73	Instructional Tech
6	Athletic	13	Title V	24	Music Elem	34	Early Childhood Ed	44	Science Sec	54	Remedial Reading K-12	64	Religious Education K-12	74	Inservice Training
7	Health Services	15	Asst Superintendent	25	Music Sec	35	Health/Phys Education	45	Math K-12	55	Remedial Reading Elem	65	Religious Education Elem	75	Marketing/Distributive
		16	Instructional Media Svcs	26	Business Education	36	Guidance Services K-12	46	Math Elem	56	Remedial Reading Sec	66	Religious Education Sec	76	Info Systems
		17	Chief Operations Officer	27	Career & Tech Ed	37	Guidance Services Elem	47	Math Sec	57	Bilingual/ELL	67	School Board President	77	Psychological Assess
		18	Chief Academic Officer	28	Technology Education	38	Guidance Services Sec	48	English/Lang Arts K-12	58	Special Education K-12	68	Teacher Personnel	78	Affirmative Action

Ohio School Directory | Mercer County

	Grd	Prgm	Enr/#Cls	
Meigs Intermediate ES	3-5	T	367	740/742-2666
36871 State Route 124 Ste 200, Middleport 45760			19	Fax 740/742-2825
Jody Howard				
Meigs Middle Sch	6-8	T	399	740/992-3058
42353 Charles Chancey Dr, Pomeroy 45769			35	Fax 740/992-6952
Vickie Jones				ⓕ
Meigs Primary Elem Sch	PK-2	T	403	740/742-3000
36871 State Route 124 Ste 100, Middleport 45760			21	Fax 740/742-2651
Kristin Baer				

● **Southern Local School Dist** PID: 00822705   740/949-2669
106 N Broadway St Ste 1, Racine 45771   Fax 740/949-2654

Schools: 2 \ *Teachers:* 45 \ *Students:* 728 \ *Special Ed Students:* 118 \
Ethnic: Hispanic 2%, Caucasian 98% \ *Exp:* $142 (Low) \ *Poverty:* 24% \
Title I: $269,172 \ *Special Education:* $152,000 \ *Open-Close:* 08/23 -
05/22 \ *DTBP:* $170 (High)

Tony Deem	...1	Christi Hendrix	...2
Charlie Wolfe	...3	Scott Wolfe	...4,11,58,296,298*
Kathy Miller	...5	Carl Wolfe	...6,88
Junie Maynard	...7,83,88*	Tricia McNickle	...8,274,288*
Russ Fields	...31,69*	Gary Evans	...67
Edward Baker	...73,76,295*	Tim Thoren	...79*
Meg Guinther	...273,280*	Elizabeth Johnson	...286*
Jenny Manuel	...297*		

Public Schs..Principal	Grd	Prgm	Enr/#Cls	SN	
Southern Elem Sch	PK-8	T	521		740/949-4222
920 Elm St, Racine 45771			25		
Tricia McNickle					
Southern High Sch	9-12	TV	220	72%	740/949-4222
920 Elm St, Racine 45771			14		Fax 740/949-2456
Dan Otto					ⓕⓣ

MEIGS PRIVATE SCHOOLS

Private Schs..Principal	Grd	Prgm	Enr/#Cls	SN	
Mid-Valley Christian Sch	PK-12		49		740/992-6249
500 N 2nd Ave, Middleport 45760					
Melissa Dailey					

MERCER COUNTY

MERCER COUNTY SCHOOLS

● **Mercer Co Ed Service Center** PID: 00823151   419/586-6628
441 E Market St, Celina 45822   Fax 419/586-3377

Shelley Vaughn	...1,11	Kurt Wendel	...2
Karen Rose	...8	Valerie Scott	...34
Chad Sapp	...58	Jeff Davis	...67
Tracy Houser	...73,295	Rachel Glass	...77
Wendi Moorman	...81		

MERCER PUBLIC SCHOOLS

● **Celina City School Dist** PID: 00822793   419/586-8300
585 E Livingston St, Celina 45822   Fax 419/586-7046

Schools: 5 \ *Teachers:* 182 \ *Students:* 2,300 \ *Special Ed Students:* 517
\ *LEP Students:* 60 \ *College-Bound:* 43% \ *Ethnic:* Asian 2%,
African American 1%, Hispanic 4%, Caucasian 93% \ *Exp:* $231 (Med)
\ *Poverty:* 13% \ *Title I:* $509,581 \ *Special Education:* $537,000 \
Open-Close: 08/21 - 05/22 \ *DTBP:* $198 (High) \ ⓕ

Dr Ken Schmiesing	...1	Connie Rose	...2
Tom Sommer	...2	Jeff Everman	...3
Deb Schroyer	...4	Greg Amspaugh	...5
Jeff Fortkamp	...6,78*	Lynne Ray	...16,82
Tim Buschur	...27,75,95	Marcia Helentjaris	...31
Amy Esser	...34	Drew Braun	...42*
Erika Draiss	...45*	Katie Gudorf	...48,51*
Tracey Dammeyer	...58	Hal Hoover	...61*
Carl Huber	...67	Kim Smith	...85*

Public Schs..Principal	Grd	Prgm	Enr/#Cls	SN	
Celina Elem Sch	3-4	T	383	53%	419/586-8300
1225 W Logan St, Celina 45822			27		Fax 419/586-6541
Cory Ahrens					
Celina High Sch	9-12	AV	878	32%	419/586-8300
715 E Wayne St, Celina 45822			80		Fax 419/584-0307
Phil Metz					
Celina Intermediate Sch	5-6	T	374	49%	419/586-8300
227 Portland St, Celina 45822			17		Fax 419/584-0353
Derek Wenning					
Celina Middle Sch	7-8		419	39%	419/586-8300
615 Holly St, Celina 45822			41		Fax 419/586-9166
Ann Esselstein					ⓕⓣ
Celina Primary Sch	K-2	T	530	50%	419/586-8300
615 E Wayne St, Celina 45822			31		Fax 419/584-0215
Michelle Duncan					ⓕ

● **Coldwater Exempted Village SD** PID: 00822858   419/678-2611
310 N 2nd St, Coldwater 45828   Fax 419/678-3100

Schools: 3 \ *Teachers:* 89 \ *Students:* 1,375 \ *Special Ed Students:* 168
\ *LEP Students:* 17 \ *College-Bound:* 76% \ *Ethnic:* Hispanic 1%,
Caucasian 98% \ *Exp:* $281 (Med) \ *Poverty:* 6% \ *Title I:* $89,391 \
Special Education: $312,000 \ *Open-Close:* 08/19 - 05/21 \ *DTBP:* $167
(High)

Jason Wood	...1	Michelle Mawer	...2
Mitch Voskuhl	...3*	Lynn Rinderle	...4*
Eric Goodwin	...6*	Sandy Hartings	...8,11,57,58,69*
Stacee Froning	...37*	Natalie Kanney	...38,88*
Sue Bills	...38*	Terry Schroyer	...67
Robert Smith	...73,295	Chip Otten	...83*

Public Schs..Principal	Grd	Prgm	Enr/#Cls	SN	
Coldwater Elem Sch	K-4		525		419/678-2613
310 N 2nd St, Coldwater 45828			30		
Michael Etzler					
Coldwater High Sch	9-12	V	452	50%	419/678-4821
310 N 2nd St, Coldwater 45828			34		Fax 419/678-4962
Jason Hemmelgarn					
Coldwater Middle Sch	5-8		409		419/678-3331
310 N 2nd St, Coldwater 45828			25		Fax 419/678-1391
Dan Pohlman					

---

79 Student Personnel	91 Safety/Security	275 Response To Intervention	298 Grant Writer/Ptnrships	**School Programs**	**Social Media**
80 Driver Ed/Safety	92 Magnet School	277 Remedial Math K-12	750 Chief Innovation Officer	A = Alternative Program	
81 Gifted/Talented	93 Parental Involvement	280 Literacy Coach	751 Chief of Staff	G = Adult Classes	ⓕ = Facebook
82 Video Services	95 Tech Prep Program	285 STEM	752 Social Emotional Learning	M = Magnet Program	
83 Substance Abuse Prev	97 Chief Information Officer	286 Digital Learning		T = Title I Schoolwide	ⓣ = Twitter
84 Erate	98 Chief Technology Officer	288 Common Core Standards	**Other School Types**	V = Career & Tech Ed Programs	
85 AIDS Education	270 Character Education	294 Accountability	Ⓐ = Alternative School		
88 Alternative/At Risk	271 Migrant Education	295 Network System	Ⓒ = Charter School	New Schools are shaded	
89 Multi-Cultural Curriculum	273 Teacher Mentor	296 Title II Programs	Ⓜ = Magnet School	New Superintendents and Principals are bold	
90 Social Work	274 Before/After Sch	297 Webmaster	Ⓨ = Year-Round School	Personnel with email addresses are underscored	

OH—143

Miami County

Ft Recovery Local School Dist PID: 00823046
400 E Butler St, Fort Recovery 45846
419/375-4139
Fax 419/375-1058

Schools: 2 \ **Teachers:** 56 \ **Students:** 920 \ **Special Ed Students:** 109 \ **LEP Students:** 5 \ **College-Bound:** 66% \ **Ethnic:** Asian 1%, Hispanic 2%, Caucasian 98% \ **Exp:** $319 (High) \ **Poverty:** 7% \ **Title I:** $82,515 \ **Open-Close:** 08/21 - 05/21 \ **DTBP:** $173 (High) \

Larry Brownlae 1,11
Kevin Will 3*
Amy Kaiser 33,38,69,83,88*
Ryan Fullencamp 73*
Deanna Knapke 2
Brent Niekamp 6,16
Greg LeFevre 67

Public Schs..Principal	Grd	Prgm	Enr/#Cls	SN	
Fort Recovery Elem Mid Sch 865 Sharpsburg Rd, Fort Recovery 45846 **Kelli Thobe** \ Tony Stahl	PK-8		720 40		419/375-2768 Fax 419/375-4231
Ft Recovery High Sch 400 E Butler St, Fort Recovery 45846 Bill Overla	9-12	V	297 20	6%	419/375-4111 Fax 419/375-2039

Marion Local School Dist PID: 00822913
7956 State Route 119, Maria Stein 45860
419/925-4294
Fax 419/925-0212

Schools: 2 \ **Teachers:** 53 \ **Students:** 860 \ **Special Ed Students:** 103 \ **College-Bound:** 77% \ **Ethnic:** Caucasian 100% \ **Exp:** $190 (Low) \ **Poverty:** 4% \ **Title I:** $28,632 \ **Special Education:** $159,000 \ **Open-Close:** 08/21 - 05/21 \ **DTBP:** $175 (High)

Mike Pohlman 1
Randy Bruns 67
Heather Cramer 2,11
Michelle Mescher 73,84,295

Public Schs..Principal	Grd	Prgm	Enr/#Cls	SN	
Marion Local Elem Sch 7956 State Route 119, Maria Stein 45860 Nick Wilker	K-8		577 60	5%	419/925-4595
Marion Local High Sch 1901 State Route 716, Maria Stein 45860 Tim Goodwin	9-12	V	270 20	5%	419/925-4597 Fax 419/925-5111

Parkway Local School Dist PID: 00823008
400 Buckeye St, Rockford 45882
419/363-3045
Fax 419/363-2595

Schools: 3 \ **Teachers:** 63 \ **Students:** 1,000 \ **Special Ed Students:** 159 \ **LEP Students:** 3 \ **College-Bound:** 54% \ **Ethnic:** African American 1%, Hispanic 1%, Caucasian 98% \ **Exp:** $278 (Med) \ **Poverty:** 13% \ **Title I:** $165,030 \ **Special Education:** $221,000 \ **Open-Close:** 08/19 - 05/20 \ **DTBP:** $184 (High)

Jeanne Osterfeld 1
Matt Triplitt 6*
Mark Esselstein 12
Curtis Hamrick 30*
Lisa Ontrop 36,69,83,88*
Melissa Burtch 67
Debra Pierce 2
Mark Esselstein 11*
Kevin Browning 16,73,84,297
Dan Cairns 35,85
Michael Gause 58

Public Schs..Principal	Grd	Prgm	Enr/#Cls	SN	
Parkway Elem Sch 400 Buckeye St, Rockford 45882 Mark Esselstein	PK-4	T	387 13		419/363-3045 Fax 419/363-2598
Parkway High Sch 400 Buckeye St, Rockford 45882 Brian Fortkamp	9-12	V	265 23	99%	419/363-3045 Fax 419/363-2596
Parkway Middle Sch 400 Buckeye St, Rockford 45882 Brian Woods	5-8		341 18		419/363-3045 Fax 419/363-2597

St Henry Cons Local Sch Dist PID: 00823101
391 E Columbus St, Saint Henry 45883
419/678-4834
Fax 419/678-1724

Schools: 3 \ **Teachers:** 62 \ **Students:** 950 \ **Special Ed Students:** 129 \ **LEP Students:** 12 \ **College-Bound:** 68% \ **Ethnic:** Asian 1%, Hispanic 3%, Caucasian 97% \ **Exp:** $233 (Med) \ **Poverty:** 4% \ **Title I:** $26,974 \ **Special Education:** $164,000 \ **Open-Close:** 08/21 - 05/21 \ **DTBP:** $174 (High)

Julie Garke 1
Terry Bills 3
Dennis Wendel 6*
Eric Rosenbeck 10*
Thomas Marchal 16,73,76,95,295,297*
Kailey Guillozet 38*
Tom Marchal 84
Jennifer Bruns 2,19
Sherri Ranly 5
Adam Puthoff 9,11,34*
Rose Harrod 16*
Betsy Armstrong 38*
Andy Fullenkamp 67

Public Schs..Principal	Grd	Prgm	Enr/#Cls	SN	
St Henry Elem Sch 251 E Columbus St, Saint Henry 45883 Adam Puthoff	PK-4		402 20	10%	419/678-4834 Fax 419/678-2544
St Henry High Sch 391 E Columbus St, Saint Henry 45883 Eric Rosenbeck	9-12	V	299 21	16%	419/678-4834
St Henry Middle Sch 381 E Columbus St, Saint Henry 45883 Kyle Kunk	5-8		294 20		419/678-4834

MERCER CATHOLIC SCHOOLS

Archdiocese Cincinnati Ed Off PID: 00808096
Listing includes only schools located in this county. See District Index for location of Diocesan Offices.

Catholic Schs..Principal	Grd	Prgm	Enr/#Cls	SN	
Immaculate Conception Grd Sch 200 W Wayne St, Celina 45822 Polly Muhlenkamp	PK-6		175 10		419/586-2379

MIAMI COUNTY

MIAMI COUNTY SCHOOLS

Miami Co Ed Service Center PID: 00823709
2000 W Stanfield Rd, Troy 45373
937/339-5100
Fax 937/339-3256

David Larson 1,11
Jay Borchers 8
Heather Lorenzo 34
Lisa Heid 58
Jenelle Hodges 67
Vern Whitt 73
Megan George 77
Vicki Kaesler 275
Cindy Hale 2
Maryann Morgret 8
Jennifer Holder 58
Megan Campbell 58
Melinda Hoffert 68
Elaine Kolber 77
Natisha Wilson 81

---

1 Superintendent	8 Curric/Instruct K-12	19 Chief Financial Officer	29 Family/Consumer Science	39 Social Studies K-12	49 English/Lang Arts Elem	59 Special Education Elem	69 Academic Assessment
2 Bus/Finance/Purchasing	9 Curric/Instruct Elem	20 Art K-12	30 Adult Education	40 Social Studies Elem	50 English/Lang Arts Sec	60 Special Education Sec	70 Research/Development
3 Buildings And Grounds	10 Curric/Instruct Sec	21 Art Elem	31 Career/Sch-to-Work K-12	41 Social Studies Sec	51 Reading K-12	61 Foreign/World Lang K-12	71 Public Information
4 Food Service	11 Federal Program	22 Art Sec	32 Career/Sch-to-Work Elem	42 Science K-12	52 Reading Elem	62 Foreign/World Lang Elem	72 Summer School
5 Transportation	12 Title I	23 Music K-12	33 Career/Sch-to-Work Sec	43 Science Elem	53 Reading Sec	63 Foreign/World Lang Sec	73 Instructional Tech
6 Athletic	13 Title V	24 Music Elem	34 Early Childhood Ed	44 Science Sec	54 Remedial Reading K-12	64 Religious Education K-12	74 Inservice Training
7 Health Services	15 Asst Superintendent	25 Music Sec	35 Health/Phys Education	45 Math K-12	55 Remedial Reading Elem	65 Religious Education Elem	75 Marketing/Distributive
	16 Instructional Media Svcs	26 Business Education	36 Guidance Services K-12	46 Math Elem	56 Remedial Reading Sec	66 Religious Education Sec	76 Info Systems
	17 Chief Operations Officer	27 Career & Tech Ed	37 Guidance Services Elem	47 Math Sec	57 Bilingual/ELL	67 School Board President	77 Psychological Assess
	18 Chief Academic Officer	28 Technology Education	38 Guidance Services Sec	48 English/Lang Arts K-12	58 Special Education K-12	68 Teacher Personnel	78 Affirmative Action

Ohio School Directory — Miami County

County Schs..Principal	Grd	Prgm	Enr/#Cls	SN
Ⓐ David L Brown Youth Center 291 S Childrens Home Rd, Troy 45373 Susan Parker	6-12		15	937/339-1858 Fax 937/335-7904
Riverside of Miami Co Sch 1625 Troy Sidney Rd, Troy 45373 Brian Greene	Spec		15 1	937/339-8313 Fax 937/335-6907

MIAMI PUBLIC SCHOOLS

● Bethel Local School Dist   PID: 00823163
7490 State Route 201, Tipp City 45371
937/845-9414
Fax 937/845-5007

Schools: 2 \ *Teachers:* 63 \ *Students:* 1,400 \ *Special Ed Students:* 111 \ *LEP Students:* 79 \ *College-Bound:* 70% \ *Ethnic:* Asian 1%, African American 1%, Hispanic 2%, Caucasian 97% \ *Exp:* $182 (Low) \ *Poverty:* 6% \ *Title I:* $72,201 \ *Special Education:* $108,000 \ *Open-Close:* 08/21 - 05/21 \ *DTBP:* $247 (High)

Justin Firks 1		Brennon Hattery 2		
James Chapman 3		Jodi Petty 4,9,12,285*		
Melissa Wolski 4		Gayle Rhoades 5,11		
Trisha Moore 7*		Holly Mills 16*		
Suzzanne Batton 58*		Jacob King 67		
Jared Ratcliff 73,76,286,295		Jared Ratliff 295		

Public Schs..Principal	Grd	Prgm	Enr/#Cls	SN
Bethel Elem Sch 7490 State Route 201, Tipp City 45371 Jodi Petty	K-5		738 22	22% 937/845-9439
Bethel Middle High Sch 7490 State Route 201, Tipp City 45371 Duane Caudill \ Barret Swope	6-12		741	29% 937/845-9487 Fax 937/845-0592

● Bradford Exempted Village SD   PID: 00823199
760 Railroad Ave, Bradford 45308
937/448-2770
Fax 937/448-2493

Schools: 2 \ *Teachers:* 36 \ *Students:* 487 \ *Special Ed Students:* 76 \ *LEP Students:* 3 \ *College-Bound:* 40% \ *Ethnic:* Caucasian 99% \ *Exp:* $114 (Low) \ *Poverty:* 14% \ *Title I:* $123,247 \ *Special Education:* $137,000 \ *Open-Close:* 08/20 - 05/22 \ *DTBP:* $183 (High)

Joe Hurst 1	Carla Surber 2
Skip Miller 3	Cheryl Clark 4*
Chloe Shell 5,6	Moniqua Skinner 7*
Michelle Lavey 9,11,288*	Matt Triplett 10,288
Tabitha Breexe 12,280	Wendy Ray 36,69*
Dr Scott Swabb 67	Logan Looker 73

Public Schs..Principal	Grd	Prgm	Enr/#Cls	SN
Bradford Elem Sch 740 Railroad Ave, Bradford 45308 Michelle Lavey	K-5	T	246 14	937/448-2811 Fax 937/448-2742
Bradford High Sch 750 Railroad Ave, Bradford 45308 Matt Triplet	6-12	T	225 22	99% 937/448-2719 Fax 937/448-2742

● Covington Exempted Village SD   PID: 00823228
807 Chestnut St Ste A, Covington 45318
937/473-2249
Fax 937/473-3730

Schools: 2 \ *Teachers:* 47 \ *Students:* 850 \ *Special Ed Students:* 84 \ *College-Bound:* 56% \ *Ethnic:* Hispanic 1%, Caucasian 99% \ *Exp:* $398 (High) \ *Poverty:* 13% \ *Title I:* $138,671 \ *Special Education:* $165,000 \ *Open-Close:* 08/20 - 05/22

Gene Gooding 1	Carol Forsythe 2,68*
Bonnie Flora 4	Ashley Johnson 6*
Lisa McCord 7*	Bridgit Kerber 8,74,92
Paula Jurgens 11,51,54*	Dave Tobias 35*
Karen Brackman 36,69*	Brian Bohlander 57*
Cindy Johnson 58*	Dr Dean Pond 67
Kim Dunn 285*	Eric Griffith 295

Public Schs..Principal	Grd	Prgm	Enr/#Cls	SN
Covington Elem Sch 807 Chestnut St, Covington 45318 Josh Long	PK-8		720 19	937/473-2252 Fax 937/473-3685
Covington High Sch 807 Chestnut St, Covington 45318 Josh Meyer	9-12		228 18	937/473-3746 Fax 937/473-3435

● Miami East Local School Dist   PID: 00823266
3825 N State Route 589, Casstown 45312
937/335-7505
Fax 937/335-6309

Schools: 3 \ *Teachers:* 63 \ *Students:* 1,300 \ *Special Ed Students:* 121 \ *College-Bound:* 71% \ *Ethnic:* Hispanic 1%, Caucasian 98% \ *Exp:* $200 (Med) \ *Poverty:* 6% \ *Title I:* $107,973 \ *Special Education:* $138,000 \ *Open-Close:* 08/21 - 05/22 \ *DTBP:* $180 (High)

Dr Todd Rappold 1,11,83	Lisa Fahncke 2,84
Kathy Knoop 5	Scott Donaldson 6*
Wade Meyers 16,82*	Brian Rohrer 59*
Todd Gentis 60*	Brandon Fellers 67
Matthew Rutledge 69*	Zach Tyre 73*

Public Schs..Principal	Grd	Prgm	Enr/#Cls	SN
Miami East Elem Sch 4025 N State Route 589, Casstown 45312 Brian Rohrer	K-5		590 10	937/335-5439 Fax 937/332-9488
Miami East High Sch 3925 N State Route 589, Casstown 45312 Todd Gentis	9-12	V	366 27	13% 937/335-7070 Fax 937/440-9581
Miami East Junior High Sch 4025 N State Route 589, Casstown 45312 Allen Mack	6-8		327	55% 937/335-5439 Fax 937/332-7927

● Milton-Union Exempted Vlg SD   PID: 00823333
7610 Milton Potsdam Rd, West Milton 45383
937/884-7910
Fax 937/884-7911

Schools: 3 \ *Teachers:* 90 \ *Students:* 1,500 \ *Special Ed Students:* 166 \ *College-Bound:* 50% \ *Ethnic:* African American 1%, Hispanic 1%, Caucasian 98% \ *Exp:* $80 (Low) \ *Poverty:* 10% \ *Title I:* $208,580 \ *Special Education:* $284,000 \ *Open-Close:* 08/21 - 05/28 \ *DTBP:* $240 (High)

Dr Brad Ritchey 1	Dan Baisden 2
Larry Smith 3,91	Brenda DeHart 4
Jodell Garrison 5	Mark Lane 6
Lori Thompson 7,83,85	Jessica Mumau 8,11,69,88,273,285,298*
Laurie Grube 11,58	Heather Galentine 16*
Paula Shaw 36*	Lori Parsons 67
Leah Blackburn 68	Mick Nealeigh 73,76,95,98,286,295

---

79 Student Personnel	91 Safety/Security	275 Response To Intervention	298 Grant Writer/Ptnrships	**School Programs**	**Social Media**	
80 Driver Ed/Safety	92 Magnet School	277 Remedial Math K-12	750 Innovation Officer	A = Alternative Program		
81 Gifted/Talented	93 Parental Involvement	280 Literacy Coach	751 Chief of Staff	G = Adult Classes	🛇 = Facebook	
82 Video Services	95 Tech Prep Program	285 STEM	752 Social Emotional Learning	M = Magnet Program		
83 Substance Abuse Prev	97 Chief Information Officer	286 Digital Learning		T = Title I Schoolwide	🛇 = Twitter	
84 Erate	98 Chief Technology Officer	288 Common Core Standards	**Other School Types**	V = Career & Tech Ed Programs		
85 AIDS Education	270 Character Education	294 Accountability	Ⓐ = Alternative School			
86 Alternative/At Risk	271 Migrant Education	295 Network System	Ⓒ = Charter School	**New Schools are shaded**		
89 Multi-Cultural Curriculum	273 Teacher Mentor	296 Title II Programs	Ⓜ = Magnet School	**New Superintendents and Principals are bold**		
90 Social Work	274 Before/After Sch	297 Webmaster	Ⓨ = Year-Round School	Personnel with email addresses are underscored		

OH-145

Miami County

Market Data Retrieval

Public Schs..Principal	Grd	Prgm	Enr/#Cls	SN	
Milton-Union Elem Sch 7620 Milton Potsdam Rd, West Milton 45383 Loretta Henderson	K-5	T	687 47		937/884-7920 Fax 937/884-7921
Milton-Union High Sch 7640 Milton Potsdam Rd, West Milton 45383 Jessica Mumau	9-12		416 40	99%	937/884-7940 Fax 937/884-7941
Milton-Union Middle Sch 7630 Milton Potsdam Rd, West Milton 45383 Katie Hartley	6-8	T	325 15		937/884-7930 Fax 937/884-7931

• **Newton Local School Dist** PID: 00823383   937/676-2002
201 N Long St, Pleasant Hill 45359   Fax 937/676-2054

Schools: 1 \ *Teachers:* 37 \ *Students:* 600 \ *Special Ed Students:* 53 \ *College-Bound:* 58% \ *Ethnic:* African American 2%, Hispanic 1%, Caucasian 98% \ *Exp:* $425 (High) \ *Poverty:* 7% \ *Title I:* $50,426 \ *Special Education:* $102,000 \ *Open-Close:* 08/21 - 05/22 \ *DTBP:* $183 (High) \

Pat McBride 1		Nick Hamilton 2	
Bryce Baker 3*		Teresa Alexander 4*	
Jeanie Via 5		Gavin Spitler 6*	
Vicki Wehrley 7*		Danielle Davis 8,11,57,273,286,288,298*	
Stan Fessler 16,28,73,76,295*		Tab LaFollette 35*	
Steve Fisher 36,85,88*		Judy Krise 58*	
Nate Oburn 67		Steve Fisher 83	
Megan Lacey 280*			

Public Schs..Principal	Grd	Prgm	Enr/#Cls	SN	
Newton Sch 201 N Long St, Pleasant Hill 45359 Danielle Davis	K-12	V	600 13	46%	937/676-2002 Fax 937/676-2397

• **Piqua City School Dist** PID: 00823412   937/773-4321
215 Looney Rd, Piqua 45356   Fax 937/778-4517

Schools: 5 \ *Teachers:* 171 \ *Students:* 3,500 \ *Special Ed Students:* 524 \ *LEP Students:* 4 \ *College-Bound:* 48% \ *Ethnic:* Asian 1%, African American 3%, Hispanic 3%, Caucasian 93% \ *Exp:* $268 (Med) \ *Poverty:* 17% \ *Title I:* $972,577 \ *Special Education:* $990,000 \ *Open-Close:* 08/19 - 05/29 \ *DTBP:* $208 (High) \

Dwayne Thompson 1		Jeremie Hittle 2	
Sean Shumaker 3		Jennifer Garland 4	
Beth Cain 5		Edward Hare 6*	
Teresa Anderson 9		Scott Bloom 10,285,288	
Anthony Lyons 15		Amy Todd 57,58,68,79,81	
Andy Hite 67		Erich Heidenreich 73,76,295	
Mindy Gearhardt 79		Jessica Sizemore 81	
Tracy Mumaw 294			

Public Schs..Principal	Grd	Prgm	Enr/#Cls	SN	
Piqua Central Interm Sch 807 Nicklin Ave, Piqua 45356 Joshua Kauffman	4-6	T	800	55%	937/773-2017 Fax 937/778-2988
Piqua High Sch 1 Indian Trl, Piqua 45356 Rob Messick	9-12	ATV	908 60	43%	937/773-6314 Fax 937/778-4514
Piqua Junior High Sch 1 Tomahawk Trl, Piqua 45356 Jeff Clark	7-8	TV	550 40	57%	937/778-2997 Fax 937/773-2574
Springcreek Primary Sch 145 E US Route 36, Piqua 45356 Ross Loudenback	PK-3	T	495 12	61%	937/773-6540 Fax 937/778-2995

Public Schs..Principal	Grd	Prgm	Enr/#Cls	SN	
Washington Primary Sch 800 N Sunset Dr, Piqua 45356 Tracy Trogdlon	K-3	T	530 17		937/773-8472 Fax 937/778-2992

• **Tipp City Exempted Village SD** PID: 00823539   937/667-8444
90 S Tippecanoe Dr, Tipp City 45371   Fax 937/667-6886

Schools: 5 \ *Teachers:* 145 \ *Students:* 2,605 \ *Special Ed Students:* 349 \ *LEP Students:* 32 \ *College-Bound:* 75% \ *Ethnic:* Asian 1%, African American 1%, Hispanic 3%, Caucasian 95% \ *Exp:* $218 (Med) \ *Poverty:* 5% \ *Title I:* $190,243 \ *Special Education:* $395,000 \ *Open-Close:* 08/20 - 05/28 \ *DTBP:* $193 (High) \

Dr Gretta Kumpf 1		David Stevens 2	
Art Hoff 3,91		Gary Pfister 4,73,286,297	
Jane Thompson 5		Kregg Cremer 6	
Galen Gingerich 8,11,58,68,88,273,296,298		Liz Robbins 16,71	
Crystal Luce 57		Andy Venters 67	
Katie Sullivan 69		Natisha Wilson 81	

Public Schs..Principal	Grd	Prgm	Enr/#Cls	SN	
Broadway Elem Sch 223 W Broadway St, Tipp City 45371 Tina Smith	2-3		400 19	21%	937/667-6216 Fax 937/669-9405
L T Ball Intermediate Sch 575 N Hyatt St, Tipp City 45371 Mike Vagedes	4-5		390 18	21%	937/667-3719 Fax 937/669-5487
Nevin Coppock Elem Sch 525 N Hyatt St, Tipp City 45371 **Galen Gingerich**	K-1		368 18	22%	937/667-2275 Fax 937/669-5508
Tippecanoe High Sch 615 E Kessler Cowlesville Rd, Tipp City 45371 Steve Verhoff	9-12	V	777 60	16%	937/667-8448 Fax 937/667-0912
Tippecanoe Middle Sch 555 N Hyatt St, Tipp City 45371 Greg Southers	6-8		616 35	19%	937/667-8454 Fax 937/667-9120

• **Troy City School Dist** PID: 00823591   937/332-6700
500 N Market St, Troy 45373   Fax 937/332-6771

Schools: 9 \ *Teachers:* 243 \ *Students:* 4,400 \ *Special Ed Students:* 533 \ *LEP Students:* 103 \ *College-Bound:* 61% \ *Ethnic:* Asian 3%, African American 5%, Hispanic 3%, Caucasian 88% \ *Exp:* $265 (Med) \ *Poverty:* 11% \ *Title I:* $699,086 \ *Special Education:* $986,000 \ *Open-Close:* 08/21 - 05/28 \ *DTBP:* $199 (High)

Chris Piper 1		Mark Barhorst 2,68	
Tytus Jacobs 3,5		Clint Huffard 4*	
David Palmer 6*		Michael Moore 8,12	
Eric Sweetman 28*		Paul Delwiche 36*	
Kellie Shephard 57*		Beth Marshal 58,83	
Doug Trostle 67		Amanda Peck 81*	
Joshua Patterson 88		Pam Salsberry 295	

Public Schs..Principal	Grd	Prgm	Enr/#Cls	SN	
Concord Elem Sch 3145 State Route 718, Troy 45373 Dan Hake	K-5		647 35	13%	937/332-6730 Fax 937/332-3840
Cookson Elem Sch 921 Mystic Ln, Troy 45373 Stephanie Johnson	K-5	T	323 21	42%	937/332-6740 Fax 937/332-3980
Forest Elem Sch 413 E Canal St, Troy 45373 Paul Hohlbein	K-5	T	257 13	53%	937/332-6746 Fax 937/332-3976

1	Superintendent	8	Curric/Instruct K-12	19	Chief Financial Officer	29	Family/Consumer Science
2	Bus/Finance/Purchasing	9	Curric/Instruct Elem	20	Art K-12	30	Adult Education
3	Buildings And Grounds	10	Curric/Instruct Sec	21	Art Elem	31	Career/Sch-to-Work K-12
4	Food Service	11	Federal Program	22	Art Sec	32	Career/Sch-to-Work Elem
5	Transportation	12	Title I	23	Music K-12	33	Career/Sch-to-Work Sec
6	Athletic	13	Title V	24	Music Elem	34	Early Childhood Ed
7	Health Services	14	Asst Superintendent	25	Music Sec	35	Health/Phys Education
		15	Instructional Media Svcs	26	Business Education	36	Guidance Services K-12
		16	Chief Operations Officer	27	Career & Tech Ed	37	Guidance Services Elem
		17	Chief Academic Officer	28	Technology Education	38	Guidance Services Sec

39	Social Studies K-12	49	English/Lang Arts Elem	59	Special Education Elem	69	Academic Assessment
40	Social Studies Elem	50	English/Lang Arts Sec	60	Special Education Sec	70	Research/Development
41	Social Studies Sec	51	Reading K-12	61	Foreign/World Lang K-12	71	Public Information
42	Science K-12	52	Reading Elem	62	Foreign/World Lang Elem	72	Summer School
43	Science Elem	53	Reading Sec	63	Foreign/World Lang Sec	73	Instructional Tech
44	Science Sec	54	Remedial Reading K-12	64	Religious Education K-12	74	Inservice Training
45	Math K-12	55	Remedial Reading Elem	65	Religious Education Elem	75	Marketing/Distributive
46	Math Elem	56	Remedial Reading Sec	66	Religious Education Sec	76	Info Systems
47	Math Sec	57	Bilingual/ELL	67	School Board President	77	Psychological Assess
48	English/Lang Arts K-12	58	Special Education K-12	68	Teacher Personnel	78	Affirmative Action

OH-146

Ohio School Directory

Monroe County

	Grd	Prgm	Enr/#Cls	SN	
Heywood Elem Sch 260 S Ridge Ave, Troy 45373 Maurice Sadler	K-5	T	294 15	57%	937/332-6750 Fax 937/332-3891
Hook Elem Sch 729 Trade Sq W, Troy 45373 Penny Johnson	K-5	T	251 13	40%	937/332-6760 Fax 937/332-3911
Kyle Elem Sch 501 S Plum St, Troy 45373 Matthew Dillon	K-5	T	224 12	59%	937/332-6770 Fax 937/335-9585
Troy High Sch 151 Staunton Rd, Troy 45373 Dave Dilbone	9-12	A	1,160 72	32%	937/332-6710 Fax 937/332-6738
Troy Junior High Sch 556 Adams St, Troy 45373 Jeff Greulich	7-8		700 60	34%	937/332-6720 Fax 937/332-3812
Van Cleve 6th Grade Sch 617 E Main St, Troy 45373 Matt Siefring	6-6		340 15	40%	937/332-6780 Fax 937/332-3951

● **Upper Valley JT Voc Sch Dist** PID: 01417523　　937/778-1980
　8811 Career Dr, Piqua 45356　　Fax 937/778-4677

Schools: 1 \ **Teachers:** 86 \ **Students:** 780 \ **College-Bound:** 41% \
Exp: $534 (High) \ **Open-Close:** 08/16 - 05/21 \ **DTBP:** $242 (High) \ f t

Dr Nancy Luce	...1,11	Anthony Fraley	...2,10,18	
Pat Gibson	...2	Michelle Brunson	...10*	
Matt Meyer	...13,60,79,88	Eric Bowser	...16,73,82,295*	
Scott Naill	...30	Maria Bayless	...33*	
Bill Ankney	...67			

Public Schs..Principal	Grd	Prgm	Enr/#Cls	SN	
Upper Valley Career Center 8811 Career Dr, Piqua 45356 Jason Haak	Voc	G	780 50		937/778-1980

MIAMI CATHOLIC SCHOOLS

● **Archdiocese Cincinnati Ed Off** PID: 00808096
Listing includes only schools located in this county. See District Index for location of Diocesan Offices.

Catholic Schs..Principal	Grd	Prgm	Enr/#Cls	SN	
Piqua Catholic Sch 503 W North St, Piqua 45356 Brad Zimmerman	K-8		120 10		937/773-1564 Fax 937/773-0380
St Patrick Catholic Sch 420 E Water St, Troy 45373 Cynthia Cathcart	K-8		150 7		937/339-3705 Fax 937/339-1158

MIAMI PRIVATE SCHOOLS

Private Schs..Principal	Grd	Prgm	Enr/#Cls	SN	
Miami Montessori Sch 86 Troy Town Dr, Troy 45373 Sharon Prais	PK-6		75 4		937/339-0025 Fax 937/339-0055
Piqua SDA Christian Sch 4020 W State Route 185, Piqua 45356 Anita Brown	K-8		9 1		937/778-0223

	Grd	Prgm	Enr/#Cls	SN	
Tipp City Enrichment Center 223 W Broadway St, Tipp City 45371 Melissa Price	K-6		122		937/667-8800 Fax 937/667-8802
Troy Christian Schools 700 S Dorset Rd, Troy 45373 Amy Long	PK-12		706 40		937/339-5692 Fax 937/335-6258

MONROE COUNTY

MONROE COUNTY SCHOOLS

County Schs..Principal	Grd	Prgm	Enr/#Cls	SN	
Monroe Achievement Center 47011 State Route 26, Woodsfield 43793 Helen Ring	Spec	G	18 3		740/472-1712 Fax 740/472-1684

MONROE PUBLIC SCHOOLS

● **Switzerland of Ohio Local SD** PID: 00823711　　740/472-5801
　304 Mill St, Woodsfield 43793　　Fax 740/472-5806

Schools: 9 \ **Teachers:** 146 \ **Students:** 2,300 \ **Special Ed Students:** 483
\ **LEP Students:** 3 \ **College-Bound:** 49% \ **Ethnic:** African American 1%, Hispanic 1%, Caucasian 98% \ **Exp:** $372 (High) \ **Poverty:** 21% \
Title I: $816,935 \ **Special Education:** $576,000 \ **Open-Close:** 08/27 - 05/29 \ **DTBP:** $195 (High)

Bob Caldwell	...1	Connie Cress	...2	
Jason Clutter	...3,5	Tina Hogue	...4	
Larry Koslik	...8,13,58,275	Zac Housley	...8	
Curtis Wisvari	...12,70,81	Sarah Smith	...67	
Terry Wells	...68,83	Terry Wells	...68,83*	
Chad Stevens	...71	Tess Hill	...73,84	
George Wells	...81	Amy Shreve	...273*	

Public Schs..Principal	Grd	Prgm	Enr/#Cls	SN	
Beallsville Elem Sch 43822 Oh-556, Beallsville 43716 Kellie Hayden	PK-6	T	165 13		740/926-1302 Fax 740/926-2487
Beallsville High Sch 43822 State Route 556, Beallsville 43716 Casey Tolzda	7-12	GT	150 17	98%	740/926-1302 Fax 740/926-2487
Monroe Central High Sch 469 Lewisville Rd, Woodsfield 43793 Joe Semple	9-12	T	235 26	55%	740/472-0414 Fax 740/472-2055
Powhatan Elem Sch 54685 Mount Victory Rd, Powhatan Pt 43942 Robert Medlyn	PK-8	T	137 22	67%	740/795-5665 Fax 740/795-5830
River Elem Sch 52558 River High School Rd, Hannibal 43931 Rob Cadwell	PK-8	T	379 10		740/483-1358 Fax 740/486-1630
River High Sch 52560 River High School Rd, Hannibal 43931 Ed Trifonoff	9-12	T	218 28	99%	740/483-1358 Fax 740/483-1031
Skyvue Elem Sch 33329 Hartshorn Ridge Rd, Graysville 45734 Chris Caldwell	PK-8	T	206 35	61%	740/567-3312 Fax 740/567-3498

79 Student Personnel	91 Safety/Security	275 Response To Intervention	298 Grant Writer/Ptnrships	**School Programs**	**Social Media**	
80 Driver Ed/Safety	92 Magnet School	277 Remedial Math K-12	750 Chief Innovation Officer	A = Alternative Program		
81 Gifted/Talented	93 Parental Involvement	280 Literacy Coach	751 Chief of Staff	G = Adult Classes	f = Facebook	
82 Video Services	95 Tech Prep Program	285 STEM	752 Social Emotional Learning	M = Magnet Program		
83 Substance Abuse Prev	97 Chief Infomation Officer	286 Digital Learning		T = Title I Schoolwide	t = Twitter	
84 Erate	98 Chief Technology Officer	288 Common Core Standards	**Other School Types**	V = Career & Tech Ed Programs		
85 AIDS Education	270 Character Education	294 Accountability	Ⓐ = Alternative School			
86 Alternative/At Risk	271 Migrant Education	295 Network System	Ⓒ = Charter School	New Schools are shaded		
89 Multi-Cultural Curriculum	273 Teacher Mentor	296 Title II Programs	Ⓜ = Magnet School	New Superintendents and Principals are bold		
90 Social Work	274 Before/After Sch	297 Webmaster	Ⓨ = Year-Round School	Personnel with email addresses are underscored		

OH-147

Montgomery County

Market Data Retrieval

Swiss Hills Career Center 46601 State Route 78, Woodsfield 43793 Marc Ring	10-12	T	147 25	62%	740/472-0722 Fax 740/472-0367
Woodsfield Elem Sch 473 Lewisville Rd, Woodsfield 43793 Kathyrn Anderson	PK-8	T	445 23	75%	740/472-0953 Fax 740/472-1646

MONROE CATHOLIC SCHOOLS

- **Diocese of Steubenville Ed Off** PID: 00812671
  Listing includes only schools located in this county. See District Index for location of Diocesan Offices.

Catholic Schs..Principal	Grd	Prgm	Enr/#Cls	SN	
St Sylvester Sch 119 Wayne St, Woodsfield 43793 Robyn Guiler	PK-8		113 9		740/472-0321

MONTGOMERY COUNTY

MONTGOMERY COUNTY SCHOOLS

- **Montgomery Co Ed Service Ctr** PID: 00825991 937/225-4598
  200 S Keowee St, Dayton 45402 Fax 937/496-7426

Frank DePalma 1,11	Christopher Fox 2
Rusty Clifford 3	Shannon Cox 8,15
Jessica Davies 58,752	Marion Stout 68
Jennifer Beam 71	Lahela Snyder 81
Lesley McClain 275*	Matt Lewis 295

County Schs..Principal	Grd	Prgm	Enr/#Cls	SN	
⊚ Emerson Academy of Dayton [203] 501 Hickory St, Dayton 45410 Alison Foreman	K-8	T	655 40		937/223-2889 Fax 937/660-6386
McEsc Learning Center East 2528 Wilmington Pike, Dayton 45419 Holly Pressley	Spec		100		937/293-7559 Fax 937/299-5422
McEsc Learning Center Presch 5654 Longford Rd, Dayton 45424 Beth Pendergast	Spec		10		937/225-4598
McEsc Learning Center West 3500 Kettering Blvd, Dayton 45439 Stefanie Deisher	Spec		200		937/253-4178 Fax 937/259-5764
⊚ North Dayton Sch of Discovery [203] 3901 Turner Rd, Dayton 45415	K-8	T	634		937/278-6671 Fax 937/278-6964
Northview Sch 8114 N Main St, Dayton 45415 Pj Arndts	Spec		200 10		937/890-0730 Fax 937/890-7456
⊚ Pathway School of Discovery [203] 173 Avondale Dr, Dayton 45404 Keith Cobert	K-8	T	767 28	74%	937/235-5498 Fax 937/716-2160
Southview Child & Family Ctr 25 Thorpe Dr, Dayton 45420 Nancy Banks	Spec		500 4		937/258-1446 Fax 937/258-2706
⊚ Summit Academy Cmty Sch-Dayton [248] 4128 Cedar Ridge Rd, Dayton 45414 Megan Fagan	K-8	T	61		937/278-4298 Fax 937/278-4613

MONTGOMERY PUBLIC SCHOOLS

- **Brookville Local School Dist** PID: 00823905 937/833-2181
  75 June Pl, Brookville 45309 Fax 937/833-2787

Schools: 3 \ *Teachers:* 73 \ *Students:* 1,500 \ *Special Ed Students:* 167 \ *LEP Students:* 4 \ *College-Bound:* 75% \ *Ethnic:* Asian 1%, African American 1%, Hispanic 1%, Caucasian 97% \ *Exp:* $80 (Low) \ *Poverty:* 8% \ *Title I:* $179,776 \ *Special Education:* $192,000 \ *Open-Close:* 08/15 - 05/28 \ *DTBP:* $251 (High) \

Tim Hopkins 1	Tiffany Hiser 2,298
Jeff Requarth 3,4,5,91	Brian Sprada 6
Kathy Dafler 7,35,85*	Stephanie Hinds 8,76,286*
Mona Bailey 11*	Richard Dobberstein 16,73*
Anna Duckro 31,38,69,79,93	Jamie Neely ....
Sherril Spangler 36*	Marti Early 57*
Chelsea Hoelzle 58,752	Joe Mellon 67
Chris Bronner 88,270*	Denise Kump 274*
Lauren Henry 285	

Public Schs..Principal	Grd	Prgm	Enr/#Cls	SN	
Brookville Elem Sch 3 Blue Pride Dr, Brookville 45309 Chelsea Tiley	PK-3		473 21	28%	937/833-6796 Fax 937/833-5354
Brookville High Sch 1 Blue Pride Dr, Brookville 45309 Chris Bronner	9-12	V	414 35	57%	937/833-6761 Fax 937/833-6302
Brookville Intermediate Sch 2 Blue Pride Dr, Brookville 45309 Erin Wheat	4-8		586 30		937/833-6731 Fax 937/833-6756

- **Centerville City School Dist** PID: 00823955 937/433-8841
  111 Virginia Ave, Centerville 45458 Fax 937/438-6057

Schools: 13 \ *Teachers:* 501 \ *Students:* 8,200 \ *Special Ed Students:* 1,152 \ *LEP Students:* 195 \ *College-Bound:* 81% \ *Ethnic:* Asian 10%, African American 7%, Hispanic 3%, Caucasian 80% \ *Exp:* $236 (Med) \ *Poverty:* 6% \ *Title I:* $740,288 \ *Special Education:* $1,722,000 \ *Open-Close:* 08/14 - 05/28 \ *DTBP:* $189 (High) \

Dr Tom Henderson 1	Jon Wesney 2
Olivia Stone 4	Andy Trick 5
Rob Dement 6*	Robert Yux 8,15,69
Cherie Colopy 9	Adam Ciarlariello 10*
Craig Suttman 27,31*	Jeff Ochs 58
Tara Sira 58	Annie Self 67
Dan Tarpey 68	Shannon Morgan 73,76,295
Tammy Drerup 79	Kathy Spyrou 81*
Linda Bruner 294	

Public Schs..Principal	Grd	Prgm	Enr/#Cls	SN	
Centerville High Sch 500 E Franklin St, Centerville 45459 John Carroll	9-12	AV	2,760	12%	937/439-3500 Fax 937/260-4416
Centerville Prim Vlg Sch North 6450 Marshall Rd, Centerville 45459 Mindy Cline	PK-1		628 18	14%	937/438-6062 Fax 937/438-6076
Centerville Prim Vlg Sch South 8388 Paragon Rd, Centerville 45458 Amy Allen	PK-1		780	20%	937/312-1270 Fax 937/312-1274
Dr John Hole Elem Sch 180 W Whipp Rd, Centerville 45459 Lisa Mays	2-5		375 16	9%	937/434-0725 Fax 937/434-0557

OH—148

1 Superintendent	8 Curric/Instruct K-12	19 Chief Financial Officer	29 Family/Consumer Science	39 Social Studies K-12	49 English/Lang Arts Elem	59 Special Education Elem	69 Academic Assessment
2 Bus/Finance/Purchasing	9 Curric/Instruct Elem	20 Art K-12	30 Adult Education	40 Social Studies Elem	50 English/Lang Arts Sec	60 Special Education Sec	70 Research/Development
3 Buildings And Grounds	10 Curric/Instruct Sec	21 Art Elem	31 Career/Sch-to-Work Elem	41 Social Studies Sec	51 Reading K-12	61 Foreign/World Lang K-12	71 Public Information
4 Food Service	11 Federal Program	22 Art Sec	32 Career/Sch-to-Work Elem	42 Science K-12	52 Reading Elem	62 Foreign/World Lang Elem	72 Summer School
5 Transportation	12 Title I	23 Music K-12	33 Career/Sch-to-Work Sec	43 Science Elem	53 Reading Sec	63 Foreign/World Lang Sec	73 Instructional Tech
6 Athletic	13 Title V	24 Music Elem	34 Early Childhood Ed	44 Science Sec	54 Remedial Reading K-12	64 Religious Education K-12	74 Inservice Training
7 Health Services	15 Asst Superintendent	25 Music Sec	35 Health/Phys Education	45 Math K-12	55 Remedial Reading Elem	65 Religious Education Elem	75 Marketing/Distributive
	16 Instructional Media Svcs	26 Business Education	36 Guidance Services K-12	46 Math Elem	56 Remedial Reading Sec	66 Religious Education Sec	76 Info Systems
	17 Chief Operations Officer	27 Career & Tech Ed	37 Guidance Services Elem	47 Math Sec	57 Bilingual/ELL	67 School Board President	77 Psychological Assess
	18 Chief Academic Officer	28 Technology Education	38 Guidance Services Sec	48 English/Lang Arts K-12	58 Special Education K-12	68 Teacher Personnel	78 Affirmative Action

Ohio School Directory — Montgomery County

School	Grd	Prgm	Enr/#Cls	SN	Phone
Driscoll Elem Sch 5767 Marshall Rd, Dayton 45429 Erin Bucher	2-5		261 22	20%	937/434-0562 Fax 937/434-0393
Hadley E Watts Middle Sch 7056 McEwen Rd, Centerville 45459 Brian Miller	6-8	V	701 55	12%	937/434-0370 Fax 937/434-2907
Magsig Middle Sch 192 W Franklin St, Centerville 45459 Stacey Westendorf	6-8	V	605 35	18%	937/433-0965 Fax 937/433-5256
Normandy Elem Sch 401 Normandy Ridge Rd, Dayton 45459 Rebecca O'Neil	2-5		461 22	27%	937/434-0917 Fax 937/434-0953
Ⓐ School of Possibilities 105 Virginia Ave, Dayton 45458 Eric Gearhart	10-12		40		937/438-6092 Fax 937/438-6095
Stingley Elem Sch 95 Linden Dr, Centerville 45459 Diana Keller	2-5		289 16	14%	937/434-1054 Fax 937/438-6049
Tower Heights Middle Sch 195 N Johanna Dr, Centerville 45459 Clint Freese	6-8	V	560 36	12%	937/434-0383 Fax 937/434-3033
W O Cline Elem Sch 99 Virginia Ave, Centerville 45458 **Katy Barker**	2-5		385 20	30%	937/435-1315 Fax 937/435-3893
Weller Elem Sch 9600 Sheehan Rd, Centerville 45458 Andrew Boeke	2-5		516 20	6%	937/885-3273 Fax 937/885-5092

● **Dayton Public School Dist** PID: 00824064
115 S Ludlow St, Dayton 45402
937/542-3000
Fax 937/542-3175

Schools: 25 \ **Teachers:** 941 \ **Students:** 13,792 \
Special Ed Students: 2,959 \ **LEP Students:** 872 \ **College-Bound:** 47%
\ **Ethnic:** Asian 1%, African American 69%, Hispanic 4%, Caucasian 26% \ **Exp:** $393 (High) \ **Poverty:** 36% \ **Title I:** $19,888,312 \
Special Education: $3,683,000 \ **Open-Close:** 08/12 - 05/21 \ **DTBP:** $244 (High) \ f

Elizabeth Lolli 1
Terri Allen 2
Thomas Gray 5
Cynthia Abbott 7
Lashawn Gram 11
Dr Sheilia Burton 15,69,70,79,294
Michelle Rammel 27
Amy McKenny-Janev 57
William Harris 67
Gregory Taylor 69,70,294
Richard Wright 91
Hiwot Abraha 2
Cathie Defehr 4
Shawna Welch 6,35*
Carolyn Mack 8,74*
Dr Michael Sullivan 15
David Andrews 27
Karen Lombard 34
Angela Nichols 58*
Judith Spurlock 68*
Ryan Tait 74

Public Schs..Principal	Grd	Prgm	Enr/#Cls	SN	Phone
Ⓜ Belle Haven Elem Sch Ⓨ 4401 Free Pike, Dayton 45416 Joy Stokes	PK-6	MT	465 18		937/542-4220 Fax 937/542-4221
Belmont High Sch 2615 Wayne Ave, Dayton 45420 Melanie Walter	7-12	GTV	1,132 60		937/542-6460 Fax 937/542-6461
Ⓨ Charity Adams Earley Girl Acad 440 Shoup Mill Rd, Dayton 45415 Karla Goins	PK-8	MT	340 14		937/542-5840 Fax 937/542-5841
Ⓨ Cleveland PK-6 Sch 1102 Pursell Ave, Dayton 45420 Laura Busse	PK-6	MT	431 25		937/542-4340 Fax 937/542-4341
David Ponitz Career Tech Ctr 741 Washington St, Dayton 45402 Nelson Stone	9-12	GT	760 50		937/542-7180 Fax 937/542-7181
Dunbar Early College HS 1400 Albritton Dr, Dayton 45417 **Sean Henry**	9-12	TV	606 37		937/542-6760 Fax 937/542-6761
Ⓨ Eastmont Elem Sch 1480 Edendale Rd, Dayton 45432 Celeste Hoerner	PK-6	MT	448 30		937/542-4490 Fax 937/542-4491
Ⓨ Edison Elem Sch 228 N Broadway St, Dayton 45402 Basharus Simmons	PK-6	MT	414 15		937/542-4540 Fax 937/542-4541
Ⓜ Edwin Joel Brown Mid Sch Ⓨ 31 Willowwood Dr, Dayton 45405 Channey Goode	7-8	MT	349 45		937/542-5740
Ⓜ Fairview Elem Sch Ⓨ 2314 Elsmere Ave, Dayton 45406 Monica Utley	PK-6	MT	451 28		937/542-4590 Fax 937/542-4591
Ⓜ Horace Mann Elem Sch 715 Krebs Ave, Dayton 45419 Sheri Moss	PK-6	MT	411 15		937/542-4890 Fax 937/542-4891
Ⓜ Kemp PK-6 Sch Ⓨ 1923 Gondert Ave, Dayton 45403 Stacy Maney	K-6	MT	452 22		937/542-5090 Fax 937/542-5091
Ⓜ Kiser Elem Sch Ⓨ 1401 Leo St, Dayton 45404 James Fowler	PK-6	MT	545 25		937/542-6130 Fax 937/542-6131
Ⓜ Louise Troy Elem Sch Ⓨ 1630 Miami Chapel Rd, Dayton 45417 Dale Robinson	PK-6	MT	439 25		937/542-4290 Fax 937/542-4291
Meadowdale High Sch 3873 Whitestone Ct, Dayton 45416 Donetrus Hill	7-12	TV	466 80		937/542-7030 Fax 937/542-7031
Ⓨ Rivers Edge Mont Elem Sch 108 Linwood St, Dayton 45405 Lisa Keane	PK-6	MT	517 21		937/542-4640 Fax 937/542-4641
Ⓨ Roosevelt Elem Sch 1923 W 3rd St, Dayton 45417 Ladawn Mims-Morrow	PK-6	MT	337 23		937/542-5340 Fax 937/542-5341
Ⓨ Rosa Parks Early Learning Ctr 3705 Lori Sue Ave, Dayton 45406 Michelle Fulcher	PK-PK	MT	167 20		937/542-4390 Fax 937/542-4391
Ruskin Elem Sch 407 Ambrose Ct, Dayton 45410 **Bryan Ertsgaard**	PK-6	T	557 23		937/542-5680 Fax 937/542-5681
Ⓜ Stivers School for Arts Ⓨ 1313 E 5th St, Dayton 45402 **Gerry Griffith**	7-12	MV	869		937/542-7380 Fax 937/542-7381
Ⓨ Thurgood Marshall STEM HS 4447 Hoover Ave, Dayton 45417 Sharon Goins	9-12	MT	561		937/542-6610 Fax 937/542-6611
Ⓨ Valerie PK-6 Sch 3871 Yellowstone Ave, Dayton 45416 Shawnkeida Whitlow	PK-6	MT	420 19		937/542-5390 Fax 937/542-5391
Ⓨ Westwood Elem Sch 2805 Oakridge Dr, Dayton 45417 Akisha Shehee	PK-6	MT	379 20		937/542-4990 Fax 937/542-4991
Ⓨ Wogaman Middle Sch 920 McArthur Ave, Dayton 45417 Renaldo O'Neal	7-8	MT	360 20		937/542-5890 Fax 937/542-5891
Ⓨ Wright Brothers Middle Sch 1361 Huffman Ave, Dayton 45403 Shawna Welch	7-8	MT	398 23		937/542-5940 Fax 937/542-5941

79 Student Personnel
30 Driver Ed/Safety
31 Gifted/Talented
32 Video Services
33 Substance Abuse Prev
34 Erate
35 AIDS Education
38 Alternative/At Risk
39 Multi-Cultural Curriculum
90 Social Work
91 Safety/Security
92 Magnet School
93 Parental Involvement
95 Tech Prep Program
97 Chief Information Officer
98 Chief Technology Officer
270 Character Education
271 Migrant Education
273 Teacher Mentor
274 Before/After Sch
275 Response To Intervention
277 Remedial Math K-12
280 Literacy Coach
285 STEM
286 Digital Learning
288 Common Core Standards
294 Accountability
295 Network System
296 Title II Programs
297 Webmaster
298 Grant Writer/Ptnrships
750 Chief Innovation Officer
751 Chief of Staff
752 Social Emotional Learning

School Programs
A = Alternative Program
G = Adult Classes
M = Magnet Program
T = Title I Schoolwide
V = Career & Tech Ed Programs

Other School Types
Ⓐ = Alternative School
Ⓒ = Charter School
Ⓜ = Magnet School
Ⓨ = Year-Round School

Social Media
f = Facebook
t = Twitter

New Schools are shaded
New Superintendents and Principals are bold
Personnel with email addresses are underscored

Montgomery County

Market Data Retrieval

Huber Heights City School Dist PID: 00825721   937/237-6300
5954 Longford Rd, Huber Heights 45424   Fax 937/237-2178

Schools: 8 \ *Teachers:* 297 \ *Students:* 6,100 \ *Special Ed Students:* 901 \ *LEP Students:* 165 \ *College-Bound:* 61% \ *Ethnic:* Asian 2%, African American 23%, Hispanic 6%, Caucasian 68% \ *Exp:* $182 (Low) \ *Poverty:* 16% \ *Title I:* $1,778,839 \ *Special Education:* $907,000 \ *Open-Close:* 08/14 - 05/22 \ *DTBP:* $90 (Med)

Name	Code
Mario Basora	1
Regina Helmick	2,19
Kasey Wonderly	4
Nate Baker	6
Kate Little	12,58
Derrick Williams	68,298
Gary Doll	2,3
Tony Cochren	3,67
William Peck	5
Vanisa Turney	8,11,70,288,296
Kelly Bolin	58
Matt Mowery	73,84

Public Schs..Principal	Grd	Prgm	Enr/#Cls	SN	
Charles Huber Elem Sch 8895 Emeraldgate Dr, Huber Heights 45424 Tamara Granata	K-6	T	628 15	51%	937/237-6375 Fax 937/669-3529
Monticello Elem Sch 6523 Alter Rd, Huber Heights 45424 Dwon Bush	K-6	T	637 26	53%	937/237-6360 Fax 937/237-8833
Rushmore Elem Sch 7701 Berchman Dr, Huber Heights 45424 Benjamin Ayers	K-6	T	660 25	55%	937/237-6365 Fax 937/237-8585
Studebaker Pre-School 5954 Longford Rd, Huber Heights 45424 Pamela Bitsko	PK-PK		194		937/237-6345 Fax 937/376-6307
Valley Forge Elem Sch 7191 Troy Manor Rd, Huber Heights 45424 Rebecca Molfenter	K-6	T	563 22	61%	937/237-6380 Fax 937/237-8679
Wayne High Sch 5400 Chambersburg Rd, Huber Heights 45424 Jeffrey Berk	9-12	TV	1,655 100	48%	937/233-6431 Fax 937/237-6321
Weisenborn Junior High Sch 6061 Troy Pike, Huber Heights 45424 Brent Carey	7-8	T	901 51	53%	937/237-6350 Fax 937/237-7491
Wright Brothers Elem Sch 5758 Harshmanville Rd, Huber Heights 45424 Chip Holloway	K-6	T	638 18	63%	937/237-6392 Fax 937/237-2741

Jefferson Twp Local Sch Dist PID: 00824777   937/835-5682
2625 S Union Rd, Dayton 45417   Fax 937/835-5955

Schools: 2 \ *Teachers:* 32 \ *Students:* 345 \ *Special Ed Students:* 66 \ *College-Bound:* 60% \ *Ethnic:* African American 77%, Hispanic 4%, Native American: 1%, Caucasian 18% \ *Exp:* $342 (High) \ *Poverty:* 25% \ *Title I:* $387,293 \ *Open-Close:* 08/08 - 05/18 \ *DTBP:* $135 (High)

Name	Code
C Mitchell	1
Dr Richard Gates	11,83,288
Dr Pat Hoyal	58
Kim Potter	73
Laura Sauber	2
Chavin Lewis	36
Vilma Helms	67

Public Schs..Principal	Grd	Prgm	Enr/#Cls	SN	
Blairwood Elem Sch 1241 Blairwood Ave, Dayton 45417 Walter Sledte	PK-6	T	195 24		937/263-3504 Fax 937/262-3450
Jefferson Jr Sr High Sch 2701 S Union Rd, Dayton 45417 Walter Sledge	7-12	T	150 36		937/835-5691 Fax 937/835-5693

Kettering City School Dist PID: 00824832   937/499-1400
3750 Far Hills Ave, Kettering 45429   Fax 937/499-1465

Schools: 12 \ *Teachers:* 464 \ *Students:* 7,400 \ *Special Ed Students:* 1,124 \ *LEP Students:* 189 \ *College-Bound:* 66% \ *Ethnic:* Asian 2%, African American 7%, Hispanic 3%, Caucasian 88% \ *Exp:* $152 (Low) \ *Poverty:* 12% \ *Title I:* $1,604,425 \ *Special Education:* $1,387,000 \ *Open-Close:* 08/14 - 05/21 \ *DTBP:* $192 (High) \ f t

Name	Code
Scott Inskeep	1
Stacey Pabst	4
Christopher Weaver	6*
Sherry Alexander	10
Liz Jenson	27,31*
Jennifer Smith	58
Ken Miller	68
Kari Basson	71
Julia Timberlake	93
Andy Ayres	295*
Debra Mears	298
Kenneth Lackey	2,3,91
Todd Silverthorn	5
Dan Vonhandorf	8,12,15,16,57,288
Molly Carmosino	11
Katie Miller	30
Jennifer Kane	67
Dawn Caldwell	69,81
Chris Merritt	73,98
Kathy Rudd	274*
Mark Pupo	295

Public Schs..Principal	Grd	Prgm	Enr/#Cls	SN	
Beavertown Elem Sch 2700 Wilmington Pike, Kettering 45419 Carmella Friz	PK-5	T	373 20	49%	937/499-1740 Fax 937/499-1779
Greenmont Elem Sch 1 E Wren Cir, Kettering 45420 Brian Zawodny	PK-5	T	379 50	54%	937/499-1850 Fax 937/499-1859
Indian Riffle Elem Sch 3090 Glengarry Dr, Kettering 45420 Debbie Beiter	PK-5	T	584 22	39%	937/499-1720 Fax 937/499-1739
J E Prass Elem Sch 2601 Parklawn Dr, Kettering 45440 Jennifer Paxson	K-5		425 22	26%	937/499-1780 Fax 937/499-1799 f t
John F Kennedy Elem Sch 5030 Polen Dr, Kettering 45440 Monica Enix	PK-5	T	606 27	52%	937/499-1830 Fax 937/499-1839
Kettering ECC Center 2600 Holman St, Moraine 45439 Cindy Smith	PK-PK	T	126		937/499-1450 Fax 937/499-1517 t
Kettering Fairmont High Sch 3301 Shroyer Rd, Kettering 45429 Tyler Alexander	9-12		2,299	34%	937/499-1600 Fax 937/499-1661
Kettering Middle Sch 3000 Glengarry Dr, Kettering 45420 Brian Snyder	6-8	T	1,020 54	46%	937/499-1550 Fax 937/499-1598 f t
Oakview Elem Sch 4001 Ackerman Blvd, Kettering 45429 Aaron Smith	PK-5	T	446 20	34%	937/499-1870 Fax 937/499-1885
Orchard Park Elem Sch 600 E Dorothy Ln, Kettering 45419 Micki Ambrose	K-5	T	328 25	39%	937/499-1910 Fax 937/499-1929 f t
Southdale Elem Sch 1200 W Dorothy Ln, Kettering 45409 Dan Palmer	K-5	T	508 30	41%	937/499-1890 Fax 937/499-1909
Van Buren Middle Sch 3775 Shroyer Rd, Kettering 45429 Sarah Adams	6-8	T	729 38	35%	937/499-1800 Fax 937/499-1820

1 Superintendent	8 Curric/Instruct K-12	19 Chief Financial Officer	29 Family/Consumer Science	39 Social Studies K-12	49 English/Lang Arts Elem	59 Special Education Elem	69 Academic Assessment
2 Bus/Finance/Purchasing	9 Curric/Instruct Elem	20 Art K-12	30 Adult Education	40 Social Studies Elem	50 English/Lang Arts Sec	60 Special Education Sec	70 Research/Development
3 Buildings And Grounds	10 Curric/Instruct Sec	21 Art Elem	31 Career/Sch-to-Work K-12	41 Social Studies Sec	51 Reading K-12	61 Foreign/World Lang K-12	71 Public Information
4 Food Service	11 Federal Program	22 Art Sec	32 Career/Sch-to-Work Elem	42 Science K-12	52 Reading Elem	62 Foreign/World Lang Elem	72 Summer School
5 Transportation	12 Title I	23 Music K-12	33 Career/Sch-to-Work Sec	43 Science Elem	53 Reading Sec	63 Foreign/World Lang Sec	73 Instructional Tech
6 Athletic	13 Title V	24 Music Elem	34 Early Childhood Ed	44 Science Sec	54 Remedial Reading K-12	64 Religious Education K-12	74 Inservice Training
7 Health Services	15 Asst Superintendent	25 Music Sec	35 Health/Phys Education	45 Math K-12	55 Remedial Reading Elem	65 Religious Education Elem	75 Marketing/Distributive
	16 Instructional Media Svcs	26 Business Education	36 Guidance Services K-12	46 Math Elem	56 Remedial Reading Sec	66 Religious Education Sec	76 Info Systems
	17 Chief Operations Officer	27 Career & Tech Ed	37 Guidance Services Elem	47 Math Sec	57 Bilingual/ELL	67 School Board President	77 Psychological Assess
	18 Chief Academic Officer	28 Technology Education	38 Guidance Services Sec	48 English/Lang Arts K-12	58 Special Education K-12	68 Teacher Personnel	78 Affirmative Action

Ohio School Directory — Montgomery County

Mad River Local School Dist PID: 00825056   937/259-6606
801 Old Harshman Rd, Riverside 45431   Fax 937/259-6607

Schools: 8 \ **Teachers:** 215 \ **Students:** 3,800 \ **Special Ed Students:** 494 \ **LEP Students:** 142 \ **College-Bound:** 56% \ **Ethnic:** Asian 3%, African American 9%, Hispanic 5%, Caucasian 83% \ **Exp:** $182 (Low) \ **Poverty:** 18% \ **Title I:** $1,095,237 \ **Special Education:** $796,000 \ **Open-Close:** 08/14 - 05/22 \ **DTBP:** $210 (High) \ f t

Chad Wyen 1	Gerald Ellender 2
Stan Bochenek 3,91	Tom Zsembik 4
Brent Speas 5	Paul Neves 6*
Pam Roberts 12,34*	Krista Wagner 15
Dustin Freeman 16,28,73,76,84,295	Jesse Maxfield 27,95*
Laurie Jacob 57*	Jack Stephens 58,77,275
Scott Huddle 67	Jennifer Alexander 71

Public Schs..Principal	Grd	Prgm	Enr/#Cls	SN	
Beverly Gardens Elem Sch 5555 Enright Ave, Riverside 45431 Cristal Fields	K-4	T	339 22	48%	937/259-6620 Fax 937/259-6614
Brantwood Elem Sch 4350 Schwinn Dr, Dayton 45404 Misha Monnin	K-4	T	428 16	65%	937/237-4270 Fax 937/237-4277
Mad River Early Childhood Ctr 801 Old Harshman Rd, Riverside 45431 Pam Roberts	PK-PK	T	149		937/259-6640 Fax 937/259-6612
Mad River Middle Sch 1801 Harshman Rd, Dayton 45424 Laurie Plank	7-8	ATV	518 31	63%	937/237-4265 Fax 937/237-4273
Saville Elem Sch 5800 Burkhardt Rd, Riverside 45431 Steve Kandel	K-4	T	387 19	72%	937/259-6625 Fax 937/259-6648
Spinning Hills Middle Sch 5001 Eastman Ave, Dayton 45432 Michael Combs	5-6	AT	586 45	66%	937/259-6635 Fax 937/259-6644 f t
Stebbins High Sch 1900 Harshman Rd, Dayton 45424 Tina Simpson	9-12	ATV	1,162 75	57%	937/237-4250 Fax 937/237-4262
Virginia Stevenson Elem Sch 805 Old Harshman Rd, Riverside 45431 Cory Miller	K-4	T	357 20	77%	937/259-6630 Fax 937/425-6783 t

Miami Valley Career Tech VSD PID: 00825977   937/854-6291
6800 Hoke Rd, Englewood 45315   Fax 937/837-5318

Schools: 2 \ **Teachers:** 138 \ **Students:** 2,100 \ **LEP Students:** 3 \ **College-Bound:** 70% \ **Exp:** $604 (High) \ **Open-Close:** 08/15 - 05/19 \ **DTBP:** $235 (High) \ f t

Dr Nick Weldy 1,11	Debbie Gossett 2
Dr Kevin Lacey 2,68	Sharon Bergman 2,19
Curtis Philpot 3,17	Mike Study 5*
Beth Manor 10,18	Rhonda Phillips 10,286,288*
Jack Poore 15,79	Tammie King 16*
Amy Leedy 30*	Joe Idzakovich 67
Kelly Herzog 71	Randy Schmidt 73*
Sandy Barker 76*	Carl Bush 91

Public Schs..Principal	Grd	Prgm	Enr/#Cls	SN	
Miami Valley Career Tech Ctr 6800 Hoke Rd, Clayton 45315 Dale Winner	Voc	G	1,980 125		937/854-6291 f t
Ⓐ Mvctc Youth Connect Alt Sch 1133 S Edwin C Moses Blvd 280, Dayton 45417 Jay Byrne	8-12		100 5		937/226-1741

Miamisburg City School Dist PID: 00825240   937/866-3381
540 Park Ave, Miamisburg 45342   Fax 937/865-5250

Schools: 10 \ **Teachers:** 325 \ **Students:** 5,500 \ **Special Ed Students:** 876 \ **LEP Students:** 150 \ **College-Bound:** 66% \ **Ethnic:** Asian 3%, African American 8%, Hispanic 3%, Caucasian 85% \ **Exp:** $130 (Low) \ **Poverty:** 14% \ **Title I:** $1,357,987 \ **Special Education:** $975,000 \ **Open-Close:** 08/08 - 05/20 \ **DTBP:** $194 (High)

Dr David Vail 1	Scott Gilbert 2
Tina Hageman 2,19,294	Rich Baker 3
Ravella Lawson 4	Mechael Reed 5
Jason Osborne 6	Stacie Moore 8,30,288
Amy Dobson 9,54,69,74,288	Katy Lucas 11,36,57,58,68,79,296
Steve Homan 15,68	Dale Toadvine 67

Public Schs..Principal	Grd	Prgm	Enr/#Cls	SN	
Bauer Elem Sch 701 Springboro Pike, Dayton 45449 Tammy Sundermann	K-5	T	451 27	35%	937/434-9191 Fax 937/434-8879
Bear Elem Sch 545 School St, Miamisburg 45342 Shannon Ruppert	K-5	T	202 10	48%	937/866-4691 Fax 937/866-4065
Jane Chance Elem Sch 10661 Wood Rd, Miamisburg 45342 Dale Geyer	K-5	T	364 12	47%	937/384-0510 Fax 937/384-0566
Kinder Elem Sch 536 E Central Ave, Miamisburg 45342 Jeremy Saylor	K-5	T	362	60%	937/866-4461 Fax 937/865-5268
Maddux-Lang Primary Sch 4010 Crains Run Rd, Miamisburg 45342 Sarah Buzek	PK-PK		172		937/847-2766 Fax 937/847-8349
Mark Twain Elem Sch 822 N 9th St, Miamisburg 45342 Kelly Marker	K-5	T	334 14	44%	937/866-2581 Fax 937/866-4085
Medlar View Elem Sch 4400 Medlar Rd, Miamisburg 45342 Susan Woods	K-5		277 31	24%	937/865-5257 Fax 937/865-5295
Miamisburg High Sch 1860 Belvo Rd, Miamisburg 45342 Michael Black	9-12	V	1,559 85	27%	937/866-0771 Fax 937/865-5267
Miamisburg Middle Sch 8668 Miamisburg Springboro Rd, Miamisburg 45342 Kelly Thomas	6-8	T	1,232 18	36%	937/865-0011 Fax 937/865-0114
Mound Elem Sch 1108 Range Ave, Miamisburg 45342 Michael Black	K-5	T	312 24	34%	937/866-4641 Fax 937/866-6767

New Lebanon Local School Dist PID: 00825331   937/687-1301
320 S Fuls Rd, New Lebanon 45345   Fax 937/687-7321

Schools: 3 \ **Teachers:** 78 \ **Students:** 1,100 \ **Special Ed Students:** 156 \ **College-Bound:** 56% \ **Ethnic:** Hispanic 1%, Caucasian 98% \ **Exp:** $320 (High) \ **Poverty:** 21% \ **Title I:** $379,935 \ **Special Education:** $232,000 \ **Open-Close:** 08/21 - 05/28 \ **DTBP:** $165 (High)

Dr Greg Williams 1	Rob Wannemacher 2,84
Lance Hoop 3,91	Charissa Brombaugh 5
Kregg Creamer 6*	Dena Shepard 8,35,54,74,277,288
Christy Howard 11,58,69,77*	Thomas Maxwell 11,296*
Keith Quillen 16,73,295	Chris Tipton 27,31,36*
David Woodgeard 67	Debbie Teater 79,298
Margie Loyacano 81*	Melissa McCartney 83,88*

---

79 Student Personnel	91 Safety/Security	275 Response To Intervention	298 Grant Writer/Ptnrships	**School Programs**	**Social Media**
60 Driver Ed/Safety	92 Magnet School	277 Remedial Math K-12	750 Chief Innovation Officer	A = Alternative Program	
61 Gifted/Talented	93 Parental Involvement	280 Literacy Coach	751 Chief of Staff	G = Adult Classes	f = Facebook
62 Video Services	95 Tech Prep Program	285 STEM	752 Social Emotional Learning	M = Magnet Program	
63 Substance Abuse Prev	97 Chief Infomation Officer	286 Digital Learning		T = Title I Schoolwide	t = Twitter
64 Erate	98 Chief Technology Officer	288 Common Core Standards	**Other School Types**	V = Career & Tech Ed Programs	
65 AIDS Education	270 Character Education	294 Accountability	Ⓐ = Alternative School		
68 Alternative/At Risk	271 Migrant Education	295 Network System	Ⓒ = Charter School	New Schools are shaded	
69 Multi-Cultural Curriculum	273 Teacher Mentor	296 Title II Programs	Ⓜ = Magnet School	New Superintendents and Principals are bold	
90 Social Work	274 Before/After Sch	297 Webmaster	Ⓨ = Year-Round School	Personnel with email addresses are underscored	

OH-151

Montgomery County

Market Data Retrieval

Public Schs..Principal	Grd	Prgm	Enr/#Cls	SN
Dixie Elem Sch 1150 W Main St, New Lebanon 45345 Holly Keadle	PK-4	T	429 21	53% 937/687-3511 Fax 937/687-7804
Dixie High Sch 300 S Fuls Rd, New Lebanon 45345 Brad Wolgast	9-12	AT	319 24	49% 937/687-1366 Fax 937/687-7074
Dixie Middle Sch 200 S Fuls Rd, New Lebanon 45345 Thomas Maxwell	5-8	T	350 28	47% 937/687-3508 Fax 937/687-7705

- **Northmont City School Dist** PID: 00825379 937/832-5000
  4001 Old Salem Rd, Englewood 45322 Fax 937/832-5001

Schools: 8 \ *Teachers:* 275 \ *Students:* 5,800 \ *Special Ed Students:* 720 \ *LEP Students:* 94 \ *College-Bound:* 77% \ *Ethnic:* Asian 2%, African American 23%, Hispanic 2%, Caucasian 73% \ *Exp:* $103 (Low) \ *Poverty:* 9% \ *Title I:* $702,412 \ *Special Education:* $937,000 \ *Open-Close:* 08/14 - 05/20 \ *DTBP:* $191 (High) \ f t

Tony Thomas 1,11,288
Jason Watson 3,5,91
Eric Shafner 5
Leslie Hobbs 7,36,57,58,77,79,271
Jennifer Zumwalt 12,13*
Brian Wissman 23*
Kristy Geiger 51*
Amy Sipes 68,270,294,296
Jessie Zink 81,298*
Jenny Wood 297
Brandon Knecht 2,70,76
Pamela Pearson 4
Micah Harding 6*
Susanne Lintz 8,11,27,31,69,285,286,288
Sean Kaiser 16,295
Dottie Woodard 34
Linda Blum 67
Brad Bush 73,95
Sheree Coffman 83,85,275*

Public Schs..Principal	Grd	Prgm	Enr/#Cls	SN
Englewood Elem Sch 702 Albert St, Englewood 45322 Joe Johnston	2-6		331 15	30% 937/832-5900 Fax 937/832-5901 t
Englewood Hills Elem Sch 508 Durst Dr, Englewood 45322 Katie Grothaus	2-6	T	226 20	46% 937/832-5950 Fax 937/832-5951
Kleptz Early Learning Center 1100 W National Rd, Clayton 45315 Beth Wyandt	PK-1	T	874	29% 937/832-6750 Fax 937/832-6786
Northmont High Sch 4916 National Rd, Clayton 45315 Dr Jason Inkrott	9-12	AV	1,462	31% 937/832-6000 Fax 937/832-6001
Northmont Middle Sch 4810 W National Rd, Clayton 45315 Jarrod Brumbaugh	7-8		776 50	37% 937/832-6500 Fax 937/832-6501
Northmoor Elem Sch 4421 Old Salem Rd, Englewood 45322 David Lawrence	2-6	T	450 26	32% 937/832-6800 Fax 937/832-6801 t
Northwood Elem Sch 6200 Noranda Dr, Dayton 45415 Sally Moore	2-6	T	363 22	48% 937/832-6240 Fax 937/832-6241
Union Elem Sch 418 W Martindale Rd, Union 45322 Kevin Grone	2-6	T	470 12	41% 937/832-6700 Fax 937/832-6701

- **Northridge Local School Dist** PID: 00825484 937/278-5885
  2008 Timber Ln, Dayton 45414 Fax 937/276-8351

Schools: 4 \ *Teachers:* 96 \ *Students:* 1,500 \ *Special Ed Students:* 233 \ *LEP Students:* 22 \ *College-Bound:* 40% \ *Ethnic:* African American 25%, Hispanic 3%, Caucasian 72% \ *Exp:* $159 (Low) \ *Poverty:* 42% \ *Title I:* $1,784,603 \ *Special Education:* $397,000 \ *Open-Close:* 09/03 - 06/12 \ *DTBP:* $252 (High)

Dave Jackson 1
Donna Maggard 5
Shane Allison 7*
Pamela Thompson 58,77*
Heather Zacharias 73,76,295,297*
Judi Hunter 4*
Nathan Farmer 6*
Laura Inkrott 8,11,273,288
Margie Lairson 67

Public Schs..Principal	Grd	Prgm	Enr/#Cls	SN
Esther Dennis MS at G Kennedy 2655 Wagner Ford Rd, Dayton 45414 Nick Elam	4-6	T	367 25	937/275-6833 Fax 937/276-8357
John H Morrison Elem Sch 2235 Arthur Ave, Dayton 45414 Derrick Thomas	1-3	T	386 22	937/276-8341 Fax 937/276-8343
Northridge High Sch 2251 Timber Ln, Dayton 45414 Tim Whitestone	7-12	T	627 46	937/275-7469 Fax 937/275-8434
Timberlane Learning Center 2131 Timber Ln, Dayton 45414 T Hardin	PK-K	T	167 13	937/278-0689 Fax 937/278-4029

- **Oakwood City School Dist** PID: 00825549 937/297-5332
  20 Rubicon Rd, Oakwood 45409 Fax 937/297-5345

Schools: 5 \ *Teachers:* 122 \ *Students:* 1,988 \ *Special Ed Students:* 224 \ *LEP Students:* 7 \ *College-Bound:* 87% \ *Ethnic:* Asian 5%, African American 1%, Hispanic 4%, Caucasian 90% \ *Exp:* $288 (Med) \ *Poverty:* 8% \ *Title I:* $214,657 \ *Special Education:* $345,000 \ *Open-Close:* 08/13 - 05/28 \ *DTBP:* $231 (High)

Dr Kyle Ramey 1
Allyson Couch 5,11,34,57
Dr Kimbe Lange 8,69,74,273,285,288,298*
Kelly Owens 31*
Todd Duwel 67
Tim Badenhop 72*
Amy Samosky 77*
Mary Barnett 85*
Julie Belden 2,3,4,19
Laura Connor 6*
Mindy Ashworth 16*
Frank Eaton 58,88*
Traci Hale 71
Matt Sproat 73,286,295*
Joan Bline 83,275*

Public Schs..Principal	Grd	Prgm	Enr/#Cls	SN
Edwin Smith Elem Sch 1701 Shafor Blvd, Dayton 45419 Chrissy Elliott	PK-6		481 26	5% 937/297-5335 Fax 937/297-1841
Harman Elem Sch 735 Harman Ave, Dayton 45419 Sarah Patterson	1-6		419 24	1% 937/297-5338 Fax 937/297-1514
Juliann Lange Sch 219 W Dorothy Ln, Dayton 45429 Frank Eaton	K-K		125 7	4% 937/299-8730 Fax 937/299-8734
Oakwood High Sch 1200 Far Hills Ave, Oakwood 45419 Paul Waller	9-12	V	690 55	937/297-5325 Fax 937/297-5348
Oakwood Junior High Sch 1200 Far Hills Ave, Dayton 45419 Tim Badenhop	7-8		334 100	937/297-5328 Fax 937/297-7807

- **Trotwood-Madison City SD** PID: 00825161 937/854-3050
  3594 N Snyder Rd, Trotwood 45426 Fax 937/854-3057

Schools: 5 \ *Teachers:* 138 \ *Students:* 2,300 \ *Special Ed Students:* 428 \ *LEP Students:* 12 \ *College-Bound:* 60% \ *Ethnic:* African American 92%, Hispanic 1%, Caucasian 7% \ *Exp:* $235 (Med) \ *Poverty:* 35% \ *Title I:* $2,880,954 \ *Special Education:* $707,000 \ *Open-Close:* 08/12 - 05/22 \ *DTBP:* $191 (High)

Marlon Howard 1
Scott Mayes 3
Janice Allen 2,8,18
James Putnam 4

---

1 Superintendent	8 Curric/Instruct K-12	19 Chief Financial Officer	29 Family/Consumer Science	39 Social Studies K-12	49 English/Lang Arts Elem	59 Special Education Elem	69 Academic Assessment
2 Bus/Finance/Purchasing	9 Curric/Instruct Elem	20 Art K-12	30 Adult Education	40 Social Studies Elem	50 English/Lang Arts Sec	60 Special Education Sec	70 Research/Development
3 Buildings And Grounds	10 Curric/Instruct Sec	21 Art Elem	31 Career/Sch-to-Work K-12	41 Social Studies Sec	51 Reading K-12	61 Foreign/World Lang K-12	71 Public Information
4 Food Service	11 Federal Program	22 Art Sec	32 Career/Sch-to-Work Elem	42 Science K-12	52 Reading Elem	62 Foreign/World Lang Elem	72 Summer School
5 Transportation	12 Title I	23 Music K-12	33 Career/Sch-to-Work Sec	43 Science Elem	53 Reading Sec	63 Foreign/World Lang Sec	73 Instructional Tech
6 Athletic	13 Title V	24 Music Elem	34 Early Childhood Ed	44 Science Sec	54 Remedial Reading K-12	64 Religious Education K-12	74 Inservice Training
7 Health Services	15 Asst Superintendent	25 Music Sec	35 Health/Phys Education	45 Math K-12	55 Remedial Reading Elem	65 Religious Education Elem	75 Marketing/Distributive
	16 Instructional Media Svcs	26 Business Education	36 Guidance Services K-12	46 Math Elem	56 Remedial Reading Sec	66 Religious Education Sec	76 Info Systems
	17 Chief Operations Officer	27 Career & Tech Ed	37 Guidance Services Elem	47 Math Sec	57 Bilingual/ELL	67 School Board President	77 Psychological Assess
	18 Chief Academic Officer	28 Technology Education	38 Guidance Services Sec	48 English/Lang Arts K-12	58 Special Education K-12	68 Teacher Personnel	78 Affirmative Action

Ohio School Directory — Montgomery County

Alicia Starks 5
Lisa Minor 8,79,288
Denise Moore 67
Luke Tults 295
Kiara Williams 8
Edward Sample 58
Rana Aljanby 285

Public Schs..Principal	Grd	Prgm	Enr/#Cls	SN	
Early Learning Center 4400 N Union Rd, Dayton 45426 Mary Martin	PK-1	T	469		937/854-4511 Fax 937/854-4624
Madison Park Elem Sch 301 S Broadway St, Trotwood 45426 Tamara Rizzo-Sterner	2-3	TV	391 50		937/854-4456 Fax 937/854-4493
Trotwood-Madison Middle Sch 4420 N Union Rd, Trotwood 45426 Phillitia Charlton	6-8	T	564		937/854-0017 Fax 937/854-8433
Trotwood-Madison Sr High Sch 4440 N Union Rd, Trotwood 45426 David White	9-12	TV	765 85		937/854-0878 Fax 937/854-0594
Westbrooke Village Elem Sch 6500 Westford Rd, Trotwood 45426 Tracey Mallory	4-5	T	380		937/854-3196 Fax 937/854-8704

- **Valley View Local School Dist** PID: 00825587   937/855-6581
  59 Peffley St, Germantown 45327   Fax 937/855-0266

Schools: 4 \ *Teachers:* 113 \ *Students:* 1,900 \ *Special Ed Students:* 256 \ *LEP Students:* 8 \ *College-Bound:* 68% \ *Ethnic:* Asian 1%, African American 1%, Hispanic 2%, Caucasian 96% \ *Exp:* $72 (Low) \ *Poverty:* 10% \ *Title I:* $292,450 \ *Special Education:* $260,000 \ *Open-Close:* 08/14 - 05/21 \ *DTBP:* $239 (High) \ f

Ben Richards 1
Erick Depew 3
Mark Kozarec 6*
Bill Lawson 11*
Kevin Phillips 34,58,77*
Angie Valenti 67
Lindsey Schmidt 288
Dan Schall 2,11
Rick Wharton 5
Candice Sears 8,69,72,273*
Penny Green 16*
Shannon Hayes 37*
Debra Landis 71,298*
Josh Frantz 295

Public Schs..Principal	Grd	Prgm	Enr/#Cls	SN	
Valley View High Sch 6027 Germantown-Farmersvile Pk, Germantown 45327 Todd Kozarec	9-12	V	517 40	25%	937/855-4116 Fax 937/855-4739
Valley View Intermediate Sch 64 Comstock St, Germantown 45327 Bill Lauson	4-6		475 30	65%	937/855-4203 Fax 937/855-0267
Valley View Junior High 202 Jackson St, Farmersville 45325 Nichole Thomas	7-8		294 33	30%	937/696-2591 Fax 937/696-1007
Valley View Primary Sch 110 Comstock St, Germantown 45327 Bill Lawson	K-3		481 40		937/855-6571 Fax 937/855-6283

- **Vandalia Butler City Sch Dist** PID: 00825630   937/415-6400
  500 S Dixie Dr, Vandalia 45377   Fax 937/415-6429

Schools: 5 \ *Teachers:* 154 \ *Students:* 3,225 \ *Special Ed Students:* 451 \ *LEP Students:* 34 \ *College-Bound:* 71% \ *Ethnic:* Asian 2%, African American 8%, Hispanic 4%, Caucasian 86% \ *Exp:* $75 (Low) \ *Poverty:* 10% \ *Title I:* $543,131 \ *Special Education:* $251,000 \ *Open-Close:* 08/21 - 05/28 \ *DTBP:* $194 (High) \ t

Robert O'Leary 1
Marcus O'Brien 3,91
Rebecca Bush 4*
Brandon Hartley ... 8,13,31,34,69,273,288,298
Rob O'Leary 2,7,8,11,57,58,77,83*
Patricia Mattix 4
Jordan Shumaker 6
Russ Garman 12

Jennifer Cornell 29*
Anaka Johnson 71
Ron Mandelik 73,295*
Rodney Washburn 67
David Mohler 73,76,98,286

Public Schs..Principal	Grd	Prgm	Enr/#Cls	SN	
Butler High Sch 600 S Dixie Dr, Vandalia 45377 Thomas Luebbe	9-12		880 87	24%	937/415-6300 Fax 937/415-6457
Demmitt Elem Sch 1010 E National Rd, Vandalia 45377 Garry Martin	PK-3	T	515 26	29%	937/415-6500 Fax 937/415-6538 t
Helke Elem Sch 611 Randler Ave, Vandalia 45377 Brian Tregoning	K-3		403	37%	937/415-3000 Fax 937/415-3031
Morton Middle Sch 8555 Peters Pike, Vandalia 45377 Shannon White	6-8		680 35	32%	937/415-6600 Fax 937/415-6648
Smith Middle Sch 3625 Little York Rd, Dayton 45414 Ryan Rogers	4-5		456 35	36%	937/415-7000 Fax 937/415-7051

- **West Carrollton City Sch Dist** PID: 00825848   937/859-5121
  430 E Pease Ave, W Carrollton 45449   Fax 937/859-5250

Schools: 6 \ *Teachers:* 211 \ *Students:* 3,700 \ *Special Ed Students:* 641 \ *LEP Students:* 171 \ *College-Bound:* 62% \ *Ethnic:* Asian 1%, African American 17%, Hispanic 8%, Caucasian 73% \ *Exp:* $178 (Low) \ *Poverty:* 20% \ *Title I:* $1,354,066 \ *Special Education:* $744,000 \ *Open-Close:* 08/20 - 05/28 \ *DTBP:* $191 (High)

Andrea Townsend 1
Ryan Sloan 2
Belinda Cox 5*
Craig Myers 8
Leslie Miller 67
Janine Corbett 71
Kimberly Harvey 76
Jack Haag 2,3,91
Tina Pett 4
Evan Ivory 6
Melissa Theis 11,15,58,275
Devon Berry 68
Robert Johnson 73

Public Schs..Principal	Grd	Prgm	Enr/#Cls	SN	
C F Holliday Elem Sch 4100 S Dixie Dr, Dayton 45439 Dorian Glover	1-5	T	550 19	70%	937/859-5121 Fax 937/643-5460
Y Harold Schnell Elem Sch 5995 Student St, W Carrollton 45449 Pamela Dudley	1-5	MT	442 33	50%	937/859-5121 Fax 937/859-2775
Harry Russell Elem Sch 123 Elementary Dr, W Carrollton 45449 Brad Thobe	1-5	T	381 20	69%	937/859-5121 Fax 937/865-5720
Walter Shade Early Chldhd Ctr 510 E Pease Ave, W Carrollton 45449 Janet Schieman	PK-K	T	390 22	48%	937/859-5121 Fax 937/859-2768
West Carrollton High Sch 5833 Student St, W Carrollton 45449 Candice Haffner	9-12	ATV	902 80	57%	937/859-5121 Fax 937/435-2315
West Carrollton Middle Sch 424 E Main St, W Carrollton 45449 Doug Mescher	6-8	TV	808 70	67%	937/859-5121 Fax 937/859-2780

MONTGOMERY CATHOLIC SCHOOLS

- **Archdiocese Cincinnati Ed Off** PID: 00808096
  Listing includes only schools located in this county. See District Index for location of Diocesan Offices.

---

79 Student Personnel	91 Safety/Security	275 Response To Intervention	298 Grant Writer/Ptnrships	**School Programs**	**Social Media**
80 Driver Ed/Safety	92 Magnet School	277 Remedial Math K-12	750 Chief Innovation Officer	A = Alternative Program	
81 Gifted/Talented	93 Parental Involvement	280 Literacy Coach	751 Chief of Staff	G = Adult Classes	f = Facebook
82 Video Services	95 Tech Prep Program	285 STEM	752 Social Emotional Learning	M = Magnet Program	
83 Substance Abuse Prev	97 Chief Infomation Officer	286 Digital Learning		T = Title I Schoolwide	t = Twitter
84 Erate	98 Chief Technology Officer	288 Common Core Standards	**Other School Types**	V = Career & Tech Ed Programs	
85 AIDS Education	270 Character Education	294 Accountability	A = Alternative School		
68 Alternative/At Risk	271 Migrant Education	295 Network System	C = Charter School	New Schools are shaded	
69 Multi-Cultural Curriculum	273 Teacher Mentor	296 Title II Programs	M = Magnet School	New Superintendents and Principals are bold	
90 Social Work	274 Before/After Sch	297 Webmaster	Y = Year-Round School	Personnel with email addresses are underscored	

OH–153

Morgan County

Market Data Retrieval

Catholic Schs..Principal	Grd	Prgm	Enr/#Cls	SN
Archbishop Alter High Sch 940 E David Rd, Kettering 45429 Lourdes Lambert	9-12		649 36	937/434-4434 Fax 937/434-0507
Ascension Sch 2001 Woodman Dr, Kettering 45420 Susan DiGiorgio	K-8		380 16	937/254-5411 Fax 937/254-1150
Bishop Leibold Sch East 6666 Springboro Pike, Dayton 45449 Theodore Wallace	4-8		200 11	937/434-9343 Fax 937/436-3048
Bishop Leibold Sch W Campus 24 S 3rd St, Miamisburg 45342 Dr Theodore Wallace	PK-3		165 12	937/866-3021
Holy Angels Sch 223 L St, Dayton 45409 Jake LaForge	PK-8		285 17	937/229-5959 Fax 937/229-5960
Immaculate Conception Sch 2268 S Smithville Rd, Dayton 45420 Tammy Haus	PK-8		342 9	937/253-8831
Incarnation Sch 45 Williamsburg Ln, Dayton 45459 Leah Coghlan	PK-8		852 32	937/433-1051 Fax 937/433-9796
Mother Maria Anna Brunner CS 4870 Denlinger Rd, Dayton 45426 Robin Johnson	PK-8		213 21	937/277-2291 Fax 937/277-2217
Our Lady of the Rosary Sch 40 Notre Dame Ave, Dayton 45404 Jacki Loffer	K-8		214 9	937/222-7231 Fax 937/222-7393
St Albert the Great Sch 104 W Dorothy Ln, Kettering 45429 Sherry Gabert	PK-8		300 20	937/293-9452 Fax 937/293-7525
St Anthony Catholic Sch 1824 Saint Charles Ave, Dayton 45410 Alana Campion	PK-8		200 9	937/253-6251 Fax 937/253-1541
St Benedict the Moor Cath Sch 138 Gramont Ave, Dayton 45417 Debra Johnson	PK-5		130 9	937/268-6391 Fax 937/268-9775
St Charles Borromeo Sch 4600 Ackerman Blvd, Dayton 45429 Dave Bogle	PK-8		500 20	937/434-4933 Fax 937/434-6692
St Christopher Sch 405 E National Rd, Vandalia 45377 Mary Kincaid	K-8		290 20	937/898-5104 Fax 937/454-4790
St Peter Sch 6185 Chambersburg Rd, Huber Heights 45424 Ron Albino	K-8		500 25	937/233-8710 Fax 937/237-3974

MONTGOMERY PRIVATE SCHOOLS

Private Schs..Principal	Grd	Prgm	Enr/#Cls	SN
Alexandria Montessori Sch 175 E Franklin St, Centerville 45459 Karen Graham	PK-6		42 3	937/435-5392 Fax 937/435-5397
Applied Behavioral Services 2570 Technical Dr, Dayton 45458 Kylea Frei	Spec		63 12	937/847-8750
Chaminade Julienne High Sch 505 S Ludlow St, Dayton 45402 John Marshall	9-12		636	937/461-3740 Fax 937/461-6256
Chess Christian Sch 208 Nutt Rd, Centerville 45458 Amy Frederick	PK-12		189	937/343-1130
Dayton Christian Sch 9391 Washington Church Rd, Miamisburg 45342 James Holliday \ Rich Garrett	PK-12	V	650	937/291-7201 Fax 937/291-7274
Dayton Islamic Sch 3662 E Patterson Rd, Dayton 45430 Shaad Ahmed	PK-8		76 10	937/429-9477 Fax 937/429-9512
Evangel Academy 132 N Smithville Rd, Dayton 45403 Dr Jack McIntosh	K-12		35	937/253-8342 Fax 937/253-1856
Gloria Dei Montessori Sch 615 Shiloh Dr, Dayton 45415 Laurie Kemp	PK-8		90	937/274-7195
Hillel Academy of Dayton 305 Sugar Camp Cir, Dayton 45409 Dan Mecoli	K-6		35 20	937/277-8966 Fax 937/835-6065
Miami Valley Sch 5151 Denise Dr, Dayton 45429 Jay Scheurle	PK-12		475 51	937/434-4444 Fax 937/434-1033
Montessori School-Centerville 5515 Brandt Pike, Huber Heights 45424 Mary Van Loveren	PK-6		25 1	937/435-4572
Salem Christian Academy 6500 Southway Rd Unit 1, Clayton 45315 Karen Tanto	K-6		225 15	937/836-9910 Fax 937/836-7630
South Community Yph 3155 Alby Rd, Dayton 45439 Melissa Buck	Adult		35 5	937/252-0100 Fax 937/258-4261
Spring Valley Academy 1461 E Spring Valley Pike, Centerville 45458 Darren Wilkins	PK-12	V	330 25	937/433-0790 Fax 937/433-0914
Temple Christian Sch 1617 Ohmer Ave, Dayton 45410 Ken Fultz	PK-12		115 13	937/253-5288 Fax 937/256-7911

MONTGOMERY REGIONAL CENTERS

- **Meta Solutions Branch** PID: 04499532   937/223-1112
  225 Linwood St, Dayton 45405

Dean Reineke 1   Jimmy Battrell 16,73,76

MORGAN COUNTY

MORGAN PUBLIC SCHOOLS

- **Morgan Local School Dist** PID: 00826012   740/962-2377
  65 W Union Ave, McConnelsvle 43756   Fax 740/962-4931

Schools: 5 \ *Teachers:* 128 \ *Students:* 1,763 \ *Special Ed Students:* 304 \ *LEP Students:* 3 \ *College-Bound:* 45% \ *Ethnic:* African American 4%, Caucasian 95% \ *Exp:* $320 (High) \ *Poverty:* 24% \ *Title I:* $824,684 \ *Special Education:* $400,000 \ *Open-Close:* 08/21 - 05/27 \ *DTBP:* $174 (High)

Lori Snyder-Lowe 1   Dean Wright 2,3,15
Susan Gable 2   Phil Moore 4
Greg Moore 5   Adam Copeland 6*
Thomas Musgraves 8,12,16,69,275,288,294,296 .... Amanda Pierce 11,298
Beverly Steinbrecher 13,57,58,83,88   Anita Eldridge 31*
Dawn Nesselroad .... 38*   Rick Rose 67
Dr Jim Johnson 73

1	Superintendent	8	Curric/Instruct K-12	19	Chief Financial Officer	29	Family/Consumer Science	39	Social Studies K-12	49	English/Lang Arts Elem	59	Special Education Elem	69	Academic Assessment
2	Bus/Finance/Purchasing	9	Curric/Instruct Elem	20	Art K-12	30	Adult Education	40	Social Studies Elem	50	English/Lang Arts Sec	60	Special Education Sec	70	Research/Development
3	Buildings And Grounds	10	Curric/Instruct Sec	21	Art Elem	31	Career/Sch-to-Work K-12	41	Social Studies Sec	51	Reading K-12	61	Foreign/World Lang K-12	71	Public Information
4	Food Service	11	Federal Program	22	Art Sec	32	Career/Sch-to-Work Elem	42	Science K-12	52	Reading Elem	62	Foreign/World Lang Elem	72	Summer School
5	Transportation	12	Title I	23	Music K-12	33	Career/Sch-to-Work Sec	43	Science Elem	53	Reading Sec	63	Foreign/World Lang Sec	73	Instructional Tech
6	Athletic	13	Title V	24	Music Elem	34	Early Childhood Ed	44	Science Sec	54	Remedial Reading K-12	64	Religious Education K-12	74	Inservice Training
7	Health Services	15	Asst Superintendent	25	Music Sec	35	Health/Phys Education	45	Math K-12	55	Remedial Reading Elem	65	Religious Education Elem	75	Marketing/Distributive
		16	Instructional Media Svcs	26	Business Education	36	Guidance Services K-12	46	Math Elem	56	Remedial Reading Sec	66	Religious Education Sec	76	Info Systems
		17	Chief Operations Officer	27	Career & Tech Ed	37	Guidance Services Elem	47	Math Sec	57	Bilingual/ELL	67	School Board President	77	Psychological Assess
		18	Chief Academic Officer	28	Technology Education	38	Guidance Services Sec	48	English/Lang Arts K-12	58	Special Education K-12	68	Teacher Personnel	78	Affirmative Action

Ohio School Directory

Morrow County

Public Schs..Principal	Grd	Prgm	Enr/#Cls	SN	
Morgan East Elem Sch 4265 N State Route 376 NW, McConnelsvle 43756 Lynn Copeland	PK-6	T	355 21	57%	740/962-3361 Fax 740/962-6804
Morgan High Sch 800 Raider Dr, McConnelsvle 43756 Anita Eldridge	9-12	T	541 50	50%	740/962-2944 Fax 740/962-6005
Morgan Junior High Sch 820 Junior Raider Dr, McConnelsvle 43756 Jeff Bragg	7-8	T	272 21	57%	740/962-2833 Fax 740/962-3389
Morgan South Elem Sch 3555 State Route 792, Stockport 43787 Joel Fox	PK-6	T	292 20	60%	740/559-2377 Fax 740/559-2864
Morgan West Elem Sch 9675 State Route 37, Malta 43758 Greg Gifford	PK-6	T	303 16	56%	740/342-4873 Fax 740/342-7326

MORROW COUNTY

MORROW COUNTY SCHOOLS

County Schs..Principal	Grd	Prgm	Enr/#Cls	SN	
Whetstone Sch 406 Bank St, Mount Gilead 43338 Julie Borchers	Spec		132 5		419/947-7045 Fax 419/947-1187

MORROW PUBLIC SCHOOLS

• **Cardington-Lincoln Local SD** PID: 00826103 419/864-3691
121 Nichols St, Cardington 43315 Fax 419/864-0946

Schools: 4 \ **Teachers:** 62 \ **Students:** 1,200 \ **Special Ed Students:** 184 \ **College-Bound:** 47% \ **Ethnic:** Hispanic 1%, Caucasian 98% \ **Exp:** $141 (Low) \ **Poverty:** 14% \ **Title I:** $243,937 \ **Special Education:** $186,000 \ **Open-Close:** 08/20 - 06/04 \ **DTBP:** $178 (High)

Brian Petrie 1,11,73
John Nippert 3
Jennifer Zierden 9*
Kathleen Porteus 16,82*
Jon Mason 2
Tom Hack 6*
Joe Mills 10
Troy Ruehrmund 67

Public Schs..Principal	Grd	Prgm	Enr/#Cls	SN	
Cardington Interm Sch 349 Chesterville Ave, Cardington 43315 Jennifer Zierden	5-8	T	178		419/864-3152 Fax 419/864-3168
Cardington-Lincoln Elem Sch 121 Nichols St, Cardington 43315 Scott Hardwick	PK-4	T	444 17	46%	419/864-6692 Fax 419/864-8701
Cardington-Lincoln High Sch 349 Chesterville Ave, Cardington 43315 Joseph Mills	9-12	V	274 24	82%	419/864-2691 Fax 419/864-9515
Cardington-Lincoln Middle Sch 349 Chesterville Ave, Cardington 43315 Joseph Mills	7-8	T	171 22		419/864-0609 Fax 419/864-3168

• **Highland Local School Dist** PID: 00826141 419/768-2206
6506 State Route 229, Marengo 43334 Fax 419/768-3115

Schools: 3 \ **Teachers:** 107 \ **Students:** 1,850 \ **Special Ed Students:** 198 \ **LEP Students:** 3 \ **College-Bound:** 52% \ **Ethnic:** African American 1%, Hispanic 2%, Caucasian 97% \ **Exp:** $104 (Low) \ **Poverty:** 13% \ **Title I:** $339,331 \ **Special Education:** $275,000 \ **Open-Close:** 09/03 - 06/03 \ **DTBP:** $174 (High)

Daniel Freund 1
Tood Belcher 3
Vicky Nelson 5
Amber Clay-Mowry 8,69*
Wayne Hinkle 67
Jessie Clark 76
Jon Mason 2,11
Deborah Hart 4
Mike DeLaney 6*
Amy Randolph 58*
Dana Lehman 73*

Public Schs..Principal	Grd	Prgm	Enr/#Cls	SN	
Highland Elem Sch 1250 Township Road 16, Marengo 43334 Shawn Winkelfoos	PK-5	T	821 20	40%	419/768-3040 Fax 419/768-2127
Highland High Sch 1300 State Route 314, Marengo 43334 Chad Carpenter	9-12	V	550 30	28%	419/768-3101 Fax 419/768-3560
Highland Middle Sch 6506 State Route 229, Marengo 43334 Matthew Bradley	6-8		430 24	35%	419/768-2781 Fax 419/768-2742

• **Mt Gilead Exempted Village SD** PID: 00826191 419/946-1646
145 N Cherry St, Mount Gilead 43338 Fax 419/946-3651

Schools: 3 \ **Teachers:** 72 \ **Students:** 1,200 \ **Special Ed Students:** 214 \ **LEP Students:** 8 \ **College-Bound:** 49% \ **Ethnic:** Hispanic 3%, Caucasian 96% \ **Exp:** $234 (Med) \ **Poverty:** 15% \ **Title I:** $271,425 \ **Special Education:** $141,000 \ **Open-Close:** 09/04 - 06/05 \ **DTBP:** $255 (High)

Jeffrey Thompson 1
Ryan Newman 3
Lorena Bowler 5
Brant Hosack 38,83,88*
Jennifer Mills 76
Tonya Boyd 2,13
Mindy Delp 4
Matt Gomps 27
Brian Barnett 67

Public Schs..Principal	Grd	Prgm	Enr/#Cls	SN	
Mt Gilead High Sch 338 W Park Ave, Mount Gilead 43338 Debra Clauss	9-12	ATV	319 40	40%	419/947-6065 Fax 419/946-3263
Mt Gilead Middle Sch 324 W Park Ave, Mount Gilead 43338 Jon Grega	6-8	T	273 13	54%	419/947-9517 Fax 419/947-9518
Park Avenue Elem Sch 335 W Park Ave, Mount Gilead 43338 Chris Kamenski	PK-5	T	553 12	54%	419/946-5736 Fax 419/946-2336

• **Northmor Local School Dist** PID: 00826256 419/946-8861
5247 County Road 29, Galion 44833 Fax 419/947-6255

Schools: 1 \ **Teachers:** 60 \ **Students:** 1,042 \ **Special Ed Students:** 122 \ **College-Bound:** 46% \ **Ethnic:** African American 1%, Hispanic 3%, Caucasian 95% \ **Exp:** $129 (Low) \ **Poverty:** 18% \ **Title I:** $374,639 \ **Special Education:** $196,000 \ **Open-Close:** 09/04 - 05/29 \ **DTBP:** $162 (High) \

Chad Redmon 1
Haven Shenefield 3*
Anne Pfister 8,69,273,288,298*
Eve Miller 16,27,73*
Tammi Cowell 2,11,19,296
Justin Hershberger 6*
Amanda Albert 11*
Nicole Miller 31*

---

79 Student Personnel	91 Safety/Security	275 Response To Intervention	298 Grant Writer/Ptnrships	**School Programs**	**Social Media**	
30 Driver Ed/Safety	92 Magnet School	277 Remedial Math K-12	750 Chief Innovation Officer	A = Alternative Program		
31 Gifted/Talented	93 Parental Involvement	280 Literacy Coach	751 Chief of Staff	G = Adult Classes	= Facebook	
32 Video Services	95 Tech Prep Program	285 STEM	752 Social Emotional Learning	M = Magnet Program		
33 Substance Abuse Prev	97 Chief Infomation Officer	286 Digital Learning		T = Title I Schoolwide	= Twitter	
34 Erate	98 Chief Technology Officer	288 Common Core Standards	**Other School Types**	V = Career & Tech Ed Programs		
35 AIDS Education	270 Character Education	294 Accountability	Ⓐ = Alternative School			
38 Alternative/At Risk	271 Migrant Education	295 Network System	Ⓒ = Charter School	New Schools are shaded		
39 Multi-Cultural Curriculum	273 Teacher Mentor	296 Title II Programs	Ⓜ = Magnet School	New Superintendents and Principals are bold		
90 Social Work	274 Before/After Sch	297 Webmaster	Ⓨ = Year-Round School	Personnel with email addresses are underscored		

Muskingum County

Sara Skelton 58*
Peggy Webb 81*
David Morgan 85*
Jeff Whisler 67
Hilary Ward 83,88*

Public Schs..Principal	Grd	Prgm	Enr/#Cls	SN	
Northmor Sch 7819 State Route 19, Galion 44833 **Brendan Gwirtz** \ Amanda Albert	K-12		1,042 15	36%	419/946-3946 Fax 419/946-2397

MORROW PRIVATE SCHOOLS

Private Schs..Principal	Grd	Prgm	Enr/#Cls	SN	
Gilead Christian School-North 220 S Main St, Mount Gilead 43338 Bryan Potteiger	K-6		69 7		419/947-5739 Fax 419/947-5010
Gilead Christian School-South 4863 US Highway 42, Mount Gilead 43338 Bryan Potteiger	7-12		100		419/946-5900 Fax 419/946-1103 ⓕ

MUSKINGUM COUNTY

MUSKINGUM COUNTY SCHOOLS

● **Muskingum Valley ESC** PID: 02094708 740/452-4518
205 N 7th St, Zanesville 43701 Fax 740/455-6702

David Branch 1
Cathy Morgan 8,69
Larry Good 67
Mike Fain 77
Mike Fuller 295
Nan Nolder 2
Caren Maniaci 58,79
Tim Deetz 73
Susan Larson 81

County Schs..Principal	Grd	Prgm	Enr/#Cls	SN	
Starlight Sch 1330 Newark Rd, Zanesville 43701 Mary Ann Cluse	Spec	G	125 10		740/455-4176 Fax 740/450-9225

MUSKINGUM PUBLIC SCHOOLS

● **East Muskingum Local Sch Dist** PID: 00826309 740/826-7655
13505 John Glenn School Rd, New Concord 43762 Fax 740/826-7194

Schools: 6 \ *Teachers:* 116 \ *Students:* 2,200 \ *Special Ed Students:* 267 \ *LEP Students:* 3 \ *College-Bound:* 62% \ *Ethnic:* Asian 1%, African American 1%, Hispanic 1%, Caucasian 97% \ *Exp:* $102 (Low) \ *Poverty:* 13% \ *Title I:* $378,074 \ *Special Education:* $331,000 \ *Open-Close:* 08/21 - 05/21 \ *DTBP:* $176 (High)

Dave Adams 1
Linda Jones 4
Michael Dunlap 6*
Chad Orecchio 37*
Ken Blood 67
Randy McFerren 76
Lottie Fisher 2
Bob Baier 5
Anne Troendly 8,11*
Mike House 58*
Kimberly Van Wey 73,76*

Public Schs..Principal	Grd	Prgm	Enr/#Cls	SN	
East Muskingum Middle Sch 13120 John Glenn School Rd, New Concord 43762 Trent Cubbison	6-8		534 38	32%	740/826-7631 Fax 740/826-4392
John Glenn High Sch 13115 John Glenn School Rd, New Concord 43762 Steve Brooks	9-12	V	587 40	32%	740/826-7641 Fax 740/826-3039
Larry Miller Intermediate Sch 13125 John Glenn School Rd, New Concord 43762 Eric Harshbarger	3-5		511 25	35%	740/826-2271 Fax 740/826-7443
New Concord Elem Sch 4 Stormont St, New Concord 43762 Chad Briggs	K-2	T	265 12	47%	740/826-4453 Fax 740/826-1332
Perry Elem Sch 6975 East Pike, Zanesville 43701 Leigh Ann Atkins	K-2		119 9	37%	740/872-3436 Fax 740/872-3372
Pike Elem Sch 4533 Peters Creek Rd, Cambridge 43725 Leigh Atkins	K-2		118 7	47%	740/439-1645 Fax 740/432-3201

● **Franklin Local School Dist** PID: 00826505 740/674-5203
360 Cedar St, Duncan Falls 43734 Fax 740/674-5214

Schools: 5 \ *Teachers:* 127 \ *Students:* 2,000 \ *Special Ed Students:* 274 \ *College-Bound:* 50% \ *Ethnic:* African American 1%, Caucasian 98% \ *Exp:* $96 (Low) \ *Poverty:* 20% \ *Title I:* $685,145 \ *Special Education:* $412,000 \ *Open-Close:* 08/20 - 05/27 \ *DTBP:* $184 (High) \ ⓣ

Sharon McDermott 1,83
Rob Preston 3,15,78,95
Don Beardsley 5
Alissa Daley 7
Cassie McLendon ... 11,57,286,288,298
Michelle Moyer 38
Mark Carpenter 67
Thelma Leese-Graham 285*
Scott Paul 2
Phillip Moore 4
Kara Harris 6,88
Dustan Henderson 8*
Leslie Smith 31,36*
Steven Rice 58
Nicholas Hansel 73,76,84,295

Public Schs..Principal	Grd	Prgm	Enr/#Cls	SN	
Duncan Falls Elem Sch 397 Oak St, Duncan Falls 43734 Pam Hartman	PK-5	T	732 33	52%	740/674-5211 Fax 740/674-4117
⊙ Franklin Local Cmty Sch 76 W Athens Rd, Roseville 43777 Jennifer Woodard	7-12	T	30 6		740/697-7317 Fax 740/697-0793
Philo High Sch 4000 Millers Ln, Duncan Falls 43734 Troy Dawson	9-12	ATV	459 30	41%	740/674-4355 Fax 740/674-5202
Philo Junior High Sch 225 Market Street, Philo 43771 David Harper	6-8	T	453 25	48%	740/674-5210 Fax 740/674-5217 ⓕⓣ
Roseville Elem Sch 35 Elm St, Roseville 43777 Frank Van Kirk	PK-6	T	250 14	38%	740/697-7216 Fax 740/697-7143 ⓕⓣ

● **Maysville Local School Dist** PID: 00826373 740/453-0754
3715 Panther Dr, Zanesville 43701 Fax 740/455-4081

Schools: 3 \ *Teachers:* 120 \ *Students:* 2,200 \ *Special Ed Students:* 356 \ *College-Bound:* 49% \ *Ethnic:* African American 1%, Hispanic 1%, Caucasian 98% \ *Exp:* $151 (Low) \ *Poverty:* 16% \ *Title I:* $522,890 \ *Special Education:* $446,000 \ *Open-Close:* 08/20 - 05/21 \ *DTBP:* $177 (High) \ ⓕ

Ruth Zitnik 1
Greg Gibson 5
Lou Sidwell 2
Mark Rider 6

---

1 Superintendent	8 Curric/Instruct K-12	19 Chief Financial Officer	29 Family/Consumer Science	39 Social Studies K-12	49 English/Lang Arts Elem	59 Special Education Elem	69 Academic Assessment
2 Bus/Finance/Purchasing	9 Curric/Instruct Elem	20 Art K-12	30 Adult Education	40 Social Studies Elem	50 English/Lang Arts Sec	60 Special Education Sec	70 Research/Development
3 Buildings And Grounds	10 Curric/Instruct Sec	21 Art Elem	31 Career/Sch-to-Work K-12	41 Social Studies Sec	51 Reading K-12	61 Foreign/World Lang K-12	71 Public Information
4 Food Service	11 Federal Program	22 Art Sec	32 Career/Sch-to-Work Elem	42 Science K-12	52 Reading Elem	62 Foreign/World Lang Elem	72 Summer School
5 Transportation	12 Title I	23 Music K-12	33 Career/Sch-to-Work Sec	43 Science Elem	53 Reading Sec	63 Foreign/World Lang Sec	73 Instructional Tech
6 Athletic	13 Title V	24 Music Elem	34 Early Childhood Ed	44 Science Sec	54 Remedial Reading K-12	64 Religious Education K-12	74 Inservice Training
7 Health Services	14 Asst Superintendent	25 Music Sec	35 Health/Phys Education	45 Math K-12	55 Remedial Reading Elem	65 Religious Education Elem	75 Marketing/Distributive
	15 Instructional Media Svcs	26 Business Education	36 Guidance Services K-12	46 Math Elem	56 Remedial Reading Sec	66 Religious Education Sec	76 Info Systems
	17 Chief Operations Officer	27 Career & Tech Ed	37 Guidance Services Elem	47 Math Sec	57 Bilingual/ELL	67 School Board President	77 Psychological Assess
	18 Chief Academic Officer	28 Technology Education	38 Guidance Services Sec	48 English/Lang Arts K-12	58 Special Education K-12	68 Teacher Personnel	78 Affirmative Action

Ohio School Directory   Muskingum County

Joe Daniels .... 8,11,15 Cindy Miller 34,288*
Jamie Sines 58   Kerry Hartman 67
Eric Smith .... 73*   Sue Stall 274

Public Schs..Principal	Grd	Prgm	Enr/#Cls SN	
Maysville Elem Sch 3850 Panther Dr, Zanesville 43701 Erik Winland	PK-5	T	1,090	740/454-4490 Fax 740/454-2109
Maysville High Sch 3725 Panther Dr, Zanesville 43701 Jason Bunting	9-12	T	474 50	740/454-7999 Fax 740/452-9921
Maysville Middle Sch 3725 Panther Dr, Zanesville 43701 Jackie Farnsworth	6-8	T	481	740/454-7982 Fax 740/454-9921

● **Mideast Career & Tech Ctrs** PID: 00826842   740/454-0105
  400 Richards Rd, Zanesville 43701   Fax 740/454-0731

Schools: 3 \ *Teachers:* 66 \ *Students:* 1,100 \ *College-Bound:* 49% \
Exp: $375 (High) \ *Open-Close:* 08/22 - 05/25 \ *DTBP:* $198 (High) \ [f]

Dr Richard Hall 1   Jeff Jones 2,91
Pamela Lyons .... 4*   Jeremy Beardmore 10,15,79,83,270
Michael Hawley .... 30*   Shannon Kenily 33,71
Debbie Manning .... 60*   Doug Bruner 60*
Dennis Doutt 67   Stacey Snider 71
Penny Fletcher 76   Vickie Stamm 91*
Richard White 298

Public Schs..Principal	Grd	Prgm	Enr/#Cls SN	
Adult Center for Education 920 Moxahala Ave, Zanesville 43701 Michael Hawley	Adult	V	100 12	740/455-3111 Fax 740/455-2043
Mideast CTC Buffalo Campus 57090 Vocational Rd, Senecaville 43780 Keith Arnold	Voc	AG	255 15	740/685-2516 Fax 740/685-2518
Mideast CTC Zanesville Campus 400 Richards Rd, Zanesville 43701 Scott Sabino	Voc	AG	795 40	740/454-0101 Fax 740/454-0723

● **Tri-Valley Local School Dist** PID: 00826440   740/754-1442
  36 E Muskingum Ave, Dresden 43821   Fax 740/754-6400

Schools: 6 \ *Teachers:* 147 \ *Students:* 3,100 \ *Special Ed Students:* 451
\ *LEP Students:* 6 \ *College-Bound:* 58% \ *Ethnic:* Asian 1%, African American 1%, Hispanic 1%, Caucasian 97% \ *Exp:* $166 (Low) \ *Poverty:* 16%
\ *Title I:* $719,911 \ *Special Education:* $255,000 \ *Open-Close:* 08/21 - 05/22 \ *DTBP:* $195 (High)

Mark Neal 1   Ryan Smith 2
Craig Strohacker .... 3,4,5,91 Rodney Ashcraft 5
Erin Nezbeth .... 6*   Jamie Campbell 11*
Helen O'Flaherty .... 16*   Todd Woodard 58
Jenny Cox 67   Christopher Irvin 73*

Public Schs..Principal	Grd	Prgm	Enr/#Cls SN	
Adamsville Elem Sch 7950 East St, Adamsville 43802 Doug Smith	K-6	T	258 25	67% 740/796-2153 Fax 740/796-4781
Dresden Elem Sch 1318 Main St, Dresden 43821 Heather Campbell	K-6	T	509 24	50% 740/754-4001 Fax 740/754-6405
Frazeysburg Elem Sch 120 E 3rd St, Frazeysburg 43822 Rebecca Norris	K-6	T	307 14	53% 740/828-2781 Fax 740/828-3666
Nashport Elem Sch 3775 Creamery Rd, Nashport 43830 Larry Bevard	K-6		598 22	33% 740/452-3977 Fax 740/452-7101
Tri-Valley High Sch 46 E Muskingum Ave, Dresden 43821 John Harris	9-12		825 45	38% 740/754-2921 Fax 740/754-6415
Tri-Valley Middle Sch 1360 Main St, Dresden 43821 Patrick Hopkins	7-8	T	471 30	43% 740/754-3531 Fax 740/754-1879

● **West Muskingum Local Sch Dist** PID: 00826581   740/455-4052
  4880 West Pike, Zanesville 43701   Fax 740/455-4063

Schools: 3 \ *Teachers:* 92 \ *Students:* 1,400 \ *Special Ed Students:* 218
\ *LEP Students:* 9 \ *College-Bound:* 58% \ *Ethnic:* Asian 2%, African American 4%, Hispanic 1%, Caucasian 93% \ *Exp:* $99 (Low) \ *Poverty:* 15%
\ *Title I:* $380,694 \ *Special Education:* $307,000 \ *Open-Close:* 08/21 - 05/21 \ *DTBP:* $224 (High) \ [f] [t]

Chad Shawger 1   Kimberly Moyer-Downs 2
Bryan Karling 3,4,5,83,85   Pete Woods 6
Kelli Wohlgamuth .... 8,12,288,296* Meredith McDonell 38
Ryan McLane 58   Ab Vousden 67
Ted Harrison 73,295*

Public Schs..Principal	Grd	Prgm	Enr/#Cls SN	
West Muskingum Elem Sch 200 Kimes Rd, Zanesville 43701 Ryan McLane	PK-4	T	571 12	49% 740/455-4058 Fax 740/455-2592
West Muskingum High Sch 150 Kimes Rd, Zanesville 43701 Kevin Smith	9-12	V	385 38	34% 740/452-6312 Fax 740/452-7648
West Muskingum Middle Sch 100 Kimes Rd, Zanesville 43701 Lindsay Rayner	5-8	TV	430 29	42% 740/455-4055 Fax 740/455-9717 [f]

● **Zanesville City School Dist** PID: 00826658   740/454-9751
  956 Moxahala Ave, Zanesville 43701   Fax 740/455-4325

Schools: 6 \ *Teachers:* 190 \ *Students:* 3,307 \ *Special Ed Students:* 949
\ *LEP Students:* 3 \ *College-Bound:* 45% \ *Ethnic:* African American 13%, Hispanic 2%, Caucasian 84% \ *Exp:* $191 (Low) \ *Poverty:* 29% \
Title I: $2,210,167 \ *Special Education:* $1,110,000 \ *Open-Close:* 08/19 - 05/21 \ *DTBP:* $195 (High) \ [f]

Dr Douglas Baker 1   Michael Young 2
Kevin Appleman .... 3,17,76,79,91 Matt Hittle 3
Vicki Wheeler 4   Jane Ford 5
Scott Aronhalt .... 6,35,80,83,85* Michelle Jordan 7,58,79,88
Laura Tompkins .... 8*   Mark Stallard 8
Dr Robert Dalton .... 8*   Steven Foreman 11,15,51,54,288,296,298
Jacob Fisher .... 28,295*   Jacob Fisher 28,295
Colby Schmitt .... 36*   Colby Schmitt 36
Brian Swope 67   Debbie Grubb 274*
Jim Rudloff 297   Jim Rudloff 297*

Public Schs..Principal	Grd	Prgm	Enr/#Cls SN	
John McIntire Elem Sch 1275 Roosevelt Ave, Zanesville 43701 Michael Emmert	PK-6	T	757 19	740/453-2851 Fax 740/588-0714
National Road Elem Sch 3505 East Pike, Zanesville 43701 Libby Hitchens	PK-6	T	364 25	740/450-1538 Fax 740/450-1544 [f]
Zane Grey Elem Sch 711 Fess St, Zanesville 43701 Mark Stallard	PK-6	T	820 27	740/453-0576 Fax 740/453-3540 [f]

79 Student Personnel	91 Safety/Security	275 Response To Intervention	298 Grant Writer/Ptnrships	**School Programs**	**Social Media**		
60 Driver Ed/Safety	92 Magnet School	277 Remedial Math K-12	750 Chief Innovation Officer	A = Alternative Program			
81 Gifted/Talented	93 Parental Involvement	280 Literacy Coach	751 Chief of Staff	G = Adult Classes	[f] = Facebook		
82 Video Services	95 Tech Prep Program	285 STEM	752 Social Emotional Learning	M = Magnet Program			
83 Substance Abuse Prev	97 Chief Infomation Officer	286 Digital Learning		T = Title I Schoolwide	[t] = Twitter		
84 Erate	98 Chief Technology Officer	288 Common Core Standards	**Other School Types**	V = Career & Tech Ed Programs			
85 AIDS Education	270 Character Education	294 Accountability	Ⓐ = Alternative School				
88 Alternative/At Risk	271 Migrant Education	295 Network System	Ⓒ = Charter School	New Schools are shaded			
89 Multi-Cultural Curriculum	273 Teacher Mentor	296 Title II Programs	Ⓜ = Magnet School	New Superintendents and Principals are bold			
90 Social Work	274 Before/After Sch	297 Webmaster	Ⓨ = Year-Round School	Personnel with email addresses are underscored			

OH–157

Noble County

	Grd	Prgm	Enr/#Cls	SN	
© Zanesville Community High Sch	9-12	AGT	88		740/588-5685
920 Moxahala Ave, Zanesville 43701			6		Fax 740/588-0732
Jeff Moore					
Zanesville High Sch	9-12	TV	747		740/453-0335
1701 Blue Ave, Zanesville 43701					Fax 740/455-4329
Laura Tompkins					
Zanesville Middle Sch	7-8	T	482		740/453-0711
1429 Blue Ave, Zanesville 43701			30		Fax 740/454-7005
Dr Robert Dalton					[f]

MUSKINGUM CATHOLIC SCHOOLS

• **Diocese of Columbus Ed Office** PID: 00802717
Listing includes only schools located in this county. See District Index for location of Diocesan Offices.

Catholic Schs..Principal	Grd	Prgm	Enr/#Cls	SN	
Bishop Fenwick Elem Sch	PK-8		260		740/454-9731
1030 E Main St, Zanesville 43701			9		Fax 740/454-0653
Kelly Sagan					
Bishop Fenwick Middle Sch	K-8		240		740/453-2637
1030 E Main St, Zanesville 43701			6		Fax 740/454-0653
Kelly Sagan					
Bishop Rosecrans High Sch	9-12		126		740/452-7504
1040 E Main St, Zanesville 43701			18		Fax 740/455-5080

MUSKINGUM PRIVATE SCHOOLS

Private Schs..Principal	Grd	Prgm	Enr/#Cls	SN	
Zanesville Christian Sch	K-12	V	7		740/454-2509
2400 Chandlersville Rd, Zanesville 43701			10		Fax 740/454-2989
Paul Shaver					
Zanesville SDA Sch	K-8		16		740/453-6050
824 Taylor St, Zanesville 43701			3		
Clare Hoover					[f][t]

NOBLE COUNTY

NOBLE PUBLIC SCHOOLS

• **Caldwell Exempted Village SD** PID: 00826878   740/732-5637
516 Fairground St, Caldwell 43724   Fax 740/732-7303

Schools: 2 \ *Teachers:* 54 \ *Students:* 800 \ *Special Ed Students:* 139 \ *College-Bound:* 46% \ *Ethnic:* Asian 1%, Hispanic 1%, Caucasian 99% \ *Exp:* $222 (Med) \ *Poverty:* 22% \ *Title I:* $303,933 \ *Special Education:* $214,000 \ *Open-Close:* 08/19 - 05/22 \ *DTBP:* $204 (High)

Kacey Cottrill 1	J Croucher 2,19*		
Rich Trisler 3	Elaine Hummerich 5		
Carey Block 8,11,58,296	Terry Rataiczak 67		
Troy Abramt 73,84,98			

Public Schs..Principal	Grd	Prgm	Enr/#Cls	SN	
Caldwell Elem Sch	K-8	T	638	50%	740/732-4614
44350 Fairground Rd, Caldwell 43724			30		Fax 740/732-2799
Tiffany Speck \ Halle Randles					
Caldwell High Sch	9-12	TV	191	48%	740/732-5634
516 Fairground St, Caldwell 43724			20		Fax 740/732-2532
Ben Rutherford					

• **Noble Local School Dist** PID: 00826921   740/732-4120
20977 Zep Rd E, Sarahsville 43779   Fax 740/732-7669

Schools: 2 \ *Teachers:* 61 \ *Students:* 900 \ *Special Ed Students:* 118 \ *College-Bound:* 43% \ *Ethnic:* Hispanic 1%, Caucasian 99% \ *Exp:* $278 (Med) \ *Poverty:* 13% \ *Title I:* $196,163 \ *Special Education:* $182,000 \ *Open-Close:* 08/14 - 05/19 \ *DTBP:* $190 (High) \ [f][t]

Dan Leffingwell 1	Trenda Rice 2,84
Jim Rayner 3	Lauren Thompson 7*
Justin Denius 8*	Daniel Schwieterman 9,31,37,83,88*
Bonnie Slynn 22*	Cathy Williams 58
Ed McKee 67	Philip Theobald 73,295

Public Schs..Principal	Grd	Prgm	Enr/#Cls	SN	
Shenandoah Elem Sch	K-8	T	623	54%	740/732-5661
20977 Zep Rd E, Sarahsville 43779			52		Fax 740/732-4362
Cindy Vanscyoc \ Dan Wesson					
Shenandoah High Sch	9-12	TV	213	40%	740/732-2361
49346 Seneca Lake Rd, Sarahsville 43779			21		Fax 740/732-6479
Justin Denius					

OTTAWA COUNTY

OTTAWA PUBLIC SCHOOLS

• **Benton-Carroll-Salem Local SD** PID: 00826983   419/898-6210
11685 W State Route 163, Oak Harbor 43449   Fax 419/898-4303

Schools: 3 \ *Teachers:* 74 \ *Students:* 1,500 \ *Special Ed Students:* 224 \ *LEP Students:* 3 \ *College-Bound:* 54% \ *Ethnic:* Hispanic 4%, Caucasian 95% \ *Exp:* $117 (Low) \ *Poverty:* 10% \ *Title I:* $200,557 \ *Special Education:* $346,000 \ *Open-Close:* 08/21 - 05/29 \ *DTBP:* $251 (High)

Guy Parmigian 1	Cajon Keeton 2
Vicky Coffman 4*	Dan Hoover 6
Angie Lewis 16,82*	Jim Boss 58*
Kim Dusseau 67	Devin Seslar 73*
Liz Guerin 273	

Public Schs..Principal	Grd	Prgm	Enr/#Cls	SN	
Oak Harbor High Sch	8-12	GV	583	23%	419/898-6216
11661 W State Route 163, Oak Harbor 43449			47		Fax 419/898-0116
Cheryl Schell					
Oak Harbor Middle Sch	4-7	V	472	35%	419/898-6217
315 N Church St, Oak Harbor 43449			32		Fax 419/898-1613
Laramie Spurlock					
R C Waters Elem Sch	PK-3	T	424	35%	419/898-6219
220 E Ottawa St, Oak Harbor 43449			23		Fax 419/898-1412
Dawn Bryant					

Ohio School Directory
Ottawa County

● **Danbury Local School Dist** PID: 00827042 419/798-5185
9451 East Harbor Rd, Lksid Marblhd 43440 Fax 419/798-2260

Schools: 1 \ *Teachers:* 34 \ *Students:* 543 \ *Special Ed Students:* 78 \ *LEP Students:* 3 \ *College-Bound:* 62% \ *Ethnic:* Asian 3%, Hispanic 3%, Caucasian 94% \ *Exp:* $428 (High) \ *Poverty:* 14% \ *Title I:* $137,626 \ *Special Education:* $89,000 \ *Open-Close:* 09/03 - 05/21 \ *DTBP:* $186 (High)

Cari Buehler 1,11,288
Tim Sypherd 5
Heidi Oglesbee 12*
Victoria Ward 38,69*
Paul Sowers 67
Shane Baumgardner 2
Keith Mora 6
Rose Tibbels 37,69,83*
Mercedes Wise 58*
Daniel Nitecki 73,295*

Public Schs..Principal	Grd	Prgm	Enr/#Cls	SN	
Danbury Local Sch 9451 East Harbor Rd, Lksid Marblhd 43440 Dan Humphrey \ Joe Miller	K-12		543	98%	419/798-5185

● **Genoa Area Local School Dist** PID: 00827078 419/855-7741
2810 N Genoa Clay Center Rd, Genoa 43430 Fax 419/855-4030

Schools: 3 \ *Teachers:* 67 \ *Students:* 1,323 \ *Special Ed Students:* 144 \ *College-Bound:* 57% \ *Ethnic:* Hispanic 8%, Caucasian 91% \ *Exp:* $255 (Med) \ *Poverty:* 7% \ *Title I:* $120,334 \ *Special Education:* $333,000 \ *Open-Close:* 08/27 - 05/28 \ *DTBP:* $175 (High) \ 📘

Michael Ferguson 1
Daniel Kalisik 3
Daniel Harstel 6
Elizabeth Wilcox 16,82*
Christina Lewis 67
Bill Nye 2
Lisa Cruickshank 4
Karen Whitt 8,69*
Tom Baker 16,73,297*

Public Schs..Principal	Grd	Prgm	Enr/#Cls	SN	
Genoa Area High Sch 2980 N Genoa Clay Center Rd, Genoa 43430 Ben Ohlemacher	9-12	V	374 15	65%	419/855-7741 Fax 419/855-7739
Genoa Elem Sch 2820 N Genoa Clay Center Rd, Genoa 43430 Yolanda Carmony-Mies	PK-5		638 15	31%	419/855-7741 Fax 419/855-8194
Genoa Middle Sch 2950 N Genoa Clay Center Rd, Genoa 43430 Kevin Katafias	6-8		311 30		419/855-7741 Fax 419/855-7784

● **Port Clinton City School Dist** PID: 00827171 419/732-2103
811 Jefferson St, Port Clinton 43452 Fax 419/734-4527

Schools: 4 \ *Teachers:* 103 \ *Students:* 1,700 \ *Special Ed Students:* 364 \ *LEP Students:* 3 \ *College-Bound:* 47% \ *Ethnic:* African American 2%, Hispanic 12%, Caucasian 86% \ *Exp:* $199 (Low) \ *Poverty:* 16% \ *Title I:* $403,651 \ *Special Education:* $478,000 \ *Open-Close:* 08/26 - 06/03 \ *DTBP:* $236 (High)

Patrick Adkins 1
Aaron Dibucci 3
Bill Lowe 5,91
Jack Nitz 8,11,54,69,81,270,271*
Heidi Steyer 36*
Jan Gluth 70,76,79*
Susan Parker 83,85,88*
Jackie Warnike 274*
Jeff Dornbusch 2
Pam Bacon 4
Rick Dominick 6,36*
Mercedes Wise 34,58,77*
Beth Benko 67
Kevin Lutz 73*
Diane Rosiar 273*

Public Schs..Principal	Grd	Prgm	Enr/#Cls	SN	
Bataan Intermediate Sch 525 W 6th St, Port Clinton 43452 Geoff Halsey	3-5	T	335 16		419/734-3931 Fax 419/734-3705
Bataan Memorial Primary Sch 525 W 6th St, Port Clinton 43452 Kendra Van Doren	PK-2	T	378 19	94%	419/734-2815 Fax 419/960-7672
Port Clinton High Sch 821 Jefferson St, Port Clinton 43452 Gary Steyer	9-12	TV	564 54	42%	419/734-2147 Fax 419/734-4276
Port Clinton Middle Sch 807 Jefferson St, Port Clinton 43452 Carrie Sanchez	6-8	T	403 30	49%	419/734-4448 Fax 419/734-4440

● **Put-In-Bay Local School Dist** PID: 00827248 419/285-3614
548 Catawba Ave, Put In Bay 43456 Fax 419/285-2137

Schools: 1 \ *Teachers:* 17 \ *Students:* 72 \ *Special Ed Students:* 4 \ *College-Bound:* 90% \ *Ethnic:* Caucasian 100% \ *Exp:* $396 (High) \ *Poverty:* 4% \ *Open-Close:* 09/03 - 05/28 \ *DTBP:* $178 (High)

Steven Poe 1,11
Craig Schuffenesker 6*
Susan Harrington 35,85*
Carol Cerny 73,95*
Joy Cooper 2,71,97
Veronica Van Ness 8,288*
John Donger 67

Public Schs..Principal	Grd	Prgm	Enr/#Cls	SN	
Put-In-Bay Sch 548 Catawba Ave, Put In Bay 43456 Steven Poe	PK-12		72 18		419/285-3614

● **Woodmore Local School Dist** PID: 00830776 419/862-1060
349 Rice St, Elmore 43416 Fax 419/862-1951

Schools: 2 \ *Teachers:* 55 \ *Students:* 974 \ *Special Ed Students:* 116 \ *LEP Students:* 3 \ *College-Bound:* 64% \ *Ethnic:* Hispanic 12%, Caucasian 87% \ *Exp:* $211 (Med) \ *Poverty:* 7% \ *Title I:* $97,414 \ *Special Education:* $165,000 \ *Open-Close:* 08/27 - 06/04 \ *DTBP:* $188 (High)

Tim Rettig 1
Jeff Sandwisch 3,5*
Sonia Reyes 7,83,85
Kevin Ball 8,58*
Jean Schultz 16,82*
Aaron Miller 67
Amy Bittel 81*
Dan Rusfomanno 2
Steve Barr 6*
Cammy Kissell 8
Brandi Cunningham 12*
Andrew Hemminger 31,38,88*
Michael Byrd 73,295*

Public Schs..Principal	Grd	Prgm	Enr/#Cls	SN	
Woodmore Elementary/Middle Sch 800 W Main St, Woodville 43469 Gary Haas \ Kevin Ball	PK-8	A	686 50	43%	419/862-1070 Fax 419/849-2132
Woodmore High Sch 633 Fremont St, Elmore 43416 Nolan Wickard	9-12	A	288 40	23%	419/862-2721 Fax 419/862-3835

OTTAWA CATHOLIC SCHOOLS

● **Diocese of Toledo Ed Office** PID: 00818297
Listing includes only schools located in this county. See District Index for location of Diocesan Offices.

---

79 Student Personnel	91 Safety/Security	275 Response To Intervention	298 Grant Writer/Ptnrships	**School Programs**	**Social Media**		
80 Driver Ed/Safety	92 Magnet School	277 Remedial Math K-12	750 Chief Innovation Officer	A = Alternative Program			
81 Gifted/Talented	93 Parental Involvement	280 Literacy Coach	751 Chief of Staff	G = Adult Classes	📘 = Facebook		
82 Video Services	95 Tech Prep Program	285 STEM	752 Social Emotional Learning	M = Magnet Program			
83 Substance Abuse Prev	97 Chief Infomation Officer	286 Digital Learning		T = Title I Schoolwide	🅣 = Twitter		
84 Erate	98 Chief Technology Officer	288 Common Core Standards	**Other School Types**	V = Career & Tech Ed Programs			
85 AIDS Education	270 Character Education	294 Accountability	Ⓐ = Alternative School				
88 Alternative/At Risk	271 Migrant Education	295 Network System	Ⓒ = Charter School	New Schools are shaded			
89 Multi-Cultural Curriculum	273 Teacher Mentor	296 Title II Programs	Ⓜ = Magnet School	New Superintendents and Principals are bold			
90 Social Work	274 Before/After Sch	297 Webmaster	Ⓨ = Year-Round School	Personnel with email addresses are underscored			

Paulding County

Catholic Schs..Principal	Grd	Prgm	Enr/#Cls	SN	
Immaculate Conception Sch 109 W 4th St, Port Clinton 43452 Connie Snyder	PK-6		154 8		419/734-3315 Fax 419/734-6172
St Boniface Catholic Sch 215 W Oak St, Oak Harbor 43449 Millie Greggila	PK-8		50 5		419/898-1340

OTTAWA PRIVATE SCHOOLS

Private Schs..Principal	Grd	Prgm	Enr/#Cls	SN	
Ottawa Co Christian Academy 325 S Toussaint Portage Rd, Oak Harbor 43449 Jeremy Bickelhaupt	PK-10		401		419/898-3888

PAULDING COUNTY

PAULDING COUNTY SCHOOLS

- **Western Buckeye Ed Service Ctr** PID: 00829399 419/399-4711
  202 N Cherry St, Paulding 45879

David Bagley 1		Tricia Taylor 2	
Jill Welch 34		Laura DeLong 58	
Maria Clawson 58		Jerry Zielke 67	
Ashley Shepherd 81			

County Schs..Principal	Grd	Prgm	Enr/#Cls	SN	
Parc Lane Training Center 900 Fairground Dr, Paulding 45879 Deb Guilford	Spec	G	30 2		419/399-4800 Fax 419/399-4820

PAULDING PUBLIC SCHOOLS

- **Antwerp Local School Dist** PID: 00827286 419/258-5421
  303 S Harrmann Rd, Antwerp 45813 Fax 419/258-4041

Schools: 1 \ **Teachers:** 47 \ **Students:** 800 \ **Special Ed Students:** 115 \ **College-Bound:** 49% \ **Ethnic:** Hispanic 3%, Caucasian 97% \ **Exp:** $355 (High) \ **Poverty:** 11% \ **Title I:** $88,245 \ **Special Education:** $139,000 \ **Open-Close:** 08/21 - 05/20

Dr Martin Miller 1		Kristine Stuart 2	
Dan Wiedman 3*		Deb Altic 4*	
Chris Hounshell 5*		Drew Altimus 6*	
Elise Boyer 8,73*		Tracy Strokes 11,274*	
Josh Hoeppner 58		Sara Schuette 67	

Public Schs..Principal	Grd	Prgm	Enr/#Cls	SN	
Antwerp Local Sch 303 S Harrmann Rd, Antwerp 45813 Travis Lichty \ Tracey Stokes	PK-12		800 60	98%	419/258-5421

- **Paulding Exempted Village SD** PID: 00827315 419/399-4656
  405 N Water St, Paulding 45879 Fax 419/399-2404

Schools: 4 \ **Teachers:** 92 \ **Students:** 1,475 \ **Special Ed Students:** 316 \ **LEP Students:** 3 \ **College-Bound:** 53% \ **Ethnic:** Hispanic 6%, Caucasian 93% \ **Exp:** $340 (High) \ **Poverty:** 13% \ **Title I:** $311,445 \ **Special Education:** $333,000 \ **Open-Close:** 08/20 - 05/21 \ **DTBP:** $136 (High)

Ken Amstutz 1,11		Kimberly Jones 2	
Brock Bergman 6		Todd Harmon 8	
Loni Porinchok 11,34,58,69,88,91,275,286		Justin Yant 16,73,76,295	
Staci Miller 27		Brett Foster 31,36,51,69*	
Tony Schaffer 31,51,69		Carolyn Connelly 57*	
Mark Manz 67		David Lamb 77*	

Public Schs..Principal	Grd	Prgm	Enr/#Cls	SN	
Oakwood Elem Sch 309 N 1st St, Oakwood 45873 Jennifer Manz	PK-6	T	269 24	45%	419/594-3346 Fax 419/594-3929
Paulding Elem Sch 405 N Water St, Paulding 45879 Greg Puthoff	PK-5	T	495 35	43%	419/399-4656
Paulding High Sch 405 N Water St, Paulding 45879 Chris Etzler	9-12	T	356 31	77%	419/399-4656
Paulding Middle Sch 405 N Water St, Paulding 45879 Matthew Carr	6-8	T	295 28		419/399-4656

- **Wayne Trace Local School Dist** PID: 00827365 419/622-6300
  4915 US Route 127, Haviland 45851 Fax 419/263-2377

Schools: 3 \ **Teachers:** 64 \ **Students:** 1,000 \ **Special Ed Students:** 174 \ **LEP Students:** 3 \ **College-Bound:** 56% \ **Ethnic:** Hispanic 1%, Caucasian 99% \ **Exp:** $396 (High) \ **Poverty:** 14% \ **Title I:** $177,698 \ **Special Education:** $224,000 \ **Open-Close:** 08/21 - 05/27 \ **DTBP:** $174 (High)

Benjamin Winans 1		Lori Davis 2	
Karen Wagonrod 4*		Sean Pfeiffer 5	
Jim Linder 6		Tim Manz 8,11,69,286,288,296,298	
Paul Jones 12		Susan Johnson 16*	
Lori Heiby 27*		Sarah Franz 36*	
Laurie DeLong 58		Duane Sinn 67	
Ashton Duer 73*		Sabrina Roth 83,85*	

Public Schs..Principal	Grd	Prgm	Enr/#Cls	SN	
Payne Elem Sch 501 W Townline St, Payne 45880 Paul Jones	K-6	T	220 15	49%	419/263-2512 Fax 419/263-1313
Wayne Trace Groverhill ES 101 N Monroe St, Grover Hill 45849 Kevin Wilson	K-6	T	246 20	48%	419/587-3414 Fax 419/587-3415
Wayne Trace Jr Sr High Sch 4915 US Route 127, Haviland 45851 Mike Myers	7-12	T	426 40	31%	419/622-5171 Fax 419/622-3037

PAULDING CATHOLIC SCHOOLS

- **Diocese of Toledo Ed Office** PID: 00818297
  Listing includes only schools located in this county. See District Index for location of Diocesan Offices.

---

1 Superintendent	8 Curric/Instruct K-12	19 Chief Financial Officer	29 Family/Consumer Science	39 Social Studies K-12	49 English/Lang Arts Elem	59 Special Education Elem	69 Academic Assessment
2 Bus/Finance/Purchasing	9 Curric/Instruct Elem	20 Art K-12	30 Adult Education	40 Social Studies Elem	50 English/Lang Arts Sec	60 Special Education Sec	70 Research/Development
3 Buildings And Grounds	10 Curric/Instruct Sec	21 Art Elem	31 Career/Sch-to-Work K-12	41 Social Studies Sec	51 Reading K-12	61 Foreign/World Lang K-12	71 Public Information
4 Food Service	11 Federal Program	22 Art Sec	32 Career/Sch-to-Work Elem	42 Science K-12	52 Reading Elem	62 Foreign/World Lang Elem	72 Summer School
5 Transportation	12 Title I	23 Music K-12	33 Career/Sch-to-Work Sec	43 Science Elem	53 Reading Sec	63 Foreign/World Lang Sec	73 Instructional Tech
6 Athletic	13 Title V	24 Music Elem	34 Early Childhood Ed	44 Science Sec	54 Remedial Reading K-12	64 Religious Education K-12	74 Inservice Training
7 Health Services	14 Asst Superintendent	25 Music Sec	35 Health/Phys Education	45 Math K-12	55 Remedial Reading Elem	65 Religious Education Elem	75 Marketing/Distributive
	15 Instructional Media Svcs	26 Business Education	36 Guidance Services K-12	46 Math Elem	56 Remedial Reading Sec	66 Religious Education Sec	76 Info Systems
	16 Chief Operations Officer	27 Career & Tech Ed	37 Guidance Services Elem	47 Math Sec	57 Bilingual/ELL	67 School Board President	77 Psychological Assess
	18 Chief Academic Officer	28 Technology Education	38 Guidance Services Sec	48 English/Lang Arts K-12	58 Special Education K-12	68 Teacher Personnel	78 Affirmative Action

Ohio School Directory — Perry County

Catholic Schs..Principal	Grd	Prgm	Enr/#Cls SN	
Divine Mercy Elem Sch	PK-6		56	419/263-2114
120 Arturus St, Payne 45880			6	
Joe Linder				

PERRY COUNTY

PERRY PUBLIC SCHOOLS

● **Crooksville Exempted Vlg SD** PID: 00827418   740/982-7040
4065 Ceramic Way, Crooksville 43731   Fax 740/982-3551

Schools: 3 \ **Teachers:** 60 \ **Students:** 1,100 \ **Special Ed Students:** 155
\ **College-Bound:** 41% \ **Ethnic:** African American 1%, Caucasian 99% \ **Exp:** $563 (High) \ **Poverty:** 20% \ **Title I:** $319,161 \
Special Education: $212,000 \ **Open-Close:** 08/15 - 05/20 \ **DTBP:** $145 (High)

Matt Sheridan 1   Robert Ogg 2,11,19
Albert Reed 3   Debbie Reed 5
Greg Williams ....6*   Jody Paul 7,85
Alea Barker .... 8,11,296,298*   Joe Winninberg 16,73*
Lisa Baughman ....36*   Kim Hearing 58*
Rhonda Moyer 67   Kathy Lackney 76

Public Schs..Principal	Grd	Prgm	Enr/#Cls SN	
Crooksville Elem Sch	PK-4		464	740/982-7010
12400 Tunnel Hill Rd, Crooksville 43731			43	Fax 740/982-5087
John Toeller				
Crooksville High Sch	9-12	V	298	740/982-7015
4075 Ceramic Way, Crooksville 43731			30	Fax 740/982-3086
Kevin Smith				
Crooksville Middle Sch	5-8		322	740/982-7010
12400 Tunnel Hill Rd, Crooksville 43731				Fax 740/982-5087
John Toeller				

● **New Lexington School Dist** PID: 00827470   740/342-4133
2549 Panther Dr NE, New Lexington 43764   Fax 740/342-6051

Schools: 4 \ **Teachers:** 113 \ **Students:** 1,980 \ **Special Ed Students:** 272
\ **College-Bound:** 48% \ **Ethnic:** Hispanic 1%, Caucasian 98% \ **Exp:** $279 (Med) \ **Poverty:** 25% \ **Title I:** $784,885 \ **Special Education:** $446,000 \
Open-Close: 08/22 - 05/21 \ **DTBP:** $163 (High)

Casey Coffey 1,83   Christy Barnette 2
David Rupe 3,5,91   Anthony Stephens 6
Molly Dupler ....7*   Rich Warren 8,11,58,88,286,296,298*
Billy Hohe ....16*   Adam Fink 27*
Bev Watson 57   John McGaughey 67
Tim Householder 73,84,295   Michael Stilwell 76
Tracy Smith 77

Public Schs..Principal	Grd	Prgm	Enr/#Cls SN	
Junction City Elem Sch	PK-5	T	360	740/987-3751
307 W Poplar St, Junction City 43748			15	Fax 740/987-3752
Maggie Cannon				
New Lexington Elem Sch	K-5	T	391	740/342-2556
2550 Panther Dr NE, New Lexington 43764			22	Fax 740/342-6062
Gregory Grant				
New Lexington Middle Sch	6-8	TV	415	740/342-4128
2549 Panther Dr NE, New Lexington 43764			35	Fax 740/342-6071
James Watts				
New Lexington Senior High Sch	9-12	TV	497	740/342-3528
2547 Panther Dr NE, New Lexington 43764			40	Fax 740/342-4765
Tony Thorngate				

● **Northern Local School Dist** PID: 00827535   740/743-1303
8700 Sheridan Dr, Thornville 43076   Fax 740/743-3301

Schools: 5 \ **Teachers:** 135 \ **Students:** 2,251 \ **Special Ed Students:** 250
\ **College-Bound:** 52% \ **Ethnic:** Caucasian 99% \ **Exp:** $131 (Low)
\ **Poverty:** 12% \ **Title I:** $419,734 \ **Special Education:** $445,000 \
Open-Close: 08/19 - 05/21 \ **DTBP:** $153 (High)

Thomas Perkins 1   Elizabeth Clark 2,4
George Helser 3   Dale Factor 5
Lance Dupler ....6*   Angela Gussler 8,273,285,288
Lisa Marton 11,296,298   Diane Christensen 16,82*
Alicia Stockler ....27,31,38,69*   Mandy Fox 37*
Stephanie Winters ....38*   Kelly Wright 58,77
Dale Derolph 67   Phillip Jones 73,76,84,295
Susan Larson 81   Jill McGee 280
Matt Gutridge 286*

Public Schs..Principal	Grd	Prgm	Enr/#Cls SN	
Glenford Elem Sch	K-5	AT	357	50% 740/659-2209
128 E High St, Glenford 43739			18	Fax 740/659-2228
Lisa Householder				
Sheridan High Sch	9-12	AV	654	35% 740/743-1335
8725 Sheridan Dr, Thornville 43076			50	Fax 740/743-3311
Lisa Householder				
Sheridan Middle Sch	6-8	AT	509	44% 740/743-1315
8660 Sheridan Dr, Thornville 43076			40	Fax 740/743-3319
Kirk Washburn				
Somerset Elem Sch	K-5	AT	265	39% 740/743-1454
100 High St, Somerset 43783			18	Fax 740/743-3324
Ed Wolfel				
Thornville Elem Sch	PK-5	AT	404	34% 740/246-6636
70 E Columbus St, Thornville 43076			18	Fax 740/246-5399
Clint Rhodes				

● **Southern Local School Dist** PID: 00827597   740/394-2402
10397 State Route 155 SE, Corning 43730   Fax 740/394-2083

Schools: 2 \ **Teachers:** 43 \ **Students:** 664 \ **Special Ed Students:** 142
\ **College-Bound:** 54% \ **Ethnic:** Caucasian 100% \ **Exp:** $122 (Low) \
Poverty: 24% \ **Title I:** $373,671 \ **Special Education:** $195,000 \
Open-Close: 08/22 - 05/25 \ **DTBP:** $174 (High)

Scott Christman 1   Janet Arkley 2
Jeffrey Kaaz 2   John Arkley 3,73,295*
Steve Janiszewski 4   Charles Hopps 5
Marylou Wycinski ....9*   Jackie Casey 11*
John Phipps ....38*   Guy Williams 58
Wendy Aichele 67   Kathy Sampson 76
Suzanne Rauch-Wittman ....81*   Jesse Harvey 295

Public Schs..Principal	Grd	Prgm	Enr/#Cls SN	
Millcreek Elem Sch	PK-6	T	403	740/721-0522
10397 State Route 155 SE, Corning 43730			22	Fax 740/394-3003
Annette Losco				
Miller High Sch	7-12	TV	261	740/721-0521
10397 State Route 155 SE, Corning 43730			35	
Tony Losco				

---

79 Student Personnel   91 Safety/Security   275 Response To Intervention   298 Grant Writer/Ptnrships   **School Programs**   **Social Media**
80 Driver Ed/Safety   92 Magnet School   277 Remedial Math K-12   750 Chief Innovation Officer   A = Alternative Program
81 Gifted/Talented   93 Parental Involvement   280 Literacy Coach   751 Chief of Staff   G = Adult Classes   = Facebook
82 Video Services   95 Tech Prep Program   285 STEM   752 Social Emotional Learning   M = Magnet Program
83 Substance Abuse Prev   97 Chief Information Officer   286 Digital Learning   T = Title I Schoolwide   = Twitter
84 Erate   98 Chief Technology Officer   288 Common Core Standards   **Other School Types**   V = Career & Tech Ed Programs
85 AIDS Education   270 Character Education   294 Accountability   Ⓐ = Alternative School
88 Alternative/At Risk   271 Migrant Education   295 Network System   Ⓒ = Charter School   New Schools are shaded
89 Multi-Cultural Curriculum   273 Teacher Mentor   296 Title II Programs   Ⓜ = Magnet School   New Superintendents and Principals are bold
90 Social Work   274 Before/After Sch   297 Webmaster   Ⓨ = Year-Round School   Personnel with email addresses are underscored

OH–161

Pickaway County

PERRY CATHOLIC SCHOOLS

- **Diocese of Columbus Ed Office** PID: 00802717
  Listing includes only schools located in this county. See District Index for location of Diocesan Offices.

Catholic Schs..Principal	Grd	Prgm	Enr/#Cls	SN	
Holy Trinity Sch 225 S Columbus St, Somerset 43783 William Noll	PK-8		156 9		740/743-1324
St Rose of Lima Sch 119 W Water St, New Lexington 43764 Michael Lollo	K-8		105 9		740/342-3043 Fax 740/342-1082

PICKAWAY COUNTY

PICKAWAY COUNTY SCHOOLS

- **Pickaway Co Ed Service Center** PID: 00827949   740/474-7529
  2050 Stoneridge Dr, Circleville 43113   Fax 740/474-7251

Ty Ankrom 1,11   Kristin O'Dell 2
Michael Hoffner 5

County Schs..Principal	Grd	Prgm	Enr/#Cls	SN	
Brooks Yates Sch 200 E High St, Circleville 43113 Christine Croyle	Spec	GV	22 3		740/474-1124 Fax 740/420-6405

PICKAWAY PUBLIC SCHOOLS

- **Circleville City School Dist** PID: 00827664   740/474-4340
  388 Clark Dr, Circleville 43113   Fax 740/474-6600

Schools: 3 \ *Teachers:* 116 \ *Students:* 2,174 \ *Special Ed Students:* 335 \ *College-Bound:* 40% \ *Ethnic:* Asian 1%, African American 2%, Hispanic 2%, Caucasian 94% \ *Exp:* $152 (Low) \ *Poverty:* 23% \ *Title I:* $815,675 \ *Special Education:* $476,000 \ *Open-Close:* 08/14 - 05/21 \ *DTBP:* $235 (High)

Jonathan Davis 1   Kristen Rhoads 2
Jerry Mogan 3,5,274   Suzie Gerhardt 4*
Chad Spradlin 6   Jaime McKeiver 7,83,85*
Lisa Heins 8,81   Karen Bullock 11
Jill Sims .... 34*   Kyle Uhrig 57,58,88,285
Todd Stevens 67   Nathan Garman 73*

Public Schs..Principal	Grd	Prgm	Enr/#Cls	SN	
Circleville Elem Sch 100 Tiger Dr, Circleville 43113 Jill Sims	PK-5	T	1,136		740/474-2495 Fax 740/477-6681
Circleville High Sch 380 Clark Dr, Circleville 43113 Chris Thornsley	9-12	TV	554 50		740/474-4846 Fax 740/477-5571
Circleville Middle Sch 360 Clark Dr, Circleville 43113 Kevin Fox	6-8	TV	484		740/474-2345 Fax 740/477-6684

- **Logan Elm Local School Dist** PID: 00827755   740/474-7501
  9579 Tarlton Rd, Circleville 43113   Fax 740/477-6525

Schools: 6 \ *Teachers:* 122 \ *Students:* 1,880 \ *Special Ed Students:* 306 \ *College-Bound:* 51% \ *Ethnic:* African American 1%, Hispanic 1%, Caucasian 98% \ *Exp:* $172 (Low) \ *Poverty:* 14% \ *Title I:* $424,864 \ *Special Education:* $429,000 \ *Open-Close:* 08/19 - 05/22 \ *DTBP:* $241 (High) \

Tim Williams 1   Trey Fausnaugh 2
Chris Yingling 3,5,91   Ginger Selin 4
Eric Karshner .... 6*   Amy Colburn 8,11,72,288
Kim Glick .... 16,82*   Tanne Gruve 37*
Megan Michalski .... 57,273*   Sandy Elsea 60
Deborah Shaw 67   John Rundag 73,84,295

Public Schs..Principal	Grd	Prgm	Enr/#Cls	SN	
George McDowell Middle Sch 9579 Tarlton Rd, Circleville 43113 Bret King	7-8		265 25	35%	740/474-7538 Fax 740/474-8539
Laurelville Elem Sch 16138 Pike St, Laurelville 43135 Bret King	PK-4	T	253 25	57%	740/332-2021 Fax 740/332-1401
Logan Elm High Sch 9575 Tarlton Rd, Circleville 43113 Nate Smith	9-12		568 40	36%	740/474-7503 Fax 740/477-3592
Pickaway Elem Sch 28158 Kingston Pike, Circleville 43113 James Wolfe	K-4		181 13	36%	740/474-3877 Fax 740/477-1324
Salt Creek Intermediate Sch 13190 State Route 56, Kingston 45644 Ted Dille	5-6	T	276 14	49%	740/332-4212 Fax 740/332-1751
Washington Elem Sch 7990 Stoutsville Pike, Circleville 43113 Jim Wolfe	K-4		219 13	32%	740/474-2851 Fax 740/474-7693

- **Teays Valley Local School Dist** PID: 00827822   740/983-5000
  385 Vicking Way, Ashville 43103   Fax 740/983-4158

Schools: 7 \ *Teachers:* 202 \ *Students:* 4,350 \ *Special Ed Students:* 441 \ *LEP Students:* 13 \ *College-Bound:* 48% \ *Ethnic:* Asian 1%, African American 1%, Hispanic 2%, Caucasian 96% \ *Exp:* $168 (Low) \ *Poverty:* 9% \ *Title I:* $412,575 \ *Special Education:* $605,000 \ *Open-Close:* 08/14 - 05/22 \ *DTBP:* $195 (High)

Robin Halley 1   Stacey Overly 2
Ron Teeters 3,5,91   Jannette Fausnaugh 4*
Randy Hageman .... 6*   Michelle Chafin 7,35,83,85*
Kyle Wolf 8,11,34,58,69,88,296,298   Beth Keplar 10*
Lisa Campbell .... 16,82*   Julie Samlow 31,36,79*
Charles Morisson 67   Julie Delisio 71
Trent Stoddard 73,295

Public Schs..Principal	Grd	Prgm	Enr/#Cls	SN	
Ashville Elem Sch 90 Walnut St, Ashville 43103 Gretchen Weiler	PK-5	T	442 24	43%	740/983-5066 Fax 740/983-5073
Scioto Elem Sch 20 W Scioto St, Commercial Pt 43116 Devin Anderson	PK-5		625 27	19%	740/983-5059 Fax 740/983-5088

1 Superintendent	8 Curric/Instruct K-12	19 Chief Financial Officer	29 Family/Consumer Science	39 Social Studies K-12	49 English/Lang Arts Elem	59 Special Education Elem	69 Academic Assessment
2 Bus/Finance/Purchasing	9 Curric/Instruct Elem	20 Art K-12	30 Adult Education	40 Social Studies Elem	50 English/Lang Arts Sec	60 Special Education Sec	70 Research/Development
3 Buildings And Grounds	10 Curric/Instruct Sec	21 Art Elem	31 Career/Sch-to-Work K-12	41 Social Studies Sec	51 Reading K-12	61 Foreign/World Lang K-12	71 Public Information
4 Food Service	11 Federal Program	22 Art Sec	32 Career/Sch-to-Work Elem	42 Science K-12	52 Reading Elem	62 Foreign/World Lang Elem	72 Summer School
5 Transportation	12 Title I	23 Music K-12	33 Career/Sch-to-Work Sec	43 Science Elem	53 Reading Sec	63 Foreign/World Lang Sec	73 Instructional Tech
6 Athletic	13 Title V	24 Music Elem	34 Early Childhood Ed	44 Science Sec	54 Remedial Reading K-12	64 Religious Education K-12	74 Inservice Training
7 Health Services	15 Asst Superintendent	25 Music Sec	35 Health/Phys Education	45 Math K-12	55 Remedial Reading Elem	65 Religious Education Elem	75 Marketing/Distributive
	16 Instructional Media Svcs	26 Business Education	36 Guidance Services K-12	46 Math Elem	56 Remedial Reading Sec	66 Religious Education Sec	76 Info Systems
	17 Chief Operations Officer	27 Career & Tech Ed	37 Guidance Services Elem	47 Math Sec	57 Bilingual/ELL	67 School Board President	77 Psychological Assess
	18 Chief Academic Officer	28 Technology Education	38 Guidance Services Sec	48 English/Lang Arts K-12	58 Special Education K-12	68 Teacher Personnel	78 Affirmative Action

Ohio School Directory — Pike County

South Bloomfield Elem Sch 194 Dowler Dr, Ashville 43103 Bruce Bryant	PK-5	T	415	47%	740/983-5003 Fax 740/983-5004
Teays Valley East Middle Sch 655 Circleville Ave, Ashville 43103 Shannon Helser	6-8		470 59	31%	740/983-5078 Fax 740/983-5037
Teays Valley High Sch 3887 State Route 752, Ashville 43103 John Keel	9-12	A	1,159 64	30%	740/983-5053 Fax 740/983-5074
Teays Valley West Middle Sch 200 Grove Run Rd, Commercial Pt 43116 Michael Kauffeld	6-8		490	29%	740/983-5000 Fax 740/983-5040
Walnut Elem Sch 7150 Ashville Fairfield Rd, Ashville 43103 Greg Kovack	PK-5		481 22	24%	740/983-5061 Fax 740/983-5049

• **Westfall Local School Dist** PID: 00827884 740/986-3671
  19463 Pherson Pike, Williamsport 43164 Fax 740/986-8375

Schools: 3 \ *Teachers:* 83 \ *Students:* 1,432 \ *Special Ed Students:* 184 \ *LEP Students:* 4 \ *College-Bound:* 60% \ *Ethnic:* African American 1%, Hispanic 2%, Caucasian 96% \ *Exp:* $244 (Med) \ *Poverty:* 15% \ *Title I:* $344,280 \ *Special Education:* $286,000 \ *Open-Close:* 08/21 - 05/28 \ *DTBP:* $196 (High)

Dr Lynn Landis 1   Brian Ramsay 2
Eric Gillispie 3   Becky Shaw 4,5
Amy Noltemeyer ....6*   Nancy Downing 7*
Amy Fox 8   Deborah Younge 8,11,69,296,298*
Janice Gearhart ....12,13*   Cheryl Lorson 16*
Andrea Brown ....38*   Beverly Kern 57*
Mary Mace-Miller 58   Judith Cook 67
JD Williamson 73,286,295*

Public Schs..Principal	Grd	Prgm	Enr/#Cls	SN	
Westfall Elem Sch 9391 State Route 56, Williamsport 43164 Joseph Patete	PK-5	T	655 30	49%	740/986-4008 Fax 740/986-4018
Westfall High Sch 19463 Pherson Pike, Williamsport 43164 Billy Dennis	9-12	AV	425 40	41%	740/986-2911 Fax 740/986-8897
Westfall Middle Sch 19545 Pherson Pike, Williamsport 43164 Jason Fife	6-8	AT	352 32	47%	740/986-2941 Fax 740/986-8882

PICKAWAY PRIVATE SCHOOLS

Private Schs..Principal	Grd	Prgm	Enr/#Cls	SN	
Crossroads Christian Academy 5679 Tarlton Rd, Circleville 43113 Wayne Gray	K-8		50 4		740/474-7265 Fax 740/474-4027
New Hope Christian Academy 2264 Walnut Creek Pike, Circleville 43113 Allison Catlos \ Kim Shepherd	PK-12		300		740/477-6427

PIKE COUNTY

PIKE COUNTY SCHOOLS

County Schs..Principal	Grd	Prgm	Enr/#Cls	SN	
Pike Co Early Childhood Center 10 American Blvd, Piketon 45661 Tammy Fyffe	Spec		50 1		740/289-1681 Fax 740/289-8923

PIKE PUBLIC SCHOOLS

• **Eastern Local School Dist** PID: 00827951 740/226-4851
  1170 Tile Mill Rd, Beaver 45613 Fax 740/226-1331

Schools: 3 \ *Teachers:* 58 \ *Students:* 901 \ *Special Ed Students:* 171 \ *College-Bound:* 75% \ *Ethnic:* Asian 1%, African American 1%, Hispanic 2%, Caucasian 96% \ *Exp:* $244 (Med) \ *Poverty:* 28% \ *Title I:* $393,162 \ *Special Education:* $177,000 \ *Open-Close:* 08/15 - 05/20 \ *DTBP:* $176 (High)

Neil Leist 1   Rodney Schilling 2,19
Gary Lee 3,4,5,11   Lance Allen 4,5,9,11,15,295
Autumn Risner ....7,85*   Chris Adkins 16,273,286*
Terry Keeton ....16,73,76 Teresa Southworth 36,69,83,270*
Shirley Walters ....57*   Rick Bowman 58
Brad Bapst 67

Public Schs..Principal	Grd	Prgm	Enr/#Cls	SN	
Eastern Elem Sch 1170 Tile Mill Rd, Beaver 45613 Matthew Hines	PK-5	T	434 18		740/226-6402 Fax 740/226-6122
Eastern High Sch 1170 Tile Mill Rd, Beaver 45613 Robie Day	9-12	TV	177 23		740/226-1544 Fax 740/226-6322
Eastern Middle Sch 1170 Tile Mill Rd, Beaver 45613 Robie Day	6-8	T	211 18		740/226-1544 Fax 740/226-6322

• **Pike Co Area JT Voc Sch Dist** PID: 00828137 740/289-2721
  175 Beaver Creek Rd, Piketon 45661 Fax 740/289-8891

Schools: 1 \ *Teachers:* 31 \ *Students:* 500 \ *Exp:* $1,622 (High) \ *Open-Close:* 08/15 - 05/25 \ *DTBP:* $174 (High)

Eric Meredith 1   Tonya Cooper 2
Chris Norman ....10,88*   Shon Tackett 27,33,288*
Lathe Moore ....30*   Nancy Bloomfield 38,79*
Connie Tackett ....60*   Jan Leeth 67
Ryan Satterfield 73,295*

Public Schs..Principal	Grd	Prgm	Enr/#Cls	SN	
Pike Co Career Tech Center 175 Beaver Creek Rd, Piketon 45661 Shon Tackett	Voc	G	400 32		740/289-2721 Fax 740/289-2527

---

79 Student Personnel
80 Driver Ed/Safety
81 Gifted/Talented
82 Video Services
83 Substance Abuse Prev
84 Erate
85 AIDS Education
88 Alternative/At Risk
89 Multi-Cultural Curriculum
90 Social Work

91 Safety/Security
92 Magnet School
93 Parental Involvement
95 Tech Prep Program
97 Chief Information Officer
98 Chief Technology Officer
270 Character Education
271 Migrant Education
273 Teacher Mentor
274 Before/After Sch

275 Response To Intervention
277 Remedial Math K-12
280 Literacy Coach
285 STEM
286 Digital Learning
288 Common Core Standards
294 Accountability
295 Network System
296 Title II Programs
297 Webmaster

298 Grant Writer/Ptnrships
750 Chief Innovation Officer
751 Chief of Staff
752 Social Emotional Learning

Other School Types
Ⓐ = Alternative School
Ⓒ = Charter School
Ⓜ = Magnet School
Ⓨ = Year-Round School

School Programs
A = Alternative Program
G = Adult Classes
M = Magnet Program
T = Title I Schoolwide
V = Career & Tech Ed Programs

New Schools are shaded
New Superintendents and Principals are bold
Personnel with email addresses are underscored

Social Media
 = Facebook
 = Twitter

Portage County — Market Data Retrieval

- **Scioto Valley Local Sch Dist** PID: 00827999   740/289-4456
  1414 Piketon Rd, Piketon 45661   Fax 740/289-3065

Schools: 2 \ **Teachers:** 70 \ **Students:** 1,300 \ **Special Ed Students:** 253 \ **College-Bound:** 36% \ **Ethnic:** Caucasian 99% \ **Exp:** $189 (Low) \ **Poverty:** 26% \ **Title I:** $637,020 \ **Special Education:** $315,000 \ **Open-Close:** 08/14 - 05/20 \ **DTBP:** $174 (High)

Megan Williams 2,19,298	Leroy Howard 3
Kandi Reed 4	Jason Mantal 5
Keith Dettwiller 6*	Mandy Day 7*
James Roberts 10,58,88,275	Libby Crothers 35*
Cheri Crabtree 37*	Sherry Fout 38*
Brandon Wooldridge 67	Kathy Lansing 68
Josh Anato 73,297	Jessica Wheeler 90

Public Schs..Principal	Grd	Prgm	Enr/#Cls SN	
Jasper Elem Sch 3185 Jasper Rd, Piketon 45661 Krista Conley	PK-5	T	575 28	87% 740/289-2425 Fax 740/289-4437
Piketon Jr Sr High Sch 1414 Piketon Rd, Piketon 45661 Jeff Reuter	6-12	AT	607 45	58% 740/289-2254 Fax 740/289-1514

- **Waverly City School Dist** PID: 00828034   740/947-4770
  1 Tiger Dr, Waverly 45690   Fax 740/947-4483

Schools: 4 \ **Teachers:** 96 \ **Students:** 1,825 \ **Special Ed Students:** 293 \ **College-Bound:** 42% \ **Ethnic:** Asian 1%, African American 2%, Hispanic 2%, Caucasian 95% \ **Exp:** $174 (Low) \ **Poverty:** 22% \ **Title I:** $682,544 \ **Special Education:** $381,000 \ **Open-Close:** 08/22 - 05/28 \ **DTBP:** $169 (High)

Edward Dickens 1	Claudia Zaler 2,11,19,68,298
Rodney Leffler 3	Lari Patton 4
Bill Hoover 5,83	Larry Arnett 6
Denise Adams 7*	Melissa Marquez .8,11,58,72,270,271,273,288
Ashlee Stulley 11,57	Brenda Walls 16*
Terry Wood 36*	Josh Hobbs 67
Patrick Williams 73*	Patrick Williams 84

Public Schs..Principal	Grd	Prgm	Enr/#Cls SN	
Waverly High Sch 1 Tiger Dr, Waverly 45690 Ashlee Stulley	9-12	T	496 35	740/947-7701 Fax 740/941-5899
Waverly Intermediate Sch 5 Tiger Dr, Waverly 45690 Travis Robertson	3-5	T	430 22	740/947-5173 Fax 740/947-2236
Waverly Junior High Sch 3 Tiger Dr, Waverly 45690 Ferdie Marquez	6-8	T	455 32	740/947-4527 Fax 740/947-8047
Waverly Primary Sch 7 Tiger Dr, Waverly 45690 Sara Turner	PK-2	T	445 35	740/947-2813 Fax 740/947-8284

- **Western Local School Dist** PID: 00828084   740/493-3113
  7959 State Route 124, Latham 45646   Fax 740/493-2065

Schools: 2 \ **Teachers:** 36 \ **Students:** 790 \ **Special Ed Students:** 135 \ **College-Bound:** 24% \ **Ethnic:** African American 1%, Caucasian 99% \ **Exp:** $327 (High) \ **Poverty:** 30% \ **Title I:** $527,344 \ **Special Education:** $213,000 \ **Open-Close:** 08/15 - 05/20 \ **DTBP:** $174 (High)

Brock Brewster 1	Rockford Lambert 2
Wayne Grooms 3*	Sonja Rittenhause 5*
Rachel Henderson 6,270*	Holly Tackett 7,85
Heather Thompson 8,280,286,288*	Peter Dunn 11,57,83,88,294,296,298
Kimberlee Runions 16,82*	Crystal Guilkey 31,38,67*
Doug McFarland 35*	Beth Alexander 58*
Brad Marhoover 67	Lynn Odell 73,76,295
Debra Collins 273*	

Public Schs..Principal	Grd	Prgm	Enr/#Cls SN	
Western Elem Sch 7959 State Route 124, Latham 45646 Bethany Whitt	K-6	T	447 40	740/493-2881 Fax 740/493-1059
Western High Sch 7959 State Route 124, Latham 45646 Carrie Gast	7-12	TV	304 30	740/493-2514 Fax 740/493-8513

PIKE PRIVATE SCHOOLS

Private Schs..Principal	Grd	Prgm	Enr/#Cls SN	
Miracle City Academy 204 Commercial Blvd, Piketon 45661 Kathy Struckel	PK-12		45 3	740/289-2787 Fax 740/289-2013

PORTAGE COUNTY

PORTAGE COUNTY SCHOOLS

- **Portage Co Ed Service Center** PID: 00828826   330/297-1436
  326 E Main St 3rd Fl, Ravenna 44266   Fax 330/297-1113

Joseph Iacano 1	Tom Morehouse 2
James Rykaceski 3,4,5	Cheryl Emrich 15,68
Mike Tornow 58,81	

County Schs..Principal	Grd	Prgm	Enr/#Cls SN	
Happy Day Sch 2500 Brady Lake Rd, Ravenna 44266 Alicea Hall	Spec		190 12	330/678-2400 Fax 330/673-3714

PORTAGE PUBLIC SCHOOLS

- **Aurora City School Dist** PID: 00828163   330/562-6106
  102 E Garfield Rd, Aurora 44202   Fax 330/562-4892

Schools: 5 \ **Teachers:** 154 \ **Students:** 3,000 \ **Special Ed Students:** 281 \ **LEP Students:** 31 \ **College-Bound:** 77% \ **Ethnic:** Asian 4%, African American 3%, Hispanic 3%, Caucasian 90% \ **Exp:** $85 (Low) \ **Poverty:** 4% \ **Title I:** $84,689 \ **Special Education:** $434,000 \ **Open-Close:** 08/15 - 05/28 \ **DTBP:** $187 (High)

Pat Ciccantelli 1	William Volosin 2
Sal Arquilla 3,4,5,91	Paul Powers 6
Sandy Petti 7*	Mike Roberto 8,11,15,16,31,57,270
Jennifer Kinkoph 16*	Kim Menza 34
Stacie Levey 57*	Mike Maglioico 58,69,77
Gerald Kohanski 67	Stacey Deanna 71
Shannon Gagel 81	Andrew Sams 84
Bob Mihliak 88	Andy Sams 95,295*

1	Superintendent	8	Curric/Instruct K-12	19	Chief Financial Officer	29	Family/Consumer Science	39	Social Studies K-12	49	English/Lang Arts Elem	59	Special Education Elem
2	Bus/Finance/Purchasing	9	Curric/Instruct Elem	20	Art K-12	30	Adult Education	40	Social Studies Elem	50	English/Lang Arts Sec	60	Special Education Sec
3	Buildings And Grounds	10	Curric/Instruct Sec	21	Art Elem	31	Career/Sch-to-Work K-12	41	Social Studies Sec	51	Reading K-12	61	Foreign/World Lang K-12
4	Food Service	11	Federal Program	22	Art Sec	32	Career/Sch-to-Work Elem	42	Science K-12	52	Reading Elem	62	Foreign/World Lang Elem
5	Transportation	12	Title I	23	Music K-12	33	Career/Sch-to-Work Sec	43	Science Elem	53	Reading Sec	63	Foreign/World Lang Sec
6	Athletic	13	Title V	24	Music Elem	34	Early Childhood Ed	44	Science Sec	54	Remedial Reading K-12	64	Religious Education K-12
7	Health Services	14	Asst Superintendent	25	Music Sec	35	Health/Phys Education	45	Math K-12	55	Remedial Reading Elem	65	Religious Education Elem
		15	Instructional Media Svcs	26	Business Education	36	Guidance Services K-12	46	Math Elem	56	Remedial Reading Sec	66	Religious Education Sec
		17	Chief Operations Officer	27	Career & Tech Ed	37	Guidance Services Elem	47	Math Sec	57	Bilingual/ELL	67	School Board President
		18	Chief Academic Officer	28	Technology Education	38	Guidance Services Sec	48	English/Lang Arts K-12	58	Special Education K-12	68	Teacher Personnel

69	Academic Assessment
70	Research/Development
71	Public Information
72	Summer School
73	Instructional Tech
74	Inservice Training
75	Marketing/Distributive
76	Info Systems
77	Psychological Assess
78	Affirmative Action

Ohio School Directory — Portage County

Public Schs..Principal	Grd	Prgm	Enr/#Cls	SN	
Aurora High Sch 109 W Pioneer Trl, Aurora 44202 Paul Milcetich	9-12	V	978 52	8%	330/562-3501 Fax 330/954-2810
Craddock Elem Sch 105 Hurd Rd, Aurora 44202 **Kim Menta**	1-2		400 16	9%	330/562-3175 Fax 330/954-2087
Harmon Middle Sch 130 Aurora Hudson Rd, Aurora 44202 Mark Abramovich	6-8		675 20	8%	330/562-3375 Fax 330/562-4796
Leighton Elem Sch 121 Aurora Hudson Rd, Aurora 44202 Mike Janatovich	3-5		669 27	9%	330/562-2209 Fax 330/562-2265
Miller Elem Sch 646 S Chillicothe Rd, Aurora 44202 Julie Troman	PK-K		262 13	4%	330/562-6199 Fax 330/995-5459

• **Crestwood Local School Dist** PID: 00828230   330/357-8206
  11260 Bowen Rd, Mantua 44255   Fax 330/274-3710

Schools: 4 \ **Teachers:** 103 \ **Students:** 1,600 \ **Special Ed Students:** 213 \ **LEP Students:** 3 \ **College-Bound:** 56% \ **Ethnic:** Hispanic 1%, Caucasian 99% \ **Exp:** $173 (Low) \ **Poverty:** 8% \ **Title I:** $206,288 \ **Special Education:** $401,000 \ **Open-Close:** 08/26 - 06/03 \ **DTBP:** $174 (High)

David Toth 1
Jennifer Bujak Hirsch 4
Bret Coke 6
Karen Graves 38*
Julie Schmidt 288*
Jeff Woolard 2,3,73,91
Sharon Dove 5
Sherry Peters 11,58,79,83,296
Bonnie Lovejoy 67

Public Schs..Principal	Grd	Prgm	Enr/#Cls	SN	
Crestwood High Sch 10919 Main St, Mantua 44255 Dave McMahon	9-12		449 60	25%	330/357-8205 Fax 330/274-3150
Crestwood Intermediate Sch 11260 Bowen Rd, Mantua 44255 Michelle Gerbrick	3-5		379 11	39%	330/357-8203 Fax 330/274-3825
Crestwood Middle Sch 10880 John Edward Dr, Mantua 44255 **Edward Kosek**	6-8		391 30	29%	330/357-8204 Fax 330/274-3705
Crestwood Primary Sch 11256 Bowen Rd, Mantua 44255 Cindy Ducca	PK-2		426 10	33%	330/357-8202 Fax 330/274-3824

• **Field Local School Dist** PID: 00828319   330/673-2659
  2900 State Route 43, Mogadore 44260   Fax 330/673-0270

Schools: 4 \ **Teachers:** 117 \ **Students:** 1,900 \ **Special Ed Students:** 271 \ **LEP Students:** 49 \ **College-Bound:** 56% \ **Ethnic:** Asian 2%, African American 3%, Hispanic 1%, Caucasian 94% \ **Exp:** $136 (Low) \ **Poverty:** 8% \ **Title I:** $277,808 \ **Special Education:** $479,000 \ **Open-Close:** 08/28 - 06/04

David Heflinger 1
Todd Carpenter 2
Michael Geraghty 6*
Alene Rayl 7*
Megan Longfellow 58
Beth Bable 68
Caitlyn Bayda 83*
Jason Vancura 2,3,5,37,91
Kelly Peterson 4
Nicole Kosewick 6
Bethany Hudson 8,11,57,288
Randy Porter 67
Alex Grad 73
Meagan Casper 83*

Public Schs..Principal	Grd	Prgm	Enr/#Cls	SN	
Brimfield Elem Sch 4170 State Route 43, Kent 44240 Barbara Hawley	K-5		544 24	74%	330/673-8581 Fax 330/677-2519
Field High Sch 2900 State Route 43, Mogadore 44260 Michael Geraghty	9-12	V	494 33	33%	330/673-9591 Fax 330/677-2520
Field Middle Sch 1379 Saxe Rd, Mogadore 44260 Susan Blake	6-8		477 35	36%	330/673-4176 Fax 330/673-5024
Suffield Elem Sch 1128 Waterloo Rd, Mogadore 44260 Shawn Bookman	K-5	T	393 30	40%	330/552-5252 Fax 330/628-9160

• **James A Garfield Local SD** PID: 00828371   330/527-4336
  10235 State Route 88, Garrettsville 44231   Fax 330/527-5941

Schools: 3 \ **Teachers:** 83 \ **Students:** 1,379 \ **Special Ed Students:** 184 \ **College-Bound:** 47% \ **Ethnic:** Caucasian 99% \ **Exp:** $100 (Low) \ **Poverty:** 11% \ **Title I:** $219,957 \ **Special Education:** $239,000 \ **Open-Close:** 08/27 - 06/04 \ **DTBP:** $174 (High)

Ted Lysiak 1,11,83
Susan Boyle 7,58
Keri Leindecker 12*
Guy Pietra 67
Tracy Knauer 2,84
Derek Hatcher 10,73*
Stephanie Damron 36

Public Schs..Principal	Grd	Prgm	Enr/#Cls	SN	
James A Garfield Elem Sch 10207 State Route 88, Garrettsville 44231 Keri Leindecker	PK-6	T	736 30	39%	330/527-2184 Fax 330/527-3015
James A Garfield High Sch 10233 State Route 88, Garrettsville 44231 Kathleen Kisabeth	9-12		403 30	61%	330/527-4341 Fax 330/527-5636
James A Garfield Middle Sch 10231 State Route 88, Garrettsville 44231 Derek Hatcher	7-8		240 14		330/527-2151 Fax 330/527-2601

• **Kent City School Dist** PID: 00828412   330/673-6515
  321 N Depeyster St, Kent 44240   Fax 330/677-6166

Schools: 6 \ **Teachers:** 216 \ **Students:** 3,400 \ **Special Ed Students:** 474 \ **LEP Students:** 93 \ **College-Bound:** 67% \ **Ethnic:** Asian 3%, African American 14%, Hispanic 3%, Caucasian 80% \ **Exp:** $250 (Med) \ **Poverty:** 17% \ **Title I:** $792,787 \ **Special Education:** $762,000 \ **Open-Close:** 08/21 - 05/29 \ **DTBP:** $214 (High)

George Joseph 1
Robert Munroe 3,91
Mark Pfaff 6
Tom Larkin 15
Justin Gates 57,58,88,275
Linda Paulus 76
Jim Soyars 2,76,84,295
Rick Lewis 5
Karen Rumley 8,11,34,69,71,288,296,298
Brian Bachtel 27,33*
Rebecca Wright-Cullis 67
Chip Hawks 285*

Public Schs..Principal	Grd	Prgm	Enr/#Cls	SN	
Davey Elem Sch 196 N Prospect St, Kent 44240 Abby Bolton	PK-5	T	481 26	52%	330/676-7400 Fax 330/677-6190
Holden Elem Sch 132 W School St, Kent 44240 Todd Poole	K-5	T	265 11	60%	330/676-8400 Fax 330/676-8405
Longcoy Elem Sch 1069 Elno Ave, Kent 44240 Janice Swan	K-5	T	280 17	49%	330/676-8350 Fax 330/677-6198

---

79 Student Personnel	91 Safety/Security	275 Response To Intervention	298 Grant Writer/Ptnrships	**School Programs**
60 Driver Ed/Safety	92 Magnet School	277 Remedial Math K-12	750 Chief Innovation Officer	A = Alternative Program
81 Gifted/Talented	93 Parental Involvement	280 Literacy Coach	751 Chief of Staff	G = Adult Classes
82 Video Services	95 Tech Prep Program	285 STEM	752 Social Emotional Learning	M = Magnet Program
83 Substance Abuse Prev	97 Chief Infomation Officer	286 Digital Learning		T = Title I Schoolwide
84 Erate	98 Chief Technology Officer	288 Common Core Standards	**Other School Types**	V = Career & Tech Ed Programs
65 AIDS Education	270 Character Education	294 Accountability	Ⓐ = Alternative School	
68 Alternative/At Risk	271 Migrant Education	295 Network System	Ⓒ = Charter School	**Social Media**
69 Multi-Cultural Curriculum	273 Teacher Mentor	296 Title II Programs	Ⓜ = Magnet School	❂ = Facebook
90 Social Work	274 Before/After Sch	297 Webmaster	Ⓨ = Year-Round School	❂ = Twitter

New Schools are shaded
New Superintendents and Principals are bold
Personnel with email addresses are underscored

Portage County

Market Data Retrieval

Roosevelt High Sch — 9-12 — 1,294 — 28% — 330/676-8700
1400 N Mantua St, Kent 44240 — 70 — Fax 330/673-9217
Dennis Love

Stanton Middle Sch — 6-8 — T — 686 — 43% — 330/676-8600
1175 Hudson Rd, Kent 44240 — 40 — Fax 330/678-1561
Anthony Horton

Walls Elem Sch — K-5 — T — 403 — 44% — 330/676-8300
900 Doramor St, Kent 44240 — 18 — Fax 330/676-8305
Heidi Singer

● **Maplewood JT Voc School Dist** PID: 00828802 — 330/296-2892
7075 State Route 88, Ravenna 44266 — Fax 330/296-5680

Schools: 1 \ *Teachers:* 45 \ *Students:* 700 \ *Exp:* $340 (High) \
Open-Close: 08/26 - 06/02 \ *DTBP:* $253 (High)

Randy Griffith 1	Michael Lenzo 2,3
Joe Hinton 4*	Craig Morgan 10,27,38,75*
Michael Hinton 30*	Brian Violi 67
Michele McPherson 69*	Jennifer Smith 73*
John Feeney 88*	

Public Schs..Principal	Grd	Prgm	Enr/#Cls	SN
Maplewood Career Center 7075 State Route 88, Ravenna 44266 Craig Morgan	Voc	AG	700 53	330/296-2892

● **Mogadore Local School Dist** PID: 00835154 — 330/628-9946
1 S Cleveland Ave, Mogadore 44260 — Fax 330/628-6661

Schools: 2 \ *Teachers:* 54 \ *Students:* 875 \ *Special Ed Students:* 79 \
College-Bound: 65% \ *Ethnic:* Hispanic 1%, Caucasian 99% \ *Exp:* $225
(Med) \ *Poverty:* 14% \ *Title I:* $125,789 \ *Special Education:* $153,000 \
Open-Close: 08/22 - 05/29 \ *DTBP:* $174 (High) \

John Knapp 1	Christopher Adams 2
Krysten Crew 3,5	Stephen Lutz 6*
Lori Grimaldi 8	Theresa Garner 16*
Ann Phillips 58	Rodger Sansom 67

Public Schs..Principal	Grd	Prgm	Enr/#Cls	SN
Mogadore Jr Sr High Sch 130 S Cleveland Ave, Mogadore 44260 Russ Swartz	7-12	M	392 22	44% 330/628-9943 Fax 330/628-6657
O H Somers Elem Sch 3600 Herbert St, Mogadore 44260 Sandra Isabella	K-6	M	465 21	34% 330/628-9947 Fax 330/628-6662

● **Ravenna School Dist** PID: 00828503 — 330/296-9679
507 E Main St, Ravenna 44266 — Fax 330/297-4158

Schools: 7 \ *Teachers:* 154 \ *Students:* 2,200 \ *Special Ed Students:* 536
\ *LEP Students:* 14 \ *College-Bound:* 35% \ *Ethnic:* African American
11%, Hispanic 3%, Caucasian 86% \ *Exp:* $270 (Med) \ *Poverty:* 20% \
Title I: $906,740 \ *Special Education:* $619,000 \ *Open-Close:* 08/19 -
05/28 \ *DTBP:* $191 (High)

Dennis Honkala 1	William Wisniewski 2,3,91
Lori Tontimonia 4	Jeanie Knapp 5
Jim Leonardy 6,35*	Susan Huth 8,11,57,69,274,294,298
Ben Ribelin 9,12,15,68,79,273,288,296	Nicholas Petresino 16*
Jessica Haynes 58,77,83,88,90	Joan Seman 67
Steven York 73,95,295,297*	Stephen York 84

Public Schs..Principal	Grd	Prgm	Enr/#Cls	SN
Brown Middle Sch 228 S Scranton St, Ravenna 44266 Jonathan Lane	6-8	T	460 50	330/296-3849 Fax 330/297-4146
Carlin Elem Sch 531 Washington Ave, Ravenna 44266 Robert Mittiga	1-5	T	242 12	330/296-6622 Fax 330/297-4144
Ravenna Early Childhood Ctr 3590 State Route 59, Ravenna 44266 Jessica Scheeser	PK-PK		120	330/297-4139
Ravenna High Sch 6589 N Chestnut St, Ravenna 44266 Beth Coleman	9-12		578	330/296-3844 Fax 330/296-1855
West Main Elem Sch 639 W Main St, Ravenna 44266 Lee Smith	1-5	T	378 24	330/296-6522 Fax 330/297-4149
West Park Elem Sch 1071 Jones St, Ravenna 44266 Frank Sciarabba	K-K	T	184 11	330/297-1744 Fax 330/297-4167
Willyard Elem Sch 680 Summit Rd, Ravenna 44266 Joseph Kuzior	1-5	T	320 16	330/296-6481 Fax 330/297-4151

● **Rootstown Local School Dist** PID: 00828591 — 330/325-9911
4140 State Route 44, Rootstown 44272 — Fax 330/325-4105

Schools: 3 \ *Teachers:* 70 \ *Students:* 1,200 \ *Special Ed Students:* 173
\ *LEP Students:* 16 \ *College-Bound:* 58% \ *Ethnic:* Asian 1%, African
American 1%, Hispanic 1%, Caucasian 97% \ *Exp:* $140 (Low) \ *Poverty:* 7%
\ *Title I:* $122,626 \ *Special Education:* $206,000 \ *Open-Close:* 08/27 -
06/03 \ *DTBP:* $238 (High)

Andrew Hawkins 1	Connie Baldwin 2,19
Peggy Shewell 4	Kelly Varga 5
Matt Collins 5	Keith Waesch 6
Terri Trehearn 8,15,69,273,274,288	Kelli Coffman 12*
Robert Campbell 13*	Danielle Ray 37*
Amelia Mohan 38*	Marcia Spence 58
Amanda Waesch 67	Lee Boring 73

Public Schs..Principal	Grd	Prgm	Enr/#Cls	SN
Bertha Bradshaw Elem Sch 4190 State Route 44, Rootstown 44272 Jeff Turner	K-5		525 23	30% 330/325-7971 Fax 330/325-2683
Rootstown High Sch 4190 State Route 44, Rootstown 44272 James Conley	9-12		324 32	26% 330/325-7911 Fax 330/325-8506
Rootstown Middle Sch 4190 State Route 44, Rootstown 44272 Robert Campbell	6-8		284 18	25% 330/325-9956 Fax 330/325-8505

● **Southeast Local School Dist** PID: 00828632 — 330/654-5841
8245 Tallmadge Rd, Ravenna 44266 — Fax 330/654-9110

Schools: 4 \ *Teachers:* 105 \ *Students:* 1,484 \ *Special Ed Students:* 254
\ *LEP Students:* 3 \ *College-Bound:* 40% \ *Ethnic:* African American
1%, Hispanic 1%, Caucasian 97% \ *Exp:* $115 (Low) \ *Poverty:* 12% \
Title I: $311,866 \ *Special Education:* $361,000 \ *Open-Close:* 08/30 -
06/04 \ *DTBP:* $201 (High)

Robert Dunn 1	Cassie Bergman 2
Denise Torres 4	Henry Michael 5
Steven Sigworth 6*	John Lamanna 12
Ben Campbell 27*	Jeff McElfresh 67
Cathy Buck 69*	Chris Formit 76

---

1 Superintendent	19 Chief Financial Officer	39 Social Studies K-12	59 Special Education Elem	69 Academic Assessment
2 Bus/Finance/Purchasing	20 Art K-12	40 Social Studies Elem	60 Special Education Sec	70 Research/Development
3 Buildings And Grounds	21 Art Elem	41 Social Studies Sec	61 Foreign/World Lang K-12	71 Public Information
4 Food Service	22 Art Sec	42 Science K-12	62 Foreign/World Lang Elem	72 Summer School
5 Transportation	23 Title I	43 Science Elem	63 Foreign/World Lang Sec	73 Instructional Tech
6 Athletic	24 Music Elem	44 Science Sec	64 Religious Education K-12	74 Inservice Training
7 Health Services	25 Music Sec	45 Math K-12	65 Religious Education Elem	75 Marketing/Distributive
8 Curric/Instruct K-12	26 Business Education	46 Math Elem	66 Religious Education Sec	76 Info Systems
9 Curric/Instruct Elem	27 Career & Tech Ed	47 Math Sec	67 School Board President	77 Psychological Assess
10 Curric/Instruct Sec	28 Technology Education	48 English/Lang Arts K-12	58 Special Education K-12	78 Affirmative Action
11 Federal Program	29 Family/Consumer Science	49 English/Lang Arts Elem	68 Teacher Personnel	
12 Title I	30 Adult Education	50 English/Lang Arts Sec		
13 Title V	31 Career/Sch-to-Work K-12	51 Reading K-12		
14 (blank)	32 Career/Sch-to-Work Elem	52 Reading Elem		
15 Asst Superintendent	33 Career/Sch-to-Work Sec	53 Reading Sec		
16 Instructional Media Svcs	34 Early Childhood Ed	54 Remedial Reading K-12		
17 Chief Operations Officer	35 Health/Phys Education	55 Remedial Reading Elem		
18 Chief Academic Officer	36 Guidance Services K-12	56 Remedial Reading Sec		
	37 Guidance Services Elem	57 Bilingual/ELL		
	38 Guidance Services Sec			

Ohio School Directory — Portage County

Public Schs..Principal	Grd	Prgm	Enr/#Cls	SN	
Southeast High Sch 8423 Tallmadge Rd, Ravenna 44266 David Kennedy	9-12	V	456 60	41%	330/654-1960
Southeast Intermediate Sch 8301 Tallmadge Rd, Ravenna 44266 Jamie Brawley	3-5	T	359 27		330/654-1940
Southeast Middle Sch 8540 Tallmadge Rd, Diamond 44412 Craig Nettleton	6-8	T	329 30	49%	330/654-1950
Southeast Primary Sch 8301 Tallmadge Rd, Ravenna 44266 David Fesemyer	K-2	T	340 19	99%	330/654-1930

● **Streetsboro City School Dist** PID: 00828668   330/626-4900
9000 Kirby Ln, Streetsboro 44241   Fax 330/626-8102

Schools: 4 \ *Teachers:* 133 \ *Students:* 2,200 \ *Special Ed Students:* 285 \ *LEP Students:* 32 \ *College-Bound:* 50% \ *Ethnic:* Asian 1%, African American 16%, Hispanic 3%, Caucasian 80% \ *Exp:* $252 (Med) \ *Poverty:* 10% \ *Title I:* $280,780 \ *Special Education:* $443,000 \ *Open-Close:* 08/21 - 06/01 \ *DTBP:* $252 (High)

Mike Daulbaugh 1   C J Scarcpino 2
Randy Tevepaugh 3,91   Darlene Wheeler 4
Andreas Johannson 5,73,76,295   Ira Campbell 31,38*
Cindy Deevers 58   Brian Violi 67
Pamela Beech 68   Lucene Leech 274*

Public Schs..Principal	Grd	Prgm	Enr/#Cls	SN	
Henry Defer Intermediate Sch 1895 Annalane Dr, Streetsboro 44241 Matt Bryan	4-5		350	34%	330/422-2480 Fax 330/626-4192
Streetsboro Elem Sch 8955 Kirby Ln, Streetsboro 44241 Greg McClellan	PK-3		685 12	34%	330/626-4907 Fax 330/626-8106
Streetsboro High Sch 8585 State Route 14, Streetsboro 44241 James Hogue	9-12	AV	614 35	33%	330/626-4902 Fax 330/626-8103
Streetsboro Middle Sch 1900 Annalane Dr, Streetsboro 44241 Vincent Suber	6-8		506 24	32%	330/626-4905 Fax 330/626-8104

● **Waterloo Local School Dist** PID: 00828723   330/947-2664
1464 Industry Rd, Atwater 44201   Fax 330/947-2847

Schools: 3 \ *Teachers:* 74 \ *Students:* 1,100 \ *Special Ed Students:* 155 \ *College-Bound:* 56% \ *Ethnic:* Asian 1%, Hispanic 1%, Caucasian 98% \ *Exp:* $68 (Low) \ *Poverty:* 10% \ *Title I:* $182,221 \ *Special Education:* $300,000 \ *Open-Close:* 08/27 - 06/04 \ *DTBP:* $155 (High)

Shawn Braman 1,11   Todd Carpenter 2
Robin Ferguson 5   Mike Devies 6
Diahn Carpenter ....7,85*   Lori Sandel 8,12,288*
Aaron Walker ....9*   Laura Mori 13,38,83,88,286*
Peggy Shaver 37   Lauren Willis 59*
Victoria Brock 67   Paul Schmidt 69,79,275
Matt Dockery ....73,76,82,295*   Martha Dragelevich 81

Public Schs..Principal	Grd	Prgm	Enr/#Cls	SN	
Waterloo Elem Sch 1464 Industry Rd, Atwater 44201 Aaron Walker	PK-5	T	472 18	65%	330/947-2153 Fax 330/947-3331
Waterloo High Sch 1464 Industry Rd, Atwater 44201 Lori Sandel	9-12		315 25	34%	330/947-2124 Fax 330/947-1911
Waterloo Middle Sch 1464 Industry Rd, Atwater 44201 Lauren Willis	6-8		252 25		330/947-0033 Fax 330/947-4073

● **Windham Exempted Vlg Sch Dist** PID: 00828761   330/326-2711
9530 Bauer Ave, Windham 44288   Fax 330/326-2134

Schools: 3 \ *Teachers:* 44 \ *Students:* 600 \ *Special Ed Students:* 113 \ *College-Bound:* 29% \ *Ethnic:* African American 8%, Hispanic 1%, Caucasian 90% \ *Exp:* $279 (Med) \ *Poverty:* 18% \ *Title I:* $225,762 \ *Special Education:* $200,000 \ *Open-Close:* 08/26 - 05/28 \ *DTBP:* $209 (High)

Aireane Curtis 1   Samantha Pochedly 2,4
Jake Eye 3,5   Dj Gross 6*
Sherri Gross ....9,11,73*   Kathy Lovejoy 16,82*
Andrea Urso ....31*   Rose Stacy 31,36,83*
Alysia Tinker ....58*   Melissa Roubic 67
Melissa Jenkins 77   Sarah Isler 81
Andrew Rosebaugh ....280*   Amandra Brundage 285*

Public Schs..Principal	Grd	Prgm	Enr/#Cls	SN	
Katherine Thomas Elem Sch 9032 Maple Grove Rd, Windham 44288 Melissa Malone	PK-4	T	200 25		330/326-9800 Fax 330/326-9810
Windham High Sch 9530 Bauer Ave, Windham 44288 Justin Christopher	9-12	T	145 15		330/326-2711 Fax 330/326-2052
Windham Junior High Sch 9530 Bauer Ave, Windham 44288 Marco Marinucci	5-8	T	150 18		330/326-3490 Fax 330/326-3713

PORTAGE CATHOLIC SCHOOLS

● **Diocese of Youngstown Ed Off** PID: 00820915
Listing includes only schools located in this county. See District Index for location of Diocesan Offices.

Catholic Schs..Principal	Grd	Prgm	Enr/#Cls	SN	
St Joseph School-Randolph 2617 Waterloo Rd, Mogadore 44260 James Holzapfel	PK-8		163 9		330/628-9555 Fax 330/628-2709
St Patrick Sch 127 Portage St, Kent 44240 Howard Mancini	K-8		220 18		330/673-7232 Fax 330/678-6612

PORTAGE PRIVATE SCHOOLS

Private Schs..Principal	Grd	Prgm	Enr/#Cls	SN	
Bethel Baptist Christian Acad 745 N Freedom St, Ravenna 44266 Dr Daviid Ballert	K-12		90 12		330/296-9845
Harbor Education Serv Leap Prg 200 N Mantua St, Kent 44240 David Cooper	K-12		50		330/676-8674 Fax 330/676-8673
Valley Christian Academy 1037 East Blvd, Aurora 44202 Rachel Zook \ Sarah Telepak	K-8		282 16		330/562-8191 Fax 330/562-9257

79	Student Personnel	91	Safety/Security	275	Response To Intervention	298	Grant Writer/Ptnrships	**School Programs**
80	Driver Ed/Safety	92	Magnet School	277	Remedial Math K-12	750	Chief Innovation Officer	A = Alternative Program
81	Gifted/Talented	93	Parental Involvement	280	Literacy Coach	751	Chief of Staff	G = Adult Classes
82	Video Services	95	Tech Prep Program	285	STEM	752	Social Emotional Learning	M = Magnet Program
83	Substance Abuse Prev	97	Chief Information Officer	286	Digital Learning			T = Title I Schoolwide
84	Erate	98	Chief Technology Officer	288	Common Core Standards	**Other School Types**		V = Career & Tech Ed Programs
85	AIDS Education	270	Character Education	294	Accountability	Ⓐ = Alternative School		
88	Alternative/At Risk	271	Migrant Education	295	Network System	Ⓒ = Charter School		**Social Media**
89	Multi-Cultural Curriculum	273	Teacher Mentor	296	Title II Programs	Ⓜ = Magnet School		📘 = Facebook
90	Social Work	274	Before/After Sch	297	Webmaster	Ⓨ = Year-Round School		🇹 = Twitter

New Schools are shaded
New Superintendents and Principals are bold
Personnel with email addresses are underscored

Preble County

PREBLE COUNTY

PREBLE COUNTY SCHOOLS

- **Preble Co Ed Service Center** PID: 00829076 937/456-1187
  597 Hillcrest Dr, Eaton 45320 Fax 937/456-3253

Mike Gray	1	Kerry Borger	2
Shawn Huff	15	Rhonda Schaar	67

County Schs..Principal	Grd	Prgm	Enr/#Cls	SN	
Third Street Sch 45 N Main St, W Alexandria 45381 Shawn Hoff	Spec		25 4		937/839-3128

PREBLE PUBLIC SCHOOLS

- **Eaton Cmty School Dist** PID: 00828905 937/456-1107
  306 Eaton Lewisburg Rd, Eaton 45320 Fax 937/472-1057

  Schools: 4 \ **Teachers:** 113 \ **Students:** 1,943 \ **Special Ed Students:** 232 \ **LEP Students:** 15 \ **College-Bound:** 58% \ **Ethnic:** Asian 1%, African American 1%, Hispanic 2%, Caucasian 96% \ **Exp:** $165 (Low) \ **Poverty:** 10% \ **Title I:** $392,665 \ **Special Education:** $407,000 \ **Open-Close:** 08/21 - 06/02 \ **DTBP:** $229 (High)

Jeff Parker	1	Rachael Tait	2,84
Matt Robbins	3,5	Travis Miller	6
Dalene Sadowski	7*	Marvin Horton	8,11,57,58,77,81,288,296
Missy Imhoss	15,88,280,298	Lisa Noble	67
Stephen Woods	73,76		

Public Schs..Principal	Grd	Prgm	Enr/#Cls	SN	
Bruce Elem Sch 506B Aukerman St, Eaton 45320 Kip Powell	3-5	T	474 26	42%	937/456-3874 Fax 937/472-2092
Eaton High Sch 600 Hillcrest Dr, Eaton 45320 Scott Couch	9-12	V	566 50	36%	937/456-1141 Fax 937/456-1143
Eaton Middle Sch 814 Camden Rd, Eaton 45320 Brian Camp	6-8	T	479 25	34%	937/456-2286 Fax 937/456-9687
Hollingsworth East Elem Sch 506 Aukerman St, Eaton 45320 Teresa Woodin	K-2	T	424 22	43%	937/456-5173 Fax 937/456-4656

- **National Trail Local Sch Dist** PID: 00828838 937/437-3333
  6940 Oxford Gettysburg Rd, New Paris 45347 Fax 937/437-7865

  Schools: 3 \ **Teachers:** 65 \ **Students:** 1,100 \ **Special Ed Students:** 126 \ **College-Bound:** 52% \ **Ethnic:** Hispanic 2%, Caucasian 98% \ **Exp:** $167 (Low) \ **Poverty:** 16% \ **Title I:** $266,396 \ **Special Education:** $199,000 \ **Open-Close:** 08/20 - 05/28 \ **DTBP:** $186 (High)

Robert Fischer	1	Carrie Warger	2,19
Kerry Borger	2	Cindy Lee	67
Brian Pool	73,286*		

Public Schs..Principal	Grd	Prgm	Enr/#Cls	SN	
National Trail Elem Sch 6940 Oxford Gettysburg Rd, New Paris 45347 Ed Eales	K-4	T	356 26		937/437-3333 Fax 937/437-7306
National Trail High Sch 6940 Oxford Gettysburg Rd, New Paris 45347 Michael Eyler	9-12	TV	309 35	64%	937/437-3333 Fax 937/437-8270
National Trail Middle Sch 6940 Oxford Gettysburg Rd, New Paris 45347 Mike Eyler	5-8	T	333 25	84%	937/437-3333 Fax 937/437-7306

- **Preble-Shawnee Local Sch Dist** PID: 00828955 937/452-1283
  124 Bloomfield St, Camden 45311 Fax 937/452-3926

  Schools: 3 \ **Teachers:** 79 \ **Students:** 1,430 \ **Special Ed Students:** 184 \ **LEP Students:** 3 \ **College-Bound:** 46% \ **Ethnic:** Caucasian 99% \ **Exp:** $261 (Med) \ **Poverty:** 11% \ **Title I:** $228,770 \ **Special Education:** $292,000 \ **Open-Close:** 08/14 - 05/22 \ **DTBP:** $169 (High)

Dr Matt Bishop	1,11	Laurie Green	2,19
Luke Barnett	3	Kitty Line	5
Jaime Ranly	8	Rich Godfrey	36*
Ami Stevenson	38,69*	Jennifer Taulbee	58,88,270*
Julie Singleton	67	Jeff Johnson	73*

Public Schs..Principal	Grd	Prgm	Enr/#Cls	SN	
Camden Primary Sch 120 Bloomfield St, Camden 45311 Heather Campbell	PK-3	T	478 26	45%	937/452-1204 Fax 937/452-3787
Preble Shawnee Jr/Sr High Sch 5495 Somers Gratis Rd, Camden 45311 Dianna Whitis	7-12	T	597 40	46%	937/787-3541 Fax 937/787-3664
West Elkton Intermediate Sch 11751 State Rd 503, West Elkton 45070 Robert Morton	4-6	T	300 35	53%	937/787-4102 Fax 937/787-3453

- **Tri-Co North School Dist** PID: 02199487 937/962-2671
  436 N Commerce St, Lewisburg 45338 Fax 937/962-4731

  Schools: 3 \ **Teachers:** 47 \ **Students:** 786 \ **Special Ed Students:** 72 \ **College-Bound:** 49% \ **Ethnic:** Hispanic 1%, Caucasian 98% \ **Exp:** $282 (Med) \ **Poverty:** 12% \ **Title I:** $181,542 \ **Special Education:** $179,000 \ **Open-Close:** 08/19 - 05/28 \ **DTBP:** $30 (Low)

William Derringer	1	Lynn Ferguson	2
Denny Dyer	3,5	Angie Hodapp	4*
Kristen Mills	6*	Lisa Galpin	8,286,288*
Joe Finkbine	11,58,296,298*	James Norman	16,73,76*
Charity McMullen	27*	Vickie Woodyard	67
Elaina Ferriell	81*		

Public Schs..Principal	Grd	Prgm	Enr/#Cls	SN	
Tri-Co North Elem Sch 436 N Commerce St, Lewisburg 45338 Joe Finkbine	K-4	T	295 20		937/962-2673 Fax 937/833-4330
Tri-Co North High Sch 500 Panther Way, Lewisburg 45338 Joe Hoelzle	9-12	ATV	210 15		937/833-4830 Fax 937/833-4860
Tri-Co North Middle Sch 436 N Commerce St, Lewisburg 45338 Joe Hoelzle	5-8	TV	281 16	99%	937/962-2675 Fax 937/833-4860

1 Superintendent	8 Curric/Instruct K-12	19 Chief Financial Officer	29 Family/Consumer Science	39 Social Studies K-12	49 English/Lang Arts Elem	59 Special Education Elem	69 Academic Assessment
2 Bus/Finance/Purchasing	9 Curric/Instruct Elem	20 Art K-12	30 Adult Education	40 Social Studies Elem	50 English/Lang Arts Sec	60 Special Education Sec	70 Research/Development
3 Buildings And Grounds	10 Curric/Instruct Sec	21 Art Elem	31 Career/Sch-to-Work K-12	41 Social Studies Sec	51 Reading K-12	61 Foreign/World Lang K-12	71 Public Information
4 Food Service	11 Federal Program	22 Art Sec	32 Career/Sch-to-Work Elem	42 Science K-12	52 Reading Elem	62 Foreign/World Lang Elem	72 Summer School
5 Transportation	12 Title I	23 Music K-12	33 Career/Sch-to-Work Sec	43 Science Elem	53 Reading Sec	63 Foreign/World Lang Sec	73 Instructional Tech
6 Athletic	13 Title V	24 Music Elem	34 Early Childhood Ed	44 Science Sec	54 Remedial Reading K-12	64 Religious Education K-12	74 Inservice Training
7 Health Services	15 Asst Superintendent	25 Music Sec	35 Health/Phys Education	45 Math K-12	55 Remedial Reading Elem	65 Religious Education Elem	75 Marketing/Distributive
	16 Instructional Media Svcs	26 Business Education	36 Guidance Services K-12	46 Math Elem	56 Remedial Reading Sec	66 Religious Education Sec	76 Info Systems
	17 Chief Operations Officer	27 Career & Tech Ed	37 Guidance Services Elem	47 Math Sec	57 Bilingual/ELL	67 School Board President	77 Psychological Assess
	18 Chief Academic Officer	28 Technology Education	38 Guidance Services Sec	48 English/Lang Arts K-12	58 Special Education K-12	68 Teacher Personnel	78 Affirmative Action

Ohio School Directory   Putnam County

- **Twin Valley Cmty Local SD** PID: 00829002   937/839-4688
  100 Education Dr, W Alexandria 45381   Fax 937/839-4898

Schools: 2 \ **Teachers:** 57 \ **Students:** 837 \ **Special Ed Students:** 108 \ **LEP Students:** 4 \ **College-Bound:** 55% \ **Ethnic:** Hispanic 1%, Caucasian 99% \ **Exp:** $333 (High) \ **Poverty:** 13% \ **Title I:** $177,068 \ **Special Education:** $167,000 \ **Open-Close:** 08/19 - 05/28 \ **DTBP:** $53 (Low)

Scott Cottingim 1,11	Tearalee Riddlebarger 2
Jeff Tully 3,5	Anthony Augspurger 6*
Vicki Unger 7	Patti Holly 9,12*
W Joe Schaller 11	Kathy Oaster 16,82
Ben Carpenter 35,85*	Jane Cottingim 38,83*
Jim Pemberton 67	Derrick Myers 297*

Public Schs..Principal	Grd	Prgm	Enr/#Cls	SN	
Twin Valley Middle High Sch	7-12	V	288	99%	937/839-4693
100 Education Dr, W Alexandria 45381			44		Fax 937/839-4165
Derek Flatter					
Twin Valley South Elem Sch	K-6	T	446		937/839-4315
100 Education Dr, W Alexandria 45381			33		Fax 937/839-5541
Patti Holly					

PUTNAM COUNTY

PUTNAM COUNTY SCHOOLS

- **Putnam Co Ed Service Center** PID: 02089260   419/523-5951
  124 Putnam Pkwy, Ottawa 45875   Fax 419/523-6126

Dr Jan Osborn 1,11	Mike Siebeneck 2
Melissa Basinger 9,81	Gary Herman 10
Karen Maag 27,58	Emily Lammers 34
Tricia Boss 58	William Goecke 67
Alex Hughes 73,76,295	Daniel Vonderembse 77,79

PUTNAM PUBLIC SCHOOLS

- **Columbus Grove Local Sch Dist** PID: 00829088   419/659-2639
  201 W Cross St, Columbus GRV 45830   Fax 419/659-5134

Schools: 2 \ **Teachers:** 56 \ **Students:** 879 \ **Special Ed Students:** 145 \ **College-Bound:** 68% \ **Ethnic:** Asian 1%, African American 1%, Hispanic 5%, Caucasian 92% \ **Exp:** $222 (Med) \ **Poverty:** 8% \ **Title I:** $104,290 \ **Special Education:** $177,000 \ **Open-Close:** 08/21 - 05/22 \ **DTBP:** $53 (Low)

Nicholas Verhoff 1	Mark Ellerbrock 2
Dale Schroeder 3*	Kristen Hertel 4*
Terry Schnipke 6*	Katie Zimmerman 7
Brian Best 8,285*	Sally Spitnale 12
Sue Ricker 16,82*	Ann Fought 29
Brenda Bruce 31,36,83*	Brad Brudakor 67
Mike Keehn 73,76*	Mike Keehn 84

Public Schs..Principal	Grd	Prgm	Enr/#Cls	SN	
Columbus Grove Elem Sch	K-6	T	399		419/659-2631
201 W Cross St, Columbus GRV 45830			20		Fax 419/659-4327
Brad Calvelage					
Columbus Grove High Sch	7-12	AV	400	85%	419/659-2156
201 W Cross St, Columbus GRV 45830			35		
Brian Best					

- **Continental Local School Dist** PID: 00829129   419/596-3671
  5211 State Route 634, Continental 45831   Fax 419/596-3861

Schools: 2 \ **Teachers:** 38 \ **Students:** 480 \ **Special Ed Students:** 107 \ **LEP Students:** 3 \ **College-Bound:** 34% \ **Ethnic:** Hispanic 4%, Caucasian 96% \ **Exp:** $326 (High) \ **Poverty:** 8% \ **Title I:** $60,740 \ **Special Education:** $117,000 \ **Open-Close:** 08/20 - 05/21

Danny Kissell 1	Katelyn Adams 2
Mark Siebeneck 3*	Sarah Goedde 4*
Jordan Striker 6	Tracy Potts 12,274
Erin Schmidt 38	Debra McIntyre 57,69,83,85,88*
Dean Bidlick 67	Keith Schnipke 73,76*

Public Schs..Principal	Grd	Prgm	Enr/#Cls	SN	
Continental Local Elem Sch	K-6	T	266	42%	419/596-3860
5211 State Route 634, Continental 45831			18		Fax 419/596-2652
Tracy Potts					
Continental Local High Sch	7-12		194	44%	419/596-3871
5211 State Route 634, Continental 45831			30		Fax 419/596-2651
Tim Eding					

- **Jennings Local School Dist** PID: 00829155   419/286-2238
  1 Musketeer Dr, Fort Jennings 45844   Fax 419/286-2240

Schools: 1 \ **Teachers:** 27 \ **Students:** 400 \ **Special Ed Students:** 38 \ **College-Bound:** 78% \ **Exp:** $362 (High) \ **Poverty:** 5% \ **Title I:** $30,058 \ **Special Education:** $72,000 \ **Open-Close:** 08/19 - 05/21 \ **DTBP:** $183 (High)

Nicholas Langhals 1,288	Valerie Maag 2
Rodney Ricker 3*	Todd Hoehn 6,35*
Matthew Dube 11*	Rob Warnecke 16,73,295*
Mike Leach 36,69*	Cliff Wieging 67

Public Schs..Principal	Grd	Prgm	Enr/#Cls	SN	
Ⓨ Jennings Local Sch	K-12	M	400		419/286-2238
1 Musketeer Dr, Fort Jennings 45844			35		
Matthew Dube \ Nick Langhals					

- **Kalida Local School Dist** PID: 00829181   419/532-3534
  301 N 3rd St, Kalida 45853   Fax 419/532-2277

Schools: 2 \ **Teachers:** 39 \ **Students:** 605 \ **Special Ed Students:** 73 \ **College-Bound:** 88% \ **Ethnic:** Caucasian 100% \ **Exp:** $230 (Med) \ **Poverty:** 2% \ **Title I:** $14,025 \ **Special Education:** $101,000 \ **Open-Close:** 08/19 - 05/20 \ **DTBP:** $13 (Low)

Karl Lammers 1,11,83	Cindy Webken 2
Sarah Neidert 4*	Adam Huber 6*
Denise Scherer 16*	Samantha Norman 27
Jeff Clement 36,69*	Kevin Deitering 63*
Craig Schmenk 67	Jeremy Okuley 73,76,295*

79 Student Personnel	91 Safety/Security	275 Response To Intervention	298 Grant Writer/Ptnrships	**School Programs**	**Social Media**
80 Driver Ed/Safety	92 Magnet School	277 Remedial Math K-12	750 Chief Innovation Officer	A = Alternative Program	
81 Gifted/Talented	93 Parental Involvement	280 Literacy Coach	751 Chief of Staff	G = Adult Classes	🅕 = Facebook
82 Video Services	95 Tech Prep Program	285 STEM	752 Social Emotional Learning	M = Magnet Program	
83 Substance Abuse Prev	97 Chief Information Officer	286 Digital Learning		T = Title I Schoolwide	🅣 = Twitter
84 Erate	98 Chief Technology Officer	288 Common Core Standards	**Other School Types**	V = Career & Tech Ed Programs	
85 AIDS Education	270 Character Education	294 Accountability	Ⓐ = Alternative School		
88 Alternative/At Risk	271 Migrant Education	295 Network System	Ⓒ = Charter School	New Schools are shaded	
89 Multi-Cultural Curriculum	273 Teacher Mentor	296 Title II Programs	Ⓜ = Magnet School	New Superintendents and Principals are bold	
90 Social Work	274 Before/After Sch	297 Webmaster	Ⓨ = Year-Round School	Personnel with email addresses are underscored	

OH–169

Putnam County

Public Schs..Principal	Grd	Prgm	Enr/#Cls	SN	
Kalida Elem Sch 208 N 4th St, Kalida 45853 Kathleen Verhoff	K-4		250 16	10%	419/532-3845 Fax 419/532-3541
Kalida High Sch 301 N 3rd St, Kalida 45853 Dean Brinkman	5-12	V	338 25	11%	419/532-3529 Fax 419/532-3581

● **Leipsic Local School Dist** PID: 00829210 419/943-2165
232 Oak St, Leipsic 45856 Fax 419/943-4331

Schools: 2 \ *Teachers:* 48 \ *Students:* 650 \ *Special Ed Students:* 129 \ *LEP Students:* 37 \ *College-Bound:* 52% \ *Ethnic:* Asian 1%, Hispanic 45%, Caucasian 53% \ *Exp:* $203 (Med) \ *Poverty:* 13% \ *Title I:* $129,867 \ *Special Education:* $148,000 \ *Open-Close:* 08/20 - 05/22 \ *DTBP:* $164 (High) \ 🅕 🅣

Greg Williamson 1,11	David Miller 2
Sam Walther 3,67	Christa Lammers 5
Gary Kreinbrink 6*	Darren Henry 9*
Brian Bennett 10*	Judy Dukes 12*
Julie Recker 31,36,69,83,88,270*	Andrea Wagner 57*
Megan Tobe 58,79,285,298	Sharon Siebeneck 73,295*

Public Schs..Principal	Grd	Prgm	Enr/#Cls	SN	
Leipsic High Sch 232 Oak St, Leipsic 45856 Brian Bennett	6-12	TV	318 50	43%	419/943-2165 Fax 419/943-2185
Leipsic Local Sch 232 Oak St, Leipsic 45856 Darren Henry	K-5	T	335 40	58%	419/943-2165 Fax 419/943-2185

● **Miller City-New Cleveland SD** PID: 00829246 419/876-3172
200 N Main St, Miller City 45864 Fax 419/876-2020

Schools: 3 \ *Teachers:* 34 \ *Students:* 485 \ *Special Ed Students:* 51 \ *College-Bound:* 98% \ *Ethnic:* Hispanic 1%, Caucasian 99% \ *Exp:* $145 (Low) \ *Poverty:* 4% \ *Title I:* $11,009 \ *Special Education:* $78,000 \ *Open-Close:* 08/19 - 05/21 \ *DTBP:* $172 (High) \ 🅕

Kerry Johnson 1	Mike Siebeneck 2
Deb Lammage 6*	Jamie Nuveman 6*
Dustin Pester 11*	Katie Lehman 12*
Kristi Hoffman 36,69,83,88*	Michael Klear 67
Jared Kern 73*	

Public Schs..Principal	Grd	Prgm	Enr/#Cls	SN	
Miller City Elem Sch 200 North Main Street, Miller City 45864 Dustin Pester	K-5		225 20		419/876-3174
Miller City High Sch 200 N Main Street, Miller City 45864 Kerry Johnson	9-12	V	140 15	18%	419/876-3173
Miller City Middle Sch 200 N Main Street, Miller City 45864 Dustin Pester	6-8		118 8		419/876-3173

● **Ottawa-Glandorf Local Sch Dist** PID: 00829284 419/523-5261
630 Glendale Ave, Ottawa 45875 Fax 419/523-5978

Schools: 4 \ *Teachers:* 87 \ *Students:* 1,400 \ *Special Ed Students:* 218 \ *LEP Students:* 9 \ *College-Bound:* 62% \ *Ethnic:* African American 1%, Hispanic 13%, Caucasian 86% \ *Exp:* $267 (Med) \ *Poverty:* 6% \ *Title I:* $130,251 \ *Special Education:* $303,000 \ *Open-Close:* 08/21 - 05/21 \ *DTBP:* $199 (High)

Don Horseman 1,11	Kathy Fruchey 2
Colleen Halker 4*	Tyson McLoughlin 6*
Paula Ruhe 7*	Jennifer Croy 8,11,58,69,274,296*
Kelly Vonsossan 16*	Brent Schroeder 67
Justin Closson 73,295*	

Public Schs..Principal	Grd	Prgm	Enr/#Cls	SN	
Glandorf Elem Sch 140 Church St, Glandorf 45848 Scott Ketner	K-8		585 35	8%	419/538-6880 Fax 419/538-6115
Ottawa Elem Sch 123 Putnam Pkwy, Ottawa 45875 Audrey Beining	K-8	T	421 48	50%	419/523-4290 Fax 419/523-6032
Ottawa-Glandorf High Sch 630 Glendale Ave, Ottawa 45875 Jayson Selgo	9-12		495 32	20%	419/523-5702 Fax 419/523-6346
Titan Tikes Pre-School 630 Glendale Ave, Ottawa 45875 Dawn Hunt	PK-PK		49 1		419/523-6464

● **Ottoville Local School Dist** PID: 00829325 419/453-3356
650 W 3rd St, Ottoville 45876 Fax 419/453-3367

Schools: 2 \ *Teachers:* 33 \ *Students:* 430 \ *Special Ed Students:* 61 \ *College-Bound:* 67% \ *Ethnic:* Caucasian 99% \ *Exp:* $330 (High) \ *Poverty:* 2% \ *Title I:* $12,521 \ *Special Education:* $83,000 \ *Open-Close:* 08/20 - 05/21 \ *DTBP:* $176 (High) \ 🅕

Scott Mangas 1,288	Robert Weber 2
Mark Odenweller 6,90*	Jon Thorbahn 10*
Diane Worth 11	Sharon Rellinger 16,82*
Shelley Mumaw 16,73,298*	Michelle Leach 36,58,69,85,270*
Kevin Landin 67	Connie Rhodes 69,83,275
Denny Mumahl 286	

Public Schs..Principal	Grd	Prgm	Enr/#Cls	SN	
Ottoville Elem Sch 650 W 3rd St, Ottoville 45876 Scott Mangas	K-5	A	233 19		419/453-3357 🅕
Ottoville High Sch 650 W 3rd St, Ottoville 45876 Jon Thorbahn	6-12	AV	215	27%	419/453-3358 Fax 419/453-3368 🅕

● **Pandora Gilboa Local Sch Dist** PID: 00829351 419/384-3225
410 Rocket Rdg, Pandora 45877 Fax 419/384-3230

Schools: 3 \ *Teachers:* 43 \ *Students:* 524 \ *Special Ed Students:* 81 \ *College-Bound:* 64% \ *Ethnic:* Hispanic 5%, Caucasian 95% \ *Exp:* $354 (High) \ *Poverty:* 5% \ *Title I:* $42,404 \ *Special Education:* $103,000 \ *Open-Close:* 08/19 - 05/20 \ *DTBP:* $176 (High)

Todd Schmutz 1	Brad Deleruyelle 2
Mary Miller 4*	Zach Weber 5,6
Lori Traxler 13,16,82*	Cheryl Schmiesing 36*
Jodi Schroeder 59*	Kati Amstutz 67
Eric Vennekotter 73*	Eric Vennekotter 84,295

1	Superintendent	8	Curric/Instruct K-12	19	Chief Financial Officer	29	Family/Consumer Science	39	Social Studies K-12	49	English/Lang Arts Elem	59	Special Education Elem	69	Academic Assessment
2	Bus/Finance/Purchasing	9	Curric/Instruct Elem	20	Art K-12	30	Adult Education	40	Social Studies Elem	50	English/Lang Arts Sec	60	Special Education Sec	70	Research/Development
3	Buildings And Grounds	10	Curric/Instruct Sec	21	Art Elem	31	Career/Sch-to-Work K-12	41	Social Studies Sec	51	Reading K-12	61	Foreign/World Lang K-12	71	Public Information
4	Food Service	11	Federal Program	22	Art Sec	32	Career/Sch-to-Work Elem	42	Science K-12	52	Reading Elem	62	Foreign/World Lang Elem	72	Summer School
5	Transportation	12	Title I	23	Music K-12	33	Career/Sch-to-Work Sec	43	Science Elem	53	Reading Sec	63	Foreign/World Lang Sec	73	Instructional Tech
6	Athletic	13	Title V	24	Music Elem	34	Early Childhood Ed	44	Science Sec	54	Remedial Reading K-12	64	Religious Education K-12	74	Inservice Training
7	Health Services	15	Asst Superintendent	25	Music Sec	35	Health/Phys Education	45	Math K-12	55	Remedial Reading Elem	65	Religious Education Elem	75	Marketing/Distributive
		16	Instructional Media Svcs	26	Business Education	36	Guidance Services K-12	46	Math Elem	56	Remedial Reading Sec	66	Religious Education Sec	76	Info Systems
		17	Chief Operations Officer	27	Career & Tech Ed	37	Guidance Services Elem	47	Math Sec	57	Bilingual/ELL	67	School Board President	77	Psychological Assess
		18	Chief Academic Officer	28	Technology Education	38	Guidance Services Sec	48	English/Lang Arts K-12	58	Special Education K-12	68	Teacher Personnel	78	Affirmative Action

Ohio School Directory — Richland County

Public Schs..Principal	Grd	Prgm	Enr/#Cls	SN	
Pandora Gilboa Elem Sch 410 Rocket Rdg, Pandora 45877 Jodi Schroeder	K-4		184 18		419/384-3225 Fax 419/384-2330
Pandora Gilboa High Sch 410 Rocket Rdg, Pandora 45877 Jeff Wise	9-12		160 9	73%	419/384-3225 Fax 419/384-3220
Pandora Gilboa Middle Sch 410 Rocket Rdg, Pandora 45877 Jodi Schroeder	5-8		180 10		419/384-3225

PUTNAM CATHOLIC SCHOOLS

● **Diocese of Toledo Ed Office** PID: 00818297
Listing includes only schools located in this county. See District Index for location of Diocesan Offices.

Catholic Schs..Principal	Grd	Prgm	Enr/#Cls	SN	
SS Peter & Paul Sch 320 N Locust St, Ottawa 45875 Connie Niese	K-8		240 16		419/523-3697 Fax 419/523-3463
St Anthony of Padua Sch 520 W Sycamore St, Columbus GRV 45830 Nancy Dukes	K-8		100 9		419/659-2103 Fax 419/659-4194
St Mary Sch 129 Saint Marys St, Leipsic 45856 Michelle Knippen	K-8		80 9		419/943-2801 Fax 419/943-3555

RICHLAND COUNTY

RICHLAND COUNTY SCHOOLS

● **Mid-Ohio Ed Service Center** PID: 00830075   419/774-5520
890 W 4th St Ste 100, Mansfield 44906   Fax 419/774-5523

Linda Keller 1   Lorraine Earnest 2
Amanda Mahon 8,16   Adrian Randall 27,58,79
Toni Zehe 34   Lisa Cook 68
Mark Donnelly 73   Leanna Ferreira 81

County Schs..Principal	Grd	Prgm	Enr/#Cls	SN	
Mid Ohio Pre-School 890 W 4th St Ste 200, Mansfield 44906 Christy Roqueplot	Spec		125 4		419/774-5556 Fax 419/774-6394
Richland Academy of Excellence 75 N Walnut St, Mansfield 44902 Sandra Sutherland	K-8		196		419/522-8224 Fax 419/522-8228
Richland-New Hope Sch 255 Hedges St, Mansfield 44902 Julie Litt	Spec		85 8		419/774-4277

RICHLAND PUBLIC SCHOOLS

● **Clear Fork Vly Local Sch Dist** PID: 00829404   419/886-3855
211 School St, Bellville 44813   Fax 419/886-2237

Schools: 4 \ *Teachers:* 103 \ *Students:* 1,692 \ *Special Ed Students:* 244 \ *LEP Students:* 3 \ *College-Bound:* 60% \ *Ethnic:* Hispanic 2%, Caucasian 97% \ *Exp:* $226 (Med) \ *Poverty:* 12% \ *Title I:* $273,904 \ *Special Education:* $319,000 \ *Open-Close:* 08/20 - 05/19 \ *DTBP:* $169 (High) \ f

Janice Wyckoff 1,11   Bradd Stevens 2,30
Kevin Carr 3   Jennifer Stallard 4
Lisa Yarger 5   Jeffrey Gottfried 6*
Cindy Ridenour .... 12* Adam Staley 27*
Cindy Truex .... 38,69,83,85* Heidi McDaniel 58
Amy Weekley 67   Cindy Kochheiser 73,82*
Kathy Quickle 81*

Public Schs..Principal	Grd	Prgm	Enr/#Cls	SN	
Bellville Elem Sch 195 School St, Bellville 44813 Stacey Swank	K-5	T	414 22	32%	419/886-3244 Fax 419/886-3851
Butler Elem Sch 125 College St, Butler 44822 Libby Nickoli	K-5	T	298 18	43%	419/883-3451 Fax 419/883-3395
Clear Fork High Sch 987 State Route 97 E, Bellville 44813 Brian Brown	9-12	V	497 45	63%	419/886-2601 Fax 419/886-4749
Clear Fork Middle Sch 987 State Route 97 E, Bellville 44813 Jennifer Klaus	6-8	T	400 40		419/886-3111 Fax 419/886-4749

● **Crestview Local School Dist** PID: 00829442   419/895-1700
1575 State Route 96, Ashland 44805   Fax 419/895-1733

Schools: 3 \ *Teachers:* 71 \ *Students:* 1,100 \ *Special Ed Students:* 131 \ *Ethnic:* Hispanic 1%, Caucasian 99% \ *Exp:* $302 (High) \ *Poverty:* 17% \ *Title I:* $356,082 \ *Special Education:* $188,000 \ *Open-Close:* 08/21 - 05/28 \ *DTBP:* $181 (High)

Randy Dunlap 1,11   Beth Lykins 2
Gene Esbenshade 3   Ray Cunningham 5
Timothy Kuhn .... 6*   Christi Barker 8,11,34,58,288*
Christopher Gilbert 9   Adrew Ditlevson 10
Chad Ditlevson 10   David Ditlevson 10
Kayla Brooks 38,83   Debbie Reidy 67
Sherry Rickter 81   Dave Stevens 84,95

Public Schs..Principal	Grd	Prgm	Enr/#Cls	SN	
Crestview Elem Sch 1575 State Route 96, Ashland 44805 **Chris Gilbert**	K-3	T	276 18	38%	419/895-1700 f
Crestview High Sch 1575 State Route 96, Ashland 44805 Andrew Ditlevson	9-12	V	321 28	35%	419/895-1700 Fax 419/895-3103
Crestview Middle Sch 1575 State Route 96, Ashland 44805 Chad Lemon	4-8	T	443 45	38%	419/895-1700

---

79 Student Personnel	91 Safety/Security	275 Response To Intervention	298 Grant Writer/Ptnrships
80 Driver Ed/Safety	92 Magnet School	277 Remedial Math K-12	750 Chief Innovation Officer
81 Gifted/Talented	93 Parental Involvement	280 Literacy Coach	751 Chief of Staff
82 Video Services	95 Tech Prep Program	285 STEM	752 Social Emotional Learning
83 Substance Abuse Prev	97 Chief Infomation Officer	286 Digital Learning	
84 Erate	98 Chief Technology Officer	288 Common Core Standards	**Other School Types**
85 AIDS Education	270 Character Education	294 Accountability	Ⓐ = Alternative School
88 Alternative/At Risk	271 Migrant Education	295 Network System	Ⓒ = Charter School
89 Multi-Cultural Curriculum	273 Teacher Mentor	296 Title II Programs	Ⓜ = Magnet School
90 Social Work	274 Before/After Sch	297 Webmaster	Ⓨ = Year-Round School

School Programs
A = Alternative Program
G = Adult Classes
M = Magnet Program
T = Title I Schoolwide
V = Career & Tech Ed Programs

Social Media
f = Facebook
t = Twitter

New Schools are shaded
New Superintendents and Principals are bold
Personnel with email addresses are underscored

Richland County

Market Data Retrieval

- **Lexington Local School Dist** PID: 00829480   419/884-2132
  103 Clever Ln, Lexington 44904   Fax 419/884-3129

Schools: 5 \ *Teachers:* 126 \ *Students:* 2,510 \ *Special Ed Students:* 312 \ *LEP Students:* 24 \ *College-Bound:* 74% \ *Ethnic:* Asian 2%, African American 1%, Hispanic 3%, Caucasian 94% \ *Exp:* $165 (Low) \ *Poverty:* 10% \ *Title I:* $338,082 \ *Special Education:* $494,000 \ *Open-Close:* 08/21 - 05/28 \ *DTBP:* $185 (High)

J Michael Ziegelhofer 1,11	Jason Whitesel 2
Tricia Volz 4*	Robin Boggs 5
Michael Grist 6	Joy Bowman 8,57*
Tucker Bacquet 10*	Jeremy Secrist 15
Emily Patterson 16,82*	Tracy McDaniel 58
Robert Whitney 67	Levi Mowry 73,76,95*

Public Schs..Principal	Grd	Prgm	Enr/#Cls	SN	
Central Elem Sch 124 Frederick St, Lexington 44904 Kathleen Weidig	K-4		376 20	33%	419/884-1308 Fax 419/884-6154
Eastern Elem Sch 155 Castor Rd, Lexington 44904 Buddy Miller	4-6		500 20	30%	419/884-3610 Fax 419/884-2987
Lexington High Sch 103 Clever Ln, Lexington 44904 Kevin Young	9-12		800 65	19%	419/884-1111 Fax 419/884-2340
Lexington Junior High Sch 90 Frederick St, Lexington 44904 Taylor Gerhardt	7-8		405 30	26%	419/884-2112 Fax 419/884-0134
Western Elem Sch 385 W Main St, Lexington 44904 Genelle Eggerton	PK-3		400 19	22%	419/884-2765 Fax 419/884-2221

- **Lucas Local School Dist** PID: 00829545   419/892-2338
  84 Lucas North Rd, Lucas 44843   Fax 419/892-1138

Schools: 3 \ *Teachers:* 36 \ *Students:* 565 \ *Special Ed Students:* 50 \ *College-Bound:* 55% \ *Ethnic:* Hispanic 1%, Caucasian 98% \ *Exp:* $369 (High) \ *Poverty:* 10% \ *Title I:* $75,639 \ *Special Education:* $138,000 \ *Open-Close:* 08/20 - 05/28 \ *DTBP:* $178 (High)

Bradley Herman 1	Larry Lifer 2,11
Brian Sauder 3	Nancy Sgambellone 4
Mark Sauder 5	Eric Teague 6*
Dale Deschner 12*	Bob Lewis 16,71,73,295*
Kelly Mongold 36,83,88*	Lillie Shelby 59*
Ron Saunders 60*	Tim Cooper 67
Mark Roseberry 273*	

Public Schs..Principal	Grd	Prgm	Enr/#Cls	SN	
Lucas Elem Sch 84 Lucas North Rd, Lucas 44843 Kari Case	K-5		237 12	74%	419/892-2338
Lucas Heritage Middle Sch 80 Lucas North Rd, Lucas 44843 Kari Case	6-7		80 7		419/892-2338
Lucas High Sch 5 1st Ave, Lucas 44843 **Dr Jim Metcalf**	8-12	A	199 24		419/892-2338

- **Madison Local School Dist** PID: 00829571   419/589-2600
  1379 Grace St, Mansfield 44905   Fax 419/589-3653

Schools: 5 \ *Teachers:* 214 \ *Students:* 2,956 \ *Special Ed Students:* 466 \ *LEP Students:* 3 \ *College-Bound:* 60% \ *Ethnic:* African American 4%, Hispanic 3%, Caucasian 92% \ *Exp:* $156 (Low) \ *Poverty:* 19% \ *Title I:* $998,841 \ *Special Education:* $677,000 \ *Open-Close:* 08/15 - 05/20 \ *DTBP:* $197 (High)

John Thomas 1	Robin Klenk 2
Steve Crist 3,91	Kim Pfleiderer 4
Michael Yost 5	Renee Neron 8,69,285,288
Lisa Gonzales 11,296,298	Michelle Frederick 16,82*
Scott Musser 27,75	Sonja Pluck 30*
Olivia Sigfreid 34	Dr Patricia Tresey 34,57,58,88,90,275*
Jeff Meyers 67	Steve Barr 73,76,286,295*

Public Schs..Principal	Grd	Prgm	Enr/#Cls	SN	
Eastview Elem Sch 1262 Eastview Dr, Mansfield 44905 Missy Wigton	K-4	T	283 20	59%	419/589-7335 Fax 419/589-3031
Madison Comprehensive High Sch 600 Esley Ln, Mansfield 44905 Robert Peterson	9-12	T	900 60	56%	419/589-2112 Fax 419/589-2533
Madison Middle Sch 1419 Grace St, Mansfield 44905 Jonathan Muro	5-8	T	956 80	59%	419/522-0471 Fax 419/522-1463
Madison South Elem Sch 700 S Illinois Ave, Mansfield 44907 Melissa Warner	PK-4	T	553 35	76%	419/522-4319 Fax 419/526-2911
Mifflin Elem Sch 441 Reed Rd, Mansfield 44903 Nathan Stump	K-4	T	287 18	51%	419/589-6517 Fax 419/589-6659

- **Mansfield City Schools** PID: 00829674   419/525-6400
  856 W Cook Rd, Mansfield 44907   Fax 419/525-6415

Schools: 8 \ *Teachers:* 229 \ *Students:* 3,350 \ *Special Ed Students:* 947 \ *LEP Students:* 12 \ *College-Bound:* 30% \ *Ethnic:* Asian 1%, African American 34%, Hispanic 4%, Caucasian 62% \ *Exp:* $185 (Low) \ *Poverty:* 32% \ *Title I:* $2,830,921 \ *Special Education:* $1,085,000 \ *Open-Close:* 08/22 - 06/01 \ *DTBP:* $271 (High)

Stan Jefferson 1	Robert Kuehmle 2
Erin Mudra 4	Lauren Moran 4
Deb Rickert 5	Kevin Porter 6*
Stephen Rizzo 8,12,18,73,288	Holly Christie 11,51,55,79,81,296
Jonathan Burras 58	Benda Clien 67
Mark Wilchuck 68	Larry Gibbs 71
Fayette Adams 73	Ken Abshire 295

Public Schs..Principal	Grd	Prgm	Enr/#Cls	SN	
Malabar Intermediate Sch 205 W Cook Rd, Mansfield 44907 Andrea Moyer	4-6	T	710 65	89%	419/525-6374 Fax 419/525-6376
Mansfield Middle Sch 124 N Linden Rd, Mansfield 44906 **Dr Milton Folson**	7-8	TV	467	84%	419/525-6307 Fax 419/525-6306
Mansfield Senior High Sch 124 N Linden Rd, Mansfield 44906 Dr Milton Folson	9-12	ATV	797 50	82%	419/525-6369 Fax 419/524-2210
Prospect Elem Sch 485 Gilbert Ave, Mansfield 44907 Jason Douglas	K-3	T	221 14	95%	419/525-6313 Fax 419/525-6312
Sherman Elem Sch 1138 Springmill St, Mansfield 44906 Michael Brennan	K-3	T	418 32	90%	419/525-6337 Fax 419/525-6340

1	Superintendent	8	Curric/Instruct K-12	19	Chief Financial Officer	29	Family/Consumer Science	39	Social Studies K-12	49	English/Lang Arts Elem	59	Special Education Elem	69	Academic Assessment
2	Bus/Finance/Purchasing	9	Curric/Instruct Elem	20	Art K-12	30	Adult Education	40	Social Studies Elem	50	English/Lang Arts Sec	60	Special Education Sec	70	Research/Development
3	Buildings And Grounds	10	Curric/Instruct Sec	21	Art Elem	31	Career/Sch-to-Work K-12	41	Social Studies Sec	51	Reading K-12	61	Foreign/World Lang K-12	71	Public Information
4	Food Service	11	Federal Program	22	Art Sec	32	Career/Sch-to-Work Elem	42	Science K-12	52	Reading Elem	62	Foreign/World Lang Elem	72	Summer School
5	Transportation	12	Title I	23	Music K-12	33	Career/Sch-to-Work Sec	43	Science Elem	53	Reading Sec	63	Foreign/World Lang Sec	73	Instructional Tech
6	Athletic	13	Title V	24	Music Elem	34	Early Childhood Ed	44	Science Sec	54	Remedial Reading K-12	64	Religious Education K-12	74	Inservice Training
7	Health Services	14	Instructional Media Svcs	25	Music Sec	35	Health/Phys Education	45	Math K-12	55	Remedial Reading Elem	65	Religious Education Elem	75	Marketing/Distributive
		15	Asst Superintendent	26	Business Education	36	Guidance Services K-12	46	Math Elem	56	Remedial Reading Sec	66	Religious Education Sec	76	Info Systems
		16	Chief Operations Officer	27	Career & Tech Ed	37	Guidance Services Elem	47	Math Sec	57	Bilingual/ELL	67	School Board President	77	Psychological Assess
		18	Chief Academic Officer	28	Technology Education	38	Guidance Services Sec	48	English/Lang Arts K-12	58	Special Education K-12	68	Teacher Personnel	78	Affirmative Action

Ohio School Directory
Richland County

Spanish Immersion Sch	K-8	T	250	48%	419/525-6321
240 Euclid Ave, Mansfield 44903					Fax 419/525-6386
Gabriel Costa					
Springmill STEM Elem Sch	PK-2	T	250	85%	419/525-6348
1200 Nestor Dr, Mansfield 44906					Fax 419/747-6284
Regina Sackman					
Woodland Elem Sch	K-3	T	184	84%	419/525-6325
460 Davis Rd, Mansfield 44907			15		Fax 419/525-6392
Michael Brennan					

● **Ontario Local School Dist** PID: 00829997   419/747-4311
457 Shelby Ontario Rd, Ontario 44906   Fax 419/747-6859

> *Schools:* 3 \ *Teachers:* 93 \ *Students:* 2,158 \ *Special Ed Students:* 171 \ *LEP Students:* 18 \ *College-Bound:* 63% \ *Ethnic:* Asian 3%, African American 5%, Hispanic 3%, Caucasian 89% \ *Exp:* $268 (Med) \ *Poverty:* 9% \ *Title I:* $199,411 \ *Special Education:* $236,000 \ *Open-Close:* 08/19 - 05/29 \ *DTBP:* $100 (High) \ 🅵 🆃

Lisa Carmichael 1		Randy Harvey 2,11		
Pat Duffner 3,5		Eva Harmon 4*		
Jeff Fisher 6		Mike Ream 8,11,288,296*		
Julia Miller 16*		Karling Ward 58*		
Heidi Zimmerman 67		Brendan Cain 73		
Amy Nagel 83		Natalie Thomas 273*		

Public Schs..Principal	Grd	Prgm	Enr/#Cls	SN	
Ontario High Sch	9-12		555	29%	419/529-3969
467 Shelby Ontario Rd, Ontario 44906			26		Fax 419/529-5649
Christopher Smith					
Ontario Middle Sch	6-8		517	34%	419/529-5507
447 Shelby Ontario Rd, Mansfield 44906			40		Fax 419/529-7058
Sue Weirich					
Stingel Elem Sch	PK-5	T	962		419/529-4955
426 Shelby Ontario Rd, Ontario 44906			15		Fax 419/529-2392
Mike Ream					

● **Pioneer Joint Voc School Dist** PID: 00830051   419/347-7926
27 Ryan Rd, Shelby 44875   Fax 419/347-4709

> *Schools:* 1 \ *Teachers:* 95 \ *Students:* 1,250 \ *LEP Students:* 4 \ *Exp:* $265 (Med) \ *Open-Close:* 08/20 - 05/28 \ *DTBP:* $256 (High) \ 🅵 🆃

Gregory Nickoli 1	Lynda Schumacher 2,19	
Mike Grimwood 3	Jason Fortman 4*	
Karrie Davison 16,82*	Donald Paullin 26,75	
Matt Parr 29	Jennifer Magers 60	
Douglas Theaker 67	Luke Brenneman 73*	

Public Schs..Principal	Grd	Prgm	Enr/#Cls	SN	
Pioneer Career & Tech Center	Voc	G	1,250		419/347-7744
27 Ryan Rd, Shelby 44875			125		Fax 419/347-4977
Gregory Nickoli					🅵🆃

● **Plymouth-Shiloh Local Sch Dist** PID: 00829882   419/687-4733
365 Sandusky St, Plymouth 44865   Fax 419/687-1541

> *Schools:* 3 \ *Teachers:* 50 \ *Students:* 681 \ *Special Ed Students:* 110 \ *LEP Students:* 6 \ *College-Bound:* 51% \ *Ethnic:* African American 1%, Hispanic 5%, Caucasian 94% \ *Exp:* $155 (Low) \ *Poverty:* 19% \ *Title I:* $287,384 \ *Special Education:* $126,000 \ *Open-Close:* 08/20 - 05/28 \ *DTBP:* $18 (Low)

Jim Metcalf 1	Gavyn Bazley 2,11	
Todd Arnold 3	Jenny Blankenship 4*	
Sam Carder 5	Josh Calame 6*	
Josh Calame 6	Jennifer Green 8	
Chuck Neal 31,69*	Amy Buzard 37,83,88	
Cathy Csanyi 58	Cathy Csanyi 58*	
Doug Hamman 67	Dave Gilbert 273	
Dave Gilbert 273*		

Public Schs..Principal	Grd	Prgm	Enr/#Cls	SN	
Plymouth High Sch	9-12	ATV	167	89%	419/687-8200
400 Trux St, Plymouth 44865			25		Fax 419/687-8175
Greg Sigg					
Shiloh Elem Sch	K-5	T	335	61%	419/687-8200
26 Mechanics St, Shiloh 44878			21		Fax 419/896-8195
Mr Gilbert					
Shiloh Middle Sch	6-8	T	179		419/687-8200
400 Trux St, Plymouth 44865			24		Fax 419/687-8195
Brad Turson					

● **Shelby City School Dist** PID: 00829923   419/342-3520
25 High School Ave, Shelby 44875   Fax 419/347-3586

> *Schools:* 5 \ *Teachers:* 94 \ *Students:* 1,918 \ *Special Ed Students:* 287 \ *LEP Students:* 8 \ *College-Bound:* 48% \ *Ethnic:* African American 1%, Hispanic 3%, Caucasian 96% \ *Exp:* $149 (Low) \ *Poverty:* 13% \ *Title I:* $386,188 \ *Special Education:* $420,000 \ *Open-Close:* 08/19 - 05/27 \ *DTBP:* $241 (High)

Timothy Tarvin 1	Barbara Donohue 2,19	
Scott Harvey 3,91	Kelly Stanford 4	
Patrick Lewis 6*	Quincy Shears 7*	
Paul Walker 8,11,275,280,288,296,298*	Sheri Mitchell 13,58,81*	
Tawny Cox 16*	Edie Lerback 36,69,83,85*	
Scott Rose 67	Luke Foley 73,297	
Nate Coffey 295		

Public Schs..Principal	Grd	Prgm	Enr/#Cls	SN	
Auburn Elem Sch	K-4	T	356	60%	419/342-5456
109 Auburn Ave, Shelby 44875			21		Fax 419/342-3023
Kelly Kuhn					
Dowds Elem Sch	K-4	T	341	44%	419/342-4641
18 Seneca Dr, Shelby 44875			14		Fax 419/342-2825
Kristin Kaple-Jones					
Little Whippets Pre-School	PK-PK		109		419/342-6593
25 High School Ave, Shelby 44875					
Paul Walker					
Shelby High Sch	9-12	V	498	35%	419/342-5065
1 Whippet Way, Shelby 44875			45		Fax 419/342-5095
John Gies					
Shelby Middle Sch	5-8	T	614	45%	419/347-5451
109 W Smiley Ave, Shelby 44875			34		Fax 419/347-2095
Barbara Green					

RICHLAND CATHOLIC SCHOOLS

● **Diocese of Toledo Ed Office** PID: 00818297
Listing includes only schools located in this county. See District Index for location of Diocesan Offices.

Catholic Schs..Principal	Grd	Prgm	Enr/#Cls	SN	
Sacred Heart Sch	PK-8		100		419/342-2797
5754 State Route 61 S, Shelby 44875			5		Fax 419/683-1697
Lisa Myers					

---

9 Student Personnel	91 Safety/Security	275 Response To Intervention	298 Grant Writer/Ptnrships	**School Programs**	**Social Media**		
10 Driver Ed/Safety	92 Magnet School	277 Remedial Math K-12	750 Chief Innovation Officer	A = Alternative Program			
1 Gifted/Talented	93 Parental Involvement	280 Literacy Coach	751 Chief of Staff	G = Adult Classes	🅵 = Facebook		
2 Video Services	95 Tech Prep Program	285 STEM	752 Social Emotional Learning	M = Magnet Program			
3 Substance Abuse Prev	97 Chief Information Officer	286 Digital Learning		T = Title I Schoolwide	🆃 = Twitter		
4 Erate	98 Chief Technology Officer	288 Common Core Standards	**Other School Types**	V = Career & Tech Ed Programs			
5 AIDS Education	270 Character Education	294 Accountability	Ⓐ = Alternative School				
8 Alternative/At Risk	271 Migrant Education	295 Network System	Ⓒ = Charter School	New Schools are shaded			
9 Multi-Cultural Curriculum	273 Teacher Mentor	296 Title II Programs	Ⓜ = Magnet School	New Superintendents and Principals are bold			
0 Social Work	274 Before/After Sch	297 Webmaster	Ⓨ = Year-Round School	Personnel with email addresses are underscored			

OH–173

Ross County

St Mary Elem Sch 26 West St, Shelby 44875 Kim Stover	PK-6		97 8	419/342-2626 Fax 419/347-2763
St Mary Sch 1630 Ashland Rd, Mansfield 44905 Christa Brubaker	PK-8		80 9	419/589-2114
St Peter Elem Sch 63 S Mulberry St, Mansfield 44902 Ashley Rastorfer	PK-6		541 30	419/524-2572
St Peter Jr Sr High Sch 104 W 1st St, Mansfield 44902 Jon Cuttitta	7-12	V	250 30	419/524-0979

RICHLAND PRIVATE SCHOOLS

Private Schs..Principal	Grd	Prgm	Enr/#Cls SN	
Discovery Sch 855 Millsboro Rd, Mansfield 44903 Julie Schwartz	PK-8		101 8	419/756-8880 Fax 419/756-7479
Mansfield Christian Sch 500 Logan Rd, Mansfield 44907 Mandy Wushinske \ Craig Klotzbach	PK-12		450 51	419/756-5651 Fax 419/756-7470
Mansfield SDA Sch 1040 W Cook Rd, Mansfield 44906 Christina Dotson	K-8		22 2	419/756-9947 Fax 419/756-8977
Temple Christian Sch 752 Stewart Rd N, Mansfield 44905 Jessica Day	K-12		172 16	419/589-9707

RICHLAND REGIONAL CENTERS

- **Ncocc-N Ctrl Ohio Co-op CA** PID: 04499568   419/747-8660
  1495 W Longview Ave Ste 100, Mansfield 44906   Fax 419/747-8680

Dr Brent Winard 1,11   Tammy Bole 2
Terry Baker 73,295   Kalin Wilburn 74
Loann Trumpower 79

- **State Support Team-Region 7** PID: 02228272   419/747-4808
  1495 W Longview Ave Ste 200, Mansfield 44906   Fax 419/747-3806

Dr George Csanyi 1   Ed Kapel 15

ROSS COUNTY

ROSS COUNTY SCHOOLS

- **Ross-Pike Co Ed Service Center** PID: 00830489   740/702-3120
  475 Western Ave Ste E, Chillicothe 45601   Fax 740/702-3123

Steve Martin 1,11   Erin Kirby 2
Tom Kitchen 8,74   Lori Lowe 58
Sue Hopkins 67   Nathan Crawford 73,295
June Allred-Smith 81

County Schs..Principal	Grd	Prgm	Enr/#Cls SN	
Pioneer Center 11268 County Road 550, Chillicothe 45601 Stacy Guerra	Spec		58 10	740/773-2165 Fax 740/775-0515

ROSS PUBLIC SCHOOLS

- **Adena Local School Dist** PID: 00830087   740/998-4633
  3367 County Road 550, Frankfort 45628   Fax 740/998-4632

Schools: 3 \ *Teachers:* 58 \ *Students:* 1,200 \ *Special Ed Students:* 166 \ *College-Bound:* 54% \ *Ethnic:* African American 1%, Hispanic 2%, Caucasian 97% \ *Exp:* $233 (Med) \ *Poverty:* 16% \ *Title I:* $270,387 \ *Special Education:* $238,000 \ *Open-Close:* 08/21 - 05/28 \ *DTBP:* $177 (High) \

John Balzer 1   Kell Morton 2
Nick McDonald 3   Tonyia Hyland 4
Joan Muntz 5   Scott Hurt 6
Kristen Earich 8,11,288   Lisa Wayland 9*
Angie Williams 16   Josh Bluck 27*
Samantha Shea .... 36*   Susan Glandon 37,69*
Kasey Shaffer 58,72,274   Nathan Huff 67
Ben Buchwalter 73,82,295   Mila Rowe 298

Public Schs..Principal	Grd	Prgm	Enr/#Cls SN	
Adena Elem Sch 3367 County Road 550, Frankfort 45628 Lisa Wayland	PK-4	T	582 40	99% 740/998-5293 Fax 740/998-2359
Adena High Sch 3367 County Road 550, Frankfort 45628 Josh Jones	9-12	TV	321 25	740/998-2313 Fax 740/998-2317
Adena Middle Sch 3367 County Road 550, Frankfort 45628 Dustin England	5-8	T	394 30	740/998-2313 Fax 740/998-2317

- **Chillicothe City School Dist** PID: 00830128   740/775-4250
  425 Yoctangee Pkwy, Chillicothe 45601   Fax 740/775-4270

Schools: 5 \ *Teachers:* 147 \ *Students:* 2,800 \ *Special Ed Students:* 426 \ *College-Bound:* 40% \ *Ethnic:* Asian 1%, African American 7%, Hispanic 3%, Caucasian 89% \ *Exp:* $156 (Low) \ *Poverty:* 27% \ *Title I:* $1,529,786 \ *Special Education:* $738,000 \ *Open-Close:* 08/21 - 05/27 \ *DTBP:* $202 (High) \

Debbie Swinehart 1   Debby Lawwell 2
Larry Pritchard 3   Mary Montgomery 4
Bobbi Lowry 5   Michael Barron 6
Alissa Putnam 8,11,288,296,298   Josh Montgomery 16,73*
Steve Mullins 67   Obadiah Harris 83,88*
Aaron Brown 91   Todd Tinker 93
Nancy Thornsberry 280*

Public Schs..Principal	Grd	Prgm	Enr/#Cls SN	
Chillicothe High Sch 421 Yoctangee Pkwy, Chillicothe 45601 Dustin Weaver	9-12	ATV	835 60	740/702-2287 Fax 740/773-1097
Chillicothe Intermediate Sch 345 Arch St, Chillicothe 45601 Todd Shoemaker	3-6	T	800 15	740/774-1119
Chillicothe Middle Sch 381 Yoctangee Pkwy, Chillicothe 45601 Matthew Ballentine	7-8	T	417 36	740/773-2241 Fax 740/774-9482

1	Superintendent	8	Curric/Instruct K-12	19	Chief Financial Officer	29	Family/Consumer Science	39	Social Studies K-12	49	English/Lang Arts Elem	59	Special Education Elem	69	Academic Assessment
2	Bus/Finance/Purchasing	9	Curric/Instruct Elem	20	Art K-12	30	Adult Education	40	Social Studies Elem	50	English/Lang Arts Sec	60	Special Education Sec	70	Research/Development
3	Buildings And Grounds	10	Curric/Instruct Sec	21	Art Elem	31	Career/Sch-to-Work K-12	41	Social Studies Sec	51	Reading K-12	61	Foreign/World Lang K-12	71	Public Information
4	Food Service	11	Federal Program	22	Art Sec	32	Career/Sch-to-Work Elem	42	Science K-12	52	Reading Elem	62	Foreign/World Lang Elem	72	Summer School
5	Transportation	12	Title I	23	Music K-12	33	Career/Sch-to-Work Sec	43	Science Elem	53	Reading Sec	63	Foreign/World Lang Sec	73	Instructional Tech
6	Athletic	13	Title V	24	Music Elem	34	Early Childhood Ed	44	Science Sec	54	Remedial Reading K-12	64	Religious Education K-12	74	Inservice Training
7	Health Services	15	Asst Superintendent	25	Music Sec	35	Health/Phys Education	45	Math K-12	55	Remedial Reading Elem	65	Religious Education Elem	75	Marketing/Distributive
		16	Instructional Media Svcs	26	Business Education	36	Guidance Services K-12	46	Math Elem	56	Remedial Reading Sec	66	Religious Education Sec	76	Info Systems
		17	Chief Operations Officer	27	Career & Tech Ed	37	Guidance Services Elem	47	Math Sec	57	Bilingual/ELL	67	School Board President	77	Psychological Assess
		18	Chief Academic Officer	28	Technology Education	38	Guidance Services Sec	48	English/Lang Arts K-12	58	Special Education K-12	68	Teacher Personnel	78	Affirmative Action

Ohio School Directory — Ross County

Chillicothe Primary Sch	K-2	T	587	740/774-3307
235 Cherry St, Chillicothe 45601			15	Fax 740/774-9460
David Bennett				

Mt Logan Learning Center	PK-PK	T	114	740/773-2638
841 E Main St, Chillicothe 45601			32	Fax 740/774-9480
Kim Suwannasing				

Huntington Local School Dist   PID: 00830245
188 Huntsman Rd, Chillicothe 45601   740/663-5892   Fax 740/663-6078

Schools: 3 \ *Teachers:* 70 \ *Students:* 1,120 \ *Special Ed Students:* 177 \ *College-Bound:* 36% \ *Ethnic:* African American 1%, Hispanic 1%, Caucasian 98% \ *Exp:* $212 (Med) \ *Poverty:* 24% \ *Title I:* $478,774 \ *Special Education:* $261,000 \ *Open-Close:* 08/15 - 05/21 \ *DTBP:* $176 (High)

Pete Ruby 1		Becki Peden 2,19	
Ron Carroll 3		Bonnie Mills 4*	
Susan Whitcomb 5		Molly Montgomery 6*	
Spenser Smith 7,83,85		Craig Kerns 8*	
Dan Riddle 11,58,91,296,298		Pam O'Neill 16*	
Anita Rogers 27,38,69*		Sarah Kohls 37*	
Kim Rittenour 57,271,273*		Carl McCloskey 67	
Mark Grashel 73,295*			

Public Schs..Principal	Grd	Prgm	Enr/#Cls	SN
Huntington Elem Sch	K-4	T	418	740/663-2191
188 Huntsman Rd, Chillicothe 45601			30	Fax 740/663-4584
Heidi Gray				
Huntington High Sch	9-12	TV	277	740/663-2230
188 Huntsman Rd, Chillicothe 45601			22	Fax 740/663-5042
Craig Kerns				
Huntington Middle Sch	5-8	T	378	740/663-6079
188 Huntsman Rd, Chillicothe 45601			25	
Matt Murphy				

Paint Valley Local School Dist   PID: 00830271
7454 US Highway 50 W, Bainbridge 45612   740/634-2826   Fax 740/634-2890

Schools: 3 \ *Teachers:* 51 \ *Students:* 890 \ *Special Ed Students:* 134 \ *College-Bound:* 49% \ *Ethnic:* Hispanic 1%, Caucasian 99% \ *Exp:* $180 (Low) \ *Poverty:* 22% \ *Title I:* $349,237 \ *Special Education:* $262,000 \ *Open-Close:* 08/15 - 05/19 \ *DTBP:* $175 (High)

Tim Winland 1	Evan Keaton 2
Kendal Evans 3,91	Rachel Osborne 4
Greg Pennington 5	Pete Hollon 6*
Leighanne Johnson 9*	Heather Bowles 11,288*
Shawn Skaggs 67	Tyler Cantrell 73
Dara Smith 271*	

Public Schs..Principal	Grd	Prgm	Enr/#Cls	SN
Paint Valley Elem Sch	PK-5	T	398	740/634-3454
7454 US Rte 50, Bainbridge 45612			26	Fax 740/634-3459
Heather Bowles				
Paint Valley High Sch	9-12	ATV	267	740/634-3582
7454 US Rte 50, Bainbridge 45612			35	Fax 740/634-3518
Lewis Ewry				
Paint Valley Middle Sch	6-8	AT	194	740/634-3512
7454 US Rte 50, Bainbridge 45612			15	Fax 740/634-3459
Lewis Ewry				

Pickaway-Ross Co JT Voc SD   PID: 00830465
895 Crouse Chapel Rd, Chillicothe 45601   740/642-1200   Fax 740/642-1399

Schools: 1 \ *Teachers:* 96 \ *Students:* 800 \ *College-Bound:* 27% \ *Exp:* $135 (Low) \ *Open-Close:* 08/15 - 05/22 \ *DTBP:* $174 (High) \

Laura Vancuren 1	Todd Stahr 2,19
Craig Jones 3*	Dana Anderson 10,33,60*
Allen Kiger 29*	Carrie Fife 30
Toby Walls-Waller 38*	Byron Lloyd 67
Vince Perhach 73*	Shara Cochenour 88*
Jason Vesey 294	Dana Anderson 298

Public Schs..Principal	Grd	Prgm	Enr/#Cls	SN
Pickaway-Ross Career Tech Ctr	Voc	G	800	740/642-1200
895 Crouse Chapel Rd, Chillicothe 45601			25	
Shara Cochenour				

Southeastern Local Sch Dist   PID: 00830312
2003 Lancaster Rd, Chillicothe 45601   740/774-2003   Fax 740/774-2012

Schools: 3 \ *Teachers:* 62 \ *Students:* 1,040 \ *Special Ed Students:* 160 \ *College-Bound:* 63% \ *Ethnic:* African American 1%, Hispanic 1%, Caucasian 98% \ *Exp:* $325 (High) \ *Poverty:* 19% \ *Title I:* $326,847 \ *Special Education:* $241,000 \ *Open-Close:* 08/21 - 05/27 \ *DTBP:* $174 (High)

Brian Justice 1	Philip Hartman 2,84
Mike Osborn 3,91	Ronald Adams 5
Rick Strausbaugh 6*	Vicki Snyder 7*
Leonard Steyer 8,88*	Zach Pfeifer 10,12,58,298*
John Evans 38,83*	Jeff Stauffer 67
Arthur McCray 73	Brian Marks 81*

Public Schs..Principal	Grd	Prgm	Enr/#Cls	SN
Southeastern Elem Sch	K-4	T	388	740/774-2003
2003 Lancaster Rd, Chillicothe 45601			5	Fax 740/774-1673
Mrs Wills				
Southeastern High Sch	9-12	V	284	740/774-2003
2003 Lancaster Rd, Chillicothe 45601			36	Fax 740/774-1684
Leonard Steyer				
Southeastern Middle Sch	5-8	T	368	99% 740/774-2003
2003 Lancaster Rd, Chillicothe 45601			64	Fax 740/774-1684
Zach Pfeifer				

Union Scioto Local Sch Dist   PID: 00830374
1565 Egypt Pike, Chillicothe 45601   740/773-4102   Fax 740/775-2852

Schools: 3 \ *Teachers:* 113 \ *Students:* 2,175 \ *Special Ed Students:* 279 \ *LEP Students:* 3 \ *College-Bound:* 51% \ *Ethnic:* Asian 1%, African American 2%, Hispanic 2%, Caucasian 95% \ *Exp:* $182 (Low) \ *Poverty:* 18% \ *Title I:* $574,521 \ *Special Education:* $410,000 \ *Open-Close:* 08/15 - 05/28 \ *DTBP:* $175 (High) \

Matt Thornsberry 1	John Rose 2,11,68,294
Steve Malone 3	Tracey Forcum 4*
Shawn Ost 5	Mike White 6
Sydney Carver 7,83*	Wilma Gillote 8,12,298*
Melissa Lawson 16*	Michelle Bowdle 28,73,76,286,295
Lisa Corcoran 29*	Sara Williams 36,69,88*
Lori Collins 37,83*	Kerri Bryant 38,69*
Jeff Miller 58	Laura Uhrig 67
Amy Martin 74*	

---

79 Student Personnel	91 Safety/Security	275 Response To Intervention	298 Grant Writer/Ptnrships	**School Programs**	**Social Media**		
80 Driver Ed/Safety	92 Magnet School	277 Remedial Math K-12	750 Chief Innovation Officer	A = Alternative Program	⬛ = Facebook		
81 Gifted/Talented	93 Parental Involvement	280 Literacy Coach	751 Chief of Staff	G = Adult Classes			
82 Video Services	95 Tech Prep Program	285 STEM	752 Social Emotional Learning	M = Magnet Program	⬛ = Twitter		
83 Substance Abuse Prev	97 Chief Information Officer	286 Digital Learning		T = Title I Schoolwide			
84 Erate	98 Chief Technology Officer	288 Common Core Standards	**Other School Types**	V = Career & Tech Ed Programs			
85 AIDS Education	270 Character Education	294 Accountability	Ⓐ = Alternative School				
88 Alternative/At Risk	271 Migrant Education	295 Network System	Ⓒ = Charter School	New Schools are shaded			
89 Multi-Cultural Curriculum	273 Teacher Mentor	296 Title II Programs	Ⓜ = Magnet School	New Superintendents and Principals are bold			
90 Social Work	274 Before/After Sch	297 Webmaster	Ⓨ = Year-Round School	Personnel with email addresses are underscored			

OH–175

Sandusky County

Market Data Retrieval

Public Schs..Principal	Grd	Prgm	Enr/#Cls	SN	
Unioto Elem Sch 138 Sandusky Rd, Chillicothe 45601 Karen Mercer	PK-5	T	1,092 50	50%	740/773-4103 Fax 740/775-4074
Unioto High Sch 14193 Pleasant Valley Rd, Chillicothe 45601 Nathan Caplinger	9-12	T	538 45	84%	740/773-4105 Fax 740/774-9158
Unioto Junior High Sch 160 Moundsville Rd, Chillicothe 45601 Wilma Gillote	6-8	T	524 20		740/773-5211 Fax 740/772-2974

• **Zane Trace Local School Dist** PID: 00830427   740/775-1355
946 State Route 180, Chillicothe 45601   Fax 740/773-0249

Schools: 3 \ *Teachers:* 75 \ *Students:* 1,301 \ *Special Ed Students:* 205 \ *College-Bound:* 57% \ *Ethnic:* African American 1%, Caucasian 98% \ *Exp:* $128 (Low) \ *Poverty:* 12% \ *Title I:* $237,231 \ *Special Education:* $325,000 \ *Open-Close:* 08/20 - 05/25 \ *DTBP:* $175 (High)

Jerry Mowery 1		Tammy Irwin 2,11	
Joe Dunkle 3		Robert Dunn 4	
Dustin Britton 5		Todd Holdren 6*	
Ty Wertman 31,38,69*		Kathy Gillespie 36*	
Dana Myers 37*		Robin Ayres 58*	
Cathy Chester 67		Krista McCorkle 76	

Public Schs..Principal	Grd	Prgm	Enr/#Cls	SN	
Zane Trace Elem Sch 946 State Route 180, Chillicothe 45601 Susan Congrove	K-4	T	468 30		740/775-1304 Fax 740/775-2092
Zane Trace High Sch 946 State Route 180, Chillicothe 45601 Ty Wertman	9-12	V	389 30	99%	740/775-1809 Fax 740/773-5107
Zane Trace Middle Sch 946 State Route 180, Chillicothe 45601 Bret Mavis	5-8	TV	444 45		740/773-5842 Fax 740/773-9998

ROSS CATHOLIC SCHOOLS

• **Diocese of Columbus Ed Office** PID: 00802717
Listing includes only schools located in this county. See District Index for location of Diocesan Offices.

Catholic Schs..Principal	Grd	Prgm	Enr/#Cls	SN	
Bishop Flaget Sch 570 Parsons Ave, Chillicothe 45601 Laura Corcoran	PK-8		203 10		740/774-2970 Fax 740/774-2998

ROSS PRIVATE SCHOOLS

Private Schs..Principal	Grd	Prgm	Enr/#Cls	SN	
Ross Co Christian Academy 2215 Egypt Pike, Chillicothe 45601 Jarod Lloyd	PK-11		300		740/772-4532 Fax 740/422-1622

SANDUSKY COUNTY

SANDUSKY COUNTY SCHOOLS

County Schs..Principal	Grd	Prgm	Enr/#Cls	SN	
School of Hope 1001 Castalia St, Fremont 43420 Becky Holtgerven	Spec		55 7		419/332-9296 Fax 419/332-9571

SANDUSKY PUBLIC SCHOOLS

• **Clyde-Green Spgs Exmpt Vlg SD** PID: 00830491   419/547-0588
106 S Main St, Clyde 43410   Fax 419/547-0909

Schools: 4 \ *Teachers:* 144 \ *Students:* 2,300 \ *Special Ed Students:* 340 \ *College-Bound:* 65% \ *Ethnic:* African American 1%, Hispanic 10%, Caucasian 89% \ *Exp:* $194 (Low) \ *Poverty:* 12% \ *Title I:* $375,039 \ *Special Education:* $431,000 \ *Open-Close:* 08/27 - 05/27 \ *DTBP:* $216 (High)

Dennis Haft 1	Meghan Rohde 2
Randy Hawk 3,91*	Vicky Nieset 4
Dan Shafer 5	Ryan Greenslade 6*
Karen Horn 7,85*	Joseph Letterhos ..8,11,57,83,88,285,288,298
Melissa Detwiler 16*	Brooke Michael 37*
Kendal Wass 58,77*	Matt Nicely 67
Jordan Hasselbach 73,76,295*	

Public Schs..Principal	Grd	Prgm	Enr/#Cls	SN	
Clyde Elem Sch 821 S Main St, Clyde 43410 Jacqueline Davis	PK-3	T	467 20	47%	419/547-9868 Fax 419/547-4885
Clyde High Sch 1015 Race St, Clyde 43410 William Webb	9-12	TV	672 48	41%	419/547-9511 Fax 419/547-7593
Green Springs Elem Sch 420 N Broadway St, Green Springs 44836 Randy Stockmaster	K-5	T	507 40	53%	419/547-4902 Fax 419/547-4906
McPherson Middle Sch 4230 Limerick Rd, Clyde 43410 Brian Cannon	6-8	T	535 40	50%	419/547-9150 Fax 419/547-9173

• **Fremont City School Dist** PID: 00830556   419/332-6454
500 W State St Ste A, Fremont 43420   Fax 419/334-5454

Schools: 9 \ *Teachers:* 234 \ *Students:* 3,843 \ *Special Ed Students:* 642 \ *LEP Students:* 101 \ *College-Bound:* 52% \ *Ethnic:* African American 10%, Hispanic 26%, Caucasian 64% \ *Exp:* $92 (Low) \ *Poverty:* 17% \ *Title I:* $1,122,537 \ *Special Education:* $855,000 \ *Open-Close:* 08/27 - 05/22 \ *DTBP:* $153 (High)

Jon Detwiler 1	Tom Anway 3,91
Abby Berndt 4	Justin Eilrich 5
Chad Berndt 6*	Abby Abernathy 7,58,83,88
Denice Hirt 8,11,16,36,69,288,296,298	Bonnie Weaver 57*
Shantel Laird 67	Susan King 68
Mandi Miller 76	Nancy McKillip 76
Rhonda Schmidt 84	

1 Superintendent	8 Curric/Instruct K-12	19 Chief Financial Officer	29 Family/Consumer Science	39 Social Studies K-12	49 English/Lang Arts Elem	59 Special Education Elem	69 Academic Assessment
2 Bus/Finance/Purchasing	9 Curric/Instruct Elem	20 Art K-12	30 Adult Education	40 Social Studies Elem	50 English/Lang Arts Sec	60 Special Education Sec	70 Research/Development
3 Buildings And Grounds	10 Curric/Instruct Sec	21 Art Elem	31 Career/Sch-to-Work K-12	41 Social Studies Sec	51 Reading K-12	61 Foreign/World Lang K-12	71 Public Information
4 Food Service	11 Federal Program	22 Art Sec	32 Career/Sch-to-Work Elem	42 Science K-12	52 Reading Elem	62 Foreign/World Lang Elem	72 Summer School
5 Transportation	12 Title I	23 Music K-12	33 Career/Sch-to-Work Sec	43 Science Elem	53 Reading Sec	63 Foreign/World Lang Sec	73 Instructional Tech
6 Athletic	13 Title V	24 Music Elem	34 Early Childhood Ed	44 Science Sec	54 Remedial Reading K-12	64 Religious Education K-12	74 Inservice Training
7 Health Services	15 Asst Superintendent	25 Music Sec	35 Health/Phys Education	45 Math K-12	55 Remedial Reading Elem	65 Religious Education Elem	75 Marketing/Distributive
	16 Instructional Media Svcs	26 Business Education	36 Guidance Services K-12	46 Math Elem	56 Remedial Reading Sec	66 Religious Education Sec	76 Info Systems
	17 Chief Operations Officer	27 Career & Tech Ed	37 Guidance Services Elem	47 Math Sec	57 Bilingual/ELL	67 School Board President	77 Psychological Assess
	18 Chief Academic Officer	28 Technology Education	38 Guidance Services Sec	48 English/Lang Arts K-12	58 Special Education K-12	68 Teacher Personnel	78 Affirmative Action

Ohio School Directory

Sandusky County

Public Schs..Principal	Grd	Prgm	Enr/#Cls		SN
Atkinson Elem Sch 1100 Delaware Ave, Fremont 43420 Chris Ward	PK-5	T	261 16		419/332-5361 Fax 419/334-6749
Croghan Elem Sch 1110 Chestnut St, Fremont 43420 Dr Lori Pierce	PK-5	T	271 20		419/332-1511 Fax 419/332-4314
Fremont Middle Sch 1250 North St, Fremont 43420 Erin Parker	6-8	T	851 68	52%	419/332-5569 Fax 419/334-5494
Fremont Ross High Sch 1100 North St, Fremont 43420 Brian Zeller	9-12	T	1,072 100	45%	419/332-8221 Fax 419/334-5450
Hayes Elem Sch 916 Hayes Ave, Fremont 43420 Joshua Matz	PK-5	T	260 14		419/332-6371 Fax 419/334-6761
Lutz Elem Sch 1929 Buckland Ave, Fremont 43420 Randy Macko	PK-5		248 15		419/332-0091 Fax 419/334-5499
Otis Elem Sch 718 N Brush St, Fremont 43420 Christine Opelt	PK-5	T	255 22		419/332-8964 Fax 419/334-6788
Stamm Elem Sch 1038 Miller St, Fremont 43420 Bridget Smith	PK-5	T	318 32		419/332-5538 Fax 419/334-6746
Washington Elem Sch 109 W Lincoln St, Lindsey 43442 Susan Gray	PK-5		91 7		419/665-2327 Fax 419/665-2241

• **Gibsonburg Exempted Village SD** PID: 00830661   419/637-2479
301 S Sunset Ave, Gibsonburg 43431   Fax 419/637-3029

Schools: 3 \ **Teachers:** 53 \ **Students:** 950 \ **Special Ed Students:** 126 \
College-Bound: 58% \ **Ethnic:** Hispanic 13%, Caucasian 86% \ **Exp:** $162 (Low) \ **Poverty:** 13% \ **Title I:** $160,027 \ **Special Education:** $192,000 \
Open-Close: 08/28 - 06/04 \ **DTBP:** $176 (High)

Tim Murray 1,11   John Common 2
Joe King 3,5   Missy Bauer 4
Jay Morlock 6   Elizabeth Kohler 33,38,69
Brian Jackson ....37*   Tabatha Elson 58,77,83*
Scott Pertner 67   Christy Goosland 73

Public Schs..Principal	Grd	Prgm	Enr/#Cls		SN
Gibsonburg High Sch 740 S Main St, Gibsonburg 43431 Sonia Herman	9-12	AV	252 18	63%	419/637-2873 Fax 419/637-2046
Gibsonburg Middle Sch 740 S Main St, Gibsonburg 43431 Sonia Herman	6-8	AV	228 14		419/637-7954 Fax 419/637-2046
James J Hilfiker Elem Sch 301 S Sunset Ave, Gibsonburg 43431 Emily Sisco	PK-5		420 32	43%	419/637-7249 Fax 419/637-2478

• **Lakota Local School Dist** PID: 00830702   419/986-6650
5200 County Road 13, Kansas 44841   Fax 419/986-6651

Schools: 3 \ **Teachers:** 53 \ **Students:** 1,140 \ **Special Ed Students:** 130 \
College-Bound: 75% \ **Ethnic:** Hispanic 5%, Caucasian 94% \ **Exp:** $173 (Low) \ **Poverty:** 12% \ **Title I:** $199,319 \ **Special Education:** $306,000 \
Open-Close: 08/27 - 05/29 \ **DTBP:** $168 (High) \ f

Chad Coffman 1   Norm Elchert 2
Tim Kern 5   Kevin Yeckley 6
Ashley Michaels 7   Beth Crawford 7*
Candy Wingert 8,69,270   Elaine Chalfin 11
Pam Bibler 58   Pam Dibler 58,270,296
Chris Chalfin 67   Russ Abott 73,286

Public Schs..Principal	Grd	Prgm	Enr/#Cls		SN
Lakota Elem Sch 5200 County Road 13, Kansas 44841 Dana Ward	PK-4	T	393 23	53%	419/986-6640 Fax 419/986-6631
Lakota High Sch 5200 County Road 13, Kansas 44841 Sherry Sprow	9-12	TV	328 25	52%	419/986-6620 Fax 419/986-6621
Lakota Middle Sch 5200 County Road 13, Kansas 44841 Patrick Flanagan	5-8	T	359 15	50%	419/986-6630 Fax 419/986-6631

• **Vanguard-Sentinel JT Voc SD** PID: 00830831   419/332-2626
1306 Cedar St, Fremont 43420   Fax 419/334-4308

Schools: 2 \ **Teachers:** 58 \ **Students:** 2,300 \ **Exp:** $419 (High) \
Open-Close: 08/20 - 05/21 \ **DTBP:** $174 (High)

Greg Edinger 1,11   Alan Binger 2
Rosemary Kreiger 12,30,57,273   Tim Damschroder 67
Kevin Dwight 73*

Public Schs..Principal	Grd	Prgm	Enr/#Cls	SN
Sentinel Career Center 793 E Township Road 201, Tiffin 44883 Elissa Heal	Voc	AG	600 16	419/448-1212 Fax 419/447-2544 f
Vanguard Technology Center 1306 Cedar St, Fremont 43420 Dave Bueing	Voc		500 6	419/332-2626 Fax 419/334-2609

SANDUSKY CATHOLIC SCHOOLS

• **Diocese of Toledo Ed Office** PID: 00818297
Listing includes only schools located in this county. See District Index for location of Diocesan Offices.

Catholic Schs..Principal	Grd	Prgm	Enr/#Cls	SN
Sacred Heart Sch-Bshp Hoffman 500 Smith Rd 550, Fremont 43420 David Perin	PK-6		385 8	419/332-7102 Fax 419/332-1542
St Joseph Ctl Cath Jr Sr HS 702 Croghan St, Fremont 43420 Anthony Fontana	7-12		200 22	419/332-9947 Fax 419/332-4945

SANDUSKY PRIVATE SCHOOLS

Private Schs..Principal	Grd	Prgm	Enr/#Cls	SN
Harvest Temple Christian Acad 1022 S Main St, Clyde 43410 Melanie Weasner	K-12		40 5	419/547-8251 Fax 419/547-7195
Solomon Lutheran Sch 305 W Main St, Woodville 43469 Natalie Schiets	PK-6		66 8	419/849-3600 Fax 419/849-2260 f
Temple Christian Academy 1150 S County Road 198, Fremont 43420 Rick Ash	K-12		40 8	419/332-6114

OH-177

Scioto County

SCIOTO COUNTY

SCIOTO COUNTY SCHOOLS

- **South Central Ohio Ed Svc Ctr** PID: 00831419 — 740/354-7761
  522 Glenwood Ave, New Boston 45662 — Fax 740/354-6778

Sandy Mers 1	Andrew Riehl 2,68
Scott Holstein 15	Rebecca Wheelersburg 34,83,85,88
Dr Paul Crabtree 67	Ryan Ottney 71
Sharee Price 81	

County Schs..Principal	Grd	Prgm	Enr/#Cls	SN	
Vern Riffe Sch 2619 Gallia St, Portsmouth 45662 Mark Cornwell	Spec		70 9		740/353-1876 Fax 740/353-0780

SCIOTO PUBLIC SCHOOLS

- **Bloom-Vernon Local Sch Dist** PID: 00830867 — 740/778-2281
  10529 Main St, South Webster 45682 — Fax 740/778-2526

  Schools: 2 \ *Teachers:* 60 \ *Students:* 900 \ *Special Ed Students:* 99 \ *LEP Students:* 3 \ *College-Bound:* 50% \ *Ethnic:* Caucasian 100% \ *Exp:* $142 (Low) \ *Poverty:* 17% \ *Title I:* $217,918 \ *Special Education:* $201,000 \ *Open-Close:* 08/20 - 05/20 \ *DTBP:* $181 (High)

Marc Kreischer 1,83	Ty Robert 2
Charlie Boggs 3	Krystal Hill 4
Adam Howe 5,274*	Greg Sullivan 6
Sandy Smith 9,11,296*	Cathy McCoy 38,69*
Dr Tim Horner 67	Tim Conley 73,295*
Tim Conley 84	

Public Schs..Principal	Grd	Prgm	Enr/#Cls	SN	
Bloom-Vernon Elem Sch 10529A Main St, South Webster 45682 Sandy Smith	PK-6	T	484 31	61%	740/778-2339 Fax 740/778-7600
South Webster Jr Sr High Sch 10529 Main St, South Webster 45682 Brett Roberts	7-12	T	365 25	67%	740/778-2320 Fax 740/778-3227

- **Clay Local School Dist** PID: 00830910 — 740/354-6645
  44 Clay High St, Portsmouth 45662 — Fax 740/354-5746

  Schools: 1 \ *Teachers:* 35 \ *Students:* 714 \ *Special Ed Students:* 82 \ *College-Bound:* 34% \ *Ethnic:* Asian 1%, Caucasian 99% \ *Exp:* $278 (Med) \ *Poverty:* 19% \ *Title I:* $173,348 \ *Special Education:* $110,000 \ *Open-Close:* 08/21 - 05/21 \ *DTBP:* $161 (High)

Todd Warnock 1	Brandi Blackburn 2
Gerald Penix 5	Mark Rose 6*
Tony Piquet 9*	Ron Goodson 11,52,55*
Cindy Parkes 16,82*	Bob Hayes 36,83,88*
Donald Caseman 67	Matt Kuehne 73,76*

Public Schs..Principal	Grd	Prgm	Enr/#Cls	SN	
Clay Local Sch 44 Clay High St, Portsmouth 45662 Russ Breech | Tony Piquet	PK-12	T	714 30	47%	740/354-6644 Fax 740/354-6105

- **Green Local School Dist** PID: 00830958 — 740/354-9221
  4070 Gallia Pike, Franklin Frnce 45629 — Fax 740/355-8975

  Schools: 2 \ *Teachers:* 39 \ *Students:* 600 \ *Special Ed Students:* 110 \ *Ethnic:* Hispanic 1%, Caucasian 99% \ *Exp:* $360 (High) \ *Poverty:* 24% \ *Title I:* $343,742 \ *Special Education:* $136,000 \ *Open-Close:* 08/20 - 05/21 \ *DTBP:* $174 (High)

Jodi Armstrong 1,11	Brodi Merrill 2
Jason McIlhenny 3	Myra Clark 4
Keri Emnett 36,69,83,88*	Rachael Ramey 58
Sandi Cherry 67	Gary Arthurs 73,295*
Jessica McIlhenny 288*	John Dicks 296*

Public Schs..Principal	Grd	Prgm	Enr/#Cls	SN	
Green Elem Sch 46 Braunlin Rd, Franklin Frnce 45629 John Biggs	PK-6	T	317 20		740/354-9290 Fax 740/354-9904
Green High Sch 4057 Gallia Pike, Franklin Frnce 45629 Matthew McCorkle	7-12	TV	269 25	32%	740/354-9150 Fax 740/355-4094

- **Minford Local School Dist** PID: 00830984 — 740/820-3896
  491 Bond Rd, Minford 45653 — Fax 740/820-3334

  Schools: 3 \ *Teachers:* 80 \ *Students:* 1,401 \ *Special Ed Students:* 217 \ *College-Bound:* 50% \ *Ethnic:* African American 1%, Hispanic 1%, Caucasian 99% \ *Exp:* $125 (Low) \ *Poverty:* 24% \ *Title I:* $553,358 \ *Special Education:* $309,000 \ *Open-Close:* 08/21 - 05/22 \ *DTBP:* $174 (High)

Jeremy Litteral 1	Ashley Roberts 2
Tim Dever 3	Sharon Hardaman 4
Ann Shirey 5	Kristen Ruby 6*
Deborah Daniels 7*	Amy Odell 8,11,74,286,288,296,298*
Dee-Anna Veach 16*	Brent Howard 37*
Erica Thomson 38,69,88	Marin Applegate 58*
Joseph Stockham 67	Ryan Stockham 73,76,295*

Public Schs..Principal	Grd	Prgm	Enr/#Cls	SN	
Minford Elem Primary Sch 215 Falcon Rd, Minford 45653 Ryan McGraw	PK-3	T	455 24	99%	740/820-2287 Fax 740/820-2466
Minford High Sch 491 Bond Rd, Minford 45653 Jeff Pica	9-12		393 35	39%	740/820-3445 Fax 740/820-4484
Minford Middle Sch 135 Falcon Rd, Minford 45653 Dennis Evans	4-8	T	553 28		740/820-2181 Fax 740/820-2466

- **New Boston Local School Dist** PID: 00831029 — 740/456-4626
  1 Glenwood Tiger Trl, New Boston 45662 — Fax 740/456-6402

  Schools: 3 \ *Teachers:* 28 \ *Students:* 500 \ *Special Ed Students:* 68 \ *College-Bound:* 39% \ *Ethnic:* Hispanic 2%, Native American: 1%, Caucasian 97% \ *Exp:* $260 (Med) \ *Poverty:* 43% \ *Title I:* $303,531 \ *Special Education:* $55,000 \ *Open-Close:* 08/19 - 05/20 \ *DTBP:* $21 (Low)

Melinda Burnside 1,73	Samantha Hamilton 2,79
Todd Grant 3,5	Pam Madden 4

---

1 Superintendent	8 Curric/Instruct K-12	19 Chief Financial Officer	29 Family/Consumer Science	39 Social Studies K-12	49 English/Lang Arts Elem	59 Special Education Elem	69 Academic Assessment
2 Bus/Finance/Purchasing	9 Curric/Instruct Elem	20 Art K-12	30 Adult Education	40 Social Studies Elem	50 English/Lang Arts Sec	60 Special Education Sec	70 Research/Development
3 Buildings And Grounds	10 Curric/Instruct Sec	21 Art Elem	31 Career/Sch-to-Work K-12	41 Social Studies Sec	51 Reading K-12	61 Foreign/World Lang K-12	71 Public Information
4 Food Service	11 Federal Program	22 Art Sec	32 Career/Sch-to-Work Elem	42 Science K-12	52 Reading Elem	62 Foreign/World Lang Elem	72 Summer School
5 Transportation	12 Title I	23 Music K-12	33 Career/Sch-to-Work Sec	43 Science Elem	53 Reading Sec	63 Foreign/World Lang Sec	73 Instructional Tech
6 Athletic	13 Title V	24 Music Elem	34 Early Childhood Ed	44 Science Sec	54 Remedial Reading K-12	64 Religious Education K-12	74 Inservice Training
7 Health Services	14 Instructional Media Svcs	25 Music Sec	35 Health/Phys Education	45 Math K-12	55 Remedial Reading Elem	65 Religious Education Elem	75 Marketing/Distributive
	15 Asst Superintendent	26 Business Education	36 Guidance Services K-12	46 Math Elem	56 Remedial Reading Sec	66 Religious Education Sec	76 Info Systems
	16 Chief Operations Officer	27 Career & Tech Ed	37 Guidance Services Elem	47 Math Sec	57 Bilingual/ELL	67 School Board President	77 Psychological Assess
	18 Chief Academic Officer	28 Technology Education	38 Guidance Services Sec	48 English/Lang Arts K-12	58 Special Education K-12	68 Teacher Personnel	78 Affirmative Action

Ohio School Directory — Scioto County

Donald Stapleton 6,10*
Zack Meeker 16
Greg Mauk 35*
Christina Logan 58*
Paul Mayberry 83,273*

Christina Dever 8,11,57,285,294,295,296*
Jimmy Bailey 29*
Jennifer Scherer 36,69,88,275*
Jeff Moore 67

Public Schs..Principal	Grd	Prgm	Enr/#Cls	SN	
Glenwood High Sch 1 Glenwood Tiger Trl, New Boston 45662 Donald Stapleton	7-12	TV	158 20		740/456-4559 Fax 740/566-6402
Oak Intermediate Sch 1 Glenwood Tiger Trl, New Boston 45662 Christina Dever	4-6	T	94 8		740/456-4559 Fax 740/566-6402
Stanton Primary Sch 1 Glenwood Tiger Trl, New Boston 45662 Christina Dever	PK-3	T	155 10		740/456-4559 Fax 740/566-6402

- **Northwest Local School Dist** PID: 00831067   740/259-5558
  800 Mohawk Dr, Mc Dermott 45652   Fax 740/259-3476

Schools: 3 \ **Teachers:** 91 \ **Students:** 1,373 \ **Special Ed Students:** 299 \ **Ethnic:** Hispanic 1%, Caucasian 98% \ **Exp:** $177 (Low) \ **Poverty:** 23% \ **Title I:** $625,378 \ **Special Education:** $367,000 \ **Open-Close:** 08/22 - 05/22 \ **DTBP:** $178 (High)

Anthony Jenkins 1,83
Alan Sexton 3
Dave Frantz 6*
Terri Freeman 8,11,58,73,285,288,296,298
Jarred Lute 67

Julie Smith 2
Sharon Conley 5
Mary Stiverson 7,85*
Alyssa Bach Enz 16*
Rebecca Ketter 77*

Public Schs..Principal	Grd	Prgm	Enr/#Cls	SN	
Northwest Elem Sch 4738 Henley Deemer Rd, Mc Dermott 45652 Brian Martin	PK-5	T	670 41	72%	740/259-2250 Fax 740/259-2337
Northwest High Sch 914 Mohawk Dr, Mc Dermott 45652 Richard Burton	9-12	TV	379 45	63%	740/259-2366 Fax 740/259-8544
Northwest Middle Sch 692 Mohawk Dr, Mc Dermott 45652 Todd Shoemaker	6-8	T	324 24	70%	740/259-2528 Fax 740/259-5731

- **Portsmouth City School Dist** PID: 00831122   740/354-5663
  724 Findlay St, Portsmouth 45662   Fax 740/355-4496

Schools: 3 \ **Teachers:** 116 \ **Students:** 1,700 \ **Special Ed Students:** 519 \ **LEP Students:** 8 \ **College-Bound:** 34% \ **Ethnic:** African American 5%, Hispanic 9%, Caucasian 85% \ **Exp:** $140 (Low) \ **Poverty:** 36% \ **Title I:** $2,145,114 \ **Special Education:** $494,000 \ **Open-Close:** 08/22 - 05/28 \ **DTBP:** $178 (High)

Scott Dutey 1
Ralph Applegate 3,4
Joseph Albrecht 6*
Heather Walker 35,83*
Ali Shultz 37*
Johnda Connally 58
Mark O'Brien 73,84

Dianna Reedy 2,11,296,298
Jeanie Miller 5
Erin Birkhimer 16,82,286,297
Ali Shultz 37
Beth Burke 38*
Barbara Barden-Gibson 67
Josh Morris 91,298

Public Schs..Principal	Grd	Prgm	Enr/#Cls	SN	
East Portsmouth Elem Sch 5929 Harding Ave, Sciotoville 45662 Kristi Toppins	PK-6	T	159 18		740/776-6444 Fax 740/776-6296
Portsmouth Elem Sch 514 Union St, Portsmouth 45662 Beth Born	PK-6	T	911 25		740/353-6719 Fax 740/353-1778
Portsmouth High Sch 1225 Gallia St, Portsmouth 45662 Doug Poage	7-12	V	615 35		740/353-2398 Fax 740/354-3494

- **Scioto Co Joint Vocational SD** PID: 00831392   740/259-5522
  951 Vern Riffe Dr, Lucasville 45648   Fax 740/259-5892

Schools: 1 \ **Teachers:** 48 \ **Students:** 540 \ **Exp:** $719 (High) \ **Open-Close:** 08/20 - 05/21 \ **DTBP:** $157 (High)

Stan Jennings 1,11
Josh Shoemaker 12,298
Kyle Copley 28,288*
Noel Frank 38*
Douglas Bell 73*

Brett Butler 2
Elizabeth Claxon 16*
Derek Brown 30
Barb Gibson 67

Public Schs..Principal	Grd	Prgm	Enr/#Cls	SN	
Scioto Co Career Tech Center 951 Vern Riffe Dr, Lucasville 45648 Kyle Copley	Voc	G	540 42		740/259-5522

- **Valley Local School Dist** PID: 00831251   740/259-3115
  1821 State Route 728, Lucasville 45648   Fax 740/259-2314

Schools: 3 \ **Teachers:** 52 \ **Students:** 1,020 \ **Special Ed Students:** 161 \ **College-Bound:** 57% \ **Ethnic:** African American 1%, Hispanic 1%, Caucasian 99% \ **Exp:** $170 (Low) \ **Poverty:** 21% \ **Title I:** $289,766 \ **Special Education:** $232,000 \ **Open-Close:** 08/19 - 05/20 \ **DTBP:** $182 (High)

Scott Rolfe 1
Scott Thayer 3,5*
Daren Crabtree 6*
Jeremy Clark 8,69,294,296*
Karrie Daniels 16*
David Flowers 67
Danette Hagans 77*

Freda Cyrus 2
Shanna Cox 4*
Debbie Baughman 7*
Jane Thayer 11*
Lisa Harley 58*
Ryan Hawk 73,295
Bruce Ottens 84

Public Schs..Principal	Grd	Prgm	Enr/#Cls	SN	
Valley Elem Sch 1821A State Route 728, Lucasville 45648 Jeremy Clark	PK-4	T	479 22	53%	740/259-2611 Fax 740/259-6645
Valley High Sch 1821 State Route 728, Lucasville 45648 Jane Thayer	9-12	TV	265 20	47%	740/259-5551 Fax 740/259-6639
Valley Middle Sch 393 Indian Dr, Lucasville 45648 Aaron Franke	5-8		313 25	60%	740/259-2651 Fax 740/259-6624

- **Washington-Nile Local Sch Dist** PID: 00831304   740/858-1111
  15332 US Highway 52, W Portsmouth 45663   Fax 740/858-1110

Schools: 3 \ **Teachers:** 80 \ **Students:** 1,449 \ **Special Ed Students:** 235 \ **College-Bound:** 50% \ **Ethnic:** Hispanic 2%, Caucasian 97% \ **Exp:** $220 (Med) \ **Poverty:** 27% \ **Title I:** $593,195 \ **Special Education:** $295,000 \ **Open-Close:** 08/19 - 05/20 \ **DTBP:** $186 (High)

Anthony Bazler 1
Jeff Fite 3,5
Ben Johnson 6*
Anthony Bazler 27,72,88*
Eric Nichols 58*
Jane Kouns 67
Chris Rapp 274*

Sherry Paterson 2,84
Barb Ingles 4*
Alison Sayre 8,11,36*
Andrea Ketaey 54,273*
Wilma Erwin 58
Bill Bekan 73*
Ben Johnson 285

---

79 Student Personnel	91 Safety/Security	275 Response To Intervention	298 Grant Writer/Ptnrships	**School Programs**	**Social Media**	
80 Driver Ed/Safety	92 Magnet School	277 Remedial Math K-12	750 Chief Innovation Officer	A = Alternative Program		
81 Gifted/Talented	93 Parental Involvement	280 Literacy Coach	751 Chief of Staff	G = Adult Classes	= Facebook	
82 Video Services	95 Tech Prep Program	285 STEM	752 Social Emotional Learning	M = Magnet Program		
83 Substance Abuse Prev	97 Chief Infomation Officer	286 Digital Learning		T = Title I Schoolwide	= Twitter	
84 Erate	98 Chief Technology Officer	288 Common Core Standards	**Other School Types**	V = Career & Tech Ed Programs		
85 AIDS Education	270 Accountability	294 Accountability	Ⓐ = Alternative School			
88 Alternative/At Risk	271 Migrant Education	295 Network System	Ⓒ = Charter School	New Schools are shaded		
89 Multi-Cultural Curriculum	273 Teacher Mentor	296 Title II Programs	Ⓜ = Magnet School	New Superintendents and Principals are bold		
90 Social Work	274 Before/After Sch	297 Webmaster	Ⓨ = Year-Round School	Personnel with email addresses are underscored		

Seneca County

Public Schs..Principal	Grd	Prgm	Enr/#Cls	SN		
Portsmouth West Elem Sch 15332 US Highway 52 Unit A, W Portsmouth 45663 Bill Platzer	PK-4	T	603 37	79%	740/858-1116 Fax 740/858-1118	
Portsmouth West High Sch 15332 US Highway 52 Frnt, W Portsmouth 45663 Kevin Llyod	9-12	T	371 50	80%	740/858-1103 Fax 740/858-3054	
Portsmouth West Middle Sch 1533 B US Highway 52, W Portsmouth 45663 Christopher Jordan	5-8	T	475 40	70%	740/858-6668 Fax 740/858-0331	

- **Wheelersburg Local School Dist** PID: 00831366   740/574-8484
  620 Center St, Wheelersburg 45694   Fax 740/574-6134

> Schools: 3 \ Teachers: 82 \ Students: 1,600 \ Special Ed Students: 168
> \ College-Bound: 69% \ Ethnic: Asian 1%, Hispanic 2%, Caucasian
> 96% \ Exp: $172 (Low) \ Poverty: 22% \ Title I: $421,558 \
> Special Education: $266,000 \ Open-Close: 08/20 - 05/21 \ DTBP: $32
> (Low)

Mark Knapp 1,11		George Grice 2		
Alex Prater 3,91		Kellie Reinhardt 5		
Jarod Shaw 6*		Melissa Bibbey 16,73,295*		
Aimee Hall 37,58,69*		Barry Spradlin 38*		
Rebecca Davis 38*		Matthew Miller 67		
Tom Vallance 73,295		Melissa Bibbey 84		

Public Schs..Principal	Grd	Prgm	Enr/#Cls	SN	
Wheelersburg Elem Sch 800 Pirate Dr, Wheelersburg 45694 Janeen Spradlin	PK-3	T	577 25	37%	740/574-8130 Fax 740/574-9201
Wheelersburg High Sch 800 Pirate Dr, Wheelersburg 45694 Chris Porter	9-12		385 30	30%	740/574-2527 Fax 740/574-6178
Wheelersburg Middle Sch 800 Pirate Dr, Wheelersburg 45694 David Rucker	4-8	T	633	37%	740/574-2515 Fax 740/574-9201

SCIOTO CATHOLIC SCHOOLS

- **Diocese of Columbus Ed Office** PID: 00802717
  Listing includes only schools located in this county. See District Index for location of Diocesan Offices.

Catholic Schs..Principal	Grd	Prgm	Enr/#Cls	SN	
Notre Dame Elem Sch 1401 Gallia St, Portsmouth 45662 Josh McMackin	PK-6		179 20		740/353-2354 Fax 740/353-6769
Notre Dame Jr Sr High Sch 2220 Sunrise Ave, Portsmouth 45662 Thomas Walker	7-12		160 17		740/353-2354 Fax 740/353-2526

SCIOTO PRIVATE SCHOOLS

Private Schs..Principal	Grd	Prgm	Enr/#Cls	SN	
Franklin Furnace Christn Acad 100 Seneak Ave, Frankln Frnce 45629 Dennis Hankinns	K-12		30 4		740/354-9301 Fax 740/354-9341
Portsmouth STEM Academy 614 3rd St, Portsmouth 45662 Megan Warnock	K-8		21		740/351-0591

Truth Christian Academy PO Box 366, Wheelersburg 45694 Robert Davis	K-12		25 3	740/574-8449 Fax 740/574-4799

SENECA COUNTY

SENECA COUNTY SCHOOLS

- **North Ctrl Ohio Ed Service Ctr** PID: 00830855   419/447-2927
  928 W Market St Ste A, Tiffin 44883   Fax 419/447-2825

Dr Jim Lahoski 1,11		Timothy Chaney 3	
Dr Kristi Graves 8		Brenda Luhring 15,751	
Cynthia Moore 15,58		Heather Justen 34,79	
Kimberly Fisher 68		Kathleen Mohr 73,74,295	

County Schs..Principal	Grd	Prgm	Enr/#Cls	SN	
Family Learning Center 797 E Township Road 201, Tiffin 44883 Heather Justen	Spec		100 6		419/448-5079 Fax 419/448-5082
ⓐ North Central Academy ⓒ 928 W Market St Ste B, Tiffin 44883 Matt Wolph	6-12	T	100	72%	419/448-5786 Fax 419/448-5789
Seneca Co Opportunity Ctr 780 E County Road 20, Tiffin 44883 Rick Gagnon	Spec	G	250 7		419/447-7521 Fax 419/448-5294

SENECA PUBLIC SCHOOLS

- **Fostoria City School Dist** PID: 00831457   419/435-8163
  1001 Park Ave, Fostoria 44830   Fax 419/436-4109

> Schools: 2 \ Teachers: 115 \ Students: 1,845 \ Special Ed Students: 374
> \ LEP Students: 23 \ College-Bound: 24% \ Ethnic: Asian 1%, African
> American 6%, Hispanic 26%, Caucasian 68% \ Exp: $363 (High) \
> Poverty: 27% \ Title I: $1,050,548 \ Special Education: $534,000 \
> Open-Close: 09/03 - 05/29 \ DTBP: $181 (High) \ f

Andrew Sprang 1		Sue Lehmann 2,19	
David Hossler 3,5,91		Hollis Reinbolt 4	
Tara Matz 8,11,286,288,298		Anne Warriner 12	
Jennifer Abell 34,36,58*		Teresa Vogel 36*	
Dr Thomas Guernsey 67		Jeremy Smith 73,295*	
Sandra Ellis 81*			

Public Schs..Principal	Grd	Prgm	Enr/#Cls	SN	
Fostoria Elem Sch 1202 H L Ford Dr, Fostoria 44830 Kori Bernal	PK-6	T	584 37	75%	419/436-4125 Fax 419/436-4169
Fostoria Jr Sr High Sch 1001 Park Ave, Fostoria 44830 Drew Bauman	7-12	TV	729 40	72%	419/436-4110 Fax 419/436-4118

---

1 Superintendent	8 Curric/Instruct K-12	19 Chief Financial Officer	29 Family/Consumer Science	39 Social Studies K-12	49 English/Lang Arts Elem	59 Special Education Elem	69 Academic Assessment
2 Bus/Finance/Purchasing	9 Curric/Instruct Elem	20 Art K-12	30 Adult Education	40 Social Studies Elem	50 English/Lang Arts Sec	60 Special Education Sec	70 Research/Development
3 Buildings And Grounds	10 Curric/Instruct Sec	21 Art Elem	31 Career/Sch-to-Work K-12	41 Social Studies Sec	51 Reading K-12	61 Foreign/World Lang K-12	71 Public Information
4 Food Service	11 Federal Program	22 Art Sec	32 Career/Sch-to-Work Elem	42 Science K-12	52 Reading Elem	62 Foreign/World Lang Elem	72 Summer School
5 Transportation	12 Title I	23 Music K-12	33 Career/Sch-to-Work Sec	43 Science Elem	53 Reading Sec	63 Foreign/World Lang Sec	73 Instructional Tech
6 Athletic	13 Title V	24 Music Elem	34 Early Childhood Ed	44 Science Sec	54 Remedial Reading K-12	64 Religious Education K-12	74 Inservice Training
7 Health Services	14 Asst Superintendent	25 Music Sec	35 Health/Phys Education	45 Math K-12	55 Remedial Reading Elem	65 Religious Education Elem	75 Marketing/Distributive
	15 Instructional Media Svcs	26 Business Education	36 Guidance Services K-12	46 Math Elem	56 Remedial Reading Sec	66 Religious Education Sec	76 Info Systems
	16 Chief Operations Officer	27 Career & Tech Ed	37 Guidance Services Elem	47 Math Sec	57 Bilingual/ELL	67 School Board President	77 Psychological Assess
	17 Chief Academic Officer	28 Technology Education	38 Guidance Services Sec	48 English/Lang Arts K-12	58 Special Education K-12	68 Teacher Personnel	78 Affirmative Action

Ohio School Directory — Seneca County

Hopewell-Loudon Local SD PID: 00831548
181 N County Rd 7, Bascom 44809
419/937-2216 Fax 419/937-2516

Schools: 1 \ **Teachers:** 48 \ **Students:** 821 \ **Special Ed Students:** 118 \ **College-Bound:** 44% \ **Ethnic:** Hispanic 4%, Caucasian 95% \ **Exp:** $430 (High) \ **Poverty:** 8% \ **Title I:** $66,470 \ **Special Education:** $140,000 \ **Open-Close:** 08/19 - 05/21 \ **DTBP:** $178 (High)

Jeffrey Holbrook 1	Veronica Reinhart 2
Doug Depinet 3,5	Steve Suter 6*
Bill Dobbins 10*	Sue Bodart 16*
Ruth Stiverson 35,85	Heather Stockmaster 36,69*
Kevin Kreais 67	Steve Acton 73,295*
Eric Speicelsehies 83	

Public Schs..Principal	Grd	Prgm	Enr/#Cls	SN	
Hopewell-Loudon Local Sch 181 N County Rd 7, Bascom 44809 Kendra Nelson \ Jason Miller	K-12		821 46	50%	419/937-2804

New Riegel Local School Dist PID: 00831574
44 N Perry St, New Riegel 44853
419/595-2256 Fax 419/595-2901

Schools: 1 \ **Teachers:** 27 \ **Students:** 500 \ **Special Ed Students:** 39 \ **College-Bound:** 60% \ **Ethnic:** Hispanic 1%, Caucasian 99% \ **Exp:** $283 (Med) \ **Poverty:** 8% \ **Title I:** $35,527 \ **Special Education:** $81,000 \ **Open-Close:** 08/21 - 05/22 \ **DTBP:** $174 (High)

David Rombach 1	Jane Schalk 2,84
Judy Smith 4*	Keith Piper 5*
Mark Theis 5	Steve Bouillon 6*
David Rombach 8,12,58,74,78,273,288*	Elaine Nye 11
Diane Clouse 16,82*	Kristin Forman 31,36,69,83,85*
Shilo Clouse 35*	Margaret Schalk 54*
Beth Kummerer 67	John Krammer 73,295*

Public Schs..Principal	Grd	Prgm	Enr/#Cls	SN	
New Riegel K-12 Sch 44 N Perry St, New Riegel 44853 Justin Johnson	K-12		500 12	42%	419/595-2265

Old Fort Local School Dist PID: 00831615
7635 N County Road 51, Tiffin 44883
419/992-4291 Fax 419/992-4293

Schools: 2 \ **Teachers:** 46 \ **Students:** 750 \ **Special Ed Students:** 77 \ **LEP Students:** 3 \ **College-Bound:** 71% \ **Ethnic:** African American 1%, Hispanic 7%, Caucasian 92% \ **Exp:** $220 (Med) \ **Poverty:** 9% \ **Title I:** $60,740 \ **Special Education:** $126,000 \ **Open-Close:** 08/26 - 05/22 \ **DTBP:** $235 (High) \ ▮

Tom Peiffer 1	Thomas Siloy 2
Jared Bilger 3*	John Miller 5*
Gregg Molyet 6	Tammy Wasserman 12*
Larry Bowman 67	Erica Cobb 275*

Public Schs..Principal	Grd	Prgm	Enr/#Cls	SN	
Old Fort Elem Sch 118 Washington St, Bettsville 44815 Laura Bryant	K-6	T	336 14	37%	419/986-5166 Fax 419/986-6039
Old Fort High Sch 7635 N County Road 51, Tiffin 44883 Erica Cobb	7-12	V	308 25	22%	419/992-4291

Seneca East Local School Dist PID: 00831641
13343 E US Highway 224, Attica 44807
419/426-7041 Fax 419/426-5514

Schools: 1 \ **Teachers:** 62 \ **Students:** 880 \ **Special Ed Students:** 127 \ **LEP Students:** 3 \ **College-Bound:** 66% \ **Ethnic:** Hispanic 3%, Caucasian 97% \ **Exp:** $208 (Med) \ **Poverty:** 9% \ **Title I:** $96,268 \ **Special Education:** $202,000 \ **Open-Close:** 08/21 - 05/22 \ **DTBP:** $149 (High)

Dr Laura Kagy 1	Laura Brickner 2
Donald Shawn Branham 3	Brenda Ruffing 4*
Tammy Rogers 5	Doug Mason 6*
Laurie Hunker 8,288*	Melody Margraf 11,83,296,298*
Andrea Schimpf 16*	Heather Stockmaster 38,69,88*
Dan Stacklin 67	Jean Schank 76*

Public Schs..Principal	Grd	Prgm	Enr/#Cls	SN	
Seneca East Local Sch 13343 E US Highway 224, Attica 44807 Don Vogt \ Bradley Powers	K-12		880 30	83%	419/426-7041 Fax 419/426-5400

Tiffin City School Dist PID: 00831706
244 S Monroe St, Tiffin 44883
419/447-2515 Fax 419/448-5202

Schools: 6 \ **Teachers:** 129 \ **Students:** 2,800 \ **Special Ed Students:** 537 \ **LEP Students:** 25 \ **College-Bound:** 63% \ **Ethnic:** Asian 1%, African American 2%, Hispanic 5%, Caucasian 93% \ **Exp:** $135 (Low) \ **Poverty:** 15% \ **Title I:** $639,813 \ **Special Education:** $645,000 \ **Open-Close:** 08/22 - 05/22 \ **DTBP:** $193 (High)

Gary Barber 1	Sharon Perry 2
Scott Daniel 3,91	Janet Beard 4*
Randy Conger 5	Brad Scheiber 6*
Jennifer Losey 8	Michelle Tuite 8,11,83,88,288,298*
Robert Boes 15	Maryl Hill 57,58,275
Chris Widman 67	Jene Roiger 71
Timothy Weber 73,76,84	Nicholas Smith 77*
Paula Zirm 81*	

Public Schs..Principal	Grd	Prgm	Enr/#Cls	SN	
Charles Krout Elem Sch 20 Glenn St, Tiffin 44883 William Beaston	2-3	T	349 26	64%	419/447-2652 Fax 419/448-5223
Columbian Senior High Sch 300 S Monroe St, Tiffin 44883 Forrest Trisler	9-12	A	829 50	33%	419/447-6331 Fax 419/448-5252
Lincoln Pre-Kindergarten Ctr 124 Ohio Ave, Tiffin 44883 Michelle Tuite	PK-PK		88	81%	419/455-9107 Fax 419/448-5221
Noble Elem Sch 130 Minerva St, Tiffin 44883 Mike Newlove	4-5	T	370 12	54%	419/447-1566 Fax 419/448-5219 ▮
Tiffin Middle Sch 103 Shepherd Dr, Tiffin 44883 Shawn Murphy	6-8	T	635 75	49%	419/447-3358 Fax 419/448-5250 ▮
Washington Elem Sch 151 Elmer St, Tiffin 44883 Nicki Jiran	K-1	T	375 13	65%	419/447-1072 Fax 419/448-5217 ▮

---

79 Student Personnel	91 Safety/Security	275 Response To Intervention	298 Grant Writer/Ptnrships
80 Driver Ed/Safety	92 Magnet School	277 Remedial Math K-12	750 Chief Innovation Officer
81 Gifted/Talented	93 Parental Involvement	280 Literacy Coach	751 Chief of Staff
82 Video Services	95 Tech Prep Program	285 STEM	752 Social Emotional Learning
83 Substance Abuse Prev	97 Chief Infomation Officer	286 Digital Learning	
84 Erate	98 Chief Technology Officer	288 Common Core Standards	**Other School Types**
85 AIDS Education	270 Character Education	294 Accountability	Ⓐ = Alternative School
88 Alternative/At Risk	271 Migrant Education	295 Network System	Ⓒ = Charter School
89 Multi-Cultural Curriculum	273 Teacher Mentor	296 Title II Programs	Ⓜ = Magnet School
90 Social Work	274 Before/After Sch	297 Webmaster	Ⓨ = Year-Round School

School Programs
A = Alternative Program
G = Adult Classes
M = Magnet Program
T = Title I Schoolwide
V = Career & Tech Ed Programs

Social Media
▮ = Facebook
▮ = Twitter

New Schools are shaded
New Superintendents and Principals are bold
Personnel with email addresses are underscored

OH-181

Shelby County

SENECA CATHOLIC SCHOOLS

- **Diocese of Toledo Ed Office** PID: 00818297
  Listing includes only schools located in this county. See District Index for location of Diocesan Offices.

Catholic Schs..Principal	Grd	Prgm	Enr/#Cls	SN	
Calvert Catholic Schools 152 Madison St, Tiffin 44883 Ted Willman \ Marilyn Seislove	PK-12		560 50		419/447-3844 Fax 419/447-2922
St Wendelin Catholic Sch 533 N Countyline St, Fostoria 44830 Teresa Kitchen	K-8		110 30		419/435-8144

SHELBY COUNTY

SHELBY PUBLIC SCHOOLS

- **Anna Local School Dist** PID: 00831811   937/394-2011
  1 McRill Way, Anna 45302   Fax 937/394-7658

Schools: 2 \ Teachers: 66 \ Students: 1,200 \ Special Ed Students: 164 \ LEP Students: 3 \ College-Bound: 71% \ Ethnic: Asian 1%, Hispanic 1%, Caucasian 98% \ Exp: $206 (Med) \ Poverty: 4% \ Title I: $37,089 \ Special Education: $191,000 \ Open-Close: 09/03 - 05/29 \ DTBP: $171 (High)

Andrew Bixler 1	Cathy Doseck 2
Dave Baumer 3,5,91*	Angie Harvey 4
Michael Muehlfeld 6	Linda Daniel 7*
Heather Wuebker 8,288,298*	John Holtzapple 9,11,296*
Joel Staudter 10*	Melissa Rivera 16*
Sarah Heilers 27*	Scott Swartz 28*
Brenda Wuebker 29*	Michele Holsinger ... 38,69,83,85,88*
Krista Pettus 52,55*	Kimberly Grewe 57*
Cindy Endsley 58*	Matt Murray 67
Brenda Littlefield 73,76,286,295*	K C Needles 285

Public Schs..Principal	Grd	Prgm	Enr/#Cls	SN	
Anna Elem Sch 607 N Pike St, Anna 45302 John Holtzapple	K-5		514 22	16%	937/394-2584 Fax 937/394-3119
Anna Middle High Sch 1 McRill Way, Anna 45302 Cindy Endsley \ Joel Staudter	6-12	V	640 62	19%	937/394-2011

- **Botkins Local School Dist** PID: 00831861   937/693-4241
  404 E State St, Botkins 45306   Fax 937/693-2557

Schools: 1 \ Teachers: 39 \ Students: 644 \ Special Ed Students: 39 \ LEP Students: 9 \ College-Bound: 81% \ Ethnic: Hispanic 2%, Caucasian 98% \ Exp: $243 (Med) \ Poverty: 4% \ Title I: $12,813 \ Special Education: $138,000 \ Open-Close: 08/20 - 05/15

Jeff McPheron 1,11,83	Joanna Jones 2*
Mick Jones 3*	Annette Hensley 4
Brad Bergman 6	Ryan Loy 10*
Michele Meyer 12,52*	Keith Puschel 16,73*

Norman Leugars 28*	Jena Holtcamp 29*
Krista Meyer 36,69*	Jeremy Pleiman 53*
Rob Berryman 58*	Neil Boerger 67
Chris Abke 81*	

Public Schs..Principal	Grd	Prgm	Enr/#Cls	SN	
Botkins Local Sch 404 E State St, Botkins 45306 Chris Abke \ Ryan Loy	K-12	V	644 38	23%	937/693-4241

- **Fairlawn Local School Dist** PID: 00831902   937/492-1974
  18800 Johnston Rd, Sidney 45365   Fax 937/492-5225

Schools: 2 \ Teachers: 27 \ Students: 650 \ Special Ed Students: 64 \ College-Bound: 50% \ Ethnic: Hispanic 1%, Caucasian 99% \ Exp: $155 (Low) \ Poverty: 15% \ Title I: $83,910 \ Special Education: $130,000 \ Open-Close: 08/20 - 05/21 \ DTBP: $49 (Low)

Jeff Hobbs 1,83	Keith Doseck 2
Matt Dankworth 3*	Zack Freiling 6
John Stekli 8*	Rycki Schmiesing 16*
Raechel Genert 37	Cary Smith 38
Connie Schnider 58	Bob Gold 67
Aaron Cox 73,295*	

Public Schs..Principal	Grd	Prgm	Enr/#Cls	SN	
Fairlawn Elem Sch 18800 Johnston Rd, Sidney 45365 Karen McRill	PK-5	T	308 20		937/492-1654
Fairlawn Middle High Sch 18800 Johnston Rd, Sidney 45365 John Stekli	6-12	V	300 20	73%	937/492-5930

- **Ft Loramie Local School Dist** PID: 00831940   937/295-3931
  575 Greenback Rd, Fort Loramie 45845   Fax 937/295-2758

Schools: 2 \ Teachers: 48 \ Students: 793 \ Special Ed Students: 117 \ College-Bound: 61% \ Ethnic: Caucasian 99% \ Exp: $282 (Med) \ Poverty: 3% \ Title I: $26,758 \ Special Education: $163,000 \ Open-Close: 08/20 - 05/20 \ DTBP: $164 (High)

Daniel Holland 1	Janet Kemper 2
Michelle Barhorst 16,82*	Ryan Goldschmidt 28*
Katie Francis 36*	Tracy Drees 67
Brad Frilling 73*	

Public Schs..Principal	Grd	Prgm	Enr/#Cls	SN	
Ft Loramie Elem Sch 35 Elm St, Fort Loramie 45845 Scott Rodeahffer	K-6		410 25	11%	937/295-2931
Ft Loramie Jr Sr High Sch 600 E Park St, Fort Loramie 45845 Kreg Hollenbacher	7-12	V	333 30	6%	937/295-3342

- **Hardin-Houston Local Sch Dist** PID: 00831976   937/295-3010
  5300 Houston Rd, Houston 45333   Fax 937/295-3737

Schools: 1 \ Teachers: 58 \ Students: 860 \ Special Ed Students: 147 \ College-Bound: 42% \ Ethnic: Hispanic 1%, Caucasian 99% \ Exp: $240 (Med) \ Poverty: 8% \ Title I: $120,510 \ Special Education: $166,000 \ Open-Close: 08/15 - 05/15 \ DTBP: $172 (High)

Ryan Maier 1	Amy Ayers 2
Dave Ewing 3*	Andrea Roberts 4,12*
Craig Knouff 6*	Andrea Kittel 11,296*

Ohio School Directory — Shelby County

Janet McClurg 16,82*	Stephanie Merickel 36*
Jennifer Hoying 58*	Bill Clark 67
Matt Stephens 73,76*	Sara Roseberry 298*

Public Schs..Principal	Grd	Prgm	Enr/#Cls	SN
Hardin-Houston Local Sch 5300 Houston Rd, Houston 45333 Sara Roseberry \ Jeff Judy	K-12		860 24	77% 937/295-3010

- **Jackson Center Local Sch Dist** PID: 00832009   937/596-6053
  204 S Linden St, Jackson CTR 45334   Fax 937/596-6490

Schools: 1 \ *Teachers:* 37 \ *Students:* 600 \ *Special Ed Students:* 90 \ *College-Bound:* 58% \ *Ethnic:* Hispanic 1%, Caucasian 98% \ *Exp:* $237 (Med) \ *Poverty:* 11% \ *Title I:* $65,324 \ *Special Education:* $96,000 \ *Open-Close:* 08/15 - 05/20 \ *DTBP:* $190 (High)

William Reichert 1,73	Tony Meyer 2
Ted Rostorfer 3*	Lacresha Clark 4*
Scott Elchert 6*	Stephanie Watercutter 9*
Jeff Reese 10*	Sheri Emerson 11*
Nancy Nolan 16*	Marilyn Kohler 36,57,69,83,85,88,270*
Beth Dickson 58*	Brad Wren 67
Ginger Heuker 288*	

Public Schs..Principal	Grd	Prgm	Enr/#Cls	SN
Jackson Center Sch 204 S Linden St, Jackson CTR 45334 Ginger Heuker \ Jeff Reese	PK-12	V	600 14	78% 937/596-6053

- **Russia Local School Dist** PID: 00832035   937/526-3156
  100 School St, Russia 45363   Fax 937/526-0045

Schools: 1 \ *Teachers:* 28 \ *Students:* 430 \ *Special Ed Students:* 39 \ *College-Bound:* 77% \ *Ethnic:* Caucasian 100% \ *Exp:* $289 (Med) \ *Poverty:* 2% \ *Title I:* $11,581 \ *Special Education:* $81,000 \ *Open-Close:* 08/20 - 05/21 \ *DTBP:* $174 (High)

Steve Rose 1	Jean Borchers 2
Lynn Blakeley 12*	Carrie Schutze 58*
Joshua Francis 67	Rachel Gregg 69
Marcus Petitjean 73*	

Public Schs..Principal	Grd	Prgm	Enr/#Cls	SN
Russia Local Sch 100 School St, Russia 45363 Marcus Bixler	K-12	V	430 30	17% 937/526-3156

- **Sidney City School Dist** PID: 00832061   937/497-2200
  750 S 4th Ave, Sidney 45365   Fax 937/497-2211

Schools: 6 \ *Teachers:* 164 \ *Students:* 3,350 \ *Special Ed Students:* 797 \ *LEP Students:* 50 \ *College-Bound:* 40% \ *Ethnic:* Asian 2%, African American 5%, Hispanic 3%, Caucasian 91% \ *Exp:* $196 (Low) \ *Poverty:* 14% \ *Title I:* $867,943 \ *Special Education:* $825,000 \ *Open-Close:* 09/03 - 05/21

Bob Humble 1	Mike Watkins 2
Jason McClain 3,4	Joni Renner 5
Mitch Hoying 6*	Brooke Gessler 8*
Brooke Gessler 8,11,285,288,298	Tammi Johnson 16*
Chris Barr 58*	Robert Smith 67
Tiffany Rank 71	John Michalos 73,286,295

Public Schs..Principal	Grd	Prgm	Enr/#Cls	SN
Emerson Elem Sch 901 Campbell Rd, Sidney 45365 Stephanie Klingshirn	K-4	T	340 16	64% 937/497-2261 Fax 937/497-2262
Longfellow Elem Sch 1250 Park St, Sidney 45365 Fran Dembski	K-5	T	278 14	80% 937/497-2264 Fax 937/497-2263
Northwood Elem Sch 1152 Saint Marys Rd, Sidney 45365 Michael Moore	K-5	T	453 24	66% 937/497-2231 Fax 937/497-2232
Sidney High Sch 1215 Campbell Rd, Sidney 45365 Denny Morrison	9-12	AV	967 60	54% 937/497-2238 Fax 937/497-2216
Sidney Middle Sch 980 Fair Rd, Sidney 45365 Diane Voress	5-8	T	900 60	60% 937/497-2225 Fax 937/497-2204 f t
Whittier Elem Sch 425 Belmont St, Sidney 45365 Keith Helmlinger	K-5	T	293 15	61% 937/497-2275 Fax 937/497-2276

SHELBY CATHOLIC SCHOOLS

- **Archdiocese Cincinnati Ed Off** PID: 00808096
  Listing includes only schools located in this county. See District Index for location of Diocesan Offices.

Catholic Schs..Principal	Grd	Prgm	Enr/#Cls	SN
Holy Angels Sch 120 E Water St, Sidney 45365 Beth Spicer	K-8		204 16	937/492-9293 Fax 937/492-8578 f
Lehman Catholic High Sch 2400 Saint Marys Rd, Sidney 45365 Denise Stauffer	9-12		200 30	937/498-1161 Fax 937/492-9877

SHELBY PRIVATE SCHOOLS

Private Schs..Principal	Grd	Prgm	Enr/#Cls	SN
Christian Academy Sch 2151 W Russell Rd, Sidney 45365 Dick Dray	K-12		150 14	937/492-7556 Fax 937/492-5399

SHELBY REGIONAL CENTERS

- **Woco-W Ohio Computer Org** PID: 04499518   937/498-2161
  129 E Court St 1st Fl, Sidney 45365   Fax 937/497-7233

Donn Walls 1,73	Marcia Wierwille 2
Julie Ellis 79	Mike Wagner 295

---

79 Student Personnel	91 Safety/Security	275 Response To Intervention	298 Grant Writer/Ptnrships	**School Programs**	**Social Media**	
80 Driver Ed/Safety	92 Magnet School	277 Remedial Math K-12	750 Chief Innovation Officer	A = Alternative Program	f = Facebook	
81 Gifted/Talented	93 Parental Involvement	280 Literacy Coach	751 Chief of Staff	G = Adult Classes		
82 Video Services	95 Tech Prep Program	285 STEM	752 Social Emotional Learning	M = Magnet Program	t = Twitter	
83 Substance Abuse Prev	97 Chief Information Officer	286 Digital Learning		T = Title I Schoolwide		
84 Erate	98 Chief Technology Officer	288 Common Core Standards	**Other School Types**	V = Career & Tech Ed Programs		
85 AIDS Education	270 Character Education	294 Accountability	Ⓐ = Alternative School			
88 Alternative/At Risk	271 Migrant Education	295 Network System	Ⓒ = Charter School	New Schools are shaded		
89 Multi-Cultural Curriculum	273 Teacher Mentor	296 Title II Programs	Ⓜ = Magnet School	New Superintendents and Principals are bold		
90 Social Work	274 Before/After Sch	297 Webmaster	Ⓨ = Year Round School	Personnel with email addresses are underscored		

Stark County

STARK COUNTY

STARK COUNTY SCHOOLS

- **Stark Co Ed Service Center** PID: 00833819   330/492-8136
  6057 Strip Ave NW, Canton 44720   Fax 330/492-6381

Joe Chaddock 1,11	Tamra Hurst 2
Jim Nicademo 8,15,34,58,73	Jean Fight 67
Tom Piccari 81	

County Schs..Principal	Grd	Prgm	Enr/#Cls	SN
ⓒ Canton College Prep Sch [238] 101 Cleveland Ave NW, Canton 44702 Daryl Lindsay	K-8		260	330/455-0498 Fax 330/915-2330
Eastgate Sch 2121 Ashland St, Louisville 44641 Tammy Maney	Spec		200 15	330/479-3440 Fax 330/875-5368
Southgate Sch 3057 Cleveland Ave S, Canton 44707 Myrna Blosser	Spec		168 21	330/484-2547 Fax 330/484-3431
ⓒ Summit Academy Sec Sch-Canton [248] 2400 Cleveland Ave NW, Canton 44709 Lisa Cook	Spec	T	90 5	330/453-8547 Fax 330/453-8924

STARK PUBLIC SCHOOLS

- **Alliance City School Dist** PID: 00832190   330/821-2100
  200 Glamorgan St, Alliance 44601   Fax 330/821-0202

Schools: 6 \ *Teachers:* 170 \ *Students:* 3,100 \ *Special Ed Students:* 591 \ *LEP Students:* 9 \ *College-Bound:* 38% \ *Ethnic:* African American 14%, Hispanic 4%, Caucasian 82% \ *Exp:* $302 (High) \ *Poverty:* 31% \ *Title I:* $1,684,031 \ *Special Education:* $643,000 \ *Open-Close:* 08/21 - 05/28 \ *DTBP:* $192 (High)

Jeffery Talbert 1	Kirk Heath 2
Nick Cowles 3,4,5,91	Mike Schott 6*
Christine Gibowicz 8,275	Jason Dixon 15,79
Cathy Brookes 57,81,88*	Jane Stoner 58
Sally Ailes 67	Chad Morris 73,84,295

Public Schs..Principal	Grd	Prgm	Enr/#Cls	SN
Alliance Early Learning Sch 285 W Oxford St, Alliance 44601 Tim Calfee	PK-K	T	422 22	330/829-2266 Fax 330/823-8106
Alliance High Sch 400 Glamorgan St, Alliance 44601 Shawn Jackson	9-12	AV	954	330/829-2245 Fax 330/823-4920
Alliance Middle Sch 3205 S Union Ave, Alliance 44601 Troy Russell	6-8	T	630 35	330/829-2254 Fax 330/823-0872
Northside Intermediate Sch 701 Johnson Ave, Alliance 44601 Stephanie Garren	4-5	T	414 17	330/829-2269 Fax 330/823-0761
Parkway Elem Sch 1490 Parkway Blvd, Alliance 44601 Cory Muller	1-3	T	267 15	330/829-2264 Fax 330/823-7350
Rockhill Elem Sch 2400 S Rockhill Ave, Alliance 44601 Michelle Balderson	1-3	T	300 18	330/829-2260 Fax 330/829-8829

- **Canton City School Dist** PID: 00832396   330/438-2500
  305 McKinley Ave NW, Canton 44702   Fax 330/455-0682

Schools: 27 \ *Teachers:* 539 \ *Students:* 9,500 \ *Special Ed Students:* 1,603 \ *LEP Students:* 164 \ *College-Bound:* 36% \ *Ethnic:* African American 44%, Hispanic 6%, Caucasian 50% \ *Exp:* $294 (Med) \ *Poverty:* 44% \ *Title I:* $8,999,721 \ *Special Education:* $2,452,000 \ *Open-Close:* 08/12 - 05/28 \ *DTBP:* $240 (High)

Dr Jeffery Graham 1	Dennie Poje 2
Tad Ellsworth 2	Dan Bailey 3
Erin Cole 4	Nicole Kizer 5
Sean Stranger 6	Kim Kinsbury 8
Mallory Floyd 8,15,68	Diedra Stokes-Davis 11,79,296
Trudy Walker 16,73,76,295	Ben Carter 27,31
Jane Meyer 30	Marilyn Vanalmen 30
Chastity Trumpower 34,58,81*	Kathleen Brooks 57
John Rinaldi 67	Barbara Maceyak 68
Robyn Matulich 71	Heather Heater 73
Steve Humphrey 91	Joellen Esber 93
Cherie Culp 298	

Public Schs..Principal	Grd	Prgm	Enr/#Cls	SN
ⓥ Aim Academy 2701 Coventry Blvd NE, Canton 44705 Annie Arvidson	K-6	M	345	330/456-3167
Allen Reading & Math Prep Sch 1326 Sherrick Rd SE, Canton 44707 Christin Sedmock	PK-2	T	229 21	330/453-2782 Fax 330/588-2127
Arts Academy at Summit 1100 10th St NW, Canton 44703 Jeanie Bowling	K-8		295	330/452-6537 Fax 330/580-3190
Belden Leadership Sch 2115 Georgetown Rd NE, Canton 44704 Angela Seders	3-5	T	250 23	330/453-6902 Fax 330/588-2128
C2RA at Lehman 1400 Broad Ave NW, Canton 44708 Shawn Monahan	6-8	TV	589 75	330/456-1963 Fax 330/456-8121
Cedar Leadership Sch 2823 9th St SW, Canton 44710 Kathy Kisha-Wise	3-5	T	357 25	330/580-3502 Fax 330/580-3165
Choices Alternative Sch 401 14th St SE, Canton 44707 Tim Henderson	Adult	T	136	330/456-1189 Fax 330/580-2404
Clarendon Leadership Sch 412 Clarendon Ave NW, Canton 44708 Nicole Herberghs	3-5	T	287 20	330/453-7681 Fax 330/588-2130
Ⓐ Connections Academy 401 14th St SE, Canton 44707 Timothy Henderson	6-8		25 4	330/456-1189 Fax 330/580-2404
ⓒ Digital Academy 401 14th St SE, Canton 44707 James Pappas	9-12	T	52 2	330/456-1189 Fax 330/580-2404
Dueber Reading & Math Prep Sch 815 Dueber Ave SW, Canton 44706 Lori Kochan	PK-2	T	231 15	330/580-3517
Early College Acad at Crenshaw 2525 19th St NE, Canton 44705 Tiffany Joseph	6-8	TV	609 52	330/454-7717 Fax 330/588-2120
Gibbs Leadership Sch 1320 Gibbs Ave NE, Canton 44705 Nicole Bush	3-5	T	258 21	330/456-1521 Fax 330/580-3164

1	Superintendent	8	Curric/Instruct K-12	19	Chief Financial Officer	29	Family/Consumer Science	39	Social Studies K-12	49	English/Lang Arts Elem	59	Special Education Elem	69	Academic Assessment
2	Bus/Finance/Purchasing	9	Curric/Instruct Elem	20	Art K-12	30	Adult Education	40	Social Studies Elem	50	English/Lang Arts Sec	60	Special Education Sec	70	Research/Development
3	Buildings And Grounds	10	Curric/Instruct Sec	21	Art Elem	31	Career/Sch-to-Work K-12	41	Social Studies Sec	51	Reading K-12	61	Foreign/World Lang K-12	71	Public Information
4	Food Service	11	Federal Program	22	Art Sec	32	Career/Sch-to-Work Elem	42	Science K-12	52	Reading Elem	62	Foreign/World Lang Elem	72	Summer School
5	Transportation	12	Title I	23	Music K-12	33	Career/Sch-to-Work Sec	43	Science Elem	53	Reading Sec	63	Foreign/World Lang Sec	73	Instructional Tech
6	Athletic	13	Title V	24	Music Elem	34	Early Childhood Ed	44	Science Sec	54	Remedial Reading K-12	64	Religious Education K-12	74	Inservice Training
7	Health Services	15	Asst Superintendent	25	Music Sec	35	Health/Phys Education	45	Math K-12	55	Remedial Reading Elem	65	Religious Education Elem	75	Marketing/Distributive
		16	Instructional Media Svcs	26	Business Education	36	Guidance Services K-12	46	Math Elem	56	Remedial Reading Sec	66	Religious Education Sec	76	Info Systems
		17	Chief Operations Officer	27	Career & Tech Ed	37	Guidance Services Elem	47	Math Sec	57	Bilingual/ELL	67	School Board President	77	Psychological Assess
		18	Chief Academic Officer	28	Technology Education	38	Guidance Services Sec	48	English/Lang Arts K-12	58	Special Education K-12	68	Teacher Personnel	78	Affirmative Action

Ohio School Directory — Stark County

School	Grd	Prgm	Enr/#Cls	Phone/Fax
ⒶGraduation Academy 401 14th St SE, Canton 44707 Minerva Morrow	9-12		100 10	330/456-1189 Fax 330/580-2404
Harter Reading & Math Prep Sch 317 Raff Rd NW, Canton 44708 Deborah Wensel	PK-2	T	399 21	330/456-1001 Fax 330/588-2132
Mason Leadership Sch 316 30th St NW, Canton 44709 Renee Brown	3-5	T	190 12	330/588-2156 Fax 330/580-3038
McGregor Reading & Math Prep 2339 17th St SW, Canton 44706 Annie Arvidson	PK-2	T	177 17	330/452-7069 Fax 330/588-2133
McKinley Downtown Campus 521 Tuscarawas St W, Canton 44702 Kenneth Brunner	9-9	GV	550 60	330/438-2602 Fax 330/580-3508
McKinley Sr High Sch 2323 17th St NW, Canton 44708 Corey Grubbs	9-12	GTV	2,237	330/438-2712 Fax 330/580-3507
ⒶPassages Sch 401 14th St SE, Canton 44707 Timothy Henderson	9-12		53 6	330/456-1189 Fax 330/580-2404
Portage Collaborative Mont Sch 1000 55th St NE, Canton 44721 Jane Reifsnyder	PK-8		216 7	330/966-1912 Fax 330/966-0737
Schreiber Reading & Math Prep 1503 Woodland Ave NW, Canton 44703 Chastity Trumpower	PK-2	T	292 22	330/452-1672 Fax 330/580-3031
Steamm Academy at Hartford 1824 3rd St SE, Canton 44707 David Thompson	6-8	TV	419 40	330/453-6012 Fax 330/453-5096
Stone Reading & Math Prep Sch 2100 Rowland Ave NE, Canton 44714 Charla Malone	PK-2	T	319 22	330/452-6521 Fax 330/452-6858
ⒶTimken Early College HS 231 McKinley Ave NW, Canton 44702 Ken Brunner	9-12		366 10	330/458-3950 Fax 330/458-3980
Worley Reading & Math Prep Sch 1340 23rd St NW, Canton 44709 Elena Monahan	PK-2	T	259 17	330/452-5748 Fax 330/588-2150
Youtz Leadership Sch 1901 Midway Ave NE, Canton 44705 Nikki Cebula	3-5	T	301 25	330/452-7601 Fax 330/588-2159

● **Canton Local School Dist** PID: 00832308
600 Faircrest St SE, Canton 44707
330/484-8010 Fax 330/484-8032

Schools: 3 \ *Teachers:* 116 \ *Students:* 2,000 \ *Special Ed Students:* 238 \ *LEP Students:* 3 \ *College-Bound:* 43% \ *Ethnic:* African American 8%, Hispanic 1%, Caucasian 90% \ *Exp:* $348 (High) \ *Poverty:* 20% \ *Title I:* $603,352 \ *Special Education:* $437,000 \ *Open-Close:* 08/20 - 05/27 \ *DTBP:* $120 (High) \ f t

Steve Milano 1		Jason Schatzel 2,68	
Chris Noll 3,74,91		Ashely Ritz 4	
Joyce Kirkpatrick 5		Andrew Harms 6	
Victoria Hessey 7,11,58,83,85,88,275		Tricia Couts Everett 8,280,285,288,298	
Krista Gearhart 27		Rick Knight 67	
Nick Stepanovich 73,76,84,95,286,295		David Norman 297	

Public Schs..Principal	Grd	Prgm	Enr/#Cls	SN
Canton South High Sch 600 Faircrest St SE, Canton 44707 Jeff Moore	9-12	GTV	769 50	45% 330/484-8000 Fax 330/484-8013
Faircrest Memorial Middle Sch 616 Faircrest St SW, Canton 44706 Gay Welker	5-8	T	592 35	330/484-8015 Fax 330/484-8033
Walker Elem Sch 3525 Sandy Ave SE, Canton 44707 Ann Bartley	PK-4	T	655 24	330/484-8020 Fax 330/484-8134

● **Fairless Local School Dist** PID: 00832712
11885 Navarre Rd SW, Navarre 44662
330/767-3577 Fax 330/767-3298

Schools: 3 \ *Teachers:* 80 \ *Students:* 1,501 \ *Special Ed Students:* 274 \ *LEP Students:* 3 \ *College-Bound:* 48% \ *Ethnic:* African American 1%, Hispanic 1%, Caucasian 98% \ *Exp:* $240 (Med) \ *Poverty:* 18% \ *Title I:* $459,179 \ *Special Education:* $327,000 \ *Open-Close:* 08/21 - 05/28 \ *DTBP:* $189 (High)

Broc Bidlack 1	Mark Phillips 2*
Valerie Wiles 3,5*	Julie Miller 4*
Michael Hearn 8,11*	Tammy Zalesinsky 16,82*
Philip Glasgow 38*	Ryan Murphy 58*
Ken Killian 67	

Public Schs..Principal	Grd	Prgm	Enr/#Cls	SN
Fairless Elem Sch 12000 Navarre Rd SW, Navarre 44662 Colleen Kornish	K-5	T	693 14	56% 330/767-3913 Fax 330/767-4398
Fairless High Sch 11885 Navarre Rd SW, Navarre 44662 Dr Larry Chambliss	9-12	TV	399 65	43% 330/767-3444 Fax 330/767-3447
Fairless Middle Sch 11836 Navarre Rd SW, Navarre 44662 Cynthia Class	6-8	T	382	47% 330/767-4293 Fax 330/767-3807

● **Green Local School Dist** PID: 00835025
1755 Town Park Blvd, Uniontown 44685
330/896-7500 Fax 330/896-7529

Schools: 5 \ *Teachers:* 218 \ *Students:* 4,253 \ *Special Ed Students:* 526 \ *LEP Students:* 24 \ *College-Bound:* 70% \ *Ethnic:* Asian 2%, African American 2%, Hispanic 1%, Caucasian 94% \ *Exp:* $86 (Low) \ *Poverty:* 9% \ *Title I:* $526,033 \ *Special Education:* $635,000 \ *Open-Close:* 08/21 - 05/29 \ *DTBP:* $190 (High) \ f t

Jeffrey Miller 1	Alicia Austin 2
Eydie Snowberger 2,19	Wendall Jackson 3,4,91
Shanna Cable 5	Erich Muzi 6*
Carrie Marochino 8,13*	Kim Brueck 11,27,57,69,72,74,270,288
Joya Mitchell 12,34,58,77,88,285*	Alana Niemiec 15
Daniel Lowmiller 15	Mary Ann Stahr 16*
Marilyn Russ-Miller 38*	Bob Campbell 67
Marc Clendaniel 73,286	Julie McMahan 298

Public Schs..Principal	Grd	Prgm	Enr/#Cls	SN
Green High Sch 1474 Boettler Rd, Uniontown 44685 Cynthia Brown	9-12	V	1,240 80	21% 330/896-7575 Fax 330/896-7549
Green Intermediate Sch 1737 Steese Rd, Uniontown 44685 Mark Booth	4-6		968 37	20% 330/896-7700 Fax 330/896-7725
Green Middle Sch 1711 Steese Road, Uniontown 44685 Jeff Wells	7-8		613 50	18% 330/896-7710 Fax 330/896-7760
Green Primary Sch 2300 Graybill Rd, Uniontown 44685 Krista Seals	1-3		881 26	24% 330/899-8700 Fax 330/899-8799
Greenwood Early Learning Ctr 2250 Graybill Rd, Uniontown 44685 Scott Shank	PK-K		372 16	17% 330/896-7474 Fax 330/896-7554

Legend:

79 Student Personnel 80 Driver Ed/Safety 81 Gifted/Talented 82 Video Services 83 Substance Abuse Prev 84 Erate 85 AIDS Education 88 Alternative/At Risk 89 Multi-Cultural Curriculum 90 Social Work 91 Safety/Security 92 Magnet School 93 Parental Involvement 95 Tech Prep Program 97 Chief Information Officer 98 Chief Technology Officer 270 Character Education 271 Migrant Education 273 Teacher Mentor 274 Before/After Sch 275 Response To Intervention 277 Remedial Math K-12 280 Literacy Coach 285 STEM 286 Digital Learning 288 Common Core Standards 294 Accountability 295 Network System 296 Title II Programs 297 Webmaster 298 Grant Writer/Ptnrships 750 Chief Innovation Officer 751 Chief of Staff 752 Social Emotional Learning

Other School Types: Ⓐ = Alternative School Ⓒ = Charter School Ⓜ = Magnet School Ⓨ = Year Round School

School Programs: A = Alternative Program G = Adult Classes M = Magnet Program T = Title I Schoolwide V = Career & Tech Ed Programs

Social Media: f = Facebook t = Twitter

New Schools are shaded
New Superintendents and Principals are bold
Personnel with email addresses are underscored

Stark County

Market Data Retrieval

● **Jackson Local School Dist** PID: 00832798 330/830-8000
7602 Fulton Dr NW, Massillon 44646 Fax 330/830-8008

Schools: 6 \ **Teachers:** 261 \ **Students:** 5,817 \ **Special Ed Students:** 634 \ **LEP Students:** 66 \ **College-Bound:** 82% \ **Ethnic:** Asian 4%, African American 2%, Hispanic 2%, Caucasian 92% \ **Exp:** $148 (Low) \ **Poverty:** 6% \ **Title I:** $513,427 \ **Special Education:** $862,000 \ **Open-Close:** 08/19 - 05/28 \ **DTBP:** $222 (High) \ f

Name	Ref
Christoper DiLoreto	1,11
Harley Neftzer	3
David Morgan	5,91
Dan Michel	6
Rebecca Gribble	8,12,81,273,280,294
Christina Conti	16,82*
Kathy Brand	34,57,58,69,77,88,90,275
Paula Blangger	71
Janet Thompson	73,76*
Monica Myers	288*
Linda Paris	2
Marsha Escola	4
Eli Rivera	5,91
Lori Fisher	7*
Barry Mason	15*
Michelle Monigold	23
Thomas Winkhart	67
George Woods	73
Richard Dinko	95*

Public Schs..Principal	Grd	Prgm	Enr/#Cls	SN	
Amherst Elem Sch 8750 Jane St NW, Massillon 44646 William Hayden	K-5		526 22	32%	330/830-8024 Fax 330/830-8071 f
Jackson High Sch 7600 Fulton Dr NW, Massillon 44646 Jeff Kracker	9-12	V	1,971 90	14%	330/837-3501 Fax 330/830-8020 f
Jackson Memorial Middle Sch 7355 Mudbrook St NW, Massillon 44646 Kacy Carter	6-8		1,403 85	17%	330/830-8034 Fax 330/830-8068
Lake Cable Elem Sch 5335 Villa Padova Dr NW, Canton 44718 Angela Leggett	K-5		580 24	25%	330/834-4673 Fax 330/834-4528 f
Sauder Elem Sch 7503 Mudbrook St NW, Massillon 44646 John Reindel	K-5		634 31	12%	330/830-8028 Fax 330/830-8032 f
Strausser Elem Sch 8646 Strausser St NW, Massillon 44646 Susanne Waltman	K-5		758 29	10%	330/830-8056 Fax 330/834-4656

● **Lake Local School Dist** PID: 00832853 330/877-9383
436 King Church Ave SW, Uniontown 44685 Fax 330/877-4754

Schools: 3 \ **Teachers:** 181 \ **Students:** 3,300 \ **Special Ed Students:** 390 \ **LEP Students:** 19 \ **College-Bound:** 90% \ **Ethnic:** Asian 1%, Hispanic 2%, Caucasian 97% \ **Exp:** $175 (Low) \ **Poverty:** 7% \ **Title I:** $316,308 \ **Special Education:** $663,000 \ **Open-Close:** 08/20 - 05/28 \ **DTBP:** $183 (High) \ f t

Name	Ref
Kevin Tobin	1
Nicole Nichols	2
Angela Harbaugh	9
Gary Kandel	13,36,57,58,88
David Poling	67
Jeff Breit	2,3,5,91
Lauri Livingston	5
Pat Carroll	10,11,15,16,69,73,288,295
Nannette Peterson	16,82*
Karen Koch	71

Public Schs..Principal	Grd	Prgm	Enr/#Cls	SN	
Lake Elem Sch 225 Lincoln St SW, Hartville 44632 Donna Bruner	2-6		1,252 40		330/877-4276 Fax 330/877-4738 f t
Lake Middle High Sch 709 Market Ave, Uniontown 44685 Dan Harold	7-12	V	1,682 60	24%	330/877-4282 Fax 330/877-0853
Lake Primary Sch 13244 Cleveland Ave NW, Uniontown 44685 Frank Gant	PK-1		458 23	13%	330/877-4298 Fax 330/699-3101 f t

● **Louisville City School Dist** PID: 00832906 330/875-1666
407 E Main St, Louisville 44641 Fax 330/875-7603

Schools: 4 \ **Teachers:** 148 \ **Students:** 2,797 \ **Special Ed Students:** 453 \ **LEP Students:** 9 \ **College-Bound:** 64% \ **Ethnic:** Hispanic 1%, Caucasian 99% \ **Exp:** $134 (Low) \ **Poverty:** 11% \ **Title I:** $436,642 \ **Special Education:** $533,000 \ **Open-Close:** 08/21 - 05/28 \ **DTBP:** $195 (High)

Name	Ref
Michele Shaffer	1
Willard Berkebile	3
Doug Haines	5
Sue Gronow	7
Justin Haren	11,58,296
Jason Siegfried	73
Monica Shadle	81*
Dereck Nottingham	2
Stacey Bettis	4
John Twinem	6*
Anna Minor	8
Dr Brenda L'Amoreaux	67
Amy Ward	77

Public Schs..Principal	Grd	Prgm	Enr/#Cls	SN	
Louisville Elem Sch 415 N Nickelplate St, Louisville 44641 Michael Norris	K-5	T	989 20	40%	330/875-1177 Fax 330/875-7608
Louisville Middle Sch 1300 S Chapel St, Louisville 44641 Jason Orin	6-8	T	678 35	42%	330/875-5597 Fax 330/875-7620
Louisville Senior High Sch 1201 S Nickelplate St, Louisville 44641 Kenneth Faye	9-12		825 84	37%	330/875-1438 Fax 330/875-7671
North Nimishillen Elem Sch 7337 Easton St, Louisville 44641 Melanie Davis	PK-2	T	305 19	39%	330/875-2661 Fax 330/875-7614

● **Marlington Local School Dist** PID: 00832970 330/823-7458
10320 Moulin Ave NE, Alliance 44601 Fax 330/823-7759

Schools: 5 \ **Teachers:** 131 \ **Students:** 2,300 \ **Special Ed Students:** 278 \ **LEP Students:** 66 \ **College-Bound:** 57% \ **Ethnic:** African American 2%, Hispanic 5%, Caucasian 93% \ **Exp:** $207 (Med) \ **Poverty:** 15% \ **Title I:** $536,248 \ **Special Education:** $376,000 \ **Open-Close:** 09/03 - 06/03 \ **DTBP:** $233 (High)

Name	Ref
Joel Knoll	1,57
Rojean Cole	4
Steve Miller	6*
Kirt Hamilton	41*
Chris Locke	45*
Mark Ryan	67
Erick Cyders	73
Stephanie Rosselli	81
Gary Bush	286*
Al Incerpi	3,91
Sheri Sickles	5
Carole Sutton	8,11,76,273,288,298
Lynn Francis	42*
Dan Swisher	58,69,274*
Lea Packey	71
Dan Swisher	79
Tina Hoffman	85*

Public Schs..Principal	Grd	Prgm	Enr/#Cls	SN	
Dukes Digital Academy 10450 Moulin Ave, Alliance 44601 **Gary Bush**	6-12		401		330/823-1000
Lexington Elem Sch 12333 Atwater Ave NE, Alliance 44601 David Rogers	K-5	T	345 29	67%	330/823-7570 Fax 330/829-1980
Marlington High Sch 10450 Moulin Ave NE, Alliance 44601 Yianni Spondyl	9-12	T	734 60	40%	330/823-1300 Fax 330/823-1644
Marlington Middle Sch 10325 Moulin Ave NE, Alliance 44601 Nick Evanich	6-8	T	529 45	46%	330/823-7566 Fax 330/823-7594
Washington Elem Sch 5786 Beechwood Ave, Alliance 44601 Michael Groholy	K-5	T	298 15	36%	330/823-7586 Fax 330/823-7465

#		#		#		#		#		#		#	
1	Superintendent	8	Curric/Instruct K-12	19	Chief Financial Officer	29	Family/Consumer Science	39	Social Studies K-12	49	English/Lang Arts Elem	59	Special Education Elem	69	Academic Assessment
2	Bus/Finance/Purchasing	9	Curric/Instruct Elem	20	Art K-12	30	Adult Education	40	Social Studies Elem	50	English/Lang Arts Sec	60	Special Education Sec	70	Research/Development
3	Buildings And Grounds	10	Curric/Instruct Sec	21	Art Elem	31	Career/Sch-to-Work K-12	41	Social Studies Sec	51	Reading K-12	61	Foreign/World Lang K-12	71	Public Information
4	Food Service	11	Federal Program	22	Art Sec	32	Career/Sch-to-Work Elem	42	Science K-12	52	Reading Elem	62	Foreign/World Lang Elem	72	Summer School
5	Transportation	12	Title I	23	Music K-12	33	Career/Sch-to-Work Sec	43	Science Elem	53	Reading Sec	63	Foreign/World Lang Sec	73	Instructional Tech
6	Athletic	13	Title V	24	Music Elem	34	Early Childhood Ed	44	Science Sec	54	Remedial Reading K-12	64	Religious Education K-12	74	Inservice Training
7	Health Services	14	Instructional Media Svcs	25	Music Sec	35	Health/Phys Education	45	Math K-12	55	Remedial Reading Elem	65	Religious Education Elem	75	Marketing/Distributive
		15	Asst Superintendent	26	Business Education	36	Guidance Services K-12	46	Math Elem	56	Remedial Reading Sec	66	Religious Education Sec	76	Info Systems
		16	Chief Operations Officer	27	Career & Tech Ed	37	Guidance Services Elem	47	Math Sec	57	Bilingual/ELL	67	School Board President	77	Psychological Assess
		18	Chief Academic Officer	28	Technology Education	38	Guidance Services Sec	48	English/Lang Arts K-12	58	Special Education K-12	68	Teacher Personnel	78	Affirmative Action

Ohio School Directory — Stark County

Massillon City School Dist   PID: 00833039   330/830-3900
930 17th St NE, Massillon 44646   Fax 330/830-6537

Schools: 7 \ **Teachers:** 232 \ **Students:** 3,900 \ **Special Ed Students:** 624 \ **LEP Students:** 101 \ **College-Bound:** 45% \ **Ethnic:** African American 12%, Hispanic 5%, Caucasian 82% \ **Exp:** $233 (Med) \ **Poverty:** 26% \ **Title I:** $1,903,086 \ **Special Education:** $977,000 \ **Open-Close:** 08/20 - 05/29 \ **DTBP:** $236 (High) \ f

Paul Salvino	1	Sandy Moeglin	2,19
John Petro	3	Amy Coyle	4
Amy Voight	4	Daniel McGrath	5
Nate Moore	6*	Ryan Spicer	7,57,58,83,286,288
Chris Blaire	8	Jamie Palma	11,30,78,296,298*
Mark Fortner	15	David Scheetz	16*
Anthony Thornsberry	31*	Tom Radel	67
Olivia Bronczek	71	James Thom	73,76
Marie Ricker	76	Mark Forther	91*
Rebecca Moore	93		

Public Schs..Principal	Grd	Prgm	Enr/#Cls	SN
Franklin Elem Sch 1237 16th St SE, Massillon 44646 Michael Medure	K-3	T	374 17	330/830-3907 Fax 330/830-6532
Gorrell Elem Sch 2420 Schuler Ave NW, Massillon 44647 Alyssia Kappas	K-3	T	393 21	330/830-3905 Fax 330/830-6533
Massillon Digital Academy 930 17th St NE, Massillon 44646 Nicki Howard	4-12	T	75 1	330/830-3900 Fax 330/832-6661
Massillon Intermediate Sch 250 29th St NW, Massillon 44647 Jarred Zapolnik	4-6	T	877	330/830-3902 Fax 330/830-3952
Massillon Junior High Sch 250 29th St NW, Massillon 44647 Vincent Lindsey	7-8	T	570 25	330/830-3902 Fax 330/830-3952
Massillon Washington High Sch 1 Paul E Brown Dr SE, Massillon 44646 Dave Lautenschleger	9-12	ATV	1,203 100	330/830-3901 Fax 330/830-1954
Whittier Elem Sch 1212 10th St NE, Massillon 44646 Matt Plybon	K-3	T	336 20	330/830-3904 Fax 330/830-6592

Minerva Local School Dist   PID: 00833170   330/868-4332
406 East St, Minerva 44657   Fax 330/868-4731

Schools: 3 \ **Teachers:** 97 \ **Students:** 1,900 \ **Special Ed Students:** 293 \ **LEP Students:** 3 \ **College-Bound:** 42% \ **Ethnic:** African American 1%, Hispanic 1%, Caucasian 98% \ **Exp:** $183 (Low) \ **Poverty:** 19% \ **Title I:** $498,738 \ **Special Education:** $439,000 \ **Open-Close:** 08/20 - 05/28 \ **DTBP:** $235 (High)

Gary Chaddock	1	Larry Pottorf	2
Aaron Hawk	3	Stacey Bettis	4*
Teri Hollar	5	Andy Mamgun	6
Rebecca Miller	8,11,288	Andrew Burman	13,34,57,58,271
Jenny White	36*	Robert Foltz	67
Amie Davis	77	Richard Hart	83,85*
Diane Ruff	273*		

Public Schs..Principal	Grd	Prgm	Enr/#Cls	SN
Minerva Elem Sch 130 Bonnieview Ave, Minerva 44657 Mark Scott	K-5	T	849 34	62% 330/868-4011 Fax 330/868-3681
Minerva High Sch 501 Almeda Ave, Minerva 44657 Brett Yeagley	9-12	V	506 50	61% 330/868-4134 Fax 330/868-5973
Minerva Middle Sch 600 E Line St, Minerva 44657 Scott Cassidy	6-8	T	466 40	61% 330/868-4497 Fax 330/868-3144

North Canton City School Dist   PID: 00833247   330/497-5600
525 7th St NE, North Canton 44720   Fax 330/497-5618

Schools: 7 \ **Teachers:** 222 \ **Students:** 4,437 \ **Special Ed Students:** 554 \ **LEP Students:** 32 \ **College-Bound:** 79% \ **Ethnic:** Asian 2%, African American 2%, Hispanic 2%, Caucasian 94% \ **Exp:** $38 (Low) \ **Poverty:** 7% \ **Title I:** $416,013 \ **Special Education:** $997,000 \ **Open-Close:** 08/20 - 05/29 \ **DTBP:** $213 (High) \ f t

Jeff Wendorf	1	Todd Henne	2,3
Jill Lauter	4	Debbie Dalton	5
Tim Walker	6*	Brenda Ramey	7*
Michelle Hostetler	8,12	Dave Pilati	11,15,275,288
Pat Topper	16*	Christopher Triner	20*
Ron Varn	23*	Jeff Kreis	45*
John Welch	58,296	Jordan Greenwald	67
Kim Knidy	73,76	Denise Cooley	81
Kimberly Nidy	84	Michael Bluey	286*

Public Schs..Principal	Grd	Prgm	Enr/#Cls	SN
Clearmount Elem Sch 150 Clearmount Ave SE, North Canton 44720 **Gary Kandel**	K-2		385 17	34% 330/497-5640 Fax 330/966-0801 f t
Greentown Intermediate Sch 3330 State St NW, North Canton 44720 Ryan Kumpf	3-5		494 25	17% 330/497-5645 Fax 330/966-1603 f t
Hoover High Sch 525 7th St NE, North Canton 44720 Eric Bornstine	9-12		1,495 90	17% 330/497-5620 Fax 330/497-5606 f t
Mary L Evans Early Chldhd Ctr 301 Portage St NW, North Canton 44720 Janet Peare	PK-PK		105	330/497-5608 Fax 330/966-0703
North Canton Middle Sch 605 Fair Oaks Ave SW, North Canton 44720 David Eby	6-8		955	23% 330/497-5635 Fax 330/497-5659
Northwood Elem Sch 1500 School Ave NE, North Canton 44720 Matt Donaldson	K-2		444 2	19% 330/497-5650 Fax 330/966-1503 f t
Orchard Hill Intermediate Sch 1305 Jonathan Ave SW, North Canton 44720 Darlene Howald	3-5		408 17	35% 330/497-5655 Fax 330/966-1701 f t

Northwest Local School Dist   PID: 00833326   330/854-2291
2309 Locust St S, Canal Fulton 44614   Fax 330/854-3591

Schools: 4 \ **Teachers:** 102 \ **Students:** 1,783 \ **Special Ed Students:** 278 \ **LEP Students:** 4 \ **College-Bound:** 56% \ **Ethnic:** Asian 1%, African American 1%, Hispanic 1%, Caucasian 97% \ **Exp:** $335 (High) \ **Poverty:** 9% \ **Title I:** $279,668 \ **Special Education:** $332,000 \ **Open-Close:** 08/20 - 05/29 \ **DTBP:** $20 (Low)

Dennis Lambes	1,288	Dan Levengood	2
Stacy Frase	3	Jason Hathaway	6,83
Debora Clark	8,11,69,88,296,298	Scott Burnett	58
Jim Gindlesberger	67	Jeff Ludwig	73,295
Jessica Brown	76	Dr Alex Christ	270,273*

Public Schs..Principal	Grd	Prgm	Enr/#Cls	SN
Northwest High Sch 8580 Erie Ave NW, Canal Fulton 44614 Larry Tausch	9-12		551 36	30% 330/854-2205 Fax 330/854-2030

---

79 Student Personnel	91 Safety/Security	275 Response To Intervention	298 Grant Writer/Ptnrships	**School Programs**	**Social Media**	
80 Driver Ed/Safety	92 Magnet School	277 Remedial Math K-12	750 Chief Innovation Officer	A = Alternative Program		
81 Gifted/Talented	93 Parental Involvement	280 Literacy Coach	751 Chief of Staff	G = Adult Classes	f = Facebook	
82 Video Services	95 Tech Prep Program	285 STEM	752 Social Emotional Learning	M = Magnet Program		
83 Substance Abuse Prev	97 Chief Information Officer	286 Digital Learning		T = Title I Schoolwide	t = Twitter	
84 Erate	98 Chief Technology Officer	288 Common Core Standards	**Other School Types**	V = Career & Tech Ed Programs		
85 AIDS Education	270 Character Education	294 Accountability	Ⓐ = Alternative School			
88 Alternative/At Risk	271 Migrant Education	295 Network System	Ⓒ = Charter School	New Schools are shaded		
89 Multi-Cultural Curriculum	273 Teacher Mentor	296 Title II Programs	Ⓜ = Magnet School	New Superintendents and Principals are bold		
90 Social Work	274 Before/After Sch	297 Webmaster	Ⓨ = Year-Round School	Personnel with email addresses are underscored		

OH-187

Stark County

Northwest Middle Sch 8614 Erie Ave NW, Canal Fulton 44614 Greg Ramos	6-8		439 31	33% 330/854-3303 Fax 330/854-5883
Northwest Primary 8436 Erie Ave NW, Canal Fulton 44614 James Lariccia	K-2		388 17	37% 330/854-5405 Fax 330/854-5809
William S Stinson Elem Sch 8454 Erie Ave NW, Canal Fulton 44614 Lori Mariani	3-5		405 19	39% 330/854-4646 Fax 330/854-7136

• **Osnaburg Local School Dist** PID: 00833388   330/488-1609
310 Browning Ct N, East Canton 44730   Fax 330/488-4001

Schools: 3 \ *Teachers:* 55 \ *Students:* 850 \ *Special Ed Students:* 120 \ *LEP Students:* 8 \ *College-Bound:* 45% \ *Ethnic:* African American 2%, Hispanic 1%, Native American: 1%, Caucasian 96% \ *Exp:* $165 (Low) \ *Poverty:* 14% \ *Title I:* $132,941 \ *Special Education:* $118,000 \ *Open-Close:* 08/21 - 05/28

Kevin Finefrock .... 1 Larry Bonam 3
Megan Depelomo .... 4 Doug Miller 6
Elaine Barkan .... 8* Cierra Barwick 36*
Sheri Kreutzer .... 38* Stephan Kimbel 67
Jason Hall .... 73* Jay Moody 73
Christine Robenstine .... 84 Gary Hinton 88
Stacy Duskey 273*

Public Schs..Principal	Grd	Prgm	Enr/#Cls	SN
East Canton Elem Sch 310 Browning Ct N, East Canton 44730 Rebecca Carter	PK-5	T	396 30	330/488-0392 Fax 330/488-4014
East Canton High Sch 310 Browning Ct N, East Canton 44730 Gary Hinton	9-12	V	286 26	99% 330/488-0316 Fax 330/488-4015
East Canton Middle Sch 310 Browning Ct N, East Canton 44730 Gregory Dente	6-8		182 22	330/488-0334 Fax 330/488-4015

• **Perry Local School Dist** PID: 00833417   330/477-8121
4201 13th St SW, Massillon 44646   Fax 330/478-6184

Schools: 8 \ *Teachers:* 266 \ *Students:* 4,500 \ *Special Ed Students:* 502 \ *LEP Students:* 23 \ *College-Bound:* 72% \ *Ethnic:* Asian 1%, African American 3%, Hispanic 3%, Caucasian 93% \ *Exp:* $224 (Med) \ *Poverty:* 13% \ *Title I:* $707,108 \ *Special Education:* $1,066,000 \ *Open-Close:* 08/20 - 05/29 \ *DTBP:* $217 (High)

Scott Beatty .... 1,11 Darrell Wolff 2
Mark Randulic .... 3 Janet McLeese 4
Mitzi Wagner .... 5 Rebecca Embly 7
Debbie Poland .... 8,11,288,296,298 Janelle Schuler 8
Janelle Simcic .... 9 Jennifer Reese 10,27,31*
Nathan Stutz .... 15 Rebekah Silla 36,57,58
Doug Brown .... 67 Brian Paisley 73,297
Joe Hug .... 81* Chantil Frederick 93*
Jeremy Stangelo .... 286* Mike Medley 295*

Public Schs..Principal	Grd	Prgm	Enr/#Cls	SN
Edison Middle Sch 4201 13th St SW, Massillon 44646 Diane Kittleberger	7-8	TV	734 35	38% 330/478-6167 Fax 330/477-4612
Genoa Elem Sch 519 Genoa Ave SW, Massillon 44646 Danita Berry	K-4	T	341 34	63% 330/478-6171 Fax 330/478-6173
Lohr Elem Sch 5300 Richville Dr SW, Navarre 44662 Nicholas Huskins	K-4		243 12	28% 330/484-3924 Fax 330/484-4987
Perry High Sch 3737 13th St SW, Massillon 44646 David Riley	9-12	AV	1,467 85	38% 330/477-3486 Fax 330/478-6160
Pfeiffer Intermediate Sch 4315 13th St SW, Massillon 44646 Bill Hildebrand	5-6	T	731 45	43% 330/478-6163 Fax 330/478-6800
T C Knapp Elem Sch 5151 Oakcliff St SW, Canton 44706 Tricia Self	PK-4	T	460 13	34% 330/478-6174 Fax 330/477-4542
Watson Elem Sch 515 Marion Ave NW, Massillon 44646 Stacy Daugherty	K-4	T	343 14	42% 330/832-8100 Fax 330/832-1427
Whipple Heights Elem Sch 4800 12th St NW, Canton 44708 Joe Hug	K-4	T	386 17	43% 330/478-6177 Fax 330/478-6179

• **Plain Local School Dist** PID: 00833510   330/492-3500
901 44th St NW, Canton 44709   Fax 330/493-5542

Schools: 9 \ *Teachers:* 291 \ *Students:* 6,000 \ *Special Ed Students:* 861 \ *LEP Students:* 71 \ *College-Bound:* 60% \ *Ethnic:* Asian 1%, African American 16%, Hispanic 4%, Caucasian 79% \ *Exp:* $244 (Med) \ *Poverty:* 16% \ *Title I:* $1,575,791 \ *Open-Close:* 08/22 - 05/29 \ *DTBP:* $220 (High)

Brent May .... 1,11 N Jordan 2,19
Tom Brabson .... 2,91 Jennifer Rex 4
Glenna Romine .... 5 Scott Garcia 6*
Brian Matthews .... 8,15 Jill Collet 12
Mark Parent .... 34,36,57,58,69,77,79* Kristin Gardata 67
Mary Beddell .... 71 Jason Patterson 73,286
Kim Hert 298

Public Schs..Principal	Grd	Prgm	Enr/#Cls	SN
Avondale Elem Sch 3933 Eaton Rd NW, Canton 44708 Jennifer Moff	K-4	T	270 19	43% 330/491-3720 Fax 330/491-3721
C L Warstler Elem Sch 2500 Schneider St NE, N Canton 44721 Mark Yocum	K-4	T	354 19	50% 330/491-3770 Fax 330/491-3771
Frazer Elem Sch 3900 Frazer Ave NW, Canton 44709 Jill Downing	K-4	T	345 22	45% 330/491-3740 Fax 330/491-3741
Glenoak High Sch 1801 Schneider St NE, Canton 44721 Mike Babics	9-12	V	2,022	39% 330/491-3800 Fax 330/491-3801
Glenwood Intermediate Sch 1015 44th St NW, Canton 44709 Brett Niarchos	5-6		983 30	52% 330/491-3780 Fax 330/491-3781
Middlebranch Elem Sch 7500 Middlebranch Ave NE, Canton 44721 J Easterling	K-4	T	533 19	43% 330/491-3750 Fax 330/491-3751
Oakwood Middle Sch 2300 Schneider St NE, Canton 44721 Jeanne McNeal	7-8	T	909 55	50% 330/491-3790 Fax 330/491-3791
Ransom H Barr Elem Sch 2000 47th St NE, Canton 44705 Trisha Williams	K-4	T	359 21	65% 330/491-3730 Fax 330/491-3731
Robert Taft Elem Sch 3829 Guilford Ave NW, Canton 44718 Kortney Milford	K-4	T	377	78% 330/491-3760 Fax 330/491-3761

1	Superintendent	8	Curric/Instruct K-12	19	Chief Financial Officer	29	Family/Consumer Science	39 Social Studies K-12	49 English/Lang Arts Elem	59 Special Education Elem	69 Academic Assessment
2	Bus/Finance/Purchasing	9	Curric/Instruct Elem	20	Art K-12	30	Adult Education	40 Social Studies Elem	50 English/Lang Arts Sec	60 Special Education Sec	70 Research/Development
3	Buildings And Grounds	10	Curric/Instruct Sec	21	Art Elem	31	Career/Sch-to-Work K-12	41 Social Studies Sec	51 Reading K-12	61 Foreign/World Lang K-12	71 Public Information
4	Food Service	11	Federal Program	22	Art Sec	32	Career/Sch-to-Work Elem	42 Science K-12	52 Reading Elem	62 Foreign/World Lang Elem	72 Summer School
5	Transportation	12	Title I	23	Music K-12	33	Career/Sch-to-Work Sec	43 Science Elem	53 Reading Sec	63 Foreign/World Lang Sec	73 Instructional Tech
6	Athletic	13	Title V	24	Music Elem	34	Early Childhood Ed	44 Science Sec	54 Remedial Reading K-12	64 Religious Education K-12	74 Inservice Training
7	Health Services	15	Asst Superintendent	25	Music Sec	35	Health/Phys Education	45 Math K-12	55 Remedial Reading Elem	65 Religious Education Elem	75 Marketing/Distributive
		16	Instructional Media Svcs	26	Business Education	36	Guidance Services K-12	46 Math Elem	56 Remedial Reading Sec	66 Religious Education Sec	76 Info Systems
		17	Chief Operations Officer	27	Career & Tech Ed	37	Guidance Services Elem	47 Math Sec	57 Bilingual/ELL	67 School Board President	77 Psychological Assess
		18	Chief Academic Officer	28	Technology Education	38	Guidance Services Sec	48 English/Lang Arts K-12	58 Special Education K-12	68 Teacher Personnel	78 Affirmative Action

Ohio School Directory — Stark County

• Portage Lakes Joint Voc SD   PID: 01601554
4401 Shriver Rd, Uniontown 44685
330/896-8200
Fax 330/896-8297

Schools: 1 \ **Teachers:** 33 \ **Students:** 650 \ **Exp:** $447 (High) \
Open-Close: 08/21 - 05/29 \ **DTBP:** $230 (High)

Kim Redmond 1
William Stauffer 11,73,288
Tina Sailey 60*
Krista Haubert 71
Christopher Wright 2
Lisa Tripney 27,286*
David Andrews 67

Public Schs..Principal	Grd	Prgm	Enr/#Cls	SN
Portage Lakes Career Center 4401 Shriver Rd, Uniontown 44685 Mike Kaschak	Voc	G	650 30	330/896-8200

• Sandy Valley Local School Dist   PID: 00833649
5362 State Route 183 NE, Magnolia 44643
330/866-3339
Fax 330/866-5238

Schools: 3 \ **Teachers:** 81 \ **Students:** 1,500 \ **Special Ed Students:** 234 \ **College-Bound:** 42% \ **Ethnic:** African American 1%, Caucasian 98% \ **Exp:** $319 (High) \ **Poverty:** 17% \ **Title I:** $340,218 \ **Special Education:** $246,000 \ **Open-Close:** 08/20 - 05/29 \ **DTBP:** $85 (Med)

David Fischer 1
Doug Neading 3,5*
Patty Main 8,11,288,296*
David Poteet 58
Michael McCahan 73*
Craig McKendry 2
Gary Hinton 6
Lori Trachsel 16*
Dennis Corsi 67
Bill Graham 286*

Public Schs..Principal	Grd	Prgm	Enr/#Cls	SN
Sandy Valley Elem Sch 5018 State Route 183 NE, Magnolia 44643 Vic Johnson	PK-5	T	595 11	57% 330/866-9225 Fax 330/866-2572
Sandy Valley High Sch 5130 State Route 183 NE, Magnolia 44643 Matt Whitted	9-12	ATV	420	91% 330/866-9371 Fax 330/866-2490
Sandy Valley Middle Sch 5130 State Route 183 NE, Magnolia 44643 Melissa Kiehl	6-8	T	321 40	330/866-9416 Fax 330/866-2490

• Stark Co Area Voc Sch Dist   PID: 01601530
2800 Richville Dr SE, Massillon 44646
330/832-1591
Fax 330/832-9850

Schools: 1 \ **Teachers:** 39 \ **Students:** 700 \ **Exp:** $285 (Med) \
Open-Close: 08/20 - 05/29 \ **DTBP:** $117 (High)

Joe Chaddock 1
Douglas Tucker 3
Dan Murphy 10,11,273,298*
Victoria Crockett 60*
Jan Cotterman 88*
Tamra Hurst 2
Pam Metzger 4*
Michele Rocco 34
Robert Foltz 67

Public Schs..Principal	Grd	Prgm	Enr/#Cls	SN
R G Drage Career Tech Center 2800 Richville Dr SE, Massillon 44646 Dan Murphy	Voc	AG	700 44	330/832-9856

• Tuslaw Local School Dist   PID: 00833699
1835 Manchester Ave NW, Massillon 44647
330/837-7813
Fax 330/837-7804

Schools: 3 \ **Teachers:** 69 \ **Students:** 1,390 \ **Special Ed Students:** 171 \ **LEP Students:** 3 \ **College-Bound:** 57% \ **Ethnic:** African American 1%, Hispanic 1%, Caucasian 98% \ **Exp:** $149 (Low) \ **Poverty:** 10% \ **Title I:** $193,681 \ **Special Education:** $199,000 \ **Open-Close:** 08/21 - 06/02 \ **DTBP:** $116 (High)

Melissa Marconi 1
Mark Lau 3
David Burkett 6*
Ryan Rodocker 16,73,285,286
Randy Bleigh 67
Sue Seidler 274*
Matt Jordan 2
Linda Earp 4,5
Joy Sama 8,11*
Mike Hamm 58
Chelsy Jackson 83*

Public Schs..Principal	Grd	Prgm	Enr/#Cls	SN
Tuslaw Elem Sch 1920 Manchester Ave NW, Massillon 44647 Shelly Menuez	K-4	T	507 25	35% 330/837-7809 Fax 330/837-7810
Tuslaw High Sch 1847 Manchester Ave NW, Massillon 44647 Adam McKenzie	9-12		386	21% 330/837-7800 Fax 330/837-6016
Tuslaw Middle Sch 1723 Manchester Ave NW, Massillon 44647 Richard Dinko	5-8	T	413 30	34% 330/837-7807 Fax 330/837-6015

STARK CATHOLIC SCHOOLS

• Diocese of Youngstown Ed Off   PID: 00820915
Listing includes only schools located in this county. See District Index for location of Diocesan Offices.

Catholic Schs..Principal	Grd	Prgm	Enr/#Cls	SN
Central Catholic High Sch 4824 Tuscarawas St W, Canton 44708 Dave Oates	9-12		350 50	330/478-2131 Fax 330/478-6086 f
Our Lady of Peace Sch 1001 39th St NW, Canton 44709 Kevin Henderson	PK-8		340	330/492-0622 Fax 330/492-0959
Regina Coeli Catholic Sch 733 Fernwood Blvd, Alliance 44601 Marcy Watry	PK-5	G	131 14	330/823-9239 Fax 330/823-1877
SS Philip & James Sch 532 High St NE, Canal Fulton 44614 Matthew Monter	PK-8		140 13	330/854-2823 Fax 330/854-7081
St Barbara Sch 2809 Lincoln Way NW, Massillon 44647 Marisa Stoll	PK-8		90 12	330/833-9510 Fax 330/833-3297 f
St James Sch 400 W Lisbon St, Waynesburg 44688 Kathleen Kettler	PK-6		51 7	330/866-9556 Fax 330/866-1750
St Joan of Arc Sch 120 Bordner Ave SW, Canton 44710 Christopher Pollard	PK-8		225 16	330/477-2972 Fax 330/478-2606
St Louis Sch 214 N Chapel St, Louisville 44641 Mario Calandros	PK-5		60 12	330/875-1467 Fax 330/875-2511
St Mary Sch 640 1st St NE, Massillon 44646 Jennifer Fischer	PK-8		200 17	330/832-9355 Fax 330/832-9030

---

79 Student Personnel	91 Safety/Security	275 Response To Intervention	298 Grant Writer/Ptnrships	**School Programs**	**Social Media**
80 Driver Ed/Safety	92 Magnet School	277 Remedial Math K-12	750 Chief Innovation Officer	A = Alternative Program	f = Facebook
81 Gifted/Talented	93 Parental Involvement	280 Literacy Coach	751 Chief of Staff	G = Adult Classes	
82 Video Services	95 Tech Prep Program	285 STEM	752 Social Emotional Learning	M = Magnet Program	t = Twitter
83 Substance Abuse Prev	97 Chief Information Officer	286 Digital Learning		T = Title I Schoolwide	
84 Erate	98 Chief Technology Officer	288 Common Core Standards	**Other School Types**	V = Career & Tech Ed Programs	
85 AIDS Education	270 Character Education	294 Accountability	Ⓐ = Alternative School		
88 Alternative/At Risk	271 Migrant Education	295 Network System	Ⓒ = Charter School	New Schools are shaded	
89 Multi-Cultural Curriculum	273 Teacher Mentor	296 Title II Programs	Ⓜ = Magnet School	New Superintendents and Principals are bold	
90 Social Work	274 Before/After Sch	297 Webmaster	Ⓨ = Year-Round School	Personnel with email addresses are underscored	

Summit County

St Michael Sch 3431 Saint Michaels Blvd NW, Canton 44718 Claire Gatti	PK-8	421 20	330/492-2657 Fax 330/492-9618	
St Paul Sch 303 S Main St, North Canton 44720 Amie Hale	K-8	327 20	330/494-0223 Fax 330/494-3226	
St Peter Sch 702 Cleveland Ave NW, Canton 44702 Sandie Fusillo	PK-5	142 10	330/452-0125 Fax 330/452-0253	
St Thomas Aquinas Mid High Sch 2121 Reno Dr, Louisville 44641 Cara Pribula	6-12	285 35	330/875-1631 Fax 330/875-8469	

STARK PRIVATE SCHOOLS

Private Schs..Principal	Grd	Prgm	Enr/#Cls	SN
Canton Country Day Sch 3000 Demington Ave NW, Canton 44718 Mike Brown	PK-8		160 24	330/453-8279 Fax 330/453-6038
Hartville Christian Sch 10515 Market Ave N, Hartville 44632 Ruth Schrock	K-12		56 9	330/877-2529
Heritage Christian Sch 2107 6th St SW, Canton 44706 Karla Robinson	PK-12	V	250 20	330/452-8271 Fax 330/452-0672
Lake Center Christian Sch 12893 Kaufman Ave NW, Hartville 44632 Jeff Knori \ Dannon Stock	PK-12		665 55	330/877-2049 Fax 330/877-2040
Massillon Christian Sch 965 Overlook Ave SW, Massillon 44647 Rebecca Hartline	K-12		75 15	330/833-1039 Fax 330/830-5981
Mayfair Christian Sch 2350 Graybill Rd, Uniontown 44685 H Clifford Reynolds	K-9		88 7	330/896-3184 Fax 330/896-0703
New Franklin Christian Academy 16310 Lisbon St SE, Minerva 44657 David DuVall	2-12		21 2	330/862-2491
Weaver Child Development Ctr 515 48th St NW, Canton 44709 Miss Susie	PK-3		90	330/433-8881

STARK REGIONAL CENTERS

Sparcc PID: 04499635   330/492-8136
6057 Strip Ave NW, North Canton 44720   Fax 330/492-6175

Marty Bowe 1   Dack Warner 73
Tyler Smith 76   Terri Lynn Hesled 79

State Support Team-Region 9 PID: 02228246   330/492-8136
6057 Strip Ave NW, North Canton 44720   Fax 330/492-6381

Marty Bowe 1   Laurie Langenfeld 15,58

SUMMIT COUNTY

SUMMIT COUNTY SCHOOLS

Summit Co Ed Service Center PID: 00835788   330/945-5600
420 Washington Ave Ste 2, Cuyahoga FLS 44221   Fax 330/945-6222

Joesph Iacano 1   Thomas Jansen 16
John Wachovec 27   Kimberly Meeker 34
Kristen Favio 36,79,83,88   Shawn Jividen 81
Kay Sonoda 88

County Schs..Principal	Grd	Prgm	Enr/#Cls	SN
Akron Digital Academy 133 Merriman Rd, Akron 44303 Teresa Sales	6-12	T	236 6	330/237-2200 Fax 330/237-2207
Akros Middle Sch 265 Park St, Akron 44304 Todd Blain	6-8	T	127	330/374-6704 Fax 330/374-6713
Edge Academy 92 N Union St, Akron 44304 Joshua Rogers	K-5	T	237 14	330/535-4581 Fax 330/535-5074

SUMMIT PUBLIC SCHOOLS

Akron Public Schools PID: 00833833   330/761-1661
10 N Main St, Akron 44308   Fax 330/761-3225

Schools: 45 \ *Teachers:* 1,394 \ *Students:* 21,343 \
Special Ed Students: 4,161 \ *LEP Students:* 1,721 \ *College-Bound:* 42%
\ *Ethnic:* Asian 8%, African American 50%, Hispanic 4%, Caucasian
38% \ *Exp:* $310 (High) \ *Poverty:* 30% \ *Title I:* $16,175,388 \
Special Education: $5,338,000 \ *Open-Close:* 08/29 - 06/04 \ *DTBP:* $250
(High) \

David James 1   Debra Foulk 2
Robert Boxler 3,91   Laura Kepler 4
William Andexler 5   Joseph Vassalotti 6,35
Ellen McWilliams 8,15   Karen Gegick 8,74
Mary Outley-Kelly 9   Mark Black 10*
Peggy Greiner 11,298   Tamiko Hatcher 11
Megan Mannion 16,82   Nathaniel Duvuvuei 20,23
Rachel Tecca 27,31   Adam Motter 35,39*
Katrina Halasa .... 35,42*   Ruth Hotchkiss 45
Toan Dang-Nguyen .... 48,89*   Loi Dang-Nguyen 57,61
Tammy Brady .... 58,275*   Dr Curtis Walker 67
Howard Lawson 69,73,294   Carla Chapman 71
Mark Williamson 71   Dan Rambler 79,91

Public Schs..Principal	Grd	Prgm	Enr/#Cls	SN
Ⓐ Akron Alternative Academy 77 W Thornton St, Akron 44311 Rebecca Green-Pallotta	9-12	T	276	330/761-1609 Fax 330/761-1349
Akron Early College High Sch 225 S Main St, Akron 44325 Cheryl Connolly	9-12	T	398 10	330/972-6450 Fax 330/972-5305
Barber Community Learning Ctr 665 Garry Rd, Akron 44305 Ranea Williams	K-6	T	322 19	330/761-7911 Fax 330/784-0451

1	Superintendent	8	Curric/Instruct K-12	19	Chief Financial Officer	29	Family/Consumer Science
2	Bus/Finance/Purchasing	9	Curric/Instruct Elem	20	Art K-12	30	Adult Education
3	Buildings And Grounds	10	Curric/Instruct Sec	21	Art Elem	31	Career/Sch-to-Work K-12
4	Food Service	11	Federal Program	22	Art Sec	32	Career/Sch-to-Work Elem
5	Transportation	12	Title I	23	Music K-12	33	Career/Sch-to-Work Sec
6	Athletic	13	Title V	24	Music Elem	34	Early Childhood Ed
7	Health Services	14	Asst Superintendent	25	Music Sec	35	Health/Phys Education
		15	Instructional Media Svcs	26	Business Education	36	Guidance Services K-12
		16	Chief Operations Officer	27	Career & Tech Ed	37	Guidance Services Elem
		17	Chief Academic Officer	28	Technology Education	38	Guidance Services Sec

39	Social Studies K-12	49	English/Lang Arts Elem	59	Special Education Elem	69	Academic Assessment
40	Social Studies Elem	50	English/Lang Arts Sec	60	Special Education Sec	70	Research/Development
41	Social Studies Sec	51	Reading K-12	61	Foreign/World Lang K-12	71	Public Information
42	Science K-12	52	Reading Elem	62	Foreign/World Lang Elem	72	Summer School
43	Science Elem	53	Reading Sec	63	Foreign/World Lang Sec	73	Instructional Tech
44	Science Sec	54	Remedial Reading K-12	64	Religious Education K-12	74	Inservice Training
45	Math K-12	55	Remedial Reading Elem	65	Religious Education Elem	75	Marketing/Distributive
46	Math Elem	56	Remedial Reading Sec	66	Religious Education Sec	76	Info Systems
47	Math Sec	57	Bilingual/ELL	67	School Board President	77	Psychological Assess
48	English/Lang Arts K-12	58	Special Education K-12	68	Teacher Personnel	78	Affirmative Action

OH–190

Ohio School Directory — Summit County

School	Grades	Programs	Enrollment/Staff	Phone/Fax
Betty Jane Cmty Learning Ctr 444 Darrow Rd, Akron 44305 Jennifer Lucas	K-5	T	416 23	330/794-4117 Fax 330/794-6970
Bridges Learning Center 77 W Thornton St, Akron 44311 Stephanie Davis	Spec	T	105	330/794-4191
Buchtel Community Learning Ctr 1040 Copley Rd, Akron 44320 Byron Hopkins	9-12	ATV	879 60	330/761-7945 Fax 330/761-7947
Case Community Learning Ctr 1420 Garmon Rd, Akron 44313 Danjile Henderson	K-5	T	312 23	330/761-1670 Fax 330/873-3360
Crouse Community Learning Ctr 1000 Diagonal Rd, Akron 44320 Angela Harper-Brooks	K-6	T	395 10	330/761-1625 Fax 330/761-1371
David Hill Community Lrng Ctr 1060 E Archwood Ave, Akron 44306 Kristen Booth	K-6	T	350 23	330/773-1129 Fax 330/773-7308
East Community Learning Ctr 80 Brittain Rd, Akron 44305 Vyrone Finney	7-8	ATV	1,054	330/761-7928 Fax 330/784-2015
Ellet High Sch 309 Woolf Ave, Akron 44312 Michelle Kearans	9-12	ATV	980 60	330/794-4120 Fax 330/794-4130
Findley Community Learning Ctr 65 W Tallmadge Ave, Akron 44310 Sherry Bennington	K-5	T	565 27	330/761-7909 Fax 330/761-1327
Firestone Cmty Learning Center 470 Castle Blvd, Akron 44313 Larry Johnson	9-12	ATV	1,273 70	330/761-3270 Fax 330/836-2001
Firestone Park Elem Sch 1479 Girard St, Akron 44301 Sharon Hill-Jones	K-5	T	332 24	330/773-1308 Fax 330/773-1025
Forest Hill Cmty Learning Ctr 850 Damon St, Akron 44310 Gregory Blondheim	K-5	T	376 16	330/761-1645 Fax 330/761-3175
Glover Community Learning Ctr 395 Hammel St, Akron 44306 Nancy Ritch	K-5	T	313 33	330/773-1245 Fax 330/773-1065
Harris-Jackson Cmty Lrng Ctr 1085 Clifton Ave, Akron 44310 Andrea Aller	K-5	T	563 24	330/761-1315 Fax 330/916-9090
Hatton Cmty Learning Center 1933 Baker Ave, Akron 44312 Darcy Candido	K-5	T	494 21	330/761-7980 Fax 330/794-4208
Helen Arnold Cmty Lrng Center 450 Vernon Odom Blvd, Akron 44307 LaMonica Davis	K-6	T	273	330/376-0153 Fax 330/376-7765
Hyre Cmty Learning Center 2385 Wedgewood Dr, Akron 44312 James Retton	6-8	AT	830 52	330/761-7930 Fax 330/761-7932
Ⓐ I Promise Sch 400 W Market St, Akron 44303 Brandi Davis	3-4		222	330/761-1516 Fax 330/761-3197
Innes Cmty Learning Ctr 1999 East Ave, Akron 44314 **David Kurzen**	6-8	ATV	729 36	330/761-7900 Fax 330/848-5212
Jennings Cmty Learning Ctr 227 E Tallmadge Ave, Akron 44310 Charles Jones	6-8	ATV	751 50	330/761-2002 Fax 330/761-2611
Judith A Resnik Cmty Lrng Ctr 65 N Meadowcroft Dr, Akron 44313 Kristen Booth	K-5	T	395 19	330/873-3370 Fax 330/873-3325
Kenmore-Garfield High Sch 2140 13th St SW, Akron 44314 Frank Kalain	9-12	ATV	864	330/848-4141 Fax 330/848-5270
King Cmty Learning Center 805 Memorial Pkwy, Akron 44303 Mary Dean	K-5	T	416 18	330/761-7962 Fax 330/873-3364
Leggett Cmty Learning Center 333 E Thornton St, Akron 44311 Philomena Vincente	K-5	T	360 19	330/761-1735 Fax 330/761-1351
Litchfield Cmty Learning Ctr 470 Castle Blvd, Akron 44313 Dyan Floyd	6-8	AT	675 40	330/761-2775 Fax 330/836-2293
Mason Cmty Learning Ctr 700 E Exchange St, Akron 44306 Angela Harper	K-6	T	265 17	330/761-2237 Fax 330/761-3309
McEbright Cmty Learning Center 349 Cole Ave, Akron 44301 Deborah Musiek	K-5	T	229 18	330/761-7940 Fax 330/761-7942
Ⓜ Miller South School-Vpa 1055 East Ave, Akron 44307 Maria Meeker	4-8	T	467 20	330/761-1765 Fax 330/761-1764
Nihf STEM High Sch 123 S Forge St, Akron 44308 Dina Popa	9-12	T	320	330/761-7965 Fax 330/761-7966
Nihf STEM Middle Sch 199 S Broadway St, Akron 44308 Amanda Morgan	5-8	T	391 12	330/761-3195 Fax 330/761-5576
North High Sch 985 Gorge Blvd, Akron 44310 Rachel Tect	9-12	ATV	887 65	330/761-2665 Fax 330/761-2661
Pfeiffer Elem Sch 2081 9th St SW, Akron 44314 Regina Llewellyn	K-5	T	224 16	330/848-5244 Fax 330/848-5249
Portage Path Cmty Lrng Ctr 55 S Portage Path, Akron 44303 Kimberly Summers	K-5	T	278 17	330/761-2795 Fax 330/761-1383
Rimer Cmty Learning Ctr 2370 Manchester Rd, Akron 44314 Rebecca Cacioppo	K-5	T	320 12	330/761-7905 Fax 330/848-3614
Ritzman Cmty Learning Ctr 629 Canton Rd, Akron 44312 Ione McIntosh	K-5	T	340 20	330/761-7903 Fax 330/794-4106
Robinson Cmty Learning Center 1156 4th Ave, Akron 44306 Anthony Lane	K-6	T	254 16	330/761-2785 Fax 330/761-5566
Sam Salem Cmty Learning Center 1222 W Waterloo Rd, Akron 44314 Anna Panning	K-5	T	369 26	330/848-5231 Fax 330/848-5213
Schumacher Cmty Learning Ctr 1020 Hartford Ave, Akron 44320 Laxmi Chari	K-6	T	428 28	330/761-7934 Fax 330/761-4103
Seiberling Cmty Learning Ctr 400 Brittain Rd, Akron 44305 Jennifer Moff	K-6	T	505 25	330/761-7956 Fax 330/794-4103
Stewart Early Learning Center 1199 Vernon Odom Blvd, Akron 44307 Patricia Cronin	PK-PK		125	330/873-3396 Fax 330/873-3392
Voris Cmty Learning Center 1885 Glenmount Ave, Akron 44301 Jennifer Douglas	K-5	T	354	330/773-6926 Fax 330/773-8073
Windemere Cmty Learning Center 2283 Windemere Ave, Akron 44312 Megan Lee-Wilfong	K-5	T	254 20	330/761-7937 Fax 330/761-7939

79 Student Personnel
80 Driver Ed/Safety
81 Gifted/Talented
82 Video Services
83 Substance Abuse Prev
84 Erate
85 AIDS Education
88 Alternative/At Risk
89 Multi-Cultural Curriculum
90 Social Work
91 Safety/Security
92 Magnet School
93 Parental Involvement
95 Tech Prep Program
97 Chief Infomation Officer
98 Chief Technology Officer
270 Character Education
271 Migrant Education
273 Teacher Mentor
274 Before/After Sch
275 Response To Intervention
277 Remedial Math K-12
280 Literacy Coach
285 STEM
286 Digital Learning
288 Common Core Standards
294 Accountability
295 Network System
296 Title II Programs
297 Webmaster
298 Grant Writer/Ptnrships
750 Chief Innovation Officer
751 Chief of Staff
752 Social Emotional Learning

Other School Types
Ⓐ = Alternative School
Ⓒ = Charter School
Ⓜ = Magnet School
Ⓨ = Year-Round School

School Programs
A = Alternative Program
G = Adult Classes
M = Magnet Program
T = Title I Schoolwide
V = Career & Tech Ed Programs

Social Media
= Facebook
= Twitter

New Schools are shaded
New Superintendents and Principals are bold
Personnel with email addresses are underscored

OH—191

Summit County

Market Data Retrieval

• Barberton City School Dist PID: 00834502
633 Brady Ave, Barberton 44203
330/753-1025
Fax 330/848-0826

Schools: 5 \ *Teachers:* 214 \ *Students:* 3,813 \ *Special Ed Students:* 788 \ *LEP Students:* 31 \ *College-Bound:* 38% \ *Ethnic:* African American 14%, Hispanic 2%, Caucasian 83% \ *Exp:* $217 (Med) \ *Poverty:* 22% \ *Title I:* $1,448,745 \ *Special Education:* $883,000 \ *Open-Close:* 08/21 - 05/28 \ *DTBP:* $188 (High)

Jeffrey Ramnytz 1	Shawnna Jones 2
Mark Brown 3	Jill Orris 4
Richard Fillmore 5	John Sabol 6
Wendy Ray 7*	Shelly Habegger 8,11,54,69,296,298
Jason Ondrus 15,68	Bill Fearigo 16,73
Joan Tonathy 37*	Deidre Parson 57,58,77,79,85,271
David Polacek 67	James Jensen 81,274*

Public Schs..Principal	Grd	Prgm	Enr/#Cls	SN	
Barberton Elem Sch-East 292 Robinson Ave, Barberton 44203 Matt Saunders	K-4	T	639 15	68%	330/745-5492 Fax 330/745-8378
Barberton Elem Sch-West 1151 Shannon Ave, Barberton 44203 Brenda Sincel	K-4	T	651 21		330/825-2183 Fax 330/825-2195
Barberton High Sch 555 Barber Rd, Barberton 44203 Henry Muren	9-12	TV	1,405 80	58%	330/753-1084 Fax 330/848-5517
Barberton Middle Sch 477 4th St NW, Barberton 44203 Michael Andric	5-8	T	1,118 40	71%	330/745-9950 Fax 330/745-9962
Barberton Preschool 633 Brady Ave, Barberton 44203 Rachel Boulder	PK-PK		401		330/753-1025 Fax 330/780-2043

• Copley-Fairlawn City Sch Dist PID: 00834681
3797 Ridgewood Rd, Copley 44321
330/664-4800
Fax 330/664-4811

Schools: 5 \ *Teachers:* 172 \ *Students:* 2,886 \ *Special Ed Students:* 301 \ *LEP Students:* 58 \ *College-Bound:* 80% \ *Ethnic:* Asian 5%, African American 13%, Hispanic 2%, Caucasian 80% \ *Exp:* $314 (High) \ *Poverty:* 6% \ *Title I:* $288,803 \ *Special Education:* $568,000 \ *Open-Close:* 08/21 - 05/28 \ *DTBP:* $191 (High) \

Brian Poe 1	John Wheadon 2,19
Steven Robinson 3,4,84,91	Mary Sharnsky 5
Andy Jalwan 6*	Brian Williams 8,15
Fiona Casida 16,82*	Dianna Ashcraft 27,75
James Borchik 67	Lance Green 73*
Jacque Cook 77	Aimee Kirsch 79

Public Schs..Principal	Grd	Prgm	Enr/#Cls	SN	
Arrowhead Primary Sch 1600 Raleigh Blvd, Copley 44321 Roman Capper	K-4		367 18	15%	330/664-4885 Fax 330/664-4927
Copley High Sch 3807 Ridgewood Rd, Copley 44321 Michael Coury	9-12	G	966	19%	330/664-4822 Fax 330/664-4951
Copley-Fairlawn Middle Sch 1531 S Cleveland Massillon Rd, Copley 44321 Kathleen Ashcroft	5-8		888 57	22%	330/664-4875 Fax 330/664-4912
Ft Island Primary Sch 496 Trunko Rd, Fairlawn 44333 Robert Whitaker	K-4		353 27	21%	330/664-4890 Fax 330/664-4921
Herberich Primary Sch 2645 Smith Rd, Akron 44333 William Kerrigan	K-4		239 28	25%	330/664-4991 Fax 330/664-4989

• Coventry Local School Dist PID: 00834758
3257 Cormany Rd, Akron 44319
330/644-8489
Fax 330/644-0159

Schools: 3 \ *Teachers:* 107 \ *Students:* 1,900 \ *Special Ed Students:* 298 \ *LEP Students:* 32 \ *College-Bound:* 56% \ *Ethnic:* Asian 2%, African American 5%, Hispanic 2%, Caucasian 91% \ *Exp:* $59 (Low) \ *Poverty:* 12% \ *Title I:* $317,018 \ *Special Education:* $277,000 \ *Open-Close:* 08/19 - 05/29 \ *DTBP:* $237 (High)

Lisa Blough 1,11	Sherry Tyson 2
Gary Olson 3	Mark Bindus 4
Kelly Smith 5	Victoria Dorsey 7
Shannon Demita 8,69,294	Sarah Wulff 12,275
Kelly Kendrick 16,73,84,295	Melissa Ostrowski 34,57,58,95
Chris Davis 67	Susan Oldham 79

Public Schs..Principal	Grd	Prgm	Enr/#Cls	SN	
Coventry Elem Sch 3089 Manchester Rd, Akron 44319 Timothy Bryan	K-4	T	541 25	52%	330/644-8469 Fax 330/644-1215
Coventry High Sch 1135 Portage Lakes Dr, Akron 44319 Neal Kopp	9-12	ATV	664 35	39%	330/644-3004 Fax 330/644-4222
Coventry Middle Sch 3257 Cormany Rd, Akron 44319 Tina Norris	5-8	TV	659 22		330/644-2232 Fax 330/644-0331

• Cuyahoga Falls City Sch Dist PID: 00834825
431 Stow Ave, Cuyahoga FLS 44221
330/926-3800
Fax 330/920-1074

Schools: 10 \ *Teachers:* 319 \ *Students:* 4,500 \ *Special Ed Students:* 617 \ *LEP Students:* 176 \ *College-Bound:* 62% \ *Ethnic:* Asian 5%, African American 5%, Hispanic 2%, Caucasian 88% \ *Exp:* $71 (Low) \ *Poverty:* 10% \ *Title I:* $684,187 \ *Special Education:* $1,159,000 \ *Open-Close:* 08/14 - 05/22 \ *DTBP:* $191 (High) \

Dr Todd Nichols 1	Kristy Stoicoiu 2
Joseph Bagatti 3	William Bailey 4*
Marjorie Johnson 5	Tom DiFrancesco 6,35,85*
Julie Dudones 8	James Marras 16,73,82,286
Courtney Marcucci 57	Amy McDougal 58
Cameron Lazar 58	Karen Schofield 67
Christine Shaw 79	Robert Vaughn 82
Allison Bogdan 83,88,95,270*	

Public Schs..Principal	Grd	Prgm	Enr/#Cls	SN	
Bolich Middle Sch 2630 13th St, Cuyahoga FLS 44223 Ryan Huch	6-8	TV	544 40	50%	330/926-3801 Fax 330/920-3737
Cuyahoga Falls High Sch 2300 4th St, Cuyahoga FLS 44221 **Kevin Vargyas**	9-12	GV	1,496	38%	330/926-3808 Fax 330/916-6013
Elizabeth Price Elem Sch 2610 Delmore St, Cuyahoga FLS 44221 John Musat	K-5	T	338 19	62%	330/926-3806 Fax 330/929-3171
Gordon DeWitt Elem Sch 425 Falls Ave, Cuyahoga FLS 44221 Catherine Perrow	K-5	T	417 40	51%	330/926-3802 Fax 330/916-6016
Lincoln Elem Sch 3131 Bailey Rd, Cuyahoga FLS 44221 **Kevin Vargyas**	K-5	T	492 32	44%	330/926-3803 Fax 330/916-6024
Preston Elem Sch 800 Tallmadge Rd, Cuyahoga FLS 44221 Tammy Brown	K-5	T	285 21	59%	330/926-3805 Fax 330/916-6027
Richardson Elem Sch 2226 23rd St, Cuyahoga FLS 44223 Julie Hall	K-5	T	397 12	42%	330/926-3807 Fax 330/916-6022

1	Superintendent	8	Curric/Instruct K-12	19	Chief Financial Officer	29	Family/Consumer Science	39	Social Studies K-12	49 English/Lang Arts Elem	59 Special Education Elem	69 Academic Assessment
2	Bus/Finance/Purchasing	9	Curric/Instruct Elem	20	Art K-12	30	Adult Education	40	Social Studies Elem	50 English/Lang Arts Sec	60 Special Education Sec	70 Research/Development
3	Buildings And Grounds	10	Curric/Instruct Sec	21	Art Elem	31	Career/Sch-to-Work K-12	41	Social Studies Sec	51 Reading K-12	61 Foreign/World Lang K-12	71 Public Information
4	Food Service	11	Federal Program	22	Art Sec	32	Career/Sch-to-Work Elem	42	Science K-12	52 Reading Elem	62 Foreign/World Lang Elem	72 Summer School
5	Transportation	12	Title I	23	Music K-12	33	Career/Sch-to-Work Sec	43	Science Elem	53 Reading Sec	63 Foreign/World Lang Sec	73 Instructional Tech
6	Athletic	13	Title V	24	Music Elem	34	Early Childhood Ed	44	Science Sec	54 Remedial Reading K-12	64 Religious Education K-12	74 Inservice Training
7	Health Services	15	Asst Superintendent	25	Music Sec	35	Health/Phys Education	45	Math K-12	55 Remedial Reading Elem	65 Religious Education Elem	75 Marketing/Distributive
		16	Instructional Media Svcs	26	Business Education	36	Guidance Services K-12	46	Math Elem	56 Remedial Reading Sec	66 Religious Education Sec	76 Info Systems
		17	Chief Operations Officer	27	Career & Tech Ed	37	Guidance Services Elem	47	Math Sec	57 Bilingual/ELL	67 School Board President	77 Psychological Assess
		18	Chief Academic Officer	28	Technology Education	38	Guidance Services Sec	48	English/Lang Arts K-12	58 Special Education K-12	68 Teacher Personnel	78 Affirmative Action

OH—192

Ohio School Directory — Summit County

School	Grd	Prgm	Enr/#Cls	SN	Phone
Roberts Middle Sch 3333 Charles St, Cuyahoga FLS 44221 Kris Gaijer	6-8	TV	404 31	45%	330/926-3809 Fax 330/920-3748
ⓒ Schnee Learning Center 2222 Issaquah St, Cuyahoga FLS 44221 Tony Pallija	9-12		69		330/922-1966 Fax 330/945-4059
Silver Lake Elem Sch 2970 Overlook Rd, Cuyahoga FLS 44224 Hillary Freitag-Geiger	K-5		231 15	31%	330/926-3811 Fax 330/916-6023

• Hudson City School Dist PID: 00835099
2400 Hudson Aurora Rd, Hudson 44236
330/653-1200 Fax 330/653-1366

Schools: 6 \ *Teachers:* 279 \ *Students:* 4,600 \ *Special Ed Students:* 641 \ *LEP Students:* 61 \ *College-Bound:* 88% \ *Ethnic:* Asian 5%, African American 1%, Hispanic 3%, Caucasian 91% \ *Exp:* $272 (Med) \ *Poverty:* 2% \ *Title I:* $127,034 \ *Special Education:* $973,000 \ *Open-Close:* 08/14 - 05/22 \ *DTBP:* $195 (High)

Phillip Herman 1	Steve Marlow 2,4,5,91
Chris Kelling 3	Kim Ciborek 4
Michael Chubba 6	Kelly Kempf 7,34,58,83,88,90,275
Doreen Osmun 8,11,16,57,69,73,95,288	Meredith Zaffrann 30
David Zuro 67	Lisa Hunt 68,85,273
Sheryl Sheatzley 71	

Public Schs..Principal	Grd	Prgm	Enr/#Cls	SN	Phone
East Woods Sch 120 N Hayden Pkwy, Hudson 44236 Michael Sedlak	4-5		666 33	5%	330/653-1256 Fax 330/653-1269
Ellsworth Hill Elem Sch 7750 Stow Rd, Hudson 44236 Jen Filomena	PK-2		411	6%	330/653-1236 Fax 330/653-1235
Evamere Elem Sch 76 N Hayden Pkwy, Hudson 44236 Beth Trivelli	K-1		599 39	4%	330/653-1226 Fax 330/653-1234
Hudson High Sch 2500 Hudson Aurora Rd, Hudson 44236 Brian Wilch	9-12		1,522	5%	330/653-1416 Fax 330/653-1481
Hudson Middle Sch 77 N Oviatt St, Hudson 44236 Kimberly Cockley	6-8		1,083 66	5%	330/653-1316 Fax 330/653-1368
McDowell Elem Sch 280 N Hayden Pkwy, Hudson 44236 Natalie Wininger	3-3		327 22	6%	330/653-1246 Fax 330/653-1238

• Manchester Local School Dist PID: 00834978
6075 Manchester Rd, Akron 44319
330/882-6926 Fax 330/882-0013

Schools: 3 \ *Teachers:* 80 \ *Students:* 1,400 \ *Special Ed Students:* 216 \ *LEP Students:* 5 \ *College-Bound:* 99% \ *Ethnic:* African American 1%, Caucasian 98% \ *Exp:* $118 (Low) \ *Poverty:* 6% \ *Title I:* $148,577 \ *Special Education:* $261,000 \ *Open-Close:* 08/20 - 05/29 \ *DTBP:* $233 (High)

Dr James Robinson 1,11,83	Jennifer Rucker 2
Michael Stafford 3	Shannon Belcher 4*
Darla Hooper 5	Mike Ankrom 6*
Rachel Willis 8	Lisa Barnes-Prince 16*
Richard Sponseller 67	Scott Ross 73*

Public Schs..Principal	Grd	Prgm	Enr/#Cls	SN	Phone
Manchester High Sch 437 W Nimisila Rd, Akron 44319 James France	9-12	AV	416 32	23%	330/882-3291 Fax 330/882-5696
Manchester Middle Sch 760 W Nimisila Rd, Akron 44319 James Miller	5-8		407 22	27%	330/882-3812 Fax 330/882-2013
Nolley Elem Sch 6285 Renninger Rd, Akron 44319 Christina Pappas	K-4		483 19	25%	330/882-4133 Fax 330/882-2001

• Nordonia Hills City Sch Dist PID: 00835180
9370 Olde 8 Rd, Northfield 44067
330/467-0580 Fax 330/468-0152

Schools: 6 \ *Teachers:* 198 \ *Students:* 3,585 \ *Special Ed Students:* 432 \ *LEP Students:* 67 \ *College-Bound:* 72% \ *Ethnic:* Asian 4%, African American 12%, Hispanic 2%, Caucasian 82% \ *Exp:* $285 (Med) \ *Poverty:* 6% \ *Title I:* $347,251 \ *Special Education:* $669,000 \ *Open-Close:* 08/22 - 06/02 \ *DTBP:* $194 (High)

Dr Joseph Clark 1,11	Matt Gagler 2,3,91
Susan Petonic 4	Rob Eckenrode 6,35*
Carrie Hutchinson 7,77,79,90	Todd Stuart 8,31,57,69,271,286,288*
Deborah Wallace 29,83,88*	Tammy Strong 67
Mike Russ 73,295*	Casey Wright 270*

Public Schs..Principal	Grd	Prgm	Enr/#Cls	SN	Phone
Ledgeview Elem Sch 9130 Shepard Rd, Macedonia 44056 Kristen Cottrell	K-4		468 23	18%	330/467-0583 Fax 330/468-4647
Lee Eaton Elem Sch 115 Ledge Rd, Northfield 44067 Rob Schrembeck	5-6		620 30	18%	330/467-0582 Fax 330/468-5218
Nordonia High Sch 8006 S Bedford Rd, Macedonia 44056 Casey Wright	9-12	V	1,215 100	17%	330/468-4601 Fax 330/468-1359
Nordonia Middle Sch 73 Leonard Ave, Northfield 44067 Bryan Seward	7-8	V	560 60	19%	330/467-0584 Fax 330/468-6719
Northfield Elem Sch 9374 Olde 8 Rd, Northfield 44067 Marc Kaminicki	K-4		368 19	15%	330/467-2010 Fax 330/468-5216
Rushwood Elem Sch 8200 Rushwood Ln, Northfield 44067 Dr Jacqueline O'Mara	K-4		385 22	21%	330/467-0581 Fax 330/468-4631

• Norton City School Dist PID: 00835269
4128 S Cleveland Massillon Rd, Norton 44203
330/825-0863 Fax 330/825-0929

Schools: 4 \ *Teachers:* 138 \ *Students:* 2,500 \ *Special Ed Students:* 329 \ *LEP Students:* 13 \ *College-Bound:* 60% \ *Ethnic:* Asian 1%, African American 3%, Hispanic 1%, Caucasian 95% \ *Exp:* $76 (Low) \ *Poverty:* 8% \ *Title I:* $250,983 \ *Special Education:* $419,000 \ *Open-Close:* 08/20 - 05/28 \ *DTBP:* $193 (High)

Dana Addis 1	Stephanie Hangenbush 2
Judy Johnsen 4*	Paulette Gemind 5
Don Shimek 6	Amy Olivieri 8,11,16,69,288,296,298*
Tom Chiera 23*	Jacquelyn McDonnell 37*
Eric Morris 58,79*	Jennifer Bennett 67
Angela Wagler 73,76,286,295*	Tricia Ebner 81
Jonathan Steiner 295	

Public Schs..Principal	Grd	Prgm	Enr/#Cls	SN	Phone
Norton Elem Sch 3390 S Cleveland Massillon Rd, Norton 44203 Brady Sackett	1-4		658 12		330/825-3828 Fax 330/825-3817
Norton High Sch 1 Panther Way, Norton 44203 Ryan Shanor	9-12		861	31%	330/825-7300 Fax 330/706-0369

---

79 Student Personnel	91 Safety/Security	275 Response To Intervention	298 Grant Writer/Ptnrships	**School Programs**	**Social Media**
80 Driver Ed/Safety	92 Magnet School	277 Remedial Math K-12	750 Chief Innovation Officer	A = Alternative Program	
81 Gifted/Talented	93 Parental Involvement	280 Literacy Coach	751 Chief of Staff	G = Adult Classes	= Facebook
82 Video Services	95 Tech Prep Program	285 STEM	752 Social Emotional Learning	M = Magnet Program	
83 Substance Abuse Prev	97 Chief Information Officer	286 Digital Learning		T = Title I Schoolwide	= Twitter
84 Erate	98 Chief Technology Officer	288 Common Core Standards	**Other School Types**	V = Career & Tech Ed Programs	
85 AIDS Education	270 Accountability	294 Accountability	Ⓐ = Alternative School		
88 Alternative/At Risk	271 Migrant Education	295 Network System	Ⓒ = Charter School	New Schools are shaded	
89 Multi-Cultural Curriculum	273 Teacher Mentor	296 Title II Programs	Ⓜ = Magnet School	New Superintendents and Principals are bold	
90 Social Work	274 Before/After Sch	297 Webmaster	Ⓨ = Year-Round School	Personnel with email addresses are underscored	

OH-193

Summit County

Market Data Retrieval

Norton Middle Sch	5-8	769	35%	330/825-5607
4108 S Cleveland Massillon Rd, Norton 44203		45		Fax 330/825-1461
Joyce Gerber				
Norton Primary Sch	PK-K	259	30%	330/825-5133
3163 Greenwich Rd, Norton 44203		15		Fax 330/825-0794
Eric Morris				

● **Revere Local School Dist** PID: 00835348   330/659-6111
3496 Everett Rd, Richfield 44286   Fax 330/659-3127

Schools: 4 \ **Teachers:** 160 \ **Students:** 2,700 \ **Special Ed Students:** 249 \ **LEP Students:** 32 \ **College-Bound:** 82% \ **Ethnic:** Asian 6%, African American 2%, Hispanic 2%, Caucasian 90% \ **Exp:** $148 (Low) \ **Poverty:** 3% \ **Title I:** $84,293 \ **Special Education:** $114,000 \ **Open-Close:** 09/03 - 06/11 \ **DTBP:** $206 (High) \

Matthew Montgomery 1
Mike Critchfield 3
Tom McKinnon 6
Abby Kassel 36,51,54,57,58,88,271,275
George Seifert 67
Bonnie Simonelli 83*
Rick Berdine 2
Justin Miller 5
Kathy Nolan 8,11,69,285,288,298
Nick Depompei 38*
Jennifer Reece 71

Public Schs..Principal	Grd	Prgm	Enr/#Cls	SN	
Bath Elem Sch	4-5		480	7%	330/523-3802
1246 N Cleveland Massillon Rd, Akron 44333			20		Fax 330/666-3058
Dan Fry					
Revere High Sch	9-12	V	857	6%	330/523-3202
3420 Everett Rd, Richfield 44286			43		Fax 330/659-6407
Phil King					
Revere Middle Sch	6-8		654	8%	330/523-3403
3195 Spring Valley Road, Bath 44210			45		Fax 330/659-3795
Bill Conley					
Richfield Elem Sch	K-3		749	5%	330/523-3603
3080 Revere Rd, Richfield 44286					Fax 330/659-6701
Julie Gulley					

● **Springfield Local School Dist** PID: 00835403   330/798-1111
2410 Massillon Rd, Akron 44312   Fax 330/798-1161

Schools: 4 \ **Teachers:** 136 \ **Students:** 2,222 \ **Special Ed Students:** 409 \ **LEP Students:** 19 \ **College-Bound:** 71% \ **Ethnic:** Asian 2%, African American 3%, Hispanic 2%, Caucasian 93% \ **Exp:** $92 (Low) \ **Poverty:** 15% \ **Title I:** $607,346 \ **Special Education:** $595,000 \ **Open-Close:** 08/22 - 05/29 \ **DTBP:** $230 (High)

Charles Sincere 1
Michael Smith 3
Kevin Vaughn 6*
Mary Meadows 8,11,69,288*
Melinda Hamilton 91
Dustin Boswell 2,3,4,73,76,91,295
Randy Silica 5
Brad Beun 7,58
Mary Lou Dodson 67

Public Schs..Principal	Grd	Prgm	Enr/#Cls	SN	
Schrop Intermediate Sch	4-6	T	510	65%	330/798-1007
2215 Pickle Rd, Akron 44312			18		Fax 330/798-1167
Lisa Vardon					
Spring Hill Elem Sch	PK-3	T	431	61%	330/798-1006
660 Lessig Ave, Akron 44312			13		Fax 330/798-1166
David Jurmanovich					
Springfield High Sch	7-12	T	1,016	59%	330/798-1002
1880 Canton Rd, Akron 44312			85		Fax 330/798-1162
Shaun Morgan					
Young Elem Sch	K-3	T	265	54%	330/798-1008
3258 Nidover Dr, Akron 44312			14		Fax 330/798-1168
Jennifer Ganzer					

● **Stow-Munroe Falls City SD** PID: 00835506   330/689-5445
4350 Allen Rd, Stow 44224   Fax 330/689-5448

Schools: 10 \ **Teachers:** 301 \ **Students:** 5,158 \ **Special Ed Students:** 641 \ **LEP Students:** 106 \ **College-Bound:** 72% \ **Ethnic:** Asian 3%, African American 4%, Hispanic 2%, Caucasian 91% \ **Exp:** $181 (Low) \ **Poverty:** 6% \ **Title I:** $465,293 \ **Special Education:** $916,000 \ **Open-Close:** 08/20 - 06/01 \ **DTBP:** $198 (High) \

Thomas Bratten 1
Robert Gress 3,84,91
Brandi Hollis 5
Julie Miller 8
Kristie Prough 13,58,77
Wendy Paul-Mikulski 31*
Kelly Toppin 67
Laura Forchione 73,295
Susan Walker 298
Trevor Gumnere 2
Allison Daugherty 4*
Cyle Feldman 6*
Happy Bengston 12
Robert Oress 17
Marykay Misterka 34
Dr Jeff Hartmann 72*
Rebeca Stanek 285

Public Schs..Principal	Grd	Prgm	Enr/#Cls	SN	
Bulldog Online Academy	6-12		42		330/689-5443
4350 Allen Rd, Stow 44224					Fax 330/689-5291
Jim Gotshall					
Echo Hills Elem Sch	K-4		337	26%	330/689-5450
4405 Stow Rd, Stow 44224			23		Fax 330/689-5455
David Ulbricht					
Fishcreek Elem Sch	K-4		334	15%	330/689-5460
5080 Fishcreek Rd, Stow 44224			20		Fax 330/689-5467
Joanne Bratten					
Highland Elem Sch	K-4		323	21%	330/689-5330
1843 Graham Rd, Stow 44224			15		Fax 330/689-5335
Meghan Graziano					
Indian Trail Elem Sch	K-4		296	27%	330/689-5320
3512 Kent Rd, Stow 44224			15		Fax 330/689-5325
John Lacoste					
Kimpton Middle Sch	7-8		809	19%	330/689-5288
380 N River Rd, Munroe Falls 44262			40		Fax 330/689-5291
Susan Palchesko					
Lakeview Intermediate Sch	5-6		778		330/689-5250
1819 Graham Rd, Stow 44224			40		Fax 330/689-5265
Andrew Yanchunas					
Riverview Elem Sch	K-4		320	25%	330/689-5310
240 N River Rd, Munroe Falls 44262			17		Fax 330/689-5317
Traci Kosmach					
Stow-Munroe Falls High Sch	9-12	V	1,791	18%	330/689-5300
3227 Graham Rd, Stow 44224					Fax 330/678-3899
Dr Jeff Hartmann					
Woodland Elem Sch	K-4		277	19%	330/689-5470
2908 Graham Rd, Stow 44224			23		Fax 330/689-5471
Mary Lou Muckleroy					

● **Tallmadge City School Dist** PID: 00835594   330/633-3291
486 East Ave, Tallmadge 44278   Fax 330/633-5331

Schools: 4 \ **Teachers:** 134 \ **Students:** 2,412 \ **Special Ed Students:** 314 \ **LEP Students:** 21 \ **College-Bound:** 76% \ **Ethnic:** Asian 1%, African American 5%, Hispanic 3%, Caucasian 91% \ **Exp:** $152 (Low) \ **Poverty:** 9% \ **Title I:** $389,394 \ **Special Education:** $621,000 \ **Open-Close:** 08/15 - 05/29 \ **DTBP:** $200 (High)

Jeffrey Ferguson 1
Don Seeker 6
Karen Kallotz 11,58,81
Kelley Smith 29*
Mike Srodawa 35,85
Richard Kellar 67
Rebecca Furbay 79
Steve Wood 2,3,4,17,78,91
Shelley Monachino 8
Kim Brendel 27*
Jim Barbera 31*
Jennifer Stewart 36,83*
Curt Gwin 73
Sharon Hall 81

1	Superintendent	8	Curric/Instruct K-12	19	Chief Financial Officer	29	Family/Consumer Science	39	Social Studies K-12	49	English/Lang Arts Elem	59	Special Education Elem	69	Academic Assessment
2	Bus/Finance/Purchasing	9	Curric/Instruct Elem	20	Art K-12	30	Adult Education	40	Social Studies Elem	50	English/Lang Arts Sec	60	Special Education Sec	70	Research/Development
3	Buildings And Grounds	10	Curric/Instruct Sec	21	Art Elem	31	Career/Sch-to-Work K-12	41	Social Studies Sec	51	Reading K-12	61	Foreign/World Lang K-12	71	Public Information
4	Food Service	11	Federal Program	22	Art Sec	32	Career/Sch-to-Work Elem	42	Science K-12	52	Reading Elem	62	Foreign/World Lang Elem	72	Summer School
5	Transportation	12	Title I	23	Music K-12	33	Career/Sch-to-Work Sec	43	Science Elem	53	Reading Sec	63	Foreign/World Lang Sec	73	Instructional Tech
6	Athletic	13	Title V	24	Music Elem	34	Early Childhood Ed	44	Science Sec	54	Remedial Reading K-12	64	Religious Education K-12	74	Inservice Training
7	Health Services	14	Asst Superintendent	25	Music Sec	35	Health/Phys Education	45	Math K-12	55	Remedial Reading Elem	65	Religious Education Elem	75	Marketing/Distributive
		15	Instructional Media Svcs	26	Business Education	36	Guidance Services K-12	46	Math Elem	56	Remedial Reading Sec	66	Religious Education Sec	76	Info Systems
		16	Chief Operations Officer	27	Career & Tech Ed	37	Guidance Services Elem	47	Math Sec	57	Bilingual/ELL	67	School Board President	77	Psychological Assess
		17	Chief Academic Officer	28	Technology Education	38	Guidance Services Sec	48	English/Lang Arts K-12	58	Special Education K-12	68	Teacher Personnel	78	Affirmative Action

Ohio School Directory — Summit County

Tim Blough 295

Public Schs..Principal	Grd	Prgm	Enr/#Cls	SN	
Dunbar Primary Sch 731 Dunbar Rd, Tallmadge 44278 Courtney Davis	K-2		497 15	29%	330/633-4515 Fax 330/630-5981
Munroe Elem Sch 230 N Munroe Rd, Tallmadge 44278 Courtney Davis	3-5		547 18	27%	330/633-5427 Fax 330/630-5983
Tallmadge High Sch 140 N Munroe Rd, Tallmadge 44278 Mike Householder	9-12		772 55	24%	330/633-5505 Fax 330/475-0567
Tallmadge Middle Sch 484 East Ave, Tallmadge 44278 Jeffrey Manion	6-8		596 54	30%	330/633-4994 Fax 330/630-5986

• Twinsburg City School Dist PID: 00835661
11136 Ravenna Rd, Twinsburg 44087
330/486-2000
Fax 330/425-7216

Schools: 5 \ *Teachers:* 195 \ *Students:* 4,200 \ *Special Ed Students:* 425 \ *LEP Students:* 147 \ *College-Bound:* 80% \ *Ethnic:* Asian 9%, African American 26%, Hispanic 3%, Caucasian 62% \ *Exp:* $76 (Low) \ *Poverty:* 8% \ *Title I:* $427,474 \ *Special Education:* $908,000 \ *Open-Close:* 08/21 - 06/02 \ *DTBP:* $187 (High)

Katherine Powers 1
Martin Aho 2,19
Mark Bindus 4*
Brian Fantone 6*
Denise Traphagen 7,58,77,79,93,274,275
Norman Potter 8
Timothy Sullen 68
Carol Friihauf 76*
Donna Kelly 2
Chad Welker 3,4,5,91,295
Adam House 5
Dominic Schwed 6
Jennifer Farthing 8,11,16,57,69,74*
Matt Cellura 67
Matthew McGing 73*
Marcus Madden 295*

Public Schs..Principal	Grd	Prgm	Enr/#Cls	SN	
George G Dodge Interm Sch 10225 Ravenna Rd, Twinsburg 44087 Reginald Holland	4-6		950 37	20%	330/486-2200 Fax 330/963-8323
R B Chamberlin Middle Sch 10270 Ravenna Rd, Twinsburg 44087 James Ries	7-8		682 45	16%	330/486-2281 Fax 330/963-8313
Samuel Bissell Elem Sch 1811 Glenwood Dr, Twinsburg 44087 Misty Johnson	2-3		581 27	17%	330/486-2100 Fax 330/963-8333
Twinsburg High Sch 10084 Ravenna Rd, Twinsburg 44087 Laura Hebert	9-12	AV	1,305 75	17%	330/486-2400 Fax 330/405-7406
Wilcox Primary Sch 9198 Darrow Rd, Twinsburg 44087 Lynn Villa	PK-1		715 26	20%	330/486-2030 Fax 330/963-8332

• Woodridge Local School Dist PID: 00834643
4411 Quick Rd, Peninsula 44264
330/928-9074
Fax 330/928-1542

Schools: 3 \ *Teachers:* 128 \ *Students:* 2,000 \ *Special Ed Students:* 262 \ *LEP Students:* 74 \ *College-Bound:* 64% \ *Ethnic:* Asian 4%, African American 23%, Hispanic 3%, Caucasian 70% \ *Exp:* $160 (Low) \ *Poverty:* 13% \ *Title I:* $449,964 \ *Special Education:* $388,000 \ *Open-Close:* 08/14 - 05/20 \ *DTBP:* $165 (High)

Walter Davis 1
Vincent Spitali 3
Terry Heard 5
Heather Edwards 7
Dina Edwards 57*
N'Ecole Ast 58,79
Tom Morehouse 2
Tina Hastings 4
Nick Mayer 6*
Kristin Jagger 8,11,51,54,69,74,273,288
Susan Keyes 57*
Jeff McHugh 67

Eric Unangst 73,76,84,286,295

Public Schs..Principal	Grd	Prgm	Enr/#Cls	SN	
Woodridge Elem Sch 4351 Quick Rd, Peninsula 44264 Beth Harrington	PK-5	T	797 19	53%	330/928-1223 Fax 330/928-2050
Woodridge High Sch 4440 Quick Rd, Peninsula 44264 Joel Morgan	9-12	V	676 30	29%	330/929-3191 Fax 330/928-5036
Woodridge Middle Sch 4451 Quick Rd, Peninsula 44264 Jesse Hosford	6-8	T	419 40	38%	330/928-7420 Fax 330/928-5645

SUMMIT CATHOLIC SCHOOLS

• Diocese of Cleveland Ed Office PID: 00795308
Listing includes only schools located in this county. See District Index for location of Diocesan Offices.

Catholic Schs..Principal	Grd	Prgm	Enr/#Cls	SN	
Archbishop Hoban High Sch 1 Holy Cross Blvd, Akron 44306 Emily Ramos	9-12		830 45		330/773-6658 Fax 330/773-9100
Holy Family Sch 3163 Kent Rd, Stow 44224 Sharon Fournier	PK-8		407 23		330/688-3816 Fax 330/688-3474
Immaculate Heart of Mary Sch 2859 Lillis Dr, Cuyahoga FLS 44223 Kathleen Friess	PK-8		300 18		330/923-1220
Our Lady of the Elms Elem Sch 1290 W Market St, Akron 44313 Michael Gavin	PK-5		153 12		330/864-7210 Fax 330/867-1262
Our Lady of the Elms Sch 1375 W Exchange St, Akron 44313 Michael Gavin	PK-12		270		330/867-0880 Fax 330/864-6488
Seton Catholic Sch 6923 Stow Rd, Hudson 44236 Karen Alestock	K-8		425 18		330/342-4200 Fax 330/342-4276
St Anthony of Padua Sch 80 E York St, Akron 44310 Sr Elizabeth Szilvasi	K-8		170 9		330/253-6918 Fax 330/762-2229
St Augustine Sch 195 7th St NW, Barberton 44203 Elaine Faessel	K-8		200 16		330/753-6435 Fax 330/753-4095
St Barnabas Parish Sch 9200 Olde 8 Rd, Northfield 44067 Erin Faetanini	PK-8		450 27		330/467-7921 Fax 330/468-1926
St Francis DeSales Sch 4009 Manchester Rd, Akron 44319 Katie Buzzelli	PK-8		315 18		330/644-0638
St Hilary Sch 645 Moorfield Rd, Fairlawn 44333 Jennifer Woodman	K-8		689 32		330/867-8720 Fax 330/867-5081
St Joseph Sch-Cuyahoga Falls 1909 3rd St, Cuyahoga FLS 44221 Carrie DePasquale	PK-8		200 18		330/928-2151 Fax 330/928-3139
St Mary Sch 750 S Main St, Akron 44311 Dr Patricia Nugent	K-8		200 10		330/253-1233 Fax 330/253-1472
St Matthew Parish Sch 2580 Benton Ave, Akron 44312 John Czaplicki	PK-8		200 16		330/784-1711 Fax 330/733-1004

---

79 Student Personnel	91 Safety/Security	275 Response To Intervention	298 Grant Writer/Ptnrships	**School Programs**	**Social Media**
80 Driver Ed/Safety	92 Magnet School	277 Remedial Math K-12	750 Chief Innovation Officer	A = Alternative Program	
81 Gifted/Talented	93 Parental Involvement	280 Literacy Coach	751 Chief of Staff	G = Adult Classes	▓ = Facebook
82 Video Services	95 Tech Prep Program	285 STEM	752 Social Emotional Learning	M = Magnet Program	
83 Substance Abuse Prev	97 Chief Information Officer	286 Digital Learning		T = Title I Schoolwide	▓ = Twitter
84 Erate	98 Chief Technology Officer	288 Common Core Standards	**Other School Types**	V = Career & Tech Ed Programs	
85 AIDS Education	270 Character Education	294 Accountability	Ⓐ = Alternative School		
88 Alternative/At Risk	271 Migrant Education	295 Network System	Ⓒ = Charter School	New Schools are shaded	
89 Multi-Cultural Curriculum	273 Teacher Mentor	296 Title II Programs	Ⓜ = Magnet School	New Superintendents and Principals are bold	
90 Social Work	274 Before/After Sch	297 Webmaster	Ⓨ = Year-Round School	Personnel with email addresses are underscored	

Trumbull County

School	Grade		Enr/#Cls	Phone
St Sebastian Parish Sch 500 Mull Ave, Akron 44320 Anthony Rohr	K-8		340 19	330/836-9107 Fax 330/836-7690
St Vincent De Paul Sch 17 S Maple St, Akron 44303 Diane Solomon	PK-8		251 12	330/762-5912 Fax 330/535-2515
St Vincent St Mary HS 15 N Maple St, Akron 44303 Robert Brownfield	9-12		650 37	330/253-9113 Fax 330/996-0020
Walsh Jesuit High Sch 4550 Wyoga Lake Rd, Cuyahoga FLS 44224 Mark Carr	9-12		1,015 72	330/929-4205 Fax 330/929-9749

SUMMIT PRIVATE SCHOOLS

Private Schs..Principal	Grd	Prgm	Enr/#Cls SN	Phone
Arlington Christian Academy 539 S Arlington St, Akron 44306 Lawrence Swoope	K-8		120 6	330/785-9116 Fax 330/785-9361
Chapel Hill Chrn School-North 1090 Howe Ave, Cuyahoga FLS 44221 Cathy Shafer	PK-6		320 19	330/929-1901 Fax 330/929-1737
Chapel Hill Chrn School-South 1639 Killian Rd, Akron 44312 Linda Wise	PK-6		220 13	330/896-0852 Fax 330/896-9918
Cornerstone Community Sch 90 W Overdale Dr, Tallmadge 44278 Dave Smith	PK-5		135 8	330/686-8900 Fax 330/686-8224
Cuyahoga Vly Christian Academy 4687 Wyoga Lake Rd, Stow 44224 Scott Iannetta	6-12		850 42	330/929-0575 Fax 330/929-0156
Discovery Montessori Sch 707 Schocalog Rd, Akron 44320 Lakshmi Mohan	PK-6		70	330/867-6222
Emmanuel Christian Academy 350 S Portage Path, Akron 44320 V Rena Suber	PK-8		222 11	330/836-7182 Fax 330/836-7274
Faith Islamic Elem Academy 152 E Steels Corners Rd, Cuyahoga FLS 44224 Br Ahmad Amawi	PK-8		26	330/926-9407 Fax 330/923-9630
Hudson Montessori Sch 7545 Darrow Rd, Hudson 44236 Matt Virgil	PK-8		250 10	330/650-0424 Fax 330/656-1870
Lawrence Upper Sch 10036 Olde 8 Rd, Northfield 44067 Jason Culp	Spec		202	440/832-7830 Fax 330/908-7006
Leap Sch 1105 E Turkeyfoot Lake Rd, Akron 44312 Amanda Talbot	Spec		75	330/899-9423 Fax 330/899-9429
Lippman Day Sch 750 White Pond Dr, Akron 44320 Sam Chestnut	K-8		100 25	330/836-0419 Fax 330/869-2514
Mogadore Christian Academy 3603 Carper Ave, Akron 44312 Rob Seymour	1-12		14 3	330/628-8482
Northfield Bapt Christian Sch 311 W Aurora Rd, Northfield 44067 Terry Mencarini	PK-6		113 9	330/467-8918 Fax 330/467-4248
Old Trail Sch 2315 Ira Rd, Akron 44333 Sarah Johnston	PK-8		600 40	330/666-1118 Fax 330/666-2187
Phoenix Sch 888 Jonathan Ave, Akron 44306 Wendy Neloms	6-12		52 7	330/784-0408 Fax 330/784-8477
Redeemer Christian Sch 2141 5th St, Cuyahoga FLS 44221 Ken Krueger	PK-8		225 10	330/923-1445 Fax 330/923-4517
Spring Garden Waldorf Sch 1791 Jacoby Rd, Copley 44321 Jennell Woodard	PK-8		180 17	330/666-0574 Fax 330/666-9210
Summit Christian Sch 3313 Northampton Rd, Cuyahoga FLS 44223 Stephanie Fleser	PK-8		142 11	330/762-3382 Fax 330/926-9058
Super Learning Center 1584 Wilson St, Lakemore 44250 Lyn Goodwin	Spec		97	330/889-4119
Western Reserve Academy 115 College St, Hudson 44236 Suzanne Buck	9-12	V	400 26	330/650-4400 Fax 330/650-9754

SUMMIT REGIONAL CENTERS

• **Neonet-NE Ohio Ed Tech** PID: 04499439   330/926-3900
  700 Graham Rd, Cuyahoga FLS 44221   Fax 330/926-3901

  Matthew Gdovin 1   Kim Fassnacht 2
  Christopher Zolla 15,73   Michele Baker 68,71

• **State Support Team-Region 8** PID: 02228260   330/929-6634
  420 Washington Ave, Cuyahoga FLS 44221   Fax 330/945-6222

  Jenine Sansosti 1   Sarah Jackson 34

• **Summit Co Educational Svc Ctr** PID: 02100993   330/945-5600
  420 Washington Ave, Cuyahoga FLS 44221   Fax 330/945-6222

  Joe Iacano 1   Laurel Young 2
  Matthew Young 8   Kristin Fazio 58,68,77
  Tom Jansen 73

TRUMBULL COUNTY

TRUMBULL COUNTY SCHOOLS

• **Trumbull Co Ed Service Center** PID: 00837059   330/505-2800
  6000 Youngstown Warren Rd, Niles 44446   Fax 330/505-2814

  Michael Hanshaw 1   Lori Simione 2
  Bryan O'Hara 8,69,74,81,285,286   Dr Robert Marino 11,15
  Kathy Vilsack 58   Don Bishop 67
  Carlotta Sheets 68   Christopher Hubinski 73

County Schs..Principal	Grd	Prgm	Enr/#Cls SN	Phone
Fairhaven Sch 420 Lincoln Way, Niles 44446 Rosanne Morell	Spec		300 25	330/652-5811 Fax 330/652-5864
© Summit Academy Cmty Sch-Warren [248] 2106 Arbor Ave SE, Warren 44484 Allison Glass	K-7	T	110 15	330/369-4233 Fax 330/369-4299
Trumbull Career & Tech Center 528 Educational Hwy NW, Warren 44483 Mary Flint	Voc	AG	950	330/847-0503 Fax 330/847-0339

1 Superintendent	8 Curric/Instruct K-12	19 Chief Financial Officer	29 Family/Consumer Science	39 Social Studies K-12	49 English/Lang Arts Elem	59 Special Education Elem	69 Academic Assessment
2 Bus/Finance/Purchasing	9 Curric/Instruct Elem	20 Art K-12	30 Adult Education	40 Social Studies Elem	50 English/Lang Arts Sec	60 Special Education Sec	70 Research/Development
3 Buildings And Grounds	10 Curric/Instruct Sec	21 Art Elem	31 Career/Sch-to-Work K-12	41 Social Studies Sec	51 Reading K-12	61 Foreign/World Lang K-12	71 Public Information
4 Food Service	11 Federal Program	22 Art Sec	32 Career/Sch-to-Work Elem	42 Science K-12	52 Reading Elem	62 Foreign/World Lang Elem	72 Summer School
5 Transportation	12 Title I	23 Music K-12	33 Career/Sch-to-Work Sec	43 Science Elem	53 Reading Sec	63 Foreign/World Lang Sec	73 Instructional Tech
6 Athletic	13 Title V	24 Music Elem	34 Early Childhood Ed	44 Science Sec	54 Remedial Reading K-12	64 Religious Education K-12	74 Inservice Training
7 Health Services	15 Asst Superintendent	25 Music Sec	35 Health/Phys Education	45 Math K-12	55 Remedial Reading Elem	65 Religious Education Elem	75 Marketing/Distributive
	16 Instructional Media Svcs	26 Business Education	36 Guidance Services K-12	46 Math Elem	56 Remedial Reading Sec	66 Religious Education Sec	76 Info Systems
	17 Chief Operations Officer	27 Career & Tech Ed	37 Guidance Services Elem	47 Math Sec	57 Bilingual/ELL	67 School Board President	77 Psychological Assess
	18 Chief Academic Officer	28 Technology Education	38 Guidance Services Sec	48 English/Lang Arts K-12	58 Special Education K-12	68 Teacher Personnel	78 Affirmative Action

Ohio School Directory — Trumbull County

TRUMBULL PUBLIC SCHOOLS

● **Bloomfield-Mespo Local SD** PID: 00835817 — 440/685-4711
2077 Park West Rd, N Bloomfield 44450 — Fax 440/685-4751

Schools: 2 \ **Teachers:** 27 \ **Students:** 314 \ **Special Ed Students:** 43 \ **LEP Students:** 44 \ **College-Bound:** 27% \ **Ethnic:** African American 2%, Caucasian 98% \ **Exp:** $286 (Med) \ **Poverty:** 13% \ **Title I:** $479,911 \ **Special Education:** $81,000 \ **Open-Close:** 08/21 - 05/27 \ **DTBP:** $197 (High)

John Sheets 1,11,288
Kerry Kerns 3
Joanna Lukz 12,58
Mike Foster 67
Rob Hollida 2
Patricia Anderson 6*
David Schnurrenberg 16,73*

Public Schs..Principal	Grd	Prgm	Enr/#Cls	SN	
Bloomfield Jr Sr High Sch 2077 Park West Rd, N Bloomfield 44450 Richard Stevens	6-12	T	104 18	53%	440/685-4711
Mesopotamia Elem Sch 4466 Kinsman Road, Mesopotamia 44439 Russell McQuaide	PK-5	T	145 11	60%	440/693-4125

● **Bristol Local School Dist** PID: 00835855 — 330/889-3882
1845 Greenville Rd NW, Bristolville 44402 — Fax 330/889-2529

Schools: 2 \ **Teachers:** 41 \ **Students:** 550 \ **Special Ed Students:** 90 \ **LEP Students:** 29 \ **College-Bound:** 44% \ **Ethnic:** Hispanic 1%, Caucasian 99% \ **Exp:** $274 (Med) \ **Poverty:** 15% \ **Title I:** $234,669 \ **Special Education:** $167,000 \ **Open-Close:** 08/19 - 05/21 \ **DTBP:** $209 (High)

Christopher Dray 1,11
Roger Prior 3
Dan Collins 6*
Timothy Fairfield 58,69,88*
Ted Ragan 73,76,295*
Mario Nero 2,296,298
Debbie Dale 4*
Kim Miller 31,36,83*
Don Mickel 67

Public Schs..Principal	Grd	Prgm	Enr/#Cls	SN	
Bristol Elem Sch 1845 Greenville Rd, Bristolville 44402 Ryan Stowell	K-6	T	281 21	45%	330/889-2621
Bristol High Sch 1845 Greenville Rd NW, Bristolville 44402 Timothy Fairfield	7-12	T	220 25	39%	330/889-2621

● **Brookfield Local School Dist** PID: 00835881 — 330/448-4930
614 Bedford Rd SE, Brookfield 44403 — Fax 330/448-5026

Schools: 3 \ **Teachers:** 58 \ **Students:** 900 \ **Special Ed Students:** 149 \ **College-Bound:** 53% \ **Ethnic:** African American 2%, Hispanic 1%, Caucasian 96% \ **Exp:** $89 (Low) \ **Poverty:** 20% \ **Title I:** $363,011 \ **Special Education:** $381,000 \ **Open-Close:** 08/26 - 05/29 \ **DTBP:** $245 (High)

Toby Gibson 1,11
Rhonda Thompson 3,5
Tim Taylor 6*
Robert Cireddu 16,73
Ronda Bonekovic 67
Craig Yaniglos 2
Donna Bailey 4*
Rhonda Zebroski 7*
Jeri Hamilton 58

Public Schs..Principal	Grd	Prgm	Enr/#Cls	SN	
Brookfield Elem Sch 614 Bedford Rd SE, Brookfield 44403 Stacey Filicky	K-4	T	381 15	60%	330/619-5240 Fax 330/619-5242
Brookfield High Sch 614 Bedford Rd SE, Brookfield 44403 Adam Lewis	9-12	T	263 29	47%	330/448-3001 Fax 330/448-3004
Brookfield Middle Sch 614 Bedford Rd SE, Brookfield 44403 Toby Gibson	5-8	T	325 25	49%	330/448-3003 Fax 330/448-3012

● **Champion Local School Dist** PID: 00835946 — 330/847-2330
5976 Mahoning Ave NW Ste B, Warren 44483 — Fax 330/847-2336

Schools: 2 \ **Teachers:** 82 \ **Students:** 1,525 \ **Special Ed Students:** 186 \ **LEP Students:** 4 \ **College-Bound:** 65% \ **Ethnic:** Hispanic 1%, Caucasian 99% \ **Exp:** $378 (High) \ **Poverty:** 13% \ **Title I:** $242,155 \ **Special Education:** $274,000 \ **Open-Close:** 08/27 - 05/29 \ **DTBP:** $104 (High) \ f

John Grabowski 1
Mark Harper 3,4,5
Alexandra Nannicola 11,296*
Holly Sandy 37*
Noeleen Miller 38*
John Pitts 67
Laurena Rouan 2
Tim Cope 6
Andrea Trendent 16,73
Danielle Fahmy 38*
Christy Pompoco 58*

Public Schs..Principal	Grd	Prgm	Enr/#Cls	SN	
Champion High Sch 5976 Mahoning Ave NW, Warren 44483 Tracy Herrholtz	9-12		389 44	37%	330/847-2305 Fax 330/847-2353
Champion K-8 Elementery Sch 5976 Mahoning Ave NW, Warren 44483 Alexandra Nannicola \ Heather Campbell	K-8		930 30		330/847-2328 Fax 330/847-2322

● **Girard City School Dist** PID: 00836079 — 330/545-2596
100 W Main St Ste 2, Girard 44420 — Fax 330/545-2597

Schools: 4 \ **Teachers:** 95 \ **Students:** 1,699 \ **Special Ed Students:** 248 \ **LEP Students:** 3 \ **College-Bound:** 51% \ **Ethnic:** African American 7%, Hispanic 4%, Caucasian 89% \ **Exp:** $246 (Med) \ **Poverty:** 23% \ **Title I:** $542,653 \ **Special Education:** $385,000 \ **Open-Close:** 08/20 - 05/22 \ **DTBP:** $211 (High)

Bryan O'Hara 1
Sam Buonavolonta 3
Renny Paolone 27,31,39*
Dianne Kosco 58
John Bello 73
Mark Bello 2
Nick Cochran 6*
Angie Cochran 36*
Mark Zuppo 67
Diane Costco 76

Public Schs..Principal	Grd	Prgm	Enr/#Cls	SN	
Girard High Sch 1244 Shannon Rd, Girard 44420 William Ryser	9-12	T	547	84%	330/545-5431 Fax 330/545-5440
Girard Intermediate Sch 702 E Prospect St, Girard 44420 Greg Bonamase	4-6	T	391 18		330/545-5219 Fax 330/545-7026
Girard Junior High Sch 1244 Shannon Rd, Girard 44420 Jennifer Santangelo	7-8	T	261 40		330/545-5431 Fax 330/545-5440
Prospect Elem Sch 700 E Prospect St, Girard 44420 Debra Gratz	PK-3	T	500 35	99%	330/545-3854 Fax 330/545-5219

---

79 Student Personnel
80 Driver Ed/Safety
81 Gifted/Talented
82 Video Services
83 Substance Abuse Prev
84 Erate
85 AIDS Education
88 Alternative/At Risk
89 Multi-Cultural Curriculum
90 Social Work
91 Safety/Security
92 Magnet School
93 Parental Involvement
95 Tech Prep Program
97 Chief Information Officer
98 Chief Technology Officer
270 Character Education
271 Migrant Education
273 Teacher Mentor
274 Before/After Sch
275 Response To Intervention
277 Remedial Math K-12
280 Literacy Coach
285 STEM
286 Digital Learning
288 Common Core Standards
294 Accountability
295 Network System
296 Title II Programs
297 Webmaster
298 Grant Writer/Ptnrships
750 Chief Innovation Officer
751 Chief of Staff
752 Social Emotional Learning

Other School Types
Ⓐ = Alternative School
Ⓒ = Charter School
Ⓜ = Magnet School
Ⓨ = Year-Round School

School Programs
A = Alternative Program
G = Adult Classes
M = Magnet Program
T = Title I Schoolwide
V = Career & Tech Ed Programs

Social Media
f = Facebook
t = Twitter

New Schools are shaded
New Superintendents and Principals are bold
Personnel with email addresses are underscored

Trumbull County

Market Data Retrieval

- **Howland Local School Dist** PID: 00836146   330/856-8200
  8200 South St SE, Warren 44484   Fax 330/856-8214

Schools: 6 \ **Teachers:** 168 \ **Students:** 2,685 \ **Special Ed Students:** 359 \ **LEP Students:** 29 \ **College-Bound:** 60% \ **Ethnic:** Asian 2%, African American 4%, Hispanic 3%, Caucasian 91% \ **Exp:** $87 (Low) \ **Poverty:** 14% \ **Title I:** $547,661 \ **Special Education:** $518,000 \ **Open-Close:** 08/27 - 05/29 \ **DTBP:** $221 (High)

Kevin Spicher 1
Keith Spiker 3
Andrea Ferenac 6,37*
Erin Pierce 8,11,69,83,88,288,298*
Jon Mosora 38,83*
Ken Jones 67
Rhonda Amorganos 2,19
Jeff McVicker 5,74,91
Karen Kunkle 7,35,85*
Sandra Williams 27,88,270*
Michelle Dohar 58*
Robert Blevins 73,76,95*

Public Schs..Principal	Grd	Prgm	Enr/#Cls	SN	
H C Mines Elem Sch 850 Howland Wilson Rd NE, Warren 44484 Jennifer Stephenson	3-4		260 25	40%	330/856-8270 Fax 330/856-8288
Howland Glen Primary Sch 8000 Bridle Ln NE, Warren 44484 Carl Clark	K-2		282 25	40%	330/856-8275 Fax 330/856-8289
Howland High Sch 200 Shaffer Dr NE, Warren 44484 Joe Simko	9-12	AV	818 40	39%	330/856-8220 Fax 330/856-7827
Howland Middle Sch 8100 South St SE, Warren 44484 Stephen Kovach	6-8		646 49	36%	330/856-8250 Fax 330/856-2157
Howland Springs Primary Sch 9500 Howland Springs Rd SE, Warren 44484 Travis Roth	K-1	T	245 20	45%	330/856-8280 Fax 330/856-2475
North Road Intermediate Sch 863 North Rd SE, Warren 44484 Sandy Williams	5-5	T	215 19	39%	330/856-8265 Fax 330/856-8287

- **Hubbard Exempted Village SD** PID: 00836237   330/534-1921
  108 Orchard Ave, Hubbard 44425   Fax 330/534-0522

Schools: 3 \ **Teachers:** 103 \ **Students:** 1,932 \ **Special Ed Students:** 190 \ **LEP Students:** 5 \ **College-Bound:** 64% \ **Ethnic:** African American 4%, Hispanic 2%, Caucasian 94% \ **Exp:** $96 (Low) \ **Poverty:** 13% \ **Title I:** $345,645 \ **Special Education:** $390,000 \ **Open-Close:** 08/27 - 05/29 \ **DTBP:** $236 (High)

Raymond Soloman 1
Raymond DeLuco 3
Mona Jones 5
Tricia Lockso 8,11,57,296,298*
Mary Mathews-Bebech 58,68,79*
Mary Sainato 69,77
Amber Babik 2
Sam Mantas 4*
Kevin Hogue 6
Megan Phiel 16*
James Adams 67
David Duffield 73,76,295

Public Schs..Principal	Grd	Prgm	Enr/#Cls	SN	
Hubbard Elem Sch 150 Hall Ave Ste A, Hubbard 44425 Shawn Marcello	K-4	T	659 34	46%	330/534-1921 Fax 330/534-6197
Hubbard High Sch 350 Hall Ave, Hubbard 44425 Bradilyn Yobe	9-12		608 48	46%	330/534-1921 Fax 330/534-6191
Hubbard Middle Sch 250 Hall Ave, Hubbard 44425 Brian Hoffman	5-8	T	638 51	47%	330/534-1921 Fax 330/534-6196

- **Joseph Badger Local Sch Dist** PID: 00836287   330/876-2810
  7119 State Route 7, Kinsman 44428   Fax 330/876-2811

Schools: 3 \ **Teachers:** 38 \ **Students:** 750 \ **Special Ed Students:** 112 \ **LEP Students:** 3 \ **College-Bound:** 56% \ **Ethnic:** Hispanic 1%, Caucasian 99% \ **Exp:** $197 (Low) \ **Poverty:** 14% \ **Title I:** $230,923 \ **Special Education:** $175,000 \ **Open-Close:** 08/20 - 05/22 \ **DTBP:** $170 (High) \ T

Edwin Baldwin 1
Pat Carney 6
Ray Anne Abramovich 36,83,88*
Andrea Steiner 69*
Greg Sciola 2
Mary Williams 9,58*
Eltha Logan 67
Eric Brugler 73*

Public Schs..Principal	Grd	Prgm	Enr/#Cls	SN	
Badger Elem Sch 7119 State Route 7, Kinsman 44428 Dr Mary Gough	PK-4	T	246 16	43%	330/876-2860 Fax 330/876-2861
Badger High Sch 7119 State Route 7, Kinsman 44428 Steven Kochemba	9-12		205 20	33%	330/876-2840 Fax 330/876-2841
Badger Middle Sch 7119 State Route 7, Kinsman 44428 Bill Hamilton	5-8	T	225 18	38%	330/876-2840 Fax 330/876-2841

- **Labrae Local School Dist** PID: 00836330   330/898-0800
  1001 N Leavitt Rd, Leavittsburg 44430   Fax 330/898-6112

Schools: 4 \ **Teachers:** 83 \ **Students:** 1,078 \ **Special Ed Students:** 175 \ **College-Bound:** 46% \ **Ethnic:** African American 5%, Hispanic 1%, Caucasian 94% \ **Exp:** $103 (Low) \ **Poverty:** 21% \ **Title I:** $399,061 \ **Special Education:** $267,000 \ **Open-Close:** 08/27 - 05/29 \ **DTBP:** $237 (High) \ T

Anthony Calderone 1
Rick Jones 3
Todd Rowe 6*
Milajean Harkabus 12,73,271*
John Zelneck 31
Amy Frederick 58*
Carol Jones 2
Alisa Propri 4*
Jeff Starkey 11,69,286*
Carol Sturgeon 16*
Linda Nogales 38*
Russell Sewell 67

Public Schs..Principal	Grd	Prgm	Enr/#Cls	SN	
Bascom Elem Sch 1015 N Leavitt Rd, Leavittsburg 44430 Maggie Kowach	K-2	T	223 18	78%	330/898-0800 Fax 330/898-1448
Labrae High Sch 1001 N Leavitt Rd, Leavittsburg 44430 Jeff Starkey	9-12	TV	320 40	42%	330/898-0800 Fax 330/898-7808
Labrae Intermediate Sch 1001 N Leavitt Rd, Leavittsburg 44430 Milajean Harkabus	3-5	T	257 19	63%	330/898-0800 Fax 330/898-7808
Labrae Middle Sch 1001 N Leavitt Rd, Leavittsburg 44430 Martin Kelly	6-8	T	278	55%	330/898-0800 Fax 330/898-7808

- **Lakeview Local School Dist** PID: 00836392   330/637-8741
  300 Hillman Dr, Cortland 44410   Fax 330/282-4260

Schools: 3 \ **Teachers:** 86 \ **Students:** 1,732 \ **Special Ed Students:** 179 \ **LEP Students:** 8 \ **College-Bound:** 69% \ **Ethnic:** Asian 1%, African American 2%, Hispanic 1%, Caucasian 96% \ **Exp:** $381 (High) \ **Poverty:** 15% \ **Title I:** $394,235 \ **Special Education:** $383,000 \ **Open-Close:** 08/15 - 05/21 \ **DTBP:** $186 (High)

Jo Taylor 1
Sean Miller 2

---

1 Superintendent	8 Curric/Instruct K-12	19 Chief Financial Officer	29 Family/Consumer Science	39 Social Studies K-12	49 English/Lang Arts Elem	59 Special Education Elem	69 Academic Assessment
2 Bus/Finance/Purchasing	9 Curric/Instruct Elem	20 Art K-12	30 Adult Education	40 Social Studies Elem	50 English/Lang Arts Sec	60 Special Education Sec	70 Research/Development
3 Buildings And Grounds	10 Curric/Instruct Sec	21 Art Elem	31 Career/Sch-to-Work K-12	41 Social Studies Sec	51 Reading K-12	61 Foreign/World Lang K-12	71 Public Information
4 Food Service	11 Federal Program	22 Art Sec	32 Career/Sch-to-Work Elem	42 Science K-12	52 Reading Elem	62 Foreign/World Lang Elem	72 Summer School
5 Transportation	12 Title I	23 Music K-12	33 Career/Sch-to-Work Sec	43 Science Elem	53 Reading Sec	63 Foreign/World Lang Sec	73 Instructional Tech
6 Athletic	13 Title V	24 Music Elem	34 Early Childhood Ed	44 Science Sec	54 Remedial Reading K-12	64 Religious Education K-12	74 Inservice Training
7 Health Services	15 Asst Superintendent	25 Music Sec	35 Health/Phys Education	45 Math K-12	55 Remedial Reading Elem	65 Religious Education Elem	75 Marketing/Distributive
	16 Instructional Media Svcs	26 Business Education	36 Guidance Services K-12	46 Math Elem	56 Remedial Reading Sec	66 Religious Education Sec	76 Info Systems
	17 Chief Operations Officer	27 Career & Tech Ed	37 Guidance Services Elem	47 Math Sec	57 Bilingual/ELL	67 School Board President	77 Psychological Assess
	18 Chief Academic Officer	28 Technology Education	38 Guidance Services Sec	48 English/Lang Arts K-12	58 Special Education K-12	68 Teacher Personnel	78 Affirmative Action

even
Ohio School Directory

Trumbull County

Mary Pehanich 4
Ron Dejulio 6*
Joanne Ogurchak 11,275,288*
Donna Zuga 67
Dan Falatic 5
Maureen Paczak 7*
Jennifer Merkich 58
Lisa Collins 73,84

Public Schs..Principal	Grd	Prgm	Enr/#Cls	SN	
Lakeview Elem Sch 640 Wakefield Dr, Cortland 44410 Scott Taylor	K-4		630 23	25%	330/638-2145 Fax 330/638-6727
Lakeview High Sch 300 Hillman Dr, Cortland 44410 Lawrence Herrholtz	9-12		600 55	19%	330/637-4921 Fax 330/637-8812
Lakeview Middle Sch 640 Wakefield Dr, Cortland 44410 Ashley Handrych	5-8		525 19	25%	330/637-4360 Fax 330/638-1913

• Liberty Local School Dist PID: 00836433   330/759-0807
4115 Shady Rd, Youngstown 44505   Fax 330/759-1209

Schools: 3 \ **Teachers:** 70 \ **Students:** 1,244 \ **Special Ed Students:** 178 \ **LEP Students:** 8 \ **College-Bound:** 59% \ **Ethnic:** Asian 1%, African American 37%, Hispanic 7%, Caucasian 55% \ **Exp:** $309 (High) \ **Poverty:** 20% \ **Title I:** $563,097 \ **Special Education:** $245,000 \ **Open-Close:** 09/03 - 06/03 \ **DTBP:** $17 (Low)

Joseph Nohra 1
Tony Daniels 3,73,76,295*
Steve Stohla ....
Pamela McCurdy 8,11,57,69,273,288
Pati Fergus 16
Bradley Panak 2
Jonette Wilson 4
James Detoro 6*
Jessica Kohler 13,58,83,88
David Malone 67

Public Schs..Principal	Grd	Prgm	Enr/#Cls	SN	
Blott Guy Elem Sch 4115 Shady Rd, Youngstown 44505 Michael Palmer	PK-6	T	502 23	69%	330/759-1733 Fax 330/759-9151
Guy Jr High Sch 1 Leopard Way, Youngstown 44505 Andrew Scarmack	7-8	T	388 40	60%	330/759-3909 Fax 330/759-4507
Liberty High Sch 1 Leopard Way, Youngstown 44505 Akesha Joseph	9-12	T	354 46	55%	330/759-2301 Fax 330/759-4506

• Lordstown Local School Dist PID: 00836483   330/824-2534
1824 Salt Springs Rd, Warren 44481   Fax 330/824-2847

Schools: 2 \ **Teachers:** 36 \ **Students:** 500 \ **Special Ed Students:** 82 \ **College-Bound:** 61% \ **Ethnic:** African American 4%, Hispanic 1%, Caucasian 95% \ **Exp:** $191 (Low) \ **Poverty:** 17% \ **Title I:** $121,664 \ **Special Education:** $100,000 \ **Open-Close:** 09/03 - 05/27 \ **DTBP:** $180 (High)

Terry Armstrong 1
Charles Worley 3
Brian Rust 6*
Jessica Lee 36,69,83,88
William Catlin 67
Mark Ferrara 2,11
Kathy Baltes 5
Genevieve Gigliotti 16*
Rich Zigarovich 58*
Rod Reiner 73

Public Schs..Principal	Grd	Prgm	Enr/#Cls	SN	
Lordstown Elem Sch 1776 Salt Springs Rd, Warren 44481 Rich Zigarovich	K-6	T	258 14	54%	330/824-2572 Fax 330/824-2568
Lordstown High Sch 1824 Salt Springs Rd, Warren 44481 James Vivo	7-12		215 30	45%	330/824-2581 Fax 330/824-2586

• Maplewood Local School Dist PID: 00836524   330/637-7506
2414 Greenville Rd, Cortland 44410

Schools: 2 \ **Teachers:** 49 \ **Students:** 750 \ **Special Ed Students:** 99 \ **LEP Students:** 3 \ **College-Bound:** 48% \ **Ethnic:** Hispanic 1%, Caucasian 98% \ **Exp:** $311 (High) \ **Poverty:** 14% \ **Title I:** $170,333 \ **Special Education:** $158,000 \ **Open-Close:** 08/21 - 05/27 \ **DTBP:** $261 (High)

Perry Nicholas 1,11
John Brown 3
Dennis Bresenhan 16,73
Merri Smith 2
Mark Yoder 6*
Dan Denman 67

Public Schs..Principal	Grd	Prgm	Enr/#Cls	SN	
Maplewood Elem Sch 4174 Greenville Rd, Cortland 44410 Kevin O'Connell	PK-6	T	371 21	52%	330/583-2321 Fax 330/583-3321
Maplewood High Sch 2414 Greenville Rd, Cortland 44410 Gordon Hitchcock	7-12		316 28	37%	330/637-8466 Fax 330/637-0496

• Mathews Local School Dist PID: 00836029   330/637-7000
4096 Cadwallader Sonk Rd, Vienna 44473   Fax 330/394-1930

Schools: 3 \ **Teachers:** 50 \ **Students:** 675 \ **Special Ed Students:** 107 \ **LEP Students:** 3 \ **College-Bound:** 71% \ **Ethnic:** African American 1%, Hispanic 1%, Caucasian 99% \ **Exp:** $284 (Med) \ **Poverty:** 17% \ **Title I:** $201,577 \ **Special Education:** $165,000 \ **Open-Close:** 08/21 - 05/22 \ **DTBP:** $174 (High)

Russell McQuaide 1
Chuck Pulice 3,5,91
Michael King 11,296
Julie Berkhouse 38,69*
Tarin Brown 67
Terry Gettemy 77*
Ryan Jones 2
Robert Rozycki 6*
James Parry 16*
Jennifer Soulcenik 58*
Steven Rudge 73*

Public Schs..Principal	Grd	Prgm	Enr/#Cls	SN	
Baker Elem Sch 4095 Sheridan Dr, Vienna 44473 Mike King	3-6	T	208 15	42%	330/637-3500 Fax 330/539-9036
Currie Elem Sch 3306 Ridge Rd, Cortland 44410 Mike King	K-2	T	130 9	45%	330/637-3500 Fax 330/637-2341
Mathews High Sch 4429 Warren Sharon Rd, Vienna 44473 James Stitt	7-12		250 25	42%	330/637-3500 Fax 330/394-3665

• McDonald Local School Dist PID: 00836574   330/530-8051
600 Iowa Ave, Mc Donald 44437   Fax 330/530-7041

Schools: 2 \ **Teachers:** 48 \ **Students:** 768 \ **Special Ed Students:** 75 \ **College-Bound:** 72% \ **Ethnic:** African American 1%, Hispanic 4%, Caucasian 94% \ **Exp:** $200 (Med) \ **Poverty:** 16% \ **Title I:** $151,039 \ **Special Education:** $153,000 \ **Open-Close:** 08/21 - 05/28 \ **DTBP:** $238 (High)

Kevin O'Connell 1,11
Carol Augustine 7*
Gary Carkido 10*
Tracy Bosheff 31,36,69,83*
Megan Titus 2
Eric Jones 9,12,90*
Jeff Studer 16,84
John Saganich 67

Public Schs..Principal	Grd	Prgm	Enr/#Cls	SN	
McDonald High Sch 600 Iowa Ave, Mc Donald 44437 Gary Carkido	7-12	V	362 25		330/530-8051

---

79 Student Personnel	91 Safety/Security	275 Response To Intervention	298 Grant Writer/Ptnrships	**School Programs**	**Social Media**
80 Driver Ed/Safety	92 Magnet School	277 Remedial Math K-12	750 Chief Innovation Officer	A = Alternative Program	
81 Gifted/Talented	93 Parental Involvement	280 Literacy Coach	751 Chief of Staff	G = Adult Classes	f = Facebook
82 Video Services	95 Tech Prep Program	285 STEM	752 Social Emotional Learning	M = Magnet Program	
83 Substance Abuse Prev	97 Chief Information Officer	286 Digital Learning		T = Title I Schoolwide	t = Twitter
84 Erate	98 Chief Technology Officer	288 Common Core Standards	**Other School Types**	V = Career & Tech Ed Programs	
85 AIDS Education	270 Character Education	294 Accountability	Ⓐ = Alternative School		
88 Alternative/At Risk	271 Migrant Education	295 Network System	Ⓒ = Charter School	New Schools are shaded	
89 Multi-Cultural Curriculum	273 Teacher Mentor	296 Title II Programs	Ⓜ = Magnet School	New Superintendents and Principals are bold	
90 Social Work	274 Before/After Sch	297 Webmaster	Ⓨ = Year-Round School	Personnel with email addresses are underscored	

OH–199

Trumbull County

Market Data Retrieval

Roosevelt Elem Sch 410 W 7th St, Mc Donald 44437 Eric Jones	K-6	T	406 26	41%	330/530-8051 Fax 330/530-7033

● **Newton Falls Exempted Vlg SD** PID: 00836603   330/872-5445
909 1/2 Milton Blvd, Newton Falls 44444   Fax 330/872-3351

Schools: 4 \ *Teachers:* 68 \ *Students:* 1,100 \ *Special Ed Students:* 173 \ *LEP Students:* 3 \ *College-Bound:* 55% \ *Ethnic:* Caucasian 99% \ *Exp:* $206 (Med) \ *Poverty:* 16% \ *Title I:* $328,900 \ *Special Education:* $217,000 \ *Open-Close:* 08/20 - 05/25 \ *DTBP:* $233 (High) \ f

Paul Woodard	1	Julie Sloan		2
Lynn Thiry	4*	Terri Pigg		5
Roy Sembach	16*	Robin Langley		58
Debra Davis	67	Shawn Donley		73,76,295
Shawn Donley	73,76,295*			

Public Schs..Principal	Grd	Prgm	Enr/#Cls	SN	
ⓐ Falls Learning Academy 907 Milton Blvd Rm 323, Newton Falls 44444 John Crowder	7-12		25		330/872-5121
Newton Falls Elem Mid Sch 909 Milton Blvd, Newton Falls 44444 Thomas Sullivan	K-5	T	424 18	61%	330/872-0695 Fax 330/872-8327 f
Newton Falls High Sch 907 Milton Blvd, Newton Falls 44444 John Crowder	9-12	TV	285 25	75%	330/872-5121 Fax 330/872-5013
Newton Falls Junior High Sch 907 1/2 Milton Blvd, Newton Falls 44444 Angelina Berilla	6-8	T	300 20		330/872-0905 Fax 330/872-0964

● **Niles City School Dist** PID: 00836653   330/989-5095
309 N Rhodes Ave, Niles 44446   Fax 330/989-5096

Schools: 4 \ *Teachers:* 146 \ *Students:* 2,209 \ *Special Ed Students:* 356 \ *LEP Students:* 5 \ *College-Bound:* 43% \ *Ethnic:* African American 5%, Hispanic 2%, Caucasian 92% \ *Exp:* $173 (Low) \ *Poverty:* 27% \ *Title I:* $1,170,840 \ *Special Education:* $583,000 \ *Open-Close:* 08/26 - 05/21 \ *DTBP:* $196 (High) \ f t

Ann Marie Thigapin	1	Lori Hudzik		2
Jones John	3	Dawn Carkido		5
Marc Fritz	6*	Scott Libert		11,69,72,74,288,298
Caroline Hines	16*	Mary Ann McMahon		67
Eric Ulrich	73	Dori MacMillian		77
Kayla Adair	83			

Public Schs..Principal	Grd	Prgm	Enr/#Cls	SN	
Niles Intermediate Sch 120 E Margaret Ave, Niles 44446 Christopher Staph	3-5	T	503 23	70%	330/989-5093 Fax 330/989-5094
Niles McKinley High Sch 616 Dragon Dr, Niles 44446 Tracie Parry	9-12	TV	718 30	55%	330/652-9968 Fax 330/505-0755
Niles Middle Sch 411 Brown St, Niles 44446 Samuel Reigle	6-8	T	510 38	63%	330/652-5656 Fax 330/652-9158
Niles Primary Sch 960 Frederick St, Niles 44446 Joanna Lukz Gatta	PK-2	T	478 13	73%	330/989-5091 Fax 330/989-5092 f

● **Southington Local School Dist** PID: 00836756   330/898-7480
2482 State Route 534, Southington 44470   Fax 330/898-4828

Schools: 1 \ *Teachers:* 35 \ *Students:* 500 \ *Special Ed Students:* 70 \ *LEP Students:* 12 \ *College-Bound:* 50% \ *Exp:* $119 (Low) \ *Poverty:* 11% \ *Title I:* $94,903 \ *Special Education:* $76,000 \ *Open-Close:* 08/21 - 05/28 \ *DTBP:* $199 (High)

Rocco Nero	1,11,288	Janet Ward		2
Mark Hertzer	3	Donna Sharpes		4*
Craig Lefkowitz	6*	Rhonda Shaffer		16*
Marilyn Dadisman	31,36,69*	Robert Kujala		58*
Elizabeth Dunn	67	Renee Karr		73*

Public Schs..Principal	Grd	Prgm	Enr/#Cls	SN	
Southington Local Sch 2482 State Route 534, Southington 44470 Robert Kujala	PK-12		500 26		330/898-7480

● **Warren City School Dist** PID: 00836782   330/841-2321
105 High St NE, Warren 44481   Fax 330/841-2434

Schools: 5 \ *Teachers:* 296 \ *Students:* 4,300 \ *Special Ed Students:* 917 \ *LEP Students:* 16 \ *College-Bound:* 46% \ *Ethnic:* African American 46%, Hispanic 4%, Caucasian 50% \ *Exp:* $219 (Med) \ *Poverty:* 39% \ *Title I:* $4,999,960 \ *Special Education:* $1,663,000 \ *Open-Close:* 08/21 - 05/29 \ *DTBP:* $195 (High) \ t

Steve Chiaro	1	Michael Wasser		2,91
Shawn Shimco	3	Laureen Postlethwait		4
Sue Harcarik	4	Dora Selbe		5
William Nicholson	6*	Ragina Teutch		8,280,288
Christine Bero	11,16,73,95	Karin Kilpatrick		12
Wendy Hartzell	15	Kelly Hutchinson		34
Nikki Littleton	45	Patricia Fisher		45
Jacqueline Lawrence	48	Paula Yauger		48
Jenniieer Meyers	58	Patricia Limperos		67
Deb Bufano	76	Christine DePascale		81*
Jill Merolla	83,298	Danielle Miller		84

Public Schs..Principal	Grd	Prgm	Enr/#Cls	SN	
Jefferson PK-8 Sch 1543 Tod Ave SW, Warren 44485 **Carrie Boyer** \ **Gary Israel**	PK-8	AT	748 16		330/675-6960 Fax 330/675-6961 t
Lincoln PK-8 Sch 2253 Atlantic St NE, Warren 44483 **Dani Burns** \ **Josh Guthrie**	PK-8	AT	1,194 45		330/373-4500 Fax 330/373-4510 t
McGuffey PK-8 Sch 3465 Tod Ave NW, Warren 44485 Jeanne Reighard \ Tracey Ryser	PK-8	AT	773 14		330/675-6980 Fax 330/675-6981
Warren G Harding High Sch 860 Elm Rd NE, Warren 44483 Dante Capers	9-12	AT	1,274 100		330/841-2316 Fax 330/841-2289
Willard PK-8 Sch 2020 Willard Ave SE, Warren 44484 Vicki Raptis \ Carly Polder	PK-8	AT	818 15		330/675-8700 Fax 330/675-8710 t

● **Weathersfield Local Sch Dist** PID: 00837011   330/652-0287
1334 Seaborn St, Mineral Ridge 44440   Fax 330/544-7476

Schools: 2 \ *Teachers:* 52 \ *Students:* 992 \ *Special Ed Students:* 123 \ *LEP Students:* 3 \ *College-Bound:* 64% \ *Ethnic:* Asian 1%, African American 1%, Hispanic 2%, Caucasian 95% \ *Exp:* $176 (Low) \ *Poverty:* 18% \ *Title I:* $191,463 \ *Special Education:* $169,000 \ *Open-Close:* 08/29 - 05/22 \ *DTBP:* $233 (High)

#		#		#		#		#		#		#		#	
1	Superintendent	8	Curric/Instruct K-12	19	Chief Financial Officer	29	Family/Consumer Science	39	Social Studies K-12	49	English/Lang Arts Elem	59	Special Education Elem	69	Academic Assessment
2	Bus/Finance/Purchasing	9	Curric/Instruct Elem	20	Art K-12	30	Adult Education	40	Social Studies Elem	50	English/Lang Arts Sec	60	Special Education Sec	70	Research/Development
3	Buildings And Grounds	10	Curric/Instruct Sec	21	Art Elem	31	Career/Sch-to-Work K-12	41	Social Studies Sec	51	Reading K-12	61	Foreign/World Lang K-12	71	Public Information
4	Food Service	11	Federal Program	22	Art Sec	32	Career/Sch-to-Work Elem	42	Science K-12	52	Reading Elem	62	Foreign/World Lang Elem	72	Summer School
5	Transportation	12	Title I	23	Music K-12	33	Career/Sch-to-Work Sec	43	Science Elem	53	Reading Sec	63	Foreign/World Lang Sec	73	Instructional Tech
6	Athletic	13	Title V	24	Music Elem	34	Early Childhood Ed	44	Science Sec	54	Remedial Reading K-12	64	Religious Education K-12	74	Inservice Training
7	Health Services	14	Asst Superintendent	25	Music Sec	35	Health/Phys Education	45	Math K-12	55	Remedial Reading Elem	65	Religious Education Elem	75	Marketing/Distributive
		15	Instructional Media Svcs	26	Business Education	36	Guidance Services K-12	46	Math Elem	56	Remedial Reading Sec	66	Religious Education Sec	76	Info Systems
		16	Chief Operations Officer	27	Career & Tech Ed	37	Guidance Services Elem	47	Math Sec	57	Bilingual/ELL	67	School Board President	77	Psychological Assess
		17	Chief Academic Officer	28	Technology Education	38	Guidance Services Sec	48	English/Lang Arts K-12	58	Special Education K-12	68	Teacher Personnel	78	Affirmative Action

Ohio School Directory

Tuscarawas County

Damon Dohar 1
Lew Cappitte 3,5
Cynthia Mulgrew 11*
Diana Wrataric 37*
Jessica Krumpak 58
Jennifer Staunton 83,85*
Laurena Rouan 2
Tim Porter 6*
Holly Buente 16*
Terri Baer 38,69*
Tim Gleason 67
Robert Martinko 93*

Public Schs..Principal	Grd	Prgm	Enr/#Cls	SN
Mineral Ridge High Sch 1334 Seaborn St, Mineral Ridge 44440 Randy Cameron	7-12	T	438 22	41% 330/652-1451 Fax 330/505-9374
Seaborn Elem Sch 3800 Niles Carver Rd, Mineral Ridge 44440 T Koniowsky	PK-6	T	554 16	54% 330/652-9695 Fax 330/544-7482

TRUMBULL CATHOLIC SCHOOLS

● **Diocese of Youngstown Ed Off** PID: 00820915
Listing includes only schools located in this county. See District Index for location of Diocesan Offices.

Catholic Schs..Principal	Grd	Prgm	Enr/#Cls	SN
JFK Lower Campus 3000 Reeves Rd NE, Warren 44483 Jacquelyn Venzeio	PK-5		305 15	330/372-2375 Fax 330/372-2465
John F Kennedy Catholic Sch 2550 Central Parkway Ave SE, Warren 44484 Alyse Consiglio	6-12		350	330/369-1804 Fax 330/369-1125
St Rose Sch 61 E Main St, Girard 44420 Linda Borton	K-8		320 13	330/545-1163 Fax 330/545-6187

TRUMBULL PRIVATE SCHOOLS

Private Schs..Principal	Grd	Prgm	Enr/#Cls	SN
Holy Trinity Christian Academy 175 Laird Ave NE Ste A, Warren 44483 Afrodete Gentis	K-4		26	330/399-7642
Hope Academy for Autism 1628 Niles Rd SE, Warren 44484 Kimberly Clinkscale	Spec		44	330/469-9501 Fax 330/369-2455
Victory Christian Sch 2053 Pleasant Valley Rd, Niles 44446 Colleen McCullough	K-12		75 13	330/539-9827 Fax 330/539-9828

TRUMBULL REGIONAL CENTERS

● **Neomin-NE Ohio Mgmt Info NET** PID: 04499570 330/847-6464
528 Educational Hwy NW, Warren 44483 Fax 330/847-8568

Brian Greathouse 1
Robert Falatic 15

TUSCARAWAS COUNTY

TUSCARAWAS COUNTY SCHOOLS

● **East Central Ohio ESC-N Phil** PID: 00837592 330/308-9939
834 E High Ave, New Phila 44663 Fax 330/308-0964

Randy Lucas 1
Melanie Cronebach 58,275
Nicholas Brown 73
Matt King 2
Jennifer Deam 67

County Schs..Principal	Grd	Prgm	Enr/#Cls	SN
© Beacon Hill Community Sch 10470 Winesburg Rd, Dundee 44624 Brad Herman	7-12	T	56	26% 330/359-5600 Fax 330/359-6197
E Central Ohio Ed Svc Center 834 E High Ave, New Phila 44663 Scott Young	Spec		150	330/308-9939
Starlight Sch 518 Church Ave SW, New Phila 44663 Holly Lawver	Spec		70 6	330/339-3577 Fax 330/339-2351

TUSCARAWAS PUBLIC SCHOOLS

● **Buckeye Joint Voc School Dist** PID: 00837580 330/339-2288
545 University Dr NE, New Phila 44663 Fax 330/308-5661

Schools: 1 \ *Teachers:* 67 \ *Students:* 975 \ *LEP Students:* 14 \
College-Bound: 65% \ *Exp:* $758 (High) \ *Open-Close:* 08/19 - 05/28 \
DTBP: $173 (High) \

Robert Alsept 1,11
Phyllis Willison 4*
Jake Kula 16,82,297*
John Fisher 33*
Cyndy Host 67
John Barr 298*
Cheryl Pritts 2
Kelly Luneborg 7,12,13
Matt Fockler 27,38,75,79,83,288*
Megan Zimmerman 57*
Kay Wise 286*

Public Schs..Principal	Grd	Prgm	Enr/#Cls	SN
Buckeye Career Center 545 University Dr NE, New Phila 44663 Matt Fockler	Voc	G	975 75	330/339-2288

● **Claymont City School Dist** PID: 00837061 740/922-5478
201 N 3rd St, Dennison 44621 Fax 740/922-7325

Schools: 6 \ *Teachers:* 128 \ *Students:* 2,000 \ *Special Ed Students:* 375
\ *LEP Students:* 3 \ *College-Bound:* 40% \ *Ethnic:* African American
1%, Hispanic 2%, Caucasian 97% \ *Exp:* $292 (Med) \ *Poverty:* 22% \
Title I: $703,840 \ *Special Education:* $512,000 \ *Open-Close:* 08/26 -
06/04 \ *DTBP:* $208 (High) \

Scott Golec 1
Beth Lint 3,73,84,286
Tracey Peterman 4,5
Jodie Miles 8,11,296
Vonda Garabrandt 36*
Austin Beckley 67
Kimberly Beckley 2
Andrea Burlison 4
Justin Jones 6
Torey Conner 13
Holly Hall 58,81,88*

OH—201

Tuscarawas County

Public Schs..Principal	Grd	Prgm	Enr/#Cls	SN	
Claymont Elem Sch 1200 Eastport Ave, Uhrichsville 44683 Richard Page	2-3	T	300 17	68%	740/922-4641 Fax 740/922-7428
Claymont High Sch 4205 Indian Hill Rd SE, Uhrichsville 44683 Lisa Brown	9-12	T	482 60	51%	740/922-3471 Fax 740/922-1031
Claymont Intermediate Sch 220 N 3rd St, Dennison 44621 Beth DiDonato	4-5	T	301 36	60%	740/922-1901 Fax 740/922-6302
Claymont Middle Sch 215 E 6th St, Uhrichsville 44683 Brian Watkins	6-8	T	427 35	61%	740/922-5241 Fax 740/922-7330
Claymont Preschool 200 Jewett Ave, Dennison 44621 Holly Hall	PK-PK	T	89		740/922-5888 Fax 740/922-6256
Claymont Primary Sch 320 Trenton Ave, Uhrichsville 44683 Eric Seiberd	K-1	T	278 17	67%	740/922-5641 Fax 740/922-7427

- **Dover City School Dist** PID: 00837140 330/364-1906
  219 W 6th St, Dover 44622   Fax 330/343-7070

Schools: 5 \ *Teachers:* 130 \ *Students:* 2,712 \ *Special Ed Students:* 429 \ *LEP Students:* 243 \ *College-Bound:* 61% \ *Ethnic:* African American 2%, Hispanic 10%, Caucasian 88% \ *Exp:* $112 (Low) \ *Poverty:* 11% \ *Title I:* $380,826 \ *Special Education:* $590,000 \ *Open-Close:* 08/21 - 05/29 \ *DTBP:* $192 (High) \

Carla Birney	1,11	Andrew Bache	2
Colin Eichel	3,5,91*	Angie Welsh	4
Barbara White	5	Tim McCrate	6*
Sherry Patterson	7*	Karie McCrate	15
Paula Fritz	16*	Brenda Wherley	29
Gina Franks	57,58,79,88,275,296,298*	Jeannine Kennedy	67
Cindy Hay	73,295*	Dan Ifft	88*
Beth Maybaugh	273		

Public Schs..Principal	Grd	Prgm	Enr/#Cls	SN	
Dover Ave Elem Sch 125 W 13th St, Dover 44622 Renee Sattler	K-5		314 20	40%	330/364-7117 Fax 330/343-7636
Dover High Sch 520 N Walnut St, Dover 44622 Teresa Alberts	9-12	V	796 55	28%	330/364-7148 Fax 330/364-7142
Dover Middle Sch 2131 N Wooster Ave, Dover 44622 Jack Edwards	6-8		635 40	32%	330/364-7121 Fax 330/364-7127
East Elem Sch 325 Betscher Ave, Dover 44622 Zachary Zesiger	K-5		509 20	32%	330/364-7114 Fax 330/343-8526
South Elem Sch 280 E Shafer Ave, Dover 44622 Tracie Murphy	PK-5	T	458 22	52%	330/364-7111 Fax 330/343-3976

- **Garaway Local School Dist** PID: 00837205 330/852-2421
  146 Dover Rd NW, Sugarcreek 44681   Fax 330/852-2991

Schools: 5 \ *Teachers:* 68 \ *Students:* 1,300 \ *Special Ed Students:* 200 \ *LEP Students:* 8 \ *College-Bound:* 54% \ *Ethnic:* Hispanic 3%, Caucasian 96% \ *Exp:* $234 (Med) \ *Poverty:* 13% \ *Title I:* $414,199 \ *Special Education:* $276,000 \ *Open-Close:* 08/21 - 05/27 \ *DTBP:* $173 (High)

Dr James Millet	1,83	Sheryl Hardesty	2
James Meek	3	Melissa Biltz	4

Kevin Roberts	5	Anthony Amicone	6*
Jeff Williams	8,11,57,58,288	Jeff Williams	8,11,57,58,288*
Linda Hochstetler	36	Dick Marshall	67
Connie Froman	76	Sherry Bichsel	273
Charles Zobel	286		

Public Schs..Principal	Grd	Prgm	Enr/#Cls	SN	
⊘ Baltic Elem Sch 300 E Main St, Baltic 43804 Mollie Parisi	K-6	MT	152 7	70%	330/897-7261 Fax 330/897-3201
⊘ Dundee Elem Sch 8072 School St, Dundee 44624 Curtis Fisher	K-6	MT	172 7	37%	330/852-2022 Fax 330/852-9952
⊘ Garaway 7-12 Sch 146 Dover Rd NW, Sugarcreek 44681 Ryan Taggart	7-12	M	515 30	28%	330/852-4292 Fax 330/852-4382
⊘ Miller Avenue Elem Sch 840 Miller Ave SW, Sugarcreek 44681 Curtis Fisher	K-6	MT	196 11	36%	330/852-2441 Fax 330/852-7702
Ragersville Elem Sch 2405 Ragersville Rd SW, Sugarcreek 44681 Mollie Parisi	K-6		154 7	30%	330/897-5021 Fax 330/897-9941

- **Indian Valley Local Sch Dist** PID: 00837267 740/254-4334
  100 N Walnut St, Gnadenhutten 44629   Fax 740/254-9271

Schools: 5 \ *Teachers:* 104 \ *Students:* 1,900 \ *Special Ed Students:* 230 \ *LEP Students:* 3 \ *College-Bound:* 46% \ *Ethnic:* Hispanic 1%, Caucasian 99% \ *Exp:* $210 (Med) \ *Poverty:* 17% \ *Title I:* $463,166 \ *Special Education:* $348,000 \ *Open-Close:* 08/21 - 05/28 \ *DTBP:* $177 (High) \

Ira Wentworth	1	Bradley Maholm	2
Nick Swoldo	3,4,5,6	Ryan Burrier	8,61,74,273,274,298
Talia St Claire	11,58,69,88,296	Wanda Krocker	16,82*
Keely Kochman	36*	Kathy Roth	67
Brian Dittfeld	73,84,295	Jodi Hillyer	76
Jody Dittcherd	81		

Public Schs..Principal	Grd	Prgm	Enr/#Cls	SN	
Indian Valley Digital Academy 188 Southern Gateway St, Gnadenhutten 44629 Juli Arnett	K-12		50		740/561-4034
Indian Valley High Sch 253 S Walnut St, Gnadenhutten 44629 Robert Clark	9-12		457 35	34%	740/254-4262 Fax 740/254-4911
Indian Valley Middle Sch 261 School St, Tuscarawas 44682 Brent Carter	6-8		456 28		740/922-4226 Fax 740/922-2493
Midvale Elem Sch 4259 W State St, Midvale 44653 Ryan Wells	K-5	T	423 18	54%	330/339-1191 Fax 330/339-1194
Port Washington Elem Sch 304 E Arch St, Prt Washingtn 43837 Troy Page	K-5	T	394 18	36%	740/498-8389 Fax 740/498-6312

- **New Philadelphia City Sch Dist** PID: 00837334 330/364-0600
  248 Front Ave SW, New Phila 44663   Fax 330/364-9310

Schools: 8 \ *Teachers:* 172 \ *Students:* 3,800 \ *Special Ed Students:* 477 \ *LEP Students:* 189 \ *College-Bound:* 58% \ *Ethnic:* Asian 1%, African American 2%, Hispanic 10%, Caucasian 88% \ *Exp:* $341 (High) \ *Poverty:* 17% \ *Title I:* $808,751 \ *Special Education:* $610,000 \ *Open-Close:* 08/22 - 05/29 \ *DTBP:* $236 (High) \

Dave Brand	1	Julie Erwin	2

1 Superintendent	8 Curric/Instruct K-12	19 Chief Financial Officer	29 Family/Consumer Science	39 Social Studies K-12	49 English/Lang Arts Elem	59 Special Education Elem	69 Academic Assessment
2 Bus/Finance/Purchasing	9 Curric/Instruct Elem	20 Art K-12	30 Adult Education	40 Social Studies Elem	50 English/Lang Arts Sec	60 Special Education Sec	70 Research/Development
3 Buildings And Grounds	10 Curric/Instruct Sec	21 Art Elem	31 Career/Sch-to-Work K-12	41 Social Studies Sec	51 Reading K-12	61 Foreign/World Lang K-12	71 Public Information
4 Food Service	11 Federal Program	22 Art Sec	32 Career/Sch-to-Work Elem	42 Science K-12	52 Reading Elem	62 Foreign/World Lang Elem	72 Summer School
5 Transportation	12 Title I	23 Music K-12	33 Career/Sch-to-Work Sec	43 Science Elem	53 Reading Sec	63 Foreign/World Lang Sec	73 Instructional Tech
6 Athletic	13 Title V	24 Music Elem	34 Early Childhood Ed	44 Science Sec	54 Remedial Reading K-12	64 Religious Education K-12	74 Inservice Training
7 Health Services	15 Asst Superintendent	25 Music Sec	35 Health/Phys Education	45 Math K-12	55 Remedial Reading Elem	65 Religious Education Elem	75 Marketing/Distributive
	16 Instructional Media Svcs	26 Business Education	36 Guidance Services K-12	46 Math Elem	56 Remedial Reading Sec	66 Religious Education Sec	76 Info Systems
	17 Chief Operations Officer	27 Career & Tech Ed	37 Guidance Services Elem	47 Math Sec	57 Bilingual/ELL	67 School Board President	77 Psychological Assess
	18 Chief Academic Officer	28 Technology Education	38 Guidance Services Sec	48 English/Lang Arts K-12	58 Special Education K-12	68 Teacher Personnel	78 Affirmative Action

Ohio School Directory
Tuscarawas County

Trent Lenhart 3,17	Cindy Jones 4*
Julia Espenschied 5	Matt Dennison 6*
Amy Wentworth .. 8,11,15,74,274,285,288,298	Ashley Claxon 16*
Heidi Briggs 31,38*	Lori Hall 57
Christina Ziga-Bud 58,69,77,270,271	Chris Weaver 67
Frank Cikach 73,295*	Kathy Joseph 76
Micheal Bucher 76	Tina Morris 273*

Public Schs..Principal	Grd	Prgm	Enr/#Cls	SN	
Central Elem Sch 145 Ray Ave NW, New Phila 44663 John Zucal	K-5	T	281 13	56%	330/364-0700 Fax 330/343-6890 f t
East Elem Sch 470 Fair Ave NE, New Phila 44663 Ryan Holmes	PK-5	T	345 13	46%	330/364-0715 Fax 330/343-6891
Joseph Welty Middle Sch 315 4th St NW, New Phila 44663 Ryan Range	6-8	T	704 40	43%	330/364-0645 Fax 330/364-0677
New Philadelphia High Sch 343 Ray Ave NW, New Phila 44663 Eric Jurkovic	9-12	T	802 60	34%	330/364-0644 Fax 330/364-0633
© Quaker Digital Academy 400 Mill Ave SE Ste 901, New Phila 44663 Steve Eckert	K-12	T	610		866/968-7032 Fax 330/364-0680
South Elem Sch 132 Providence Ave SW, New Phila 44663 Jaclyn Triplet	PK-5		511 20	22%	330/364-0725 Fax 330/364-0730
West Elem Sch 232 Tuscarawas Ave NW, New Phila 44663 Christa Frantz	PK-5	T	315 14	64%	330/364-0755 Fax 330/364-0758 f t
York Elem Sch 938 Stonecreek Rd SW, New Phila 44663 Kevin Wolf	K-5	T	125 6	29%	330/364-0770 Fax 330/364-0773 f t

• **Newcomerstown Exempted Vlg SD** PID: 00837437 740/498-8373
702 S River St, Newcomerstown 43832 Fax 740/498-8375

Schools: 4 \ **Teachers:** 73 \ **Students:** 1,100 \ **Special Ed Students:** 172
\ **LEP Students:** 10 \ **College-Bound:** 37% \ **Ethnic:** Asian 1%,
African American 1%, Hispanic 3%, Caucasian 96% \ **Exp:** $220 (Med)
\ **Poverty:** 20% \ **Title I:** $420,272 \ **Special Education:** $260,000 \
Open-Close: 08/19 - 05/22 \ **DTBP:** $178 (High)

Jeff Staggs 1,83	Christie Green 2
Brian Collins 3,5*	Scott Blind 4
Chad Elliott 6	Seth Corder 11,288*
Sacsha Durben 16*	Christopher Lipinski 58
Randy Addy 67	Shawn Dakin 73,76*
Tim Sherman 76	

Public Schs..Principal	Grd	Prgm	Enr/#Cls	SN	
East Elem Sch 137 S College St, Newcomerstown 43832 Brian Collins	K-1	T	140 8		740/498-6601 Fax 740/498-4997
Newcomerstown High Sch 659 Beaver St, Newcomerstown 43832 Josh Branch	9-12	TV	269 30	51%	740/498-5111 Fax 740/498-4994
Newcomerstown Middle Sch 325 W State St, Newcomerstown 43832 Jason Peoples	6-8	T	231 25	61%	740/498-8151 Fax 740/498-4991
West Elem Sch 517 Beaver St, Newcomerstown 43832 Erin Peoples	2-5	T	344 18		740/498-4151 Fax 740/498-4998

• **Strasburg Franklin Local SD** PID: 00837499 330/878-5571
140 N Bodmer Ave, Strasburg 44680 Fax 330/878-7900

Schools: 2 \ **Teachers:** 35 \ **Students:** 534 \ **Special Ed Students:** 77
\ **LEP Students:** 3 \ **College-Bound:** 59% \ **Ethnic:** Asian 1%, Hispanic
3%, Caucasian 96% \ **Exp:** $185 (Low) \ **Poverty:** 15% \ **Title I:** $135,043 \
Special Education: $108,000 \ **Open-Close:** 08/21 - 05/29 \ **DTBP:** $174
(High)

Cindy Brown 1	Tricia Schreffler 2,11
Robert Niedenthal 3*	Lana Williams 4*
Sharon Smith 5	Gary Spinell 6*
Kelly Britton 8,58,81	Veronica Videll 67
Cameron Lewis 73	Dawn Pelcoma 286

Public Schs..Principal	Grd	Prgm	Enr/#Cls	SN	
Strasburg Franklin Elem Sch 140 N Bodmer Ave, Strasburg 44680 Sheila Doerschuk	K-5	T	265 16	63%	330/878-6503 Fax 330/878-5983
Strasburg Franklin High Sch 140 N Bodmer Ave, Strasburg 44680 Adam Hall	6-12	V	269 25		330/878-5571

• **Tuscarawas Valley Local SD** PID: 00837528 330/859-2213
2637 Tusky Valley Rd NE, Zoarville 44656

Schools: 4 \ **Teachers:** 76 \ **Students:** 1,380 \ **Special Ed Students:** 138
\ **LEP Students:** 3 \ **College-Bound:** 59% \ **Ethnic:** Hispanic 1%,
Caucasian 98% \ **Exp:** $208 (Med) \ **Poverty:** 9% \ **Title I:** $218,063 \
Special Education: $285,000 \ **Open-Close:** 08/21 - 05/27 \ **DTBP:** $179
(High) \ f

Mark Murphy 1	Mark Phillips 2
Mike Spillman 3,5,91*	Stacey Betties 4
Derek Varansky 8,11	Katy Wells 9,58*
Andrea Clements 11,34*	Tiffany Shaw 13*
Julie Peterson 57*	Susan Kaschak 67
Courtney Vesco 69	Chris Lewis 73,295*
Tessa Lambert 76	Lisa Burrell 81
Becky Dickerhoof 83,85,88,270*	Sean Paisley 273*
Jim Lindon 286	Mike Horger 297*

Public Schs..Principal	Grd	Prgm	Enr/#Cls	SN	
Tuscarawas Valley Primary Sch 8647 1st St NE, Mineral City 44656 Andrea Clements	PK-1	T	230 13	67%	330/859-2461 Fax 330/859-8885
Tuscarawas Vly Interm Sch 216 Park Ave NW, Bolivar 44612 Andrea Clements	2-4	T	299 17	58%	330/874-3234 Fax 330/859-8875
Tuscarawas Vly Middle Sch 2633 Tuscarawas Vly Rd NE, Zoarville 44656 Erica Knowles	5-8	T	417 25	46%	330/859-2427 Fax 330/859-8845 f
Tuscarawas Vly Senior High Sch 2637 Tuscarawas Vly NE, Zoarville 44656 Jason Phillips	9-12	T	369 35	41%	330/859-2421 Fax 330/859-8805

TUSCARAWAS CATHOLIC SCHOOLS

• **Diocese of Columbus Ed Office** PID: 00802717
Listing includes only schools located in this county. See District Index for
location of Diocesan Offices.

---

79 Student Personnel	91 Safety/Security	275 Response To Intervention	298 Grant Writer/Ptnrships	**School Programs**	**Social Media**
80 Driver Ed/Safety	92 Magnet School	277 Remedial Math K-12	750 Chief Innovation Officer	A = Alternative Program	
81 Gifted/Talented	93 Parental Involvement	280 Literacy Coach	751 Chief of Staff	G = Adult Classes	f = Facebook
82 Video Services	95 Tech Prep Program	285 STEM	752 Social Emotional Learning	M = Magnet Program	
83 Substance Abuse Prev	97 Chief Information Officer	286 Digital Learning		T = Title I Schoolwide	t = Twitter
84 Erate	98 Chief Technology Officer	288 Common Core Standards	**Other School Types**	V = Career & Tech Ed Programs	
85 AIDS Education	270 Character Education	294 Accountability	Ⓐ = Alternative School		
88 Alternative/At Risk	271 Migrant Education	295 Network System	Ⓒ = Charter School	New Schools are shaded	
89 Multi-Cultural Curriculum	273 Teacher Mentor	296 Title II Programs	Ⓜ = Magnet School	New Superintendents and Principals are bold	
90 Social Work	274 Before/After Sch	297 Webmaster	Ⓨ = Year-Round School	Personnel with email addresses are underscored	

Union County

Market Data Retrieval

Catholic Schs..Principal	Grd	Prgm	Enr/#Cls SN	
Immaculate Conception Sch 100 Sherman St, Dennison 44621 Matt Ritzert	PK-6		115 10	740/922-3539 Fax 740/922-2486
Tuscarawas Central Catholic HS 777 3rd St NE, New Philo 44663 Annette Civiello	7-12		160 20	330/343-3302 Fax 330/343-6388
Tuscarawas Ctrl Catholic ES 600 N Tuscarawas Ave, Dover 44622 Matt Ritzert	PK-6		151 13	330/343-9134 Fax 330/364-6509

TUSCARAWAS PRIVATE SCHOOLS

Private Schs..Principal	Grd	Prgm	Enr/#Cls SN	
Legacy Christian Sch 2772 Simons Dr NW, Sugarcreek 44681 Mark Miller	K-12		105	330/852-4322

UNION COUNTY

UNION COUNTY SCHOOLS

County Schs..Principal	Grd	Prgm	Enr/#Cls SN	
Harold Lewis Center 1280 Charles Ln, Marysville 43040 Sue LaMendola	Spec		150 7	937/645-6733 Fax 937/642-9909

UNION PUBLIC SCHOOLS

• **Fairbanks Local School Dist** PID: 00837607   937/349-3731
11158 State Route 38, Milford CTR 43045   Fax 937/349-8885

Schools: 3 \ *Teachers:* 58 \ *Students:* 1,072 \ *Special Ed Students:* 115 \ *LEP Students:* 4 \ *College-Bound:* 70% \ *Ethnic:* Asian 2%, African American 2%, Hispanic 1%, Caucasian 95% \ *Exp:* $124 (Low) \ *Poverty:* 4% \ *Title I:* $45,851 \ *Special Education:* $203,000 \ *Open-Close:* 08/14 - 05/21 \ *DTBP:* $91 (Med)

Adham Schirg 1		Aaron Johnson 2*	
Scott Shively 3		Lorri Mowery 4	
Beth Wyckoff 5		Larry Morriss 6*	
Teri Dunlap 7*		Ann Arthur 8,11,31,58,69,273	
Teresa Goins 8		Amy Sines 12*	
Ed Rebmann 16,271*		Kendra Elliot 37*	
Mark Lippencott 67		Carol Stillings 68	
Bj Thaman 73*		Steve Smith 73	
Tom Montgomery 83*		Janet Bardin 274	

Public Schs..Principal	Grd	Prgm	Enr/#Cls SN	
Fairbanks Elem Sch 11140 State Route 38, Milford CTR 43045 Mark Lotycz	K-5		464 15	15% 937/349-9000 Fax 937/349-9001
Fairbanks High Sch 11158 State Route 38, Milford CTR 43045 Tom Montgomery	9-12		344 20	13% 937/349-3721 Fax 937/349-2011
Fairbanks Middle Sch 11158 State Route 38, Milford CTR 43045 Joe Newell	6-8		264 20	15% 937/349-6841 Fax 937/349-2013

• **Marysville Exempted Village SD** PID: 00837657   937/578-6100
1000 Edgewood Dr, Marysville 43040   Fax 937/578-6113

Schools: 10 \ *Teachers:* 261 \ *Students:* 5,100 \ *Special Ed Students:* 910 \ *LEP Students:* 58 \ *College-Bound:* 66% \ *Ethnic:* Asian 3%, African American 2%, Hispanic 2%, Caucasian 93% \ *Exp:* $121 (Low) \ *Poverty:* 5% \ *Title I:* $375,902 \ *Open-Close:* 08/15 - 05/21 \ *DTBP:* $183 (High)

Diane Mankins 1		Ryan Walker 2,91	
Todd Johnson 2,19		Jeff Wargo 3	
Lorie Pennington 4		Tina Sharrock 5	
Joey Day 6		Megan Stevens 7*	
Jonathan Langhals 8,11,18,27,74,288,296		Steven Griffin 8,54,69,277,280	
Kim Jude 13,34,58,77,79		Linda Proehl 38,88*	
Amy Brown 57*		Sue DeVine 67	
Tom Powers 71,73,76,97		Kelly Walker 274	
Kelly Walker 274*		Ken Chaffin 285	

Public Schs..Principal	Grd	Prgm	Enr/#Cls SN	
Bunsold Middle Sch 14198 State Route 4, Marysville 43040 Michelle Kaffenbarger	7-8		862 40	22% 937/578-6400 Fax 937/578-6413
Creekview Intermediate Sch 2000 Creekview Dr, Marysville 43040 Timothy Kannally	5-6		766 56	24% 937/578-6600 Fax 937/578-6613
Edgewood Elem Sch 203 Grove St, Marysville 43040 Thomas Holdren	K-4		333 18	30% 937/578-6800 Fax 937/578-6813
Marysville Early College HS 833 N Maple St, Marysville 43040 Karen Chaffin	9-12	V	521	9% 937/578-7300 Fax 937/578-7313
Marysville High Sch 800 Amrine Mill Rd, Marysville 43040 Thomas Cochran	9-12	V	1,098 85	24% 937/578-6200 Fax 937/578-6213
Mill Valley Elem Sch 633 Mill Wood Blvd, Marysville 43040 Amey McGlenn	PK-4		393 30	23% 937/578-6900 Fax 937/578-6913
Navin Elem Sch 16265 County Home Rd, Marysville 43040 Lynette Lewis	K-4		454	31% 937/578-7000 Fax 937/578-7013
Northwood Elem Sch 2100 Creekview Dr, Marysville 43040 David Hensinger	K-4		498 24	19% 937/578-7100 Fax 937/578-7113
Raymond Elem Sch 21511 State Route 347, Raymond 43067 Carol Lentz	K-4		249 17	20% 937/578-7200 Fax 937/578-7213
@ Tri Academy 212 Chestnut St, Marysville 43040 Ashley Thompson	9-12		60	937/578-6191

• **North Union Local School Dist** PID: 00837712   740/943-2509
12920 State Route 739, Richwood 43344   Fax 740/943-2534

Schools: 3 \ *Teachers:* 85 \ *Students:* 1,540 \ *Special Ed Students:* 230 \ *College-Bound:* 48% \ *Ethnic:* Hispanic 1%, Caucasian 98% \ *Exp:* $176 (Low) \ *Poverty:* 7% \ *Title I:* $151,278 \ *Special Education:* $263,000 \ *Open-Close:* 08/14 - 05/29 \ *DTBP:* $177 (High)

Richard Baird 1		Scott Maruniak 2,19	
Bev Wasserbeck 4		Brian Nauman 5	
Nick Hajjar 6,69		Erika Bower 8,18,30	
Pam Ensign 11*		Thomas Brown 34,58	

1 Superintendent	8 Curric/Instruct K-12	19 Chief Financial Officer	29 Family/Consumer Science	39 Social Studies K-12	49 English/Lang Arts Elem	59 Special Education Elem	69 Academic Assessment
2 Bus/Finance/Purchasing	9 Curric/Instruct Elem	20 Art K-12	30 Adult Education	40 Social Studies Elem	50 English/Lang Arts Sec	60 Special Education Sec	70 Research/Development
3 Buildings And Grounds	10 Curric/Instruct Sec	21 Art Elem	31 Career/Sch-to-Work K-12	41 Social Studies Sec	51 Reading K-12	61 Foreign/World Lang K-12	71 Public Information
4 Food Service	11 Federal Program	22 Art Sec	32 Career/Sch-to-Work Elem	42 Science K-12	52 Reading Elem	62 Foreign/World Lang Elem	72 Summer School
5 Transportation	12 Title I	23 Music K-12	33 Career/Sch-to-Work Sec	43 Science Elem	53 Reading Sec	63 Foreign/World Lang Sec	73 Instructional Tech
6 Athletic	13 Title V	24 Music Elem	34 Early Childhood Ed	44 Science Sec	54 Remedial Reading K-12	64 Religious Education K-12	74 Inservice Training
7 Health Services	14 Instructional Media Svcs	25 Music Sec	35 Health/Phys Education	45 Math K-12	55 Remedial Reading Elem	65 Religious Education Elem	75 Marketing/Distributive
	15 Asst Superintendent	26 Business Education	36 Guidance Services K-12	46 Math Elem	56 Remedial Reading Sec	66 Religious Education Sec	76 Info Systems
	16 Instructional Media Svcs	27 Career & Tech Ed	37 Guidance Services Elem	47 Math Sec	57 Bilingual/ELL	67 School Board President	77 Psychological Assess
	17 Chief Operations Officer	28 Technology Education	38 Guidance Services Sec	48 English/Lang Arts K-12	58 Special Education K-12	68 Teacher Personnel	78 Affirmative Action
	18 Chief Academic Officer						

Ohio School Directory

Tammy Borders	37
Brian Davis	67

Tammy Borders	37*
Jared Evans	73,297

Public Schs..Principal	Grd	Prgm	Enr/#Cls	SN	
North Union Elem Sch 420 Grove St, Richwood 43344 Darlene Allison	PK-5	T	741 20	45%	740/943-3113 Fax 740/943-1010
North Union High Sch 401 N Franklin St, Richwood 43344 Janel Chapman	9-12	V	406 31	38%	740/943-3012 Fax 740/943-2046
North Union Middle Sch 12555 Mulvane Rd, Richwood 43344 Matt Burggraf	6-8	T	359 25	46%	740/943-2369 Fax 740/943-9279

UNION PRIVATE SCHOOLS

Private Schs..Principal	Grd	Prgm	Enr/#Cls	SN
St John's Lutheran Sch 12809 State Route 736, Marysville 43040 Rich Rausch	PK-8		250 12	937/644-5540 Fax 937/644-1086
St Paul Lutheran Sch 7960 State Route 38, Milford CTR 43045 Cathy McNabb	PK-7		50 5	937/349-5939 Fax 937/349-5702
Trinity Lutheran Sch 220 S Walnut St, Marysville 43040 Lori Poling	PK-6		319 15	937/642-1726 Fax 937/642-1875

VAN WERT COUNTY

VAN WERT COUNTY SCHOOLS

- **Western Buckeye Ed Service Ctr** PID: 00838027   419/238-4746
  813A N Franklin St, Van Wert 45891   Fax 419/238-6259

David Basley	1
Jerry Zielke	67
Ashley Shepherd	81

Tricia Taylor	2
Cindy Lamb	77

County Schs..Principal	Grd	Prgm	Enr/#Cls	SN
Ⓐ Synergy Learning Center 620 N Cherry St, Van Wert 45891 Tony Langhals	5-12		35 3	419/623-5380 Fax 419/238-6228
Thomas Edison Center Pre-Sch 813 N Franklin St, Van Wert 45891 Jill Welch	Spec	G	170 9	419/238-4019 Fax 419/238-6255

VAN WERT PUBLIC SCHOOLS

- **Crestview Local School Dist** PID: 00837815   419/749-9100
  531 E Tully St, Convoy 45832   Fax 419/749-4235

Schools: 1 \ *Teachers:* 61 \ *Students:* 820 \ *Special Ed Students:* 160 \ *College-Bound:* 57% \ *Ethnic:* African American 1%, Hispanic 3%, Caucasian 96% \ *Exp:* $471 (High) \ *Poverty:* 7% \ *Title I:* $80,223 \ *Special Education:* $181,000 \ *Open-Close:* 08/21 - 05/28 \ *DTBP:* $186 (High)

Kathy Mollenkopf	1,11,84
Geoff Waddlef	3
Kaye Barns	12*
Erika Priest	27*
John Auld	67

Ashley Whetsel	2,19
Trent Kreischer	6,8*
Kristie McCormick	16,286*
Amy Eickholt	58,69,71
Shane Leeth	73,295*

Public Schs..Principal	Grd	Prgm	Enr/#Cls	SN	
Crestview Local Sch 531 E Tully St, Convoy 45832 Jessica Schuette \ Trent Kreischer \ David Bowen	K-12	V	820 53	99%	419/749-9100 f

- **Lincolnview Local School Dist** PID: 00837853   419/968-2226
  15945 Middle Point Rd, Van Wert 45891   Fax 419/968-2227

Schools: 3 \ *Teachers:* 53 \ *Students:* 900 \ *Special Ed Students:* 97 \ *LEP Students:* 3 \ *College-Bound:* 62% \ *Ethnic:* Hispanic 3%, Caucasian 97% \ *Exp:* $219 (Med) \ *Poverty:* 9% \ *Title I:* $88,245 \ *Special Education:* $157,000 \ *Open-Close:* 08/14 - 05/21 \ *DTBP:* $147 (High)

Jeff Snyder	1
Jason Maples	3*
Cindy DuVall	5,11,69,270
Brenda Leeth	8,31,36*
Maria Clawson	58*
Eric Miglin	73*
Robbie Breese	88*

Troy Bowersock	2,84
Deb Miller	4
Greg Leap	6
Nita Meyer	11*
Kirk Berryman	67
Rhonda Rank	85

Public Schs..Principal	Grd	Prgm	Enr/#Cls	SN	
Lincolnview Elem Sch 15945 Middle Point Rd, Van Wert 45891 Nita Meyer	K-6	T	435 20		419/968-2351
Lincolnview Jr Sr High Sch 15945 Middle Point Rd, Van Wert 45891 Brad Mendenhall	7-12	V	394 35	86%	419/968-2214
Ⓐ Marsh Foundation Sch 1229 Lincoln Hwy, Van Wert 45891 Robbie Breese	3-12		43 5		419/238-1695 Fax 419/238-3986

- **Van Wert City School Dist** PID: 00837932   419/238-0648
  205 W Crawford St, Van Wert 45891   Fax 419/238-3974

Schools: 4 \ *Teachers:* 127 \ *Students:* 2,084 \ *Special Ed Students:* 410 \ *LEP Students:* 8 \ *College-Bound:* 59% \ *Ethnic:* Asian 1%, African American 1%, Hispanic 5%, Caucasian 93% \ *Exp:* $171 (Low) \ *Poverty:* 15% \ *Title I:* $430,038 \ *Special Education:* $435,000 \ *Open-Close:* 08/20 - 05/22 \ *DTBP:* $175 (High)

Vicki Brunn	1
Mark Carter	3
Becky Proffitt	4*
Craig Hershey	6
Ken Amstutz	11
Nelly Schmidt	16*
Frankie Bowen	38*
Debbie Compton	67
Jamie Gibson	76
Tricia Ridenour	81*

Michael Ruen	2
Randy Stemen	3
Ed Wells	5
Chris Covey	8,288*
Bill Clifton	15
Lori Bittner	30,34,88*
Doug Grooms	57,58,69,83*
Justin Bragg	73
Barb Rhinehart	77
John Basinger	90*

Public Schs..Principal	Grd	Prgm	Enr/#Cls	SN	
Van Wert Early Childhood Ctr 1120 Buckeye Dr, Van Wert 45891 Lori Bittner	PK-K	T	373	45%	419/238-0384 Fax 419/238-2137
Van Wert Elem Sch 10992 State Route 118, Van Wert 45891 Justin Krogman	1-5	T	701 11	57%	419/238-1761 Fax 419/238-5055

79 Student Personnel	91 Safety/Security	275 Response To Intervention	298 Grant Writer/Ptnrships	School Programs	Social Media		
80 Driver Ed/Safety	92 Magnet School	277 Remedial Math K-12	750 Chief Innovation Officer	A = Alternative Program			
81 Gifted/Talented	93 Parental Involvement	280 Literacy Coach	751 Chief of Staff	G = Adult Classes	f = Facebook		
82 Video Services	95 Tech Prep Program	285 STEM	752 Social Emotional Learning	M = Magnet Program			
83 Substance Abuse Prev	97 Chief Information Officer	286 Digital Learning		T = Title I Schoolwide	t = Twitter		
84 Erate	98 Chief Technology Officer	288 Common Core Standards	Other School Types	V = Career & Tech Ed Programs			
85 AIDS Education	270 Character Education	294 Accountability	Ⓐ = Alternative School				
88 Alternative/At Risk	271 Migrant Education	295 Network System	Ⓒ = Charter School	New Schools are shaded			
89 Multi-Cultural Curriculum	273 Teacher Mentor	296 Title II Programs	Ⓜ = Magnet School	New Superintendents and Principals are bold			
90 Social Work	274 Before/After Sch	297 Webmaster	Ⓨ = Year-Round School	Personnel with email addresses are underscored			

Vinton County

Van Wert High Sch 10708 State Route 118, Van Wert 45891 Bob Priest	9-12		539 40	75%	419/238-3350 Fax 419/238-0526
Van Wert Middle Sch 10694 State Route 118, Van Wert 45891 Mark Bagley	6-8	T	471 30		419/238-0727 Fax 419/238-7166

- **Vantage Career Center Sch Dist** PID: 01537800   419/238-5411
  818 N Franklin St, Van Wert 45891   Fax 419/238-4058

Schools: 1 \ *Teachers:* 37 \ *Students:* 480 \ *College-Bound:* 42% \
Exp: $758 (High) \ *Open-Close:* 08/20 - 05/22 \ *DTBP:* $169 (High) \ f t

Rick Turner 1
Pam Knodel 16,82*
James Fisher 38,83*
Tony Unverferth 68*
Stacie Lippi 73*
Laura Peters 2
Melissa McClury 30
Pat Bulme 67
Maryjo Wilhlem 71*

Public Schs..Principal	Grd	Prgm	Enr/#Cls SN	
Vantage Career Center High Sch 818 N Franklin St, Van Wert 45891 Tony Unverferth	Voc	G	480 13	419/238-5411 f t

VAN WERT CATHOLIC SCHOOLS

- **Diocese of Toledo Ed Office** PID: 00818297
  Listing includes only schools located in this county. See District Index for location of Diocesan Offices.

Catholic Schs..Principal	Grd	Prgm	Enr/#Cls SN	
St Mary Asumption Catholic ES 611 Jennings Rd, Van Wert 45891 Daniel Metzger	K-6		100 6	419/238-5186 Fax 419/238-5842

VINTON COUNTY

VINTON PUBLIC SCHOOLS

- **Vinton Co Local School Dist** PID: 00838039   740/596-5218
  307 W High St, Mc Arthur 45651   Fax 740/596-3142

Schools: 5 \ *Teachers:* 156 \ *Students:* 2,100 \ *Special Ed Students:* 363
\ *LEP Students:* 3 \ *College-Bound:* 41% \ *Ethnic:* Hispanic 1%,
Caucasian 99% \ *Exp:* $178 (Low) \ *Poverty:* 25% \ *Title I:* $897,258 \
Special Education: $511,000 \ *Open-Close:* 08/15 - 05/22 \ *DTBP:* $195
(High)

Rick Brooks 1
Eddie Mullins 3
Michael Ogier 5
Val Rahamut 7,85
Michael Waggoner 15
Aimee Jones 31*
Kellie Abele 36*
Jeff Thacker 67
John Zinn 91
Chad Carpenter 2,76
Bobbie Jo Harper 4
Matt Combs 6,88*
Terry Snider 8,11,57,83,273,288,294*
Andee Caudill 16,274,275*
Jeran Cox 35*
Larry Arthur 58,77*
Tracy Fee 73,84,295,297

Public Schs..Principal	Grd	Prgm	Enr/#Cls SN	
Central Elem Sch 507 Jefferson Ave, Mc Arthur 45651 Kim Arthur	PK-5	T	357 16	740/596-4386 Fax 740/596-4027
South Elem Sch 38234 State Route 93, Hamden 45634 Miranda Smith	PK-5	T	281 22	740/384-2731 Fax 740/384-4001
Vinton Co High Sch 63910 US Highway 50, Mc Arthur 45651 Jj Milliken	9-12	ATV	572 35	62% 740/596-5258 Fax 740/596-3003
Vinton Co Middle Sch 63780 Locker Plant Rd, Mc Arthur 45651 Jeremy Ward	6-8	T	461 55	64% 740/596-5243 Fax 740/596-3815
West Elem Sch 57772 US Highway 50, Mc Arthur 45651 Kevin Waddell	PK-5	T	313 25	740/596-5236 Fax 740/596-5237

WARREN COUNTY

WARREN COUNTY SCHOOLS

- **Warren Co Ed Service Center** PID: 00838560   513/695-2900
  1879 Deerfield Rd, Lebanon 45036   Fax 513/695-2961

Tom Isaacs 1
Brandon Anness 5
Jiles Farley 67
Dr Kathie MacNeil 77,83,275
Alleyn Unversaw 2
Christy Even 58
Tyler McCall 73
Shelley Brown 88

WARREN PUBLIC SCHOOLS

- **Carlisle Local School Dist** PID: 00838106   937/746-0710
  724 Fairview Dr, Carlisle 45005   Fax 937/746-0438

Schools: 4 \ *Teachers:* 87 \ *Students:* 1,593 \ *Special Ed Students:* 193
\ *LEP Students:* 3 \ *College-Bound:* 51% \ *Ethnic:* Asian 1%, African
American 1%, Hispanic 2%, Caucasian 96% \ *Exp:* $159 (Low) \ *Poverty:* 11%
\ *Title I:* $233,793 \ *Special Education:* $287,000 \ *Open-Close:* 08/14 -
05/22 \ *DTBP:* $242 (High)

Larry Hook 1,11,83
Chad Allen 3,5
Gail French 4
Rebecca Baker 7*
Michael Milner 12*
Kim Perkins 58
Bruce Terry 73,84,295
Karen McKinley 81
Jill French 273*
Dan Bassler 2
Ken Sprinkles 3
John Augustine 6*
Shane Estep 8
Heather Allison 31*
William Jewell 67
Brenda Wilson 76
Quentin Hammock 82

Public Schs..Principal	Grd	Prgm	Enr/#Cls SN	
Alden R Brown Elem Sch 310 Jamaica Rd, Carlisle 45005 Michael Milner	PK-2	T	380 22	38% 937/746-7610 Fax 937/746-0511
Bobby F Grigsby Interm Sch 100 Jamaica Rd, Carlisle 45005 Jennifer Dearwester	3-5	T	378 17	39% 937/746-8969 Fax 937/746-0512

Ohio School Directory

Warren County

Public Schs..Principal	Grd	Prgm	Enr/#Cls	SN	
Carlisle High Sch 250 Jamaica Rd, Carlisle 45005 **Dave Slamer**	9-12	V	445 40	33%	937/746-4481 Fax 937/746-6578
Chamberlain Middle Sch 720 Fairview Dr, Carlisle 45005 **Daniel Turner**	6-8		390 30	31%	937/746-3227 Fax 937/746-0519

• Franklin City School Dist PID: 00838247
150 E 6th St, Franklin 45005
937/746-1699
Fax 937/743-8620

Schools: 8 \ **Teachers:** 154 \ **Students:** 2,750 \ **Special Ed Students:** 566 \ **LEP Students:** 6 \ **College-Bound:** 46% \ **Ethnic:** Asian 1%, African American 2%, Hispanic 1%, Caucasian 96% \ **Exp:** $295 (Med) \ **Poverty:** 12% \ **Title I:** $596,246 \ **Special Education:** $622,000 \ **Open-Close:** 08/20 - 05/29 \ **DTBP:** $193 (High) \ f t

Dr Michael Sander 1
Lori Feltner 4
Bryan Bales 6*
Jim McFarland 58*
Craig Irgens 73,295
Rodney Roberts 2
Tamara Centers 5
Robyn Donisi 8,15
Kevin Sizemore 67
Caroline Ferguson 81

Public Schs..Principal	Grd	Prgm	Enr/#Cls	SN	
Anthony Wayne Elem Sch 16 Farm Ave, Franklin 45005 **James Rhodes**	1-6	T	226 20	68%	937/743-8640 Fax 937/743-8642
Franklin High Sch 750 E 4th St, Franklin 45005 **Kelli Fromm**	9-12	TV	786 45	39%	937/743-8610 Fax 937/743-8625
Franklin Junior High Sch 136 E 6th St, Franklin 45005 **Tammy Burchfield**	7-8	TV	487 35	42%	937/743-8630 Fax 937/743-8635
George H Gerke Elem Sch 312 Sherman Dr, Franklin 45005 **Steve Greenwood**	1-6	T	262 14	60%	937/743-8650 Fax 937/743-8649
Hampton Bennett ECC 150 E 6th St, Franklin 45005 **Julie Ratliff**	PK-K	T	250	79%	937/743-5290
Hunter Elem Sch 4418 State Route 122, Franklin 45005 **Erin Truesdell**	1-6		330 14	20%	937/743-8655 Fax 937/743-8608
Pennyroyal Elem Sch 4203 Pennyroyal Rd, Franklin 45005 **Jeremy Ward**	1-6	T	264 16	73%	937/743-8660 Fax 937/743-8609
W C Schenck Elem Sch 350 Arlington Ave, Franklin 45005 **Deborah Kienle**	1-6	T	230 12	39%	937/743-8665 Fax 937/743-8644

• Kings Local School Dist PID: 00838194
1797 King Ave, Kings Mills 45034
513/459-2900
Fax 513/229-7590

Schools: 7 \ **Teachers:** 233 \ **Students:** 4,650 \ **Special Ed Students:** 605 \ **LEP Students:** 179 \ **College-Bound:** 74% \ **Ethnic:** Asian 3%, African American 2%, Hispanic 6%, Caucasian 89% \ **Exp:** $218 (Med) \ **Poverty:** 4% \ **Title I:** $155,099 \ **Special Education:** $899,000 \ **Open-Close:** 08/14 - 05/21 \ **DTBP:** $186 (High)

Tim Ackermann 1
Matt Lucke 3,91
Dave Smith 5
Eva Garchar 7*
Jane Boehm 11,296,298*
Dana Martin 58
Peggy Phillips 67
Angela Thompson 81*
Kim Sellers 752
Cary Furniss 2
Jennifer Arlinghaus 4*
Tyler Miller 6
Tim Spinner 8,16,57,69,73,95,288
Heidi Murray 36*
Mary Fosse 58
Dawn Gould 71
Susan Guckert 274*

Public Schs..Principal	Grd	Prgm	Enr/#Cls	SN	
ⓎColumbia Intermediate Sch 8263 Columbia Rd, Kings Mills 45034 **Shelley Detmer-Bogaert**	5-6	M	710 24	20%	513/398-8050 Fax 513/459-2961
J F Burns Elem Sch 8471 Columbia Rd, Maineville 45039 **Cheryl Montag**	K-4		778 30	20%	513/398-8050 Fax 513/683-8367
Kings High Sch 5500 Columbia Rd, Kings Mills 45034 **Doug Leist**	9-12	V	1,343 30	18%	513/398-8050 Fax 513/459-2938
Kings Junior High Sch 5620 Columbia Rd, Kings Mills 45034 **Eric Dunn**	7-8		650 38	19%	513/398-8050 Fax 513/229-7974
Kings Mills Elem Sch 1780 King Ave, Kings Mills 45034 **Shawn Rosekrans**	K-4		499 22	13%	513/398-8050 Fax 513/398-4863
Kings Preschool 1797 King Ave, Kings Mills 45034 **Susan Guckert**	PK-PK		270		513/398-8050
South Lebanon Elem Sch 50 Ridgeview Ln, Maineville 45039 **Belinda Atkins**	K-4		533 15	32%	513/398-8050 Fax 513/494-1469

• Lebanon City School Dist PID: 00838340
700 Holbrook Ave, Lebanon 45036
513/934-5770
Fax 513/932-5906

Schools: 5 \ **Teachers:** 252 \ **Students:** 6,000 \ **Special Ed Students:** 710 \ **LEP Students:** 125 \ **College-Bound:** 66% \ **Ethnic:** Asian 1%, African American 2%, Hispanic 6%, Caucasian 91% \ **Exp:** $122 (Low) \ **Poverty:** 5% \ **Title I:** $459,563 \ **Special Education:** $763,000 \ **Open-Close:** 08/13 - 05/21 \ **DTBP:** $185 (High)

Todd Yohey 1
Patsy Tibbs 4
Mark Graler 8,11,83,88,288,294,298
Donna Davidson-North 67
Robyn Buskirk 68*
Jesse Murnahan 295
Eric Sotzing 2
William Stewart 6*
Krista Foley 11,58,77,79,81,271,275
Robert Buskirk 68
Casey Greene 73,295*

Public Schs..Principal	Grd	Prgm	Enr/#Cls	SN	
Berry Intermediate Sch 160 Miller Rd, Lebanon 45036 **Elizabeth Kletzy**	5-6		880 5	24%	513/934-5700 Fax 513/932-9436
Bowman Primary Sch 825 Hart Rd, Lebanon 45036 **Laura Michaels**	PK-2		1,298 24	26%	513/934-5800 Fax 513/934-2466
Donovan Elem Sch 401 Justice Dr, Lebanon 45036 **Clifton Franz**	3-4		820 31	29%	513/934-5400 Fax 513/934-2467
Lebanon High Sch 1916 Drake Rd, Lebanon 45036 **Scott Butler**	9-12	AV	1,625 90	16%	513/934-5100 Fax 513/933-2150
Lebanon Junior High Sch 160 A Miller Rd, Lebanon 45036 **Brian Dalton**	7-8		900 75	20%	513/934-5300 Fax 513/228-1043

• Little Miami Local School Dist PID: 00838405
95 E US 22-3, Maineville 45039
513/899-2264
Fax 513/899-3244

Schools: 6 \ **Teachers:** 231 \ **Students:** 5,020 \ **Special Ed Students:** 613 \ **LEP Students:** 34 \ **College-Bound:** 67% \ **Ethnic:** Asian 1%, African American 4%, Hispanic 4%, Caucasian 93% \ **Exp:** $236 (Med) \ **Poverty:** 3% \ **Title I:** $161,168 \ **Special Education:** $851,000 \ **Open-Close:** 08/15 - 05/21 \ **DTBP:** $194 (High) \ f t

---

79 Student Personnel
80 Driver Ed/Safety
81 Gifted/Talented
82 Video Services
83 Substance Abuse Prev
84 Erate
85 AIDS Education
88 Alternative/At Risk
89 Multi-Cultural Curriculum
90 Social Work

91 Safety/Security
92 Magnet School
93 Parental Involvement
95 Tech Prep Program
97 Chief Information Officer
98 Chief Technology Officer
270 Character Education
271 Migrant Education
273 Teacher Mentor
274 Before/After Sch

275 Response To Intervention
277 Remedial Math K-12
280 Literacy Coach
285 STEM
286 Digital Learning
288 Common Core Standards
294 Accountability
295 Network System
296 Title II Programs
297 Webmaster

298 Grant Writer/Ptnrships
750 Chief Innovation Officer
751 Chief of Staff
752 Social Emotional Learning

Other School Types
Ⓐ = Alternative School
Ⓒ = Charter School
Ⓜ = Magnet School
Ⓨ = Year-Round School

School Programs
A = Alternative Program
G = Adult Classes
M = Magnet Program
T = Title I Schoolwide
V = Career & Tech Ed Programs

Social Media
f = Facebook
t = Twitter

New Schools are shaded
New Superintendents and Principals are bold
Personnel with email addresses are underscored

OH–207

Warren County

Market Data Retrieval

Gregory Power 1	Terry Gonda 2,19
David Florea 3	Rachel Tilford 4
Larry Bennington 5	Keith Pantling 6
Regina Morgan 8,11,15,296,298	Donna Chilcote 16,82*
Karen Dumais 57*	Deedee Walker 58,85
Jennifer Dafoe 63*	Randy Haas 67
Pam Coates 68	Melinda Briggs 71
Steven Collins 73,95	Susan Ganim 76
Marla Timmerman 79	Carrie Suttle 280*
Rick Schuster 295	

Public Schs..Principal	Grd	Prgm	Enr/#Cls	SN	
Hamilton-Maineville Prim Sch 373 E Fosters Maineville Rd, Maineville 45039 Teresa Reynolds	1-2		500	11%	513/899-4760 Fax 513/683-3879
Harlan-Butlerville Prim Sch 8276 State Route 132, Blanchester 45107 **Jamie Miles**	1-2	T	272	28%	513/899-5200 Fax 513/877-3200
Little Miami High Sch 3001 E US Highway 22 and 3, Morrow 45152 Catherine Trevathan	9-12	V	1,309 40	17%	513/899-3781 Fax 513/899-4912
Little Miami Intermediate Sch 7247 Zoar Rd, Maineville 45039 Alison Gates	5-6		828 20	23%	513/899-2334 Fax 513/899-4020
Little Miami Junior High Sch 5290 Morrow Cozaddale Rd, Morrow 45152 Ryan Cherry	7-8		740 35	20%	513/899-3408 Fax 513/899-2048
Salem Township Elem Sch 605 Welch Rd, Morrow 45152 Lisa Smith	PK-4		1,223	19%	513/899-5275 Fax 513/899-3196

● **Mason City School Dist** PID: 00838467   513/398-0474
211 N East St, Mason 45040

Schools: 5 \ **Teachers:** 474 \ **Students:** 10,396 \ **Special Ed Students:** 978 \ **LEP Students:** 751 \ **College-Bound:** 82% \ **Ethnic:** Asian 24%, African American 4%, Hispanic 5%, Caucasian 67% \ **Exp:** $151 (Low) \ **Poverty:** 2% \ **Title I:** $196,234 \ **Special Education:** $1,405,000 \ **Open-Close:** 08/20 - 05/29 \ **DTBP:** $203 (High)

Dr Gail Kist-Kline 1	Todd Petrey 2,3,17,91
George Highfill 3	Tamara Earl 4
Carolyn Thornton 5	Dr Heather Sass 8,11,18,57,69,88,288,296
Jonathan Cooper 15	Thurman Allen 23,274*
Shannon Homeoelle 49	Milena Varbanova 57*
Jessica Stevens 58,294	Matt Steele 67
Marla Niebiling 68	Tracy Carson 71,298
Cristine McCormick 73,76,286,295	

Public Schs..Principal	Grd	Prgm	Enr/#Cls	SN	
Mason Early Childhood Center 4631 Hickory Woods Ln, Mason 45040 Melissa Bly	PK-2		2,079 23	6%	513/398-3741 Fax 513/398-2169
Mason Intermediate Sch 6307 S Mason Montgomery Rd, Mason 45040 Eric Messer	5-6		1,648	10%	513/459-2850 Fax 513/459-2873
Mason Middle Sch 6370 S Mason Montgomery Rd, Mason 45040 Lauren Gentene	7-8		1,714 40	8%	513/398-9035 Fax 513/459-0904
Western Elem Sch 6307 Mason Montgomery Rd, Mason 45040 Vivian Alvarez	3-4		1,480 40	9%	513/398-5821 Fax 513/459-1072
William Mason High Sch 6100 S Mason Montgomery Rd, Mason 45040 Bobby Dodd	9-12	V	3,475 80	6%	513/398-5025 Fax 513/336-6823

● **Springboro Cmty School Dist** PID: 00838156   937/748-3960
1685 S Main St, Springboro 45066   Fax 937/748-3956

Schools: 6 \ **Teachers:** 268 \ **Students:** 6,093 \ **Special Ed Students:** 574 \ **LEP Students:** 19 \ **College-Bound:** 82% \ **Ethnic:** Asian 3%, African American 2%, Hispanic 1%, Caucasian 94% \ **Exp:** $167 (Low) \ **Poverty:** 2% \ **Title I:** $123,405 \ **Special Education:** $840,000 \ **Open-Close:** 08/14 - 05/21 \ **DTBP:** $182 (High)

Dan Schroer 1	Terrah Floyd 2
John Pennell 3,4,5	Kathleen Poor 4
Michelle Palmer 5	Austin Rhoads 6
Andrea Cook 8,11,16,73	Emily Hill 12,58
Matt Blair 57*	Kim Perkins 58
David Stuckey 67	Wendy Ford 90*

Public Schs..Principal	Grd	Prgm	Enr/#Cls	SN	
Clearcreek Elem Sch 750 S Main St, Springboro 45066 Carrie Corder	PK-1		943 20	3%	937/748-3958 Fax 937/748-3980
Dennis Elem Sch 1695 S Main St, Springboro 45066 Terrah Hunter	2-5		760		937/748-6070 Fax 937/748-6077
Five-Points Elememtary Sch 650 E Lytle 5 Points Rd, Centerville 45458 Traci Griffen	2-5		1,000		937/748-6090 Fax 937/748-6068
Springboro High Sch 1675 S Main St, Springboro 45066 Kyle Martin	9-12	V	1,925 45	5%	937/748-3950 Fax 937/748-3983
Springboro Intermediate Sch 705 S Main St, Springboro 45066 Brooke Coulter	6-6		494 28	6%	937/748-4113 Fax 937/748-8498
Springboro Junior High Sch 1605 S Main St, Springboro 45066 Jon Franks	7-8		1,000 50	6%	937/748-3953 Fax 937/748-3964

● **Warren Co Voc School Dist** PID: 01537824   513/932-5677
3525 N State Route 48, Lebanon 45036   Fax 513/932-3810

Schools: 1 \ **Teachers:** 68 \ **Students:** 775 \ **LEP Students:** 8 \ **College-Bound:** 58% \ **Exp:** $376 (High) \ **Open-Close:** 08/16 - 05/22 \ **DTBP:** $249 (High) \

Rick Smith 1	Bob Wysong 3
Kim Fladung 3	Shari Jones 4*
Gary Patton 10*	Tom Harris 30
Bobbie Grice 67	Melissa Solazzo 68
Peg Allen 71	John Reeder 73,295
Kim Gambill 79*	

Public Schs..Principal	Grd	Prgm	Enr/#Cls	SN	
Warren Co Career Center 3525 N State Route 48, Lebanon 45036 Gary Patton	Voc	G	775 75		513/932-5677 Fax 513/932-0775

● **Wayne Local School Dist** PID: 00838510   513/897-6971
659 Dayton Rd, Waynesville 45068   Fax 513/897-9605

Schools: 3 \ **Teachers:** 72 \ **Students:** 1,473 \ **Special Ed Students:** 154 \ **LEP Students:** 11 \ **College-Bound:** 72% \ **Ethnic:** Hispanic 2%, Caucasian 97% \ **Exp:** $502 (High) \ **Poverty:** 3% \ **Title I:** $50,643 \ **Special Education:** $229,000 \ **Open-Close:** 08/15 - 05/21 \ **DTBP:** $238 (High) \

Patrick Dubbs 1	Ronald James 2,8,18
Mark McKeehan 3	Ryan Hill 6

1 Superintendent	8 Curric/Instruct K-12	19 Chief Financial Officer	29 Family/Consumer Science	39 Social Studies K-12	49 English/Lang Arts Elem	59 Special Education Elem	69 Academic Assessment
2 Bus/Finance/Purchasing	9 Curric/Instruct Elem	20 Art K-12	30 Adult Education	40 Social Studies Elem	50 English/Lang Arts Sec	60 Special Education Sec	70 Research/Development
3 Buildings And Grounds	10 Curric/Instruct Sec	21 Art Elem	31 Career/Sch-to-Work K-12	41 Social Studies Sec	51 Reading K-12	61 Foreign/World Lang K-12	71 Public Information
4 Food Service	11 Federal Program	22 Art Sec	32 Career/Sch-to-Work Elem	42 Science K-12	52 Reading Elem	62 Foreign/World Lang Elem	72 Summer School
5 Transportation	12 Title I	23 Music K-12	33 Career/Sch-to-Work Sec	43 Science Elem	53 Reading Sec	63 Foreign/World Lang Sec	73 Instructional Tech
6 Athletic	13 Title V	24 Music Elem	34 Early Childhood Ed	44 Science Sec	54 Remedial Reading K-12	64 Religious Education K-12	74 Inservice Training
7 Health Services	15 Asst Superintendent	25 Music Sec	35 Health/Phys Education	45 Math K-12	55 Remedial Reading Elem	65 Religious Education Elem	75 Marketing/Distributive
	16 Instructional Media Svcs	26 Business Education	36 Guidance Services K-12	46 Math Elem	56 Remedial Reading Sec	66 Religious Education Sec	76 Info Systems
	17 Chief Operations Officer	27 Career & Tech Ed	37 Guidance Services Elem	47 Math Sec	57 Bilingual/ELL	67 School Board President	77 Psychological Assess
	18 Chief Academic Officer	28 Technology Education	38 Guidance Services Sec	48 English/Lang Arts K-12	58 Special Education K-12	68 Teacher Personnel	78 Affirmative Action

Ohio School Directory

Tammy Burchfield 11*
Cathy Joefreda-Wells 36,69,88*
Brad Conner 67
Jim Lucas 73,297*

Kelley Purkey 16*
Charnelle Bees 36*
Dee Wilms 68*
Jennifer Royalty 83*

Public Schs..Principal	Grd	Prgm	Enr/#Cls	SN	
Waynesville Elem Sch 659 Dayton Rd, Waynesville 45068 Tammy Burchfield	K-5		672 31	20%	513/897-2761 Fax 513/897-3938
Waynesville High Sch 735 Dayton Rd, Waynesville 45068 Samuel Ison	9-12		454 35	22%	513/897-2776 Fax 513/897-2713
Waynesville Middle Sch 723 Dayton Rd, Waynesville 45068 Tracey Poole	6-8		347 20		513/897-4706 Fax 513/897-2083

WARREN CATHOLIC SCHOOLS

• **Archdiocese Cincinnati Ed Off** PID: 00808096
Listing includes only schools located in this county. See District Index for location of Diocesan Offices.

Catholic Schs..Principal	Grd	Prgm	Enr/#Cls	SN	
Bishop Fenwick High Sch 4855 State Route 122, Franklin 45005 Blane Collison	9-12		537 30		513/423-0723 Fax 513/420-8690
St Francis DeSales Sch 20 DeSales Ave, Lebanon 45036 Dan Stringer	K-8		172 9		513/932-6501 Fax 513/932-9919
St Susanna Sch 500 Reading Rd, Mason 45040 Dan Albrinck	1-8		673 20		513/398-3821 Fax 513/398-1657

WARREN PRIVATE SCHOOLS

Private Schs..Principal	Grd	Prgm	Enr/#Cls	SN	
Cinday Academy 11 Sycamore Creek Dr, Springboro 45066 Gina Pangalangan	PK-12		250		937/748-1991 Fax 937/748-2091
Emmanuel Baptist Sch 495 Old 122 Rd, Lebanon 45036 Richard Ross	K-12		79		513/932-5205 Fax 513/932-5206
Lebanon Christian Sch 1436 Deerfield Rd, Lebanon 45036 Kent Jurgenson	PK-5		182		513/932-5590 Fax 513/934-5698
Liberty Bible Academy 4900 Old Irwin Simpson Rd, Mason 45040 Dana Garwood	PK-12		475 12		513/754-1234 Fax 513/754-1237
Mars Hill Academy 4230 Aero Dr, Mason 45040 James Waldy	K-12		298 19		513/770-3223 Fax 513/770-3443
Middletown Christian Sch 3011 Union Rd, Franklin 45005 Thomas Coats \ Jennifer Fluegge	K-12		445 20		513/423-4542 Fax 513/261-6841
Montessori Academy Cincinnati 8293 Duke Blvd, Mason 45040 Megan Ball	PK-8		250		513/398-7773
Royalmont Academy 200 Northcrest Dr, Mason 45040 Veronica Murphy	PK-12		181		513/754-0555 Fax 513/754-0009

Washington County

Village Christian Sch PK-12 108 513/877-2014
4581 Long Spurling Rd, Pleasant PLN 45162 16 Fax 513/877-2102
Kelly Magill

WASHINGTON COUNTY

WASHINGTON COUNTY SCHOOLS

• **Ohio Valley Ed Service Ctr** PID: 00838998 740/373-6669
1338A Colegate Dr, Marietta 45750 Fax 740/376-5809

Andy Brooks 1   Megan Atkinson 2,11

County Schs..Principal	Grd	Prgm	Enr/#Cls	SN	
Ewing Sch 1701 Colegate Dr, Marietta 45750 Melissa Nething	Spec		100 6		740/373-3781
Ohio Valley Educ ESC 115 Victory Pl, Marietta 45750 Chris Keylor	Spec		25 2		740/374-5873 Fax 740/376-5809

WASHINGTON PUBLIC SCHOOLS

• **Belpre City School Dist** PID: 00838572 740/423-9511
2014 Rockland Ave, Belpre 45714 Fax 740/423-3050

Schools: 2 \ *Teachers:* 54 \ *Students:* 1,000 \ *Special Ed Students:* 199 \ *College-Bound:* 46% \ *Ethnic:* African American 2%, Hispanic 1%, Caucasian 96% \ *Exp:* $136 (Low) \ *Poverty:* 21% \ *Title I:* $360,211 \ *Special Education:* $246,000 \ *Open-Close:* 08/14 - 05/20 \ *DTBP:* $217 (High)

Jeffery Greenley 1   Lance Erlwin 2
Fred Meredith 3   Kimmy Odonnell 4
Stephanie Evans .... 6* Allie True 8,73,296
Jeffrey Greenleigh 11   Kellie Krason 16,82*
Cathy O'Donnell 67   Bernie Boice 69
Tyler Leasure 286   Matt Morris 295

Public Schs..Principal	Grd	Prgm	Enr/#Cls	SN	
Belpre Elem Sch 2000 Rockland Ave, Belpre 45714 Lauren Keeling	K-6	T	555 23	58%	740/423-3010 Fax 740/423-3012
Belpre High Sch 612 3rd St, Belpre 45714 Samuel Pepper	7-12	T	405 32	62%	740/423-3000 Fax 740/423-3003

• **Frontier Local School Dist** PID: 00838687 740/865-3473
44870 State Route 7, New Matamoras 45767 Fax 740/865-2010

Schools: 3 \ *Teachers:* 46 \ *Students:* 625 \ *Special Ed Students:* 124 \ *College-Bound:* 53% \ *Ethnic:* African American 1%, Hispanic 1%, Caucasian 98% \ *Exp:* $377 (High) \ *Poverty:* 16% \ *Title I:* $170,931 \ *Special Education:* $197,000 \ *Open-Close:* 08/20 - 05/26 \ *DTBP:* $184 (High)

Brian Rentsch 1   Lee Howard 2,294,296
Rick Barber 3   Bill Creighton 4,11*

---

79 Student Personnel	91 Safety/Security	275 Response To Intervention	298 Grant Writer/Ptnrships	School Programs	Social Media		
80 Driver Ed/Safety	92 Magnet School	277 Remedial Math K-12	750 Chief Innovation Officer	A = Alternative Program			
81 Gifted/Talented	93 Parental Involvement	280 Literacy Coach	751 Chief of Staff	G = Adult Classes	f = Facebook		
82 Video Services	95 Tech Prep Program	285 STEM	752 Social Emotional Learning	M = Magnet Program			
83 Substance Abuse Prev	97 Chief Infomation Officer	286 Digital Learning		T = Title I Schoolwide	t = Twitter		
84 Erate	98 Chief Technology Officer	288 Common Core Standards	Other School Types	V = Career & Tech Ed Programs			
85 AIDS Education	270 Character Education	294 Accountability	Ⓐ = Alternative School				
88 Alternative/At Risk	271 Migrant Education	295 Network System	Ⓒ = Charter School	New Schools are shaded			
89 Multi-Cultural Curriculum	273 Teacher Mentor	296 Title II Programs	Ⓜ = Magnet School	New Superintendents and Principals are bold			
90 Social Work	274 Before/After Sch	297 Webmaster	Ⓨ = Year-Round School	Personnel with email addresses are underscored			

OH–209

Washington County

Market Data Retrieval

Danny Riggs 5	Roger Kirkpatrick 6*
Tammie Rinard 7*	Frank McCreery 8,74,298
Beth Brown 10,83*	Laurie Mullen 11,58*
Holly Cunningham 36,69*	Amy Powell 54,273*
Jeff Nolton 67	Bruce Cassady 73,295

Public Schs..Principal	Grd	Prgm	Enr/#Cls	SN	
Frontier High Middle Sch 44870 State Route 7, New Matamoras 45767 Beth Brown	7-12	TV	315 35	86%	740/865-3441 Fax 740/865-2011
Matamoras Elem Sch 1000 Stover Dr, New Matamoras 45767 Bill Creighton	K-6	T	107 13	59%	740/865-3422 Fax 740/865-3423
Newport Elem Sch 100 Harrison St, Newport 45768 Brian Williams	K-6	T	197 7	46%	740/473-2667 Fax 740/473-2963

● **Ft Frye Local School Dist** PID: 00838625   740/984-2497
540 5th St, Beverly 45715   Fax 740/984-8784

Schools: 4 \ Teachers: 53 \ Students: 1,031 \ Special Ed Students: 189 \ College-Bound: 59% \ Ethnic: Caucasian 99% \ Exp: $177 (Low) \ Poverty: 12% \ Title I: $181,988 \ Special Education: $195,000 \ Open-Close: 08/22 - 05/26 \ DTBP: $161 (High)

Stephanie Starcher 1	Stacy Bolden 2
Ryan Henry 16,73,76,286,295*	Stephanie Lang 67

Public Schs..Principal	Grd	Prgm	Enr/#Cls	SN	
Beverly-Center Elem Sch 540 5th St, Beverly 45715 Megan Miller	K-6	T	256 14	53%	740/984-2371 Fax 740/984-8167
Ft Frye Jr Sr High Sch 420 5th St, Beverly 45715 Andy Schob	7-12	V	427 38	53%	740/984-2376 Fax 740/984-4361
Lowell Elem Sch 305 Market St, Lowell 45744 Krista Ross	K-6	T	149 12	61%	740/896-2523 Fax 740/896-3425
Salem Liberty Elem Sch 10930 State Route 821, Lower Salem 45745 Krista Ross	K-6	T	115 7	52%	740/585-2252 Fax 740/585-2638

● **Marietta City School Dist** PID: 00838730   740/374-6500
111 Academy Dr, Marietta 45750   Fax 740/374-6506

Schools: 6 \ Teachers: 151 \ Students: 2,580 \ Special Ed Students: 462 \ LEP Students: 3 \ College-Bound: 54% \ Ethnic: Asian 1%, African American 1%, Hispanic 2%, Caucasian 96% \ Exp: $100 (Low) \ Poverty: 25% \ Title I: $1,202,770 \ Special Education: $585,000 \ Open-Close: 08/21 - 06/29 \ DTBP: $219 (High) \ 📘 📧

Will Hampton 1	Frank Antell 2
Daryl Prim 3,5,73,91	Pat Snider 4*
Caleb McElroy 5,76	Cody Venderlic 6
Dr Jona Hall 8,11,31,38,286,296	Matthew Dehmlow 11,58,79
Christy Boothby 16,82*	Jason Schob 35*
Doug Mallett 67	Lindsey West 81
Lynn Doebrich 83*	Tasha Werry 288,298

Public Schs..Principal	Grd	Prgm	Enr/#Cls	SN	
Harmar Elem Sch 100 Fort Sq, Marietta 45750 Cheryl Cook	K-5	T	261 13	74%	740/374-6510 Fax 740/376-2465
Marietta High Sch 115 Academy Dr, Marietta 45750 Chad Rinard	9-12	AV	773 56	39%	740/374-6540 Fax 740/376-2462
Marietta Middle Sch 242 N 7th St, Marietta 45750 Brittany Schob	6-8	AT	601 60	46%	740/374-6530 Fax 740/374-6531
Phillips Elem Sch 300 Pike St, Marietta 45750 Kristi Lantz	K-5	T	352 20	56%	740/374-6514 Fax 740/374-6523
Putnam Elem Sch 598 Masonic Park Rd, Marietta 45750 Scott Kratche	K-5	T	227 14	24%	740/374-6516 Fax 740/374-6517
Washington Elem Sch 401 Washington St, Marietta 45750 Alicia McIntire	K-5	T	320 15	65%	740/374-6520 Fax 740/374-6521

● **Warren Local School Dist** PID: 00838857   740/678-2366
220 Sweetapple Rd, Vincent 45784   Fax 740/678-8275

Schools: 4 \ Teachers: 110 \ Students: 2,022 \ Special Ed Students: 264 \ College-Bound: 59% \ Ethnic: African American 1%, Hispanic 1%, Caucasian 98% \ Exp: $284 (Med) \ Poverty: 13% \ Title I: $411,746 \ Special Education: $568,000 \ Open-Close: 08/15 - 05/28

Kyle Newton 1,11	Melcie Wells 2
Lisa Spence 3,5	Charlene Fronko 4
Melissa Kemper 7	Angela Dunn 8,12,275,288
Robin Testerman 16	Scott Elzey 16,73,82,273*
Barbara Augustine 36,83*	Larry Ryan 58*
Debbie West 67	

Public Schs..Principal	Grd	Prgm	Enr/#Cls	SN	
Little Hocking Elem Sch 95 Federal Rd, Little Hockng 45742 Robin Carter	PK-4	T	386 19	39%	740/989-2000 Fax 740/989-2585
Warren Elem Sch 16855 State Route 550, Marietta 45750 Robin Carter	PK-4	T	370 26	47%	740/445-5300 Fax 740/373-0517
Warren High Sch 130 Warrior Dr, Vincent 45784 Ryan Lemley	9-12	V	622 40	33%	740/678-2393 Fax 740/678-2783
Warren Middle Sch 70 Warrior Dr, Vincent 45784 Brent Taylor	5-8		633	35%	740/678-2395 Fax 740/678-0118

● **Washington Co JT Voc Sch Dist** PID: 00838962   740/373-2766
21740 State Route 676, Marietta 45750   Fax 740/373-9026

Schools: 1 \ Teachers: 28 \ Students: 487 \ College-Bound: 48% \ Exp: $462 (High) \ Open-Close: 08/22 - 05/22 \ DTBP: $112 (High)

Dennis Blatt 1,11	Joe Crone 2,294
Pete Spaziani 3*	Becky Jones 7*
Stacy Bradford 16,286*	Dr Anthony Huffman 30
Cindy Schwendeman 38,69*	Debbie West 67
Jerry Bradford 73,84*	Anastasia Elliott 88*

Public Schs..Principal	Grd	Prgm	Enr/#Cls	SN	
Washington Co Career Center 21740 State Route 676, Marietta 45750 Michael Elliot	Voc	G	487 20		740/373-2766 Fax 740/376-2244

1	Superintendent	8	Curric/Instruct K-12	19	Chief Financial Officer	29	Family/Consumer Science	39 Social Studies K-12 49 English/Lang Arts Elem 59 Special Education Elem 69 Academic Assessment
2	Bus/Finance/Purchasing	9	Curric/Instruct Elem	20	Art K-12	30	Adult Education	40 Social Studies Elem 50 English/Lang Arts Sec 60 Special Education Sec 70 Research/Development
3	Buildings And Grounds	10	Curric/Instruct Sec	21	Art Elem	31	Career/Sch-to-Work K-12	41 Social Studies Sec 51 Reading K-12 61 Foreign/World Lang K-12 71 Public Information
4	Food Service	11	Federal Program	22	Art Sec	32	Career/Sch-to-Work Elem	42 Science K-12 52 Reading Elem 62 Foreign/World Lang Elem 72 Summer School
5	Transportation	12	Title I	23	Music K-12	33	Career/Sch-to-Work Sec	43 Science Elem 53 Reading Sec 63 Foreign/World Lang Sec 73 Instructional Tech
6	Athletic	13	Title V	24	Music Elem	34	Early Childhood Ed	44 Science Sec 54 Remedial Reading K-12 64 Religious Education K-12 74 Inservice Training
7	Health Services	15	Asst Superintendent	25	Music Sec	35	Health/Phys Education	45 Math K-12 55 Remedial Reading Elem 65 Religious Education Elem 75 Marketing/Distributive
		16	Instructional Media Svcs	26	Business Education	36	Guidance Services K-12	46 Math Elem 56 Remedial Reading Sec 66 Religious Education Sec 76 Info Systems
		17	Chief Operations Officer	27	Career & Tech Ed	37	Guidance Services Elem	47 Math Sec 57 Bilingual/ELL 67 School Board President 77 Psychological Assess
		18	Chief Academic Officer			38	Guidance Services Sec	48 English/Lang Arts K-12 58 Special Education K-12 68 Teacher Personnel 78 Affirmative Action

OH—210

Ohio School Directory

Wayne County

• **Wolf Creek Local School Dist** PID: 00838924 740/984-2373
330 Main St, Waterford 45786 Fax 740/984-4420

Schools: 2 \ **Teachers:** 42 \ **Students:** 606 \ **Special Ed Students:** 104 \ **College-Bound:** 65% \ **Ethnic:** Hispanic 1%, Caucasian 99% \ **Exp:** $104 (Low) \ **Poverty:** 11% \ **Title I:** $87,099 \ **Special Education:** $76,000 \ **Open-Close:** 08/21 - 05/22 \ **DTBP:** $181 (High)

Douglas Baldwin .... 1,11 Rachel Miller 2
Dale Hill .... 3 Cathy Crock 4*
Tim Rankin .... 5 Juwan Hollins 6
Joan Smith .... 12* Lisa Wagner 13,16,73,82,295*
Beth Morris .... 36,69,83* Hugh Arnold 67
Suellen Coleman 298*

Public Schs..Principal	Grd	Prgm	Enr/#Cls SN	
Waterford Elem Sch 19700 State Route 339, Waterford 45786 Jana Thomas	K-8	T	417 40	39% 740/984-2342 Fax 740/984-4608
Waterford High Sch 330 Main St, Waterford 45786 Suellen Coleman	9-12	V	189 20	38% 740/984-2373

WASHINGTON CATHOLIC SCHOOLS

• **Diocese of Steubenville Ed Off** PID: 00812671
Listing includes only schools located in this county. See District Index for location of Diocesan Offices.

Catholic Schs..Principal	Grd	Prgm	Enr/#Cls SN	
St John Central Sch State Rte 676, Marietta 45750 Dr Larry Moegling	PK-8		118 9	740/896-2697 Fax 740/896-2555
St Mary Sch 320 Marion St, Marietta 45750 Molly Frye	PK-8		201 16	740/374-8181 Fax 740/374-8602

WASHINGTON PRIVATE SCHOOLS

Private Schs..Principal	Grd	Prgm	Enr/#Cls SN	
Belpre Christian Academy 200 1st Ln, Belpre 45714 Eric Fullerton	K-12		35 3	740/423-7741
Marietta Christian Sch 4070 State Route 60, Marietta 45750 Cecilia Fair	K-12		30 4	740/373-5551 Fax 740/373-4314
Veritas Classical Academy 115 Victory Pl, Marietta 45750 Melissa Nayak	PK-12		150	740/885-2033

WAYNE COUNTY

WAYNE COUNTY SCHOOLS

• **Tri-Co Ed Service Center** PID: 00839631 330/345-6771
741 Winkler Dr, Wooster 44691 Fax 330/345-7622

James Ritchie .... 1 Mary Workman 2,11,68
Kris Pipes-Perone .... 8,58 Sandy Stebly 34

County Schs..Principal	Grd	Prgm	Enr/#Cls SN	
Ida Sue Sch 266 Oldman Rd, Wooster 44691 Timothy Frye	Spec		76 12	330/345-7251 Fax 330/345-0917
© Liberty Preparatory Sch 243 N Milton St, Smithville 44677 Brian Hessey	7-12	T	66	330/669-0055
Tri-County International Acad 515 Oldman Rd, Wooster 44691 Tyler Keener	9-12		300	330/345-4000 Fax 330/345-3510

WAYNE PUBLIC SCHOOLS

• **Chippewa Local School Dist** PID: 00839007 330/658-6368
56 N Portage St, Doylestown 44230 Fax 330/658-5842

Schools: 3 \ **Teachers:** 74 \ **Students:** 1,290 \ **Special Ed Students:** 145 \ **College-Bound:** 62% \ **Ethnic:** African American 1%, Hispanic 2%, Caucasian 97% \ **Exp:** $240 (Med) \ **Poverty:** 9% \ **Title I:** $184,513 \ **Special Education:** $569,000 \ **Open-Close:** 08/20 - 05/28 \ **DTBP:** $174 (High)

Todd Osborn .... 1 Molly Koch 2,71
Laurie Sizemore .... 3,5 Christine Schafrath 4
Matthew Rodriguez .... 8,11,69,288* Kimberly Roth-Kimbre 36
Caity Schrock .... 58 T DeAngelis 67
Leslie Marshall .... 273* Sean Linder 286

Public Schs..Principal	Grd	Prgm	Enr/#Cls SN	
Chippewa Intermediate Sch 100 Valley View Rd, Doylestown 44230 Jamie Zollinger	3-6		376 25	36% 330/658-2214 Fax 330/658-2241
Chippewa Jr Sr High Sch 466 S Portage St, Doylestown 44230 Matthew Rodriguez	7-12	A	631 26	330/658-6368
Hazel Harvey Elem Sch 165 Brooklyn Ave, Doylestown 44230 Jodie Hughes	PK-2		283 24	36% 330/658-2522 Fax 330/658-3644

• **Dalton Local School Dist** PID: 00839045 330/828-2267
177 Mill St N, Dalton 44618 Fax 330/828-2801

Schools: 2 \ **Teachers:** 49 \ **Students:** 875 \ **Special Ed Students:** 104 \ **LEP Students:** 17 \ **College-Bound:** 67% \ **Ethnic:** Asian 2%, Hispanic 1%, Caucasian 96% \ **Exp:** $410 (High) \ **Poverty:** 20% \ **Title I:** $383,550 \ **Special Education:** $176,000 \ **Open-Close:** 08/19 - 05/29 \ **DTBP:** $184 (High)

---

79 Student Personnel	91 Safety/Security	275 Response To Intervention	298 Grant Writer/Ptnrships	**School Programs**	**Social Media**	
80 Driver Ed/Safety	92 Magnet School	277 Remedial Math K-12	750 Chief Innovation Officer	A = Alternative Program		
81 Gifted/Talented	93 Parental Involvement	280 Literacy Coach	751 Chief of Staff	G = Adult Classes	= Facebook	
82 Video Services	95 Tech Prep Program	285 STEM	752 Social Emotional Learning	M = Magnet Program		
83 Substance Abuse Prev	97 Chief Infomation Officer	286 Digital Learning		T = Title I Schoolwide	= Twitter	
84 Erate	98 Chief Technology Officer	288 Common Core Standards	**Other School Types**	V = Career & Tech Ed Programs		
85 AIDS Education	270 Character Education	294 Accountability	Ⓐ = Alternative School			
88 Alternative/At Risk	271 Migrant Education	295 Network System	Ⓒ = Charter School	New Schools are shaded		
89 Multi-Cultural Curriculum	273 Teacher Mentor	296 Title II Programs	Ⓜ = Magnet School	New Superintendents and Principals are bold		
90 Social Work	274 Before/After Sch	297 Webmaster	Ⓨ = Year-Round School	Personnel with email addresses are underscored		

Wayne County — Market Data Retrieval

Jim Saxer 1
Craig McGinty 3*
Tim Prasse 4
John Gregory 6*
Steve Watkins 8,11,288,298
Lisa Zona 58,88,275,296*
Seth Sullivan 73,98*
Elizabeth Combs 77
Sheryl Shawstewart 2,71,97
Sheryl Stewart 3,17
Jason Byrnes 5
Diann King 7*
Luke Grau 31,38,69,83*
Phil Schlabach 67
Kristi Nussbaum 76

Public Schs..Principal	Grd	Prgm	Enr/#Cls	SN	
Dalton High Sch 177 Mill St N, Dalton 44618 Chris Black	9-12		236 18	16%	330/828-2261 Fax 330/828-2904
Dalton Local Elem Middle Sch 250 N Church St, Dalton 44618 Steven Watkins	K-8	V	620		330/828-2405

● **Green Local School Dist** PID: 00839095   330/669-3921
100 Smithie Dr, Smithville 44677   Fax 330/669-2121

> *Schools:* 3 \ *Teachers:* 67 \ *Students:* 1,056 \ *Special Ed Students:* 120 \ *College-Bound:* 60% \ *Ethnic:* African American 1%, Hispanic 2%, Caucasian 97% \ *Exp:* $269 (Med) \ *Poverty:* 12% \ *Title I:* $193,681 \ *Special Education:* $165,000 \ *Open-Close:* 08/21 - 05/29

Dean Frank 1
Lindsey Welch 8,11
Derrick Hochstetler 73*
Barb Markland 2
Brad Yochheim 67
Lori Ebert 81*

Public Schs..Principal	Grd	Prgm	Enr/#Cls	SN	
Green Elem Sch 200 Smithie Dr, Smithville 44677 Christine Miller	K-5	T	441 8		330/669-3501 Fax 330/669-2974
Green Middle Sch 200 Smithie Dr, Smithville 44677 Andy Bratcher	6-8		296 17		330/669-3165 Fax 330/669-2069
Smithville High Sch 200 Smithie Dr, Smithville 44677 Andy Bratcher	9-12	V	319 29	39%	330/669-3165 Fax 330/669-2069

● **Northwestern Local School Dist** PID: 00839198   419/846-3151
7571 N Elyria Rd, West Salem 44287   Fax 419/846-3361

> *Schools:* 3 \ *Teachers:* 91 \ *Students:* 1,320 \ *Special Ed Students:* 147 \ *LEP Students:* 6 \ *College-Bound:* 64% \ *Ethnic:* Hispanic 2%, Caucasian 97% \ *Exp:* $344 (High) \ *Poverty:* 14% \ *Title I:* $287,513 \ *Special Education:* $283,000 \ *Open-Close:* 08/20 - 05/28 \ *DTBP:* $56 (Low)

Jeffrey Layton 1
Wendi Mole 4
Jamie Imhoff 5
Diana Rogers 8
Maria Hines 16*
Joyce Bowman 37*
Chris Sykes 58
Kevin Brazee 73,286*
Rusty Yarman 3
Armand Massary 5
Randall Hafner 6*
Julie McCumber 8,15
Levi Myers 27*
Juliet Thomas 38*
Laura Woodring 67
Luann Stefanuik 83,88*

Public Schs..Principal	Grd	Prgm	Enr/#Cls	SN	
Northwestern Elem Sch 7334 N Elyria Rd, West Salem 44287 Joey Brightbill	PK-5	T	666 30	47%	419/846-3519 Fax 419/846-3584
Northwestern High Sch 7473 N Elyria Rd, West Salem 44287 Mike Burkholder	9-12	TV	368 34	43%	419/846-3833 Fax 419/846-3163
Northwestern Middle Sch 7569 N Elyria Rd, West Salem 44287 Rachel Beun	6-8	T	304 24	44%	419/846-3974 Fax 419/846-3750

● **Norwayne Local School Dist** PID: 00839148   330/435-6382
350 S Main St, Creston 44217   Fax 330/435-4633

> *Schools:* 3 \ *Teachers:* 74 \ *Students:* 1,400 \ *Special Ed Students:* 175 \ *LEP Students:* 3 \ *College-Bound:* 56% \ *Ethnic:* Asian 1%, Hispanic 1%, Caucasian 98% \ *Exp:* $58 (Low) \ *Poverty:* 11% \ *Title I:* $263,819 \ *Special Education:* $241,000 \ *Open-Close:* 08/20 - 05/29 \ *DTBP:* $166 (High)

Karen O'Hare 1
Terry Valentine 3,5
Vincent Sette 11*
Amy Frary 69,83*
Sandy Hadsell 2
Ann Gerber 8*
Jon Widmer 67
Ryan Wile 73,76

Public Schs..Principal	Grd	Prgm	Enr/#Cls	SN	
Norwayne Elem Sch 286 S Main St, Creston 44217 Dave Dreher	PK-5		704 10	31%	330/435-6383
Norwayne High Sch 350 S Main St, Creston 44217 Doug Zimmerly	9-12	V	414 25	59%	330/435-6384
Norwayne Middle Sch 350 S Main St, Creston 44217 Kevin Leatherman	6-8		333 20		330/435-1195

● **Orrville City School Dist** PID: 00839241   330/682-5811
815 N Ella St, Orrville 44667   Fax 330/682-0073

> *Schools:* 3 \ *Teachers:* 90 \ *Students:* 1,600 \ *Special Ed Students:* 268 \ *LEP Students:* 83 \ *College-Bound:* 60% \ *Ethnic:* Asian 2%, African American 5%, Hispanic 12%, Caucasian 81% \ *Exp:* $248 (Med) \ *Poverty:* 14% \ *Title I:* $372,350 \ *Special Education:* $289,000 \ *Bilingual Education:* $5,000 \ *Open-Close:* 08/19 - 05/28 \ *DTBP:* $174 (High)

James Ritchie 1
Debra Byrnes 4*
Audreay Zuercher 6*
Denise Rehm 16*
Dr Greg Roadruck 67
Mark Dickerhoof 2
Matt Wyatt 5
Brett Lanz 8,11,69,73,83,271,288,294
Amy Meredith 58
Amy Wilson 81

Public Schs..Principal	Grd	Prgm	Enr/#Cls	SN	
Orrville Elem Sch 605 Mineral Springs St, Orrville 44667 Beverly Waseman	K-4	T	661 18	58%	330/682-1851 Fax 330/682-2143
Orrville High Sch 841 N Ella St, Orrville 44667 Tim Adams	9-12	T	500 35	45%	330/682-4661 Fax 330/682-4662
Orrville Middle Sch 801 Mineral Springs St, Orrville 44667 Dave Sovacool	5-8	T	498 20	56%	330/682-1791 Fax 330/682-2743

● **Rittman Exempted Village SD** PID: 00839306   330/927-7400
100 Saurer St, Rittman 44270   Fax 330/927-7405

> *Schools:* 4 \ *Teachers:* 53 \ *Students:* 999 \ *Special Ed Students:* 144 \ *LEP Students:* 3 \ *College-Bound:* 52% \ *Ethnic:* African American 1%, Hispanic 1%, Caucasian 97% \ *Exp:* $262 (Med) \ *Poverty:* 18% \ *Title I:* $317,020 \ *Special Education:* $225,000 \ *Open-Close:* 08/21 - 05/29 \ *DTBP:* $60 (Low)

Ohio School Directory — Wayne County

James Ritchie	1	Mark Dickerhoof		2
Rick Campbell	3,4	Kathy Yannayon		5
Joe Staley	6*	Dr Shawna DeVoe		9*
Amy Wilson	10	Jennifer Dziczkowski		16*
Dr Amy Meredith	58,83	Doug Stuart		67
Sandi Trogdon	73*			

Public Schs..Principal	Grd	Prgm	Enr/#Cls	SN
ⓒ Rittman Academy 100 Saurer St, Rittman 44270 Kent Smith	9-12		35	330/927-7162
Rittman Elem Sch 131 N Metzger Ave, Rittman 44270 Dr Shawna DeVoe	K-5	T	440 13	54% 330/927-7460 Fax 330/927-7465
Rittman High Sch 50 Saurer St, Rittman 44270 Nick Evans	9-12	TV	255 30	99% 330/927-7140 Fax 330/927-7145
Rittman Middle Sch 50 Saurer St, Rittman 44270 Nick Evans	6-8	T	269 14	330/927-7100 Fax 330/927-7145

● **Southeast Local School Dist** PID: 00839356   330/698-3001
9048 Dover Rd, Apple Creek 44606   Fax 330/698-5000

Schools: 6 \ **Teachers:** 91 \ **Students:** 1,400 \ **Special Ed Students:** 219 \ **LEP Students:** 141 \ **College-Bound:** 56% \ **Ethnic:** Hispanic 3%, Caucasian 97% \ **Exp:** $79 (Low) \ **Poverty:** 16% \ **Title I:** $1,005,674 \ **Open-Close:** 08/20 - 05/28 \ **DTBP:** $169 (High)

Jon Ritchie	1	Mark Dickerhoof		2
Dave Thomas	3	Luann Suppes		4*
Mark Williams	5	Chris Lapish		6*
Holly Mastrine	8,11,72,88,288,296	Jennifer Troyer		36*
Lisa Gwinn	57	Jaimie Ticconetti		58
Sue Williams	67	Glenn Caudill		73
Darcy Bennett	77			

Public Schs..Principal	Grd	Prgm	Enr/#Cls	SN
Apple Creek Elem Sch 173 W Main St, Apple Creek 44606 Matt Karolewski	PK-6	T	417 21	45% 330/698-3111 Fax 330/698-2922
Fredericksburg Elem Sch 160 W Clay St, Fredericksbrg 44627 Shawn Snyder	K-8	T	134 11	38% 330/695-2741 Fax 330/695-2116
Holmesville Elem Sch 8141 E Jackson St, Holmesville 44633 Shawn Snyder	K-6	T	142 9	52% 330/279-2341 Fax 330/279-2023
John R Lea Middle Sch 9130 Dover Rd, Apple Creek 44606 Erich Riebe	7-8	T	173 15	45% 330/698-3151 Fax 330/698-1922
Mt Eaton Elem Sch 8746 Market St, Mount Eaton 44659 Samantha Miglich	K-8	T	140 16	33% 330/857-5313 Fax 330/857-3703
Waynedale High Sch 9050 Dover Rd, Apple Creek 44606 Richard Roth	9-12	V	351 35	45% 330/698-3071 Fax 330/698-1432

● **Triway Local School Dist** PID: 00839423   330/264-9491
3205 Shreve Rd, Wooster 44691   Fax 330/262-3955

Schools: 4 \ **Teachers:** 116 \ **Students:** 1,637 \ **Special Ed Students:** 217 \ **LEP Students:** 13 \ **College-Bound:** 50% \ **Ethnic:** African American 1%, Hispanic 2%, Caucasian 97% \ **Exp:** $139 (Low) \ **Poverty:** 18% \ **Title I:** $553,646 \ **Special Education:** $343,000 \ **Open-Close:** 08/20 - 05/29 \ **DTBP:** $174 (High)

Nanthan Schindewolf	1,83	Denny Wells		3*
Sue Kruse	4	Tracy Piper		5
Sean Carmichael	6*	Joshua Stutz		8
Lisa Acker	11,296,298*	Kimberly Mitchell		38*
Benjanim Holt	60	Eric Walter		67
Erik Johnson	73*	Melissa Radich		285

Public Schs..Principal	Grd	Prgm	Enr/#Cls	SN
Shreve Elem Sch 598 N Market St, Shreve 44676 Adam Stein	PK-6	T	447 25	45% 330/567-2837 Fax 330/567-9107
Triway High Sch 3205 Shreve Rd, Wooster 44691 Scott Wharton	9-12	V	438 32	36% 330/264-8685 Fax 330/262-2620
Triway Junior High Sch 3145 Shreve Rd, Wooster 44691 Joshua Stutz	7-8	T	264 20	41% 330/264-2114 Fax 330/264-6025
Wooster Twp Elem Sch 1071 Dover Rd, Wooster 44691 Angela Carmichael	PK-6	T	321 28	46% 330/264-6252 Fax 330/263-7078

● **Wayne Co Joint Voc School Dist** PID: 00839617   330/669-2134
518 W Prospect St, Smithville 44677   Fax 330/669-7001

Schools: 1 \ **Teachers:** 50 \ **Students:** 879 \ **College-Bound:** 27% \ **Exp:** $534 (High) \ **Open-Close:** 08/19 - 05/28 \ **DTBP:** $174 (High) \ 🅵 🆃

Dr Kip Crain	1	Mary Workman		2,11
Sean Havalotti	3*	Cheryl Boyer		16,73*
Lynn Moomaw	30*	Dr Gregory Roadruck		67
Nate Gaubatz	288*			

Public Schs..Principal	Grd	Prgm	Enr/#Cls	SN
Wayne Co Schools Career Center 518 W Prospect St, Smithville 44677 Matthew Brown	Voc	G	879 70	330/669-2134

● **Wooster City School Dist** PID: 00839485   330/264-0869
144 N Market St, Wooster 44691   Fax 330/262-3407

Schools: 7 \ **Teachers:** 203 \ **Students:** 3,650 \ **Special Ed Students:** 624 \ **LEP Students:** 38 \ **College-Bound:** 55% \ **Ethnic:** Asian 2%, African American 3%, Hispanic 3%, Caucasian 92% \ **Exp:** $237 (Med) \ **Poverty:** 16% \ **Title I:** $978,254 \ **Special Education:** $729,000 \ **Open-Close:** 08/19 - 05/27 \ **DTBP:** $198 (High)

Dr Michael Tefs	1	Bonnie West		2
Michael Foore	3,5,91	Dawn Lewis		4,57
Vic Cole	5	Heidi Haas		8,11,58,79,88
Karen Arbogast	9,280	Richard Leone		10,273
Rebecca Furlong	16,73*	William Gantz		67
Racheal Workman	68			

Public Schs..Principal	Grd	Prgm	Enr/#Cls	SN
Boys Village Sch 1494 Old Mansfield Rd, Wooster 44691 Anita Jorney-Gifford	5-12		46 13	330/262-3442 Fax 330/202-3890
Cornerstone Elem Sch 101 W Bowman St, Wooster 44691 Eric Vizzo	PK-4	T	375 17	72% 330/988-1111 Fax 330/262-7611
Edgewood Middle Sch 2695 Graustark Path, Wooster 44691 Brad Warner	5-7	T	796 55	46% 330/988-1111 Fax 330/345-8237
Kean Elem Sch 432 Oldman Rd, Wooster 44691 Brandon Cobb	K-4	T	323 15	37% 330/345-6634 Fax 330/345-7845

79	Student Personnel	91	Safety/Security	275	Response To Intervention	298 Grant Writer/Ptnrships
80	Driver Ed/Safety	92	Magnet School	277	Remedial Math K-12	750 Chief Innovation Officer
81	Gifted/Talented	93	Parental Involvement	280	Literacy Coach	751 Chief of Staff
82	Video Services	95	Tech Prep Program	285	STEM	752 Social Emotional Learning
83	Substance Abuse Prev	97	Chief Information Officer	286	Digital Learning	
84	Erate	98	Chief Technology Officer	288	Common Core Standards	**Other School Types**
85	AIDS Education	270	Character Education	294	Accountability	Ⓐ = Alternative School
88	Alternative/At Risk	271	Migrant Education	295	Network System	Ⓒ = Charter School
89	Multi-Cultural Curriculum	273	Teacher Mentor	296	Title II Programs	Ⓜ = Magnet School
90	Social Work	274	Before/After Sch	297	Webmaster	Ⓨ = Year-Round School

School Programs
A = Alternative Program
G = Adult Classes
M = Magnet Program
T = Title I Schoolwide
V = Career & Tech Ed Programs

Social Media
🅵 = Facebook
🆃 = Twitter

New Schools are shaded
New Superintendents and Principals are bold
Personnel with email addresses are underscored

Williams County

Melrose Elem Sch K-4 T 298 46% 330/988-1111
1641 Sunset Ln, Wooster 44691   15   Fax 330/345-7868
Kaylee Harrell

Parkview Elem Sch K-4 T 330 50% 330/262-3821
773 Parkview Dr, Wooster 44691   17   Fax 330/262-4655
Steve Furlong

Wooster High Sch 8-12 ATV 1,300 43% 330/988-1111
515 Oldman Rd, Wooster 44691   100   Fax 330/345-3501
Tyler Keener

WAYNE CATHOLIC SCHOOLS

- **Diocese of Cleveland Ed Office** PID: 00795308
  Listing includes only schools located in this county. See District Index for location of Diocesan Offices.

Catholic Schs..Principal	Grd	Prgm	Enr/#Cls	SN	
SS Peter & Paul Sch 169 W Clinton St, Doylestown 44230 Theresa Williams	PK-8		67 9		330/658-2804 Fax 330/658-2287
St Mary of the Imm Concep Sch 515 Beall Ave, Wooster 44691 Laura Marvin	PK-8		175 9		330/262-8671

WAYNE PRIVATE SCHOOLS

Private Schs..Principal	Grd	Prgm	Enr/#Cls	SN	
Central Christian Sch 3970 Kidron Road, Kidron 44636 Joyce Taylor \ Craig Martin	PK-12		270 28		330/857-7311 Fax 330/857-7331
Rock of Ages Sch 4407 S Kansas Rd, Apple Creek 44606 Trent Troyer	K-8		32 3		330/698-2298 Fax 330/698-2299
Wooster Christian Sch 480 Fry Rd, Wooster 44691 Randy Claes	PK-8		212 16		330/345-6436 Fax 330/345-4330

WAYNE REGIONAL CENTERS

- **Tccsa-Tri-Co Comp Svcs** PID: 04499647   330/264-6047
  2125 Eagle Pass, Wooster 44691   Fax 330/264-5703

Stuart Workman 1   Joe Picking 73
Jim Franks 295

Market Data Retrieval

WILLIAMS COUNTY

WILLIAMS PUBLIC SCHOOLS

- **Bryan City School Dist** PID: 00839643   419/636-6973
  1350 Fountain Grove Dr, Bryan 43506   Fax 419/633-6280

Schools: 2 \ *Teachers:* 116 \ *Students:* 2,200 \ *Special Ed Students:* 339 \ *LEP Students:* 9 \ *College-Bound:* 51% \ *Ethnic:* Asian 2%, Hispanic 6%, Caucasian 92% \ *Exp:* $187 (Low) \ *Poverty:* 12% \ *Title I:* $351,472 \ *Special Education:* $309,000 \ *Open-Close:* 08/14 - 05/22 \ *DTBP:* $182 (High) \

Diana Savage 1   Kevin Schaffer 2,19
Chad Bassett .... 3,4,8,11,57,69,296,298*   Ryan Eberley 5
Chad Savage 6   Rhonda Samples 37,83*
Julie Taylor 60   Cindra Teller 67
Tom Karnes 73   Shandra Swank 77
Gary Wyse 84   Denise Collins 297

Public Schs..Principal	Grd	Prgm	Enr/#Cls	
Bryan Elem Sch 1301 Center St, Bryan 43506 Karyn Cox	PK-5		923 15	419/636-6931 Fax 419/633-6285
Bryan Middle High Sch 1000 W Fountain Grove Dr, Bryan 43506 Stephen Alspaugh	6-12		1,004 60	419/636-4536 Fax 419/633-6281

- **Edgerton Local School Dist** PID: 00839708   419/298-2112
  111 E River St, Edgerton 43517   Fax 419/298-1322

Schools: 2 \ *Teachers:* 38 \ *Students:* 599 \ *Special Ed Students:* 65 \ *College-Bound:* 59% \ *Ethnic:* African American 1%, Hispanic 5%, Caucasian 94% \ *Exp:* $136 (Low) \ *Poverty:* 17% \ *Title I:* $167,766 \ *Special Education:* $143,000 \ *Open-Close:* 08/20 - 05/29 \ *DTBP:* $161 (High)

Kermit Riehle 1   William Blakely 2
Jim Saul 3,5   Beth Winsler 4
Keith Merrille 6   Kelli Seiler 12*
Shari Saneda .... 16,73,295*   Kimberly Stark 36*
Chris Herman 67   Kevin Wolfe 270
Tracy Rendelman .... 273*   Melinda Cooley 286

Public Schs..Principal	Grd	Prgm	Enr/#Cls	SN	
Edgerton Elem Sch 111 E River St, Edgerton 43517 Brett Grieser	K-6	T	293 17	45%	419/298-2332 Fax 419/298-3466
Edgerton High Sch 111 E River St, Edgerton 43517 Kevin Wolfe	7-12	V	300 24	37%	419/298-2331

1	Superintendent	8	Curric/Instruct K-12	19	Chief Financial Officer	29	Family/Consumer Science	39	Social Studies K-12	49	English/Lang Arts Elem	59	Special Education Elem	69	Academic Assessment
2	Bus/Finance/Purchasing	9	Curric/Instruct Elem	20	Art K-12	30	Adult Education	40	Social Studies Elem	50	English/Lang Arts Sec	60	Special Education Sec	70	Research/Development
3	Buildings And Grounds	10	Curric/Instruct Sec	21	Art Elem	31	Career/Sch-to-Work K-12	41	Social Studies Sec	51	Reading K-12	61	Foreign/World Lang K-12	71	Public Information
4	Food Service	11	Federal Program	22	Art Sec	32	Career/Sch-to-Work Elem	42	Science K-12	52	Reading Elem	62	Foreign/World Lang Elem	72	Summer School
5	Transportation	12	Title I	23	Music K-12	33	Career/Sch-to-Work Sec	43	Science Elem	53	Reading Sec	63	Foreign/World Lang Sec	73	Instructional Tech
6	Athletic	13	Title V	24	Music Elem	34	Early Childhood Ed	44	Science Sec	54	Remedial Reading K-12	64	Religious Education K-12	74	Inservice Training
7	Health Services	14	Asst Superintendent	25	Music Sec	35	Health/Phys Education	45	Math K-12	55	Remedial Reading Elem	65	Religious Education Elem	75	Marketing/Distributive
		15	Instructional Media Svcs	26	Business Education	36	Guidance Services K-12	46	Math Elem	56	Remedial Reading Sec	66	Religious Education Sec	76	Info Systems
		16	Chief Operations Officer	27	Career & Tech Ed	37	Guidance Services Elem	47	Math Sec	57	Bilingual/ELL	67	School Board President	77	Psychological Assess
		18	Chief Academic Officer	28	Technology Education	38	Guidance Services Sec	48	English/Lang Arts K-12	58	Special Education K-12	68	Teacher Personnel	78	Affirmative Action

Ohio School Directory — Williams County

Edon Northwest Local Sch Dist PID: 00839746
802 W Indiana St, Edon 43518
419/272-3213
Fax 419/272-2240

Schools: 1 \ **Teachers:** 37 \ **Students:** 500 \ **Special Ed Students:** 104 \ **College-Bound:** 53% \ **Ethnic:** Hispanic 1%, Native American: 1%, Caucasian 97% \ **Exp:** $159 (Low) \ **Poverty:** 10% \ **Title I:** $96,394 \ **Special Education:** $108,000 \ **Open-Close:** 08/21 - 05/28 \ **DTBP:** $164 (High)

Anthony Stevens 1,73
Laurence Walker 6
Jessica Foltis 58*
Debra Nester 2
Alicia Graham 36,69,83,88
Cody Best 67

Public Schs..Principal	Grd	Prgm	Enr/#Cls	SN	
Edon Northwest Local Sch 802 W Indiana St, Edon 43518 Jennifer Ripke \ Kayla Lapham	K-12		500 30	99%	419/272-3213

Millcreek-West Unity Local SD PID: 00839784
1401 W Jackson St, West Unity 43570
419/924-2366
Fax 419/924-2367

Schools: 1 \ **Teachers:** 38 \ **Students:** 520 \ **Special Ed Students:** 84 \ **LEP Students:** 3 \ **College-Bound:** 58% \ **Exp:** $431 (High) \ **Poverty:** 9% \ **Title I:** $84,385 \ **Special Education:** $110,000 \ **Open-Close:** 08/20 - 05/28 \ **DTBP:** $173 (High)

Jim Wyse 1,11,288
Bill Williams 3*
Nathan Seigal 5*
Vicki Rhodes 12*
Amber Metzger 36,69,88*
Heather Jones 67
Steven Riley 83,85*
Traci Thompson 2,19
Ellie Shinhearl 4*
Anthony Gerig 6*
Mary Sauder 16*
Bill Boyer 58,752*
Alex Cummins 73
Cameron Thompson 286

Public Schs..Principal	Grd	Prgm	Enr/#Cls	SN	
Millcreek-West Unity Local Sch 1401 W Jackson St, West Unity 43570 Steven Riley \ Laurie Worline	K-12	V	520		419/924-2366

Montpelier Exempted Village SD PID: 00839825
1015 E Brown Rd, Montpelier 43543
419/485-3676
Fax 419/485-4318

Schools: 1 \ **Teachers:** 56 \ **Students:** 1,100 \ **Special Ed Students:** 155 \ **LEP Students:** 3 \ **College-Bound:** 43% \ **Ethnic:** Asian 2%, Hispanic 2%, Caucasian 95% \ **Exp:** $206 (Med) \ **Poverty:** 14% \ **Title I:** $198,510 \ **Special Education:** $196,000 \ **Open-Close:** 08/19 - 05/21 \ **DTBP:** $174 (High)

Jamison Grime 1,11,288
Don Schlosser 3*
Joe Brigle 6
Lance Thorp 12*
Darrell Higbie 67
James Lee 73,76
Sue Thorp 286*
Carla Rice 2
Dianne Sanders 5*
Michael Bumb 8
Monica Brigle 58*
Stephanie Friend 69,88*
Jennifer Hodapp 81*

Public Schs..Principal	Grd	Prgm	Enr/#Cls	SN	
Montpelier Sch 1015 E Brown Rd, Montpelier 43543 Lance Thorp \ Sue Thorp	PK-12	T	1,100 20		419/485-6700 Fax 419/485-3487

North Central Local Sch Dist PID: 00839863
400 E Baubice St, Pioneer 43554
419/737-2392
Fax 419/737-3361

Schools: 1 \ **Teachers:** 39 \ **Students:** 600 \ **Special Ed Students:** 91 \ **LEP Students:** 22 \ **College-Bound:** 28% \ **Ethnic:** Asian 1%, Hispanic 6%, Caucasian 92% \ **Exp:** $447 (High) \ **Poverty:** 8% \ **Title I:** $85,779 \ **Special Education:** $120,000 \ **Open-Close:** 08/22 - 05/29 \ **DTBP:** $181 (High)

William Hanak 1
Eric Moreland 3,5*
Greg Waidelich 6,11*
Deb Meyers 16,73*
Linda Cochran 57*
Eric Smeltzer 2
Rob Taylor 4*
Sharon Deetz 12*
Diane Veres 38,69,83*
Homer Hendricks 67

Public Schs..Principal	Grd	Prgm	Enr/#Cls	SN	
North Central Local Sch 400 E Baubice St, Pioneer 43554 Andrew Morr \ Marcia Rozevink	K-12	T	600 60	99%	419/737-2366 Fax 419/737-2531

Stryker Local School Dist PID: 00839904
400 S Defiance St, Stryker 43557
419/682-2841
Fax 419/682-3508

Schools: 2 \ **Teachers:** 37 \ **Students:** 407 \ **Special Ed Students:** 63 \ **LEP Students:** 3 \ **College-Bound:** 37% \ **Ethnic:** Asian 1%, African American 1%, Hispanic 11%, Caucasian 87% \ **Exp:** $418 (High) \ **Poverty:** 7% \ **Title I:** $112,955 \ **Special Education:** $69,000 \ **Open-Close:** 08/15 - 05/21 \ **DTBP:** $174 (High)

Nate Johnson 1
Kim Miller 6
Lisa Arnold 58
Kirsten Meyer 73*
Jill Peters 2,84
David Schultz 8,11,31*
Jason Leupp 67

Public Schs..Principal	Grd	Prgm	Enr/#Cls	SN	
Stryker Elem Sch 400 S Defiance St, Stryker 43557 David Schultz	PK-6	T	235 12		419/682-2841
Stryker High Sch 400 S Defiance St, Stryker 43557 David Schultz	7-12	T	172 16	98%	419/682-4591

WILLIAMS CATHOLIC SCHOOLS

Diocese of Toledo Ed Office PID: 00818297
Listing includes only schools located in this county. See District Index for location of Diocesan Offices.

Catholic Schs..Principal	Grd	Prgm	Enr/#Cls	SN	
St Mary Sch 314 S Locust St, Edgerton 43517 Julie Taylor	1-6		98 6		419/298-2531 Fax 419/298-3123
St Patrick Sch 610 S Portland St, Bryan 43506 Tracy Koenig	PK-8		120 10		419/636-3592 Fax 419/633-9112

- 79 Student Personnel
- 80 Driver Ed/Safety
- 81 Gifted/Talented
- 82 Video Services
- 83 Substance Abuse Prev
- 84 Erate
- 85 AIDS Education
- 88 Alternative/At Risk
- 89 Multi-Cultural Curriculum
- 90 Social Work
- 91 Safety/Security
- 92 Magnet School
- 93 Parental Involvement
- 95 Tech Prep Program
- 97 Chief Information Officer
- 98 Chief Technology Officer
- 270 Character Education
- 271 Migrant Education
- 273 Teacher Mentor
- 274 Before/After Sch
- 275 Response To Intervention
- 277 Remedial Math K-12
- 280 Literacy Coach
- 285 STEM
- 286 Digital Learning
- 288 Common Core Standards
- 294 Accountability
- 295 Network System
- 296 Title II Programs
- 297 Webmaster
- 298 Grant Writer/Ptnrships
- 750 Chief Innovation Officer
- 751 Chief of Staff
- 752 Social Emotional Learning

Other School Types
- Ⓐ = Alternative School
- Ⓒ = Charter School
- Ⓜ = Magnet School
- Ⓨ = Year-Round School

School Programs
- A = Alternative Program
- G = Adult Classes
- M = Magnet Program
- T = Title I Schoolwide
- V = Career & Tech Ed Programs

Social Media
- = Facebook
- = Twitter

New Schools are shaded
New Superintendents and Principals are bold
Personnel with email addresses are underscored

Wood County

Market Data Retrieval

WILLIAMS PRIVATE SCHOOLS

Private Schs..Principal	Grd	Prgm	Enr/#Cls SN	
Fountain City Christian Sch	K-12		67	419/636-2333
120 S Beech St, Bryan 43506			9	Fax 419/636-2888
Troy Cummins				

WOOD COUNTY

WOOD COUNTY SCHOOLS

- **Wood Co Ed Service Center** PID: 00840549   419/354-9010
  1867 N Research Dr, Bowling Green 43402   Fax 419/354-1146

Mark North 1	Gina Fernbaugh 2
Susan Spencer 11	Joe Taylor 34,58
Susan Shaffer 81	Kyle Clark 83
Christy Spontelli 88	

County Schs..Principal	Grd	Prgm	Enr/#Cls SN	
Children's Resource Center	Spec		60	419/352-7588
1045 Klotz Rd, Bowling Green 43402			6	Fax 419/354-4977
Kaleb Kuhlman				
Wood Lane Sch	Spec		29	419/352-9577
545 Pearl St Ste A, Bowling Green 43402			7	Fax 419/352-9602
Jessica Miller-Blakely				

WOOD PUBLIC SCHOOLS

- **Bowling Green City Sch Dist** PID: 00839942   419/352-3576
  137 Clough St, Bowling Green 43402   Fax 419/352-1701

Schools: 6 \ *Teachers:* 168 \ *Students:* 3,450 \ *Special Ed Students:* 520 \ *LEP Students:* 49 \ *College-Bound:* 61% \ *Ethnic:* Asian 2%, African American 3%, Hispanic 11%, Caucasian 84% \ *Exp:* $259 (Med) \ *Poverty:* 11% \ *Title I:* $510,680 \ *Special Education:* $684,000 \ *Open-Close:* 08/21 - 05/29 \ *DTBP:* $188 (High) \ f

Francis Scruci 1	Cathy Schuller 2
Charles Martin 3,91	Anne Forschmer 4
Toby Snow 5	Dirk Conner 6*
Dr Ann McCarty .. 8,11,57,83,286,288,296,298	Zebulon Kellough 9
Jodi Anderson 10*	Brittany Howard 35
Melanie Garbig 36,77,79*	Christie Walendzak 58*
Jill Carr 67	Dawn Dazell 68
Beth Krolak 73,76,95,295*	Melanie Garbig 79
Jeff Taylor 295	

Public Schs..Principal	Grd	Prgm	Enr/#Cls SN	
Bowling Green High Sch	9-12	A	864	35% 419/354-0100
530 W Poe Rd, Bowling Green 43402			80	Fax 419/354-1839
Jeffrey Dever				
Bowling Green Middle Sch	6-8		683	36% 419/354-0200
1079 Fairview Ave, Bowling Green 43402			40	Fax 419/353-1958
Eric Radabaugh				
Bowling Green Pre-School	PK-PK		115	419/354-0300
542 Haskins Rd, Bowling Green 43402				Fax 419/352-7675
Jim Lang				
Conneaut Elem Sch	K-5		447	22% 419/354-0300
542 Haskins Rd, Bowling Green 43402			20	Fax 419/352-6661
James Lang				
Crim Elem Sch	K-5	T	484	419/354-0400
1020 Scott Hamilton Ave, Bowling Green 43402			13	Fax 419/352-7675
Zeb Kellough				
Kenwood Elem Sch	K-5	T	386	42% 419/354-0500
710 Kenwood Ave, Bowling Green 43402			29	Fax 419/352-8261
Kathleen Daney				

- **Eastwood Local School Dist** PID: 00840044   419/833-6411
  120 College Ave, Pemberville 43450   Fax 419/287-4245

Schools: 3 \ *Teachers:* 77 \ *Students:* 1,500 \ *Special Ed Students:* 171 \ *LEP Students:* 3 \ *College-Bound:* 63% \ *Ethnic:* Asian 1%, African American 1%, Hispanic 4%, Caucasian 93% \ *Exp:* $444 (High) \ *Poverty:* 10% \ *Title I:* $191,389 \ *Special Education:* $251,000 \ *Open-Close:* 08/21 - 06/02 \ *DTBP:* $190 (High) \ f t

Brent Welker 1,83	Kris Wagoner 3
Karen Brown 4*	Susan Volschow 5
Jeff Hill 6	Ann McVey 8,58,69,79,81,275
Matthew Bostdorff 16,295	Donna Schuessler 36*
Tutsy Asmus 37	Sherri Sheffler 67

Public Schs..Principal	Grd	Prgm	Enr/#Cls SN	
Eastwood Elem Sch	PK-5		676	419/833-2821
4700 Sugar Ridge Rd, Pemberville 43450			11	Fax 419/833-8404
Joe Wank				
Eastwood High Sch	9-12	V	415	18% 419/833-3611
4900 Sugar Ridge Rd, Pemberville 43450			40	Fax 419/833-6014
Jim Kieper				
Eastwood Middle Sch	6-8	V	374	28% 419/833-6011
4800 Sugar Ridge Rd, Pemberville 43450			26	Fax 419/833-7454
Dwight Fertig				

- **Elmwood Local School Dist** PID: 00840111   419/655-2583
  7650 Jerry City Rd, Bloomdale 44817   Fax 419/655-3995

Schools: 3 \ *Teachers:* 77 \ *Students:* 1,275 \ *Special Ed Students:* 193 \ *College-Bound:* 51% \ *Ethnic:* African American 1%, Hispanic 5%, Caucasian 94% \ *Exp:* $270 (Med) \ *Poverty:* 6% \ *Title I:* $91,575 \ *Special Education:* $241,000 \ *Open-Close:* 08/21 - 05/29 \ *DTBP:* $170 (High)

Tony Borton 1	Luann Vanek 2
Gregg Abke 3	Terry Rothenbuhler 4
Laurie Lee 5	Ty Traxler 6*
Angela Missig 7,85	Julie Iannantuono 8
Gary Dulle 11,34,296*	Sonja Brand 16*
Brenda Schnitker 58	Debbie Reynolds 67
Gregg Bishop 73,286,295	David Fawcett 84
Thomas Bentley 88*	

Public Schs..Principal	Grd	Prgm	Enr/#Cls SN	
Elmwood Elem Sch	PK-4	T	535	419/655-2583
7650 Jerry City Rd, Bloomdale 44817			19	
Gary Dulle				
Elmwood High Sch	9-12	V	321	99% 419/655-2583
7650 Jerry City Rd, Bloomdale 44817			25	
Thomas Bentley				
Elmwood Middle Sch	5-8	TV	373	419/655-2583
7650 Jerry City Rd, Bloomdale 44817			27	
Roger Frank				

---

1 Superintendent	8 Curric/Instruct K-12	19 Chief Financial Officer	29 Family/Consumer Science	39 Social Studies K-12	49 English/Lang Arts Elem	59 Special Education Elem	69 Academic Assessment
2 Bus/Finance/Purchasing	9 Curric/Instruct Elem	20 Art K-12	30 Adult Education	40 Social Studies Elem	50 English/Lang Arts Sec	60 Special Education Sec	70 Research/Development
3 Buildings And Grounds	10 Curric/Instruct Sec	21 Art Elem	31 Career/Sch-to-Work Elem	41 Social Studies Sec	51 Reading K-12	61 Foreign/World Lang K-12	71 Public Information
4 Food Service	11 Federal Program	22 Art Sec	32 Career/Sch-to-Work Elem	42 Science K-12	52 Reading Elem	62 Foreign/World Lang Elem	72 Summer School
5 Transportation	12 Title I	23 Music K-12	33 Career/Sch-to-Work Sec	43 Science Elem	53 Reading Sec	63 Foreign/World Lang Sec	73 Instructional Tech
6 Athletic	13 Title V	24 Music Elem	34 Early Childhood Ed	44 Science Sec	54 Remedial Reading K-12	64 Religious Education K-12	74 Inservice Training
7 Health Services	15 Asst Superintendent	25 Music Sec	35 Health/Phys Education	45 Math K-12	55 Remedial Reading Elem	65 Religious Education Elem	75 Marketing/Distributive
	16 Instructional Media Svcs	26 Business Education	36 Guidance Services K-12	46 Math Elem	56 Remedial Reading Sec	66 Religious Education Sec	76 Info Systems
	17 Chief Operations Officer	27 Career & Tech Ed	37 Guidance Services Elem	47 Math Sec	57 Bilingual/ELL	67 School Board President	77 Psychological Assess
	18 Chief Academic Officer	28 Technology Education	38 Guidance Services Sec	48 English/Lang Arts K-12	58 Special Education K-12	68 Teacher Personnel	78 Affirmative Action

Ohio School Directory — Wood County

Lake Local School Dist PID: 00840173
28090 Lemoyne Rd, Millbury 43447
419/661-6690
Fax 419/661-6678

Schools: 3 \ **Teachers:** 91 \ **Students:** 1,679 \ **Special Ed Students:** 193 \ **LEP Students:** 12 \ **College-Bound:** 59% \ **Ethnic:** African American 2%, Hispanic 9%, Caucasian 89% \ **Exp:** $194 (Low) \ **Poverty:** 11% \ **Title I:** $233,793 \ **Special Education:** $278,000 \ **Open-Close:** 08/21 - 05/28 \

Jim Witt	1	Jeff Carpenter		2
Dave Shaffer	3,6*	Trudy Foster		5
Jodi Takats	8*	Jessica Wilson		16
Tracy Orians	38*	Jodi Laktaks		58
Timothy Krugh	67	Wes Bartlett		73*
Hollie Parsons	76			

Public Schs..Principal	Grd	Prgm	Enr/#Cls	SN	
Lake Elem Sch 28150 Lemoyne Rd, Millbury 43447 Missy Wagoner	PK-4		700 30	39%	419/661-6680 Fax 419/661-6683
Lake High Sch 28080 Lemoyne Rd, Millbury 43447 Lee Herman	8-12	TV	670 35	60%	419/661-6640 Fax 419/661-6650
Lake Middle Sch 28100 Lemoyne Rd, Millbury 43447 Katie Beard	5-7	V	420 16		419/661-6660 Fax 419/661-6664

North Baltimore Local Sch Dist PID: 00840238
201 S Main St, N Baltimore 45872
419/257-3531
Fax 419/257-2008

Schools: 2 \ **Teachers:** 41 \ **Students:** 700 \ **Special Ed Students:** 136 \ **College-Bound:** 37% \ **Ethnic:** African American 1%, Hispanic 8%, Caucasian 90% \ **Exp:** $221 (Med) \ **Poverty:** 12% \ **Title I:** $139,017 \ **Special Education:** $174,000 \ **Open-Close:** 08/21 - 05/29 \ **DTBP:** $239 (High)

Ryan DeLaney	1,11	Steven Stewart		2
Georgianna Lanning	4	Sandy Stewart		5
Dan Davis	6	Brent Hermiller		16,73
Michael Kipplen	31,36,69*	Martin Vamundio		57
Rodney Hopten	58	Tami Thomas		67
Lauren Napier	77	Sarah Bugner		83,273*
Dr Robert Falkenenstein	88*	Jonelle Semancik		298

Public Schs..Principal	Grd	Prgm	Enr/#Cls	SN	
E A Powell Elem Sch 500 N Main St, N Baltimore 45872 Mark Lange	K-6	T	364 18	58%	419/257-2124 Fax 419/257-3044
North Baltimore Jr Sr High Sch 201 Tiger Dr, N Baltimore 45872 Dr Robert Falkenenstein	7-12		266 55	75%	419/257-3464 Fax 419/257-0084

Northwood Local School Dist PID: 00840288
600 Lemoyne Rd, Northwood 43619
419/691-3888
Fax 419/697-2470

Schools: 2 \ **Teachers:** 50 \ **Students:** 950 \ **Special Ed Students:** 131 \ **College-Bound:** 57% \ **Ethnic:** Asian 2%, African American 2%, Hispanic 13%, Caucasian 84% \ **Exp:** $166 (Low) \ **Poverty:** 11% \ **Title I:** $122,626 \ **Special Education:** $157,000 \ **Open-Close:** 08/20 - 05/28 \ **DTBP:** $180 (High) \

Jason Kozina	1	Angel Adamski		2
Greg Hornstein	3,5	Emilia Bires		4
Kenneth James	6*	Kristel James		16,82*
Michelle Reid	38,69*	Amy Rondstadt		67
Brad Lindquist	73*	Dr Ann McVey		79,288,298
Bill Hamilton	83,88*			

Public Schs..Principal	Grd	Prgm	Enr/#Cls	SN	
Northwood Elem Sch 500 Lemoyne Rd, Northwood 43619 Lindsey Krontz	PK-6	T	495 20	54%	419/691-4621 Fax 419/697-2479
Northwood High Sch 700 Lemoyne Rd, Northwood 43619 Jason Kozina	7-12	T	417 20	58%	419/691-4651 Fax 419/691-2846

Otsego Local School Dist PID: 00840331
18505 Tontogany Creek Rd Ste 1, Bowling Green 43402
419/823-4381
Fax 419/823-3035

Schools: 3 \ **Teachers:** 77 \ **Students:** 1,650 \ **Special Ed Students:** 218 \ **LEP Students:** 3 \ **College-Bound:** 51% \ **Ethnic:** African American 1%, Hispanic 7%, Caucasian 92% \ **Exp:** $201 (Med) \ **Poverty:** 9% \ **Title I:** $202,849 \ **Special Education:** $344,000 \ **Open-Close:** 08/21 - 05/29 \ **DTBP:** $170 (High)

Adam Koch	1	Steve Carroll		2*
Eva Vasher	3,5	Jeannie Jeffers		4*
Tom Ferdig	6*	Katrina Baughman		11,34,288,298
Pam Heyman	16,82*	Christen Zender		37
Jen Clark	38*	Lauri Dunham		58*
Brad Anderson	67	Luke Swartz		73*
Mary Gase	83	Stephen Mohr		286*

Public Schs..Principal	Grd	Prgm	Enr/#Cls	SN	
Otsego Elem Sch 18505 Tontogany Creek Rd Ste 4, Bowling Green 43402 Katrina Baughman	PK-5		832 14		419/823-4381 Fax 419/823-1703
Otsego High Sch 18505 Tontogany Creek Rd Ste 2, Bowling Green 43402 Kevin O'Shea	9-12	ATV	399 27	48%	419/823-4381 Fax 419/823-1397
Otsego Junior High Sch 18505 Tontogany Creek Rd Ste 3, Bowling Green 43402 Jon Rife	6-8	V	350 18		419/823-4381 Fax 419/823-0944

Penta Co JT Voc School Dist PID: 00840513
9301 Buck Rd, Perrysburg 43551
419/666-1120
Fax 419/666-6049

Schools: 1 \ **Teachers:** 167 \ **Students:** 1,500 \ **College-Bound:** 30% \ **Exp:** $771 (High) \ **Open-Close:** 08/27 - 05/29 \ **DTBP:** $245 (High)

Ronald Matter	1,11	Carrie Herringshaw		2
Kevin Baker	3,5*	Kelsey Yosick		4*
Christine Kerns	10*	Edward Ewers		15
Tara Schenkenberger	16*	Jeffrey Kurtz		27*
Debra Morris	30*	Daniel Weirich		38,79*
Ryan Myers	60*	Judy Paredez		67
Caleb Grills	73,76*	Linda Logue		83
Mark Smith	273*			

Public Schs..Principal	Grd	Prgm	Enr/#Cls	SN	
Penta Career Center 9301 Buck Rd, Perrysburg 43551 Jeffrey Kurtz	Voc	G	1,500		419/666-1120 Fax 419/661-6479

---

79 Student Personnel	91 Safety/Security	275 Response To Intervention	298 Grant Writer/Ptnrships	**School Programs**
80 Driver Ed/Safety	92 Magnet School	277 Remedial Math K-12	750 Chief Innovation Officer	A = Alternative Program
81 Gifted/Talented	93 Parental Involvement	280 Literacy Coach	751 Chief of Staff	G = Adult Classes
82 Video Services	95 Tech Prep Program	285 STEM	752 Social Emotional Learning	M = Magnet Program
83 Substance Abuse Prev	97 Chief Information Officer	286 Digital Learning		T = Title I Schoolwide
84 Erate	98 Chief Technology Officer	288 Common Core Standards	**Other School Types**	V = Career & Tech Ed Programs
85 AIDS Education	270 Character Education	294 Accountability	Ⓐ = Alternative School	
88 Alternative/At Risk	271 Migrant Education	295 Network System	Ⓒ = Charter School	
89 Multi-Cultural Curriculum	273 Teacher Mentor	296 Title II Programs	Ⓜ = Magnet School	
90 Social Work	274 Before/After Sch	297 Webmaster	Ⓨ = Year-Round School	

Social Media = Facebook   = Twitter

New Schools are shaded
New Superintendents and Principals are bold
Personnel with email addresses are underscored

Wyandot County

Market Data Retrieval

- **Perrysburg Exempted Village SD** PID: 00840408   419/874-9131
  140 E Indiana Ave, Perrysburg 43551   Fax 419/872-8820

Schools: 7 \ *Teachers:* 257 \ *Students:* 5,400 \ *Special Ed Students:* 514 \ *LEP Students:* 41 \ *College-Bound:* 78% \ *Ethnic:* Asian 4%, African American 2%, Hispanic 6%, Caucasian 87% \ *Exp:* $293 (Med) \ *Poverty:* 3% \ *Title I:* $132,171 \ *Special Education:* $740,000 \ *Open-Close:* 08/15 - 05/21 \ *DTBP:* $188 (High) \ 🅕 🅣

Thomas Hosler 1	Pamela Harrington 2
Stacie Feix 2	Greg Clarke 3
Lila Szozda 4	James Mapus 5
Chuck Jaco 6,35*	Brent Swartzmiller 8,11,288,298
Joe Sarnes 8,286	Sara Stockwell 13,57,79,296
Dr Kadee Anstadt 15	Andrea Glesser 58
Jarman Davis 67	Kelly Johnson 68,74,91,273
Kathryn Anstadt 69,275	Rachel Zickar 71
Brent Shafer 73,295	Cathy Kronmann 76
Brian Billings 81	

Public Schs..Principal	Grd	Prgm	Enr/#Cls	SN	
Frank Elem Sch 401 W South Boundary St, Perrysburg 43551 Dr Chad Warnimont	PK-4		474 21	9%	419/874-8721 Fax 419/874-1808 🅕 🅣
Ft Meigs Elem Sch 26431 Fort Meigs Rd, Perrysburg 43551 Kellie Johnson	PK-4		565 24	8%	419/872-8822 Fax 419/872-8825
Hull Prairie Interm Sch 25480 Hull Prairie Rd, Perrysburg 43551 Scott Best	5-6		873		419/873-6293
Perrysburg High Sch 13385 Roachton Rd, Perrysburg 43551 Dr Michael Short	9-12		1,570 73	11%	419/874-3181 Fax 419/872-8813
Perrysburg Junior High Sch 550 E South Boundary St, Perrysburg 43551 Donald Christie	7-8		838 80	10%	419/874-9193 Fax 419/872-8812
Toth Elem Sch 200 E 7th St, Perrysburg 43551 Dale Wiltse	PK-4		494 23	11%	419/874-3123 Fax 419/872-8828
Woodland Elem Sch 27979 White Rd, Perrysburg 43551 Brook Price	PK-4		574 21	13%	419/874-8736 Fax 419/874-2964

- **Rossford Exempted Village SD** PID: 00840458   419/666-2010
  325 Superior St, Rossford 43460   Fax 419/463-9088

Schools: 3 \ *Teachers:* 94 \ *Students:* 1,650 \ *Special Ed Students:* 191 \ *LEP Students:* 3 \ *College-Bound:* 56% \ *Ethnic:* Asian 2%, African American 1%, Hispanic 11%, Caucasian 86% \ *Exp:* $178 (Low) \ *Poverty:* 10% \ *Title I:* $250,983 \ *Special Education:* $379,000 \ *Open-Close:* 09/03 - 06/04 \ *DTBP:* $225 (High)

Dan Creps 1,11	James Rossler 2
Dave Duhamel 3	Julie Kalisik 4,5*
Chris Lucius 6	Erin Perry 58,77
Dawn Burks 67	Sandra Smith 73,84

Public Schs..Principal	Grd	Prgm	Enr/#Cls	SN	
ⓥ Rossford Elem Sch 28500 Lime City Rd, Rossford 43460 Jeff Taylor	PK-5	MT	600 15	51%	419/666-8130
Rossford High Sch 701 Superior St, Rossford 43460 Tony Brashear	9-12		420 40	73%	419/666-5262 Fax 419/661-2831
Rossford Junior High Sch 401 Glenwood Rd, Rossford 43460 Bryan Skrzyniecki	6-8	T	384 24		419/666-5254 Fax 419/661-5432 🅕 🅣

WOOD CATHOLIC SCHOOLS

- **Diocese of Toledo Ed Office** PID: 00818297
  Listing includes only schools located in this county. See District Index for location of Diocesan Offices.

Catholic Schs..Principal	Grd	Prgm	Enr/#Cls	SN	
All Saints Catholic Sch 630 Lime City Rd, Rossford 43460 Teri Fischer	PK-8		210 10		419/661-2070 Fax 419/661-2077
St Aloysius Sch 148 S Enterprise St, Bowling Green 43402 Andrea Puhl	K-8		209 11		419/352-8614 Fax 419/352-4738
St Louis Sch 22776 Defiance Pike, Custar 43511 Jennie Tussing	PK-6		33 5		419/669-1875 Fax 419/669-2878 🅕
St Rose Sch 217 E Front St, Perrysburg 43551 Dr Bryon Borgelt	PK-8		431 22		419/874-5631 Fax 419/874-1002

WOOD PRIVATE SCHOOLS

Private Schs..Principal	Grd	Prgm	Enr/#Cls	SN	
Bowling Green Chrn Academy 1165 Haskins Rd, Bowling Green 43402 Bo Kessler	PK-12		156 19		419/354-2422 Fax 419/354-0232
Islamic Sch of Greater Toledo 25877 Scheider Rd, Perrysburg 43551 Catherine Hammoud	PK-6		30 5		419/874-8820 Fax 419/874-8824

WOOD REGIONAL CENTERS

- **Northwest Ohio Ed Tech** PID: 02101052   419/372-7033
  245 Troup Ave Rm 119, Bowling Green 43403   Fax 419/372-0220

Roger Minier 1	Judy Tucker 15,16,74
Larry Busdeker 67	Tonya Sanders 73,76

WYANDOT COUNTY

WYANDOT COUNTY SCHOOLS

County Schs..Principal	Grd	Prgm	Enr/#Cls	SN	
Angeline Sch 11028 County Highway 44, Upper Sandsky 43351 Todd Dilley	Spec		30 4		419/294-4901 Fax 419/294-2054

---

1 Superintendent	8 Curric/Instruct K-12	19 Chief Financial Officer	29 Family/Consumer Science	39 Social Studies K-12	49 English/Lang Arts Elem	59 Special Education Elem	69 Academic Assessment
2 Bus/Finance/Purchasing	9 Curric/Instruct Elem	20 Art K-12	30 Adult Education	40 Social Studies Elem	50 English/Lang Arts Sec	60 Special Education Sec	70 Research/Development
3 Buildings And Grounds	10 Curric/Instruct Sec	21 Art Elem	31 Career/Sch-to-Work K-12	41 Social Studies Sec	51 Reading K-12	61 Foreign/World Lang K-12	71 Public Information
4 Food Service	11 Federal Program	22 Art Sec	32 Career/Sch-to-Work Elem	42 Science K-12	52 Reading Elem	62 Foreign/World Lang Elem	72 Summer School
5 Transportation	12 Title I	23 Music K-12	33 Career/Sch-to-Work Sec	43 Science Elem	53 Reading Sec	63 Foreign/World Lang Sec	73 Instructional Tech
6 Athletic	13 Title V	24 Music Elem	34 Early Childhood Ed	44 Science Sec	54 Remedial Reading K-12	64 Religious Education K-12	74 Inservice Training
7 Health Services	15 Asst Superintendent	25 Music Sec	35 Health/Phys Education	45 Math K-12	55 Remedial Reading Elem	65 Religious Education Elem	75 Marketing/Distributive
	16 Instructional Media Svcs	26 Business Education	36 Guidance Services K-12	46 Math Elem	56 Remedial Reading Sec	66 Religious Education Sec	76 Info Systems
	17 Chief Operations Officer	27 Career & Tech Ed	37 Guidance Services Elem	47 Math Sec	57 Bilingual/ELL	67 School Board President	77 Psychological Assess
	18 Chief Academic Officer	28 Technology Education	38 Guidance Services Sec	48 English/Lang Arts K-12	58 Special Education K-12	68 Teacher Personnel	78 Affirmative Action

Wyandot County

WYANDOT PUBLIC SCHOOLS

● **Carey Exempted Village SD** PID: 00840551   419/396-7922
2016 Blue Devil Dr, Carey 43316   Fax 419/396-3158

Schools: 1 \ **Teachers:** 58 \ **Students:** 850 \
Special Ed Students: 157 \ **College-Bound:** 36% \ **Ethnic:** Asian 2%, Hispanic 4%, Caucasian 93% \ **Exp:** $307 (High) \ **Poverty:** 7% \ **Title I:** $82,515 \ **Special Education:** $184,000 \ **Open-Close:** 08/26 - 05/29 \ **DTBP:** $177 (High)

Michael Wank	1	Karen Phillips	2*
Stan Stombaugh	3*	Rob Alexander	4
Kevin Kirkpatrick	5*	Lenny Orians	5*
Kent Asher	6	Rachel Nedacore	7,85*
Rachel Neidorkohr	7,85	Jen Barrett	8*
Dr Tammy Elchert	11*	Derek Cunningham	27,75*
Shannon Darby	36,69*	Tony Wenzinger	67
Nick Rider	73,76,295*	Steve Kozel	83*

Public Schs..Principal	Grd	Prgm	Enr/#Cls	SN	
Carey Exempted Village Sch 2016 Blue Devil Dr, Carey 43316 **Dr Tammy Elchert** \ Peter Cole	PK-12	V	850 30	29%	419/396-7922

● **Mohawk Local School Dist** PID: 00840599   419/927-2595
605 State Highway 231, Sycamore 44882   Fax 419/927-2393

Schools: 1 \ **Teachers:** 48 \ **Students:** 930 \ **Special Ed Students:** 92 \ **College-Bound:** 69% \ **Ethnic:** Hispanic 1%, Caucasian 99% \ **Exp:** $237 (Med) \ **Poverty:** 8% \ **Title I:** $97,414 \ **Special Education:** $180,000 \ **Open-Close:** 08/20 - 05/20 \ **DTBP:** $177 (High)

Mark Burke	1,11	Rhonda Feasel	2
Pam Dyer	4*	Jason Price	5
Chip Dietrich	6*	Gina Wyman	12,54*
Kaycee Hallett	16*	Lisa Zellner	36*
Brooke Bowlin	58	Sam Flood	67
Jake Molyet	73*	Angie McGinnis	85*
Kristie Graves	288		

Public Schs..Principal	Grd	Prgm	Enr/#Cls	SN	
Mohawk Local Sch 605 State Highway 231, Sycamore 44882 Mark Vehre \ Tami Wallace	PK-12		930 69	66%	419/927-2595

● **Upper Sandusky Exempted Vlg SD** PID: 00840642   419/294-2306
800 N Sandusky Ave Ste A, Upper Sandsky 43351   Fax 419/294-6891

Schools: 5 \ **Teachers:** 94 \ **Students:** 1,600 \ **Special Ed Students:** 268 \ **LEP Students:** 40 \ **College-Bound:** 55% \ **Ethnic:** Asian 1%, Hispanic 6%, Caucasian 93% \ **Exp:** $180 (Low) \ **Poverty:** 10% \ **Title I:** $256,777 \ **Special Education:** $336,000 \ **Open-Close:** 08/22 - 05/21 \ **DTBP:** $179 (High) \ f

Laurie Vent	1,11	Nathan Lynch	2
Michael Courtad	4	Kim Graboski	5
Brad Ehrman	6	Janine McMillan	8,270,288*
Wendy Searfoss	16*	Kristal Dunlap	33,38*
Andrea Schnieder	58	Jim Morris	67
Rhonda Caudill	68,71,83	Alison Cheney	69*
Tasha Stanton	72	Jim Frye	73,76,286,295*
Corrina Waggy	88		

Public Schs..Principal	Grd	Prgm	Enr/#Cls	SN	
East Elem Sch 401 N 3rd St, Upper Sandusky 43351 Angela Murphy	K-5		128 12	36%	419/294-2396 Fax 419/294-6895
South Elem Sch 444 S 8th St, Upper Sandusky 43351 Angela Murphy	K-5	T	138 8	51%	419/294-2304 Fax 419/294-6892
Union Elem Sch 390 W Walker St, Upper Sandusky 43351 Janine McMillan	K-3	T	266 52	46%	419/294-5721 Fax 419/294-2586 f
Upper Sandusky Middle Sch 390 W Walker St, Upper Sandusky 43351 James Wheeler	4-8		542	28%	419/294-5721 Fax 419/294-2856
Upper Sandusky Senior High Sch 800 N Sandusky Ave, Upper Sandusky 43351 Tasha Stanton	9-12		522 35	38%	419/294-2308 Fax 419/294-6889

WYANDOT CATHOLIC SCHOOLS

● **Diocese of Toledo Ed Office** PID: 00818297
Listing includes only schools located in this county. See District Index for location of Diocesan Offices.

Catholic Schs..Principal	Grd	Prgm	Enr/#Cls	SN	
Our Lady of Consolation Sch 401 Clay St, Carey 43316 Brian Gerber	PK-8		176 9		419/396-6166 Fax 419/396-3355
St Peter Catholic Sch 310 N 8th St, Upper Sandusky 43351 Mary Alice Harbour	K-6		125 8		419/294-1395 Fax 419/209-0295

Ohio School Directory

DISTRICT INDEX

SCHOOL DISTRICT	NO. OF SCHOOLS	ENROLL-MENT	COUNTY	PAGE
PUBLIC SCHOOL DISTRICTS				
ADA Exempted Village Sch Dist	1	890	Hardin	99
Adams Co Ohio Valley Sch Dist	7	3,800	Adams	6
Adena Local School Dist	3	1,200	Ross	174
Akron Public Schools	45	21,343	Summit	190
Alexander Local School Dist	2	1,495	Athens	14
Allen East Local School Dist	3	1,200	Allen	7
Alliance City School Dist	6	3,100	Stark	184
Amanda-Clearcreek Local SD	4	1,445	Fairfield	62
Amherst Exempted Village SD	4	3,800	Lorain	122
Anna Local School Dist	2	1,200	Shelby	182
Ansonia Local School Dist	2	700	Darke	55
Anthony Wayne Local Sch Dist	6	4,400	Lucas	127
Antwerp Local School Dist	1	800	Paulding	160
Apollo Joint Voc School Dist	1	600	Allen	8
Arcadia Local School Dist	1	575	Hancock	97
Arcanum Butler Local Sch Dist	4	1,125	Darke	55
Archbold Area Local Sch Dist	3	1,212	Fulton	78
Arlington Local School Dist	1	570	Hancock	97
Ashland City School Dist	5	3,800	Ashland	10
Ashland Co-West Holmes JVSD	1	450	Ashland	10
Ashtabula Area City Sch Dist	8	3,600	Ashtabula	12
Ashtabula Co Tech & Career SD	1	694	Ashtabula	12
Athens City School Dist	6	2,483	Athens	14
Auburn Vocational School Dist	1	745	Lake	112
Aurora City School Dist	5	3,000	Portage	164
Austintown Local School Dist	4	4,567	Mahoning	133
Avon Lake City School Dist	7	3,819	Lorain	122
Avon Local School Dist	5	4,650	Lorain	122
Ayersville Local School Dist	3	700	Defiance	56
Barberton City School Dist	5	3,813	Summit	192
Barnesville Exempted Vlg SD	3	1,480	Belmont	17
Batavia Local School Dist	3	2,289	Clermont	29
Bath Local School Dist	3	1,900	Allen	8
Bay Village City School Dist	4	2,442	Cuyahoga	40
Beachwood City School Dist	5	1,612	Cuyahoga	40
Beaver Local School Dist	3	1,800	Columbiana	34
Beavercreek City School Dist	11	7,200	Greene	83
Bedford City School Dist	6	3,292	Cuyahoga	40
Bellaire Local School Dist	3	1,159	Belmont	17
Bellbrook-Sugarcreek Schools	5	2,875	Greene	83
Bellefontaine City School Dist	4	2,600	Logan	120
Bellevue City School Dist	3	2,000	Huron	105
Belmont-Harrison Voc Sch Dist	2	408	Belmont	17
Belpre City School Dist	2	1,000	Washington	209
Benjamin Logan Local Sch Dist	3	1,750	Logan	121
Benton-Carroll-Salem Local SD	3	1,500	Ottawa	158
Berea City School Dist	7	5,817	Cuyahoga	41
Berkshire Local School Dist	3	1,200	Geauga	81
Berne Union Local School Dist	2	950	Fairfield	63
Bethel Local School Dist	2	1,400	Miami	145
Bethel-Tate Local School Dist	4	1,600	Clermont	30
Bexley City School Dist	5	2,463	Franklin	66
Big Walnut Local School Dist	7	4,000	Delaware	58
Black River Local School Dist	2	631	Medina	139
Blanchester Local School Dist	4	1,650	Clinton	32
Bloom-Carroll Local Sch Dist	4	2,000	Fairfield	63
Bloom-Vernon Local Sch Dist	2	900	Scioto	178
Bloomfield-Mespo Local SD	2	314	Trumbull	197
Bluffton Exempted Village Sch	3	1,220	Allen	8
Boardman Local School Dist	6	4,000	Mahoning	134
Botkins Local School Dist	1	644	Shelby	182
Bowling Green City Sch Dist	6	3,450	Wood	216
Bradford Exempted Village SD	2	487	Miami	145
Brecksville Broadview Hts CSD	5	3,850	Cuyahoga	41
Bridgeport School Dist	3	820	Belmont	18
Bright Local School Dist	2	700	Highland	102
Bristol Local School Dist	2	550	Trumbull	197
Brookfield Local School Dist	3	900	Trumbull	197
Brooklyn City School Dist	2	1,300	Cuyahoga	41
Brookville Local School Dist	3	1,500	Montgomery	148
Brown Local School Dist	3	630	Carroll	25
Brunswick City School Dist	11	7,123	Medina	140
Bryan City School Dist	2	2,200	Williams	214
Buckeye Central Local Sch Dist	3	650	Crawford	38
Buckeye Joint Voc School Dist	1	975	Tuscarawas	201
Buckeye Local School Dist	4	1,800	Ashtabula	12
Buckeye Local School Dist	5	1,700	Jefferson	108
Buckeye Local School Dist	4	2,300	Medina	140
Buckeye Valley Local Sch Dist	4	2,202	Delaware	58
Bucyrus City School Dist	2	1,300	Crawford	38
Butler Tech Career Dev Schs	1	900	Butler	21
Caldwell Exempted Village SD	2	800	Noble	158
Cambridge City School Dist	4	1,954	Guernsey	86
Campbell City School Dist	2	1,071	Mahoning	134
Canal Winchester Local SD	4	3,600	Franklin	66
Canfield Local School Dist	4	2,600	Mahoning	134
Canton City School Dist	27	9,500	Stark	184
Canton Local School Dist	3	2,000	Stark	185
Cardinal Local School Dist	3	1,000	Geauga	81
Cardington-Lincoln Local SD	4	1,200	Morrow	155
Carey Exempted Village SD	1	850	Wyandot	219
Carlisle Local School Dist	4	1,593	Warren	206
Carrollton Exempted Village SD	2	2,150	Carroll	25
Cedar Cliff Local School Dist	2	650	Greene	84
Celina City School Dist	5	2,300	Mercer	143
Centerburg Local School Dist	2	1,088	Knox	110
Centerville City School Dist	13	8,200	Montgomery	148
Central Local School Dist	3	1,050	Defiance	57
Chagrin Falls Exempted Vlg SD	4	2,000	Cuyahoga	42
Champion Local School Dist	2	1,525	Trumbull	197
Chardon Local School Dist	4	2,772	Geauga	82
Chesapeake Union Exempt Vlg SD	3	1,400	Lawrence	115
Chillicothe City School Dist	5	2,800	Ross	174
Chippewa Local School Dist	3	1,290	Wayne	211
Cincinnati City School Dist	61	35,000	Hamilton	87
Circleville City School Dist	3	2,174	Pickaway	162
Clark-Shawnee Local Sch Dist	5	2,057	Clark	27
Clay Local School Dist	1	714	Scioto	178
Claymont City School Dist	6	2,000	Tuscarawas	201
Clear Fork Vly Local Sch Dist	4	1,692	Richland	171
Clearview Local School Dist	3	1,644	Lorain	123
Clermont Northeastern Local SD	3	1,350	Clermont	30
Cleveland Hts-Univ Hts City SD	11	5,200	Cuyahoga	42
Cleveland Metro School Dist	112	38,949	Cuyahoga	42
Clinton-Massie Local Sch Dist	3	1,800	Clinton	33
Cloverleaf Local School Dist	3	2,264	Medina	140
Clyde-Green Spgs Exmpt Vlg SD	4	2,300	Sandusky	176
Coldwater Exempted Village SD	3	1,375	Mercer	143
Colonel Crawford Local SD	3	920	Crawford	38
Columbia Local School Dist	3	900	Lorain	123
Columbiana Co Voc Sch Dist	1	450	Columbiana	34
Columbiana Exempted Village SD	3	1,077	Columbiana	34
Columbus City School Dist	113	52,000	Franklin	66
Columbus Grove Local Sch Dist	2	879	Putnam	169
Conneaut Area City Sch Dist	4	1,604	Ashtabula	12
Conotton Valley Union Local SD	2	402	Harrison	100
Continental Local School Dist	2	480	Putnam	169
Copley-Fairlawn City Sch Dist	5	2,886	Summit	192
Cory-Rawson Local School Dist	2	550	Hancock	97
Coshocton City School Dist	2	1,600	Coshocton	36
Coshocton Co Joint Voc SD	1	246	Coshocton	37
Coventry Local School Dist	3	1,900	Summit	192
Covington Exempted Village SD	2	850	Miami	145
Crestline Exempted Village SD	1	570	Crawford	38
Crestview Local School Dist	3	1,100	Richland	171
Crestview Local School Dist	3	1,245	Columbiana	34
Crestview Local School Dist	1	820	Van Wert	205
Crestwood Local School Dist	4	1,600	Portage	165
Crooksville Exempted Vlg SD	3	1,100	Perry	161
Cuyahoga Falls City Sch Dist	10	4,500	Summit	192
Cuyahoga Heights Local SD	3	900	Cuyahoga	45
Cuyahoga Vly Career Ctr Voc SD	1	1,000	Cuyahoga	45

School Year 2019-2020 800-333-8802 OH-Q1

DISTRICT INDEX

Market Data Retrieval

SCHOOL DISTRICT	NO. OF SCHOOLS	ENROLLMENT	COUNTY	PAGE
Dalton Local School Dist	2	875	Wayne	211
Danbury Local School Dist	1	543	Ottawa	159
Danville Local School Dist	2	615	Knox	110
Dawson-Bryant Local Sch Dist	3	1,200	Lawrence	115
Dayton Public School Dist	25	13,792	Montgomery	149
Deer Park Cmty School Dist	2	1,261	Hamilton	89
Defiance City School Dist	3	2,400	Defiance	57
Delaware City School Dist	7	5,459	Delaware	58
Delaware Joint Voc Sch Dist	2	1,000	Delaware	59
Delphos City School Dist	3	1,050	Allen	8
Dover City School Dist	5	2,712	Tuscarawas	202
Dublin City School Dist	20	16,200	Franklin	69
East Cleveland City Sch Dist	6	2,300	Cuyahoga	45
East Clinton Local School Dist	4	1,300	Clinton	33
East Guernsey Local Sch Dist	3	1,200	Guernsey	86
East Holmes Local School Dist	8	1,615	Holmes	104
East Knox Local School Dist	2	1,100	Knox	111
East Liverpool City Sch Dist	4	2,050	Columbiana	34
East Muskingum Local Sch Dist	6	2,200	Muskingum	156
East Palestine City Sch Dist	3	1,087	Columbiana	35
Eastern Local School Dist	3	820	Meigs	142
Eastern Local School Dist	4	1,350	Adams	7
Eastern Local School Dist	3	901	Pike	163
Eastland-Ffld Career Tech VSD	3	1,500	Franklin	70
Eastwood Local School Dist	3	1,500	Wood	216
Eaton Cmty School Dist	4	1,943	Preble	168
Edgerton Local School Dist	2	599	Williams	214
Edgewood City School Dist	5	3,800	Butler	21
Edison Local School Dist	3	2,000	Jefferson	109
Edison Local Schools Dist	3	1,650	Erie	60
Edon Northwest Local Sch Dist	1	500	Williams	215
Ehove Joint Voc School Dist	1	850	Erie	60
Elgin Local School Dist	3	1,200	Marion	138
Elida Local School Dist	3	2,500	Allen	8
Elmwood Local School Dist	3	1,275	Wood	216
Elyria City School Dist	13	7,010	Lorain	123
Euclid City School Dist	7	5,100	Cuyahoga	46
Evergreen Local School Dist	3	1,300	Fulton	78
Fairbanks Local School Dist	3	1,072	Union	204
Fairborn City School Dist	4	4,300	Greene	84
Fairfield City School Dist	11	10,000	Butler	21
Fairfield Local Sch Dist	3	950	Highland	102
Fairfield Union Local Sch Dist	4	2,000	Fairfield	63
Fairland Local School Dist	4	1,569	Lawrence	116
Fairlawn Local School Dist	2	650	Shelby	182
Fairless Local School Dist	3	1,501	Stark	185
Fairport Harbor Exempt Vlg SD	2	720	Lake	112
Fairview Park City Sch Dist	4	1,702	Cuyahoga	46
Fayette Local Sch Dist	1	370	Fulton	79
Fayetteville Perry Local SD	3	855	Brown	19
Federal Hocking Local Sch Dist	3	1,000	Athens	14
Felicity-Franklin Local SD	3	800	Clermont	30
Field Local School Dist	4	1,900	Portage	165
Findlay City School Dist	15	6,000	Hancock	97
Finneytown Local School Dist	3	1,400	Hamilton	89
Firelands Local School Dist	4	1,626	Lorain	124
Forest Hills School Dist	9	7,450	Hamilton	89
Fostoria City School Dist	2	1,845	Seneca	180
Four-Co Joint Voc School Dist	1	1,000	Fulton	79
Franklin City School Dist	8	2,750	Warren	207
Franklin Local School Dist	5	2,000	Muskingum	156
Franklin-Monroe Local Sch Dist	2	625	Darke	55
Fredericktown Local Sch Dist	3	1,197	Knox	111
Fremont City School Dist	9	3,843	Sandusky	176
Frontier Local School Dist	3	625	Washington	209
Ft Frye Local School Dist	4	1,031	Washington	210
Ft Loramie Local School Dist	2	793	Shelby	182
Ft Recovery Local School Dist	2	920	Mercer	144
Gahanna-Jefferson Public SD	11	7,543	Franklin	70
Galion City School Dist	4	1,817	Crawford	38
Gallia Co Local School Dist	8	2,200	Gallia	80
Gallia-Jackson-Vinton JVSD	1	500	Gallia	80
Gallipolis City School Dist	5	2,052	Gallia	81
Garaway Local School Dist	5	1,300	Tuscarawas	202
Garfield Heights City SD	6	3,721	Cuyahoga	46
Geneva Area City School Dist	5	2,415	Ashtabula	13
Genoa Area Local School Dist	3	1,323	Ottawa	159
Georgetown Exempted Village SD	2	1,100	Brown	19
Gibsonburg Exempted Village SD	3	950	Sandusky	177
Girard City School Dist	4	1,699	Trumbull	197
Goshen Local School Dist	4	2,800	Clermont	30
Graham Local School Dist	3	1,836	Champaign	25
Grand Valley Local School Dist	3	1,075	Ashtabula	13
Grandview Heights City SD	4	1,075	Franklin	70
Granville Exempted Village SD	4	2,500	Licking	117
Great Oaks Career Campuses	4	3,000	Hamilton	89
Green Local School Dist	2	600	Scioto	178
Green Local School Dist	5	4,253	Stark	185
Green Local School Dist	3	1,056	Wayne	212
Greene Co Voc School Dist	1	685	Greene	84
Greeneview Local School Dist	3	1,400	Greene	84
Greenfield Exempted Village SD	5	2,250	Highland	103
Greenon Local School Dist	3	1,486	Clark	27
Greenville City School Dist	3	2,507	Darke	55
Groveport Madison Local SD	11	7,200	Franklin	71
Hamilton City School Dist	13	10,300	Butler	21
Hamilton Local School Dist	4	3,200	Franklin	71
Hardin Northern Local Sch Dist	2	405	Hardin	100
Hardin-Houston Local Sch Dist	1	860	Shelby	182
Harrison Hills City Sch Dist	3	1,600	Harrison	101
Heath City School Dist	4	1,730	Licking	117
Hicksville Exempted Village SD	2	1,000	Defiance	57
Highland Local School Dist	5	3,233	Medina	141
Highland Local School Dist	3	1,850	Morrow	155
Hilliard City School Dist	25	16,600	Franklin	71
Hillsboro City School Dist	3	2,300	Highland	103
Hillsdale Local School Dist	3	850	Ashland	11
Holgate Local School Dist	1	470	Henry	101
Hopewell-Loudon Local SD	1	821	Seneca	181
Howland Local School Dist	6	2,685	Trumbull	198
Hubbard Exempted Village SD	3	1,932	Trumbull	198
Huber Heights City School Dist	8	6,100	Montgomery	150
Hudson City School Dist	6	4,600	Summit	193
Huntington Local School Dist	3	1,120	Ross	175
Huron City School Dist	4	1,324	Erie	60
Independence Local School Dist	3	1,075	Cuyahoga	46
Indian Creek Local Sch Dist	4	2,300	Jefferson	109
Indian Hill Exempted Vlg SD	4	2,030	Hamilton	90
Indian Lake Local School Dist	3	1,516	Logan	121
Indian Valley Local Sch Dist	5	1,900	Tuscarawas	202
Ironton City School Dist	3	1,400	Lawrence	116
Jackson Center Local Sch Dist	1	600	Shelby	183
Jackson City School Dist	5	2,450	Jackson	107
Jackson Local School Dist	6	5,817	Stark	186
Jackson-Milton Local Sch Dist	2	700	Mahoning	134
James A Garfield Local SD	3	1,379	Portage	165
Jefferson Area Local SD	4	1,651	Ashtabula	13
Jefferson Co JT Voc Sch Dist	1	350	Jefferson	109
Jefferson Local School Dist	3	1,200	Madison	132
Jefferson Twp Local Sch Dist	2	345	Montgomery	150
Jennings Local School Dist	1	400	Putnam	169
Johnstown-Monroe Local SD	3	1,600	Licking	118
Jonathan Alder Local Sch Dist	5	2,270	Madison	132
Joseph Badger Local Sch Dist	3	750	Trumbull	198
Kalida Local School Dist	2	605	Putnam	169
Kelleys Island Local Sch Dist	1	5	Erie	61
Kenston Local School Dist	4	2,858	Geauga	82
Kent City School Dist	6	3,400	Portage	165
Kenton City School Dist	3	1,848	Hardin	100
Kettering City School Dist	12	7,400	Montgomery	150
Keystone Local School Dist	3	1,500	Lorain	124
Kings Local School Dist	7	4,650	Warren	207
Kirtland Local School Dist	3	1,155	Lake	112
Knox Co Voc School Dist	1	640	Knox	111

OH-Q2   800-333-8802   School Year 2019-2020

Ohio School Directory

DISTRICT INDEX

SCHOOL DISTRICT	NO. OF SCHOOLS	ENROLL-MENT	COUNTY	PAGE
Labrae Local School Dist	4	1,078	Trumbull	198
Lake Local School Dist	3	3,300	Stark	186
Lake Local School Dist	3	1,679	Wood	217
Lakeview Local School Dist	3	1,732	Trumbull	198
Lakewood City School Dist	12	4,000	Cuyahoga	47
Lakewood Local School Dist	4	1,900	Licking	118
Lakota Local School Dist	23	16,500	Butler	22
Lakota Local School Dist	3	1,140	Sandusky	177
Lancaster City School Dist	9	6,300	Fairfield	63
Lawrence Co Joint Voc Sch Dist	1	475	Lawrence	116
Lebanon City School Dist	5	6,000	Warren	207
Leetonia Exempted Village SD	1	780	Columbiana	35
Leipsic Local School Dist	2	650	Putnam	170
Lexington Local School Dist	5	2,510	Richland	172
Liberty Center Local Sch Dist	3	1,174	Henry	101
Liberty Local School Dist	3	1,244	Trumbull	199
Liberty Union-Thurstn Sch Dist	3	1,350	Fairfield	64
Liberty-Benton Local Sch Dist	3	1,242	Hancock	98
Licking Co Joint Voc Sch Dist	1	750	Licking	118
Licking Heights Local Sch Dist	5	4,700	Licking	118
Licking Valley Local Sch Dist	3	2,000	Licking	118
Lima City School Dist	9	4,000	Allen	9
Lincolnview Local School Dist	3	900	Van Wert	205
Lisbon Exempted Village SD	2	850	Columbiana	35
Little Miami Local School Dist	6	5,020	Warren	207
Lockland School Dist	3	550	Hamilton	90
Logan Elm Local School Dist	6	1,880	Pickaway	162
Logan-Hocking Local Sch Dist	7	3,945	Hocking	104
London City School Dist	3	2,103	Madison	132
Lorain City School Dist	14	6,500	Lorain	124
Lorain Co Joint Voc Sch Dist	1	1,500	Lorain	125
Lordstown Local School Dist	2	500	Trumbull	199
Loudonville-Perrysville SD	3	1,100	Ashland	11
Louisville City School Dist	4	2,797	Stark	186
Loveland City School Dist	6	4,700	Hamilton	90
Lowellville Local School Dist	1	499	Mahoning	135
Lucas Local School Dist	3	565	Richland	172
Lynchburg-Clay Local Sch Dist	3	1,150	Highland	103
Mad River Local School Dist	8	3,800	Montgomery	151
Madeira City School Dist	3	1,400	Hamilton	90
Madison Local School Dist	2	1,600	Butler	23
Madison Local School Dist	5	3,120	Lake	112
Madison Local School Dist	5	2,956	Richland	172
Madison Plains Local Sch Dist	4	1,173	Madison	133
Mahoning Co Joint Voc Sch Dist	2	778	Mahoning	135
Manchester Local School Dist	2	856	Adams	7
Manchester Local School Dist	3	1,400	Summit	193
Mansfield City Schools	8	3,350	Richland	172
Maple Heights City School Dist	5	3,800	Cuyahoga	47
Mapleton Local School Dist	3	890	Ashland	11
Maplewood JT Voc School Dist	1	700	Portage	166
Maplewood Local School Dist	2	750	Trumbull	199
Margaretta Local School Dist	3	2,602	Erie	61
Mariemont City School Dist	4	1,700	Hamilton	90
Marietta City School Dist	6	2,580	Washington	210
Marion City School Dist	9	4,200	Marion	138
Marion Local School Dist	2	860	Mercer	144
Marlington Local School Dist	5	2,300	Stark	186
Martins Ferry City School Dist	3	1,500	Belmont	18
Marysville Exempted Village SD	10	5,100	Union	204
Mason City School Dist	5	10,396	Warren	208
Massillon City School Dist	7	3,900	Stark	187
Mathews Local School Dist	3	675	Trumbull	199
Maumee City School Dist	5	2,222	Lucas	127
Mayfield City School Dist	6	4,000	Cuyahoga	47
Maysville Local School Dist	3	2,200	Muskingum	156
McComb Local School Dist	3	700	Hancock	98
McDonald Local School Dist	2	768	Trumbull	199
Mechanicsburg Exempted Vlg SD	2	900	Champaign	26
Medina City School Dist	11	7,100	Medina	141
Medina Co Joint Voc Sch Dist	1	1,100	Medina	141
Meigs Local School Dist	4	1,700	Meigs	142
Mentor Exempted Village SD	11	7,415	Lake	113
Miami East Local School Dist	3	1,300	Miami	145
Miami Trace Local School Dist	3	2,582	Fayette	65
Miami Valley Career Tech VSD	2	2,100	Montgomery	151
Miamisburg City School Dist	10	5,500	Montgomery	151
Middletown City School Dist	10	6,561	Butler	23
Mideast Career & Tech Ctrs	3	1,100	Muskingum	157
Midview Local School Dist	5	3,000	Lorain	125
Milford Exempted Village SD	10	6,600	Clermont	30
Millcreek-West Unity Local SD	1	520	Williams	215
Miller City-New Cleveland SD	3	485	Putnam	170
Milton-Union Exempted Vlg SD	3	1,500	Miami	145
Minerva Local School Dist	3	1,900	Stark	187
Minford Local School Dist	3	1,401	Scioto	178
Minster Local School Dist	2	849	Auglaize	15
Mississinawa Valley Sch Dist	2	700	Darke	56
Mogadore Local School Dist	2	875	Portage	166
Mohawk Local School Dist	1	930	Wyandot	219
Monroe Local School Dist	4	2,900	Butler	23
Monroeville Local School Dist	2	593	Huron	105
Montpelier Exempted Village SD	1	1,100	Williams	215
Morgan Local School Dist	5	1,763	Morgan	154
Mt Gilead Exempted Village SD	3	1,200	Morrow	155
Mt Healthy City School Dist	3	3,300	Hamilton	91
Mt Vernon City School Dist	8	4,000	Knox	111
Napoleon Area City School Dist	3	1,700	Henry	101
National Trail Local Sch Dist	3	1,100	Preble	168
Nelsonville-York City Sch Dist	3	1,206	Athens	15
New Albany-Plain Local SD	5	5,100	Franklin	72
New Boston Local School Dist	3	500	Scioto	178
New Bremen Local School Dist	2	760	Auglaize	16
New Knoxville Local Sch Dist	1	392	Auglaize	16
New Lebanon Local School Dist	3	1,100	Montgomery	151
New Lexington School Dist	4	1,980	Perry	161
New London Local School Dist	4	900	Huron	105
New Miami Local School Dist	2	620	Butler	23
New Philadelphia City Sch Dist	8	3,800	Tuscarawas	202
New Richmond Exempted Vlg SD	4	2,400	Clermont	31
New Riegel Local School Dist	1	500	Seneca	181
Newark City School Dist	13	6,500	Licking	119
Newbury Local School Dist	2	270	Geauga	82
Newcomerstown Exempted Vlg SD	4	1,100	Tuscarawas	203
Newton Falls Exempted Vlg SD	4	1,100	Trumbull	200
Newton Local School Dist	1	600	Miami	146
Niles City School Dist	4	2,209	Trumbull	200
Noble Local School Dist	2	900	Noble	158
Nordonia Hills City Sch Dist	6	3,585	Summit	193
North Baltimore Local Sch Dist	2	700	Wood	217
North Canton City School Dist	7	4,437	Stark	187
North Central Local Sch Dist	1	600	Williams	215
North College Hill City SD	3	1,650	Hamilton	91
North Fork Local School Dist	4	1,800	Licking	119
North Olmsted City School Dist	8	3,900	Cuyahoga	48
North Ridgeville City Sch Dist	5	4,600	Lorain	125
North Royalton City Sch Dist	5	4,060	Cuyahoga	48
North Union Local School Dist	3	1,540	Union	204
Northeastern Local School Dist	7	3,300	Clark	27
Northeastern Local School Dist	4	1,082	Defiance	57
Northern Local School Dist	5	2,251	Perry	161
Northmont City School Dist	8	5,800	Montgomery	152
Northmor Local School Dist	1	1,042	Morrow	155
Northridge Local School Dist	4	1,300	Licking	119
Northridge Local School Dist	4	1,500	Montgomery	152
Northwest Local School Dist	11	9,000	Hamilton	91
Northwest Local School Dist	3	1,373	Scioto	179
Northwest Local School Dist	4	1,783	Stark	187
Northwestern Local School Dist	2	1,643	Clark	27
Northwestern Local School Dist	3	1,320	Wayne	212
Northwood Local School Dist	2	950	Wood	217
Norton City School Dist	4	2,500	Summit	193
Norwalk City School Dist	6	2,750	Huron	106
Norwayne Local School Dist	3	1,400	Wayne	212

School Year 2019-2020 800-333-8802

DISTRICT INDEX

SCHOOL DISTRICT	NO. OF SCHOOLS	ENROLLMENT	COUNTY	PAGE
Norwood City School Dist	5	2,000	Hamilton	92
Oak Hill Union Local Sch Dist	2	1,220	Jackson	107
Oak Hills Local School Dist	9	8,700	Hamilton	92
Oakwood City School Dist	5	1,988	Montgomery	152
Oberlin City School Dist	4	1,200	Lorain	125
Ohio Hi-Point Joint Voc SD	1	500	Logan	121
Old Fort Local School Dist	2	750	Seneca	181
Olentangy Local School Dist	25	22,125	Delaware	59
Olmsted Falls City School Dist	5	3,628	Cuyahoga	48
Ontario Local School Dist	3	2,158	Richland	173
Orange City School Dist	4	2,000	Cuyahoga	48
Oregon City School Dist	8	3,800	Lucas	128
Orrville City School Dist	3	1,600	Wayne	212
Osnaburg Local School Dist	3	850	Stark	188
Otsego Local School Dist	3	1,650	Wood	217
Ottawa Hills Local Sch Dist	2	1,000	Lucas	128
Ottawa-Glandorf Local Sch Dist	4	1,400	Putnam	170
Ottoville Local School Dist	2	430	Putnam	170
Painesville City Local SD	6	3,000	Lake	113
Paint Valley Local School Dist	3	890	Ross	175
Pandora Gilboa Local Sch Dist	3	524	Putnam	170
Parkway Local School Dist	3	1,000	Mercer	144
Parma City School Dist	15	10,712	Cuyahoga	49
Patrick Henry Local Sch Dist	3	855	Henry	102
Paulding Exempted Village SD	4	1,475	Paulding	160
Penta Co JT Voc School Dist	1	1,500	Wood	217
Perkins Local School Dist	4	1,950	Erie	61
Perry Local School Dist	2	753	Allen	9
Perry Local School Dist	3	1,700	Lake	113
Perry Local School Dist	8	4,500	Stark	188
Perrysburg Exempted Village SD	7	5,400	Wood	218
Pettisville Local School Dist	2	525	Fulton	79
Pickaway-Ross Co JT Voc SD	1	800	Ross	175
Pickerington Local School Dist	15	10,600	Fairfield	64
Pike Co Area JT Voc Sch Dist	1	500	Pike	163
Pike-Delta-York Local Sch Dist	3	1,100	Fulton	79
Pioneer Joint Voc School Dist	1	1,250	Richland	173
Piqua City School Dist	5	3,500	Miami	146
Plain Local School Dist	9	6,000	Stark	188
Pleasant Local School Dist	4	1,320	Marion	138
Plymouth-Shiloh Local Sch Dist	3	681	Richland	173
Poland Local School Dist	3	1,888	Mahoning	135
Polaris Joint Voc School Dist	1	1,000	Cuyahoga	49
Port Clinton City School Dist	4	1,700	Ottawa	159
Portage Lakes Joint Voc SD	1	650	Stark	189
Portsmouth City School Dist	3	1,700	Scioto	179
Preble-Shawnee Local Sch Dist	3	1,430	Preble	168
Princeton City School Dist	10	6,500	Hamilton	92
Put-In-Bay Local School Dist	1	72	Ottawa	159
Pymatuning Valley Local SD	3	1,200	Ashtabula	13
Ravenna School Dist	7	2,200	Portage	166
Reading Cmty City School Dist	4	1,535	Hamilton	93
Revere Local School Dist	4	2,700	Summit	194
Reynoldsburg City School Dist	16	7,572	Franklin	72
Richmond Heights Local SD	2	850	Cuyahoga	49
Ridgedale Local School Dist	2	642	Marion	138
Ridgemont Local School Dist	2	511	Hardin	100
Ridgewood Local School Dist	3	1,275	Coshocton	37
Ripley-Union-Lewis-Huntngtn SD	3	850	Brown	20
Rittman Exempted Village SD	4	999	Wayne	212
River Valley Local School Dist	4	2,260	Marion	139
River View Local School Dist	5	2,100	Coshocton	37
Riverdale Local School Dist	3	1,030	Hancock	98
Riverside Local School Dist	2	633	Logan	121
Riverside Local School Dist	6	3,987	Lake	113
Rock Hill Local School Dist	3	1,450	Lawrence	116
Rocky River City School Dist	5	2,610	Cuyahoga	50
Rolling Hills Local Sch Dist	6	1,650	Guernsey	86
Rootstown Local School Dist	3	1,200	Portage	166
Ross Local School Dist	4	2,500	Butler	24
Rossford Exempted Village SD	3	1,650	Wood	218
Russia Local School Dist	1	430	Shelby	183
Salem City School Dist	5	2,100	Columbiana	35
Sandusky City School Dist	7	3,250	Erie	61
Sandy Valley Local School Dist	3	1,500	Stark	189
Scioto Co Joint Vocational SD	1	540	Scioto	179
Scioto Valley Local Sch Dist	2	1,300	Pike	164
Sebring Local School Dist	2	600	Mahoning	135
Seneca East Local School Dist	1	880	Seneca	181
Shadyside Local School Dist	3	800	Belmont	18
Shaker Heights City Sch Dist	9	5,180	Cuyahoga	50
Shawnee Local School Dist	4	2,500	Allen	9
Sheffield-Sheffield Lake CSD	5	1,747	Lorain	125
Shelby City School Dist	5	1,918	Richland	173
Sidney City School Dist	6	3,350	Shelby	183
Solon City School Dist	7	4,547	Cuyahoga	50
South Central Local Sch Dist	3	750	Huron	106
South Euclid-Lyndhurst City SD	6	3,500	Cuyahoga	50
South Point Local School Dist	4	1,500	Lawrence	116
South Range Local School Dist	3	1,247	Mahoning	135
South-Western City School Dist	33	22,790	Franklin	73
Southeast Local School Dist	6	1,400	Wayne	213
Southeast Local School Dist	4	1,484	Portage	166
Southeastern Local Sch Dist	3	1,040	Ross	175
Southeastern Local School Dist	2	778	Clark	28
Southern Hills Joint Voc SD	1	380	Brown	20
Southern Local School Dist	2	920	Columbiana	35
Southern Local School Dist	2	728	Meigs	143
Southern Local School Dist	2	664	Perry	161
Southington Local School Dist	1	500	Trumbull	200
Southwest Licking Local SD	6	4,300	Licking	120
Southwest Local School Dist	6	4,044	Hamilton	93
Spencerville Local School Dist	3	965	Allen	9
Springboro Cmty School Dist	6	6,093	Warren	208
Springfield City School Dist	16	7,583	Clark	28
Springfield Local School Dist	4	2,222	Summit	194
Springfield Local School Dist	6	4,000	Lucas	128
Springfield Local School Dist	3	942	Mahoning	135
Springfield-Clark Co JVSD	1	700	Clark	28
St Bernard-Elmwood Place Schs	3	1,000	Hamilton	93
St Clairsville-Richland CSD	3	1,700	Belmont	18
St Henry Cons Local Sch Dist	3	950	Mercer	144
St Mary's City School Dist	4	1,996	Auglaize	16
Stark Co Area Voc Sch Dist	1	700	Stark	189
Steubenville City School Dist	6	2,600	Jefferson	109
Stow-Munroe Falls City SD	10	5,158	Summit	194
Strasburg Franklin Local SD	2	534	Tuscarawas	203
Streetsboro City School Dist	4	2,200	Portage	167
Strongsville City School Dist	8	5,553	Cuyahoga	51
Struthers City School Dist	3	1,785	Mahoning	136
Stryker Local School Dist	2	407	Williams	215
Swanton Local School Dist	3	1,300	Fulton	79
Switzerland of Ohio Local SD	9	2,300	Monroe	147
Sycamore Cmty School Dist	7	5,481	Hamilton	93
Sylvania City School Dist	12	7,704	Lucas	128
Symmes Valley Local Sch Dist	2	743	Lawrence	117
Talawanda School Dist	5	3,100	Butler	24
Tallmadge City School Dist	4	2,412	Summit	194
Teays Valley Local School Dist	7	4,350	Pickaway	162
Tecumseh Local School Dist	5	3,130	Clark	28
Three Rivers Local School Dist	2	2,200	Hamilton	94
Tiffin City School Dist	6	2,800	Seneca	181
Tipp City Exempted Village SD	5	2,605	Miami	146
Toledo Public Schools	52	24,000	Lucas	129
Tolles Career & Tech Sch Dist	1	640	Madison	133
Toronto City School Dist	2	891	Jefferson	109
Tri-Co Joint Voc Sch Dist	1	450	Athens	15
Tri-Co North School Dist	3	786	Preble	168
Tri-Rivers Joint Voc Sch Dist	1	550	Marion	139
Tri-Valley Local School Dist	6	3,100	Muskingum	157
Tri-Village Local Sch Dist	1	827	Darke	56
Triad Local School Dist	3	830	Champaign	26
Trimble Local School Dist	3	900	Athens	15
Triway Local School Dist	4	1,637	Wayne	213

Market Data Retrieval

OH-Q4 800-333-8802 School Year 2019-2020

Ohio School Directory — DISTRICT INDEX

SCHOOL DISTRICT	NO. OF SCHOOLS	ENROLLMENT	COUNTY	PAGE
Trotwood-Madison City SD	5	2,300	Montgomery	152
Troy City School Dist	9	4,400	Miami	146
Tuscarawas Valley Local SD	4	1,380	Tuscarawas	203
Tuslaw Local School Dist	3	1,390	Stark	189
Twin Valley Cmty Local SD	2	837	Preble	169
Twinsburg City School Dist	5	4,200	Summit	195
U S Grant Career School Dist	1	400	Clermont	31
Union Local School Dist	3	1,521	Belmont	18
Union Scioto Local Sch Dist	3	2,175	Ross	175
United Local School Dist	2	1,300	Columbiana	36
Upper Arlington City Sch Dist	8	6,000	Franklin	74
Upper Sandusky Exempted Vlg SD	5	1,600	Wyandot	219
Upper Scioto Valley Local SD	1	450	Hardin	100
Upper Valley JT Voc Sch Dist	1	780	Miami	147
Urbana City School Dist	3	2,000	Champaign	26
Valley Local School Dist	3	1,020	Scioto	179
Valley View Local School Dist	4	1,900	Montgomery	153
Van Buren Local School Dist	3	1,080	Hancock	99
Van Wert City School Dist	4	2,084	Van Wert	205
Vandalia Butler City Sch Dist	5	3,225	Montgomery	153
Vanguard-Sentinel JT Voc SD	2	2,300	Sandusky	177
Vanlue Local School Dist	1	180	Hancock	99
Vantage Career Center Sch Dist	1	480	Van Wert	206
Vermilion Local School Dist	3	1,900	Erie	62
Versailles Exempted Village SD	3	1,305	Darke	56
Vinton Co Local School Dist	5	2,100	Vinton	206
Wadsworth City School Dist	8	4,800	Medina	141
Walnut Twp Local School Dist	2	490	Fairfield	64
Wapakoneta City School Dist	4	3,081	Auglaize	16
Warren City School Dist	5	4,300	Trumbull	200
Warren Co Voc School Dist	1	775	Warren	208
Warren Local School Dist	4	2,022	Washington	210
Warrensville Heights City SD	5	1,700	Cuyahoga	51
Washington Co JT Voc Sch Dist	1	487	Washington	210
Washington Court House City SD	4	2,200	Fayette	65
Washington Local School Dist	13	7,042	Lucas	130
Washington-Nile Local Sch Dist	3	1,449	Scioto	179
Waterloo Local School Dist	3	1,100	Portage	167
Wauseon Exempted Village SD	4	1,770	Fulton	79
Waverly City School Dist	4	1,825	Pike	164
Wayne Co Joint Voc School Dist	1	879	Wayne	213
Wayne Local School Dist	3	1,473	Warren	208
Wayne Trace Local School Dist	3	1,000	Paulding	160
Waynesfield-Goshen Local SD	2	500	Auglaize	16
Weathersfield Local Sch Dist	2	992	Trumbull	200
Wellington Exempted Village SD	3	1,304	Lorain	126
Wellston City School Dist	4	1,450	Jackson	108
Wellsville Local Sch Dist	3	850	Columbiana	36
West Branch Local School Dist	5	2,100	Mahoning	136
West Carrollton City Sch Dist	6	3,700	Montgomery	153
West Clermont Local Sch Dist	10	9,500	Clermont	31
West Geauga Local School Dist	4	1,874	Geauga	82
West Holmes Local School Dist	6	2,100	Holmes	105
West Liberty-Salem Local SD	1	1,250	Champaign	26
West Muskingum Local Sch Dist	3	1,400	Muskingum	157
Western Brown Local Sch Dist	4	3,400	Brown	20
Western Local School Dist	2	790	Pike	164
Western Reserve Local Sch Dist	3	994	Huron	106
Western Reserve Local Sch Dist	1	850	Mahoning	136
Westerville City School Dist	24	15,000	Franklin	74
Westfall Local School Dist	3	1,432	Pickaway	163
Westlake City School Dist	4	3,500	Cuyahoga	51
Wheelersburg Local School Dist	3	1,600	Scioto	180
Whitehall City School Dist	6	3,200	Franklin	75
Wickliffe City School Dist	3	1,290	Lake	114
Willard City School Dist	2	1,520	Huron	106
Williamsburg Local School Dist	2	994	Clermont	32
Willoughby-Eastlake City SD	13	8,090	Lake	114
Wilmington City School Dist	5	3,000	Clinton	33
Windham Exempted Vlg Sch Dist	3	600	Portage	167
Winton Woods City School Dist	7	3,500	Hamilton	94
Wolf Creek Local School Dist	2	606	Washington	211
Woodmore Local School Dist	2	974	Ottawa	159
Woodridge Local School Dist	3	2,000	Summit	195
Wooster City School Dist	7	3,650	Wayne	213
Worthington School Dist	20	12,500	Franklin	75
Wynford Local School Dist	2	1,200	Crawford	39
Wyoming City School Dist	5	1,950	Hamilton	94
Xenia Community School Dist	8	4,600	Greene	84
Yellow Springs Exempted Vlg SD	2	696	Greene	85
Youngstown City School Dist	15	5,275	Mahoning	136
Zane Trace Local School Dist	3	1,301	Ross	176
Zanesville City School Dist	6	3,307	Muskingum	157

CATHOLIC DIOCESE

SCHOOL DISTRICT	NO. OF SCHOOLS	ENROLLMENT	COUNTY	PAGE
Archdiocese Cincinnati Ed Off	107	42,000	Hamilton	94
Diocese of Cleveland Ed Office	106	40,303	Cuyahoga	52
Diocese of Columbus Ed Office	53	15,418	Franklin	76
Diocese of Steubenville Ed Off	12	1,900	Jefferson	110
Diocese of Toledo Ed Office	68	15,000	Lucas	131
Diocese of Youngstown Ed Off	27	6,100	Mahoning	137

COUNTY CENTERS

SCHOOL DISTRICT	COUNTY	PAGE
Allen Co Ed Service Center	Allen	7
Ashtabula Co Ed Service Center	Ashtabula	11
Athens Meigs Ed Service Center	Athens	14
Auglaize Co Ed Service Center	Auglaize	15
Brown Co Ed Service Center	Brown	19
Butler Co Ed Service Center	Butler	20
Clark Co Ed Service Center	Clark	27
Clermont Co Ed Service Center	Clermont	29
Columbiana Co Ed Service Ctr	Columbiana	33
Cuyahoga Co Ed Service Center	Cuyahoga	39
Darke Co Ed Service Center	Darke	55
East Central Ohio ESC-N Phil	Tuscarawas	201
East Central Ohio ESC-St Clair	Belmont	17
Ed Service Center Lorain Co	Lorain	122
Ed Service Ctr Lake Erie West	Lucas	127
Ed Svc Center of Medina Co	Medina	139
Educational Serv Ctr-Ctl Ohio	Franklin	65
Fairfield Co Ed Service Center	Fairfield	62
Gallia-Vinton Ed Svc Center	Gallia	80
Geauga Co Ed Service Center	Geauga	81
Greene Co Ed Service Center	Greene	83
Hamilton Co Ed Service Center	Hamilton	87
Hancock Co Ed Service Center	Hancock	97
Jefferson Co Ed Service Center	Jefferson	108
Knox Co Ed Service Center	Knox	110
Lawrence Co Ed Service Center	Lawrence	115
Licking Co Ed Service Center	Licking	117
Madison-Champaign Ed Svc Ctr	Champaign	25
Mahoning Co Ed Service Center	Mahoning	133
Mercer Co Ed Service Center	Mercer	143
Miami Co Ed Service Center	Miami	144
Mid-Ohio Ed Service Center	Richland	171
Midwest Reg Ed Service Center	Logan	120
Montgomery Co Ed Service Ctr	Montgomery	148
Muskingum Valley ESC	Muskingum	156
North Central Ohio Ed Svc Ctr	Marion	137
North Ctrl Ohio Ed Service Ctr	Seneca	180
North Point Ed Svc Ctr	Erie	60
North West Ohio Ed Service Ctr	Fulton	78
Ohio Valley Ed Service Center	Guernsey	85
Ohio Valley Ed Service Ctr	Washington	209
Pickaway Co Ed Service Center	Pickaway	162
Portage Co Ed Service Center	Portage	164
Preble Co Ed Service Center	Preble	168
Putnam Co Ed Service Center	Putnam	169
Ross-Pike Co Ed Service Center	Ross	174

DISTRICT INDEX

SCHOOL DISTRICT	NO. OF SCHOOLS	ENROLLMENT	COUNTY	PAGE
South Central Ohio Ed Svc Ctr			Scioto	178
Southern Ohio Ed Serv Ctr			Clinton	32
Stark Co Ed Service Center			Stark	184
State Support Team-Region 4			Lake	112
Summit Co Ed Service Center			Summit	190
Tri-Co Ed Service Center			Wayne	211
Trumbull Co Ed Service Center			Trumbull	196
Warren Co Ed Service Center			Warren	206
Western Buckeye Ed Service Ctr			Paulding	160
Western Buckeye Ed Service Ctr			Van Wert	205
Wood Co Ed Service Center			Wood	216

REGIONAL CENTERS

SCHOOL DISTRICT	NO. OF SCHOOLS	ENROLLMENT	COUNTY	PAGE
Access			Mahoning	137
Connect Information Tech Ctr			Cuyahoga	54
Connect Information Tech Ctr			Lorain	126
Hamilton County ESC			Hamilton	97
Hamilton-Clermont Co-op OCA			Clermont	32
Laca-Licking Area Cmop Assoc			Licking	120
Lgca-Lake Geauga Ohio OCA			Lake	115
Medina Co Sch Educl Svcs Ctr			Medina	142
Meta Solutions			Franklin	78
Meta Solutions			Marion	139
Meta Solutions Branch			Montgomery	154
Miami Valley Educational CA			Greene	85
Ncocc-N Ctrl Ohio Co-op CA			Richland	174
Neomin-NE Ohio Mgmt Info NET			Trumbull	201
Neonet-NE Ohio Ed Tech			Summit	196
Noeca-Northern Ohio Ed CA			Erie	62
North Coast Ed Media Center			Cuyahoga	54
Northwest Ohio Computer Assoc			Fulton	80
Northwest Ohio Computer Co-op			Allen	10
Northwest Ohio Ed Tech			Wood	218
Ohio Mid-Eastern RESA			Jefferson	110
SE Ohio Voluntary Ed Co-op			Athens	15
Southwest Ohio OCA			Butler	25
Sparcc			Stark	190
State Support Team 3			Cuyahoga	54
State Support Team 11			Franklin	78
State Support Team-Region 1			Lucas	132
State Support Team-Region 2			Lorain	126
State Support Team-Region 5			Mahoning	137
State Support Team-Region 6			Auglaize	17
State Support Team-Region 7			Richland	174
State Support Team-Region 8			Summit	196
State Support Team-Region 9			Stark	190
State Support Team-Region 10			Greene	85
State Support Team-Region 12			Guernsey	86
State Support Team-Region 13			Hamilton	97
State Support Team-Region 14			Highland	103
State Support Team-Region 16			Athens	15
Summit Co Educational Svc Ctr			Summit	196
Tccsa-Tri-Co Comp Svcs			Wayne	214
Woco-W Ohio Computer Org			Shelby	183

Ohio School Directory

COUNTY INDEX

COUNTY District/City	NO. OF SCHOOLS	ENROLL-MENT	PAGE
ADAMS			
Adams Co Ohio Valley Sch Dist/*West Union*	7	3,800	6
Eastern Local School Dist/*Winchester*	4	1,350	7
Manchester Local School Dist/*Manchester*	2	856	7
ALLEN			
Allen Co Ed Service Center/*Lima*			7
Allen East Local School Dist/*Harrod*	3	1,200	7
Apollo Joint Voc School Dist/*Lima*	1	600	8
Bath Local School Dist/*Lima*	3	1,900	8
Bluffton Exempted Village Sch/*Bluffton*	3	1,220	8
Delphos City School Dist/*Delphos*	3	1,050	8
Elida Local School Dist/*Elida*	3	2,500	8
Lima City School Dist/*Lima*	9	4,000	9
Northwest Ohio Computer Co-op/*Lima*			10
Perry Local School Dist/*Lima*	2	753	9
Shawnee Local School Dist/*Lima*	4	2,500	9
Spencerville Local School Dist/*Spencerville*	3	965	9
ASHLAND			
Ashland City School Dist/*Ashland*	5	3,800	10
Ashland Co-West Holmes JVSD/*Ashland*	1	450	10
Hillsdale Local School Dist/*Jeromesville*	3	850	11
Loudonville-Perrysville SD/*Loudonville*	3	1,100	11
Mapleton Local School Dist/*Ashland*	3	890	11
ASHTABULA			
Ashtabula Area City Sch Dist/*Ashtabula*	8	3,600	12
Ashtabula Co Ed Service Center/*Ashtabula*			11
Ashtabula Co Tech & Career SD/*Jefferson*	1	694	12
Buckeye Local School Dist/*Ashtabula*	4	1,800	12
Conneaut Area City Sch Dist/*Conneaut*	4	1,604	12
Geneva Area City School Dist/*Geneva*	5	2,415	13
Grand Valley Local School Dist/*Orwell*	3	1,075	13
Jefferson Area Local SD/*Jefferson*	4	1,651	13
Pymatuning Valley Local SD/*Andover*	3	1,200	13
ATHENS			
Alexander Local School Dist/*Albany*	2	1,495	14
Athens City School Dist/*The Plains*	6	2,483	14
Athens Meigs Ed Service Center/*Chauncey*			14
Federal Hocking Local Sch Dist/*Stewart*	3	1,000	14
Nelsonville-York City Sch Dist/*Nelsonville*	3	1,206	15
SE Ohio Voluntary Ed Co-op/*Athens*			15
State Support Team-Region 16/*Chauncey*			15
Tri-Co Joint Voc Sch Dist/*Nelsonville*	1	450	15
Trimble Local School Dist/*Glouster*	3	900	15
AUGLAIZE			
Auglaize Co Ed Service Center/*Wapakoneta*			15
Minster Local School Dist/*Minster*	2	849	15
New Bremen Local School Dist/*New Bremen*	2	760	16
New Knoxville Local Sch Dist/*New Knoxville*	1	392	16
St Mary's City School Dist/*Saint Marys*	4	1,996	16
State Support Team-Region 6/*Wapakoneta*			17
Wapakoneta City School Dist/*Wapakoneta*	4	3,081	16
Waynesfield-Goshen Local SD/*Waynesfield*	2	500	16
BELMONT			
Barnesville Exempted Vlg SD/*Barnesville*	3	1,480	17
Bellaire Local School Dist/*Bellaire*	3	1,159	17
Belmont-Harrison Voc Sch Dist/*St Clairsvle*	2	408	17
Bridgeport School Dist/*Bridgeport*	3	820	18
East Central Ohio ESC-St Clair/*St Clairsvle*			17
Martins Ferry City School Dist/*Martins Ferry*	3	1,500	18
Shadyside Local School Dist/*Shadyside*	3	800	18
St Clairsville-Richland CSD/*St Clairsvle*	3	1,700	18
Union Local School Dist/*Belmont*	3	1,521	18
BROWN			
Brown Co Ed Service Center/*Georgetown*			19
Fayetteville Perry Local SD/*Fayetteville*	3	855	19
Georgetown Exempted Village SD/*Georgetown*	2	1,100	19
Ripley-Union-Lewis-Huntngtn SD/*Ripley*	3	850	20
Southern Hills Joint Voc SD/*Georgetown*	1	380	20
Western Brown Local Sch Dist/*Mount Orab*	4	3,400	20
BUTLER			
Butler Co Ed Service Center/*Hamilton*			20
Butler Tech Career Dev Schs/*Hamilton*	1	900	21
Edgewood City School Dist/*Trenton*	5	3,800	21
Fairfield City School Dist/*Fairfield*	11	10,000	21
Hamilton City School Dist/*Hamilton*	13	10,300	21
Lakota Local School Dist/*Liberty Twp*	23	16,500	22
Madison Local School Dist/*Middletown*	2	1,600	23
Middletown City School Dist/*Middletown*	10	6,561	23

COUNTY District/City	NO. OF SCHOOLS	ENROLL-MENT	PAGE
Monroe Local School Dist/*Monroe*	4	2,900	23
New Miami Local School Dist/*Hamilton*	2	620	23
Ross Local School Dist/*Hamilton*	4	2,500	24
Southwest Ohio OCA/*Hamilton*			25
Talawanda School Dist/*Oxford*	5	3,100	24
CARROLL			
Brown Local School Dist/*Malvern*	3	630	25
Carrollton Exempted Village SD/*Carrollton*	2	2,150	25
CHAMPAIGN			
Graham Local School Dist/*Saint Paris*	3	1,836	25
Madison-Champaign Ed Svc Ctr/*Urbana*			25
Mechanicsburg Exempted Vlg SD/*Mechanicsburg*	2	900	26
Triad Local School Dist/*N Lewisburg*	3	830	26
Urbana City School Dist/*Urbana*	3	2,000	26
West Liberty-Salem Local SD/*West Liberty*	1	1,250	26
CLARK			
Clark Co Ed Service Center/*Springfield*			27
Clark-Shawnee Local Sch Dist/*Springfield*	5	2,057	27
Greenon Local School Dist/*Enon*	3	1,486	27
Northeastern Local School Dist/*Springfield*	7	3,300	27
Northwestern Local School Dist/*Springfield*	2	1,643	27
Southeastern Local School Dist/*S Charleston*	2	778	28
Springfield City School Dist/*Springfield*	16	7,583	28
Springfield-Clark Co JVSD/*Springfield*	1	700	28
Tecumseh Local School Dist/*New Carlisle*	5	3,130	28
CLERMONT			
Batavia Local School Dist/*Batavia*	3	2,289	29
Bethel-Tate Local School Dist/*Bethel*	4	1,600	30
Clermont Co Ed Service Center/*Batavia*			29
Clermont Northeastern Local SD/*Batavia*	3	1,350	30
Felicity-Franklin Local SD/*Felicity*	3	800	30
Goshen Local School Dist/*Goshen*	4	2,800	30
Hamilton-Clermont Co-op OCA/*Loveland*			32
Milford Exempted Village SD/*Milford*	10	6,600	30
New Richmond Exempted Vlg SD/*New Richmond*	4	2,400	31
U S Grant Career School Dist/*Bethel*	1	400	31
West Clermont Local Sch Dist/*Cincinnati*	10	9,500	31
Williamsburg Local School Dist/*Williamsburg*	2	994	32
CLINTON			
Blanchester Local School Dist/*Blanchester*	4	1,650	32
Clinton-Massie Local Sch Dist/*Clarksville*	3	1,800	33
East Clinton Local School Dist/*Sabina*	4	1,300	33
Southern Ohio Ed Serv Ctr/*Wilmington*			32
Wilmington City School Dist/*Wilmington*	5	3,000	33
COLUMBIANA			
Beaver Local School Dist/*E Liverpool*	3	1,800	34
Columbiana Co Ed Service Ctr/*Lisbon*			33
Columbiana Co Voc Sch Dist/*Lisbon*	1	450	34
Columbiana Exempted Village SD/*Columbiana*	3	1,077	34
Crestview Local School Dist/*Columbiana*	3	1,245	34
East Liverpool City Sch Dist/*E Liverpool*	4	2,050	34
East Palestine City Sch Dist/*E Palestine*	3	1,087	35
Leetonia Exempted Village SD/*Leetonia*	1	780	35
Lisbon Exempted Village SD/*Lisbon*	2	850	35
Salem City School Dist/*Salem*	5	2,100	35
Southern Local School Dist/*Salineville*	2	920	35
United Local School Dist/*Hanoverton*	2	1,300	36
Wellsville Local Sch Dist/*Wellsville*	3	850	36
COSHOCTON			
Coshocton City School Dist/*Coshocton*	2	1,600	36
Coshocton Co Joint Voc SD/*Coshocton*	1	246	37
Ridgewood Local School Dist/*W Lafayette*	3	1,275	37
River View Local School Dist/*Warsaw*	5	2,100	37
CRAWFORD			
Buckeye Central Local Sch Dist/*New Washingtn*	3	650	38
Bucyrus City School Dist/*Bucyrus*	2	1,300	38
Colonel Crawford Local SD/*N Robinson*	3	920	38
Crestline Exempted Village SD/*Crestline*	1	570	38
Galion City School Dist/*Galion*	4	1,817	38
Wynford Local School Dist/*Bucyrus*	2	1,200	39
CUYAHOGA			
Bay Village City School Dist/*Bay Village*	4	2,442	40
Beachwood City School Dist/*Beachwood*	5	1,612	40
Bedford City School Dist/*Bedford*	6	3,292	40
Berea City School Dist/*Berea*	7	5,817	41
Brecksville Broadview Hts CSD/*Brecksville*	5	3,850	41
Brooklyn City School Dist/*Brooklyn*	2	1,300	41
Chagrin Falls Exempted Vlg SD/*Chagrin Falls*	4	2,000	42

School Year 2019-2020   800-333-8802   OH-R1

COUNTY INDEX

Market Data Retrieval

COUNTY District/City	NO. OF SCHOOLS	ENROLL- MENT	PAGE
Cleveland Hts-Univ Hts City SD/University Ht	11	5,200	42
Cleveland Metro School Dist/Cleveland	112	38,949	42
Connect Information Tech Ctr/Valley View			54
Cuyahoga Co Ed Service Center/Independence			39
Cuyahoga Heights Local SD/Cleveland	3	900	45
Cuyahoga Vly Career Ctr Voc SD/Brecksville	1	1,000	45
Diocese of Cleveland Ed Office/Cleveland	106	40,303	52
East Cleveland City Sch Dist/E Cleveland	6	2,300	45
Euclid City School Dist/Euclid	7	5,100	46
Fairview Park City Sch Dist/Fairview Park	4	1,702	46
Garfield Heights City SD/Garfield HTS	6	3,721	46
Independence Local School Dist/Independence	3	1,075	46
Lakewood City School Dist/Lakewood	12	4,000	47
Maple Heights City School Dist/Maple Heights	5	3,800	47
Mayfield City School Dist/Mayfield HTS	6	4,000	47
North Coast Ed Media Center/Valley View			54
North Olmsted City School Dist/North Olmsted	8	3,900	48
North Royalton City School Dist/N Royalton	5	4,060	48
Olmsted Falls City School Dist/Olmsted Falls	5	3,628	48
Orange City School Dist/Pepper Pike	4	2,000	48
Parma City School Dist/Parma	15	10,712	49
Polaris Joint Voc School Dist/Middlebrg HTS	1	1,000	49
Richmond Heights Local SD/Richmond HTS	2	850	49
Rocky River City School Dist/Rocky River	5	2,610	50
Shaker Heights City Sch Dist/Shaker HTS	9	5,180	50
Solon City School Dist/Solon	7	4,547	50
South Euclid-Lyndhurst City SD/Lyndhurst	6	3,500	50
State Support Team 3/Independence			54
Strongsville City School Dist/Strongsville	8	5,553	51
Warrensville Heights City SD/Warrensvl HTS	5	1,700	51
Westlake City School Dist/Westlake	4	3,500	51
DARKE			
Ansonia Local School Dist/Ansonia	2	700	55
Arcanum Butler Local Sch Dist/Arcanum	4	1,125	55
Darke Co Ed Service Center/Greenville			55
Franklin-Monroe Local Sch Dist/Arcanum	2	625	55
Greenville City School Dist/Greenville	3	2,507	55
Mississinawa Valley Sch Dist/Union City	2	700	56
Tri-Village Local Sch Dist/New Madison	1	827	56
Versailles Exempted Village SD/Versailles	3	1,305	56
DEFIANCE			
Ayersville Local School Dist/Defiance	3	700	56
Central Local School Dist/Sherwood	3	1,050	57
Defiance City School Dist/Defiance	3	2,400	57
Hicksville Exempted Village SD/Hicksville	2	1,000	57
Northeastern Local School Dist/Defiance	4	1,082	57
DELAWARE			
Big Walnut Local School Dist/Sunbury	7	4,000	58
Buckeye Valley Local Sch Dist/Delaware	4	2,202	58
Delaware City School Dist/Delaware	7	5,459	58
Delaware Joint Voc Sch Dist/Delaware	2	1,000	59
Olentangy Local School Dist/Lewis Center	25	22,125	59
ERIE			
Edison Local Schools Dist/Milan	3	1,650	60
Ehove Joint Voc School Dist/Milan	1	850	60
Huron City School Dist/Huron	4	1,324	60
Kelleys Island Local Sch Dist/Kelleys Is	1	5	61
Margaretta Local School Dist/Castalia	3	2,602	61
Noeca-Northern Ohio Ed CA/Sandusky			62
North Point Ed Svc Ctr/Sandusky			60
Perkins Local School Dist/Sandusky	4	1,950	61
Sandusky City School Dist/Sandusky	7	3,250	61
Vermilion Local School Dist/Vermilion	3	1,900	62
FAIRFIELD			
Amanda-Clearcreek Local SD/Amanda	4	1,445	62
Berne Union Local School Dist/Sugar Grove	2	950	63
Bloom-Carroll Local Sch Dist/Carroll	4	2,000	63
Fairfield Co Ed Service Center/Lancaster			62
Fairfield Union Local Sch Dist/Lancaster	4	2,000	63
Lancaster City School Dist/Lancaster	9	6,300	63
Liberty Union-Thurstn Sch Dist/Baltimore	3	1,350	64
Pickerington Local School Dist/Pickerington	15	10,600	64
Walnut Twp Local School Dist/Millersport	2	490	64
FAYETTE			
Miami Trace Local School Dist/Wshngtn Ct Hs	3	2,582	65
Washington Court House City SD/Wshngtn Ct Hs	4	2,200	65
FRANKLIN			
Bexley City School Dist/Bexley	5	2,463	66
Canal Winchester Local SD/Canal Wnchstr	4	3,600	66
Columbus City School Dist/Columbus	113	52,000	66

COUNTY District/City	NO. OF SCHOOLS	ENROLL- MENT	PAGE
Diocese of Columbus Ed Office/Columbus	53	15,418	76
Dublin City School Dist/Dublin	20	16,200	69
Eastland-Ffld Career Tech VSD/Groveport	3	1,500	70
Educational Serv Ctr-Ctl Ohio/Columbus			65
Gahanna-Jefferson Public SD/Gahanna	11	7,543	70
Grandview Heights City SD/Columbus	4	1,075	70
Groveport Madison Local SD/Groveport	11	7,200	71
Hamilton Local School Dist/Columbus	4	3,200	71
Hilliard City School Dist/Columbus	25	16,600	71
Meta Solutions/Columbus			78
New Albany-Plain Local SD/New Albany	5	5,100	72
Reynoldsburg City School Dist/Reynoldsburg	16	7,572	72
South-Western City School Dist/Grove City	33	22,790	73
State Support Team 11/Columbus			78
Upper Arlington City Sch Dist/Upper Arlngtn	8	6,000	74
Westerville City School Dist/Westerville	24	15,000	74
Whitehall City School Dist/Whitehall	6	3,200	75
Worthington School Dist/Worthington	20	12,500	75
FULTON			
Archbold Area Local Sch Dist/Archbold	3	1,212	78
Evergreen Local School Dist/Metamora	3	1,300	78
Fayette Local Sch Dist/Fayette	1	370	79
Four-Co Joint Voc School Dist/Archbold	1	1,000	79
North West Ohio Ed Service Ctr/Archbold			78
Northwest Ohio Computer Assoc/Archbold			80
Pettisville Local School Dist/Pettisville	2	525	79
Pike-Delta-York Local Sch Dist/Delta	3	1,100	79
Swanton Local School Dist/Swanton	3	1,300	79
Wauseon Exempted Village SD/Wauseon	4	1,770	79
GALLIA			
Gallia Co Local School Dist/Patriot	8	2,200	80
Gallia-Jackson-Vinton JVSD/Rio Grande	1	500	80
Gallia-Vinton Ed Svc Center/Rio Grande			80
Gallipolis City School Dist/Gallipolis	5	2,052	81
GEAUGA			
Berkshire Local School Dist/Burton	3	1,200	81
Cardinal Local School Dist/Middlefield	3	1,000	81
Chardon Local School Dist/Chardon	4	2,772	82
Geauga Co Ed Service Center/Chardon			81
Kenston Local School Dist/Chagrin Falls	4	2,858	82
Newbury Local School Dist/Newbury	2	270	82
West Geauga Local School Dist/Chesterland	4	1,874	82
GREENE			
Beavercreek City School Dist/Beavercreek	11	7,200	83
Bellbrook-Sugarcreek Schools/Bellbrook	5	2,875	83
Cedar Cliff Local School Dist/Cedarville	2	650	84
Fairborn City School Dist/Fairborn	4	4,300	84
Greene Co Ed Service Center/Yellow Spgs			83
Greene Co Voc School Dist/Xenia	1	685	84
Greeneview Local School Dist/Jamestown	3	1,400	84
Miami Valley Educational CA/Yellow Spgs			85
State Support Team-Region 10/Dayton			85
Xenia Community School Dist/Xenia	8	4,600	84
Yellow Springs Exempted Vlg SD/Yellow Spgs	2	696	85
GUERNSEY			
Cambridge City School Dist/Cambridge	4	1,954	86
East Guernsey Local Sch Dist/Lore City	3	1,200	86
Ohio Valley Ed Service Center/Cambridge			85
Rolling Hills Local Sch Dist/Cambridge	6	1,650	86
State Support Team-Region 12/Byesville			86
HAMILTON			
Archdiocese Cincinnati Ed Off/Cincinnati	107	42,000	94
Cincinnati City School Dist/Cincinnati	61	35,000	87
Deer Park Cmty School Dist/Cincinnati	2	1,261	89
Finneytown Local School Dist/Cincinnati	3	1,400	89
Forest Hills School Dist/Cincinnati	9	7,450	89
Great Oaks Career Campuses/Cincinnati	4	3,000	89
Hamilton Co Ed Service Center/Cincinnati			87
Hamilton County ESC/Cincinnati			97
Indian Hill Exempted Vlg SD/Cincinnati	4	2,030	90
Lockland School Dist/Lockland	3	550	90
Loveland City School Dist/Loveland	6	4,700	90
Madeira City School Dist/Cincinnati	3	1,400	90
Mariemont City School Dist/Cincinnati	4	1,700	90
Mt Healthy City School Dist/Cincinnati	3	3,300	91
North College Hill City SD/Cincinnati	3	1,650	91
Northwest Local School Dist/Cincinnati	11	9,000	91
Norwood City School Dist/Norwood	5	2,000	92
Oak Hills Local School Dist/Cincinnati	9	8,700	92
Princeton City School Dist/Cincinnati	10	6,500	92

Ohio School Directory — COUNTY INDEX

COUNTY / District/City	NO. OF SCHOOLS	ENROLLMENT	PAGE
Reading Cmty City School Dist/*Reading*	4	1,535	93
Southwest Local School Dist/*Harrison*	6	4,044	93
St Bernard-Elmwood Place Schs/*Saint Bernard*	3	1,000	93
State Support Team-Region 13/*Cincinnati*			97
Sycamore Cmty School Dist/*Cincinnati*	7	5,481	93
Three Rivers Local School Dist/*Cleves*	2	2,200	94
Winton Woods City School Dist/*Cincinnati*	7	3,500	94
Wyoming City School Dist/*Wyoming*	5	1,950	94
HANCOCK			
Arcadia Local School Dist/*Arcadia*	1	575	97
Arlington Local School Dist/*Arlington*	1	570	97
Cory-Rawson Local School Dist/*Rawson*	2	550	97
Findlay City School Dist/*Findlay*	15	6,000	97
Hancock Co Ed Service Center/*Findlay*			97
Liberty-Benton Local Sch Dist/*Findlay*	3	1,242	98
McComb Local School Dist/*Mc Comb*	3	700	98
Riverdale Local School Dist/*Mt Blanchard*	3	1,030	98
Van Buren Local School Dist/*Van Buren*	3	1,080	99
Vanlue Local School Dist/*Vanlue*	1	180	99
HARDIN			
ADA Exempted Village Sch Dist/*Ada*	1	890	99
Hardin Northern Local Sch Dist/*Dola*	2	405	100
Kenton City School Dist/*Kenton*	3	1,848	100
Ridgemont Local School Dist/*Mount Victory*	2	511	100
Upper Scioto Valley Local SD/*Mc Guffey*	1	450	100
HARRISON			
Conotton Valley Union Local SD/*Sherrodsville*	2	402	100
Harrison Hills City Sch Dist/*Cadiz*	3	1,600	101
HENRY			
Holgate Local School Dist/*Holgate*	1	470	101
Liberty Center Local Sch Dist/*Liberty CTR*	3	1,174	101
Napoleon Area City School Dist/*Napoleon*	3	1,700	101
Patrick Henry Local Sch Dist/*Hamler*	3	855	102
HIGHLAND			
Bright Local School Dist/*Mowrystown*	2	700	102
Fairfield Local Sch Dist/*Leesburg*	3	950	102
Greenfield Exempted Village SD/*Greenfield*	5	2,250	103
Hillsboro City School Dist/*Hillsboro*	3	2,300	103
Lynchburg-Clay Local Sch Dist/*Lynchburg*	3	1,150	103
State Support Team-Region 14/*Hillsboro*			103
HOCKING			
Logan-Hocking Local Sch Dist/*Logan*	7	3,945	104
HOLMES			
East Holmes Local School Dist/*Millersburg*	8	1,615	104
West Holmes Local School Dist/*Millersburg*	6	2,100	105
HURON			
Bellevue City School Dist/*Bellevue*	3	2,000	105
Monroeville Local School Dist/*Monroeville*	2	593	105
New London Local School Dist/*New London*	4	900	105
Norwalk City School Dist/*Norwalk*	6	2,750	106
South Central Local Sch Dist/*Greenwich*	3	750	106
Western Reserve Local Sch Dist/*Collins*	3	994	106
Willard City School Dist/*Willard*	2	1,520	106
JACKSON			
Jackson City School Dist/*Jackson*	5	2,450	107
Oak Hill Union Local Sch Dist/*Oak Hill*	2	1,220	107
Wellston City School Dist/*Wellston*	4	1,450	108
JEFFERSON			
Buckeye Local School Dist/*Dillonvale*	5	1,700	108
Diocese of Steubenville Ed Off/*Steubenville*	12	1,900	110
Edison Local School Dist/*Hammondsville*	3	2,000	109
Indian Creek Local Sch Dist/*Wintersville*	4	2,300	109
Jefferson Co Ed Service Center/*Steubenville*			108
Jefferson Co JT Voc Sch Dist/*Bloomingdale*	1	350	109
Ohio Mid-Eastern RESA/*Steubenville*			110
Steubenville City School Dist/*Steubenville*	6	2,600	109
Toronto City School Dist/*Toronto*	2	891	109
KNOX			
Centerburg Local School Dist/*Centerburg*	2	1,088	110
Danville Local School Dist/*Danville*	2	615	110
East Knox Local School Dist/*Howard*	2	1,100	111
Fredericktown Local Sch Dist/*Fredericktown*	3	1,197	111
Knox Co Ed Service Center/*Mount Vernon*			110
Knox Co Voc School Dist/*Mount Vernon*	1	640	111
Mt Vernon City School Dist/*Mount Vernon*	8	4,000	111
LAKE			
Auburn Vocational School Dist/*Painesville*	1	745	112
Fairport Harbor Exempt Vlg SD/*Fairport Hbr*	2	720	112
Kirtland Local School Dist/*Kirtland*	3	1,155	112
Lgca-Lake Geauga Ohio OCA/*Painesville*			115
Madison Local School Dist/*Madison*	5	3,120	112
Mentor Exempted Village SD/*Mentor*	11	7,415	113
Painesville City Local SD/*Painesville*	6	3,000	113
Perry Local School Dist/*Perry*	3	1,700	113
Riverside Local School Dist/*Painesville*	6	3,987	113
State Support Team-Region 4/*Concord Twp*			112
Wickliffe City School Dist/*Wickliffe*	3	1,290	114
Willoughby-Eastlake City SD/*Eastlake*	13	8,090	114
LAWRENCE			
Chesapeake Union Exempt Vlg SD/*Chesapeake*	3	1,400	115
Dawson-Bryant Local Sch Dist/*Coal Grove*	3	1,200	115
Fairland Local School Dist/*Proctorville*	4	1,569	116
Ironton City School Dist/*Ironton*	3	1,400	116
Lawrence Co Ed Service Center/*Ironton*			115
Lawrence Co Joint Voc Sch Dist/*Chesapeake*	1	475	116
Rock Hill Local School Dist/*Ironton*	3	1,450	116
South Point Local School Dist/*South Point*	4	1,500	116
Symmes Valley Local Sch Dist/*Willow Wood*	2	743	117
LICKING			
Granville Exempted Village SD/*Granville*	4	2,500	117
Heath City School Dist/*Heath*	4	1,730	117
Johnstown-Monroe Local SD/*Johnstown*	3	1,600	118
Laca-Licking Area Cmop Assoc/*Newark*			120
Lakewood Local School Dist/*Hebron*	4	1,900	118
Licking Co Ed Service Center/*Newark*			117
Licking Co Joint Voc Sch Dist/*Newark*	1	750	118
Licking Heights Local Sch Dist/*Pataskala*	5	4,700	118
Licking Valley Local Sch Dist/*Newark*	3	2,000	118
Newark City School Dist/*Newark*	13	6,500	119
North Fork Local School Dist/*Utica*	4	1,800	119
Northridge Local School Dist/*Johnstown*	4	1,300	119
Southwest Licking Local SD/*Pataskala*	6	4,300	120
LOGAN			
Bellefontaine City School Dist/*Bellefontaine*	4	2,600	120
Benjamin Logan Local Sch Dist/*Bellefontaine*	3	1,750	121
Indian Lake Local School Dist/*Lewistown*	3	1,516	121
Midwest Reg Ed Service Center/*Bellefontaine*			120
Ohio Hi-Point Joint Voc SD/*Bellefontaine*	1	500	121
Riverside Local School Dist/*De Graff*	2	633	121
LORAIN			
Amherst Exempted Village SD/*Amherst*	4	3,800	122
Avon Lake City School Dist/*Avon Lake*	7	3,819	122
Avon Local School Dist/*Avon*	5	4,650	122
Clearview Local School Dist/*Lorain*	3	1,644	123
Columbia Local School Dist/*Columbia Sta*	3	900	123
Connect Information Tech Ctr/*Elyria*			126
Ed Service Center Lorain Co/*Elyria*			122
Elyria City School Dist/*Elyria*	13	7,010	123
Firelands Local School Dist/*South Amherst*	4	1,626	124
Keystone Local School Dist/*Lagrange*	3	1,500	124
Lorain City School Dist/*Lorain*	14	6,500	124
Lorain Co Joint Voc Sch Dist/*Oberlin*	1	1,500	125
Midview Local School Dist/*Grafton*	5	3,000	125
North Ridgeville City Sch Dist/*N Ridgeville*	5	4,600	125
Oberlin City School Dist/*Oberlin*	4	1,200	125
Sheffield-Sheffield Lake CSD/*Sheffield VLG*	5	1,747	125
State Support Team-Region 2/*Elyria*			126
Wellington Exempted Village SD/*Wellington*	3	1,304	126
LUCAS			
Anthony Wayne Local Sch Dist/*Whitehouse*	6	4,400	127
Diocese of Toledo Ed Office/*Toledo*	68	15,000	131
Ed Service Ctr Lake Erie West/*Toledo*			127
Maumee City School Dist/*Maumee*	5	2,222	127
Oregon City School Dist/*Oregon*	8	3,800	128
Ottawa Hills Local Sch Dist/*Toledo*	2	1,000	128
Springfield Local School Dist/*Holland*	6	4,000	128
State Support Team-Region 1/*Toledo*			132
Sylvania City School Dist/*Sylvania*	12	7,704	128
Toledo Public Schools/*Toledo*	52	24,000	129
Washington Local School Dist/*Toledo*	13	7,042	130
MADISON			
Jefferson Local School Dist/*W Jefferson*	3	1,200	132
Jonathan Alder Local Sch Dist/*Plain City*	5	2,270	132
London City School Dist/*London*	3	2,103	132
Madison Plains Local Sch Dist/*London*	4	1,173	133
Tolles Career & Tech Sch Dist/*Plain City*	1	640	133

COUNTY INDEX

Market Data Retrieval

COUNTY District/City	NO. OF SCHOOLS	ENROLL- MENT	PAGE
MAHONING			
Access/*Canfield*			137
Austintown Local School Dist/*Youngstown*	4	4,567	133
Boardman Local School Dist/*Boardman*	6	4,000	134
Campbell City School Dist/*Campbell*	2	1,071	134
Canfield Local School Dist/*Canfield*	4	2,600	134
Diocese of Youngstown Ed Off/*Youngstown*	27	6,100	137
Jackson-Milton Local Sch Dist/*North Jackson*	2	700	134
Lowellville Local School Dist/*Lowellville*	1	499	135
Mahoning Co Ed Service Center/*Canfield*			133
Mahoning Co Joint Voc Sch Dist/*Canfield*	2	778	135
Poland Local School Dist/*Poland*	3	1,888	135
Sebring Local School Dist/*Sebring*	2	600	135
South Range Local School Dist/*Canfield*	3	1,247	135
Springfield Local School Dist/*New Middletwn*	3	942	135
State Support Team-Region 5/*Canfield*			137
Struthers City School Dist/*Struthers*	3	1,785	136
West Branch Local School Dist/*Beloit*	5	2,100	136
Western Reserve Local Sch Dist/*Berlin Center*	1	850	136
Youngstown City School Dist/*Youngstown*	15	5,275	136
MARION			
Elgin Local School Dist/*Marion*	3	1,200	138
Marion City School Dist/*Marion*	9	4,200	138
Meta Solutions/*Marion*			139
North Central Ohio Ed Svc Ctr/*Marion*			137
Pleasant Local School Dist/*Marion*	4	1,320	138
Ridgedale Local School Dist/*Morral*	2	642	138
River Valley Local School Dist/*Caledonia*	4	2,260	139
Tri-Rivers Joint Voc Sch Dist/*Marion*	1	550	139
MEDINA			
Black River Local School Dist/*Sullivan*	2	631	139
Brunswick City School Dist/*Brunswick*	11	7,123	140
Buckeye Local School Dist/*Medina*	4	2,300	140
Cloverleaf Local School Dist/*Lodi*	3	2,264	140
Ed Svc Center of Medina Co/*Medina*			139
Highland Local School Dist/*Medina*	5	3,233	141
Medina City School Dist/*Medina*	11	7,100	141
Medina Co Joint Voc Sch Dist/*Medina*	1	1,100	141
Medina Co Sch Educl Svcs Ctr/*Medina*			142
Wadsworth City School Dist/*Wadsworth*	8	4,800	141
MEIGS			
Eastern Local School Dist/*Reedsville*	3	820	142
Meigs Local School Dist/*Pomeroy*	4	1,700	142
Southern Local School Dist/*Racine*	2	728	143
MERCER			
Celina City School Dist/*Celina*	5	2,300	143
Coldwater Exempted Village SD/*Coldwater*	3	1,375	143
Ft Recovery Local School Dist/*Fort Recovery*	2	920	144
Marion Local School Dist/*Maria Stein*	2	860	144
Mercer Co Ed Service Center/*Celina*			143
Parkway Local School Dist/*Rockford*	3	1,000	144
St Henry Cons Local Sch Dist/*Saint Henry*	3	950	144
MIAMI			
Bethel Local School Dist/*Tipp City*	2	1,400	145
Bradford Exempted Village SD/*Bradford*	2	487	145
Covington Exempted Village SD/*Covington*	2	850	145
Miami Co Ed Service Center/*Troy*			144
Miami East Local School Dist/*Casstown*	3	1,300	145
Milton-Union Exempted Vlg SD/*West Milton*	3	1,500	145
Newton Local School Dist/*Pleasant Hill*	1	600	146
Piqua City School Dist/*Piqua*	5	3,500	146
Tipp City Exempted Village SD/*Tipp City*	5	2,605	146
Troy City School Dist/*Troy*	9	4,400	146
Upper Valley JT Voc Sch Dist/*Piqua*	1	780	147
MONROE			
Switzerland of Ohio Local SD/*Woodsfield*	9	2,300	147
MONTGOMERY			
Brookville Local School Dist/*Brookville*	3	1,500	148
Centerville City School Dist/*Centerville*	13	8,200	148
Dayton Public School Dist/*Dayton*	25	13,792	149
Huber Heights City School Dist/*Huber Heights*	8	6,100	150
Jefferson Twp Local Sch Dist/*Dayton*	2	345	150
Kettering City School Dist/*Kettering*	12	7,400	150
Mad River Local School Dist/*Riverside*	8	3,800	151
Meta Solutions Branch/*Dayton*			154
Miami Valley Career Tech VSD/*Englewood*	2	2,100	151
Miamisburg City School Dist/*Miamisburg*	10	5,500	151
Montgomery Co Ed Service Ctr/*Dayton*			148
New Lebanon Local School Dist/*New Lebanon*	3	1,100	151
Northmont City School Dist/*Englewood*	8	5,800	152

COUNTY District/City	NO. OF SCHOOLS	ENROLL- MENT	PAGE
Northridge Local School Dist/*Dayton*	4	1,500	152
Oakwood City School Dist/*Oakwood*	5	1,988	152
Trotwood-Madison City SD/*Trotwood*	5	2,300	152
Valley View Local School Dist/*Germantown*	4	1,900	153
Vandalia Butler City Sch Dist/*Vandalia*	5	3,225	153
West Carrollton City Sch Dist/*W Carrollton*	6	3,700	153
MORGAN			
Morgan Local School Dist/*McConnelsvle*	5	1,763	154
MORROW			
Cardington-Lincoln Local SD/*Cardington*	4	1,200	155
Highland Local School Dist/*Marengo*	3	1,850	155
Mt Gilead Exempted Village SD/*Mount Gilead*	3	1,200	155
Northmor Local School Dist/*Galion*	1	1,042	155
MUSKINGUM			
East Muskingum Local Sch Dist/*New Concord*	6	2,200	156
Franklin Local School Dist/*Duncan Falls*	5	2,000	156
Maysville Local School Dist/*Zanesville*	3	2,200	156
Mideast Career & Tech Ctrs/*Zanesville*	3	1,100	157
Muskingum Valley ESC/*Zanesville*			156
Tri-Valley Local School Dist/*Dresden*	6	3,100	157
West Muskingum Local Sch Dist/*Zanesville*	3	1,400	157
Zanesville City School Dist/*Zanesville*	6	3,307	157
NOBLE			
Caldwell Exempted Village SD/*Caldwell*	2	800	158
Noble Local School Dist/*Sarahsville*	2	900	158
OTTAWA			
Benton-Carroll-Salem Local SD/*Oak Harbor*	3	1,500	158
Danbury Local School Dist/*Lksid Marblhd*	1	543	159
Genoa Area Local School Dist/*Genoa*	3	1,323	159
Port Clinton City School Dist/*Port Clinton*	4	1,700	159
Put-In-Bay Local School Dist/*Put In Bay*	1	72	159
Woodmore Local School Dist/*Elmore*	2	974	159
PAULDING			
Antwerp Local School Dist/*Antwerp*	1	800	160
Paulding Exempted Village SD/*Paulding*	4	1,475	160
Wayne Trace Local School Dist/*Haviland*	3	1,000	160
Western Buckeye Ed Service Ctr/*Paulding*			160
PERRY			
Crooksville Exempted Vlg SD/*Crooksville*	3	1,100	161
New Lexington School Dist/*New Lexington*	4	1,980	161
Northern Local School Dist/*Thornville*	5	2,251	161
Southern Local School Dist/*Corning*	2	664	161
PICKAWAY			
Circleville City School Dist/*Circleville*	3	2,174	162
Logan Elm Local School Dist/*Circleville*	6	1,880	162
Pickaway Co Ed Service Center/*Circleville*			162
Teays Valley Local School Dist/*Ashville*	7	4,350	162
Westfall Local School Dist/*Williamsport*	3	1,432	163
PIKE			
Eastern Local School Dist/*Beaver*	3	901	163
Pike Co Area JT Voc Sch Dist/*Piketon*	1	500	163
Scioto Valley Local Sch Dist/*Piketon*	2	1,300	164
Waverly City School Dist/*Waverly*	4	1,825	164
Western Local School Dist/*Latham*	2	790	164
PORTAGE			
Aurora City School Dist/*Aurora*	5	3,000	164
Crestwood Local School Dist/*Mantua*	4	1,600	165
Field Local School Dist/*Mogadore*	4	1,900	165
James A Garfield Local SD/*Garrettsville*	3	1,379	165
Kent City School Dist/*Kent*	6	3,400	165
Maplewood JT Voc School Dist/*Ravenna*	1	700	166
Mogadore Local School Dist/*Mogadore*	2	875	166
Portage Co Ed Service Center/*Ravenna*			164
Ravenna School Dist/*Ravenna*	7	2,200	166
Rootstown Local School Dist/*Rootstown*	3	1,200	166
Southeast Local School Dist/*Ravenna*	4	1,484	166
Streetsboro City School Dist/*Streetsboro*	4	2,200	167
Waterloo Local School Dist/*Atwater*	3	1,100	167
Windham Exempted Vlg Sch Dist/*Windham*	3	600	167
PREBLE			
Eaton Cmty School Dist/*Eaton*	4	1,943	168
National Trail Local Sch Dist/*New Paris*	3	1,100	168
Preble Co Ed Service Center/*Eaton*			168
Preble-Shawnee Local Sch Dist/*Camden*	3	1,430	168
Tri-Co North School Dist/*Lewisburg*	3	786	168
Twin Valley Cmty Local SD/*W Alexandria*	2	837	169

OH-R4 800-333-8802 School Year 2019-2020

Ohio School Directory

COUNTY INDEX

COUNTY District/City	NO. OF SCHOOLS	ENROLL- MENT	PAGE
PUTNAM			
Columbus Grove Local Sch Dist/*Columbus GRV*	2	879	169
Continental Local School Dist/*Continental*	2	480	169
Jennings Local School Dist/*Fort Jennings*	1	400	169
Kalida Local School Dist/*Kalida*	2	605	169
Leipsic Local School Dist/*Leipsic*	2	650	170
Miller City-New Cleveland SD/*Miller City*	3	485	170
Ottawa-Glandorf Local Sch Dist/*Ottawa*	4	1,400	170
Ottoville Local School Dist/*Ottoville*	2	430	170
Pandora Gilboa Local Sch Dist/*Pandora*	3	524	170
Putnam Co Ed Service Center/*Ottawa*			169
RICHLAND			
Clear Fork Vly Local Sch Dist/*Bellville*	4	1,692	171
Crestview Local School Dist/*Ashland*	3	1,100	171
Lexington Local School Dist/*Lexington*	5	2,510	172
Lucas Local School Dist/*Lucas*	3	565	172
Madison Local School Dist/*Mansfield*	5	2,956	172
Mansfield City Schools/*Mansfield*	8	3,350	172
Mid-Ohio Ed Service Center/*Mansfield*			171
Ncocc-N Ctrl Ohio Co-op CA/*Mansfield*			174
Ontario Local School Dist/*Ontario*	3	2,158	173
Pioneer Joint Voc School Dist/*Shelby*	1	1,250	173
Plymouth-Shiloh Local Sch Dist/*Plymouth*	3	681	173
Shelby City School Dist/*Shelby*	5	1,918	173
State Support Team-Region 7/*Mansfield*			174
ROSS			
Adena Local School Dist/*Frankfort*	3	1,200	174
Chillicothe City School Dist/*Chillicothe*	5	2,800	174
Huntington Local School Dist/*Chillicothe*	3	1,120	175
Paint Valley Local School Dist/*Bainbridge*	3	890	175
Pickaway-Ross Co JT Voc SD/*Chillicothe*	1	800	175
Ross-Pike Co Ed Service Center/*Chillicothe*			174
Southeastern Local Sch Dist/*Chillicothe*	3	1,040	175
Union Scioto Local Sch Dist/*Chillicothe*	3	2,175	175
Zane Trace Local School Dist/*Chillicothe*	3	1,301	176
SANDUSKY			
Clyde-Green Spgs Exmpt Vlg SD/*Clyde*	4	2,300	176
Fremont City School Dist/*Fremont*	9	3,843	176
Gibsonburg Exempted Village SD/*Gibsonburg*	3	950	177
Lakota Local School Dist/*Kansas*	3	1,140	177
Vanguard-Sentinel JT Voc SD/*Fremont*	2	2,300	177
SCIOTO			
Bloom-Vernon Local Sch Dist/*South Webster*	2	900	178
Clay Local School Dist/*Portsmouth*	1	714	178
Green Local School Dist/*Franklin Frnce*	2	600	178
Minford Local School Dist/*Minford*	3	1,401	178
New Boston Local School Dist/*New Boston*	3	500	178
Northwest Local School Dist/*Mc Dermott*	3	1,373	179
Portsmouth City School Dist/*Portsmouth*	3	1,700	179
Scioto Co Joint Vocational SD/*Lucasville*	1	540	179
South Central Ohio Ed Svc Ctr/*New Boston*			178
Valley Local School Dist/*Lucasville*	3	1,020	179
Washington-Nile Local Sch Dist/*W Portsmouth*	3	1,449	179
Wheelersburg Local School Dist/*Wheelersburg*	3	1,600	180
SENECA			
Fostoria City School Dist/*Fostoria*	2	1,845	180
Hopewell-Loudon Local SD/*Bascom*	1	821	181
New Riegel Local School Dist/*New Riegel*	1	500	181
North Ctrl Ohio Ed Service Ctr/*Tiffin*			180
Old Fort Local School Dist/*Tiffin*	2	750	181
Seneca East Local School Dist/*Attica*	1	880	181
Tiffin City School Dist/*Tiffin*	6	2,800	181
SHELBY			
Anna Local School Dist/*Anna*	2	1,200	182
Botkins Local School Dist/*Botkins*	1	644	182
Fairlawn Local School Dist/*Sidney*	2	650	182
Ft Loramie Local School Dist/*Fort Loramie*	2	793	182
Hardin-Houston Local Sch Dist/*Houston*	1	860	182
Jackson Center Local Sch Dist/*Jackson CTR*	1	600	183
Russia Local School Dist/*Russia*	1	430	183
Sidney City School Dist/*Sidney*	6	3,350	183
Woco-W Ohio Computer Org/*Sidney*			183
STARK			
Alliance City School Dist/*Alliance*	6	3,100	184
Canton City School Dist/*Canton*	27	9,500	184
Canton Local School Dist/*Canton*	3	2,000	185
Fairless Local School Dist/*Navarre*	3	1,501	185
Green Local School Dist/*Uniontown*	5	4,253	185
Jackson Local School Dist/*Massillon*	6	5,817	186
Lake Local School Dist/*Uniontown*	3	3,300	186
Louisville City School Dist/*Louisville*	4	2,797	186
Marlington Local School Dist/*Alliance*	5	2,300	186
Massillon City School Dist/*Massillon*	7	3,900	187
Minerva Local School Dist/*Minerva*	3	1,900	187
North Canton City School Dist/*North Canton*	7	4,437	187
Northwest Local School Dist/*Canal Fulton*	4	1,783	187
Osnaburg Local School Dist/*East Canton*	3	850	188
Perry Local School Dist/*Massillon*	8	4,500	188
Plain Local School Dist/*Canton*	9	6,000	188
Portage Lakes Joint Voc SD/*Uniontown*	1	650	189
Sandy Valley Local School Dist/*Magnolia*	3	1,500	189
Sparcc/*North Canton*			190
Stark Co Area Voc Sch Dist/*Massillon*	1	700	189
Stark Co Ed Service Center/*Canton*			184
State Support Team-Region 9/*North Canton*			190
Tuslaw Local School Dist/*Massillon*	3	1,390	189
SUMMIT			
Akron Public Schools/*Akron*	45	21,343	190
Barberton City School Dist/*Barberton*	5	3,813	192
Copley-Fairlawn City Sch Dist/*Copley*	5	2,886	192
Coventry Local School Dist/*Akron*	3	1,900	192
Cuyahoga Falls City Sch Dist/*Cuyahoga FLS*	10	4,500	192
Hudson City School Dist/*Hudson*	6	4,600	193
Manchester Local School Dist/*Akron*	3	1,400	193
Neonet-NE Ohio Ed Tech/*Cuyahoga FLS*			196
Nordonia Hills City Sch Dist/*Northfield*	6	3,585	193
Norton City School Dist/*Norton*	4	2,500	193
Revere Local School Dist/*Richfield*	4	2,700	194
Springfield Local School Dist/*Akron*	4	2,222	194
State Support Team-Region 8/*Cuyahoga FLS*			196
Stow-Munroe Falls City SD/*Stow*	10	5,158	194
Summit Co Ed Service Center/*Cuyahoga FLS*			190
Summit Co Educational Svc Ctr/*Cuyahoga FLS*			196
Tallmadge City School Dist/*Tallmadge*	4	2,412	194
Twinsburg City School Dist/*Twinsburg*	5	4,200	195
Woodridge Local School Dist/*Peninsula*	3	2,000	195
TRUMBULL			
Bloomfield-Mespo Local SD/*N Bloomfield*	2	314	197
Bristol Local School Dist/*Bristolville*	2	550	197
Brookfield Local School Dist/*Brookfield*	3	900	197
Champion Local School Dist/*Warren*	2	1,525	197
Girard City School Dist/*Girard*	4	1,699	197
Howland Local School Dist/*Warren*	6	2,685	198
Hubbard Exempted Village SD/*Hubbard*	3	1,932	198
Joseph Badger Local Sch Dist/*Kinsman*	3	750	198
Labrae Local School Dist/*Leavittsburg*	4	1,078	198
Lakeview Local School Dist/*Cortland*	3	1,732	198
Liberty Local School Dist/*Youngstown*	3	1,244	199
Lordstown Local School Dist/*Warren*	2	500	199
Maplewood Local School Dist/*Cortland*	2	750	199
Mathews Local School Dist/*Vienna*	3	675	199
McDonald Local School Dist/*Mc Donald*	2	768	199
Neomin-NE Ohio Mgmt Info NET/*Warren*			201
Newton Falls Exempted Vlg SD/*Newton Falls*	4	1,100	200
Niles City School Dist/*Niles*	4	2,209	200
Southington Local School Dist/*Southington*	1	500	200
Trumbull Co Ed Service Center/*Niles*			196
Warren City School Dist/*Warren*	5	4,300	200
Weathersfield Local Sch Dist/*Mineral Ridge*	2	992	200
TUSCARAWAS			
Buckeye Joint Voc School Dist/*New Phila*	1	975	201
Claymont City School Dist/*Dennison*	6	2,000	201
Dover City School Dist/*Dover*	5	2,712	202
East Central Ohio ESC-N Phil/*New Phila*			201
Garaway Local School Dist/*Sugarcreek*	5	1,300	202
Indian Valley Local Sch Dist/*Gnadenhutten*	5	1,900	202
New Philadelphia City Sch Dist/*New Phila*	8	3,800	202
Newcomerstown Exempted Vlg SD/*Newcomerstown*	4	1,100	203
Strasburg Franklin Local SD/*Strasburg*	2	534	203
Tuscarawas Valley Local SD/*Zoarville*	4	1,380	203
UNION			
Fairbanks Local School Dist/*Milford CTR*	3	1,072	204
Marysville Exempted Village SD/*Marysville*	10	5,100	204
North Union Local School Dist/*Richwood*	3	1,540	204
VAN WERT			
Crestview Local School Dist/*Convoy*	1	820	205
Lincolnview Local School Dist/*Van Wert*	3	900	205
Van Wert City School Dist/*Van Wert*	4	2,084	205
Vantage Career Center Sch Dist/*Van Wert*	1	480	206
Western Buckeye Ed Service Ctr/*Van Wert*			205

COUNTY INDEX

COUNTY District/City	NO. OF SCHOOLS	ENROLL- MENT	PAGE
VINTON			
Vinton Co Local School Dist/*Mc Arthur*	5	2,100	206
WARREN			
Carlisle Local School Dist/*Carlisle*	4	1,593	206
Franklin City School Dist/*Franklin*	8	2,750	207
Kings Local School Dist/*Kings Mills*	7	4,650	207
Lebanon City School Dist/*Lebanon*	5	6,000	207
Little Miami Local School Dist/*Maineville*	6	5,020	207
Mason City School Dist/*Mason*	5	10,396	208
Springboro Cmty School Dist/*Springboro*	6	6,093	208
Warren Co Ed Service Center/*Lebanon*			206
Warren Co Voc School Dist/*Lebanon*	1	775	208
Wayne Local School Dist/*Waynesville*	3	1,473	208
WASHINGTON			
Belpre City School Dist/*Belpre*	2	1,000	209
Frontier Local School Dist/*New Matamoras*	3	625	209
Ft Frye Local School Dist/*Beverly*	4	1,031	210
Marietta City School Dist/*Marietta*	6	2,580	210
Ohio Valley Ed Service Ctr/*Marietta*			209
Warren Local School Dist/*Vincent*	4	2,022	210
Washington Co JT Voc Sch Dist/*Marietta*	1	487	210
Wolf Creek Local School Dist/*Waterford*	2	606	211
WAYNE			
Chippewa Local School Dist/*Doylestown*	3	1,290	211
Dalton Local School Dist/*Dalton*	2	875	211
Green Local School Dist/*Smithville*	3	1,056	212
Northwestern Local School Dist/*West Salem*	3	1,320	212
Norwayne Local School Dist/*Creston*	3	1,400	212
Orrville City School Dist/*Orrville*	3	1,600	212
Rittman Exempted Village SD/*Rittman*	4	999	212
Southeast Local School Dist/*Apple Creek*	6	1,400	213
Tccsa-Tri-Co Comp Svcs/*Wooster*			214
Tri-Co Ed Service Center/*Wooster*			211
Triway Local School Dist/*Wooster*	4	1,637	213
Wayne Co Joint Voc School Dist/*Smithville*	1	879	213
Wooster City School Dist/*Wooster*	7	3,650	213
WILLIAMS			
Bryan City School Dist/*Bryan*	2	2,200	214
Edgerton Local School Dist/*Edgerton*	2	599	214
Edon Northwest Local Sch Dist/*Edon*	1	500	215
Millcreek-West Unity Local SD/*West Unity*	1	520	215
Montpelier Exempted Village SD/*Montpelier*	1	1,100	215
North Central Local Sch Dist/*Pioneer*	1	600	215
Stryker Local School Dist/*Stryker*	2	407	215
WOOD			
Bowling Green City Sch Dist/*Bowling Green*	6	3,450	216
Eastwood Local School Dist/*Pemberville*	3	1,500	216
Elmwood Local School Dist/*Bloomdale*	3	1,275	216
Lake Local School Dist/*Millbury*	3	1,679	217
North Baltimore Local Sch Dist/*N Baltimore*	2	700	217
Northwest Ohio Ed Tech/*Bowling Green*			218
Northwood Local School Dist/*Northwood*	2	950	217
Otsego Local School Dist/*Bowling Green*	3	1,650	217
Penta Co JT Voc School Dist/*Perrysburg*	1	1,500	217
Perrysburg Exempted Village SD/*Perrysburg*	7	5,400	218
Rossford Exempted Village SD/*Rossford*	3	1,650	218
Wood Co Ed Service Center/*Bowling Green*			216
WYANDOT			
Carey Exempted Village SD/*Carey*	1	850	219
Mohawk Local School Dist/*Sycamore*	1	930	219
Upper Sandusky Exempted Vlg SD/*Upper Sandusky*	5	1,600	219

Ohio School Directory

DISTRICT PERSONNEL INDEX

A

NAME/District	JOB FUNCTIONS	PAGE
Abbott, Cynthia/*Dayton Public School Dist*	7	149
Abbott, Joe/*Bloom-Carroll Local Sch Dist*	67	63
Abbott, Travis/*Meigs Local School Dist*	27,75	142
Abele, Kellie/*Vinton Co Local School Dist*	36	206
Abell, Jennifer/*Fostoria City School Dist*	34,36,58	180
Abernathy, Abby/*Fremont City School Dist*	7,58,83,88	176
Abke, Chris/*Botkins Local School Dist*	81	182
Abke, Gregg/*Elmwood Local School Dist*	3	216
Abott, Russ/*Lakota Local School Dist*	73,286	177
Abraha, Hiwot/*Dayton Public School Dist*	2	149
Abraham, Jill/*Bexley City School Dist*	8,11,16,69,288,296,298	66
Abraham, Jill/*Dublin City School Dist*	9	69
Abramovich, Ray Anne/*Joseph Badger Local Sch Dist*	36,83,88	198
Abramt, Troy/*Caldwell Exempted Village SD*	73,84,98	158
Abshire, Ken/*Mansfield City Schools*	295	172
Accavallo, Amanda/*New London Local School Dist*	12,34	105
Acker, Lisa/*Triway Local School Dist*	11,296,298	213
Ackerman, Jill/*Lima City School Dist*	1,11,57,83	9
Ackerman, Nancy/*Buckeye Central Local Sch Dist*	2,11,296	38
Ackermann, Doug/*Lockland School Dist*	2	90
Ackermann, Tim/*Kings Local School Dist*	1	207
Acton, Steve/*Hopewell-Loudon Local SD*	73,295	181
Adair, Kayla/*Niles City School Dist*	83	200
Adams, Bradley, Dr/*Riverside Local School Dist*	67	121
Adams, Brenda/*Wynford Local School Dist*	58	39
Adams, Christopher/*Mogadore Local School Dist*	2	166
Adams, Dave/*East Muskingum Local Sch Dist*	1	156
Adams, Dave/*South Point Local School Dist*	6	116
Adams, Denise/*Waverly City School Dist*	7	164
Adams, Don/*Canfield Local School Dist*	3,91	134
Adams, Edward/*Boardman Local School Dist*	285,298	134
Adams, Fayette/*Mansfield City Schools*	73	172
Adams, Greg/*St Mary's City School Dist*	3	16
Adams, James/*Hubbard Exempted Village SD*	67	198
Adams, Jennifer/*Pleasant Local School Dist*	1	138
Adams, Katelyn/*Continental Local School Dist*	2	169
Adams, Kimberly/*London City School Dist*	5	132
Adams, Kimberly/*Southern Ohio Ed Serv Ctr*	8	32
Adams, Melissa/*Lisbon Exempted Village SD*	4	35
Adams, Natalie/*South Point Local School Dist*	67	116
Adams, Natasha/*West Clermont Local Sch Dist*	1	31
Adams, Ronald/*Southeastern Local Sch Dist*	5	175
Adamski, Angel/*Northwood Local School Dist*	2	217
Adamski, Donald/*Maumee City School Dist*	83	127
Addington, Amy/*Sylvania City School Dist*	71	128
Addis, Dana/*Norton City School Dist*	1	193
Adduci, Rocco/*Buckeye Local School Dist*	8,11,72	12
Addy, Randy/*Newcomerstown Exempted Vlg SD*	67	203
Adelsberger, Eric/*Ohio Hi-Point Joint Voc SD*	2	121
Adkins, Chris/*Eastern Local School Dist*	16,273,286	163
Adkins, Ellen/*Dawson-Bryant Local Sch Dist*	8,11,58,69,83,88,288	115
Adkins, Heidi/*Clearview Local School Dist*	67	123
Adkins, Michael/*Whitehall City School Dist*	67	75
Adkins, Patrick/*Port Clinton City School Dist*	1	159
Adkins, Willard/*Columbiana Co Voc Sch Dist*	1	34
Adkinson, Colleen/*Grandview Heights City SD*	274	71
Adrean, Angie/*Worthington School Dist*	8,11,18,88,285,288,294,296	75
Agnew, Mike/*Beaver Local School Dist*	36	34
Agosto, Diane/*Lorain City School Dist*	11	124
Agresta, Carolyn/*Greenon Local School Dist*	7	27
Agresta, Jennifer/*Steubenville City School Dist*	36,83,85,88,270,275	109
Ahlers, Jill/*New Bremen Local School Dist*	2	16
Aho, Martin/*Twinsburg City School Dist*	2,19	195
Ahrens, Hollie/*Versailles Exempted Village SD*	38,83	56
Aichele, Wendy/*Southern Local School Dist*	67	161
Aichholz, Nancy/*Indian Hill Exempted Vlg SD*	67	90
Ailes, Sally/*Alliance City School Dist*	67	184
Aills, Joyce/*Clark-Shawnee Local Sch Dist*	16	27
Aker, Crystal/*Springfield City School Dist*	69,294	28
Albanese, Anthony/*Springfield Local School Dist*	9,34	135
Albert, Amanda/*Northmor Local School Dist*	11	155
Albrecht, Joseph/*Portsmouth City School Dist*	6	179
Aldrich, Chris/*Findlay City School Dist*	67	98
Aldrich, Nate/*Beaver Local School Dist*	73,84	34
Alekna, Cindy/*Orange City School Dist*	4	48
Alexander, Beth/*Western Local School Dist*	58	164
Alexander, Jennifer/*Mad River Local School Dist*	71	151
Alexander, Joseph/*Laca-Licking Area Cmop Assoc*	76,295	120
Alexander, Linda/*London City School Dist*	30	132
Alexander, Rob/*Carey Exempted Village SD*	4	219
Alexander, Sherry/*Kettering City School Dist*	10	150
Alexander, Teresa/*Newton Local School Dist*	4	146
Alferio, Leann/*Brunswick City School Dist*	58	140
Alford, Paul/*Amanda-Clearcreek Local SD*	8,58	62
Alford, Paul/*Berne Union Local School Dist*	8,273	63
Alford, Paul/*Fairfield Co Ed Service Center*	8	62
Alig, Susan/*Oberlin City School Dist*	58,79	125
Aljanby, Rana/*Trotwood-Madison City SD*	285	153
Allen, Amy, Dr/*Toledo Public Schools*	34,58	129
Allen, Chad/*Carlisle Local School Dist*	3,5	206
Allen, Janice/*Trotwood-Madison City SD*	2,8,18	152
Allen, Jeffery/*Cleveland Metro School Dist*	20,23	42
Allen, Lance/*Eastern Local School Dist*	4,5,9,11,15,295	163
Allen, Peg/*Warren Co Voc School Dist*	71	208
Allen, Sally/*Shawnee Local School Dist*	4	9
Allen, Steve/*Madison-Champaign Ed Svc Ctr*	298	25
Allen, Susan/*Benjamin Logan Local Sch Dist*	67	121
Allen, Terri/*Dayton Public School Dist*	2	149
Allen, Thurman/*Mason City School Dist*	23,274	208
Allerding, Jennifer/*Galion City School Dist*	8,288	38
Allessandro, Joe/*South Euclid-Lyndhurst City SD*	73	51
Alliod, Dianna/*Xenia Community School Dist*	58,275	84
Allison, Heather/*Carlisle Local School Dist*	31	206
Allison, Melody/*Wellsville Local Sch Dist*	36	36
Allison, Shane/*Northridge Local School Dist*	7	152
Allison, Sue/*Columbiana Co Voc Sch Dist*	38	34
Allred-Smith, June/*Ross-Pike Co Ed Service Center*	81	174
Alsept, Robert/*Buckeye Joint Voc School Dist*	1,11	201
Alter, Mark/*Grandview Heights City SD*	286	71
Althiser, Gary/*Wellsville Local Sch Dist*	67	36
Altic, Deb/*Antwerp Local School Dist*	4	160
Altier, Connie/*Tri-Co Joint Voc Sch Dist*	1,11	15
Altimus, Drew/*Antwerp Local School Dist*	6	160
Amat-Outlaw, Tianay/*Cincinnati City School Dist*	15	87
Amato, Donna/*Brunswick City School Dist*	8,11,270,288,298	140
Ameen, Sam/*North Ridgeville City Sch Dist*	71	125
Ames, John/*Loveland City School Dist*	2,73,91,295	90
Amicone, Anthony/*Garaway Local School Dist*	6	202
Amlin, Jonathan/*Federal Hocking Local Sch Dist*	58	14
Amorganos, Rhonda/*Howland Local School Dist*	2,19	198
Amspaugh, Greg/*Celina City School Dist*	5	143
Amster, Karen/*Clermont Northeastern Local SD*	16	30
Amstutz, Kati/*Pandora Gilboa Local Sch Dist*	67	170
Amstutz, Ken/*Paulding Exempted Village SD*	1,11	160
Amstutz, Ken/*Van Wert City School Dist*	11	205
Amstutz, Leah/*Ohio Department of Education*	27	1
Anato, Josh/*Scioto Valley Local Sch Dist*	73,297	164
Anderson, Alicia/*Lima City School Dist*	67	9
Anderson, Brad/*Otsego Local School Dist*	67	217
Anderson, Carol/*North College Hill City SD*	6	91
Anderson, Dana/*Pickaway-Ross Co JT Voc SD*	298	175
Anderson, Dana/*Pickaway-Ross Co JT Voc SD*	10,33,60	175
Anderson, Elizabeth/*Rocky River City School Dist*	8,11,15,73,81,273,288,296	50
Anderson, Eva/*Greene Co Voc School Dist*	2	84
Anderson, Jodi/*Bowling Green City Sch Dist*	10	216
Anderson, Kathryn/*Eastland-Ffld Career Tech VSD*	16,82	70
Anderson, Pam/*Conneaut Area City Sch Dist*	4	12
Anderson, Patricia/*Bloomfield-Mespo Local SD*	6	197
Anderson, Teresa/*Piqua City School Dist*	9	146
Andexler, William/*Akron Public Schools*	5	190
Andrews, Chris/*Edgewood City School Dist*	73	21
Andrews, David/*Dayton Public School Dist*	27	149
Andrews, David/*Portage Lakes Joint Voc SD*	67	189
Andrews, Jennifer/*Coshocton City School Dist*	4,5	36
Andrews, Kayley/*State Support Team-Region 12*	93	86
Andrews, Mary Kay/*Lakewood Local School Dist*	1	118
Andrews, Sondra/*Lawrence Co Joint Voc Sch Dist*	298	116
Angelini, Jamie/*Hamilton Local School Dist*	34,58	71
Anger, Christine/*Loudonville-Perrysville SD*	2,11	11

DISTRICT PERSONNEL INDEX

Market Data Retrieval

NAME/District	JOB FUNCTIONS	PAGE
Angney, Keri/*Firelands Local School Dist*	2	124
Ankney, Bill/*Upper Valley JT Voc Sch Dist*	67	147
Ankrom, Mike/*Manchester Local School Dist*	6	193
Ankrom, Ty/*Pickaway Co Ed Service Center*	1,11	162
Anness, Brandon/*Warren Co Ed Service Center*	5	206
Anon, Jill/*Fairborn City School Dist*	58,275	84
Anspach, Christina/*Madison Local School Dist*	7,83,85	23
Anstadt, Kadee/*Washington Local School Dist*	1	130
Anstadt, Kadee, Dr/*Perrysburg Exempted Village SD*	15	218
Anstadt, Kathryn/*Perrysburg Exempted Village SD*	69,275	218
Antell, Frank/*Marietta City School Dist*	2	210
Anway, Tom/*Fremont City School Dist*	3,91	176
Apisa, Andrea/*Austintown Local School Dist*	2,68,79	133
Apolito, Betsy/*State Support Team-Region 10*	1	85
Appel, Lynda/*Westlake City School Dist*	297	51
Applegate, Marin/*Minford Local School Dist*	58	178
Applegate, Ralph/*Portsmouth City School Dist*	3,4	179
Appleman, Kevin/*Zanesville City School Dist*	3,17,76,79,91	157
Appolloni, Kim/*Martins Ferry City School Dist*	6,16,76,79	18
Arbogast, Angela/*Columbiana Co Ed Service Ctr*	5	33
Arbogast, Angie/*Lisbon Exempted Village SD*	5	35
Arbogast, Karen/*Wooster City School Dist*	9,280	213
Archer, Mickie/*Licking Valley Local Sch Dist*	5	118
Arganbright, Marty/*Olentangy Local School Dist*	11,58,77,79	59
Arkley, Janet/*Southern Local School Dist*	2	161
Arkley, John/*Southern Local School Dist*	3,73,295	161
Arledge, Robert/*Greene Co Ed Service Center*	2	83
Arlinghaus, Jennifer/*Kings Local School Dist*	4	207
Arlinghaus, Jennifer/*Lockland School Dist*	4	90
Armentrout, Diane/*Bath Local School Dist*	84	8
Armstrong, Betsy/*St Henry Cons Local Sch Dist*	38	144
Armstrong, Dean/*Hillsboro City School Dist*	3	103
Armstrong, Donald/*Gallia-Jackson-Vinton JVSD*	27,30,73,88	80
Armstrong, Jodi/*Green Local School Dist*	1,11	178
Armstrong, Terry/*Lordstown Local School Dist*	1	199
Armstrong, Troy/*Wauseon Exempted Village SD*	1	79
Arndt, Richard/*Geneva Area City School Dist*	67	13
Arnett, Jo Heather/*Lynchburg-Clay Local Sch Dist*	16,73	103
Arnett, Larry/*Waverly City School Dist*	6	164
Arnett, Trevor/*Greenfield Exempted Village SD*	6	103
Arnold, Anne/*Edison Local Schools District*	2	60
Arnold, Dwayne/*North Point Ed Svc Ctr*	81	60
Arnold, Hugh/*Wolf Creek Local School Dist*	67	211
Arnold, Lisa/*Stryker Local School Dist*	58	215
Arnold, Steve/*Central Local School Dist*	1,83	57
Arnold, Todd/*Plymouth-Shiloh Local Sch Dist*	3	173
Arnone, Tracey/*Diocese of Cleveland Ed Office*	9	52
Arnott, Billi/*Meigs Local School Dist*	76	142
Aronhalt, Scott/*Zanesville City School Dist*	6,35,80,83,85	157
Arps, Brenda/*Northeastern Local School Dist*	73	57
Arquilla, Sal/*Aurora City School Dist*	3,4,5,91	164
Arthur, Ann/*Fairbanks Local School Dist*	8,11,31,58,69,273	204
Arthur, Jerri/*Springfield City School Dist*	4	28
Arthur, Larry/*Vinton Co Local School Dist*	58,77	206
Arthur, Suzanne/*Greeneview Local School Dist*	67	84
Arthurs, Gary/*Green Local School Dist*	73,295	178
Ash, Theresa/*Beaver Local School Dist*	7	34
Ashbrook, Kaitlyn/*Coshocton City School Dist*	8,11,69,74,273,288,296	36
Ashcraft, Dianna/*Copley-Fairlawn City Sch Dist*	27,75	192
Ashcraft, Rodney/*Tri-Valley Local School Dist*	5	157
Asher, Kent/*Carey Exempted Village SD*	6	219
Ashley, Joshua/*Beavercreek City School Dist*	4	83
Ashmore, Michael/*Batavia Local School Dist*	2	29
Ashworth, Mindy/*Oakwood City School Dist*	16	152
Askew, Kelly/*Richmond Heights Local SD*	298	49
Asmus, Tutsy/*Eastwood Local School Dist*	37	216
Ast, N'Ecole/*Woodridge Local School Dist*	58,79	195

NAME/District	JOB FUNCTIONS	PAGE
Astroino, Mark/*Ashtabula Area City Sch Dist*	2,3,17,19,73,91	12
Atchison, Tracy/*State Support Team-Region 13*	1	97
Atchley, James/*Ansonia Local School Dist*	1	55
Atkinson, Carrie/*Columbia Local School Dist*	8,12,73,76,285,286,288,298	123
Atkinson, Megan/*Ohio Valley Ed Service Center*	2	85
Atkinson, Megan/*Ohio Valley Ed Service Ctr*	2,11	209
Atkinson, Timothy/*Olmsted Falls City School Dist*	2,3,5,91	48
Atwell, Joe/*Auburn Vocational School Dist*	3	112
Atwell, Kirk/*Lgca-Lake Geauga Ohio OCA*	3	115
Auble, Duane/*Lorain Co Joint Voc Sch Dist*	3	125
Auck, Judy/*Buckeye Central Local Sch Dist*	4	38
Aug, Mandy/*Fairfield City School Dist*	8	21
Aug, Mandy/*Three Rivers Local School Dist*	11,18,57,73,271,288,296	94
Augsburger, Emiko/*Darke Co Ed Service Center*	2	55
Augspurger, Anthony/*Twin Valley Cmty Local SD*	6	169
Augustine, Barbara/*Warren Local School Dist*	36,83	210
Augustine, Carol/*McDonald Local School Dist*	7	199
Augustine, John/*Carlisle Local School Dist*	6	206
Aukerman, Catherine/*Highland Local School Dist*	1	141
Auld, John/*Crestview Local School Dist*	67	205
Aulet, Ronald/*Campbell City School Dist*	6	134
Ault, Mark, Dr/*Indian Hill Exempted Vlg SD*	15	90
Austin, Alicia/*Green Local School Dist*	2	185
Austin, Jason/*Salem City School Dist*	3	35
Austin, Karen/*Hamilton Co Ed Service Center*	81	87
Austin, Karen/*Hamilton County ESC*	8,74	97
Avery, Mark/*Dublin City School Dist*	7,13,34,58,83	69
Axe, Doug/*Minster Local School Dist*	73	15
Axe, Jon/*Connect Information Tech Ctr*	295	54
Ayers, Amy/*Hardin-Houston Local Sch Dist*	2	182
Ayers, Andy/*Hardin Northern Local Sch Dist*	4	100
Ayres, Andy/*Kettering City School Dist*	295	150
Ayres, Laura/*Franklin-Monroe Local Sch Dist*	31,36,69,83	55
Ayres, Robin/*Zane Trace Local School Dist*	58	176

B

NAME/District	JOB FUNCTIONS	PAGE
Baar, Lindsay/*Cleveland Hts-Univ Hts City SD*	79	42
Babcock, Sandy/*Archbold Area Local Sch Dist*	4	78
Babik, Amber/*Hubbard Exempted Village SD*	2	198
Bable, Beth/*Field Local School Dist*	68	165
Bach Enz, Alyssa/*Northwest Local School Dist*	16	179
Bache, Andrew/*Dover City School Dist*	2	202
Bachman, Rick/*Four-Co Joint Voc School Dist*	3,27,34,75,288	79
Bachmann, Susan/*Hamilton Local School Dist*	76	22
Bacho, Alan/*Sylvania City School Dist*	3	128
Bachtel, Brian/*Kent City School Dist*	27,33	165
Backer, Yovona/*Felicity-Franklin Local SD*	67	30
Bacon, Pam/*Port Clinton City School Dist*	4	159
Bacquet, Tucker/*Lexington Local School Dist*	10	172
Badanjek, Jim/*Berkshire Local School Dist*	3	81
Badawi, Najwa/*Sylvania City School Dist*	30	128
Badenhop, Tim/*Oakwood City School Dist*	72	152
Badertscher, Pete/*Lima City School Dist*	73	9
Baer, Terri/*Weathersfield Local Sch Dist*	38,69	201
Baetjer, Carolyn/*North Royalton City Sch Dist*	7	48
Bagatti, Joseph/*Cuyahoga Falls City Sch Dist*	3	192
Bagley, Brian/*Licking Heights Local Sch Dist*	67	118
Bagley, David/*Western Buckeye Ed Service Ctr*	1	160
Bagrowski, Michele/*Archbold Area Local Sch Dist*	8,273	78
Bahorek, Stanley/*Columbus City School Dist*	2,19	66
Baier, Bob/*East Muskingum Local Sch Dist*	5	156
Bailey, Amanda/*Gallipolis City School Dist*	16	81
Bailey, Brad/*Ayersville Local School Dist*	4	56
Bailey, Brian/*Goshen Local School Dist*	15,36,57,69,79,83,88,285	30
Bailey, Dan/*Canton City School Dist*	3	184
Bailey, Dan/*New London Local School Dist*	5	105
Bailey, Donna/*Brookfield Local School Dist*	4	197

---

1 Superintendent	16 Instructional Media Svcs	30 Adult Education	44 Science Sec	58 Special Education K-12	72 Summer School	88 Alternative/At Risk	277 Remedial Math K-12
2 Bus/Finance/Purchasing	17 Chief Operations Officer	31 Career/Sch-to-Work K-12	45 Math K-12	59 Special Education Elem	73 Instructional Tech	89 Multi-Cultural Curriculum	280 Literacy Coach
3 Buildings And Grounds	18 Chief Academic Officer	32 Career/Sch-to-Work Elem	46 Math Elem	60 Special Education Sec	74 Inservice Training	90 Social Work	285 STEM
4 Food Service	19 Chief Financial Officer	33 Career/Sch-to-Work Sec	47 Math Sec	61 Foreign/World Lang K-12	75 Marketing/Distributive	91 Safety/Security	286 Digital Learning
5 Transportation	20 Art K-12	34 Early Childhood Ed	48 English/Lang Arts K-12	62 Foreign/World Lang Elem	76 Info Systems	92 Magnet School	288 Common Core Standards
6 Athletic	21 Art Elem	35 Health/Phys Education	49 English/Lang Arts Elem	63 Foreign/World Lang Sec	77 Psychological Assess	93 Parental Involvement	294 Accountability
7 Health Services	22 Art Sec	36 Guidance Services K-12	50 English/Lang Arts Sec	64 Religious Education K-12	78 Affirmative Action	95 Tech Prep Program	295 Network System
8 Curric/Instruct K-12	23 Music K-12	37 Guidance Services Elem	51 Reading K-12	65 Religious Education Elem	79 Student Personnel	97 Chief Infomation Officer	296 Title II Programs
9 Curric/Instruct Elem	24 Music Elem	38 Guidance Services Sec	52 Reading Elem	66 Religious Education Sec	80 Driver Ed/Safety	98 Chief Technology Officer	297 Webmaster
10 Curric/Instruct Sec	25 Music Sec	39 Social Studies K-12	53 Reading Sec	67 School Board President	81 Gifted/Talented	270 Character Education	298 Grant Writer/Ptnrshps
11 Federal Program	26 Business Education	40 Social Studies Elem	54 Remedial Reading K-12	68 Teacher Personnel	82 Video Services	271 Migrant Education	750 Chief Innovation Officer
12 Title I	27 Career & Tech Ed	41 Social Studies Sec	55 Remedial Reading Elem	69 Academic Assessment	83 Substance Abuse Prev	273 Teacher Mentor	751 Chief of Staff
13 Title V	28 Technology Education	42 Science K-12	56 Remedial Reading Sec	70 Research/Development	84 Erate	274 Before/After Sch	752 Social Emotional Learning
15 Asst Superintendent	29 Family/Consumer Science	43 Science Elem	57 Bilingual/ELL	71 Public Information	85 AIDS Education	275 Response To Intervention	

OH-T2

Ohio School Directory

DISTRICT PERSONNEL INDEX

NAME/District	JOB FUNCTIONS	PAGE
Bailey, Jimmy/New Boston Local School Dist	29	179
Bailey, Lloyd/Rock Hill Local School Dist	73,297	116
Bailey, Mona/Brookville Local School Dist	11	148
Bailey, Richard/Dublin City School Dist	68,70	69
Bailey, Shari/Garfield Heights City SD	16,73,295,297	46
Bailey, Tom/Washington Court House City SD	1,11	65
Bailey, William/Cuyahoga Falls City Sch Dist	4	192
Bailis, Scott/Riverside Local School Dist	27,31,36	114
Bails, Nathan/Urbana City School Dist	3	26
Bain, Steve/Oak Hills Local School Dist	2	92
Bainter, Monty/Logan-Hocking Local Sch Dist	1	104
Baird, Kristin/Felicity-Franklin Local SD	31,36,69,83,88	30
Baird, Pete/Reading Cmty City School Dist	73	93
Baird, Richard/North Union Local School Dist	1	204
Baisden, Dan/Milton-Union Exempted Vlg SD	2	145
Baker, Alyson/Hillsdale Local School Dist	8	11
Baker, Brian/Four-Co Joint Voc School Dist	67	79
Baker, Bryce/Newton Local School Dist	3	146
Baker, Caley/Westerville City School Dist	81	74
Baker, David/Arcanum Butler Local Sch Dist	84	55
Baker, Doug/Dublin City School Dist	71	69
Baker, Douglas, Dr/Zanesville City School Dist	1	157
Baker, Edward/Southern Local School Dist	73,76,295	143
Baker, Frank/United Local School Dist	83	36
Baker, Gary/Columbus City School Dist	67	67
Baker, Kevin/Penta Co JT Voc School Dist	3,5	217
Baker, Kirk/Jackson-Milton Local Sch Dist	1	134
Baker, Lisa/State Support Team-Region 12	1	86
Baker, Matt/Clinton-Massie Local Sch Dist	1	33
Baker, Melissa/Adams Co Ohio Valley Sch Dist	5	6
Baker, Melissa/United Local School Dist	2	36
Baker, Michele/Neonet-NE Ohio Ed Tech	68,71	196
Baker, Nate/Huber Heights City School Dist	6	150
Baker, Nathan/Yellow Springs Exempted Vlg SD	6	85
Baker, Rebecca/Carlisle Local School Dist	7	206
Baker, Rich/Miamisburg City School Dist	3	151
Baker, Terri/South Point Local School Dist	2	116
Baker, Terry/Ncocc-N Ctrl Ohio Co-op CA	73,295	174
Baker, Tom/Genoa Area Local School Dist	16,73,297	159
Baker, Trish/Laca-Licking Area Cmop Assoc	16	120
Bakos, Patsy/Campbell City School Dist	298	134
Bakos, Patsy/Campbell City School Dist	84	134
Baldwin, Anne/Westerville City School Dist	27,38,95	74
Baldwin, Chelsea/West Liberty-Salem Local SD	2	26
Baldwin, Connie/Rootstown Local School Dist	2,19	166
Baldwin, Douglas/Wolf Creek Local School Dist	1,11	211
Baldwin, Edwin/Joseph Badger Local Sch Dist	1	198
Baldwin, Ervin/Tolles Career & Tech Sch Dist	3,5	133
Baldwin, Jessica/Cleveland Metro School Dist	58,275	42
Balelt, Paul/Sycamore Cmty School Dist	67	93
Bales, Bryan/Franklin City School Dist	6	207
Ball, Kevin/Woodmore Local School Dist	8,58	159
Ball, Paula/Southwest Licking Local SD	298	120
Ball, Peggy/Ridgewood Local School Dist	58	37
Ballard, Marissa/Johnstown-Monroe Local SD	286	118
Ballard, Mark/Lorain City School Dist	67	124
Ballentine, Lori/Northwestern Local School Dist	81	27
Ballinger, Patrick/Ridgedale Local School Dist	67,288	138
Ballmer, Janna/Fayette Local Sch Dist	36,69	79
Balotta, Jim/Vermilion Local School Dist	8,11,57,69,91,273,285,288	62
Baltes, Kathy/Lordstown Local School Dist	5	199
Balzer, Dorothy/Greenfield Exempted Village SD	4	103
Balzer, John/Adena Local School Dist	1	174
Bame, Robin/Kenton City School Dist	286	100
Bandow, John/Hilliard City School Dist	10	71
Banfield, Brian/Poland Local School Dist	6	135
Banfield, Cindy/New Richmond Exempted Vlg SD	83	31
Banfield, Mara/Mahoning Co Joint Voc Sch Dist	10,38,60,79,88,288	135
Banfield, Mara/Mahoning Co Joint Voc Sch Dist	27	135
Banks, Art/Bexley City School Dist	5	66
Banks, Laurie/Finneytown Local School Dist	79	89
Banks, Michelle/Upper Arlington City Sch Dist	7,8,57	74
Banks, Randy/Worthington School Dist	15,79,273	75
Bansek, Graig/Columbia Local School Dist	1,84	123
Bapst, Brad/Eastern Local School Dist	67	163
Barber, Brad/Lynchburg-Clay Local Sch Dist	2,4	103
Barber, Gary/Tiffin City School Dist	1	181
Barber, Julie/New Miami Local School Dist	38	23
Barber, Kelley/Marion City School Dist	7,57,58	138
Barber, Rick/Frontier Local School Dist	3	209
Barbera, Jim/Tallmadge City School Dist	31	194
Barbon, Erik/Pickerington Local School Dist	57	64
Barch, Charles/Chagrin Falls Exempted Vlg SD	6	42
Barden-Gibson, Barbara/Portsmouth City School Dist	67	179
Bardin, Janet/Fairbanks Local School Dist	274	204
Barga, Jerry/Ansonia Local School Dist	5	55
Barhorst, Mark/Troy City School Dist	2,68	146
Barhorst, Michelle/Ft Loramie Local School Dist	16,82	182
Barkan, Elaine/Osnaburg Local School Dist	8	188
Barker, Alea/Crooksville Exempted Vlg SD	8,11,296,298	161
Barker, Bill/Rock Hill Local School Dist	5	116
Barker, Christi/Crestview Local School Dist	8,11,34,58,288	171
Barker, Kristin/Whitehall City School Dist	296	75
Barker, Sandy/Miami Valley Career Tech VSD	76	151
Barnaclo, Mary/Northwest Local School Dist	58	91
Barnes-Prince, Lisa/Manchester Local School Dist	16	193
Barnes, Carey/Southern Hills Joint Voc SD	2	20
Barnes, Michael, Dr/Lakewood City School Dist	1	47
Barnes, Neil/Highland Local School Dist	2	141
Barnes, Sarah/Jackson-Milton Local Sch Dist	27,29	134
Barnett, Brian/Mt Gilead Exempted Village SD	67	155
Barnett, Jerry/Beaver Local School Dist	67	34
Barnett, Luke/Preble-Shawnee Local Sch Dist	3	168
Barnett, Mary/Oakwood City School Dist	85	152
Barnett, Michael/Meigs Local School Dist	11,83,288,298	142
Barnette, Christy/New Lexington School Dist	2	161
Barnhart, Michael/Findlay City School Dist	2	97
Barnhizer, Ellen/Springfield Local School Dist	16	128
Barnier, Jaimie/Elyria City School Dist	68,74,273	123
Barno, John/Bexley City School Dist	67	66
Barnott, Billi/Meigs Local School Dist	76	142
Barns, Deirdre/Fredericktown Local Sch Dist	7,83,85	111
Barns, Kaye/Crestview Local School Dist	12	205
Barone, Jeffrey/Boardman Local School Dist	67	134
Barone, Thomas/Avon Lake City School Dist	2,3	122
Barr, Chris/Sidney City School Dist	58	183
Barr, John/Buckeye Joint Voc School Dist	298	201
Barr, Steve/Madison Local School Dist	73,76,286,295	172
Barr, Steve/Woodmore Local School Dist	6	159
Barr, Wendy/Ohio Mid-Eastern RESA	2	110
Barrell, Trina/Logan-Hocking Local Sch Dist	8,11,273,286	104
Barrett, Alisa/Greenfield Exempted Village SD	8	103
Barrett, Jen/Carey Exempted Village SD	8	219
Barrett, Robert/Wellsville Local Sch Dist	2,4,84	36
Barrett, Steve/Gahanna-Jefferson Public SD	1	70
Barron, Michael/Chillicothe City School Dist	6	174
Barth, Lawrence/South Range Local School Dist	33	135
Bartlett, Wes/Lake Local School Dist	73	217
Barto, Christopher/Carrollton Exempted Village SD	273	25
Barton, Terri/East Clinton Local School Dist	8,11,73,285,288,296	33
Bartos, Danielle/Canal Winchester Local SD	81	66
Barwick, Cierra/Osnaburg Local School Dist	36	188
Basalla, Bruce/Cuyahoga Co Ed Service Center	2	39
Basinger, John/Van Wert City School Dist	90	205
Basinger, Melissa/Putnam Co Ed Service Center	9,81	169
Basit, Arneice/Warrensville Heights City SD	11,294,298	51
Basley, David/Western Buckeye Ed Service Ctr	1	205
Basora, Mario/Huber Heights City School Dist	1	150
Basora, Mario/Yellow Springs Exempted Vlg SD	1	85
Bassett, Chad/Bryan City School Dist	3,4,8,11,57,69,296,298	214
Bassett, Eric/Hicksville Exempted Village SD	3	57
Bassler, Dan/Carlisle Local School Dist	2	206
Basson, Kari/Kettering City School Dist	71	150
Bastian, Matt/Beaver Local School Dist	3	34
Bates, Aaron/East Guernsey Local Sch Dist	6	86
Battaglia, Gina/Orange City School Dist	3	48
Battlagia, Anthony/Cleveland Metro School Dist	27,30,31	42
Batton, Suzzanne/Bethel Local School Dist	58	145
Battrell, Jimmy/Meta Solutions	71,97	78
Battrell, Jimmy/Meta Solutions Branch	16,73,76	154
Battrell, Jimmy/SE Ohio Voluntary Ed Co-op	1	15
Batty, Hope/Versailles Exempted Village SD	67	56

DISTRICT PERSONNEL INDEX

Market Data Retrieval

NAME/District	JOB FUNCTIONS	PAGE
Bauer, Christina/Cleveland Hts-Univ Hts City SD	73,286	42
Bauer, Matt/North Point Ed Svc Ctr	2	60
Bauer, Missy/Gibsonburg Exempted Village SD	4	177
Baughman, Brian/West Holmes Local School Dist	8,11,16,57,69,280,296,298	105
Baughman, Debbie/Valley Local School Dist	7	179
Baughman, Katrina/Otsego Local School Dist	11,34,288,298	217
Baughman, Lisa/Crooksville Exempted Vlg SD	36	161
Baughman, Travis/Licking Valley Local Sch Dist	73,286,295	119
Baughman, Wayne/Carrollton Exempted Village SD	5	25
Baughn, Kyle/Galion City School Dist	6	38
Baumann, Judy/Firelands Local School Dist	4	124
Baumer, Dave/Anna Local School Dist	3,5,91	182
Baumgardner, Sarah/Conneaut Area City Sch Dist	11,34,57,58,271,286	12
Baumgardner, Shane/Danbury Local School Dist	2	159
Baumgartner, Diane/Cardinal Local School Dist	5	81
Baumgartner, Jane/Spencerville Local School Dist	31,38,69,85	9
Baumgartner, Keith/Allen East Local School Dist	58	7
Bawn, Damien/Federal Hocking Local Sch Dist	295	14
Baxter, Jason/Ashtabula Area City Sch Dist	6	12
Bayda, Caitlyn/Field Local School Dist	83	165
Bayless, Maria/Upper Valley JT Voc Sch Dist	33	147
Baylis, William/Oberlin City School Dist	8,11,57,74,273,285,298	125
Baylog, Kathy/Garfield Heights City SD	81	46
Baz, Paulette/Springfield Local School Dist	11	128
Bazler, Anthony/Washington-Nile Local Sch Dist	1	179
Bazler, Anthony/Washington-Nile Local Sch Dist	27,72,88	179
Bazley, Gavyn/Plymouth-Shiloh Local Sch Dist	2,11	173
Bazzarri, Jeffrey/Union Local School Dist	16,73,95,295	18
Beach, Mark/Oregon City School Dist	6	128
Beach, Ruth/Rocky River City School Dist	67	50
Beadle, Liz/Middletown City School Dist	71	23
Beam, Jennifer/Montgomery Co Ed Service Ctr	71	148
Beam, Jennifer/State Support Team-Region 10	71	85
Beard, Elmer/Greenon Local School Dist	5	27
Beard, Janet/Tiffin City School Dist	4	181
Beardmore, Jeremy/Mideast Career & Tech Ctrs	10,15,79,83,270	157
Beardsley, Don/Franklin Local School Dist	5	156
Bearman, Marylynn/Reading Cmty City School Dist	4	93
Beattie, Bill/Edison Local School Dist	1,11	109
Beatty, Scott/Perry Local School Dist	1,11	188
Beaufort, Tricia/Mariemont City School Dist	11,57,79,83	91
Bebout, Carol/Tri-Rivers Joint Voc Sch Dist	270	139
Becerra, Mickey/Lorain City School Dist	15	124
Becher, Amy/Auglaize Co Ed Service Center	58	15
Beck, Don/Monroeville Local School Dist	5	105
Beck, Doug/Four-Co Joint Voc School Dist	30	79
Beck, Heather/Elyria City School Dist	6	123
Beck, Joe/Sylvania City School Dist	5	128
Beckemeyer, John/Oak Hills Local School Dist	3,7	92
Beckenhaupt, Dan/Oak Hills Local School Dist	68	92
Becker, Dan/Columbiana Exempted Village SD	91	34
Becker, Karen/Brunswick City School Dist	4	140
Beckett, Alesia/Edgewood City School Dist	68	21
Beckley, Austin/Claymont City School Dist	67	201
Beckley, Kimberly/Claymont City School Dist	2	201
Beckstrom, Dennis/Diocese of Cleveland Ed Office	2	52
Beckwith, Amy/Jefferson Area Local SD	7,85	13
Beddell, Mary/Plain Local School Dist	71	188
Beebe, Linda/Lakewood City School Dist	67	47
Beech, Pamela/Streetsboro City School Dist	68	167
Beegle, Carrie/Cloverleaf Local School Dist	4	140
Beegle, Carrie/Wellington Exempted Village SD	4,295	126
Beeman, Douglas/Wadsworth City School Dist	2	141
Beerman, Chris/Deer Park Cmty School Dist	88	89
Bees, Charnelle/Wayne Local School Dist	36	209
Beeson, Emmy/Tolles Career & Tech Sch Dist	1	133
Begeny, Joe/Reynoldsburg City School Dist	67	72

NAME/District	JOB FUNCTIONS	PAGE
Beiser, Jill/Black River Local School Dist	8,11,288	139
Bekan, Bill/Washington-Nile Local Sch Dist	73	179
Belako, Julie/Riverside Local School Dist	274	114
Belcher, Angie/Fayette Local Sch Dist	1,11	79
Belcher, Shannon/Manchester Local School Dist	4	193
Belcher, Tood/Highland Local School Dist	3	155
Belden, Julie/Oakwood City School Dist	2,3,4,19	152
Bell, Alison/Western Reserve Local Sch Dist	16,82	106
Bell, Christopher/Delaware Joint Voc Sch Dist	2	59
Bell, Douglas/Scioto Co Joint Vocational SD	73	179
Bell, Heather/McComb Local School Dist	37	98
Bell, Jason/Riverside Local School Dist	3,4,5	121
Bell, Lance/Logan-Hocking Local Sch Dist	67	104
Bella, Brian/Struthers City School Dist	2,5,294	136
Bella, Jeff/Swanton Local School Dist	5	79
Bello, John/Girard City School Dist	73	197
Bello, Mark/Girard City School Dist	2	197
Bellville, Chad/Fairfield Union Local Sch Dist	1	63
Belt, John/Indian Creek Local Sch Dist	15	109
Bemus, Laura/Greenville City School Dist	81	55
Bengston, Happy/Stow-Munroe Falls City SD	12	194
Benincasa, Nancy/West Geauga Local School Dist	8,48,51,54,69,74,273,298	82
Benko, Beth/Port Clinton City School Dist	67	159
Bennet, Lisa/Licking Valley Local Sch Dist	38	119
Bennett, Brian/Leipsic Local School Dist	10	170
Bennett, Daniel/Clark Co Ed Service Center	1	27
Bennett, Darcy/Southeast Local School Dist	77	213
Bennett, Jennifer/Norton City School Dist	67	193
Bennett, John/Martins Ferry City School Dist	16,38,45,83,88	18
Bennett, Margie, Dr/Mt Vernon City School Dist	67	111
Bennington, Larry/Little Miami Local School Dist	5	208
Benthien, John/Goshen Local School Dist	67	30
Bentley, Amy/Athens City School Dist	81	14
Bentley, Kelly/Fayette Local Sch Dist	2,84	79
Bentley, Thomas/Elmwood Local School Dist	88	216
Benton, Janis/Cardinal Local School Dist	4	81
Benton, Sherrell/Euclid City School Dist	79,92	46
Benway, Cheryl/Ashland City School Dist	67	10
Berdine, Richard/Cuyahoga Vly Career Ctr Voc SD	2	45
Berdine, Rick/Revere Local School Dist	2	194
Berding, Michael/Fairfield City School Dist	67	21
Berding, Mike/Butler Tech Career Dev Schs	67	21
Bereschik, Richard/Wellsville Local Sch Dist	1	36
Beresford, Lisa/Bright Local School Dist	58	102
Bergan, Dave/Deer Park Cmty School Dist	8,11,15,57,58,71,288,298	89
Bergan, Dave/Madeira City School Dist	8,11,69,79,83,88,288	90
Bergen, Karen/Cuyahoga Heights Local SD	16	45
Berger, Karla/Great Oaks Career Campuses	68,273	89
Bergholz, Carrie/Garfield Heights City SD	5	46
Bergman, Brad/Botkins Local School Dist	6	182
Bergman, Brock/Paulding Exempted Village SD	6	160
Bergman, Cassie/Southeast Local School Dist	2	166
Bergman, Sharon/Miami Valley Career Tech VSD	2,19	151
Bergman, Shawn/Vermilion Local School Dist	73,295	62
Berkebile, Willard/Louisville City School Dist	3	186
Berkemeyer, Bonnie/Southwest Local School Dist	4,5	93
Berkhouse, Julie/Mathews Local School Dist	38,69	199
Berkley, Jennie/Milford Exempted Village SD	58	30
Bernans, John/Dublin City School Dist	6	69
Bernath, Ryan/Granville Exempted Village SD	8,15,273,288	117
Berndt, Abby/Fremont City School Dist	4	176
Berndt, Chad/Fremont City School Dist	6	176
Bernier, Mary Ann/Archdiocese Cincinnati Ed Off	11	94
Berning, Michele/Fairborn City School Dist	77	84
Bero, Christine/Warren City School Dist	11,16,73,95	200
Berry, Bruce/Black River Local School Dist	5	139
Berry, Devon/West Carrollton City Sch Dist	68	153

1 Superintendent	16 Instructional Media Svcs	30 Adult Education	44 Science Sec	58 Special Education K-12	72 Summer School	88 Alternative/At Risk	277 Remedial Math K-12
2 Bus/Finance/Purchasing	17 Chief Operations Officer	31 Career/Sch-to-Work K-12	45 Math K-12	59 Special Education Elem	73 Instructional Tech	89 Multi-Cultural Curriculum	280 Literacy Coach
3 Buildings And Grounds	18 Chief Academic Officer	32 Career/Sch-to-Work Elem	46 Math Elem	60 Special Education Sec	74 Inservice Training	90 Social Work	285 STEM
4 Food Service	19 Chief Financial Officer	33 Career/Sch-to-Work Sec	47 Math Sec	61 Foreign/World Lang K-12	75 Marketing/Distributive	91 Safety/Security	286 Digital Learning
5 Transportation	20 Art K-12	34 Early Childhood Ed	48 English/Lang Arts K-12	62 Foreign/World Lang Elem	76 Info Systems	92 Magnet School	288 Common Core Standards
6 Athletic	21 Art Elem	35 Health/Phys Education	49 English/Lang Arts Elem	63 Foreign/World Lang Sec	77 Psychological Assess	93 Parental Involvement	294 Accountability
7 Health Services	22 Art Sec	36 Guidance Services K-12	50 English/Lang Arts Sec	64 Religious Education K-12	78 Affirmative Action	95 Tech Prep Program	295 Network System
8 Curric/Instruct K-12	23 Music K-12	37 Guidance Services Elem	51 Reading K-12	65 Religious Education Elem	79 Student Personnel	96 Title II Programs	296 Title II Programs
9 Curric/Instruct Elem	24 Music Elem	38 Guidance Services Sec	52 Reading Elem	66 Religious Education Sec	80 Driver Ed/Safety	98 Chief Technology Officer	297 Webmaster
10 Curric/Instruct Sec	25 Music Sec	39 Social Studies K-12	53 Reading Sec	67 School Board President	81 Gifted/Talented	270 Character Education	298 Grant Writer/Ptnrships
11 Federal Program	26 Business Education	40 Social Studies Elem	54 Remedial Reading K-12	68 Teacher Personnel	82 Video Services	271 Migrant Education	750 Chief Innovation Officer
12 Title I	27 Career & Tech Ed	41 Social Studies Sec	55 Remedial Reading Elem	69 Academic Assessment	83 Substance Abuse Prev	273 Teacher Mentor	751 Chief of Staff
13 Title V	28 Technology Education	42 Science K-12	56 Remedial Reading Sec	70 Research/Development	84 Erate	274 Before/After Sch	752 Social Emotional Learning
15 Asst Superintendent	29 Family/Consumer Science	43 Science Elem	57 Bilingual/ELL	71 Public Information	85 AIDS Education	275 Response To Intervention	

Ohio School Directory

DISTRICT PERSONNEL INDEX

NAME/District	JOB FUNCTIONS	PAGE
Berry, Michelle/*Heath City School Dist*	73	117
Berryman, Kirk/*Lincolnview Local School Dist*	67	205
Berryman, Laura/*Washington Local School Dist*	68	130
Berryman, Rob/*Botkins Local School Dist*	58	182
Bertani, Brad/*Grandview Heights City SD*	6	71
Bertke, Jamie/*Fairfield City School Dist*	3	21
Bertke, Ken/*Liberty-Benton Local Sch Dist*	3	98
Bertram, Amy/*Northwest Local School Dist*	58	91
Bertram, Randy/*Middletown City School Dist*	2	23
Berwald, Gavin/*Westlake City School Dist*	5	51
Bess, Charile/*Adams Co Ohio Valley Sch Dist*	67	6
Best, Brian/*Columbus Grove Local Sch Dist*	8,285	169
Best, Cody/*Edon Northwest Local Sch Dist*	67	215
Best, Jennifer/*Worthington School Dist*	67	75
Best, Leslie/*Columbiana Exempted Village SD*	5	34
Betties, Stacey/*Tuscarawas Valley Local SD*	4	203
Bettis, Stacey/*Louisville City School Dist*	4	186
Bettis, Stacey/*Minerva Local School Dist*	4	187
Betts, Dawn, Dr/*Clermont Co Ed Service Center*	15,36,68	29
Betts, John/*Edison Local Schools District*	67	60
Betz, Elizabeth/*Bellbrook-Sugarcreek Schools*	67	83
Beumer, Michelle/*Hillsboro City School Dist*	8	103
Beun, Brad/*Springfield Local School Dist*	7,58	194
Beun, Erik/*East Holmes Local School Dist*	1	104
Beverly, Edward/*Milford Exempted Village SD*	3	30
Bianca, Petie/*North Ridgeville City Sch Dist*	79	125
Bibbey, Melissa/*Wheelersburg Local School Dist*	16,73,295	180
Bibbey, Melissa/*Wheelersburg Local School Dist*	84	180
Biber, Keith/*Ashtabula Co Tech & Career SD*	2	12
Bibler, Pam/*Lakota Local School Dist*	58	177
Bican, Deb/*Cloverleaf Local School Dist*	83	140
Bichel, Tom/*Tolles Career & Tech Sch Dist*	67	133
Bichsel, Sherry/*Garaway Local School Dist*	273	202
Biddle, Jeffrey/*Southwest Local School Dist*	67	93
Bidlack, Broc/*Fairless Local School Dist*	1	185
Bidlick, Dean/*Continental Local School Dist*	67	169
Biecheler, Jamie/*Sandusky City School Dist*	79	61
Biederstedt, Joshua/*Patrick Henry Local Sch Dist*	1	102
Biehl, Mark/*Washington Court House City SD*	6	65
Bierman, Mary Lynne/*Deer Park Cmty School Dist*	4	89
Bierman, Marylynn/*Talawanda School Dist*	4	24
Bigam, Travis/*Bloom-Carroll Local Sch Dist*	2,11,84,298	63
Biggs, Susan/*Diocese of Cleveland Ed Office*	9,15	52
Bihn, Rebecca/*Oregon City School Dist*	27,31	128
Bilger, Jared/*Old Fort Local School Dist*	3	181
Billaplain, Robert/*Xenia Community School Dist*	67	84
Billings, Brian/*Perrysburg Exempted Village SD*	81	218
Bills, Sue/*Coldwater Exempted Village SD*	38	143
Bills, Terry/*St Henry Cons Local Sch Dist*	3	144
Bils, Tina/*Cory-Rawson Local School Dist*	57	97
Biltz, Melissa/*East Holmes Local School Dist*	4	104
Biltz, Melissa/*Garaway Local School Dist*	4	202
Bindus, Mark/*Coventry Local School Dist*	4	192
Bindus, Mark/*Twinsburg City School Dist*	4	195
Bing, Kyle/*Lisbon Exempted Village SD*	6	35
Binger, Alan/*Vanguard-Sentinel JT Voc SD*	2	177
Binger, Alex/*Van Buren Local School Dist*	2	99
Bingham, Anne/*Cleveland Metro School Dist*	67	42
Binkley, David/*Strongsville City School Dist*	16,73	51
Binkley, David/*Strongsville City School Dist*	16,73	51
Binkley, Diane/*Spencerville Local School Dist*	12,52,55	9
Bir, Carrie/*Clinton-Massie Local Sch Dist*	2	33
Birchwell, Beth/*Edgewood City School Dist*	7,72,85	21
Bires, Emilia/*Northwood Local School Dist*	4	217
Birkemeier, Robert/*Bath Local School Dist*	67	8
Birkhimer, Erin/*Portsmouth City School Dist*	16,82,286,297	179
Birney, Carla/*Dover City School Dist*	1,11	202
Bishop, Don/*Trumbull Co Ed Service Center*	67	196
Bishop, Gregg/*Elmwood Local School Dist*	73,286,295	216
Bishop, Matt, Dr/*Preble-Shawnee Local Sch Dist*	1,11	168
Bittel, Amy/*Woodmore Local School Dist*	81	159
Bittner, Lori/*Van Wert City School Dist*	30,34,88	205
Bixler, Andrew/*Anna Local School Dist*	1	182
Bizzarri, Jeff/*Union Local School Dist*	84	18
Blabolil, Ginger/*Jefferson Area Local SD*	58	13
Blabolil, Glen/*Grand Valley Local School Dist*	58	13

NAME/District	JOB FUNCTIONS	PAGE
Black, Annette/*Tri-Village Local Sch Dist*	8,34,38,57,69,83,88	56
Black, Debbie/*Miami Trace Local School Dist*	2,19,71	65
Black, Mark/*Akron Public Schools*	10	190
Blackburn, Bob/*Pickerington Local School Dist*	15,79,83,91	64
Blackburn, Brandi/*Clay Local School Dist*	2	178
Blackburn, Karen/*Vermilion Local School Dist*	58	62
Blackburn, Leah/*Milton-Union Exempted Vlg SD*	68	145
Blackstone, Jayme/*North Fork Local School Dist*	8,58,79,288	119
Blackstone, Jenifer/*Liberty Union-Thurstn Sch Dist*	8,57,288,296	64
Blackwell, Krista/*Buckeye Local School Dist*	58	108
Blackwood, Sandy/*Pettisville Local School Dist*	4	79
Blahnik, Rick/*Hillsdale Local School Dist*	2	11
Blair, Cory/*Logan-Hocking Local Sch Dist*	3,17	104
Blair, Matt/*Springboro Cmty School Dist*	57	208
Blaire, Chris/*Massillon City School Dist*	8	187
Blake, Jenette/*Madison Local School Dist*	7,85	112
Blake, Karen/*Martins Ferry City School Dist*	2	18
Blakeley, Lynn/*Russia Local School Dist*	12	183
Blakely, William/*Edgerton Local School Dist*	2	214
Blalock, Eugene/*North College Hill City SD*	1	91
Blanchard, Terri/*Loudonville-Perrysville SD*	4	11
Blandin, Matt/*Batavia Local School Dist*	6	29
Blangger, Paula/*Jackson Local School Dist*	71	186
Blankenship, Aaron/*Fairfield City School Dist*	6	21
Blankenship, Jenny/*Plymouth-Shiloh Local Sch Dist*	4	173
Blankenship, Julie/*Ed Service Center Lorain Co*	275	122
Blascoe, Mark/*Toronto City School Dist*	3	109
Blatt, Denise/*Elyria City School Dist*	58	123
Blatt, Dennis/*Washington Co JT Voc Sch Dist*	1,11	210
Blaze, Leah/*North Olmsted City School Dist*	73	48
Blazek, Michelle/*Toronto City School Dist*	273	109
Blazer, Shawn/*Northeastern Local School Dist*	8,15,69,288	27
Bleigh, Randy/*Tuslaw Local School Dist*	67	189
Blevins, Andrea/*Hamilton City School Dist*	9	22
Blevins, Lilly/*Gallia Co Local School Dist*	2	80
Blevins, Lily/*Gallia-Vinton Ed Svc Center*	2	80
Blevins, Robert/*Howland Local School Dist*	73,76,95	198
Blind, Scott/*Newcomerstown Exempted Vlg SD*	4	203
Bline, Joan/*Oakwood City School Dist*	83,275	152
Block, Carey/*Caldwell Exempted Village SD*	8,11,58,296	158
Blodgett, Jim/*Avon Local School Dist*	5	122
Blood, Ken/*East Muskingum Local Sch Dist*	67	156
Bloom, Scott/*Piqua City School Dist*	10,285,288	146
Bloomfield, Crystal/*Symmes Valley Local Sch Dist*	38	117
Bloomfield, Nancy/*Pike Co Area JT Voc Sch Dist*	38,79	163
Bloomstrom, Gretchen/*Three Rivers Local School Dist*	8,69	94
Blosser, Jacqueline/*Lima City School Dist*	12	9
Blosser, Vicki/*Madison Plains Local Sch Dist*	68	133
Blotler, John/*Barnesville Exempted Vlg SD*	3,5	17
Blough, Lisa/*Coventry Local School Dist*	1,11	192
Blough, Tim/*Tallmadge City School Dist*	295	195
Blubaugh, Philip/*Danville Local School Dist*	5	110
Bluck, Josh/*Adena Local School Dist*	27	174
Blue, Mike/*Hicksville Exempted Village SD*	38,69,83	57
Bluey, Michael/*North Canton City School Dist*	286	187
Blum, Linda/*Northmont City School Dist*	67	152
Blust, Jenny/*Northwest Local School Dist*	8,11,34,35,36,77,286,288	91
Boatman, Roger/*River View Local School Dist*	3,91	37
Bober, Ronald/*Union Local School Dist*	273	18
Bobic, Michael/*Campbell City School Dist*	5	134
Bobincheck, Lori/*Berea City School Dist*	58,79	41
Boch, Karen/*Wellston City School Dist*	1,11	108
Bochenek, Stan/*Mad River Local School Dist*	3,91	151
Bock, Joseph/*Lorain City School Dist*	16,82	124
Bock, Liz/*Cory-Rawson Local School Dist*	88	97
Bodart, Sue/*Hopewell-Loudon Local SD*	16	181
Bodin, Colleen/*Benjamin Logan Local Sch Dist*	9,69	121
Bodnarik, Tim/*Hancock Co Ed Service Center*	8,74	97
Boedicker, Laurie/*Highland Local School Dist*	8,11,57,69,88,288	141
Boehm, Jane/*Kings Local School Dist*	11,296,298	207
Boehmer, Tracy/*Licking Valley Local School Dist*	16	118
Boeke, Brenda/*Minster Local School Dist*	1,11	15
Boerger, Karl/*Adams Co Ohio Valley Sch Dist*	275	6
Boerger, Neil/*Botkins Local School Dist*	67	182
Boes, Robert/*Tiffin City School Dist*	15	181
Boettcher, Lauren/*Lakota Local School Dist*	16,71	22

School Year 2019-2020   800-333-8802   OH-T5

DISTRICT PERSONNEL INDEX

Market Data Retrieval

NAME/District	JOB FUNCTIONS	PAGE
Boettner, Rich/Hilliard City School Dist	73,95,98,295	71
Bogart, Travis/Bright Local School Dist	16,73	102
Bogdan, Allison/Cuyahoga Falls City Sch Dist	83,88,95,270	192
Bogden, Julie/North Royalton City Sch Dist	36,58,81,83	48
Bogenrife, Jen/Springfield City School Dist	58	28
Boggs, Charlie/Bloom-Vernon Local Sch Dist	3	178
Boggs, Kim/Madison Local School Dist	5	112
Boggs, Penny/Ohio Valley Ed Service Center	81	85
Boggs, Robin/Lexington Local School Dist	5	172
Boggs, Shari/Canal Winchester Local SD	16,82	66
Boggs, Todd/Perkins Local School Dist	1	61
Bogielski, Richard/Bay Village City School Dist	77	40
Bohannon, Rhonda/Edgewood City School Dist	68	21
Bohl, Jina/Western Brown Local Sch Dist	8,11,15,288,296,298	20
Bohlander, Brian/Covington Exempted Village SD	57	145
Bohrer, Jennifer/Western Brown Local Sch Dist	34,58	20
Boice, Bernie/Belpre City School Dist	69	209
Bojc, Taylor/Jonathan Alder Local Sch Dist	280	132
Bolden, Fred/Solon City School Dist	2,15,68	50
Bolden, Stacy/Ft Frye Local School Dist	2	210
Bole, Tammy/Ncocc-N Ctrl Ohio Co-op CA	2	174
Bolender, Ron/Greene Co Voc School Dist	27,71,75	84
Boles, Joshua/Bellbrook-Sugarcreek Schools	16,73,286,295	83
Bolin, Kelly/Huber Heights City School Dist	58	150
Bolyard, April/Liberty Union-Thurstn Sch Dist	2,11	64
Bomar, Eric/Lorain City School Dist	71	124
Bonam, Larry/Osnaburg Local School Dist	3	188
Bonar, Robin/New Miami Local School Dist	2	23
Bonbright, Mallory/Sycamore Cmty School Dist	71	93
Bond, April/Colonel Crawford Local SD	12	38
Bond, Barbara/Ridgewood Local School Dist	7,85	37
Bone, Curt/Wilmington City School Dist	2	33
Bonekovic, Ronda/Brookfield Local School Dist	67	197
Bonner, Lisa/Athens Meigs Ed Service Center	58	14
Bonnes, Barb/Mentor Exempted Village SD	8,81,286,288,296	113
Bontempo, Brian, Dr/Auburn Vocational School Dist	1	112
Bonvissuto, Kim/Westlake City School Dist	71	51
Boobek, Nate/Hilliard City School Dist	6,35	71
Boothby, Blinda/Brown Co Ed Service Center	2	19
Boothby, Christy/Marietta City School Dist	16,82	210
Boothe, Todd/Gallia Co Local School Dist	3,73,295	80
Borba, Marie/Bellefontaine City School Dist	76,295	121
Borchers, Jay/Miami Co Ed Service Center	8	144
Borchers, Jean/Russia Local School Dist	2	183
Borchik, James/Copley-Fairlawn City Sch Dist	67	192
Borders, Tammy/North Union Local School Dist	37	205
Borders, Tammy/North Union Local School Dist	37	205
Borger, Kerry/National Trail Local Sch Dist	2	168
Borger, Kerry/Preble Co Ed Service Center	2	168
Borgerding, Ron/Indian Lake Local School Dist	73	121
Borges, Donna/Minster Local School Dist	4	15
Boring, Lee/Rootstown Local School Dist	73	166
Bornino-Elwell, Terrilynn/Lakewood City School Dist	88	47
Bors, Dave/Riverside Local School Dist	6	114
Borton, Tony/Elmwood Local School Dist	1	216
Bosch, Christy/Logan-Hocking Local Sch Dist	11,15,74,83	104
Bosch, Mike/Shawnee Local School Dist	5	9
Bosheff, Tracy/McDonald Local School Dist	31,36,69,83	199
Boss, Jim/Benton-Carroll-Salem Local SD	58	158
Boss, Tricia/Putnam Co Ed Service Center	58	169
Bosse, Peggy/Deer Park Cmty School Dist	67	89
Bosser, Pam/Lancaster City School Dist	6	63
Bostdorff, Matthew/Eastwood Local School Dist	16,295	216
Bostian, Matthew/Austintown Local School Dist	3,91	133
Bostic, Chuck/Northwest Local School Dist	3,91	91
Bostleman, Mike/Napoleon Area City School Dist	2	101
Boston, Amy/Miami Trace Local School Dist	9,11,280,296	65
Boston, Randy/Eastern Local School Dist	3,5	142
Boswell, Dustin/Springfield Local School Dist	2,3,4,73,76,91,295	194
Bott, Anna/Boardman Local School Dist	27,36,69,77,83	134
Bottoni, Mary/Maumee City School Dist	4,5	127
Boughton, Heather, Dr/Ohio Department of Education	69,70,294	1
Bouillon, Steve/New Riegel Local School Dist	6	181
Bourelle, Katherine/Arcanum Butler Local Sch Dist	38	55
Bowdle, Michelle/Union Scioto Local Sch Dist	28,73,76,286,295	175
Bowe, Marty/Sparcc	1	190
Bowe, Marty/State Support Team-Region 9	1	190
Bowen, Frankie/Van Wert City School Dist	38	205
Bowen, Matthew/Campbell City School Dist	1	134
Bower, Andrea/Vanlue Local School Dist	59	99
Bower, Chris/Conotton Valley Union Local SD	67	100
Bower, Erika/North Union Local School Dist	8,18,30	204
Bower, Jeanette/Grand Valley Local School Dist	4	13
Bowers, Eileen/Willoughby-Eastlake City SD	11,58,79,271	114
Bowers, Greg/Steubenville City School Dist	45	109
Bowers, Sharon/Allen Co Ed Service Center	81	7
Bowers, Stacey/Liberty Center Local Sch Dist	285	101
Bowers, Trent, Dr/Worthington School Dist	1	75
Bowersock, Troy/Lincolnview Local School Dist	2,84	205
Bowler, Lorena/Mt Gilead Exempted Village SD	5	155
Bowles, Heather/Paint Valley Local School Dist	11,288	175
Bowlin, Brooke/Mohawk Local School Dist	58	219
Bowlin, David, Dr/Ohio Department of Education	5	1
Bowling, Becky/Lawrence Co Ed Service Center	8	115
Bowling, Kathy/Rock Hill Local School Dist	8,15,76	116
Bowling, Scott/Brown Local School Dist	1	25
Bowling, Todd/Northwest Local School Dist	1	91
Bowman, Dan/Perkins Local School Dist	2	61
Bowman, Georgine/Butler Co Ed Service Center	8	20
Bowman, Jessica/Columbia Local School Dist	81	123
Bowman, John/Wellington Exempted Village SD	6	126
Bowman, Joseph/Ashland Co-West Holmes JVSD	3	11
Bowman, Joy/Lexington Local School Dist	8,57	172
Bowman, Joyce/Northwestern Local School Dist	37	212
Bowman, Larry/Old Fort Local School Dist	67	181
Bowman, Rick/Eastern Local School Dist	58	163
Bowser, Brian/South-Western City School Dist	9,34	73
Bowser, Eric/Upper Valley JT Voc Sch Dist	16,73,82,295	147
Bowser, Kerry/Mentor Exempted Village SD	58	113
Boxler, Robert/Akron Public Schools	3,91	190
Boyarko, Maria/South-Western City School Dist	74,273	73
Boyd, Jim/Berkshire Local School Dist	67	81
Boyd, Mitzi/Groveport Madison Local SD	58	71
Boyd, Noah/East Holmes Local School Dist	38	104
Boyd, Tonya/Mt Gilead Exempted Village SD	2,13	155
Boyer, Bill/Millcreek-West Unity Local SD	58,752	215
Boyer, Cheryl/Wayne Co Joint Voc School Dist	16,73	213
Boyer, David/Shaker Heights City Sch Dist	3	50
Boyer, Dawn/Yellow Springs Exempted Vlg SD	298	85
Boyer, Elise/Antwerp Local School Dist	8,73	160
Boyer, Sam/Elida Local School Dist	80	8
Boyer, Tara/Newark City School Dist	11,69,74,294,296,298	119
Boyle, Colleen, Dr/Columbus City School Dist	81	67
Boyle, Susan/James A Garfield Local SD	7,58	165
Brabson, Tom/Plain Local School Dist	2,91	188
Bracken, Kimberly/Ashland City School Dist	81	10
Brackenhoff, Sue, Dr/Fairborn City School Dist	8,11,280,285,286,288,294,296	84
Brackman, Karen/Covington Exempted Village SD	36,69	145
Bradac, Ed/Kirtland Local School Dist	16	112
Brader, Lorinda/Archbold Area Local Sch Dist	73	78
Bradford, Jerry/Washington Co JT Voc Sch Dist	73,84	210
Bradford, Jill/Amanda-Clearcreek Local SD	2	62
Bradford, Randy/Centerburg Local School Dist	3,5	110
Bradford, Stacy/Washington Co JT Voc Sch Dist	16,286	210

1 Superintendent
2 Bus/Finance/Purchasing
3 Buildings And Grounds
4 Food Service
5 Transportation
6 Athletic
7 Health Services
8 Curric/Instruct K-12
9 Curric/Instruct Elem
10 Curric/Instruct Sec
11 Federal Program
12 Title I
13 Title V
15 Asst Superintendent
16 Instructional Media Svcs
17 Chief Operations Officer
18 Chief Academic Officer
19 Chief Financial Officer
20 Art K-12
21 Art Elem
22 Art Sec
24 Music Elem
25 Music Sec
26 Business Education
27 Career & Tech Ed
28 Technology Education
29 Family/Consumer Science
30 Adult Education
31 Career/Sch-to-Work K-12
32 Career/Sch-to-Work Elem
33 Career/Sch-to-Work Sec
34 Early Childhood Ed
35 Health/Phys Education
36 Guidance Services K-12
37 Guidance Services Elem
38 Guidance Services Sec
39 Social Studies K-12
40 Social Studies Elem
41 Social Studies Sec
42 Science K-12
43 Science Elem
44 Science Sec
45 Math K-12
46 Math Elem
47 Math Sec
48 English/Lang Arts K-12
49 English/Lang Arts Elem
50 English/Lang Arts Sec
51 Reading K-12
52 Reading Elem
53 Reading Sec
54 Remedial Reading K-12
55 Remedial Reading Elem
56 Remedial Reading Sec
57 Bilingual/ELL
58 Special Education K-12
59 Special Education Elem
60 Special Education Sec
61 Foreign/World Lang K-12
62 Foreign/World Lang Elem
63 Foreign/World Lang Sec
64 Religious Education K-12
65 Religious Education Elem
66 Religious Education Sec
67 School Board President
68 Teacher Personnel
69 Academic Assessment
70 Research/Development
71 Public Information
72 Summer School
73 Instructional Tech
74 Inservice Training
75 Marketing/Distributive
76 Info Systems
77 Psychological Assess
78 Affirmative Action
79 Student Personnel
80 Driver Ed/Safety
81 Gifted/Talented
82 Video Services
83 Substance Abuse Prev
84 Erate
85 AIDS Education
88 Alternative/At Risk
89 Multi-Cultural Curriculum
90 Social Work
91 Safety/Security
92 Magnet School
93 Parental Involvement
95 Tech Prep Program
97 Chief Information Officer
98 Chief Technology Officer
270 Character Education
271 Migrant Education
273 Teacher Mentor
274 Before/After Sch
275 Response To Intervention
277 Remedial Math K-12
280 Literacy Coach
285 STEM
286 Digital Learning
288 Common Core Standards
294 Accountability
295 Network System
296 Title II Programs
297 Webmaster
298 Grant Writer/Ptnrships
750 Chief Innovation Officer
751 Chief of Staff
752 Social Emotional Learning

OH-T6

Ohio School Directory

DISTRICT PERSONNEL INDEX

NAME/District	JOB FUNCTIONS	PAGE
Bradley, Brett/Grandview Heights City SD	3,91	70
Bradley, Kraft/Sandusky City School Dist	4	61
Bradley, Stephanie/Edison Local Schools District	11,57,58	60
Bradshaw, Curt/East Clinton Local School Dist	81	33
Bradshaw, Curt/Southern Ohio Ed Serv Ctr	81	32
Brady, Andrea/Indian Hill Exempted Vlg SD	71,75,91	90
Brady, Joe/Jefferson Area Local SD	3,91	13
Brady, Laura/Central Local School Dist	4	57
Brady, Tammy/Akron Public Schools	58,275	190
Bragg, Justin/Van Wert City School Dist	73	205
Brahler, Kim/Brown Local School Dist	68	25
Braman, Shawn/Waterloo Local School Dist	1,11	167
Brammer, Sharon/Dawson-Bryant Local Sch Dist	4	115
Branch, David/Muskingum Valley ESC	1	156
Brand, Dave/New Philadelphia City Sch Dist	1	202
Brand, Kassi/Grand Valley Local School Dist	76,79	13
Brand, Kathy/Jackson Local School Dist	34,57,58,69,77,88,90,275	186
Brand, Sonja/Elmwood Local School Dist	16	216
Brandt, Cheri/Wapakoneta City School Dist	12	16
Brandt, Jeff/Oak Hills Local School Dist	1	92
Brandt, Michael/Clermont Northeastern Local SD	1	30
Branham, Donald Shawn/Seneca East Local School Dist	3	181
Branham, Ricky/Willard City School Dist	7	106
Brannock, David/Bethel-Tate Local School Dist	67	30
Brannon, Lynn/Educational Serv Ctr-Ctl Ohio	58,79,88	65
Brassell, Wayne/Columbia Local School Dist	67	123
Brately, Adam/West Holmes Local School Dist	6	105
Bratten, Thomas/Stow-Munroe Falls City SD	1	194
Brauer, David/Ohio Department of Education	57,271	1
Braun, Brenda/Versailles Exempted Village SD	69,270,288	56
Braun, Drew/Celina City School Dist	42	143
Braxton, Shawn/Cleveland Metro School Dist	16,73	42
Bray, Tonya/Winton Woods City School Dist	7,11,58,79	94
Brazee, Kevin/Northwestern Local School Dist	73,286	212
Brebberman, Karen/Maumee City School Dist	16	127
Breckner, Stephen/Strongsville City School Dist	2,3,4,5,76,91,286	51
Breehl, Kelly/North Fork Local School Dist	2,19,76	119
Breese, Robbie/Lincolnview Local School Dist	88	205
Breexe, Tabitha/Bradford Exempted Village SD	12,280	145
Brehm, Amanda/Evergreen Local School Dist	37,69	78
Breit, Jeff/Lake Local School Dist	2,3,5,91	186
Bremer, Steve/Swanton Local School Dist	67	79
Brendel, Kim/Tallmadge City School Dist	27	194
Brenneman, Luke/Pioneer Joint Voc School Dist	73	173
Brenneman, Tirrell/Toledo Public Schools	74	129
Brents, Johanna/Northwestern Local School Dist	5	27
Bresenhan, Dennis/Maplewood Local School Dist	16,73	199
Brewer, Edwina/Marion City School Dist	4	138
Brewer, Philip/Great Oaks Career Campuses	5	89
Brewster, Brock/Western Local School Dist	1	164
Breymaier, Su, Dr/Toledo Public Schools	69	129
Breymier, Gayle/Mississinawa Valley Sch Dist	67	56
Brice, Keva/Northwest Local School Dist	7,83,85	91
Brickey, Kathy/Hamilton Local School Dist	7,83,85	71
Brickner, Laura/Seneca East Local School Dist	2	181
Bridges, Chandra/Southern Hills Joint Voc SD	60,83	20
Briggs, Chris, Dr/Pickerington Local School Dist	1	64
Briggs, Deb/Buckeye Central Local Sch Dist	5	38
Briggs, Heidi/New Philadelphia City Sch Dist	31,38	203
Briggs, Melinda/Little Miami Local School Dist	71	208
Bright, Casey/Allen East Local School Dist	286	7
Bright, Gary/Columbus City School Dist	5	66
Brigle, Joe/Montpelier Exempted Village SD	6	215
Brigle, Monica/Montpelier Exempted Village SD	58	215
Bringman, Linda/Toledo Public Schools	68	129
Britton, Dustin/Zane Trace Local School Dist	5	176
Britton, Kelly/Strasburg Franklin Local SD	8,58,81	203
Britton, Robert/Ridgedale Local School Dist	1	138
Broadwater, Mike/Forest Hills School Dist	15	89
Brock, Victoria/Waterloo Local School Dist	67	167
Brockway, Jerome, Dr/Ashtabula Co Tech & Career SD	1,11	12
Brockway, Tom/Pymatuning Valley Local SD	2	13
Brockwell, Lisa/Beachwood Local School Dist	5	40
Broderick, Lauren/Beachwood City School Dist	7,11,57,58,69,88,275,296	40
Brodman, Duane/Riverdale Local School Dist	3	98
Brombaugh, Charissa/New Lebanon Local School Dist	5	151
Bronczek, Olivia/Massillon City School Dist	71	187
Bronner, Chris/Brookville Local School Dist	88,270	148
Brookes, Cathy/Alliance City School Dist	57,81,88	184
Brookes, Dave/Lisbon Exempted Village SD	58	35
Brookhart, Tom/Waynesfield-Goshen Local SD	67	16
Brooks, Andy/Ohio Valley Ed Service Center	1	85
Brooks, Andy/Ohio Valley Ed Service Ctr	1	209
Brooks, Kathleen/Canton City School Dist	57	184
Brooks, Kayla/Crestview Local School Dist	38,83	171
Brooks, Rebecca/Mt Healthy City School Dist	2	91
Brooks, Rick/Vinton Co Local School Dist	1	206
Brooks, Vera/Cincinnati City School Dist	34	87
Broome, Melissa/Madeira City School Dist	16	90
Brothers, Debbie/Springfield Local School Dist	5	135
Brotzki, Paul/Maumee City School Dist	2	127
Broughton, Chris/Cleveland Metro School Dist	294	42
Brown, Aaron/Chillicothe City School Dist	91	174
Brown, Amy/Marysville Exempted Village SD	57	204
Brown, Andrea/Westfall Local School Dist	38	163
Brown, Beth/Frontier Local School Dist	10,83	210
Brown, Carl/Greenville City School Dist	69	55
Brown, Carrie/Evergreen Local School Dist	5	78
Brown, Chris/Butler Co Ed Service Center	1	20
Brown, Cindy/Strasburg Franklin Local SD	1	203
Brown, Curtis/Campbell City School Dist	3,91	134
Brown, Darryl/London City School Dist	67	132
Brown, Derek/Scioto Co Joint Vocational SD	30	179
Brown, Doug/Perry Local School Dist	67	188
Brown, Elisa/Edison Local Schools District	38	60
Brown, Elysa/Edison Local Schools District	31,36	60
Brown, Eric, Dr/Mt Vernon City School Dist	9	111
Brown, Giles/Clearview Local School Dist	5	123
Brown, Greg/Edgewood City School Dist	6	21
Brown, Jacquinette, Dr/Cleveland Metro School Dist	74	42
Brown, Jeffery/Granville Exempted Village SD	1	117
Brown, Jeffrey/Arcanum Butler Local Sch Dist	3	55
Brown, Jessica/Northwest Local School Dist	76	187
Brown, John/Maplewood Local School Dist	3	199
Brown, Karen/Eastwood Local School Dist	4	216
Brown, Karen/Euclid City School Dist	70	46
Brown, Karla/Meigs Local School Dist	58	142
Brown, Kimberly/Worthington School Dist	58,79	75
Brown, Lakim/Lorain City School Dist	15,751	124
Brown, Mark/Barberton City School Dist	3	192
Brown, Matthew/Euclid City School Dist	2	46
Brown, Melvin/Reynoldsburg City School Dist	1	72
Brown, Nancy/Monroeville Local School Dist	67	105
Brown, Nicholas/East Central Ohio ESC-N Phil	73	201
Brown, Nicholas/East Central Ohio ESC-St Clair	73	17
Brown, Robert/Meta Solutions	76	78
Brown, Ryan/Ohio Mid-Eastern RESA	73,76	110
Brown, Sandi/Hicksville Exempted Village SD	273	57
Brown, Shawn/Auglaize Co Ed Service Center	1	15
Brown, Shelley/Warren Co Ed Service Center	88	206
Brown, Sherrie/Central Local School Dist	9,11,285,296,298	57
Brown, Steve/Ayersville Local School Dist	3,5	56
Brown, Tarin/Mathews Local School Dist	67	199
Brown, Thomas/North Union Local School Dist	34,58	204
Browne, Bradley/Ottawa Hills Local Sch Dist	2	128
Brownfield, Joe/Walnut Twp Local School Dist	73	64
Browning, Kevin/Parkway Local School Dist	16,73,84,297	144
Brownlae, Larry/Ft Recovery Local School Dist	1,11	144
Brownlee, Lynette/Canfield Local School Dist	76	134
Bruce, Brenda/Columbus Grove Local Sch Dist	31,36,83	169
Brudakor, Brad/Columbus Grove Local Sch Dist	67	169
Brueck, Kim/Green Local School Dist	11,27,57,69,72,74,270,288	185
Bruening, Lisa/Lakewood City School Dist	7,11,35,36,77,79,83,296	47
Brugler, Eric/Joseph Badger Local Sch Dist	73	198
Brundage, Amandra/Windham Exempted Vlg Sch Dist	285	167
Brundo, Ashley/Chagrin Falls Exempted Vlg SD	2	42
Brunell, Karl/Buckeye Local School Dist	5,8	12
Bruner, Dan/Pettisville Local School Dist	67	79
Bruner, Doug/Mideast Career & Tech Ctrs	60	157
Bruner, Linda/Centerville City School Dist	294	148
Bruning, Mike/Canal Winchester Local SD	5	66
Brunn, Vicki/Van Wert City School Dist	1	205

School Year 2019-2020   800-333-8802   **OH-T7**

DISTRICT PERSONNEL INDEX

Market Data Retrieval

NAME/District	JOB FUNCTIONS	PAGE
Bruns, Jennifer/*St Henry Cons Local Sch Dist*	2,19	144
Bruns, Randy/*Marion Local School Dist*	67	144
Brunson, Michelle/*Upper Valley JT Voc Sch Dist*	10	147
Brunton, Paula/*Southwest Licking Local SD*	11,31,57,58,79,88,271,275	120
Bruzzese, Lisa/*Edison Local School Dist*	2	109
Bryan, Anne/*Van Buren Local School Dist*	57	99
Bryan, Mason/*Riverside Local School Dist*	8,13,285,288	121
Bryant, Joanna/*Centerburg Local School Dist*	73,295	110
Bryant, Kerri/*Union Scioto Local Sch Dist*	38,69	175
Bryson, Hayley/*North Ridgeville City Sch Dist*	23	125
Bucher, Micheal/*New Philadelphia City Sch Dist*	76	203
Buchman, Amy/*Federal Hocking Local Sch Dist*	38,69,286	14
Buchwalter, Ben/*Adena Local School Dist*	73,82,295	174
Buck, Cathy/*Southeast Local School Dist*	69	166
Buck, Chuck/*West Liberty-Salem Local SD*	67	26
Buck, Robert/*Forest Hills School Dist*	9,11,51,54,92,296	89
Buckalew, Melissa/*Forest Hills School Dist*	59	89
Buckey, James/*Rolling Hills Local Sch Dist*	73,98	86
Buckingham, Dustin/*East Knox Local School Dist*	67	111
Buckingham, Jane/*Campbell City School Dist*	8,11,58,69,72	134
Buckley, Emily/*Oak Hills Local School Dist*	71	92
Buehler, Cari/*Danbury Local School Dist*	1,11,288	159
Buell, Jamie/*Apollo Joint Voc School Dist*	38,60,79	8
Buenger, Janell/*Liberty Center Local Sch Dist*	2,19	101
Buente, Holly/*Weathersfield Local Sch Dist*	16	201
Buescher, Andrea/*Jefferson Local School Dist*	9	132
Buettner, Bev/*Kenston Local School Dist*	16	82
Buettner, Kathy/*Delphos City School Dist*	9,58	8
Bufano, Deb/*Warren City School Dist*	76	200
Buffenbarger, Tim/*Waynesfield-Goshen Local SD*	3	16
Buffington, Bonny/*Mt Vernon City School Dist*	79	111
Bugner, Sarah/*North Baltimore Local Sch Dist*	83,273	217
Bujak Hirsch, Jennifer/*Crestwood Local School Dist*	4	165
Bull, David/*Madison Local School Dist*	15	112
Bullock, Karen/*Circleville City School Dist*	11	162
Bulme, Pat/*Vantage Career Center Sch Dist*	67	206
Bumb, Michael/*Montpelier Exempted Village SD*	8	215
Bunkley, Dennis/*East Cleveland City Sch Dist*	7,36,58,79,90	45
Bunte, Susan/*Cincinnati City School Dist*	15,58	87
Bunting, Jared/*Trimble Local School Dist*	2,11	15
Bunting, Matt/*Athens City School Dist*	2	14
Buonavolonta, Sam/*Girard City School Dist*	3	197
Burbick, Richard/*Crestview Local School Dist*	5	34
Burch, Debra/*Princeton City School Dist*	76	92
Burcham, Kendell/*Urbana City School Dist*	16	26
Burchfield, Tammy/*Wayne Local School Dist*	11	209
Burda, Larry/*Maumee City School Dist*	3,91	127
Burden, Chelsea/*Van Buren Local School Dist*	16,82	99
Burden, Ray/*Northwest Ohio Computer Co-op*	1	10
Burdick, Beth/*North Royalton City Sch Dist*	81	48
Burdick, Elizabeth/*Strongsville City School Dist*	81	51
Burdick, Gina/*Granville Exempted Village SD*	7	117
Burgard, Gerald/*Geneva Area City School Dist*	73	13
Burgett, PJ/*Franklin-Monroe Local Sch Dist*	38	55
Burich, George/*Cuyahoga Heights Local SD*	58	45
Burk, Ben/*Chesapeake Union Exempt Vlg SD*	3	115
Burke, Beth/*Portsmouth City School Dist*	38	179
Burke, Mark/*Mohawk Local School Dist*	1,11	219
Burkett, Brian/*Liberty-Benton Local Sch Dist*	9,57	98
Burkett, David/*Tuslaw Local School Dist*	6	189
Burkey, Ericka/*South Range Local School Dist*	36,69	135
Burkhardt, Chris/*Cleveland Metro School Dist*	4	42
Burkhart, Jackie/*Conotton Valley Union Local SD*	76	100
Burkhart, Jon/*Medina City School Dist*	2	141
Burkholder, Carol/*Fayette Local Sch Dist*	12	79
Burkholder, Ron/*Pettisville Local School Dist*	3	79
Burks, Dawn/*Rossford Exempted Village SD*	67	218
Burley, Don/*Graham Local School Dist*	3,4,5,73,76	25
Burlison, Andrea/*Claymont City School Dist*	4	201
Burman, Andrew/*Minerva Local School Dist*	13,34,57,58,271	187
Burnett, Kathy/*Mentor Exempted Village SD*	68	113
Burnett, Scott/*Northwest Local School Dist*	58	187
Burns, Barbara/*Carrollton Exempted Village SD*	4	25
Burns, John/*Bethel-Tate Local School Dist*	3,73,295,297	30
Burnside, Melinda/*New Boston Local School Dist*	1,73	178
Burras, Jonathan/*Mansfield City Schools*	58	172
Burrell, Lisa/*Tuscarawas Valley Local SD*	81	203
Burrier, Ryan/*Indian Valley Local Sch Dist*	8,61,74,273,274,298	202
Burrma, Morgan/*Elgin Local School Dist*	11,296	138
Burtch, Melissa/*Parkway Local School Dist*	67	144
Burton, Sheilia, Dr/*Dayton Public School Dist*	15,69,70,79,294	149
Burton, Tom/*Princeton City School Dist*	1	92
Burzanko, Amy/*Geneva Area City School Dist*	31,34	13
Busby, Amy/*Medina City School Dist*	71	141
Busch, Becky/*Avon Lake City School Dist*	7	122
Buschur, Tim/*Celina City School Dist*	27,75,95	143
Busdeker, Larry/*Hancock Co Ed Service Center*	1,11	97
Busdeker, Larry/*Northwest Ohio Ed Tech*	67	218
Busenburg, Jessi/*East Knox Local School Dist*	2	111
Bush, Brad/*Northmont City School Dist*	73,95	152
Bush, Carl/*Miami Valley Career Tech VSD*	91	151
Bush, Gary/*Marlington Local School Dist*	286	186
Bush, Rebecca/*Vandalia Butler City Sch Dist*	4	153
Buskirk, Jeremy/*Big Walnut Local School Dist*	2	58
Buskirk, Robert/*Lebanon City School Dist*	68	207
Buskirk, Robyn/*Lebanon City School Dist*	68	207
Busse, Shelly/*New Bremen Local School Dist*	67	16
Busskin, Katie/*Bellefontaine City School Dist*	7,85	121
Butcher, Eddie/*Adams Co Ohio Valley Sch Dist*	295	6
Butcher, Jere, Dr/*Coshocton City School Dist*	67	36
Butchko, Jennifer/*Firelands Local School Dist*	71	124
Buti, Jerry/*Defiance City School Dist*	6	57
Butlar, Katie/*Pike-Delta-York Local Sch Dist*	37	79
Butler, Brett/*Scioto Co Joint Vocational SD*	2	179
Butler, Cari/*Granville Exempted Village SD*	71	117
Butler, Jane/*Cedar Cliff Local School Dist*	81	84
Butler, Seanna/*Jefferson Area Local SD*	5	13
Butler, Tammy/*North Ridgeville City Sch Dist*	5	125
Butterfield, Mark/*Talawanda Local School Dist*	67	24
Butts, Aaron/*Medina Co Joint Voc Sch Dist*	2	141
Buzard, Amy/*Plymouth-Shiloh Local Sch Dist*	37,83,88	173
Buzzard, David/*Columbiana Exempted Village SD*	10,288	34
Byers, Amanda/*Findlay City School Dist*	77	98
Byers, Kevin/*Danville Local School Dist*	3,91	110
Byrd, Allison/*Cleveland Hts-Univ Hts City SD*	70	42
Byrd, Michael/*Woodmore Local School Dist*	73,295	159
Byrnes, Debra/*Orrville City School Dist*	4	212
Byrnes, Jason/*Dalton Local School Dist*	5	212

C

NAME/District	JOB FUNCTIONS	PAGE
Cable, Shanna/*Green Local School Dist*	5	185
Caccimelio, Sharon/*Pickerington Local School Dist*	8	64
Cade, Vilicia, Dr/*Sandusky City School Dist*	12	61
Cahall, Krista/*Georgetown Exempted Village SD*	4	19
Cain, Beth/*Piqua City School Dist*	5	146
Cain, Brendan/*Ontario Local School Dist*	73	173
Cain, Donald/*Columbus City School Dist*	35	66
Cairns, Dan/*Parkway Local School Dist*	35,85	144
Caito, Caryl/*Liberty Union-Thurstn Sch Dist*	67	64
Cakall, Holly/*Monroe Local School Dist*	2,19	23
Calame, Josh/*Plymouth-Shiloh Local Sch Dist*	6	173
Calame, Josh/*Plymouth-Shiloh Local Sch Dist*	6	173
Calderon, Elizabeth/*Poland Local School Dist*	31,38,69	135
Calderone, Anthony/*Labrae Local School Dist*	1	198

---

1 Superintendent	16 Instructional Media Svcs	30 Adult Education	44 Science Sec	58 Special Education K-12
2 Bus/Finance/Purchasing	17 Chief Operations Officer	31 Career/Sch-to-Work K-12	45 Math K-12	59 Special Education Elem
3 Buildings And Grounds	18 Chief Academic Officer	32 Career/Sch-to-Work Elem	46 Math Elem	60 Special Education Sec
4 Food Service	19 Chief Financial Officer	33 Career/Sch-to-Work Sec	47 Math Sec	61 Foreign/World Lang K-12
5 Transportation	20 Art K-12	34 Early Childhood Ed	48 English/Lang Arts K-12	62 Foreign/World Lang Elem
6 Athletic	21 Art Elem	35 Health/Phys Education	49 English/Lang Arts Elem	63 Foreign/World Lang Sec
7 Health Services	22 Art Sec	36 Guidance Services K-12	50 English/Lang Arts Sec	64 Religious Education K-12
8 Curric/Instruct K-12	23 Music K-12	37 Guidance Services Elem	51 Reading K-12	65 Religious Education Elem
9 Curric/Instruct Elem	24 Music Elem	38 Guidance Services Sec	52 Reading Elem	66 Religious Education Sec
10 Curric/Instruct Sec	25 Music Sec	39 Social Studies K-12	53 Reading Sec	67 School Board President
11 Federal Program	26 Business Education	40 Social Studies Elem	54 Remedial Reading K-12	68 Teacher Personnel
12 Title I	27 Career & Tech Ed	41 Social Studies Sec	55 Remedial Reading Elem	69 Academic Assessment
13 Title V	28 Technology Education	42 Science K-12	56 Remedial Reading Sec	70 Research/Development
15 Asst Superintendent	29 Family/Consumer Science	43 Science Elem	57 Bilingual/ELL	71 Public Information

72 Summer School	88 Alternative/At Risk	277 Remedial Math K-12
73 Instructional Tech	89 Multi-Cultural Curriculum	280 Literacy Coach
74 Inservice Training	90 Social Work	285 STEM
75 Marketing/Distributive	91 Safety/Security	286 Digital Learning
76 Info Systems	92 Magnet School	288 Common Core Standards
77 Psychological Assess	93 Parental Involvement	294 Accountability
78 Affirmative Action	95 Tech Prep Program	295 Network System
79 Student Personnel	97 Chief Information Officer	296 Title II Programs
80 Driver Ed/Safety	98 Chief Technology Officer	297 Webmaster
81 Gifted/Talented	270 Character Education	298 Grant Writer/Ptnrships
82 Video Services	271 Migrant Education	750 Chief Innovation Officer
83 Substance Abuse Prev	273 Teacher Mentor	751 Chief of Staff
84 Erate	274 Before/After Sch	752 Social Emotional Learning
85 AIDS Education	275 Response To Intervention	

OH-T8

Ohio School Directory

DISTRICT PERSONNEL INDEX

NAME/District	JOB FUNCTIONS	PAGE
Calderone, Karla/*Southern Local School Dist*	57,61	36
Caldwell, Bob/*Switzerland of Ohio Local SD*	1	147
Caldwell, Cynthia/*Shadyside Local School Dist*	4,273	18
Caldwell, Dave/*Cambridge City School Dist*	2	86
Caldwell, Dawn/*Kettering City School Dist*	69,81	150
Caleris, Chris/*North Olmsted City School Dist*	79	48
Caleris, Ted, Dr/*Cuyahoga Heights Local SD*	8,15,84,273,288,296,752	45
Call, Cindy/*Brown Co Ed Service Center*	81	19
Call, Jason/*Avon Local School Dist*	11,36,58,77	122
Call, Thomas/*Gallipolis City School Dist*	4	81
Callaghan, Patrick/*Worthington School Dist*	9	75
Callahan, Elaine/*Warrensville Heights City SD*	5	51
Callan, Jamie/*Springfield-Clark Co JVSD*	67	28
Callender, Bradley/*Cleveland Hts-Univ Hts City SD*	27	42
Calloway, Virgil/*Maple Heights City School Dist*	3	47
Campbell, Barry/*Upper Scioto Valley Local SD*	67	100
Campbell, Ben/*Southeast Local School Dist*	27	166
Campbell, Bob/*Green Local School Dist*	67	185
Campbell, Charlene/*Cedar Cliff Local School Dist*	67	84
Campbell, Denise/*East Knox Local School Dist*	7	111
Campbell, Dwight/*Winton Woods City School Dist*	83	94
Campbell, Emily/*Cincinnati City School Dist*	45	87
Campbell, Gary/*Miami Trace Local School Dist*	4	65
Campbell, Ira/*Streetsboro City School Dist*	31,38	167
Campbell, Jamie/*Tri-Valley Local School Dist*	11	157
Campbell, Kristyn/*Mechanicsburg Exempted Vlg SD*	16,82	26
Campbell, Lisa/*Teays Valley Local School Dist*	16,82	162
Campbell, Lynn, Dr/*Orange City School Dist*	1	48
Campbell, Matt/*Mahoning Co Joint Voc Sch Dist*	26	135
Campbell, Megan/*Miami Co Ed Service Center*	58	144
Campbell, Rick/*Rittman Exempted Village SD*	3,4	213
Campbell, Robert/*Rootstown Local School Dist*	13	166
Camper, Wendy/*Painesville City Local SD*	42,45	113
Camper, Wendy/*Painesville City Local SD*	8,280,285,288	113
Camstock, Regina/*Kenton City School Dist*	4	100
Canfora, Roseann, Dr/*Cleveland Metro School Dist*	71	42
Cano, Andrew/*Hardin Northern Local Sch Dist*	58	100
Cantrell, Alan/*Columbia Local School Dist*	5	123
Cantrell, Tyler/*Paint Valley Local School Dist*	73	175
Cantu, Cory/*Springfield Local School Dist*	73,84,286	128
Caplinger, Shannon/*Washington Court House City SD*	34,58	65
Cappitte, Lew/*Weathersfield Local Sch Dist*	3,5	201
Cappozzello, David/*Austintown Local School Dist*	1	133
Capucini, Morgan/*Williamsburg Local School Dist*	31,36,69	32
Cardelein, Chris/*East Liverpool City Sch Dist*	73,84	35
Carden, Mark/*Springfield Local School Dist*	6	135
Carder, Sam/*Plymouth-Shiloh Local Sch Dist*	5	173
Cardillo, Jared/*Boardman Local School Dist*	8,11,51,54,81,273,288,296	134
Cardinal, Melissa/*Cardinal Local School Dist*	280	81
Carkido, Dawn/*Niles City School Dist*	5	200
Carkido, Gary/*McDonald Local School Dist*	10	199
Carlier, Tim/*Fayetteville Perry Local SD*	1	19
Carlisle, Mark/*Gallia-Vinton Ed Svc Center*	73	80
Carlson, Autumn/*Nelsonville-York City Sch Dist*	7,83,85	15
Carman, James/*Brown Local School Dist*	2,11	25
Carman, Lori/*Colonel Crawford Local SD*	69,93	38
Carmichael, Lisa/*Ontario Local School Dist*	1	173
Carmichael, Sean/*Triway Local School Dist*	6	213
Carmosino, Molly/*Kettering City School Dist*	11	150
Carnahan, Tamela/*Forest Hills School Dist*	68,78,79	89
Carney, Pat/*Joseph Badger Local Sch Dist*	6	198
Carney, Patrick/*Bedford City School Dist*	5	40
Carosielli, Cristina/*Berea City School Dist*	70,71	41
Carpenter, Ben/*Twin Valley Cmty Local SD*	35,85	169
Carpenter, Carol/*Mechanicsburg Exempted Vlg SD*	37,88	26
Carpenter, Chad/*Vinton Co Local School Dist*	2,76	206
Carpenter, Diahn/*Waterloo Local School Dist*	7,85	167
Carpenter, Jeff/*Lake Local School Dist*	2	217
Carpenter, Mark/*Franklin Local School Dist*	67	156
Carpenter, Matthew/*Georgetown Exempted Village SD*	16	19
Carpenter, Mike/*Shawnee Local School Dist*	67	9
Carpenter, Paul/*Butler Tech Career Dev Schs*	2,19	21
Carpenter, Steve/*Oak Hill Union Local Sch Dist*	5	107
Carpenter, Todd/*Field Local School Dist*	2	165
Carpenter, Todd/*Waterloo Local School Dist*	2	167
Carr, Jill/*Bowling Green City Sch Dist*	67	216

NAME/District	JOB FUNCTIONS	PAGE
Carr, Kevin/*Clear Fork Vly Local Sch Dist*	3	171
Carr, Melisa/*Ashland Co-West Holmes JVSD*	30	11
Carrabine, Nicholas/*Riverside Local School Dist*	71	114
Carraher, Joanne/*Williamsburg Local School Dist*	2	32
Carras, Mary Ellen/*Cleveland Metro School Dist*	81	42
Carrington, Vickie/*Southern Hills Joint Voc SD*	30	20
Carroll, Kenny/*Loudonville-Perrysville SD*	5	11
Carroll, Pam/*St Bernard-Elmwood Place Schs*	76	93
Carroll, Pat/*Lake Local School Dist*	10,11,15,16,69,73,288,295	186
Carroll, Ron/*Huntington Local School Dist*	3	175
Carroll, Steve/*Otsego Local School Dist*	2	217
Carson, Chad/*Laca-Licking Area Cmop Assoc*	1	120
Carson, Deanna/*Butler Co Ed Service Center*	88	20
Carson, Rhonda/*North Ridgeville City Sch Dist*	7	125
Carson, Tracy/*Mason City School Dist*	71,298	208
Carter Evans, Lori/*Olentangy Local School Dist*	5	59
Carter, Adreana/*Southwest Licking Local SD*	34	120
Carter, Ben/*Canton City School Dist*	27,31	184
Carter, Craig/*Yellow Springs Exempted Vlg SD*	3	85
Carter, John/*Oberlin City School Dist*	6	125
Carter, Jolene/*Pleasant Local School Dist*	2	138
Carter, Larry/*Gallia Co Local School Dist*	5	80
Carter, Mark/*Van Wert City School Dist*	3	205
Carter, Neil/*Liberty Center Local Sch Dist*	67	101
Cartwright, Michael/*Johnstown-Monroe Local SD*	4	118
Carver, Sydney/*Union Scioto Local Sch Dist*	7,83	175
Carvi, Julianna/*Bexley City School Dist*	4	66
Case, John/*Ohio Hi-Point Joint Voc SD*	73	121
Caseman, Donald/*Clay Local School Dist*	67	178
Casey, Jackie/*Southern Local School Dist*	11	161
Cash, Don/*Bridgeport School Dist*	67	18
Casida, Fiona/*Copley-Fairlawn City Sch Dist*	16,82	192
Casper, Meagan/*Field Local School Dist*	83	165
Cassady, Bruce/*Frontier Local School Dist*	73,295	210
Cassell, Laura/*Fairfield Co Ed Service Center*	2	62
Cassella, Jeffery/*Mentor Exempted Village SD*	6	113
Cassidy, Tina/*Medina City School Dist*	8	141
Cassidy, Veronica/*Tecumseh Local School Dist*	73,295,297	28
Catanzaro, Jessie/*Monroe Local School Dist*	2	23
Cates, Briana/*Berea City School Dist*	4	41
Catlin, William/*Lordstown Local School Dist*	67	199
Caudill, Andee/*Vinton Co Local School Dist*	16,274,275	206
Caudill, Glenn/*Southeast Local School Dist*	73	213
Caudill, Rhonda/*Upper Sandusky Exempted Vlg SD*	68,71,83	219
Cavanagh, Ruth/*Newbury Local School Dist*	7	82
Caver, Tamea, Dr/*Warrensville Heights City SD*	8,15,288	51
Cawley, Connie/*McComb Local School Dist*	73,295	98
Celestin, Scott/*Buckeye Local School Dist*	5,91	108
Celico, Andrea/*Bedford City School Dist*	1	40
Cellura, Matt/*Twinsburg City School Dist*	67	195
Centers, Tamara/*Franklin City School Dist*	5	207
Ceredue, Bob/*Fairport Harbor Exempt Vlg SD*	73	112
Cereghini, Lenore/*Dublin City School Dist*	79	69
Cerny, Carol/*Put-In-Bay Local School Dist*	73,95	159
Chadd, Betsy/*Bellbrook-Sugarcreek Schools*	12	83
Chadd, Betsy/*Bellbrook-Sugarcreek Schools*	8,11,88,273,288,294	83
Chaddock, Gary/*Minerva Local School Dist*	1	187
Chaddock, Joe/*Stark Co Area Voc Sch Dist*	1	189
Chaddock, Joe/*Stark Co Ed Service Center*	1,11	184
Chaffee, Benjamin/*South Central Local Sch Dist*	1,11,83	106
Chaffin, Ken/*Marysville Exempted Village SD*	285	204
Chafin, Jaime/*Lawrence Co Joint Voc Sch Dist*	69,294	116
Chafin, Michelle/*Teays Valley Local School Dist*	7,35,83,85	162
Chalfin, Chris/*Lakota Local School Dist*	67	177
Chalfin, Elaine/*Lakota Local School Dist*	11	177
Chambers, David/*Medina City School Dist*	2	141
Chandler, Edward/*West Geauga Local School Dist*	16,73,295	82
Chandler, Greg/*Bethel-Tate Local School Dist*	12,69	30
Chaney, Kim/*Mahoning Co Joint Voc Sch Dist*	30	135
Chaney, Timothy/*North Ctrl Ohio Ed Service Ctr*	3	180
Chanoski, Edward/*East Central Ohio ESC-St Clair*	88	17
Chapman, Ana/*Berea City School Dist*	67	41
Chapman, Carla/*Akron Public Schools*	71	190
Chapman, Gary/*Jonathan Alder Local Sch Dist*	1	132
Chapman, James/*Bethel Local School Dist*	3	145
Chapman, Jana/*Tri-Co Joint Voc Sch Dist*	16,82	15

School Year 2019-2020

DISTRICT PERSONNEL INDEX

Market Data Retrieval

NAME/District	JOB FUNCTIONS	PAGE
Chappelear, Thomas, Dr/*Indian Creek Local Sch Dist*	1	109
Charville, Holly/*Huron City School Dist*	12,58,88	60
Chase, Brian/*Conneaut Area City Sch Dist*	73	12
Chatfield, Beth/*Licking Heights Local Sch Dist*	38	118
Cheney, Alison/*Upper Sandusky Exempted Vlg SD*	69	219
Cherry, Sandi/*Green Local School Dist*	67	178
Cheslock, Krissy/*Four-Co Joint Voc School Dist*	16,33,38,60,83,88	79
Chesson, Kristina/*Norwood City School Dist*	8,11,57,73,88,288,296,298	92
Chester, Cathy/*Zane Trace Local School Dist*	67	176
Cheyney, Rodney/*Ashland Co-West Holmes JVSD*	1	10
Chhay, Maraday/*Richmond Heights Local SD*	57	49
Chiaro, Steve/*Warren City School Dist*	1	200
Chiera, Tom/*Norton City School Dist*	23	193
Chilcote, Donna/*Little Miami Local School Dist*	16,82	208
Childress, Tracey/*Union Local School Dist*	7	18
Chio, Jason/*Ashland Co-West Holmes JVSD*	67	11
Choksi, Michael/*Painesville City Local SD*	15	113
Chonich, Wenonah/*Conneaut Area City Sch Dist*	7	12
Chowning, Kim/*Tri-Village Local Sch Dist*	2	56
Chrisman, Steven/*Medina Co Joint Voc Sch Dist*	1	141
Chrispin, Matthew/*Bucyrus City School Dist*	1,11	38
Chrispin, Matthew/*Fredericktown Local School Dist*	1	111
Christ, Alex, Dr/*Northwest Local School Dist*	270,273	187
Christensen, Diane/*Northern Local School Dist*	16,82	161
Christensen, Nancy/*Groveport Madison Local SD*	60	71
Christian, Mark/*South Point Local School Dist*	1	116
Christie, Holly/*Mansfield City Schools*	11,51,55,79,81,296	172
Christman, Scott/*Southern Local School Dist*	1	161
Christophel, Debbie/*Ross Local School Dist*	4	24
Christopher, Norman, Dr/*Highland Local School Dist*	67	141
Chubba, Michael/*Hudson City School Dist*	6	193
Chumney, Kristi/*Johnstown-Monroe Local SD*	6	118
Churchwell, Brigitte/*Sandusky City School Dist*	67	61
Ciarlariello, Adam/*Centerville City School Dist*	10	148
Ciborek, Kim/*Hudson City School Dist*	4	193
Ciccantelli, Pat/*Aurora City School Dist*	1	164
Ciferno, Alison/*Willoughby-Eastlake City SD*	12	114
Ciferno, Alison/*Willoughby-Eastlake City SD*	11,81,92,296	114
Cikach, Frank/*New Philadelphia City Sch Dist*	73,295	203
Cipollone, Tony/*Westlake City School Dist*	6	51
Cipriani, Ann/*Toledo Public Schools*	7,83,85	129
Cireddu, Bob/*Auburn Vocational School Dist*	73	112
Cireddu, Bob/*Madison Local School Dist*	73,286,295	112
Cireddu, Robert/*Brookfield Local School Dist*	16,73	197
Cireddu, Robert/*Newbury Local School Dist*	73	82
Cirino, Denise/*Mayfield City School Dist*	7,36,57,58,69,81,88,275	47
Cirino, Erin/*Painesville City Local SD*	10	113
Claar, Cindy/*Clark-Shawnee Local Sch Dist*	2	27
Clady, Jarrod/*Buckeye Central Local Sch Dist*	3	38
Clady, Lori/*Holgate Local School Dist*	4	101
Clapsadle, Ryan/*Leetonia Exempted Village SD*	73,295	35
Clarckson, Alex/*Sylvania City School Dist*	8,13,27,31,288	128
Clark, Adam/*Gallipolis City School Dist*	6	81
Clark, Allyson/*Ashtabula Co Tech & Career SD*	60	12
Clark, Andy/*Fairfield Union Local Sch Dist*	6	63
Clark, Bill/*Hardin-Houston Local Sch Dist*	67	183
Clark, Brian/*North Royalton City Sch Dist*	3	48
Clark, Brian/*Sebring Local School Dist*	6	135
Clark, Cheryl/*Bradford Exempted Village SD*	4	145
Clark, Chris/*Bath Local School Dist*	59	8
Clark, Chris/*Black River Local School Dist*	1	139
Clark, Debora/*Northwest Local School Dist*	8,11,69,88,296,298	187
Clark, Edward/*Sycamore Cmty School Dist*	35	93
Clark, Elizabeth/*Northern Local School Dist*	2,4	161
Clark, Jen/*Otsego Local School Dist*	38	217
Clark, Jeremy/*Valley Local School Dist*	8,69,294,296	179
Clark, Jessie/*Highland Local School Dist*	76	155
Clark, Joseph, Dr/*Nordonia Hills City Sch Dist*	1,11	193
Clark, Kyle/*Wood Co Ed Service Center*	83	216
Clark, Lacresha/*Jackson Center Local Sch Dist*	4	183
Clark, Lisa/*Bridgeport School Dist*	11,16,73,280,285,286	18
Clark, Marsha/*East Holmes Local School Dist*	2	104
Clark, Myra/*Green Local School Dist*	4	178
Clark, Nancy/*Noeca-Northern Ohio Ed CA*	2	62
Clark, Steve/*Springfield-Clark Co JVSD*	2	28
Clark, Tara/*Heath City School Dist*	36	117
Clark, Vicky/*Hilliard City School Dist*	15	71
Clarke, Greg/*Perrysburg Exempted Village SD*	3	218
Clary, Kim/*Granville Exempted Village SD*	5	117
Clawson, Bryan/*Kenton City School Dist*	5	100
Clawson, Maria/*Lincolnview Local School Dist*	58	205
Clawson, Maria/*Western Buckeye Ed Service Ctr*	58	160
Claxon, Ashley/*New Philadelphia City Sch Dist*	16	203
Claxon, Elizabeth/*Scioto Co Joint Vocational SD*	16	179
Clay-Mowry, Amber/*Highland Local School Dist*	8,69	155
Clay, Nick/*South Point Local School Dist*	73	116
Claypool, Lee/*Triad Local School Dist*	9,11	26
Cleary, Pegeen/*Columbus City School Dist*	27,30,31,95	66
Cleghorn, Amanda/*Columbiana Exempted Village SD*	38,88	34
Clemens, Joyce/*Ed Service Ctr Lake Erie West*	298	127
Clemens, Tom/*United Local School Dist*	3	36
Clement, Jeff/*Kalida Local School Dist*	36,69	169
Clements, Andrea/*Tuscarawas Valley Local SD*	11,34	203
Clemons, Vikki/*Hamilton Co Ed Service Center*	11	87
Clendaniel, Marc/*Green Local School Dist*	73,286	185
Cleveland, Mary/*Princeton City School Dist*	67	92
Clien, Benda/*Mansfield City Schools*	67	172
Clifford, Rusty/*Montgomery Co Ed Service Ctr*	3	148
Clifton, Bill/*Van Wert City School Dist*	15	205
Clonch, Sandy/*Alexander Local School Dist*	8,11,69,286,288,296	14
Close, Christine/*Buckeye Central Local Sch Dist*	38,79	38
Closson, Justin/*Ottawa-Glandorf Local Sch Dist*	73,295	170
Closson, Tim/*Bluffton Exempted Village Sch*	11	8
Clouse, Diane/*New Riegel Local School Dist*	16,82	181
Clouse, Shilo/*New Riegel Local School Dist*	35	181
Clumen, Robert/*Sebring Local School Dist*	58	135
Clune, Josh/*Minster Local School Dist*	5,6	15
Clutter, Jason/*Switzerland of Ohio Local SD*	3,5	147
Cluxton, Jeff/*Ripley-Union-Lewis-Huntngtn SD*	67	20
Clyde, Dru/*Struthers City School Dist*	4	136
Clymer, Linda/*McComb Local School Dist*	2,296,298	98
Coad, Chris/*Brecksville Broadview Hts CSD*	2	41
Coad, Linda/*Black River Local School Dist*	38,58	139
Coakley, Shawn/*Sandusky City School Dist*	6	61
Coates, Pam/*Little Miami Local School Dist*	68	208
Cobb, Erica/*Old Fort Local School Dist*	275	181
Coble, Sonja/*Federal Hocking Local Sch Dist*	73	14
Cochenour, Shara/*Pickaway-Ross Co JT Voc SD*	88	175
Cochran, Angie/*Girard City School Dist*	36	197
Cochran, Debbie/*Hilliard City School Dist*	7,36,58,77,79,85,88	71
Cochran, Linda/*North Central Local Sch Dist*	57	215
Cochran, Michael/*Canfield Local School Dist*	6	134
Cochran, Nick/*Girard City School Dist*	6	197
Cochren, Tony/*Huber Heights City School Dist*	3,67	150
Coffey, Casey/*New Lexington School Dist*	1,83	161
Coffey, Nate/*Shelby City School Dist*	295	173
Coffman, Chad/*Lakota Local School Dist*	1	177
Coffman, Dan/*Cambridge City School Dist*	1	86
Coffman, Kelli/*Rootstown Local School Dist*	12	166
Coffman, Sheree/*Northmont City School Dist*	83,85,275	152
Coffman, Tim/*Ehove Joint Voc School Dist*	2,19	60
Coffman, Vicky/*Benton-Carroll-Salem Local SD*	4	158
Cogan, Kelli/*Olmsted Falls City School Dist*	8,15,69,74,273,288	48
Cogdell, Doug/*Amherst Exempted Village SD*	73,295	122

1 Superintendent	16 Instructional Media Svcs	30 Adult Education	44 Science Sec	58 Special Education K-12	72 Summer School	88 Alternative/At Risk	277 Remedial Math K-12
2 Bus/Finance/Purchasing	17 Chief Operations Officer	31 Career/Sch-to-Work K-12	45 Math K-12	59 Special Education Elem	73 Instructional Tech	89 Multi-Cultural Curriculum	280 Literacy Coach
3 Buildings And Grounds	18 Chief Academic Officer	32 Career/Sch-to-Work Elem	46 Math Elem	60 Special Education Sec	74 Inservice Training	90 Social Work	285 STEM
4 Food Service	19 Chief Financial Officer	33 Career/Sch-to-Work Sec	47 Math Sec	61 Foreign/World Lang K-12	75 Marketing/Distributive	91 Safety/Security	286 Digital Learning
5 Transportation	20 Art K-12	34 Early Childhood Ed	48 English/Lang Arts K-12	62 Foreign/World Lang Elem	76 Info Systems	92 Magnet School	288 Common Core Standards
6 Athletic	21 Art Elem	35 Health/Phys Education	49 English/Lang Arts Elem	63 Foreign/World Lang Sec	77 Psychological Assess	93 Parental Involvement	294 Accountability
7 Health Services	22 Art Sec	36 Guidance Services K-12	50 English/Lang Arts Sec	64 Religious Education K-12	78 Affirmative Action	95 Tech Prep Program	295 Network System
8 Curric/Instruct K-12	23 Music K-12	37 Guidance Services Elem	51 Reading K-12	65 Religious Education Elem	79 Student Personnel	96 Title II Programs	296 Title II Programs
9 Curric/Instruct Elem	24 Music Elem	38 Guidance Services Sec	52 Reading Elem	66 Religious Education Sec	80 Driver Ed/Safety	97 Chief Information Officer	297 Webmaster
10 Curric/Instruct Sec	25 Music Sec	39 Social Studies K-12	53 Reading Sec	67 School Board President	81 Gifted/Talented	98 Chief Technology Officer	298 Character Education
11 Federal Program	26 Business Education	40 Social Studies Elem	54 Remedial Reading K-12	68 Teacher Personnel	82 Video Services	270 Character Education	750 Chief Innovation Officer
12 Title I	27 Career & Tech Ed	41 Social Studies Sec	55 Remedial Reading Elem	69 Academic Assessment	83 Substance Abuse Prev	271 Migrant Education	751 Chief of Staff
13 Title V	28 Technology Education	42 Science K-12	56 Remedial Reading Sec	70 Research/Development	84 Erate	273 Teacher Mentor	752 Social Emotional Learning
15 Asst Superintendent	29 Family/Consumer Science	43 Science Elem	57 Bilingual/ELL	71 Public Information	85 AIDS Education	274 Before/After Sch	
						275 Response To Intervention	

OH-T10

Ohio School Directory

DISTRICT PERSONNEL INDEX

NAME/District	JOB FUNCTIONS	PAGE
Cogley, Greg/Bath Local School Dist	3,91	8
Cohn, Connie/Triad Local School Dist	2	26
Coke, Bret/Crestwood Local School Dist	6	165
Colburn, Amy/Logan Elm Local School Dist	8,11,72,288	162
Coldsnow, Jennifer/Leetonia Exempted Village SD	2,84	35
Cole, Amy/Kenton City School Dist	83	100
Cole, Bill/Loveland City School Dist	3	90
Cole, Erin/Canton City School Dist	4	184
Cole, Jay/Southern Local School Dist	67	36
Cole, Jodi/Kenton City School Dist	8,16,82,288	100
Cole, Rojean/Marlington Local School Dist	4	186
Cole, Sue/Avon Lake City School Dist	5	122
Cole, Vic/Wooster City School Dist	5	213
Cole, Wes/Talawanda School Dist	6	24
Coleman, Rex/Berne Union Local School Dist	67	63
Coleman, Suellen/Wolf Creek Local School Dist	298	211
Coleman, Vicky/Northwest Local School Dist	93	91
Colins, Courtney/North College Hill City SD	8,11,273	91
Collet, Jill/Plain Local School Dist	12	188
Collett, Jeff/Gahanna-Jefferson Public SD	73	70
Collier, Adam/Hamilton Local School Dist	2	71
Collier, Beth/Grandview Heights City SD	2,296	70
Collier, Mike/Clearview Local School Dist	6	123
Collins, Brian/Eastern Local School Dist	4	142
Collins, Brian/Newcomerstown Exempted Vlg SD	3,5	203
Collins, Christina, Dr/Buckeye Local School Dist	8,16,74,81	140
Collins, Dan/Bristol Local School Dist	6	197
Collins, Debra/Western Local School Dist	273	164
Collins, Denise/Bryan City School Dist	297	214
Collins, James/Gallia-Jackson-Vinton JVSD	3	80
Collins, James/West Clermont Local Sch Dist	6	31
Collins, Lisa/Lakeview Local School Dist	73,84	199
Collins, Lori/Union Scioto Local Sch Dist	37,83	175
Collins, Matt/Rootstown Local School Dist	5	166
Collins, Ryan/Kenton City School Dist	73	100
Collins, Ryan/Lynchburg-Clay Local Sch Dist	5	103
Collins, Stephanie/Gahanna-Jefferson Public SD	76	70
Collins, Stephanie/Upper Arlington City Sch Dist	76	74
Collins, Steven/Little Miami Local School Dist	73,95	208
Collins, Thomas/Hamilton-Clermont Co-op OCA	1	32
Colon, Lorraine/Boardman Local School Dist	7	134
Colopy, Cherie/Centerville City School Dist	9	148
Colucci, Patrick/Buckeye Local School Dist	1	12
Colvin, Matt/Ridgewood Local School Dist	6	37
Combs, Elizabeth/Dalton Local School Dist	77	212
Combs, Jessica/Buckeye Valley Local Sch Dist	36	58
Combs, John/Bright Local School Dist	6	102
Combs, Kurtis/Greenville City School Dist	3	55
Combs, Matt/Vinton Co Local School Dist	6,88	206
Combs, Teressa/Hardin Northern Local Sch Dist	5,71	100
Common, John/Gibsonburg Exempted Village SD	2	177
Compton, Debbie/Van Wert City School Dist	67	205
Compton, Linda/East Clinton Local School Dist	67	33
Compton, Molly/Fredericktown Local Sch Dist	37,69	111
Comstock, Doug/Kenton City School Dist	3	100
Comstock, Matt/Bellefontaine City School Dist	6	121
Conant, Todd/Mt Vernon City School Dist	5	111
Conatser, Brian/Loveland City School Dist	6	90
Conaway, Randy/Perkins Local School Dist	5	61
Conger, Randy/Tiffin City School Dist	5	181
Congleton, Denise/London City School Dist	57	132
Coniglio, Melody/Kenston Local School Dist	5	82
Conkle, Jennifer/Oregon City School Dist	8,286,288	128
Conley, Sharon/Northwest Local School Dist	5	179
Conley, Tim/Bloom-Vernon Local Sch Dist	73,295	178
Conley, Tim/Bloom-Vernon Local Sch Dist	84	178
Conley, Traci/Vanlue Local School Dist	1	99
Conn, Steve/Yellow Springs Exempted Vlg SD	67	85
Connally, Johnda/Portsmouth City School Dist	58	179
Connaughton, Steve/Hamilton City School Dist	48,51	22
Connell, Matt/Fairfield Co Ed Service Center	73	62
Connelly, Carolyn/Paulding Exempted Village SD	57	160
Conner, Brad/Wayne Local School Dist	67	209
Conner, Dirk/Bowling Green City Sch Dist	6	216
Conner, Jennifer/Napoleon Area City School Dist	4	101
Conner, Jim/Anthony Wayne Local Sch Dist	285,288,298	127
Conner, Torey/Claymont City School Dist	13	201
Connor, Laura/Oakwood City School Dist	6	152
Conover, Dave/Deer Park Cmty School Dist	3	89
Conroy, Jennifer/Elgin Local School Dist	67	138
Conroy, Rogina/Southern Ohio Ed Serv Ctr	68	32
Conti, Christina/Jackson Local School Dist	16,82	186
Cook, Andrea/Springboro Cmty School Dist	8,11,16,73	208
Cook, Barbara/Apollo Joint Voc School Dist	7	8
Cook, Jacque/Copley-Fairlawn City Sch Dist	77	192
Cook, Jeff/Parma City School Dist	10,18	49
Cook, Joe/Symmes Valley Local Sch Dist	5	117
Cook, Judith/Westfall Local School Dist	67	163
Cook, Lisa/Mid-Ohio Ed Service Center	68	171
Cook, Mark/Barnesville Exempted Vlg SD	6	17
Cook, Mark/Barnesville Exempted Vlg SD	4	17
Cook, Michael/Sheffield-Sheffield Lake CSD	1	125
Cook, Randy/New Miami Local School Dist	67	23
Cook, Renee/Eastland-Ffld Career Tech VSD	16,82	70
Cook, Ryan/Bucyrus City School Dist	2,19	38
Cook, Timothy/Western Brown Local Sch Dist	6	20
Cooke-Porter, Carrie/Logan-Hocking Local Sch Dist	58,77,79,88	104
Cool, Aimee/Conneaut Area City Sch Dist	69,77	12
Cooley, Denise/North Canton City School Dist	81	187
Cooley, Melinda/Edgerton Local School Dist	286	214
Coomer, Ami/Franklin-Monroe Local Sch Dist	16	55
Cooper, Bonnie/Black River Local School Dist	4	139
Cooper, Jonathan/Mason City School Dist	15	208
Cooper, Joy/Put-In-Bay Local School Dist	2,71,97	159
Cooper, Mark/Big Walnut Local School Dist	15	58
Cooper, Tim/Lucas Local School Dist	67	172
Cooper, Tonya/Pike Co Area JT Voc Sch Dist	2	163
Cooperider, Farrah/North Fork Local School Dist	67	119
Copas, Joni/Hamilton City School Dist	71	22
Cope, Tim/Champion Local School Dist	6	197
Copeland, Adam/Morgan Local School Dist	6	154
Copeland, Jeff/Jefferson Co JT Voc Sch Dist	30	109
Copelandshaw, Cheri/Springfield Local School Dist	16	128
Copley, Kyle/Scioto Co Joint Vocational SD	28,288	179
Copps, Luana/Bellevue City School Dist	34	105
Copus, Cory/Georgetown Exempted Village SD	6	19
Corbett, Janine/West Carrollton City Sch Dist	71	153
Corbin, Mary Beth/Wyoming City School Dist	38	94
Corcoran, Lisa/Union Scioto Local Sch Dist	29	175
Corcoran, Mike/Darke Co Ed Service Center	73,295	55
Corder, Seth/Newcomerstown Exempted Vlg SD	11,288	203
Core, Brenda/Spencerville Local School Dist	2	9
Core, Deb/Cory-Rawson Local School Dist	67	97
Core, Sheila/Jonathan Alder Local Sch Dist	77	132
Corfman, Joseph/Toledo Public Schools	11	129
Corley, Larry/Forest Hills School Dist	3	89
Cornell, Jennifer/Vandalia Butler City Sch Dist	29	153
Cornett, Rachel/Clinton-Massie Local Sch Dist	36	33
Corrani, Dana/Keystone Local School Dist	7,85	124
Corsi, Dennis/Sandy Valley Local School Dist	67	189
Cosby, Reva, Dr/Mt Healthy City School Dist	1	91
Cosgrave, Jocelyn/Reynoldsburg City School Dist	8,18	72
Cosgrove, Timothy/Kirtland Local School Dist	67	112
Costal, Leslie/Columbiana Exempted Village SD	7	34
Costco, Diane/Girard City School Dist	76	197
Cotner, Randy/Walnut Twp Local School Dist	1	64
Cotter, Gerrie/Westerville City School Dist	67	74
Cotterman, Jan/Stark Co Area Voc Sch Dist	88	189
Cottingim, Jane/Twin Valley Cmty Local SD	38,83	169
Cottingim, Scott/Twin Valley Cmty Local SD	1,11	169
Cottrell, Nicole/Springfield City School Dist	2	28
Cottrill, Kacey/Caldwell Exempted Village SD	1	158
Couch, Allyson/Oakwood City School Dist	5,11,34,57	152
Couch, Cj/Vanlue Local School Dist	3,5	99
Countryman, Keith/Hicksville Exempted Village SD	1	57
Courtad, Michael/Upper Sandusky Exempted Vlg SD	4	219
Courtad, Michelle/Riverdale Local School Dist	67	98
Courter, Jeff/Indian Lake Local School Dist	6	121
Couts Everett, Tricia/Canton Local School Dist	8,280,285,288,298	185
Covert, Micah/Nelsonville-York City Sch Dist	67	15
Covey, Chris/Van Wert City School Dist	8,288	205
Cowell, Tammi/Northmor Local School Dist	2,11,19,296	155

School Year 2019-2020   800-333-8802   OH-T11

DISTRICT PERSONNEL INDEX

Market Data Retrieval

NAME/District	JOB FUNCTIONS	PAGE
Cowles, Nick/Alliance City School Dist	3,4,5,91	184
Cox, Aaron/Fairlawn Local School Dist	73,295	182
Cox, Belinda/West Carrollton City Sch Dist	5	153
Cox, Dan/Great Oaks Career Campuses	12,27	89
Cox, Jenny/Tri-Valley Local School Dist	67	157
Cox, Jeran/Vinton Co Local School Dist	35	206
Cox, Richard/Ed Service Ctr Lake Erie West	2	127
Cox, Shanna/Valley Local School Dist	4	179
Cox, Shannon/Montgomery Co Ed Service Ctr	8,15	148
Cox, Tawny/Shelby City School Dist	16	173
Cox, Tim/South-Western City School Dist	5	73
Coxon, Rob/Olmsted Falls City School Dist	6	48
Coyle, Amy/Massillon City School Dist	4	187
Cozad, Doug, Dr/Bellbrook-Sugarcreek Schools	1	83
Crabtree, Cheri/Scioto Valley Local Sch Dist	37	164
Crabtree, Daren/Valley Local School Dist	6	179
Crabtree, Deborah/Jackson City School Dist	11,93,286,288,296,298	107
Crabtree, Paul, Dr/South Central Ohio Ed Svc Ctr	67	178
Craft, Paul/Delaware City School Dist	1	58
Crain, Kip, Dr/Wayne Co Joint Voc School Dist	1	213
Crall, Steve/Wynford Local School Dist	67	39
Cramer, Heather/Marion Local School Dist	2,11	144
Cramer, Todd, Dr/Maumee City School Dist	1	127
Crantz, Mickey/Shaker Heights City Sch Dist	8,11,15,57	50
Crawford, Beth/Lakota Local School Dist	7	177
Crawford, Joe/Willard City School Dist	6	106
Crawford, Kay/Danville Local School Dist	16	110
Crawford, Kimberly/Kirtland Local School Dist	7	112
Crawford, Nathan/Ross-Pike Co Ed Service Center	73,295	174
Creamer, Kregg/New Lebanon Local School Dist	6	151
Creighton, Bill/Frontier Local School Dist	4,11	209
Cremer, Kregg/Tipp City Exempted Village SD	6	146
Creps, Dan/Rossford Exempted Village SD	1,11	218
Cress, Connie/Switzerland of Ohio Local SD	2	147
Crew, Curt/Wauseon Exempted Village SD	73	80
Crew, Krysten/Mogadore Local School Dist	3,5	166
Crew, Paula/Tecumseh Local School Dist	1	28
Crews, Pam/Maple Heights City School Dist	67	47
Crist, Steve/Madison Local School Dist	3,91	172
Critchfield, Mike/Revere Local School Dist	3	194
Crock, Cathy/Wolf Creek Local School Dist	4	211
Crockett, Victoria/Stark Co Area Voc Sch Dist	60	189
Crofford, Lori/Diocese of Youngstown Ed Off	73	137
Croley, Belitta/Sycamore Cmty School Dist	90	93
Crone, Joe/Washington Co JT Voc Sch Dist	2,294	210
Cronebach, Melanie/East Central Ohio ESC-N Phil	58,275	201
Cronebach, Melanie/East Central Ohio ESC-St Clair	58	17
Crooks, Douglas/North Point Ed Svc Ctr	1,11	60
Cropper, Alana/Forest Hills School Dist	2,294	89
Cross, Christina/Shawnee Local School Dist	2,91	9
Crossley, Jeniffer/Geneva Area City School Dist	6	13
Crossley, Randy/Lima City School Dist	3,5	9
Crothers, Libby/Scioto Valley Local Sch Dist	35	164
Croucher, J/Caldwell Exempted Village SD	2,19	158
Crouse, Amy, Dr/Loveland City School Dist	1,11,83	90
Crowder, Tim/Fairfield Local Sch Dist	73	102
Crowe, Jason/Mentor Exempted Village SD	26,27,31	113
Croxall, Josh/Beaver Local School Dist	5	34
Croy, Jennifer/Ottawa-Glandorf Local Sch Dist	8,11,58,69,274,296	170
Crozier, Robert/Shadyside Local School Dist	3,5	18
Cruickshank, Lisa/Genoa Area Local School Dist	4	159
Cruse, Amy/Highland Local School Dist	81	141
Csanyi, Cathy/Plymouth-Shiloh Local Sch Dist	58	173
Csanyi, Cathy/Plymouth-Shiloh Local Sch Dist	58	173
Csanyi, George, Dr/State Support Team-Region 7	1	174
Csillag, John/Beavercreek City School Dist	3	83
Culp, Andrew/Grandview Heights City SD	1	70
Culp, Cherie/Canton City School Dist	298	184
Culwell, Jeff/Meta Solutions	2	78
Cummins, Alex/Millcreek-West Unity Local SD	73	215
Cunningham, Andi/Hilliard City School Dist	5	71
Cunningham, Brandi/Woodmore Local School Dist	12	159
Cunningham, Derek/Carey Exempted Village SD	27,75	219
Cunningham, Holly/Frontier Local School Dist	36,69	210
Cunningham, Ray/Crestview Local School Dist	5	171
Cunningham, Thomas/Southern Local School Dist	1	35
Cunninghamn, Julia/East Guernsey Local Sch Dist	5	86
Curlette, Angela/Cedar Cliff Local School Dist	36,69,274	84
Curran, Robin/Beaver Local School Dist	273	34
Currence, Tom/Geneva Area City School Dist	3,5	13
Curtin, Chris/Clermont Co Ed Service Center	58	29
Curtis, Aireane/Windham Exempted Vlg Sch Dist	1	167
Curtis, Becky/Greenville City School Dist	38	55
Curtis, Dan/Evergreen Local School Dist	10	78
Curtis, Dan/Evergreen Local School Dist	10	78
Curtis, Erin/Big Walnut Local School Dist	79	58
Curtis, Matt/Graham Local School Dist	1	25
Curtis, Matt/Trimble Local School Dist	8	15
Curtis, Rhonda/Loudonville-Perrysville SD	77	11
Curtis, Russ/Ripley-Union-Lewis-Huntngtn SD	8,73,295	20
Cusick, Paul/Crestview Local School Dist	6	34
Custar, Katie/Wellington Exempted Village SD	273	126
Custis, Barry/Lynchburg-Clay Local Sch Dist	3	103
Cybulski, Tim, Dr/Oak Hills Local School Dist	8,11,15,57,58,69,88,298	92
Cyders, Erick/Marlington Local School Dist	73	186
Cygnor, Matt/Groveport Madison Local SD	68	71
Cyrus, Freda/Valley Local School Dist	2	179

D

NAME/District	JOB FUNCTIONS	PAGE
D'Alberti, Julie/North Ridgeville City Sch Dist	79	125
D'Amato, Joe/Cleveland Hts-Univ Hts City SD	6	42
D'Arcy, Patty/Finneytown Local School Dist	58	89
D'Aurora, Shana, Dr/Steubenville City School Dist	11,31,78,89	109
Dackin, Rich/Bath Local School Dist	1	8
Dadisman, Marilyn/Southington Local School Dist	31,36,69	200
Dafler, Kathy/Brookville Local School Dist	7,35,85	148
Dafoe, Jennifer/Little Miami Local School Dist	63	208
Dailey, Jonathan/Keystone Local School Dist	6	124
Dakin, Shawn/Newcomerstown Exempted Vlg SD	73,76	203
Dalby, Anne/Cardinal Local School Dist	37	81
Dale, Debbie/Bristol Local School Dist	4	197
Daley, Alissa/Franklin Local School Dist	7	156
Dalluge, Anita/Hilliard City School Dist	2	71
Dalton, Debbie/North Canton City School Dist	5	187
Dalton, Robert, Dr/Zanesville City School Dist	8	157
Dammeyer, Tracey/Celina City School Dist	58	143
Damron, Stephanie/James A Garfield Local SD	36	165
Damschroder, Tim/Vanguard-Sentinel JT Voc SD	67	177
Dang-Nguyen, Loi/Akron Public Schools	57,61	190
Dang-Nguyen, Toan/Akron Public Schools	48,89	190
Daniel, Linda/Anna Local School Dist	7	182
Daniel, Scott/Tiffin City School Dist	3,91	181
Daniels-Blouse, Joni/Miami Trace Local School Dist	5	65
Daniels, Deborah/Minford Local School Dist	7	178
Daniels, Joe/Maysville Local School Dist	8,11,15	157
Daniels, Jonathan/Forest Hills School Dist	5	89
Daniels, Karrie/Valley Local School Dist	16	179
Daniels, Paul/Milford Exempted Village SD	10	30
Daniels, Tony/Liberty Local School Dist	3,73,76,295	199
Dankworth, Matt/Fairlawn Local School Dist	3	182
Darby, Shannon/Carey Exempted Village SD	36,69	219
Daring, Kyle/Bellefontaine City School Dist	57,58	121
Daring, Tiffany/Upper Scioto Valley Local SD	4	100
Darney, Kelly/Columbiana Co Voc Sch Dist	16,30	34

#		#		#		#		#		#	
1	Superintendent	16	Instructional Media Svcs	30	Adult Education	44	Science Sec	58	Special Education K-12	72	Summer School
2	Bus/Finance/Purchasing	17	Chief Operations Officer	31	Career/Sch-to-Work K-12	45	Math K-12	59	Special Education Elem	74	Inservice Training
3	Buildings And Grounds	18	Chief Academic Officer	32	Career/Sch-to-Work Elem	46	Math Elem	60	Special Education Sec	75	Marketing/Distributive
4	Food Service	19	Chief Financial Officer	33	Career/Sch-to-Work Sec	47	Math Sec	61	Foreign/World Lang K-12	76	Info Systems
5	Transportation	20	Art K-12	34	Early Childhood Ed	48	English/Lang Arts K-12	62	Foreign/World Lang Elem	77	Psychological Assess
6	Athletic	21	Art Elem	35	Health/Phys Education	49	English/Lang Arts Elem	63	Foreign/World Lang Sec	78	Student Personnel
7	Health Services	22	Art Sec	36	Guidance Services K-12	50	English/Lang Arts Sec	64	Religious Education K-12	79	Affirmative Action
8	Curric/Instruct K-12	23	Music K-12	37	Guidance Services Elem	51	Reading K-12	65	Religious Education Elem	80	Driver Ed/Safety
9	Curric/Instruct Elem	24	Music Elem	38	Guidance Services Sec	52	Reading Elem	66	Religious Education Sec	81	Gifted/Talented
10	Curric/Instruct Sec	25	Music Sec	39	Social Studies K-12	53	Reading Sec	67	School Board President	82	Video Services
11	Federal Program	26	Business Education	40	Social Studies Elem	54	Remedial Reading K-12	68	Teacher Personnel	83	Substance Abuse Prev
12	Title I	27	Career & Tech Ed	41	Social Studies Sec	55	Remedial Reading Elem	69	Academic Assessment	84	Erate
13	Title V	28	Technology Education	42	Science K-12	56	Remedial Reading Sec	70	Research/Development	85	AIDS Education
15	Asst Superintendent	29	Family/Consumer Science	43	Science Elem	57	Bilingual/ELL	71	Public Information		

#		#	
88	Alternative/At Risk	277	Remedial Math K-12
89	Multi-Cultural Curriculum	280	Literacy Coach
90	Social Work	285	STEM
91	Safety/Security	286	Digital Learning
92	Magnet School	288	Common Core Standards
93	Parental Involvement	294	Accountability
95	Tech Prep Program	295	Network System
97	Chief Information Officer	296	Title II Programs
98	Chief Technology Officer	297	Webmaster
270	Character Education	298	Grant Writer/Ptnrships
271	Migrant Education	750	Chief Innovation Officer
273	Teacher Mentor	751	Chief of Staff
274	Before/After Sch	752	Social Emotional Learning
275	Response To Intervention		

Ohio School Directory

DISTRICT PERSONNEL INDEX

NAME/District	JOB FUNCTIONS	PAGE
Darnold, Heather/*Fredericktown Local Sch Dist*	2	111
Darr, Cassiee/*Greene Co Ed Service Center*	58	83
Darrah, Merrie/*State Support Team-Region 4*	1	112
Daugherty, Allison/*Stow-Munroe Falls City SD*	4	194
Daugherty, Andrew/*Barnesville Exempted Vlg SD*	73,76,286	17
Daugherty, Dan/*Cambridge City School Dist*	5	86
Daugherty, Mike/*Chagrin Falls Exempted Vlg SD*	73,286,295	42
Daulbaugh, Mike/*Streetsboro City School Dist*	1	167
Daulton, Mitch/*Jefferson Local School Dist*	6	132
Daurora, Brian/*Steubenville City School Dist*	73,84,91,286	109
Davenport, Lavern/*Brown Local School Dist*	4	25
Daves, Amy/*West Geauga Local School Dist*	11,31,34,58,88,271,275	82
Davidson-North, Donna/*Lebanon City School Dist*	67	207
Davidson, Kim/*New Miami Local School Dist*	8	23
Davies, Jessica/*Montgomery Co Ed Service Ctr*	58,752	148
Davies, Kathy/*Columbiana Exempted Village SD*	2	34
Davies, Lakisha/*Richmond Heights Local SD*	58	49
Davies, Tom/*Access*	16,295	137
Davis, Amie/*Minerva Local School Dist*	77	187
Davis, Brian/*North Union Local School Dist*	67	205
Davis, Brian/*Washington Local School Dist*	15	130
Davis, Chris/*Coventry Local School Dist*	67	192
Davis, Christine/*Bethel-Tate Local School Dist*	83	30
Davis, Crystal/*Pickerington Local School Dist*	71	64
Davis, Dan/*North Baltimore Local Sch Dist*	6	217
Davis, Danielle/*Newton Local School Dist*	8,11,57,273,286,288,298	146
Davis, Debra/*Newton Falls Exempted Vlg SD*	67	200
Davis, Donna/*Southwest Ohio OCA*	1	25
Davis, Gary/*Triad Local School Dist*	6	26
Davis, Jamie/*Buckeye Local School Dist*	2	12
Davis, Janell/*River View Local School Dist*	16	37
Davis, Jarman/*Perrysburg Exempted Village SD*	67	218
Davis, Jeff/*Mercer Co Ed Service Center*	67	143
Davis, Jerome/*Clearview Local School Dist*	1	123
Davis, John/*Ashland Co-West Holmes JVSD*	69	11
Davis, John/*Cincinnati City School Dist*	5	87
Davis, Jonathan/*Circleville City School Dist*	1	162
Davis, Kayla/*River View Local School Dist*	7,85	37
Davis, Kim/*London City School Dist*	16	132
Davis, Kim/*Mahoning Co Ed Service Center*	8	133
Davis, Krista/*Olentangy Local School Dist*	71	59
Davis, Larry/*Boardman Local School Dist*	42	134
Davis, Liah/*Amanda-Clearcreek Local SD*	37	62
Davis, Lori/*Wayne Trace Local School Dist*	2	160
Davis, Matt/*Westerville City School Dist*	297	74
Davis, Mick/*Indian Hill Exempted Vlg SD*	2	90
Davis, Mike/*Talawanda School Dist*	2,11,19	24
Davis, Nikole/*Lorain City School Dist*	88	124
Davis, Rebecca/*Wheelersburg Local School Dist*	38	180
Davis, Ryan/*Chesapeake Union Exempt Vlg SD*	6	115
Davis, Sue/*Ridgewood Local School Dist*	27	37
Davis, Tanya, Dr/*Reynoldsburg City School Dist*	68	72
Davis, Terry/*Cincinnati City School Dist*	298	87
Davis, Thomas/*Greeneview Local School Dist*	73	84
Davis, Tiffany/*Leetonia Exempted Village SD*	280	35
Davis, Tim/*Hillsboro City School Dist*	1	103
Davis, Tod/*Highland Local School Dist*	3	141
Davis, Walter/*Woodridge Local School Dist*	1	195
Davison, Karrie/*Pioneer Joint Voc School Dist*	16,82	173
Dawson, Brad/*Grand Valley Local School Dist*	73	13
Dawson, John/*East Liverpool City Sch Dist*	7	35
Dawson, Shelly, Dr/*Pleasant Local School Dist*	60,79	138
Day, Janice/*Adams Co Ohio Valley Sch Dist*	81	6
Day, Joey/*Marysville Exempted Village SD*	6	204
Day, Joseph/*Kenton City School Dist*	6	100
Day, Kelly/*Western Brown Local Sch Dist*	5	20
Day, Mandy/*Scioto Valley Local Sch Dist*	7	164
Daymut, Jacquelynn/*Keystone Local School Dist*	285	124
Daymut, Rose/*Cambridge City School Dist*	8,11,69,72,288,296,298	86
Dazell, Dawn/*Bowling Green City Sch Dist*	68	216
De Roche, Phil/*Upper Arlington City Sch Dist*	3	74
Deagle, Tracey, Dr/*Dublin City School Dist*	8,15,68	69
Deal, Judy/*Upper Arlington City Sch Dist*	16	74
Deam, Jennifer/*East Central Ohio ESC-N Phil*	67	201
Dean, Bren/*Southeastern Local School Dist*	16,82	28
Dean, Stanfield/*Edison Local Schools District*	8	60
DeAngelis, T/*Chippewa Local School Dist*	67	211
Deanna, Stacey/*Aurora City School Dist*	71	164
Debevoise, Stephanie/*Newark City School Dist*	81	119
Debevoise, Ty/*Whitehall City School Dist*	71	75
Deboas, Rey/*Toledo Public Schools*	4	129
Debold, Joe/*Edison Local School Dist*	3,5	109
Decker, Lynn/*Bright Local School Dist*	5	102
Decker, Lynn/*Wadsworth City School Dist*	7	141
Deeble, Jeff/*South Central Local Sch Dist*	3,5	106
Deem, Tony/*Southern Local School Dist*	1	143
Deere, Audra/*Dawson-Bryant Local Sch Dist*	2	115
Deetz, Sharon/*North Central Local Sch Dist*	12	215
Deetz, Tim/*Muskingum Valley ESC*	73	156
Deevers, Cindy/*Streetsboro City School Dist*	58	167
Defehr, Cathie/*Dayton Public School Dist*	4	149
DeFelice, Anthony/*Springfield Local School Dist*	10	135
DeHart, Brenda/*Milton-Union Exempted Vlg SD*	4	145
Dehmlow, Matthew/*Marietta City School Dist*	11,58,79	210
Deis, Chris/*Grandview Heights City SD*	16,73,76,98,295,297	71
Deitering, Kevin/*Kalida Local School Dist*	63	169
Deitsch, Brion/*Dublin City School Dist*	2,3	69
Dejulio, Ron/*Lakeview Local School Dist*	6	199
DeLaney, Lora/*Gallia Co Local School Dist*	4	80
DeLaney, Mike/*Highland Local School Dist*	6	155
DeLaney, Ryan/*North Baltimore Local Sch Dist*	1,11	217
Delehanty-Koen, Ann/*Sycamore Cmty School Dist*	38	93
Deleruyelle, Brad/*Pandora Gilboa Local Sch Dist*	2	170
Delisio, Julie/*Teays Valley Local School Dist*	71	162
Dell, John/*Findlay City School Dist*	5	97
Dellamorte, Anne/*Solon City School Dist*	93	50
Dellapina, Michael/*Springfield City School Dist*	6	28
Dellinger, Abby/*Waynesfield-Goshen Local SD*	37	16
Dellinger, Terry/*Oregon City School Dist*	5	128
DeLong, Laura/*Western Buckeye Ed Service Ctr*	58	160
DeLong, Laurie/*Wayne Trace Local School Dist*	58	160
DeLong, Scott/*Mechanicsburg Exempted Vlg SD*	67	26
Delp, Mindy/*Mt Gilead Exempted Village SD*	4	155
DeLuco, Raymond/*Hubbard Exempted Village SD*	3	198
Delury, Keith/*Connect Information Tech Ctr*	16,73,76	54
Delury, Keith/*Connect Information Tech Ctr*	15,16,73	126
Delwiche, Paul/*Troy City School Dist*	36	146
DeMaria, Paolo/*Ohio Department of Education*	1	1
Demell, Ann/*Richmond Heights Local SD*	4	49
Dement, Rob/*Centerville City School Dist*	6	148
Demers, Cathy/*Monroe Local School Dist*	1	23
Demita, Shannon/*Coventry Local School Dist*	8,69,294	192
Demmler, Sally/*Hamilton County ESC*	58,275	97
Demotte, John/*Riverdale Local School Dist*	73	98
Denecker, Greg/*Bluffton Exempted Village Sch*	1	8
Deniro, Anthony/*Youngstown City School Dist*	2	136
Denius, Justin/*Noble Local School Dist*	8	158
Denman, Dan/*Maplewood Local School Dist*	67	199
Dennis, Betsy/*London City School Dist*	31	132
Dennis, Curt/*Jefferson Local School Dist*	73,76,286	132
Dennison, Matt/*New Philadelphia City Sch Dist*	6	203
Denny, Corina/*Winton Woods City School Dist*	71	94
Denny, Steve/*Winton Woods City School Dist*	2,11,91,288,294,296,298	94
Denton, Ron/*Pickerington Local School Dist*	76	64
DePalma, Frank/*Montgomery Co Ed Service Ctr*	1,11	148
DePascale, Christine/*Warren City School Dist*	81	200
Depelomo, Megan/*Osnaburg Local School Dist*	4	188
Depew, Erick/*Valley View Local School Dist*	3	153
Depew, Linda/*Buckeye Local School Dist*	38	140
Depinet, Doug/*Hopewell-Loudon Local SD*	3,5	181
Depompei, Nick/*Revere Local School Dist*	38	194
Deppert, Gina/*Sandusky City School Dist*	2,19	61
Deramo, Jill/*Cardinal Local School Dist*	38	81
Derby-Lovell, Karen/*Bay Village City School Dist*	71	40
Derolph, Dale/*Northern Local School Dist*	67	161
Derringer, William/*Tri-Co North School Dist*	1	168
Deschner, Dale/*Lucas Local School Dist*	12	172
Deskins, David/*Greene Co Voc School Dist*	1,11	84
Detoro, James/*Liberty Local School Dist*	6	199
Detterman, Monte/*South-Western City School Dist*	2,4,5	73
Dettwiller, Keith/*Scioto Valley Local Sch Dist*	6	164
Dettwiller, Tim/*Fairfield Local Sch Dist*	1	102

DISTRICT PERSONNEL INDEX

Market Data Retrieval

NAME/District	JOB FUNCTIONS	PAGE
Detwiler, Jon/Fremont City School Dist	1	176
Detwiler, Melissa/Clyde-Green Spgs Exmpt Vlg SD	16	176
Detzel, Pam/Northwest Local School Dist	67	91
Deuber, John, Dr/Highland Local School Dist	6	141
Dever, Christina/New Boston Local School Dist	8,11,57,285,294,295,296	179
Dever, Tim/Minford Local School Dist	3	178
Devies, Mike/Waterloo Local School Dist	6	167
DeVincentis, Lou/Orange City School Dist	71	48
DeVine, Sue/Marysville Exempted Village SD	67	204
DeVito, Tina/State Support Team-Region 5	34	137
DeVoe, Shawna, Dr/Rittman Exempted Village SD	9	213
Devooght, Lindy/Vanlue Local School Dist	82	99
DeWeese, Kim/Wilmington City School Dist	2	33
Dewey, David/Wickliffe City School Dist	81	114
Dexter, Elden/Nelsonville-York City Sch Dist	5	15
Deyarman, Jennifer/Toledo Public Schools	8	129
Dezarn, Cindy/Middletown City School Dist	4	23
Dial, Sue Ann/Chesapeake Union Exempt Vlg SD	2,11	115
Dianetti, Joe/Fairview Park City Sch Dist	6	46
DiBlasi, Kathy/Butler Tech Career Dev Schs	10,285	21
Dibler, Pam/Lakota Local Sch Dist	58,270,296	177
Dibucci, Aaron/Port Clinton City School Dist	3	159
Dick, Denise/Youngstown City School Dist	71	136
Dick, JB/Amanda-Clearcreek Local SD	1	62
Dick, Matt/Anthony Wayne Local Sch Dist	3,91	127
Dick, William/Pymatuning Valley Local SD	3,5,91	13
Dicken, Tamra/Athens City School Dist	4	14
Dickens, Edward/Waverly City School Dist	1	164
Dickerhoof, Becky/Tuscarawas Valley Local SD	83,85,88,270	203
Dickerhoof, Mark/Orrville City School Dist	2	212
Dickerhoof, Mark/Rittman Exempted Village SD	2	213
Dickerhoof, Mark/Southeast Local School Dist	2	213
Dickerson, Steven/Hillsdale Local School Dist	1,84	11
Dickinson, Brice/Blanchester Local School Dist	76	32
Dicks, John/Green Local School Dist	296	178
Dicks, Joyce/Springfield Local School Dist	4	135
Dickson, Beth/Jackson Center Local Sch Dist	58	183
Dickson, Dale/Johnstown-Monroe Local SD	1	118
Dickson, Dustin/Gallipolis City School Dist	295	81
Dickson, Rhonda/State Support Team 11	1	78
Didinger, Elaine/Danville Local School Dist	4	110
DiDonato, Dave/Conotton Valley Union Local SD	6	100
Diekmann, Lori/Clermont Northeastern Local SD	7,85	30
Diels, Troy/Wilmington City School Dist	6	33
Dieringer, Sara/St Mary's City School Dist	77	16
Dietrich, Chip/Mohawk Local School Dist	6	219
Dietrich, Joe/Allen Co Ed Service Center	5	7
Dietrick, Dave/Hillsboro City School Dist	6	103
Dietz, Monica/Diocese of Cleveland Ed Office	9,15	52
DiFrancesco, Tom/Cuyahoga Falls City Sch Dist	6,35,85	192
Diglia, Don/Ayersville Local School Dist	1	56
Dikowicz, Sheila/Kirtland Local School Dist	5	112
Dikowicz, Sheila/Perry Local School Dist	5	113
Diller, Roger/Tecumseh Local School Dist	3	28
Dillon, Clint/Arlington Local School Dist	84,295	97
DiLoreto, Christoper/Jackson Local School Dist	1,11	186
Dimacchia, Gordana/Lakewood City School Dist	79	47
Dimacio, William/Lakewood City School Dist	27	47
DiMarzio, Kayla/Steubenville City School Dist	42	109
DiMattia, Joe/Cardinal Local School Dist	85	81
Dimetren, Thomas/Toledo Public Schools	27	129
Dinko, Richard/Jackson Local School Dist	95	186
Dishop, Jan/Liberty Center Local Sch Dist	51,54	101
Distel, Dave/Hamilton County ESC	1	97
Distel, David/Hamilton Co Ed Service Center	1	87
Ditlevson, Adrew/Crestview Local School Dist	10	171
Ditlevson, Chad/Crestview Local School Dist	10	171
Ditlevson, David/Crestview Local School Dist	10	171
Dittcherd, Jody/Indian Valley Local Sch Dist	81	202
Dittfeld, Brian/Indian Valley Local Sch Dist	73,84,295	202
Dixon, Jason/Alliance City School Dist	15,79	184
Dixon, Talisa, Dr/Columbus City School Dist	1	66
Dobbelaere, Kris/North West Ohio Ed Service Ctr	8,74	78
Dobberstein, Richard/Brookville Local School Dist	16,73	148
Dobbins, Andi/Ridgewood Local School Dist	81	37
Dobbins, Bill/Hopewell-Loudon Local SD	10	181
Dobbins, Lisa/Liberty-Benton Local Sch Dist	2	98
Dobie, Dustin/Elida Local School Dist	286	8
Dobson, Amy/Miamisburg City School Dist	9,54,69,74,288	151
Dockery, Matt/Waterloo Local School Dist	73,76,82,295	167
Docter, Mark/Winton Woods City School Dist	4	94
Dodd, Jennifer/Cuyahoga Co Ed Service Center	298	39
Dodgion, Stephen/Lawrence Co Joint Voc Sch Dist	1	116
Dodson, Mary Lou/Springfield Local School Dist	67	194
Doebrich, Lynn/Marietta City School Dist	83	210
Dohar, Damon/Weathersfield Local Sch Dist	1	201
Dohar, Michelle/Howland Local School Dist	58	198
Dolejs, Mary/Independence Local School Dist	36	46
Doll, Gary/Huber Heights City School Dist	2,3	150
Dominick, Rick/Port Clinton City School Dist	6,36	159
Dominique, Glen/Swanton Local School Dist	3	79
Donahoe, Christopher/Lakewood City School Dist	3,5	47
Donahue, Donald/Jefferson Co Ed Service Center	2	108
Donaldson, Scott/Miami East Local School Dist	6	145
Donato, Benjamin/Toledo Public Schools	295	129
Donda, Jared/Riverside Local School Dist	76	114
Donger, John/Put-In-Bay Local School Dist	67	159
Donisi, Robyn/Franklin City School Dist	8,15	207
Donley, Sarah/Bridgeport School Dist	57	18
Donley, Shawn/Newton Falls Exempted Vlg SD	73,76,295	200
Donley, Shawn/Newton Falls Exempted Vlg SD	73,76,295	200
Donley, Tom/Mapleton Local School Dist	67	11
Donnelly, Mark/Mid-Ohio Ed Service Center	73	171
Donofrio, Bonnie/North College Hill City SD	27,69	91
Donohue, Barbara/Shelby City School Dist	2,19	173
Dool, Eric/Loveland City School Dist	11,58	90
Dopp, Christopher/Toronto City School Dist	8	109
Dornbusch, Jeff/Port Clinton City School Dist	2	159
Dorne, Scott/Westerville City School Dist	3	74
Dorsey, Victoria/Coventry Local School Dist	7	192
Doseck, Cathy/Anna Local School Dist	2	182
Doseck, Keith/Fairlawn Local School Dist	2	182
Doss, Andy/Fairfield Union Local Sch Dist	295	63
Dotson, Angela/Oberlin City School Dist	2	125
Dotson, Micheal/Georgetown Exempted Village SD	3	19
Dotson, Peter/Groveport Madison Local SD	73,76,98	71
Douglas, Carolyn/Cuyahoga Heights Local SD	36,275	45
Douglas, Cindy/Austintown Local School Dist	76	133
Douglas, Kimberly/Southern Ohio Ed Serv Ctr	79,275	32
Douglas, Linda/Ripley-Union-Lewis-Huntngtn SD	57	20
Douglas, Lindy/Alexander Local School Dist	1	14
Douglas, Michael/Salem City School Dist	2	35
Douglas, Shawn/Madison Local School Dist	87	112
Doulton, Barry/U S Grant Career School Dist	27,75,288	31
Douthwaite, Jennifer/West Liberty-Salem Local SD	7	26
Doutt, Dennis/Mideast Career & Tech Ctrs	67	157
Dove, Sharon/Crestwood Local School Dist	5	165
Dovenbarger, Eddie/Coshocton Co Joint Voc SD	10,31,69,88	37
Dowdell, Laura/Ehove Joint Voc School Dist	30	60
Downard, Tami/Wellston City School Dist	2	108
Downing, Nancy/Westfall Local School Dist	7	163
Downing, Pamela/Greene Co Voc School Dist	10,288	84
Downing, Shannon/Elgin Local School Dist	5	138
Downing, Ted/Bright Local School Dist	1,11,83	102

#		#		#		#		#		#	
1	Superintendent	16	Instructional Media Svcs	30	Adult Education	44	Science Sec	58	Special Education K-12	72	Summer School	88	Alternative/At Risk	277	Remedial Math K-12
2	Bus/Finance/Purchasing	17	Chief Operations Officer	31	Career/Sch-to-Work K-12	45	Math K-12	59	Special Education Elem	73	Instructional Tech	89	Multi-Cultural Curriculum	280	Literacy Coach
3	Buildings And Grounds	18	Chief Academic Officer	32	Career/Sch-to-Work Elem	46	Math Elem	60	Special Education Sec	74	Inservice Training	90	Social Work	285	STEM
4	Food Service	19	Chief Financial Officer	33	Career/Sch-to-Work Sec	47	Math Sec	61	Foreign/World Lang K-12	75	Marketing/Distributive	91	Safety/Security	286	Digital Learning
5	Transportation	20	Art K-12	34	Early Childhood Ed	48	English/Lang Arts K-12	62	Foreign/World Lang Elem	76	Info Systems	92	Magnet School	288	Common Core Standards
6	Athletic	21	Art Elem	35	Health/Phys Education	49	English/Lang Arts Elem	63	Foreign/World Lang Sec	77	Psychological Assess	93	Parental Involvement	294	Accountability
7	Health Services	22	Art Sec	36	Guidance Services K-12	50	English/Lang Arts Sec	64	Religious Education K-12	78	Affirmative Action	95	Tech Prep Program	295	Network System
8	Curric/Instruct K-12	23	Music K-12	37	Guidance Services Elem	51	Reading K-12	65	Religious Education Elem	79	Student Personnel	96	Title II Programs	296	Title II Programs
9	Curric/Instruct Elem	24	Music Elem	38	Guidance Services Sec	52	Reading Elem	66	Religious Education Sec	80	Driver Ed/Safety	98	Chief Technology Officer	297	Webmaster
10	Curric/Instruct Sec	25	Music Sec	39	Social Studies K-12	53	Reading Sec	67	School Board President	81	Gifted/Talented	270	Character Education	298	Grant Writer/Ptnrships
11	Federal Program	26	Business Education	40	Social Studies Elem	54	Remedial Reading K-12	68	Teacher Personnel	82	Video Services	271	Migrant Education	750	Chief Innovation Officer
12	Title I	27	Career & Tech Ed	41	Social Studies Sec	55	Remedial Reading Elem	69	Academic Assessment	83	Substance Abuse Prev	273	Teacher Mentor	751	Chief of Staff
13	Title V	28	Technology Education	42	Science K-12	56	Remedial Reading Sec	70	Research/Development	84	Erate	274	Before/After Sch	752	Social Emotional Learning
15	Asst Superintendent	29	Family/Consumer Science	43	Science Elem	57	Bilingual/ELL	71	Public Information	85	AIDS Education	275	Response To Intervention		

OH-T14

Ohio School Directory

DISTRICT PERSONNEL INDEX

NAME/District	JOB FUNCTIONS	PAGE
Downour, Nathan/*Amanda-Clearcreek Local SD*	295	62
Downs, Austin/*Trimble Local School Dist*	6	15
Downs, Druien/*Madeira City School Dist*	3	90
Doyle, Ben/*Bellaire Local School Dist*	285	17
Dragas, John/*Madison Local School Dist*	6	112
Dragelevich, Martha/*Waterloo Local School Dist*	81	167
Draheim, Jane/*Evergreen Local School Dist*	9,11,51,273,280,285,296	78
Draiss, Erika/*Celina City School Dist*	45	143
Drake, Mike/*Western Brown Local Sch Dist*	73,76	20
Draper, Carrie/*Graham Local School Dist*	73	26
Dratwa, Heather/*Greenfield Exempted Village SD*	12,58,83,88,273,274	103
Draves, Michael/*Brunswick City School Dist*	68	140
Draves, Michale/*Berea City School Dist*	15	41
Drawl, David/*West Branch Local School Dist*	11	136
Dray, Christopher/*Bristol Local School Dist*	1,11	197
Drees, Tracy/*Ft Loramie Local School Dist*	67	182
Drerup, Tammy/*Centerville City School Dist*	79	148
Dress, Jenna/*Conotton Valley Union Local SD*	58	100
Dressel, William/*Ironton City School Dist*	8,11,15,83,273	116
Dresser, Courtney/*Margaretta Local School Dist*	5	61
Drewery, Meliisa/*Berne Union Local School Dist*	298	63
Droerman, Scott/*Versailles Exempted Village SD*	6	56
Drost, Bryan, Dr/*Rocky River City School Dist*	71,73,76,91,286,295	50
Drought, Cindy/*Geneva Area City School Dist*	7	13
Drummey, Felicia/*Coshocton City School Dist*	2	36
Dubbs, Patrick/*Wayne Local School Dist*	1	208
Dube, Matthew/*Jennings Local School Dist*	11	169
Duckro, Anna/*Brookville Local School Dist*	31,38,69,79,93	148
Dudones, Julie/*Cuyahoga Falls City Sch Dist*	8	192
Duer, Ashton/*Wayne Trace Local School Dist*	73	160
Dufau, Tim/*New Richmond Exempted Vlg SD*	67	31
Dufault, Adam/*Diocese of Columbus Ed Office*	1	76
Duff, Kevin/*East Holmes Local School Dist*	5	104
Duffield, David/*Hubbard Exempted Village SD*	73,76,295	198
Duffner, Pat/*Ontario Local School Dist*	3,5	173
Duffy, Beth/*Wellston City School Dist*	8,288	108
Dugan, Jason/*Maumee City School Dist*	73,286,295	127
Duhamel, Dave/*Rossford Exempted Village SD*	3	218
Dukes, Judy/*Leipsic Local School Dist*	12	170
Dukes, Laura/*Tri-Co Joint Voc Sch Dist*	2	15
Duko, Ed/*Lisbon Exempted Village SD*	3	35
Dulle, Gary/*Elmwood Local School Dist*	11,34,296	216
Dumais, Karen/*Little Miami Local School Dist*	57	208
Dunfee, James/*Diocese of Steubenville Ed Off*	2	110
Dunham, Dennis/*South Range Local School Dist*	1	135
Dunham, Doug/*Mississinawa Valley Sch Dist*	1,11	56
Dunham, Lauri/*Otsego Local School Dist*	58	217
Dunkle, Joe/*Zane Trace Local School Dist*	3	176
Dunlap, Dennis/*Western Brown Local Sch Dist*	2	20
Dunlap, Kristal/*Upper Sandusky Exempted Vlg SD*	33,38	219
Dunlap, Matt/*Liberty Park City Sch Dist*	16,73,295	46
Dunlap, Michael/*East Muskingum Local Sch Dist*	6	156
Dunlap, Randy/*Crestview Local School Dist*	1,11	171
Dunlap, Teri/*Fairbanks Local School Dist*	7	204
Dunlavy, Jessica/*Triad Local School Dist*	294	26
Dunlevy, Joseph/*Indian Creek Local Sch Dist*	6	109
Dunn, Angela/*Warren Local School Dist*	8,12,275,288	210
Dunn, Douglas/*Meigs Local School Dist*	16	142
Dunn, Douglas/*Meigs Local School Dist*	16	142
Dunn, Elizabeth/*Southington Local School Dist*	67	200
Dunn, Kim/*Covington Exempted Village SD*	285	145
Dunn, Liz/*Miami Valley Educational CA*	2	85
Dunn, Peter/*Western Local School Dist*	11,57,83,88,294,296,298	164
Dunn, Robert/*Southeast Local School Dist*	1	166
Dunn, Robert/*Zane Trace Local School Dist*	4	176
Dunn, Ryan/*Boardman Local School Dist*	5	134
Dunn, Stacy/*West Liberty-Salem Local SD*	8,69,294	26
Duplay, John/*Mayfield City School Dist*	16,73,286	47
Dupler, Jeff/*Liberty Union-Thurstn Sch Dist*	7	64
Dupler, Lance/*Northern Local School Dist*	6	161
Dupler, Molly/*New Lexington School Dist*	7	161
Duplinsky, Thomas/*Liberty Union-Thurstn Sch Dist*	38	64
DuPont, Joyce/*Norwalk City School Dist*	2	106
DuPree, Gordon, Dr/*Garfield Heights City SD*	57,79,91	46
Durant, Romules, Dr/*Toledo Public Schools*	1	129
Durben, Sacsha/*Newcomerstown Exempted Vlg SD*	16	203

NAME/District	JOB FUNCTIONS	PAGE
Durbin, Pat/*Canal Winchester Local SD*	6	66
Durham, Marni/*Butler Tech Career Dev Schs*	15,68	21
Durkin, Melissa/*North Ridgeville City Sch Dist*	285	125
Durkin, Teresa/*Eastland-Ffld Career Tech VSD*	38,60,79,85	70
Durliat, Craig/*Arlington Local School Dist*	67	97
Duskey, Stacy/*Osnaburg Local School Dist*	273	188
Dusseau, Kim/*Benton-Carroll-Salem Local SD*	67	158
Dusthimer, David/*Danville Local School Dist*	67	110
Dutey, Scott/*Portsmouth City School Dist*	1	179
Dutt, Barry/*River Valley Local School Dist*	10,83,88	139
Duval, Barb/*Delphos City School Dist*	8,273	8
DuVall, Cindy/*Lincolnview Local School Dist*	5,11,69,270	205
Duvuvuei, Nathaniel/*Akron Public Schools*	20,23	190
Duwel, Todd/*Oakwood City School Dist*	67	152
Dwight, Kevin/*Vanguard-Sentinel JT Voc SD*	73	177
Dyer, Denny/*Tri-Co North School Dist*	3,5	168
Dyer, Pam/*Mohawk Local School Dist*	4	219
Dysinger, Jeffery/*Fairborn City School Dist*	3	84
Dziczkowski, Jennifer/*Rittman Exempted Village SD*	16	213

E

NAME/District	JOB FUNCTIONS	PAGE
Eachus, Susan/*Gallipolis City School Dist*	11,34,58,88,296	81
Eades, David/*Mechanicsburg Exempted Vlg SD*	3	26
Earich, Kristen/*Adena Local School Dist*	8,11,288	174
Earick, Max/*Bellefontaine City School Dist*	3	121
Earl, Tamara/*Mason City School Dist*	4	208
Earley, Matthew/*Williamsburg Local School Dist*	1,83	32
Earley, Mike/*Xenia Community School Dist*	68,79	84
Early, Marti/*Brookville Local School Dist*	57	148
Early, Nancy/*Lakewood City School Dist*	4	47
Early, Pam/*East Clinton Local School Dist*	16,82,271	33
Earnest, Lorraine/*Mid-Ohio Ed Service Center*	2	171
Earnest, Steve/*Tri-Rivers Joint Voc Sch Dist*	2,19	139
Earnhart, Sharon/*Middletown City School Dist*	5	23
Earp, Linda/*Tuslaw Local School Dist*	4,5	189
Easterling, Steve/*Dawson-Bryant Local Sch Dist*	1	115
Eaton, Frank/*Oakwood City School Dist*	58,88	152
Ebbrecht, Scott, Dr/*Westerville City School Dist*	83,88	74
Eberhart, Rhonda/*Union Local School Dist*	36,83,85,88	18
Eberley, Ryan/*Bryan City School Dist*	5	214
Ebert, Lori/*Green Local School Dist*	81	212
Eble, Jeffrey/*Worthington School Dist*	4,5,7,91	75
Ebner, Tricia/*Norton City School Dist*	81	193
Ebrecht, Scott, Dr/*Westerville City School Dist*	72	74
Eby, Victoria/*Chardon Local School Dist*	16,82	82
Eckenrode, Eric/*Sandusky City School Dist*	73,98	61
Eckenrode, Rob/*Nordonia Hills City Sch Dist*	6,35	193
Eckert, John/*Forest Hills School Dist*	3,91	89
Eckhart, Andrew/*Defiance City School Dist*	73	57
Eddy, Jason/*Carrollton Exempted Village SD*	6	25
Eddy, Keith/*Harrison Hills City Sch Dist*	73,76,84,295	101
Eddy, Pat/*Columbia Local School Dist*	2,11	123
Eden, Anthony/*Bridgeport School Dist*	3,5	18
Edens, Leslie/*Symmes Valley Local Sch Dist*	16,82	117
Edie, Troy/*Finneytown Local School Dist*	8	89
Edinger, Greg/*Vanguard-Sentinel JT Voc SD*	1,11	177
Edison, Chris/*Pymatuning Valley Local SD*	1,11	13
Edmonds, Pam/*Parma City School Dist*	79	49
Edwards, Darrell/*Goshen Local School Dist*	1	30
Edwards, Dina/*Woodridge Local School Dist*	57	195
Edwards, Heather/*Woodridge Local School Dist*	7	195
Edwards, Kelly/*Conotton Valley Union Local SD*	36,79	100
Edwards, Rick/*Nelsonville-York City Sch Dist*	1	15
Edy, Jerry/*Laca-Licking Area Cmop Assoc*	73	120
Eff, Leah/*Edison Local School Dist*	38	109
Eft, Steve/*Indian Creek Local Sch Dist*	37	109
Eggbert, Shawn/*New Knoxville Local Sch Dist*	67	16
Eghbalnia, Cynthia/*Cincinnati City School Dist*	7,83,85	87
Egli, Maryjane/*West Branch Local School Dist*	12,34,36,57,58,83,88,296	136
Ehnsperger, Jane/*Kelleys Island Local Sch Dist*	7	61
Ehrhardt, Matthew/*Ehove Joint Voc School Dist*	60,83,88	60
Ehrman, Brad/*Upper Sandusky Exempted Vlg SD*	6	219
Eichel, Colin/*Dover City School Dist*	3,5,91	202
Eick, Jeff/*River View Local School Dist*	73,76	37
Eickholt, Amy/*Crestview Local School Dist*	58,69,71	205
Eickholt, Donna/*Liberty Center Local Sch Dist*	4	101

DISTRICT PERSONNEL INDEX

Market Data Retrieval

NAME/District	JOB FUNCTIONS	PAGE
Eier, Craig/Tecumseh Local School Dist	6	28
Eifert, Nicholas/Ansonia Local School Dist	35,85	55
Eikenberry, John/Bexley City School Dist	2,84	66
Eilrich, Justin/Fremont City School Dist	5	176
Eisler, Chad/Madison Plains Local Sch Dist	1	133
Elchert, Norm/Lakota Local School Dist	2	177
Elchert, Scott/Jackson Center Local Sch Dist	6	183
Elchert, Tammy, Dr/Carey Exempted Village SD	11	219
Elder, Kenneth/Bedford City School Dist	79,752	40
Elder, Mary/Fredericktown Local Sch Dist	16,82	111
Elder, Paula/East Cleveland City Sch Dist	8,69,296	45
Elder, Rebecca/Berea City School Dist	7	41
Eldridge, Anita/Morgan Local School Dist	31	154
Eldridge, Ryan/Delaware Joint Voc Sch Dist	10,69	59
Elegante, Linda/Chardon Local School Dist	57,58,81	82
Elek, Greg/Elyria City School Dist	67	123
Elkins, Christine/Jefferson Local School Dist	4	132
Ellender, Gerald/Mad River Local School Dist	2	151
Ellerbrock, Mark/Columbus Grove Local Sch Dist	2	169
Elliot, Kendra/Fairbanks Local School Dist	37	204
Elliott, Anastasia/Washington Co JT Voc Sch Dist	88	210
Elliott, Chad/Newcomerstown Exempted Vlg SD	6	203
Elliott, Don/Wellsville Local Sch Dist	6	36
Elliott, Eva/Manchester Local School Dist	2	7
Elliott, Jill/Gahanna-Jefferson Public SD	15	70
Elliott, Lisa/Painesville City Local SD	77	113
Elliott, Sarah/Steubenville City School Dist	58,69,77,90	109
Elliott, Tracy/Knox Co Voc School Dist	2,11	111
Ellis, Brad/Felicity-Franklin Local SD	58	30
Ellis, Julie/Woco-W Ohio Computer Org	79	183
Ellis, Rick/East Palestine City Sch Dist	2,84	35
Ellis, Sandra/Fostoria City School Dist	81	180
Ellis, Tami/Bright Local School Dist	10	102
Ellis, William/Meigs Local School Dist	3,91	142
Ellsworth, Tad/Canton City School Dist	2	184
Ellyson, Mike/United Local School Dist	67	36
Elsea, Sandy/Logan Elm Local School Dist	60	162
Elson, Tabatha/Gibsonburg Exempted Village SD	58,77,83	177
Ely, Roger/Bellefontaine City School Dist	2,5,91	121
Elzey, Scott/Warren Local School Dist	16,73,82,273	210
Embly, Rebecca/Perry Local School Dist	7	188
Emerine, Andy/Hardin Northern Local Sch Dist	73,295	100
Emerson, Sheri/Jackson Center Local Sch Dist	11	183
Emery, Rebecca/Edison Local Schools District	7	60
Emery, Scott/New Albany-Plain Local SD	9	72
Emick, Lou/Groveport Madison Local SD	4	71
Emnett, Keri/Green Local School Dist	36,69,83,88	178
Emrich, Cheryl/Portage Co Ed Service Center	15,68	164
Emrick, Tammy/Yellow Springs Exempted Vlg SD	2,11,296	85
Enders, Todd/Wynford Local School Dist	16,82	39
Endsley, Cindy/Anna Local School Dist	58	182
Engle, Kandee/Southwest Licking Local SD	67	120
Engle, Rex/Amherst Exempted Village SD	67	122
Englehart, Joshua, Dr/Painesville City Local SD	1,73	113
Englehart, Mari/Medina Co Joint Voc Sch Dist	73	141
Engleman, Lawanda/Mt Healthy City School Dist	76	91
Enix, Jason/Beavercreek City School Dist	8,15	83
Enochs, Jennifer/East Liverpool City Sch Dist	58	35
Enriquez, Michael/Batavia Local School Dist	67	29
Ensign, Pam/North Union Local School Dist	11	204
Entler, Tony/Southeastern Local School Dist	67	28
Enyart, Marilyn/Bloom-Carroll Local Sch Dist	4	63
Epperson, Annie/Laca-Licking Area Cmop Assoc	58	120
Erb, Kristy/Salem City School Dist	58,81	35
Erlwin, Lance/Belpre City School Dist	2	209
Ernst, Jane/Loveland City School Dist	16,82	90
Ervin, Sharon/Athens City School Dist	5	14

NAME/District	JOB FUNCTIONS	PAGE
Erwin, Julie/New Philadelphia City Sch Dist	2	202
Erwin, Laura/Toronto City School Dist	4	109
Erwin, Wilma/Washington-Nile Local Sch Dist	58	179
Erwine, Moira/Ed Service Center Lorain Co	8,74,275	122
Esbenshade, Gene/Crestview Local School Dist	3	171
Esber, Joellen/Canton City School Dist	93	184
Escola, Marsha/Jackson Local School Dist	4	186
Eshleman, Anita/Forest Hills School Dist	57,69,88	89
Eshman, Shannon/Norwood City School Dist	58,271	92
Espenschied, Julia/New Philadelphia City Sch Dist	5	203
Esselstein, Mark/Parkway Local School Dist	11	144
Esselstein, Mark/Parkway Local School Dist	12	144
Esser, Amy/Celina City School Dist	34	143
Estep, Shane/Carlisle Local School Dist	8	206
Estepp, Steven/Mariemont City School Dist	1	90
Evans, Christopher/Toledo Public Schools	295	129
Evans, Dan/Riverdale Local School Dist	10	98
Evans, Dave/Elida Local School Dist	6	8
Evans, Gary/Southern Local School Dist	67	143
Evans, Jane/Carrollton Exempted Village SD	7,85	25
Evans, Jared/North Union Local School Dist	73,297	205
Evans, John/Southeastern Local Sch Dist	38,83	175
Evans, Kendal/Paint Valley Local School Dist	3,91	175
Evans, Michelle, Dr/Wadsworth City School Dist	8,11,69,73,270,285	141
Evans, Stephanie/Belpre City School Dist	6	209
Evans, Tom/Cuyahoga Heights Local SD	1	45
Evanston, Rebecca/Ashtabula Area City Sch Dist	34	12
Even, Christy/Warren Co Ed Service Center	58	206
Everhart, L'Taundra/Parma City School Dist	58	49
Everman, Ed/Arcanum Butler Local School Dist	67	55
Everman, Jeff/Celina City School Dist	3	143
Ewart, John/Cloverleaf Local School Dist	5	140
Ewers, Edward/Penta Co JT Voc School Dist	15	217
Ewing, Dave/Hardin-Houston Local Sch Dist	3	182
Ewing, Luke/McComb Local School Dist	3,5	98
Eye, Jake/Windham Exempted Vlg Sch Dist	3,5	167
Eyerman, Christie/Johnstown-Monroe Local SD	12,58,273	118
Ezzo, Marylou/Wickliffe City School Dist	8,11,16,58	114

F

NAME/District	JOB FUNCTIONS	PAGE
Fabino, Diane/Access	79	137
Fackler, Amanda/Noeca-Northern Ohio Ed CA	16	62
Factor, Ben/Lancaster City School Dist	23	63
Factor, Dale/Northern Local School Dist	5	161
Fagnani, Morgan/Triad Local School Dist	8,69,285,296,298	26
Fahle, Brenda/Benjamin Logan Local Sch Dist	5	121
Fahmy, Danielle/Champion Local School Dist	38	197
Fahncke, Lisa/Miami East Local School Dist	2,84	145
Fahner, Frank/Granville Exempted Village SD	3	117
Fain, Mike/Muskingum Valley ESC	77	156
Fairchild, Lana/Bright Local School Dist	2	102
Faircloth, Glenn, Dr/Lorain Co Joint Voc Sch Dist	1,11	125
Fairfield, Timothy/Bristol Local School Dist	58,69,88	197
Falatic, Dan/Lakeview Local School Dist	5	199
Falatic, Robert/Neomin-NE Ohio Mgmt Info NET	15	201
Falcone, Vicki/Bridgeport School Dist	31,38,69	18
Falk, Darren/New Albany-Plain Local SD	23	72
Falk, Kori/New London Local School Dist	71	106
Falkenberg, Dana/Springfield Local School Dist	8,15,69,288	128
Falkenenstein, Robert, Dr/North Baltimore Local Sch Dist	88	217
Falknor, Ryan/Western Reserve Local Sch Dist	6	106
Fallo, Katie/Boardman Local School Dist	58	134
Fangman, Tonja/New Miami Local School Dist	7,83,85	23
Fangmeyer, Dave/Blanchester Local School Dist	3	32
Fankhauser, Karissa/Colonel Crawford Local SD	16	38
Fantone, Brian/Twinsburg City School Dist	6	195
Farkas, Susanne/Cleveland Metro School Dist	76	42

---

1 Superintendent	16 Instructional Media Svcs	30 Adult Education	44 Science Sec	58 Special Education K-12	72 Summer School	88 Alternative/At Risk	277 Remedial Math K-12
2 Bus/Finance/Purchasing	17 Chief Operations Officer	31 Career/Sch-to-Work K-12	45 Math K-12	59 Special Education Elem	73 Instructional Tech	89 Multi-Cultural Curriculum	280 Literacy Coach
3 Buildings And Grounds	18 Chief Academic Officer	32 Career/Sch-to-Work Elem	46 Math Elem	60 Special Education Sec	74 Inservice Training	90 Social Work	285 STEM
4 Food Service	19 Chief Financial Officer	33 Career/Sch-to-Work Sec	47 Math Sec	61 Foreign/World Lang K-12	75 Marketing/Distributive	91 Safety/Security	286 Digital Learning
5 Transportation	20 Art K-12	34 Early Childhood Ed	48 English/Lang Arts K-12	62 Foreign/World Lang Elem	76 Info Systems	92 Magnet School	288 Common Core Standards
6 Athletic	21 Art Elem	35 Health/Phys Education	49 English/Lang Arts Elem	63 Foreign/World Lang Sec	77 Psychological Assess	93 Parental Involvement	294 Accountability
7 Health Services	22 Art Sec	36 Guidance Services K-12	50 English/Lang Arts Sec	64 Religious Education K-12	78 Affirmative Action	95 Tech Prep Program	295 Network System
8 Curric/Instruct K-12	23 Music K-12	37 Guidance Services Elem	51 Reading K-12	65 Religious Education Elem	79 Student Personnel	96 Title II Programs	296 Title II Programs
9 Curric/Instruct Elem	24 Music Elem	38 Guidance Services Sec	52 Reading Elem	66 Religious Education Sec	80 Driver Ed/Safety	97 Chief Information Officer	297 Webmaster
10 Curric/Instruct Sec	25 Music Sec	39 Social Studies K-12	53 Reading Sec	67 School Board President	81 Gifted/Talented	98 Chief Technology Officer	298 Grant Writer/Ptnrships
11 Federal Program	26 Business Education	40 Social Studies Elem	54 Remedial Reading K-12	68 Teacher Personnel	82 Video Services	270 Character Education	750 Chief Innovation Officer
12 Title I	27 Career & Tech Ed	41 Social Studies Sec	55 Remedial Reading Elem	69 Academic Assessment	83 Substance Abuse Prev	271 Migrant Education	751 Chief of Staff
13 Title V	28 Technology Education	42 Science K-12	56 Remedial Reading Sec	70 Research/Development	84 Erate	273 Teacher Mentor	752 Social Emotional Learning
15 Asst Superintendent	29 Family/Consumer Science	43 Science Elem	57 Bilingual/ELL	71 Public Information	85 AIDS Education	274 Before/After Sch	
						275 Response To Intervention	

Ohio School Directory

DISTRICT PERSONNEL INDEX

NAME/District	JOB FUNCTIONS	PAGE
Farley, Frank/*Washington Local School Dist*	76	130
Farley, Jiles/*Warren Co Ed Service Center*	67	206
Farmer, Nathan/*Northridge Local School Dist*	6	152
Farrell, Patrick/*North Royalton City Sch Dist*	68	48
Farrell, Trina/*Clermont Northeastern Local SD*	12	30
Farthing, Jennifer/*Twinsburg City School Dist*	8,11,16,57,69,74	195
Fassnacht, Kim/*Neonet-NE Ohio Ed Tech*	2	196
Fausnaugh, Jannette/*Teays Valley Local School Dist*	4	162
Fausnaugh, Trey/*Logan Elm Local School Dist*	2	162
Faust, Brad/*South-Western City School Dist*	8,12,13,15,275	73
Faust, Mark/*Lynchburg-Clay Local Sch Dist*	6	103
Favio, Kristen/*Summit Co Ed Service Center*	36,79,83,88	190
Fawcett, David/*Elmwood Local School Dist*	84	216
Fazio, Kristin/*Summit Co Educational Svc Ctr*	58,68,77	196
Fearigo, Bill/*Barberton City School Dist*	16,73	192
Feasel, Matt/*Pike-Delta-York Local Sch Dist*	2,19	79
Feasel, Rhonda/*Mohawk Local School Dist*	2	219
Fee, Tracy/*Vinton Co Local School Dist*	73,84,295,297	206
Feeney, John/*Maplewood JT Voc School Dist*	88	166
Feix, Stacie/*Perrysburg Exempted Village SD*	2	218
Feldman, Cyle/*Stow-Munroe Falls City SD*	6	194
Feldner, Carmen/*Cambridge City School Dist*	34,58	86
Felker, Jennifer/*Geauga Co Ed Service Center*	1,11	81
Feller, Molly/*Bellaire Local School Dist*	6	17
Fellers, Brandon/*Miami East Local School Dist*	67	145
Feltman, John/*Knox Co Voc School Dist*	38	111
Feltner, Lori/*Franklin City School Dist*	4	207
Fenik, Mark/*Jonathan Alder Local Sch Dist*	91	132
Fenstermaker, Tony/*McComb Local School Dist*	1,11	98
Fenwick, Mary/*Beavercreek City School Dist*	51,54	83
Fenwick, Maryann/*Cedar Cliff Local School Dist*	54,57,58	84
Ferdig, Tom/*Otsego Local School Dist*	6	217
Feren, Don/*South Range Local School Dist*	6	135
Ferenac, Andrea/*Howland Local School Dist*	6,37	198
Ferencie, Joseph/*Solon City School Dist*	82	50
Fergus, Pati/*Liberty Local School Dist*	16	199
Ferguson, Caroline/*Franklin City School Dist*	81	207
Ferguson, Jeffrey/*Tallmadge City School Dist*	1	194
Ferguson, Lisa/*Wellsville Local Sch Dist*	11,296	36
Ferguson, Lynn/*Tri-Co North School Dist*	2	168
Ferguson, Melissa/*Jefferson Local School Dist*	7	132
Ferguson, Michael/*Genoa Area Local School Dist*	1	159
Ferguson, Robin/*Waterloo Local School Dist*	5	167
Ferlito, Ken/*Euclid City School Dist*	11,54	46
Fernbaugh, Gina/*Wood Co Ed Service Center*	2	216
Ferrara, Mark/*Lordstown Local School Dist*	2,11	199
Ferreira, Leanna/*Mid-Ohio Ed Service Center*	81	171
Ferrel, Frank/*Bridgeport School Dist*	76,295	18
Ferrell, Vic/*Shaker Heights City Sch Dist*	91	50
Ferrelli, Sue/*Martins Ferry City School Dist*	8,11,57,69,288	18
Ferriell, Elaina/*Tri-Co North School Dist*	81	168
Ferris, Greg/*Hamilton County ESC*	3	97
Ferritto, Don/*Richmond Heights Local SD*	3	49
Fessler, Stan/*Newton Local School Dist*	16,28,73,76,295	146
Fetchik, Andrew/*Mayfield City School Dist*	2,68,79	47
Fette, Jack/*Olentangy Local School Dist*	8,18,69,288	59
Fiala, Mary/*Diocese of Youngstown Ed Off*	1	137
Fields, Corinne/*Gahanna-Jefferson Public SD*	58	70
Fields, Marissa/*Ironton City School Dist*	38	116
Fields, Russ/*Southern Local School Dist*	31,69	143
Fields, Thadius/*Trimble Local School Dist*	58	15
Fife, Carrie/*Pickaway-Ross Co JT Voc SD*	30	175
Figalkowski, Mark/*Shadyside Local School Dist*	67	18
Figgi, Mary Ellen/*North Royalton City Sch Dist*	4	48
Fight, Jean/*Stark Co Ed Service Center*	67	184
Figueroa, Ruben/*Lorain City School Dist*	27	124
Figy, Jim/*Wauseon Exempted Village SD*	3	79
Fihoner, Cindy/*Brecksville Broadview Hts CSD*	4	41
Filipovich, Timothy/*Youngstown City School Dist*	69,294	136
Fill, Adam/*Lisbon Exempted Village SD*	73	35
Fillmore, Richard/*Barberton City School Dist*	5	192
Filon, Michele/*Eastern Local School Dist*	1	7
Filut, Toni/*Keystone Local School Dist*	69,81	124
Finch, Joe/*Jackson City School Dist*	38	107
Fine, Tiffany/*Greenville City School Dist*	37	55
Finefrock, Kevin/*Osnaburg Local School Dist*	1	188
Fink, Adam/*New Lexington School Dist*	27	161
Finkbine, Joe/*Tri-Co North School Dist*	11,58,296,298	168
Finkes, Paul/*St Bernard-Elmwood Place Schs*	3	93
Finley, Richard/*Holgate Local School Dist*	6	101
Finseke, Adam, Dr/*Ottawa Hills Local Sch Dist*	1	128
Fiori, Bobby/*Beavercreek City School Dist*	11,58,79	83
Firks, Justin/*Bethel Local School Dist*	1	145
Fischer, David/*Sandy Valley Local School Dist*	1	189
Fischer, Matt/*Northwest Local School Dist*	6,71,73,74,295	91
Fischer, Robert/*National Trail Local Sch Dist*	1	168
Fish, Larry/*Avon Local School Dist*	73	122
Fisher, Jack/*Belmont-Harrison Voc Sch Dist*	275	18
Fisher, Jacob/*Zanesville City School Dist*	28,295	157
Fisher, Jacob/*Zanesville City School Dist*	28,295	157
Fisher, James/*Vantage Career Center Sch Dist*	38,83	206
Fisher, Jeff/*Ontario Local School Dist*	6	173
Fisher, John/*Buckeye Joint Voc School Dist*	33	201
Fisher, Kimberly/*North Ctrl Ohio Ed Service Ctr*	68	180
Fisher, Lori/*Jackson Local School Dist*	7	186
Fisher, Lottie/*East Muskingum Local Sch Dist*	2	156
Fisher, Michele/*Salem City School Dist*	4	35
Fisher, Michelle/*Ashland City School Dist*	76	10
Fisher, Patricia/*Warren City School Dist*	45	200
Fisher, Steve/*Newton Local School Dist*	83	146
Fisher, Steve/*Newton Local School Dist*	36,85,88	146
Fisk, George/*Norwalk City School Dist*	1	106
Fisk, Kim/*Jackson-Milton Local Sch Dist*	12,58	134
Fite, Jeff/*Washington-Nile Local Sch Dist*	3,5	179
Fitts, Vicki/*Diocese of Toledo Ed Office*	73	131
Fitzgerald, Anndrat/*East Cleveland City Sch Dist*	11,298	45
Fitzgerald, Ryan/*Hamilton Local School Dist*	6	71
Fitzpatrick, Bethany/*Georgetown Exempted Village SD*	36	20
Fitzpatrick, Ronnie/*Riverside Local School Dist*	2,298	121
Fladung, Kim/*Warren Co Voc School Dist*	3	208
Flamm, Doug/*U S Grant Career School Dist*	91	31
Flanigan, Michael/*Wilmington City School Dist*	67	33
Flannigan, Greg/*Colonel Crawford Local SD*	16,73	38
Flecher, Ken/*Cloverleaf Local School Dist*	3,91	140
Fleckinger, Al/*Clermont Co Ed Service Center*	2	29
Fleharty, Todd/*Bath Local School Dist*	6	8
Fleming Krall, Elizabeth/*Ed Service Center Lorain Co*	34	122
Fleming, Dave/*Wauseon Exempted Village SD*	2	79
Fleming, Dawn/*Berkshire Local School Dist*	8,11,58,81,296	81
Flemming, Alex/*Westlake City School Dist*	8,12,74,273,296	51
Fletcher, Chelsey/*Toronto City School Dist*	6	109
Fletcher, Gina/*Fairfield City School Dist*	71	21
Fletcher, Kenneth/*Cloverleaf Local School Dist*	3	140
Fletcher, Penny/*Mideast Career & Tech Ctrs*	76	157
Flicker, Tammy/*Bellevue City School Dist*	2	105
Flickinger, Ora/*Hillsdale Local School Dist*	4,5	11
Flood, Sam/*Mohawk Local School Dist*	67	219
Flora, Bonnie/*Covington Exempted Village SD*	4	145
Florea, David/*Little Miami Local School Dist*	3	208
Flowers, David/*Valley Local School Dist*	67	179
Floyd, Eric/*Rock Hill Local School Dist*	11,15,69,288	116
Floyd, Kim/*Swanton Local School Dist*	273	79
Floyd, Mallory/*Canton City School Dist*	8,15,68	184
Floyd, Terrah/*Springboro Cmty School Dist*	2	208
Fockler, Matt/*Buckeye Joint Voc School Dist*	27,38,75,79,83,288	201
Fogle, Jim/*Martins Ferry City School Dist*	1	18
Fogo, Steve, Dr/*Napoleon Area City School Dist*	1,11	101
Folds, Sherry/*Berne Union Local School Dist*	4	63
Foley, Krista/*Lebanon City School Dist*	11,58,77,79,81,271,275	207
Foley, Luke/*Shelby City School Dist*	73,297	173
Folger, Josh/*Eastern Local School Dist*	6	142
Folino, Wendy/*Butler Co Ed Service Center*	58,77	20
Folkerth, Matt/*Bethel-Tate Local School Dist*	6	30
Foltis, Jessica/*Edon Northwest Local Sch Dist*	58	215
Foltz, Robert/*Minerva Local School Dist*	67	187
Foltz, Robert/*Stark Co Area Voc Sch Dist*	67	189
Fonders, Sharon/*Northwestern Local School Dist*	8,57	27
Fontaine, Kim/*Bethel-Tate Local School Dist*	5	30
Foore, Michael/*Wooster City School Dist*	3,5,91	213
Foote, Doug/*New Richmond Exempted Vlg SD*	6	31
Foraker, Angela/*Cleveland Metro School Dist*	2	42
Forby, Stacy/*Washington Court House City SD*	8,13,16,69,74	65

DISTRICT PERSONNEL INDEX

Market Data Retrieval

NAME/District	JOB FUNCTIONS	PAGE
Forchione, Laura/Stow-Munroe Falls City SD	73,295	194
Forcum, Tracey/Union Scioto Local Sch Dist	4	175
Ford, Jane/Zanesville City School Dist	5	157
Ford, Mary/Bloom-Carroll Local Sch Dist	16,82	63
Ford, Meredith/Triad Local School Dist	12	26
Ford, Mike/Pike-Delta-York Local Sch Dist	67	79
Ford, Sharri/Clinton-Massie Local Sch Dist	16,82	33
Ford, Shonteea/Lorain City School Dist	5	124
Ford, Stephen/Clinton-Massie Local Sch Dist	3,5	33
Ford, Wendy/Springboro Cmty School Dist	90	208
Fordham, Allan/Gahanna-Jefferson Public SD	3,91	70
Foreman, Steven/Zanesville City School Dist	11,15,51,54,288,296,298	157
Forfia, Anthony/Newbury Local School Dist	6	82
Forinash, Leonard/Wickliffe City School Dist	3	114
Forman, Ashlee/Ansonia Local School Dist	9,11,51,54,88	55
Forman, Kristin/New Riegel Local School Dist	31,36,69,83,85	181
Formit, Chris/Southeast Local School Dist	76	166
Forney, Judy/Mt Vernon City School Dist	2	111
Forschmer, Anne/Bowling Green City Sch Dist	4	216
Forshey, Stephanie/East Guernsey Local Sch Dist	36	86
Forsthoefel, Frank/Sycamore Cmty School Dist	1	93
Forsthoesfel, Kurt/Minster Local School Dist	67	15
Forsythe, Carol/Covington Exempted Village SD	2,68	145
Forsythe, Cathy/Bright Local School Dist	76	102
Forther, Mark/Massillon City School Dist	91	187
Fortkamp, Jeff/Celina City School Dist	6,78	143
Fortman, Jason/Pioneer Joint Voc School Dist	4	173
Fortner, Mark/Massillon City School Dist	15	187
Fortney, Tim/Coshocton City School Dist	6	36
Fortune, Sheri/River View Local School Dist	34,58,78,81	37
Fosse, Mary/Kings Local School Dist	58	207
Foster, Brett/Paulding Exempted Village SD	31,36,51,69	160
Foster, David/Sycamore Cmty School Dist	3,91	93
Foster, Jay/Toronto City School Dist	67	109
Foster, Mike/Bloomfield-Mespo Local SD	67	197
Foster, Rick/Manchester Local School Dist	67	7
Foster, Steven/Connect Information Tech Ctr	76	54
Foster, Steven/Connect Information Tech Ctr	76	126
Foster, Trudy/Lake Local School Dist	5	217
Fouch, Holly/Lynchburg-Clay Local Sch Dist	57	103
Fought, Ann/Columbus Grove Local Sch Dist	29	169
Fouke, Jefferey/Washington Local School Dist	2,19	130
Foulk, Debra/Akron Public Schools	2	190
Foust, Jd/Middletown City School Dist	6	23
Fout, Sherry/Scioto Valley Local Sch Dist	38	164
Fowler-Mack, Christine/Cleveland Metro School Dist	69	42
Fowler, Cheryl/West Geauga Local School Dist	5	82
Fox, Amy/Westfall Local School Dist	8	163
Fox, Christopher/Montgomery Co Ed Service Ctr	2	148
Fox, Fred/Wynford Local School Dist	1	39
Fox, Mandy/Northern Local School Dist	37	161
Fox, Sara/Franklin-Monroe Local Sch Dist	12,55	55
Fraker, Amy/Northwestern Local School Dist	38,69,83,88	27
Fraley, Anthony/Upper Valley JT Voc Sch Dist	2,10,18	147
Fraley, Susan/Reading Cmty City School Dist	12	93
Francis, Beth/Felicity-Franklin Local SD	285	30
Francis, Joshua/Russia Local School Dist	67	183
Francis, Katie/Ft Loramie Local School Dist	36	182
Francis, Lynn/Marlington Local School Dist	42	186
Frandt, Mandie/Benjamin Logan Local Sch Dist	2	121
Frank, Dean/Green Local School Dist	1	212
Frank, Noel/Scioto Co Joint Vocational SD	38	179
Frankart, Brenda/Liberty-Benton Local Sch Dist	270,273	98
Franke, Bill/Miami Trace Local School Dist	2,3,4,5,79,91	65
Franks, Gina/Dover City School Dist	57,58,79,88,275,296,298	202
Franks, Jim/Tccsa-Tri-Co Comp Svcs	295	214
Frantz, Dave/Northwest Local School Dist	6	179
Frantz, Josh/Valley View Local School Dist	295	153
Frantz, Mary/Greene Co Voc School Dist	67	84
Franz, Sarah/Wayne Trace Local School Dist	36	160
Frary, Amy/Norwayne Local School Dist	69,83	212
Frase, Stacy/Northwest Local School Dist	3	187
Fraunfelter, Steve/Cambridge City School Dist	73	86
Frazier, Bill/Ripley-Union-Lewis-Huntngtn SD	5	20
Frazier, James/Brown Co Ed Service Center	1,11	19
Frdley, Tara/Euclid City School Dist	4	46
Frederick, Amy/Labrae Local School Dist	58	198
Frederick, Chantil/Perry Local School Dist	93	188
Frederick, Michelle/Madison Local School Dist	16,82	172
Fredrick, Debra/Grand Valley Local School Dist	29	13
Freedy, Marci/Columbiana Exempted Village SD	57,58,275	34
Freeh, Mark/Margaretta Local School Dist	73	61
Freeman, Cynthia/Bloom-Carroll Local Sch Dist	58,88	63
Freeman, Dustin/Mad River Local School Dist	16,28,73,76,84,295	151
Freeman, Marybeth/Delaware Joint Voc Sch Dist	1	59
Freeman, Matt/Salem City School Dist	6	35
Freeman, Terri/Northwest Local School Dist	8,11,58,73,285,288,296,298	179
Freiling, Zack/Fairlawn Local School Dist	6	182
French, David/Madison Local School Dist	67	23
French, Elizabeth/Western Reserve Local Sch Dist	38	106
French, Gail/Carlisle Local School Dist	4	206
French, Jill/Carlisle Local School Dist	273	206
Frere, Corby/East Knox Local School Dist	58	111
Freshour, Pam/Pleasant Local School Dist	67	138
Freund, Daniel/Highland Local School Dist	1	155
Frey, Mary/Versailles Exempted Village SD	16	56
Friedrich, Jan/Liberty Union-Thurstn Sch Dist	4	64
Friend, Stephanie/Montpelier Exempted Village SD	69,88	215
Fries, Douglas/Greenville City School Dist	1	55
Friess, Derek/Pike-Delta-York Local Sch Dist	73,76,295	79
Friess, Joe/Wauseon Exempted Village SD	72	80
Friihauf, Carol/Twinsburg City School Dist	76	195
Frilling, Brad/Ft Loramie Local School Dist	73	182
Frimmel, Karen/Berea City School Dist	8,11,54,61,69,81	41
Frisch, Sandra/Ed Service Ctr Lake Erie West	1,11	127
Frist, Donna/Yellow Springs Exempted Vlg SD	58	85
Fritz, Bill/Sycamore Cmty School Dist	28,73,84,286	93
Fritz, Jim, Dr/Anthony Wayne Local Sch Dist	1	127
Fritz, Marc/Niles City School Dist	6	200
Fritz, Paula/Dover City School Dist	16	202
Froelich, Amy/Cambridge City School Dist	67	86
Froelich, Lindsey/Central Local School Dist	37	57
Frolick, Jeremy/Buckeye Valley Local Sch Dist	3,4,5	58
Froman, Connie/Garaway Local School Dist	76	202
Frombach, Erich/Avon Local School Dist	6	122
Froning, Stacee/Coldwater Exempted Village SD	37	143
Fronko, Charlene/Warren Local School Dist	4	210
Fruchey, Kathy/Ottawa-Glandorf Local Sch Dist	2	170
Fruth, Todd/Defiance City School Dist	7,57,58,83,85,88,271,274	57
Frye, Jim/Upper Sandusky Exempted Vlg SD	73,76,286,295	219
Frye, John/New Richmond Exempted Vlg SD	8,11,58,69,74,271,288,296	31
Fryman, Tom/Bellbrook-Sugarcreek Schools	3	83
Fuchs, Micah/Barnesville Exempted Vlg SD	8,11,58,69,288,296,298	17
Fuge, Dennis/Spencerville Local School Dist	1	9
Fullencamp, Ryan/Ft Recovery Local School Dist	73	144
Fullenkamp, Andy/St Henry Cons Local Sch Dist	67	144
Fuller, Mike/Muskingum Valley ESC	295	156
Fuller, Rebecca/Washington Local School Dist	5	130
Fulton, Sarah/Fairborn City School Dist	81	84
Fultz, Lester/Cleveland Metro School Dist	91	42
Funk, Brian/Fairfield Union Local Sch Dist	37,273	84
Furbay, Rebecca/Tallmadge City School Dist	79	194
Furlong, Rebecca/Wooster City School Dist	16,73	213
Furman, Terry/Jefferson Area Local SD	16	13

---

1 Superintendent	16 Instructional Media Svcs	30 Adult Education	44 Science Sec	58 Special Education K-12	72 Summer School	88 Alternative/At Risk	277 Remedial Math K-12
2 Bus/Finance/Purchasing	17 Chief Operations Officer	31 Career/Sch-to-Work K-12	45 Math K-12	59 Special Education Elem	73 Instructional Tech	89 Multi-Cultural Curriculum	280 Literacy Coach
3 Buildings And Grounds	18 Chief Academic Officer	32 Career/Sch-to-Work Elem	46 Math Elem	60 Special Education Sec	74 Inservice Training	90 Social Work	285 STEM
4 Food Service	19 Chief Financial Officer	33 Career/Sch-to-Work Sec	47 Math Sec	61 Foreign/World Lang K-12	75 Marketing/Distributive	91 Safety/Security	286 Digital Learning
5 Transportation	20 Art K-12	34 Early Childhood Ed	48 English/Lang Arts K-12	62 Foreign/World Lang Elem	76 Info Systems	92 Magnet School	288 Common Core Standards
6 Athletic	21 Art Elem	35 Health/Phys Education	49 English/Lang Arts Elem	63 Foreign/World Lang Sec	77 Psychological Assess	93 Parental Involvement	294 Accountability
7 Health Services	22 Art Sec	36 Guidance Services K-12	50 English/Lang Arts Sec	64 Religious Education K-12	78 Affirmative Action	94 Tech Prep Program	295 Network System
8 Curric/Instruct K-12	23 Music K-12	37 Guidance Services Elem	51 Reading K-12	65 Religious Education Elem	79 Student Personnel	96 Chief Information Officer	296 Title II Programs
9 Curric/Instruct Elem	24 Music Elem	38 Guidance Services Sec	52 Reading Elem	66 Religious Education Sec	80 Driver Ed/Safety	97 Chief Technology Officer	297 Webmaster
10 Curric/Instruct Sec	25 Music Sec	39 Social Studies K-12	53 Reading Sec	67 School Board President	81 Gifted/Talented	270 Character Education	298 Grant Writer/Ptnrships
11 Federal Program	26 Business Education	40 Social Studies Elem	54 Remedial Reading K-12	68 Teacher Personnel	82 Video Services	271 Migrant Education	750 Chief Innovation Officer
12 Title I	27 Career & Tech Ed	41 Social Studies Sec	55 Remedial Reading Elem	69 Academic Assessment	83 Substance Abuse Prev	273 Teacher Mentor	751 Chief of Staff
13 Title V	28 Technology Education	42 Science K-12	56 Remedial Reading Sec	70 Research/Development	84 Erate	274 Before/After Sch	752 Social Emotional Learning
15 Asst Superintendent	29 Family/Consumer Science	43 Science Elem	57 Bilingual/ELL	71 Public Information	85 AIDS Education	275 Response To Intervention	

OH-T18

Ohio School Directory

DISTRICT PERSONNEL INDEX

NAME/District	JOB FUNCTIONS	PAGE
Furniss, Cary/*Kings Local School Dist*	2	207
Furniss, Cary/*Reading Cmty City School Dist*	2	93
Fussnecker, Russ/*Edgewood City School Dist*	1	21
Fussnecker, Scott/*Edgewood City School Dist*	8	21
Fyffe, Heidi/*Painesville City Local SD*	11	113
Fyffeyocum, Heidi/*Painesville City Local SD*	9,11,76,88,273,286,296,298	113

G

NAME/District	JOB FUNCTIONS	PAGE
Gabbard, Gary/*Edgewood City School Dist*	67	21
Gable, Susan/*Morgan Local School Dist*	2	154
Gabler, Tina/*Wellington Exempted Village SD*	2,11	126
Gaddis, Lydia/*Springfield City School Dist*	68,74,78,83,273,275	28
Gadison, Lavora/*Cleveland Metro School Dist*	39	42
Gagel, Shannon/*Aurora City School Dist*	81	164
Gagler, Matt/*Nordonia Hills City Sch Dist*	2,3,91	193
Gagnon, Lynn/*Keystone Local School Dist*	16	124
Gaietto, Jodi/*Tri-Rivers Joint Voc Sch Dist*	38,88	139
Gaiffe, Rose/*Sylvania City School Dist*	58	128
Gainer, Mark/*Cedar Cliff Local School Dist*	11,298	84
Gainer, Scott/*Cleveland Hts-Univ Hts City SD*	2,19	42
Galante, Lew/*Perry Local School Dist*	2,19	113
Galante, Lewis/*Kirtland Local School Dist*	2	112
Galbincea, Elaine/*Berea City School Dist*	274	41
Gale, Cathy/*Amherst Exempted Village SD*	5	122
Gale, Laura/*Great Oaks Career Campuses*	69	89
Galentine, Heather/*Milton-Union Exempted Vlg SD*	16	145
Gallagher, Lisa/*Barnesville Exempted Vlg SD*	16	17
Gallaway, Patrick/*New Albany-Plain Local SD*	71	72
Gallion, Patrick/*Wellington Exempted Village SD*	31	126
Gallo, Eugene/*Lisbon Exempted Village SD*	67	35
Gallo, Franco/*Ed Service Center Lorain Co*	1	122
Galloway, Charles/*Firelands Local School Dist*	3,91	124
Gallup, Todd/*Newark City School Dist*	4	119
Gallwitz, Crystal/*East Knox Local School Dist*	4	111
Gallwitz, Gail/*State Support Team-Region 12*	34	86
Galpin, Lisa/*Tri-Co North School Dist*	8,286,288	168
Gambill, Kim/*Warren Co Voc School Dist*	79	208
Gamertsfelder, Thomas/*Licking Co Joint Voc Sch Dist*	3,5,10	118
Ganim, Susan/*Little Miami Local School Dist*	76	208
Gant, James/*Toledo Public Schools*	2,3,5,15,73,91,296	129
Gantz, William/*Wooster City School Dist*	67	213
Garabrandt, Vonda/*Claymont City School Dist*	36	201
Garbig, Melanie/*Bowling Green City Sch Dist*	79	216
Garbig, Melanie/*Bowling Green City Sch Dist*	36,77,79	216
Garchar, Eva/*Kings Local School Dist*	7	207
Garcia, Jason/*Ed Service Ctr Lake Erie West*	73,295	127
Garcia, Scott/*Plain Local School Dist*	6	188
Gardata, Kristin/*Plain Local School Dist*	67	188
Gardner, Angela/*Anthony Wayne Local Sch Dist*	60	127
Garison, Michael/*Bellbrook-Sugarcreek Schools*	57	83
Garke, Julie/*St Henry Cons Local Sch Dist*	1	144
Garland, Jennifer/*Piqua City School Dist*	4	146
Garlinger, Dianne/*Lancaster City School Dist*	67	63
Garlock, Nathan/*Lima City School Dist*	91	9
Garlock, Scott/*Liberty-Benton Local Sch Dist*	6	98
Garman, Nathan/*Circleville City School Dist*	73	162
Garman, Russ/*Vandalia Butler City School Dist*	12	153
Garman, Tammie/*Bellefontaine City School Dist*	5	121
Garmyn, Susan/*Northeastern Local School Dist*	2	57
Garner, Theresa/*Mogadore Local School Dist*	16	166
Garrett, Karen/*Goshen Local School Dist*	7	30
Garrett, Michelle/*Clark-Shawnee Local Sch Dist*	67	27
Garrison, Dana/*Bridgeport School Dist*	2,4,11,296,298	18
Garrison, Jodell/*Milton-Union Exempted Vlg SD*	5	145
Garrison, Nicole/*Newark City School Dist*	60	119
Garrott, Stephanie/*Conotton Valley Union Local SD*	8,11	100
Garside, Hugh/*South-Western City School Dist*	19	73
Garton, Michelle/*North College Hill City SD*	12	91
Garven, Holly/*Bridgeport School Dist*	83,85,88	18
Garverick, Grant/*Galion City School Dist*	67	38
Garverick, Mindy/*South-Western City School Dist*	67	73
Garvey, Kathryn/*Chagrin Falls Exempted Vlg SD*	67	42
Garvic, Don/*Knox Co Ed Service Center*	81	110
Garvic, Donald/*Mt Vernon City School Dist*	81	111
Gase, Mary/*Otsego Local School Dist*	83	217
Gaski, Michele/*State Support Team 3*	1	54

NAME/District	JOB FUNCTIONS	PAGE
Gaskins, Barbara/*Fairfield Union Local Sch Dist*	5	63
Gaskins, Heather/*State Support Team-Region 1*	34	132
Gast, Bruce/*Elgin Local School Dist*	1	138
Gast, Kirsten/*Cory-Rawson Local School Dist*	4	97
Gast, Tony/*Finneytown Local School Dist*	67	89
Gates, Justin/*Kent City School Dist*	57,58,88,275	165
Gates, Richard/*Crestview Local School Dist*	12	34
Gates, Richard, Dr/*Jefferson Twp Local Sch Dist*	11,83,288	150
Gates, Scott/*Ross Local School Dist*	1,83	24
Gatll, Michael/*Ashtabula Area City Sch Dist*	5	12
Gaubatz, Nate/*Wayne Co Joint Voc School Dist*	288	213
Gauche, John/*Fayetteville Perry Local SD*	3,5	19
Gaulke, Richard/*Bloom-Carroll Local Sch Dist*	36,69	63
Gault, Bernard/*Columbia Local School Dist*	3	123
Gault, Dawn/*Arlington Local School Dist*	4	97
Gault, Jim/*Toledo Public Schools*	8,11,69,70,88,274,288,294	129
Gause, Michael/*Parkway Local School Dist*	58	144
Gaydos, Rory/*Delaware Joint Voc Sch Dist*	73,76,295	59
Gayheart, Pam/*Fairborn City School Dist*	71,298	84
Gdovin, Matthew/*Neonet-NE Ohio Ed Tech*	1	196
Gearhardt, Mindy/*Piqua City School Dist*	79	146
Gearhart, Janice/*Westfall Local School Dist*	12,13	163
Gearhart, Kerri/*North West Ohio Ed Service Ctr*	1	78
Gearhart, Krista/*Canton Local School Dist*	27	185
Geason, Shelly/*Edison Local Schools District*	4	60
Geers, Judy/*Graham Local School Dist*	2,84	25
Gegick, Karen/*Akron Public Schools*	8,74	190
Geha, Bill/*Springfield Local School Dist*	83	128
Geha, Bill/*Sylvania City School Dist*	83,88,275	128
Geha, Matt/*Springfield Local School Dist*	1,11	128
Gehret, Deanna/*Tecumseh Local School Dist*	298	28
Gehret, Ivan/*Tecumseh Local School Dist*	8,11,15,16,18,69	28
Gehring, Dustin/*Northwest Local School Dist*	79,88	91
Gehring, Timothy/*Worthington School Dist*	3	75
Geiger, Elli/*West Branch Local School Dist*	6	136
Geiger, Jay/*Hicksville Exempted Village SD*	57	57
Geiger, Kristy/*Northmont City School Dist*	51	152
Geis, Sue/*Northwestern Local School Dist*	4	27
Geis, Suzanne/*Central Local School Dist*	11	57
Geisler, Cheryl/*Fairfield City School Dist*	76	21
Geissinger, J Mac/*Ridgemont Local School Dist*	3,5	100
Geistfeld, Andrew/*Upper Arlington City Sch Dist*	2	74
Geletka, Joseph/*Ironton City School Dist*	1	116
Gemind, Paulette/*Norton City School Dist*	5	193
Gendreau, Andre/*Hamilton City School Dist*	34,58,77,88,275	22
Genert, Raechel/*Fairlawn Local School Dist*	37	182
Geniusz, Brian/*Worthington School Dist*	42	75
Gentile, Matt/*Springfield Local School Dist*	67	136
Gentis, Todd/*Miami East Local School Dist*	60	145
Geordan, Alex/*Canfield Local School Dist*	1	134
George, Ben/*Patrick Henry Local Sch Dist*	6	102
George, Bradley/*Greenfield Exempted Village SD*	5	103
George, Jacob/*Greeneview Local School Dist*	58	84
George, Megan/*Miami Co Ed Service Center*	77	144
George, Mike/*Northridge Local School Dist*	6	119
George, Nic/*Benjamin Logan Local Sch Dist*	73	121
George, Richard/*Tri-Rivers Joint Voc Sch Dist*	30	139
George, Robert/*Jefferson Co JT Voc Sch Dist*	67	109
George, Ryan/*Arcadia Local School Dist*	67	97
Gephart, Scott/*Spencerville Local School Dist*	5	9
Geraghty, Michael/*Field Local School Dist*	6	165
Gerber, Adam/*Monroeville Local School Dist*	73,295	105
Gerber, Ann/*Norwayne Local School Dist*	8	212
Gerhardstein, Adam/*Bellevue City School Dist*	3	105
Gerhardt, Suzie/*Circleville City School Dist*	4	162
Gerhart, Monica/*New Albany-Plain Local SD*	2	72
Gerig, Anthony/*Millcreek-West Unity Local SD*	6	215
Gerken, Brittani/*Wauseon Exempted Village SD*	4	79
Gerspacher, Kay/*Xenia Community School Dist*	16	84
Gerstner, Todd/*Wapakoneta City School Dist*	3	16
Gertz, James/*East Holmes Local School Dist*	67	104
Geschke, Patrick/*Brunswick City School Dist*	8	140
Gessler, Brooke/*Sidney City School Dist*	8	183
Gessler, Brooke/*Sidney City School Dist*	8,11,285,288,298	183
Gettemy, Terry/*Mathews Local School Dist*	77	199
Gettinger, Brad/*Greenville City School Dist*	67	55

School Year 2019-2020   800-333-8802   **OH-T19**

DISTRICT PERSONNEL INDEX

Market Data Retrieval

NAME/District	JOB FUNCTIONS	PAGE
Gheen, Scot/*Meigs Local School Dist*	1	142
Gibbons, Susan/*Archdiocese Cincinnati Ed Off*	1	94
Gibbs, Angie/*Athens Meigs Ed Service Center*	34	14
Gibbs, Angie/*State Support Team-Region 16*	34	15
Gibbs, Larry/*Mansfield City Schools*	71	172
Gibbs, Thomas, Dr/*Athens City School Dist*	1	14
Giblin, Gary/*Winton Woods City School Dist*	57	94
Gibowicz, Christine/*Alliance City School Dist*	8,275	184
Gibson, Amanda/*Geneva Area City School Dist*	57	13
Gibson, Barb/*Scioto Co Joint Vocational SD*	67	179
Gibson, David/*Felicity-Franklin Local SD*	1,11	30
Gibson, Greg/*Maysville Local School Dist*	5	156
Gibson, Jamie/*Van Wert City School Dist*	76	205
Gibson, Jenny/*Harrison Hills City Sch Dist*	79	101
Gibson, Julie/*Northwestern Local School Dist*	2	27
Gibson, Justin/*Lockland School Dist*	12,58	90
Gibson, Pam/*Riverside Local School Dist*	58	121
Gibson, Pat/*Upper Valley JT Voc Sch Dist*	2	147
Gibson, Terry/*Lockland School Dist*	67	90
Gibson, Toby/*Brookfield Local School Dist*	1,11	197
Giesler, Emly/*Fairborn City School Dist*	73,76,295	84
Giesting, Lindsey/*Northwest Local School Dist*	58	91
Gifford, Michelle/*Riverside Local School Dist*	4	114
Gifford, Sam/*Rocky River City School Dist*	68,298	50
Gift, Brenda/*Ed Service Ctr Lake Erie West*	58,81	127
Gigliotti, Genevieve/*Lordstown Local School Dist*	16	199
Gilbert, Christopher/*Crestview Local School Dist*	9	171
Gilbert, Cynthia/*Elgin Local School Dist*	16,73	138
Gilbert, Dave/*Plymouth-Shiloh Local Sch Dist*	273	173
Gilbert, Dave/*Plymouth-Shiloh Local Sch Dist*	273	173
Gilbert, Deborah/*Lynchburg-Clay Local Sch Dist*	37,69,77	103
Gilbert, Kathy/*Fairfield City School Dist*	34,58	21
Gilbert, Scott/*Miamisburg City School Dist*	2	151
Gilbride, James/*Cuyahoga Vly Career Ctr Voc SD*	67	45
Gill, Scott/*Dublin City School Dist*	76	69
Gill, Terry/*Wellston City School Dist*	67	108
Gille, Al/*Great Oaks Career Campuses*	7	89
Gille, Michele/*Eastland-Ffld Career Tech VSD*	76	70
Gillespie, Kathy/*Zane Trace Local School Dist*	36	176
Gillespie, Mary/*Ashtabula Co Ed Service Center*	2	11
Gilliam, Dan/*Elgin Local School Dist*	3	138
Gilliam, David/*Delaware Joint Voc Sch Dist*	60,79	59
Gillies, Cheryl/*Clearview Local School Dist*	4	123
Gillig, Janet/*Educational Serv Ctr-Ctl Ohio*	79,81	65
Gilliland, Jill/*North West Ohio Ed Service Ctr*	58	78
Gillison, Alesia/*Columbus City School Dist*	8,18	66
Gillispie, Eric/*Westfall Local School Dist*	3	163
Gillote, Wilma/*Union Scioto Local Sch Dist*	8,12,298	175
Gilmore, Deanna/*Hillsdale Local School Dist*	58	11
Gilroy, Breanna/*Forest Hills School Dist*	71	89
Gindlesberger, Jim/*Northwest Local School Dist*	67	187
Ginetti, A J/*Youngstown City School Dist*	19	136
Gingerich, Galen/*Tipp City Exempted Village SD*	8,11,58,68,88,273,296,298	146
Ginise, Russell/*Granville Exempted Village SD*	67	117
Ginther, Megan/*Goshen Local School Dist*	280	30
Gioffredo, Amelia/*Amherst Exempted Village SD*	2	122
Giovannelli, Jeanna/*Granville Exempted Village SD*	81	117
Gissel, Jeanne/*Diocese of Columbus Ed Office*	68,71	76
Giuffre, Lisa/*Darke Co Ed Service Center*	59,77	55
Given, William/*New London Local School Dist*	67	106
Glacier, Stephanie/*Carrollton Exempted Village SD*	8	25
Gladden, John/*Cloverleaf Local School Dist*	71	140
Gladieux, Allan/*Archbold Area Local Sch Dist*	6	78
Glandon, Susan/*Adena Local School Dist*	37,69	174
Glasgow, Philip/*Fairless Local School Dist*	38	185
Glasner, David, Dr/*Shaker Heights City Sch Dist*	1	50
Glass, Guerdie/*Westerville City School Dist*	59	74
Glass, Rachel/*Mercer Co Ed Service Center*	77	143
Gleason, Tim/*Weathersfield Local Sch Dist*	67	201
Gleichauf, Mark/*Brooklyn City School Dist*	1	41
Glesenkamp, Steve/*Delaware City School Dist*	6	58
Glesser, Andrea/*Perrysburg Exempted Village SD*	58	218
Glick, Kim/*Logan Elm Local School Dist*	16,82	162
Gluth, Jan/*Port Clinton City School Dist*	70,76,79	159
Gnap, Kelly/*Wadsworth City School Dist*	4	141
Gnezda, Victoria/*Worthington School Dist*	71	75
Godby, Angie/*Lynchburg-Clay Local Sch Dist*	8	103
Godfrey, Rich/*Preble-Shawnee Local Sch Dist*	36	168
Goecke, John/*Spencerville Local School Dist*	67	9
Goecke, William/*Putnam Co Ed Service Center*	67	169
Goedde, Sarah/*Continental Local School Dist*	4	169
Goggin, Scott/*Westlake City School Dist*	1	51
Gogolski, Jeanne/*Upper Arlington City Sch Dist*	27,31	74
Goings, Jason/*Ashland City School Dist*	6	10
Goins, Teresa/*Fairbanks Local School Dist*	8	204
Gold, Bob/*Fairlawn Local School Dist*	67	182
Goldberger, Eli/*Bexley City School Dist*	6	66
Goldsberry, Kim/*Athens City School Dist*	67	14
Goldschmidt, Ryan/*Ft Loramie Local School Dist*	28	182
Golec, Scott/*Claymont City School Dist*	1	201
Golen, Julie/*Versailles Exempted Village SD*	57	56
Golinar, Tom/*Mariemont City School Dist*	2,11,19	90
Gollinar, Kelley/*Auburn Vocational School Dist*	294	112
Gomps, Matt/*Mt Gilead Exempted Village SD*	27	155
Gonda, Terry/*Little Miami Local School Dist*	2,19	208
Gonterman, Debbie/*Riverside Local School Dist*	36,83,88	121
Gonzales, Lisa/*Madison Local School Dist*	11,296,298	172
Gonzalez, Eric/*Campbell City School Dist*	73	134
Gonzalez, Jose/*Cleveland Metro School Dist*	57,89	42
Gonzalez, Kelly/*Avon Local School Dist*	16	122
Good, Larry/*Muskingum Valley ESC*	67	156
Goodill, Michael/*Cleveland Metro School Dist*	297	42
Gooding, Gene/*Covington Exempted Village SD*	1	145
Gooding, Scott/*Columbus City School Dist*	2	66
Goodman, Justin/*Wilmington City School Dist*	37	33
Goodney, Tom/*Educational Serv Ctr-Ctl Ohio*	1	65
Goodson, Ron/*Clay Local School Dist*	11,52,55	178
Goodwin, Eric/*Coldwater Exempted Village SD*	6	143
Goodwin, Jeff/*Edison Local Schools District*	88	60
Goodwin, Tresa/*Medina Co Joint Voc Sch Dist*	26,273	141
Goosey, Becky/*Hamilton City School Dist*	5	22
Goosland, Christy/*Gibsonburg Exempted Village SD*	73	177
Gorbandt, Cinde/*Hamilton City School Dist*	4	22
Gordillo, Christine/*Lakewood City School Dist*	71	47
Gordon, Eric/*Cleveland Metro School Dist*	1	42
Gordon, Jeffrey/*Olentangy Local School Dist*	2	59
Gordon, Ted/*Black River Local School Dist*	6	139
Gorius, Michele/*North Fork Local School Dist*	11,35,83,85	119
Gorman, Kevin, Dr/*Upper Arlington City Sch Dist*	11,58,77,88,275,296	74
Gorman, Robert/*Parma City School Dist*	4	49
Gorrell, Annette/*Loudonville-Perrysville SD*	12,34,296	11
Gorski, Dennise/*Boardman Local School Dist*	6	134
Gorsuch, Amy/*Fayette Local Sch Dist*	4	79
Goss, Shannon/*Olmsted Falls City School Dist*	11,54,58,77,79,81,92,296	48
Gossett, Debbie/*Miami Valley Career Tech VSD*	2	151
Gottfried, Jeffrey/*Clear Fork Vly Local Sch Dist*	6	171
Goubeaux, Michael/*Versailles Exempted Village SD*	73,286,295	56
Gough, Tim/*Bath Local School Dist*	286	8
Gould, Dawn/*Kings Local School Dist*	71	207
Gould, Felisha/*Cleveland Hts-Univ Hts City SD*	15,57,74,288	42
Gozur, Richard/*Campbell City School Dist*	31	134
Graber, Deb/*Pettisville Local School Dist*	5	79
Graboski, Kim/*Upper Sandusky Exempted Vlg SD*	5	219
Grabowski, John/*Champion Local School Dist*	1	197

#		#		#		#		#	
1	Superintendent	16	Instructional Media Svcs	30	Adult Education	44	Science Sec	58	Special Education K-12
2	Bus/Finance/Purchasing	17	Chief Operations Officer	31	Career/Sch-to-Work K-12	45	Math K-12	59	Special Education Elem
3	Buildings And Grounds	18	Chief Academic Officer	32	Career/Sch-to-Work Elem	46	Math Elem	60	Special Education Sec
4	Food Service	19	Chief Financial Officer	33	Career/Sch-to-Work Sec	47	Math Sec	61	Foreign/World Lang K-12
5	Transportation	20	Art K-12	34	Early Childhood Ed	48	English/Lang Arts K-12	62	Foreign/World Lang Elem
6	Athletic	21	Art Elem	35	Health/Phys Education	49	English/Lang Arts Elem	63	Foreign/World Lang Sec
7	Health Services	22	Art Sec	36	Guidance Services K-12	50	English/Lang Arts Sec	64	Religious Education K-12
8	Curric/Instruct K-12	23	Music K-12	37	Guidance Services Elem	51	Reading K-12	65	Religious Education Elem
9	Curric/Instruct Elem	24	Music Elem	38	Guidance Services Sec	52	Reading Elem	66	Religious Education Sec
10	Curric/Instruct Sec	25	Music Sec	39	Social Studies K-12	53	Reading Sec	67	School Board President
11	Federal Program	26	Business Education	40	Social Studies Elem	54	Remedial Reading K-12	68	Teacher Personnel
12	Title I	27	Career & Tech Ed	41	Social Studies Sec	55	Remedial Reading Elem	69	Academic Assessment
13	Title V	28	Technology Education	42	Science K-12	56	Remedial Reading Sec	70	Research/Development
15	Asst Superintendent	29	Family/Consumer Science	43	Science Elem	57	Bilingual/ELL	71	Public Information

#		#		#	
72	Summer School	88	Alternative/At Risk	277	Remedial Math K-12
73	Instructional Tech	89	Multi-Cultural Curriculum	280	Literacy Coach
74	Inservice Training	90	Social Work	285	STEM
75	Marketing/Distributive	91	Safety/Security	286	Digital Learning
76	Info Systems	92	Magnet School	288	Common Core Standards
77	Psychological Assess	93	Parental Involvement	294	Accountability
78	Affirmative Action	95	Tech Prep Program	295	Network System
79	Student Personnel	96	Chief Information Officer	296	Title II Programs
80	Driver Ed/Safety	97	Chief Technology Officer	297	Webmaster
81	Gifted/Talented	98	Chief Technology Officer	298	Grant Writer/Ptnrships
82	Video Services	270	Character Education	750	Chief Innovation Officer
83	Substance Abuse Prev	271	Migrant Education	751	Chief of Staff
84	Erate	273	Teacher Mentor	752	Social Emotional Learning
85	AIDS Education	274	Before/After Sch		
		275	Response To Intervention		

OH-T20

Ohio School Directory

DISTRICT PERSONNEL INDEX

NAME/District	JOB FUNCTIONS	PAGE
Grad, Alex/*Field Local School Dist*	73	165
Graft, Jon/*Butler Tech Career Dev Schs*	1	21
Graham, Alicia/*Edon Northwest Local Sch Dist*	36,69,83,88	215
Graham, Bill/*Sandy Valley Local School Dist*	286	189
Graham, Jeffery, Dr/*Canton City School Dist*	1	184
Graham, Jim/*West Branch Local School Dist*	73,76	136
Graham, Kevin/*Northwestern Local School Dist*	73	27
Grahl, Drew/*Margaretta Local School Dist*	6	61
Graler, Mark/*Lebanon City School Dist*	8,11,83,88,288,294,298	207
Gram, Lashawn/*Dayton Public School Dist*	11	149
Granatir, Rachael/*Edison Local School Dist*	73,84	109
Grandstaff, Randall/*Norwood City School Dist*	295	92
Grandy, Kirk/*Berne Union Local School Dist*	2	63
Granger, A/*Liberty-Benton Local Sch Dist*	67	98
Grant, Todd/*New Boston Local School Dist*	3,5	178
Grantier, Claire/*Sandusky City School Dist*	73,295	61
Grashel, Mark/*Huntington Local School Dist*	73,295	175
Grasty, Andrew/*Greenville City School Dist*	5	55
Gratz, Stacy/*Upper Scioto Valley Local SD*	2	100
Grau, Jacob/*Bucyrus City School Dist*	3	38
Grau, Luke/*Dalton Local School Dist*	31,38,69,83	212
Graves, Barbara/*North College Hill City SD*	67	91
Graves, Karen/*Crestwood Local School Dist*	38	165
Graves, Kristi, Dr/*North Ctrl Ohio Ed Service Ctr*	8	180
Graves, Kristie/*Mohawk Local School Dist*	288	219
Gray, Angela/*Southern Hills Joint Voc SD*	38	20
Gray, Bradley/*Tri-Village Local Sch Dist*	6	56
Gray, Dave/*Cambridge City School Dist*	6	86
Gray, Mike/*Darke Co Ed Service Center*	1	55
Gray, Mike/*Preble Co Ed Service Center*	1	168
Gray, Quincey/*Greenfield Exempted Village SD*	1	103
Gray, Rodney/*Cambridge City School Dist*	36	86
Gray, Thomas/*Dayton Public School Dist*	5	149
Grdic, Liz/*Austintown Local School Dist*	7	133
Greathouse, Brian/*Neomin-NE Ohio Mgmt Info NET*	1	201
Green, Brett/*Liberty Center Local Sch Dist*	286	101
Green, Christie/*Newcomerstown Exempted Vlg SD*	2	203
Green, Debra/*Sebring Local School Dist*	67	135
Green, Erin/*Strongsville City School Dist*	8,11,57,69,81,288,296,298	51
Green, Jennifer/*Plymouth-Shiloh Local Sch Dist*	8	173
Green, Karen/*Mt Healthy City School Dist*	68	91
Green, Karla/*Graham Local School Dist*	85	26
Green, Lance/*Copley-Fairlawn City Sch Dist*	73	192
Green, Laurie/*Preble-Shawnee Local Sch Dist*	2,19	168
Green, Linda/*Gahanna-Jefferson Public SD*	4	70
Green, Penny/*Valley View Local School Dist*	16	153
Green, Tricia/*Carrollton Exempted Village SD*	58,275	25
Greenawalt, Mike/*United Local School Dist*	5	36
Greene, Casey/*Lebanon City School Dist*	73,295	207
Greene, Ce/*Mechanicsburg Exempted Vlg SD*	58	26
Greene, Glenda/*Clermont Northeastern Local SD*	11,58	30
Greene, William/*Parma City School Dist*	3,17	49
Greenich, Katherine/*Knox Co Voc School Dist*	1	111
Greenleigh, Jeffrey/*Belpre City School Dist*	11	209
Greenley, Jeffery/*Belpre City School Dist*	1	209
Greenslade, Ryan/*Clyde-Green Spgs Exmpt Vlg SD*	6	176
Greenwald, Jordan/*North Canton City School Dist*	67	187
Greer, Julie/*Riverdale Local School Dist*	9,11	98
Greer, Katie/*Hillsboro City School Dist*	7	103
Greg, Lindsey/*Talawanda School Dist*	8,12,57,76,285,286,288	24
Gregg, Rachel/*Russia Local School Dist*	69	183
Gregory, Hal/*Oregon City School Dist*	1,11,57,83	128
Gregory, John/*Dalton Local School Dist*	6	212
Greiner, Peggy/*Akron Public Schools*	11,298	190
Grengbondai, Tya/*Cincinnati City School Dist*	11,298	87
Grennan, Paulette/*Wickliffe City School Dist*	5	114
Gress, Robert/*Stow-Munroe Falls City SD*	3,84,91	194
Gresta, Greg/*Steubenville City School Dist*	67	109
Greve, Jordan/*Arcanum Butler Local Sch Dist*	4	55
Grewe, Kimberly/*Anna Local School Dist*	57	182
Grezlik, Matt/*Conotton Valley Union Local SD*	91	101
Gribble, Rebecca/*Jackson Local School Dist*	8,12,81,273,280,294	186
Grice, Bobbie/*Warren Co Voc School Dist*	67	208
Grice, George/*Wheelersburg Local School Dist*	2	180
Grida, Salvatore/*Brunswick City School Dist*	2	140
Griesmer, Raquel/*Painesville City Local SD*	31,83	113

NAME/District	JOB FUNCTIONS	PAGE
Griffin, Steven/*Marysville Exempted Village SD*	8,54,69,277,280	204
Griffith, Eric/*Covington Exempted Village SD*	295	145
Griffith, Jim/*Van Buren Local School Dist*	67	99
Griffith, Randy/*Maplewood JT Voc School Dist*	1	166
Griffith, Todd/*Licking Heights Local Sch Dist*	2	118
Griffiths, Courtney/*Lorain Co Joint Voc Sch Dist*	69	125
Griggs, Sandra/*Wauseon Exempted Village SD*	67	80
Grigsby, Karen/*Madison Plains Local Sch Dist*	8,12,273,288	133
Grigsby, Kristina/*North Fork Local School Dist*	31	119
Grillot, Rob/*Ansonia Local School Dist*	3	55
Grills, Caleb/*Penta Co JT Voc School Dist*	73,76	217
Grimaldi, Lori/*Mogadore Local School Dist*	8	166
Grime, Jamison/*Montpelier Exempted Village SD*	1,11,288	215
Grime, Jennifer/*Wauseon Exempted Village SD*	58	79
Grime, Shawn/*Archbold Area Local Sch Dist*	69,88	78
Grimes, Jennifer/*Adams Co Ohio Valley Sch Dist*	27	6
Grimm, Terry/*State Support Team-Region 5*	73	137
Grimm, Todd/*Hamilton City School Dist*	6	22
Grimmept, Chuck/*Amherst Exempted Village SD*	3	122
Grimwood, Mike/*Pioneer Joint Voc School Dist*	3	173
Grinch, John/*Shadyside Local School Dist*	73	18
Grist, Michael/*Lexington Local School Dist*	6	172
Groden, Terry/*North Olmsted City School Dist*	67	48
Groman, Cindy/*New Richmond Exempted Vlg SD*	77	31
Gronow, Sue/*Louisville City School Dist*	7	186
Groob, Jaime/*Groveport Madison Local SD*	3,91	71
Grooms, Doug/*Van Wert City School Dist*	57,58,69,83	205
Grooms, Greg/*Adams Co Ohio Valley Sch Dist*	68,78,79	6
Grooms, Wayne/*Western Local School Dist*	3	164
Gross, Dj/*Windham Exempted Vlg Sch Dist*	6	167
Gross, Renae/*Carrollton Exempted Village SD*	31,38	25
Gross, Rosemarie/*Parma City School Dist*	274	49
Gross, Sherri/*Windham Exempted Vlg Sch Dist*	9,11,73	167
Grosse, Jeff/*Berea City School Dist*	2	41
Grosse, Jeff/*Shaker Heights City Sch Dist*	17	50
Groszek, Sue/*Mayfield City School Dist*	67	47
Grothause, Dan/*St Mary's City School Dist*	5,91	16
Grove, Wendy, Dr/*Ohio Department of Education*	34	1
Grubb, Cale/*Fredericktown Local Sch Dist*	5	111
Grubb, Debbie/*Zanesville City School Dist*	274	157
Grubb, Jeannie/*Groveport Madison Local SD*	274	71
Grubbs, Jim/*Galion City School Dist*	1	38
Grube, Jamie/*Meta Solutions*	1	78
Grube, Laurie/*Milton-Union Exempted Vlg SD*	11,58	145
Gruve, Tanne/*Logan Elm Local School Dist*	37	162
Guarnieri, Reed/*Kenston Local School Dist*	6	82
Guckert, Susan/*Kings Local School Dist*	274	207
Gudorf, Katie/*Celina City School Dist*	48,51	143
Guerin, Liz/*Benton-Carroll-Salem Local SD*	273	158
Guernsey, Thomas, Dr/*Fostoria City School Dist*	67	180
Guilkey, Crystal/*Western Local School Dist*	31,38,69	164
Guillozet, Kailey/*St Henry Cons Local Sch Dist*	38	144
Guimond, Richard/*Athens City School Dist*	6	14
Guinther, Meg/*Southern Local School Dist*	273,280	143
Gummel, John/*Greenon Local School Dist*	4	27
Gummere, Sally/*Granville Exempted Village SD*	16,82	117
Gummere, Trevor/*London City School Dist*	2	132
Gumnere, Trevor/*Stow-Munroe Falls City SD*	2	194
Gunderson, Steve/*Athens City School Dist*	73,84,295	14
Gundler, Alice/*Three Rivers Local School Dist*	2	94
Gundolf, Andy/*Northwestern Local School Dist*	67	27
Gunkleman, Barbara/*Buckeye Local School Dist*	67	140
Gupta, Neil, Dr/*Worthington School Dist*	10	75
Gurka, Greg/*North Royalton City Sch Dist*	1	48
Gurtsak, Maridi/*Olmsted Falls City School Dist*	36	48
Guse, Karen/*Heath City School Dist*	4	117
Guss, Chris/*Perkins Local School Dist*	58	61
Gussler, Angela/*Northern Local School Dist*	8,273,285,288	161
Gustin, Amy/*Miami Trace Local School Dist*	73,295	65
Gutierrez, Christine/*Tri-Village Local Sch Dist*	285	56
Gutridge, Matt/*Northern Local School Dist*	286	161
Guy, Jennifer/*Felicity-Franklin Local SD*	296	30
Guy, Krista/*Fairborn City School Dist*	16	84
Gwin, Curt/*Tallmadge City School Dist*	73	194
Gwinn, Lisa/*Southeast Local School Dist*	57	213

School Year 2019-2020   800-333-8802   **OH-T21**

DISTRICT PERSONNEL INDEX

Market Data Retrieval

NAME/District	JOB FUNCTIONS	PAGE
H		
Haag, Jack/*West Carrollton City Sch Dist*	2,3,91	153
Haas, Heidi/*Wooster City School Dist*	8,11,58,79,88	213
Haas, Randy/*Little Miami Local School Dist*	67	208
Habegger, Shelly/*Barberton City School Dist*	8,11,54,69,296,298	192
Hack, Tom/*Cardington-Lincoln Local SD*	6	155
Hacker, Jim/*North West Ohio Ed Service Ctr*	2	78
Haddad, Luann/*Salem City School Dist*	67	35
Hadden, Patricia/*Deer Park Cmty School Dist*	79	89
Hadsell, Sandy/*Norwayne Local School Dist*	2	212
Hafer, Brian/*Northwest Local School Dist*	76	91
Haffa, James/*Riverside Local School Dist*	5	114
Haffey, Susan/*Wickliffe City School Dist*	2,73	114
Hafner, Randall/*Northwestern Local School Dist*	6	212
Haft, Dennis/*Clyde-Green Spgs Exmpt Vlg SD*	1	176
Hagans, Danette/*Valley Local School Dist*	77	179
Hageman, Ben/*Oak Hills Local School Dist*	6	92
Hageman, Ben/*Oak Hills Local School Dist*	6	92
Hageman, Randy/*Teays Valley Local School Dist*	6	162
Hageman, Tina/*Miamisburg City School Dist*	2,19,294	151
Haines, Doug/*Louisville City School Dist*	5	186
Haines, Ruth/*Painesville City Local SD*	57,271	113
Hajjar, Nick/*North Union Local School Dist*	6,69	204
Hakel, Susan/*U S Grant Career Dev Schs*	60	31
Halasa, Katrina/*Akron Public Schools*	35,42	190
Halco, Diana/*St Mary's City School Dist*	7,85	16
Hale, Brenda/*Arcanum Butler Local Sch Dist*	2	55
Hale, Cindy/*Miami Co Ed Service Center*	2	144
Hale, Nathan/*Lancaster City School Dist*	68	63
Hale, Traci/*Oakwood City School Dist*	71	152
Haley, Tom/*Pleasant Local School Dist*	5	138
Halker, Colleen/*Ottawa-Glandorf Local Sch Dist*	4	170
Hall, Aimee/*Wheelersburg Local School Dist*	37,58,69	180
Hall, Bradley/*Bellefontaine City School Dist*	1	121
Hall, Brian/*Greene Co Voc School Dist*	73,84	84
Hall, David, Dr/*Oberlin City School Dist*	1	125
Hall, Dorinda/*Lorain City School Dist*	58	124
Hall, Holly/*Claymont City School Dist*	58,81,88	201
Hall, Jason/*Osnaburg Local School Dist*	73	188
Hall, Jona, Dr/*Marietta City School Dist*	8,11,31,38,286,296	210
Hall, Kathleen/*Margaretta Local School Dist*	58,77,275	61
Hall, Lori/*New Philadelphia City Sch Dist*	57	203
Hall, Mariah/*Sheffield-Sheffield Lake CSD*	58,77,88,275	125
Hall, Richard, Dr/*Mideast Career & Tech Ctrs*	1	157
Hall, Sharon/*Tallmadge City School Dist*	81	194
Hall, Susan/*Holgate Local School Dist*	274	101
Hall, Tammy/*Delaware Joint Voc Sch Dist*	11,288,298	59
Hallas, Howard/*Poland Local School Dist*	3	135
Hallett, Kaycee/*Mohawk Local School Dist*	16	219
Halley, Kimberly/*Reynoldsburg City School Dist*	15	72
Halley, Robin/*Teays Valley Local School Dist*	1	162
Halley, Rochelle/*Gallia Co Local School Dist*	8,16,51,68,74	80
Halley, Wendy/*Gallia Co Local School Dist*	58,88,275	80
Halley, Wendy/*Gallia-Vinton Ed Svc Center*	58,74	80
Halliburton, Betty/*Lorain Co Joint Voc Sch Dist*	71	125
Halls, Mark/*Western Reserve Local Sch Dist*	67	136
Halsey, Brett/*Hardin Northern Local Sch Dist*	288	100
Halstead, Sam/*East Liverpool City Sch Dist*	3,91	34
Ham, Andy/*Napoleon Area City School Dist*	6	101
Hamady, Chris/*Anthony Wayne Local Sch Dist*	73	127
Hamberg, Angie/*Big Walnut Local School Dist*	1,11	58
Hamelic, James/*Strongsville City School Dist*	84	51
Hamilton, Bill/*Northwood Local School Dist*	83,88	217
Hamilton, Carol/*New Albany-Plain Local SD*	4	72
Hamilton, Dustin/*Springfield Local School Dist*	3,91	128
Hamilton, Jeri/*Brookfield Local School Dist*	58	197
Hamilton, Kip/*Butler Tech Career Dev Schs*	286	21

NAME/District	JOB FUNCTIONS	PAGE
Hamilton, Kirt/*Marlington Local School Dist*	41	186
Hamilton, Melinda/*Springfield Local School Dist*	91	194
Hamilton, Mindy/*Fairfield Local Sch Dist*	11,58,288	102
Hamilton, Nicholas/*Mississinawa Valley Sch Dist*	2	56
Hamilton, Nick/*Ansonia Local School Dist*	2	55
Hamilton, Nick/*Newton Local School Dist*	2	146
Hamilton, Samantha/*New Boston Local School Dist*	2,79	178
Hamilton, Shirley, Dr/*New Albany-Plain Local SD*	8	72
Hamler, Brian/*Whitehall City School Dist*	1	75
Hamlin, Pam/*Findlay City School Dist*	34	97
Hamm, Eric/*Bellefontaine City School Dist*	36	121
Hamm, Mike/*Tuslaw Local School Dist*	58	189
Hamman, Doug/*Plymouth-Shiloh Local Sch Dist*	67	173
Hamman, Tim/*Mentor Exempted Village SD*	15	113
Hammock, Quentin/*Carlisle Local School Dist*	82	206
Hammond, Aaron/*Miami Trace Local School Dist*	6	65
Hammond, Richard/*Canfield Local School Dist*	5	134
Hammond, Steve/*Galion City School Dist*	76,295	38
Hammond, Tirzah/*Southwest Licking Local SD*	7,85	120
Hampton, Will/*Marietta City School Dist*	1	210
Hamrick, Curtis/*Parkway Local School Dist*	30	144
Hamrick, Lisa/*South-Western City School Dist*	4	73
Hamstra, John/*Southwest Local School Dist*	1	93
Hanahs, Angela/*Barnesville Exempted Vlg SD*	1	17
Hanak, William/*North Central Local Sch Dist*	1	215
Hancock, Robert/*Hamilton City School Dist*	2	21
Hange, Andrew/*Pike-Delta-York Local Sch Dist*	6	79
Hange, Connie/*Black River Local School Dist*	2,84	139
Hangenbush, Stephanie/*Norton City School Dist*	2	193
Hanger, Tammy/*Ohio Valley Ed Service Center*	93	85
Hanifan, Susan/*Evergreen Local School Dist*	27	78
Hanke, Chris/*Garfield Heights City SD*	1	46
Hankins, Dave/*Riverdale Local School Dist*	5	98
Hankinson, Jason/*Licking Co Ed Service Center*	8,68	117
Hanlon, Michael, Dr/*Chardon Local School Dist*	1,11	82
Hanna, Erin/*Cleveland Hts-Univ Hts City SD*	58,273	42
Hanna, Stephanie/*Monroeville Local School Dist*	2	105
Hannah, Alex/*Bluffton Exempted Village Sch*	6	8
Hanning, David/*Federal Hocking Local Sch Dist*	1	14
Hansel, Nicholas/*Franklin Local School Dist*	73,76,84,295	156
Hanshaw, Michael/*Trumbull Co Ed Service Center*	1	196
Hanson, Heather/*Belmont-Harrison Voc Sch Dist*	10,68	18
Hanson, Jackie/*Southern Hills Joint Voc SD*	7,85	20
Hanson, Kurt/*Urbana City School Dist*	73	26
Hanstine, Lauren/*Conotton Valley Union Local SD*	58	100
Hanus, Kathy/*Garfield Heights City SD*	2	46
Harbaugh, Angela/*Lake Local School Dist*	9	186
Harbaugh, Jonathan/*Granville Exempted Village SD*	4	117
Harcarik, Sue/*Warren City School Dist*	4	200
Hardaman, Sharon/*Minford Local School Dist*	4	178
Harden, Jennifer/*Riverside Local School Dist*	67	114
Harden, Mark/*Sycamore Cmty School Dist*	6	93
Hardesty, Cyndi/*Archdiocese Cincinnati Ed Off*	15,45	94
Hardesty, Sheryl/*Garaway Local School Dist*	2	202
Hardin, Josh/*Cincinnati City School Dist*	6	87
Harding, Micah/*Northmont City School Dist*	6	152
Harding, Roxane/*Harrison Hills City Sch Dist*	2,298	101
Hardis, Robert, Dr/*Beachwood City School Dist*	1	40
Hardy, David/*Lorain City School Dist*	1	124
Hardy, Matt/*East Guernsey Local Sch Dist*	73	86
Hare, Edward/*Piqua City School Dist*	6	146
Haren, Justin/*Louisville City School Dist*	11,58,296	186
Harkabus, Milajean/*Labrae Local School Dist*	12,73,271	198
Harkness, Greg/*Bridgeport School Dist*	6	18
Harless, Kim/*Jackson City School Dist*	67	107
Harley, Lisa/*Valley Local School Dist*	58	179
Harmeling, Natalie/*Wilmington City School Dist*	31,58,81,83,93	33

1 Superintendent	16 Instructional Media Svcs	30 Adult Education	44 Science Sec	58 Special Education K-12	72 Summer School	88 Alternative/At Risk	277 Remedial Math K-12
2 Bus/Finance/Purchasing	17 Chief Operations Officer	31 Career/Sch-to-Work K-12	45 Math K-12	59 Special Education Elem	73 Instructional Tech	89 Multi-Cultural Curriculum	280 Literacy Coach
3 Buildings And Grounds	18 Chief Academic Officer	32 Career/Sch-to-Work Elem	46 Math Elem	60 Special Education Sec	74 Inservice Training	90 Social Work	285 STEM
4 Food Service	19 Chief Financial Officer	33 Career/Sch-to-Work Sec	47 Math Sec	61 Foreign/World Lang K-12	75 Marketing/Distributive	91 Safety/Security	286 Digital Learning
5 Transportation	20 Art K-12	34 Early Childhood Ed	48 English/Lang Arts K-12	62 Foreign/World Lang Elem	76 Info Systems	92 Magnet School	288 Common Core Standards
6 Athletic	21 Art Elem	35 Health/Phys Education	49 English/Lang Arts Elem	63 Foreign/World Lang Sec	77 Psychological Assess	93 Parental Involvement	294 Accountability
7 Health Services	22 Art Sec	36 Guidance Services K-12	50 English/Lang Arts Sec	64 Religious Education K-12	78 Affirmative Action	95 Tech Prep Program	295 Network System
8 Curric/Instruct K-12	23 Music K-12	37 Guidance Services Elem	51 Reading K-12	65 Religious Education Elem	79 Student Personnel	96 Title II Programs	296 Title II Programs
9 Curric/Instruct Elem	24 Music Elem	38 Guidance Services Sec	52 Reading Elem	66 Religious Education Sec	80 Driver Ed/Safety	98 Chief Technology Officer	297 Webmaster
10 Curric/Instruct Sec	25 Music Sec	39 Social Studies K-12	53 Reading Sec	67 School Board President	81 Gifted/Talented	270 Character Education	298 Grant Writer/Ptnrships
11 Federal Program	26 Business Education	40 Social Studies Elem	54 Remedial Reading K-12	68 Teacher Personnel	82 Video Services	271 Migrant Education	750 Chief Innovation Officer
12 Title I	27 Career & Tech Ed	41 Social Studies Sec	55 Remedial Reading Elem	69 Academic Assessment	83 Substance Abuse Prev	273 Teacher Mentor	751 Chief of Staff
13 Title V	28 Technology Education	42 Science K-12	56 Remedial Reading Sec	70 Research/Development	84 Erate	274 Before/After Sch	752 Social Emotional Learning
15 Asst Superintendent	29 Family/Consumer Science	43 Science Elem	57 Bilingual/ELL	71 Public Information	85 AIDS Education	275 Response To Intervention	

OH-T22

Ohio School Directory — DISTRICT PERSONNEL INDEX

NAME/District	JOB FUNCTIONS	PAGE
Harmon, David/*Benjamin Logan Local Sch Dist*	1	121
Harmon, Eva/*Ontario Local School Dist*	4	173
Harmon, Todd/*Paulding Exempted Village SD*	8	160
Harms, Andrew/*Canton Local School Dist*	6	185
Harner, Melissa/*Deer Park Cmty School Dist*	2	89
Harper, Bobbie Jo/*Vinton Co Local School Dist*	4	206
Harper, David/*Jefferson Local School Dist*	67	132
Harper, Kathy/*Greene Co Ed Service Center*	8,11,15,34	83
Harper, Kathy/*Greeneview Local School Dist*	34	84
Harper, Mark/*Champion Local School Dist*	3,4,5	197
Harper, Mark/*Rock Hill Local School Dist*	67	116
Harpring, Rita/*Edison Local Schools District*	5	60
Harr, Linda/*West Liberty-Salem Local SD*	5	26
Harr, Tammy/*Northeastern Local School Dist*	31	57
Harrell, Kevin/*East Cleveland City Sch Dist*	68	45
Harrington, Pamela/*Perrysburg Exempted Village SD*	2	218
Harrington, Susan/*Put-In-Bay Local School Dist*	35,85	159
Harrington, Tom/*Buckeye Local School Dist*	6	140
Harris, Abby/*Meigs Local School Dist*	38	142
Harris, Apollos, Dr/*Mt Healthy City School Dist*	7,58,79,88	91
Harris, Buddy/*Ohio Department of Education*	285	1
Harris, Dean/*Meigs Local School Dist*	5	142
Harris, E/*Logan-Hocking Local Sch Dist*	3,91	104
Harris, Kara/*Franklin Local School Dist*	6,88	156
Harris, Obadiah/*Chillicothe City School Dist*	83,88	174
Harris, Scott/*Lakewood Local School Dist*	6	118
Harris, Tom/*Warren Co Voc School Dist*	30	208
Harris, William/*Dayton Public School Dist*	67	149
Harrison, Brady/*Dawson-Bryant Local Sch Dist*	67	115
Harrison, Jenny/*Berkshire Local School Dist*	4	81
Harrison, Rhonda/*Oak Hill Union Local Sch Dist*	2,11,19,84	107
Harrison, Ted/*West Muskingum Local Sch Dist*	73,295	157
Harrod, Rose/*St Henry Cons Local Sch Dist*	16	144
Harstel, Daniel/*Genoa Area Local School Dist*	6	159
Hart, Brian/*Hilliard City School Dist*	34	71
Hart, Deborah/*Highland Local School Dist*	4	155
Hart, Doug/*Northridge Local School Dist*	67	119
Hart, Richard/*Minerva Local School Dist*	83,85	187
Hartings, Michelle/*Versailles Exempted Village SD*	37	56
Hartings, Sandy/*Coldwater Exempted Village SD*	8,11,57,58,69	143
Hartley, Brandon/*Vandalia Butler City Sch Dist*	8,13,31,34,69,273,288,298	153
Hartley, Scott/*North Fork Local School Dist*	1	119
Hartman, Brian/*South Range Local School Dist*	91	135
Hartman, Holly/*Licking Co Ed Service Center*	81	117
Hartman, Holly/*North Fork Local School Dist*	81	119
Hartman, Jean/*Bridgeport School Dist*	77	18
Hartman, Kerry/*Maysville Local School Dist*	67	157
Hartman, Philip/*Southeastern Local Sch Dist*	2,84	175
Hartmann, Jeff, Dr/*Stow-Munroe Falls City SD*	72	194
Hartsel, Julie/*West Liberty-Salem Local SD*	58,275	26
Hartzell, Wendy/*Warren City School Dist*	15	200
Harvey, Angie/*Anna Local School Dist*	4	182
Harvey, Curt/*Pymatuning Valley Local SD*	67	13
Harvey, Jesse/*Southern Local School Dist*	295	161
Harvey, Kimberly/*West Carrollton City Sch Dist*	76	153
Harvey, Randy/*Ontario Local School Dist*	2,11	173
Harvey, Scott/*Shelby City School Dist*	3,91	173
Harwell, John/*Ohio Mid-Eastern RESA*	67	110
Haselman, Ted/*Pike-Delta-York Local Sch Dist*	1	79
Haselman, Wade/*Swanton Local School Dist*	6	79
Hassan, Toni/*McComb Local School Dist*	285	98
Hasselbach, Jordan/*Clyde-Green Spgs Exmpt Vlg SD*	73,76,295	176
Hasselbach, Robin/*Bellevue City School Dist*	31	105
Hastings, Tina/*Woodridge Local School Dist*	4	195
Haswell, John/*Shadyside Local School Dist*	1	18
Hatch, Audra/*Columbiana Exempted Village SD*	81	34
Hatcher, Derek/*James A Garfield Local SD*	10,73	165
Hatcher, Tamiko/*Akron Public Schools*	11	190
Hatert, Jack/*Yellow Springs Exempted Vlg SD*	10,83,88	85
Hatfield, Brendan/*Blanchester Local School Dist*	16,73,295	32
Hatfield, Craig/*Lakota Local School Dist*	4	22
Hathaway, Jason/*Northwest Local School Dist*	6,83	187
Hatley, Connie/*Centerburg Local School Dist*	11,58,83,88,275,296	110
Hatmaker, Anthony/*Ed Svc Center of Medina Co*	2	139
Hattery, Brennon/*Bethel Local School Dist*	2	145
Hatton, Andrew/*Dublin City School Dist*	285	69
Hatton, Andrew/*Upper Arlington City Sch Dist*	83	74
Haubert, Krista/*Portage Lakes Joint Voc SD*	71	189
Haughn, Shawn/*Bloom-Carroll Local Sch Dist*	1	63
Haught, Kevin/*Arlington Local School Dist*	1,11,83,288	97
Haupt, Kevin/*Lorain City School Dist*	3	124
Hause, Alida/*Liberty-Benton Local Sch Dist*	16	98
Hauser, Emily/*Madeira City School Dist*	2	90
Hauser, Emily/*St Bernard-Elmwood Place Schs*	2	93
Haushalter, Joan/*Bellefontaine City School Dist*	67	121
Hausknecht, Sheila/*Cory-Rawson Local School Dist*	2	97
Hausmann, Dave/*Whitehall City School Dist*	3,5,16,73,76,82,91,295	75
Hausmann, Jodi/*Bay Village City School Dist*	1	40
Havalotti, Sean/*Wayne Co Joint Voc School Dist*	3	213
Havert, Jodie/*Wilmington City School Dist*	4	33
Hawk, Aaron/*Minerva Local School Dist*	3	187
Hawk, Kim/*Ridgemont Local School Dist*	31	100
Hawk, Randy/*Clyde-Green Spgs Exmpt Vlg SD*	3,91	176
Hawk, Richard/*Lynchburg-Clay Local Sch Dist*	2,84	103
Hawk, Ryan/*Valley Local School Dist*	73,295	179
Hawk, Tammy/*Athens City School Dist*	16,73,95,297	14
Hawkins, Andrew/*Rootstown Local School Dist*	1	166
Hawkins, Valerie/*Princeton City School Dist*	78	92
Hawks, Chip/*Kent City School Dist*	285	165
Hawley, Michael/*Mideast Career & Tech Ctrs*	30	157
Hay, Cindy/*Dover City School Dist*	73,295	202
Hayden, Kim/*U S Grant Career School Dist*	67	31
Hayes, Bill/*Greeneview Local School Dist*	12	84
Hayes, Bob/*Clay Local School Dist*	36,83,88	178
Hayes, Corinne/*Southwest Local School Dist*	8,15,69,74,275	93
Hayes, Eric/*New Miami Local School Dist*	6	23
Hayes, Roni/*Fairland Local School Dist*	1,11,73,84	116
Hayes, Sara/*Liberty Union-Thurstn Sch Dist*	58	64
Hayes, Shannon/*Valley View Local School Dist*	37	153
Hayles, Robert/*Warrensville Heights City SD*	3	51
Haynes, Jessica/*Ravenna School Dist*	58,77,83,88,90	166
Healey, Rick/*Williamsburg Local School Dist*	6	32
Heard, Terry/*Woodridge Local School Dist*	5	195
Hearing, Kim/*Crooksville Exempted Vlg SD*	58	161
Hearn, Michael/*Fairless Local School Dist*	8,11	185
Heasley, Erin/*Columbiana Exempted Village SD*	6	34
Heater, Heather/*Canton City School Dist*	73	184
Heath, Craig/*Dublin City School Dist*	10	69
Heath, Kirk/*Alliance City School Dist*	2	184
Hebenthal, Mike/*Centerburg Local School Dist*	1	110
Heckman, John/*Solon City School Dist*	67	50
Hedderick, Christine/*Wellston City School Dist*	33,38	108
Hedger, Sheryll/*Tri-Village Local Sch Dist*	4,7	56
Hedrick, Jim/*Brunswick City School Dist*	5	140
Heflinger, David/*Field Local School Dist*	1	165
Hefner, Jennie/*Shawnee Local School Dist*	11,57,58,83,296,298	9
Hegedish, Ben/*Independence Local School Dist*	1	46
Heiby, Lori/*Wayne Trace Local School Dist*	27	160
Heid, Lisa/*Miami Co Ed Service Center*	58	144
Heidenreich, Erich/*Piqua City School Dist*	73,76,295	146
Heidenreich, Krista/*Lakota Local School Dist*	286	22
Heikkinen, Rebecca, Dr/*Canfield Local School Dist*	36,83,270	134
Heilers, Sarah/*Anna Local School Dist*	27	182
Heilman, Corey/*St Clairsville-Richland CSD*	77	18
Heilman, Jason/*Marion City School Dist*	5	138
Heilman, Marsha/*Four-Co Joint Voc School Dist*	4	79
Heimlich, Shawn/*Dublin City School Dist*	79	69
Heinerman, Cindy/*Toronto City School Dist*	8,11,58,83,85,288,296	109
Heinl, Matt/*Warrensville Heights City SD*	4	51
Heinlen, Elizabeth/*Wynford Local School Dist*	36	39
Heins, Lisa/*Circleville City School Dist*	8,81	162
Heinsbergen, Karen/*Cleveland Hts-Univ Hts City SD*	280	42
Heinz, Alex/*Norwood City School Dist*	6	92
Heise, Perry/*Allen East Local School Dist*	3,5	7
Heistan, Jeff/*Shawnee Local School Dist*	73	9
Heitkamp, Jennifer/*New Knoxville Local Sch Dist*	36	16
Heitman, Lee/*South Euclid-Lyndhurst City SD*	5	51
Hejduk, Terry/*Grand Valley Local School Dist*	3,6	13
Helentjaris, Marcia/*Celina City School Dist*	31	143
Helfrich, Dana/*Hancock Co Ed Service Center*	16,73	97
Heller, Randy/*Ashland City School Dist*	3,91	10
Helmecamp, James/*London City School Dist*	3	132

DISTRICT PERSONNEL INDEX

Market Data Retrieval

NAME/District	JOB FUNCTIONS	PAGE
Helmick, Regina/Huber Heights City School Dist	2,19	150
Helms, David/Butler Tech Career Dev Schs	10	21
Helms, Vilma/Jefferson Twp Local Sch Dist	67	150
Helser, George/Northern Local School Dist	3	161
Helwagen, Bruce/St Bernard-Elmwood Place Schs	73,295	93
Hemmelgorn, Jon/Versailles Exempted Village SD	8,11	56
Hemminger, Andrew/Woodmore Local School Dist	31,38,88	159
Hemsley, Joseph/Jackson City School Dist	2,4,5,15,27,69,88	107
Hench, Beth/Ayersville Local School Dist	11,93	56
Henderly, Chad/Toledo Public Schools	76	129
Hendershott, Jeff/Wellston City School Dist	5,6	108
Henderson, Dustan/Franklin Local School Dist	8	156
Henderson, Kim/Licking Heights Local Sch Dist	68	118
Henderson, Matthew/Crestline Exempted Village SD	1	38
Henderson, Rachel/Western Local School Dist	6,270	164
Henderson, Tom, Dr/Centerville City School Dist	1	148
Hendricks, Homer/North Central Local Sch Dist	67	215
Hendricks, Homer/North West Ohio Ed Service Ctr	2	78
Hendricks, Richard/Leetonia Exempted Village SD	67	35
Hendrix, Christi/Southern Local School Dist	2	143
Henes, Katie/Avon Local School Dist	2	122
Hengstebeck, Judy/Gahanna-Jefferson Public SD	71	70
Henne, Todd/North Canton City School Dist	2,3	187
Hennison, Eric/Hillsboro City School Dist	73,98	103
Henrick, Sally/Ridgemont Local School Dist	1,11,57,83	100
Henry, Darren/Leipsic Local School Dist	9	170
Henry, Dennis/Greenon Local School Dist	67	27
Henry, Lauren/Brookville Local School Dist	285	148
Henry, Leslie/Gallia Co Local School Dist	69	80
Henry, Mike/Miami Trace Local School Dist	67	65
Henry, Ryan/Ft Frye Local School Dist	16,73,76,286,295	210
Henry, Shanel/Bellefontaine City School Dist	8,11,288,296,298	121
Henry, Sharon/Midview Local School Dist	4	125
Hensley, Annette/Botkins Local School Dist	4	182
Hensley, Mike/Colonel Crawford Local SD	3	38
Henson, Jennifer/Meigs Local School Dist	273	142
Hepperly, Dee/Oregon City School Dist	58,77	128
Heramb, Ann/Mentor Exempted Village SD	36	113
Herbruck, Erin, Dr/Shaker Heights City Sch Dist	68,74	50
Herdman, Brent/River Valley Local School Dist	4	139
Herges, Larry/Three Rivers Local School Dist	6	94
Herman-Wells, Elizabeth/Sandusky City School Dist	16	61
Herman, Bradley/Lucas Local School Dist	1	172
Herman, Chris/Edgerton Local School Dist	67	214
Herman, Gary/Putnam Co Ed Service Center	10	169
Herman, Kevin/Anthony Wayne Local Sch Dist	15,69	127
Herman, Phillip/Hudson City School Dist	1	193
Herman, Todd/Conotton Valley Union Local SD	1,83	100
Hermiller, Brent/North Baltimore Local Sch Dist	16,73	217
Heronn, Barb/Perry Local School Dist	4	9
Herr, Marden/Bluffton Exempted Village Sch	84	8
Herr, Marty/Bluffton Exempted Village Sch	16,73,286	8
Herr, Tracie/Liberty-Benton Local Sch Dist	35,36,69,83,88	98
Herringshaw, Carrie/Penta Co JT Voc School Dist	2	217
Herron, Tracey/River View Local School Dist	11,296	37
Hersey, Ann/ADA Exempted Village Sch Dist	4	99
Hershberger, Deb/East Holmes Local School Dist	37	104
Hershberger, Justin/Northmor Local School Dist	6	155
Hershey, Craig/Van Wert City School Dist	6	205
Hershiser, Mark/Westerville City School Dist	15	74
Hert, Kim/Plain Local School Dist	298	188
Hertel, Kristen/Columbus Grove Local Sch Dist	4	169
Hertzer, Mark/Southington Local School Dist	3	200
Herzog, Kelly/Miami Valley Career Tech VSD	71	151
Hesled, Terri Lynn/Sparcc	79	190
Hess, Jackie/Bellevue City School Dist	4	105
Hess, Jaqueline/Bellevue City School Dist	4	105
Hess, Krystia/Adams Co Ohio Valley Sch Dist	4	6
Hessey, Victoria/Canton Local School Dist	7,11,58,83,85,88,275	185
Hester, Greg/Hamilton Co Ed Service Center	68	87
Hester, Greg/Hamilton County ESC	68	97
Hete, Thaddeus/Warrensville Heights City SD	91	51
Hetrick, Nikki/Chardon Local School Dist	36	82
Hetrik, Phil/Central Local School Dist	3,5	57
Hetzel, Cliff/Hilliard City School Dist	2	71
Heuker, Ginger/Jackson Center Local Sch Dist	288	183
Heuker, Mike/New Bremen Local School Dist	285	16
Hevener, Robert/Cloverleaf Local School Dist	8,11,72,74,93,273,296	140
Hewitt, Bill/Whitehall City School Dist	6,35	75
Heyhurst, Jamie/Cambridge City School Dist	3	86
Heyman, Pam/Otsego Local School Dist	16,82	217
Hibbard, Amy/Fayette Local Sch Dist	16	79
Hibbs, Raymond/Harrison Hills City Sch Dist	6	101
Hickman, Larry/Tri-Rivers Joint Voc Sch Dist	10,11,27,60	139
Hieronimus, Nathan/Symmes Valley Local Sch Dist	67	117
Hieronymus, Paul/North Ridgeville City Sch Dist	73,76,295	125
Higbie, Darrell/Montpelier Exempted Village SD	67	215
Higgenbotham, Michele/Conotton Valley Union Local SD	79	100
Higginbotham, Carrie/Hilliard City School Dist	72,280	71
Higgins, Amy/Elyria City School Dist	71	123
Higgins, Andy/Benjamin Logan Local Sch Dist	77	121
Higgins, Jack/Delaware Joint Voc Sch Dist	3	59
Higgins, Jodi/Bay Village City School Dist	4	40
Highfill, George/Mason City School Dist	3	208
Higley, Patrick/Euclid City School Dist	2,91	46
Hildebrandt, Joann/Western Brown Local Sch Dist	67	20
Hildreth, Dawn/Fairfield City School Dist	57	21
Hile, David, Dr/Licking Valley Local Sch Dist	1,11	118
Hill, Andrew, Dr/Wadsworth City School Dist	1	141
Hill, Betty/Columbus City School Dist	20,23	66
Hill, Brenda/Lawrence Co Ed Service Center	2	115
Hill, Dale/Wolf Creek Local School Dist	3	211
Hill, Emily/Springboro Cmty School Dist	12,58	208
Hill, Eric/Ridgemont Local School Dist	67	100
Hill, Jeff/Eastwood Local School Dist	6	216
Hill, Jim/Bellaire Local School Dist	3,4,5,91	17
Hill, Josh/Lorain City School Dist	2	124
Hill, Kassie/Wapakoneta City School Dist	58	16
Hill, Krystal/Bloom-Vernon Local Sch Dist	4	178
Hill, Ladora/Wyoming City School Dist	9,34	94
Hill, Maria/Georgetown Exempted Village SD	752	20
Hill, Maria/Orange City School Dist	34	48
Hill, Maryl/Tiffin City School Dist	57,58,275	181
Hill, Robert, Dr/Springfield City School Dist	1	28
Hill, Ryan/Wayne Local School Dist	6	208
Hill, Tess/Switzerland of Ohio Local SD	73,84	147
Hill, Thomas/Youngstown City School Dist	68	136
Hill, Tracy/Cleveland Metro School Dist	12,93	42
Hille, Laurie/Noeca-Northern Ohio Ed CA	1	62
Hiller, Marjorie/Southern Local School Dist	16,73,82	36
Hiller, Tracy/Kenton City School Dist	2,11,91,296	100
Hiller, Tracy/Vanlue Local School Dist	2,11	99
Hilliker, Chad/Hamilton County ESC	15	97
Hillman, Kathy/Bellevue City School Dist	5	105
Hillyer, Jodi/Indian Valley Local Sch Dist	76	202
Himmelein, Mary/Ed Service Ctr Lake Erie West	68	127
Hinds, Greg/Franklin-Monroe Local Sch Dist	2,11	55
Hinds, Stephanie/Brookville Local School Dist	8,76,286	148
Hines, Caroline/Niles City School Dist	16	200
Hines, Dennis/Lowellville Local School Dist	11,73,296	135
Hines, Maria/Northwestern Local School Dist	16	212
Hinkle, Scott/Hillsdale Local School Dist	3	11
Hinkle, Wayne/Highland Local School Dist	67	155
Hinson, Kristan/Hamilton City School Dist	12,52,280	22

#		#		#		#		#		#	
1	Superintendent	16	Instructional Media Svcs	30	Adult Education	44	Science Sec	58	Special Education K-12	72	Summer School
2	Bus/Finance/Purchasing	17	Chief Operations Officer	31	Career/Sch-to-Work K-12	45	Math K-12	59	Special Education Elem	73	Instructional Tech
3	Buildings And Grounds	18	Chief Academic Officer	32	Career/Sch-to-Work Elem	46	Math Elem	60	Special Education Sec	74	Inservice Training
4	Food Service	19	Chief Financial Officer	33	Career/Sch-to-Work Sec	47	Math Sec	61	Foreign/World Lang K-12	75	Marketing/Distributive
5	Transportation	20	Art K-12	34	Early Childhood Ed	48	English/Lang Arts K-12	62	Foreign/World Lang Elem	76	Info Systems
6	Athletic	21	Art Elem	35	Health/Phys Education	49	English/Lang Arts Elem	63	Foreign/World Lang Sec	77	Psychological Assess
7	Health Services	22	Art Sec	36	Guidance Services K-12	50	English/Lang Arts Sec	64	Religious Education K-12	78	Affirmative Action
8	Curric/Instruct K-12	23	Music K-12	37	Guidance Services Elem	51	Reading K-12	65	Religious Education Elem	79	Student Personnel
9	Curric/Instruct Elem	24	Music Elem	38	Guidance Services Sec	52	Reading Elem	66	Religious Education Sec	80	Driver Ed/Safety
10	Curric/Instruct Sec	25	Music Sec	39	Social Studies K-12	53	Reading Sec	67	School Board President	81	Gifted/Talented
11	Federal Program	26	Business Education	40	Social Studies Elem	54	Remedial Reading K-12	68	Teacher Personnel	82	Video Services
12	Title I	27	Career & Tech Ed	41	Social Studies Sec	55	Remedial Reading Elem	69	Academic Assessment	83	Substance Abuse Prev
13	Title V	28	Technology Education	42	Science K-12	56	Remedial Reading Sec	70	Research/Development	84	Erate
15	Asst Superintendent	29	Family/Consumer Science	43	Science Elem	57	Bilingual/ELL	71	Public Information	85	AIDS Education

#		#	
88	Alternative/At Risk	277	Remedial Math K-12
89	Multi-Cultural Curriculum	280	Literacy Coach
90	Social Work	285	STEM
91	Safety/Security	286	Digital Learning
92	Magnet School	288	Common Core Standards
93	Parental Involvement	294	Accountability
95	Tech Prep Program	295	Network System
97	Chief Information Officer	296	Title II Programs
98	Chief Technology Officer	297	Webmaster
270	Character Education	298	Grant Writer/Ptnrships
271	Migrant Education	750	Chief Innovation Officer
273	Teacher Mentor	751	Chief of Staff
274	Before/After Sch	752	Social Emotional Learning
275	Response To Intervention		

Ohio School Directory

DISTRICT PERSONNEL INDEX

NAME/District	JOB FUNCTIONS	PAGE
Hinton, Gary/Osnaburg Local School Dist	88	188
Hinton, Gary/Sandy Valley Local School Dist	6	189
Hinton, Joe/Maplewood JT Voc School Dist	4	166
Hinton, Kim/Wauseon Exempted Village SD	81	80
Hinton, Michael/Maplewood JT Voc School Dist	30	166
Hippler, Brooke/Canal Winchester Local SD	58,88	66
Hire, David, Dr/Coshocton City School Dist	1	36
Hirt, Denice/Fremont City School Dist	8,11,16,36,69,288,296,298	176
Hiscox, Brian/Berkshire Local School Dist	6	81
Hiscox, Douglas/Mahoning Co Ed Service Center	15	133
Hiser, Tiffany/Brookville Local School Dist	2,298	148
Hiss, Robert/Jefferson Local School Dist	3,5	132
Hissong, Kraig/West Liberty-Salem Local SD	1	26
Hissrich, Janet/Union Local School Dist	2	18
Hite, Andy/Piqua City School Dist	67	146
Hittle, Jeremie/Piqua City School Dist	2	146
Hittle, Matt/Zanesville City School Dist	3	157
Hix, Jason/Elgin Local School Dist	6	138
Hizer, Ginny/Southwest Local School Dist	71	93
Hoadley, Todd/Dublin City School Dist	1	69
Hobbs, Jeff/Fairlawn Local School Dist	1,83	182
Hobbs, Josh/Waverly City School Dist	67	164
Hobbs, Leslie/Northmont City School Dist	7,36,57,58,77,79,271	152
Hobbs, Rhonda/Winton Woods City School Dist	73,76,286,295	94
Hobby, Jeffrey/Northwestern Local School Dist	6	27
Hobson, Diane, Dr/Trimble Local School Dist	8,288	15
Hochstetler, Derrick/Green Local School Dist	73	212
Hochstetler, Linda/Garaway Local School Dist	36	202
Hockenberry, Craig/Three Rivers Local School Dist	1	94
Hocker, Ben/Crestline Exempted Village SD	3	38
Hodapp, Angie/Tri-Co North School Dist	4	168
Hodapp, Jennifer/Montpelier Exempted Village SD	81	215
Hodge, Benjamin/Avon Local School Dist	8,11,15,57,288,296	122
Hodges, Brenda/Winton Woods City School Dist	88	94
Hodges, Jenelle/Miami Co Ed Service Center	67	144
Hodkey, Todd/Medina City School Dist	6	141
Hoehn, Jennifer/Bellbrook-Sugarcreek Schools	4	83
Hoehn, Todd/Jennings Local School Dist	6,35	169
Hoehner, Brian/Miami Valley Educational CA	3	85
Hoelzle, Chelsea/Brookville Local School Dist	58,752	148
Hoeppner, Josh/Antwerp Local School Dist	58	160
Hoeppner, Stephanie/Williamsburg Local School Dist	73,295	32
Hoersten, Linda/Perry Local School Dist	33,36,69	9
Hoerth, Terri/Clermont Northeastern Local SD	4	30
Hoey, Linda/Youngstown City School Dist	93	136
Hoff, Art/Tipp City Exempted Village SD	3,91	146
Hoffert, Melinda/Miami Co Ed Service Center	68	144
Hoffman, Callie/Sycamore Cmty School Dist	45	93
Hoffman, Christie/Hicksville Exempted Village SD	16,82	57
Hoffman, Jane/Chardon Local School Dist	7	82
Hoffman, John-Paul/Canal Winchester Local SD	73	66
Hoffman, Kristi/Miller City-New Cleveland SD	36,69,83,88	170
Hoffman, Scott/River Valley Local School Dist	3,5	139
Hoffman, Tina/Marlington Local School Dist	85	186
Hoffman, Vickie/Triad Local School Dist	1	26
Hoffner, Michael/Pickaway Co Ed Service Center	5	162
Hogue, Kevin/Hubbard Exempted Village SD	6	198
Hogue, Tina/Switzerland of Ohio Local SD	4	147
Hohe, Billy/New Lexington School Dist	16	161
Hohler, Kelly/Hillsdale Local School Dist	36	11
Holbrook, Jeffrey/Hopewell-Loudon Local SD	1	181
Holbrook, Kelly/Heath City School Dist	8,11,15,57,69	117
Holbrook, Mike/Hamilton City School Dist	1	21
Holden, Terri, Dr/Winton Woods City School Dist	8	94
Holder, Jennifer/Miami Co Ed Service Center	58	144
Holdren, Todd/Zane Trace Local School Dist	6	176
Holewinski, Cassie/Buckeye Valley Local Sch Dist	16,73,82,286,295	58
Holland, Daniel/Ft Loramie Local School Dist	1	182
Hollander, Lance/Mariemont City School Dist	3	90
Hollandsworth, Jill, Dr/Milford Exempted Village SD	8,11,15,16,288,294,296,298	30
Hollar, Kim/West Liberty-Salem Local SD	35,83,85,88	26
Hollar, Teri/Minerva Local School Dist	5	187
Hollida, Rob/Bloomfield-Mespo Local SD	2	197
Holliman, Tia/Gahanna-Jefferson Public SD	8	70
Hollinger, Jerry/Tri-Village Local Sch Dist	5	56
Hollins, Juwan/Wolf Creek Local School Dist	6	211
Hollis, Brandi/Stow-Munroe Falls City SD	5	194
Hollman, Tim/St Mary's City School Dist	6	16
Hollon, Pete/Paint Valley Local School Dist	6	175
Holly, Patti/Twin Valley Cmty Local SD	9,12	169
Holman, Eddie/Lorain City School Dist	295	124
Holman, Eric/Pleasant Local School Dist	6	138
Holsinger, Michele/Anna Local School Dist	38,69,83,85,88	182
Holstein, Scott/South Central Ohio Ed Svc Ctr	15	178
Holt, Benjanim/Triway Local School Dist	60	213
Holtcamp, Jena/Botkins Local School Dist	29	182
Holtzapple, John/Anna Local School Dist	9,11,296	182
Holycross, Ernin/Ridgemont Local School Dist	5	100
Homan, Steve/Miamisburg City School Dist	15,68	151
Homeoelle, Shannon/Mason City School Dist	49	208
Honaker, Linda/New Albany-Plain Local SD	5	72
Honkala, Dennis/Ravenna School Dist	1	166
Hoock, Steve/Deer Park Cmty School Dist	69	89
Hood, Dejuan/Columbus City School Dist	3	66
Hood, Jon/New Albany-Plain Local SD	79,91	72
Hook, Larry/Carlisle Local School Dist	1,11,83	206
Hoop, Lance/New Lebanon Local School Dist	3,91	151
Hooper, Darla/Manchester Local School Dist	5	193
Hooper, Jim/Greenville City School Dist	8	55
Hooper, Kristi/Winton Woods City School Dist	5	94
Hoover, Bill/Waverly City School Dist	5,83	164
Hoover, Dan/Benton-Carroll-Salem Local SD	6	158
Hoover, Hal/Celina City School Dist	61	143
Hopkins, Bonnie/Eastland-Ffld Career Tech VSD	1	70
Hopkins, Guy/Southern Hills Joint Voc SD	88,288	20
Hopkins, Marc/Southwest Ohio OCA	76	25
Hopkins, Paul, Dr/Westerville City School Dist	68	74
Hopkins, Sue/Ross-Pike Co Ed Service Center	67	174
Hopkins, Tim/Brookville Local School Dist	1	148
Hopkins, Todd/Westlake City School Dist	2,11,19,298	51
Hoppe, Heather/Kenton City School Dist	58	100
Hopper, David/Rock Hill Local School Dist	1	116
Hopps, Charles/Southern Local School Dist	5	161
Hopten, Rodney/North Baltimore Local Sch Dist	58	217
Horgan, Maura/Newark City School Dist	8,57,74,286,288	119
Horger, Mike/Tuscarawas Valley Local SD	297	203
Horn, Karen/Clyde-Green Spgs Exmpt Vlg SD	7,85	176
Horne, Sharon/Yellow Springs Exempted Vlg SD	5	85
Horner, Jennifer/Clinton-Massie Local Sch Dist	37	33
Horner, Keith/Apollo Joint Voc School Dist	1,11	8
Horner, Tim, Dr/Bloom-Vernon Local Sch Dist	67	178
Hornstein, Greg/Northwood Local School Dist	3,5	217
Horseman, Don/Ottawa-Glandorf Local Sch Dist	1,11	170
Horton, Kellsey/Wellington Exempted Village SD	83,88	126
Horton, Marvin/Eaton Cmty School Dist	8,11,57,58,77,81,288,296	168
Hortsman, Ken/Liberty-Benton Local Sch Dist	11	98
Horvath, Angela/Bellefontaine City School Dist	81	121
Horvath, Brett/Geneva Area City School Dist	8,11,16,34,88,270,285,288	13
Horvath, Madelon/Chardon Local School Dist	67	82
Horvath, Sandy/Struthers City School Dist	280	136
Horvatich, Frank/Lorain City School Dist	4	124
Hosack, Brant/Mt Gilead Exempted Village SD	38,83,88	155
Hoschak, Jackie/Northeastern Local School Dist	4	57
Hosler, Thomas/Perrysburg Exempted Village SD	1	218
Hossler, David/Fostoria City School Dist	3,5,91	180
Host, Cyndy/Buckeye Joint Voc School Dist	67	201
Hostetler, Lance/United Local School Dist	1	36
Hostetler, Michelle/North Canton City School Dist	8,12	187
Hoston, Rasheeda/Bedford City School Dist	58	40
Hotchkiss, Ruth/Akron Public Schools	45	190
Hothem, Daniel/River View Local School Dist	67	37
Hotlosz, Bruce/Martins Ferry City School Dist	73,285	18
Houck, Lori/Centerburg Local School Dist	2	110
Houdeshell, Tara/Lakewood Local School Dist	67	118
Hounshell, Chris/Antwerp Local School Dist	5	160
House, Adam/Twinsburg City School Dist	5	195
House, Mike/East Muskingum Local Sch Dist	58	156
House, Nancy/Milford Exempted Village SD	1	30
House, Susan/Wyoming City School Dist	37	94
Householder, Tim/New Lexington School Dist	73,84,295	161
Houser, Dawn/New Knoxville Local Sch Dist	54,59	16
Houser, Tracy/Mercer Co Ed Service Center	73,295	143

DISTRICT PERSONNEL INDEX

Market Data Retrieval

NAME/District	JOB FUNCTIONS	PAGE
Housh, Matt/Yellow Springs Exempted Vlg SD	9	85
Housley, Zac/Switzerland of Ohio Local SD	8	147
Housman, Kathleen/Fairborn City School Dist	4	84
Hout, Jeremy/Gallipolis City School Dist	8,12,74,273,288	81
Hovan, Greg/North Royalton City Sch Dist	5	48
Hovest, Tonia/Waynesfield-Goshen Local SD	2,11	16
Hovorka, John/Ed Svc Center of Medina Co	16,73,295	139
Howard, Adam/Berea City School Dist	6	41
Howard, Alicia/Clearview Local School Dist	69	123
Howard, Brent/Minford Local School Dist	37	178
Howard, Brittany/Bowling Green City Sch Dist	35	216
Howard, Bryan/Goshen Local School Dist	5	30
Howard, Christy/New Lebanon Local School Dist	11,58,69,77	151
Howard, Jim/Lawrence Co Joint Voc Sch Dist	27,88,274	116
Howard, Joy/Richmond Heights Local SD	73	49
Howard, Lee/Frontier Local School Dist	2,294,296	209
Howard, Leroy/Scioto Valley Local Sch Dist	3	164
Howard, Marlon/Trotwood-Madison City SD	1	152
Howard, Phil/Jackson City School Dist	1	107
Howard, T J/South Point Local School Dist	12,15,288	116
Howard, Zack/Pickerington Local School Dist	15,68	64
Howdyshell, Debbie/Liberty Union-Thurstn Sch Dist	16	64
Howe, Adam/Bloom-Vernon Local Sch Dist	5,274	178
Howell, Christopher/Northwestern Local School Dist	3	27
Howell, Kevin/Sebring Local School Dist	73	135
Howell, Scott/Midwest Reg Ed Service Center	1	120
Howell, Tom/New London Local School Dist	6,69	105
Hoy, Patrick/Parma City School Dist	68	49
Hoyal, Pat, Dr/Jefferson Twp Local Sch Dist	58	150
Hoying, Amy/Versailles Exempted Village SD	83	56
Hoying, April/Darke Co Ed Service Center	8	55
Hoying, Jennifer/Hardin-Houston Local Sch Dist	58	183
Hoying, Mitch/Sidney City School Dist	6	183
Hoynes, Jacqueline, Dr/Newbury Local School Dist	1,11	82
Hruschak, Lynn, Dr/State Support Team 3	8,74	54
Hubbard, Bill/Talawanda School Dist	3,91	24
Huber, Adam/Kalida Local School Dist	6	169
Huber, Carl/Celina City School Dist	67	143
Hubinski, Christopher/Trumbull Co Ed Service Center	73	196
Huchinson, Lyn/Solon City School Dist	4	50
Huddle, Scott/Mad River Local School Dist	67	151
Hudley, Robyn/Vanlue Local School Dist	8	99
Hudson, Bethany/Field Local School Dist	8,11,57,288	165
Hudson, Dan/Lakota Local School Dist	69	22
Hudson, James/Cloverleaf Local School Dist	2,84	140
Hudson, Jim/New London Local School Dist	2,84	105
Hudzik, Lori/Niles City School Dist	2	200
Huelsman, Bob/Urbana City School Dist	2	26
Huff, Brenda/Fairborn City School Dist	5	84
Huff, Devin/Ross Local School Dist	3	24
Huff, Nathan/Adena Local School Dist	67	174
Huff, Shawn/Preble Co Ed Service Center	15	168
Huff, Tony/Butler Tech Career Dev Schs	296	21
Huffard, Clint/Troy City School Dist	4	146
Huffman, Andy/Ashland Co-West Holmes JVSD	73	11
Huffman, Anthony, Dr/Washington Co JT Voc Sch Dist	30	210
Huffman, Heath/Cory-Rawson Local School Dist	1	97
Huffman, Mary/Mechanicsburg Exempted Vlg SD	8,11,280,285,294	26
Hufford, Amber/South-Western City School Dist	7,79,83	73
Hug, Joe/Perry Local School Dist	81	188
Hug, Tod, Dr/Northwest Ohio Computer Assoc	1	80
Hug, Trevor/Liberty Center Local Sch Dist	73,76	101
Hughes, Alex/Putnam Co Ed Service Center	73,76,295	169
Hughes, Brian/Holgate Local School Dist	10,11	101
Hughes, Mark/Washington Local School Dist	67	130
Hughes, Melissa/Jackson City School Dist	68	107
Hughes, Michelle/Mt Healthy City School Dist	8,288	91
Hughes, Scott/Oak Hill Union Local Sch Dist	91	107
Hughes, Sheila/ADA Exempted Village Sch Dist	58	99
Hughes, Sue/Sebring Local School Dist	4	135
Hulit, Tami/Brown Local School Dist	67	25
Hull, Deanna/Defiance City School Dist	4	57
Hulse, Kristina/Pickerington Local School Dist	58,296	64
Humble, Bob/Sidney City School Dist	1	183
Hummel, Tina/Licking Co Joint Voc Sch Dist	60	118
Hummell, Glenn/Euclid City School Dist	3	46
Hummerich, Elaine/Caldwell Exempted Village SD	5	158
Humphrey, Alana/Eastern Local School Dist	36,69,83	7
Humphrey, Steve/Canton City School Dist	91	184
Humphrey, Willaim/Centerburg Local School Dist	8	110
Humphreys, Darrell/Symmes Valley Local Sch Dist	1,11,57,83	117
Hunker, Laurie/Seneca East Local School Dist	8,288	181
Hunnicutt, Tajuana/Euclid City School Dist	79	46
Hunt, Brian/Benjamin Logan Local Sch Dist	11,274	121
Hunt, Brian/Dublin City School Dist	4	69
Hunt, Brian/Worthington School Dist	4	75
Hunt, Darren/South Central Local Sch Dist	6	106
Hunt, Denise/Ashtabula Co Ed Service Center	81	11
Hunt, Irene/Upper Arlington City Sch Dist	4	74
Hunt, Kenya/Warrensville Heights City SD	68	51
Hunt, Kiya/Canal Winchester Local SD	15	66
Hunt, Lisa/Hudson City School Dist	68,85,273	193
Hunt, Robert/Chagrin Falls Exempted Vlg SD	1	42
Hunt, Travis/Oak Hills Local School Dist	270	92
Hunter, Carrie/Madison Local School Dist	58,77	23
Hunter, Jeremy/Lgca-Lake Geauga Ohio OCA	8	115
Hunter, Judi/Northridge Local School Dist	4	152
Huntshield, Mike/Lakewood Local School Dist	73,76	118
Hupe, Rick/Four-Co Joint Voc School Dist	11,28,73,79	79
Hupp, Corey/Ottawa Hills Local Sch Dist	67	128
Hurd, John/Trimble Local School Dist	1	15
Hurd, Sandi/Nelsonville-York City Sch Dist	2,294	15
Hurley, Craig/Upper Scioto Valley Local SD	8,12,58,270,273,288	100
Hurley, Craig/Upper Scioto Valley Local SD	1	100
Hurley, Matt/Indian Lake Local School Dist	3	121
Hurst, Jeremy/Archbold Area Local Sch Dist	67	78
Hurst, Joe/Bradford Exempted Village SD	1	145
Hurst, Tamra/Stark Co Area Voc Sch Dist	2	189
Hurst, Tamra/Stark Co Ed Service Center	2	184
Hurt, Scott/Adena Local School Dist	6	174
Hurwitz, Eli/Yellow Springs Exempted Vlg SD	16	85
Huss, James/Sylvania City School Dist	6	128
Huster, Greg/Deer Park Cmty School Dist	6	89
Huston, Dave/Hilliard City School Dist	3	71
Huston, Paul/Nelsonville-York City Sch Dist	3,91	15
Huston, Tim/Arlington Local School Dist	3	97
Hutcheson, Marybeth/Arlington Local School Dist	31,38,79,88	97
Hutchinson, Alan/Educational Serv Ctr-Ctl Ohio	2	65
Hutchinson, Carrie/Nordonia Hills City Sch Dist	7,77,79,90	193
Hutchinson, Kelly/Warren City School Dist	34	200
Hutchinson, Matt/Wauseon Exempted Village SD	6	79
Hutchinson, Terri/Canfield Local School Dist	4	134
Hutchison, John/Alexander Local School Dist	67	14
Huth, Susan/Ravenna School Dist	8,11,57,69,274,294,298	166
Hutson, Laura/Cloverleaf Local School Dist	30	140
Hutson, Mark/Columbiana Exempted Village SD	67	34
Hyatt, Sara/Madison Plains Local Sch Dist	77	133
Hyland, Tonyia/Adena Local School Dist	4	174

I

Iacano, Joe/Summit Co Educational Svc Ctr	1	196
Iacano, Joesph/Summit Co Ed Service Center	1	190
Iacano, Joseph/Portage Co Ed Service Center	1	164
Iammarino, Debra/Geauga Co Ed Service Center	27,31	81

---

1 Superintendent
2 Bus/Finance/Purchasing
3 Buildings And Grounds
4 Food Service
5 Transportation
6 Athletic
7 Health Services
8 Curric/Instruct K-12
9 Curric/Instruct Elem
10 Curric/Instruct Sec
11 Federal Program
12 Title I
13 Title V
15 Asst Superintendent
16 Instructional Media Svcs
17 Chief Operations Officer
18 Chief Academic Officer
19 Chief Financial Officer
20 Art K-12
21 Art Elem
22 Art Sec
23 Music K-12
24 Music Elem
25 Music Sec
26 Business Education
27 Career & Tech Ed
28 Technology Education
29 Family/Consumer Science
30 Adult Education
31 Career/Sch-to-Work K-12
32 Career/Sch-to-Work Elem
33 Career/Sch-to-Work Sec
34 Early Childhood Ed
35 Health/Phys Education
36 Guidance Services K-12
37 Guidance Services Elem
38 Guidance Services Sec
39 Social Studies K-12
40 Social Studies Elem
41 Social Studies Sec
42 Science K-12
43 Science Elem
44 Science Sec
45 Math K-12
46 Math Elem
47 Math Sec
48 English/Lang Arts K-12
49 English/Lang Arts Elem
50 English/Lang Arts Sec
51 Reading K-12
52 Reading Elem
53 Reading Sec
54 Remedial Reading K-12
55 Remedial Reading Elem
56 Remedial Reading Sec
57 Bilingual/ELL
58 Special Education K-12
59 Special Education Elem
60 Special Education Sec
61 Foreign/World Lang K-12
62 Foreign/World Lang Elem
63 Foreign/World Lang Sec
64 Religious Education K-12
65 Religious Education Elem
66 Religious Education Sec
67 School Board President
68 Teacher Personnel
69 Academic Assessment
70 Research/Development
71 Public Information
72 Summer School
73 Instructional Tech
74 Inservice Training
75 Marketing/Distributive
76 Info Systems
77 Psychological Assess
78 Affirmative Action
79 Student Personnel
80 Driver Ed/Safety
81 Gifted/Talented
82 Video Services
83 Substance Abuse Prev
84 Erate
85 AIDS Education
88 Alternative/At Risk
89 Multi-Cultural Curriculum
90 Social Work
91 Safety/Security
92 Magnet School
93 Parental Involvement
95 Tech Prep Program
97 Chief Information Officer
98 Chief Technology Officer
270 Character Education
271 Migrant Education
273 Teacher Mentor
274 Before/After Sch
275 Response To Intervention
277 Remedial Math K-12
280 Literacy Coach
285 STEM
286 Digital Learning
288 Common Core Standards
294 Accountability
295 Network System
296 Title II Programs
297 Webmaster
298 Grant Writer/Ptnrships
750 Chief Innovation Officer
751 Chief of Staff
752 Social Emotional Learning

Ohio School Directory

DISTRICT PERSONNEL INDEX

NAME/District	JOB FUNCTIONS	PAGE
Iannantuono, Julie/*Elmwood Local School Dist*	8	216
Iarussi, Ronald, Dr/*Mahoning Co Ed Service Center*	1	133
Iarussi, Ronald, Dr/*Marion City School Dist*	1	138
Idzakovich, Joe/*Miami Valley Career Tech VSD*	67	151
Ifft, Dan/*Dover City School Dist*	88	202
Ignaczak, Ron/*Midview Local School Dist*	3	125
Iiames, Mary/*Perry Local School Dist*	37	9
Imes, Keith/*Conotton Valley Union Local SD*	73,295	100
Imes, Keith/*Conotton Valley Union Local SD*	84	101
Imhoff, Jamie/*Northwestern Local School Dist*	5	212
Imhoff, Paul/*Upper Arlington City Sch Dist*	1	74
Imhoss, Missy/*Eaton Cmty School Dist*	15,88,280,298	168
Immelt, Devon/*Olentangy Local School Dist*	71	59
Incerpi, Al/*Marlington Local School Dist*	3,91	186
Infante, Angela/*Evergreen Local School Dist*	73,76,84,286,295	78
Ingles, Barb/*Washington-Nile Local Sch Dist*	4	179
Ingram, Mindy/*Tri-Co Joint Voc Sch Dist*	76	15
Inkrott, Laura/*Northridge Local School Dist*	8,11,273,288	152
Inskeep, Scott/*Kettering City School Dist*	1	150
Ionno, Stacy/*Ridgewood Local School Dist*	38	37
Irby, Daphne/*Diocese of Columbus Ed Office*	9	76
Ireland, Christie/*River View Local School Dist*	8,72,273,274,286,288	37
Irgens, Craig/*Franklin City School Dist*	73,295	207
Irish-Glass, Jeannette/*Orange City School Dist*	73,76,295,297	49
Irvin, Christopher/*Tri-Valley Local School Dist*	73	157
Irwin, Chris/*Sylvania City School Dist*	6	128
Irwin, Tammy/*Zane Trace Local School Dist*	2,11	176
Isaacs, Jeffrey/*Shaker Heights City Sch Dist*	67	50
Isaacs, Tom/*Warren Co Ed Service Center*	1	206
Isgro, Steven/*Hamilton City School Dist*	67	22
Isler, Sarah/*Windham Exempted Vlg Sch Dist*	81	167
Ives, Valerie/*Trimble Local School Dist*	81	15
Ivory, Evan/*West Carrollton City Sch Dist*	6	153

J

NAME/District	JOB FUNCTIONS	PAGE
Jablonka, Emily/*Springfield City School Dist*	8,74	28
Jackfert, Jodi/*Martins Ferry City School Dist*	58,77	18
Jacks, Winnie/*Bellefontaine City School Dist*	4	121
Jackson, Brian/*Gibsonburg Exempted Village SD*	37	177
Jackson, Chelsy/*Tuslaw Local School Dist*	83	189
Jackson, Dan/*Pymatuning Valley Local SD*	79	13
Jackson, Dave/*Northridge Local School Dist*	1	152
Jackson, Jason/*Madison Local School Dist*	12	23
Jackson, Mary/*Sebring Local School Dist*	36	135
Jackson, Sarah/*State Support Team-Region 8*	34	196
Jackson, Sean/*Lakewood City School Dist*	6	47
Jackson, Wendall/*Green Local School Dist*	3,4,91	185
Jaco, Chuck/*Perrysburg Exempted Village SD*	6,35	218
Jacob, Laurie/*Mad River Local School Dist*	57	151
Jacob, Michael/*St Clairsville-Richland CSD*	67	18
Jacobs, Carletta/*Reading Cmty City School Dist*	273	93
Jacobs, Cindy/*Batavia Local School Dist*	57,58,81	29
Jacobs, Dawn/*Huron City School Dist*	2,84	60
Jacobs, Dawn/*North Central Ohio Ed Svc Ctr*	2	137
Jacobs, Mark/*Shaker Heights City Sch Dist*	4	50
Jacobs, Steve/*Great Oaks Career Campuses*	28,76	89
Jacobs, Tytus/*Troy City School Dist*	3,5	146
Jacobson, Marti/*Chagrin Falls Exempted Vlg SD*	4	42
Jagger, Kristin/*Woodridge Local School Dist*	8,11,51,54,69,74,273,288	195
Jalwan, Andy/*Copley-Fairlawn City Sch Dist*	6	192
James, Alice/*Perkins Local School Dist*	37	61
James, Beth/*Gallia Co Local School Dist*	67	80
James, Chris/*Springfield-Clark Co JVSD*	27	28
James, David/*Akron Public Schools*	1	190
James, Jessica/*SE Ohio Voluntary Ed Co-op*	2	15
James, Kathy/*Talawanda School Dist*	280	24
James, Kenneth/*Northwood Local School Dist*	6	217
James, Kristel/*Northwood Local School Dist*	16,82	217
James, Phil/*Columbiana Co Voc Sch Dist*	73,295,297	34
James, Ronald/*Wayne Local School Dist*	2,8,18	208
Jameson, Angie/*Chagrin Falls Exempted Vlg SD*	16,82	42
Jamison, Nora/*Western Reserve Local Sch Dist*	7	136
Janiszewski, Patrick/*Nelsonville-York City Sch Dist*	4	15
Janiszewski, Steve/*Southern Local School Dist*	4	161
Janofa, David/*Poland Local School Dist*	1	135
Janosek, Laura/*Independence Local School Dist*	16	46

NAME/District	JOB FUNCTIONS	PAGE
Jansen, Thomas/*Summit Co Ed Service Center*	16	190
Jansen, Tom/*Summit Co Educational Svc Ctr*	73	196
Jaramillo, Amy/*Cuyahoga Vly Career Ctr Voc SD*	38,83,85	45
Jaroscak, Susan/*Maple Heights City School Dist*	8,11,69,275,285,288,296,298	47
Jarrett, Kevin/*Granville Exempted Village SD*	6	117
Jarvais, Art/*Loveland City School Dist*	67	90
Jarvis, Kim/*Tri-Co Joint Voc Sch Dist*	273	15
Jaunzemis, Don/*Ohio Hi-Point Joint Voc SD*	4	121
Javins, Mary/*Fairport Harbor Exempt Vlg SD*	67	112
Jaynes, Kevin/*Berea City School Dist*	73,84	41
Jeffers, Dan/*Fairfield City School Dist*	73	21
Jeffers, Jeannie/*Otsego Local School Dist*	4	217
Jefferson, Stan/*Mansfield City Schools*	1	172
Jenkins, Anthony/*Northwest Local School Dist*	1,83	179
Jenkins, Darren/*Bellaire Local School Dist*	1	17
Jenkins, Darrin/*Bellaire Local School Dist*	11	17
Jenkins, David/*Ehove Joint Voc School Dist*	3,73,76,84,295	60
Jenkins, Melissa/*Windham Exempted Vlg Sch Dist*	77	167
Jenkins, Rebecca/*New Albany-Plain Local SD*	2,19	72
Jennell, Robert/*Southwest Licking Local SD*	1	120
Jenney, Kathleen/*Upper Arlington City Sch Dist*	15,68	74
Jennings, Crystal/*Wynford Local School Dist*	29	39
Jennings, Jan/*Licking Valley Local Sch Dist*	4	118
Jennings, Stan/*Scioto Co Joint Vocational SD*	1,11	179
Jensen, James/*Barberton City School Dist*	81,274	192
Jenson, Liz/*Kettering City School Dist*	27,31	150
Jermer, Randy/*Williamsburg Local School Dist*	3	32
Jetter, Kathy/*Greenville City School Dist*	7	55
Jewell, David/*Edgewood City School Dist*	4	21
Jewell, Melissa/*Clark-Shawnee Local Sch Dist*	58	27
Jewell, William/*Carlisle Local School Dist*	67	206
Jividen, Shawn/*Summit Co Ed Service Center*	81	190
Jodfrey, Jared/*Eastern Local School Dist*	6	7
Joefreda-Wells, Cathy/*Wayne Local School Dist*	36,69,88	209
Johannson, Andreas/*Streetsboro City School Dist*	5,73,76,295	167
John, Jones/*Niles City School Dist*	3	200
Johns, Gwen/*Elida Local School Dist*	58	8
Johnsen, Judy/*Norton City School Dist*	4	193
Johnson, Aaron/*Fairbanks Local School Dist*	2	204
Johnson, Aaron/*Jonathan Alder Local Sch Dist*	2	132
Johnson, Anaka/*Vandalia Butler City Sch Dist*	71	153
Johnson, Andrea/*Pike-Delta-York Local Sch Dist*	8,11,288	79
Johnson, April/*Ed Svc Center of Medina Co*	5	139
Johnson, Ashley/*Covington Exempted Village SD*	6	145
Johnson, Ben/*Washington-Nile Local Sch Dist*	285	179
Johnson, Ben/*Washington-Nile Local Sch Dist*	6	179
Johnson, Bruce/*Apollo Joint Voc School Dist*	286	8
Johnson, Cassandra/*Bedford City School Dist*	15	40
Johnson, Cindy/*Covington Exempted Village SD*	58	145
Johnson, Cindy/*East Guernsey Local Sch Dist*	58,88	86
Johnson, Coreena/*West Holmes Local School Dist*	5	105
Johnson, David/*Vermilion Local School Dist*	5	62
Johnson, Elizabeth/*Southern Local School Dist*	286	143
Johnson, Erik/*Triway Local School Dist*	73	213
Johnson, Greg/*Ridgemont Local School Dist*	35	100
Johnson, H Tad/*Coshocton Co Joint Voc SD*	67	37
Johnson, Jeff/*Great Oaks Career Campuses*	3,4,5,73,95	89
Johnson, Jeff/*Milford Exempted Village SD*	2	30
Johnson, Jeff/*Preble-Shawnee Local Sch Dist*	73	168
Johnson, Jim, Dr/*Morgan Local School Dist*	73	154
Johnson, Kelly/*Perrysburg Exempted Village SD*	68,74,91,273	218
Johnson, Kerri/*Anthony Wayne Local Sch Dist*	2	127
Johnson, Kerry/*Miller City-New Cleveland SD*	1	170
Johnson, Leighanne/*Paint Valley Local School Dist*	9	175
Johnson, Lynnea/*Groveport Madison Local SD*	81	71
Johnson, Marjorie/*Cuyahoga Falls City Sch Dist*	5	192
Johnson, Mike/*Liberty Union-Thurstn Sch Dist*	1	64
Johnson, Nate/*Stryker Local School Dist*	1	215
Johnson, Paul, Dr/*Bucyrus City School Dist*	67	38
Johnson, Peggy/*Loveland City School Dist*	36	90
Johnson, Rhonda/*Wyoming City School Dist*	2,5,11	94
Johnson, Rich/*West Liberty-Salem Local SD*	73	26
Johnson, Robert/*West Carrollton City Sch Dist*	73	153
Johnson, Ron/*Oak Hill Union Local Sch Dist*	73	107
Johnson, Ron/*South Euclid-Lyndhurst City SD*	69	51
Johnson, Roy/*Meigs Local School Dist*	2	142

DISTRICT PERSONNEL INDEX

Market Data Retrieval

NAME/District	JOB FUNCTIONS	PAGE
Johnson, Susan/Wayne Trace Local School Dist	16	160
Johnson, Tammi/Sidney City School Dist	16	183
Johnson, Tim/Ironton City School Dist	67	116
Johnson, Todd/Coshocton City School Dist	3,58	36
Johnson, Todd/Marysville Exempted Village SD	2,19	204
Johnson, Tracy/Fayetteville Perry Local SD	7	19
Johnson, Troy/Gallipolis City School Dist	5,91	81
Johnson, Viola/Winton Woods City School Dist	67	94
Johnston, Elissa/Licking Co Joint Voc Sch Dist	33,294	118
Johnston, Larry/Cleveland Metro School Dist	2	42
Jokinen, Beth/Lima City School Dist	76	9
Jolliss, Stephanie/Ridgemont Local School Dist	27	100
Jolly, Donald/Warrensville Heights City SD	1	51
Jones, Aimee/Vinton Co Local School Dist	31	206
Jones, Ashley/Lancaster City School Dist	81	63
Jones, Becky/Leetonia Exempted Village SD	16	35
Jones, Becky/Washington Co JT Voc Sch Dist	7	210
Jones, Ben/Reynoldsburg City School Dist	73,84	72
Jones, Carol/Labrae Local School Dist	2	198
Jones, Carolyn/Cincinnati City School Dist	67	87
Jones, Cindy/New Philadelphia City Sch Dist	4	203
Jones, Courtney/East Cleveland City Sch Dist	58	45
Jones, Craig/Pickaway-Ross Co JT Voc SD	3	175
Jones, Eric/McDonald Local School Dist	9,12,90	199
Jones, Heather/Millcreek-West Unity Local SD	67	215
Jones, Jeff/Mideast Career & Tech Ctrs	2,91	157
Jones, Jennifer/Xenia Community School Dist	58	84
Jones, Jeremy/SE Ohio Voluntary Ed Co-op	295	15
Jones, Joanna/Botkins Local School Dist	2	182
Jones, Justin/Claymont City School Dist	6	201
Jones, Ken/Howland Local School Dist	67	198
Jones, Kimberly/Paulding Exempted Village SD	2	160
Jones, Laura/Geneva Area City School Dist	4	13
Jones, Lauren/Chagrin Falls Exempted Vlg SD	72	42
Jones, Linda/East Muskingum Local Sch Dist	4	156
Jones, Lori/Mt Healthy City School Dist	67	91
Jones, Marvin, Dr/Euclid City School Dist	1	46
Jones, Matt/Madeira City School Dist	73,295	90
Jones, Matt/Winton Woods City School Dist	295	94
Jones, Mick/Botkins Local School Dist	3	182
Jones, Minda/Hicksville Exempted Village SD	67	57
Jones, Mona/Hubbard Exempted Village SD	5	198
Jones, Nicole/Berne Union Local School Dist	77	63
Jones, Paul/Wayne Trace Local School Dist	12	160
Jones, Paula/Brooklyn City School Dist	12,58,79	41
Jones, Phillip/Northern Local School Dist	73,76,84,295	161
Jones, Richard/Southwest Licking Local SD	2,84	120
Jones, Rick/Labrae Local School Dist	3	198
Jones, Ryan/Mathews Local School Dist	2	199
Jones, Sam/Buckeye Local School Dist	6	108
Jones, Shari/Warren Co Voc School Dist	4	208
Jones, Shawnna/Barberton City School Dist	2	192
Jones, Terri/Ehove Joint Voc School Dist	12,30	60
Jones, Tina/Evergreen Local School Dist	16,82	78
Jordan, Kyley/Waynesfield-Goshen Local SD	57	16
Jordan, Matt/Tuslaw Local School Dist	2	189
Jordan, Michelle/Zanesville City School Dist	7,58,79,88	157
Jordan, N/Plain Local School Dist	2,19	188
Jordan, Tammy/Big Walnut Local School Dist	36,72,88,270	58
Joseph, George/Kent City School Dist	1	165
Joseph, Kathy/New Philadelphia City Sch Dist	76	203
Jude, Joe/Graham Local School Dist	9	26
Jude, Kim/Marysville Exempted Village SD	13,34,58,77,79	204
Jump, Jeff/Columbia Local School Dist	6	123
Jump, Kristi/Grandview Heights City SD	16,82	71
Junkins, Chelsea/Waynesfield-Goshen Local SD	31	16
Jurgens, Paula/Covington Exempted Village SD	11,51,54	145
Jurick, Michelle/Fairport Harbor Exempt Vlg SD	36,69	112
Jurkowitz, Leeanne/Fredericktown Local Sch Dist	38	111
Jurosic, Jenna/Greenville City School Dist	2	55
Justen, Heather/North Central Ohio Ed Svc Ctr	34	137
Justen, Heather/North Ctrl Ohio Ed Service Ctr	34,79	180
Justice, Beth/Southern Ohio Ed Serv Ctr	1	32
Justice, Brett/Lynchburg-Clay Local Sch Dist	1	103
Justice, Brian/Southeastern Local Sch Dist	1	175
Justice, John/Brunswick City School Dist	6	140

K

NAME/District	JOB FUNCTIONS	PAGE
Kaaz, Jeffrey/Southern Local School Dist	2	161
Kaczor, Jennifer/Bellaire Local School Dist	81	17
Kaesler, Vicki/Miami Co Ed Service Center	275	144
Kaffenbarger, Daniel, Dr/Madison-Champaign Ed Svc Ctr	1	25
Kaffenberger, Jenny/Bellbrook-Sugarcreek Schools	7	83
Kagy, Laura, Dr/Seneca East Local School Dist	1	181
Kahlik, Sue/Highland Local School Dist	274	141
Kaiser, Amy/Ft Recovery Local School Dist	33,38,69,83,88	144
Kaiser, Curt/Columbiana Co Voc Sch Dist	60,88	34
Kaiser, Kevin/Reading Cmty City School Dist	67	93
Kaiser, Megan/Mayfield City School Dist	5	47
Kaiser, Sean/Northmont City School Dist	16,295	152
Kalis, Jim/Riverside Local School Dist	1	113
Kalish, Michele/Brooklyn City School Dist	8,11,15,74,273,288	41
Kalisik, Daniel/Genoa Area Local School Dist	3	159
Kalisik, Julie/Rossford Exempted Village SD	4,5	218
Kaliszewski, Nicholas/Maple Heights City School Dist	6	47
Kallotz, Karen/Tallmadge City School Dist	11,58,81	194
Kalzo, Karrie/East Holmes Local School Dist	58,79,275	104
Kamelesky, Kimberly/Liberty Center Local Sch Dist	58	101
Kamenik, Leslie/Loudonville-Perrysville SD	73,295	11
Kamets, Jamie/Salem City School Dist	8,11	35
Kaminski, Katherine/Madison Local School Dist	36	112
Kaminski, Shelby/Auburn Vocational School Dist	13	112
Kaminski, Valerie/Avon Local School Dist	8	122
Kamphaus, Julie/Norwood City School Dist	2	92
Kanable, James/Shawnee Local School Dist	1	9
Kanapki, Darren/Greenon Local School Dist	275	27
Kandel, Gary/Lake Local School Dist	13,36,57,58,88	186
Kandel, Jordan/Knox Co Voc School Dist	3	111
Kane, Jennifer/Kettering City School Dist	67	150
Kane, Kathy/Archdiocese Cincinnati Ed Off	15,68,273	94
Kanensky, Marsha/Lowellville Local School Dist	16	135
Kanney, Natalie/Coldwater Exempted Village SD	38,88	143
Kantzer, Heather/River Valley Local School Dist	58	139
Kapel, Ed/State Support Team-Region 7	15	174
Kaper, Angela/Liberty Union-Thurstn Sch Dist	12	64
Kariofiles, Pam/Butler Tech Career Dev Schs	69	21
Karl-Thompson, Jennifer/Anthony Wayne Local Sch Dist	59	127
Karling, Bryan/West Muskingum Local Sch Dist	3,4,5,83,85	157
Karlovic, Blaise/Austintown Local School Dist	11	133
Karlovic, Blaise/Mahoning Co Ed Service Center	2	133
Karlovic, Blaise/Mahoning Co Joint Voc Sch Dist	2,19	135
Karmony, Jacob/Elyria City School Dist	2,3,5,91	123
Karnes, Tom/Bryan City School Dist	73	214
Karr, Renee/Southington Local School Dist	73	200
Karshner, Eric/Logan Elm Local School Dist	6	162
Karsok, Jill/Orange City School Dist	30	48
Kaschak, Susan/Tuscarawas Valley Local SD	67	203
Kasler, Kathy/Mt Vernon City School Dist	10	111
Kassel, Abby/Revere Local School Dist	36,51,54,57,58,88,271,275	194
Kassner, Darlene/Blanchester Local School Dist	2	32
Katterheinrich, Marna/New Knoxville Local Sch Dist	12	16
Kauffman, Bruce/Avon Lake City School Dist	3,91	122
Kaufman, Dawn/Brown Local School Dist	8,58,270	25
Kaylor, Austin/Minster Local School Dist	10	15

#	Function	#	Function	#	Function	#	Function	#	Function	#	Function
1	Superintendent	16	Instructional Media Svcs	30	Adult Education	44	Science Sec	58	Special Education K-12	72	Summer School
2	Bus/Finance/Purchasing	17	Chief Operations Officer	31	Career/Sch-to-Work K-12	45	Math K-12	59	Special Education Elem	73	Instructional Tech
3	Buildings And Grounds	18	Chief Academic Officer	32	Career/Sch-to-Work Elem	46	Math Elem	60	Special Education Sec	74	Inservice Training
4	Food Service	19	Chief Financial Officer	33	Career/Sch-to-Work Sec	47	Math Sec	61	Foreign/World Lang K-12	75	Marketing/Distributive
5	Transportation	20	Art K-12	34	Early Childhood Ed	48	English/Lang Arts K-12	62	Foreign/World Lang Elem	76	Info Systems
6	Athletic	21	Art Elem	35	Health/Phys Education	49	English/Lang Arts Elem	63	Foreign/World Lang Sec	77	Psychological Assess
7	Health Services	22	Art Sec	36	Guidance Services K-12	50	English/Lang Arts Sec	64	Religious Education K-12	78	Affirmative Action
8	Curric/Instruct K-12	23	Music K-12	37	Guidance Services Elem	51	Reading K-12	65	Religious Education Elem	79	Student Personnel
9	Curric/Instruct Elem	24	Music Elem	38	Guidance Services Sec	52	Reading Elem	66	Religious Education Sec	80	Driver Ed/Safety
10	Curric/Instruct Sec	25	Music Sec	39	Social Studies K-12	53	Reading Sec	67	School Board President	81	Gifted/Talented
11	Federal Program	26	Business Education	40	Social Studies Elem	54	Remedial Reading K-12	68	Teacher Personnel	82	Video Services
12	Title I	27	Career & Tech Ed	41	Social Studies Sec	55	Remedial Reading Elem	69	Academic Assessment	83	Substance Abuse Prev
13	Title V	28	Technology Education	42	Science K-12	56	Remedial Reading Sec	70	Research/Development	84	Erate
15	Asst Superintendent	29	Family/Consumer Science	43	Science Elem	57	Bilingual/ELL	71	Public Information	85	AIDS Education

#	Function	#	Function	#	Function
88	Alternative/At Risk	277	Remedial Math K-12		
89	Multi-Cultural Curriculum	280	Literacy Coach		
90	Social Work	285	STEM		
91	Safety/Security	286	Digital Learning		
92	Magnet School	288	Common Core Standards		
93	Parental Involvement	294	Accountability		
95	Tech Prep Program	295	Network System		
97	Chief Information Officer	296	Title II Programs		
98	Chief Technology Officer	297	Webmaster		
270	Character Education	298	Grant Writer/Ptnrships		
271	Migrant Education	750	Chief Innovation Officer		
273	Teacher Mentor	751	Chief of Staff		
274	Before/After Sch	752	Social Emotional Learning		
275	Response To Intervention				

OH-T28

Ohio School Directory

DISTRICT PERSONNEL INDEX

NAME/District	JOB FUNCTIONS	PAGE
Kearns, Kristin/Jefferson Local School Dist	16	132
Kearns, Sean/Marion City School Dist	6	138
Keaton, Evan/Paint Valley Local School Dist	2	175
Keegan, Diane/Margaretta Local School Dist	2,3	61
Keehn, Mike/Columbus Grove Local Sch Dist	84	169
Keehn, Mike/Columbus Grove Local Sch Dist	73,76	169
Keenan, Charles, Dr/Maple Heights City School Dist	1	47
Keenan, Heather, Dr/North Olmsted City School Dist	81	48
Keeney, Tim/Grand Valley Local School Dist	67	13
Keenon, Una, Dr/East Cleveland City Sch Dist	67	45
Keeton, Cajon/Benton-Carroll-Salem Local SD	2	158
Keeton, Terry/Eastern Local School Dist	16,73,76	163
Kegley, Heidi/Delaware City School Dist	8,15,69	58
Kehoe, Karen/Buckeye Valley Local Sch Dist	11,34,57,58,79,275	58
Keir, Amy/Elyria City School Dist	8	123
Keisel, Nick/Reynoldsburg City School Dist	91	72
Keiser, Kirk/Fayette Local Sch Dist	67	79
Kelber, Ryan/Cuyahoga Heights Local SD	6	45
Kellar, Richard/Tallmadge City School Dist	67	194
Keller, Beth/Washington Court House City SD	16	65
Keller, Brittany/Knox Co Ed Service Center	2	110
Keller, Karen/Walnut Twp Local School Dist	67	64
Keller, Ken/Northeastern Local School Dist	67	57
Keller, Leanne/Minster Local School Dist	9	15
Keller, Linda/Mid-Ohio Ed Service Center	1	171
Kelley, Debbie/Heath City School Dist	67	117
Kelley, Greg/Pickerington Local School Dist	5	64
Kelley, Jon/Van Buren Local School Dist	3,5	99
Kelley, Laura/Rock Hill Local School Dist	58	116
Kelling, Chris/Hudson City School Dist	3	193
Kellogg, John, Dr/Westerville City School Dist	1	74
Kellough, Zebulon/Bowling Green City Sch Dist	9	216
Kelly, Donna/Twinsburg City School Dist	2	195
Kelly, Emeline/Tri-Rivers Joint Voc Sch Dist	7	139
Kelly, Jan/Northridge Local School Dist	16,82,273	119
Kelly, John, Dr/North Royalton City Sch Dist	67	48
Kelly, Keith, Dr/Mayfield City School Dist	1	47
Kelly, Kevin/Euclid City School Dist	91	46
Kelly, Leslie/Columbus City School Dist	16,285	66
Kelly, Melinda/Ross Local School Dist	81	24
Kelly, Mike/Licking Valley Local Sch Dist	16,71,84	118
Kelly, Patrick/Diocese of Youngstown Ed Off	2	137
Kelly, Robert/Brunswick City School Dist	3,91	140
Kelly, Tony/Campbell City School Dist	67	134
Kemats, Daniel/Lisbon Exempted Village SD	11	35
Kemper, Janet/Ft Loramie Local School Dist	2	182
Kemper, Melissa/Warren Local School Dist	7	210
Kempf, Kelly/Hudson City School Dist	7,34,58,83,88,90,275	193
Kendall, Kevin/Eastern Local School Dist	2	7
Kendrick, Kelly/Coventry Local School Dist	16,73,84,295	192
Kendziorski, Dana/Union Local School Dist	12	18
Kenily, Shannon/Mideast Career & Tech Ctrs	33,71	157
Kennard, Kathy/Logan-Hocking Local Sch Dist	7	104
Kennedy, Ed/South-Western City School Dist	57,89	73
Kennedy, Jeannine/Dover City School Dist	67	202
Kenny, Deborah/Harrison Hills City Sch Dist	67	101
Keplar, Beth/Teays Valley Local School Dist	10	162
Kepler, Laura/Akron Public Schools	4	190
Kerber, Bridgit/Covington Exempted Village SD	8,74,92	145
Kermavner, Bill/Cardinal Local School Dist	1	81
Kern, Beverly/Westfall Local School Dist	57	163
Kern, Brandon/Amanda-Clearcreek Local SD	67	62
Kern, Brian/Dublin City School Dist	2	69
Kern, Jared/Miller City-New Cleveland SD	73	170
Kern, Tim/Lakota Local School Dist	5	177
Kerner, Kendra/Delphos City School Dist	69	8
Kerns, Christine/Penta Co JT Voc School Dist	10	217
Kerns, Craig/Elida Local School Dist	73,76,295	8
Kerns, Craig/Huntington Local School Dist	8	175
Kerns, Kerry/Bloomfield-Mespo Local SD	3	197
Kerns, Samantha/East Palestine City Sch Dist	37,83	35
Kerschbaum, Richard/Sheffield-Sheffield Lake CSD	6	125
Kessler, Corey/Oak Hills Local School Dist	9,294	92
Kessling, Stephanie/Northwest Local School Dist	57,68,273	91
Ketaey, Andrea/Washington-Nile Local Sch Dist	54,273	179
Ketcham, Matthew/Madison-Champaign Ed Svc Ctr	2	25
Ketchum, Denise/Conotton Valley Union Local SD	2,294	100
Ketter, Rebecca/Northwest Local School Dist	77	179
Kettlehake, Kristen/Springfield City School Dist	8,74	28
Keuvern, Gina/Willoughby-Eastlake City SD	8,57,69,285	114
Keyes, Susan/Woodridge Local School Dist	57	195
Kfuvern, Gina/Willoughby-Eastlake City SD	8,79	114
Kidd, Heather/Northwest Local School Dist	45	91
Kidd, Paul/Lakewood City School Dist	79	47
Kidder, Bruce/Arcadia Local School Dist	1,11	97
Kiefer, Nora/Evergreen Local School Dist	67	78
Kiger, Allen/Pickaway-Ross Co JT Voc SD	29	175
Kight, Michelle/Wellston City School Dist	11,69,72,74,273,294	108
Kilby, Jeffrey/Hamilton City School Dist	2,11,91,274,296,298	21
Kilfoyle, Heather/Riverside Local School Dist	57	114
Kilgore, Alan/Cuyahoga Vly Career Ctr Voc SD	76	45
Kill, Debb/Spencerville Local School Dist	4	9
Kill, Jesse/Perry Local School Dist	8,57,83,271	9
Killian, Ken/Fairless Local School Dist	67	185
Kilpatrick, Karin/Warren City School Dist	12	200
Kimbel, Stephan/Osnaburg Local School Dist	67	188
Kimble, Brenda/Youngstown City School Dist	67	136
Kime, Mark/Mt Vernon City School Dist	4	111
Kimling, Joe/Madeira City School Dist	6,35,80,91	90
Kimmel, Elizabeth/Shaker Heights City Sch Dist	79	50
Kimmerly, Kylea/Beavercreek City School Dist	76	83
Kimpel, Stephanie/North Fork Local School Dist	69	119
Kinch, Patty/North Olmsted City School Dist	4	48
Kindl, Cori/Hilliard City School Dist	74,273	71
King, Angel/Licking Heights Local Sch Dist	280	118
King, Diann/Dalton Local School Dist	7	212
King, Jacob/Bethel Local School Dist	67	145
King, Jennifer/Norwalk City School Dist	31,34,58,77,88	106
King, Joe/Gibsonburg Exempted Village SD	3,5	177
King, Karen/Evergreen Local School Dist	7,35	78
King, Kari/Vanlue Local School Dist	4	99
King, Kate/Columbus City School Dist	7	66
King, Matt/East Central Ohio ESC-N Phil	2	201
King, Matt/East Central Ohio ESC-St Clair	2	17
King, Michael/Mathews Local School Dist	11,296	199
King, Pamela/Ohio Department of Education	68	1
King, Shannon/Willard City School Dist	4	106
King, Susan/Fremont City School Dist	68	176
King, Tammie/Miami Valley Career Tech VSD	16	151
King, Tina/Wellston City School Dist	4	108
King, Villa/Hillsdale Local School Dist	67	11
Kinkoph, Jennifer/Aurora City School Dist	16	164
Kinnick, Christine/Austintown Local School Dist	26	133
Kinsbury, Kim/Canton City School Dist	8	184
Kinsel, John/Ross Local School Dist	2	24
Kinsman, Joyce/Swanton Local School Dist	2,11,84,296	79
Kinyo, Krista/Buckeye Local School Dist	38	108
Kipp, Rodger/Norwood City School Dist	4	92
Kipplen, Michael/North Baltimore Local Sch Dist	31,36,69	217
Kirby, Elizabeth, Dr/Cleveland Hts-Univ Hts City SD	1	42
Kirby, Erin/Ross-Pike Co Ed Service Center	2	174
Kircher, Melissa/Bethel-Tate Local School Dist	1	30
Kireta, Julie/Edison Local School Dist	8,12,288	109
Kiriakis, Sean/Springfield City School Dist	286	28
Kirk-Chappa, Barbara/Buckeye Valley Local Sch Dist	7	58
Kirkland, Sean/Salem City School Dist	1	35
Kirkpatrick, Joyce/Canton Local School Dist	5	185
Kirkpatrick, Kevin/Carey Exempted Village SD	5	219
Kirkpatrick, Neil/Fredericktown Local Sch Dist	3	111
Kirkpatrick, Roger/Frontier Local School Dist	6	210
Kirsch, Aimee/Copley-Fairlawn City Sch Dist	79	192
Kish, Dave/Keystone Local School Dist	8,11	124
Kish, Jim/West Geauga Local School Dist	72	82
Kish, Paul, Dr/Clearview Local School Dist	8,270,296	123
Kiss, Karri/Springfield City School Dist	274	28
Kissell, Cammy/Woodmore Local School Dist	8	159
Kissell, Danny/Continental Local School Dist	1	169
Kist-Kline, Gail, Dr/Mason City School Dist	1	208
Kitchen, Ben/Southeastern Local School Dist	2	28
Kitchen, Tom/Ross-Pike Co Ed Service Center	8,74	174
Kittel, Andrea/Hardin-Houston Local Sch Dist	11,296	182
Kitzmiller, Joy/Cedar Cliff Local School Dist	2	84

School Year 2019-2020   800-333-8802   OH-T29

DISTRICT PERSONNEL INDEX

Market Data Retrieval

NAME/District	JOB FUNCTIONS	PAGE
Kizer, Nicole/Canton City School Dist	5	184
Klaber, Andy/Ross Local School Dist	73,295	24
Klag, David/Berea City School Dist	295	41
Klamfoth, Jodell/Canal Winchester Local SD	12	66
Klamfoth, Linda/Big Walnut Local School Dist	4	58
Klammer, Tamara/Berea City School Dist	58	41
Klatt, Vicki/Barnesville Exempted Vlg SD	77	17
Klaustermeyer, Dennis/United Local School Dist	73,295	36
Klear, Michael/Miller City-New Cleveland SD	67	170
Klei, Katie/New Miami Local School Dist	58	23
Klein, Ed/Chardon Local School Dist	15	82
Klein, Kaitlyn/United Local School Dist	4	36
Klein, William/Austintown Local School Dist	23	133
Klempa, Susan/Bellaire Local School Dist	72	17
Klenk, Robin/Madison Local School Dist	2	172
Klima, Ken/Cardinal Local School Dist	67	81
Kline, Jennifer/Fredericktown Local Sch Dist	11,58,275,288	111
Kline, Machelle, Dr/Columbus City School Dist	294	67
Klinefelter, Keith/Ross Local School Dist	67	24
Klingensmith, Barbara/Ashtabula Co Tech & Career SD	67	12
Klinger, Wes/Bluffton Exempted Village Sch	67	8
Klingshirn, Justin/Vermilion Local School Dist	2	62
Klingshirn, Stephanie/Mississinawa Valley Sch Dist	12	56
Kloepfer, Jeremy/Vanlue Local School Dist	6	99
Klosterman, Laura/Minster Local School Dist	2	15
Kluiber, Brett/Lorain City School Dist	73,295	124
Kmitt, Joe/Black River Local School Dist	3	139
Knabe, Robert/Ashland City School Dist	2	10
Knapke, Deanna/Ft Recovery Local School Dist	2	144
Knapp, David/Loveland City School Dist	76,286	90
Knapp, Jeanie/Ravenna School Dist	5	166
Knapp, Jennifer/Buckeye Local School Dist	2,68	140
Knapp, Jennifer/Westerville City School Dist	8,285	74
Knapp, John/Mogadore Local School Dist	1	166
Knapp, Mark/Wheelersburg Local School Dist	1,11	180
Knauer, Tracy/James A Garfield Local SD	2,84	165
Knechely, Dale/Southern Hills Joint Voc SD	73,76,295	20
Knecht, Brandon/Northmont City School Dist	2,70,76	152
Knechtly, Dale/Brown Co Ed Service Center	73	19
Knick, Thomas/Bay Village City School Dist	5	40
Knidy, Kim/North Canton City School Dist	73,76	187
Knight, Missy/Finneytown Local School Dist	71	89
Knight, Nancy/Struthers City School Dist	6	136
Knight, Rick/Canton Local School Dist	67	185
Kniss, Chris/Van Buren Local School Dist	73	99
Knoblauch, Daniel/Bright Local School Dist	3	102
Knoch, Carrie/Wapakoneta City School Dist	54,69,273,274,280	16
Knodel, Pam/Vantage Career Center Sch Dist	16,82	206
Knoll, Joel/Marlington Local School Dist	1,57	186
Knoop, Kathy/Miami East Local School Dist	5	145
Knop Buchanan, Merriha/Franklin-Monroe Local Sch Dist	5	55
Knose, Sandy/Southwest Local School Dist	79	93
Knouff, Craig/Hardin-Houston Local Sch Dist	6	182
Knowlton, Ashley/Licking Valley Local Sch Dist	8,12,13,58,69,275,285,296	118
Knuckles, Merry Lou/Cardinal Local School Dist	2	81
Knueven, Michael/Patrick Henry Local Sch Dist	67	102
Kocar, Michelle/Parma City School Dist	9	49
Kocevar, Dave/Westlake City School Dist	3,4,84,91	51
Koch, Adam/Otsego Local School Dist	1	217
Koch, Karen/Lake Local School Dist	71	186
Koch, Molly/Chippewa Local School Dist	2,71	211
Kochheiser, Cindy/Clear Fork Vly Local Sch Dist	73,82	171
Kochman, Keely/Indian Valley Local Sch Dist	36	202
Koehler, Craig, Dr/Avon Local School Dist	83,88	122
Koehler, Eric/Independence Local School Dist	2	46
Koehne, Keith/Lakota Local School Dist	8	22
Kofol, Steven/Chardon Local School Dist	2,3,15,91,271	82
Kohanski, Gerald/Aurora City School Dist	67	164
Kohl, Amy/Kenton City School Dist	83	100
Kohler, Elizabeth/Gibsonburg Exempted Village SD	33,38,69	177
Kohler, James/Keystone Local School Dist	27,31	124
Kohler, Jessica/Liberty Local School Dist	13,58,83,88	199
Kohler, Laura/Ohio Department of Education	67	1
Kohler, Marilyn/Jackson Center Local Sch Dist	36,57,69,83,85,88,270	183
Kohls, Sarah/Huntington Local School Dist	37	175
Kokai, Brian/Elyria City School Dist	73	123
Kokiko, Chuck, Dr/Jefferson Co Ed Service Center	1	108
Kolar, Rick/Mentor Exempted Village SD	3	113
Kolber, Elaine/Miami Co Ed Service Center	77	144
Konkle, Chad, Dr/Hamilton City School Dist	15,68,74,78	22
Konkoe, Brent/Wynford Local School Dist	6	39
Kopp, Nathan/Xenia Community School Dist	6	84
Koran, William/Ed Svc Center of Medina Co	1,11	139
Koran, William/Medina Co Sch Educl Svcs Ctr	1	142
Korn, Jen/Jonathan Alder Local Sch Dist	57,58,88	132
Koronich, Jan/Gallipolis City School Dist	7	81
Kosanovic, Leslie/Bridgeport School Dist	8,288	18
Kosanovic, Leslie/Shadyside Local School Dist	8	18
Kosco, Dianne/Girard City School Dist	58	197
Kosewick, Nicole/Field Local School Dist	6	165
Koslik, Larry/Switzerland of Ohio Local SD	8,13,58,275	147
Kosman, Mary/Highland Local School Dist	274	141
Koss, Brian/Beachwood City School Dist	3,91	40
Kosuda, Jim/Garfield Heights City SD	295	46
Kotechi, Krista/Sheffield-Sheffield Lake CSD	8,11,69,74,298	125
Kotowski, Ben/West Geauga Local School Dist	67	82
Kouns, Jane/Washington-Nile Local Sch Dist	67	179
Koury, Bryan/Lorain City School Dist	6,35	124
Kovach, Darian/Licking Heights Local Sch Dist	73,76	118
Kovach, Gayle/Western Reserve Local Sch Dist	273	106
Kovacs, Rob/Hamilton County ESC	71	97
Kovar, Sally/Fayette Local Sch Dist	8	79
Kovin, Kim/Washington Local School Dist	81	130
Kowalczyk, Nancy/Avon Local School Dist	4	122
Kowalski, Mark/Liberty-Benton Local Sch Dist	1	98
Kozar Kocsis, Stacy/Rocky River City School Dist	77	50
Kozarec, Mark/Valley View Local School Dist	6	153
Kozel, Steve/Carey Exempted Village SD	83	219
Kozina, Jason/Northwood Local School Dist	1	217
Kozman, Ruth/Granville Exempted Village SD	12	117
Kraft, Brad/Sandusky City School Dist	4	61
Krakowiak, Heath/Olmsted Falls City School Dist	5	48
Kramer, Amy/Pike-Delta-York Local Sch Dist	58,275	79
Kramer, Diane/New Bremen Local School Dist	9,12,51,54,85	16
Kramer, Linda/Wadsworth City School Dist	67	141
Kramer, Lou, Dr/London City School Dist	1	132
Kramer, Rachel/Springfield Local School Dist	58	128
Kramer, Rob/Lakota Local School Dist	68,74,273	22
Kramer, Tracy/Eastern Local School Dist	7,85	7
Krammer, John/New Riegel Local School Dist	73,295	181
Kramp, Lori/Pleasant Local School Dist	4	138
Krason, Kellie/Belpre City School Dist	16,82	209
Kratzer, Carrie/Georgetown Exempted Village SD	68	20
Kratzer, Charlotte/Blanchester Local School Dist	2	32
Kratzer, Kevin/Southern Hills Joint Voc SD	1	20
Krause, Beth/Kenston Local School Dist	67	82
Krauss, Rachel/Ed Svc Center of Medina Co	58	139
Krauss, Rachel/Medina Co Sch Educl Svcs Ctr	58,275	142
Kray, Steven/Buckeye Local School Dist	6	12
Kreais, Kevin/Hopewell-Loudon Local SD	67	181
Kreiger, Rosemary/Vanguard-Sentinel JT Voc SD	12,30,57,273	177
Kreinbrink, Gary/Leipsic Local School Dist	6	170
Kreis, Jeff/North Canton City School Dist	45	187
Kreischer, Adam/Norwalk City School Dist	273	106

1 Superintendent	16 Instructional Media Svcs	30 Adult Education	44 Science Sec	58 Special Education K-12	72 Summer School	88 Alternative/At Risk	277 Remedial Math K-12
2 Bus/Finance/Purchasing	17 Chief Operations Officer	31 Career/Sch-to-Work K-12	45 Math K-12	59 Special Education Elem	73 Instructional Tech	89 Multi-Cultural Curriculum	280 Literacy Coach
3 Buildings And Grounds	18 Chief Academic Officer	32 Career/Sch-to-Work Elem	46 Math Elem	60 Special Education Sec	74 Inservice Training	90 Social Work	285 STEM
4 Food Service	19 Chief Financial Officer	33 Career/Sch-to-Work Sec	47 Math Sec	61 Foreign/World Lang K-12	75 Marketing/Distributive	91 Safety/Security	286 Digital Learning
5 Transportation	20 Art K-12	34 Early Childhood Ed	48 English/Lang Arts K-12	62 Foreign/World Lang Elem	76 Info Systems	92 Magnet School	288 Common Core Standards
6 Athletic	21 Art Elem	35 Health/Phys Education	49 English/Lang Arts Elem	63 Foreign/World Lang Sec	77 Psychological Assess	93 Parental Involvement	294 Accountability
7 Health Services	22 Art Sec	36 Guidance Services K-12	50 English/Lang Arts Sec	64 Religious Education K-12	78 Affirmative Action	95 Tech Prep Program	295 Network System
8 Curric/Instruct K-12	23 Music K-12	37 Guidance Services Elem	51 Reading K-12	65 Religious Education Elem	79 Student Personnel	96 Chief Information Officer	296 Title II Programs
9 Curric/Instruct Elem	24 Music Elem	38 Guidance Services Sec	52 Reading Elem	66 Religious Education Sec	80 Driver Ed/Safety	97 Chief Technology Officer	297 Webmaster
10 Curric/Instruct Sec	25 Music Sec	39 Social Studies K-12	53 Reading Sec	67 School Board President	81 Gifted/Talented	270 Character Education	298 Grant Writer/Ptnrships
11 Federal Program	26 Business Education	40 Social Studies Elem	54 Remedial Reading K-12	68 Teacher Personnel	82 Video Services	271 Migrant Education	750 Chief Innovation Officer
12 Title I	27 Career & Tech Ed	41 Social Studies Sec	55 Remedial Reading Elem	69 Academic Assessment	83 Substance Abuse Prev	273 Teacher Mentor	751 Chief of Staff
13 Title V	28 Technology Education	42 Science K-12	56 Remedial Reading Sec	70 Research/Development	84 Erate	274 Before/After Sch	752 Social Emotional Learning
15 Asst Superintendent	29 Family/Consumer Science	43 Science Elem	57 Bilingual/ELL	71 Public Information	85 AIDS Education	275 Response To Intervention	

OH-T30

Ohio School Directory

DISTRICT PERSONNEL INDEX

NAME/District	JOB FUNCTIONS	PAGE
Kreischer, Marc/*Bloom-Vernon Local Sch Dist*	1,83	178
Kreischer, Trent/*Crestview Local School Dist*	6,8	205
Kreutzer, Sheri/*Osnaburg Local School Dist*	38	188
Krieg, Jeremy/*New Bremen Local School Dist*	3,91	16
Krieg, Leslie/*New Knoxville Local Sch Dist*	76	16
Krise, Judy/*Newton Local School Dist*	58	146
Krocker, Wanda/*Indian Valley Local Sch Dist*	16,82	202
Kroetz, Jessica/*Dublin City School Dist*	69	69
Krol, Christine, Dr/*Cuyahoga Co Ed Service Center*	67	39
Krolak, Beth/*Bowling Green City Sch Dist*	73,76,95,295	216
Kromer, Kitty/*Columbiana Co Ed Service Ctr*	275	33
Kromer, Mike/*Warrensville Heights City SD*	295	51
Kromer, Shannon/*Mariemont City School Dist*	8,288	91
Kronmann, Cathy/*Perrysburg Exempted Village SD*	76	218
Kronour, John, Dr/*Northeastern Local School Dist*	1	27
Krosnosky, Stephanie/*Bexley City School Dist*	38	66
Krugh, Timothy/*Lake Local School Dist*	67	217
Krulik, Laura/*Southern Local School Dist*	11,58,298	36
Krumpak, Jessica/*Weathersfield Local Sch Dist*	58	201
Kruse, Jack/*Northridge Local School Dist*	73	119
Kruse, Sue/*Triway Local School Dist*	4	213
Krzynowek, Dale/*Garfield Heights City SD*	6	46
Kuba, Angelique/*Black River Local School Dist*	58	139
Kubec, John/*Geneva Area City School Dist*	58,69,77	13
Kubilus, Daryl/*Cloverleaf Local School Dist*	1	140
Kucinic, Paula/*Cuyahoga Co Ed Service Center*	74	39
Kuehmle, Robert/*Mansfield City Schools*	2	172
Kuehne, Matt/*Clay Local School Dist*	73,76	178
Kuffel, Jackie/*Tolles Career & Tech Sch Dist*	69	133
Kuhn, Brian/*Clark-Shawnee Local Sch Dist*	1	27
Kuhn, Pam/*Four-Co Joint Voc School Dist*	69	79
Kuhn, Timothy/*Crestview Local School Dist*	6	171
Kujala, Eric/*Geneva Area City School Dist*	1	13
Kujala, Robert/*Southington Local School Dist*	58	200
Kula, Jake/*Buckeye Joint Voc School Dist*	16,82,297	201
Kummerer, Beth/*New Riegel Local School Dist*	67	181
Kump, Denise/*Brookville Local School Dist*	274	148
Kumpf, Gretta, Dr/*Tipp City Exempted Village SD*	1	146
Kunkle, Karen/*Howland Local School Dist*	7,35,85	198
Kunzler, Michael/*Trimble Local School Dist*	16,73,273,295	15
Kupfereerg, Craig/*Allen Co Ed Service Center*	1	7
Kurt, Edward/*Findlay City School Dist*	1,11	97
Kurtz, Jeffrey/*Penta Co JT Voc School Dist*	27	217

L

NAME/District	JOB FUNCTIONS	PAGE
L'Amoreaux, Brenda, Dr/*Louisville City School Dist*	67	186
La Civita, Jason/*Edison Local Schools District*	73	60
LaBelle, John/*Liberty Union-Thurstn Sch Dist*	73,295	64
Lacey, Kevin, Dr/*Miami Valley Career Tech VSD*	2,68	151
Lacey, Megan/*Newton Local School Dist*	280	146
Lackey, Kenneth/*Kettering City School Dist*	2,3,91	150
Lackney, Kathy/*Crooksville Exempted Vlg SD*	76	161
Laconis, Rob/*Edison Local Schools District*	76,295,297	60
LaFata, Chuck/*Reading Cmty City School Dist*	1,11,57,288	93
LaFollette, Tab/*Newton Local School Dist*	35	146
LaFon, Mark/*Ironton City School Dist*	4,59	116
Lahoski, James, Dr/*North Central Ohio Ed Svc Ctr*	1,11	137
Lahoski, Jim, Dr/*North Ctrl Ohio Ed Service Ctr*	1,11	180
Laird, Shantel/*Fremont City School Dist*	67	176
Lairson, Margie/*Northridge Local School Dist*	67	152
Lake, Chris/*Swanton Local School Dist*	1	79
Laktaks, Jodi/*Lake Local School Dist*	58	217
Lally, Beth/*Bay Village City School Dist*	67	40
Lamanna, John/*Southeast Local School Dist*	12	166
Lamb, Cindy/*Western Buckeye Ed Service Ctr*	77	205
Lamb, David/*Paulding Exempted Village SD*	77	160
Lamb, Jeremy/*Clinton-Massie Local Sch Dist*	67	33
Lamb, Scott/*Southeastern Local School Dist*	16,73	28
Lambert, Heather/*Ironton City School Dist*	7,85	116
Lambert, Natalie/*Evergreen Local School Dist*	57	78
Lambert, Paul/*Hilliard City School Dist*	67	71
Lambert, Rockford/*Western Local School Dist*	2	164
Lambert, Tessa/*Tuscarawas Valley Local SD*	76	203
Lambes, Dennis/*Northwest Local School Dist*	1,288	187
Lammage, Deb/*Miller City-New Cleveland SD*	6	170
Lammers, Christa/*Leipsic Local School Dist*	5	170

NAME/District	JOB FUNCTIONS	PAGE
Lammers, Emily/*Putnam Co Ed Service Center*	34	169
Lammers, Karl/*Kalida Local School Dist*	1,11,83	169
Lammert, Mr/*Columbiana Co Voc Sch Dist*	67	34
Lampton, Michael/*Cory-Rawson Local Sch Dist*	35,83,85	97
Lance, David/*Loudonville-Perrysville SD*	38,83,85	11
Landin, Kevin/*Ottoville Local School Dist*	67	170
Landis, Debra/*Valley View Local School Dist*	71,298	153
Landis, Lynn, Dr/*Westfall Local School Dist*	1	163
Landry, Sam/*South Range Local School Dist*	83	135
Lane, Mark/*Milton-Union Exempted Vlg SD*	6	145
Lane, Michael/*Pettisville Local School Dist*	8,69	79
Lang, Stephanie/*Ft Frye Local School Dist*	67	210
Langdon, Jeff/*Three Rivers Local School Dist*	3,68	94
Langdon, Kevin/*Danville Local School Dist*	73	110
Lange, Alexander/*Mariemont City School Dist*	71	91
Lange, Kimbe, Dr/*Oakwood City School Dist*	8,69,74,273,285,288,298	152
Langenfeld, Laurie/*State Support Team-Region 9*	15,58	190
Langford, Keith/*Shaker Heights City Sch Dist*	93	50
Langhals, Jonathan/*Marysville Exempted Village SD*	8,11,18,27,74,288,296	204
Langhals, Nicholas/*Jennings Local School Dist*	1,288	169
Langley, Robin/*Newton Falls Exempted Vlg SD*	58	200
Lanko, Bethany/*Olentangy Local School Dist*	4	59
Lanman, Justin/*Miami Trace Local School Dist*	60	65
Lanning, Cheryl/*Riverside Local School Dist*	13,58	114
Lanning, Georgianna/*North Baltimore Local Sch Dist*	4	217
Lanning, Gerald/*Polaris Joint Voc School Dist*	27,69,75	49
Lanning, Stephanie/*Washington Court House City SD*	4	65
Lansing, Kathy/*Scioto Valley Local Sch Dist*	68	164
Lantz, Doug/*Finneytown Local School Dist*	2	89
Lanz, Brett/*Orrville City School Dist*	8,11,69,73,83,271,288,294	212
Lapish, Chris/*Southeast Local School Dist*	6	213
LaPlante, John/*Youngstown City School Dist*	73,76,97,98	136
LaPoint, Julie/*Swanton Local School Dist*	73	79
Larcomb, Steve/*East Knox Local School Dist*	1,11	111
Larkin, Tom/*Kent City School Dist*	15	165
LaRoche, John/*Bellaire Local School Dist*	67	17
Larson, David/*Miami Co Ed Service Center*	1,11	144
Larson, Susan/*Muskingum Valley ESC*	81	156
Larson, Susan/*Northern Local School Dist*	81	161
Laski, Lynne/*Independence Local School Dist*	67	46
Lasso, Nathan/*Springfield-Clark Co JVSD*	10	28
Lau, Mark/*Tuslaw Local School Dist*	3	189
Laub, Michael/*Avon Local School Dist*	1	122
Laubach, Christina/*Felicity-Franklin Local SD*	2	30
Lauber, Tyler/*South Central Local Sch Dist*	58	106
Laughbaum, Neil/*Triad Local School Dist*	3,5	26
Laughlin, Kathy Jo/*East Liverpool City School Dist*	2	34
Laura, Ball/*Lima City School Dist*	30	9
Laurell, Vicki/*Oregon City School Dist*	4	128
Lauter, Jill/*North Canton City School Dist*	4	187
Lavey, Michelle/*Bradford Exempted Village SD*	9,11,288	145
Lavik, Kate/*Lockland School Dist*	77,275	90
LaVin, Jeff/*Knox Co Voc School Dist*	288	111
Lawhorn, Marketta/*Adams Co Ohio Valley Sch Dist*	16,73,76,84,95	6
Lawless, Dave/*Ironton City School Dist*	5	116
Lawley, Sharon/*Elida Local School Dist*	84	8
Lawrence, Jacqueline/*Warren City School Dist*	48	200
Lawrence, Laura/*Big Walnut Local School Dist*	58	58
Lawrence, Marvin/*Athens City School Dist*	3	14
Lawson, Bill/*Valley View Local School Dist*	11	153
Lawson, Howard/*Akron Public Schools*	69,73,294	190
Lawson, Jennifer/*Marion City School Dist*	8,15,16,74,280	138
Lawson, Melissa/*Union Scioto Local Sch Dist*	16	175
Lawson, Ravella/*Miamisburg City School Dist*	4	151
Lawton, Kathy/*Upper Arlington City Sch Dist*	34	74
Lawwell, Debby/*Chillicothe City School Dist*	2	174
Lay, John/*Tri-Village Local Sch Dist*	76,295	56
Layton, Jeffrey/*Northwestern Local School Dist*	1	212
Lazar, Cameron/*Cuyahoga Falls City Sch Dist*	58	192
Lazar, Kelly/*Brecksville Broadview Hts CSD*	83,88	41
Leach, Cherie/*Ridgedale Local School Dist*	85	138
Leach, Leigh Ann/*Logan-Hocking Local Sch Dist*	69	104
Leach, Michelle/*Ottoville Local School Dist*	36,58,69,85,270	170
Leach, Mike/*Jennings Local School Dist*	36,69	169
Leamy, Judy/*Loveland City School Dist*	35	90
Leap, Greg/*Lincolnview Local School Dist*	6	205

DISTRICT PERSONNEL INDEX

Market Data Retrieval

NAME/District	JOB FUNCTIONS	PAGE
Leasure, Tyler/*Belpre City School Dist*	286	209
Leatherman, Michelle/*Wauseon Exempted Village SD*	8,11	79
Leavitt, Nicholas/*Ashtabula Co Tech & Career SD*	295	12
Lee, Chris/*Pettisville Local School Dist*	2	79
Lee, Cindy/*National Trail Local Sch Dist*	67	168
Lee, Gary/*Eastern Local School Dist*	3,4,5,11	163
Lee, James/*Montpelier Exempted Village SD*	73,76	215
Lee, Jessica/*Lordstown Local School Dist*	36,69,83,88	199
Lee, Jordyn/*Amanda-Clearcreek Local SD*	5	62
Lee, Kristin/*Lima City School Dist*	20,23,92	9
Lee, Laurie/*Elmwood Local School Dist*	5	216
Lee, Steven/*Maumee City School Dist*	15,68	127
Leech, Lucene/*Streetsboro City School Dist*	274	167
Leedy, Amy/*Miami Valley Career Tech VSD*	30	151
Leedy, Trent/*Toledo Public Schools*	12	129
Lees, Christine/*Centerburg Local School Dist*	16	110
Leese-Graham, Thelma/*Franklin Local School Dist*	285	156
Leese, Chris/*Lawrence Co Joint Voc Sch Dist*	28,73,295	116
Leeth, Brenda/*Lincolnview Local School Dist*	8,31,36	205
Leeth, Jan/*Pike Co Area JT Voc Sch Dist*	67	163
Leeth, Jason/*Wilmington City School Dist*	5	33
Leeth, Shane/*Crestview Local School Dist*	73,295	205
LeFevre, Greg/*Ft Recovery Local School Dist*	67	144
Leffingwell, Dan/*Noble Local School Dist*	1	158
Leffler, Katherine/*Columbus City School Dist*	58,79	67
Leffler, Kelly/*Tri-Co Joint Voc Sch Dist*	3,30	15
Leffler, Rodney/*Waverly City School Dist*	3	164
Lefkowitz, Craig/*Southington Local School Dist*	6	200
LeGault, Kimberly/*Madison Plains Local Sch Dist*	11,58,88,275	133
LeGere, Pete, Dr/*Kelleys Island Local Sch Dist*	67	61
Lehman, Dana/*Highland Local School Dist*	73	155
Lehman, Jennifer/*Berne Union Local School Dist*	58	63
Lehman, Katie/*Miller City-New Cleveland SD*	12	170
Lehmann, Peggy/*Ross Local School Dist*	5	24
Lehmann, Sue/*Fostoria City School Dist*	2,19	180
Leibhardt, Patricia/*Madison Local School Dist*	54,57,58,271,275	112
Leigh, David/*North Olmsted City School Dist*	5	48
Leigh, James/*Parma City School Dist*	3,5	49
Leindecker, Keri/*James A Garfield Local SD*	12	165
Leist, Emily/*Amanda-Clearcreek Local SD*	7	62
Leist, Neil/*Eastern Local School Dist*	1	163
Leith, Adam/*Liberty Union-Thurstn Sch Dist*	5	64
Lemley, Dawn/*Eastland-Ffld Career Tech VSD*	2	70
Lengacher, Morgan/*Mapleton Local School Dist*	58	11
Lengyel, Cynthia/*Columbiana Co Ed Service Ctr*	2	33
Lenhart, Mike/*ADA Exempted Village Sch Dist*	3,5	99
Lenhart, Trent/*New Philadelphia City Sch Dist*	3,17	203
Lennartz, Eric/*Clark-Shawnee Local Sch Dist*	27,73	27
Lenzi, Linda/*Jefferson Co Ed Service Center*	81	108
Lenzo, Michael/*Maplewood JT Voc School Dist*	2,3	166
Leonard, Barb/*Indian Hill Exempted Vlg SD*	5	90
Leonard, Charlotte/*Geneva Area City School Dist*	5	13
Leonard, Dick/*Arlington Local School Dist*	6	97
Leonard, Kimberley/*Buckeye Local School Dist*	1	108
Leonard, Valerie/*Urbana City School Dist*	36,83	26
Leonardy, Jim/*Ravenna School Dist*	6,35	166
Leone, Richard/*Wooster City School Dist*	10,273	213
Leopold, Michael/*Dublin City School Dist*	79	69
Leppelmeier, Brian/*Pettisville Local School Dist*	6	79
Leppert, Erica/*Indian Hill Exempted Vlg SD*	12,13,58,79,296,298	90
Lerback, Edie/*Shelby City School Dist*	36,69,83,85	173
Lerch, Larry/*Orange City School Dist*	5	48
Lerose, Jeff/*Westerville City School Dist*	3	74
Leskovec, Darci/*Perry Local School Dist*	73,76	113
Lessing, Candice/*Oak Hills Local School Dist*	34	92
Lessler, Keith/*Mayfield City School Dist*	6	47
Leszczuk, Amanda/*Mariemont City School Dist*	31	91
Leszynski, Barb/*Westlake City School Dist*	67	51
Letterhos, Joseph/*Clyde-Green Spgs Exmpt Vlg SD*	8,11,57,83,88,285,288,298	176
Leu, Denise/*Evergreen Local School Dist*	2	78
Leugars, Norman/*Botkins Local School Dist*	28	182
Leupp, Jason/*Stryker Local School Dist*	67	215
LeVan, Scott/*Benjamin Logan Local Sch Dist*	58,275	121
Levengood, Dan/*Northwest Local School Dist*	2	187
Leventhal, Ed/*Springfield City School Dist*	67	28
Levering, Jim/*Brown Local School Dist*	16,73,76,295	25
Levey, Stacie/*Aurora City School Dist*	57	164
Levins, Trina/*Cincinnati City School Dist*	2	87
Levy, Geraldine/*Milford Exempted Village SD*	4	30
Levy, Gerry/*Wyoming City School Dist*	4	94
Lewellen, Dale/*Licking Co Ed Service Center*	1	117
Lewis, Angie/*Benton-Carroll-Salem Local SD*	16,82	158
Lewis, Bob/*Lucas Local School Dist*	16,71,73,295	172
Lewis, Britt/*Northridge Local School Dist*	2,19	119
Lewis, Cameron/*Strasburg Franklin Local SD*	73	203
Lewis, Carley/*Northridge Local School Dist*	4	119
Lewis, Chad/*Sycamore Cmty School Dist*	2	93
Lewis, Chavin/*Jefferson Twp Local Sch Dist*	36	150
Lewis, Chris/*Hilliard City School Dist*	76	71
Lewis, Chris/*Tuscarawas Valley Local SD*	73,295	203
Lewis, Christina/*Genoa Area Local School Dist*	67	159
Lewis, David/*Miami Trace Local School Dist*	1	65
Lewis, Dawn/*Wooster City School Dist*	4,57	213
Lewis, Erin/*Kenston Local School Dist*	73	82
Lewis, Greg/*Westerville City School Dist*	76,84	74
Lewis, Jay/*Graham Local School Dist*	6	25
Lewis, Jeff/*Bellbrook-Sugarcreek Schools*	2	83
Lewis, Leesa/*Gallia-Jackson-Vinton JVSD*	10,33,60,69,79	80
Lewis, Matt/*Montgomery Co Ed Service Ctr*	295	148
Lewis, Patrick/*Shelby City School Dist*	6	173
Lewis, Rick/*Kent City School Dist*	5	165
Lewis, Shari/*South Range Local School Dist*	8,11,58,275,286,288,296,298	135
Lewis, Whitney/*Lynchburg-Clay Local Sch Dist*	36	103
Libert, Scott/*Niles City School Dist*	11,69,72,74,288,298	200
Lichtenauer, Courtney/*Licking Valley Local Sch Dist*	38,83	119
Lichtenfels, Tracy/*State Support Team-Region 2*	1,11	126
Lichty, Travis/*Hicksville Exempted Village SD*	9,12	57
Liddell-Anders, Karen/*Cleveland Hts-Univ Hts City SD*	36,58,79	42
Liebrecht, Phil/*Ayersville Local School Dist*	73	57
Lifer, Larry/*Lucas Local School Dist*	2,11	172
Liggett, David/*Northridge Local School Dist*	3	119
Light, Kim/*ADA Exempted Village Sch Dist*	2	99
Lillie, Kevin/*Geneva Area City School Dist*	2	13
Lillo, Michael/*Willard City School Dist*	3,5	106
Limes, Kieth/*Sylvania City School Dist*	15,68	128
Liming, Kevin/*Bellbrook-Sugarcreek Schools*	2	83
Limo, Billie/*Trimble Local School Dist*	4	15
Limperos, Patricia/*Warren City School Dist*	67	200
Linder, Jim/*Wayne Trace Local School Dist*	6	160
Linder, Sean/*Chippewa Local School Dist*	286	211
Lindon, Jim/*Tuscarawas Valley Local SD*	286	203
Lindquist, Brad/*Northwood Local School Dist*	73	217
Lindsey, Jamie/*Warrensville Heights City SD*	58	51
Lindsey, Mike/*Marion City School Dist*	6	138
Lindsey, Rod/*River View Local School Dist*	6	37
Line, Kitty/*Preble-Shawnee Local Sch Dist*	5	168
Lingrell, Gina/*Urbana City School Dist*	37	26
Linick, Matt/*Cleveland Metro School Dist*	70	42
Link, Lauren/*New Bremen Local School Dist*	37	16
Linkenbach, Greg/*Perkins Local School Dist*	3	61
Linscott, Jamie/*Federal Hocking Local Sch Dist*	4	14
Linson, Lennie/*Northeastern Local School Dist*	81	27
Linson, Steve/*Northeastern Local School Dist*	57,58,83,88,275,280,294,298	27

#		#		#		#		#		#	
1	Superintendent	16	Instructional Media Svcs	30	Adult Education	44	Science Sec	58	Special Education K-12	72	Summer School
2	Bus/Finance/Purchasing	17	Chief Operations Officer	31	Career/Sch-to-Work K-12	45	Math K-12	59	Special Education Elem	73	Instructional Tech
3	Buildings And Grounds	18	Chief Academic Officer	32	Career/Sch-to-Work Elem	46	Math Elem	60	Special Education Sec	74	Inservice Training
4	Food Service	19	Chief Financial Officer	33	Career/Sch-to-Work Sec	47	Math Sec	61	Foreign/World Lang K-12	75	Marketing/Distributive
5	Transportation	20	Art K-12	34	Early Childhood Ed	48	English/Lang Arts K-12	62	Foreign/World Lang Elem	76	Info Systems
6	Athletic	21	Art Elem	35	Health/Phys Education	49	English/Lang Arts Elem	63	Foreign/World Lang Sec	77	Psychological Assess
7	Health Services	22	Art Sec	36	Guidance Services K-12	50	English/Lang Arts Sec	64	Religious Education K-12	78	Affirmative Action
8	Curric/Instruct K-12	23	Music K-12	37	Guidance Services Elem	51	Reading K-12	65	Religious Education Elem	79	Student Personnel
9	Curric/Instruct Elem	24	Music Elem	38	Guidance Services Sec	52	Reading Elem	66	Religious Education Sec	80	Driver Ed/Safety
10	Curric/Instruct Sec	25	Music Sec	39	Social Studies K-12	53	Reading Sec	67	School Board President	81	Gifted/Talented
11	Federal Program	26	Business Education	40	Social Studies Elem	54	Remedial Reading K-12	68	Teacher Personnel	82	Video Services
12	Title I	27	Career & Tech Ed	41	Social Studies Sec	55	Remedial Reading Elem	69	Academic Assessment	83	Substance Abuse Prev
13	Title V	28	Technology Education	42	Science K-12	56	Remedial Reading Sec	70	Research/Development	84	Erate
15	Asst Superintendent	29	Family/Consumer Science	43	Science Elem	57	Bilingual/ELL	71	Public Information	85	AIDS Education

#		#	
88	Alternative/At Risk	277	Remedial Math K-12
89	Multi-Cultural Curriculum	280	Literacy Coach
90	Social Work	285	STEM
91	Safety/Security	286	Digital Learning
92	Magnet School	288	Common Core Standards
94	Parental Involvement	294	Accountability
95	Tech Prep Program	295	Network System
97	Chief Information Officer	296	Title II Programs
98	Chief Technology Officer	297	Webmaster
270	Character Education	298	Grant Writer/Ptnrships
271	Migrant Education	750	Chief Innovation Officer
273	Teacher Mentor	751	Chief of Staff
274	Before/After Sch	752	Social Emotional Learning
275	Response To Intervention		

OH-T32

Ohio School Directory

DISTRICT PERSONNEL INDEX

NAME/District	JOB FUNCTIONS	PAGE
Lint, Beth/*Claymont City School Dist*	3,73,84,286	201
Lintz, Susanne/*Northmont City School Dist*	8,11,27,31,69,285,286,288	152
Lipinski, Christopher/*Newcomerstown Exempted Vlg SD*	58	203
Lipke, Paula/*Austintown Local School Dist*	5	133
Lippencott, Mark/*Fairbanks Local School Dist*	67	204
Lippi, Stacie/*Vantage Career Center Sch Dist*	73	206
List, Jon/*Medina Co Joint Voc Sch Dist*	3	141
Liston, Sharon/*Bridgeport School Dist*	273	18
Liston, Todd/*Southwest Licking Local SD*	5	120
Litteral, Barry/*Rock Hill Local School Dist*	6	116
Litteral, Jeremy/*Minford Local School Dist*	1	178
Little, Brian/*St Mary's City School Dist*	67	16
Little, Chad/*Bloom-Carroll Local Sch Dist*	6	63
Little, Kate/*Edgewood City School Dist*	58	21
Little, Kate/*Huber Heights City School Dist*	12,58	150
Littlefield, Brenda/*Anna Local School Dist*	73,76,286,295	182
Littleton, Nikki/*Warren City School Dist*	45	200
Livengood, Kyle/*Cuyahoga Vly Career Ctr Voc SD*	73	45
Livingston, Lauri/*Lake Local School Dist*	5	186
Lloyd, Amanda/*Fairview Park City Sch Dist*	71	46
Lloyd, Byron/*Pickaway-Ross Co JT Voc SD*	67	175
Lloyd, James, Dr/*Olmsted Falls City School Dist*	1	48
Lloyd, Maureen/*Lowellville Local School Dist*	2	135
Lobosco, Marc/*Kenston Local School Dist*	3	82
Locke, Chris/*Marlington Local School Dist*	45	186
Lockett, Ann/*Columbus City School Dist*	34	66
Lockhart, Chris/*Princeton City School Dist*	73,286	92
Lockso, Tricia/*Hubbard Exempted Village SD*	8,11,57,296,298	198
Lockwood, Paul/*Ehove Joint Voc School Dist*	67	60
Lockwood, Ryan/*Springfield Local School Dist*	2	128
Locy, Steve/*Jefferson Area Local SD*	6	13
Lodovico, Jenifer/*Lakota Local School Dist*	68	22
Loescher, Scott/*Mapleton Local School Dist*	3	11
Lofton, Gabriel, Dr/*Xenia Community School Dist*	1	84
Lofton, Lori/*New Albany-Plain Local SD*	15,68	72
Lofton, Scott/*Gahanna-Jefferson Public SD*	2	70
Logan, Christina/*New Boston Local School Dist*	58	179
Logan, Eltha/*Joseph Badger Local Sch Dist*	67	198
Logan, Jenni/*Lakota Local School Dist*	2,19	22
Logan, Laura/*Carrollton Exempted Village SD*	27	25
Logaobo, Linda/*Beachwood City School Dist*	8	40
Logue, Linda/*Penta Co JT Voc School Dist*	83	217
Lokai, Karen/*Tecumseh Local School Dist*	5	28
Lolli, Elizabeth/*Dayton Public School Dist*	1	149
Lolli, Gene/*Fairborn City School Dist*	1	84
Lombard, Karen/*Dayton Public School Dist*	34	149
Lombardo, Paul, Dr/*Cleveland Hts-Univ Hts City SD*	15,68,78	42
Lonaker, Lynnett/*Williamsburg Local School Dist*	16	32
Loncar, Victoria/*Mayfield City School Dist*	8,12,273	47
Long, Christen/*Oak Hills Local School Dist*	16,73,286,295	92
Long, Danielle/*Clearview Local School Dist*	16,82	123
Long, Jodi/*Hillsdale Local School Dist*	6	11
Long, Jody/*Monroe Local School Dist*	11,51,69,296	23
Long, Katy/*Toronto City School Dist*	7	109
Longberry, Bret/*Jonathan Alder Local Sch Dist*	76,295	132
Longfellow, Megan/*Field Local School Dist*	58	165
Longworth, Andrea/*Lakota Local School Dist*	58	22
Longworth, Bob/*Lockland School Dist*	1	90
Looker, Logan/*Bradford Exempted Village SD*	73	145
Loomis, David/*Oak Hill Union Local Sch Dist*	57	107
Loomis, Lisa/*Buckeye Local School Dist*	4	12
Loomis, Lisa/*Jefferson Area Local SD*	4	13
Looney, Chris/*Ridgedale Local School Dist*	57	138
Loose, Jeremy/*Monroeville Local School Dist*	3	105
Loper, Gretchen/*Sheffield-Sheffield Lake CSD*	9	125
Loper, Susan/*Clearview Local School Dist*	7	123
Lopez, Sheila/*Sheffield-Sheffield Lake CSD*	67	125
Lorenzo, Heather/*Miami Co Ed Service Center*	34	144
Lorson, Cheryl/*Westfall Local School Dist*	16	163
Lorta, Eric/*Northwest Local School Dist*	16,297	91
Losey, Jennifer/*Tiffin City School Dist*	8	181
Losiewicz, Donna/*Hancock Co Ed Service Center*	34	97
Lott, Heather/*Margaretta Local School Dist*	36	61
Loucka, Stephanie/*Gahanna-Jefferson Public SD*	68	70
Lovejoy, Bonnie/*Crestwood Local School Dist*	67	165
Lovejoy, Dee/*Chesapeake Union Exempt Vlg SD*	4	115

NAME/District	JOB FUNCTIONS	PAGE
Lovejoy, Kathy/*Windham Exempted Vlg Sch Dist*	16,82	167
Lovonni, Jim/*Poland Local School Dist*	67	135
Lowden, Marnie/*Apollo Joint Voc School Dist*	33,88	8
Lowe, Bill/*Port Clinton City School Dist*	5,91	159
Lowe, Eric/*Beaver Local School Dist*	1	34
Lowe, Lori/*Ross-Pike Co Ed Service Center*	58	174
Lowe, Scott/*Jackson City School Dist*	11,36,57,58,81	107
Lowe, Thomas/*Southwest Local School Dist*	2	93
Lowery, Bob/*Trimble Local School Dist*	5	15
Lowmiller, Daniel/*Green Local School Dist*	15	185
Lowry, Bobbi/*Chillicothe City School Dist*	5	174
Loy, Phil/*Buckeye Central Local Sch Dist*	6	38
Loy, Ryan/*Botkins Local School Dist*	10	182
Loyacano, Margie/*New Lebanon Local School Dist*	81	151
Lucarelli, Santina/*Kenston Local School Dist*	38	82
Lucas, George/*Milford Exempted Village SD*	67	30
Lucas, Jim/*Wayne Local School Dist*	73,297	209
Lucas, Katy/*Miamisburg City School Dist*	11,36,57,58,68,79,296	151
Lucas, Kristina/*Delaware Joint Voc Sch Dist*	273	59
Lucas, Mark/*Belmont-Harrison Voc Sch Dist*	2	18
Lucas, Randy/*East Central Ohio ESC-N Phil*	1	201
Lucas, Randy/*East Central Ohio ESC-St Clair*	1	17
Lucas, Robin/*Adams Co Ohio Valley Sch Dist*	11,83,88,298	6
Lucas, Wade, Dr/*Meta Solutions*	1	139
Lucci, David/*Toronto City School Dist*	16	109
Luce, Crystal/*Tipp City Exempted Village SD*	57	146
Luce, Nancy, Dr/*Upper Valley JT Voc Sch Dist*	1,11	147
Lucha, Thomas/*South Central Local Sch Dist*	67	106
Lucius, Chris/*Rossford Exempted Village SD*	6	218
Lucke, Matt/*Kings Local School Dist*	3,91	207
Ludban, Chris/*Hilliard City School Dist*	6	71
Ludeman, Allison/*Patrick Henry Local Sch Dist*	79	102
Luderman, Rob/*Ayersville Local School Dist*	6	56
Ludwig, Jeff/*Northwest Local School Dist*	73,295	187
Ludwig, Vicki/*Buckeye Local School Dist*	37	140
Luhring, Brenda/*North Central Ohio Ed Svc Ctr*	15	137
Luhring, Brenda/*North Ctrl Ohio Ed Service Ctr*	15,751	180
Lukus, Daniel/*Union Local School Dist*	67	18
Lukz, Joanna/*Bloomfield-Mespo Local SD*	12,58	197
Lumpkin, David/*Winton Woods City School Dist*	6	94
Lumpkins, Kathy/*Knox Co Ed Service Center*	34	110
Luna, Jose/*Toledo Public Schools*	57,271	129
Luneborg, Kelly/*Buckeye Joint Voc School Dist*	7,12,13	201
Lunsford, Johnna/*Lawrence Co Ed Service Center*	58	115
Lupia, Kati/*Jonathan Alder Local Sch Dist*	37	132
Lusher, Jamie/*Grandview Heights City SD*	8,18,68,74,273,288	71
Lute, Jarred/*Northwest Local School Dist*	67	179
Luther, Gale/*Buckeye Local School Dist*	4	140
Luther, William/*Buckeye Local School Dist*	8,11,16,27,74,88,273,275	108
Luttrel, Amy/*Southern Ohio Ed Serv Ctr*	58	32
Lutz, Denise/*Upper Arlington City Sch Dist*	73,295	74
Lutz, Kevin/*Port Clinton City School Dist*	73	159
Lutz, M Denise/*Upper Arlington City Sch Dist*	73,98	74
Lutz, Stephen/*Mogadore Local School Dist*	6	166
Lybarger, Lori/*Centerburg Local School Dist*	90	110
Lykins, Beth/*Crestview Local School Dist*	2	171
Lyle, Dave/*Springfield City School Dist*	91	28
Lynch, Dean/*Blanchester Local School Dist*	1	32
Lynch, Nathan/*Upper Sandusky Exempted Vlg SD*	2	219
Lynde, Bob/*Westerville City School Dist*	2,5	74
Lynn, Brian/*Forest Hills School Dist*	10,27,31,61,271,273	89
Lyons, Anthony/*Piqua City School Dist*	15	146
Lyons, Mary/*Colonel Crawford Local SD*	273	38
Lyons, Pamela/*Mideast Career & Tech Ctrs*	4	157
Lysiak, Ted/*James A Garfield Local SD*	1,11,83	165

M

NAME/District	JOB FUNCTIONS	PAGE
Maag, Karen/*Putnam Co Ed Service Center*	27,58	169
Maag, Valerie/*Jennings Local School Dist*	2	169
Maassen, Jamie/*Ed Service Center Lorain Co*	58	122
Mace-Miller, Mary/*Westfall Local School Dist*	58	163
Macechko, Amy/*Talawanda School Dist*	7,83	24
Maceyak, Barbara/*Canton City School Dist*	68	184
Mack, Carolyn/*Dayton Public School Dist*	8,74	149
Mack, Kathleen/*Brecksville Broadview Hts CSD*	67	41
Mack, Kyle/*Forest Hills School Dist*	286	89

DISTRICT PERSONNEL INDEX

Market Data Retrieval

NAME/District	JOB FUNCTIONS	PAGE
Mackley, Timm, Dr/Knox Co Ed Service Center	1	110
MacMillian, Dori/Niles City School Dist	77	200
MacNeil, Kathie, Dr/Warren Co Ed Service Center	77,83,275	206
MacNicol, Sharon/Ehove Joint Voc School Dist	273	60
Macon, Yzvetta/Mt Healthy City School Dist	10	91
Macwhinney, Angie/Delaware City School Dist	58	58
Macy, Matt/Ansonia Local School Dist	6	55
Madden, Corrie/Deer Park Cmty School Dist	38	89
Madden, Marcus/Twinsburg City School Dist	295	195
Madden, Pam/New Boston Local School Dist	4	178
Maddox, Jeffrey/Worthington School Dist	11,36,68,79,83,270,296	75
Maffett, Cathy/Brown Local School Dist	16,82	25
MaGee, Eric/East Clinton Local School Dist	1,83	33
Magers, Jennifer/Pioneer Joint Voc School Dist	60	173
Maggard, Donna/Northridge Local School Dist	5	152
Magier, Tom/Ed Svc Center of Medina Co	88	139
Magistrale, Nick/Dublin City School Dist	6	69
Maglioico, Mike/Aurora City School Dist	58,69,77	164
Magrey, Joseph/Olmsted Falls City School Dist	73,95,295	48
Magyar, Joelle/Brecksville Broadview Hts CSD	1	41
Mahan, Kyle/Grandview Heights City SD	4	70
Mahnke, Linda/Four-Co Joint Voc School Dist	85	79
Maholm, Bradley/Indian Valley Local Sch Dist	2	202
Mahon, Amanda/Mid-Ohio Ed Service Center	8,16	171
Mahone, Kyle/Hilliard City School Dist	4	71
Mahoney, Timothy/Diocese of Toledo Ed Office	8	131
Mahovlich, Kirsten/Cleveland Metro School Dist	44,285	42
Mahr, Ryan/Meigs Local School Dist	67	142
Maier, Ryan/Hardin-Houston Local Sch Dist	1	182
Main, Patty/Sandy Valley Local School Dist	8,11,288,296	189
Major, Frank/Maple Heights City School Dist	11,68,79	47
Majoy, Kim/Norwalk City School Dist	29	106
Makarek, Evelyn/Highland Local School Dist	4	141
Makowski, Alysha/Cardinal Local School Dist	7	81
Makowski, Bonnie/Berkshire Local School Dist	294	81
Malainy, Joyce, Dr/Licking Co Joint Voc Sch Dist	1,11	118
Malchesky, Betty Jo, Dr/Perry Local School Dist	8,15,288,296	113
Malich, George/Canfield Local School Dist	73	134
Malinas, Becky/Kirtland Local School Dist	11,285,288	112
Malito, Greg/Western Reserve Local Sch Dist	38,69,83	136
Mallett, Doug/Marietta City School Dist	67	210
Mallory, Suzy/Indian Lake Local School Dist	37	121
Malloy, Sherri/West Branch Local School Dist	5	136
Malone, Bridget/Rock Hill Local School Dist	38	116
Malone, David/Liberty Local School Dist	67	199
Malone, Dennis/Talawanda School Dist	4,68	24
Malone, Steve/Union Scioto Local School Dist	3	175
Malwich, Kevin/Loudonville-Perrysville SD	6,35,286	11
Mamais, Jessica/New Albany-Plain Local SD	69,294	72
Mamgun, Andy/Minerva Local School Dist	6	187
Mandelik, Ron/Vandalia Butler City Sch Dist	73,295	153
Mandrick, Thomas/Greeneview Local School Dist	77	84
Mangan, Connie/Cuyahoga Vly Career Ctr Voc SD	16	45
Mangas, David/Cuyahoga Vly Career Ctr Voc SD	1	45
Mangas, Scott/Ottoville Local School Dist	1,288	170
Mangerink, Bob/Connect Information Tech Ctr	67	54
Mangus, Debrorah/Fairfield Local Sch Dist	36,83	102
Maniaci, Caren/Muskingum Valley ESC	58,79	156
Manik, Greg/Avon Local School Dist	3	122
Manist, Josh/Southern Local School Dist	16	36
Mankins, Diane/Marysville Exempted Village SD	1	204
Manley, Matthew/Crestview Local School Dist	1,11	34
Mann, Scott/Riverside Local School Dist	1,11	121
Manning, Debbie/Mideast Career & Tech Ctrs	60	157
Manning, Elaine/Ripley-Union-Lewis-Huntngtn SD	7,35,85	20
Mannion, Megan/Akron Public Schools	16,82	190
Manor, Beth/Miami Valley Career Tech VSD	10,18	151

NAME/District	JOB FUNCTIONS	PAGE
Mansfield, Jeanie/Defiance City School Dist	16	57
Mansfield, Lisa/McComb Local School Dist	67	98
Mantal, Jason/Scioto Valley Local Sch Dist	5	164
Mantas, Sam/Hubbard Exempted Village SD	4	198
Manuel, Jenny/Southern Local School Dist	297	143
Manz, Mark/Paulding Exempted Village SD	67	160
Manz, Tim/Wayne Trace Local School Dist	8,11,69,286,288,296,298	160
Maples, Jason/Lincolnview Local School Dist	3	205
Mapus, James/Perrysburg Exempted Village SD	5	218
Mara, Tom/North College Hill City SD	3	91
Marchal, Thomas/St Henry Cons Local Sch Dist	16,73,76,95,295,297	144
Marchal, Tom/St Henry Cons Local Sch Dist	84	144
Marchetti, Tom/Delaware Joint Voc School Dist	30	59
Marconi, Melissa/Tuslaw Local School Dist	1	189
Marcucci, Courtney/Cuyahoga Falls City Sch Dist	57	192
Marcum, Scott/Arlington Local School Dist	11,58	97
Margraf, Melody/Seneca East Local School Dist	11,83,296,298	181
Marhoover, Brad/Western Local School Dist	67	164
Mariano, Nick/Liberty Center Local Sch Dist	298	101
Marino, Robert, Dr/Trumbull Co Ed Service Center	11,15	196
Marinucci, Marco/Boardman Local School Dist	6	134
Marion, Steve/Jackson City School Dist	16,73,84,295	107
Markham, Adam/Butler Co Ed Service Center	71	20
Markijohn, Anthony/Geneva Area City School Dist	91	13
Markland, Barb/Green Local School Dist	2	212
Marks, Brian/Southeastern Local Sch Dist	81	175
Marks, Jeremy/Ohio Department of Education	11	1
Markus, Greg/Rocky River City School Dist	2	50
Markwardt, Richard/West Geauga Local School Dist	1	82
Marlow, Jane/Knox Co Voc School Dist	30	111
Marlow, Steve/Hudson City School Dist	2,4,5,91	193
Marochino, Carrie/Green Local School Dist	8,13	185
Maroni, Joe/Canfield Local School Dist	9	134
Marple, Lori/Dublin City School Dist	45	69
Marquez, Melissa/Waverly City School Dist	8,11,58,72,270,271,273,288	164
Marra, Robert/Southern Local School Dist	5	35
Marrah, Doug, Dr/Ashland City School Dist	1	10
Marras, James/Cuyahoga Falls City Sch Dist	16,73,82,286	192
Marschhausen, John, Dr/Hilliard City School Dist	1	71
Marsh, Gale/Dublin City School Dist	68	69
Marsh, Jim/East Clinton Local School Dist	6	33
Marsh, Kelli/Urbana City School Dist	286	26
Marshal, Beth/Troy City School Dist	58,83	146
Marshall, Charlie/Felicity-Franklin Local SD	73,98,295,297	30
Marshall, Debbie/Brunswick City School Dist	83	140
Marshall, Dick/Garaway Local School Dist	67	202
Marshall, Leslie/Chippewa Local School Dist	273	211
Marshall, Nicole/Westerville City School Dist	2,19	74
Marthe, Alice/Mentor Exempted Village SD	12,51	113
Martin, Amy/Union Scioto Local School Dist	74	175
Martin, Charles/Bowling Green City School Dist	3,91	216
Martin, Cooper/Richmond Heights Local SD	2,19	49
Martin, Dana/Kings Local School Dist	58	207
Martin, David/Brecksville Broadview Hts CSD	8,69,288,298	41
Martin, David/East Cleveland City Sch Dist	3	45
Martin, Dawn/West Holmes Local School Dist	4	105
Martin, Jason/Columbiana Exempted Village SD	286,295,297	34
Martin, Leigh/West Branch Local School Dist	16,82	136
Martin, Mary Kay/Licking Valley Local Sch Dist	67	119
Martin, Mike/Buckeye Central Local Sch Dist	10	38
Martin, Nicholas/North College Hill City SD	2	91
Martin, Rachel/Eastern Local School Dist	8,11,57,58,286,288	142
Martin, Roger/Fairfield City School Dist	15	21
Martin, Steve/Ross-Pike Co Ed Service Center	1,11	174
Martin, Susan/Groveport Madison Local SD	11,296	71
Martin, Tessa/Wynford Local School Dist	27	39
Martin, Todd/Colonel Crawford Local SD	1	38

#	Function	#	Function	#	Function	#	Function	#	Function	#	Function
1	Superintendent	16	Instructional Media Svcs	30	Adult Education	44	Science Sec	58	Special Education K-12	72	Summer School
2	Bus/Finance/Purchasing	17	Chief Operations Officer	31	Career/Sch-to-Work K-12	45	Math K-12	59	Special Education Elem	73	Instructional Tech
3	Buildings And Grounds	18	Chief Academic Officer	32	Career/Sch-to-Work Elem	46	Math Elem	60	Special Education Sec	74	Inservice Training
4	Food Service	19	Chief Financial Officer	33	Career/Sch-to-Work Sec	47	Math Sec	61	Foreign/World Lang K-12	75	Marketing/Distributive
5	Transportation	20	Art K-12	34	Early Childhood Ed	48	English/Lang Arts K-12	62	Foreign/World Lang Elem	76	Info Systems
6	Athletic	21	Art Elem	35	Health/Phys Education	49	English/Lang Arts Elem	63	Foreign/World Lang Sec	77	Psychological Assess
7	Health Services	22	Art Sec	36	Guidance Services K-12	50	English/Lang Arts Sec	64	Religious Education K-12	78	Affirmative Action
8	Curric/Instruct K-12	23	Music K-12	37	Guidance Services Elem	51	Reading K-12	65	Religious Education Elem	79	Student Personnel
9	Curric/Instruct Elem	24	Music Elem	38	Guidance Services Sec	52	Reading Elem	66	Religious Education Sec	80	Driver Ed/Safety
10	Curric/Instruct Sec	25	Music Sec	39	Social Studies K-12	53	Reading Sec	67	School Board President	81	Gifted/Talented
11	Federal Program	26	Business Education	40	Social Studies Elem	54	Remedial Reading K-12	68	Teacher Personnel	82	Video Services
12	Title I	27	Career & Tech Ed	41	Social Studies Sec	55	Remedial Reading Elem	69	Academic Assessment	83	Substance Abuse Prev
13	Title V	28	Technology Education	42	Science K-12	56	Remedial Reading Sec	70	Research/Development	84	Erate
15	Asst Superintendent	29	Family/Consumer Science	43	Science Elem	57	Bilingual/ELL	71	Public Information	85	AIDS Education

#	Function	#	Function
88	Alternative/At Risk	277	Remedial Math K-12
89	Multi-Cultural Curriculum	280	Literacy Coach
90	Social Work	285	STEM
91	Safety/Security	286	Digital Learning
92	Magnet School	288	Common Core Standards
93	Parental Involvement	294	Accountability
95	Tech Prep Program	295	Network System
97	Chief Information Officer	296	Title II Programs
98	Chief Technology Officer	297	Webmaster
270	Character Education	298	Grant Writer/Ptnrships
271	Migrant Education	750	Chief Innovation Officer
273	Teacher Mentor	751	Chief of Staff
274	Before/After Sch	752	Social Emotional Learning
275	Response To Intervention		

OH-T34

Ohio School Directory

DISTRICT PERSONNEL INDEX

NAME/District	JOB FUNCTIONS	PAGE
Martindale, Deanna/*Lakewood Local School Dist*	285	118
Martindale, Dee/*Lakewood Local School Dist*	13	118
Martinez, Christian/*Swanton Local School Dist*	4	79
Martinko, Robert/*Weathersfield Local Sch Dist*	93	201
Marton, Lisa/*Northern Local School Dist*	11,296,298	161
Maruniak, Scott/*Mechanicsburg Exempted Vlg SD*	2,19	26
Maruniak, Scott/*North Union Local School Dist*	2,19	204
Marvin, Sharon/*Swanton Local School Dist*	8,12,58	79
Mascioli, Mitch/*Jackson-Milton Local Sch Dist*	67	134
Masella, Florence/*Euclid City School Dist*	9,77	46
Maslona, Mark/*Brecksville Broadview Hts CSD*	6	41
Masloski, Mark/*Jefferson Co Ed Service Center*	73	108
Masloski, Mike/*Ridgewood Local School Dist*	1	37
Mason, Barry/*Jackson Local School Dist*	15	186
Mason, Chad/*Cedar Cliff Local School Dist*	1	84
Mason, Doug/*Seneca East Local School Dist*	6	181
Mason, Jon/*Cardington-Lincoln Local SD*	2	155
Mason, Jon/*Highland Local School Dist*	2,11	155
Mason, Julie/*Tolles Career & Tech Sch Dist*	4	133
Mason, Mark/*Madison Plains Local Sch Dist*	67	133
Mason, Matt/*Madison Plains Local School Dist*	6	133
Mass, Tony/*Diocese of Toledo Ed Office*	10	131
Massary, Armand/*Northwestern Local School Dist*	5	212
Masse, Lindsey/*Loveland City School Dist*	2	90
Masser, Brian/*Clark-Shawnee Local Sch Dist*	11,15,72	27
Massie, Lauren/*Licking Co Joint Voc Sch Dist*	30	118
Massie, Leah/*Wellston City School Dist*	58,79,275	108
Massingill, Donna/*Maumee City School Dist*	36	127
Mast, Jodi/*Huron City School Dist*	67	60
Mastrine, Holly/*Southeast Local School Dist*	8,11,72,88,288,296	213
Mastroianni, Sharon/*Ehove Joint Voc School Dist*	1,11	60
Matheson, Ashley/*Arcanum Butler Local Sch Dist*	38	55
Mathews-Bebech, Mary/*Hubbard Exempted Village SD*	58,68,79	198
Mathews, Gregory/*State Support Team 11*	15	78
Mathews, Tracy/*Clinton-Massie Local Sch Dist*	2,4	33
Matos, Danielle/*Western Reserve Local Sch Dist*	37	136
Matson, Robert/*North Olmsted City School Dist*	2,11	48
Matsudo, Kenji/*Madeira City School Dist*	1	90
Matter, Ronald/*Penta Co JT Voc School Dist*	1,11	217
Mattern, Jacob/*Clark-Shawnee Local Sch Dist*	5	27
Matthews, Brian/*Plain Local School Dist*	8,15	188
Matthews, Kyle/*Lakewood Local School Dist*	3	118
Matthews, Merri/*Buckeye Local School Dist*	2	108
Matthews, Michael/*Fairview Park City Sch Dist*	3,5,68,74	46
Matthews, Rindy/*Fairfield Local Sch Dist*	67	102
Matthews, Samantha/*New London Local School Dist*	4	105
Matthies, Rosie/*Clark-Shawnee Local Sch Dist*	45	27
Mattix, Patricia/*Vandalia Butler City Sch Dist*	4	153
Matulich, Robyn/*Canton City School Dist*	71	184
Matz, Tara/*Fostoria City School Dist*	8,11,286,288,298	180
Mauk, Greg/*New Boston Local School Dist*	35	179
Maul, Jim/*Indian Creek Local Sch Dist*	38	109
Mauro, Mary/*Grandview Heights City SD*	7	71
Mautz, Lisa/*Hamilton Local School Dist*	16,73,84	71
Mawer, Michelle/*Coldwater Exempted Village SD*	2	143
Maxfield, Jesse/*Mad River Local School Dist*	27,95	151
Maxwell, Kathi/*Westlake City School Dist*	15	51
Maxwell, Lisa/*Northeastern Local School Dist*	72	57
Maxwell, Mike/*North Fork Local School Dist*	4,5	119
Maxwell, Thomas/*New Lebanon Local School Dist*	11,296	151
May, Brent/*Plain Local School Dist*	1,11	188
May, Daniel/*Midview Local School Dist*	6	125
May, Michael/*Maple Heights City School Dist*	11,68,79	47
May, Tamara/*Hamilton Local School Dist*	5	71
Maybaugh, Beth/*Dover City School Dist*	273	202
Mayberry, Matt/*Mechanicsburg Exempted Vlg SD*	5	26
Mayberry, Paul/*New Boston Local School Dist*	83,273	179
Mayell, Michael/*Brunswick City School Dist*	1	140
Mayer, Nick/*Woodridge Local School Dist*	6	195
Mayes, John/*Defiance City School Dist*	3,91	57
Mayes, Scott/*Trotwood-Madison City SD*	3	152
Mayle, Amanda/*Lorain Co Joint Voc Sch Dist*	7,83,85	125
Mayle, Mary-Kay/*Buckeye Local School Dist*	7	108
Maynard, Junie/*Southern Local School Dist*	7,83,88	143
Mayo, Julie/*Lawrence Co Ed Service Center*	58	115
Mays, Andrew/*New Richmond Exempted Vlg SD*	5	31
Mazur, Patricia/*Toledo Public Schools*	16,71	129
Mazur, Roxanne/*Carrollton Exempted Village SD*	2,296	25
Mazzi, Steven/*Westerville City School Dist*	68	74
McAfee, Steve/*Whitehall City School Dist*	2	75
McArthur, Cheryl/*Mahoning Co Ed Service Center*	2,68	133
McBride, Laura/*Springfield Local School Dist*	58,81	136
McBride, Pat/*Newton Local School Dist*	1	146
McBride, Tom/*Diocese of Cleveland Ed Office*	73	52
McBrien, Jann/*Benjamin Logan Local Sch Dist*	4	121
McBroom, Tammy/*Tecumseh Local School Dist*	274	28
McCaffrey, Beth/*Berkshire Local School Dist*	2	81
McCahan, Michael/*Sandy Valley Local School Dist*	73	189
McCall, Harrison/*Wickliffe City School Dist*	6	114
McCall, Tyler/*Warren Co Ed Service Center*	73	206
McCallister, Marilyn/*Campbell City School Dist*	38	134
McCance, Donna/*Lancaster City School Dist*	58	63
McCandlish, Sally/*Fairfield Union Local Sch Dist*	4	63
McCarthy, Amy/*Ohio Hi-Point Joint Voc SD*	7,91	121
McCarthy, Kelly/*North Ridgeville City Sch Dist*	67	125
McCartney, Melissa/*New Lebanon Local School Dist*	83,88	151
McCarty, Ann, Dr/*Bowling Green City Sch Dist*	8,11,57,83,286,288,296,298	216
McCaskey, Shane/*Loudonville-Perrysville SD*	3,91	11
McCaughtry, Michele/*Youngstown City School Dist*	81	136
McClain, Jason/*Sidney City School Dist*	3,4	183
McClain, Lesley/*Montgomery Co Ed Service Ctr*	275	148
McClain, Lisa/*Grand Valley Local School Dist*	38	13
McClanahan, Cheri/*Manchester Local School Dist*	5	7
McClanahan, Cheri/*Manchester Local School Dist*	6	7
McCleese, Tiffany/*West Clermont Local Sch Dist*	4	31
McClelan, Rena/*Perkins Local School Dist*	8,69,280	61
McClelland, John/*New Albany-Plain Local SD*	67	72
McCloskey, Carl/*Huntington Local School Dist*	67	175
McClure, Ron/*Big Walnut Local School Dist*	3,4,5	58
McClurg, Janet/*Hardin-Houston Local Sch Dist*	16,82	183
McClury, Melissa/*Vantage Career Center Sch Dist*	30	206
McCollough, Brenda/*Pike-Delta-York Local Sch Dist*	4	79
McCollum, Bryan/*Alexander Local School Dist*	3	14
McComas, Jennifer/*Heath City School Dist*	58,77	117
McConnell, Jerry/*Chesapeake Union Exempt Vlg SD*	1	115
McCord, Lisa/*Covington Exempted Village SD*	7	145
McCorkle, Krista/*Zane Trace Local School Dist*	76	176
McCormick, Cathy/*Northridge Local School Dist*	271	119
McCormick, Cristine/*Mason City School Dist*	73,76,286,295	208
McCormick, Kristie/*Crestview Local School Dist*	16,286	205
McCormick, Zach/*Wyoming City School Dist*	73,98,286	94
McCoy, Brooke/*Wilmington City School Dist*	37	33
McCoy, Cathy/*Bloom-Vernon Local Sch Dist*	38,69	178
McCoy, Kesia/*Fairfield Local Sch Dist*	8	102
McCoy, Michael/*Oak Hill Union Local Sch Dist*	1	107
McCoy, Samuel/*Vanlue Local School Dist*	16,73,76,295	99
McCrate, Karie/*Dover City School Dist*	15	202
McCrate, Tim/*Dover City School Dist*	6	202
McCray, Arthur/*Southeastern Local School Dist*	73	175
McCrea, Cathy/*Ridgewood Local School Dist*	67	37
McCreary, Mike/*North Central Ohio Ed Svc Ctr*	15	137
McCreery, Frank/*Frontier Local School Dist*	8,74,298	210
McCuen, Jeffrey/*Worthington School Dist*	2	75
McCullough, Mark/*Licking Valley Local Sch Dist*	6	118
McCullough, Sandra/*Independence Local School Dist*	58,275	46
McCully, Chris/*Polaris Joint Voc School Dist*	15	49
McCumber, Julio/*Northwestern Local School Dist*	8,15	212
McCurdy, Jackie/*Lancaster City School Dist*	76	63
McCurdy, Pamela/*Liberty Local School Dist*	8,11,57,69,273,288	199
McCutchen, David/*Diocese of Toledo Ed Office*	64	131
McDade, Michael/*North Olmsted City School Dist*	5,73	48
McDaniel-Brown, Jayna/*Delaware City School Dist*	67	58
McDaniel, Heidi/*Clear Fork Vly Local Sch Dist*	58	171
McDaniel, Nicole/*Elyria City School Dist*	5	123
McDaniel, Tracy/*Lexington Local School Dist*	58	172
McDaniels, Ginger/*River Valley Local School Dist*	274	139
McDermott, Nancy/*Washington Court House City SD*	81	65
McDermott, Sharon/*Franklin Local School Dist*	1,83	156
McDevitt, Jeremy/*Kenston Local School Dist*	15	82
McDole, Paul/*Cincinnati City School Dist*	68	87
McDonald, Charinita/*Maple Heights City School Dist*	5	47
McDonald, Julie/*Huron City School Dist*	8,11,31,273,296,298	60

School Year 2019-2020   800-333-8802   OH-T35

DISTRICT PERSONNEL INDEX

Market Data Retrieval

NAME/District	JOB FUNCTIONS	PAGE
McDonald, Julie/Sandusky City School Dist	8,11,81,288,296	61
McDonald, Nick/Adena Local School Dist	3	174
McDonald, Nicole/Indian Creek Local Sch Dist	288	109
McDonald, Stan/Delaware City School Dist	73	58
McDonell, Meredith/West Muskingum Local Sch Dist	38	157
McDonnell, Jacquelyn/Norton City School Dist	37	193
McDonnell, Tom/Dublin City School Dist	79	69
McDonough, Mike/Hilliard City School Dist	3,15,91	71
McDougal, Amy/Cuyahoga Falls City Sch Dist	58	192
McDougal, Melissa/Buckeye Central Local Sch Dist	67	38
McDowell, Chris/Dublin City School Dist	2,10	69
McDowell, Jim/East Clinton Local School Dist	3	33
McElfresh, Jeff/Southeast Local School Dist	67	166
McElroy, Caleb/Marietta City School Dist	5,76	210
McEvoy, Rick/Clermont Northeastern Local SD	3	30
McFarland, Doug/Western Local School Dist	35	164
McFarland, Jim/Franklin City School Dist	58	207
McFarland, Jim/Tri-Rivers Joint Voc Sch Dist	67	139
McFarland, Melissa/Cory-Rawson Local School Dist	8,11,36	97
McFarland, Rodney/Dawson-Bryant Local School Dist	73	115
McFarland, Susan/Brown Co Ed Service Center	34	19
McFerren, Randy/East Muskingum Local Sch Dist	76	156
McGaughey, John/New Lexington School Dist	67	161
McGee, Jill/Northern Local School Dist	280	161
McGhee, Annie/Independence Local School Dist	6,83,88	46
McGill, Andy/West Liberty-Salem Local SD	91	26
McGill, Micheal/Western Reserve Local Sch Dist	73,295	106
McGing, Matthew/Twinsburg City School Dist	73	195
McGinnis, Angie/Mohawk Local School Dist	85	219
McGinnis, Lisa/Buckeye Central Local Sch Dist	58	38
McGinty, Craig/Dalton Local School Dist	3	212
McGinty, Kathryn/Westlake City School Dist	83	51
McGlynn, Doug/Western Reserve Local Sch Dist	1	136
McGlynn, Maribeth/Austintown Local School Dist	36,69	133
McGowan, Bill/Eastland-Ffld Career Tech VSD	67	70
McGowan, Cassie/Logan-Hocking Local Sch Dist	4	104
McGowan, Kim/Lakota Local School Dist	11	22
McGraph, Jacob/Greeneview Local School Dist	2,11	84
McGrath, Cheryl/Columbiana Co Ed Service Ctr	58,88	33
McGrath, Daniel/Massillon City School Dist	5	187
McGrath, Katy/Kenston Local School Dist	71	82
McGregor, Roger/Southwest Local School Dist	76	93
McHugh, Jeff/Woodridge Local School Dist	67	195
McIlhenny, Jason/Green Local School Dist	3	178
McIlhenny, Jessica/Green Local School Dist	288	178
McIntosh, Heidi/Southern Local School Dist	7	36
McIntyre, Debra/Continental Local School Dist	57,69,83,85,88	169
McJecee, Michell/Northridge Local School Dist	57,275	119
McKahan, Lynn/State Support Team-Region 1	1	132
McKean, Lori/Wapakoneta City School Dist	4	16
McKee, Brad/Greenon Local School Dist	2,11	27
McKee, Christopher/Northwest Local School Dist	2	91
McKee, Ed/Noble Local School Dist	67	158
McKee, Gregg/Arcadia Local School Dist	73,95,286	97
McKee, Mary/South Central Local Sch Dist	8,36,57,69	106
McKee, Tari/Hamilton City School Dist	20,23	22
McKeegan, Barb/Martins Ferry City School Dist	81	18
McKeehan, Mark/Wayne Local School Dist	3	208
McKeiver, Jaime/Circleville City School Dist	7,83,85	162
McKendry, Craig/Sandy Valley Local School Dist	2	189
McKenny-Janev, Amy/Dayton Public School Dist	57	149
McKenzie, Gregg/Western Brown Local Sch Dist	16	20
McKenzie, Matt/Boardman Local School Dist	3	134
McKenzie, Mike/Beaver Local School Dist	6	34
McKibben, Brad/Colonel Crawford Local SD	67	38
McKibben, Linda/Ashland City School Dist	8,11,54,57,273,296,298	10
McKillip, Nancy/Fremont City School Dist	76	176
McKinley, Karen/Carlisle Local School Dist	81	206
McKinney, Patrick/Willoughby-Eastlake City SD	73,286	114
McKinniss, Ted/Marion City School Dist	67	138
McKinnon, Tom/Revere Local School Dist	6	194
McKlaskey, Janet/Liberty Union-Thurstn Sch Dist	6	64
McLane, Ryan/West Muskingum Local Sch Dist	58	157
McLarnan, Richard/Knox Co Ed Service Center	67	110
McLarnan, Richard/Knox Co Voc School Dist	67	111
McLaughlin, Lori/West Branch Local School Dist	67	136
McLean, Rebecca/Ottawa Hills Local Sch Dist	16	128
McLeese, Janet/Perry Local School Dist	4	188
McLendon, Cassie/Franklin Local School Dist	11,57,286,288,298	156
McLoughlin, Tyson/Ottawa-Glandorf Local Sch Dist	6	170
McMahan, Julie/Green Local School Dist	298	185
McMahon, Jennifer/Newark City School Dist	59	119
McMahon, Mary Ann/Niles City School Dist	67	200
McMannis, David/Berne Union Local School Dist	73,76,295	63
McMasters, Samantha/Bexley City School Dist	57,58	66
McMichael, Georgia/Spencerville Local School Dist	16	9
McMillan, Janine/Upper Sandusky Exempted Vlg SD	8,270,288	219
McMillen, Dianna/Loudonville-Perrysville SD	54,58,275	11
McMillen, Melissa/Barnesville Exempted Vlg SD	12	17
McMullen, Charity/Tri-Co North School Dist	27	168
McMurry, Peggy/Olentangy Local School Dist	8	59
McNamara, Keanna/Bath Local School Dist	5	8
McNaull, Phillip/Ashland City School Dist	73	10
McNeely, Kristin/Yellow Springs Exempted Vlg SD	12	85
McNeely, Michelle/Licking Co Joint Voc Sch Dist	38,83,88	118
McNichols, Catherina/Sheffield-Sheffield Lake CSD	38,83	125
McNickle, Tricia/Southern Local School Dist	8,274,288	143
McNier, Chuck/Southeastern Local School Dist	5	28
McNinch, Amanda/Struthers City School Dist	11,58,69,77,296	136
McPheron, Dennis/Findlay City School Dist	3,91	97
McPheron, Jeff/Botkins Local School Dist	1,11,83	182
McPherson, Mary Ann/Madeira City School Dist	34	90
McPherson, Michele/Maplewood JT Voc School Dist	69	166
McQuade, Timothy/Wauseon Exempted Village SD	77	80
McQuaide, Russell/Mathews Local School Dist	1	199
McVey, Ann/Eastwood Local School Dist	8,58,69,79,81,275	216
McVey, Ann, Dr/Northwood Local School Dist	79,288,298	217
McVicker, Jeff/Howland Local School Dist	5,74,91	198
McVicker, Jill/Jefferson Co JT Voc Sch Dist	60	109
McWilliams, Ellen/Akron Public Schools	8,15	190
McWilliams, Tina/Nelsonville-York City Sch Dist	11,34,54,58,83,296,298	15
Mead, Shane/Tri-Village Local Sch Dist	12,296	56
Meade, J Michael/Hamilton Local School Dist	3,4,5,91	71
Meade, Pam/Cuyahoga Heights Local SD	4	45
Meadows, Mary/Springfield Local School Dist	8,11,69,288	194
Means, Heidi/Brecksville Broadview Hts CSD	5	41
Mears, Debra/Kettering City School Dist	298	150
Medley, Mike/Perry Local School Dist	295	188
Meece, Stephen/Forest Hills School Dist	73,76	89
Meek, James/Garaway Local School Dist	3	202
Meeker, Kimberly/Summit Co Ed Service Center	34	190
Meeker, Zack/New Boston Local School Dist	16	179
Meeks, Dawn/Sebring Local School Dist	2,84	135
Megger, Juanita/Willard City School Dist	31,58,83,88,271	106
Mehno, Rob/Leetonia Exempted Village SD	1,11,288	35
Meissner, Deborah/Westerville City School Dist	7,91	74
Meister, Tim/Four-Co Joint Voc School Dist	1	79
Melda, Deborah/Lorain Co Joint Voc Sch Dist	67	125
Mellon, Joe/Brookville Local School Dist	67	148
Melody, Scott/Dublin City School Dist	67	69
Menabb-Welsh, Kathi/Mahoning Co Joint Voc Sch Dist	67	135
Menchhofer, Kyle/St Mary's City School Dist	73,295	16
Mendak, Ramona/Elyria City School Dist	8,81	123
Mendenhall, Janet/Versailles Exempted Village SD	4	56

1 Superintendent
2 Bus/Finance/Purchasing
3 Buildings And Grounds
4 Food Service
5 Transportation
6 Athletic
7 Health Services
8 Curric/Instruct K-12
9 Curric/Instruct Elem
10 Curric/Instruct Sec
11 Federal Program
12 Title I
13 Title V
15 Asst Superintendent
16 Instructional Media Svcs
17 Chief Operations Officer
18 Chief Academic Officer
19 Chief Financial Officer
20 Art K-12
21 Art Elem
22 Art Sec
23 Music K-12
24 Music Elem
25 Music Sec
26 Business Education
27 Career & Tech Ed
28 Technology Education
29 Family/Consumer Science
30 Adult Education
31 Career/Sch-to-Work K-12
32 Career/Sch-to-Work Elem
33 Career/Sch-to-Work Sec
34 Early Childhood Ed
35 Health/Phys Education
36 Guidance Services Elem
37 Guidance Services Elem
38 Guidance Services Sec
39 Social Studies K-12
40 Social Studies Elem
41 Social Studies Sec
42 Science K-12
43 Science Elem
44 Science Sec
45 Math K-12
46 Math Elem
47 Math Sec
48 English/Lang Arts K-12
49 English/Lang Arts Elem
50 English/Lang Arts Sec
51 Reading K-12
52 Reading Elem
53 Reading Sec
54 Remedial Reading K-12
55 Remedial Reading Elem
56 Remedial Reading Sec
57 Bilingual/ELL
58 Special Education K-12
59 Special Education Elem
60 Special Education Sec
61 Foreign/World Lang K-12
62 Foreign/World Lang Elem
63 Foreign/World Lang Sec
64 Religious Education K-12
65 Religious Education Elem
66 Religious Education Sec
67 School Board President
68 Teacher Personnel
69 Academic Assessment
70 Research/Development
71 Public Information
72 Summer School
73 Instructional Tech
74 Inservice Training
75 Marketing/Distributive
76 Info Systems
77 Psychological Assess
78 Affirmative Action
79 Student Personnel
80 Driver Ed/Safety
81 Gifted/Talented
82 Video Services
83 Substance Abuse Prev
84 Erate
85 AIDS Education
88 Alternative/At Risk
89 Multi-Cultural Curriculum
90 Social Work
91 Safety/Security
92 Magnet School
93 Parental Involvement
95 Tech Prep Program
97 Chief Information Officer
98 Chief Technology Officer
270 Character Education
271 Migrant Education
273 Teacher Mentor
274 Before/After Sch
275 Response To Intervention
277 Remedial Math K-12
280 Literacy Coach
285 STEM
286 Digital Learning
288 Common Core Standards
294 Accountability
295 Network System
296 Title II Programs
297 Webmaster
298 Grant Writer/Ptnrships
750 Chief Innovation Officer
751 Chief of Staff
752 Social Emotional Learning

OH-T36

Ohio School Directory

DISTRICT PERSONNEL INDEX

NAME/District	JOB FUNCTIONS	PAGE
Mendenhall, Robert/*Toledo Public Schools*	8	129
Mendez, Andrew/*Kenston Local School Dist*	4	82
Mendoza, Victoria/*Indian Hill Exempted Vlg SD*	16	90
Mengerink, Joel/*Elida Local School Dist*	1	8
Mengerink, Robert, Dr/*Cuyahoga Co Ed Service Center*	1,11	39
Menges, Mike/*Union Local School Dist*	91	18
Menna, Anthony/*Swanton Local School Dist*	69	79
Menza, Kim/*Aurora City School Dist*	34	164
Menzie, Greg/*Marion Local School Dist*	294	138
Meranto, Joseph/*Youngstown City School Dist*	1	136
Merb, Jennifer/*Jefferson Local School Dist*	58,285	132
Mercure, Charlene/*Crestview Local School Dist*	2,84	34
Meredith, Amy/*Orrville City School Dist*	58	212
Meredith, Amy, Dr/*Rittman Exempted Village SD*	58,83	213
Meredith, Eric/*Pike Co Area JT Voc Sch Dist*	1	163
Meredith, Fred/*Belpre City School Dist*	3	209
Meredith, Liz/*Rolling Hills Local Sch Dist*	280,298	86
Meredith, Scott/*Black River Local School Dist*	73	139
Merenda, Trisha/*Worthington School Dist*	280	75
Merickel, Stephanie/*Hardin-Houston Local Sch Dist*	36	183
Merillat, Troy/*Ayersville Local School Dist*	58	56
Meriwether, Cheryl/*Parma City School Dist*	298	49
Merkich, Jennifer/*Lakeview Local School Dist*	58	199
Merolla, Jill/*Warren City School Dist*	83,298	200
Merrill, Brodi/*Green Local School Dist*	2	178
Merrille, Keith/*Edgerton Local School Dist*	6	214
Merritt, Chris/*Kettering City School Dist*	73,98	150
Merritt, Jay/*Washington Local School Dist*	3	130
Merritt, Jennifer/*Mahoning Co Ed Service Center*	88	133
Mers, Sandy/*South Central Ohio Ed Svc Ctr*	1	178
Mertig, Jeff/*Salem City School Dist*	5	35
Mertz, Ronald/*Wapakoneta City School Dist*	67	16
Mescher, Michelle/*Marion Local School Dist*	73,84,295	144
Mesera, Rich/*Steubenville City School Dist*	4	109
Messenger, Ellen/*Tri-Rivers Joint Voc Sch Dist*	71	139
Metcalf, Jim/*Plymouth-Shiloh Local Sch Dist*	1	173
Metz, Jovi/*River View Local School Dist*	4	37
Metz, Kim/*Wapakoneta City School Dist*	36	16
Metzger, Amber/*Millcreek-West Unity Local SD*	36,69,88	215
Metzger, Carl/*South-Western City School Dist*	15,68	73
Metzger, Deb/*Riverdale Local School Dist*	76,295	98
Metzger, Pam/*Stark Co Area Voc Sch Dist*	4	189
Meyer, James/*Bedford City School Dist*	76	40
Meyer, Jane/*Canton City School Dist*	30	184
Meyer, Jennifer/*Monroeville Local School Dist*	58	105
Meyer, Kirsten/*Stryker Local School Dist*	73	215
Meyer, Krista/*Botkins Local School Dist*	36,69	182
Meyer, Lynn/*Steubenville City School Dist*	6	109
Meyer, Matt/*Upper Valley JT Voc Sch Dist*	13,60,79,88	147
Meyer, Michele/*Botkins Local School Dist*	12,52	182
Meyer, Mike/*Patrick Henry Local Sch Dist*	3,5	102
Meyer, Nita/*Lincolnview Local School Dist*	11	205
Meyer, Rachel/*Southern Ohio Ed Serv Ctr*	2	32
Meyer, Todd/*Olentangy Local School Dist*	3,17,68	59
Meyer, Tony/*Jackson Center Local Sch Dist*	2	183
Meyers, Deb/*North Central Local Sch Dist*	16,73	215
Meyers, Jeff/*Madison Local School Dist*	67	172
Meyers, Jennifeer/*Warren City School Dist*	58	200
Meyers, Jude/*Gallia Co Local School Dist*	1	80
Meyers, Kelly/*Holgate Local School Dist*	1	101
Meyers, Lara/*Southwest Local School Dist*	11,57,58,79,296	93
Meyers, Wade/*Miami East Local School Dist*	16,82	145
Michael, Aaron/*Oak Hill Union Local Sch Dist*	67	107
Michael, Adam/*Oak Hill Union Local Sch Dist*	8,11,31,83,288,296	107
Michael, Beth/*Oak Hill Union Local Sch Dist*	58	107
Michael, Brooke/*Clyde-Green Spgs Exmpt Vlg SD*	37	176
Michael, Dayne/*Brown Co Ed Service Center*	74	19
Michael, Diane/*Hillsboro City School Dist*	11,57,68,69,74,88,296,298	103
Michael, Henry/*Southeast Local School Dist*	5	166
Michael, Kristine/*Buckeye Valley Local Sch Dist*	8,12,79,288	58
Michaels, Ashley/*Lakota Local School Dist*	4	177
Michaelson, Jill/*Ottawa Hills Local Sch Dist*	11,58,88	128
Michalos, John/*Sidney City School Dist*	73,286,295	183
Michalski, Megan/*Logan Elm Local School Dist*	57,273	162
Michel, Dan/*Jackson Local School Dist*	6	186
Micho, Richard/*Polaris Joint Voc School Dist*	67	49

NAME/District	JOB FUNCTIONS	PAGE
Mickel, Don/*Bristol Local School Dist*	67	197
Mickley, Tonya/*Danville Local School Dist*	2	110
Middleton, Kathy/*Madison Local School Dist*	5	23
Miglin, Eric/*Lincolnview Local School Dist*	73	205
Migliore, Shirley/*Licking Co Joint Voc Sch Dist*	60	118
Miguel-Keith, Erin/*Upper Arlington City Sch Dist*	273	74
Mihalich, Katherine/*Columbiana Co Voc Sch Dist*	2	34
Mihliak, Bob/*Aurora City School Dist*	88	164
Milano, Steve/*Canton Local School Dist*	1	185
Miles, Jodie/*Claymont City School Dist*	8,11,296	201
Miles, Mark, Dr/*Indian Hill Exempted Vlg SD*	1	90
Miley, Taryn/*Springfield Local School Dist*	9	128
Millar, Mark/*Wellington Exempted Village SD*	81	126
Millard, Abbie/*West Branch Local School Dist*	273	136
Millard, Keith/*Batavia Local School Dist*	1,11	29
Miller, Aaron/*Woodmore Local School Dist*	67	159
Miller, Andrew/*Buckeye Valley Local Sch Dist*	1	58
Miller, Bill/*Ottawa Hills Local Sch Dist*	8,12,57,288,298	128
Miller, Brenda/*Northwest Local School Dist*	8,69,270,294	91
Miller, Brent/*Evergreen Local School Dist*	3,91	78
Miller, Brock/*South Range Local School Dist*	273	135
Miller, Chrissy/*Northwestern Local School Dist*	58	27
Miller, Cindy/*Maysville Local School Dist*	34,288	157
Miller, Dale/*Northeastern Local School Dist*	2,11	27
Miller, Danielle/*Warren City School Dist*	84	200
Miller, Daryl/*Crestview Local School Dist*	73,88,295	34
Miller, Dave/*Ed Service Center Lorain Co*	73,76,295	122
Miller, David/*Leipsic Local School Dist*	2	170
Miller, Deb/*Lincolnview Local School Dist*	4	205
Miller, Deborah/*Wadsworth City School Dist*	5	141
Miller, Doug/*Osnaburg Local School Dist*	6	188
Miller, Doug/*Polaris Joint Voc School Dist*	71	49
Miller, Edward, Dr/*Crestview Local School Dist*	67	34
Miller, Eric/*Allen East Local School Dist*	73,84,295	7
Miller, Erica/*Cambridge City School Dist*	37	86
Miller, Erin/*Southwest Licking Local SD*	83	120
Miller, Eve/*Northmor Local School Dist*	16,27,73	155
Miller, Jackie/*Brown Co Ed Service Center*	74	19
Miller, Jeanie/*Portsmouth City School Dist*	5	179
Miller, Jeff/*Union Scioto Local Sch Dist*	58	175
Miller, Jeffrey/*Green Local School Dist*	1	185
Miller, John/*Old Fort Local School Dist*	5	181
Miller, Julia/*Ontario Local School Dist*	16	173
Miller, Julie/*Fairless Local School Dist*	4	185
Miller, Julie/*Stow-Munroe Falls City SD*	8	194
Miller, Justin/*Revere Local School Dist*	5	194
Miller, Kathy/*Southern Local School Dist*	5	143
Miller, Katie/*Kettering City School Dist*	30	150
Miller, Katie/*Urbana City School Dist*	36,83	26
Miller, Ken/*Kettering City School Dist*	68	150
Miller, Kevin/*Fairfield Union Local Sch Dist*	2	63
Miller, Kim/*Bristol Local School Dist*	31,36,83	197
Miller, Kim/*Dublin City School Dist*	8,11,16,27,35,36,298	69
Miller, Kim/*Stryker Local School Dist*	6	215
Miller, Kirk/*Solon City School Dist*	28,73,76,84,95,286,295	50
Miller, Krista/*Findlay City School Dist*	12,54,296	97
Miller, Leslie/*West Carrollton City Sch Dist*	67	153
Miller, Linda/*Blanchester Local School Dist*	7	32
Miller, Lynn/*Milford Exempted Village SD*	12	30
Miller, Mandi/*Fremont City School Dist*	76	176
Miller, Martin, Dr/*Antwerp Local School Dist*	1	160
Miller, Mary/*Pandora Gilboa Local Sch Dist*	4	170
Miller, Matthew/*Lakota Local School Dist*	1	22
Miller, Matthew/*Wheelersburg Local School Dist*	67	180
Miller, Melissa/*Kenston Local School Dist*	58	82
Miller, Michael/*Sycamore Cmty School Dist*	5	93
Miller, Nicole/*Northmor Local School Dist*	31	155
Miller, Nina/*Georgetown Exempted Village SD*	11,288,296	19
Miller, Noeleen/*Champion Local School Dist*	38	197
Miller, Phil/*Eastland-Ffld Career Tech VSD*	83,88	70
Miller, Rachel/*Jonathan Alder Local Sch Dist*	5	132
Miller, Rachel/*Wolf Creek Local School Dist*	2	211
Miller, Rebecca/*Minerva Local School Dist*	8,11,288	187
Miller, Robert/*Barnesville Exempted Vlg SD*	67	17
Miller, Salina/*Warrensville Heights City SD*	93	51
Miller, Sally/*Central Local School Dist*	16	57

School Year 2019-2020 800-333-8802 OH-T37

DISTRICT PERSONNEL INDEX

Market Data Retrieval

NAME/District	JOB FUNCTIONS	PAGE
Miller, Sean/*Lakeview Local School Dist*	2	198
Miller, Skip/*Bradford Exempted Village SD*	3	145
Miller, Staci/*Paulding Exempted Village SD*	27	160
Miller, Stephanie/*Bath Local School Dist*	38	8
Miller, Steve/*Marlington Local School Dist*	6	186
Miller, Tracey/*Dublin City School Dist*	91	69
Miller, Tracey/*New Richmond Exempted Vlg SD*	1	31
Miller, Travis/*Eaton Cmty School Dist*	6	168
Miller, Tyler/*Kings Local School Dist*	6	207
Miller, Vikki/*State Support Team-Region 13*	34	97
Miller, William/*South Euclid-Lyndhurst City SD*	68,78	51
Millet, James, Dr/*Garaway Local School Dist*	1,83	202
Millice, Chris/*Triad Local School Dist*	67	26
Mills, Bonnie/*Huntington Local School Dist*	4	175
Mills, Holly/*Bethel Local School Dist*	16	145
Mills, Jennifer/*Mt Gilead Exempted Village SD*	76	155
Mills, Joe/*Cardington-Lincoln Local SD*	10	155
Mills, Kristen/*Tri-Co North School Dist*	6	168
Mills, Michele/*Beachwood City School Dist*	2,19	40
Mills, Nancy/*Central Local School Dist*	81	57
Milner, Michael/*Carlisle Local School Dist*	12	206
Minamyer, Tina/*Columbiana Exempted Village SD*	4	34
Minick, Elise/*Wapakoneta City School Dist*	13,34,77	16
Minier, Roger/*Northwest Ohio Ed Tech*	1	218
Minnich, Dan/*Ohio Department of Education*	16,71	1
Minnick, Kelly/*Madison Local School Dist*	4	112
Minnick, Kelly/*Painesville City Local SD*	4	113
Minnig, Scott/*Wapakoneta City School Dist*	57	16
Minor, Anna/*Louisville City School Dist*	8	186
Minor, Lisa/*Trotwood-Madison City SD*	8,79,288	153
Miranda, Jaclynne/*Conneaut Area City Sch Dist*	2	12
Miroglotta, Jenny/*Diocese of Cleveland Ed Office*	8	52
Mirone, Dana/*Springfield Local School Dist*	3	135
Misch, Kelly/*Chardon Local School Dist*	76	82
Missig, Angela/*Elmwood Local School Dist*	7,85	216
Misterka, Marykay/*Stow-Munroe Falls City SD*	34	194
Mitchel, Bradley, Dr/*Perkins Local School Dist*	67	61
Mitchell, Brian/*Marion City School Dist*	3	138
Mitchell, C/*Jefferson Twp Local Sch Dist*	1	150
Mitchell, Jesse/*Greenfield Exempted Village SD*	73,76	103
Mitchell, John/*Connect Information Tech Ctr*	1	54
Mitchell, John/*Connect Information Tech Ctr*	1	126
Mitchell, Joya/*Green Local School Dist*	12,34,58,77,88,285	185
Mitchell, Kimberly/*Triway Local School Dist*	38	213
Mitchell, Laura/*Cincinnati City School Dist*	1	87
Mitchell, Mary/*Federal Hocking Local Sch Dist*	9	14
Mitchell, Megan/*Ridgedale Local School Dist*	4	138
Mitchell, Sheri/*Shelby City School Dist*	13,58,81	173
Mitchell, Tad/*Adams Co Ohio Valley Sch Dist*	10,33,270	6
Mitchell, Traci/*Warrensville Heights City SD*	67	51
Mittendorf, Steve/*Perry Local School Dist*	73	9
Mlakar, Melissa/*Riverside Local School Dist*	8	114
Moats, Wesley/*Defiance City School Dist*	67	57
Mock, Dennis/*Margaretta Local School Dist*	1,83	61
Moeglin, Sandy/*Massillon City School Dist*	2,19	187
Moehring, Bill/*Cincinnati City School Dist*	3,91	87
Mogan, Jerry/*Circleville City School Dist*	3,5,274	162
Mohan, Amelia/*Rootstown Local School Dist*	38	166
Mohler, David/*Vandalia Butler City Sch Dist*	73,76,98,286	153
Mohller, Michael/*Lakewood Local School Dist*	31,88	118
Mohr, Kathleen/*North Ctrl Ohio Ed Service Ctr*	73,74,295	180
Mohr, Kathy/*North Central Ohio Ed Svc Ctr*	73,74	137
Mohr, Stephen/*Otsego Local School Dist*	286	217
Mole, Wendi/*Northwestern Local School Dist*	4	212
Moles, Jen/*South Euclid-Lyndhurst City SD*	34,57,58,69,77	51
Mollenkopf, Kathy/*Crestview Local School Dist*	1,11,84	205
Mollica, Corrina/*Berea City School Dist*	5	41

NAME/District	JOB FUNCTIONS	PAGE
Molnar, Carol/*Oregon City School Dist*	67	128
Molnar, Deborah/*Clearview Local School Dist*	273	123
Molnar, John/*Kenston Local School Dist*	76,84	82
Molnar, Michael/*Amherst Exempted Village SD*	8,11,15,286,288,294,296	122
Molyet, Gregg/*Old Fort Local School Dist*	6	181
Molyet, Jake/*Mohawk Local School Dist*	73	219
Monachino, Kim, Dr/*Ohio Department of Education*	58,81	1
Monachino, Shelley/*Tallmadge City School Dist*	8	194
Mongold, Kelly/*Lucas Local School Dist*	36,83,88	172
Monigold, Michelle/*Jackson Local School Dist*	23	186
Montague, Jamie/*Lorain City School Dist*	91	124
Montanaro, John/*Jefferson Area Local SD*	1	13
Montanez, Nora/*Campbell City School Dist*	2	134
Montel, Barth/*ADA Exempted Village Sch Dist*	286	99
Montgomery, Jacquie/*Bellevue City School Dist*	57,58,79	105
Montgomery, Jacquline/*Bellevue City School Dist*	79	105
Montgomery, Josh/*Chillicothe City School Dist*	16,73	174
Montgomery, Mary/*Chillicothe City School Dist*	4	174
Montgomery, Matthew/*Revere Local School Dist*	1	194
Montgomery, Molly/*Huntington Local School Dist*	6	175
Montgomery, Tom/*Fairbanks Local School Dist*	83	204
Moodt, Lisa/*Grand Valley Local School Dist*	2	13
Moodt, Lowell/*Grand Valley Local School Dist*	27	13
Moody, Jay/*Osnaburg Local School Dist*	73	188
Moody, Paula/*Ansonia Local School Dist*	4	55
Mook, Donald/*Columbiana Exempted Village SD*	1	34
Moomaw, Lynn/*Wayne Co Joint Voc School Dist*	30	213
Moore, Ali/*Princeton City School Dist*	91	92
Moore, Amy/*Bloom-Carroll Local Sch Dist*	27,30	63
Moore, Beth/*Tecumseh Local School Dist*	8,91,285	28
Moore, Cathy/*Bellaire Local School Dist*	2	17
Moore, Cherie/*Springfield City School Dist*	71	28
Moore, Christy/*Walnut Twp Local School Dist*	2,294	64
Moore, Corbin/*Hamilton City School Dist*	57,69,81,288	22
Moore, Cynthia/*North Central Ohio Ed Svc Ctr*	58	137
Moore, Cynthia/*North Ctrl Ohio Ed Service Ctr*	15,58	180
Moore, David/*Hillsdale Local School Dist*	73	11
Moore, Deborah/*Cleveland Hts-Univ Hts City SD*	79	42
Moore, Denise/*Trotwood-Madison City SD*	67	153
Moore, Greg/*Morgan Local School Dist*	5	154
Moore, Jeff/*New Boston Local School Dist*	67	179
Moore, Jessica/*Talawanda School Dist*	81	24
Moore, Joel/*River View Local School Dist*	5	37
Moore, Kacy/*Triad Local School Dist*	38	26
Moore, Karen/*Orange City School Dist*	11,288	48
Moore, Katrina/*Columbiana Co Ed Service Ctr*	27	33
Moore, Lathe/*Pike Co Area JT Voc Sch Dist*	30	163
Moore, Lori/*Jackson City School Dist*	7,83	107
Moore, Matt/*Danville Local School Dist*	6	110
Moore, Michael/*Troy City School Dist*	8,12	146
Moore, Michele/*State Support Team-Region 5*	1	137
Moore, Nate/*Massillon City School Dist*	6	187
Moore, Paula/*Southern Hills Joint Voc SD*	4	20
Moore, Phil/*Morgan Local School Dist*	4	154
Moore, Phillip/*Franklin Local School Dist*	4	156
Moore, Ralph/*Monroeville Local School Dist*	1,11,83	105
Moore, Rebecca/*Massillon City School Dist*	93	187
Moore, Rob/*South-Western City School Dist*	73,286,295	73
Moore, Scott/*North Olmsted City School Dist*	8	48
Moore, Stacie/*Miamisburg City School Dist*	8,30,288	151
Moore, Tanya/*Southwest Licking Local SD*	71	120
Moore, Trisha/*Bethel Local School Dist*	7	145
Moorman, Ken/*Versailles Exempted Village SD*	3	56
Moorman, Wendi/*Mercer Co Ed Service Center*	81	143
Mora, Keith/*Danbury Local School Dist*	6	159
Moran, Aaron/*Versailles Exempted Village SD*	1	56
Moran, Kelly/*Chardon Local School Dist*	8,12	82

---

1 Superintendent	16 Instructional Media Svcs	30 Adult Education	44 Science Sec	58 Special Education K-12	72 Summer School	88 Alternative/At Risk	277 Remedial Math K-12
2 Bus/Finance/Purchasing	17 Chief Operations Officer	31 Career/Sch-to-Work K-12	45 Math K-12	59 Special Education Elem	73 Instructional Tech	89 Multi-Cultural Curriculum	280 Literacy Coach
3 Buildings And Grounds	18 Chief Academic Officer	32 Career/Sch-to-Work Elem	46 Math Elem	60 Special Education Sec	74 Inservice Training	90 Social Work	285 STEM
4 Food Service	19 Chief Financial Officer	33 Career/Sch-to-Work Sec	47 Math Sec	61 Foreign/World Lang K-12	75 Marketing/Distributive	91 Safety/Security	286 Digital Learning
5 Transportation	20 Art K-12	34 Early Childhood Ed	48 English/Lang Arts K-12	62 Foreign/World Lang Elem	76 Info Systems	92 Magnet School	288 Common Core Standards
6 Athletic	21 Art Elem	35 Health/Phys Education	49 English/Lang Arts Elem	63 Foreign/World Lang Sec	77 Psychological Assess	93 Parental Involvement	294 Accountability
7 Health Services	22 Art Sec	36 Guidance Services K-12	50 English/Lang Arts Sec	64 Religious Education K-12	78 Affirmative Action	95 Tech Prep Program	295 Network System
8 Curric/Instruct K-12	23 Music K-12	37 Guidance Services Elem	51 Reading K-12	65 Religious Education Elem	79 Student Personnel	96 Chief Information Officer	296 Title II Programs
9 Curric/Instruct Elem	24 Music Elem	38 Guidance Services Sec	52 Reading Elem	66 Religious Education Sec	80 Driver Ed/Safety	97 Chief Technology Officer	297 Webmaster
10 Curric/Instruct Sec	25 Music Sec	39 Social Studies K-12	53 Reading Sec	67 School Board President	81 Gifted/Talented	270 Character Education	298 Grant Writer/Ptnrships
11 Federal Program	26 Business Education	40 Social Studies Elem	54 Remedial Reading K-12	68 Teacher Personnel	82 Video Services	271 Migrant Education	750 Chief Innovation Officer
12 Title I	27 Career & Tech Ed	41 Social Studies Sec	55 Remedial Reading Elem	69 Academic Assessment	83 Substance Abuse Prev	272 Teacher Mentor	751 Chief of Staff
13 Title V	28 Technology Education	42 Science K-12	56 Remedial Reading Sec	70 Research/Development	84 Erate	274 Before/After Sch	752 Social Emotional Learning
15 Asst Superintendent	29 Family/Consumer Science	43 Science Elem	57 Bilingual/ELL	71 Public Information	85 AIDS Education	275 Response To Intervention	

Ohio School Directory

DISTRICT PERSONNEL INDEX

NAME/District	JOB FUNCTIONS	PAGE
Moran, Lauren/*Mansfield City Schools*	4	172
Morbitzer, Carole/*Hamilton Local School Dist*	8,11,57,68,69,288,296,298	71
Morbitzer, Michael/*Hamilton Local School Dist*	296,298	71
Morehouse, Tom/*Portage Co Ed Service Center*	2	164
Morehouse, Tom/*Woodridge Local School Dist*	2	195
Morel, Ed/*Diocese of Cleveland Ed Office*	4	52
Moreland, Eric/*North Central Local Sch Dist*	3,5	215
Morell, Doreen/*Clearview Local School Dist*	58,271	123
Morell, Doreen/*Lorain City School Dist*	79	124
Morelli-Nutter, Lisa/*Southwest Licking Local SD*	6	120
Morgan, Cathy/*Muskingum Valley ESC*	8,69	156
Morgan, Craig/*Maplewood JT Voc School Dist*	10,27,38,75	166
Morgan, David/*Jackson Local School Dist*	5,91	186
Morgan, David/*Northmor Local School Dist*	85	156
Morgan, Dennis/*Logan-Hocking Local Sch Dist*	5	104
Morgan, Duran/*Harrison Hills City Sch Dist*	8,11,58,88,275,288,294	101
Morgan, Kent/*Buckeye Local School Dist*	1	140
Morgan, Michael/*Chagrin Falls Exempted Vlg SD*	5	42
Morgan, Regina/*Little Miami Local School Dist*	8,11,15,296,298	208
Morgan, Shannon/*Centerville City School Dist*	73,76,295	148
Morgan, Stephanie/*Westlake City School Dist*	36,58,69,79,81	51
Morgan, Tom/*Cedar Cliff Local School Dist*	5	84
Morgan, Tommy/*Greeneview Local School Dist*	5	84
Morgret, Maryann/*Miami Co Ed Service Center*	8	144
Mori, Laura/*Waterloo Local School Dist*	13,38,83,88,286	167
Morisson, Charles/*Teays Valley Local School Dist*	67	162
Morlock, Jay/*Gibsonburg Exempted Village SD*	6	177
Morman, Annette/*Bath Local School Dist*	2	8
Morman, Kate/*Lima City School Dist*	7	9
Morres, Bailey/*Warrensville Heights City SD*	69	51
Morris, Beth/*Wolf Creek Local School Dist*	36,69,83	211
Morris, Chad/*Alliance City School Dist*	73,84,295	184
Morris, Debra/*Penta Co JT Voc School Dist*	30	217
Morris, Eric/*Norton City School Dist*	58,79	193
Morris, Jim/*Upper Sandusky Exempted Vlg SD*	67	219
Morris, Josh/*Portsmouth City School Dist*	91,298	179
Morris, Matt/*Belpre City School Dist*	295	209
Morris, Mike/*Southwest Local School Dist*	3	93
Morris, Tina/*New Philadelphia City Sch Dist*	273	203
Morrish, Holli/*Talawanda School Dist*	79,298	24
Morrison, Amy/*Lakewood Local School Dist*	7	118
Morrison, Debbie/*Madison Local School Dist*	77	23
Morrison, Fran/*Middletown City School Dist*	11,57,69,285,286,288,296,298	23
Morrison, Matt/*Madison Local School Dist*	3,6	23
Morrison, Sherri/*Hamilton City School Dist*	45,277	22
Morriss, Julie/*Rocky River City School Dist*	36	50
Morriss, Larry/*Fairbanks Local School Dist*	6	204
Morrissey, Kerry/*Southern Local School Dist*	4	35
Morrow, Michael/*Fairfield Local Sch Dist*	2	102
Mortine, Darlene/*Licking Heights Local Sch Dist*	5	118
Morton, Kell/*Adena Local School Dist*	2	174
Morton, Robert/*Defiance City School Dist*	1	57
Morvay, William/*Youngstown City School Dist*	91	136
Moser, Rob/*West Holmes Local School Dist*	73,295	105
Moses, Kathy/*Madeira City School Dist*	5	90
Mosora, Jon/*Howland Local School Dist*	38,83	198
Moss, David/*Clinton-Massie Local Sch Dist*	73,76,295	33
Mossing, Karen/*Cedar Cliff Local School Dist*	13,16,82	84
Motley, Veronica, Dr/*South Euclid-Lyndhurst City SD*	8,12,15,16,72,73,74,81	51
Motter, Adam/*Akron Public Schools*	35,39	190
Mowery, Adam/*Graham Local School Dist*	10	26
Mowery, Jerry/*Zane Trace Local School Dist*	1	176
Mowery, Lorri/*Fairbanks Local School Dist*	4	204
Mowery, Matt/*Huber Heights City School Dist*	73,84	150
Mowry, Alicia/*Delaware Joint Voc Sch Dist*	71	59
Mowry, Levi/*Lexington Local School Dist*	73,76,95	172
Moyer-Downs, Kimberly/*West Muskingum Local Sch Dist*	2	157
Moyer, Michelle/*Franklin Local School Dist*	38	156
Moyer, Rhonda/*Crooksville Exempted Vlg SD*	67	161
Mquaide, Jim/*Solon City School Dist*	6	50
Mraz, Angie/*Austintown Local School Dist*	5	133
Mucchio, Matt/*Cuyahoga Heights Local SD*	2,11	45
Mucci, Kris/*Conneaut Area City Sch Dist*	8,12,296	12
Mudra, Erin/*Mansfield City Schools*	4	172
Muehlfeld, Michael/*Anna Local School Dist*	6	182
Mulcahey, Michael/*Southwest Ohio OCA*	295	25
Mulcahy, Marge/*Dublin City School Dist*	81	69
Mulgrew, Cynthia/*Weathersfield Local Sch Dist*	11	201
Mulkey, Brian/*Dawson-Bryant Local Sch Dist*	6,274	115
Mullane, William/*Ashtabula Co Ed Service Center*	9	11
Mullane, William/*Jefferson Area Local SD*	8,11,57,83,286,288,296,298	13
Mullen, Cathy/*Greene Co Voc School Dist*	16	84
Mullen, Laurie/*Frontier Local School Dist*	11,58	210
Mullett, Bill/*Jefferson Local School Dist*	1	132
Mullett, Denise/*Licking Valley Local Sch Dist*	88	119
Mullins, Amy, Dr/*ADA Exempted Village Sch Dist*	67	99
Mullins, Becky/*Washington Court House City SD*	2	65
Mullins, Eddie/*Vinton Co Local School Dist*	3	206
Mullins, Jerry/*Jackson City School Dist*	3,91	107
Mullins, Steve/*Chillicothe City School Dist*	67	174
Mulvany, Bryan/*South-Western City School Dist*	76,294	73
Mulvey, Nancy/*Great Oaks Career Campuses*	10,30,72,285,288	89
Mumahl, Denny/*Ottoville Local School Dist*	286	170
Mumau, Jessica/*Milton-Union Exempted Vlg SD*	8,11,69,88,273,285,298	145
Mumaw, Shelley/*Ottoville Local School Dist*	16,73,298	170
Mumaw, Tracy/*Piqua City School Dist*	294	146
Muniz, Samantha/*United Local School Dist*	38,69,294	36
Munroe, Robert/*Kent City School Dist*	3,91	165
Muntean, Janet/*Poland Local School Dist*	2,19	135
Muntz, Joan/*Adena Local School Dist*	5	174
Muratori, Dennis/*Huron City School Dist*	1	60
Muratori, Rebecca/*Sandusky City School Dist*	274	61
Murdock, Daniel, Dr/*Avon Lake City School Dist*	31,57,58,69,88	122
Murdock, Melissa/*Greenfield Exempted Village SD*	37	103
Murnahan, Jesse/*Lebanon City School Dist*	295	207
Murphy-Penk, Colleen/*Youngstown City School Dist*	5	136
Murphy, Charles/*Willoughby-Eastlake City SD*	15	114
Murphy, Dan/*Stark Co Area Voc Sch Dist*	10,11,273,298	189
Murphy, Mark/*Tuscarawas Valley Local SD*	1	203
Murphy, Mike/*South Euclid-Lyndhurst City SD*	6,35,85	51
Murphy, Ryan/*Fairless Local School Dist*	58	185
Murray, Carol/*Toronto City School Dist*	38,69,88	109
Murray, Heidi/*Kings Local School Dist*	36	207
Murray, Matt/*Anna Local School Dist*	67	182
Murray, Teresa/*London City School Dist*	4	132
Murray, Tiffani/*Findlay City School Dist*	274	98
Murray, Tim/*Gibsonburg Exempted Village SD*	1,11	177
Murray, Zach/*Indian Creek Local Sch Dist*	73,295	109
Musgrave, Brad/*Wadsworth City School Dist*	6	141
Musgraves, Thomas/*Morgan Local School Dist*	8,12,16,69,275,288,294,296	154
Musser, Chrissy/*Meigs Local School Dist*	4	142
Musser, Scott/*Madison Local School Dist*	27,75	172
Mustain, Todd/*Madison Plains Local Sch Dist*	2,19	133
Mustain, Tom/*Ridgemont Local School Dist*	73,295	100
Mustovich, Pamela/*Clark Co Ed Service Center*	2	27
Muterspaw, Betsy/*Clinton-Massie Local Sch Dist*	58	33
Muzi, Erich/*Green Local School Dist*	6	185
Myer, Adrian/*Evergreen Local School Dist*	4,31,38,79,83,88	78
Myers, Ben/*Fairfield Union Local Sch Dist*	67	63
Myers, Bill/*Hillsboro City School Dist*	67	103
Myers, Craig/*West Carrollton City Sch Dist*	8	153
Myers, Dana/*Zane Trace Local School Dist*	37	176
Myers, Derrick/*Twin Valley Cmty Local SD*	297	169
Myers, Jason/*Cloverleaf Local School Dist*	67	140
Myers, Jessica/*Ayersville Local School Dist*	67	56
Myers, Katie/*Fairfield City School Dist*	68	21
Myers, Levi/*Northwestern Local School Dist*	27	212
Myers, Monica/*Jackson Local School Dist*	288	186
Myers, Ryan/*Penta Co JT Voc School Dist*	60	217
Myers, Scott/*Franklin-Monroe Local School Dist*	67	55
Myers, Tim/*Van Buren Local School Dist*	1	99
Myers, Tracey/*Centerburg Local School Dist*	67	110

N

NAME/District	JOB FUNCTIONS	PAGE
Naber, Karen/*Sycamore Cmty School Dist*	12,15,280,288,296,298	93
Nace, James/*Chagrin Falls Exempted Vlg SD*	3	42
Nagel, Amy/*Ontario Local School Dist*	83	173
Naidu, Kershini/*Orange City School Dist*	58	48
Naill, Scott/*Upper Valley JT Voc Sch Dist*	30	147
Nannicola, Alexandra/*Champion Local School Dist*	11,296	197
Napier, Holley/*Buckeye Valley Local Sch Dist*	274	58
Napier, Lauren/*North Baltimore Local Sch Dist*	77	217

DISTRICT PERSONNEL INDEX

Market Data Retrieval

NAME/District	JOB FUNCTIONS	PAGE
Napier, Paul/Knox Co Voc School Dist	73,286	111
Nardo, Nick/Union Local School Dist	6	18
Narvaez, Lourdes/Springfield City School Dist	61	28
Nash, Jaime/Gallia-Jackson-Vinton JVSD	1,11,83	80
Nashu, Wendy/Napoleon Area City School Dist	8,69,288,296	101
Naso, Carl/Strongsville City School Dist	67	51
Natiello, Rich/Madison Local School Dist	2,298	23
Naughton, Robin/Perry Local School Dist	71,97	113
Nauman, Brian/North Union Local School Dist	5	204
Naveaux, Thomas/Ed Service Ctr Lake Erie West	77,79	127
Neading, Doug/Sandy Valley Local School Dist	3,5	189
Neal-Miller, Patricia/Cincinnati City School Dist	93	87
Neal, Chevonne/Northwest Local School Dist	58	91
Neal, Chuck/Plymouth-Shiloh Local Sch Dist	31,69	173
Neal, Mark/Tri-Valley Local School Dist	1	157
Neale, Rocky/Brooklyn City School Dist	67	41
Neale, Sandra/Brooklyn City School Dist	2,3	41
Nealeigh, Mick/Milton-Union Exempted Vlg SD	73,76,95,98,286,295	145
Neargarder, Tony/Mississinawa Valley Sch Dist	3	56
Nease, Joshua/Pleasant Local School Dist	3	138
Neasel, Joseph/Madison Local School Dist	16	112
Nedacore, Rachel/Carey Exempted Village SD	7,85	219
Nedlik, Steve/Mayfield City School Dist	2	47
Neece, Mitch/West Holmes Local School Dist	3,91	105
Needham, Carol/Perry Local School Dist	38	113
Needham, Kevin/South Euclid-Lyndhurst City SD	4	51
Needles, K C/Anna Local School Dist	285	182
Neely, Amy/Steubenville City School Dist	7	109
Neely, Jamie/Brookville Local School Dist	36	148
Neff, Suzie/Columbia Local School Dist	38	123
Neftzer, Harley/Jackson Local School Dist	3	186
Neidert, Sarah/Kalida Local School Dist	4	169
Neidorkohr, Rachel/Carey Exempted Village SD	7,85	219
Neifer, Chris/East Palestine City Sch Dist	1	35
Neilson, Steve/Oberlin City School Dist	73,295	125
Nekoloff, Sandra/South-Western City School Dist	71	73
Nellis, Kim/Allen Co Ed Service Center	58	7
Nells, Bill/Chardon Local School Dist	73,84	82
Nelson-Creel, Elizabeth/Cleveland Metro School Dist	8,45	42
Nelson, Angela/Columbus City School Dist	274	67
Nelson, Luke/St Clairsville-Richland CSD	6	18
Nelson, Scott/Groveport Madison Local SD	8,11,69,273,288,294,298	71
Nelson, Vicky/Highland Local School Dist	5	155
Nemick, Alena/Crestline Exempted Village SD	2	38
Neni, William/Ashtabula Area City Sch Dist	67	12
Nerl, Tom/Mariemont City School Dist	6	90
Nero, Mario/Bristol Local School Dist	2,296,298	197
Nero, Rocco/Southington Local School Dist	1,11,288	200
Neron, Renee/Madison Local School Dist	8,69,285,288	172
Nesselroad, Dawn/Morgan Local School Dist	38	154
Nester, Debra/Edon Northwest Local Sch Dist	2	215
Neufarth, Jayne/Ross Local School Dist	16	24
Neuman, Taya/Brunswick City School Dist	79	140
Neumann, Holly/Olmsted Falls City School Dist	67	48
Neuoff, Rhonda/Amherst Exempted Village SD	57	122
Neves, Paul/Mad River Local School Dist	6	151
Neville, Kelli/Mariemont City School Dist	67	91
Newcomb, Katie/Conneaut Area City Sch Dist	29	12
Newcomer, Michael/Van Buren Local School Dist	9,11,52,55,296	99
Newland, Sara/Elida Local School Dist	4	8
Newlon, Angela/Johnstown-Monroe Local SD	73	118
Newman, Ryan/Mt Gilead Exempted Village SD	3	155
Newton, Chris/Forest Hills School Dist	6	89
Newton, Kyle/Warren Local School Dist	1,11	210
Nezbeth, Erin/Tri-Valley Local School Dist	6	157
Niamke, Muata/Maple Heights City School Dist	2,4	47
Niblick, Zach/Johnstown-Monroe Local SD	2	118
Nicademo, Jim/Stark Co Ed Service Center	8,15,34,58,73	184
Niccum, Bev/Licking Co Joint Voc Sch Dist	67	118
Nicely, Connie/Four-Co Joint Voc School Dist	2	79
Nicely, Jeff/Napoleon Area City School Dist	5	101
Nicely, Matt/Clyde-Green Spgs Exmpt Vlg SD	67	176
Niceswanger, Brian/Canal Winchester Local SD	67	66
Nicholas, Perry/Maplewood Local School Dist	1,11	199
Nicholason, Diane/Holgate Local School Dist	7	101
Nichols, Angela/Dayton Public School Dist	58	149
Nichols, Diane/Madeira City School Dist	71	90
Nichols, Eric/Washington-Nile Local Sch Dist	58	179
Nichols, Jacy/Westlake City School Dist	16,82	51
Nichols, Nicole/Lake Local School Dist	2	186
Nichols, Roberta/McComb Local School Dist	16,82	98
Nichols, Todd, Dr/Cuyahoga Falls City Sch Dist	1	192
Nicholson, William/Warren City School Dist	6	200
Nickell, John/North Royalton City Sch Dist	73,76	48
Nickoli, Gregory/Pioneer Joint Voc School Dist	1	173
Nicodemus, Todd/Cuyahoga Vly Career Ctr Voc SD	88	45
Nidy, Kimberly/North Canton City School Dist	84	187
Niebiling, Marla/Mason Local School Dist	68	208
Niedenthal, Robert/Strasburg Franklin Local SD	3	203
Niedzwicki, Maggie/Lakewood City School Dist	15	47
Niekamp, Brent/Ft Recovery Local School Dist	6,16	144
Niekamp, Cory/Napoleon Area City School Dist	3	101
Niekamp, Terry/Mississinawa Valley Sch Dist	35	56
Nielsen, Steve/Oberlin City School Dist	295	125
Nielson, Heather/Vanlue Local School Dist	12,54	99
Niemiec, Alana/Green Local School Dist	15	185
Niese, Augusta/Ayersville Local School Dist	38	56
Nieset, Vicky/Clyde-Green Spgs Exmpt Vlg SD	4	176
Nimene, Jrayene/Lorain City School Dist	83	124
Nimmo, Nancy/Wellington Exempted Village SD	57,58	126
Nippert, John/Cardington-Lincoln Local SD	3	155
Nitecki, Daniel/Danbury Local School Dist	73,295	159
Nitz, Jack/Port Clinton City School Dist	8,11,54,69,81,270,271	159
Nizen, Michele/Cardinal Local School Dist	11	81
Noble, Lisa/Eaton Cmty School Dist	67	168
Noe, Terri/Finneytown Local School Dist	1,11	89
Nofbaum, James/Sylvania City School Dist	67	128
Nogales, Linda/Labrae Local School Dist	38	198
Nohra, Joseph/Liberty Local School Dist	1	199
Nolan, Kathy/Revere Local School Dist	8,11,69,285,288,298	194
Nolan, Nancy/Jackson Center Local Sch Dist	16	183
Nolder, Nan/Muskingum Valley ESC	2	156
Noll, Chris/Canton Local School Dist	3,74,91	185
Noll, Susan/Georgetown Exempted Village SD	57	20
Noltemeyer, Amy/Westfall Local School Dist	6	163
Nolton, Jeff/Frontier Local School Dist	67	210
Norman, Amy/Newark City School Dist	73,295	119
Norman, Chris/Pike Co Area JT Voc Sch Dist	10,88	163
Norman, David/Canton Local School Dist	297	185
Norman, James/Tri-Co North School Dist	16,73,76	168
Norman, Jennifer/Rocky River City School Dist	11,27,34,57,58,69,83,88	50
Norman, Paula/Belmont-Harrison Voc Sch Dist	60,69	18
Norman, Samantha/Kalida Local School Dist	27	169
Norris, Donna/Southwest Ohio OCA	15	25
Norris, Stephanie/Talawanda School Dist	34,58	24
North, Mark/Wood Co Ed Service Center	1	216
North, Marlene/Arcadia Local School Dist	58	97
North, Marlene/Hancock Co Ed Service Center	58	97
Northup, Shaun/Gallipolis City School Dist	73	81
Norton, Joan/Conneaut Area City Sch Dist	67	12
Nottingham, Dereck/Louisville City School Dist	2	186
Nottke, Bruce/Tri-Co Joint Voc Sch Dist	67	15
Novak, Sharon/Midview Local School Dist	58,77,79	125
Novotni, Wendy/Reynoldsburg City School Dist	4	72

1 Superintendent	16 Instructional Media Svcs	30 Adult Education	44 Science Sec	58 Special Education K-12	72 Summer School	88 Alternative/At Risk	277 Remedial Math K-12
2 Bus/Finance/Purchasing	17 Chief Operations Officer	31 Career/Sch-to-Work K-12	45 Math K-12	59 Special Education Elem	73 Instructional Tech	89 Multi-Cultural Curriculum	280 Literacy Coach
3 Buildings And Grounds	18 Chief Academic Officer	32 Career/Sch-to-Work Elem	46 Math Elem	60 Special Education Sec	74 Inservice Training	90 Social Work	285 STEM
4 Food Service	19 Chief Financial Officer	34 Career/Sch-to-Work Sec	47 Math Sec	61 Foreign/World Lang K-12	75 Marketing/Distributive	91 Safety/Security	286 Digital Learning
5 Transportation	20 Art K-12	34 Early Childhood Ed	48 English/Lang Arts K-12	62 Foreign/World Lang Elem	76 Info Systems	92 Magnet School	288 Common Core Standards
6 Athletic	21 Art Elem	35 Health/Phys Education	49 English/Lang Arts Elem	63 Foreign/World Lang Sec	77 Psychological Assess	93 Parental Involvement	294 Accountability
7 Health Services	22 Art Sec	36 Guidance Services K-12	50 English/Lang Arts Sec	64 Religious Education K-12	78 Affirmative Action	95 Tech Prep Program	295 Network System
8 Curric/Instruct K-12	23 Music K-12	37 Guidance Services Elem	51 Reading K-12	65 Religious Education Elem	79 Student Personnel	97 Chief Information Officer	296 Title II Programs
9 Curric/Instruct Elem	24 Music Elem	38 Guidance Services Sec	52 Reading Elem	66 Religious Education Sec	80 Driver Ed/Safety	98 Chief Technology Officer	297 Webmaster
10 Curric/Instruct Sec	25 Music Sec	39 Social Studies K-12	53 Reading Sec	67 School Board President	81 Gifted/Talented	270 Character Education	298 Grant Writer/Ptnrships
11 Federal Program	26 Business Education	40 Social Studies Elem	54 Remedial Reading K-12	68 Teacher Personnel	82 Video Services	271 Migrant Education	750 Chief Innovation Officer
12 Title I	27 Career & Tech Ed	41 Social Studies Sec	55 Remedial Reading Elem	69 Academic Assessment	83 Substance Abuse Prev	273 Teacher Mentor	751 Chief of Staff
13 Title V	28 Technology Education	42 Science K-12	56 Remedial Reading Sec	70 Research/Development	84 Erate	274 Before/After Sch	752 Social Emotional Learning
15 Asst Superintendent	29 Family/Consumer Science	43 Science Elem	57 Bilingual/ELL	71 Public Information	85 AIDS Education	275 Response To Intervention	

Ohio School Directory

DISTRICT PERSONNEL INDEX

NAME/District	JOB FUNCTIONS	PAGE
Nowak, Maryann/*Clearview Local School Dist*	2,11,19,298	123
Nowosielski, Michael/*Strongsville City School Dist*	4	51
Nuccio, Sean/*Parma City School Dist*	2,19	49
Nuggud, Vishtasp/*Avon Lake City School Dist*	285	122
Nuss, Don/*Eastland-Ffld Career Tech VSD*	73	70
Nussbaum, Kristi/*Dalton Local School Dist*	76	212
Nuveman, Jamie/*Miller City-New Cleveland SD*	6	170
Nye, Bill/*Genoa Area Local School Dist*	2	159
Nye, Elaine/*New Riegel Local School Dist*	11	181
Nye, William, Dr/*Grand Valley Local School Dist*	1	13

O

NAME/District	JOB FUNCTIONS	PAGE
O'Brien, Marcus/*Vandalia Butler City Sch Dist*	3,91	153
O'Brien, Mark/*Portsmouth City School Dist*	73,84	179
O'Connell, Karen/*Mt Healthy City School Dist*	11,31,69,298	91
O'Connell, Kevin/*McDonald Local School Dist*	1,11	199
O'Connell, Shelley/*Williamsburg Local School Dist*	4	32
O'Connor, Wesley/*Austintown Local School Dist*	25	133
O'Cull, Ryan/*Medina City School Dist*	73,295	141
O'Dell, Charlie/*Bellbrook-Sugarcreek Schools*	6,72	83
O'Dell, Kristin/*Pickaway Co Ed Service Center*	2	162
O'Dierno, Amy/*Miami Trace Local School Dist*	59	65
O'Donnell, Cathy/*Belpre City School Dist*	67	209
O'Donnell, Dawne/*West Holmes Local School Dist*	38	105
O'Donnell, Kerri/*United Local School Dist*	37	36
O'Flaherty, Helen/*Tri-Valley Local School Dist*	16	157
O'Hara, Bryan/*Girard City School Dist*	1	197
O'Hara, Bryan/*Trumbull Co Ed Service Center*	8,69,74,81,285,286	196
O'Hare, Jenny/*Lancaster City School Dist*	8,11,16,69,275	63
O'Hare, Karen/*Norwayne Local School Dist*	1	212
O'Keefe, Kim/*Mentor Exempted Village SD*	5	113
O'Keefe, Mike/*Firelands Local School Dist*	67	124
O'Leary, Rob/*Vandalia Butler City Sch Dist*	2,7,8,11,57,58,77,83	153
O'Leary, Robert/*Vandalia Butler City Sch Dist*	1	153
O'Linn, Frank/*Diocese of Cleveland Ed Office*	1	52
O'Neill, Pam/*Huntington Local School Dist*	16	175
O'Shea, Sheryl/*Sylvania City School Dist*	16,73,286,295	128
Oaster, Kathy/*Twin Valley Cmty Local SD*	16,82	169
Obenour, Michelle/*Hardin Northern Local Sch Dist*	67	100
Oblak, Jeff/*Jefferson Co Ed Service Center*	58	108
Oburn, Nate/*Newton Local School Dist*	67	146
Ochs, Jeff/*Centerville City School Dist*	58	148
Oconner, Corey/*Greenon Local School Dist*	73	27
Oconnor, Melissa/*Georgetown Exempted Village SD*	58	20
Odell, Amy/*Minford Local School Dist*	8,11,74,286,288,296,298	178
Odell, Lynn/*Western Local School Dist*	73,76,295	164
Odenweller, Mark/*Ottoville Local School Dist*	6,90	170
Odonnell, Kimmy/*Belpre City School Dist*	4	209
Ogden, Garilee/*Groveport Madison Local SD*	1	71
Ogg, Robert/*Crooksville Exempted Vlg SD*	2,11,19	161
Ogier, Michael/*Vinton Co Local School Dist*	5	206
Ogilvie, Dj/*United Local School Dist*	6	36
Oglesbee, Heidi/*Danbury Local School Dist*	12	159
Ogurchak, Joanne/*Lakeview Local School Dist*	11,275,288	199
Ohle, Willie/*Lorain City School Dist*	76	124
Ohlinger, Steve/*Eastern Local School Dist*	1	142
Ohlinger, Vanessa/*Dublin City School Dist*	34	69
Okuley, Jeremy/*Kalida Local School Dist*	73,76,295	169
Oldham, Maurice/*Columbus City School Dist*	3,17	66
Oldham, Susan/*Coventry Local School Dist*	79	192
Olinger, Jason/*Coshocton City School Dist*	73,84	36
Olinger, Rose/*River View Local School Dist*	33,36,69	37
Oliver, Alison/*Bright Local School Dist*	36,69	102
Olivieri, Amy/*Norton City School Dist*	8,11,16,69,288,296,298	193
Olle, Frank/*Polaris Joint Voc School Dist*	73,295	49
Olson, Gary/*Coventry Local School Dist*	3	192
Omen, Deborah/*Jefferson Local School Dist*	273	132
Ondrus, Chris/*Dublin City School Dist*	79	69
Ondrus, Jason/*Barberton City School Dist*	15,68	192
Ontrop, Lisa/*Parkway Local School Dist*	36,69,83,88	144
Orecchio, Chad/*East Muskingum Local Sch Dist*	37	156
Oremus, Donneta/*Dublin City School Dist*	27	69
Oress, Robert/*Stow-Munroe Falls City SD*	17	194
Orians, Lenny/*Carey Exempted Village SD*	5	219
Orians, Tracy/*Lake Local School Dist*	38	217
Orris, Jill/*Barberton City School Dist*	4	192

NAME/District	JOB FUNCTIONS	PAGE
Orseno, Jill/*Ed Service Center Lorain Co*	2	122
Ortiz, Shelby/*Mapleton Local School Dist*	288	11
Orza, Valerie/*Norwood City School Dist*	67	92
Osborn, Jan, Dr/*Putnam Co Ed Service Center*	1,11	169
Osborn, Justin/*Buckeye Valley Local Sch Dist*	67	58
Osborn, Mike/*Southeastern Local Sch Dist*	3,91	175
Osborn, Todd/*Chippewa Local School Dist*	1	211
Osborne, Angie/*Marion City School Dist*	81,298	138
Osborne, Carole/*Fairfield Union Local Sch Dist*	7,85	63
Osborne, Jason/*Miamisburg City School Dist*	6	151
Osborne, Paul/*Greene Co Ed Service Center*	73	83
Osborne, Rachel/*Paint Valley Local School Dist*	4	175
Osbourne, Yvonne/*Whitehall City School Dist*	37	75
Oser, Chris/*Three Rivers Local School Dist*	67	94
Osman, Jasmine/*Ripley-Union-Lewis-Huntngtn SD*	36	20
Osmun, Doreen/*Hudson City School Dist*	8,11,16,57,69,73,95,288	193
Ost, Shawn/*Union Scioto Local Sch Dist*	5	175
Osterfeld, Jeanne/*Parkway Local School Dist*	1	144
Ostrowski, Melissa/*Coventry Local School Dist*	34,57,58,95	192
Ott, Lauren/*Gallipolis City School Dist*	69,77	81
Otten, Chip/*Coldwater Exempted Village SD*	83	143
Otten, Paul/*Beavercreek City School Dist*	1	83
Ottens, Bruce/*Valley Local School Dist*	84	179
Ottney, Ryan/*South Central Ohio Ed Svc Ctr*	71	178
Otto, Ty/*Napoleon Area City School Dist*	67	101
Outley-Kelly, Mary/*Akron Public Schools*	9	190
Ouzts, Pamela/*Diocese of Cleveland Ed Office*	11	52
Overbey, Michale/*West Clermont Local Sch Dist*	15	31
Overley, Nathan/*St Mary's City School Dist*	295	16
Overly, Stacey/*Teays Valley Local School Dist*	2	162
Overman, Kim/*St Mary's City School Dist*	8,12,81	16
Overman, Marcus/*New Bremen Local School Dist*	10,31,83	16
Overmyer, Paul/*Hicksville Exempted Village SD*	6	57
Owen, Dave/*Trimble Local School Dist*	67	15
Owens, Kelly/*Oakwood City School Dist*	31	152

P

NAME/District	JOB FUNCTIONS	PAGE
Pabst, Stacey/*Kettering City School Dist*	4	150
Packer, Jara/*Dublin City School Dist*	79	69
Packey, Lea/*Marlington Local School Dist*	71	186
Paczak, Maureen/*Lakeview Local School Dist*	7	199
Page, Tebra/*Solon City School Dist*	7,36,57,58,77,79,92,294	50
Pagnotta, Dean/*South Range Local School Dist*	3,73,84,295	135
Paisley, Brian/*Perry Local School Dist*	73,297	188
Paisley, Sean/*Tuscarawas Valley Local SD*	273	203
Palazzo, Joe/*Jefferson Local School Dist*	38	132
Pallas, Kayla/*Warrensville Heights City SD*	71	51
Palm, Sarah/*Newbury Local School Dist*	2	82
Palma, Jamie/*Massillon City School Dist*	11,30,78,296,298	187
Palmer, David/*Garfield Heights City SD*	3	46
Palmer, David/*Troy City School Dist*	6	146
Palmer, Michelle/*Springboro Cmty School Dist*	5	208
Palmer, Richard/*Madeira City School Dist*	67	90
Palmer, Susanne/*Worthington School Dist*	81	75
Palmison, Lisa/*Olmsted Falls City School Dist*	38	48
Palumbo, Christine, Dr/*Lakewood City School Dist*	8,12,288	47
Panak, Bradley/*Liberty Local School Dist*	2	199
Panapucci, Tony/*Buckeye Local School Dist*	3	108
Pantling, Keith/*Little Miami Local School Dist*	6	208
Panuto, Janice/*Findlay City School Dist*	8,18,83,88	97
Paolo, Dominic/*Fairport Harbor Exempt Vlg SD*	1	112
Paolone, Renny/*Girard City School Dist*	27,31,39	197
Paparizos, Charlene/*Chagrin Falls Exempted Vlg SD*	71	42
Paparizos, Charlene/*Independence Local School Dist*	71	46
Paparizos, Charlene/*North Royalton City Sch Dist*	71	48
Papouras, Christopher/*Euclid City School Dist*	15	46
Pardee, Susan/*Cleveland Hts-Univ Hts City SD*	11,298	42
Parece, Larry/*West Clermont Local Sch Dist*	16,73,84,91,95,270,295	31
Paredez, Judy/*Penta Co JT Voc School Dist*	67	217
Parent, Mark/*Plain Local School Dist*	34,36,57,58,69,77,79	188
Paris, Linda/*Jackson Local School Dist*	2	186
Paris, Susan/*Youngstown City School Dist*	4	136
Parish, Paula/*Bluffton Exempted Village Sch*	2	8
Parker, Debbie/*Highland Local School Dist*	5	141
Parker, Jeff/*Eaton Cmty School Dist*	1	168
Parker, Jill/*Northeastern Local School Dist*	67	27

DISTRICT PERSONNEL INDEX

Market Data Retrieval

NAME/District	JOB FUNCTIONS	PAGE
Parker, Joel/Elida Local School Dist	2	8
Parker, Ken/Harrison Hills City Sch Dist	83	101
Parker, Rhonda/New Miami Local School Dist	1,11	23
Parker, Steve/Sheffield-Sheffield Lake CSD	3,4,91	125
Parker, Susan/Port Clinton City School Dist	83,85,88	159
Parker, Teresa/Ashtabula Co Ed Service Center	58	11
Parker, Teresa/Buckeye Local School Dist	58	12
Parkes, Cindy/Clay Local School Dist	16,82	178
Parkinson, Bill/Willoughby-Eastlake City SD	2	114
Parkinson, Charlene/Galion City School Dist	2	38
Parks, Darlene/Bethel-Tate Local School Dist	4	30
Parks, Terri/Northeastern Local School Dist	4	27
Parmigian, Guy/Benton-Carroll-Salem Local SD	1	158
Parpart, Stephen/Centerburg Local School Dist	31,36,69	110
Parr, Debbie/Newbury Local School Dist	4	82
Parr, Matt/Pioneer Joint Voc School Dist	29	173
Parr, Stacy/Springfield City School Dist	16,73,76,295	28
Parrish, John/Springfield City School Dist	3	28
Parrott, Cindy/Galion City School Dist	58,752	38
Parry, James/Mathews Local School Dist	16	199
Parry, Michael/Ashland Co-West Holmes JVSD	11	11
Parry, Michael/U S Grant Career School Dist	1	31
Parson, Deidre/Barberton City School Dist	57,58,77,79,85,271	192
Parsons, Ginger/Licking Heights Local Sch Dist	4	118
Parsons, Hollie/Lake Local School Dist	76	217
Parsons, Lori/Milton-Union Exempted Vlg SD	67	145
Parsons, Tom/Athens City School Dist	8,11,36,74,286,288,294,298	14
Parthemore, Jessica/Ridgedale Local School Dist	6,83,88,275	138
Partlow, Madeline/Grandview Heights City SD	7,11,57,58,69,88,271,298	71
Passarge, Chris/Lakota Local School Dist	2,3,17,91	22
Pastre, Vince/Buckeye Local School Dist	73,295	108
Pastva, Deanne/Amherst Exempted Village SD	4	122
Patacca, Shane/Ottawa Hills Local Sch Dist	73,76	128
Pate, Richard/Hamilton City School Dist	27,31	22
Paterson, Kate/Licking Valley Local Sch Dist	4	118
Paterson, Sherry/Washington-Nile Local Sch Dist	2,84	179
Patriarca, Christy/Perry Local School Dist	280	113
Patrick, Michelle/Springfield-Clark Co JVSD	1	28
Patrick, Mindy/Olentangy Local School Dist	67	59
Patten, Patricia/U S Grant Career School Dist	2	31
Patterson, Denny/East Guernsey Local Sch Dist	67	86
Patterson, Doug/Lisbon Exempted Village SD	5	35
Patterson, Doug/Ridgewood Local School Dist	3,5	37
Patterson, Emily/Lexington Local School Dist	16,82	172
Patterson, Heather/Allen East Local School Dist	12	7
Patterson, Jason/Plain Local School Dist	73,286	188
Patterson, Joshua/Troy City School Dist	88	146
Patterson, Kent/Ed Svc Center of Medina Co	67	139
Patterson, Sarah/Fairfield Co Ed Service Center	58	62
Patterson, Sherry/Dover City School Dist	7	202
Patton, Gary/Warren Co Voc School Dist	10	208
Patton, Lari/Waverly City School Dist	4	164
Patton, Martha/Bay Village City School Dist	15,58	40
Patton, Trevor/Washington Court House City SD	71	65
Paul-Mikulski, Wendy/Stow-Munroe Falls City SD	31	194
Paul, Benjamin/Monroeville Local School Dist	6	105
Paul, Jody/Crooksville Exempted Vlg SD	7,85	161
Paul, Matthew/Kirtland Local School Dist	6	112
Paul, Scott/Franklin Local School Dist	2	156
Pauley, Autumn/Centerburg Local School Dist	4	110
Pauley, Jeff/Symmes Valley Local Sch Dist	16,73,295	117
Paullin, Donald/Pioneer Joint Voc School Dist	26,75	173
Paulsey, Alicia/Kenston Local School Dist	88	82
Paulus, Linda/Kent City School Dist	76	165
Pavkovich, Duane/East Palestine City Sch Dist	6	35
Pavlic, Janet/Bedford City School Dist	2	40
Pavlik, Jerry/Lorain Co Joint Voc Sch Dist	15	125
Pawlowski, Phil/Jefferson Area Local SD	67	13
Payne, Bev/Crestline Exempted Village SD	5	38
Payne, Jon/Reading Cmty City School Dist	6	93
Pazitka, Mine/Medina City School Dist	34,57,58,79	141
Peach, Ron/Jefferson Co JT Voc Sch Dist	73	109
Peacock, Erin/Rocky River City School Dist	5	50
Peardon, Joe/Liberty Union-Thurstn Sch Dist	3	64
Pearson, Chris/Tri-Village Local Sch Dist	3,73,91	56
Pearson, Pamela/Northmont City School Dist	4	152
Pechie, Joni/Arcanum Butler Local Sch Dist	11,69,72	55
Peck, Amanda/Troy City School Dist	81	146
Peck, Beth/Holgate Local School Dist	8,31,36,69,83	101
Peck, Pamela/Ashtabula Area City Sch Dist	4	12
Peck, William/Huber Heights City School Dist	5	150
Pedal, Trudy/Cambridge City School Dist	36	86
Peden, Becki/Huntington Local School Dist	2,19	175
Pedicino, Jeff/Solon City School Dist	91	50
Peger, Deborah/Licking Co Ed Service Center	34	117
Pegram, Nick/New Miami Local School Dist	3,91	23
Pehanich, Mary/Lakeview Local School Dist	4	199
Peiffer, Tom/Old Fort Local School Dist	1	181
Pelcoma, Dawn/Strasburg Franklin Local SD	286	203
Pelko, Jennifer/Strongsville City School Dist	15,68,74,78,273	51
Pellin, Darlene/Jackson-Milton Local Sch Dist	5	134
Pemberton, Jim/Twin Valley Cmty Local SD	67	169
Pempin, Phill/Vermilion Local School Dist	1	62
Pence, Jeff/Greenfield Exempted Village SD	3,91	103
Pence, Tim/Waynesfield-Goshen Local SD	12,58,69	16
Penczarski, Jennifer/Kenton City School Dist	1	100
Pendexter, Rita/Licking Heights Local Sch Dist	6	118
Penington, Laurie/Galion City School Dist	4	38
Penix, Gerald/Clay Local School Dist	5	178
Penk, James/Austintown Local School Dist	6	133
Penler, Karen/West Geauga Local School Dist	2,11,19	82
Pennell, John/Springboro Cmty School Dist	3,4,5	208
Penney, Joe/Madison Plains Local Sch Dist	3,4,16,73,76,82	133
Pennington, Dave/Clermont Northeastern Local SD	67	30
Pennington, Greg/Paint Valley Local School Dist	5	175
Pennington, Lorie/Marysville Exempted Village SD	4	204
Pennington, Matt/Benjamin Logan Local Sch Dist	3	121
Pennington, Mike/Independence Local School Dist	8,11,31,35,69,73,273,295	46
Pennix, Brian/Blanchester Local School Dist	6	32
Penny, Joe/Fairfield City School Dist	2	21
Penton, Tim/Lakota Local School Dist	2	22
Peoples, Juliet/Westerville City School Dist	11,296,298	74
Pequignot, Jeremy/Franklin-Monroe Local Sch Dist	1	55
Pera, Jonathan/Poland Local School Dist	16,76,295	135
Perchinske, Jim/Wellington Exempted Village SD	73	126
Perez, Elena/Norwalk City School Dist	57	106
Perhach, Vince/Pickaway-Ross Co JT Voc SD	73	175
Perkins, Eric/ADA Exempted Village Sch Dist	6	99
Perkins, Jacob/Reynoldsburg City School Dist	6	72
Perkins, Kasey/Southwest Licking Local SD	8,12,16,69,73,288,295,296	120
Perkins, Kim/Carlisle Local School Dist	58	206
Perkins, Kim/Springboro Cmty School Dist	58	208
Perkins, Lowell/St Clairsville-Richland CSD	4	18
Perkins, Thomas/Northern Local School Dist	1	161
Perry, Erin/Rossford Exempted Village SD	58,77	218
Perry, Lance/West Clermont Local School Dist	3,5	31
Perry, Sharon/Tiffin City School Dist	2	181
Persin, Norm/Oak Hill Union Local Sch Dist	6	107
Pertner, Scott/Gibsonburg Exempted Village SD	67	177
Pestello, Paul/Kenston Local School Dist	2	82
Pester, Dustin/Miller City-New Cleveland SD	11	170
Peter, John/Norwood City School Dist	3	92
Peter, Teresa/Talawanda School Dist	31,38	24
Peterman, Tracey/Claymont City School Dist	4,5	201

1 Superintendent
2 Bus/Finance/Purchasing
3 Buildings And Grounds
4 Food Service
5 Transportation
6 Athletic
7 Health Services
8 Curric/Instruct K-12
9 Curric/Instruct Elem
10 Curric/Instruct Sec
11 Federal Program
12 Title I
13 Title V
15 Asst Superintendent
16 Instructional Media Svcs
17 Chief Operations Officer
18 Chief Academic Officer
19 Chief Financial Officer
20 Art K-12
21 Art Elem
22 Art Sec
23 Music K-12
24 Music Elem
25 Music Sec
26 Business Education
27 Career & Tech Ed
28 Technology Education
29 Family/Consumer Science
30 Adult Education
31 Career/Sch-to-Work K-12
32 Career/Sch-to-Work Elem
33 Career/Sch-to-Work Sec
34 Early Childhood Ed
35 Health/Phys Education
36 Guidance Services K-12
37 Guidance Services Elem
38 Guidance Services Sec
39 Social Studies K-12
40 Social Studies Elem
41 Social Studies Sec
42 Science K-12
43 Science Elem
44 Science Sec
45 Math K-12
46 Math Elem
47 Math Sec
48 English/Lang Arts K-12
49 English/Lang Arts Elem
50 English/Lang Arts Sec
51 Reading K-12
52 Reading Elem
53 Reading Sec
54 Remedial Reading K-12
55 Remedial Reading Elem
56 Remedial Reading Sec
57 Bilingual/ELL
58 Special Education K-12
59 Special Education Elem
60 Special Education Sec
61 Foreign/World Lang K-12
62 Foreign/World Lang Elem
63 Foreign/World Lang Sec
64 Religious Education K-12
65 Religious Education Elem
66 Religious Education Sec
67 School Board President
68 Teacher Personnel
69 Academic Assessment
70 Research/Development
71 Public Information
72 Summer School
73 Instructional Tech
74 Inservice Training
75 Marketing/Distributive
76 Info Systems
77 Psychological Assess
78 Affirmative Action
79 Student Personnel
80 Driver Ed/Safety
81 Gifted/Talented
82 Video Services
83 Substance Abuse Prev
84 Erate
85 AIDS Education
88 Alternative/At Risk
89 Multi-Cultural Curriculum
90 Social Work
91 Safety/Security
92 Magnet School
93 Parental Involvement
95 Tech Prep Program
97 Chief Information Officer
98 Chief Technology Officer
270 Character Education
271 Migrant Education
273 Teacher Mentor
274 Before/After Sch
275 Response To Intervention
277 Remedial Math K-12
280 Literacy Coach
285 STEM
286 Digital Learning
288 Common Core Standards
294 Accountability
295 Network System
296 Title II Programs
297 Webmaster
298 Grant Writer/Ptnrships
750 Chief Innovation Officer
751 Chief of Staff
752 Social Emotional Learning

OH-T42

Ohio School Directory — DISTRICT PERSONNEL INDEX

NAME/District	JOB FUNCTIONS	PAGE
Peters, Jill/*Stryker Local School Dist*	2,84	215
Peters, Laura/*Vantage Career Center Sch Dist*	2	206
Peters, Michele/*Triad Local School Dist*	58,88,275	26
Peters, Richard/*Liberty Center Local Sch Dist*	1	101
Peters, Ryan/*Beachwood City School Dist*	6	40
Peters, Shawn/*Ansonia Local School Dist*	73	55
Peters, Shawn/*Mississinawa Valley Sch Dist*	16,73	56
Peters, Sherry/*Crestwood Local School Dist*	11,58,79,83,296	165
Peters, Ted/*Sandusky City School Dist*	5	61
Peters, Vickie/*Perry Local School Dist*	4	113
Peterson, Julie/*Tuscarawas Valley Local SD*	57	203
Peterson, Kelly/*Field Local School Dist*	4	165
Peterson, Nannette/*Lake Local School Dist*	16,82	186
Peterson, Neil/*Cuyahoga Heights Local SD*	3	45
Peterson, Stacy/*Buckeye Valley Local Sch Dist*	4	58
Petitjean, Marcus/*Russia Local School Dist*	73	183
Petkac, George/*Cleveland Hts-Univ Hts City SD*	2	42
Petonic, Susan/*Nordonia Hills City Sch Dist*	4	193
Petresino, Nicholas/*Ravenna School Dist*	16	166
Petrey, Todd/*Mason City School Dist*	2,3,17,91	208
Petrie, Brian/*Cardington-Lincoln Local SD*	1,11,73	155
Petrina, Kim/*Olmsted Falls City School Dist*	71	48
Petro, John/*Massillon City School Dist*	3	187
Petroff, Laura/*North Royalton City Sch Dist*	2	48
Petros, Steve/*Groveport Madison Local SD*	6	71
Petry, Dottie/*North College Hill City SD*	4	91
Pett, Tina/*West Carrollton City Sch Dist*	4	153
Petti, Sandy/*Aurora City School Dist*	7	164
Pettiegrew, Henry, Dr/*East Cleveland City Sch Dist*	1	45
Pettit, Brad/*Bexley City School Dist*	73	66
Pettus, Krista/*Anna Local School Dist*	52,55	182
Petty, Joanne/*Urbana City School Dist*	12	26
Petty, Jodi/*Bethel Local School Dist*	4,9,12,285	145
Peugeot, Megan/*Sandusky City School Dist*	8,57,58,88	61
Pfaff, Mark/*Kent City School Dist*	6	165
Pfeifer, Zach/*Southeastern Local Sch Dist*	10,12,58,298	175
Pfeiffer, Sean/*Wayne Trace Local School Dist*	5	160
Pfelman, Carmen/*Bloom-Carroll Local Sch Dist*	5	63
Pfister, Anne/*Northmor Local School Dist*	8,69,273,288,298	155
Pfister, Chris/*Waynesfield-Goshen Local SD*	1	16
Pfister, Gary/*Tipp City Exempted Village SD*	4,73,286,297	146
Pfleiderer, Kim/*Madison Local School Dist*	4	172
Phares, Randy/*Northeastern Local School Dist*	3,5,91	27
Phelps, Tammy/*Canal Winchester Local SD*	38	66
Phiel, Megan/*Hubbard Exempted Village SD*	16	198
Philabaum, Scott/*Fairfield Union Local Sch Dist*	3,8,11,15,16,69,73,297	63
Phillips, Ann/*Mogadore Local School Dist*	58	166
Phillips, Cindy/*Fayetteville Perry Local SD*	4	19
Phillips, Dan/*Alexander Local School Dist*	5	14
Phillips, Jack/*Deer Park Cmty School Dist*	1	89
Phillips, James/*South Range Local School Dist*	2,19	135
Phillips, Joe/*Keystone Local School Dist*	28,73	124
Phillips, Jud/*Milford Exempted Village SD*	5	30
Phillips, Karen/*Carey Exempted Village SD*	2	219
Phillips, Kevin/*Valley View Local School Dist*	34,58,77	153
Phillips, Mari, Dr/*Princeton City School Dist*	58	92
Phillips, Mark/*Fairless Local School Dist*	2	185
Phillips, Mark/*Tuscarawas Valley Local SD*	2	203
Phillips, Peggy/*Kings Local School Dist*	67	207
Phillips, Rhonda/*Miami Valley Career Tech VSD*	10,286,288	151
Phillipson, Todd, Dr/*Jefferson Co JT Voc Sch Dist*	1,11	109
Philpot, Curtis/*Miami Valley Career Tech VSD*	3,17	151
Phipps, John/*Southern Local School Dist*	38	161
Phipps, John/*Walnut Twp Local School Dist*	36,69	64
Piccari, Tom/*Stark Co Ed Service Center*	81	184
Piccolantonio, Beryl/*Gahanna-Jefferson Public SD*	67	70
Pickard, Mark/*Jefferson Area Local SD*	73	13
Picken, Doris/*Jefferson Local School Dist*	274	132
Pickering, Cindy/*Southwest Licking Local SD*	4	120
Pickering, Patti/*Lakewood Local School Dist*	8,11,69,79,288,294,296,298	118
Picking, Joe/*Tccsa-Tri-Co Comp Svcs*	73	214
Piedermann, Roy/*Austintown Local School Dist*	76	133
Pierce, Amanda/*Morgan Local School Dist*	11,298	154
Pierce, Debra/*Parkway Local School Dist*	2	144
Pierce, Erin/*Howland Local School Dist*	8,11,69,83,88,288,298	198
Pierre-Farid, Michelle, Dr/*Cleveland Metro School Dist*	8,18	42
Pierson, Lori/*Hamilton City School Dist*	273	22
Pietch, Sherry/*Avon Local School Dist*	69	122
Pietra, Guy/*James A Garfield Local SD*	67	165
Pietsch Miller, Kimberly, Dr/*Bexley City School Dist*	1	66
Pigg, Terri/*Newton Falls Exempted Vlg SD*	5	200
Pilati, Dave/*North Canton City School Dist*	11,15,275,288	187
Pillets, Brooke/*Garfield Heights City SD*	58	46
Pimpas, Erica/*Delphos City School Dist*	67	8
Pine, Ryan/*Graham Local School Dist*	67	26
Pinkava, Kathy/*Berkshire Local School Dist*	7,85	81
Pinter, Tess/*Archbold Area Local Sch Dist*	16,82	78
Pipa, Missy/*Medina City School Dist*	7	141
Piper, Chris/*Troy City School Dist*	1	146
Piper, Keith/*New Riegel Local School Dist*	5	181
Piper, Tracy/*Triway Local School Dist*	5	213
Pipes-Perone, Kris/*Tri-Co Ed Service Center*	8,58	211
Pipic, Michelle/*West Geauga Local School Dist*	4	82
Pipps, Kathleen/*Elida Local School Dist*	93	8
Pique, Arline/*Hamilton County ESC*	73	97
Piquet, Tony/*Clay Local School Dist*	9	178
Piro, Cj/*Beachwood City School Dist*	91	40
Pirone, Peter/*Struthers City School Dist*	1,83	136
Pisano, Kari/*Monroeville Local School Dist*	16,82	105
Pissini, Michael/*Sheffield-Sheffield Lake CSD*	2,19	125
Pittis, Adam/*East Guernsey Local Sch Dist*	1	86
Pitts, John/*Champion Local School Dist*	67	197
Pitts, Marsha/*Marion City School Dist*	11,54,69,83,88,296	138
Pittser, Kim/*Miami Trace Local School Dist*	15,273,285,286,288,294	65
Pizzola, Katleen/*South Range Local School Dist*	4	135
Plageman, Kristen/*Parma City School Dist*	27,30	49
Plaisted, Glenna/*Lakewood Local School Dist*	2,19	118
Plantz, Sandra/*Gallia Co Local School Dist*	11,81,273	80
Platko, Gary/*Riverside Local School Dist*	2,7,19,84	113
Pleasant, Robert/*Lawrence Co Joint Voc Sch Dist*	67	116
Pleiman, Jeremy/*Botkins Local School Dist*	53	182
Plikerd, Dustin/*Indian Lake Local School Dist*	3	121
Plikerd, Sue/*Bath Local School Dist*	16	8
Plotts, David/*Butler Tech Career Dev Schs*	3,5,73,295	21
Pluchinsky, Rossana/*South Range Local School Dist*	16	135
Plucinsky, Gary/*Brooklyn City School Dist*	69,83	41
Pluck, Sonja/*Madison Local School Dist*	30	172
Pochedly, Samantha/*Windham Exempted Vlg Sch Dist*	2,4	167
Poe, Brian/*Copley-Fairlawn City Sch Dist*	1	192
Poe, Kathleen/*Kenston Local School Dist*	8,11,27,69,83,288,296,298	82
Poe, Steven/*Put-In-Bay Local School Dist*	1,11	159
Poetter, Christine/*Princeton City School Dist*	2	92
Pohlman, Mark/*Hilliard City School Dist*	73	71
Pohlman, Mike/*Marion Local School Dist*	1	144
Poje, Dennie/*Canton City School Dist*	2	184
Polacek, David/*Barberton City School Dist*	67	192
Polak, Jennifer/*Fairport Harbor Exempt Vlg SD*	8,11,58	112
Poland, Debbie/*Perry Local School Dist*	8,11,288,296,298	188
Poling, Clare/*Hardin Northern Local Sch Dist*	12	100
Poling, David/*Lake Local School Dist*	67	186
Poling, Debbie/*ADA Exempted Village Sch Dist*	12	99
Polish, Janet/*Austintown Local School Dist*	9	133
Pollock, Greg/*Buckeye Local School Dist*	5	140
Pollock, Kathy/*Sylvania City School Dist*	81	128
Pollom, Melissa/*Ridgemont Local School Dist*	2	100
Polter, Lori/*Central Local School Dist*	33,38,69	57
Pomeroy, Keith/*Upper Arlington City Sch Dist*	8,18,36,74,288,298	74
Pomesky, Kaye/*Ashland City School Dist*	288	10
Pompoco, Christy/*Champion Local School Dist*	58	197
Pompos, Brad/*Beavercreek City School Dist*	6	83
Pond, Dean, Dr/*Covington Exempted Village SD*	67	145
Pool, Brian/*National Trail Local Sch Dist*	73,286	168
Poor, Kathleen/*Springboro Cmty School Dist*	4	208
Poore, Jack/*Miami Valley Career Tech VSD*	15,79	151
Pope, Carrie/*Elyria City School Dist*	58	123
Porcello, Leah/*Wickliffe City School Dist*	36	114
Porinchok, Loni/*Paulding Exempted Village SD*	11,34,58,69,88,91,275,286	160
Porter-Sawyer, Debra/*Pickerington Local School Dist*	68	64
Porter, Al/*Clermont Northeastern Local SD*	2	30
Porter, Amy/*St Clairsville-Richland CSD*	2,19	18
Porter, Ben/*Marion City School Dist*	8,288	138
Porter, Ben/*Union Local School Dist*	1,11	18

School Year 2019-2020   800-333-8802   OH-T43

DISTRICT PERSONNEL INDEX

Market Data Retrieval

NAME/District	JOB FUNCTIONS	PAGE
Porter, Ken/Ashtabula Co Tech & Career SD	31	12
Porter, Kevin/Mansfield City Schools	6	172
Porter, Randy/Field Local School Dist	67	165
Porter, Rich/Centerburg Local School Dist	6	110
Porter, Richard/Forest Hills School Dist	5	89
Porter, Sarah/East Liverpool City Sch Dist	67	35
Porter, Tim/Weathersfield Local Sch Dist	6	201
Porter, William/Mentor Exempted Village SD	1	113
Porteus, Kathleen/Cardington-Lincoln Local SD	16,82	155
Pospisil, Kathryn/Fairfield City School Dist	10	21
Postlethwait, Laureen/Warren City School Dist	4	200
Poston, Cathy/Fairfield Union Local Sch Dist	36,83	63
Poteet, David/Sandy Valley Local School Dist	58	189
Potter, Kim/Jefferson Twp Local Sch Dist	73	150
Potter, Norman/Twinsburg City School Dist	8	195
Potter, Wes/Hardin Northern Local Sch Dist	2,11	100
Pottorf, Larry/Minerva Local School Dist	2	187
Potts, Christopher/Upper Arlington City Sch Dist	3,17,91	74
Potts, Donna/Clinton-Massie Local School Dist	27,31,38,83,270	33
Potts, Jason/Greenfield Exempted Village SD	27,31,75	103
Potts, Mark/Ashtabula Area City Sch Dist	1	12
Potts, Tracy/Continental Local School Dist	12,274	169
Powell, Amy/Frontier Local School Dist	54,273	210
Powell, Desiree/Cleveland Metro School Dist	7,35	42
Powell, Kristy/Meigs Local School Dist	7	142
Powell, Susan/Athens City School Dist	38	14
Power, Gregory/Little Miami Local School Dist	1	208
Powers-Dolney, Kathleen/Painesville City Local SD	67	113
Powers, Katherine/Twinsburg Local School Dist	1	195
Powers, Paul/Aurora City School Dist	6	164
Powers, Steve/Washington Court House City SD	16,73,286	65
Powers, Tom/Marysville Exempted Village SD	71,73,76,97	204
Poynter, Rachel/Northwestern Local School Dist	38	27
Pozenel, Lucas/Urbana City School Dist	58,77	26
Pozsgai, Tricia/North Royalton City Sch Dist	73,286	48
Prairie, Connie/North College Hill City SD	58	91
Prasse, Tim/Dalton Local School Dist	4	212
Prater, Alex/Wheelersburg Local School Dist	3,91	180
Prater, Barb/Blanchester Local School Dist	5	32
Prater, Erinn/ADA Exempted Village Sch Dist	69,83,88,270	99
Prater, Jason/Coshocton Co Joint Voc SD	60	37
Prati, Beverly/Bridgeport School Dist	58	18
Pratt, Pam/Edgewood City School Dist	71	21
Prchlik, Joe/Northwest Ohio Computer Assoc	16,73	80
Prebles, Scot/Forest Hills School Dist	1	89
Prescott, Suzanne/Butler Co Ed Service Center	34	20
Presot, James/North Royalton City Sch Dist	15	48
Pressman, Rita/Kenston Local School Dist	58	82
Preston, Ellie/West Clermont Local Sch Dist	12,36,69,79,88,288,298	31
Preston, Rob/Franklin Local School Dist	3,15,78,95	156
Price, Janice/Fairview Park City Sch Dist	11,36,57,58,69,77,271,296	46
Price, Jason/Mohawk Local School Dist	5	219
Price, Jeff, Dr/Hardin Northern Local Sch Dist	1	100
Price, Jennifer/Licking Heights Local Sch Dist	7,83,88,275	118
Price, Kathryn/Ironton City School Dist	16,297	116
Price, Sharee/South Central Ohio Ed Svc Ctr	81	178
Prichard, Matt/New Richmond Exempted Vlg SD	16,73,295,297	31
Pride, Richie/Southern Hills Joint Voc SD	67	20
Priest, Erika/Crestview Local School Dist	27	205
Prim, Daryl/Marietta City School Dist	3,5,73,91	210
Prince, Patricia/Canfield Local School Dist	2	134
Pringle, Lori/East Holmes Local School Dist	16,82	104
Prior, Roger/Bristol Local School Dist	3	197
Pritchard, Kylie/London City School Dist	8,11,275,288	132
Pritchard, Larry/Chillicothe City School Dist	3	174
Pritt, David/North Ridgeville City Sch Dist	8,11,69,74,76,288,296,298	125
Pritt, David/North Ridgeville City Sch Dist	8,11,69,76,288,296,298	125
Pritt, Lynn/North Ridgeville City Sch Dist	273	125
Pritts, Cheryl/Barnesville Exempted Vlg SD	2	17
Pritts, Cheryl/Buckeye Joint Voc School Dist	2	201
Proehl, Linda/Marysville Exempted Village SD	38,88	204
Proffitt, Becky/Van Wert City School Dist	4	205
Prohaska, Danielle/Mechanicsburg Exempted Vlg SD	1	26
Proper, Matthew/Danville Local School Dist	58,69	110
Propri, Alisa/Labrae Local School Dist	4	198
Prough, Kristie/Stow-Munroe Falls City SD	13,58,77	194
Provitt, Vickie/Lisbon Exempted Village SD	2	35
Pryer, David/Allen East Local School Dist	7	7
Pryor, Katie/Greenfield Exempted Village SD	7	103
Ptacek, Michael/North Olmsted City School Dist	6	48
Pugh, John/Bloom-Carroll Local Sch Dist	3	63
Puhalla, Mike/Urbana City School Dist	5	26
Puhlman, Kaleb/Liberty Center Local Sch Dist	6	101
Pulice, Chuck/Mathews Local School Dist	3,5,91	199
Pulley, Dede/Wapakoneta City School Dist	16	16
Pullman, Cindy/Mechanicsburg Exempted Vlg SD	7	26
Puperi, Helen/Union Local School Dist	298	19
Pupo, Mark/Kettering City School Dist	295	150
Purcell, Brett/Waynesfield-Goshen Local SD	6	16
Purdon, Raechel/Blanchester Local School Dist	8,11,69,72,273,288	32
Purkey, Kelley/Wayne Local School Dist	16	209
Pursell, Brad/Southwest Ohio OCA	73	25
Pusateri, Anthony/Upper Arlington City Sch Dist	6	74
Puschel, Keith/Botkins Local School Dist	16,73	182
Push, Mark/Kenton City School Dist	67	100
Puster, Cathrine/Loudonville-Perrysville SD	1	11
Puster, Todd/Orange City School Dist	2,19	48
Puthoff, Adam/St Henry Cons Local Sch Dist	9,11,34	144
Puthoff, Brian/New Bremen Local School Dist	73,295	16
Putnam, Alissa/Chillicothe City School Dist	8,11,288,296,298	174
Putnam, James/Trotwood-Madison City SD	4	152

Q

NAME/District	JOB FUNCTIONS	PAGE
Quackenbush, Barbara/Newark City School Dist	68	119
Quackenbush, Jeff/Newark City School Dist	6	119
Quallen, Nicole/Wilmington City School Dist	8,11,57,286,288,296,298	33
Quallich, Kristine, Dr/Medina City School Dist	8,15,58,73,74,81	141
Quattrochi, David/Carrollton Exempted Village SD	1,11,83	25
Quattrone, Tracy, Dr/Wyoming City School Dist	7,13,54,57,58,79,81,88	94
Queberg, Melonie/Medina Co Joint Voc Sch Dist	7	141
Quickle, Kathy/Clear Fork Vly Local Sch Dist	81	171
Quigley, Susanne/Loveland City School Dist	71,75,97	90
Quillen, Keith/New Lebanon Local School Dist	16,73,295	151
Quinlan, Michael/Cory-Rawson Local School Dist	73,76,295	97
Quinn, Kitty/Diocese of Columbus Ed Office	34,83	76
Quinn, Rebecca/Chagrin Falls Exempted Vlg SD	8,288	42
Quires, Kathy/Elgin Local School Dist	16,58,82	138

R

NAME/District	JOB FUNCTIONS	PAGE
Raach, Kandi/Rolling Hills Local Sch Dist	2,19	86
Raach, Rick/Coshocton Co Joint Voc SD	1	37
Rabe, Don/Hamilton County ESC	2	97
Rabe, Donald/Hamilton Co Ed Service Center	2	87
Rabold, Chris/Northwest Local School Dist	16	91
Rachel, Rachelle/Jackson City School Dist	2	107
Radabaugh, Brian/North Fork Local School Dist	6	119
Radar-Brown, Lucy, Dr/Westerville City School Dist	57	74
Radel, Tom/Massillon City School Dist	67	187
Radich, Melissa/Triway Local School Dist	285	213
Radman, Jay/Crestview Local School Dist	3	34
Radtke, Linda/St Bernard-Elmwood Place Schs	67	93
Radwancky, John/Buckeye Local School Dist	73,295	12
Rae, Elizabeth/Cleveland Hts-Univ Hts City SD	12	42
Ragan, Ted/Bristol Local School Dist	73,76,295	197

---

1 Superintendent	16 Instructional Media Svcs	30 Adult Education	44 Science Sec	58 Special Education K-12	72 Summer School	88 Alternative/At Risk	277 Remedial Math K-12	
2 Bus/Finance/Purchasing	17 Chief Operations Officer	31 Career/Sch-to-Work K-12	45 Math K-12	59 Special Education Elem	74 Inservice Training	89 Multi-Cultural Curriculum	280 Literacy Coach	
3 Buildings And Grounds	18 Chief Academic Officer	32 Career/Sch-to-Work Elem	46 Math Elem	60 Special Education Sec	74 Inservice Training	90 Social Work	285 STEM	
4 Food Service	19 Chief Financial Officer	33 Career/Sch-to-Work Sec	47 Math Sec	61 Foreign/World Lang K-12	75 Marketing/Distributive	91 Safety/Security	286 Digital Learning	
5 Transportation	20 Art K-12	34 Early Childhood Ed	48 English/Lang Arts K-12	62 Foreign/World Lang Elem	76 Info Systems	92 Magnet School	288 Common Core Standards	
6 Athletic	21 Art Elem	35 Health/Phys Education	49 English/Lang Arts Elem	63 Foreign/World Lang Sec	77 Psychological Assess	93 Parental Involvement	294 Accountability	
7 Health Services	22 Art Sec	36 Guidance Services K-12	50 English/Lang Arts Sec	64 Religious Education K-12	78 Affirmative Action	95 Tech Prep Program	295 Network System	
8 Curric/Instruct K-12	23 Music K-12	37 Guidance Services Elem	51 Reading K-12	65 Religious Education Elem	79 Student Personnel	97 Chief Information Officer	296 Title II Programs	
9 Curric/Instruct Elem	24 Music Elem	38 Guidance Services Sec	52 Reading Elem	66 Religious Education Sec	80 Driver Ed/Safety	98 Chief Technology Officer	297 Webmaster	
10 Curric/Instruct Sec	25 Music Sec	40 Social Studies K-12	53 Reading Sec	67 School Board President	81 Gifted/Talented	270 Character Education	298 Grant Writer/Ptnrships	
11 Federal Program	26 Business Education	40 Social Studies Elem	54 Remedial Reading K-12	68 Teacher Personnel	82 Video Services	271 Migrant Education	750 Chief Innovation Officer	
12 Title I	27 Career & Tech Ed	41 Social Studies Sec	55 Remedial Reading Elem	69 Academic Assessment	83 Substance Abuse Prev	273 Teacher Mentor	751 Chief of Staff	
13 Title V	28 Technology Education	42 Science K-12	56 Remedial Reading Sec	70 Research/Development	84 Erate	274 Before/After Sch	752 Social Emotional Learning	
15 Asst Superintendent	29 Family/Consumer Science	43 Science Elem	57 Bilingual/ELL	71 Public Information	85 AIDS Education	275 Response To Intervention		

Ohio School Directory

DISTRICT PERSONNEL INDEX

NAME/District	JOB FUNCTIONS	PAGE
Rager, Patrick/*Access*	76	137
Rahamut, Val/*Vinton Co Local School Dist*	7,85	206
Raiff, Mark/*Olentangy Local School Dist*	1	59
Raike, Dan/*Greenfield Exempted Village SD*	38	103
Rainey, Jeff/*Pleasant Local School Dist*	16	138
Rainey, Jerry/*Lancaster City School Dist*	2,73	63
Rainey, Linda/*Liberty Union-Thurstn Sch Dist*	69	64
Rainier, Casey/*Lancaster City School Dist*	3	63
Rair, Randall/*Diocese of Youngstown Ed Off*	6,11,15	137
Rambler, Dan/*Akron Public Schools*	79,91	190
Ramey, Brenda/*North Canton City School Dist*	7	187
Ramey, Kyle, Dr/*Oakwood City School Dist*	1	152
Ramey, Rachael/*Green Local School Dist*	58	178
Rammel, Michelle/*Dayton Public School Dist*	27	149
Rammel, Shel/*U S Grant Career School Dist*	10,69	31
Ramnytz, Jeffrey/*Barberton City School Dist*	1	192
Ramos, Julie/*Wickliffe City School Dist*	285	114
Ramsay, Brian/*Westfall Local School Dist*	2	163
Ramsey, Katie/*Ashland City School Dist*	7	10
Ramsey, Linda/*Goshen Local School Dist*	4	30
Ramsey, Pat/*Arcadia Local School Dist*	38,69,83,85,88,270	97
Ramsey, Roxann/*North Ridgeville City Sch Dist*	1	125
Ramunno, Mr/*Lowellville Local School Dist*	67	135
Rand, Matthew/*Talawanda School Dist*	73,76,84	24
Randall, Adrian/*Mid-Ohio Ed Service Center*	27,58,79	171
Randolph, Amy/*Highland Local School Dist*	58	155
Randulic, Mark/*Perry Local School Dist*	3	188
Raneger, Jodi/*Bloom-Carroll Local Sch Dist*	8,11,51,54,57,286,288,296	63
Rank, Rhonda/*Lincolnview Local School Dist*	85	205
Rank, Tiffany/*Sidney City School Dist*	71	183
Rankin, Tim/*Wolf Creek Local School Dist*	5	211
Ranly, Jaime/*Preble-Shawnee Local Sch Dist*	8	168
Ranly, Sherri/*St Henry Cons Local Sch Dist*	5	144
Ransom, Sarah/*Margaretta Local School Dist*	4	61
Rapp, Chris/*Washington-Nile Local Sch Dist*	274	179
Rapp, Joey/*Wellston City School Dist*	73,295	108
Rappold, Todd, Dr/*Miami East Local School Dist*	1,11,83	145
Rasmussen, Nicole/*St Mary's City School Dist*	4	16
Rataiczak, Terry/*Caldwell Exempted Village SD*	67	158
Ratcliff, Jared/*Bethel Local School Dist*	73,76,286,295	145
Rateno, Chris/*Shaker Heights City Sch Dist*	76,294	50
Raterman, Stacie/*Hilliard City School Dist*	71	71
Rathje, Sally/*Delaware City School Dist*	4	58
Ratliff, Jared/*Bethel Local School Dist*	295	145
Ratliff, Nelle/*Wynford Local School Dist*	9	39
Rau, Brian/*Manchester Local School Dist*	1,11,73	7
Rau, Michele/*Ripley-Union-Lewis-Huntngtn SD*	4	20
Rauch-Wittman, Suzanne/*Southern Local School Dist*	81	161
Rauch, Elisabeth/*Lakewood Local School Dist*	16,82,273	118
Rauchenstein, Jenny/*Northridge Local School Dist*	38	119
Ray, Danielle/*Rootstown Local School Dist*	37	166
Ray, Lynne/*Celina City School Dist*	16,82	143
Ray, Ruth/*Warrensville Heights City SD*	10	51
Ray, Vaughn/*Auglaize Co Ed Service Center*	8	15
Ray, Wendy/*Barberton City School Dist*	7	192
Ray, Wendy/*Bradford Exempted Village SD*	36,69	145
Rayk, Karen/*Polaris Joint Voc School Dist*	30,57	49
Rayl, Alene/*Field Local School Dist*	7	165
Rayner, Jim/*Noble Local School Dist*	3	158
Readshaw, Brandon/*Liberty Center Local Sch Dist*	27	101
Ream, Corey/*Norwalk City School Dist*	8,11,83,275,285,288,296,298	106
Ream, Mike/*Ontario Local School Dist*	8,11,288,296	173
Reames, Anne/*Ohio Hi-Point Joint Voc SD*	67	121
Reasdeck, Randell/*Martins Ferry City School Dist*	5	18
Rebillot, Ashley/*Crestline Exempted Village SD*	58	38
Rebmann, Ed/*Fairbanks Local School Dist*	16,271	204
Recker, Craig/*Arcadia Local School Dist*	3	97
Recker, Julie/*Leipsic Local School Dist*	31,36,69,83,88,270	170
Recks, Erin/*Wapakoneta City School Dist*	11,288	16
Redd, John/*Bellevue City School Dist*	67	105
Redic, Darlene/*Bedford City School Dist*	90	40
Redmon, Chad/*Northmor Local School Dist*	1	155
Redmond, Kim/*Portage Lakes Joint Voc SD*	1	189
Reece, Jennifer/*Revere Local School Dist*	71	194
Reed-Brown, Katy/*Ehove Joint Voc School Dist*	16,82	60
Reed, Albert/*Crooksville Exempted Vlg SD*	3	161

NAME/District	JOB FUNCTIONS	PAGE
Reed, Autumn/*Avon Lake City School Dist*	2,11,19,288,296	122
Reed, Candy/*Canfield Local School Dist*	69	134
Reed, Chris/*Reynoldsburg City School Dist*	2,3,4,5,76,295,298	72
Reed, Debbie/*Crooksville Exempted Vlg SD*	5	161
Reed, Kandi/*Scioto Valley Local Sch Dist*	4	164
Reed, Matt/*East Guernsey Local Sch Dist*	2	86
Reed, Mechael/*Miamisburg City School Dist*	5	151
Reed, Shea/*Groveport Madison Local SD*	79,91	71
Reed, Steven/*Wilmington City School Dist*	16	33
Reed, Tammy/*East Liverpool City Sch Dist*	5	35
Reed, Tom/*Educational Serv Ctr-Ctl Ohio*	8,74,294	65
Reeder, John/*Warren Co Voc School Dist*	73,295	208
Reedy, Dianna/*Portsmouth City School Dist*	2,11,296,298	179
Reedy, Karen/*Walnut Twp Local School Dist*	4	64
Rees, Rebecca/*State Support Team-Region 6*	1	17
Reese, Brigid/*North Olmsted City School Dist*	31	48
Reese, Jeff/*Jackson Center Local Sch Dist*	10	183
Reese, Jennifer/*Perry Local School Dist*	10,27,31	188
Reeves, Andy/*Beaver Local School Dist*	11,58	34
Reeves, Jacqueline/*Steubenville City School Dist*	72,81	109
Reeves, Margaret/*Medina Co Joint Voc Sch Dist*	11	141
Reeves, Margaret/*Medina Co Joint Voc Sch Dist*	11,30,38,79	141
Reeves, Scott/*Westerville City School Dist*	6,10,31,69	74
Reffitt, Kim/*Greeneview Local School Dist*	27	84
Regano, Joseph/*Solon City School Dist*	1	50
Rehm, Denise/*Orrville City School Dist*	16	212
Reichard, Aj/*Wynford Local School Dist*	273	39
Reichert, Tina/*Great Oaks Career Campuses*	60,88	89
Reichert, William/*Jackson Center Local Sch Dist*	1,73	183
Reid, Linda/*South Euclid-Lyndhurst City SD*	1	51
Reid, Michelle/*Northwood Local School Dist*	38,69	217
Reidy, Debbie/*Crestview Local School Dist*	67	171
Reiff, Shelly/*Lima City School Dist*	2	9
Reinbolt, Hollis/*Fostoria City School Dist*	4	180
Reineke, Amy/*New Knoxville Local Sch Dist*	2	16
Reineke, Dean/*Meta Solutions Branch*	1	154
Reiner, Rod/*Lordstown Local School Dist*	73	199
Reinhard, Brianna/*Van Buren Local School Dist*	4	99
Reinhardt, Kellie/*Wheelersburg Local School Dist*	5	180
Reinhart, Jill/*Dublin City School Dist*	8	69
Reinhart, Veronica/*Hopewell-Loudon Local SD*	2	181
Reinhart, Veronica/*Marion City School Dist*	2	138
Reisland, Leanne/*Garfield Heights City SD*	8	46
Reisner, Glen/*Buckeye Local School Dist*	3	140
Relic, Grant/*Brunswick City School Dist*	67	140
Rellinger, Maria/*Apollo Joint Voc School Dist*	2,19,84	8
Rellinger, Sharon/*Ottoville Local School Dist*	16,82	170
Relsford, Cheryl/*Westerville City School Dist*	9,16,752	74
Remaklus, Brittany/*Perkins Local School Dist*	79	61
Rendelman, Tracy/*Edgerton Local School Dist*	273	214
Renner, Chris/*Bath Local School Dist*	11,296	8
Renner, Joni/*Sidney City School Dist*	5	183
Rentsch, Brian/*Frontier Local School Dist*	1	209
Rentschler, Mel/*Allen East Local School Dist*	1	7
Renwand, Mr/*Springfield Local School Dist*	6	128
Renwick, John/*Kirtland Local School Dist*	73,295	112
Reprogle, Coleen/*Indian Lake Local School Dist*	2	121
Requarth, Jeff/*Brookville Local School Dist*	3,4,5,91	148
Resar, Michael/*Keystone Local School Dist*	2	124
Rettig, Tim/*Woodmore Local School Dist*	1	159
Reucher, Alexander/*Fayette Local Sch Dist*	79	79
Reucher, Allie/*Fayette Local Sch Dist*	58	79
Reule, Scott/*Benjamin Logan Local Sch Dist*	6	121
Rex, Aaron/*Wapakoneta City School Dist*	1	16
Rex, Brad/*Wapakoneta City School Dist*	6	16
Rex, Jacqueline/*Delphos City School Dist*	16,82	8
Rex, Jared/*Napoleon Area City School Dist*	73,84,286,295	101
Rex, Jennifer/*Plain Local School Dist*	4	188
Reyes-Rao, Connie/*Hamilton County ESC*	57	97
Reyes, Sonia/*Woodmore Local School Dist*	7,83,85	159
Reynolds, Adam/*North Fork Local School Dist*	3,91	119
Reynolds, Brian/*Bay Village City School Dist*	76	40
Reynolds, Debbie/*Elmwood Local School Dist*	67	216
Reynolds, Kim/*Elgin Local School Dist*	2	138
Reynolds, Rea/*Bethel-Tate Local School Dist*	38	30
Reynolds, Regina/*Canfield Local School Dist*	7	134

School Year 2019-2020   800-333-8802   OH-T45

DISTRICT PERSONNEL INDEX

Market Data Retrieval

NAME/District	JOB FUNCTIONS	PAGE
Reynolds, Stacy/Tecumseh Local School Dist	4	28
Reynolds, Tammy/Mapleton Local School Dist	5	11
Rhine, Stephanie/South Euclid-Lyndhurst City SD	67	51
Rhinehart, Barb/Van Wert City School Dist	77	205
Rhinehart, James/Greeneview Local School Dist	4	84
Rhoades, Dave/West Holmes Local School Dist	73,295	105
Rhoades, Gayle/Bethel Local School Dist	5,11	145
Rhoads, Austin/Springboro Cmty School Dist	6	208
Rhoads, Kristen/Circleville City School Dist	2	162
Rhodes, Christopher/Boardman Local School Dist	16,73,76,82,286	134
Rhodes, Connie/Ottoville Local School Dist	69,83,275	170
Rhodes, Vicki/Millcreek-West Unity Local SD	12	215
Rhodus, Tyler/Franklin-Monroe Local Sch Dist	6,27	55
Ribelin, Ben/Ravenna School Dist	9,12,15,68,79,273,288,296	166
Ribley, Jodie/Riverdale Local School Dist	2	98
Riccardi, Amy/Nelsonville-York City Sch Dist	8,69,273,286	15
Ricciardulli, Bill/Wellsville Local Sch Dist	73	36
Rice, Carla/Montpelier Exempted Village SD	2	215
Rice, Joanna/South Point Local School Dist	4	116
Rice, Mark/Alexander Local School Dist	84,295	14
Rice, Mary/Leetonia Exempted Village SD	36,286	35
Rice, Steven/Franklin Local School Dist	58	156
Rice, Trenda/Noble Local School Dist	2,84	158
Rich, Brooke/Greeneview Local School Dist	16	84
Richard, Jason/Federal Hocking Local Sch Dist	73,76	14
Richard, John, Dr/Ohio Department of Education	8,15,69,79,294	1
Richards, Ben/Valley View Local School Dist	1	153
Richards, Jake/Ross Local School Dist	6	24
Richards, Jeffrey/Pymatuning Valley Local SD	4	13
Richards, Rob/Harrison Hills City Sch Dist	286	101
Richards, Rusty/Nelsonville-York City Sch Dist	6	15
Richards, Sandy/River Valley Local School Dist	12	139
Richardson, Aaron/Edison Local School Dist	67	109
Richardson, Andrea/Columbus City School Dist	11,296	66
Richardson, Brad/Allen East Local School Dist	67	7
Richardson, C J/Holgate Local School Dist	295	101
Richardson, Fredrika/Mt Healthy City School Dist	4	91
Richardson, Mark/Indian Hill Exempted Vlg SD	73,286	90
Richey, Derek/Cleveland Metro School Dist	2,19	42
Richey, Lowell/Eastern Local School Dist	67	7
Richey, Richard/Maple Heights City School Dist	91	47
Richmond, Amy/Geneva Area City School Dist	68	13
Richmond, Krista/Wynford Local School Dist	51	39
Ricker, Marie/Massillon City School Dist	76	187
Ricker, Rodney/Jennings Local School Dist	3	169
Ricker, Stacey/Delphos City School Dist	83,85	8
Ricker, Sue/Columbus Grove Local Sch Dist	16,82	169
Rickert, Deb/Mansfield City Schools	5	172
Rickle, Mike/Riverdale Local School Dist	3	98
Rickter, Sherry/Crestview Local School Dist	81	171
Riddle, Dan/Huntington Local School Dist	11,58,91,296,298	175
Riddlebarger, Tearalee/Twin Valley Cmty Local SD	2	169
Ridenour, Cindy/Clear Fork Vly Local Sch Dist	12	171
Ridenour, Floyd/Eastern Local School Dist	67	142
Ridenour, Tricia/Van Wert City School Dist	81	205
Rider, Mark/Maysville Local School Dist	6	156
Rider, Nick/Carey Exempted Village SD	73,76,295	219
Rider, Steve/McComb Local School Dist	4	98
Riedel, Tonya/Olentangy Local School Dist	34	59
Riehl, Andrew/South Central Ohio Ed Svc Ctr	2,68	178
Riehl, Peggy/Diocese of Toledo Ed Office	9	131
Riehle, Kermit/Edgerton Local School Dist	1	214
Riel, Jeff/West Clermont Local Sch Dist	16	31
Riera, Roger/Newbury Local School Dist	3,91	82
Rife, Stephanie/Gallia-Jackson-Vinton JVSD	2	80
Rigano, Jo Anne/Beavercreek City School Dist	67	83
Rigby, James/Southern Local School Dist	3,91	35
Riggs, Danny/Frontier Local School Dist	5	210
Righi, Pam/Liberty Center Local Sch Dist	37	101
Riley, Judy/Pickerington Local School Dist	4	64
Riley, Lori/Conneaut Area City Sch Dist	1,288	12
Riley, Maggie/Groveport Madison Local SD	59	71
Riley, Ruth/Poland Local School Dist	16	135
Riley, Steven/Millcreek-West Unity Local SD	83,85	215
Rinaldi, John/Canton City School Dist	67	184
Rinard, Tammie/Frontier Local School Dist	7	210
Rinderle, Lynn/Coldwater Exempted Village SD	4	143
Rinehart, Jodi/Darke Co Ed Service Center	60,77	55
Rinehart, Mark/Greeneview Local School Dist	6	84
Rinehart, Veronica/Galion City School Dist	73	38
Ring, Beth/Loudonville-Perrysville SD	37	11
Ringhiser, Rocky/Licking Co Joint Voc Sch Dist	28,73,76,295	118
Rings, Rebecca/Jonathan Alder Local Sch Dist	4	132
Rinkel, Tricia/Northeastern Local School Dist	38	57
Rios, Hillary/Clearview Local School Dist	297	123
Ripley, Brent/Bridgeport School Dist	1	18
Ripperman, Chuck/Northeastern Local School Dist	6	27
Risner, Autumn/Eastern Local School Dist	7,85	163
Ritchey, Brad, Dr/Milton-Union Exempted Vlg SD	1	145
Ritchie, James/Orrville City School Dist	1	212
Ritchie, James/Rittman Exempted Village SD	1	213
Ritchie, James/Tri-Co Ed Service Center	1	211
Ritchie, Jon/Southeast Local School Dist	1	213
Ritchie, Lisa/Eastern Local School Dist	2,19	142
Ritchie, Theresa/Reynoldsburg City School Dist	5	72
Rittenhause, Sonja/Western Local School Dist	5	164
Rittenour, Kim/Huntington Local School Dist	57,271,273	175
Ritz, Ashely/Canton Local School Dist	4	185
Ritz, Jeff/Willard City School Dist	1	106
Rivera, Eli/Jackson Local School Dist	5,91	186
Rivera, Melissa/Anna Local School Dist	16	182
Rivet, Megan/Three Rivers Local School Dist	34,58	94
Rizzo, John/Shaker Heights City Sch Dist	16,73	50
Rizzo, Stephen/Mansfield City Schools	8,12,18,73,288	172
Roach, James/Northeastern Local School Dist	1,11	57
Roades, Michael/Brown Co Ed Service Center	58	19
Roadruck, Greg, Dr/Orrville City School Dist	67	212
Roadruck, Gregory, Dr/Wayne Co Joint Voc School Dist	67	213
Rob-Carney, Cathi/Columbiana Exempted Village SD	37,83,270	34
Robbins, Kareen/Licking Co Ed Service Center	58	117
Robbins, Liz/Tipp City Exempted Village SD	16,71	146
Robbins, Matt/Eaton Cmty School Dist	3,5	168
Robenstine, Christine/Osnaburg Local School Dist	84	188
Roberson, Debbie/Bright Local School Dist	4	102
Robert, James/Columbiana Exempted Village SD	3	34
Robert, Ty/Bloom-Vernon Local Sch Dist	2	178
Roberto, Mike/Aurora City School Dist	8,11,15,16,31,57,270	164
Roberts, Andrea/Hardin-Houston Local School Dist	4,12	182
Roberts, Ashley/Minford Local School Dist	2	178
Roberts, Carole, Dr/Archdiocese Cincinnati Ed Off	8,69	94
Roberts, Cheryl/East Clinton Local School Dist	88	33
Roberts, James/Scioto Valley Local Sch Dist	10,58,88,275	164
Roberts, Kevin/Garaway Local School Dist	5	202
Roberts, Lori/Riverside Local School Dist	16	121
Roberts, Michele/Madison-Champaign Ed Svc Ctr	81	25
Roberts, Nick/Canal Winchester Local SD	2	66
Roberts, Pam/Mad River Local School Dist	12,34	151
Roberts, Rodney/Franklin City School Dist	2	207
Roberts, Sheila/Madison-Champaign Ed Svc Ctr	79	25
Robinson, Brian/Forest Hills School Dist	288	89
Robinson, Denise/Tecumseh Local School Dist	2,3,17	28
Robinson, Ed/Carrollton Exempted Village SD	8,57,88,285,288	25
Robinson, Elaine/Knox Co Voc School Dist	60	111
Robinson, James, Dr/Manchester Local School Dist	1,11,83	193

1 Superintendent	16 Instructional Media Svcs	30 Adult Education	44 Science Sec	58 Special Education K-12	72 Summer School	88 Alternative/At Risk	277 Remedial Math K-12
2 Bus/Finance/Purchasing	17 Chief Operations Officer	31 Career/Sch-to-Work K-12	45 Math K-12	59 Special Education Elem	73 Instructional Tech	89 Multi-Cultural Curriculum	280 Literacy Coach
3 Buildings And Grounds	18 Chief Academic Officer	32 Career/Sch-to-Work Elem	46 Math Elem	60 Special Education Sec	74 Inservice Training	90 Social Work	285 STEM
4 Food Service	19 Chief Financial Officer	33 Career/Sch-to-Work Sec	47 Math Sec	61 Foreign/World Lang K-12	75 Marketing/Distributive	91 Safety/Security	286 Digital Learning
5 Transportation	20 Art K-12	34 Early Childhood Ed	48 English/Lang Arts K-12	62 Foreign/World Lang Elem	76 Info Systems	92 Magnet School	288 Common Core Standards
6 Athletic	21 Art Elem	35 Health/Phys Education	49 English/Lang Arts Elem	63 Foreign/World Lang Sec	77 Psychological Assess	93 Parental Involvement	294 Accountability
7 Health Services	22 Art Sec	36 Guidance Services K-12	50 English/Lang Arts Sec	64 Religious Education K-12	78 Affirmative Action	95 Tech Prep Program	295 Network System
8 Curric/Instruct K-12	23 Music K-12	37 Guidance Services Elem	51 Reading K-12	65 Religious Education Elem	79 Student Personnel	96 Chief Information Officer	296 Title II Programs
9 Curric/Instruct Elem	24 Music Elem	38 Guidance Services Sec	52 Reading Elem	66 Religious Education Sec	80 Driver Ed/Safety	98 Chief Technology Officer	297 Webmaster
10 Curric/Instruct Sec	25 Music Sec	39 Social Studies K-12	53 Reading Sec	67 School Board President	81 Gifted/Talented	270 Character Education	298 Grant Writer/Ptnrships
11 Federal Program	26 Business Education	40 Social Studies Elem	54 Remedial Reading K-12	68 Teacher Personnel	82 Video Services	271 Migrant Education	750 Chief Innovation Officer
12 Title I	27 Career & Tech Ed	41 Social Studies Sec	55 Remedial Reading Elem	69 Academic Assessment	83 Substance Abuse Prev	273 Teacher Mentor	751 Chief of Staff
13 Title V	28 Technology Education	42 Science K-12	56 Remedial Reading Sec	70 Research/Development	84 Erate	274 Before/After Sch	752 Social Emotional Learning
15 Asst Superintendent	29 Family/Consumer Science	43 Science Elem	57 Bilingual/ELL	71 Public Information	85 AIDS Education	275 Response To Intervention	

OH-T46

Ohio School Directory

DISTRICT PERSONNEL INDEX

NAME/District	JOB FUNCTIONS	PAGE
Robinson, Joni/*Versailles Exempted Village SD*	58	56
Robinson, Judy/*Orange City School Dist*	79	49
Robinson, Katherine/*North Fork Local School Dist*	36	119
Robinson, Mark/*Buckeye Central Local Sch Dist*	1	38
Robinson, Marla, Dr/*Shaker Heights City Sch Dist*	18	50
Robinson, Mike/*Polaris Joint Voc School Dist*	2	49
Robinson, Pam/*Ridgemont Local School Dist*	273	100
Robinson, Randy/*Conotton Valley Union Local SD*	3,4,5	100
Robinson, Steven/*Copley-Fairlawn City Sch Dist*	3,4,84,91	192
Robinson, Thomas/*Rock Hill Local School Dist*	2	116
Robinson, Tracy/*Central Local School Dist*	273	57
Robison, Lisa/*Northwest Local School Dist*	4	91
Robson, Brett/*Western Reserve Local Sch Dist*	2	106
Robson, Jim/*Ansonia Local School Dist*	10	55
Robson, Lori/*East Central Ohio ESC-St Clair*	8,298	17
Roby, Rod/*Union Local School Dist*	3,4,5	18
Rocco, Michele/*Stark Co Area Voc Sch Dist*	34	189
Rochotte, Neil/*Washington Local School Dist*	7,11,36,58,69,77,81,83	130
Rochte, Laura/*Mt Vernon City School Dist*	16	111
Rock, Michael, Dr/*Warrensville Heights City SD*	2	51
Rockwell, TJ/*Perry Local School Dist*	6	113
Roddy, Tricia/*Princeton City School Dist*	298	92
Rodkey, Kristen/*Wadsworth City School Dist*	76	141
Rodocker, Ryan/*Tuslaw Local School Dist*	16,73,285,286	189
Rodriguez, Joseph/*East Holmes Local School Dist*	77	104
Rodriguez, Matthew/*Chippewa Local School Dist*	8,11,69,288	211
Roebuck, Celena, Dr/*Cuyahoga Vly Career Ctr Voc SD*	11	45
Roehm, Cary/*St Mary's City School Dist*	58	16
Roemer, Laureen/*Firelands Local School Dist*	8,16,73	124
Roemer, Megan/*Poland Local School Dist*	4	135
Rogaski, Steve/*Cuyahoga Co Ed Service Center*	68,79	39
Rogel, Elizabeth/*Lakewood City School Dist*	79	47
Rogers, Alison/*West Holmes Local School Dist*	38,83	105
Rogers, Anita/*Huntington Local School Dist*	27,38,69	175
Rogers, Diana/*Northwestern Local School Dist*	8	212
Rogers, Joe/*Princeton City School Dist*	6	92
Rogers, Kim/*Madison Plains Local Sch Dist*	5	133
Rogers, Quentin/*Richmond Heights Local SD*	6	49
Rogers, Tammy/*Seneca East Local School Dist*	5	181
Rohde, Meghan/*Clyde-Green Spgs Exmpt Vlg SD*	2	176
Rohrer, Brian/*Miami East Local School Dist*	59	145
Roiger, Jene/*Tiffin City School Dist*	71	181
Rolfe, Scott/*Valley Local School Dist*	1	179
Rollins, Teri/*Monroe Local School Dist*	11,57,58	23
Rolsten, Logan/*Upper Scioto Valley Local SD*	3,5	100
Romack, Cathy/*Western Reserve Local Sch Dist*	2,298	136
Romanello, Barbara, Dr/*Diocese of Columbus Ed Office*	64	76
Romano, Brad/*New London Local School Dist*	1,11	105
Rombach, David/*New Riegel Local School Dist*	1	181
Rombach, David/*New Riegel Local School Dist*	8,12,58,74,78,273,288	181
Romine, Glenna/*Plain Local School Dist*	5	188
Romito, Lynette/*Campbell City School Dist*	16	134
Roncone, Lynley/*Columbia Local School Dist*	13,69,77	123
Rondstadt, Amy/*Northwood Local School Dist*	67	217
Rooker, Rosemary/*Findlay City School Dist*	286	98
Ropos, Kristina/*State Support Team-Region 10*	27	85
Rose, Connie/*Celina City School Dist*	2	143
Rose, John/*Union Scioto Local Sch Dist*	2,11,68,294	175
Rose, Karen/*Mercer Co Ed Service Center*	8	143
Rose, Mark/*Clay Local School Dist*	6	178
Rose, Pam/*Mt Vernon City School Dist*	58	111
Rose, Rick/*Morgan Local School Dist*	67	154
Rose, Scott/*Shelby City School Dist*	67	173
Rose, Steve/*Russia Local School Dist*	1	183
Rosebaugh, Andrew/*Windham Exempted Vlg Sch Dist*	280	167
Roseberry, Kevin/*Shadyside Local School Dist*	11	18
Roseberry, Mark/*Lucas Local School Dist*	273	172
Roseberry, Sara/*Hardin-Houston Local Sch Dist*	298	183
Roseberry, Ted/*Orange City School Dist*	2,91	48
Rosecrans, Dan/*Wellington Exempted Village SD*	67	126
Rosenbeck, Eric/*St Henry Cons Local Sch Dist*	10	144
Rosendale, Anjali/*Cleveland Hts-Univ Hts City SD*	4	42
Roshaun, Edward, Dr/*Firelands Local School Dist*	58	124
Rosiar, Diane/*Port Clinton City School Dist*	273	159
Ross, Kelly/*Norwalk City School Dist*	5	106
Ross, Kelly/*Norwalk City School Dist*	3,4	106
Ross, Mariah/*Bath Local School Dist*	4	8
Ross, Ron/*Medina City School Dist*	67	141
Ross, Scott/*Manchester Local School Dist*	73	193
Rosselli, Stephanie/*Marlington Local School Dist*	81	186
Rosser, Chase/*East Guernsey Local Sch Dist*	8,11,69,74,288	86
Rossler, James/*Rossford Exempted Village SD*	2	218
Rostorfer, Brad/*Delphos City School Dist*	2,11	8
Rostorfer, Ted/*Jackson Center Local Sch Dist*	3	183
Roth-Kimbre, Kimberly/*Chippewa Local School Dist*	36	211
Roth, Gregg/*Elida Local School Dist*	5	8
Roth, Kathy/*Indian Valley Local Sch Dist*	67	202
Roth, Sabrina/*Wayne Trace Local School Dist*	83,85	160
Roth, Stephanie/*Findlay City School Dist*	9,34,35,85,270,273,280,288	97
Roth, Thomas/*Edison Local Schools District*	1	60
Roth, Troy/*Findlay City School Dist*	15,68,70,71,74,78	97
Rothenbuhler, Terry/*Elmwood Local School Dist*	4	216
Rothhaar, Chris/*Willard City School Dist*	67	106
Rotuna, Ryan/*Jackson-Milton Local Sch Dist*	73,84	134
Rouan, Laurena/*Champion Local School Dist*	2	197
Rouan, Laurena/*Weathersfield Local Sch Dist*	2	201
Roubic, Melissa/*Windham Exempted Vlg Sch Dist*	67	167
Roush, Erin/*Alexander Local School Dist*	34,58,77	14
Roush, Sheryl/*Eastern Local School Dist*	38,69	142
Rowe, Carla/*South Point Local School Dist*	5	116
Rowe, Denise/*Newark City School Dist*	280	119
Rowe, Leslie/*Midview Local School Dist*	16	125
Rowe, Mila/*Adena Local School Dist*	298	174
Rowe, Todd/*Labrae Local School Dist*	6	198
Rowley, Jeff/*Ripley-Union-Lewis-Huntngtn SD*	2	20
Roy, Seth/*Newark City School Dist*	71	119
Royalty, Jeff/*State Support Team-Region 14*	1	103
Royalty, Jennifer/*Wayne Local School Dist*	83	209
Royer, Karen/*Bethel-Tate Local School Dist*	2,19,84	30
Royer, Stacey/*Upper Arlington City Sch Dist*	67	74
Rozenk, Robin/*Buckeye Local School Dist*	84	108
Rozsnyai, Julia/*Connect Information Tech Ctr*	2	54
Rozsnyai, Julia/*Connect Information Tech Ctr*	2	126
Rozycki, Robert/*Mathews Local School Dist*	6	199
Ruane, Bill/*St Mary's City School Dist*	1	16
Rubesich, John/*Ashtabula Co Ed Service Center*	1	11
Ruby, Kristen/*Minford Local School Dist*	6	178
Ruby, Pete/*Huntington Local School Dist*	1	175
Rucker, Jennifer/*Manchester Local School Dist*	2	193
Rucker, Penny/*Beavercreek City School Dist*	2	83
Rudd, Kathy/*Kettering City School Dist*	274	150
Rudge, Steven/*Mathews Local School Dist*	73	199
Rudloff, Jim/*Zanesville City School Dist*	297	157
Rudloff, Jim/*Zanesville City School Dist*	297	157
Rudloff, Larry/*Southern Local School Dist*	37,83,88	36
Rudolph, Constance/*Warrensville Heights City SD*	79	51
Ruehrmund, Troy/*Cardington-Lincoln Local SD*	67	155
Ruen, Michael/*Van Wert City School Dist*	2	205
Ruen, Micheal/*Hicksville Exempted Village SD*	2	57
Ruf, John/*North Point Ed Svc Ctr*	15	60
Ruf, Karen/*North Point Ed Svc Ctr*	34,58	60
Ruff, Diane/*Minerva Local School Dist*	273	187
Ruffell, Dustin/*Patrick Henry Local Sch Dist*	73,295	102
Ruffing, Brenda/*Seneca East Local School Dist*	4	181
Ruffner, Brian/*Lgca-Lake Geauga Ohio OCA*	73,76	115
Ruggiero, Caitlyn/*Campbell City School Dist*	4	134
Ruhe, Esther/*Perry Local School Dist*	2	9
Ruhe, Jennifer/*Delaware City School Dist*	71	58
Ruhe, Paula/*Ottawa-Glandorf Local Sch Dist*	7	170
Ruhenkamp, Jenny/*New Knoxville Local Sch Dist*	60	16
Rule, Ben/*Worthington School Dist*	57	75
Rumley, Dave/*Lawrence Co Ed Service Center*	88	115
Rumley, Karen/*Kent City School Dist*	8,11,34,69,71,288,296,298	165
Rundag, John/*Logan Elm Local School Dist*	73,84,295	162
Runions, Kimberlee/*Western Local School Dist*	16,82	164
Running, Cindy/*Clinton-Massie Local Sch Dist*	6	33
Rupe, David/*New Lexington School Dist*	3,5,91	161
Rusfomanno, Dan/*Woodmore Local School Dist*	2	159
Rush, Daniel/*Great Oaks Career Campuses*	10	89
Russ-Miller, Marilyn/*Green Local School Dist*	38	185
Russ, Mike/*Nordonia Hills City Sch Dist*	73,295	193
Rust, Brian/*Lordstown Local School Dist*	6	199

School Year 2019-2020   800-333-8802   OH-T47

DISTRICT PERSONNEL INDEX

Market Data Retrieval

NAME/District	JOB FUNCTIONS	PAGE
Rutger, Lisa/*Sheffield-Sheffield Lake CSD*	16,82	125
Rutledge, Amy/*Brunswick City School Dist*	71	140
Rutledge, Matthew/*Miami East Local School Dist*	69	145
Rutter, Brittany/*Meta Solutions*	68	139
Rutter, Craig/*Northeastern Local School Dist*	6	57
Ryan, Betsy/*Forest Hills School Dist*	7,12,35,36,60,83,270,752	89
Ryan, Joe/*Edison Local Schools District*	5	60
Ryan, Larry/*Warren Local School Dist*	58	210
Ryan, Mark/*Marlington Local School Dist*	67	186
Ryba, Cameron, Dr/*Strongsville City School Dist*	1	51
Rykaceski, James/*Portage Co Ed Service Center*	3,4,5	164

S

NAME/District	JOB FUNCTIONS	PAGE
Sable, Aaron/*Medina City School Dist*	1	141
Sabo, Kathy, Dr/*Norwood City School Dist*	1	92
Sabol, Jennifer, Dr/*Cardinal Local School Dist*	8	81
Sabol, John/*Barberton City School Dist*	6	192
Sadowski, Dalene/*Eaton Cmty School Dist*	7	168
Saffell, Michael/*Harrison Hills City Sch Dist*	3,4,5,91	101
Saffle, Roger/*Highland Local School Dist*	73	141
Saganich, John/*McDonald Local School Dist*	67	199
Sage, Thor/*Miami Valley Educational CA*	1	85
Sagester, Josh/*Tri-Village Local Sch Dist*	1	56
Sailey, Tina/*Portage Lakes Joint Voc SD*	60	189
Sain, Michael/*Columbus City School Dist*	57	67
Sainato, Mary/*Hubbard Exempted Village SD*	69,77	198
Salay, Amy/*Dublin City School Dist*	5	69
Saldunas, Vytas/*Beachwood City School Dist*	295	40
Salsberry, Pam/*Troy City School Dist*	295	146
Saltzman, Tim/*Arcadia Local School Dist*	91	97
Salvino, Paul/*Massillon City School Dist*	1	187
Sama, Joy/*Tuslaw Local School Dist*	8,11	189
Samac, Sherri/*Painesville City Local SD*	2,294	113
Samblanet, Lindsay/*South Range Local School Dist*	76	135
Sambon, Kristy/*Southern Local School Dist*	12	36
Samlow, Julie/*Teays Valley Local School Dist*	31,36,79	162
Samosky, Amy/*Oakwood City School Dist*	77	152
Samosky, Shayna/*Medina City School Dist*	81	141
Sample, Edward/*Trotwood-Madison City SD*	58	153
Samples, Kerry/*Central Local School Dist*	2,19	57
Samples, Rhonda/*Bryan City School Dist*	37,83	214
Sampson, Kathy/*Southern Local School Dist*	76	161
Sams, Andrew/*Aurora City School Dist*	84	164
Sams, Andy/*Aurora City School Dist*	95,295	164
Sams, Rachael/*Clinton-Massie Local Sch Dist*	90,752	33
Samuel, Tricia/*Maumee City School Dist*	7,79	127
Samuels, Deanna/*Fairfield City School Dist*	274	21
Sanborn, Tina/*West Clermont Local Sch Dist*	67	31
Sanches, Cristina/*Springfield City School Dist*	9	28
Sandel, Lori/*Waterloo Local School Dist*	8,12,288	167
Sander, Debbie/*Middletown City School Dist*	58	23
Sander, Michael, Dr/*Franklin City School Dist*	1	207
Sanderman, Debra/*Bellbrook-Sugarcreek Schools*	31,38,69,83	83
Sanders, Dianne/*Montpelier Exempted Village SD*	5	215
Sanders, Eugene, Dr/*Sandusky City School Dist*	1	61
Sanders, Tonya/*Northwest Ohio Ed Tech*	73,76	218
Sandlin, Heidi/*Reading Cmty City School Dist*	7	93
Sandor, Michelle/*Norwalk City School Dist*	36,69	106
Sandwisch, Dean/*Oregon City School Dist*	2,3,84,91	128
Sandwisch, Jeff/*Woodmore Local School Dist*	3,5	159
Sandy, Holly/*Champion Local School Dist*	37	197
Saneda, Shari/*Edgerton Local School Dist*	16,73,295	214
Saner, Jay/*Nelsonville-York City Sch Dist*	73,295	15
Sanfelippo, Tammy/*Clearview Local School Dist*	57	123
Sanford, Julie/*Sylvania City School Dist*	31,69,95,285	128
Sanna, Kate/*Struthers City School Dist*	81	136
Sansom, Rodger/*Mogadore Local School Dist*	67	166
Sansosti, Jenine/*State Support Team-Region 8*	1	196
Santa, Tami/*Westerville City School Dist*	37,752	74
Santantonio, Brett/*Bexley City School Dist*	3	66
Santilli, Nancy/*Kenston Local School Dist*	1	82
Sapp, Chad/*Mercer Co Ed Service Center*	58	143
Sarbach, Doug/*Grand Valley Local School Dist*	73,84,295	13
Sargent, Tim/*Franklin-Monroe Local Sch Dist*	73	55
Sarnes, Joe/*Perrysburg Exempted Village SD*	8,286	218
Sass, Heather, Dr/*Mason City School Dist*	8,11,18,57,69,88,288,296	208
Satchell, Glen/*Cedar Cliff Local School Dist*	6	84
Satchell, Terry/*Cedar Cliff Local School Dist*	4	84
Satterfield, Ryan/*Pike Co Area JT Voc Sch Dist*	73,295	163
Sauber, Laura/*Jefferson Twp Local Sch Dist*	2	150
Sauder, Brian/*Lucas Local School Dist*	3	172
Sauder, Mark/*Lucas Local School Dist*	5	172
Sauder, Mary/*Millcreek-West Unity Local SD*	16	215
Saul, Jim/*Edgerton Local School Dist*	3,5	214
Saunders, Jeff/*Lawrence Co Ed Service Center*	1	115
Saunders, Morgan/*Gallipolis City School Dist*	67	81
Saunders, Ron/*Lucas Local School Dist*	60	172
Saunders, Sharon/*Northwestern Local School Dist*	11	27
Saunders, Sheila/*New Albany-Plain Local SD*	58,296	72
Savage, Chad/*Bryan City School Dist*	6	214
Savage, Diana/*Bryan City School Dist*	1	214
Savage, Terry/*Bellaire Local School Dist*	77	17
Savastone, Dave/*Ohio Mid-Eastern RESA*	16	110
Savvato, Greg/*Southern Local School Dist*	2	35
Saward, Teresa/*Newark City School Dist*	5	119
Sawicki, Christine/*Youngstown City School Dist*	8,18	136
Sawyers, Jerry/*Eastern Local School Dist*	73,76,84,286,295	7
Sawyers, Michael/*New Albany-Plain Local SD*	1	72
Saxer, Jim/*Dalton Local School Dist*	1	212
Saxon, Judy/*Garfield Heights City SD*	74	46
Saxton, Timothy/*Boardman Local School Dist*	1	134
Saxton, Timothy/*West Branch Local School Dist*	1	136
Sayers, Steven/*Amherst Exempted Village SD*	1	122
Sayler, Milt/*Firelands Local School Dist*	5	124
Sayre, Alison/*Washington-Nile Local Sch Dist*	8,11,36	179
Sayre, Nancy/*Maumee City School Dist*	11,296	127
Scali, Catherine/*Campbell City School Dist*	77	134
Scarberry, Steve/*Eastern Local School Dist*	16	142
Scarcpino, C J/*Streetsboro City School Dist*	2	167
Scarpucci, Denise/*Lorain Co Joint Voc Sch Dist*	58,88	125
Scarsella, Richard/*Mahoning Co Ed Service Center*	67	133
Schaar, Rhonda/*Preble Co Ed Service Center*	67	168
Schade, David/*Painesville City Local SD*	16,295,297	113
Schaffer, Cassie/*Van Buren Local School Dist*	8,11,69,88,286,288	99
Schaffer, Holly/*Bay Village City School Dist*	68	40
Schaffer, Julie/*Lakota Local School Dist*	67	22
Schaffer, Kevin/*Bryan City School Dist*	2,19	214
Schaffer, Tony/*Paulding Exempted Village SD*	31,51,69	160
Schafrath, Christine/*Chippewa Local School Dist*	4	211
Schakat, Amy/*South-Western City School Dist*	27,31	73
Schalk, Jane/*New Riegel Local School Dist*	2,84	181
Schalk, Margaret/*New Riegel Local School Dist*	54	181
Schall, Dan/*Valley View Local School Dist*	2,11	153
Schaller, W Joe/*Twin Valley Cmty Local SD*	11	169
Schank, Jean/*Seneca East Local School Dist*	76	181
Schatzel, Jason/*Canton Local School Dist*	2,68	185
Schaum, Anne/*Oberlin City School Dist*	67	125
Scheetz, David/*Massillon City School Dist*	16	187
Scheiber, Brad/*Tiffin City School Dist*	6	181
Schenkenberger, Tara/*Penta Co JT Voc School Dist*	16	217
Schentur, Diane/*Bedford City School Dist*	58	40
Scherer, Denise/*Kalida Local School Dist*	16	169
Scherer, Jennifer/*New Boston Local School Dist*	36,69,88,275	179
Scherzinger, Theresa/*Goshen Local School Dist*	8,11,69,288,296,298	30

#	Function	#	Function	#	Function	#	Function	#	Function	#	Function
1	Superintendent	16	Instructional Media Svcs	30	Adult Education	44	Science Sec	58	Special Education K-12	72	Summer School
2	Bus/Finance/Purchasing	17	Chief Operations Officer	31	Career/Sch-to-Work K-12	45	Math K-12	59	Special Education Elem	73	Instructional Tech
3	Buildings And Grounds	18	Chief Academic Officer	32	Career/Sch-to-Work Elem	46	Math Elem	60	Special Education Sec	74	Inservice Training
4	Food Service	19	Chief Financial Officer	33	Career/Sch-to-Work Sec	47	Math Sec	61	Foreign/World Lang K-12	75	Marketing/Distributive
5	Transportation	20	Art K-12	34	Early Childhood Ed	48	English/Lang Arts K-12	62	Foreign/World Lang Elem	76	Info Systems
6	Athletic	21	Art Elem	35	Health/Phys Education	49	English/Lang Arts Elem	63	Foreign/World Lang Sec	77	Psychological Assess
7	Health Services	22	Art Sec	36	Guidance Services K-12	50	English/Lang Arts Sec	64	Religious Education K-12	78	Affirmative Action
8	Curric/Instruct K-12	23	Music K-12	37	Guidance Services Elem	51	Reading K-12	65	Religious Education Elem	79	Student Personnel
9	Curric/Instruct Elem	24	Music Elem	38	Guidance Services Sec	52	Reading Elem	66	Religious Education Sec	80	Driver Ed/Safety
10	Curric/Instruct Sec	25	Music Sec	39	Social Studies K-12	53	Reading Sec	67	School Board President	81	Gifted/Talented
11	Federal Program	26	Business Education	40	Social Studies Elem	54	Remedial Reading K-12	68	Teacher Personnel	82	Video Services
12	Title I	27	Career & Tech Ed	41	Social Studies Sec	55	Remedial Reading Elem	69	Academic Assessment	83	Substance Abuse Prev
13	Title V	28	Technology Education	42	Science K-12	56	Remedial Reading Sec	70	Research/Development	84	Erate
15	Asst Superintendent	29	Family/Consumer Science	43	Science Elem	57	Bilingual/ELL	71	Public Information	85	AIDS Education

#	Function	#	Function	#	Function
88	Alternative/At Risk	277	Remedial Math K-12		
89	Multi-Cultural Curriculum	280	Literacy Coach		
90	Social Work	285	STEM		
91	Safety/Security	286	Digital Learning		
92	Magnet School	288	Common Core Standards		
93	Parental Involvement	294	Accountability		
95	Tech Prep Program	295	Network System		
97	Chief Information Officer	296	Title II Programs		
98	Chief Technology Officer	297	Webmaster		
270	Character Education	298	Grant Writer/Ptnrships		
271	Migrant Education	750	Chief Innovation Officer		
273	Teacher Mentor	751	Chief of Staff		
274	Before/After Sch	752	Social Emotional Learning		
275	Response To Intervention				

OH-T48

Ohio School Directory

DISTRICT PERSONNEL INDEX

NAME/District	JOB FUNCTIONS	PAGE
Schiavone, Dawn/*Oregon City School Dist*	73,76,295	128
Schick, Patty/*Whitehall City School Dist*	4	75
Schierloh, Jen/*Lockland School Dist*	83,85	90
Schildmeyer, Brenda/*St Bernard-Elmwood Place Schs*	273	93
Schilling, Eydie/*Fairfield Union Local Sch Dist*	11,296,298	63
Schilling, Rodney/*Eastern Local School Dist*	2,19	163
Schimpf, Andrea/*Seneca East Local School Dist*	16	181
Schindewolf, Nanthan/*Triway Local School Dist*	1,83	213
Schinker, John/*Brecksville Broadview Hts CSD*	73,76,286	41
Schinker, John/*Brecksville Broadview Hts CSD*	84	41
Schiraldi, Jennifer/*East Palestine City Sch Dist*	4	35
Schirg, Adham/*Fairbanks Local School Dist*	1	204
Schirm, Aaron/*Alexander Local School Dist*	2	14
Schlabach, Phil/*Dalton Local School Dist*	67	212
Schlade, Jeff/*Lakewood City School Dist*	68	47
Schlarb, Keith/*Worthington School Dist*	73,76	75
Schley, Tom/*Tri-Village Local Sch Dist*	67	56
Schlick, Charles/*Riverside Local School Dist*	11,15,36,57,69,79,271,294	114
Schloss, Ann/*Elyria City School Dist*	1	123
Schlosser, Don/*Montpelier Exempted Village SD*	3	215
Schlotterer, Josh/*Norwalk City School Dist*	6	106
Schmenk, Craig/*Kalida Local School Dist*	67	169
Schmid, John/*Northeastern Local School Dist*	73,76,286,295	27
Schmidlin, Kristy/*Evergreen Local School Dist*	58,275	78
Schmidt, Cindy/*Crestview Local School Dist*	76	34
Schmidt, Erin/*Continental Local School Dist*	38	169
Schmidt, Erin/*Gahanna-Jefferson Public SD*	39,48,74	70
Schmidt, Julie/*Crestwood Local School Dist*	288	165
Schmidt, Linda/*Archbold Area Local Sch Dist*	5	78
Schmidt, Lindsey/*Valley View Local School Dist*	288	153
Schmidt, Nelly/*Van Wert City School Dist*	16	205
Schmidt, Paul/*Waterloo Local School Dist*	69,79,275	167
Schmidt, Randy/*Miami Valley Career Tech VSD*	73	151
Schmidt, Rhonda/*Fremont City School Dist*	84	176
Schmidt, Scott/*Northridge Local School Dist*	1	119
Schmidt, Vincent, Dr/*Diocese of Toledo Ed Office*	1	131
Schmiesing, Cheryl/*Pandora Gilboa Local Sch Dist*	36	170
Schmiesing, Ken, Dr/*Celina City School Dist*	1	143
Schmiesing, Rycki/*Fairlawn Local School Dist*	16	182
Schmitt, Colby/*Zanesville City School Dist*	36	157
Schmitt, Colby/*Zanesville City School Dist*	36	157
Schmitz, Sharon/*Pickerington Local School Dist*	7,85	64
Schmutz, Todd/*Pandora Gilboa Local Sch Dist*	1	170
Schneider, Brad/*Big Walnut Local School Dist*	67	58
Schneider, Paul/*Springfield City School Dist*	11,57,271,296	28
Schneider, Stella/*Western Brown Local Sch Dist*	4	20
Schnider, Connie/*Fairlawn Local School Dist*	58	182
Schnieder, Andrea/*Upper Sandusky Exempted Vlg SD*	58	219
Schnipke, Keith/*Continental Local School Dist*	73,76	169
Schnipke, Terry/*Columbus Grove Local Sch Dist*	6	169
Schnitker, Brenda/*Elmwood Local School Dist*	58	216
Schnurrenberg, David/*Bloomfield-Mespo Local SD*	16,73	197
Schob, Jason/*Marietta City School Dist*	35	210
Schoen, Amy/*Greenville City School Dist*	34	55
Schoene, Richard/*Belmont-Harrison Voc Sch Dist*	1	18
Schofield, Karen/*Cuyahoga Falls City Sch Dist*	67	192
Schonauer, Susan/*Indian Hill Exempted Vlg SD*	27	90
Schondelmyer, Jason/*Arcanum Butler Local Sch Dist*	6	55
Schooler, Kelly/*Perry Local School Dist*	9,11,59,88	9
Schoonerover, Jeannie/*Oak Hills Local School Dist*	67	92
Schott, Mike/*Alliance City School Dist*	6	184
Schrader, Jason/*New Bremen Local School Dist*	1,11,57	16
Schraff, Susan/*State Support Team 3*	15,58,93	55
Schramm, Shelly/*Pettisville Local School Dist*	16	79
Schreffler, Tricia/*Strasburg Franklin Local SD*	2,11	203
Schremp, Brent/*Avon Lake City School Dist*	6	122
Schremp, Jessica/*Sheffield-Sheffield Lake CSD*	273	125
Schrock, Caity/*Chippewa Local School Dist*	58	211
Schrock, Nicole/*Jonathan Alder Local School Dist*	16,28,73,286	132
Schroeder, Ann/*Perry Local School Dist*	58	9
Schroeder, Brent/*Ottawa-Glandorf Local Sch Dist*	67	170
Schroeder, Dale/*Columbus Grove Local Sch Dist*	3	169
Schroeder, Jodi/*Pandora Gilboa Local Sch Dist*	59	170
Schroeder, Julie/*Holgate Local School Dist*	273	101
Schroeder, Ken/*Bay Village City School Dist*	36	40
Schroer, Dan/*Springboro Cmty School Dist*	1	208

NAME/District	JOB FUNCTIONS	PAGE
Schroer, Scott/*New Knoxville Local Sch Dist*	3	16
Schroth, Brandon/*Swanton Local School Dist*	76,295	79
Schroyer, Deb/*Celina City School Dist*	4	143
Schroyer, Dick/*Apollo Joint Voc School Dist*	73	8
Schroyer, Terry/*Coldwater Exempted Village SD*	67	143
Schubert, Brian/*Bellevue City School Dist*	6	105
Schubert, Kim/*Bellevue City School Dist*	1	105
Schuckert, Lyndie/*Cuyahoga Heights Local SD*	67	45
Schuessler, Donna/*Eastwood Local School Dist*	36	216
Schuette, Sara/*Antwerp Local School Dist*	67	160
Schuffenesker, Craig/*Put-In-Bay Local School Dist*	6	159
Schuler, Janelle/*Perry Local School Dist*	8	188
Schuller, Cathy/*Bowling Green City Sch Dist*	2	216
Schulte, Thomas/*Hamilton City School Dist*	3	21
Schultheiss, Theresa/*Logan-Hocking Local Sch Dist*	6	104
Schultz, David/*Stryker Local School Dist*	8,11,31	215
Schultz, Jean/*Woodmore Local School Dist*	16,82	159
Schulz, Mindy/*Allen Co Ed Service Center*	10	7
Schumacher, Lynda/*Pioneer Joint Voc School Dist*	2,19	173
Schumann, Matthew/*U S Grant Career School Dist*	73,84	31
Schumm, Marylynn/*Upper Scioto Valley Local SD*	57	100
Schumm, Robert/*Greenfield Exempted Village SD*	8,69,72,81,288	103
Schuster, Martin/*Bucyrus City School Dist*	5	38
Schuster, Rick/*Little Miami Local School Dist*	295	208
Schutte, David/*Hamilton Local School Dist*	67	71
Schutte, Jim/*Wilmington City School Dist*	3,91	33
Schutte, Karen/*Hamilton Local School Dist*	16,82	71
Schutze, Carrie/*Russia Local School Dist*	58	183
Schwartz, Beth/*Amherst Exempted Village SD*	69,274	122
Schwed, Dominic/*Twinsburg City School Dist*	6	195
Schweitzer, John/*Parma City School Dist*	67	49
Schweitzer, Lindie/*Dublin City School Dist*	73,286	69
Schwenderman, Cindy/*Washington Co JT Voc Sch Dist*	38,69	210
Schwiefert, Betty/*Kelleys Island Local School Dist*	2	61
Schwieterman, Daniel/*Noble Local School Dist*	9,31,37,83,88	158
Schwieterman, Deron/*Beavercreek City School Dist*	68,74,78	83
Schwinn, Diana/*New London Local School Dist*	16	105
Sciola, Greg/*Joseph Badger Local Sch Dist*	2	198
Scofield, Joan/*Jefferson Local School Dist*	10,11,57,74,81,88,275,288	132
Scott, Caleb/*Cory-Rawson Local School Dist*	6	97
Scott, Chad/*Dawson-Bryant Local Sch Dist*	3	115
Scott, Chad/*Northridge Local School Dist*	35,85	119
Scott, Corinne/*Tecumseh Local School Dist*	67	28
Scott, Jaime/*Northridge Local School Dist*	8	119
Scott, John/*Brecksville Broadview Hts CSD*	2,19	41
Scott, Robert/*Avon Lake City School Dist*	1	122
Scott, Valerie/*Mercer Co Ed Service Center*	34	143
Scruci, Francis/*Bowling Green City Sch Dist*	1	216
Seals, Andy/*Clermont Northeastern Local SD*	295	30
Searcy, Rachel/*Oak Hills Local School Dist*	79,93,275	92
Searfoss, Wendy/*Upper Sandusky Exempted Vlg SD*	16	219
Sears, Amanda/*Amherst Exempted Village SD*	285	122
Sears, Bill/*Hamilton Co Ed Service Center*	73,295	87
Sears, Candice/*Valley View Local School Dist*	8,69,72,273	153
Sears, Greg/*Forest Hills School Dist*	8,69	89
Seas, Richard/*Adams Co Ohio Valley Sch Dist*	1	6
Sebastian, Pam/*Hillsboro City School Dist*	58	103
Seck, Rose/*Carrollton Exempted Village SD*	67	25
Secrist, Jeremy/*Lexington Local School Dist*	15	172
Seder, Bill/*Mt Vernon City School Dist*	1	111
Seeger, Kirby/*Federal Hocking Local Sch Dist*	6	14
Seeker, Don/*Tallmadge City School Dist*	6	194
Seeman, Kent/*Holgate Local School Dist*	2	101
Seevers, Isaac/*Greeneview Local School Dist*	1	84
Seidler, Sue/*Tuslaw Local School Dist*	274	189
Seifert, George/*Revere Local School Dist*	67	194
Seigal, Nathan/*Millcreek West Unity Local SD*	5	215
Seigla, Gar/*Georgetown Exempted Village SD*	16,73	19
Seiler, Kelli/*Edgerton Local School Dist*	12	214
Selbe, Dora/*Warren City School Dist*	5	200
Self, Annie/*Centerville City School Dist*	67	148
Selgo, Jayson, Dr/*Archbold Area Local Sch Dist*	1	78
Selin, Ginger/*Logan Elm Local School Dist*	4	162
Sellars, Angie/*Medina City School Dist*	4	141
Sellers, Kim/*Kings Local School Dist*	752	207
Sellins, Alicia/*Hillsboro City School Dist*	8,288	103

School Year 2019-2020   800-333-8802   OH-T49

DISTRICT PERSONNEL INDEX

Market Data Retrieval

NAME/District	JOB FUNCTIONS	PAGE
Seman, Joan/*Ravenna School Dist*	67	166
Semancik, Jonelle/*North Baltimore Local Sch Dist*	298	217
Sembach, Roy/*Newton Falls Exempted Vlg SD*	16	200
Senic, Lori/*Strongsville City School Dist*	5	51
Senish, Annette/*Perkins Local School Dist*	76	61
Seslar, Devin/*Benton-Carroll-Salem Local SD*	73	158
Sette, Vincent/*Norwayne Local School Dist*	11	212
Severance, Mark/*Lakewood Local School Dist*	12,57,58,81	118
Sewell, Russell/*Labrae Local School Dist*	67	198
Sexton, Alan/*Northwest Local School Dist*	3	179
Sexton, Cherie/*Oregon City School Dist*	7	128
Sexton, Robert/*Olentangy Local School Dist*	73	59
Seymour, Brian/*Pickerington Local School Dist*	73	64
Sgambellone, Nancy/*Lucas Local School Dist*	4	172
Shadle, Monica/*Louisville City School Dist*	81	186
Shafer, Brent/*Perrysburg Exempted Village SD*	73,295	218
Shafer, Dan/*Clyde-Green Spgs Exmpt Vlg SD*	5	176
Shafer, Michelle/*Maumee City School Dist*	8,69,288	127
Shaffer, Connie/*Amanda-Clearcreek Local SD*	4	62
Shaffer, Dave/*Lake Local School Dist*	3,6	217
Shaffer, Jeffrey/*Hicksville Exempted Village SD*	16,73	57
Shaffer, Kasey/*Adena Local School Dist*	58,72,274	174
Shaffer, Michele/*Louisville City School Dist*	1	186
Shaffer, Rhonda/*Southington Local School Dist*	16	200
Shaffer, Rick/*Mt Vernon City School Dist*	3	111
Shaffer, Susan/*Wood Co Ed Service Center*	81	216
Shafner, Eric/*Northmont City School Dist*	5	152
Shamy, Joe/*Sylvania City School Dist*	4	128
Shanks, Lisa/*Sylvania City School Dist*	2,19	128
Shannon, Lisa/*Chagrin Falls Exempted Vlg SD*	11,57,58,69,88,275,294,296	42
Shansky, Robert/*Southern Local School Dist*	6	35
Shappie, Brian/*Versailles Exempted Village SD*	7	56
Sharnsky, Mary/*Copley-Fairlawn City Sch Dist*	5	192
Sharp, Abby/*Ayersville Local School Dist*	2,298	56
Sharpes, Donna/*Southington Local School Dist*	4	200
Sharrock, Tina/*Marysville Exempted Village SD*	5	204
Sharshan, Kimberly/*Columbiana Exempted Village SD*	9,11,51,54,273	34
Shaver, Peggy/*Waterloo Local School Dist*	37	167
Shaw, Becky/*Westfall Local School Dist*	4,5	163
Shaw, Brian/*Waynesfield-Goshen Local SD*	73	16
Shaw, Christine/*Cuyahoga Falls City Sch Dist*	79	192
Shaw, Deborah/*Logan Elm Local School Dist*	67	162
Shaw, Heidi/*Athens City School Dist*	7,35,85	14
Shaw, Jarod/*Wheelersburg Local School Dist*	6	180
Shaw, Joy/*Madison Local School Dist*	73	23
Shaw, Paul/*Logan-Hocking Local Sch Dist*	2	104
Shaw, Paula/*Milton-Union Exempted Vlg SD*	36	145
Shaw, Tiffany/*Tuscarawas Valley Local SD*	13	203
Shawger, Chad/*West Muskingum Local Sch Dist*	1	157
Shawstewart, Sheryl/*Dalton Local School Dist*	2,71,97	212
Shay, Daniel/*Urbana City School Dist*	6	26
Shea, David/*Southeastern Local School Dist*	1,11	28
Shea, Samantha/*Adena Local School Dist*	36	174
Shears, Quincy/*Shelby City School Dist*	7	173
Sheatzley, Sheryl/*Hudson City School Dist*	71	193
Sheets, Brady/*Westlake City School Dist*	68,79	51
Sheets, Carlotta/*Trumbull Co Ed Service Center*	68	196
Sheets, John/*Bloomfield-Mespo Local SD*	1,11,288	197
Sheets, Sharon/*Fayetteville Perry Local SD*	74,288	19
Sheffler, Sherri/*Eastwood Local School Dist*	67	216
Sheipline, Tasha/*Apollo Joint Voc School Dist*	30	8
Shelby, Lillie/*Lucas Local School Dist*	59	172
Shelby, Meghan, Dr/*Maple Heights City School Dist*	57,58,77,83	47
Sheldon, David/*Colonel Crawford Local SD*	6	38
Shell, Chloe/*Bradford Exempted Village SD*	5,6	145
Shelly, Jessica/*Cincinnati City School Dist*	4	87
Shelton, Brain/*Big Walnut Local School Dist*	6	58
Shelton, Brian/*Big Walnut Local School Dist*	6	58
Shelton, Matt/*Greenfield Exempted Village SD*	275	103
Shenefield, Haven/*Northmor Local School Dist*	3	155
Shepard, Dena/*New Lebanon Local School Dist*	8,35,54,74,277,288	151
Shepas, Rick/*Youngstown City School Dist*	6,35	136
Sheperd, Karry/*St Clairsville-Richland CSD*	7,83,85	18
Shephard, Kellie/*Troy City School Dist*	57	146
Shepherd, Ashley/*Western Buckeye Ed Service Ctr*	81	160
Shepherd, Ashley/*Western Buckeye Ed Service Ctr*	81	205
Sherburne, Tonya/*Granville Exempted Village SD*	2,3,68	117
Sheridan, Matt/*Crooksville Exempted Vlg SD*	1	161
Sherman, Jason/*Delaware City School Dist*	3,5,91	58
Sherman, Tim/*Newcomerstown Exempted Vlg SD*	76	203
Sherwood, Don/*Austintown Local School Dist*	67	133
Shewell, Peggy/*Rootstown Local School Dist*	4	166
Shield, Jamie/*Chesapeake Union Exempt Vlg SD*	8,11,58,77,286,288	115
Shields, Jim/*Medina City School Dist*	68	141
Shields, Lisa/*Perry Local School Dist*	58	113
Shilling, Natasha/*Barnesville Exempted Vlg SD*	38	17
Shimco, Shawn/*Warren City School Dist*	3	200
Shimek, Don/*Norton City School Dist*	6	193
Shinhearl, Ellie/*Millcreek-West Unity Local SD*	4	215
Shinkle, Todd/*Goshen Local School Dist*	2	30
Shinler, Scott/*Central Local School Dist*	67	57
Shinn, Jack/*Licking Valley Local Sch Dist*	3,91	118
Shipper, Doug/*Ashland City School Dist*	5	10
Shirey, Ann/*Minford Local School Dist*	5	178
Shirey, Bryan/*Xenia Community School Dist*	2,3,73	84
Shirkey, Lisa/*Solon City School Dist*	5	50
Shively, Gina/*Perry Local School Dist*	6,7	9
Shively, Mark/*Newark City School Dist*	2,3,78,91	119
Shively, Scott/*Fairbanks Local School Dist*	3	204
Shives, Ron/*Struthers City School Dist*	67	136
Shoaf, Michael, Dr/*Rocky River City School Dist*	1	50
Shockley, Denise, Dr/*Gallia-Vinton Ed Svc Center*	1	80
Shoemaker, Brian/*Groveport Madison Local SD*	67	71
Shoemaker, Josh/*Scioto Co Joint Vocational SD*	12,298	179
Sholl, Mark/*Washington Local School Dist*	11,296	130
Shook, Kathy/*Western Reserve Local Sch Dist*	58	136
Shoppell, Amy/*Spencerville Local School Dist*	73	9
Short, Becky/*Fayette Local Sch Dist*	73	79
Short, Royal/*Archbold Area Local Sch Dist*	83	78
Short, Susan/*Ed Service Ctr Lake Erie West*	8,69	127
Shoup, Cynthia/*Willard City School Dist*	2	106
Shoup, Kevin/*Van Buren Local School Dist*	11,273	99
Showalter, Rob/*Midview Local School Dist*	2	125
Shreve, Amy/*Switzerland of Ohio Local SD*	273	147
Shrider, Nick/*Wapakoneta City School Dist*	73,76,295	16
Shrigley, Dwight/*New Albany-Plain Local SD*	3	72
Shryock, Char/*Bay Village City School Dist*	8,11,16,69,73,273,288	40
Shucofsky, Joe/*Fairview Park City Sch Dist*	67	46
Shuey, Erik, Dr/*South-Western City School Dist*	6,10	73
Shull, Karen/*Amanda-Clearcreek Local SD*	73	62
Shultz, Ali/*Portsmouth City School Dist*	37	179
Shultz, Ali/*Portsmouth City School Dist*	37	179
Shultz, Anna/*Whitehall City School Dist*	58	75
Shultzaberger, Amanda/*Avon Local School Dist*	274	122
Shumaker, Dillan/*London City School Dist*	73	132
Shumaker, Jordan/*Vandalia Butler City Sch Dist*	6	153
Shumaker, Lindy/*Beavercreek City School Dist*	5	83
Shumaker, Sean/*Piqua City School Dist*	3	146
Shuman, Mike/*Beavercreek City School Dist*	16,73	83
Shupe, Kevin/*Sheffield-Sheffield Lake CSD*	5	125
Shupp, Brian/*Wynford Local School Dist*	5	39
Sickles, Sheri/*Marlington Local School Dist*	5	186
Sidberry, Antawn/*Groveport Madison Local SD*	5	71
Sidell, Chris/*Cedar Cliff Local School Dist*	73,76,84	84

Code	Function	Code	Function	Code	Function	Code	Function	Code	Function
1	Superintendent	16	Instructional Media Svcs	30	Adult Education	44	Science Sec	58	Special Education K-12	72	Summer School	88	Alternative/At Risk	277	Remedial Math K-12
2	Bus/Finance/Purchasing	17	Chief Operations Officer	31	Career/Sch-to-Work K-12	45	Math K-12	59	Special Education Elem	73	Instructional Tech	89	Multi-Cultural Curriculum	280	Literacy Coach
3	Buildings And Grounds	18	Chief Academic Officer	32	Career/Sch-to-Work Elem	46	Math Elem	60	Special Education Sec	74	Inservice Training	90	Social Work	285	STEM
4	Food Service	19	Chief Financial Officer	33	Career/Sch-to-Work Sec	47	Math Sec	61	Foreign/World Lang K-12	75	Marketing/Distributive	91	Safety/Security	286	Digital Learning
5	Transportation	20	Art K-12	34	Early Childhood Ed	48	English/Lang Arts K-12	62	Foreign/World Lang Elem	76	Info Systems	92	Magnet School	288	Common Core Standards
6	Athletic	21	Art Elem	35	Health/Phys Education	49	English/Lang Arts Elem	63	Foreign/World Lang Sec	77	Psychological Assess	93	Parental Involvement	294	Accountability
7	Health Services	22	Art Sec	36	Guidance Services K-12	50	English/Lang Arts Sec	64	Religious Education K-12	78	Affirmative Action	95	Tech Prep Program	295	Network System
8	Curric/Instruct K-12	23	Music K-12	37	Guidance Services Elem	51	Reading K-12	65	Religious Education Elem	79	Student Personnel	96	Chief Information Officer	296	Title II Programs
9	Curric/Instruct Elem	24	Music Elem	38	Guidance Services Sec	52	Reading Elem	66	Religious Education Sec	80	Driver Ed/Safety	98	Chief Technology Officer	297	Webmaster
10	Curric/Instruct Sec	25	Music Sec	39	Social Studies K-12	53	Reading Sec	67	School Board President	81	Gifted/Talented	270	Character Education	298	Grant Writer/Ptnrships
11	Federal Program	26	Business Education	40	Social Studies Elem	54	Remedial Reading K-12	68	Teacher Personnel	82	Video Services	271	Migrant Education	750	Chief Innovation Officer
12	Title I	27	Career & Tech Ed	41	Social Studies Sec	55	Remedial Reading Elem	69	Academic Assessment	83	Substance Abuse Prev	273	Teacher Mentor	751	Chief of Staff
13	Title V	28	Technology Education	42	Science K-12	56	Remedial Reading Sec	70	Research/Development	84	Erate	274	Before/After Sch	752	Social Emotional Learning
15	Asst Superintendent	29	Family/Consumer Science	43	Science Elem	57	Bilingual/ELL	71	Public Information	85	AIDS Education	275	Response To Intervention		

Ohio School Directory

DISTRICT PERSONNEL INDEX

NAME/District	JOB FUNCTIONS	PAGE
Sidell, Kayla/*Crestview Local School Dist*	69	34
Sidell, Linda/*Miami Valley Educational CA*	16	85
Sidesinger, Ann/*Upper Arlington City Sch Dist*	274	74
Sidner, Marc/*Perry Local School Dist*	67	9
Sidwell, Lou/*Maysville Local School Dist*	2	156
Siebeneck, Mark/*Continental Local School Dist*	3	169
Siebeneck, Mike/*Miller City-New Cleveland SD*	2	170
Siebeneck, Mike/*Putnam Co Ed Service Center*	2	169
Siebeneck, Sharon/*Leipsic Local School Dist*	73,295	170
Siefke, Joseph/*Lisbon Exempted Village SD*	1	35
Siefring, Amanda/*Benjamin Logan Local Sch Dist*	7	121
Siegel, Debbie/*Solon City School Dist*	8,11,83,88,285,288,296,298	50
Siegel, Wendy/*Whitehall City School Dist*	7	75
Siegfried, Jason/*Louisville City School Dist*	73	186
Siegler, Bill/*Fayetteville Perry Local SD*	73,76,295	19
Sigfreid, Olivia/*Madison Local School Dist*	34	172
Sigler, Mary-Alice/*United Local School Dist*	11,58,88,273,275,296	36
Sigworth, Steven/*Southeast Local School Dist*	6	166
Sikora, Aaron/*Ohio Valley Ed Service Center*	73,76	85
Silbernagel, Leslie/*Northwest Local School Dist*	8,42	91
Silica, Randy/*Springfield Local School Dist*	5	194
Silla, Rebekah/*Perry Local School Dist*	36,57,58	188
Siloy, Thomas/*Old Fort Local School Dist*	2	181
Silva, Susanne/*Lorain City School Dist*	57	124
Silverthorn, Todd/*Kettering City School Dist*	5	150
Silvus, Brad/*Greenon Local School Dist*	1	27
Simcic, Janelle/*Perry Local School Dist*	9	188
Simecek, Mary/*Solon City School Dist*	27,31	50
Simione, Lori/*Trumbull Co Ed Service Center*	2	196
Simmons, Julie/*Elida Local School Dist*	8,11,57,273,288,294,296,298	8
Simon, Eric/*Evergreen Local School Dist*	6	78
Simonelli, Bonnie/*Revere Local School Dist*	83	194
Simpson, Erin/*Wadsworth City School Dist*	280	141
Simpson, Jimmy/*Eastern Local School Dist*	3,5	7
Simpson, Matt/*Meigs Local School Dist*	73,295	142
Simpson, Sally/*Centerburg Local School Dist*	54	110
Sims, Jill/*Circleville City School Dist*	34	162
Sims, Paul/*Wellston City School Dist*	3	108
Sincere, Charles/*Springfield Local School Dist*	1	194
Sines, Amy/*Fairbanks Local School Dist*	12	204
Sines, Brynt/*Solon City School Dist*	297	50
Sines, Jamie/*Maysville Local School Dist*	58	157
Singer, Adam/*Central Local School Dist*	28,73,286,295	57
Singh, Betsy/*Cincinnati City School Dist*	81	87
Singleton, Julie/*Preble-Shawnee Local Sch Dist*	67	168
Sininger, Kelly/*West Clermont Local Sch Dist*	2	31
Sinn, Duane/*Wayne Trace Local School Dist*	67	160
Sipes, Amy/*Northmont City School Dist*	68,270,294,296	152
Sira, Tara/*Centerville City School Dist*	58	148
Sirbaugh, Christina/*St Clairsville-Richland CSD*	8	18
Sisk, Michelle/*Winton Woods City School Dist*	16,82	94
Sismondo, Ron/*Jefferson Co Ed Service Center*	8,74	108
Sizemore, Elisabeth/*Beavercreek City School Dist*	26,39,45,81	83
Sizemore, Jessica/*Piqua City School Dist*	81	146
Sizemore, Kevin/*Franklin City School Dist*	67	207
Sizemore, Laurie/*Chippewa Local School Dist*	3,5	211
Skaggs, Mike/*Washington Court House City SD*	3	65
Skaggs, Shawn/*Paint Valley Local School Dist*	67	175
Skaggs, Walt/*St Clairsville-Richland CSD*	1	18
Skelton, Sara/*Northmor Local School Dist*	58	156
Sketel, Richard/*Lawrence Co Joint Voc Sch Dist*	2,11,85	116
Skidmore, Robert/*Medina Co Joint Voc Sch Dist*	67	141
Skilliter, Meri/*ADA Exempted Village Sch Dist*	1	99
Skinner, Moniqua/*Bradford Exempted Village SD*	7	145
Skoczen, Judy/*Columbia Local School Dist*	58	123
Slade Jackson, Nneka/*Richmond Heights Local SD*	67	49
Slagle, Emily/*Goshen Local School Dist*	16,82	30
Slagle, Mark/*Goshen Local School Dist*	73,76,295	30
Slater, Kip/*Lancaster City School Dist*	5	63
Slauterbeck, Justin/*Van Buren Local School Dist*	6	99
Slavkovsky, Jeff/*Auburn Vocational School Dist*	15	112
Slazkovski, Justin/*Auburn Vocational School Dist*	91	112
Slivochka, Mike/*Berea City School Dist*	68	41
Sloan, Brian/*Ridgedale Local School Dist*	16,73,76,82,84,295	138
Sloan, Julie/*Newton Falls Exempted Vlg SD*	2	200
Sloan, Ryan/*West Carrollton City Sch Dist*	2	153
Sluka, Allen/*Garfield Heights City SD*	2	46
Sluss, Laura/*Newark City School Dist*	273	119
Slynn, Bonnie/*Noble Local School Dist*	22	158
Smarsh, Mark/*Clearview Local School Dist*	3	123
Smeal, Robin/*Mayfield City School Dist*	4	47
Smeltzer, Eric/*North Central Local Sch Dist*	2	215
Smialek, Charles/*Parma City School Dist*	1	49
Smialek, Rasheeda/*Bedford City School Dist*	58	40
Smiley, Bridgette/*Oak Hills Local School Dist*	10,16,30,73,286,295	92
Smiley, Dawnyell/*Warrensville Heights City SD*	93	51
Smith, Andrea/*North Point Ed Svc Ctr*	8,15	60
Smith, Andrew/*Chesapeake Union Exempt Vlg SD*	73,84	115
Smith, Angela/*Madison Local School Dist*	1,11,288	112
Smith, Anthony/*Winton Woods City School Dist*	1	94
Smith, Ben/*Cory-Rawson Local School Dist*	5	97
Smith, Billy/*Fairfield City School Dist*	1	21
Smith, Cary/*Fairlawn Local School Dist*	38	182
Smith, Casey, Dr/*Lynchburg-Clay Local Sch Dist*	11,31,83,88,296,298	103
Smith, Chanda/*ADA Exempted Village Sch Dist*	16,82	99
Smith, Cherie/*State Support Team-Region 6*	36,58,77	17
Smith, Chuck/*Goshen Local School Dist*	3	30
Smith, Dara/*Paint Valley Local School Dist*	271	175
Smith, Dave/*Kings Local School Dist*	5	207
Smith, Dave/*Yellow Springs Exempted Vlg SD*	31,69	85
Smith, Elizabeth/*Bluffton Exempted Village Sch*	38,69	8
Smith, Emily/*Graham Local School Dist*	12,34,58,69,88	26
Smith, Eric/*Maysville Local School Dist*	73	157
Smith, Heather/*Perry Local School Dist*	16,288	9
Smith, Jacqualine/*Allen East Local School Dist*	6,33,38,69,83,88	7
Smith, James/*Perry Local School Dist*	3	113
Smith, Jenni/*Willard City School Dist*	8,280,285,288	106
Smith, Jennifer/*Kettering City School Dist*	58	150
Smith, Jennifer/*Maplewood JT Voc School Dist*	73	166
Smith, Jeremy/*Fostoria City School Dist*	73,295	180
Smith, Jill/*Jefferson Local School Dist*	2	132
Smith, Joan/*Wolf Creek Local School Dist*	12	211
Smith, Joe Pat/*Greenfield Exempted Village SD*	2	103
Smith, Judy/*New Riegel Local School Dist*	4	181
Smith, Julie/*Ashland Co-West Holmes JVSD*	2	10
Smith, Julie/*Northwest Local School Dist*	2	179
Smith, Kara/*Lancaster City School Dist*	4	63
Smith, Karen/*Finneytown Local School Dist*	5	89
Smith, Kathy/*West Liberty-Salem Local SD*	4	26
Smith, Kelley/*Tallmadge City School Dist*	29	194
Smith, Kelly/*Coventry Local School Dist*	5	192
Smith, Kim/*Celina City School Dist*	85	143
Smith, Kristian/*Lorain Co Joint Voc Sch Dist*	30	125
Smith, Larry/*Milton-Union Exempted Vlg SD*	3,91	145
Smith, Larry/*North Fork Local School Dist*	73,286,295	119
Smith, Leesa/*Wynford Local School Dist*	2,11	39
Smith, Leisan/*Bexley City School Dist*	83,85,88,752	66
Smith, Leslie/*Franklin Local School Dist*	31,36	156
Smith, Lisa/*Access*	1	137
Smith, Mark/*Penta Co JT Voc School Dist*	273	217
Smith, Matthew/*Perkins Local School Dist*	6	61
Smith, Matthew/*Swanton Local School Dist*	294	79
Smith, Melissa/*Gahanna-Jefferson Public SD*	34	70
Smith, Merri/*Maplewood Local School Dist*	2	199
Smith, Michael/*Springfield Local School Dist*	3	194
Smith, Mitzi/*Southwest Local School Dist*	68	93
Smith, Molly/*West Liberty-Salem Local SD*	31,36	26
Smith, Nicholas/*Tiffin City School Dist*	77	181
Smith, Nikki/*Vanlue Local School Dist*	36,69	99
Smith, Patrick/*Indian Lake Local School Dist*	5	121
Smith, Patrick/*Madison Local School Dist*	3,92	112
Smith, Randy/*Forest Hills School Dist*	67	89
Smith, Rick/*Ohio Hi-Point Joint Voc SD*	1,11	121
Smith, Rick/*Warren Co Voc School Dist*	1	208
Smith, Robert/*Coldwater Exempted Village SD*	73,295	143
Smith, Robert/*Sidney City School Dist*	67	183
Smith, Robert/*Van Buren Local School Dist*	73,76,295	99
Smith, Ryan/*Tri-Valley Local School Dist*	2	157
Smith, Sandra/*Rossford Exempted Village SD*	73,84	218
Smith, Sandy/*Bloom-Vernon Local Sch Dist*	9,11,296	178
Smith, Sarah/*Switzerland of Ohio Local SD*	67	147
Smith, Scott/*Cleveland Hts-Univ Hts City SD*	5	42

DISTRICT PERSONNEL INDEX

Market Data Retrieval

NAME/District	JOB FUNCTIONS	PAGE
Smith, Scott/Mapleton Local School Dist	1	11
Smith, Sharon/Reynoldsburg City School Dist	12	72
Smith, Sharon/Strasburg Franklin Local SD	5	203
Smith, Shawn/Lakota Local School Dist	76	22
Smith, Sherry/Sandusky City School Dist	286	61
Smith, Shirley/Ridgewood Local School Dist	16,73,76	37
Smith, Spenser/Huntington Local School Dist	7,83,85	175
Smith, Stacy/Milford Exempted Village SD	73,286	30
Smith, Steve/Fairbanks Local School Dist	73	204
Smith, Taylor/Brooklyn City School Dist	73	41
Smith, Teri/Monroeville Local School Dist	12,55	105
Smith, Tracy/New Lexington School Dist	77	161
Smith, Tricia/Hamilton City School Dist	73,286,295	22
Smith, Tyler/Sparcc	76	190
Smith, Wendy/Brooklyn City School Dist	16	41
Smithberger, Denise/Diocese of Cleveland Ed Office	74	52
Smola, Eric/Evergreen Local School Dist	1	78
Smuck, Fatima/Edison Local School Dist	4,58	109
Smucker, Craig/Fayetteville Perry Local SD	67	19
Snedeker, Ben/Knox Co Ed Service Center	58	110
Snider, Dana/Harrison Hills City Sch Dist	1	101
Snider, Pat/Marietta City School Dist	4	210
Snider, Stacey/Mideast Career & Tech Ctrs	71	157
Snider, Terry/Vinton Co Local School Dist	8,11,57,83,273,288,294	206
Sniegowski, Rob/New Bremen Local School Dist	5	16
Snively, Jason/Danville Local School Dist	1	110
Snoke, James/Berne Union Local School Dist	3,5	63
Snook, Thomas/Washington Local School Dist	6,35	130
Snow, Drew/Upper Scioto Valley Local SD	73,295	100
Snow, Michelle/Licking Co Joint Voc School Dist	10	118
Snow, Toby/Bowling Green City Sch Dist	5	216
Snowberger, Eydie/Green Local School Dist	2,19	185
Snowden, Dave/Jackson-Milton Local Sch Dist	3	134
Snowden, Dave/Jackson-Milton Local Sch Dist	3	134
Snyder-Lowe, Lori/Morgan Local School Dist	1	154
Snyder, Andrea/Allen East Local School Dist	2,11,19	7
Snyder, Breanna/Patrick Henry Local Sch Dist	2,11,19	102
Snyder, Doug/Chardon Local School Dist	6	82
Snyder, Harry/Great Oaks Career Campuses	1	89
Snyder, Jeff/Lincolnview Local School Dist	1	205
Snyder, John/Anthony Wayne Local Sch Dist	6	127
Snyder, Julie/West Holmes Local School Dist	58	105
Snyder, Kevin/Lancaster City School Dist	10	63
Snyder, Lahela/Montgomery Co Ed Service Ctr	81	148
Snyder, Mike/New London Local School Dist	3	105
Snyder, Tim/Meta Solutions	73	139
Snyder, Vicki/Southeastern Local Sch Dist	7	175
Sobnosky, Edward/Springfield Local School Dist	2	135
Sobota, Michael/South Range Local School Dist	82	135
Sobul, Michael/Granville Exempted Village SD	2,11	117
Sodini, Steven/East Clinton Local School Dist	58	33
Sokol, Mike/Talawanda School Dist	5	24
Solano, Connie/Cincinnati City School Dist	69,294	87
Solano, Donna/Willoughby-Eastlake City SD	11	114
Solazzo, Melissa/Warren Co Voc School Dist	68	208
Sollars, Julie/Berkshire Local School Dist	4	81
Soloman, Raymond/Hubbard Exempted Village SD	1	198
Sommer, Erol/Cuyahoga Vly Career Ctr Voc SD	60	45
Sommer, Tom/Celina City School Dist	2	143
Sommers, John/Bedford City School Dist	3	40
Sommers, Shawn/Bath Local School Dist	77	8
Sonoda, Kay/Summit Co Ed Service Center	88	190
Sontag, George/Worthington School Dist	5	75
Sotkovsky, Sue/Geauga Co Ed Service Center	2	81
Sotlar, James/Canal Winchester Local SD	1	66
Sotzing, Eric/Lebanon City School Dist	2	207
Soulcenik, Jennifer/Mathews Local School Dist	58	199

NAME/District	JOB FUNCTIONS	PAGE
Sourini, Jodi/Cleveland Hts-Univ Hts City SD	67	42
Southworth, Teresa/Eastern Local School Dist	36,69,83,270	163
Sowards, Gary/Fairland Local School Dist	67	116
Sowders, Wyatt/Fairfield Local Sch Dist	3,5	102
Sowers, Paul/Danbury Local School Dist	67	159
Soyars, Jim/Kent City School Dist	2,76,84,295	165
Spain, Cheryl, Dr/South-Western City School Dist	69,81	73
Spangler, Karla/Toledo Public Schools	31,58,77	129
Spangler, Sherril/Brookville Local School Dist	36	148
Sparks, Don/North Ridgeville City Sch Dist	6	125
Sparks, Jean/Princeton City School Dist	4	92
Sparks, Sue/South Central Local Sch Dist	73,84,295	106
Sparks, Tim/Dawson-Bryant Local Sch Dist	5	115
Sparling, Brian/Ridgedale Local School Dist	8	138
Spaziani, Pete/Washington Co JT Voc Sch Dist	3	210
Spears, Nancy/Goshen Local School Dist	58	30
Speas, Brent/Mad River Local School Dist	5	151
Speelman, Charles/Tri-Rivers Joint Voc Sch Dist	1	139
Speese, Karen/Oak Hill Union Local Sch Dist	69	107
Speicelsehies, Eric/Hopewell-Loudon Local SD	83	181
Spence, Gwenn/Granville Exempted Village SD	58,79	117
Spence, Lisa/Warren Local School Dist	3,5	210
Spence, Marcia/Rootstown Local School Dist	58	166
Spence, Shaun/Cardinal Local School Dist	285	81
Spencer, Andrea/Jonathan Alder Local Sch Dist	7,85	132
Spencer, Clay/Franklin-Monroe Local Sch Dist	3	55
Spencer, Lauren/Greenon Local School Dist	38	27
Spencer, Robert/New Miami Local School Dist	5	23
Spencer, Stacey/Sycamore Cmty School Dist	7,11,58,83,88,285	93
Spencer, Susan/Wood Co Ed Service Center	11	216
Spenthoff, Katie/Washington Local School Dist	8	130
Sperling, Kim/Fairview Park City Sch Dist	2	46
Spero, Jennifer/Federal Hocking Local Sch Dist	8,11,296,298	14
Spevak, Erin/Shaker Heights City Sch Dist	5	50
Spiccia, Joseph/Wickliffe City School Dist	1	114
Spicer, Ryan/Massillon City School Dist	7,57,58,83,286,288	187
Spicher, Kevin/Howland Local School Dist	1	198
Spiers, Tracy/Adams Co Ohio Valley Sch Dist	58	6
Spieser, John/Milford Exempted Village SD	68	30
Spiess, Greg/Hancock Co Ed Service Center	2	97
Spiker, Keith/Howland Local School Dist	3	198
Spiller, Caitlin/Bethel-Tate Local School Dist	36,69,81	30
Spiller, Eric/Northeastern Local School Dist	12	57
Spillman, Mike/Tuscarawas Valley Local SD	3,5,91	203
Spindler, Richard/Berne Union Local School Dist	1,11	63
Spinell, Gary/Strasburg Franklin Local SD	6	203
Spinner, Tim/Kings Local School Dist	8,16,57,69,73,95,288	207
Spires, Crystal/New Albany-Plain Local SD	76	72
Spitali, Vincent/Woodridge Local School Dist	3	195
Spitler, Gavin/Newton Local School Dist	6	146
Spitnale, Sally/Columbus Grove Local Sch Dist	12	169
Spitzer, Carissa/Lakewood City School Dist	81	47
Sponseller, Richard/Manchester Local School Dist	67	193
Spontelli, Christy/Wood Co Ed Service Center	88	216
Spoonemore, Karen/Jefferson Co JT Voc Sch Dist	2	109
Sprada, Brian/Brookville Local School Dist	6	148
Spradlin, Barry/Wheelersburg Local School Dist	38	180
Spradlin, Chad/Circleville City School Dist	6	162
Spragu-Marcum, Tracy/Oak Hills Local School Dist	5	92
Sprang, Andrew/Fostoria City School Dist	1	180
Spridgeon, Angie/Arcadia Local School Dist	2	97
Spriggs, Craig/Bellbrook-Sugarcreek Schools	295	83
Spriggs, Kris/Northeastern Local School Dist	6	27
Spring, Amanda/Dublin City School Dist	7	69
Springer, Chad/Athens City School Dist	83	14
Sprinkles, Ken/Carlisle Local School Dist	3	206
Sproat, Matt/Oakwood City School Dist	73,286,295	152

---

1 Superintendent	16 Instructional Media Svcs	30 Adult Education	44 Science Sec	58 Special Education K-12	72 Summer School	88 Alternative/At Risk	277 Remedial Math K-12
2 Bus/Finance/Purchasing	17 Chief Operations Officer	31 Career/Sch-to-Work K-12	45 Math K-12	59 Special Education Elem	73 Instructional Tech	89 Multi-Cultural Curriculum	280 Literacy Coach
3 Buildings And Grounds	18 Chief Academic Officer	32 Career/Sch-to-Work Elem	46 Math Elem	60 Special Education Sec	74 Inservice Training	90 Social Work	285 STEM
4 Food Service	19 Chief Financial Officer	33 Career/Sch-to-Work Sec	47 Math Sec	61 Foreign/World Lang K-12	75 Marketing/Distributive	91 Safety/Security	286 Digital Learning
5 Transportation	20 Art K-12	34 Early Childhood Ed	48 English/Lang Arts K-12	62 Foreign/World Lang Elem	76 Info Systems	92 Magnet School	288 Common Core Standards
6 Athletic	21 Art Elem	35 Health/Phys Education	49 English/Lang Arts Elem	63 Foreign/World Lang Sec	77 Psychological Assess	93 Parental Involvement	294 Accountability
7 Health Services	22 Art Sec	36 Guidance Services K-12	50 English/Lang Arts Sec	64 Religious Education K-12	78 Affirmative Action	95 Tech Prep Program	295 Network System
8 Curric/Instruct K-12	23 Music K-12	37 Guidance Services Elem	51 Reading K-12	65 Religious Education Elem	79 Student Personnel	96 Chief Information Officer	296 Title II Programs
9 Curric/Instruct Elem	24 Music Elem	38 Guidance Services Sec	52 Reading Elem	66 Religious Education Sec	80 Driver Ed/Safety	98 Chief Technology Officer	297 Webmaster
10 Curric/Instruct Sec	25 Music Sec	39 Social Studies K-12	53 Reading Sec	67 School Board President	81 Gifted/Talented	270 Character Education	298 Grant Writer/Ptnrships
11 Federal Program	26 Business Education	40 Social Studies Elem	54 Remedial Reading K-12	68 Teacher Personnel	82 Video Services	271 Migrant Education	750 Chief Innovation Officer
12 Title I	27 Career & Tech Ed	41 Social Studies Sec	55 Remedial Reading Elem	69 Academic Assessment	83 Substance Abuse Prev	273 Teacher Mentor	751 Chief of Staff
13 Title V	28 Technology Education	42 Science K-12	56 Remedial Reading Sec	70 Research/Development	84 Erate	274 Before/After Sch	752 Social Emotional Learning
15 Asst Superintendent	29 Family/Consumer Science	43 Science Elem	57 Bilingual/ELL	71 Public Information	85 AIDS Education	275 Response To Intervention	

OH-T52

Ohio School Directory

DISTRICT PERSONNEL INDEX

NAME/District	JOB FUNCTIONS	PAGE
Spurgeon, Jane/*Sylvania City School Dist*	1	128
Spurlock, Judith/*Dayton Public School Dist*	68	149
Spyker, Jamie/*Shawnee Local School Dist*	3	9
Spyrou, Kathy/*Centerville City School Dist*	81	148
Srodawa, Mike/*Tallmadge City School Dist*	35,85	194
St Claire, Talia/*Indian Valley Local Sch Dist*	11,58,69,88,296	202
Stacey, Sheri/*Liberty Center Local Sch Dist*	5	101
Stacho, Helene/*State Support Team 11*	34	78
Stacklin, Dan/*Seneca East Local School Dist*	67	181
Stackshloney, Ned/*Apollo Joint Voc School Dist*	67	8
Stacy, Jamie/*Columbiana Co Voc Sch Dist*	273	34
Stacy, Rose/*Windham Exempted Vlg Sch Dist*	31,36,83	167
Staffilino, Brenda/*Indian Creek Local Sch Dist*	5	109
Stafford, Michael/*Manchester Local School Dist*	3	193
Stagani, Jo/*Edison Local School Dist*	6	109
Stage, Connie/*Tri-Co Joint Voc Sch Dist*	4	15
Staggs, Jeff/*Newcomerstown Exempted Vlg SD*	1,83	203
Stahr, Mary Ann/*Green Local School Dist*	16	185
Stahr, Todd/*Pickaway-Ross Co JT Voc SD*	2,19	175
Staimpel, Roni/*North Coast Ed Media Center*	1	54
Stalder, Teresa/*Alexander Local School Dist*	7	14
Staley, Adam/*Clear Fork Vly Local School Dist*	27	171
Staley, Cameron/*Bath Local School Dist*	6	8
Staley, Joe/*Rittman Exempted Village SD*	6	213
Stall, Sue/*Maysville Local School Dist*	274	157
Stallard, Jennifer/*Clear Fork Vly Local Sch Dist*	4	171
Stallard, Mark/*Zanesville City School Dist*	8	157
Stallsmith, Ron/*Columbiana Exempted Village SD*	16,82	34
Stamm, Vickie/*Mideast Career & Tech Ctrs*	91	157
Stanek, Rebeca/*Stow-Munroe Falls City SD*	285	194
Stanfield, Dean/*Edison Local Schools District*	8,11,16,69,74,83,288,298	60
Stanford, Kelly/*Shelby City School Dist*	4	173
Stangelo, Jeremy/*Perry Local School Dist*	286	188
Stankovich, Nick/*Martins Ferry City School Dist*	67	18
Stanley, John/*East Clinton Local School Dist*	2	33
Stanley, Kevin/*Arcanum Butler Local Sch Dist*	5	55
Stanley, Todd/*Pickerington Local School Dist*	81	64
Stanton, Tasha/*Upper Sandusky Exempted Vlg SD*	72	219
Stapleton, Donald/*New Boston Local School Dist*	6,10	179
Starcher, Dave/*Columbiana Co Voc Sch Dist*	3	34
Starcher, Stephanie/*Ft Frye Local School Dist*	1	210
Stark, Kimberly/*Edgerton Local School Dist*	36	214
Stark, Lynne/*Clearview Local School Dist*	12,72,274	123
Stark, Michael/*Vermilion Local School Dist*	67	62
Starkey, Jeff/*Labrae Local School Dist*	11,69,286	198
Starkey, Mark/*Western Reserve Local Sch Dist*	27	106
Starkey, Ted, Dr/*Indian Creek Local Sch Dist*	67	109
Starks, Alicia/*Trotwood-Madison City SD*	5	153
Staton, Sam/*Ridgedale Local School Dist*	9,11	138
Staudter, Joel/*Anna Local School Dist*	10	182
Stauffer, Cheryl/*London City School Dist*	58,81	132
Stauffer, Jeff/*Southeastern Local Sch Dist*	67	175
Stauffer, William/*Portage Lakes Joint Voc SD*	11,73,288	189
Staunton, Jennifer/*Weathersfield Local Sch Dist*	83,85	201
Stearns, Dana/*South Euclid-Lyndhurst City SD*	3,4,5,73,91	51
Stebly, Sandy/*Tri-Co Ed Service Center*	34	211
Steel, Elizabeth/*New Albany-Plain Local SD*	71	72
Steele, Matt/*Mason City School Dist*	67	208
Steenrod, Bruce/*Federal Hocking Local Sch Dist*	2	14
Stefanuik, Luann/*Northwestern Local School Dist*	83,88	212
Stegman, Ken/*Indian Hill Exempted Vlg SD*	3	90
Stehura, Ben/*West Geauga Local School Dist*	6	82
Steierhoff, Lakeisha/*Indian Lake Local School Dist*	38	121
Steinbrecher, Beverly/*Morgan Local School Dist*	13,57,58,83,88	154
Steiner, Andrea/*Joseph Badger Local Sch Dist*	69	198
Steiner, Jessie/*Northwestern Local School Dist*	1	27
Steiner, Jonathan/*Norton City School Dist*	295	193
Steiner, Rich/*Findlay City School Dist*	7,10,38,57,69,79,90,298	97
Steinhoff, Suzanne/*Berkshire Local School Dist*	5	81
Steinlage, Dale/*Clark Co Ed Service Center*	67	27
Stekli, John/*Fairlawn Local School Dist*	8	182
Stelzer, Donna/*Madison-Champaign Ed Svc Ctr*	15	25
Stemen, Lewis/*Educational Serv Ctr-Ctl Ohio*	68	65
Stemen, Lou/*Fairfield Co Ed Service Center*	67	62
Stemen, Randy/*Van Wert City School Dist*	3	205
Stemen, Zach/*Spencerville Local School Dist*	3	9

NAME/District	JOB FUNCTIONS	PAGE
Stenger, Cindy/*Clinton-Massie Local Sch Dist*	7,280	33
Stepanovich, Nick/*Canton Local School Dist*	73,76,84,95,286,295	185
Stephens, Anthony/*New Lexington School Dist*	6	161
Stephens, Jack/*Mad River Local School Dist*	58,77,275	151
Stephens, John/*Arcanum Butler Local Sch Dist*	1	55
Stephens, Lisa/*East Clinton Local School Dist*	7	33
Stephens, Matt/*Hardin-Houston Local Sch Dist*	73,76	183
Stephens, Scott/*Shaker Heights City Sch Dist*	71	50
Stephens, Tracey/*Willard City School Dist*	11,69,72,296	106
Sterling, Bill/*West Holmes Local School Dist*	1	105
Sternberg, Bill, Dr/*Licking Heights Local Sch Dist*	15	118
Steurer, Pam/*Delaware City School Dist*	274	58
Stevens, Anthony/*Edon Northwest Local Sch Dist*	1,73	215
Stevens, Bradd/*Clear Fork Vly Local Sch Dist*	2,30	171
Stevens, Brian/*Jefferson Area Local SD*	2	13
Stevens, Chad/*Switzerland of Ohio Local SD*	71	147
Stevens, Charles/*Jackson City School Dist*	6	107
Stevens, Dave/*Crestview Local School Dist*	84,95	171
Stevens, David/*Tipp City Exempted Village SD*	2	146
Stevens, Donnie/*Ottawa Hills Local Sch Dist*	3	128
Stevens, Drew/*Parma City School Dist*	84,95	49
Stevens, Jessica/*Madeira City School Dist*	58	90
Stevens, Jessica/*Mason City School Dist*	58,294	208
Stevens, Megan/*Marysville Exempted Village SD*	7	204
Stevens, Phil/*Richmond Heights Local SD*	3,5,91	49
Stevens, Todd/*Circleville City School Dist*	67	162
Stevenson, Ami/*Preble-Shawnee Local Sch Dist*	38,69	168
Stevenson, Carla/*Hardin Northern Local Sch Dist*	7	100
Stevenson, Garrett/*Manchester Local School Dist*	76,286,295	7
Stevenson, Jeff/*Upper Arlington City Sch Dist*	16	74
Stevenson, Luke/*Bright Local School Dist*	73,295	102
Stewart, Chris/*Mahoning Co Joint Voc Sch Dist*	16,73	135
Stewart, Connie/*South Range Local School Dist*	7	135
Stewart, Jennifer/*Tallmadge City School Dist*	36,83	194
Stewart, Jerry/*Delaware City School Dist*	68,79	58
Stewart, Melinda/*Wilmington City School Dist*	1	33
Stewart, Melissa, Dr/*Indian Hill Exempted Vlg SD*	8,11,15,34,69,288	90
Stewart, Roger/*Belmont-Harrison Voc Sch Dist*	67	18
Stewart, Sandy/*North Baltimore Local Sch Dist*	5	217
Stewart, Sheryl/*Dalton Local School Dist*	3,17	212
Stewart, Steven/*North Baltimore Local Sch Dist*	2	217
Stewart, William/*Lebanon City School Dist*	6	207
Steyer, Heidi/*Port Clinton City School Dist*	36	159
Steyer, Leonard/*Southeastern Local Sch Dist*	8,88	175
Stickney, Heidi/*Northwest Local School Dist*	8,58	91
Stidham, Brian/*Access*	2	137
Stillings, Carol/*Fairbanks Local School Dist*	68	204
Stillman, Andrew/*Vermilion Local School Dist*	6	62
Stillman, Ty/*Firelands Local School Dist*	6	124
Stilwell, Michael/*New Lexington School Dist*	76	161
Stingle, Brooke/*Buckeye Local School Dist*	67	108
Stitzel, Angela/*Butler Tech Career Dev Schs*	16,82	21
Stiver, Chuck/*Black River Local School Dist*	67	139
Stiver, Randy/*Edgewood City School Dist*	2	21
Stiverson, Mary/*Northwest Local School Dist*	7,85	179
Stiverson, Ruth/*Hopewell-Loudon Local SD*	35,85	181
Stobe, James/*Avon Lake City School Dist*	67	122
Stocker, Brenda/*Elida Local School Dist*	67	8
Stockham, Joseph/*Minford Local School Dist*	67	178
Stockham, Ryan/*Minford Local School Dist*	73,76,295	178
Stockler, Alicia/*Northern Local School Dist*	27,31,38,69	161
Stockmaster, Heather/*Hopewell-Loudon Local SD*	36,69	181
Stockmaster, Heather/*Seneca East Local School Dist*	38,69,88	181
Stockwell, Sara/*Perrysburg Exempted Village SD*	13,57,79,296	218
Stockwell, Tracy/*Cory-Rawson Local School Dist*	54	97
Stoddard, John/*Berkshire Local School Dist*	1	81
Stoddard, Trent/*Teays Valley Local School Dist*	73,295	162
Stoffer, Michelle/*Ridgewood Local School Dist*	4	37
Stohla, Steve/*Liberty Local School Dist*	5	199
Stoicoiu, Kristy/*Cuyahoga Falls City Sch Dist*	2	192
Stokes-Davis, Diedra/*Canton City School Dist*	11,79,296	184
Stoklosa, Kevin/*Struthers City School Dist*	73,295	136
Stolly, Sally/*Benjamin Logan Local Sch Dist*	8,11,16,83,298	121
Stombaugh, Stan/*Carey Exempted Village SD*	3	219
Stone, Erica/*Dublin City School Dist*	57	69
Stone, Leslie/*Monroe Local School Dist*	67	23

School Year 2019-2020 800-333-8802 OH-T53

DISTRICT PERSONNEL INDEX

Market Data Retrieval

NAME/District	JOB FUNCTIONS	PAGE
Stone, Olivia/Centerville City School Dist	4	148
Stoner, Angie/Arcadia Local School Dist	12	97
Stoner, Jane/Alliance City School Dist	58	184
Storer, Amy/West Clermont Local Sch Dist	11,57,294	31
Stork, Bryan/Grandview Heights City SD	38,83,275	71
Stotler, Nikki/Willoughby-Eastlake City SD	8	114
Stotts, Ginger/Nelsonville-York City Sch Dist	76	15
Stout, Marion/Montgomery Co Ed Service Ctr	68	148
Stove, Jennifer/Lakewood Local School Dist	4	118
Stover, Brian/River Valley Local School Dist	67	139
Strahm, Jane/Hamilton Local School Dist	273	71
Stranger, Sean/Canton City School Dist	6	184
Strasser, Kathy/Norwood City School Dist	7	92
Straub, Amber/Shawnee Local School Dist	8,69,74,88	9
Straus, Josh/Logan-Hocking Local Sch Dist	73	104
Straus, Tia/Forest Hills School Dist	4	89
Strausbaugh, Rick/Southeastern Local Sch Dist	6	175
Strebe, Connie/Tolles Career & Tech Sch Dist	27,69	133
Strebe, Connie/Tolles Career & Tech Sch Dist	10,38,83,294	133
Streby, Benjamin/Licking Co Joint Voc Sch Dist	2	118
Streby, Charles/Fredericktown Local Sch Dist	67	111
Streby, Sharon/Fredericktown Local Sch Dist	274	111
Streitenberger, Susan/Diocese of Columbus Ed Office	10	76
Strieter, Terry, Dr/Greene Co Ed Service Center	1	83
Striker, Jordan/Continental Local School Dist	6	169
Strohacker, Craig/Tri-Valley Local School Dist	3,4,5,91	157
Strohl, Shawn/Reynoldsburg City School Dist	34,57,58,81,90	72
Strokes, Tracy/Antwerp Local School Dist	11,274	160
Strom, Tamara/Solon City School Dist	16,71	50
Strong, Tammy/Nordonia Hills City Sch Dist	67	193
Strunk, Wayne/Delaware Joint Voc Sch Dist	73,76,295	59
Stuart, Doug/Rittman Exempted Village SD	67	213
Stuart, Kristine/Antwerp Local School Dist	2	160
Stuart, Todd/Nordonia Hills City Sch Dist	8,31,57,69,271,286,288	193
Stubbelbine, Rachel/Buckeye Central Local Sch Dist	69	38
Stuckey, David/Springboro Cmty School Dist	67	208
Stuckey, Larry/West Branch Local School Dist	3	136
Stucky, Ken/Ripley-Union-Lewis-Huntngtn SD	78	20
Studer, Jeff/McDonald Local School Dist	16,84	199
Studer, Tammy/Buckeye Central Local Sch Dist	73	38
Study, Mike/Miami Valley Career Tech VSD	5	151
Stufflebean, Rodney/Lakewood Local School Dist	5	118
Stulley, Ashlee/Waverly City School Dist	11,57	164
Stump, Vickie/Colonel Crawford Local SD	2,11	38
Stumph, Daryl/Bay Village City School Dist	2,3,15,298	40
Stupak, Lisa/East Central Ohio ESC-St Clair	81	17
Sturgeon, Carol/Labrae Local School Dist	16	198
Sturgill, Ashley/Wellston City School Dist	31	108
Sturgill, Stephen, Dr/Sandusky City School Dist	15,68,79,294,751	61
Sturgis, Julie/Boardman Local School Dist	39	134
Sturm, Milinda/Southwest Licking Local SD	2	120
Stutton, Don/Wilmington City School Dist	73,295	33
Stutz, Joshua/Triway Local School Dist	8	213
Stutz, Nathan/Perry Local School Dist	15	188
Styer, Sheri/Defiance City School Dist	8,11,27,31,54,69,296,298	57
Styles, Marlon/Middletown City School Dist	1	23
Sublett, Sara/Findlay City School Dist	69,90	98
Sudar, Donna/Euclid City School Dist	67	46
Suerth, Kyle/Elyria City School Dist	4	123
Suerth, Kyle/North Ridgeville City School Dist	4	125
Suever, Rick/Delphos City School Dist	73	8
Suffoletta, Robert/Toronto City School Dist	16,73,295	109
Suiter, Arthur/Chesapeake Union Exempt Vlg SD	67	115
Sullen, Timothy/Twinsburg City School Dist	68	195
Sullivan, Elsie/Fairfield Union Local Sch Dist	16,82	63
Sullivan, Greg/Bloom-Vernon Local Sch Dist	6	178
Sullivan, Katie/Tipp City Exempted Village SD	69	146
Sullivan, Michael, Dr/Dayton Public School Dist	15	149
Sullivan, Seth/Dalton Local School Dist	73,98	212
Summers, Dalton/River View Local School Dist	1	37
Suppes, Luann/Southeast Local School Dist	4	213
Surber, Carla/Bradford Exempted Village SD	2	145
Suriano, Sharon/Gahanna-Jefferson Public SD	35,42,45	70
Suter, Steve/Hopewell-Loudon Local SD	6	181
Sutherland, Missy/Ohio Mid-Eastern RESA	73,98	110
Sutter, Matt/Ansonia Local School Dist	31,36,57,69,83,270,273	55
Suttle, Carrie/Little Miami Local School Dist	280	208
Suttman, Craig/Centerville City School Dist	27,31	148
Sutton, Carole/Marlington Local School Dist	8,11,76,273,288,298	186
Sutton, Nikki/Wapakoneta City School Dist	93	16
Swabb, Cathy/Ansonia Local School Dist	16,82	55
Swabb, Scott, Dr/Bradford Exempted Village SD	67	145
Swaggard, Robert/Cleveland Hts-Univ Hts City SD	8	42
Swanger, Misty, Dr/Jonathan Alder Local Sch Dist	8,11,285,288,294,296,298	132
Swank, Shandra/Bryan City School Dist	77	214
Swann, Bryan/Athens Meigs Ed Service Center	2	14
Swann, Tim/Oak Hill Union Local Sch Dist	3	107
Swartz, Kim/Bellevue City School Dist	8,11,285	105
Swartz, Liz/Medina Co Joint Voc Sch Dist	83,88	141
Swartz, Luke/Otsego Local School Dist	73	217
Swartz, Roy/Arlington Local School Dist	2	97
Swartz, Scott/Anna Local School Dist	28	182
Swartz, Shane/Edgewood City School Dist	5	21
Swartzmiller, Brent/Perrysburg Exempted Village SD	8,11,288,298	218
Swauyck, Tim/Johnstown-Monroe Local SD	67	118
Swavel, Tessa/Riverdale Local School Dist	37,83	98
Swearlingen, Melissa/Delaware City School Dist	2,19	58
Sweet, Sharon/Hicksville Exempted Village SD	85	57
Sweetman, Eric/Troy City School Dist	28	146
Swinderman, Vanessa/Blanchester Local School Dist	4	32
Swinehart, Debbie/Chillicothe City School Dist	1	174
Swisher, Cheryl/Defiance City School Dist	2	57
Swisher, Dan/Marlington Local School Dist	79	186
Swisher, Dan/Marlington Local School Dist	58,69,274	186
Switzer, Stephen, Dr/Pettisville Local School Dist	1	79
Swoldo, Nick/Indian Valley Local Sch Dist	3,4,5,6	202
Swope, Amie/Norwalk City School Dist	73,76	106
Swope, Brian/Zanesville City School Dist	67	157
Sycks, Jeanna/Athens City School Dist	78	14
Sykes, Chris/Northwestern Local School Dist	58	212
Symsek, Gina/Brecksville Broadview Hts CSD	12	41
Symsek, Gina/Brecksville Broadview Hts CSD	11,36,58,79	41
Synder, Kelly/Deer Park Cmty School Dist	69,77,85	89
Sypherd, Tim/Danbury Local School Dist	5	159
Sywanyk, Adam/Rocky River City School Dist	3	50
Syx, Mark/Jonathan Alder Local Sch Dist	3	132
Szozda, Lila/Perrysburg Exempted Village SD	4	218

T

NAME/District	JOB FUNCTIONS	PAGE
Tabar, Denise/Olmsted Falls City School Dist	4	48
Tabler, Pat/Federal Hocking Local Sch Dist	3,5,91	14
Tackaberry, Crystal/Strongsville City School Dist	7	51
Tackett, Connie/Pike Co Area JT Voc Sch Dist	60	163
Tackett, Holly/Western Local School Dist	7,85	164
Tackett, Shon/Pike Co Area JT Voc Sch Dist	27,33,288	163
Taggert, Maureen/Toronto City School Dist	1	109
Tait, Rachael/Eaton Cmty School Dist	2,84	168
Tait, Ryan/Dayton Public School Dist	74	149
Takats, Jodi/Lake Local School Dist	8	217
Talbe, Ryan/Felicity-Franklin Local SD	6	30
Talbert, Jeffery/Alliance City School Dist	1	184
Talley, Nancy/River Valley Local School Dist	8	139
Talmage, Tammy/Ottawa Hills Local School Dist	6	128
Tangeman, David/Wapakoneta City School Dist	5	16

1	Superintendent	16	Instructional Media Svcs	30	Adult Education	44	Science Sec	58	Special Education K-12
2	Bus/Finance/Purchasing	17	Chief Operations Officer	31	Career/Sch-to-Work K-12	45	Math K-12	59	Special Education Elem
3	Buildings And Grounds	18	Chief Academic Officer	32	Career/Sch-to-Work Elem	46	Math Elem	60	Special Education Sec
4	Food Service	19	Chief Financial Officer	33	Career/Sch-to-Work Sec	47	Math Sec	61	Foreign/World Lang K-12
5	Transportation	20	Art K-12	34	Early Childhood Ed	48	English/Lang Arts K-12	62	Foreign/World Lang Elem
6	Athletic	21	Art Elem	35	Health/Phys Education	49	English/Lang Arts Elem	63	Foreign/World Lang Sec
7	Health Services	22	Art Sec	36	Guidance Services K-12	50	English/Lang Arts Sec	64	Religious Education K-12
8	Curric/Instruct K-12	23	Music K-12	37	Guidance Services Elem	51	Reading K-12	65	Religious Education Elem
9	Curric/Instruct Elem	24	Music Elem	38	Guidance Services Sec	52	Reading Elem	66	Religious Education Sec
10	Curric/Instruct Sec	25	Music Sec	39	Social Studies K-12	53	Reading Sec	67	School Board President
11	Federal Program	26	Business Education	40	Social Studies Elem	54	Remedial Reading K-12	68	Teacher Personnel
12	Title I	27	Career & Tech Ed	41	Social Studies Sec	55	Remedial Reading Elem	69	Academic Assessment
13	Title V	28	Technology Education	42	Science K-12	56	Remedial Reading Sec	70	Research/Development
15	Asst Superintendent	29	Family/Consumer Science	43	Science Elem	57	Bilingual/ELL	71	Public Information

72	Summer School	88	Alternative/At Risk	277	Remedial Math K-12
73	Instructional Tech	89	Multi-Cultural Curriculum	280	Literacy Coach
74	Inservice Training	90	Social Work	285	STEM
75	Marketing/Distributive	91	Safety/Security	286	Digital Learning
76	Info Systems	92	Magnet School	288	Common Core Standards
77	Psychological Assess	93	Parental Involvement	294	Accountability
78	Affirmative Action	95	Tech Prep Program	295	Network System
79	Student Personnel	96	Title II Programs	296	Title II Programs
80	Driver Ed/Safety	97	Chief Infomation Officer	297	Webmaster
81	Gifted/Talented	98	Chief Technology Officer	298	Character Education
82	Video Services	270	Character Education	270	Character Education
83	Substance Abuse Prev	271	Migrant Education	750	Chief Innovation Officer
84	Erate	273	Teacher Mentor	751	Chief of Staff
85	AIDS Education	274	Before/After Sch	752	Social Emotional Learning
		275	Response To Intervention		

OH-T54

Ohio School Directory

DISTRICT PERSONNEL INDEX

NAME/District	JOB FUNCTIONS	PAGE
Tansey, Rachel/*Lorain City School Dist*	11,36,274,298	124
Tapley, Tammy/*Anthony Wayne Local Sch Dist*	5	127
Tarbert, Jared/*Knox Co Ed Service Center*	73	110
Tarpey, Dan/*Centerville City School Dist*	68	148
Tarvin, Timothy/*Shelby City School Dist*	1	173
Tate, James/*Winton Woods City School Dist*	3	94
Tatman, David/*Western Brown Local Sch Dist*	3	20
Tatman, James/*Olmsted Falls City School Dist*	68	48
Tatman, Tammy/*Felicity-Franklin Local SD*	5	30
Taulbee, Jennifer/*Preble-Shawnee Local Sch Dist*	58,88,270	168
Taylor, Craig/*Riverdale Local School Dist*	6	98
Taylor, Eric/*Cleveland Metro School Dist*	5	42
Taylor, Gregory/*Dayton Public School Dist*	69,70,294	149
Taylor, Jaime/*Trimble Local School Dist*	9,12,273	15
Taylor, Jeff/*Bowling Green City Sch Dist*	295	216
Taylor, Jeremy/*Brown Local School Dist*	69	25
Taylor, Jo/*Lakeview Local School Dist*	1	198
Taylor, Joe/*Wood Co Ed Service Center*	34,58	216
Taylor, Joel/*Conneaut Area City Sch Dist*	6	12
Taylor, Julie/*Bryan City School Dist*	60	214
Taylor, Ken/*Mayfield City School Dist*	3	47
Taylor, Randy/*East Liverpool City School Dist*	1,288	34
Taylor, Rob/*North Central Local Sch Dist*	4	215
Taylor, Tim/*Brookfield Local School Dist*	6	197
Taylor, Tricia/*Western Buckeye Ed Service Ctr*	2	160
Taylor, Tricia/*Western Buckeye Ed Service Ctr*	2	205
Teague, Eric/*Lucas Local School Dist*	6	172
Teater, Debbie/*New Lebanon Local School Dist*	79,298	151
Tebbe, Kelli/*Indian Lake Local School Dist*	8,296	121
Tecca, Rachel/*Akron Public Schools*	27,31	190
Teeters, Ben/*Hillsboro City School Dist*	2	103
Teeters, Ron/*Teays Valley Local School Dist*	3,5,91	162
Tefs, Michael, Dr/*Wooster City School Dist*	1	213
Telerski, Anna/*Whitehall City School Dist*	58	75
Telford, Gayle/*Buckeye Local School Dist*	11,83,88,275	140
Telinda, Bonnie/*Northwest Local School Dist*	4	91
Teller, Cindra/*Bryan City School Dist*	67	214
Templeman, Roy/*Loudonville-Perrysville SD*	67	11
Templeton, Jim/*Northeastern Local School Dist*	23	27
Tench, Tim/*Bedford City School Dist*	67	40
Tener, Eileen/*Clark Co Ed Service Center*	58	27
Terry, Bruce/*Carlisle Local School Dist*	73,84,295	206
Terry, James/*South Range Local School Dist*	5	135
Terry, Rebecca/*Oak Hill Union Local Sch Dist*	4	107
Testerman, Robin/*Warren Local School Dist*	16	210
Teutch, Ragina/*Warren City School Dist*	8,280,288	200
Tevepaugh, Randy/*Streetsboro City School Dist*	3,91	167
Thacker, Jeff/*Vinton Co Local School Dist*	67	206
Thacker, Jeffery/*Gallia-Jackson-Vinton JVSD*	67	80
Thacker, Mary/*Gallia-Vinton Ed Svc Center*	8,11	80
Thaman, BJ/*Fairbanks Local School Dist*	73	204
Thaxton, Ben/*ADA Exempted Village Sch Dist*	13,73,84,295	99
Thayer, Jane/*Valley Local School Dist*	11	179
Thayer, Linda/*State Support Team 3*	27	55
Thayer, Scott/*Valley Local School Dist*	3,5	179
Theaker, Douglas/*Pioneer Joint Voc School Dist*	67	173
Theis, Mark/*New Riegel Local School Dist*	5	181
Theis, Melissa/*West Carrollton City Sch Dist*	11,15,58,275	153
Theiss, Laura/*Butler Co Ed Service Center*	15,68	20
Theobald, Philip/*Noble Local School Dist*	73,295	158
Theroux, Ed/*Talawanda School Dist*	1	24
Thesken, Lori/*Butler Tech Career Dev Schs*	68	21
Thiede, Phil/*Kelleys Island Local Sch Dist*	1,11,84	61
Thiel, Charles/*Union Local School Dist*	1	26
Thigapin, Ann Marie/*Niles City School Dist*	1	200
Thimmes, Sarah/*Lancaster City School Dist*	7	63
Thirion, Elaine/*Euclid City School Dist*	76	46
Thiry, Lynn/*Newton Falls Exempted Vlg SD*	4	200
This, Shelley/*New Bremen Local School Dist*	16,82	16
Thom, James/*Massillon City School Dist*	73,76	187
Thoman, Jeff/*Springfield-Clark Co JVSD*	76	28
Thomas, Angie/*Tri-Village Local Sch Dist*	60	56
Thomas, Darrell/*Urbana City School Dist*	67	26
Thomas, Dave/*Southeast Local School Dist*	3	213
Thomas, Eugene, Dr/*Lowellville Local School Dist*	1,83	135
Thomas, Greg/*Holgate Local School Dist*	67	101
Thomas, John/*Edgewood City School Dist*	3,5,91	21
Thomas, John/*Madison Local School Dist*	1	172
Thomas, Jonathon/*Vanlue Local School Dist*	67	99
Thomas, Juliet/*Northwestern Local School Dist*	38	212
Thomas, Katie/*Wickliffe City School Dist*	12	114
Thomas, Keith/*Midwest Reg Ed Service Center*	2	120
Thomas, Mark/*Bloom-Carroll Local Sch Dist*	73,76,295	63
Thomas, Natalie/*Ontario Local School Dist*	273	173
Thomas, Roberta/*Cincinnati City School Dist*	30	87
Thomas, Tami/*North Baltimore Local Sch Dist*	67	217
Thomas, Tony/*Northmont City School Dist*	1,11,288	152
Thomas, Trevor, Dr/*Heath City School Dist*	1	117
Thomassetti, Cynthia/*Ashtabula Area City Sch Dist*	8,11,58,69,74,79,81	12
Thomeier, Daniel/*Wickliffe City School Dist*	67	114
Thompkins, Adrian/*Batavia Local School Dist*	4	29
Thompson, Angela/*Kings Local School Dist*	81	207
Thompson, Brandi/*Riverside Local School Dist*	73	121
Thompson, Cameron/*Millcreek-West Unity Local SD*	286	215
Thompson, Christopher/*Talawanda School Dist*	69	24
Thompson, Cory/*Lorain Co Joint Voc Sch Dist*	2	125
Thompson, Diane/*St Clairsville-Richland CSD*	11,58,296,298	18
Thompson, Dwayne/*Piqua City School Dist*	1	146
Thompson, Greg/*Beavercreek City School Dist*	3,5,71,91	83
Thompson, Heather/*Western Local School Dist*	8,280,286,288	164
Thompson, Jack, Dr/*Perry Local School Dist*	1	113
Thompson, Jackie/*Warrensville Heights City SD*	4	51
Thompson, Jane/*Tipp City Exempted Village SD*	5	146
Thompson, Janet/*Jackson Local School Dist*	73,76	186
Thompson, Jeffrey/*Mt Gilead Exempted Village SD*	1	155
Thompson, Jennie/*Fairfield City School Dist*	9	21
Thompson, Karen/*Cleveland Metro School Dist*	751	42
Thompson, Kelly/*Conneaut Area City Sch Dist*	5	12
Thompson, Lauren/*Noble Local School Dist*	7	158
Thompson, Lori/*Milton-Union Exempted Vlg SD*	7,83,85	145
Thompson, Melissa/*South Euclid-Lyndhurst City SD*	7,79,90	51
Thompson, Miguel/*Fredericktown Local Sch Dist*	11,78	111
Thompson, Pamela/*Northridge Local School Dist*	58,77	152
Thompson, Rhonda/*Brookfield Local School Dist*	3,5	197
Thompson, Ryan/*Triad Local School Dist*	16,73,295	26
Thompson, Steve/*Willoughby-Eastlake City SD*	1	114
Thompson, Teresa/*Fredericktown Local Sch Dist*	4	111
Thompson, Tim/*Hamilton-Clermont Co-op OCA*	295	32
Thompson, Traci/*Millcreek-West Unity Local SD*	2,19	215
Thompson, Wayne/*Big Walnut Local School Dist*	73,286	58
Thomson, Erica/*Minford Local School Dist*	38,69,88	178
Thorbahn, Jon/*Ottoville Local School Dist*	10	170
Thoren, Tim/*Southern Local School Dist*	79	143
Thornburg, Pam/*Miami Trace Local School Dist*	93	65
Thorndike, Sandra/*Austintown Local School Dist*	58	133
Thornsberry, Anthony/*Massillon City School Dist*	31	187
Thornsberry, Matt/*Union Scioto Local Sch Dist*	1	175
Thornsberry, Nancy/*Chillicothe City School Dist*	280	174
Thornton, Carolyn/*Mason City School Dist*	5	208
Thornton, Tony/*Monroe Local School Dist*	73,76,84	23
Thorp, Lance/*Montpelier Exempted Village SD*	12	215
Thorp, Sue/*Montpelier Exempted Village SD*	286	215
Tibbels, Rose/*Danbury Local School Dist*	37,69,83	159
Tibbs, Patsy/*Lebanon City School Dist*	4	207
Tibbs, Vickie/*Sebring Local School Dist*	83,85	135
Ticconetti, Jaimie/*Southeast Local School Dist*	58	213
Tidwell, Meaghan/*Indian Lake Local School Dist*	58	121
Tilford, Rachel/*Little Miami Local School Dist*	4	208
Tillis, Beverly/*Lawrence Co Ed Service Center*	8	115
Timberlake, Julia/*Kettering City School Dist*	93	150
Timmerman, Marla/*Little Miami Local School Dist*	79	208
Timmerman, Mike/*Minster Local School Dist*	3	15
Timmons, Bob/*Polaris Joint Voc School Dist*	1,11	49
Timmons, Curtis/*Cleveland Metro School Dist*	73,76,84,97,295	42
Tincher, Steve/*Clark-Shawnee Local Sch Dist*	6	27
Tingelstad, Rachell/*Cedar Cliff Local School Dist*	31	84
Tingle, Jay/*Ridgewood Local School Dist*	2	37
Tinker, Alysia/*Windham Exempted Vlg Sch Dist*	58	167
Tinker, Todd/*Chillicothe City School Dist*	93	174
Tipton, Chris/*New Lebanon Local School Dist*	27,31,36	151
Tipton, Eric/*Northeastern Local School Dist*	27,31,88	57
Tirey, Kathy/*Hamilton Co Ed Service Center*	34	87

School Year 2019-2020   800-333-8802   **OH-T55**

DISTRICT PERSONNEL INDEX

Market Data Retrieval

NAME/District	JOB FUNCTIONS	PAGE
Tirey, Kathy/Hamilton County ESC	34	97
Titus, Megan/McDonald Local School Dist	2	199
Toadvine, Dale/Miamisburg City School Dist	67	151
Tobe, Megan/Leipsic Local School Dist	58,79,285,298	170
Tobias, Dave/Covington Exempted Village SD	35	145
Tobin, Kevin/Lake Local School Dist	1	186
Tobin, Lisa/Auglaize Co Ed Service Center	8	15
Todd, Amy/Piqua City School Dist	57,58,68,79,81	146
Todd, Jeffrey/Worthington School Dist	6	75
Todoroff, Denise/Indian Creek Local Sch Dist	2	109
Toledo, Cyndi/Canal Winchester Local SD	8,69,273	66
Toler, Donis, Dr/Princeton City School Dist	68	92
Tom, Mitch/Licking Heights Local Sch Dist	11,57,58,79,296	118
Tomashefski, Kim/Medina Co Sch Educl Svcs Ctr	74	142
Tomashefski, Kimberly/Ed Svc Center of Medina Co	68	139
Tomasheski, Tom/Midview Local School Dist	67	125
Tomkins, Becky/Ross Local School Dist	8,11,31,271,296	24
Tommelleo, Andrew, Dr/State Support Team-Region 5	27	137
Tompkins, Laura/Zanesville City School Dist	8	157
Toms, Kevin/Sandusky City School Dist	3,91	61
Tonathy, Joan/Barberton City School Dist	37	192
Tontimonia, Lori/Ravenna School Dist	4	166
Toole, Eric/Georgetown Exempted Village SD	2	19
Toole, Lisa/Adams Co Ohio Valley Sch Dist	9,37,72,273,288	6
Topper, Pat/North Canton City School Dist	16	187
Toppin, Kelly/Stow-Munroe Falls City SD	67	194
Torbert, Jolynn/Licking Valley Local Sch Dist	2,19	118
Torbert, Melvina/South-Western City School Dist	11,296,298	73
Tornes, Kathy/Delaware Joint Voc Sch Dist	38,83,88	59
Tornow, Mike/Portage Co Ed Service Center	58,81	164
Torrence, Dan/Federal Hocking Local Sch Dist	67	14
Torres, Denise/Southeast Local School Dist	4	166
Toth, David/Crestwood Local School Dist	1	165
Toth, Julia/New Richmond Exempted Vlg SD	2	31
Toth, Richard/Bay Village City School Dist	16,82	40
Towery, Margaret/South-Western City School Dist	16,20,23,39,48,61	73
Townsend, Andrea/Greenville City School Dist	2,27,58	55
Townsend, Andrea/West Carrollton City Sch Dist	1	153
Townsend, Robin/Ridgedale Local School Dist	5	138
Trace, Mark/Whitehall City School Dist	15,68,79	75
Trachsel, Lori/Sandy Valley Local School Dist	16	189
Tracy, Andrea/Auburn Vocational School Dist	30	112
Tracy, Chris/Loveland City School Dist	4	90
Traina, Joseph/Wellsville Local Sch Dist	3	36
Traphagen, Denise/Twinsburg City School Dist	7,58,77,79,93,274,275	195
Traubert, David/Cincinnati City School Dist	39	87
Travers, Jeff/Butler Tech Career Dev Schs	30	21
Travis, Robert/Medina City School Dist	5	141
Traxler, Lori/Pandora Gilboa Local Sch Dist	13,16,82	170
Traxler, Ty/Elmwood Local School Dist	6	216
Trego, Albert/Keystone Local School Dist	3	124
Trego, Michael/Educational Serv Ctr-Ctl Ohio	15	65
Treharn, Terri/Rootstown Local School Dist	8,15,69,273,274,288	166
Trendent, Andrea/Champion Local School Dist	16,73	197
Tresey, Patricia, Dr/Madison Local School Dist	34,57,58,88,90,275	172
Trew, Mary/Cuyahoga Vly Career Ctr Voc SD	30	45
Trick, Andy/Centerville City School Dist	5	148
Trill, Tyler/Bexley City School Dist	71	66
Trimble-Oliver, Sarah/Cincinnati City School Dist	73,98	87
Trimble-Oliver, Sarah/Cincinnati City School Dist	2,73,76,98,286,295	87
Trimmer, Kristin/Cambridge City School Dist	38	86
Triner, Christopher/North Canton City School Dist	20	187
Triplett, Matt/Bradford Exempted Village SD	10,288	145
Triplett, Matt/Mapleton Local School Dist	73,295	11
Triplitt, Matt/Parkway Local School Dist	6	144
Tripney, Lisa/Portage Lakes Joint Voc SD	27,286	189
Trisler, Rich/Caldwell Exempted Village SD	3	158
Troendly, Anne/East Muskingum Local Sch Dist	8,11	156
Trogdon, Sandi/Rittman Exempted Village SD	73	213
Trostle, Doug/Troy City School Dist	67	146
Trotter, Andy/United Local School Dist	9	36
Trousdell, Karen/New Miami Local School Dist	4	23
Troyer, Jennifer/Southeast Local School Dist	36	213
Troyer, Rebekah/West Liberty-Salem Local SD	11	26
True, Allie/Belpre City School Dist	8,73,296	209
Truett, Karen/Upper Arlington City Sch Dist	71	74
Truex, Adam/Ohio Mid-Eastern RESA	15	110
Truex, Cindy/Clear Fork Vly Local Sch Dist	38,69,83,85	171
Trujillo, Andy/Strongsville City School Dist	58,79	51
Truman, Michelle/Lynchburg-Clay Local Sch Dist	35	103
Trumpower, Chastity/Canton City School Dist	34,58,81	184
Trumpower, Loann/Ncocc-N Ctrl Ohio Co-op CA	79	174
Trurett, Jesse/Grandview Heights City SD	67	71
Trusty, Alvin/Liberty-Benton Local Sch Dist	73,295	98
Trusty, Angie/Arcadia Local School Dist	16	97
Tucci, Dave/Brown Local School Dist	6	25
Tucker, Chad/Midview Local School Dist	5	125
Tucker, Douglas/Stark Co Area Voc Sch Dist	3	189
Tucker, Judy/Northwest Ohio Ed Tech	15,16,74	218
Tucker, Mary/Bethel-Tate Local School Dist	58,298	30
Tudor, Gabe/Wadsworth City School Dist	15	141
Tuite, Michelle/Tiffin City School Dist	8,11,83,88,288,298	181
Tullio, John/Canfield Local School Dist	8	134
Tully, Jeff/Twin Valley Cmty Local SD	3,5	169
Tults, Luke/Trotwood-Madison City SD	295	153
Turco, Shelli/Ross Local School Dist	7,85	24
Turk, James/Lgca-Lake Geauga Ohio OCA	1	115
Turner, Michael/Cincinnati City School Dist	27	87
Turner, Rick/Vantage Career Center Sch Dist	1	206
Turney, Vanisa/Huber Heights City School Dist	8,11,70,288,296	150
Tussey, Lisa/Fayetteville Perry Local SD	2	19
Tuttle-Huff, Lisa/U S Grant Career School Dist	11	31
Tuttle, Phillip/Keystone Local School Dist	273	124
Tuttle, Tom/Mentor Exempted Village SD	67	113
Tuttlehuff, Lisa/Madison Local School Dist	1	23
Twinem, John/Louisville City School Dist	6	186
Tyler, Mark/Hamilton Local School Dist	1	71
Tyo, Nicole/South-Western City School Dist	58	73
Tyre, Zach/Miami East Local School Dist	73	145
Tyson, Sherry/Coventry Local School Dist	2	192

U

NAME/District	JOB FUNCTIONS	PAGE
Uehlin, Eneida/Cincinnati City School Dist	57	87
Uher, Joseph/Delaware City School Dist	9	58
Uhlir, Laurie/Mayfield City School Dist	71	47
Uhrig, Kyle/Circleville City School Dist	57,58,88,285	162
Uhrig, Laura/Union Scioto Local Sch Dist	67	175
Ulm, Ken/Butler Co Ed Service Center	2	20
Ulrich, Eric/Niles City School Dist	73	200
Ulrich, Pam/Tecumseh Local School Dist	274	28
Unangst, Eric/Woodridge Local School Dist	73,76,84,286,295	195
Underwood, Angela/Ohio Mid-Eastern RESA	1	110
Underwood, Kelley/Hamilton-Clermont Co-op OCA	73	32
Underwood, Michelle/Upper Scioto Valley Local SD	16,31,36,69	100
Underwood, Robert/Indian Lake Local School Dist	1,11	121
Unger, Vicki/Twin Valley Cmty Local SD	7	169
Unverferth, Tony/Vantage Career Center Sch Dist	68	206
Unversaw, Alleyn/Warren Co Ed Service Center	2	206
Unversaw, Kristin/Blanchester Local School Dist	58,298	32
Updegrove, Marlinda/Three Rivers Local School Dist	4	94
Updike, Timothy/Gallia-Jackson-Vinton JVSD	5	80
Upthegrove, Ken/Washington Court House City SD	67	65
Urbaniak, Heath/Cambridge City School Dist	4	86
Urso, Andrea/Windham Exempted Vlg Sch Dist	31	167

---

1 Superintendent	16 Instructional Media Svcs	30 Adult Education	44 Science Sec	58 Special Education K-12	72 Summer School	88 Alternative/At Risk	277 Remedial Math K-12	
2 Bus/Finance/Purchasing	17 Chief Operations Officer	31 Career/Sch-to-Work K-12	45 Math K-12	59 Special Education Elem	73 Instructional Tech	89 Multi-Cultural Curriculum	280 Literacy Coach	
3 Buildings And Grounds	18 Chief Academic Officer	32 Career/Sch-to-Work Elem	46 Math Elem	60 Special Education Sec	74 Inservice Training	90 Social Work	285 STEM	
4 Food Service	19 Chief Financial Officer	33 Career/Sch-to-Work Sec	47 Math Sec	61 Foreign/World Lang K-12	75 Marketing/Distributive	91 Safety/Security	286 Digital Learning	
5 Transportation	20 Art K-12	34 Early Childhood Ed	48 English/Lang Arts K-12	62 Foreign/World Lang Elem	76 Info Systems	92 Magnet School	288 Common Core Standards	
6 Athletic	21 Art Elem	35 Health/Phys Education	49 English/Lang Arts Elem	63 Foreign/World Lang Sec	77 Psychological Assess	93 Parental Involvement	294 Accountability	
7 Health Services	22 Art Sec	36 Guidance Services K-12	50 English/Lang Arts Sec	64 Religious Education K-12	78 Affirmative Action	95 Tech Prep Program	295 Network System	
8 Curric/Instruct K-12	23 Music K-12	37 Guidance Services Elem	51 Reading K-12	65 Religious Education Elem	79 Student Personnel	97 Chief Information Officer	296 Title II Programs	
9 Curric/Instruct Elem	24 Music Elem	38 Guidance Services Sec	52 Reading Elem	66 Religious Education Sec	80 Driver Ed/Safety	98 Chief Technology Officer	297 Webmaster	
10 Curric/Instruct Sec	25 Music Sec	39 Social Studies K-12	53 Reading Sec	67 School Board President	81 Gifted/Talented	270 Character Education	298 Grant Writer/Ptnrships	
11 Federal Program	26 Business Education	40 Social Studies Elem	54 Remedial Reading K-12	68 Teacher Personnel	82 Video Services	271 Migrant Education	750 Chief Innovation Officer	
12 Title I	27 Career & Tech Ed	41 Social Studies Sec	55 Remedial Reading Elem	69 Academic Assessment	83 Substance Abuse Prev	273 Teacher Mentor	751 Chief of Staff	
13 Title V	28 Technology Education	42 Science K-12	56 Remedial Reading Sec	70 Research/Development	84 Erate	274 Before/After Sch	752 Social Emotional Learning	
15 Asst Superintendent	29 Family/Consumer Science	43 Science Elem	57 Bilingual/ELL	71 Public Information	85 AIDS Education	275 Response To Intervention		

OH-T56

Ohio School Directory
DISTRICT PERSONNEL INDEX

NAME/District	JOB FUNCTIONS	PAGE
Urso, Chris/*Middletown City School Dist*	67	23
Ute, Douglas/*Newark City School Dist*	1	119
Utsinger, Joel/*Ironton City School Dist*	73	116
Utter, Michelle/*Felicity-Franklin Local SD*	4	30
Utterback, Vince/*Pickerington Local School Dist*	2	64

V

NAME/District	JOB FUNCTIONS	PAGE
Vaccariello, Mike/*Madison Local School Dist*	2	112
Vail, David, Dr/*Miamisburg City School Dist*	1	151
Valdares, Julio/*Licking Co Ed Service Center*	2	117
Valenti, Angie/*Valley View Local School Dist*	67	153
Valentine, Terry/*Norwayne Local School Dist*	3,5	212
Valenza, Karen/*South Euclid-Lyndhurst City SD*	8	51
Valenzuela, Rita/*Whitehall City School Dist*	37	75
Valerio, Denise/*Medina Co Sch Educl Svcs Ctr*	73	142
Valkosky, Missy/*Ohio Mid-Eastern RESA*	2	110
Vallance, Tom/*Wheelersburg Local School Dist*	73,295	180
Vamundio, Martin/*North Baltimore Local Sch Dist*	57	217
Van Dyke, Christina/*Tolles Career & Tech Sch Dist*	16	133
Van Horn, Jeanne/*Wapakoneta City School Dist*	7	16
Van Leeuwen, Colleen/*Lisbon Exempted Village SD*	16	35
Van Ness, Veronica/*Put-In-Bay Local School Dist*	8,288	159
Van Wey, Kimberly/*Eastwood Muskingum Local Sch Dist*	73,76	156
Vanalmen, Marilyn/*Canton City School Dist*	30	184
VanBuskirk, Robin/*ADA Exempted Village Sch Dist*	8,11,288	99
Vance, Jaqueline/*Keystone Local School Dist*	57,58	124
Vancura, Jason/*Field Local School Dist*	2,3,5,37,91	165
Vancuren, Laura/*Pickaway-Ross Co JT Voc SD*	1	175
Vanek, Debora/*Parma City School Dist*	69,76,288	49
Vanek, Luann/*Elmwood Local School Dist*	2	216
Vanek, Rick/*Parma City School Dist*	91	49
VanGorder, Alison/*Perry Local School Dist*	1	9
VanHorn, Ben/*Great Oaks Career Campuses*	2,11	89
Varansky, Derek/*Tuscarawas Valley Local SD*	8,11	203
Varbanova, Milena/*Mason City School Dist*	57	208
Varda, David/*Meta Solutions*	2	139
Varga, Kelly/*Rootstown Local School Dist*	5	166
Vargas, Mutsimi/*Fairborn City School Dist*	57	84
Vargo, Tom/*Jonathan Alder Local Sch Dist*	6	132
Varn, Ron/*North Canton City School Dist*	23	187
Vasher, Eva/*Otsego Local School Dist*	3,5	217
Vassalotti, Joseph/*Akron Public Schools*	6,35	190
Vaughn, Anna Marie/*Columbiana Co Ed Service Ctr*	1	33
Vaughn, Kevin/*Springfield Local School Dist*	6	194
Vaughn, Melinda/*Newark City School Dist*	58,275	119
Vaughn, Robert/*Cuyahoga Falls City Sch Dist*	82	192
Vaughn, Shelley/*Mercer Co Ed Service Center*	1,11	143
Veach, Dee-Anna/*Minford Local School Dist*	16	178
Velchek, Andrew/*Mahoning Co Ed Service Center*	16,73,295	133
Venderlic, Cody/*Marietta City School Dist*	6	210
Vennekotter, Eric/*Pandora Gilboa Local Sch Dist*	84,295	170
Vennekotter, Eric/*Pandora Gilboa Local Sch Dist*	73	170
Vent, Laurie/*Upper Sandusky Exempted Vlg SD*	1,11	219
Venters, Andy/*Tipp City Exempted Village SD*	67	146
Ventresco, Thomas/*Austintown Local School Dist*	73,295	133
Veon, Ken, Dr/*Beachwood City School Dist*	15,28,76	40
Verba, James/*Brooklyn City School Dist*	6	41
Veres, Diane/*North Central Local Sch Dist*	38,69,83	215
Verhelst, Bob/*Sylvania City School Dist*	7,57,79,91	128
Verhest, Kathleen/*Brunswick City School Dist*	73,76	140
Verhest, Rob/*Berea City School Dist*	3,91	41
Verhoff, Nicholas/*Columbus Grove Local Sch Dist*	1	169
Verlingo, Micheal/*North Ridgeville City Sch Dist*	2,84	125
Vermillion, Marlene/*ADA Exempted Village Sch Dist*	7	99
Vermillion, Teresa/*Elgin Local School Dist*	4	138
Vernell, Vera/*Allen East Local School Dist*	4	7
Vesco, Courtney/*Tuscarawas Valley Local SD*	69	203
Vesey, Jason/*Pickaway-Ross Co JT Voc SD*	294	175
Via, Jeanie/*Newton Local School Dist*	5	146
Vicich, Caren/*Kenston Local School Dist*	68	82
Vickers, Jeff/*River View Local School Dist*	58	37
Videll, Veronica/*Strasburg Franklin Local SD*	67	203
Viebranz, Greg/*Westerville City School Dist*	71	74
Villareal, Donna/*Ohio Department of Education*	57	1
Villinger, Esther/*Heath City School Dist*	7	117
Vilsack, Kathy/*Trumbull Co Ed Service Center*	58	196

NAME/District	JOB FUNCTIONS	PAGE
Vince, Stacey/*State Support Team-Region 2*	34	126
Violi, Brian/*Maplewood JT Voc School Dist*	67	166
Violi, Brian/*Streetsboro City School Dist*	67	167
Vipperman, Steve Vipperm/*Willard City School Dist*	36	106
Virost, Raymond/*Georgetown Exempted Village SD*	67	20
Viscounte, Toni/*Access*	67	137
Viscounte, Toni/*Sebring Local School Dist*	1,11,57	135
Visnic, Melissa/*Shadyside Local School Dist*	2	18
Visnjic, Mirka/*Canal Winchester Local SD*	57	66
Vitale, Nicole/*Cleveland Metro School Dist*	8,34	42
Vitto, John/*Canfield Local School Dist*	11,58,81,88,298	134
Vivo, Tracy/*Youngstown City School Dist*	20	136
Vlachos, Joe/*North College Hill City SD*	73,76	91
Vogel, Teresa/*Fostoria City School Dist*	36	180
Vogelmann, Robb/*Lakota Local School Dist*	15	22
Voges, Bret/*Arcadia Local School Dist*	5	97
Vogh, Aaron/*Salem City School Dist*	295	35
Voight, Amy/*Massillon City School Dist*	4	187
Vojta, Melissa/*North Royalton City Sch Dist*	8,69,288,294	48
Vollborn, Beth/*Gallipolis City School Dist*	2	81
Vollnogle, Carol/*East Palestine City Sch Dist*	11,58,298	35
Volosin, William/*Aurora City School Dist*	2	164
Volschow, Susan/*Eastwood Local School Dist*	5	216
Volz, Tricia/*Lexington Local School Dist*	4	172
Von Gunten, Mike/*Firelands Local School Dist*	1	124
Vonderembse, Daniel/*Putnam Co Ed Service Center*	77,79	169
Vonhandorf, Dan/*Kettering City School Dist*	8,12,15,16,57,288	150
Vonsossan, Kelly/*Ottawa-Glandorf Local Sch Dist*	16	170
Voorhees, Greg/*East Liverpool City Sch Dist*	6	35
Vorhies, Melissa/*New London Local School Dist*	58,79	106
Vorst, Beth/*Cory-Rawson Local School Dist*	16,37	97
Voskuhl, Mitch/*Coldwater Exempted Village SD*	3	143
Voss, Amanda/*Liberty Center Local Sch Dist*	77	101
Voss, Michael/*New Albany-Plain Local SD*	73	72
Votaw, Steve/*Jonathan Alder Local Sch Dist*	67	132
Vousden, Ab/*West Muskingum Local Sch Dist*	67	157
Vtrup, Melissa/*Minster Local School Dist*	38,83	15

W

NAME/District	JOB FUNCTIONS	PAGE
Wachovec, John/*Summit Co Ed Service Center*	27	190
Wackerly, Doug/*Brown Local School Dist*	3	25
Waddlef, Geoff/*Crestview Local School Dist*	3	205
Wade-Lyles, Terri, Dr/*Cleveland Metro School Dist*	43,285	42
Wade, Lisa/*Riverside Local School Dist*	16,82	114
Wade, Patty/*Ironton City School Dist*	2,19	116
Wade, Tiffany/*Fairfield Union Local Sch Dist*	58	63
Wade, William/*Kirtland Local School Dist*	1	112
Waesch, Amanda/*Rootstown Local School Dist*	67	166
Waesch, Keith/*Rootstown Local School Dist*	6	166
Waggoner, Michael/*Vinton Co Local School Dist*	15	206
Waggy, Corrina/*Upper Sandusky Exempted Vlg SD*	88	219
Wagler, Angela/*Norton City School Dist*	73,76,286,295	193
Wagner-Feasel, Julie/*Delaware Joint Voc Sch Dist*	67	59
Wagner, Andrea/*Leipsic Local School Dist*	57	170
Wagner, Becky/*Amanda-Clearcreek Local SD*	11	62
Wagner, Jennifer/*Cincinnati City School Dist*	2,19	87
Wagner, Krista/*Mad River Local School Dist*	15	151
Wagner, Lisa/*Wolf Creek Local School Dist*	13,16,73,82,295	211
Wagner, Mark/*Rocky River City School Dist*	6	50
Wagner, Matt/*Bethel-Tate Local School Dist*	11,52	30
Wagner, Mike/*Woco-W Ohio Computer Org*	295	183
Wagner, Mitzi/*Perry Local School Dist*	5	188
Wagner, Philip, Dr/*Licking Heights Local Sch Dist*	1	118
Wagner, Tim/*Three Rivers Local School Dist*	5	94
Wagner, William, Dr/*Fairview Park City Sch Dist*	1	46
Wagoner, Katrina/*Eastern Local School Dist*	9	7
Wagoner, Kris/*Eastwood Local School Dist*	3	216
Wagonrod, Karen/*Wayne Trace Local School Dist*	4	160
Waidelich, Greg/*North Central Local Sch Dist*	6,11	215
Wake, Scott/*Goshen Local School Dist*	6	30
Walders, Kristi/*Logan-Hocking Local Sch Dist*	34	104
Waldvogel, Jason/*Pettisville Local School Dist*	9	79
Walendzak, Christie/*Bowling Green City Sch Dist*	58	216
Walkden, Beverly/*Greeneview Local School Dist*	8,69,273,288	84
Walker, Aaron/*Waterloo Local School Dist*	9	167
Walker, Brandon/*Symmes Valley Local Sch Dist*	6	117

School Year 2019-2020 800-333-8802 **OH-T57**

DISTRICT PERSONNEL INDEX

Market Data Retrieval

NAME/District	JOB FUNCTIONS	PAGE
Walker, Curtis, Dr/Akron Public Schools	67	190
Walker, Deedee/Little Miami Local School Dist	58,85	208
Walker, Gary/Fairborn City School Dist	7,36,68,69,79,88	84
Walker, Heather/Portsmouth City School Dist	35,83	179
Walker, Jessica/Hillsboro City School Dist	4	103
Walker, Joyce/Wadsworth City School Dist	58,79	141
Walker, Karl/Buckeye Local School Dist	16,73	140
Walker, Kelly/Marysville Exempted Village SD	274	204
Walker, Kelly/Marysville Exempted Village SD	274	204
Walker, Laurence/Edon Northwest Local Sch Dist	6	215
Walker, Paul/Shelby City School Dist	8,11,275,280,288,296,298	173
Walker, Robert/Ohio Hi-Point Joint Voc SD	3	121
Walker, Roy/Hilliard City School Dist	68,78	71
Walker, Ryan/Marysville Exempted Village SD	2,91	204
Walker, Sarah/Amherst Exempted Village SD	11,34,58	122
Walker, Susan/Stow-Munroe Falls City SD	298	194
Walker, Tim/North Canton City School Dist	6	187
Walker, Trudy/Canton City School Dist	16,73,76,295	184
Walkup, Craig/Cloverleaf Local School Dist	6	140
Wallace, Barbara/Westerville City School Dist	9,34,92	74
Wallace, Brian/Sycamore Cmty School Dist	68	93
Wallace, Dawn/Eastern Local School Dist	11,34,58,61,69,81,298	7
Wallace, Deborah/Nordonia Hills City Sch Dist	29,83,88	193
Wallace, Janis/Huron City School Dist	7,83,85	60
Walling, Marwin/Painesville City Local SD	6	113
Wallis, David/Cuyahoga Heights Local SD	73	45
Walls-Waller, Toby/Pickaway-Ross Co JT Voc SD	38	175
Walls, Brenda/Waverly City School Dist	16	164
Walls, Donn/Woco-W Ohio Computer Org	1,73	183
Walls, Jim/Lynchburg-Clay Local Sch Dist	58	103
Walsh, John/Groveport Madison Local SD	2	71
Walter, Dennis/Keystone Local School Dist	67	124
Walter, Eric/Triway Local School Dist	67	213
Walters, Erik/Auburn Vocational School Dist	67	112
Walters, Katie/Mississinawa Valley Sch Dist	4	56
Walters, Shirley/Eastern Local School Dist	57	163
Walther, Sam/Leipsic Local School Dist	3,67	170
Waltz, Perry/Cambridge City School Dist	77	86
Wank, Michael/Carey Exempted Village SD	1	219
Wank, Renee/Defiance City School Dist	37	57
Wannemacher, Rob/New Lebanon Local School Dist	2,84	151
Wanyerka, Nancy/Cuyahoga Heights Local SD	56	45
Warchol, Joe/Columbiana Co Ed Service Ctr	73,295	33
Ward, Amy/Louisville City School Dist	77	186
Ward, Angela/Eastland-Ffld Career Tech VSD	30	70
Ward, Chris/Columbus City School Dist	91	67
Ward, Christopher/Columbus City School Dist	91	67
Ward, Denise/United Local School Dist	16,82	36
Ward, Hilary/Northmor Local School Dist	83,88	156
Ward, Janet/Southington Local School Dist	2	200
Ward, Karling/Ontario Local School Dist	58	173
Ward, Kristie/Ashland City School Dist	4	10
Ward, Lori/Cleveland Metro School Dist	68	42
Ward, Marie, Dr/Fairfield Co Ed Service Center	1	62
Ward, Paul/Diocese of Steubenville Ed Off	1,11	110
Ward, Ron/Hillsboro City School Dist	5	103
Ward, Victoria/Danbury Local School Dist	38,69	159
Ware, Wendy/Bellaire Local School Dist	79	17
Warger, Carrie/National Trail Local Sch Dist	2,19	168
Wargo, Jeff/Marysville Exempted Village SD	3	204
Warmack, Gerald/Finneytown Local School Dist	6	89
Warnecke, Rob/Jennings Local School Dist	16,73,295	169
Warner, Andrew/Margaretta Local School Dist	67	61
Warner, Dack/Sparcc	73	190
Warner, Jeff/Groveport Madison Local SD	71	71
Warner, Margaret/Willoughby-Eastlake City SD	67	114
Warnicke, Margaret/Perkins Local School Dist	36,83	61
Warnike, Jackie/Port Clinton City School Dist	274	159
Warniment, Larry/Toledo Public Schools	30	129
Warnock, Nancy/Greeneview Local School Dist	7,88	84
Warnock, Todd/Clay Local School Dist	1	178
Warren, Deb/Washington Local School Dist	4	130
Warren, Jane/Northeastern Local School Dist	36	27
Warren, Kelsey/Sycamore Cmty School Dist	4	93
Warren, Natalie/Rolling Hills Local Sch Dist	285	86
Warren, Rich/New Lexington School Dist	8,11,58,88,286,296,298	161
Warren, Theresa/Princeton City School Dist	58	92
Warriner, Anne/Fostoria City School Dist	12	180
Washburn, Rodney/Vandalia Butler City Sch Dist	67	153
Wasil, Todd/Brecksville Broadview Hts CSD	16	41
Wass, Kendal/Clyde-Green Spgs Exmpt Vlg SD	58,77	176
Wasser, Michael/Warren City School Dist	2,91	200
Wasserbauer, Tina/Rocky River City School Dist	4	50
Wasserbeck, Bev/North Union Local School Dist	4	204
Wasserbeck, Bev/Ridgemont Local School Dist	4	100
Wasserman, Tammy/Old Fort Local School Dist	12	181
Watercutter, Stephanie/Jackson Center Local Sch Dist	9	183
Waterhouse, Michelle/Pickerington Local School Dist	67	64
Waterman, Kimberly/New Knoxville Local Sch Dist	1,11	16
Watkins, Mike/Sidney City School Dist	2	183
Watkins, Steve/Dalton Local School Dist	8,11,288,298	212
Watson, Bev/New Lexington School Dist	57	161
Watson, Jason/Northmont City School Dist	3,5,91	152
Watson, Keith/River View Local School Dist	23	37
Watt, Mike/Wapakoneta City School Dist	2,3,5,16,27,91	16
Watts, Cory/Pymatuning Valley Local SD	73,295	13
Waugh, Kelly/Wellston City School Dist	7,83,88	108
Waugh, Pamela/Wauseon Exempted Village SD	5	79
Wayland, Lisa/Adena Local School Dist	9	174
Wayne, Dianna/Washington Court House City SD	9	65
Wayner, Dan/Riverside Local School Dist	3,91	114
Weathers, Veonta/Euclid City School Dist	68	46
Weaver, Angela/Franklin-Monroe Local Sch Dist	4	55
Weaver, Bonnie/Fremont City School Dist	57	176
Weaver, Chris/New Philadelphia City Sch Dist	67	203
Weaver, Christopher/Kettering City School Dist	6	150
Weaver, Shirley/Triad Local School Dist	4	26
Weaver, Tammie/Springfield City School Dist	5	28
Webb, Bradley/Ross Local School Dist	34,58,88,270	175
Webb, Brian/Hardin Northern Local Sch Dist	3	100
Webb, Chris/Pleasant Local School Dist	38,69,83,85	138
Webb, David/Ironton City School Dist	3	116
Webb, Jack/Symmes Valley Local Sch Dist	2	117
Webb, Kay/New Knoxville Local Sch Dist	6	16
Webb, Mimi, Dr/St Bernard-Elmwood Place Schs	1	93
Webb, Peggy/Northmor Local School Dist	81	156
Webb, Tammy/Ashland City School Dist	58,79,275	10
Weber, Alexis/Austintown Local School Dist	4	133
Weber, Beth/Sycamore Cmty School Dist	2,76	93
Weber, Edward/Wellington Exempted Village SD	1	126
Weber, Robert/Ottoville Local School Dist	2	170
Weber, Tim/Wyoming City School Dist	1	94
Weber, Timothy/Tiffin City School Dist	73,76,84	181
Weber, Warren/Newark City School Dist	67	119
Weber, Zach/Pandora Gilboa Local Sch Dist	5,6	170
Webken, Cindy/Kalida Local School Dist	2	169
Weekley, Amy/Clear Fork Vly Local Sch Dist	67	171
Weese, April/South-Western City School Dist	35,42,45	73
Wegener, Kelly/Sycamore Cmty School Dist	8,12	93
Wegley, Kelly/Worthington School Dist	72	75
Wehrley, Vicki/Newton Local School Dist	7	146
Weidlich, Jonathan/Great Oaks Career Campuses	71	89
Weidrick, Jody/Ed Service Center Lorain Co	11	122
Weigand, Cheri/Cloverleaf Local School Dist	16	140

#		#		#		#		#		#	
1	Superintendent	16	Instructional Media Svcs	30	Adult Education	44	Science Sec	58	Special Education K-12	72	Summer School
2	Bus/Finance/Purchasing	17	Chief Operations Officer	31	Career/Sch-to-Work K-12	45	Math K-12	59	Special Education Elem	73	Instructional Tech
3	Buildings And Grounds	18	Chief Academic Officer	32	Career/Sch-to-Work Elem	46	Math Elem	60	Special Education Sec	74	Inservice Training
4	Food Service	19	Chief Financial Officer	33	Career/Sch-to-Work Sec	47	Math Sec	61	Foreign/World Lang K-12	75	Marketing/Distributive
5	Transportation	20	Art K-12	34	Early Childhood Ed	48	English/Lang Arts K-12	62	Foreign/World Lang Elem	76	Info Systems
6	Athletic	21	Art Elem	35	Health/Phys Education	49	English/Lang Arts Elem	63	Foreign/World Lang Sec	77	Psychological Assess
7	Health Services	22	Art Sec	36	Guidance Services K-12	50	English/Lang Arts Sec	64	Religious Education K-12	78	Affirmative Action
8	Curric/Instruct K-12	23	Music K-12	37	Guidance Services Elem	51	Reading K-12	65	Religious Education Elem	79	Student Personnel
9	Curric/Instruct Elem	24	Music Elem	38	Guidance Services Sec	52	Reading Elem	66	Religious Education Sec	80	Driver Ed/Safety
10	Curric/Instruct Sec	25	Music Sec	39	Social Studies K-12	53	Reading Sec	67	School Board President	81	Gifted/Talented
11	Federal Program	26	Business Education	40	Social Studies Elem	54	Remedial Reading K-12	68	Teacher Personnel	82	Video Services
12	Title I	27	Career & Tech Ed	41	Social Studies Sec	55	Remedial Reading Elem	69	Academic Assessment	83	Substance Abuse Prev
13	Title V	28	Technology Education	42	Science K-12	56	Remedial Reading Sec	70	Research/Development	84	Erate
15	Asst Superintendent	29	Family/Consumer Science	43	Science Elem	57	Bilingual/ELL	71	Public Information	85	AIDS Education

#		#	
88	Alternative/At Risk	277	Remedial Math K-12
89	Multi-Cultural Curriculum	280	Literacy Coach
90	Social Work	285	STEM
91	Safety/Security	286	Digital Learning
92	Magnet School	288	Common Core Standards
93	Parental Involvement	294	Accountability
95	Tech Prep Program	295	Network System
97	Chief Infomation Officer	296	Title II Programs
98	Chief Technology Officer	297	Webmaster
270	Character Education	298	Grant Writer/Ptnrshps
271	Migrant Education	750	Chief Innovation Officer
273	Teacher Mentor	751	Chief of Staff
274	Before/After Sch	752	Social Emotional Learning
275	Response To Intervention		

Ohio School Directory
DISTRICT PERSONNEL INDEX

NAME/District	JOB FUNCTIONS	PAGE
Weigle, Barry/*East Palestine City Sch Dist*	3,5	35
Weigle, Sue/*East Palestine City Sch Dist*	67	35
Weigman, John/*Avon Local School Dist*	67	122
Weihrauch, Nate/*Findlay City School Dist*	6	97
Weiland, Cleighton/*Wyoming City School Dist*	69,77	94
Weingart, Lorie/*West Branch Local School Dist*	4	136
Weir, Jeff/*Clermont Co Ed Service Center*	1	29
Weirauch, Clarence/*Liberty Center Local Sch Dist*	3	101
Weirich, Daniel/*Penta Co JT Voc School Dist*	38,79	217
Weisal, Tammy/*St Clairsville-Richland CSD*	294	18
Weiser, Tom/*Middletown City School Dist*	2,73,76,95,294	23
Weiss, Brian, Dr/*Beachwood City School Dist*	67	40
Welage, Chad/*Lockland School Dist*	3	90
Welch, Jill/*Western Buckeye Ed Service Ctr*	34	160
Welch, John/*North Canton City School Dist*	58,296	187
Welch, Lindsey/*Green Local School Dist*	8,11	212
Welch, Mark/*Perry Local School Dist*	67	113
Welch, Shawna/*Dayton Public School Dist*	6,35	149
Weldele, Kelly/*Oak Hills Local School Dist*	4	92
Weldy, Nick, Dr/*Miami Valley Career Tech VSD*	1,11	151
Welker, Brent/*Eastwood Local School Dist*	1,83	216
Welker, Chad/*Twinsburg City School Dist*	3,4,5,91,295	195
Welker, Glen/*Granville Exempted Village SD*	73,295	117
Welker, Glenn/*Licking Co Ed Service Center*	73,295	117
Wellin, Mike/*Tri-Rivers Joint Voc Sch Dist*	16,73	139
Wellman, Sarah/*Ironton City School Dist*	36,58,69,77	116
Wells, Amy/*Northwest Local School Dist*	2,8,18,19	91
Wells, Angela/*East Knox Local School Dist*	5	111
Wells, Chad/*New Bremen Local School Dist*	6	16
Wells, Denny/*Triway Local School Dist*	3	213
Wells, Ed/*Van Wert City School Dist*	5	205
Wells, George/*Switzerland of Ohio Local SD*	81	147
Wells, Greg/*Williamsburg Local School Dist*	67	32
Wells, Karen/*Perkins Local School Dist*	4	61
Wells, Katy/*Tuscarawas Valley Local SD*	9,58	203
Wells, Kim/*Symmes Valley Local Sch Dist*	10,69,288,298	117
Wells, Melcie/*Warren Local School Dist*	2	210
Wells, Nichole/*Northeastern Local School Dist*	9	57
Wells, Terry/*Switzerland of Ohio Local SD*	68,83	147
Wells, Terry/*Switzerland of Ohio Local SD*	68,83	147
Welsh, Angie/*Dover City School Dist*	4	202
Welsh, Bradley/*West Holmes Local School Dist*	67	105
Welty, Teresa/*Findlay City School Dist*	4	97
Wendel, Dennis/*St Henry Cons Local Sch Dist*	6	144
Wendel, Kurt/*Mercer Co Ed Service Center*	2	143
Wendel, Tricia/*New Bremen Local School Dist*	38,69,88	16
Wendorf, Jeff/*North Canton City School Dist*	1	187
Wendt, Lisa/*Meta Solutions*	16	78
Wenning-Earp, Pam/*Mechanicsburg Exempted Vlg SD*	73,95,286	26
Wentworth, Amy/*New Philadelphia City Sch Dist*	8,11,15,74,274,285,288,298	203
Wentworth, Ira/*Indian Valley Local Sch Dist*	1	202
Wenzinger, Tony/*Carey Exempted Village SD*	67	219
Werry, Tasha/*Marietta City School Dist*	288,298	210
Wertman, Ty/*Zane Trace Local School Dist*	31,38,69	176
Wesley, Todd/*Lakota Local School Dist*	73,98,295	22
Wesney, Jon/*Centerville City School Dist*	2	148
Wessel, Elizabeth/*Mt Healthy City School Dist*	79	91
West, Bart/*Oak Hills Local School Dist*	91	92
West, Bonnie/*Wooster City School Dist*	2	213
West, Debbie/*Warren Local School Dist*	67	210
West, Debbie/*Washington Co JT Voc School Dist*	67	210
West, Gary/*Lynchburg-Clay Local Sch Dist*	67	103
West, Lindsey/*Marietta City School Dist*	81	210
West, Roger/*Brunswick City School Dist*	73	140
West, Scott/*Gallia Co Local School Dist*	286	80
Westbrooks, Sarah/*Lancaster City School Dist*	69	63
Westerbeck, Bill/*Fairfield City School Dist*	5	21
Westrick, Douglas/*Delphos City School Dist*	1	8
Wethington, Jennifer/*Mt Healthy City School Dist*	2	91
Wetzel, Beverly/*Bellbrook-Sugarcreek Schools*	5	83
Wharton, Rick/*Valley View Local School Dist*	9	153
Wheadon, John/*Copley-Fairlawn City Sch Dist*	2,19	192
Wheatley, Jolynn/*Jonathan Alder Local Sch Dist*	31,83	132
Wheeler, Darlene/*Streetsboro City School Dist*	4	167
Wheeler, Jessica/*Scioto Valley Local Sch Dist*	90	164
Wheeler, Laura/*Vermilion Local School Dist*	31,36,83	62

NAME/District	JOB FUNCTIONS	PAGE
Wheeler, Mike/*Miami Valley Educational CA*	73,76,295	85
Wheeler, Paul/*Galion City School Dist*	11,57,296,298	38
Wheeler, Steve/*Tri-Co Joint Voc Sch Dist*	69	15
Wheeler, Tracy/*Berea City School Dist*	1	41
Wheeler, Tracy/*Brunswick City School Dist*	15,68,81	140
Wheeler, Vicki/*Zanesville City School Dist*	4	157
Wheelersburg, Rebecca/*South Central Ohio Ed Svc Ctr*	34,83,85,88	178
Whelan, Sean/*West Geauga Local School Dist*	2	82
Wherley, Brenda/*Dover City School Dist*	29	202
Whetsel, Ashley/*Crestview Local School Dist*	2,19	205
Whipple, Jon/*Ashtabula Co Tech & Career SD*	27	12
Whisler, Jeff/*Northmor Local School Dist*	67	156
Whitaker, Sue/*Huron City School Dist*	4	60
Whitcomb, Susan/*Huntington Local School Dist*	5	175
White, Barbara/*Dover City School Dist*	5	202
White, Daniel/*Keystone Local School Dist*	1	124
White, Gary/*Connect Information Tech Ctr*	68	54
White, Jami/*Western Reserve Local Sch Dist*	67	106
White, Jenny/*Minerva Local School Dist*	36	187
White, Jody/*Keystone Local School Dist*	4	124
White, Kristina/*Springfield Local School Dist*	71	128
White, Mark/*Willard City School Dist*	73	106
White, Martin/*Findlay City School Dist*	16,73,76,84,295	97
White, Matt/*Carrollton Exempted Village SD*	73	25
White, Mike/*Union Scioto Local Sch Dist*	6	175
White, Raegan/*Western Brown Local Sch Dist*	1	20
White, Richard/*Mideast Career & Tech Ctrs*	298	157
Whiteley, Lisa/*Three Rivers Local School Dist*	71	94
Whitely, Ashley/*Wyoming City School Dist*	8,12,15,68,69,83,288	94
Whitesel, Jason/*Lexington Local School Dist*	2	172
Whitesel, Stephanie/*East Knox Local School Dist*	36	111
Whitlatch, Kala/*Steubenville City School Dist*	2,71,294	109
Whitlatch, William/*Canal Winchester Local SD*	69	66
Whitney, Robert/*Lexington Local School Dist*	67	172
Whitt, Karen/*Genoa Area Local School Dist*	8,69	159
Whitt, Vern/*Miami Co Ed Service Center*	73	144
Whittaker, Patricia/*Southern Hills Joint Voc SD*	33	20
Whittington, Mike/*Heath City School Dist*	3,5	117
Whitworth, Jane/*Rock Hill Local School Dist*	16	116
Whorten, Dave/*Springfield Local School Dist*	73	136
Whyman, Lila/*Apollo Joint Voc School Dist*	16	8
Wick, Lisa/*Norwalk City School Dist*	67	106
Wickham, Colleen/*Toronto City School Dist*	2	109
Wickline, Gabe/*Indian Lake Local School Dist*	67	121
Widenhammer, Mark/*Defiance City School Dist*	5	57
Widman, Chris/*Tiffin City School Dist*	67	181
Widman, Sarah/*West Geauga Local School Dist*	36	82
Widmer, Jon/*Norwayne Local School Dist*	67	212
Wiederhold, Paula/*Fayetteville Perry Local SD*	11,58,296,298	19
Wiedman, Dan/*Antwerp Local School Dist*	3	160
Wieging, Cliff/*Jennings Local School Dist*	67	169
Wieging, Sue/*Gahanna-Jefferson Public SD*	58	70
Wierwille, Marcia/*Woco-W Ohio Computer Org*	2	183
Wigg, Kelly/*Hilliard City School Dist*	274	71
Wiggins, Kelly/*Springfield City School Dist*	30	28
Wightman, Melanie/*Fairview Park City Sch Dist*	8,285,288	46
Wigton, Steve/*Lancaster City School Dist*	1	63
Wiiliams, Brad/*Sycamore Cmty School Dist*	26	93
Wiita, Pat/*Edgewood City School Dist*	69,77	21
Wilburn, Kalin/*Ncocc-N Ctrl Ohio Co-op CA*	74	174
Wilchuck, Mark/*Mansfield City Schools*	68	172
Wilcox, Elizabeth/*Genoa Area Local School Dist*	16,82	159
Wilcox, Gen/*Madison Local School Dist*	8,11,69,72,285,288	23
Wildenhaus, Richard/*New Albany-Plain Local SD*	6	72
Wile, Ryan/*Norwayne Local School Dist*	73,76	212
Wile, Susan/*Tecumseh Local School Dist*	58,76,83,275,296	28
Wiles, Jill/*Walnut Twp Local School Dist*	7,83,85	64
Wiles, Priscilla/*North Olmsted City School Dist*	16	48
Wiles, Valerie/*Fairless Local School Dist*	3,5	185
Wiley, Katy/*Mapleton Local School Dist*	2	11
Wiley, Mike/*Maumee City School Dist*	67	127
Wiley, Robin/*Loveland City School Dist*	15,68,79	90
Wilheigh, Jeff/*Crestline Exempted Village SD*	67	38
Wilhelm, Kay/*Delphos City School Dist*	286	8
Wilhite, Kerri/*Crestline Exempted Village SD*	4	38
Wilhlem, Maryjo/*Vantage Career Center Sch Dist*	71	206

School Year 2019-2020   800-333-8802   OH-T59

DISTRICT PERSONNEL INDEX

Market Data Retrieval

NAME/District	JOB FUNCTIONS	PAGE
Wilkeson, David/Canfield Local School Dist	67	134
Wilking, Jan/Wyoming City School Dist	6	94
Wilkins, Jamie/Ripley-Union-Lewis-Huntngtn SD	1	20
Wilkins, Leigha/Manchester Local School Dist	69	7
Will, Kevin/Ft Recovery Local School Dist	3	144
William, Emily/Sycamore Cmty School Dist	57	93
Williams, Angie/Adena Local School Dist	16	174
Williams, Bill/Millcreek-West Unity Local SD	3	215
Williams, Billie/Pymatuning Valley Local SD	8,58,298	13
Williams, Brian/Cleveland Hts-Univ Hts City SD	88	42
Williams, Brian/Copley-Fairlawn City Sch Dist	8,15	192
Williams, Cathy/Noble Local School Dist	58	158
Williams, Chris/Cedar Cliff Local School Dist	3	84
Williams, Dennis/Clark-Shawnee Local Sch Dist	3	27
Williams, Derrick/Huber Heights City School Dist	68,298	150
Williams, Don/Gahanna-Jefferson Public SD	5	70
Williams, Don/Upper Arlington City Sch Dist	5	74
Williams, Greg/Crooksville Exempted Vlg SD	6	161
Williams, Greg, Dr/New Lebanon Local School Dist	1	151
Williams, Guy/Southern Local School Dist	58	161
Williams, Harley, Dr/Bexley City School Dist	3,17,273	66
Williams, Jeff/Garaway Local School Dist	8,11,57,58,288	202
Williams, Jeff/Garaway Local School Dist	8,11,57,58,288	202
Williams, Jennifer/Cincinnati City School Dist	42	87
Williams, Kara/Ripley-Union-Lewis-Huntngtn SD	11,54,58,69,77,275	20
Williams, Kiara/Trotwood-Madison City SD	8	153
Williams, Lana/Strasburg Franklin Local SD	4	203
Williams, Marie/Columbiana Co Ed Service Ctr	8	33
Williams, Mark/Southeast Local School Dist	5	213
Williams, Mary/Joseph Badger Local Sch Dist	9,58	198
Williams, Mary/New Bremen Local School Dist	4	16
Williams, Megan/Scioto Valley Local Sch Dist	2,19,298	164
Williams, Nicole/Riverdale Local School Dist	38	98
Williams, Patrick/Waverly City School Dist	73	164
Williams, Patrick/Waverly City School Dist	84	164
Williams, Regina/Washington Court House City SD	5	65
Williams, Rhonda/Ansonia Local School Dist	67	55
Williams, Rob/Four-Co Joint Voc School Dist	76,82	79
Williams, Sandra/Howland Local School Dist	27,88,270	198
Williams, Sara/Union Scioto Local Sch Dist	36,69,88	175
Williams, Stacy/Beaver Local School Dist	2,19	34
Williams, Sue/Southeast Local School Dist	67	213
Williams, Ted/Cedar Cliff Local School Dist	8	84
Williams, Tim/Logan Elm Local School Dist	1	162
Williams, Tom/Hillsdale Local School Dist	12	11
Williams, Tony/Fairfield Local Sch Dist	6	102
Williams, Tyler/Wilmington City School Dist	38	33
Williamson, Greg/Leipsic Local School Dist	1,11	170
Williamson, James/Vermilion Local School Dist	3	62
Williamson, Jd/Westfall Local School Dist	73,286,295	163
Williamson, Lee Jane/River View Local School Dist	2	37
Williamson, Mark/Akron Public Schools	71	190
Williamson, Sherry/Auburn Vocational School Dist	2,19	112
Williamson, Sherry/Auburn Vocational School Dist	2,11	112
Willingham, Bruce, Dr/Midview Local School Dist	1	125
Willis, Felice/Bedford City School Dist	10,69,288	40
Willis, Lauren/Waterloo Local School Dist	59	167
Willis, Rachel/Manchester Local School Dist	8	193
Willis, Renee, Dr/Richmond Heights Local SD	1	49
Willison, Phyllis/Buckeye Joint Voc School Dist	4	201
Willman, Kolene/Reading Cmty City School Dist	16,82	93
Willoughby, Julie, Dr/Urbana City School Dist	8	26
Wilms, Dee/Wayne Local School Dist	68	209
Wilson-Fish, Beth/Orange City School Dist	67	48
Wilson, Amy/Orrville City School Dist	81	212
Wilson, Amy/Rittman Exempted Village SD	10	213
Wilson, Andrew/Fairborn City School Dist	67	84
Wilson, Brenda/Carlisle Local School Dist	76	206
Wilson, Brian/Hilliard City School Dist	2,19	71
Wilson, Courtney/Winton Woods City School Dist	68,79	94
Wilson, Daniel/Mentor Exempted Village SD	2,19	113
Wilson, Darlene/Hardin Northern Local Sch Dist	16	100
Wilson, David/Northeastern Local School Dist	25	27
Wilson, Donshon/East Cleveland City Sch Dist	73	45
Wilson, Jan/Greenfield Exempted Village SD	11,296	103
Wilson, Jen/Big Walnut Local School Dist	8	58
Wilson, Jessica/Lake Local School Dist	16	217
Wilson, John Andrew/Hardin Northern Local Sch Dist	8,57,69	100
Wilson, Jon/East Holmes Local School Dist	8,11,57,83,288,296,298	104
Wilson, Jonette/Liberty Local School Dist	4	199
Wilson, Kyle/Blanchester Local School Dist	67	32
Wilson, Mayra/Archdiocese Cincinnati Ed Off	271	94
Wilson, Natisha/Miami Co Ed Service Center	81	144
Wilson, Natisha/Tipp City Exempted Village SD	81	146
Wilson, Rodge/Western Reserve Local Sch Dist	1	106
Wilson, Tonya/Bellbrook-Sugarcreek Schools	58	83
Winans, Benjamin/Wayne Trace Local School Dist	1	160
Winard, Brent, Dr/Ncocc-N Ctrl Ohio Co-op CA	1,11	174
Winer, Ellen/Grand Valley Local School Dist	11,296,298	13
Wingert, Candy/Lakota Local School Dist	8,69,270	177
Winkhart, Thomas/Jackson Local School Dist	67	186
Winkle, Natalie/Boardman Local School Dist	4	134
Winland, Tim/Paint Valley Local School Dist	1	175
Winninberg, Joe/Crooksville Exempted Vlg SD	16,73	161
Winsler, Beth/Edgerton Local School Dist	4	214
Winstead, Sharon/Butler Tech Career Dev Schs	11,30	21
Winterod, Brad/Georgetown Exempted Village SD	1	19
Winters, Stephanie/Northern Local School Dist	38	161
Winters, Tanera/Cleveland Hts-Univ Hts City SD	4	42
Wiohite, Kerri/Colonel Crawford Local SD	4	38
Wireman, Karla/Allen Co Ed Service Center	2	7
Wirick, Lee/Tolles Career & Tech Sch Dist	73	133
Wirwille, Nick/New Knoxville Local Sch Dist	73	16
Wirzfeld, Loretta/Fairland Local School Dist	2	116
Wischmeyer, Brian/Lima City School Dist	58	9
Wise, Bill, Dr/South-Western City School Dist	1	73
Wise, Brent/Mariemont City School Dist	73,295	91
Wise, Kay/Buckeye Joint Voc School Dist	286	201
Wise, Kelsey/Union Local School Dist	69,77	18
Wise, Mercedes/Danbury Local School Dist	58	159
Wise, Mercedes/Port Clinton City School Dist	34,58,77	159
Wise, Rodney/Brown Local School Dist	5	25
Wise, Shawna/Greenville City School Dist	16,73,82,295	55
Wisniewski, William/Ravenna School Dist	2,3,91	166
Wisnyai, Mary/Buckeye Local School Dist	67	12
Wissman, Brian/Northmont City School Dist	23	152
Wisvari, Curtis/Switzerland of Ohio Local SD	12,70,81	147
Withrow, Judy/Findlay City School Dist	81,285	98
Witt, Jim/Lake Local School Dist	1	217
Witterstaeter, Amanda/Three Rivers Local School Dist	7,35,85	94
Wlyudyga, Robert/Pymatuning Valley Local SD	285	13
Wobser, Mike/Bellevue City School Dist	73,84,295,297	105
Wohlgamuth, Kelli/West Muskingum Local Sch Dist	8,12,288,296	157
Wolf, Allen/East Cleveland City Sch Dist	2,4	45
Wolf, Casey/Amherst Exempted Village SD	6	122
Wolf, Kyle/Teays Valley Local School Dist	8,11,34,58,69,88,296,298	162
Wolfe-Izworski, Melissa/Sycamore Cmty School Dist	48,273	93
Wolfe, Brenton/Fredericktown Local Sch Dist	73	111
Wolfe, Carl/Southern Local School Dist	6,88	143
Wolfe, Charlie/Southern Local School Dist	3	143
Wolfe, Heather/Athens Meigs Ed Service Center	1,73	14
Wolfe, Heather/State Support Team-Region 16	1	15
Wolfe, Jana/Mt Healthy City School Dist	9	91
Wolfe, Kevin/Edgerton Local School Dist	270	214

---

1 Superintendent	16 Instructional Media Svcs	30 Adult Education	44 Science Sec	58 Special Education K-12	72 Summer School	88 Alternative/At Risk	277 Remedial Math K-12
2 Bus/Finance/Purchasing	17 Chief Operations Officer	31 Career/Sch-to-Work K-12	45 Math K-12	59 Special Education Elem	73 Instructional Tech	89 Multi-Cultural Curriculum	280 Literacy Coach
3 Buildings And Grounds	18 Chief Academic Officer	32 Career/Sch-to-Work Elem	46 Math Elem	60 Special Education Sec	74 Inservice Training	90 Social Work	285 STEM
4 Food Service	19 Chief Financial Officer	33 Career/Sch-to-Work Sec	47 Math Sec	61 Foreign/World Lang K-12	75 Marketing/Distributive	91 Safety/Security	286 Digital Learning
5 Transportation	20 Art K-12	34 Early Childhood Ed	48 English/Lang Arts K-12	62 Foreign/World Lang Elem	76 Info Systems	92 Magnet School	288 Common Core Standards
6 Athletic	21 Art Elem	35 Health/Phys Education	49 English/Lang Arts Elem	63 Foreign/World Lang Sec	77 Psychological Assess	93 Parental Involvement	294 Accountability
7 Health Services	22 Art Sec	36 Guidance Services K-12	50 English/Lang Arts Sec	64 Religious Education K-12	78 Affirmative Action	95 Tech Prep Program	295 Network System
8 Curric/Instruct K-12	23 Music K-12	37 Guidance Services Elem	51 Reading K-12	65 Religious Education Elem	79 Student Personnel	97 Chief Information Officer	296 Title II Programs
9 Curric/Instruct Elem	24 Music Elem	38 Guidance Services Sec	52 Reading Elem	66 Religious Education Sec	80 Driver Ed/Safety	98 Chief Technology Officer	297 Webmaster
10 Curric/Instruct Sec	25 Music Sec	39 Social Studies K-12	53 Reading Sec	67 School Board President	81 Gifted/Talented	270 Character Education	298 Grant Writer/Ptnrships
11 Federal Program	26 Business Education	40 Social Studies Elem	54 Remedial Reading K-12	68 Teacher Personnel	82 Video Services	271 Migrant Education	750 Chief Innovation Officer
12 Title I	27 Career & Tech Ed	41 Social Studies Sec	55 Remedial Reading Elem	69 Academic Assessment	83 Substance Abuse Prev	273 Teacher Mentor	751 Chief of Staff
13 Title V	28 Technology Education	42 Science K-12	56 Remedial Reading Sec	70 Research/Development	84 Erate	274 Before/After Sch	752 Social Emotional Learning
15 Asst Superintendent	29 Family/Consumer Science	43 Science Elem	57 Bilingual/ELL	71 Public Information	85 AIDS Education	275 Response To Intervention	

OH-T60

Ohio School Directory
DISTRICT PERSONNEL INDEX

NAME/District	JOB FUNCTIONS	PAGE
Wolfe, Scott/*Southern Local School Dist*	4,11,58,296,298	143
Wolfe, Steve/*Adams Co Ohio Valley Sch Dist*	2,3,91	6
Wolfe, Tyler/*Dublin City School Dist*	9	69
Wolff, Darrell/*Perry Local School Dist*	2	188
Wolpert, Jim/*Pike-Delta-York Local Sch Dist*	3,5	79
Wolske, Gary/*Garfield Heights City SD*	67	46
Wolski, Melissa/*Bethel Local School Dist*	4	145
Wolverton, Jim/*London City School Dist*	6	132
Wonderling, Andrea/*Pymatuning Valley Local SD*	27	13
Wonderly, Kasey/*Huber Heights City School Dist*	4	150
Wood, Glen/*Steubenville City School Dist*	3,5	109
Wood, Jason/*Coldwater Exempted Village SD*	1	143
Wood, Jenny/*Northmont City School Dist*	297	152
Wood, Kurt/*U S Grant Career School Dist*	3	31
Wood, Steve/*Tallmadge City School Dist*	2,3,4,17,78,91	194
Wood, Terry/*Waverly City School Dist*	36	164
Woodall, Vince/*Archdiocese Cincinnati Ed Off*	2	94
Woodard, Dottie/*Northmont City School Dist*	34	152
Woodard, Paul/*Newton Falls Exempted Vlg SD*	1	200
Woodard, Todd/*Tri-Valley Local School Dist*	58	157
Woodgeard, David/*New Lebanon Local School Dist*	67	151
Woodring, Laura/*Northwestern Local School Dist*	67	212
Woodruff, Anne/*East Clinton Local School Dist*	4	33
Woodruff, Carrie/*Lima City School Dist*	4	9
Woodruff, Sabrina/*Xenia Community School Dist*	8,11,69,288	84
Woods, Beth/*Jonathan Alder Local Sch Dist*	37	132
Woods, George/*Jackson Local School Dist*	73	186
Woods, Pete/*West Muskingum Local Sch Dist*	6	157
Woods, Stephen/*Eaton Cmty School Dist*	73,76	168
Woodward, Julie/*Great Oaks Career Campuses*	71	89
Woodworth, Jeremy/*Mentor Exempted Village SD*	73,84,295	113
Woody, Sheila/*Bellbrook-Sugarcreek Schools*	68	83
Woodyard, Vickie/*Tri-Co North School Dist*	67	168
Woofter, Christopher/*Chagrin Falls Exempted Vlg SD*	3,68,273,298	42
Woolard, Jeff/*Crestwood Local School Dist*	2,3,73,91	165
Wooldridge, Brandon/*Scioto Valley Local Sch Dist*	67	164
Woolf, Shawn/*McComb Local School Dist*	6	98
Worick, Chris/*South Central Local Sch Dist*	2	106
Workman, Mary/*Tri-Co Ed Service Center*	2,11,68	211
Workman, Mary/*Wayne Co Joint Voc School Dist*	2,11	213
Workman, Racheal/*Wooster City School Dist*	68	213
Workman, Stuart/*Tccsa-Tri-Co Comp Svcs*	1	214
Worley, Charles/*Lordstown Local School Dist*	3	199
Worth, Diane/*Ottoville Local School Dist*	11	170
Worthen, Matt/*Butler Co Ed Service Center*	73	20
Wortman, Scott/*Cleveland Hts-Univ Hts City SD*	71,297	42
Wortman, Scott/*Columbus City School Dist*	71	67
Wrataric, Diana/*Weathersfield Local Sch Dist*	37	201
Wren, Brad/*Jackson Center Local Sch Dist*	67	183
Wright-Cullis, Rebecca/*Kent City School Dist*	67	165
Wright, Angie/*Bright Local School Dist*	67	102
Wright, Ann/*North Fork Local School Dist*	68	119
Wright, Casey/*Nordonia Hills City Sch Dist*	270	193
Wright, Christopher/*Portage Lakes Joint Voc SD*	2	189
Wright, Craig/*Gallipolis City School Dist*	1	81
Wright, Dean/*Morgan Local School Dist*	2,3,15	154
Wright, Kelly/*Northern Local School Dist*	58,77	161
Wright, Margie/*East Liverpool City Sch Dist*	4	34
Wright, Michael/*Hamilton City School Dist*	79	22
Wright, Mira/*Columbus City School Dist*	68	67
Wright, Randy/*Olentangy Local School Dist*	3,5,15,68,91	59
Wright, Richard/*Dayton Public School Dist*	91	149
Wright, Roger/*Wadsworth City School Dist*	27,31,75	141
Wright, Sarah/*Symmes Valley Local Sch Dist*	27	117
Wright, Thomas/*Wyoming City School Dist*	3	94
Wright, Tonya/*Greenville City School Dist*	4	55
Wudke, Gretchen/*Fairborn City School Dist*	88	84
Wuebker, Brenda/*Anna Local School Dist*	29	182
Wuebker, Heather/*Anna Local School Dist*	8,288,298	182
Wuensch, Scott/*Avon Lake City School Dist*	73,84,98	122
Wukeson, Raymond/*Bridgeport School Dist*	21	18
Wulff, Sarah/*Coventry Local School Dist*	12,275	192
Wulfhoop, Tim/*Olmsted Falls City School Dist*	294	48
Wunder, Valerie/*Reynoldsburg City School Dist*	71,297,298	72
Wyatt, Matt/*Orrville City School Dist*	5	212
Wycinski, Marylou/*Southern Local School Dist*	9	161
Wyckoff, Beth/*Fairbanks Local School Dist*	5	204
Wyckoff, Janice/*Clear Fork Vly Local Sch Dist*	1,11	171
Wycuff, Brian/*Brecksville Broadview Hts CSD*	68	41
Wydra, Shanna/*Steubenville City School Dist*	285,298	109
Wyen, Chad/*Mad River Local School Dist*	1	151
Wyman, Gina/*Mohawk Local School Dist*	12,54	219
Wyman, Mandy/*Pettisville Local School Dist*	36,83,88	79
Wyse, Gary/*Bryan City School Dist*	84	214
Wyse, Jim/*Millcreek-West Unity Local SD*	1,11,288	215
Wysong, Bob/*Warren Co Voc School Dist*	3	208

X

NAME/District	JOB FUNCTIONS	PAGE
Xander, Diane/*Polaris Joint Voc School Dist*	29,60,79,81	49

Y

NAME/District	JOB FUNCTIONS	PAGE
Yaist, Kathy/*Western Reserve Local Sch Dist*	273	136
Yakoobian, George/*Noeca-Northern Ohio Ed CA*	295	62
Yane, James/*Euclid City School Dist*	73	46
Yaniglos, Craig/*Brookfield Local School Dist*	2	197
Yankie, Sandy/*Perry Local School Dist*	85	113
Yannayon, Kathy/*Rittman Exempted Village SD*	5	213
Yant, Justin/*Paulding Exempted Village SD*	16,73,76,295	160
Yarger, Lisa/*Clear Fork Vly Local Sch Dist*	5	171
Yarman, Rusty/*Northwestern Local School Dist*	3	212
Yarnell, Katie/*Patrick Henry Local Sch Dist*	4	102
Yater, Darrell/*Northwest Local School Dist*	8,15	91
Yates, Jim/*St Clairsville-Richland CSD*	73,84,95,295	18
Yates, William/*Walnut Twp Local School Dist*	3,5	64
Yauger, Paula/*Warren City School Dist*	48	200
Yazvac, Thomas/*Springfield Local School Dist*	1,11	135
Yeager, Ava/*Parma City School Dist*	11	49
Yeager, Ava/*Youngstown City School Dist*	11,296	136
Yeager, Kathy/*Indian Hill Exempted Vlg SD*	83,85,88	90
Yeager, Katie/*Big Walnut Local School Dist*	81	58
Yeazel, Doug/*New Miami Local School Dist*	16,73,82	23
Yeckley, Kevin/*Lakota Local School Dist*	6	177
Yenni, Kim/*Walnut Twp Local School Dist*	9,11	64
Yinger, Michael/*Buckeye Valley Local Sch Dist*	6	58
Yingling, Chris/*Logan Elm Local School Dist*	3,5,91	162
Yingst, Dusty/*Greenville City School Dist*	6	55
Yoakam, Corey/*South Range Local School Dist*	67	135
Yochheim, Brad/*Green Local School Dist*	67	212
Yockey, David/*Great Oaks Career Campuses*	67	89
Yockey, Duane/*Clermont Co Ed Service Center*	73	29
Yockey, Evelyn/*Brown Co Ed Service Center*	298	19
Yockey, Tammy/*Upper Arlington City Sch Dist*	69,286,294	74
Yocum, Forest/*Licking Co Ed Service Center*	67	117
Yoder, Art/*East Holmes Local School Dist*	6	104
Yoder, Francine/*Bay Village City School Dist*	57	40
Yoder, Lewis/*East Holmes Local School Dist*	3	104
Yoder, Mark/*Maplewood Local School Dist*	6	199
Yoder, Rhonda/*Martins Ferry City School Dist*	4	18
Yoder, Rodney/*Riverside Local School Dist*	6	121
Yoder, Shaun/*Ohio Department of Education*	69,298	1
Yoder, Toby/*East Holmes Local School Dist*	280	104
Yoder, Todd/*Martins Ferry City School Dist*	3	18
Yohey, Todd/*Lebanon City School Dist*	1	207
Yonak, Jayme/*Union Local School Dist*	8,58	18
Yonker, Jacinda/*Ed Svc Center of Medina Co*	8,74,81	139
York, Stephen/*Ravenna School Dist*	84	166
York, Steven/*Ravenna School Dist*	73,95,295,297	166
Yorko, Deborah/*Highland Local School Dist*	34,58	141
Yosay, Linda/*Mahoning Co Ed Service Center*	34,58	133
Yosay, Linda/*Youngstown City School Dist*	58,79	136
Yosick, Kelsey/*Penta Co JT Voc School Dist*	4	217
Yost, Carol/*Brunswick City School Dist*	57	140
Yost, Michael/*Madison Local School Dist*	5	172
Young, Carol/*Canfield Local School Dist*	280	134
Young, Chris/*Ripley-Union-Lewis-Huntngtn SD*	6	20
Young, Christine/*Painesville City Local SD*	7,34,58,69	113
Young, Diane/*Noeca-Northern Ohio Ed CA*	79	62
Young, James/*East Palestine City Sch Dist*	16	35
Young, James/*Fairfield Co Ed Service Center*	81	62
Young, James/*Reynoldsburg City School Dist*	81	72
Young, Jeffrey/*Riverdale Local School Dist*	1,11	98
Young, Jen/*Big Walnut Local School Dist*	8	58

DISTRICT PERSONNEL INDEX

Market Data Retrieval

NAME/District	JOB FUNCTIONS	PAGE
Young, Kathy/Findlay City School Dist	58	97
Young, Laura/Holgate Local School Dist	9	101
Young, Laurel/Summit Co Educational Svc Ctr	2	196
Young, Matthew/Summit Co Educational Svc Ctr	8	196
Young, Melinda/Steubenville City School Dist	1,11	109
Young, Michael/Zanesville City School Dist	2	157
Young, Molly/Beaver Local School Dist	280	34
Young, Nate/Athens City School Dist	58	14
Young, Sharon/Sheffield-Sheffield Lake CSD	7	125
Young, Shawn/Batavia Local School Dist	5	29
Young, Shay/Bellaire Local School Dist	8	17
Young, Susan/Indian Lake Local School Dist	4	121
Young, Tom/Yellow Springs Exempted Vlg SD	73,295	85
Young, Wayne/Cory-Rawson Local School Dist	3,91	97
Young, William/United Local School Dist	10	36
Young, William, Dr/Austintown Local School Dist	10	133
Younge, Deborah/Westfall Local School Dist	8,11,69,296,298	163
Younglas, Amy/North Olmsted City School Dist	76	48
Younker, Jacqueline/Lorain City School Dist	68	124
Yunker, Matt/North Ridgeville City Sch Dist	3,5,91	125
Yunker, Paul/Central Local School Dist	6	57
Yurick, Tess/Lakewood City School Dist	30	47
Yurik, Teresa/Lakewood City School Dist	30	47
Yux, Robert/Centerville City School Dist	8,15,69	148

Z

NAME/District	JOB FUNCTIONS	PAGE
Zacharias, Heather/Northridge Local School Dist	73,76,295,297	152
Zaffrann, Meredith/Hudson City School Dist	30	193
Zagray, Pete/Westlake City School Dist	16,73	51
Zahneis, Karen/Oak Hills Local School Dist	76	92
Zalar, Michael, Dr/North Olmsted City School Dist	1	48
Zaler, Claudia/Waverly City School Dist	2,11,19,68,298	164
Zalesinsky, Tammy/Fairless Local School Dist	16,82	185
Zanni, Robert/Struthers City School Dist	82	136
Zaph, Andrea/Lawrence Co Joint Voc Sch Dist	10,29,74,273	116
Zarins, Karl/Heath City School Dist	2	117
Zebroski, Rhonda/Brookfield Local School Dist	7	197
Zehe, Toni/Mid-Ohio Ed Service Center	34	171
Zehentbauer, John/Mahoning Co Joint Voc Sch Dist	1,11	135
Zeigler, Jamie/West Holmes Local School Dist	2	105
Zell, John/Lima City School Dist	6	9
Zellar, Cindy/Tolles Career & Tech Sch Dist	30	133
Zellner, Lisa/Mohawk Local School Dist	36	219
Zelneck, John/Labrae Local School Dist	31	198
Zeman, Kent/Lakewood City School Dist	2,19	47
Zender, Christen/Otsego Local School Dist	37	217
Zender, Martin/Van Buren Local School Dist	38	99
Zenobi, Matt/Connect Information Tech Ctr	79	126
Zenubi, Matt/Connect Information Tech Ctr	79	54
Zepp, Brendan/Buckeye Local School Dist	58	140
Zerbe, John/Spencerville Local School Dist	6	9
Zeroff, Tim/Sylvania City School Dist	8,15	128
Zgrabik, Jerry/Bedford City School Dist	2	40
Zickar, Rachel/Perrysburg Exempted Village SD	71	218
Zidron, Jeff/Indian Hill Exempted Vlg SD	6	90
Ziebel, Anna/Pickerington Local School Dist	3	64
Ziegelhofer, J Michael/Lexington Local School Dist	1,11	172
Ziegler, Brett/Napoleon Area City School Dist	88	101
Ziegler, Chris/Archbold Area Local Sch Dist	2,19	78
Ziegler, Denny/Strongsville City School Dist	6	51
Ziegler, Elizabeth/Washington Local School Dist	16,82	130
Ziegler, Kelly/Buckeye Valley Local School Dist	2	58
Ziegler, Perry/Strongsville City School Dist	6	51
Zielke, Jerry/Western Buckeye Ed Service Ctr	67	205
Zielke, Jerry/Western Buckeye Ed Service Ctr	67	160
Zielske, Denise/Vermilion Local School Dist	4	62
Zierden, Jennifer/Cardington-Lincoln Local SD	9	155

NAME/District	JOB FUNCTIONS	PAGE
Ziga-Bud, Christina/New Philadelphia City Sch Dist	58,69,77,270,271	203
Zigarovich, Rich/Lordstown Local School Dist	58	199
Zimmer, Cathryn/River Valley Local School Dist	2	139
Zimmer, Roberta/Arcanum Butler Local Sch Dist	73	55
Zimmerman, Doug/Anthony Wayne Local Sch Dist	67	127
Zimmerman, Heidi/Ontario Local School Dist	67	173
Zimmerman, Katie/Columbus Grove Local Sch Dist	7	169
Zimmerman, Megan/Buckeye Joint Voc School Dist	57	201
Zimmerman, Mike/Pettisville Local School Dist	73	79
Zinger, John/Jackson-Milton Local Sch Dist	2	134
Zink, Jessie/Northmont City School Dist	81,298	152
Zinn, John/Vinton Co Local School Dist	91	206
Zint, Eric/Greenfield Exempted Village SD	67	103
Zipes, Jeff/Greeneview Local School Dist	38	84
Zippay, Alexis/Ayersville Local School Dist	16	56
Zirm, Paula/Tiffin City School Dist	81	181
Zitnik, Ruth/Maysville Local School Dist	1	156
Zobel, Charles/Garaway Local School Dist	286	202
Zock, Maggie/Newbury Local School Dist	67	82
Zofka, Mark/Bedford City School Dist	6	40
Zohn, Patrick/Cleveland Metro School Dist	3,17	42
Zolla, Christopher/Neonet-NE Ohio Ed Tech	15,73	196
Zoller, Chuck/Beavercreek City School Dist	295	83
Zoller, Jeanie/Wyoming City School Dist	67	94
Zona, Lisa/Dalton Local School Dist	58,88,275,296	212
Zsembik, Tom/Mad River Local School Dist	4	151
Zuercher, Audreay/Orrville City School Dist	6	212
Zuga, Donna/Lakeview Local School Dist	67	199
Zukowski, Cristina/North Royalton City Sch Dist	58	48
Zumwalt, Jennifer/Northmont City School Dist	12,13	152
Zupka, Aaron/Milford Exempted Village SD	6	30
Zuppo, Mark/Girard City School Dist	67	197
Zura, Mark/Poland Local School Dist	11,36,57,58,73,88	135
Zurbuch, Dick/Ripley-Union-Lewis-Huntngtn SD	3,91	20
Zurmehly, Leslie/Williamsburg Local School Dist	79	32
Zuro, David/Hudson City School Dist	67	193
Zwack, Rebecca/Bellaire Local School Dist	57	17
Zwiep, Sherry/New Knoxville Local Sch Dist	4	16

---

1 Superintendent
2 Bus/Finance/Purchasing
3 Buildings And Grounds
4 Food Service
5 Transportation
6 Athletic
7 Health Services
8 Curric/Instruct K-12
9 Curric/Instruct Elem
10 Curric/Instruct Sec
11 Federal Program
12 Title I
13 Title V
15 Asst Superintendent
16 Instructional Media Svcs
17 Chief Operations Officer
18 Chief Academic Officer
19 Chief Financial Officer
20 Art K-12
21 Art Elem
22 Art Sec
23 Music K-12
24 Music Elem
25 Music Sec
26 Business Education
27 Career & Tech Ed
28 Technology Education
29 Family/Consumer Science
30 Adult Education
31 Career/Sch-to-Work K-12
32 Career/Sch-to-Work Elem
33 Career/Sch-to-Work Sec
34 Early Childhood Ed
35 Health/Phys Education
36 Guidance Services Elem
37 Guidance Services Elem
38 Guidance Services Sec
39 Social Studies K-12
40 Social Studies Elem
41 Social Studies Sec
42 Science K-12
43 Science Elem
44 Science Sec
45 Math K-12
46 Math Elem
47 Math Sec
48 English/Lang Arts K-12
49 English/Lang Arts Elem
50 English/Lang Arts Sec
51 Reading K-12
52 Reading Elem
53 Reading Sec
54 Remedial Reading K-12
55 Remedial Reading Elem
56 Remedial Reading Sec
57 Bilingual/ELL
58 Special Education K-12
59 Special Education Elem
60 Special Education Sec
61 Foreign/World Lang K-12
62 Foreign/World Lang Elem
63 Foreign/World Lang Sec
64 Religious Education K-12
65 Religious Education Elem
66 Religious Education Sec
67 School Board President
68 Teacher Personnel
69 Academic Assessment
70 Research/Development
71 Public Information
72 Summer School
73 Instructional Tech
74 Inservice Training
75 Marketing/Distributive
76 Info Systems
77 Psychological Assess
78 Affirmative Action
79 Student Personnel
80 Driver Ed/Safety
81 Gifted/Talented
82 Video Services
83 Substance Abuse Prev
84 Erate
85 AIDS Education
88 Alternative/At Risk
89 Multi-Cultural Curriculum
90 Social Work
91 Safety/Security
92 Magnet School
93 Parental Involvement
95 Tech Prep Program
97 Chief Information Officer
98 Chief Technology Officer
270 Character Education
271 Migrant Education
273 Teacher Mentor
274 Before/After Sch
275 Response To Intervention
277 Remedial Math K-12
280 Literacy Coach
285 STEM
286 Digital Learning
288 Common Core Standards
294 Accountability
295 Network System
296 Title II Programs
297 Webmaster
298 Grant Writer/Ptnrships
750 Chief Innovation Officer
751 Chief of Staff
752 Social Emotional Learning

Ohio School Directory — PRINCIPAL INDEX

NAME/School	PAGE
A	
Abbott, Clinton/*Barnesville Elem Sch*	17
Abbott, Clinton/*Barnesville Ind Elem Sch*	19
Abbott, Travis/*Meigs High Sch*	142
Abdalla, Fred/*Jefferson Co Alt Sch*	108
Abdussatar, Lashonda/*Renwood Elem Sch*	49
Abel, Tina/*St Patrick-Heatherdowns Sch*	131
Aber, Allison/*Longfellow Elem Sch*	114
Aber, Allison/*Roosevelt Elem Sch*	47
Abke, Chris/*Botkins Local Sch*	182
Abraham, Gwen/*Elmwood Elem Sch*	46
Abramovich, Mark/*Harmon Middle Sch*	165
Accavallo, Amanda/*New London Elem Sch*	106
Accurso, Debra/*Clark Pre-School*	28
Acemah, Christian/*Olney Friends Sch*	19
Acomb, Mike/*Dorothy E Lewis Elem Sch*	50
Ada, Mustafa/*Horizon Sci Acad-Dayton Downtn [153]*	3
Adams, Bill/*Sacred Heart Parish Sch*	142
Adams, Jill/*Bell Creek Intermediate Sch*	83
Adams, Lisa/*Promise Academy*	44
Adams, Sarah/*Van Buren Middle Sch*	150
Adams, Tim/*Orrville High Sch*	212
Adelsberger, Krista/*Bellefontaine Intermediate Sch*	121
Adkins, Cosetta/*Digital Academy*	106
Adkins, Cosetta/*Ontario Elem Sch*	61
Adkins, Emily/*Brookside Middle Sch*	126
Adkins, Gregory/*Hannah Gibbons STEM Sch*	43
Adkins, Terry/*St Brigid Sch*	85
Ahmed, Shaad/*Dayton Islamic Sch*	154
Ahrens, Cory/*Celina Elem Sch*	143
Ahrens, Curtis/*Warrior Academy*	136
Akben, Daniel/*Horizon Sci Academy-Denison [153]*	39
Akkaya, Hasan/*Horizon Sci Acad-Columbus MS [153]*	3
Akosi, Joseph/*SS Joseph & John Sch*	52
Albanese, Anthony/*Springfield Elem Sch*	136
Albanese, James/*Buckeye Valley High Sch*	58
Albeit, Richard/*Arts & College Prep Academy*	65
Albert, Amanda/*Northmor Sch*	156
Alberts, Teresa/*Dover High Sch*	202
Albino, Ron/*St Peter Sch*	154
Albrecht, Tim/*Carrollton Elem Sch*	25
Albright, Joyce/*Hilltonia Middle Sch*	68
Albrinck, Dan/*St Susanna Sch*	209
Alestock, Karen/*Seton Catholic Sch*	195
Alexander, Missy/*Heritage Early Childhood Sch*	22
Alexander, Tyler/*Kettering Fairmont High Sch*	150
Alexandrou, Jim/*Maple Intermediate Sch*	48
Alferio, Jacob/*Keystone Elem Sch*	124
Alisson, Michael/*South Avondale Elem Sch*	88
Allen, Amy/*Centerville Prim Vlg Sch South*	148
Allen, Natasha/*Keyser Elem Sch*	129
Aller, Andrea/*Harris-Jackson Cmty Lrng Ctr*	191
Allison, Darlene/*North Union Elem Sch*	205
Allison, Michelle/*Elida Elem Sch*	8
Allshouse, Gail/*Van Gorden Elem Sch*	23
Almendinger, Kris/*Willis C Adams Middle Sch*	118
Alsharaiha, Luna/*St Agatha Sch*	76
Alspaugh, Stephen/*Bryan Middle High Sch*	214
Althof, Rachel/*Wellington Sch*	78
Altiers, Kelly/*Hamilton Intermediate Sch*	71
Alvarez, Vivian/*Western Elem Sch*	208
Amawi, Ahmad, Br/*Faith Islamic Elem Academy*	196
Ambrose, Micki/*Orchard Park Elem Sch*	150
Amen, R Scott/*Oliver Sch*	6
Amick, Oatis/*Crissey Elem Sch*	128
Amstutz, Scott/*Kirtland High Sch*	112
Amstutz, Scott/*Kirtland Middle Sch*	112
Anderson, Alex/*Geneva Middle Sch*	13
Anderson, Brittany/*Patrick Henry Sch*	44
Anderson, Devin/*Scioto Elem Sch*	162
Anderson, Grant/*Whitaker Elem Sch*	89
Anderson, Kathyrn/*Woodsfield Elem Sch*	148
Anderson, Lea/*Kairos Academy*	120
Andrachik, Elizabeth/*St Angela Merici Sch*	52
Andrews, Patrick/*Padre Pio Academy*	54
Andric, Michael/*Barberton Middle Sch*	192
Andrzejewski, Janine/*Valley Forge High Sch*	49
Annett, Anna/*Licking Heights Central MS*	118
Annett, Anna/*Licking Heights North Elem Sch*	118
Anservitz, Scott/*Lakeside Junior High Sch*	12
Anthony, Summer/*Como Elem Sch*	67
Antjas, Christopher/*Westwood Preparatory Academy*	6
Appelman, Steve/*Peebles High Sch*	6
Arck, Margy/*Dan Emmett Elem Sch*	111
Arcus-Goldberg, Rachel/*Columbus Jewish Day Sch*	77
Arick, Paul/*Foxfire East Academy*	86
Armelli, Terri/*All Saints-St John Vianney Sch*	114
Armstrong, Sabrina/*Mt Orab Middle Sch*	20
Arn, Andy/*St Michael Sch*	20
Arndts, PJ/*Northview Sch*	148
Arnett, Juli/*Indian Valley Digital Academy*	202
Arnold, Keith/*Mideast CTC Buffalo Campus*	157
Arnold, Nikki/*Sycamore Creek Elem Sch*	64
Arnold, Shaka/*Columbus Academy*	77
Arthur, Kim/*Central Elem Sch*	206
Arthurs, Brenda/*Columbus Adventist Academy*	77
Artino, Nate/*Bellevue Senior High Sch*	105
Artrip, Pamela/*Valleyview Elem Sch*	69
Arvidson, Annie/*Aim Academy*	184
Arvidson, Annie/*McGregor Reading & Math Prep*	185
Ash, Rick/*Temple Christian Academy*	177
Ashcroft, Kathleen/*Copley-Fairlawn Middle Sch*	192
Asher, Anne/*St Peter Catholic Sch*	62
Asher, Monica/*Chagrin Falls High Sch*	42
Asinjo, Tess/*Dayton Leadership Academy*	2
Aslan, Bill/*Horizon Sci Acad-Cleveland MS*	39
Assell, Mary Lou/*Success Academy*	31
Ast, Steven/*Brecksville Broadview Hts HS*	41
Atkins, Belinda/*South Lebanon Elem Sch*	207
Atkins, Leigh/*Pike Elem Sch*	156
Atkins, Leigh Ann/*Perry Elem Sch*	156
Audette, Elizabeth/*Slate Hill Elem Sch*	76
Aug, Holly/*Our Lady of Visitation Sch*	95
Aurin, Michael/*Dublin Jerome High Sch*	69
Auvil, Stacie/*East Dayton Christian Sch*	85
Aviles, Kathy/*Black River Education Center*	139
Ayers, Benjamin/*Rushmore Elem Sch*	150
B	
Babbs, Vera/*Duxberry Park Elem Sch*	67
Babics, Mike/*Glenoak High Sch*	188
Babiczuk, Timothy/*Malvern High Sch*	25
Babiczuk, Timothy/*Malvern Middle Sch*	25
Bachman, Rick/*Four Co Career Center*	79
Bacho, Linda/*Trinity High Sch*	53
Bacon, Tamra/*Ottawa River Elem Sch*	130
Badenhop, Tim/*Oakwood Junior High Sch*	152
Bader, Mike/*Timberstone Junior High Sch*	129
Baer, Kristin/*Meigs Primary Elem Sch*	143
Bagcioglu, Akan/*Horizon Sci Acad-Dayton HS [153]*	3
Bagcioglu, Hakan/*Noble Academy Cleveland [153]*	4
Bagley, Mark/*Van Wert Middle Sch*	206
Bailey, Dawn/*Lincoln Heights Elem Sch*	92
Bailey, Marianne/*Garfield Elem Sch*	138
Bailey, Mark/*New Richmond High Sch*	31
Bailey, Paul/*Westmoor Middle Sch*	69
Bailey, Paul/*Woodward Park Middle Sch*	69
Bailey, Tonya, Dr/*Encore Academy*	73
Bajorek, Celeste/*William Patrick Day EC Center*	40
Baker, Brian/*Buckeye Valley Middle Sch*	58
Baker, Carla/*Berkshire Middle Sch*	59
Baker, Christopher/*Bellbrook High Sch*	83
Baker, Cynthia/*McGuffey Elem Sch*	119
Baker, Davis/*Hillsdale High Sch*	11
Baker, Edmund/*South High Sch*	69
Baker, Kristin/*Olentangy Meadows Elem Sch*	59
Baker, Madeline/*Buckeye Online Sch-Success [240]*	33

School Year 2019-2020 — 800-333-8802

PRINCIPAL INDEX

Market Data Retrieval

NAME/School	PAGE
Baker, Meisha/Eastwood Elem Sch	125
Baker, Meredith/Brent Elem Sch	89
Baker, Stephanie/Highland Park Elem Sch	73
Baker, Terra/French Run Elem Sch	73
Balderson, Michelle/Rockhill Elem Sch	184
Baldner, Ben/Austintown Middle Sch	134
Baldwin, Paula/Frank Jacinto Elem Sch	124
Ball, Kevin/Woodmore Elementary/Middle Sch	159
Ball, Megan/Montessori Academy Cincinnati	209
Ball, Melissa/Northview Elem Sch	107
Ballentine, Matthew/Chillicothe Middle Sch	174
Ballert, Daviid, Dr/Bethel Baptist Christian Acad	167
Ballew, Larry/Hillcrest Academy	2
Ballinger, Brett/Utica Elem Sch	119
Ballinger, Kirk/Grant Middle Sch	138
Balough, Lori/Finland Middle Sch	73
Bamford, Sue/Parkwood Elem Sch	83
Banfield, Mara/Mahoning Co Career Tech Ctr	135
Banfield, Mara/Valley STEM and ME2 Academy	135
Bange, Leona/Clarksfield SDA Sch	107
Banks, Jeffrey/Babeck Early Childhood Ctr	21
Banks, Nancy/Southview Child & Family Ctr	148
Banks, Willie/University Academy [238]	5
Bankston, Iteisha/Lincoln-West High Sch	44
Barboza, Brad/Gahanna Middle School-East	70
Bare, Karen/Wyoming High Sch	94
Barhorst, Thomas/Ursuline Academy	96
Barker, Katy/W O Cline Elem Sch	149
Barker, Stacy/Heritage Elem Sch	9
Barley, Martha/Olde Sawmill Elem Sch	70
Barnett, Ward/Jones Leadership Academy	129
Barnhouse, Rick/Union Local Middle Sch	19
Barot, Brian/Greater Ohio Virtual Sch	2
Barr, Eric/Laura Woodward Elem Sch	58
Barrett, Melissa/Columbus Collegiate Acad-Main [249]	1
Barte, Sue/Norwood Elem Sch	132
Bartha, Daniel/Dempsey Middle Sch	58
Bartley, Ann/Walker Elem Sch	185
Bartley, Craig/Genoa Christian Academy	60
Bartley, Robin/Lakeshore Intergenerationl Sch	3
Bartlome, Beth/Sailorway Middle Sch	62
Barwacz, Jessica/Prospect Elem Sch	123
Basalla, Rita/St Mary Byzantine Sch	53
Basinski, Michael/Northwood Middle Sch	123
Basstock, Ray/Longfellow Middle Sch	124
Bastock, Rae/Southview Middle Sch	124
Bates, Thomas/Chapelfield Elem Sch	70
Bauer, Jeremy/Stranahan Elem Sch	129
Bauer, Lucas/Daniel Wright Elem Sch	69
Baughman, Katrina/Otsego Elem Sch	217
Baughman, Scott/Meadowbrook Middle Sch	86
Baum, Howard/Central College Christian Acad	77
Bauman, Dan/Main Street Sch	106
Bauman, Drew/Fostoria Jr Sr High Sch	180
Bauman, Eric/Liberty Junior High Sch	22
Baumgartner, Keith/Allen East High Sch	7
Baun, William/Paul C Bunn Elem Sch	136
Bavaro, Marisa/Hickory Ridge Elem Sch	140
Baxendale, Nathan/McCormick Middle Sch	126
Bay, Barry/Hilliard Memorial Middle Sch	72
Bays, Julie/Rio Grande Elem Sch	81
Beach, Nora/Glendale Primary Sch	41
Beadling, Troy/Scranton Elem Sch	45
Beal, Danene/St Francis Xavier Sch	142
Beam, Kim/Hillsboro Middle Sch	103
Beard, Karen/Golden Bridge Academy	10
Beard, Katie/Lake Middle Sch	217
Bearer, Kelly/Wickliffe Elem Sch	114
Beasley, Joy/East Preparatory Academy	39
Beaston, William/Charles Krout Elem Sch	181
Beauchamp, Alpacino/Roberts Paideia Academy	88
Beaver, Jill/Northridge Primary Sch	120
Beavers, Robin/Garfield Middle Sch	47
Bebout, Carol/Tri-Rivers Career Center HS	139
Beckman, Erika/Ehove Career Center	60

NAME/School	PAGE
Beers, Julie/Campus International Sch North	43
Beery, Scott/Licking Valley Middle Sch	119
Beining, Audrey/Ottawa Elem Sch	170
Beiter, Debbie/Indian Riffle Elem Sch	150
Belair, Craig/Liberty Elem Sch	75
Bell, Douglas/Marshall Elem Sch	130
Bell, Jacqueline/Glenville High Sch	43
Bell, Jerry/McGregor Elem Sch	130
Belmont, Michael/London Middle Sch	132
Belville, Chad/Fairland High Sch	116
Benn, Selethia/Imagine Columbus Primary Acad [245]	3
Bennett, Brian/Leipsic High Sch	170
Bennett, David/Chillicothe Primary Sch	175
Bennett, David/Pointview Elem Sch	75
Bennett, Gary/Coshocton Christian Sch	37
Bennett, Matthew/Milkovich Middle Sch	47
Bennett, Sarah/Imagine Clay Ave Cmty ES [245]	3
Bennett, Scott/Reynoldsburg HS-E STEM Academy	73
Bennetto, Kimberly/Eastern Heights Middle Sch	123
Bennington, Sherry/Findley Community Learning Ctr	191
Benns, Mary/St Mary of the Assumption Sch	115
Bentley, Mylissa/South Point Middle Sch	116
Bentley, Thomas/Elmwood High Sch	216
Berardinelli, Jennifer/Holy Family Learning Center	52
Bergant, Wendy/RE-Education Aspire Access	115
Berger, Lori/Little River Pre-School	99
Bergman, Diana/Sunbridge Sch	131
Berilla, Angelina/Newton Falls Junior High Sch	200
Berk, Jeffrey/Wayne High Sch	150
Berka, Sarah/Robert Frost Elem Sch	75
Berkemeier, Michael/Fairfield Freshman High Sch	21
Berkley, Jennie/Milford Preschool	31
Berkowitz, Rochie/Chaviva High Sch	53
Berlean, Kellie/Horizon Sci Acad-Dayton ES [153]	3
Berlean, Kellie/Snowhill Elem Sch	28
Berman, Karen/Toledo Early College High Sch	130
Bernal, Ellen/Delta Elem Sch	79
Bernal, Kori/Fostoria Elem Sch	180
Bernhardt, Albert/Hiawatha Elem Sch	130
Bernowski, Amanda/Northridge High Sch	119
Berridge, Sherri/Colonial Hills Elem Sch	75
Berry, Danita/Genoa Elem Sch	188
Bertemes, P J/Southeastern Jr Sr High Sch	28
Bertke, Pamela/Lakeview Junior High Sch	64
Bess, Simone/Southwest Ohio Prep Sch	5
Bessler, Heather/Our Lady of Lourdes Sch	95
Best, Brian/Columbus Grove High Sch	169
Best, Matthew/Wilson Vance Intermediate Sch	98
Best, Scott/Hull Prairie Interm Sch	218
Besteder, Dawn/Abraham Lincoln Elem Sch	47
Bethany, Elizabeth/Edgewater Elem Sch	129
Beun, Rachel/Northwestern Middle Sch	212
Bevard, Larry/Nashport Elem Sch	157
Beverage, Lori/Wynn Center	128
Beyer, Nicholas/Beaumont Sch	52
Bialko, Barb/St Mary Catholic Sch	62
Bick, Michael/Bright Elem Sch	102
Bickel, Dana/Crossroads Day Treatment Ctr	112
Bickel, Lukas/Immanuel Lutheran Sch	24
Bickel, Roxann/Anthony Wayne Early Chldhd Ctr	55
Bickelhaupt, Jeremy/Ottawa Co Christian Academy	160
Bickley, Theodore/Thoreau Park Elem Sch	49
Biedenbach, Adam/Three Rivers Elem Sch	94
Biederstedt, Josh/Patrick Henry High Sch	102
Biernacki, Tom/High Street Christian Academy	77
Biggs, John/Green Elem Sch	178
Bileci, Bernadette/Cornerstone Christian Academy	115
Billing, Eric/Dale Roy Sch	10
Billingsley, Gabrielle/Richard Allen Prep-Downtown	4
Billington, William/Kingsville Elem Sch	12
Binegar, Jason/Miami Trace Middle Sch	65
Birch, H/Zenith Academy East	6
Birch, H/Zenith Academy West	6
Birney, Grace/Le Chaperon Rouge Elem Sch	54
Birney, Jennifer/Harrison East Elem Sch	101

Ohio School Directory

PRINCIPAL INDEX

NAME/School	PAGE
Bishop, Andrea/Eastwood Elem Sch	51
Bishop, Jay/West Geauga High Sch	82
Bitsko, Pamela/Studebaker Pre-School	150
Bittner, Lori/Van Wert Early Childhood Ctr	205
Bixler, Marcus/Russia Local Sch	183
Black, Chris/Dalton High Sch	212
Black, Jude/Secrest Elem Sch	86
Black, Larry/Liberty Center High Sch	101
Black, Michael/Miamisburg High Sch	151
Black, Michael/Mound Elem Sch	151
Black, Neil/Monclova Christian Academy	131
Black, Twana, Dr/Waggoner Rd Junior High Sch	73
Blackburn, Ericka/Memorial Middle Sch	113
Blackburn, Scott/Warder Park Wayne Elem Sch	28
Blain, Todd/Akros Middle Sch	190
Blair, Carlos/Western Hills Univ High Sch	88
Blais, Jodi/Fairfield Co Early Chldhd Ctr	62
Blake, Susan/Field Middle Sch	165
Blakeman, Lisa/Gallia Academy Middle Sch	81
Blanc, Shelbrey/Holy Name High Sch	52
Bland, Duane/Linden-McKinley STEM Academy	68
Bland, Stephanie/Champion Middle Sch	67
Blankenship, Cathy/A Plus Children's Academy	1
Blase, Dean/Clark Montessori Sch	87
Blass, Barb/Marimor Sch	7
Blaurock, Colleen, Dr/Eastlake Middle Sch	114
Blondheim, Gregory/Forest Hill Cmty Learning Ctr	191
Bloomquist, Debra, Dr/Regina Coeli Sch	131
Blosser, Myrna/Southgate Sch	184
Blower, Cathe/Amesville Elem Sch	14
Bly, Melissa/Mason Early Childhood Center	208
Bocian, James, Dr/Fallen Timbers Middle Sch	127
Bockleman, Megan/Summit Acad Alt Lrng-Middleton [248]	20
Bodey, Doug/Apollo Career High Sch	8
Bodin, Colleen/Benjamin Logan Elem Sch	121
Bodo, Jamie/School of Bright Promise	108
Boeke, Andrew/Weller Elem Sch	149
Boggs, Melissa/Christian Life Academy	108
Bogle, Dave/St Charles Borromeo Sch	154
Bohn, Ryan/Townsend Cmty Sch	61
Boiarski, Michele/Erie Intermediate Sch	12
Boie, Angela/Louis Agassiz Elem Sch	44
Boka, Stephanie/Pleasant Valley Elem Sch	49
Boland, Daniel/Jackson Middle Sch	73
Bolchlinger, Darren/Berlin Elem Sch	104
Bolin, Kara/Athens Middle Sch	14
Bollinger, John/Bellevue Middle Sch	105
Bollmer, Ron/Princeton High Sch	92
Bolton, Abby/Davey Elem Sch	165
Bolton, Matt/The Seven Hills Sch	96
Bonamase, Greg/Girard Intermediate Sch	197
Bond, April/William Crawford Interm Sch	38
Bond, Tara/Danville Elem Middle Sch	110
Bonnell, Kari/Our Lady-Perpetual Help Sch	131
Bonner, Cliff/Federal Hocking Mid High Sch	14
Boodheshwar, Kesh/Huntington Elem Sch	140
Bookman, Shawn/Suffield Elem Sch	165
Booth, Kristen/David Hill Community Lrng Ctr	191
Booth, Kristen/Judith A Resnik Cmty Lrng Ctr	191
Booth, Mark/Green Intermediate Sch	185
Borchers, Julie/Whetstone Sch	155
Border, Lisa/Western Reserve High Sch	106
Border, Lisa/Western Reserve Middle Sch	106
Borgelt, Bryon, Dr/St Rose Sch	218
Borgman, Amy/Our Lady of Victory Sch	95
Borlaza, Stephanie/Britton Elem Sch	72
Born, Beth/Portsmouth Elem Sch	179
Bornino-Elwell, Terrilynn/Franklin School of Opportunity	47
Bornstine, Eric/Hoover High Sch	187
Boroff, Randy/Gross Schechter Day Sch	53
Borton, Linda/St Rose Sch	201
Bose, Sarah/Clermont Educ Collaborative-S	29
Bosley, Jacob/Garfield Elem Sch	43
Bossell, Larry/Harrison Career Center	18
Bostic, Edie/Hannan Trace Elem Sch	80

NAME/School	PAGE
Boulder, Rachel/Barberton Preschool	192
Bourgeois, Julie/St Paul Lutheran Sch	102
Bouscher, Peggy/East Liverpool Christian Sch	36
Bowen, Ann/Bright Beginnings Pre-School	85
Bowen, David/Crestview Local Sch	205
Bowles, Heather/Paint Valley Elem Sch	175
Bowling, Jeanie/Arts Academy at Summit	184
Bowman, Greg/Symmes Valley High Sch	117
Bowman, Mark/Utica Senior High Sch	119
Bowman, Thomas/Newark High Sch	119
Boyd, Elizabeth/Richmond Heights Elem Sch	49
Boyer, Carrie/Jefferson PK-8 Sch	200
Brack, Jane/St Vivian Sch	96
Brackman, Cheryl/Butler Tech Career Center	21
Bradesca, Dan/St Ignatius High Sch	53
Bradford, Lemon/Garfield Heights Learning Ctr	46
Bradley-Martes, Annette/Toledo Junior Academy	131
Bradley, Erin/Summit Academy Alt Lrng-Warren [248]	5
Bradley, Matthew/Highland Middle Sch	155
Brady, Barbara/Gilles-Sweet Elem Sch	46
Brady, Christopher/Hamilton STEM Academy	68
Brady, Jean/Xenia Preschool	85
Brady, Steve/Lincoln Elem Sch	142
Brady, Tom/Madison Middle Sch	112
Bragg, Jeff/Morgan Junior High Sch	155
Brakhage, Kara/New Miami Middle High Sch	24
Branch, Josh/Newcomerstown High Sch	203
Brandy, Worth/Alum Creek Elem Sch	59
Brashear, Tony/Rossford High Sch	218
Brasno, Jason/Northtowne Elem Sch	68
Bratcher, Andy/Green Middle Sch	212
Bratcher, Andy/Smithville High Sch	212
Bratten, Joanne/Fishcreek Elem Sch	194
Braun, Brenda/Versailles Elem Sch	56
Brawley, Jamie/Southeast Intermediate Sch	167
Braxton, Lisa/Warrensville Heights Mid Sch	51
Bray, April/Groveport Elem Sch	71
Brecheisen, Katie/Ohio Connections Academy [181]	4
Breech, Russ/Clay Local Sch	178
Breese, Robbie/Marsh Foundation Sch	205
Brengelman, Carol/Ohio Christian Academy	25
Brennan, Michael/Sherman Elem Sch	172
Brennan, Michael/Woodland Elem Sch	173
Bresler, Sharon/St Veronica Sch	96
Brewer, Dawn/South Western Preschool	74
Breyman, Tim/Fairview High Sch	57
Brickley, Joyce/Hilliard Darby High Sch	72
Brickner, Matthew/Bishop Ready High Sch	76
Briggs, Aideen/Mother Teresa Cath ES	24
Briggs, Aideen/St Nicholas Academy	96
Briggs, Chad/New Concord Elem Sch	156
Briggs, Ryan/Blanchester Middle Sch	32
Briggs, Ryan/Fayetteville Middle Sch	19
Brigham, Monte/Roosevelt Middle Sch	28
Brightbill, Joey/Northwestern Elem Sch	212
Brindley, Rick/Ashland Co-W Holmes Career Ctr	11
Brinkman, Chad/Jefferson Senior High Sch	8
Brinkman, Dean/Kalida High Sch	170
Brock, Theresa/Endeavor Elem Sch	22
Brockett, Paul/Ashtabula Co Tech & Career Ctr	12
Brockway, Pat/Kenston Middle Sch	82
Brodie, Nicole/Reagan Elem Sch	10
Broermann, Mark/Jackson Middle Sch	107
Brogan, Curt/Glendening Elem Sch	71
Brokamp, Stephen/Batavia Middle Sch	29
Bronikowski, Jennifer/Washington Junior High Sch	131
Bronner, Chris/Brookville High Sch	148
Brooks, Roger/St Peter Sch	126
Brooks, Selena/St John Central Academy	19
Brooks, Steve/John Glenn High Sch	156
Browarsky, Joanne/St Francis DeSales Sch	95
Brown, Anastasia/Devonshire Elem Sch	67
Brown, Anita/Piqua SDA Christian Sch	147
Brown, Ben/Ridge Junior High Sch	22
Brown, Beth/Frontier High Middle Sch	210

School Year 2019-2020   800-333-8802   OH-U3

PRINCIPAL INDEX

NAME/School	PAGE
Brown, Brian/*Clear Fork High Sch*	171
Brown, Courtney/*St Bernard Taylor Creek Sch*	95
Brown, Cynthia/*Green High Sch*	185
Brown, Donna/*Venice Heights Elem Sch*	61
Brown, Garla/*Bell Academy*	72
Brown, Greg/*Charles Sch at Ohio Dominican*	66
Brown, Greg/*Graham Elem and Middle Sch*	66
Brown, Greg/*Graham Sch*	66
Brown, John/*Groveport Madison MS Central*	71
Brown, John/*Midview Middle Sch*	125
Brown, Jonathan, Dr/*William H Taft Elem Sch*	88
Brown, Kara/*Simon Kenton Sch*	99
Brown, Lisa/*Claymont High Sch*	202
Brown, Luke/*Heritage Christian Sch*	54
Brown, Marnisha/*Richmond Heights Secondary Sch*	49
Brown, Matthew/*Wayne Co Schools Career Center*	213
Brown, Melissa/*Phoenix Cmty Learning Center*	4
Brown, Mike/*Canton Country Day Sch*	190
Brown, Odell/*Cleveland Sch of Arch & Design*	43
Brown, Rebecca/*St Peter School-Lorain*	126
Brown, Renee/*Mason Leadership Sch*	185
Brown, Robb/*Holloway Elem Sch*	128
Brown, Robert/*Grandview Heights High Sch*	71
Brown, Ryan/*Watkins Middle Sch*	120
Brown, Sherrie/*Fairview Elem Sch*	57
Brown, Tammy/*Preston Elem Sch*	192
Brown, Timothy/*Elyria High Sch*	123
Brownfield, Robert/*St Vincent St Mary HS*	196
Brownfield, Thomas/*Holy Family Catholic Sch*	52
Browning, Michael/*London High Sch*	132
Brownlow, Terry/*Solon Pre-Chool*	50
Brubaker, Christa/*St Mary Sch*	174
Bruce, Jeremy/*Fuchs Mizrachi Sch*	53
Brumbaugh, Jarrod/*Northmont Middle Sch*	152
Bruner, Donna/*Lake Elem Sch*	186
Bruner, Jacob/*Colonel Crawford High Sch*	38
Brunner, Ken/*Timken Early College HS*	185
Brunner, Kenneth/*McKinley Downtown Campus*	185
Bryan, Mason/*Riverside Elem Sch*	121
Bryan, Matt/*Henry Defer Intermediate Sch*	167
Bryan, Timothy/*Coventry Elem Sch*	192
Bryant, Bruce/*South Bloomfield Elem Sch*	163
Bryant, Dawn/*R C Waters Elem Sch*	158
Bryant, Laura/*Old Fort Elem Sch*	181
Bucher, Erin/*Driscoll Elem Sch*	149
Buchheim, Robert/*Mt Healthy Jr Sr High Sch*	91
Buchman, Kevin/*Ridgewood Elem Sch*	72
Buck, Melissa/*South Community Yph*	154
Buck, Ryan/*Carroll Hills Sch*	25
Buck, Suzanne/*Western Reserve Academy*	196
Buckman, Nancy/*Chca-Founders Campus Upper Sch*	96
Bucy, Joan/*Olde Orchard Elem Sch*	68
Buddy, Lee, Dr/*Wade Park Elem Sch*	45
Budimirovic, Brittany/*Galloway Ridge Interm Sch*	73
Bueing, Dave/*Vanguard Technology Center*	177
Buell, Whitney/*Indian Hill Elem Sch*	90
Buffer, Jim/*Tremont Elem Sch*	74
Buller, Kristina/*Avon High Sch*	123
Bunner, Troy/*Copopa Elem Sch*	123
Bunting, Jason/*Maysville High Sch*	157
Burchfield, Tammy/*Franklin Junior High Sch*	207
Burchfield, Tammy/*John E Gregg Elem Sch*	109
Burchfield, Tammy/*Waynesville Elem Sch*	209
Burgett, PJ/*Franklin-Monroe Jr Sr High Sch*	55
Burggraf, Matt/*North Union Middle Sch*	205
Burgos, Marisol/*Int'l Newcomers Acad-Jefferson*	43
Burk, Travis/*Cozaddale Baptist Academy*	32
Burke, Jill, Dr/*Central Crossing High Sch*	73
Burke, John/*St Marys Memorial High Sch*	16
Burke, Mark, Dr/*Bucyrus Secondary Sch*	38
Burke, Shannon/*Mt Pleasant Elem Sch*	64
Burkett, Brian/*Liberty-Benton Elem Sch*	98
Burkholder, Jay/*Donnelsville Elem Sch*	29

NAME/School	PAGE
Burkholder, Mike/*Northwestern High Sch*	212
Burnett, Jeremy/*Bethel Christian Academy*	53
Burney, Tashlai/*Rise & Shine Academy*	127
Burns, Dani/*Lincoln PK-8 Sch*	200
Burns, Denise/*St Leo the Great Sch*	53
Burre, Scott/*Lancaster Senior High Sch*	63
Burris, Gayle/*Granville Intermediate Sch*	117
Burroughs, John/*Heritage Christian Sch*	139
Burrow, Robin/*Eastern Elem Sch*	142
Burrows, Christopher/*Southern Hills Career Tech Ctr*	20
Burson, Bryian/*Westgate Middle Sch*	35
Burt, Larry/*Lake Erie International HS*	3
Burton, Richard/*Northwest High Sch*	179
Burzanko, Amy/*Austinburg Elem Sch*	13
Buschur, Chrissy/*St Helen Sch*	85
Busdeker, Larry/*Hancock Co MH Unit*	97
Busenburg, Derick/*Johnstown-Monroe High Sch*	118
Bush, Dwon/*Monticello Elem Sch*	150
Bush, Gary/*Dukes Digital Academy*	186
Bush, Jacob/*Celeryville Christian Sch*	107
Bush, Nicole/*Gibbs Leadership Sch*	184
Bush, Shawn/*Eastern High Sch*	142
Bush, Shawn/*Eastern Middle Sch*	142
Busold, Bryan/*North Olmsted Middle Sch*	48
Busse, Laura/*Cleveland PK-6 Sch*	149
Bussey, Maleeka/*Rowland Elem Sch*	51
Bute, Michael/*West Jefferson High Sch*	132
Butler, Aaron/*Mason Run High Sch*	4
Butler, Deshannon/*Bridge Gate Cmty Sch*	1
Butler, Mark/*Benjamin Logan High Sch*	121
Butler, Scott/*Lebanon High Sch*	207
Butler, William/*Monroeville Elem Sch*	105
Butterman, Angela/*Kenton Elem Sch*	100
Butts, Chrissie/*Loudonville High Sch*	11
Buzek, Sarah/*Maddux-Lang Primary Sch*	151
Buzzard, David/*Columbiana High Sch*	34
Buzzelli, Katie/*St Francis DeSales Sch*	195
Byrne, Jamie/*The Tomorrow Center*	5
Byrne, Jay/*Mvctc Youth Connect Alt Sch*	151

C

NAME/School	PAGE
Cable-Miller, Dena/*Ben Franklin Elem Sch*	119
Cabot, Lori/*Ridgewood Elem Sch*	37
Cacioppo, Rebecca/*Rimer Cmty Learning Ctr*	191
Cadwell, Rob/*River Elem Sch*	147
Calandros, Mario/*St Louis Sch*	189
Caldwell, Chris/*Skyvue Elem Sch*	147
Caldwell, Cynthia/*Jefferson Avenue Elem Sch*	18
Caldwell, Danielle/*Conotton Valley High Sch*	101
Caldwell, Ryan/*Belmont Career Center*	18
Calfee, Tim/*Alliance Early Learning Sch*	184
Callewaert, Wendy/*Greeneview Middle Sch*	84
Calvelage, Brad/*Columbus Grove Elem Sch*	169
Cameron, Kirk/*Kenton Middle Sch*	100
Cameron, Randy/*Mineral Ridge High Sch*	201
Camp, Brian/*Eaton Middle Sch*	168
Campana, Monica/*Washington Elem Sch*	72
Campbell-Sauer, Tamar/*Scioto Darby Elem Sch*	72
Campbell, Charmaine/*Parkmoor Elem Sch*	68
Campbell, Chris/*Bishop Watterson High Sch*	76
Campbell, Diane/*Wedgewood Middle Sch*	69
Campbell, Heather/*Camden Primary Sch*	168
Campbell, Heather/*Champion K-8 Elementery Sch*	197
Campbell, Heather/*Dresden Elem Sch*	157
Campbell, Jacob/*Tallmadge Elem Sch*	64
Campbell, Jaime/*Ohdela Academy*	4
Campbell, Mary Ann/*Four Oaks Early Intervention*	83
Campbell, Noah/*Discovery Academy*	2
Campbell, Robert/*Rootstown Middle Sch*	166
Campion, Alana/*St Anthony Catholic Sch*	154
Campisi, Margaret/*St Michael Sch*	53
Candela, Steve/*Jefferson Elem Sch*	13
Candela, Steve/*Rock Creek Elem Sch*	13

Ohio School Directory — PRINCIPAL INDEX

NAME/School	PAGE
Candido, Darcy/Hatton Cmty Learning Center	191
Cannon, Brian/McPherson Middle Sch	176
Cannon, Maggie/Junction City Elem Sch	161
Cano, Andrew/Hardin Northern High Sch	100
Cantwell, Kimberly/Royalview Elem Sch	114
Capers, Dante/Warren G Harding High Sch	200
Caplinger, Nathan/Unioto High Sch	176
Capper, Roman/Arrowhead Primary Sch	192
Capretta, Karen/Red Raiders Pre-School	113
Caputo, Matthew/Fredericktown Middle Sch	111
Caras, George/Beavercreek High Sch	83
Card, Gary/Lakota West Freshman Campus	22
Card, Gary/Lakota West High Sch	22
Cardinal, Andy/Cardinal Middle Sch	81
Carey, Brent/Weisenborn Junior High Sch	150
Carey, Janie/Michigan Primary Sch	12
Carkido, Gary/McDonald High Sch	199
Carlier, Garth/Loveland Intermediate Sch	90
Carlier, Tim/Fayetteville High Sch	19
Carmer, Todd/Licking Valley Elem Sch	119
Carmichael, Angela/Wooster Twp Elem Sch	213
Carmony-Mies, Yolanda/Genoa Elem Sch	159
Carner, Andrew/St Mary Catholic Sch	53
Caroff, Craig/Millridge Elem Sch	48
Carpenter, Chad/Highland High Sch	155
Carpenter, Craig/Fairfield Christian Academy	65
Carpenter, James/Hinckley Elem Sch	141
Carpenter, Mr/St Christine Sch	137
Carpenter, Patrick/Noble Elem Sch	42
Carpenter, Steve/Oak Hill Middle High Sch	107
Carr, Andrew/Newbridge Math Reading Academy	4
Carr, Eldrich/Springer School and Center	96
Carr, Holly/Brookpark Middle Sch	73
Carr, Mark/Walsh Jesuit High Sch	196
Carr, Matthew/Defiance Middle Sch	57
Carr, Matthew/Paulding Middle Sch	160
Carr, Michael/Glenwood Elem Sch	129
Carraher, Melissa/Charles L Seipelt Elem Sch	31
Carroll, Dreama/Imagine Harrisburg PK Cmty Sch [245]	3
Carroll, John/Centerville High Sch	148
Carroll, Joseph/Christ the King Sch	131
Carroll, Tom/Delaware Christian Sch	60
Carsolo, Melanie/Rich Center for Autism	137
Carter, Adrienne/Southwest Licking ELC	120
Carter, Brent/Indian Valley Middle Sch	202
Carter, Chad/McCormick Junior High Sch	61
Carter, Kacy/Jackson Memorial Middle Sch	186
Carter, Larry/Southwestern Elem Sch	80
Carter, Rebecca/East Canton Elem Sch	188
Carter, Robin/Little Hocking Elem Sch	210
Carter, Robin/Warren Elem Sch	210
Case, Kari/Lucas Elem Sch	172
Case, Kari/Lucas Heritage Middle Sch	172
Case, Karla/Lincoln Park Elem Sch	68
Cash, Crystal/Chambers Elem Sch	45
Casselberry, Helen/Messiah Lutheran Elem Sch	54
Cassidy, Scott/Minerva Middle Sch	187
Casson, Barbara/Our Lady of Bethlehem Sch	76
Castiglione, Kim/Harrison Street Elem Sch	58
Cathcart, Cynthia/St Patrick Catholic Sch	147
Catlos, Allison/New Hope Christian Academy	163
Caton, Joshua/Blessed Sacrament Sch	120
Caton, Terri/Liberty Tree Elem Sch	59
Caudill, Duane/Bethel Middle High Sch	145
Caudill, Jason/Bexley Middle Sch	66
Caudill, Mark/Oakland Park Elem Sch	68
Cavanaugh, Bill/St Dominic Sch	95
Cavin, Mike/Apostolic Christian Academy	131
Cebula, Nikki/Youtz Leadership Sch	185
Cecchetti, Samary/St James the Less Sch	76
Cech, Lucas/Marion-Franklin High Sch	68
Cecil, Amanda/Liberty Christian Academy	120
Celeste, Natalie/Tremont Montessori Sch	45
Cento, Terri/Cardinal Pacelli Sch	95
Cercone, Carrie/Education Alternatives	126
Cerny, Renee/St Columbkille Sch	53
Cerny, Renee/St Rocco Sch	53
Cervello, Al/West Boulevard Elem Sch	134
Chaffee, Michael/Newbury Jr Sr High Sch	82
Chaffin, Karen/Marysville Early College HS	204
Chamberlain, Carl/Walnut Ridge High Sch	69
Chambers, Beverly/Chippewa Elem Sch	41
Chambers, John/Walnut Hills High Sch	88
Chambliss, Larry, Dr/Fairless High Sch	185
Chanoski, Ed/Fox Run Sch	19
Chapman, Edna/Hayward Middle Sch	28
Chapman, Janel/North Union High Sch	205
Chari, Laxmi/Schumacher Cmty Learning Ctr	191
Charlton, Phillitia/Trotwood-Madison Middle Sch	153
Charpentier, Albert/Summit Acad Alt Lrng-Lorain	122
Chase, Paul/Beachwood High Sch	40
Chatman, Samantha/Alton Darby Elem Sch	71
Cheraso, Frank/Summit Acad Cmty Sch-Painsvlle [248]	112
Cherry, Ryan/Little Miami Junior High Sch	208
Chessler, Amy/Holy Spirit Sch	76
Chestnut, Sam/Lippman Day Sch	196
Childs, Rhonda/Linden Park Ecec	68
Chilman, Jason/Springfield-Clark Career Tech	28
Choe, Sun/Firelands Elem Sch	124
Chorba, Susan/Glendale-Feilbach Elem Sch	129
Christi, Maria, Sr/St Gertrude Sch	95
Christie, Donald/Perrysburg Junior High Sch	218
Christopher, Justin/Windham High Sch	167
Ciccarelli, Jennifer/Columbus School for Girls	77
Cicco, Cristin/Brooklyn Sch	41
Cicerchi, Janette/Incarnate Word Academy	52
Cicerchi, Jeff/North Royalton Middle Sch	48
Cinadr, Lisa/St Ambrose Sch	142
Civiello, Annette/Tuscarawas Central Catholic HS	204
Claes, Randy/Wooster Christian Sch	214
Clark, Adam/Treca Digital Academy	5
Clark, Andrea/Big Walnut Elem Sch	58
Clark, Brad/Bath Middle Sch	8
Clark, Carl/Howland Glen Primary Sch	198
Clark, Chris/Ashland Christian Sch	11
Clark, George/Lomond Elem Sch	50
Clark, Jay/Van Buren Middle Sch	99
Clark, Jeff/Piqua Junior High Sch	146
Clark, Jeremy/Valley Elem Sch	179
Clark, Kennith/Adams County Christian Sch	7
Clark, Nancy/Holy Cross Lutheran Sch	54
Clark, Robert/Indian Valley High Sch	202
Clark, Ron/Barnesville High Sch	17
Clark, Sonja/Denison Elem Sch	43
Clarke-Eagle, Monica/Reynolds Elem Sch	130
Class, Cynthia/Fairless Middle Sch	185
Class, Tabatha/New Miami Elem Sch	23
Clauss, Debra/Mt Gilead High Sch	155
Clay, Michael/Burlington Elem Sch	116
Claypool, Lee/Triad Elem Sch	26
Clements, Andrea/Tuscarawas Valley Primary Sch	203
Clements, Andrea/Tuscarawas Vly Interm Sch	203
Clements, Lauren/Corryville Catholic Elem Sch	95
Clemons, Karen/St Bernard Elem Sch	93
Clemons, Shannon/Parsons Elem Sch	68
Climer, Collin/Colerain Elem Sch	91
Cline, Mindy/Centerville Prim Vlg Sch North	148
Clinkscale, Ernest/Hawthorne Elem Sch	75
Clinkscale, Kimberly/Hope Academy for Autism	201
Closson, Tim/Bluffton Elem Sch	8
Clugh, Alissa/Lincoln Park Academy [238]	3
Clugh, Alissa/Lincoln Prepartory Academy	3
Cluse, Mary Ann/Starlight Sch	156
Coan, Susan/St Jerome Elem Sch	53
Coats, Thomas/Middletown Christian Sch	209
Cobb, Brandon/Kean Elem Sch	213
Cobb, Erica/Old Fort High Sch	181
Cobert, Keith/Pathway School of Discovery [203]	148
Cochenour, Shara/Pickaway-Ross Career Tech Ctr	175
Cochran, Aimee/Amanda-Clearcreek Middle Sch	62

PRINCIPAL INDEX

Market Data Retrieval

NAME/School	PAGE
Cochran, Thomas/Marysville High Sch	204
Cochrane, Kimberly/Washington Elem Sch	81
Cocita, Karen/St Mark Sch	53
Cockley, Kimberly/Hudson Middle Sch	193
Coddington, Charlie/Citizens Academy Southeast [239]	39
Coffee, Brian/West Branch High Sch	136
Coghlan, Leah/Incarnation Sch	154
Cole, Peter/Carey Exempted Village Sch	219
Coleman, Ben/South Point High Sch	116
Coleman, Beth/Ravenna High Sch	166
Coleman, Chet/Cherry Valley Elem Sch	119
Coleman, David/River Valley High Sch	139
Coleman, Patrick/Cuyahoga Heights High Sch	45
Coleman, Patrick/Cuyahoga Heights Middle Sch	45
Coleman, Rachel/Roxboro Middle Sch	42
Coleman, Suellen/Waterford High Sch	211
Collaros, Chris/Wickliffe Elem Sch	74
Collier, Jul'Yanna/East Bridge Acad of Excellence	2
Collier, Juliana/Gateway Academy of Ohio	2
Collins, Brian/East Elem Sch	203
Collins, Michael/St Peter In Chains Sch	24
Collison, Blane/Bishop Fenwick High Sch	209
Colon, William/Greenwood Elem Sch	130
Colson, Tracey/Mifflin Middle Sch	68
Colwell, Meg/Puritas Cmty Elememtary Sch [242]	40
Combs, Leslie/Blue Ash Elem Sch	93
Combs, Michael/Spinning Hills Middle Sch	151
Combs, Tim/Legacy Christian Academy	85
Comer, Anthony/Lockland Elem Sch	90
Comer, Anthony/Lockland High Sch	90
Comstock, Melanie/Heritage Elem Sch	139
Conaway, Melanie/Western Reserve Elem Sch	106
Condit, Brian/Ella Canavan Elem Sch	141
Congrove, Susan/Zane Trace Elem Sch	176
Conley, Bill/Revere Middle Sch	194
Conley, James/Rootstown High Sch	166
Conley, Josh/Hamilton Elem Sch	71
Conley, Krista/Jasper Elem Sch	164
Conley, Micca/Slate Ridge Elem Sch	73
Conley, Shannon/Buckeye Junior High Sch	140
Conners, Brian/C O Harrison Elem Sch	92
Conners, T/Queen of Peace Elem Sch	24
Connolly, Cheryl/Akron Early College High Sch	190
Conrad, Nathan/Bloom-Carroll High Sch	63
Conroy, Jeff/Belle Aire Intermediate Sch	65
Consiglio, Alyse/John F Kennedy Catholic Sch	201
Contat, Brad/Anthony Wayne Jr High Sch	127
Cook-Frazier, Angela/Kilgour Elem Sch	88
Cook, Cheryl/Harmar Elem Sch	210
Cook, Jenna/Columbus Collegiate Acad-Dana [249]	1
Cook, Lisa/Summit Academy Sec Sch-Canton [248]	184
Cook, Michelle/Hillside Middle Sch	49
Cookson, Aaron/Hilliard Davidson High Sch	72
Cooley, Brad/Norwalk High Sch	106
Cooper, David/Harbor Education Serv Leap Prg	167
Cooper, Ellen/Legend Elem Sch	119
Cooper, Heather/Western Brown High Sch	20
Cooper, Jason/River Gate High Sch	5
Cooper, Sharon/Robert H Jamison Sch	45
Cooper, Yolanda/Richard Allen Academy-Hamilton	4
Copas, Dorethia/Violet Elem Sch	64
Copehaver, Donald/Cas-Gerson Sch	53
Copeland-Shull, Cheri/Dorr Street Elem Sch	128
Copeland, Lynn/Morgan East Elem Sch	155
Copley, Kyle/Scioto Co Career Tech Center	179
Corbin, Emily/Ecole Kenwood FR Immersion ES	68
Corcoran, Laura/Bishop Flaget Sch	176
Corder, Carrie/Clearcreek Elem Sch	208
Cornwell, Mark/Vern Riffe Sch	178
Cosgriff, Meg/SS Robert & William Sch	52
Costa, Gabriel/Spanish Immersion Sch	173
Costello, Gregory/West High Sch	69
Costello, T/Catholic Central High Sch	110
Cothran, Ron/Mound St Info & Tech Academy	4
Cotter, Carmela/Middletown High Sch	23
Cottrell, Kristen/Ledgeview Elem Sch	193
Couch, Scott/Eaton High Sch	168
Coulter, Brooke/Springboro Intermediate Sch	208
Courtney, Lisa/Summerside Elem Sch	31
Coury, Michael/Copley High Sch	192
Cousins, Zachary/Maple Elem Sch	113
Covington, Mrs/St Dominic Sch	53
Cox, Dan/Live Oaks Career Dev Campus	89
Cox, Karyn/Bryan Elem Sch	214
Cox, Matt/Hylen Souders Elem Sch	58
Cozad, Roberta/Grand Valley Middle Sch	13
Craft, Renene/A Plus Arts Acad-Maybury	1
Crawford, Renee/Bond Hill Academy	87
Crawford, Sabrina/Harrison Elem Sch	47
Creighton, Bill/Matamoras Elem Sch	210
Cremeans, Heather/Fairwood Elem Sch	22
Croll, Tami/Terrace Park Elem Sch	91
Cronin, Patricia/Stewart Early Learning Center	191
Crook, Rapp/Bible Believers Christian Sch	10
Crosier, Shawn/Garfield East Elem Sch	109
Crosier, Shawn/Wells Academy	109
Crothers, Nichole/Liberty Middle Sch	59
Crowder, John/Falls Learning Academy	200
Crowder, John/Newton Falls High Sch	200
Crowe, Duane, Dr/Winton Preparatory Academy [238]	6
Crowe, Jason/Mentor High Sch	113
Crowe, Lori/West Clermont Middle Sch	31
Croyle, Christine/Brooks Yates Sch	162
Crum, Lori/Shaw High Sch	45
Crum, Sherry/Licking Valley Elem Sch	119
Csank, Dave/Villa Angela-St Joseph HS	53
Cubbison, Trent/East Muskingum Middle Sch	156
Cullum, Sarah/Notre Dame Academy	131
Culp, Jason/Lawrence Upper Sch	196
Cummings, Brent/Summit Academy Elem Sch-Toledo	127
Cummings, Brent/Summit Academy-Toledo	5
Cummins, Troy/Fountain City Christian Sch	216
Cunningham, Chad/Elgin High Sch	138
Cunningham, Jack/North Elem Sch	35
Cunningham, Scott/Orange Middle Sch	59
Cunningham, Thomas/Beaver Local High Sch	34
Cupp, Brandi/Wellston Middle Sch	108
Curtis, Dan/Evergreen High Sch	78
Curtis, Matt/Trimble High Sch	15
Curtis, Scott/George Washington Elem Sch	138
Cuttitta, Jon/St Peter Jr Sr High Sch	174
Czaplicki, John/St Matthew Parish Sch	195

D

NAME/School	PAGE
D'Amico, Terese/Pine Intermediate Sch	48
D'Aurora, Shana, Dr/STEM Academy	109
Dailey, Melissa/Mid-Valley Christian Sch	143
Daily, Leigh/Elmwood Primary Sch	9
Daley, Tom/Bridgeport High Sch	18
Dallio, Jim/Edgewood Middle Sch	21
Dalton, Brian/Lebanon Junior High Sch	207
Dalton, Robert, Dr/Zanesville Middle Sch	158
Damadeo, Jeff/Indian Hill High Sch	90
Danaher, T/Bishop Mussio Ctl Elem Sch	110
Danaher, Theresa/Bishop Mussio Ctl Jr High Sch	110
Dancy, Jaeda/Castle High Sch	1
Daney, Kathleen/Kenwood Elem Sch	216
Dangerfield, Marian/Crestview Elem Sch	34
Daniel, Deborah/Buckeye Central Middle Sch	38
Dansby, Matthew/Tussing Elem Sch	64
Dason, Shelly, Dr/Pleasant Cmty Digital Academy	138
Daugherty, Mrs/Richard Allen Prep-Dayton	4
Daugherty, Stacy/Watson Elem Sch	188
Davenport, Ramone/Dohn Cmty High Sch	87
Davia, Joel/Union Local High Sch	19
Davidson, Jodi/Mercer Elem Sch	89

Ohio School Directory — PRINCIPAL INDEX

NAME/School	PAGE
Davis, Brandi/*I Promise Sch*	191
Davis, Brent/*Tree of Life Christian Sch*	77
Davis, Caroline/*Metro Institute of Technology*	4
Davis, Christine/*Bethel-Tate Middle Sch*	30
Davis, Courtney/*Dunbar Primary Sch*	195
Davis, Courtney/*Munroe Elem Sch*	195
Davis, Damon/*Reading Middle Sch*	93
Davis, Danielle/*Newton Sch*	146
Davis, Dave/*Carrollton Middle High Sch*	25
Davis, DeWayne/*Fairwood Elem Sch*	68
Davis, Frank/*Mentor Christian Sch*	115
Davis, Jacqueline/*Clyde Elem Sch*	176
Davis, Jenny/*Griffith Thomas Elem Sch*	70
Davis, John/*Wilson Middle Sch*	119
Davis, Kay/*Carlton Sch*	142
Davis, LaMonica/*Helen Arnold Cmty Lrng Center*	191
Davis, Latonia/*Martin L King Career Campus*	44
Davis, Melanie/*North Nimishillen Elem Sch*	186
Davis, Quenton/*Garrett Morgan Sch*	43
Davis, Robert/*Truth Christian Academy*	180
Davis, Ryan/*Miami Trace Elem Sch*	65
Davis, Stephanie/*Bridges Learning Center*	191
Davis, Susan/*Lakota East High Sch*	22
Davis, Suzanna/*Lakota East Freshman Campus*	22
Davis, Tresa/*Norton Middle Sch*	74
Davisson, Kelli/*Buckeye Intermediate Sch*	140
Dawson, Shelly, Dr/*Pleasant Elem Sch*	138
Dawson, Troy/*Philo High Sch*	156
Day, Jeremy/*Winton Woods Interm Sch*	94
Day, Jessica/*Temple Christian Sch*	174
Day, Karen/*Mt Notre Dame High Sch*	95
Day, Lindsey/*Imagine Madison Ave Sch-Arts [245]*	3
Day, Robie/*Eastern High Sch*	163
Day, Robie/*Eastern Middle Sch*	163
Day, Roger/*Struthers High Sch*	136
Dean, Mary/*King Cmty Learning Center*	191
Dean, Nancy/*Decolores Montessori Sch*	56
Dean, Nancy, Dr/*Decolores Mnt Jr High Farm Sch*	56
DeAngelis, Melissa/*Heritage Middle Sch*	113
Dearwester, Jennifer/*Bobby F Grigsby Interm Sch*	206
Debelak, Charles/*Birchwood School of Hawken*	53
Debos, Ken/*Wright Preparatory Academy [238]*	6
DeCastro, Matthew/*East Franklin Elem Sch*	73
Dedo, Kim/*Shoreland Elem Sch*	130
Deem, Todd/*Waite High Sch*	130
DeFelice, Anthony/*Springfield High Sch*	136
Deisher, Stefanie/*McEsc Learning Center West*	148
DeLaney, Trisha/*Buckeye Trail Elem Sch*	86
Delatore, Mike/*Martins Ferry Middle Sch*	18
Deliz, Lisa/*Vermilion High Sch*	62
Delzani, Sheila/*Westpark Cmty Elem Sch [242]*	40
Delzani, Sheila/*Westpark Cmty Middle Sch [242]*	40
Dembski, Fran/*Longfellow Elem Sch*	183
Denius, Justin/*Shenandoah High Sch*	158
Dennis, Billy/*Westfall High Sch*	163
Dennis, Jennifer/*Highview 6th Grade Center*	23
Denny, Jennifer/*New Albany Interm Sch*	72
Dente, Gregory/*East Canton Middle Sch*	188
DePasquale, Carrie/*St Joseph Sch-Cuyahoga Falls*	195
Derickson, Tim/*Batavia High Sch*	29
DeRose, Lisa/*Southeast Elem Sch*	35
Deshuk, Marie/*Stevan Dohanos Elem Sch*	124
Dessler, Simcha/*Hebrew Academy of Cleveland*	54
Destino, Paul/*Mayfield Middle Sch*	47
Detmer-Bogaert, Shelley/*Columbia Intermediate Sch*	207
Dettra, Devvon/*Meadowbrook High Sch*	86
Dever, Christina/*Oak Intermediate Sch*	179
Dever, Christina/*Stanton Primary Sch*	179
Dever, Jeffrey/*Bowling Green High Sch*	216
DeVine, Krista/*Immaculate Heart of Mary Sch*	95
DeVoe, Shawna, Dr/*Rittman Elem Sch*	213
DeWeese, Shannon/*Catholic Central ES-Limestone*	29
DeWeese, Shannon/*Catholic Central Jr Sr HS*	29
DeWeese, Shannon/*Catholic Central Sch*	29
DiBacco, Shelley/*St Joan of Arc Sch*	53
Dibee, Jack, Dr/*Ely Elem Sch*	123
Dick, Matt/*Maumee High Sch*	128
DiDonato, Beth/*Claymont Intermediate Sch*	202
Diedrick, Steven/*Bessie Kinsner Elem Sch*	51
Diener, Jayme/*Granville Christian Academy*	120
Dietrich, Matt/*Napoleon Elem Sch PK-2*	101
DiFrancesco, Deborah/*Rayen Early College Interm Sch*	137
DiGiorgio, Susan/*Ascension Sch*	154
Dilbone, Dave/*Troy High Sch*	147
Dill, Matthew/*Wiggin St Elem Sch*	111
Dillard, Denecia/*Lake Erie Preparatory Sch [238]*	3
Dille, Ted/*Salt Creek Intermediate Sch*	162
Dilley, Todd/*Angeline Sch*	218
Dillians, Sheree/*Broadway Academy [238]*	1
Dillon, Matthew/*Kyle Elem Sch*	147
DiMascio, William/*West Shore Career & Tech Sch*	47
Dinan, Jennifer/*Finneytown Secondary Sch*	89
Dinkins, Maria/*Memorial Year-Round Sch*	44
Dinko, Richard/*Tuslaw Middle Sch*	189
Dipman, Victoria/*Spring Elem Sch*	130
Dippman, Doug/*Oregon Eagle Learning Center*	128
Discenza, Laila/*Chagrin Falls Middle Sch*	42
Ditlevson, Andrew/*Crestview High Sch*	171
Dixon-Harris, Lachelle/*Harvard Ave Performance Acad [247]*	2
Dixon, Brian/*Tecumseh Middle Sch*	29
Dobbelaere, Zach/*South Vienna Middle Sch*	27
Dobbins, Andrea/*Buckeye Online Sch-Success [240]*	33
Dobbins, Bill/*Arcadia Sch*	97
Dobrowolski, Gregory/*Youngstown Community Sch*	6
Dockter, Nathan/*Shawnee High Sch*	27
Dodd, Bobby/*William Mason High Sch*	208
Dodson, Erica/*Arts Impact Middle Sch*	67
Doering, Barbara/*Notre Dame Elem Sch*	83
Doerschuk, Sheila/*Strasburg Franklin Elem Sch*	203
Doherty, Melissa/*Cork Elem Sch*	13
Dolan, Matt/*Whitehall Prep & Fitness Acad [247]*	6
Donahue, Timothy/*Franklin Heights High Sch*	73
Donaldson, Matt/*Northwood Elem Sch*	187
Donley, Josh/*Gallia Academy High Sch*	81
Donnelly, Glenda/*SS Peter & Paul Academy*	96
Dorbish, Cathy/*William Holmes McGuffey ES*	137
Dorsey, Kendall/*Orion Academy [203]*	87
Dorsey, Nena/*Perrin Woods Elem Sch*	28
Dotson, Christina/*Mansfield SDA Sch*	174
Dotson, Lea/*Bard HS Early Clg East Campus*	43
Doudna, Frank/*Alexander Jr Sr High Sch*	14
Doudt, Joshua/*Ohio School for the Deaf*	4
Doughty, Mark/*Woodlands Intermediate Sch*	61
Douglas, Jason/*Prospect Elem Sch*	172
Douglas, Jennifer/*Voris Cmty Learning Center*	191
Doulton, Barry/*U S Grant Career Center*	31
Dovenbarger, Eddie/*Coshocton Co Career Center*	37
Downing, Jill/*Frazer Elem Sch*	188
Doyle, Ben/*Bellaire Elem Sch*	17
Doyle, Paula Leigh/*Hershey Montessori Sch*	83
Draheim, Jane/*Evergreen Elem Sch*	78
Drake, Donnell/*South Scioto Perform Academy [247]*	66
Drake, Susan/*Maryland Ave Elem Sch*	66
Drake, Tina/*Wellington High Sch*	126
Drakeford, Dion/*Columbus City Prep Sch-Boys*	67
Drakes, Shirley/*C Ray Williams Early Chldhd*	75
Dray, Dick/*Christian Academy Sch*	183
Dreher, Dave/*Norwayne Elem Sch*	212
Dreier, Valerie/*Old Orchard Elem Sch*	130
Drescher, Thomas/*Byrnedale Elem Sch*	129
Drouhard, Tara/*Rhodes Sch Environmental Study*	44
Drury, Doug/*Elida Middle Sch*	8
Dube, Matthew/*Jennings Local Sch*	169
Dubin, Halle/*Joseph & Florence Mandel Sch*	54
Ducca, Cindy/*Crestwood Primary Sch*	165
Dudley, Pamela/*Harold Schnell Elem Sch*	153
Dukes, Nancy/*St Anthony of Padua Sch*	171
Dulle, Gary/*Elmwood Elem Sch*	216
Dumford, Nancy/*All Children of the World Acad*	60
DuMond, Lee/*Windsor-STEM Academy*	69

PRINCIPAL INDEX

Market Data Retrieval

NAME/School	PAGE	NAME/School	PAGE
Duncan, Andrew/*Whiteford Elem Sch*	129	Erhard, Kathleen/*High Point Elem Sch*	70
Duncan, Michelle/*Celina Primary Sch*	143	Ernst, Aileen/*Deca Prep*	2
Duncan, Shawn/*Winton Place Baptist Academy*	96	Ertel, Anthony/*Annunciation Sch*	94
Dunn, Eric/*Kings Junior High Sch*	207	**Ertsgaard, Bryan**/*Ruskin Elem Sch*	149
Dunn, Kevin/*Williamsburg Elem Sch*	32	Eshleman, Anita/*Nagel Middle Sch*	89
Dunnigan, Jackie/*Leetonia Sch*	35	Eslinger, James/*Stewart Alternative Elem Sch*	69
Duplace, Polly/*St Ursula Villa Sch*	96	Esselstein, Ann/*Celina Middle Sch*	143
Durkin, Melissa/*Ranger High-Tech Academy*	125	Esselstein, Mark/*Parkway Elem Sch*	144
Durst, Matthew/*Granville High Sch*	117	Etzler, Chris/*Paulding High Sch*	160
Dutt, Arun/*Imagine Bella Acad Excellence [245]*	3	Etzler, Michael/*Coldwater Elem Sch*	143
DuVall, David/*New Franklin Christian Academy*	190	Evanich, Nick/*Marlington Middle Sch*	186
Duwve, John/*Maplewood Elem Sch*	129	**Evans, Alisha**/*Dike School of the Arts*	43
Dykstra, Nicole/*Hope Academy Northwest [238]*	2	Evans, Brian/*James F Rhodes High Sch*	43
Dzurnak, Renee/*Dentzler Elem Sch*	49	Evans, Corinne/*Willard Grizzell Middle Sch*	70
		Evans, Dan/*Riverdale Local High Sch*	98
E		Evans, Dan/*Riverdale Middle Sch*	98
Eales, Ed/*National Trail Elem Sch*	168	Evans, Dennis/*Minford Middle Sch*	178
Ealy, Sherwin/*Chase Sch*	87	Evans, Felecia/*Lander Elem Sch*	47
Easterling, J/*Middlebranch Elem Sch*	188	Evans, Fred/*Rock Hill Elem Sch*	116
Easton, Brandon/*Helen Steiner Rice Elem Sch*	124	Evans, Nick/*Rittman High Sch*	213
Eaton, Frank/*Juliann Lange Sch*	152	Evans, Nick/*Rittman Middle Sch*	213
Ebbrecht, Scott, Dr/*Academic Enrichment Center*	74	Evans, Tammy/*Worthington Christian Mid Sch*	78
Ebert, Paul/*DePaul Cristo Rey High Sch*	96	Everhart, Luke/*Northwestern Elem Sch*	28
Ebert, TJ/*Independence Primary Sch*	47	Ewry, Lewis/*Paint Valley High Sch*	175
Ebert, TJ/*Redwood Elem Sch*	122	Ewry, Lewis/*Paint Valley Middle Sch*	175
Eberts, Dana/*Bundy Elem Sch*	108	**Eyler, Michael**/*National Trail High Sch*	168
Ebie, Randall/*Boardman Center Middle Sch*	134	Eyler, Mike/*National Trail Middle Sch*	168
Eby, David/*North Canton Middle Sch*	187		
Eckert, Steve/*Quaker Digital Academy*	203	**F**	
Edenfield, Keith/*David Anderson Jr Sr High Sch*	35	Fadden, Sean/*Liberty High Sch*	3
Eding, Tim/*Continental Local High Sch*	169	Faessel, Elaine/*St Augustine Sch*	195
Edwards, Debbie/*Grove City Christian Sch*	77	Faetanini, Erin/*St Barnabas Parish Sch*	195
Edwards, Jack/*Dover Middle Sch*	202	Fagan, Megan/*Summit Academy Cmty Sch-Dayton [248]*	148
Edwards, Kee/*Miller Ridge Elem Sch*	23	Fair, Cecilia/*Marietta Christian Sch*	211
Edwards, Rick/*Athens Meigs ESC*	14	Fairfield, Timothy/*Bristol High Sch*	197
Edwards, Robert/*St Joseph Sch*	131	Falconi, Melinda/*Olmsted Falls Early Chldhd Ctr*	48
Edwards, Sherri/*Columbus Africentric EC K8 Sch*	67	Falk, Matt/*St Bridget of Kildare Sch*	53
Edwards, Timothy/*River Valley High Sch*	80	Falkenenstein, Robert, Dr/*North Baltimore Jr Sr High Sch*	217
Egan, Bridget/*Zenith Academy North*	6	Fallis, Chad/*South Science Tech Magnet Sch*	9
Eggerton, Genelle/*Western Elem Sch*	172	Fancher, Kevin/*Loveland Primary Sch*	90
Ehrsam, William/*Eli Pinney Elem Sch*	70	Fansler, Darren/*Springfield Prep-Fitness Acad [247]*	5
Eibel, Jim/*Prospect Elem Sch*	125	Farelli, Deb/*Western Reserve Local Sch*	136
Eicher, Mike/*Willard Middle High Sch*	106	Farfsing, Andy/*Purcell Marian High Sch*	95
Eichhold, Lou/*St Jude Sch*	95	Farnsworth, Jackie/*Maysville Middle Sch*	157
Eiser, Jeff/*St Clement Sch*	95	Farrington, Ron/*Emmanuel Christian Sch*	131
El-Mallawany, Ameer Kim/*Campus International Sch South*	43	Farson, Bryan/*A I Root Middle Sch*	141
Elam, Nick/*Esther Dennis MS at G Kennedy*	152	Faska, Tom/*Midview High Sch*	125
Elchert, Tammy, Dr/*Carey Exempted Village Sch*	219	Faulkner, Tricia/*Madison Elem Sch*	71
Eldridge, Anita/*Morgan High Sch*	155	Fausnaugh, Ronald/*Stewart Elem Sch*	92
Elkins, Anthony/*Chesire Elem Sch*	59	Fauver, Grant/*Coshocton High Sch*	37
Elliot, Michael/*Washington Co Career Center*	210	Favor, Kim/*Joseph & Florence Mandel Sch*	54
Elliott, Cheryl/*Summit Acad Cmty Sch-Columbus [248]*	5	Fay, John/*St Martin De Porres High Sch*	54
Elliott, Chrissy/*Edwin Smith Elem Sch*	152	Faye, Kenneth/*Louisville Senior High Sch*	186
Elliott, Jason/*Christian Life Church Academy*	60	**Feagins, Marie**/*JFK-Pact Academy*	44
Ellison, Kelli/*Meadowview Elem Sch*	31	Feasel, Suzanne/*Christian Star Academy*	111
Elsing, Deanna/*Northern Career Institute*	114	Federinko, Shannon/*Heritage Elem Sch*	141
Elson, Lisa/*St Marys Intermediate Sch*	16	Fee, Monica/*On Course*	28
Eltringham, Pamela/*St Bernadette Sch*	65	Feeling, Chelsey/*Hills & Dales Training Center*	102
Elwell, Julie/*Carson Elem Sch*	119	Feilds, Kat/*Heath High Sch*	117
Embacher, Scott/*St Francis School-Cleveland*	53	Fellows, Robert/*Anderson High Sch*	89
Embry, Stanley/*Cranbrook Elem Sch*	67	Fender, Adam/*Kenston Intermediate Sch*	82
Emery, Kenneth/*J T Karaffa Elem Sch*	109	Ferguson, Andrea/*Jacob Coy Middle Sch*	83
Emmert, Michael/*John McIntire Elem Sch*	157	Ferguson, Ashley/*KIPP Columbus Sch [246]*	3
Empie, Melissa/*Cardinal Stritch Cath HS-Acad*	131	Ferguson, Barbara/*Raymer Elem Sch*	130
Endres, Jeff/*Hamilton Middle Sch*	71	Ferguson, Letha/*Toledo School for the Arts*	5
Endsley, Cindy/*Anna Middle High Sch*	182	Ferguson, Lisa/*Garfield Elem Sch*	36
England, Dustin/*Adena Middle Sch*	174	Fernback, Cynthia/*Boardman High Sch*	134
Engle, Brandi/*Acs Early Learning Center*	14	Fertig, Dwight/*Eastwood Middle Sch*	216
Englert, Melissa/*Norwalk Catholic Elem Sch*	107	Fesemyer, David/*Southeast Primary Sch*	167
Engoglia, Marc/*Facing History New Tech Sch*	43	Fickes, Brent/*Liberty Middle Sch*	119
Enix, Monica/*John F Kennedy Elem Sch*	150	Field, Carol/*Jackson Intermediate Sch*	118
Enochs, Rob/*Miami Trace High Sch*	65	Fields, Cristal/*Beverly Gardens Elem Sch*	151
Eraybar, Theresa/*Eakin Elem Sch*	67	Fife, Jason/*Westfall Middle Sch*	163

Ohio School Directory

PRINCIPAL INDEX

NAME/School	PAGE
Fightmaster, Jason/*St Martin of Tours Sch*	95
Filicky, Stacey/*Brookfield Elem Sch*	197
Filliater, Leah/*Benjamin Harrison Elem Sch*	138
Fillman, Darren/*Groveport Madison MS South*	71
Filomena, Jen/*Ellsworth Hill Elem Sch*	193
Filut, Antonietta/*Keystone Middle Sch*	124
Fine, Jason/*Jones Middle Sch*	74
Finell, David, Dr/*Rockwern Academy*	96
Finkbine, Joe/*Tri-Co North Elem Sch*	168
Finke, Greg, Dr/*Independence Elem Sch*	22
Finley, Virmeal/*Wilbur Wright Sch*	45
Finney, Jeren/*Rising Stars Academy*	88
Finney, Vyrone/*East Community Learning Ctr*	191
Fiori, Bobbie/*Beavercreek Preschool Center*	83
Fischer, Barbara/*Burroughs Elem Sch*	129
Fischer, Doreen/*McKinley Elem Sch*	112
Fischer, Jennifer/*St Mary Sch*	189
Fischer, Teri/*All Saints Catholic Sch*	218
Fischer, Toby/*STEM Middle at Baldwin Rd JHS*	73
Fiscus, Aric/*Fayetteville Elem Sch*	19
Fisher, Curtis/*Dundee Elem Sch*	202
Fisher, Curtis/*Miller Avenue Elem Sch*	202
Fisher, Derek/*Knox County Career Center*	111
Fisher, Jack/*Colerain High Sch*	91
Fisher, Lynn/*West Side Montessori*	131
Fisher, Lynn/*Westside Montessori Middle Sch*	131
Fisher, Robyn/*Elyria Early Childhood Village*	123
Fisher, William/*Madison High Sch*	112
Fisk, Kim/*Jackson-Milton Elem Sch*	134
Fitch, Jen/*Avon Heritage Elem Sch*	123
Fitch, Virgina/*McKinley Elem Sch*	123
Flanagan, Chris/*Madeira Elem Sch*	90
Flanagan, Dorothy/*Dominion Middle Sch*	67
Flanagan, Patrick/*Lakota Middle Sch*	177
Flatter, Derek/*Twin Valley Middle High Sch*	169
Fledderjohann, Jenny/*New Knoxville Sch*	16
Fleser, Stephanie/*Summit Christian Sch*	196
Flint, Mary/*Trumbull Career & Tech Center*	196
Flood, Dan/*Buckeye High Sch*	140
Flood, Thomas/*Elyria Cmty Elem Middle Sch [242]*	122
Florence, J Lindsay/*Mercer Elem Sch*	50
Flores, Nichole/*St Ursula Academy*	131
Flowers, Julieta/*Achieve Career Prep Academy [200]*	1
Floyd, Dyan/*Litchfield Cmty Learning Ctr*	191
Fluegge, Jennifer/*Middletown Christian Sch*	209
Fluhart, Michael/*Shepherd Christian Sch*	77
Flynn, Sean/*Phoenix Middle Sch*	76
Flynn, Sean/*Worthington Academy*	76
Flynn, Wendy/*Goshen Middle Sch*	30
Fockler, Matt/*Buckeye Career Center*	201
Folson, Milton, Dr/*Mansfield Middle Sch*	172
Folson, Milton, Dr/*Mansfield Senior High Sch*	172
Fontana, Anthony/*St Joseph Ctl Cath Jr Sr HS*	177
Foos, Larry/*Maplewood Intermediate Sch*	9
Ford, Doug/*Delta Middle Sch*	79
Ford, India, Dr/*T Squared Honors Academy*	5
Foreman, Alison/*Emerson Academy of Dayton [203]*	148
Forman, Ashlee/*Ansonia Elem Sch*	55
Forman, Eric/*Onaway Elem Sch*	50
Forren, Jennifer/*Loveland Elem Sch*	90
Forrider, Dan/*Salem Wesleyan Academy*	36
Fortkamp, Brian/*Parkway High Sch*	144
Foster, Dair/*Imagine Groveport Cmty ES [245]*	3
Foster, Sarah/*North Linden Elem Sch*	68
Fountain, Sommer/*Waverly Sch*	45
Fourman, Kevin/*Crestline Sch*	38
Fournier, Sharon/*Holy Family Sch*	195
Fowler, Amren/*Applewood Elem Sch*	140
Fowler, James/*Kiser Elem Sch*	149
Fowler, Steve/*West Branch Middle Sch*	136
Fox, Cindy/*Bluffsview Elem Sch*	75
Fox, Joel/*Morgan South Elem Sch*	155
Fox, Kevin/*Circleville Middle Sch*	162
Fox, Roger/*Academy for Urban Scholars HS*	1
Fraley, Susan/*Central Elem Sch*	93

NAME/School	PAGE
Frame, Josh/*Big Walnut Middle Sch*	58
France, James/*Manchester High Sch*	193
Franchini, Kari/*Fairfield Creekside Mid Sch*	21
Francis, Jennifer/*St Thomas More Sch*	53
Francis, Kathryn/*Orchard STEM Sch*	44
Franco, Amy/*Jackman Elem Sch*	130
Frank, Brian/*Ballard Brady Middle Sch*	49
Frank, Roger/*Elmwood Middle Sch*	216
Frankart, Brenda/*Liberty-Benton High Sch*	98
Franke, Aaron/*Valley Middle Sch*	179
Franklin, Jason/*Ohio School for the Deaf*	4
Franklin, Ricardo/*Citizens Leadership Acad East [239]*	1
Franklin, Terrence/*L Hollingworth School for Tag*	3
Franko, James/*Eastview Elem Sch*	122
Franks, Jon/*Springboro Junior High Sch*	208
Frantz, Christa/*West Elem Sch*	203
Franz, Clifton/*Donovan Elem Sch*	207
Fraser, Christina/*Towpath Trail High Sch*	5
Frederick, Amy/*Chess Christian Sch*	154
Frederick, Scott/*Benjamin Logan Middle Sch*	121
Freeman, Julie/*Our Lady-Perpetual Help Sch*	76
Freeman, Kevin/*Sherwood Middle Sch*	69
Freer, Kathie/*Ruffing Montessori Ingalls Sch*	54
Freese, Clint/*Tower Heights Middle Sch*	149
Frei, Eric/*North High Sch*	114
Frei, Kylea/*Applied Behavioral Services*	154
Freitag-Geiger, Hillary/*Silver Lake Elem Sch*	193
French, Christina/*Hopewell Early Childhood Sch*	22
French, Karen/*Tcp World Academy*	5
Frentzel, Roben/*Jefferson Elem Sch*	70
Friess, Beth/*Fulton Co Bd-Dev Disabilities*	78
Friess, Joe/*Wauseon Middle Sch*	80
Friess, Kathleen/*Immaculate Heart of Mary Sch*	195
Frisby, Kelli/*Summit Acad Sec Sch-Middletown [248]*	5
Friz, Carmella/*Beavertown Elem Sch*	150
Fromm, Kelli/*Franklin High Sch*	207
Froning, Jacob, Dr/*St Patrick Sch*	133
Fruchey, Brian/*Jefferson Middle Sch*	8
Fry, Dan/*Bath Elem Sch*	194
Fry, Jessica/*Lakewood Middle Sch*	118
Frye, Molly/*St Mary Sch*	211
Frye, Timothy/*Ida Sue Sch*	211
Fulcher, Michelle/*Rosa Parks Early Learning Ctr*	149
Fulford, Jim/*Calumet Christian Sch*	77
Fuller, Mark/*Everest High Sch*	73
Fullerton, Eric/*Belpre Christian Academy*	211
Fulmer, Jeff/*St James the Greater Sch*	95
Fulton, Benjamin/*Winton Hills Academy*	88
Fulton, Kristyl/*SS Peter & Paul Cath Sch*	108
Fultz, Ken/*Temple Christian Sch*	154
Furlong, Steve/*Parkview Elem Sch*	214
Fusillo, Sandie/*St Peter Sch*	190
Fyffe, Tammy/*Pike Co Early Childhood Center*	163

G

NAME/School	PAGE
Gabbard, Mark/*Williams Avenue Elem Sch*	92
Gabert, Sherry/*St Albert the Great Sch*	154
Gabram, Thomas/*Kenston High Sch*	82
Gaddis, Scott/*Genoa Middle Sch*	74
Gage, Quint/*Montrose Elem Sch*	66
Gagnon, Rick/*Seneca Co Opportunity Ctr*	180
Gahan, Joanne/*Central Intermediate Sch*	141
Gaietto, Jodi/*Cory-Rawson High Sch*	97
Gaijer, Kris/*Roberts Middle Sch*	193
Gainer, Mark/*Cedarville Elem Sch*	84
Gale, Kevin/*White Oak Middle Sch*	91
Galecki, Charles/*St Paul's Lutheran Sch*	77
Gallagher, Patrick/*University High Sch*	54
Gallagher, Patrick/*University Sch-Shaker Campus*	54
Gallatin, Matt/*Liberty Union High Sch*	64
Gallo, Karrie/*Fairfield Central Elem Sch*	21
Gallwitz, Ryan/*Centerburg High Sch*	110
Gamber, Amy/*Rosemont Center*	77
Gamble, Jessica/*Riverside Sch*	44

PRINCIPAL INDEX

Market Data Retrieval

NAME/School	PAGE
Gamertsfelder, Thomas/Career Tech Ed Ctr Licking Co	118
Gannon, Patrick/St Helen Sch	83
Gant, Frank/Lake Primary Sch	186
Ganzer, Jennifer/Young Elem Sch	194
Garbor, Andrew/Robert Bycroft Sch	34
Garee, Brent/Fredericktown High Sch	111
Garmon, Crystal/Life Skills Center of Elyria	3
Garren, Stephanie/Northside Intermediate Sch	184
Garrett, Bill/Eastern Local High Sch	7
Garrett, Rhonda/Park Elem Sch	82
Garrett, Rich/Dayton Christian Sch	154
Garrett, Terri/Gorsuch West Elem Sch	63
Garrick, Dan/St Francis DeSales High Sch	76
Garris, Greg/Kilbourne Middle Sch	75
Garten, Chris/Seven Hills Sch-Doherty Campus	96
Garver, Christy/Dohron Wilson Elem Sch	26
Garwood, Dana/Liberty Bible Academy	209
Gast, Carrie/Western High Sch	164
Gates, Alison/Little Miami Intermediate Sch	208
Gates, Ashley/Beechwood Elem Sch	75
Gates, Thomas/Logan Christian Sch	104
Gatti, Claire/St Michael Sch	190
Gault, Juliane/Sylvan Elem Sch	129
Gausnan, Leann/Granger Elem Sch	141
Gavin, Michael/Our Lady of the Elms Elem Sch	195
Gavin, Michael/Our Lady of the Elms Sch	195
Gayheart, Amy/Fairborn High Sch	84
Gearhart, Eric/School of Possibilities	149
Gebhardt, Randy/West Clermont High Sch	31
Geis, Suzanne/Fairview Middle Sch	57
Gelonese, Robert/Struthers Middle Sch	136
Gentene, Lauren/Mason Middle Sch	208
Gentis, Afrodete/Holy Trinity Christian Academy	201
Gentis, Todd/Miami East High Sch	145
Genton, Tiffany/Maize Elem Sch	68
George, James/St Augustine Sch	102
George, Krystle/Clara E Westropp Elem Sch	43
George, Lisa/Jefferson Elem Sch	114
Gephart, Judy/Shawnee Middle Sch	9
Gephart, Scott/Spencerville High Sch	9
Gephart, Scott/Spencerville Middle Sch	9
Geraghty, Michael/Field High Sch	165
Gerber, Brian/Our Lady of Consolation Sch	219
Gerber, Joyce/Norton Middle Sch	194
Gerbrick, Michelle/Crestwood Intermediate Sch	165
Geresy, Stephen/Summit Academy Trans HS-Cinn [248]	5
Gerhardt, Taylor/Lexington Junior High Sch	172
Gersten, Diane/Children's Mtng House Mont Sch	32
Geyer, Dale/Jane Chance Elem Sch	151
Geyer, Linda/Parma Cmty Elem Sch [242]	39
Geyer, Linda/Parma Cmty High Sch [242]	40
Geyer, Linda/Parma Cmty Pearl Rd Elem Sch [242]	40
Geygan, Doug/Edgewood High Sch	21
Giardino, Claire/Lincoln Elem Sch	70
Gibbs, Kelly/Marion Sterling Elem Sch	44
Gibbs, Paul/Fassett Junior High Sch	128
Gibson, Andrew/Amherst Junior High Sch	122
Gibson, Linda, Dr/Cesar Chavez College Prep Sch [243]	1
Gibson, Linda, Dr/Cesar Chavez North Sch	65
Gibson, Toby/Brookfield Middle Sch	197
Gies, John/Shelby High Sch	173
Gifford, Greg/Morgan West Elem Sch	155
Gilbert, Chris/Crestview Elem Sch	171
Gilbert, Mr/Shiloh Elem Sch	173
Giles-Weeks, Veda/Northeast Ohio College Prep [238]	4
Gillespie, Paige/Fairfield East Elem Sch	21
Gilliam, Derrick/Hyatts Middle Sch	59
Gilliland, Melanie/Liberty Christian Academy	120
Gillote, Wilma/Unioto Junior High Sch	176
Gingerich, Galen/Nevin Coppock Elem Sch	146
Ginocchio, Nina/Spencer Ctr-Gifted	88
Ginsburg, Malkie/Fuchs Mizrachi Sch	53
Girard, Dan/Wilson Hill Elem Sch	76
Glass, Allison/Summit Academy Cmty Sch-Warren [248]	196
Glass, Latosha/Anton Grdina Sch	42
Glassmeyer, TJ/Clermont Northeastern High Sch	30
Glenn, Rick/Hayes Elem Sch	138
Gliebe, Don/River Valley Middle Sch	139
Glispie, Kyle/South Columbus Prep Acad [238]	5
Globokar, Jim/William V Fisher Catholic HS	65
Glover, Dorian/C F Holliday Elem Sch	153
Godby, Angela/Lynchburg-Clay Elem Sch	103
Goedde, Mike/St Cecilia Sch	95
Goggin, Laurie/Cambridge Interm Sch	86
Goins, Karla/Charity Adams Earley Girl Acad	149
Goins, Sharon/Thurgood Marshall STEM HS	149
Golden, Dave/Arcadia Sch	97
Golden, Virginia/Columbus Intermediate Sch	41
Golden, Virginia/Heskett Middle Sch	41
Golsby, Kelly/Kae Avenue Elem Sch	75
Gomaa, Nabila/Toledo Islamic Academy	131
Gomez, Cara/South Amherst Middle Sch	124
Gonda, Robb/Hastings Middle Sch	74
Gonzales, Manuel/Gesu Sch	131
Good, Gregg/Montessori HS-Univ Circle	54
Goode, Channey/Edwin Joel Brown Mid Sch	149
Goodman, Larry/Andrews Osborne Academy	115
Goodrich, Marci/Blanchester Intermediate Sch	32
Goodson, Mike/Milford Christian Academy	32
Goodwin, Jeff/Edison High Sch	60
Goodwin, Lyn/Super Learning Center	196
Goodwin, Maureen/St Bernadette Sch	52
Goodwin, Tim/Marion Local High Sch	144
Goodwin, Tresa/Medina Co Career Center	141
Gordon, Sonya/East High Sch	136
Gorius, Michele/Newton Elem Sch	119
Gorman, Lynnett/West Pugleise Elem Sch	109
Gorman, Ted/Steubenville High Sch	109
Gorrell, Annette/McMullen Elem Sch	11
Gosztyla, Mike/Prairie Norton Elem Sch	74
Gotshall, Jim/Bulldog Online Academy	194
Gottesman, Jamie/Columbus Mont Educational Ctr	77
Goudy, Christine/Orange Inclusive Pre-School	49
Gough, Mary, Dr/Badger Elem Sch	198
Gould, David/Bethany Sch	96
Graham, Erik/Maumee Valley Country Day Sch	131
Graham, Karen/Alexandria Montessori Sch	154
Graham, Robert/Knox Elem Sch	136
Granata, Tamara/Charles Huber Elem Sch	150
Grant, Christopher/Westwood Sch	88
Grant, Gregory/New Lexington Elem Sch	161
Grant, Joel/Binns Elem Sch	67
Grant, Ralph/Summit Academy Sec Sch-Akron [248]	5
Gratz, Debra/Prospect Elem Sch	197
Graves-Hill, Vicki/Roll Hill Sch	88
Graves, Daniel/Goshen Lane Elem Sch	70
Gray, Heather/Firelands Montessori Academy	62
Gray, Heidi/Huntington Elem Sch	175
Gray, Jerron/Withrow University High Sch	88
Gray, Susan/Washington Elem Sch	177
Gray, Wayne/Crossroads Christian Academy	163
Grayson, Karen/Struble Elem Sch	91
Graziano, Meghan/Highland Elem Sch	194
Greb, Sarah/Mulberry Elem Sch	31
Greco, Anthony/Dater Montessori Sch	87
Green-Pallotta, Rebecca/Akron Alternative Academy	190
Green, Barbara/Shelby Middle Sch	173
Green, Lance/Freedom Elem Sch	22
Green, Paul/Calvary Christian Sch	121
Green, Valerie/Worthington Adventist Academy	78
Greenberger, Esther/Yeshiva Derech Ha Torah	54
Greene, Brian/Riverside of Miami Co Sch	145
Greene, James/Almira Academy	42
Greenwood, Steve/George H Gerke Elem Sch	207
Greer, Julie/Riverdale Elem Sch	98
Grega, Jon/Mt Gilead Middle Sch	155

Ohio School Directory — PRINCIPAL INDEX

NAME/School	PAGE
Greggila, Millie/*St Boniface Catholic Sch*	160
Gregory, Kathy/*Old West End Academy*	130
Greulich, Jeff/*Troy Junior High Sch*	147
Grgic, Deborah/*St Rita Sch*	53
Grice, Cindy/*Ralph Waite Elem Sch*	141
Griebel, Pamela/*Immaculate Conception Sch*	107
Grieco, Nick/*SS Andrew-Elizabeth Seton Sch*	32
Grieger, Justin/*Northridge Middle Sch*	120
Grieser, Brett/*Edgerton Elem Sch*	214
Griffen, Traci/*Five-Points Elememtary Sch*	208
Griffey, Dave/*Parma Heights Chrn Academy*	54
Griffith, Gerry/*Stivers School for Arts*	149
Griffith, Martin/*Franklinton Preparatory Acad*	2
Griffith, Michael/*Lillian & Betty Ratner Sch*	54
Griffiths, Robert/*Olentangy High Sch*	59
Grimm, Teri/*Grindstone Elem Sch*	41
Grimsle, James/*Mound St Health Careers Acad*	4
Grimsley, James/*Mound St Tech Trade Military*	4
Groh, Jeff/*New School Montessori*	96
Groholy, Michael/*Washington Elem Sch*	186
Grondin, Diane/*Jane Addams Bus Career Center*	44
Grone, Kevin/*Union Elem Sch*	152
Groscost, Stephanie/*South Side Academy*	5
Grossman, Steve/*Crestwood Elem Sch*	123
Grote, Kristin/*Silverton Paideia Academy*	88
Grothaus, Katie/*Englewood Hills Elem Sch*	152
Grove, Larry/*Findlay Digital Academy*	98
Groves, Kristen/*Blacklick Elem Sch*	70
Grow, Chad/*Logan-Hocking Middle Sch*	104
Grubbs, Corey/*McKinley Sr High Sch*	185
Gruber, Elizabeth/*Wyandot Early Childhood Sch*	23
Gruber, Will/*St Brendan Sch*	76
Gruhin, Sydney/*Citizens Leadership Academy [239]*	1
Guckert, Susan/*Kings Preschool*	207
Guerra, Stacy/*Pioneer Center*	174
Guffey, Melissa/*Alexander Elem Sch*	14
Guiler, Robyn/*St Sylvester Sch*	148
Guilford, Deb/*Parc Lane Training Center*	160
Guliano, Patrick/*Happy Hearts Sch*	12
Gulley, Julie/*Richfield Elem Sch*	194
Gurbuz, Mehmet/*Horizon Sci Acad-Cleveland HS [153]*	3
Gurski, Rick/*Youngstown Virtual Academy*	137
Gusdanovic, Allison, Sr/*Cleveland Central Catholic HS*	52
Gustin, Julie/*Geneva Platt R Spencer ES*	13
Guthrie, Josh/*Lincoln PK-8 Sch*	200
Guzman, Jennifer/*St Joan of Arc Sch*	131
Gwirtz, Brendan/*Northmor Sch*	156

H

NAME/School	PAGE
Haak, Jason/*Upper Valley Career Center*	147
Haas, Gary/*Woodmore Elementary/Middle Sch*	159
Hacker, Eli/*Logan High Sch*	104
Hackett, Stephen/*Fairfield Local High Sch*	102
Hackett, Stephen/*Fairfield Local Middle Sch*	102
Haddow, Jennifer/*Childhood League Center*	77
Haemmerle, Chad/*Cedarville Middle High Sch*	84
Haffner, Angela/*Liberty Arts Magnet Sch*	9
Haffner, Candice/*West Carrollton High Sch*	153
Hager, Tammy/*Garfield Heights High Sch*	46
Hainer, Kevin/*Shady Lane Elem Sch*	69
Haines, Thad/*Jackson High Sch*	107
Hairston, Brian/*Garfield Academy*	2
Hairston, Jeff/*Ironton High Sch*	116
Hake, Dan/*Concord Elem Sch*	146
Hale, Amie/*St Paul Sch*	190
Hale, Tim/*Greenon Jr Sr High Sch*	27
Hall, Adam/*Strasburg Franklin High Sch*	203
Hall, Alexis/*Albert Einstein Acad-Westlake*	39
Hall, Alicea/*Happy Day Sch*	164
Hall, Beth/*Midview West Elem Sch*	125
Hall, Brianne/*Beaver Local Elem Sch*	34
Hall, Chuck/*Marshall High Sch*	4
Hall, Holly/*Claymont Preschool*	202
Hall, Jeffery/*Frederick Douglass Elem Sch*	87
Hall, John/*St Francis DeSales High Sch*	131
Hall, Julie/*Richardson Elem Sch*	192
Hall, Molly/*Indian Lake Elem Sch*	121
Hall, Tammy/*Medina Christian Academy*	142
Hallock, Kimberly/*Eliza Northrop Elem Sch*	141
Halsey, Brett/*Hardin Northern Elem Sch*	100
Halsey, Geoff/*Bataan Intermediate Sch*	159
Halsey, Jenny/*Edgewood Elem Sch*	21
Hamblen, Keith/*Lima Christian Academy*	10
Hamersley, Beth/*Keene Elem Sch*	37
Hamilton, Bill/*Badger Middle Sch*	198
Hamilton, Daniel/*Sherwood Elem Sch*	89
Hamilton, Douglas/*Lawrence Lower Sch*	54
Hammoud, Catherine/*Islamic Sch of Greater Toledo*	218
Hamstein, Dan/*Luther E Ball High Sch*	4
Handrych, Ashley/*Lakeview Middle Sch*	199
Hankinns, Dennis/*Franklin Furnace Christn Acad*	180
Hankins, Gary/*Big Walnut Intermediate Sch*	58
Hanning, David/*Athens High Sch*	14
Hansen, Mark/*Columbus Academy*	77
Hanthorn, Jeff/*Hawkins Elem Sch*	129
Harbal, Jeffrey/*Perkins High Sch*	61
Harbour, Mary Alice/*St Peter Catholic Sch*	219
Hardin, T/*Timberlane Learning Center*	152
Hardwick, Scott/*Cardington-Lincoln Elem Sch*	155
Hardy, Heather/*Bellflower Elem Sch*	113
Harkabus, Milajean/*Labrae Intermediate Sch*	198
Harkins, Michele/*Bolton Crossing Elem Sch*	73
Harmon, Brett/*Pleasant View Middle Sch*	74
Harmon, Kattie/*Marie English ECC*	137
Harning, Joshua/*Highland Community Lrng Ctr*	77
Harold, Dan/*Lake Middle High Sch*	186
Harold, Geoff/*Rapid Run Middle Sch*	92
Harper-Brooks, Angela/*Crouse Community Learning Ctr*	191
Harper, Angela/*Mason Cmty Learning Ctr*	191
Harper, David/*Philo Junior High Sch*	156
Harper, Valarie/*Huron Primary Sch*	12
Harrell, Kaylee/*Melrose Elem Sch*	214
Harrington, Amy/*Frederick Douglass High Sch*	2
Harrington, Beth/*Woodridge Elem Sch*	195
Harris, John/*Tri-Valley High Sch*	157
Harris, Kendall/*Blendon Middle Sch*	74
Harris, Trisha/*Chesapeake Elem Sch*	115
Harrison, Jeff/*Medina High Sch*	141
Harrison, Lori/*Seven Mile Elem Sch*	21
Harshbarger, Eric/*Larry Miller Intermediate Sch*	156
Hart, Brian/*Hilliard City Pre-School*	72
Hart, Carly/*Stark High Sch*	5
Hart, Linda/*St Aloysius Educational Center*	96
Harter, Jody/*Greenville Elem Sch*	55
Hartley, Katie/*Milton-Union Middle Sch*	146
Hartley, Shane/*Deer Park Jr Sr High Sch*	89
Hartline, Rebecca/*Massillon Christian Sch*	190
Hartman, Dan/*Jefferson Co Joint Voc Sch*	109
Hartman, Kevan/*All Saints Sch*	94
Hartman, Martha/*St Benedict Catholic Sch*	131
Hartman, Pam/*Duncan Falls Elem Sch*	156
Hartman, Todd/*Ayer Elem Sch*	89
Hartmann, Jeff, Dr/*Stow-Munroe Falls High Sch*	194
Hartmeyer, Bill/*Buckeye Trail Middle Sch*	86
Hartmeyer, William/*Buckeye Trail High Sch*	86
Harvey, Ann/*Auglaize Co Educational Acad*	7
Harvey, Susan/*George W Carver-STEM Sch*	43
Harville, Chad/*Eden Grove Academy*	96
Hasebrook, Chris/*Linworth Alternative High Sch*	75
Hasselbusch, Martha/*Midway Elem Sch*	88
Hatcher, Amber/*Innis Elem Sch*	68
Hatcher, Derek/*James A Garfield Middle Sch*	165
Hatfield, Stefanie/*Alton Hall Elem Sch*	73
Hatteberg, Scott/*Solon Middle Sch*	50
Hatten, Linda/*Lynchburg-Clay High Sch*	103
Haughn, Tricia/*Rushville Middle Sch*	63
Haus, Tammy/*Immaculate Conception Sch*	154
Haven, Darrell/*Walnut Creek Elem Sch*	104
Haven, Darrell/*Winesburg Elem Sch*	105

PRINCIPAL INDEX

Market Data Retrieval

NAME/School	PAGE
Havens, Megan/St Rita School for the Deaf	96
Havens, Roger/Franklin Elem Sch	141
Haverty, Anne/Bridgeport Middle Sch	18
Hawes, Garry/McKinley Elem Sch	85
Hawley, Barbara/Brimfield Elem Sch	165
Hawley, Michael/Adult Center for Education	157
Hawley, Sarah/Ilead Spring Meadows	3
Hawthorne, Nancy/McGuffey Montessori Sch	24
Hayden, Dawn/Willson Elem Sch	45
Hayden, Kellie/Beallsville Elem Sch	147
Hayden, William/Amherst Elem Sch	186
Hayes, Ariel/Michael R White STEM Sch	44
Hayes, Bill/Greeneview Elem Sch	84
Hayes, Clint/Jonathan Alder High Sch	132
Hayes, Dennis/Fairfield North Elem Sch	21
Hayward, Christopher/Fernway Elem Sch	50
Hazlett, Victoria, Dr/Wilder Elem Sch	75
Heal, Elissa/Sentinel Career Center	177
Heban, Debra/Whitmer Career & Tech Center	131
Hebert, Laura/Twinsburg High Sch	195
Heck, Andrew/Cherrington Elem Sch	74
Heddleson, Lucia/St Anthony of Padua Sch	126
Hedgepeth, Heather/Diley Middle Sch	64
Heffron, Mitchell/Liberty Sch	125
Hefner, Joel/Ft Miami Elem Sch	127
Heim, Kendra/Open Door Sch	115
Heitzman, Michael/Norwich Elem Sch	72
Held, Deanne/Defiance Elem Sch	57
Hellickson, Thomas/South Central High Sch	106
Helm-Borchers, Amy/Ohio Virtual Academy	4
Helman, Donald/Wayside Christian Sch	39
Helmlinger, Keith/Whittier Elem Sch	183
Helser, Shannon/Teays Valley East Middle Sch	163
Helton, Angela/Central Baptist Academy	96
Hemmelgarn, Jason/Coldwater High Sch	143
Hemmelgorn, Jon/Versailles Middle Sch	56
Hempelmann, Donna/Cincinnati Christian Elem Sch	24
Hempleman, Jeff/Garfield Elem Sch	117
Hench, Beth/Ayersville Elem Sch	57
Henderson, Danjile/Case Community Learning Ctr	191
Henderson, G/Madisonville Smart Elem Sch	4
Henderson, Graham/Pathways to Success	122
Henderson, Kevin/Our Lady of Peace Sch	189
Henderson, Kirk/Canal Winchester High Sch	66
Henderson, Loretta/Milton-Union Elem Sch	146
Henderson, Tim/Choices Alternative Sch	184
Henderson, Timothy/Connections Academy	184
Henderson, Timothy/Passages Sch	185
Hendricks, Beth/Amanda Elem Sch	23
Henry, Alicia/Road to Success Academy [135]	66
Henry, Darren/Leipsic Local Sch	170
Henry, Leslie/Vinton Elem Sch	80
Henry, Nicole/Hebron Elem Sch	118
Henry, Rob/Highland Middle Sch	141
Henry, Sean/Dunbar Early College HS	149
Hensinger, David/Northwood Elem Sch	204
Hensley, Keri/Wildwood Elem Sch	23
Herberghs, Nicole/Clarendon Leadership Sch	184
Herman, Brad/Beacon Hill Community Sch	201
Herman, Lee/Lake High Sch	217
Herman, Nicole/St John Baptist Sch	95
Herman, Sonia/Gibsonburg High Sch	177
Herman, Sonia/Gibsonburg Middle Sch	177
Herman, Susan/St Francis of Assisi Sch	53
Hermes, Davy/Edison Elem Sch	60
Herr, Jeremy/McComb High Sch	98
Herr, Jeremy/McComb Middle Sch	98
Herrholtz, Lawrence/Lakeview High Sch	199
Herrholtz, Tracy/Champion High Sch	197
Herron, Tracey/Warsaw Elem Sch	37
Hershberger, Paul/Mechanicsburg Jr Sr High Sch	26
Hessey, Brian/Liberty Preparatory Sch	211
Hetzler, Jeannine/Cassingham Elem Sch	66

NAME/School	PAGE
Heuker, Ginger/Jackson Center Sch	183
Heuser, Chris/Indian Springs Elem Sch	59
Hibler, Molly/St Jude Sch	126
Hickman, Keith/Cincinnati College Prep Acad	1
Hicks, Bill/St Joseph Consolidated Sch	24
Hicks, Katrina/Gearity Professional Dev Sch	42
Hicks, Kelly/Plain City Elem Sch	132
Hicks, Sheila/Langston Middle Sch	125
Hieber, Bryan/Patrick Henry Elem Sch	102
Hildebrand, Bill/Pfeiffer Intermediate Sch	188
Hilgenberg, Tom/Coshocton Opportunity Sch	2
Hilkert, Tyson/Huber Ridge Elem Sch	75
Hilko, Bryan/General Johnny Wilson Mid Sch	124
Hill-Jones, Sharon/Firestone Park Elem Sch	191
Hill-Simmons, Stacey/Evanston Academy	87
Hill, Becky/Martins Ferry Christian Sch	19
Hill, Beth/Newark Catholic High Sch	120
Hill, Donetrus/Meadowdale High Sch	149
Hill, Jeffrey/Valley Vista Elem Sch	48
Hill, John/Kenton Ridge High Sch	27
Hill, Kerry/Focus Lrng Acad-W Columbus [244]	2
Hill, Ladora/Elm Primary Sch	94
Hill, Ladora/Hilltop Primary Sch	94
Hill, Ladora/Vermont Primary Sch	94
Hilliard, Charlene/East Clark Elem Sch	43
Hilsher, Jody/Miami Valley Christian Academy	96
Hiltunen, Jovette/Madison Pre-K	112
Hines, Dennis/Lowellville K-12 Sch	135
Hines, Matthew/Eastern Elem Sch	163
Hinton, Chad/Marshall Elem Sch	24
Hinton, Gary/East Canton High Sch	188
Hinton, Scott/Amanda-Clearcreek High Sch	62
Hintze, Kyle/Bellevue Elem Sch	105
Hinze, Michael/Westerville South High Sch	75
Hiser, Jeremy/Meadowlawn Intermediate Sch	61
Hitchcock, Doug/Grand Valley High Sch	13
Hitchcock, Gordon/Maplewood High Sch	199
Hitchens, Libby/National Road Elem Sch	157
Hitzman, Melissa/Learning Ctr at North Norwood	87
Hliatzos, Peter/Riverside Campus	114
Hoban, Judy/Polaris Christian Academy	60
Hoelzle, Joe/Tri-Co North High Sch	168
Hoelzle, Joe/Tri-Co North Middle Sch	168
Hoerner, Celeste/Eastmont Elem Sch	149
Hoff, Shawn/Third Street Sch	168
Hoffman, Andrew/Whittier Elem Sch	75
Hoffman, Brian/Hubbard Middle Sch	198
Hoffman, Colleen/Tree of Life Christian Sch	77
Hogan, Brian/Waynesfield-Goshen Mid/Hi Sch	16
Hogue, James/Streetsboro High Sch	167
Hohlbein, Bob/Franklin Elem Sch	8
Hohlbein, Paul/Forest Elem Sch	146
Hohman, Belinda/Licking Heights West Elem Sch	118
Holcombe, Tim/Eisenhower Intermediate Sch	128
Holdren, Thomas/Edgewood Elem Sch	204
Holifield, Derrick/Kenneth Clement Boys Academy	44
Holland, Reginald/George G Dodge Interm Sch	195
Hollar, Aaron/West Liberty-Salem Sch	26
Hollenbacher, Kreg/Ft Loramie Jr Sr High Sch	182
Holliday, James/Dayton Christian Sch	154
Hollie, Kimberly/Cincinnati Junior Academy	96
Hollinger, Jamie/Waterville Primary Sch	127
Hollon, Joseph/Clinton-Massie Middle Sch	33
Hollon, Pam/Hillsboro Elem Sch	103
Holloway, Chip/Wright Brothers Elem Sch	150
Holly, Patti/Twin Valley South Elem Sch	169
Holmes, Damon/Ginn Academy	43
Holmes, Eric/Symmes Valley Elem Sch	117
Holmes, Ryan/East Elem Sch	203
Holop, Ted/Warner Middle Sch	85
Holowatyj, Anna/Global Village Academy	39
Holsinger, Matt/Elgin Elem Sch	138
Holsinger, Matt/McKinley Elem Sch	138

Ohio School Directory — PRINCIPAL INDEX

NAME/School	PAGE
Holt, Bradley/Baker Middle Sch	84
Holtgerven, Becky/School of Hope	176
Holthaus, Rebecca/Hilltop Elem Sch	40
Holtzapple, John/Anna Elem Sch	182
Holycross, Lynda/Bellefontaine Middle Sch	121
Holzapfel, James/St Joseph School-Randolph	167
Holzhauer, Erin/East Elem Sch	123
Holzwart, Amy/St Michael Sch	99
Homan, Nelson/Winton Woods Elem Sch	94
Honabarger, Ed/Danville High Sch	110
Hoover, Clare/Zanesville SDA Sch	158
Hopkins, Aaron/Crawford Woods Elem Sch	22
Hopkins, Byron/Buchtel Community Learning Ctr	191
Hopkins, Byron/Cleveland Heights High Sch	42
Hopkins, Patrick/Tri-Valley Middle Sch	157
Hopkins, Robin/Lorain High Sch	124
Hopkins, Robin/South High Sch	114
Hopper, David/Rock Hill High Sch	116
Horrocks, Robert/Washington Park Cmty Sch	40
Horton, Anthony/Stanton Middle Sch	166
Horton, Pamela/South Mifflin STEM Academy	69
Hosford, Jesse/Woodridge Middle Sch	195
Hosking, Patricia/Sutter Park Pre-School	76
Hoskins, Shari/Heritage Hill Elem Sch	92
Hoston, Rasheeda/Euclid Child Dev Center	46
Houchen, Joy/Cuyahoga Heights Elem Sch	45
Householder, Lisa/Glenford Elem Sch	161
Householder, Lisa/Sheridan High Sch	161
Householder, Mike/Tallmadge High Sch	195
Housel, Robert/Summit Academy Alt Lrng-Canton [248]	5
Houser, Debbie/G A T E	24
Houser, Laura/Ohio Virtual Academy	4
Housh, Matt/Mills Lawn Elem Sch	85
Howald, Darlene/Orchard Hill Intermediate Sch	187
Howard, Deborah/Fulton Elem Sch	28
Howard, Jim/Collins Career Center	116
Howard, Jody/Meigs Intermediate ES	143
Howard, Nicki/Massillon Digital Academy	187
Hoynes, Laurie/Lake Elem Sch	113
Hoyson, Richard/Jefferson Area Jr High Sch	13
Huber, Andrew/Madison Junior Senior High Sch	23
Huber, Jeremy/Jefferson Area Sr High Sch	13
Huch, Ryan/Bolich Middle Sch	192
Hudepohl, Vicki/Fairborn Primary Sch	84
Hudley, Robyn/Vanlue Local Sch	99
Huffman, Kyle/Triad High Sch	26
Hufnagel, Peg/Evolve Academy	141
Hug, Joe/Whipple Heights Elem Sch	188
Hughes, Brian/Holgate Sch	101
Hughes, Jodie/Hazel Harvey Elem Sch	211
Hughes, Michelle/Lincoln-West Sch Sci & Health	44
Hughes, Micki/Monroe Elem Sch	132
Hughes, Stan/Greenville Senior High Sch	55
Hughes, Tom/Lancaster SDA Elem Sch	65
Hull, Adam/Elda Elem Sch	24
Humphrey, Dan/Danbury Local Sch	159
Humphrey, Jessica/Sunbeam Sch	45
Humphrey, William/Centerburg High Sch	110
Hunt, Charlena/Pinnacle Academy [203]	40
Hunt, Dawn/Titan Tikes Pre-School	170
Hunt, Travis/Oak Hills High Sch	92
Hunter, Amanda/St Mary Sch	103
Hunter, Cathy/Forest Rose Sch	62
Hunter, Jack/Chase Stemm Academy	129
Hunter, Josh/Victory Christian Sch	26
Hunter, Miata/Shaker Heights Middle Sch	50
Hunter, Terrah/Dennis Elem Sch	208
Hurley, Candace/St Thomas More Sch	32
Hurley, Craig/Upper Scioto Valley Sch	100
Hursey, Lynn/Northland Prep & Fitness Acad [247]	4
Hurstman, Alissa/Etna Elem Sch	120
Huskins, Nicholas/Lohr Elem Sch	188
Hussel, Jason/Fairfield South Elem Sch	21
Hutchins, Keyonna/Riverside Academy [238]	5
Hutchinson, Stacy/High Tech Academy	43
Huth, Brenda/St Joseph Montessori Sch	76
Hutto, Pam/Ridge Elem Sch	113
Hutton, Jennifer/Youngstown Acad of Excellence [238]	6

I

NAME/School	PAGE
Iaconis, Christina/St Anthony Sch	76
Iannetta, Scott/Cuyahoga Vly Christian Academy	196
Iemmolo, Lucy/Gesu Catholic Sch	52
Ifill, Christina/West Broad Elem Sch	69
Ike, Amanda/Shawnee Middle Sch	27
Imke, Ryan/Findlay High Sch	98
Inboden, Scott, Dr/Worthington Christian High Sch	78
Ingram, Lizanne/St Bernadette Sch	32
Ingram, Sabrina/Mayfair Elem Sch	45
Inkrott, Jason, Dr/Northmont High Sch	152
Irvin, Brittani/Oliver Hazard Perry Academy	44
Isaacs, Nicole/Career Readiness Academy	22
Isabella, Sandra/O H Somers Elem Sch	166
Ison, Samuel/Waynesville High Sch	209
Israel, Gary/Jefferson PK-8 Sch	200
Ivory, Tamika/Miles Park Elem Sch	44
Izokaitis, Cory/Columbus Academy	77

J

NAME/School	PAGE
Jablonski, Cheryl/St Joseph the Provider Sch	137
Jaccaci, Anthony/Cincinnati Country Day Sch	96
Jackson, Dan/Pymatuning Valley High Sch	13
Jackson, Eric/Wadsworth Middle Sch	142
Jackson, Jason/Madison Elem Sch	23
Jackson, Joyce, Dr/McComb Elem Sch	98
Jackson, Kara/Toll Gate Middle Sch	64
Jackson, Shawn/Alliance High Sch	184
Jacobs, Nkenge/Youthbuild Columbus Cmty Sch	6
Jadallah, Maysa/AL Ihsan Islamic Sch	53
Jadallah, Maysa/AL Ihsan Sch	53
Jados, Andy/Big Walnut High Sch	58
Jaissle, Michael/Hope Academy-West	2
Jaissle, Michael/Pearl Academy	4
Jaissle, Michael/West Park Academy [238]	6
James, Dee/Mansion Day Sch	77
James, Gisele/Par Excellence Academy	119
James, Natalie/Ridgeview Middle Sch	68
James, Quatrice/Fairfax Elem Sch	42
James, Roy/Miles Elem Sch	44
James, Tiffiany/Washington Park Env Stud Acad	45
Jameson, Michael/Cypress Christian Sch	77
Jamison, Kyle/Fairfield Academy	21
Jamison, Roni/Columbus Performance Academy [247]	66
Janasov, Suzie/Highland Co Pre-School Unit	102
Janatovich, Mike/Leighton Elem Sch	165
Jarrett, Lorrie/Wintersville Elem Sch	109
Javier, Irene, Dr/Lincoln-West HS Global Studies	44
Jeffers, Christine/Mac-A-Cheek Learning Center	120
Jenkins, Michael, Dr/Boulevard Elem Sch	42
Jenkins, William/Immaculate Conception Academy	96
Jennings, Joshua/Global Impact STEM Academy	2
Jennings, Tracy/Glendale Elem Sch	92
Jesko, Brian/Bath High Sch	8
Jesse, Stuart/Glass City Academy	127
Jewell, Wendy/Parma Park Elem Sch	49
Jiovanazzo, Jill/Walter G Nord Middle Sch	122
Jiran, Nicki/Washington Elem Sch	181
Johns, Jodi/Imagine Clay Ave Cmty ES [245]	3
Johnson, Billie/Robinwood Lane Elem Sch	134
Johnson, Debra/St Benedict the Moor Cath Sch	154
Johnson, Ebone/West Mound Elem Sch	69
Johnson, Erin/Columbus Humanties Arts & Tech [238]	1
Johnson, Erin/Columbus Preparatory Academy [238]	1
Johnson, Greg/West Liberty-Salem Sch	26
Johnson, Herneika/Grove Patterson Academy	129
Johnson, Jamie/Central Academy of Ohio [195]	1
Johnson, Jamie/Taylor Road Elem Sch	73
Johnson, Jason/Northland High Sch	68
Johnson, Justin/New Riegel K-12 Sch	181

PRINCIPAL INDEX

Market Data Retrieval

NAME/School	PAGE
Johnson, Kellie/*Ft Meigs Elem Sch*	218
Johnson, Kerry/*Miller City High Sch*	170
Johnson, Larry/*Firestone Cmty Learning Center*	191
Johnson, Lawanda/*Arbor Elem Sch*	46
Johnson, Mike/*Summit Country Day Sch*	96
Johnson, Misty/*Samuel Bissell Elem Sch*	195
Johnson, Peggy/*Loveland High Sch*	90
Johnson, Penny/*Hook Elem Sch*	147
Johnson, Robin/*Mother Maria Anna Brunner CS*	154
Johnson, Samuel/*Beechcroft High Sch*	67
Johnson, Stephanie/*Cookson Elem Sch*	146
Johnson, Stephanie/*Hawthorne Elem Sch*	124
Johnson, Teresa/*Fairland West Elem Sch*	116
Johnson, Ty/*Chesapeake Middle Sch*	115
Johnson, Vic/*Sandy Valley Elem Sch*	189
Johnson, Warren/*Eastwood SDA Junior Academy*	77
Johnson, Yolanda/*Longfellow Elem Sch*	129
Johnston, Jeffrey, Dr/*Monticello Middle Sch*	42
Johnston, Jennifer/*Ohio Construction Academy*	4
Johnston, Jodi/*Julie Billiart Sch*	52
Johnston, Joe/*Englewood Elem Sch*	152
Johnston, Sarah/*Old Trail Sch*	196
Jones, Andre/*Northgate Intermediate Sch*	68
Jones, Betsy/*Toronto High Sch*	110
Jones, Charles/*Jennings Cmty Learning Ctr*	191
Jones, Cheryl/*East Linden Elem Sch*	67
Jones, Christina/*Madison Christian Sch*	77
Jones, Denise/*South Vienna Elem Sch*	27
Jones, Eric/*Roosevelt Elem Sch*	200
Jones, James/*Autism Academy of Learning*	127
Jones, James/*Robinson Elem Sch*	130
Jones, Jason/*New Vienna Elem Sch*	33
Jones, Jeffrey/*Groveport Madison MS-North*	71
Jones, Joan/*Struthers Elem Sch*	136
Jones, Josh/*Adena High Sch*	174
Jones, Joy/*Oakwood Elem Sch*	123
Jones, K Frank/*SS Agatha & Aloysius Sch*	52
Jones, Kevin/*Winton Woods Primary Sch-North*	94
Jones, Kirk/*Ayersville Middle Sch*	57
Jones, Lorenzo/*Holy Name Elem Sch*	52
Jones, Monica/*Youngstown Early College HS*	137
Jones, Paul/*Payne Elem Sch*	160
Jones, Rachel, Dr/*Gurney Elem Sch*	42
Jones, Sabrina/*Academy for Urban Scholars*	1
Jones, Shannon/*Eastland Preparatory Academy [238]*	2
Jones, Tim/*Davis Aerospace & Maritime HS*	43
Jones, Vickie/*Meigs Middle Sch*	143
Jordan, Christopher/*Portsmouth West Middle Sch*	180
Jordan, John/*Harvard Elem Sch*	129
Jordan, Kasi/*Sharonville Elem Sch*	92
Jorney-Gifford, Anita/*Boys Village Sch*	213
Joseph, Akesha/*Liberty High Sch*	199
Joseph, Tiffany/*Early College Acad at Crenshaw*	184
Jude, Joseph/*Possum Elem Sch*	27
Jude, Martha/*Pickett Academy*	130
Judy, Donna/*St Rose Catholic Sch*	10
Judy, Jeff/*Hardin-Houston Local Sch*	183
Juli, Eric/*Shaker Heights High Sch*	50
Jurgenson, Kent/*Lebanon Christian Sch*	209
Jurkovic, Eric/*New Philadelphia High Sch*	203
Jurmanovich, David/*Spring Hill Elem Sch*	194
Jurski, Jim/*Clay High Sch*	128
Justen, Heather/*Family Learning Center*	180
Justice, Todd/*Northeastern High Sch*	27

K

NAME/School	PAGE
Kaczor, James/*Monroeville High Sch*	105
Kaeser, Miriam, Sr/*St Boniface Sch*	95
Kaffenbarger, Michelle/*Bunsold Middle Sch*	204
Kahny, Shelly/*St Antoninus Sch*	95
Kaiser, Cherie/*Old Brooklyn Cmty Elem Sch [242]*	4
Kaiser, Cherie/*Old Brooklyn Cmty Middle Sch [242]*	4
Kalain, Frank/*Kenmore-Garfield High Sch*	191
Kaliszewski, Richard/*Assumption Academy*	52
Kamenski, Chris/*Park Avenue Elem Sch*	155
Kaminicki, Marc/*Northfield Elem Sch*	193
Kampschmidt, Connie/*Mercy McAuley High Sch*	95
Kandel, Gary/*Clearmount Elem Sch*	187
Kandel, Steve/*Saville Elem Sch*	151
Kannally, Timothy/*Creekview Intermediate Sch*	204
Kapki, Ferhat/*Horizon Sci Acad-Youngstwn [153]*	3
Kaple-Jones, Kristin/*Dowds Elem Sch*	173
Kaple, Dominick/*Memorial Junior High Sch*	51
Kappas, Alyssia/*Gorrell Elem Sch*	187
Kara, Aydin/*Horizon Sci Academy-Toledo [153]*	3
Karacson, Katie/*Buckeye Valley East Elem Sch*	58
Karner, Jack/*North East Center*	66
Karolewski, Matt/*Apple Creek Elem Sch*	213
Karshner, Nelson/*Eastland Career Center*	70
Kaschak, Mike/*Portage Lakes Career Center*	189
Kasner, Neal/*Greeneview High Sch*	84
Katafias, Kevin/*Genoa Middle Sch*	159
Kauffeld, Jennifer/*Buckeye Woods Elem Sch*	73
Kauffeld, Michael/*Teays Valley West Middle Sch*	163
Kauffman, Brice/*Shekinah Christian Sch*	133
Kauffman, Josh/*Milford High Sch*	31
Kauffman, Joshua/*Piqua Central Interm Sch*	146
Kauffman, Kelly/*Riverside Jr Sr High Sch*	121
Kaufman, Aaron/*West Holmes High Sch*	105
Kawczynski, Kori/*Ottawa Hills Elem Sch*	128
Keadle, Holly/*Dixie Elem Sch*	152
Keal, Heather/*Mayfield Elem Sch*	23
Keane, Lisa/*Rivers Edge Mont Elem Sch*	149
Kearans, Michelle/*Ellet High Sch*	191
Kearns, Robert/*Harding Elem Sch*	136
Keefer, Jay/*Admiral King Elem Sch*	124
Keel, John/*Teays Valley High Sch*	163
Keeling, Lauren/*Belpre Elem Sch*	209
Keener, Tyler/*Tri-County International Acad*	211
Keener, Tyler/*Wooster High Sch*	214
Keesee, Alan/*East Knox Junior Senior HS*	111
Keeton, Ginger/*Stephen Bell Elem Sch*	84
Keib, Tim/*Hillsdale Middle Sch*	11
Kellenberger, Nathan/*Worthingway Middle Sch*	76
Keller, Diana/*Stingley Elem Sch*	149
Keller, Jennifer/*Felicity-Franklin Elem Sch*	30
Keller, Lawrence/*Willoughby Middle Sch*	114
Keller, Leanne/*Minster Elem Sch*	15
Keller, Matthew/*Canaan Middle Sch*	132
Kellough, Zeb/*Crim Elem Sch*	216
Kelly, Dave/*Miamitown Elem Sch*	93
Kelly, Kristen/*John Adams Clg & Career Acad*	44
Kelly, Martin/*Labrae Middle Sch*	198
Kelty, Tim/*Austintown Elem Sch*	134
Kelty, Timothy/*Fitch High Sch*	134
Kemats, Daniel/*McKinley Elem Sch*	35
Kemp, Laurie/*Gloria Dei Montessori Sch*	154
Kemp, Stephanie/*Mississinawa Valley Elem Sch*	56
Kendziorski, Dana/*Union Local Elem Sch*	19
Kennedy, Dave/*Madeira High Sch*	90
Kennedy, David/*Southeast High Sch*	167
Kennedy, Jim/*Conneaut Middle Sch*	12
Kennedy, Michelle/*Willowville Elem Sch*	31
Kennedy, Nannette/*St Mary Central Sch*	19
Kenney, Julie/*Prairie Lincoln Elem Sch*	74
Kenny, Kathleen/*Gilmour Academy*	52
Kent, Colleen/*Immaculate Conception Sch*	76
Kernerman, Yuval/*Cincinnati Hebrew Day Sch*	96
Kerns, Craig/*Huntington High Sch*	175
Kerns, Nikki/*Oakstone Academy*	77
Kerrigan, William/*Herberich Primary Sch*	192
Kessler, Bo/*Bowling Green Chrn Academy*	218
Ketner, Scott/*Glandorf Elem Sch*	170
Ketterer, Vince/*Albion Elem Sch*	48
Kettler, Kathleen/*St James Sch*	189
Keylor, Chris/*Ohio Valley Educ ESC*	209

Ohio School Directory

PRINCIPAL INDEX

NAME/School	PAGE
Kibler, Amy-Anne/Montessori Sch-Mahoning Valley	137
Kidner, Sara/John Marshall-Civic & Business	44
Kiehl, Melissa/Sandy Valley Middle Sch	189
Kienle, Deborah/W C Schenck Elem Sch	207
Kieper, Jim/Eastwood High Sch	216
Kiger, J/Southern Local Jr Sr HS	36
Kilbane, Caitlin/Marion C Seltzer Elem Sch	44
Kile, Suzanne/Preschool Early Learning Ctr	75
Kimani, Mitzi/Foundation Academy [238]	2
Kime, Jennifer/First Baptist Christian Sch	126
Kimmons, Rhonda/Springfield High Sch	128
Kincaid, Barbara/Montessori Childrens Sch	54
Kincaid, Mary/St Christopher Sch	154
King, Ben/West Union Elem Sch	6
King, Bret/George McDowell Middle Sch	162
King, Bret/Laurelville Elem Sch	162
King, Elizabeth/Alliance Academy of Cincinnati [203]	87
King, Juliet/Bolton Elem Sch	43
King, Michael/Berkshire Jr Sr High Sch	81
King, Mike/Baker Elem Sch	199
King, Mike/Currie Elem Sch	199
King, Phil/Revere High Sch	194
King, Victoria/Douglas MacArthur Girls Ldrshp	43
Kinley, Dan/St Matthias Sch	76
Kipp, Michele/Covedale Elem Sch	87
Kireta, Julie/Stanton Elem Sch	109
Kirk, Mandy/Our Lady of Grace Sch	95
Kirkendall, Jeana/Autism Model Sch	127
Kirkland, Sean/Salem High Sch	35
Kirkland, Sean/Salem Junior High Sch	35
Kisabeth, Kathleen/James A Garfield High Sch	165
Kish, Jim/West Geauga Middle Sch	82
Kish, Paul/Berea-Midpark Middle Sch	41
Kisha-Wise, Kathy/Cedar Leadership Sch	184
Kisner, Andra/Stevenson Elem Sch	118
Kist, Daniel/Hilltop Elem Sch	93
Kitchen, Teresa/St Wendelin Catholic Sch	182
Kittleberger, Diane/Edison Middle Sch	188
Klaus, Jennifer/Clear Fork Middle Sch	171
Klein, Debra/Mt Washington Sch	88
Klein, Jennifer/Wyoming Middle Sch	94
Klemens, Joanie/Mater Dei Academy	114
Kletzy, Elizabeth/Berry Intermediate Sch	207
Klimkewicz, Patrick/St Anthony Padua Elem Sch	52
Klinar, Bob/Chaney High Sch	136
Klinar, Robert/Lakeside High Sch	12
Kline, Becky/Hathaway Brown Sch	54
Kline, Corey/Mapleton High Sch	11
Kline, Corey/Mapleton Middle Sch	11
Kline, Sheryl/Broadmoor Sch	112
Klinedinst, Angela/Mount Auburn Preparatory Acad [238]	4
Klingensmith, Jame/Campbell K-7 Sch	134
Klingshirn, Stephanie/Emerson Elem Sch	183
Klotz, Ann/Laurel Sch	54
Klotzbach, Craig/Mansfield Christian Sch	174
Klus, Richard/St Lawrence Sch	95
Knapke, Darrin/Enon Primary Sch	27
Knapke, Darrin/Indian Valley Intermediate Sch	27
Knapp, Carrie/Highland High Sch	141
Knight, April/Avondale Elem Sch	67
Knight, Christopher/St John's Jesuit High Sch	131
Knight, Dustin/Tarhe Trails Elem Sch	64
Knippen, Michelle/St Mary Sch	171
Knisely, Robert/Perry Middle Sch	113
Knittel, David/Beautiful Savior Luth Sch	77
Knori, Jeff/Lake Center Christian Sch	190
Knowles, Erica/Tuscarawas Vly Middle Sch	203
Kobel, Mary/Sacred Heart Sch	37
Koch, Eric/Ridgeview STEM Junior High Sch	64
Kochan, Lori/Dueber Reading & Math Prep Sch	184
Kochanek, Dawn/Buckeye Primary Sch	140
Kochemba, Steven/Badger High Sch	198
Koehler, Craig, Dr/Avon Middle Sch	123
Koenig, Beth/Clermont Co Hearing Hndcp Unit	29
Koenig, Rick/Lake Catholic High Sch	114
Koenig, Tracy/St Patrick Sch	215
Koeth, Brandy/Indianola K-8 Sch	68
Kohler, James/Keystone High Sch	124
Kohls, Jesse/Loveland Early Childhood Ctr	90
Kohn, Chelsey/John Marshall-Info Tech	44
Kolebuck, Chad/Hill View Elem Sch	129
Kollmorgen, Tim/St Mark's Lutheran Sch	32
Komar, Craig/Sidney Fenn Elem Sch	141
Koniowsky, T/Seaborn Elem Sch	201
Kopp, Neal/Coventry High Sch	192
Koppisch, Israel, Dr/Academy of Educ Excellence	127
Kornick, Joe/J & G Snow Sch	41
Kornish, Colleen/Fairless Elem Sch	185
Kosanovic, Leslie/Belmont Co Alt Program	17
Kosek, Edward/Crestwood Middle Sch	165
Kosmach, Traci/Riverview Elem Sch	194
Kosmerchock, Shellie/St John Lutheran Sch	58
Kostyack, Mike/Brook Park Memorial Elem Sch	41
Koth, Cindy/Dayton Smart Bilingual Academy	2
Kountz, Kathryn/Imagine Great Western Academy [245]	66
Kovach, Stephen/Howland Middle Sch	198
Kovack, Greg/Walnut Elem Sch	163
Kovalski, Jason/Buckeye Local Jr High Sch	108
Kowach, Maggie/Bascom Elem Sch	198
Kowalk, Vicki/Bridgeport Elem Sch	22
Kowza, Kathryn/Sharon Elem Sch	141
Kozak, Timothy/Sandusky Middle Sch	61
Kozarec, Todd/Valley View High Sch	153
Kozina, Jason/Northwood High Sch	217
Kozlaka, Sandra/Lincoln Elem Sch	47
Kracker, Jeff/Jackson High Sch	186
Kraemer, Ken/New Albany High Sch	72
Kramer, Charles/St John Lutheran Sch	102
Kramer, Diane/New Bremen Elem Sch	16
Kratche, Scott/Putnam Elem Sch	210
Kreischer, Adam/League Elem Sch	106
Kreischer, Trent/Crestview Local Sch	205
Kremer, Carl/Archbishop Moeller High Sch	95
Kriegmont, Shannon/Madison South Elem Sch	112
Krier, Kevin/Lakewood High Sch	118
Krier, Tim/Yellow Springs High Sch	85
Krogman, Justin/Van Wert Elem Sch	205
Kronewetter, Heather/Oakstone Cmty Sch	66
Krontz, Lindsey/Northwood Elem Sch	217
Krueger, Ken/Redeemer Christian Sch	196
Kruger, Sylvia/Intergenerational Sch	39
Krugh, Lora/Holy Rosary Sch	17
Krumpak, Joe/Sebring McKinley Jr/Sr High	135
Krupa, Kelly/Stepstone Academy	5
Krupar, Kathy/Our Lady of Angels Sch	52
Kubec, Bonnie/Walter Kidder Elem Sch	140
Kubiak, Thomas/Joseph M Gallagher Elem Sch	44
Kucbel, Brian/Shawnee Elem Sch	61
Kuchta, Kim/Holy Trinity Sch	126
Kuffel, Jackie/Tolles Career & Tech Center	133
Kuhlman, Jeremy/Ayersville High Sch	57
Kuhlman, Kaleb/Children's Resource Center	216
Kuhn, Kelly/Auburn Elem Sch	173
Kuhn, Phillip/Southview Elem Sch	107
Kujala, Robert/Southington Local Sch	200
Kulka, Brandon/Holy Trinity Sch	80
Kummer, Chris/St Catherine of Siena ECC	131
Kumpf, Ryan/Greentown Intermediate Sch	187
Kunath, Arthur, Dr/St Edmund Campion Academy	96
Kunk, Kyle/St Henry Middle Sch	144
Kunz, Jamie/Monroe Elem Sch	31
Kunze, Valerie/United Preparatory Acad-East [249]	5
Kuri, Michael/McCord Middle Sch	76
Kurty, Peter/Glacier Ridge Elem Sch	70
Kurtz, Jeffrey/Penta Career Center	217
Kurz, Mark/Olmsted Falls Middle Sch	48
Kurzen, David/Innes Cmty Learning Ctr	191
Kussmaul, Kimberly/Liberty Christian Academy	120
Kuzior, Joseph/Willyard Elem Sch	166

PRINCIPAL INDEX

Market Data Retrieval

NAME/School	PAGE
L	
Lacoste, John/*Indian Trail Elem Sch*	194
Lacy, Kyle/*Patrick Henry Middle Sch*	102
LaFon, Angela/*Dawson-Bryant Elem Sch*	115
LaForge, Jake/*Holy Angels Sch*	154
Lallathin, Max/*Winchester Trail Elem Sch*	66
Lama, Jamie/*Imagine Academy at Sullivant [245]*	3
Lamb, Tim/*Huron High Sch*	61
Lambdin, Tracey/*Black River High Sch*	140
Lambert, Dorothy/*Archbold Elem Sch*	78
Lambert, Lourdes/*Archbishop Alter High Sch*	154
LaMendola, Sue/*Harold Lewis Center*	204
Lammlein, Stephanie/*Bio-Med Science Academy*	1
Lamp, Lindsay/*Knox County Head Start*	110
Landon, Beth/*Bethlehem Lutheran Sch*	85
Landon, Kevin/*Avery Elem Sch*	72
Landskroener, Jim/*Trinity Lutheran Sch*	131
Lane, Anthony/*Robinson Cmty Learning Center*	191
Lane, Jonathan/*Brown Middle Sch*	166
Lane, Michael/*Pettisville Jr Sr High Sch*	79
Laney, Gwenda/*St Ann Catholic Sch*	24
Lang, James/*Conneaut Elem Sch*	216
Lang, Jim/*Bowling Green Pre-School*	216
Lange, Mark/*E A Powell Elem Sch*	217
Langhals, Nick/*Jennings Local Sch*	169
Langhals, Tony/*Synergy Learning Center*	205
Lanham, Bobbie/*Mt Healthy Prep & Fitness Acad [247]*	87
Lanier, Thomas/*Westerville Central High Sch*	75
Lanning, Gerald/*Polaris Career Ctr High Sch*	49
Lanning, Michelle/*Wellston Intermediate Sch*	108
Lanthorn, Robert/*Hamilton Twp High Sch*	71
Lantz, Kristi/*Phillips Elem Sch*	210
LaPaglia, Christy/*Cares Center*	113
Lapham, Kayla/*Edon Northwest Local Sch*	215
Lapp, Titus/*Antrim Mennonite Sch*	101
Lariccia, Betsy/*Heartland Christian Sch*	36
Lariccia, James/*Northwest Primary*	188
Lasky, Kenneth/*Adrian Elem Sch*	51
Lassman, James/*Maumee Valley Country Day Sch*	131
Lather, Julie/*Oak Creek Elem Sch*	59
Lauridsen, Dawn, Dr/*West Franklin Elem Sch*	74
Lauson, Bill/*Valley View Intermediate Sch*	153
Lautenschleger, Dave/*Massillon Washington High Sch*	187
Laux, Stephen/*Mercer Co Alternative Sch*	4
Lavdas, Eldora/*H G Blake Elem Sch*	141
Lavery, Travis/*C H Campbell Elem Sch*	134
Lavey, Michelle/*Bradford Elem Sch*	145
Lawrence-Jones, Cheryl/*Liberty Christian Sch*	10
Lawrence, David/*Northmoor Elem Sch*	152
Lawson, Bill/*Valley View Primary Sch*	153
Lawver, Holly/*Starlight Sch*	201
Layton, Randy/*Oak Hill Middle High Sch*	107
Leatherman, Keith/*Wauseon High Sch*	80
Leatherman, Kevin/*Norwayne Middle Sch*	212
Leatherman, Kyle/*Bluffton Middle Sch*	8
Leatherman, Kyle/*Liberty-Benton Middle Sch*	98
LeBeau, Donna/*New Albany Middle Sch*	72
Leddy, Denice/*Emerson Elem Sch*	47
Lee-Wilfong, Megan/*Windemere Cmty Learning Center*	191
Lee, Adam/*St John's High Sch*	10
Lee, Dan/*ADA Sch*	99
Lee, Jason/*Foxfire Schools*	2
Lee, Kenton/*Columbus N International Sch*	67
Lees, Tracie/*Larry Larson Middle Sch*	71
Lees, Tracie/*Thomas A Edison Interm Sch*	71
Leever, Dale/*Summit Acad Sch-Cincinnati [248]*	87
Legan, Jeffrey/*Mayfield High Sch*	47
LeGault, Kimberly/*Madison Plains Interm Sch*	133
Leggett, Angela/*Lake Cable Elem Sch*	186
Lehman, Joe/*Scenic Ridge Christian Sch*	11
Leigh-Doyle, Paula/*Hershey Montessori Sch*	115
Leindecker, Keri/*James A Garfield Elem Sch*	165
Leist, Doug/*Kings High Sch*	207
Lemaster, Allison/*Crestview Middle Sch*	34
Lemley, Ryan/*Warren High Sch*	210
Lemon, Chad/*Crestview Middle Sch*	171
Lengel, Theresa/*Westwood Middle Sch*	123
Lensman, Chad/*Graham Middle Sch*	26
Lentz, Carol/*Raymond Elem Sch*	204
Leon, Luis/*Cornerstone Academy [238]*	2
Leonard, Shaunamichele/*New Tech High School-West*	44
Leone, Paula/*City Day Community Sch*	1
Lepelley, John/*Cleveland School of the Arts*	43
Leppla, Leslie/*Cambridge Primary Sch*	86
Lerner, Michele/*Welsh Hills Sch*	120
Lester, Brittney/*Madison Cmty Elem Sch [242]*	39
Lester, Suzanne/*Elyria Catholic High Sch*	126
Lesure, Shawna/*Superior Elem Sch*	46
Leu, Elizabeth/*St Louis Sch*	32
Levy, Nicole/*Luther Memorial Sch*	54
Lewellen, Natalie/*Dunloe Elem Sch*	71
Lewin, Elizabeth/*Wildwood Environmental Acad K5 [200]*	6
Lewis Kaylor, Susan/*St Vincent Family Center*	77
Lewis, Aaron/*Fairland Middle Sch*	116
Lewis, Adam/*Brookfield High Sch*	197
Lewis, Antwan/*Hartwell Sch*	88
Lewis, Chantelle/*Larkmoor Elem Sch*	124
Lewis, Lynette/*Navin Elem Sch*	204
Lewis, Roger/*North Avondale Montessori Sch*	88
Lichey, Kyle/*Union Elem Sch*	22
Licht, Lisa/*Franklin Elem Sch*	123
Lichty, Travis/*Antwerp Local Sch*	160
Lichty, Travis/*Hicksville Elem Sch*	57
Liggens, Gretchen/*Walton Elem Sch*	45
Likely, Shalonda/*Liberty Elem Sch*	68
Lilly, Court/*New Richmond Middle Sch*	31
Linder, Joe/*Divine Mercy Elem Sch*	161
Linder, Megan/*Franklin-Monroe Elem Sch*	55
Lindley, Matt/*Greene Co Career Center*	84
Lindley, Matthew/*William Henry Harrison HS*	93
Lindsay, Daryl/*Canton College Prep Sch [238]*	184
Lindsay, Sally/*Clintonville Academy*	77
Lindsey, Vincent/*Massillon Junior High Sch*	187
Linton, Michelle/*Tri County Pre-School*	10
Litman-Hall, Sue/*Withamsville-Tobasco Elem Sch*	31
Litt, Julie/*Richland-New Hope Sch*	171
Littlefield, Jennifer/*Apex Academy [203]*	39
Llewellyn, Regina/*Pfeiffer Elem Sch*	191
Lloyd, Jarod/*Ross Co Christian Academy*	176
Llyod, Kevin/*Portsmouth West High Sch*	180
Loboschefski, Michele/*Fairfield Elem Sch*	127
Locklear, Lisa/*Willow Sch*	45
Loffer, Jacki/*Our Lady of the Rosary Sch*	154
Lofton, Darwin/*Heir Force Cmty Sch*	7
Lollo, Michael/*St Rose of Lima Sch*	162
Long, Amy/*Troy Christian Schools*	147
Long, Jenn/*Furry Elem Sch*	61
Long, Josh/*Covington Elem Sch*	145
Long, Karen/*Denver Place Elem Sch*	33
Long, Michael/*Sugar Creek Christian Academy*	117
Long, Will/*Heritage Christian Sch*	99
Longbrake, Jason/*Swanton High Sch*	79
Longworth, Bob/*Lockland Middle Sch*	90
Looney, Scott/*Hawken Lower-Middle Sch*	54
Looney, Scott/*Hawken Sch*	54
Loper, Gretchen/*Forestlawn Elem Sch*	126
Loper, Gretchen/*Knollwood Elem Sch*	126
Lopez, Alissa/*Royal Manor Elem Sch*	70
Lord, Sarah/*Sands Montessori Sch*	88
Losco, Annette/*Millcreek Elem Sch*	161
Losco, Tony/*Miller High Sch*	161
Losee, Robert/*Hubbard Mastery Sch*	68
Lotycz, Mark/*Fairbanks Elem Sch*	204
Louden, Jeremy/*St Paul Lutheran Sch*	54
Loudenback, Ross/*Springcreek Primary Sch*	146
Love, Dennis/*Roosevelt High Sch*	166

Ohio School Directory

PRINCIPAL INDEX

NAME/School	PAGE
Lowe, Angie/Open Door Christian Sch	126
Lowe, Patti/Resurrection of Our Lord Sch	95
Lower, James/St Charles Preparatory Sch	76
Lowery, Doug/Triad Middle Sch	26
Lowther, Jo/Imagine Groveport Prep Sch [245]	3
Loy, Judy/Springfield Christian Sch	29
Loy, Ryan/Botkins Local Sch	182
Lucas, Jennifer/Betty Jane Cmty Learning Ctr	191
Lucas, Kristina/Delaware Area Career Ctr-South	59
Lucas, Paul/Orange High Sch	49
Luce, Corey/Green Elem Sch	81
Luck, Robbin/East Clinton Middle Sch	33
Ludwig, Jonathan/East Liverpool Jr Sr High Sch	35
Luebbe, Thomas/Butler High Sch	153
Luehrman, Karen/Life Skills Ctr of Cincinnati	3
Luelleman, Jeff/Columbus Prep & Fitness Acad [247]	1
Lukz Gatta, Joanna/Niles Primary Sch	200
Lundin, John/Buckeye Elem Sch	35
Luneborg, James/Chestnut Ridge Elem Sch	104
Luneborg, James/Mt Hope Elem Sch	104
Lusk, Aaron/Maritime Academy of Toledo	127
Luth, Becky/Black River Education Center	139
Lutz, John/Newark Digital Academy	119
Lutz, Staci/Riverside Elem Sch	70
Lynch, Sean/Columbia High Sch	123
Lyons, Barry/Buckeye Valley West Elem Sch	58
Lyons, Lisa/Lincoln Prepartory Academy	3
Lyons, Maggie/Rainsboro Elem Sch	103

M

NAME/School	PAGE
Maag, Justine/St Vincent De Paul Sch	111
Mabry, Halsey/St Francis Seraph Sch	95
Macarthy, Stacy/Livingston Elem Sch	68
Macek, Molly/Maumee Valley Country Day Sch	131
Macik, Luke/The Lyceum	54
Mack, Allen/Miami East Junior High Sch	145
Mack, Kimberly/John P Parker Elem Sch	88
Mack, Ms/MC2 STEM HS-GE Lighting	44
Macki-Barr, Amy/South Suburban Montessori Sch	54
MacKinnon, Feowyn/MC2 STEM HS-Grt Lakes Sci Ctr	44
Macko, Randy/Lutz Elem Sch	177
Mackzum, David/Princeton Cmty Middle Sch	92
Macon, Yzvetta/South Elem Sch	91
Maddux, Craig/Cherry Hill Primary Sch	65
Mader, Dean/Dawson-Bryant High Sch	115
Mader, Doug/Sycamore High Sch	93
Madigan, Brian/Cloverleaf Middle Sch	140
Madison, Jasmin/Children's Home Sch	96
Maetin, Rebecca/Beacon Sch	14
Magill, Kelly/Village Christian Sch	209
Magyar, Robert/Columbia Middle Sch	123
Mahlmister, James/Sciotoville Cmty East High Sch	5
Mahoney, Lisa/Harvest Preparatory Sch	77
Maimone, April/Near West Intergenerationl Sch	44
Maine, David/Fairfield Crossroads Mid Sch	21
Majzun, Michael/Summit Academy Youngstown	5
Majzun, Micheal/Summit Academy-Youngstown [248]	5
Makcen, Tim/Aldersgate Christian Academy	96
Makruski, Amy/St Joseph Sch	126
Malany, Ryan/Jonathan Alder Junior High Sch	132
Malcom, Michael/Elgin Middle Sch	138
Malcom, Michael/Pleasant Middle Sch	138
Malik, Maria/Leawood Elem Sch	68
Mallory, Tracey/Westbrooke Village Elem Sch	153
Malone, Charla/Stone Reading & Math Prep Sch	185
Malone, David/Springfield Local Interm Sch	136
Malone, Heidi/Royal Redeemer Lutheran Sch	54
Malone, Melissa/Katherine Thomas Elem Sch	167
Malone, Mike/Talawanda Middle Sch	24
Maloy, Susan/St Matthew Sch	76
Maltarich, Carrie/Killbuck Elem Sch	105
Mamone, Joe/Martins Ferry High Sch	18
Mancini, Howard/St Patrick Sch	167
Mandell, Debra/Monarch Sch of Bellefaire Jcb	54

NAME/School	PAGE
Maney, Stacy/Kemp PK-6 Sch	149
Maney, Tammy/Eastgate Sch	184
Mangan, Joell/Fairbrook Elem Sch	83
Mangas, David/Cuyahoga Valley Career Center	45
Mangas, Scott/Ottoville Elem Sch	170
Mangus, Ron/Harrison Elem Sch	93
Manion, Jeffrey/Tallmadge Middle Sch	195
Manke, Dean/Invictus High Sch	3
Manley, Krist/Edison Elem Sch	10
Mann, Katie/Memorial Elem Sch	140
Manning, Laura/Durling Middle Sch	123
Manz, Jennifer/Oakwood Elem Sch	160
Marangoni, Tres/Village Academy	60
Marawi, Marie/Int'l Academy of Cincinnati	24
Marcello, Shawn/Hubbard Elem Sch	198
Marchetti, Tom/Delaware Area Career Ctr-North	59
Marconi, Jacqueline/Green Valley Elem Sch	49
Marcum, Scott/Arlington Local Sch	97
Margaret, Yitreack/Yeshiva Derech Ha Torah	54
Margerum, Joshua/Riverview Elem Sch	22
Mariani, Lori/William S Stinson Elem Sch	188
Mariano, Nick/Liberty Center Middle Sch	101
Marino, Adam/Strongsville Middle Sch	51
Marinucci, Marco/Windham Junior High Sch	167
Marion, James/South-Western Career Academy	74
Marker, Kelly/Mark Twain Elem Sch	151
Markgraf, Daniel/Beautiful Savior Luth Sch	96
Marley, Tara/Beach Sch	50
Marok, Wayne/Downtown Educational Ctr	43
Maroni, Joe/Hilltop Elem Sch	134
Marquez, Ferdie/Waverly Junior High Sch	164
Marsh, Natalie/St Rita School for the Deaf	96
Marshall, Aaron/La Salle High Sch	95
Marshall, Brooke/Amanda-Clearcreek Primary Sch	63
Marshall, Emily/Ripley-Union-Lewis-Huntngtn ES	20
Marshall, Erin/Temple Christian Sch	10
Marshall, John/Chaminade Julienne High Sch	154
Martin, Angela/Westgate Elem Sch	69
Martin, Ashely/Summit Acad Sec Sch-Youngstown [248]	133
Martin, Brian/Northwest Elem Sch	179
Martin, Brian/Ross High Sch	24
Martin, Christie/Malcolm-Bain Center	130
Martin, Craig/Central Christian Sch	214
Martin, David/Hilton Elem Sch	41
Martin, Deborah/St Stanislaus Elem Sch	53
Martin, Eric/Winton Woods HS-Global Studies	94
Martin, Eric/Winton Woods HS-New Tech Acad	94
Martin, Garry/Demmitt Elem Sch	153
Martin, Jason/Bay High Sch	40
Martin, Jason/Columbiana Middle Sch	34
Martin, Jennifer/East End Elem Sch	33
Martin, Karen/Cloverleaf Elem Sch	140
Martin, Kristine/Whitmer High Sch	131
Martin, Kyle/Springboro High Sch	208
Martin, Mary/Early Learning Center	153
Martin, Mike/Buckeye Central High Sch	38
Martindell, Kim/Bobbie B Fairfax Sch	87
Martinez, Andrea/King Academy Cmty Sch	3
Martini, Bert/Wilmington Middle Sch	33
Martz, Pat/Bellefontaine Elem Sch	121
Marvin, Laura/St Mary of the Imm Concep Sch	214
Masey, Lanicka/Life Skills Center of Dayton	3
Mason, Patrese/Trevitt Elem Sch	69
Mast, Mike/Fairhaven Sch	132
Mast, Roda/Holmes Co Training Center	104
Masucci, Michael/Union Elem Sch	135
Masur, Christine/Cincinnati Waldorf Sch	96
Matheny, Kerri/East Clinton High Sch	33
Matheny, Scott/Briar Middle Sch	61
Mathes, Chris/South Point Elem Sch	116
Matos, Steven/South Range Elem Sch	135
Mattingly, John/Adena Elem Sch	22
Matz, Joshua/Hayes Elem Sch	177
Maver, Robert/Firelands High Sch	124
Mavis, Bret/Zane Trace Middle Sch	176

PRINCIPAL INDEX

Market Data Retrieval

NAME/School	PAGE
Maxsam, Jamal/*North Elem Sch*	91
Maxwell, Lisa/*Tinora Junior High Sch*	57
Maxwell, Thomas/*Dixie Middle Sch*	152
Mayer, William/*North Elem Sch*	113
Mayo, Casey/*Barnesville Middle Sch*	17
Mays, Kristin/*Urbana High Sch*	26
Mays, Lisa/*Dr John Hole Elem Sch*	148
Maze, Jasmine/*Cleveland HS for Digital Arts*	43
Mazza, Jennifer/*Tyler Run Elem Sch*	59
McAfee, Derrick/*Bellaire High Sch*	17
McAfee, Derrick/*Bellaire Middle Sch*	17
McAndrews, Sean/*Bay Middle Sch*	40
McCann, Brett/*Willowick Middle Sch*	114
McCann, Tyrone/*Green Road Developmental Ctr*	39
McCants, Charles/*Caledonia Elem Sch*	45
McCarty, Pandy/*Blanchester High Sch*	32
McCaulla, Megan/*Hanby Elementary*	75
McClain, Nedria/*Hays-Porter Elem Sch*	88
McClain, Patricia, Sr/*Lial Sch*	131
McClellan, Greg/*Streetsboro Elem Sch*	167
McClellan, Jeffrey/*MC2 STEM HS-Cleveland State*	44
McCloud, Dawn/*Reynolds HS-HS2 STEM Academy*	73
McCloud, Dawn/*Waggoner Road Middle Sch*	73
McCorkle, Matthew/*Green High Sch*	178
McCoy, Margaret/*Brice Christian Academy*	77
McCoy, Stephanie/*Buckeye Middle Sch*	67
McCullough, Colleen/*Victory Christian Sch*	201
McCullough, Elizabeth/*St Nicholas Sch*	137
McDade, Mary/*Spruce Primary Sch*	48
McDainels, Josh/*Shanahan Middle Sch*	59
McDaniel, A Cory/*Cleveland Arts & Soc Sci Acad [238]*	1
McDaniel, Brittney/*Finland Elem Sch*	73
McDonald, Mellisa/*Arbor Hills Junior High Sch*	129
McDonnell, Stephen/*Taft Intermediate Sch*	10
McDowell, David/*St Joseph Sch*	107
McDowell, Donna/*St Francis Xavier Sch*	107
McDowell, Janet/*Case Elem Sch*	43
McDowell, Penny/*Morrison Elem Sch*	14
McDowell, Shauna/*Pleasant Hill Academy*	88
McEldowney, Roger/*Versailles High Sch*	56
McElwain, Daniel/*Bridge Academy*	53
McFadden, Shawyna/*Oakmont Elem Sch*	68
McFarland, Amanda/*Peebles Elem Sch*	6
McFarland, Susan/*Educational Svc Ctr Pre-School*	19
McGinty, Karen/*Garfield Elem Sch*	141
McGlenn, Amey/*Mill Valley Elem Sch*	204
McGrath, Cheryl/*Columbiana Co Ed Center*	33
McGraw, Ryan/*Minford Elem Primary Sch*	178
McGreevy, Tom/*Tri-Co Career Center*	15
McGuinness, William/*Independence High Sch*	46
McIntire, Alicia/*Washington Elem Sch*	210
McIntosh, Ione/*Ritzman Cmty Learning Ctr*	191
McIntosh, Jack, Dr/*Evangel Academy*	154
McIntosh, Joelle/*Nathan Hale Elem Sch*	44
McKee, Alicia/*South Central Middle Sch*	106
McKeever, Michael/*St Clairsville Middle Sch*	18
McKenna, Kc/*St Edward High Sch*	53
McKenzie, Adam/*Tuslaw High Sch*	189
McKibbin, Rhonna/*Forest Park Elem Sch*	68
McLane, Ryan/*West Muskingum Elem Sch*	157
McLaughlin, Elaine/*J C Sommer Elem Sch*	73
McMackin, Josh/*Notre Dame Elem Sch*	180
McMahan, John/*Taft Elem Sch*	137
McMahon, Dave/*Crestwood High Sch*	165
McManaway, Melissa/*Imagine Klepinger Rd Cmty Sch [245]*	3
McManaway, Melissa/*Imagine Woodbury Academy [245]*	3
McMillan, Janine/*Union Elem Sch*	219
McMillan, Jim/*Grove City Christian Sch*	77
McMillen, Bridget/*Arrowhead Elem Sch*	59
McMurray, Benjamin/*Ottawa Hills Jr Sr High Sch*	128
McNabb, Cathy/*St Paul Lutheran Sch*	205
McNally, Elizabeth, Dr/*Highland Elem Sch*	68
McNamara, John/*Ruffing Mont Rocky River Sch*	54

NAME/School	PAGE
McNeal, Jeanne/*Oakwood Middle Sch*	188
McNeil, Velma/*Mound-STEM Sch*	44
McNickle, Tricia/*Southern Elem Sch*	143
McPhail, Matt/*Fairfield Union High Sch*	63
McPherson, Gary/*Mary B Martin STEM Academy*	44
McQuaide, Russell/*Mesopotamia Elem Sch*	197
McRill, Karen/*Fairlawn Elem Sch*	182
McWhinnie, Joy/*Toledo Christian Sch*	131
McWreath, Van/*T W Harvey High Sch*	113
Mead, Shane/*Tri-Village Sch*	56
Mears, Phil/*Grace Community Sch*	60
Mecoli, Dan/*Hillel Academy of Dayton*	154
Medlyn, Robert/*Powhatan Elem Sch*	147
Medure, Michael/*Franklin Elem Sch*	187
Meeker, Maria/*Miller South School-Vpa*	191
Meeks, Marvis/*Miami Valley Academies*	4
Melton, Wade/*Hardin Cmty Sch*	2
Mencarini, Terry/*Northfield Bapt Christian Sch*	196
Mendenhall, Brad/*Lincolnview Jr Sr High Sch*	205
Menduni, Brooke/*Dr Henry Karrer Middle Sch*	69
Menefee, Terrance/*John Adams High Sch*	44
Mennel, Michael/*Central Middle Sch*	46
Menta, Kim/*Craddock Elem Sch*	165
Menta, Kim/*Robert C Lindsey Elem Sch*	82
Mental, Jack/*St Mary Sch*	139
Menuez, Shelly/*Tuslaw Elem Sch*	189
Mercer, Karen/*Unioto Elem Sch*	176
Merrill, Keith/*Brunswick High Sch*	140
Merz, Jason/*Kramer Elem Sch*	24
Mescher, Doug/*West Carrollton Middle Sch*	153
Messenheimer, Rob/*Worthington Estates Elem Sch*	76
Messer, Eric/*Mason Intermediate Sch*	208
Messick, Rob/*Piqua High Sch*	146
Metcalf, Jim, Dr/*Lucas High Sch*	172
Metsker, Shyla/*Wickliffe High Sch*	114
Metz, Jerry/*St Catharine Sch*	95
Metz, Phil/*Celina High Sch*	143
Metzger, Daniel/*St Mary Asumption Catholic ES*	206
Meyer, Bonnie/*Vermilion Elem Sch*	62
Meyer, Josh/*Covington High Sch*	145
Meyer, Nita/*Lincolnview Elem Sch*	205
Micciulla, Jim/*Darbydale Elem Sch*	73
Michael, Adam/*Oak Hill Elem Sch*	107
Michael, Jerod/*Ripley-Union-Lewis-Huntngtn MS*	20
Michael, Jordan/*Eastern Middle Sch*	7
Michael, Josh/*Sardinia Elem Sch*	7
Michaels, Laura/*Bowman Primary Sch*	207
Micheal, Heather/*Hope Haven Sch*	107
Miglich, Samantha/*Mt Eaton Elem Sch*	213
Milcetich, Paul/*Aurora High Sch*	165
Miles, Ashley/*Akron Preparatory Sch [238]*	1
Miles, Jamie/*Harlan-Butlerville Prim Sch*	208
Miley, Christine/*Hopkins Elem Sch*	113
Milford, Kortney/*Robert Taft Elem Sch*	188
Miller-Blakely, Jessica/*Wood Lane Sch*	216
Miller, Aaron/*Hamilton Christian Sch*	24
Miller, Brad/*Madison Plains Elem Sch*	133
Miller, Brian/*Hadley E Watts Middle Sch*	149
Miller, Buddy/*Eastern Elem Sch*	172
Miller, Chad/*Graham Elem Sch*	26
Miller, Christine/*Green Elem Sch*	212
Miller, Cory/*Virginia Stevenson Elem Sch*	151
Miller, Erin/*Indian Lake Middle Sch*	121
Miller, Gary/*Northridge Middle Sch*	27
Miller, Gary/*Summit Academy Trans HS-Dayton [248]*	5
Miller, James/*Manchester Middle Sch*	193
Miller, James, Dr/*Westland High Sch*	74
Miller, Jaqueline/*Stonebrook Montessori Sch*	45
Miller, Jason/*Hopewell-Loudon Local Sch*	181
Miller, Joe/*Danbury Local Sch*	159
Miller, Joe/*Norwood Middle Sch*	92
Miller, Julie/*Wynford High Sch*	39
Miller, Kate/*Brown Elem Sch*	72

OH-U18   800-333-8802   **School Year 2019-2020**

Ohio School Directory

PRINCIPAL INDEX

NAME/School	PAGE
Miller, Krista/Glenwood Middle Sch	98
Miller, Krista/Metro Early Clg Mid High Sch	4
Miller, Kyle/Ohio Avenue Elem Sch	68
Miller, Laura/All Saints Academy	76
Miller, Mark/Legacy Christian Sch	204
Miller, Mary/New Tech Collinwood	44
Miller, Mary/St Marys Middle Sch	16
Miller, Megan/Beverly-Center Elem Sch	210
Miller, Michael/Grand Lake Christian Sch	17
Miller, Nicholas/Dover Intermediate Sch	51
Miller, Nicole/Columbus Torah Academy	77
Miller, Nina/Georgetown Elem Sch	20
Miller, Shelly/Genoa Christian Academy	60
Miller, Sherry/Bryden Elem Sch	40
Miller, Sherry/Fairmount Early Childhood Ctr	40
Miller, Suzanne/Twin Oak Elem Sch	111
Miller, Vern/Easthaven Elem Sch	67
Millett, Jennifer/Our Lady of the Lake	52
Milligan, Tonya, Dr/Briggs High Sch	67
Milliken, Jj/Vinton Co High Sch	206
Millinger, Matt/Buckeye Central Elem Sch	38
Mills, Andrew/Harvest Preparatory Sch	77
Mills, Bryan/Harding Middle Sch	109
Mills, Deirdre/North Adams Elem Sch	6
Mills, Joseph/Cardington-Lincoln High Sch	155
Mills, Joseph/Cardington-Lincoln Middle Sch	155
Mills, Kimberly/Mifflin High Sch	68
Milner, Dawn/Reach Academy [200]	4
Milner, Michael/Alden R Brown Elem Sch	206
Milner, Michelle/Columbus Scioto	67
Mims-Morrow, Ladawn/Roosevelt Elem Sch	149
Minch-Hick, Holly, Dr/Indian Creek Middle Sch	109
Mineard, Cariann/Orchard Middle Sch	50
Minelli, Daniel/St John the Baptist Sch	95
Minnig, Mike/Bluffton High Sch	8
Minnig, Scott/Wapakoneta High Sch	16
Minto, Michelle/Hills Elem Sch	109
Mioni, Kathleen/Akiva Academy	137
Misty, Goetz/Milford Junior High Sch	31
Mitchell, Adam/East Richland Christian Sch	19
Mitchell, George/Academy of St Adalbert	52
Mitchell, Kyla/Berwick Alternative Elem Sch	67
Mitchell, Mary/Coolville Elem Sch	14
Mitchell, Shaun/DeVeaux Elem Sch	129
Mitchell, Tad/Ohio Valley Career Tech Ctr	6
Mitchell, Terrance/Valley View Boys Ldrshp Acad	45
Mitchem, Brandon/Addaville Elem Sch	80
Mitchnr-Asinjo, Tess/Dayton Liberty Academy	2
Mitskavich, Ken/Corpus Christi Academy	53
Mitskavich, Ken/St Raphael Sch	53
Mittiga, Robert/Carlin Elem Sch	166
Mobley, Amy/William Cullen Bryant Sch	45
Moegling, Larry, Dr/St John Central Sch	211
Moehrman, Kimber/Trinity Cath Elem Sch	77
Moeschberger, Mariann/Grace L Roxbury Elem Sch	50
Moff, Jennifer/Avondale Elem Sch	188
Moff, Jennifer/Seiberling Cmty Learning Ctr	191
Mohan, Lakshmi/Discovery Montessori Sch	196
Moldovan, Mike/Canfield High Sch	134
Molfenter, Rebecca/Valley Forge Elem Sch	150
Molina Kuhlman, Jessica/Toledo Smart Elem Sch	5
Mollenhauer, Nathan/Riverside Elem Sch	130
Molnar, Amy/Coy Elem Sch	128
Molnar, Carla/Midview North Elem Sch	125
Molter, Jon/Fayette Sch	79
Molter, Kristi/Swanton Elem Sch	79
Monahan, Elena/Worley Reading & Math Prep Sch	185
Monahan, Shawn/C2RA at Lehman	184
Monell, Ajayi/William Rainey Harper Sch	45
Monnin, Brent/Chestnut Intermediate Sch	48
Monnin, Misha/Brantwood Elem Sch	151
Monnin, Misha/Central Academy	23
Montag, Cheryl/J F Burns Elem Sch	207
Montague, Darlene/Euclid Preparatory Sch [238]	2
Monte, Chris/St Joseph High Sch	117

NAME/School	PAGE
Monte, Chris/St Lawrence Elem Sch	117
Monteleone, John/Washington Elem Sch	124
Monter, Matthew/SS Philip & James Sch	189
Montgomery, Cammie/Chca-Otto Armleder Mem Ed Ctr	96
Montgomery, Carrie/Liberty Early Childhood Sch	22
Montgomery, Tom/Fairbanks High Sch	204
Montgomery, Valerie/Cherokee Elem Sch	22
Moore-Tyler, Angela/Starling STEM PK-8 Sch	69
Moore, Amy/Howard Chapman Elem Sch	51
Moore, Cathy/Richard Avenue Elem Sch	74
Moore, Danny/Emmanuel Christian Academy	29
Moore, Dwan/Hamilton Co Math & Sci Academy	87
Moore, Ed/River Valley Middle Sch	80
Moore, Jared/Harmon Middle Sch	64
Moore, Jeff/Canton South High Sch	185
Moore, Jeff/Zanesville Community High Sch	158
Moore, Jessica/Etna Road Elem Sch	75
Moore, Ken/Maplehurst Elem Sch	106
Moore, Michael/Northwood Elem Sch	183
Moore, Nick/Westview Elem Sch	122
Moore, Sally/Northwood Elem Sch	152
Moore, Steven/Wadsworth High Sch	142
Moore, Trina/Summit Acad Trans HS-Columbus [248]	5
Moran, Lynn/Elmhurst Elem Sch	129
Moran, Trish/Parkview Early Education Ctr	46
Mordarski, Mindy/Hilliard Bradley High Sch	72
Morell, Rosanne/Fairhaven Sch	196
Moretti, Margaret/Monterey Elem Sch	73
Morgan, Amanda/Nihf STEM Middle Sch	191
Morgan, Craig/Maplewood Career Center	166
Morgan, Joel/Woodridge High Sch	195
Morgan, John/Centerburg Elem Sch	110
Morgan, Joy/Brookside High Sch	126
Morgan, Shaun/Springfield High Sch	194
Moriarty, Melissa/Pickerington Elem Sch	64
Morr, Andrew/North Central Local Sch	215
Morris, Brynn/William Foster Elem Sch	46
Morris, Eric/Norton Primary Sch	194
Morris, Lee/Tri-Village Sch	56
Morris, Travis/Granville Elem Sch	117
Morrison, Denny/Sidney High Sch	183
Morrison, Matt/Edison Jr Sr High Sch	109
Morrow, Minerva/Graduation Academy	185
Morse-Grnt, Lisa/Jefferson Junior High Sch	130
Mort, Fran/Lima Senior High Sch	9
Mortensen, Chris/Greenville Middle Sch	55
Morton, Bob/Defiance High Sch	57
Morton, Brian/Eastmoor Academy	67
Morton, Jason/Flex High Sch	2
Morton, Jason/Focus Lrng Acad-E Columbus [244]	2
Morton, Robert/West Elkton Intermediate Sch	168
Moses, William/Bethany Lutheran Sch	53
Mosholder, George/St Timothy Sch	77
Moss, Collene/Mater Dei Academy	77
Moss, Sheri/Horace Mann Elem Sch	149
Moss, Vicki/Mark Twain Elem Sch	75
Motsch, Kristi/Toll Gate Elem Sch	64
Mounts, David/Buckeye Preparatory Academy [238]	1
Mowery, Adam/Taft Elem Sch	138
Moyer, Andrea/Malabar Intermediate Sch	172
Muckleroy, Mary Lou/Woodland Elem Sch	194
Mudore, Colleen/Avon Early Learning Center	123
Mueller, David/Archbishop McNicholas HS	94
Mueller, Joseph/Avon Lake High Sch	122
Mueller, Joseph/Strongsville High Sch	51
Mueller, Marie/Ohio Virtual Academy	4
Muhlenkamp, Polly/Immaculate Conception Grd Sch	144
Muller, Cory/Parkway Elem Sch	184
Muller, Missy/Fairfield West Elem Sch	21
Mullins, Rick/Lakeville Elem Sch	105
Mumau, Jessica/Milton-Union High Sch	146
Mummey, Sally/St Francis DeSales Elem Sch	120
Munk, Shoshana/Yeshiva Derech Ha Torah	54
Munro, Renee/Batavia Elem Sch	29
Muratori, Rebecca/Osborne Elem Sch	61

School Year 2019-2020   800-333-8802   **OH-U19**

PRINCIPAL INDEX

Market Data Retrieval

NAME/School	PAGE
Murch, Tracy/*The Seven Hills Sch*	96
Murdock, Robin/*Gahanna Middle School-South*	70
Muren, Henry/*Barberton High Sch*	192
Muro, Jonathan/*Madison Middle Sch*	172
Murphy, Angela/*East Elem Sch*	219
Murphy, Angela/*South Elem Sch*	219
Murphy, Carolyn/*St Michael Sch*	95
Murphy, Dan/*R G Drage Career Tech Center*	189
Murphy, Erin/*Alfred Benesch Academy*	42
Murphy, Kelly/*Greenview Upper Elem Sch*	51
Murphy, Matt/*Huntington Middle Sch*	175
Murphy, Shauna/*Woodward Career Tech High Sch*	88
Murphy, Shawn/*Tiffin Middle Sch*	181
Murphy, Todd/*Kensington Intermediate Sch*	50
Murphy, Tracie/*South Elem Sch*	202
Murphy, Veronica/*Royalmont Academy*	209
Murray, Aimee/*Houston Early Learning Center*	91
Murray, Douglas/*Chardon High Sch*	82
Murry, Betsey/*Monclova Primary Sch*	127
Musat, John/*Elizabeth Price Elem Sch*	192
Musbach, Jennifer/*Harding High Sch*	138
Muschott, David/*Grove City Christian Sch*	77
Musiek, Deborah/*McEbright Cmty Learning Center*	191
Musselman, Amanda/*Lee Burneson Middle Sch*	52
Myers, Charlene/*Riverview East Academy*	88
Myers, Holly/*Heath Middle Sch*	117
Myers, Jane/*Defiance Elem Sch*	57
Myers, Kathryn/*Columbus Span Immersion Acad*	67
Myers, Kerri/*Scottwood Elem Sch*	68
Myers, Kimberly/*Mount Vernon SDA Elem Sch*	112
Myers, Lisa/*Sacred Heart Sch*	173
Myers, Michael/*Pleasantville Elem Sch*	63
Myers, Mike/*Wayne Trace Jr Sr High Sch*	160
Myers, Nicholas/*Hillview Elem Sch*	119
Myers, Nikki/*Salem Elem Sch*	68
Myree, Jennifer/*Rees E Price Academy*	88
Myslenski, Christopher/*Artemus Ward Sch*	43

N

NAME/School	PAGE
Nabors, Lynda/*John Clem Elem Sch*	119
Nabura, Eddie/*Oakstone Academy Mid High Sch*	77
Nachlinger, Sharma/*Main Elem Sch*	83
Nagle, Joseph/*Sacred Heart of Jesus Sch*	24
Nakonachny, Melanie/*Mary M Bethune Elem Sch*	44
Nanney, Deborah/*Westwood Elem Sch*	82
Nannicola, Alexandra/*Champion K-8 Elementery Sch*	197
Nappi, Laura/*Crestview High Sch*	34
Natko, Jon/*Steam Academy of Warren [238]*	5
Nau, Kay/*William Bick Primary Sch*	30
Nayak, Melissa/*Veritas Classical Academy*	211
Naylor, Linda/*North Adams Jr Sr High Sch*	6
Nazzarine, Laura/*Clermont Northeastern Mid Sch*	30
Neading, Arianna/*Perry Elem Sch*	113
Neal, Timothy, Dr/*Conneaut High Sch*	12
Nealy, Erin/*Bridgeway Academy*	77
Neckel, Mia/*Whitewater Valley Elem Sch*	93
Neeley, Tracy/*Rosa Parks Elem Sch*	23
Neely, Jeff/*Trotwood Prep & Fitness Acad [247]*	5
Neely, Trudie/*Rogers High Sch*	130
Neiderhouse, Nick/*Wayne Trail Elem Sch*	128
Neloms, Wendy/*Phoenix Sch*	196
Nelson, Kendra/*Hopewell-Loudon Local Sch*	181
Nesler, Michael/*Hayes Intermediate Sch*	73
Nespeca, Candace/*Colerain Sch*	67
Nething, Melissa/*Ewing Sch*	209
Nettleton, Craig/*Southeast Middle Sch*	167
Newark, Shane/*Early College High Sch*	123
Newcomer, Michael/*Van Buren Elem Sch*	99
Newell, Joe/*Fairbanks Middle Sch*	204
Newlove, Mike/*Noble Elem Sch*	181
Newsome, Lisa/*Ontario Primary Sch*	12
Newson, Lisa/*Aacs Early Lrng Center*	12
Ngom, Martin, Dr/*Hope Academy-Northcoast [238]*	2

NAME/School	PAGE
Niarchos, Brett/*Glenwood Intermediate Sch*	188
Nicholas, Dean/*Chca-Martha S Lindner High Sch*	96
Nichols, Dave/*St Joseph Sch*	131
Nichols, Jim/*Indian Hill Primary Sch*	90
Nichols, Steven/*Canton Harbor High Sch*	1
Nickerson, Christy/*New Tech High School-East*	44
Nickoli, Gregory/*Pioneer Career & Tech Center*	173
Nickoli, Libby/*Butler Elem Sch*	171
Niehaus, Gayle, Dr/*Monroe Primary Sch*	23
Niemantsverdri, Joe/*Harding Middle Sch*	47
Niese, Adam/*Napoleon Elem Sch 3-6*	101
Niese, Connie/*SS Peter & Paul Sch*	171
Nizen, Michelle/*A J Jordak Elem Sch*	81
Noble, Megan/*Indian Springs Elem Sch*	68
Noeth, Pamela, Dr/*Bellefontaine High Sch*	121
Nolan, Julie/*Windermere Elem Sch*	74
Nolan, Susan/*North Elem Sch*	108
Noll, William/*Holy Trinity Sch*	162
Nolting, Cheri/*Goal Digital Academy*	2
Normile, Patty/*Mercy Montessori Center Sch*	95
Norris, Kathleen, Dr/*St Paul Sch*	60
Norris, Michael/*Louisville Elem Sch*	186
Norris, Rebecca/*Frazeysburg Elem Sch*	157
Norris, Tina/*Coventry Middle Sch*	192
North, Marlene/*Hancock Co SBH Unit*	97
Notar, Michael/*Edgewood High Sch*	12
Novack, Jeff/*Leonard Kirtz Sch*	133
Novar, Brian/*Darby Woods Elem Sch*	73
Nugent, Patricia, Dr/*St Mary Sch*	195
Nuggud, Vishtasp/*Learwood Middle Sch*	122
Nunmarker, Rene/*Young Scholars Prep Sch*	6
Nuveman, Chandra/*Freedom Elem Sch*	9

O

NAME/School	PAGE
O'Bannon, Heather/*Westside Academy*	6
O'Brien, Chris/*Village Prep Sch-Woodland [239]*	5
O'Brien, Jennifer/*St William Sch*	96
O'Callaghan, Nova/*Steam Academy of Akron [118]*	5
O'Connell, Kevin/*Maplewood Elem Sch*	199
O'Donnell, Patrick/*Ohio Valley Christian Sch*	81
O'Mara, Eva/*Highland Drive Elem Sch*	41
O'Mara, Jacqueline, Dr/*Rushwood Elem Sch*	193
O'Neal, Renaldo/*Wogaman Middle Sch*	149
O'Neil, Rebecca/*Normandy Elem Sch*	149
O'Reilly, Edward/*ACES*	67
O'Reilly, Kathleen/*St Brigid of Kildare Elem Sch*	76
O'Shea, Bryan/*Grove City High Sch*	73
O'Shea, Kevin/*Otsego High Sch*	217
Oakes, Aaron/*Tecumseh High Sch*	29
Oates, Dave/*Central Catholic High Sch*	189
Obringer, Mary/*St Bernard Elem Sch*	39
Ochsenbein, Karen/*Westview Elem Sch*	107
Oditt, Tim/*Grand River Academy*	14
Ogdan, Charles/*Loveland Middle Sch*	90
Ogren, Amanda/*Central Trail Elem Sch*	129
Ohlemacher, Ben/*Genoa Area High Sch*	159
Olinger, Jerry/*River View Junior High Sch*	37
Olson, Tom/*Madeira Middle Sch*	90
Omen, Deborah/*West Jefferson Middle Sch*	132
Onacila, Julie/*St Brendan Sch*	52
Ondrus, Melany/*Scioto Ridge Elem Sch*	59
Opelt, Christine/*Otis Elem Sch*	177
Opsincs, Marc/*The Alternate Learning Center*	127
Orhan, Ufak/*Horizon Sci Acad-Cincinnati [153]*	2
Orin, Jason/*Louisville Middle Sch*	186
Oriti, Lisa/*St Benedict Catholic Sch*	52
Orlando, Nick/*Henry F Lamuth Middle Sch*	114
Ormond, Lisa/*Granville Middle Sch*	117
Ortiz, Sandi/*Cornerstone Christian Academy*	115
Osborne, Sean/*North Royalton High Sch*	48
Osburn, Rebecca/*Green Elem Sch*	104
Ostertag, J/*St Teresa of Avila Sch*	96
Otterson, Craig/*East Broadway Elem Sch*	129

Ohio School Directory

PRINCIPAL INDEX

NAME/School	PAGE
Otto, Dan/Southern High Sch	143
Overbeck, Linda/Montgomery Elem Sch	93
Overla, Bill/Ft Recovery High Sch	144
Overman, Marcus/New Bremen High Sch	16
Owens, Angel/Austintown Intermediate Sch	134
Owens, Jason/Rock Hill Middle Sch	116
Owens, Michael/Sch for Creative Perform Arts	88

P

NAME/School	PAGE
Pace-Sanders, Kathy/Hancock Elem Sch	61
Pacht, Benjamin/United Preparatory Acad-State [249]	5
Packer, Julie/South Elem Sch	108
Paeltz, Marty/Mt Orab Elem Sch	20
Page, Charles/General Sherman Jr High Sch	63
Page, Josh/James Conger Elem Sch	58
Page, Richard/Claymont Elem Sch	202
Page, Stefanie/Clark Preparatory Academy	1
Page, Troy/Port Washington Elem Sch	202
Palascak, Elizabeth/Academy of St Bartholomew	52
Palchesko, Susan/Kimpton Middle Sch	194
Pallija, Tony/Schnee Learning Center	193
Palmer, Dan/Southdale Elem Sch	150
Palmer, Michael/Blott Guy Elem Sch	199
Pames, Zelina/Maple Heights High Sch	47
Pammer, Joan/Eastland Performance Academy [247]	2
Pancurak, David/St Paul Sch	36
Pangalangan, Gina/Cinday Academy	209
Panneff, Page/Lucas Co Pre-School Unit	127
Pannell, Abbie/Fairland East Elem Sch	116
Pannell, Brianne/Woodcrest Elem Sch	69
Panning, Anna/Sam Salem Cmty Learning Center	191
Papouras, Chris/Chardon Hills Magnet Sch	46
Pappas, Christina/Nolley Elem Sch	193
Pappas, James/Digital Academy	184
Parisi, Mollie/Baltic Elem Sch	202
Parisi, Mollie/Ragersville Elem Sch	202
Parker, Erin/Fremont Middle Sch	177
Parker, Erin/Holly Hill Elem Sch	31
Parker, John/Berne Union High Sch	63
Parker, Ken/Harrison Centrl Jr Sr High Sch	101
Parker, Susan/David L Brown Youth Center	145
Parkins, Kevin/Central Catholic High Sch	131
Parlar, Kadir/Noble Academy-Columbus [153]	4
Parrish, Jim/Worthington Chrstn Westview ES	78
Parron, Carol/Sonshine Christian Academy	77
Parry, Tracie/Niles McKinley High Sch	200
Parsons, Lucas/Buckeye Local High Sch	108
Parsons, Lucas/West Elem Sch	108
Patete, Joseph/Westfall Elem Sch	163
Patrick, Brian/W-E School of Innovation	114
Patterson, Heather/Allen East Elem Sch	7
Patterson, Sarah/Harman Elem Sch	152
Patton, Gary/Warren Co Career Center	208
Patton, Stephanie/Columbus City Prep Sch-Girls	67
Paul, Amy/Simon Kenton Elem Sch	28
Paul, John, Sr/St Michael Sch	76
Pavelich, Kirk/Royalview Elem Sch	48
Pavlinac, Linda/Creekside Early Childhood Sch	22
Paxson, Jennifer/J E Prass Elem Sch	150
Payich, Michelle/Williamson Elem Sch	137
Payne, Eric/Northview Primary Sch	98
Payton, Kevin/Fullerton Elem Sch	43
Peace, Monica/Walbridge Elem Sch	130
Peare, Janet/Mary L Evans Early Chldhd Ctr	187
Pearn, Melanie/Fairfax Elem Sch	113
Pearson, Audra/Winterset Elem Sch	69
Pearson, Lynn/Crossgates Pre-School	129
Pease, Kenneth/Sedalia Elem Sch	71
Pease, Vicky/Bloom-Carroll Primary	63
Pecchia, Michael/Valley Christian Sch	137
Pechie, Joni/Arcanum Early Learning Center	55
Pechie, Joni/Arcanum Elem Sch	55
Peck, Amy/North Ridgeville Academic Ctr	125
Peck, David/St John Lutheran Sch	54
Peeples, Rhonda/Alpine Elem Sch	67
Peltz, Andrew/Troy Intermediate Sch	122
Pence, Tim/Waynesfield-Goshen Elem Sch	16
Pendergast, Beth/McEsc Learning Center Presch	148
Pendergest, Brian/Stephen T Badin High Sch	24
Pendry, Jeffrey/Springfield Middle Sch	128
Penley, Kristen/St Margaret of York Sch	32
Penn, Phillip/Cleveland College Prep [238]	39
Peoples, Erin/West Elem Sch	203
Peoples, Jason/Newcomerstown Middle Sch	203
Pepper, Samuel/Belpre High Sch	209
Perez, Ann, Dr/Ann Simpson Davis Middle Sch	69
Perez, Michelle/Cleveland Sch of Science & Med	43
Perin, David/Sacred Heart Sch-Bshp Hoffman	177
Perkins, Markiel/Cardinal High Sch	81
Perkins, Markiel/Cleveland Preparatory Academy [238]	1
Perozek, Edward/Start High Sch	130
Perrow, Catherine/Gordon DeWitt Elem Sch	192
Perry, Andrew/Edwards Middle Sch	140
Perry, Stephen/Ridge-Brook Elem Sch	49
Perry, Tom/Morgan Elem Sch	24
Person, Michelle/Charles A Mooney Sch	43
Pester, Dustin/Miller City Elem Sch	170
Pester, Dustin/Miller City Middle Sch	170
Peterlin, Kimberly/Citizens Academy [239]	39
Peters, Adam/Lorain Cmty Elem Sch [242]	122
Peters, Adam/Lorain Cmty Middle Sch [242]	122
Peters, Justina/Helen Muraski Elem Sch	51
Peters, Sherry/Elmwood Place Elem Sch	93
Peters, Staci/Asbury Elem Sch	71
Peters, Stephen/Glen Oak Elem Sch	59
Peterson, Lisa/Cox Elem Sch	85
Peterson, Michelle/Creekview Elem Sch	23
Peterson, Robert/Madison Comprehensive High Sch	172
Petitti, Jill/Lorain Co Joint Voc Sch	125
Petty, Jodi/Bethel Elem Sch	145
Peveler, Susan/Shaw Elem Sch	83
Pfeffer, Joe/Felicity-Franklin Middle Sch	30
Pfefferle, Kevin/Anthony Wayne High Sch	127
Pfeifer, Zach/Southeastern Middle Sch	175
Phelps, Kyle/Reid Sch	27
Phillips, Cindy/Grace Christian Sch	77
Phillips, Jason/Tuscarawas Vly Senior High Sch	203
Phillips, Tom/Pickerington Alternative Sch	64
Piazza, Deborah/Puritas Cmty Middle Sch [242]	40
Piazza, Timothy/Westside Christian Academy	54
Pica, Jeff/Minford High Sch	178
Pickerill, Dawn/John XXIII Catholic Elem Sch	24
Pierce, Lori, Dr/Croghan Elem Sch	177
Pike, Tanya/Blanchard Valley Sch	97
Pinnick, Kayla/Hilliard Crossing Elem Sch	72
Piperis, Sofia/Paul L Dunbar Elem Sch	44
Piquet, Tony/Clay Local Sch	178
Pittis, Mindy/Lakeland Academy Community Sch	100
Pitts, Janice/Acad Multilingual Immer Stud	87
Plank, Laurie/Mad River Middle Sch	151
Plantner, Greg/North Ridgeville Academic Ctr	125
Plate, Ruth Ann, Dr/Willoughby-Eastlake Preschool	114
Platzer, Bill/Portsmouth West Elem Sch	180
Plescia, Scott/St John Sch	14
Plesec, Kim/Jefferson Primary Sch	98
Plybon, Matt/Whittier Elem Sch	187
Poage, Doug/Portsmouth High Sch	179
Poe, Steven/Put-In-Bay Sch	159
Pohlman, Dan/Coldwater Middle Sch	143
Pohly, Susan/St Anselm Sch	83
Poilek, John/Shadyside High Sch	18
Poland, Duane/Cambridge Middle Sch	86
Polca, Rob/Mariemont Junior High Sch	91
Polder, Carly/Willard PK-8 Sch	200
Poling, Lori/Trinity Lutheran Sch	205
Pollard, Christopher/St Joan of Arc Sch	189
Pollard, Tyree/Columbus Africentric EC K8 Sch	67
Pollock, Dana/Manchester Local High Sch	7
Poole, Scott/Shawnee Elem Sch	85

School Year 2019-2020   800-333-8802   OH-U21

PRINCIPAL INDEX

NAME/School	PAGE
Poole, Todd/Holden Elem Sch	165
Poole, Tracey/Waynesville Middle Sch	209
Popa, Dina/Nihf STEM High Sch	191
Porcello, Todd/Perry High Sch	113
Porta, Stephanie/Centennial High Sch	67
Porter, Chris/Wheelersburg High Sch	180
Porter, Taylor/James N Gamble Montessori HS	88
Postl, Allison/Liberty Center Elem Sch	101
Poston, Steve/Thomas Ewing Jr High Sch	64
Potantus, Carolyn/Lakewood Lutheran Elem Sch	54
Potteiger, Bryan/Gilead Christian School-North	156
Potteiger, Bryan/Gilead Christian School-South	156
Potter, Andrew/St John Sch	104
Potts, Jason/McClain High Sch	103
Potts, Tracy/Continental Local Elem Sch	169
Powell, Dave/Carroll Co Christian Academy	25
Powell, Heather/Williamsburg Middle High Sch	32
Powell, Kip/Bruce Elem Sch	168
Powell, Troy/The Steel Academy	5
Powell, Zach/Union Local Elem Sch	19
Powers, Bradley/Seneca East Local Sch	181
Powers, Sandra/Hayes Elem Sch	47
Poynter, Chris/Emerson Elementary	74
Poynter, Chris/Longfellow Elem Sch	75
Prais, Sharon/Miami Montessori Sch	147
Prati, Jacki/J W Reason Elem Sch	72
Pratt, Jospeh/Pataskala Elem Sch	120
Prescott, Richard/Daw Elem Sch	36
Presley, Dawn/Summit Academy Elem Sch-Akron [248]	5
Pressley, Holly/McEsc Learning Center East	148
Preston, Nate/Winterfield Venture Academy [203]	127
Prezioso, Mathew/Munson Elem Sch	82
Pribula, Cara/St Thomas Aquinas Mid High Sch	190
Price, Brook/Woodland Elem Sch	218
Price, Melissa/Tipp City Enrichment Center	147
Price, Patricia/Clinton Elem Sch	67
Pride, Mindy/Hamersville Elem Sch	20
Priest, Bob/Van Wert High Sch	206
Prieto, Marie/Mills Elem Sch	61
Primus, Timothy/John Marshall-Engineering	44
Prince, Darin/Mt Vernon Middle Sch	111
Printup, Randy/A Plus Arts Acad-Fair Campus	1
Printy, Amy/Star Academy of Toledo [238]	127
Prohaska, Tom/Monroe High Sch	23
Proper, Matt/Danville Elem Middle Sch	110
Prusinski, Andrew/Lutheran High School East	54
Pugh, Mark/Northview High Sch	129
Puhl, Andrea/St Aloysius Sch	218
Pulling, Shelley/Roxboro Elem Sch	42
Purins, David/Poland MS-McKinley Elem Sch	135
Puthoff, Adam/St Henry Elem Sch	144
Puthoff, Greg/Paulding Elem Sch	160
Puthoff, Katie/Holy Family Catholic Sch	95
Putinski, Laura/Fairfield Christian Academy	65

Q

NAME/School	PAGE
Quaranta, Rosemary/Xavier Univ Montessori Lab Sch	96
Quatman, Matthew/Independence Elem Sch	9
Quinn, Teresa/Ella P Stewart Acad for Girls	129

R

NAME/School	PAGE
Raach, Bryan/Ridgewood Middle Sch	37
Radabaugh, Eric/Bowling Green Middle Sch	216
Radinsky, Troy/Leetonia Sch	35
Raguz, Diane/St Paschal Baylon Sch	53
Rahm, Daniel/Brookside Intermediate Sch	126
Rahm, Earl/Alcott Elem Sch	74
Raiff, Scott/St Christopher Sch	53
Rainey, Linda/Liberty Union Elem Sch	64
Rajnicek, Annemarie/St Mary of the Falls Sch	53
Rallings, Leon/Green Inspiration Academy	2
Ramey, Tonya/Ohio Hi-Point Career Center	121
Ramos, Emily/Archbishop Hoban High Sch	195
Ramos, Greg/Northwest Middle Sch	188
Ramsey, Christina/McKinley Stemm Academy	130
Ramsey, Dennis/Reading High Sch	93
Randall, Kaitlyn/Monfort Heights Elem Sch	91
Randenburg, Kathryn/New Carlisle Elem Sch	29
Randles, Halle/Caldwell Elem Sch	158
Randles, Mandy/Burton Elem Sch	81
Randolph, Amy/Oyler Sch	88
Range, Ryan/Joseph Welty Middle Sch	203
Ranginwala, Aliya/Ridgewood Sch	29
Rankin, Katy/St Thomas Aquinas Sch	53
Rankin, Rochelle/Rosemore Middle Sch	75
Ransey, Danny/Ohio State Sch for the Blind	4
Raptis, Vicki/Willard PK-8 Sch	200
Rardon, Clint/Park Street Intermediate Sch	74
Rardon, Jessica/Hilliard Tharp 6th Grade Sch	72
Raso, Sally, Dr/Edna Surrarrer Elem Sch	51
Rastorfer, Ashley/St Peter Elem Sch	174
Rateno, Katharine/Mayfield Center Elem Sch	47
Rathburn, John/Northridge Intermediate Sch	119
Ratkosky, Mary/Carylwood Intermediate Sch	41
Ratley, Tamara/Clermont Educ Collaborative-N	29
Ratliff, Julie/Hampton Bennett ECC	207
Ratliff, Nelle/Wynford Elem Sch	39
Rausch, Rich/St John's Lutheran Sch	205
Ravida, Laurel/Gates Mills Elem Sch	47
Rayner, Lindsay/West Muskingum Middle Sch	157
Rea, Traci/Sycamore Junior High Sch	93
Read, Sarah/Chagrin Falls Intermediate Sch	42
Ream, Mike/Stingel Elem Sch	173
Recker, Amy/Allen Co Pre-School Unit	7
Reed, Nadia/Gloria S Friend Christian Acad	77
Reese, Cody/East Knox Elem Sch	111
Reese, Jeff/Jackson Center Sch	183
Regnier, David/Emmanuel Christian Sch	131
Reid, Octavia, Dr/Barack Obama Sch	47
Reid, Rebecca/Risen Christ Lutheran Sch	29
Reidenbaugh, Amanda/Columbus Gifted Academy	67
Reifsnyder, Jane/Portage Collaborative Mont Sch	185
Reighard, Jeanne/McGuffey PK-8 Sch	200
Reighard, Kristie/Pike-Delta-York High Sch	79
Reigle, Samuel/Niles Middle Sch	200
Reiman, Danny/Greater Summit County ELC	2
Reindel, John/Sauder Elem Sch	186
Reinhart, Rose/Holy Cross Cath Sch-Defiance	58
Reinke, Ann/Maple Dale Elem Sch	93
Remley, Eric/Whittier Elem Sch	130
Renn, Chris/Millstream Career Center	98
Renner, Chris/Bath Elem Sch	8
Renner, James, Dr/Mariemont High Sch	91
Renner, Jarred/Conesville Elem Sch	37
Renz, Jack/Woodward High Sch	130
Ressler, Denise/Forest Primary Sch	48
Retton, James/Hyre Cmty Learning Center	191
Retton, Louie/Indian Creek High Sch	109
Reucher, Allie/Fayette Sch	79
Reuter, Jeff/Piketon Jr Sr High Sch	164
Revou, Thomas/Watkins Elem Sch	69
Reynolds, H Clifford/Mayfair Christian Sch	190
Reynolds, Richard/Warrensville Heights High Sch	51
Reynolds, Robert/St Bernard-Elmwood Place HS	93
Reynolds, Teresa/Hamilton-Maineville Prim Sch	208
Rhodes, Brad/Whitehouse Primary Sch	127
Rhodes, Clint/Thornville Elem Sch	161
Rhodes, James/Anthony Wayne Elem Sch	207
Rhoten, Jo/St Columban Sch	32
Rice, Andy/Chieftain Elem Sch	104
Rice, Andy/Hocking Hills Elem Sch	104
Rice, Cathryn/Tecumseh Elem Sch	85
Rice, Chad/Heritage Elem Sch	64
Rice, Dawn/Bremen Elem Sch	63
Rice, William/Fairfield Senior High Sch	21
Richards, Nathaniel/South Central Elem Sch	106

Ohio School Directory

PRINCIPAL INDEX

NAME/School	PAGE
Richards, Sandy/*Liberty Elem Sch*	139
Richardson, Charles/*East High Sch*	67
Richardson, Janice/*Garfield Elem Sch*	129
Richardson, Lynesha/*E Prep Woodland Hills Sch [239]*	2
Richardson, Susan/*St Pius X Sch*	131
Richburg, Angela/*Rosa Parks Elem Sch*	130
Richlen, M/*The Antioch Sch*	85
Ricksecker, Marge/*St Ignatius of Antioch ES*	53
Riddle, Eric/*Indian Trail Elem Sch*	66
Ridley, Melissa/*James N Gamble Montessori ES*	88
Ridley, Melissa/*Pleasant Ridge Montessori Sch*	88
Riebe, Erich/*John R Lea Middle Sch*	213
Riedel, Tonya/*Olentangy Spec Needs Pre-Sch*	59
Ries, James/*R B Chamberlin Middle Sch*	195
Riesenberger, Elizabeth/*John Foster Dulles Elem Sch*	92
Rife, Jon/*Otsego Junior High Sch*	217
Riley, Barb/*Our Shepherd Lutheran Sch*	115
Riley, David/*Perry High Sch*	188
Riley, John/*London Elem Sch*	132
Riley, Kimberly/*Tri-County Pre-School Unit*	104
Riley, Mike/*Ashland High Sch*	10
Riley, Steven/*Millcreek-West Unity Local Sch*	215
Rinard, Chad/*Marietta High Sch*	210
Rinehart, Kelly/*Ledgemont Elem Sch*	81
Ring, Helen/*Monroe Achievement Center*	147
Ring, Marc/*Swiss Hills Career Center*	148
Ringer, Steven/*Pleasant High Sch*	138
Rings, Todd/*Brecksville Broadview Hts MS*	41
Rinkes, Charles/*River View High Sch*	37
Ripke, Jennifer/*Edon Northwest Local Sch*	215
Rischmann, Trey/*Taylor Elem Sch*	91
Rishell, J/*A Plus Arts Acad-Napoleon*	1
Rismiller, Ryan/*Graham High Sch*	26
Ritch, Nancy/*Glover Community Learning Ctr*	191
Ritter, Shawn/*Mary Emma Bailey Elem Sch*	70
Ritzert, Matt/*Immaculate Conception Sch*	204
Ritzert, Matt/*Tuscarawas Ctrl Catholic ES*	204
Rizer, Patrick/*Catholic Central Jr Sr HS*	29
Rizi, Jean/*Maple Leaf Elem Sch*	46
Rizzo-Sterner, Tamara/*Madison Park Elem Sch*	153
Roach, Joe/*Locust Corner Elem Sch*	31
Roach, Leanora/*John Paul II Catholic Sch*	95
Roach, Rick/*Dawson-Bryant Middle Sch*	115
Robbins, Kristin/*Bexley High Sch*	66
Roberts-Schein, Yancy/*Union Furnace Elem Sch*	104
Roberts, Brett/*South Webster Jr Sr High Sch*	178
Roberts, Christopher/*Valley View Elem Sch*	142
Roberts, Nick/*Manchester Elem Sch*	7
Roberts, Pam/*Mad River Early Childhood Ctr*	151
Robertson, Jessica/*Mary Queen of Peace Sch*	52
Robertson, Travis/*Waverly Intermediate Sch*	164
Robinson-Ervin, Porsha/*Weinland Park Elem Sch*	69
Robinson, Dale/*Louise Troy Elem Sch*	149
Robinson, Diane/*Summit Academy Cmty Sch-Parma [248]*	40
Robinson, Karla/*Beacon Academy*	1
Robinson, Karla/*Heritage Christian Sch*	190
Robinson, Neal/*Boulevard Elem Sch*	50
Roblin, Michelle/*Mapleton Elem Sch*	11
Robson, Jim/*Ansonia Jr Sr High Sch*	55
Roddy, Angel/*Mt Airy Elem Sch*	88
Rodeahffer, Scott/*Ft Loramie Elem Sch*	182
Rodman, Lori/*Wickliffe Middle Sch*	114
Rodriguez, Amanda/*Clark Elem Sch*	43
Rodriguez, Matthew/*Chippewa Jr Sr High Sch*	211
Roe, Jamie/*Fayette Progressive Sch*	65
Roeth, Derek/*Fairfield Career Center*	70
Rogaliner, Dave/*Timmons Elem Sch*	82
Rogan, Thomas/*Central High Sch*	1
Rogers, David/*Lexington Elem Sch*	186
Rogers, Joshua/*Edge Academy*	190
Rogers, Kiersten/*Crosby Elem Sch*	93
Rogers, Ryan/*Smith Middle Sch*	153
Rohan, Steve/*South Range High Sch*	135
Rohr, Anthony/*St Sebastian Parish Sch*	196
Rohrer, Brian/*Miami East Elem Sch*	145
Rolland, Katherine/*Big Creek Elem Sch*	41
Rolley, Linda/*Wellsville Jr Sr High Sch*	36
Roman, Samuel/*Luis Munoz Marin Elem Sch*	44
Rook, James/*East Palestine High Sch*	35
Rook, James/*East Palestine Middle Sch*	35
Roqueplot, Christy/*Mid Ohio Pre-School*	171
Rosco, Miranda/*Windsor Elem Sch*	123
Rose-Geiling, Wendy/*Newton D Baker School of Arts*	44
Rose, Alice/*Linden Elem Sch*	22
Rose, D Kyle/*Greenview Day Treatment Center*	39
Rose, Megan/*Rocky River Middle Sch*	50
Rose, Tracy/*Washington High Sch*	65
Roseberry, Kevin/*Leona Middle Sch*	18
Roseberry, Sara/*Hardin-Houston Local Sch*	183
Rosekrans, Shawn/*Kings Mills Elem Sch*	207
Rosemond, Marianne/*St Mary Sch*	95
Rosenbeck, Eric/*St Henry High Sch*	144
Rosenbeck, Vernon/*St Mary Sch*	56
Rosiak, Carol, Dr/*Goldwood Primary Sch*	50
Ross, Davelyn/*Flying Colors Pub Sch Pre-Sch*	117
Ross, Krista/*Lowell Elem Sch*	210
Ross, Krista/*Salem Liberty Elem Sch*	210
Ross, Mo/*Wyandot Run Elem Sch*	59
Ross, Richard/*Emmanuel Baptist Sch*	209
Rossman, Greg/*Ridgedale Jr Sr High Sch*	138
Roth, Richard/*Waynedale High Sch*	213
Roth, Travis/*Howland Springs Primary Sch*	198
Rothacker, Noeleen/*Clearview High Sch*	123
Rotolo, Deborah/*Westside Cmty Sch of the Arts [242]*	6
Rouff, Jeff/*Hopewell Junior High Sch*	22
Routzong, Janet/*Whetstone High Sch*	69
Rowe, Joe/*Ironton Elem Sch*	116
Rowedder, Jacquelyn/*Academy of World Languages*	87
Rowely, Matt/*Beverly Elem Sch*	129
Roy, Kimberly/*St Vincent Ferrer Sch*	96
Rozeski, Stephen/*Bloom-Carroll Intermediate Sch*	63
Rozevink, Marcia/*North Central Local Sch*	215
Rozier, Eric/*Cincinnati Digital Academy*	87
Rozier, Eric/*Virtual High Sch*	88
Rubesich, John/*Ashtabula Co Educ Svc Ctr*	12
Rubin, Judd/*Canfield Village Middle Sch*	134
Ruckel, Brian/*West Union High Sch*	6
Ruckel, Brian/*Whiteoak Jr Sr High Sch*	102
Rucker, David/*Wheelersburg Middle Sch*	180
Rudolph, Andre/*JFK E3Agle Academy*	44
Ruffin, Milton, Dr/*Hayes Art & Academic HS*	68
Ruffing, Kurt/*Elder High Sch*	95
Rumbarger, Katie/*Harding Middle High Sch*	112
Ruppert, Shannon/*Bear Elem Sch*	151
Rush, Daniel/*Diamond Oaks Career Dev Campus*	89
Russell, Tijuana/*Millennium Community Sch*	66
Russell, Troy/*Alliance Middle Sch*	184
Russo, Kim/*East Palestine Elem Sch*	35
Rutherford, Ben/*Caldwell High Sch*	158
Rutherford, Marcia/*Utica Junior High Sch*	119
Rutz, Cristine/*Superior Intermediate Sch*	12
Ryan, Danyel/*Ridgeview Elem Sch*	12
Ryan, Lisa/*Vincent Elem Sch*	123
Rybak, Katherine/*Eastside Arts Academy [242]*	2
Rychener, Molly/*Trinity Christian Academy*	107
Rykowski, Mary/*Evening Street Elem Sch*	75
Ryser, Tracey/*McGuffey PK-8 Sch*	200
Ryser, William/*Girard High Sch*	197
Ryzner, Ryan/*Benedictine High Sch*	52

S

NAME/School	PAGE
S'Williams, Vanice/*Life Skills Center of Toledo*	3
Sabino, Scott/*Mideast CTC Zanesville Campus*	157
Sabinski, Kamaron/*Bridgeport Elem Sch*	18
Sableski, Matt/*Carroll High Sch*	85
Sachtleben, Matt/*John Sells Middle Sch*	70
Sackett, Brady/*Norton Elem Sch*	193
Sackman, Regina/*Springmill STEM Elem Sch*	173
Sadler, Maurice/*Heywood Elem Sch*	147

School Year 2019-2020   800-333-8802   OH-U23

PRINCIPAL INDEX

Market Data Retrieval

NAME/School	PAGE
Sadler, Nolan/*Heritage Middle Sch*	119
Saez, Raul/*Lorain Bilingual Academy [238]*	4
Saffell, Mike/*Harrison North Elem Sch*	101
Sagan, Kelly/*Bishop Fenwick Elem Sch*	158
Sagan, Kelly/*Bishop Fenwick Middle Sch*	158
Salazar, Ana/*Gilbert A Dater High Sch*	87
Sales, Teresa/*Akron Digital Academy*	190
Salti, Mona/*Sunrise Academy*	77
Salvati, Dan/*St Joseph Catholic Sch*	39
Salwiesz, Michael, Dr/*Global Ambassadors Language CS*	2
Salyer, Katie/*Hoffman Trails Elem Sch*	72
Samber, Michael/*Grant Elem Sch*	114
Samerigo, Frank/*Birch Primary Sch*	48
Sammartino, Matthew/*Ursuline High Sch*	137
Sampson, Eric/*Utica Shale Academy of Ohio*	34
Sampson, Kristy/*Southern Elem Sch*	36
Sams, Kimberly/*Leverette Elem Sch*	129
Sams, Ronald/*Children's Academy*	77
Sanchez, Carrie/*Port Clinton Middle Sch*	159
Sanchez, Michelle/*Buhrer Dual Language Elem Sch*	43
Sandel, Lori/*Waterloo High Sch*	167
Sanders, Darryl/*Columbus Alternative High Sch*	67
Sanders, Dessie/*Daniel E Morgan Elem Sch*	43
Sanders, Naim/*Stiles Elem Sch*	74
Sanders, Sue/*St Benedict Sch*	86
Sandy, Valerie/*Toledo Prep & Fitness Academy [247]*	5
Sanfilippo, Josie/*Westerly Elem Sch*	40
Sanifilippo, Jim/*West Lake Elem Sch*	52
Sanker, Doug/*Winton Woods Middle Sch*	94
Santangelo, Jennifer/*Girard Junior High Sch*	197
Sapanaro, Dan/*Wallace H Braden Middle Sch*	12
Sargent, Steve/*Freedom Trail Elem Sch*	59
Sattler, Greg/*Blessed Sacrament Sch*	131
Sattler, Renee/*Dover Ave Elem Sch*	202
Sauer, Chris/*Garfield Heights Middle Sch*	46
Saunders, Dallas/*Western Reserve Local Sch*	136
Saunders, Matt/*Barberton Elem Sch-East*	192
Sauner, Mike/*Western Reserve Local Sch*	136
Savage, Doug/*Boyd E Smith Elem Sch*	31
Saville, Mike/*Choffin Career & Technical Ctr*	136
Saylor, Chris/*Ross Middle Sch*	24
Saylor, Jeremy/*Kinder Elem Sch*	151
Scarcella, Christopher/*Design Lab Early College HS*	43
Scarcella, Christopher/*Max S Hayes High Sch*	44
Scarmack, Andrew/*Guy Jr High Sch*	199
Schaaf, Chris/*Willard Middle High Sch*	106
Schad, Steve/*Roger Bacon High Sch*	95
Schaffer, Natosha/*Cassady Elem Sch*	67
Schager, Colleen/*St Mary School-Avon*	126
Schalnat, Kevin/*Horace Mann Elem Sch*	28
Scharf, Scott/*Wernert Elem Sch*	131
Scharf, Stacey/*Birmingham Elem Sch*	129
Scheeser, Jessica/*Ravenna Early Childhood Ctr*	166
Scheibelhood, Nicholas/*H B Booker Wraparound Sch*	43
Scheid, Megan/*St Charles Borremo Sch*	10
Scheiderer, Kurt/*Licking Heights South Elem Sch*	118
Schell, Cheryl/*Oak Harbor High Sch*	158
Schenek, Shelley/*Our Lady Mt Carmel Sch*	52
Scherschel, Luke/*Zion Lutheran Sch*	132
Scherz, Casey/*Pleasant Run Elem Sch*	91
Scheurle, Jay/*Miami Valley Sch*	154
Schieman, Janet/*Walter Shade Early Chldhd Ctr*	153
Schiets, Natalie/*Solomon Lutheran Sch*	177
Schilling, Sandra/*Schilling Sch-Gifted Children*	96
Schindler, David/*Erieview Elem Sch*	122
Schipfer, Marlo/*Mechanicsburg Jr Sr High Sch*	26
Schissler, Jill/*Greenbriar Middle Sch*	49
Schlagel, Patti/*Granby Elem Sch*	75
Schlok, Mary/*Blue Ash Elem Charter Sch*	1
Schlueter, Fritz/*Damascus Elem Sch*	136
Schmidt, Lauren/*Hilliard Station 6th Grade Sch*	72
Schmidt, Sheri/*Primrose Sch of Lewis Center*	60
Schmidt, Tonya/*Clermont Northeastern Elem Sch*	30
Schnebelen, Laura/*Burroughs Elem Sch*	67
Schneid, Tracy/*Brookview Elem Sch*	41
Schneider, Karl/*John Muir Elem Sch*	49
Schob, Andy/*Ft Frye Jr Sr High Sch*	210
Schob, Brittany/*Marietta Middle Sch*	210
Schooler, Kelly/*Perry Elem Sch*	9
Schoonover, Natalie/*St Gerard Sch*	10
Schornack, Erin/*St Mary Sch*	65
Schreck, Toben/*Ironton Middle Sch*	116
Schreiner, Erin/*Horizon Sci Acad-Sprngfld [153]*	3
Schrembeck, Rob/*Lee Eaton Elem Sch*	193
Schrock, Ruth/*Hartville Christian Sch*	190
Schroeder, Jodi/*Pandora Gilboa Elem Sch*	171
Schroeder, Jodi/*Pandora Gilboa Middle Sch*	171
Schuette, Jessica/*Crestview Local Sch*	205
Schulke, Jamie/*Crestview Elem Sch*	140
Schulte, Chad/*Hilliard Weaver Middle Sch*	72
Schultz, David/*Stryker Elem Sch*	215
Schultz, David/*Stryker High Sch*	215
Schumm, Robert/*Greenfield Elem Sch*	103
Schutt, Shelby/*Andrew J Rickoff Elem Sch*	42
Schwanke, Jennifer/*Indian Run Elem Sch*	70
Schwartz, Beth/*Powers Elem Sch*	122
Schwartz, Julie/*Discovery Sch*	174
Schwartz, Renae/*Wyandot Elem Sch*	70
Schwieterman, Dan/*Valley Elem Sch*	83
Sciarabba, Frank/*West Park Elem Sch*	166
Scissum, Artemus/*Martin Luther King Elem Sch*	136
Scoles, Michael/*Lincoln Elem Sch*	98
Scott, Cathie/*Lagonda Elem Sch*	28
Scott, Mark/*Minerva Elem Sch*	187
Scott, Michael/*Oberlin High Sch*	125
Scott, Misha/*Kirkmere Elem Sch*	136
Scott, Misha/*Volney Rogers Elem Sch*	137
Scott, Monica/*Capital High Sch*	1
Scott, Robert/*Dublin Scioto High Sch*	70
Scruggs, Tanunya/*Life Skills HS of N Akron*	3
Scully, Peter/*Thomas Worthington High Sch*	76
Seals, Krista/*Green Primary Sch*	185
Searight, Kenny/*Firelands Digital Academy*	124
Sears, Andrew/*Dayton Regional STEM Sch*	2
Sears, Mike/*Shore Middle Sch*	113
Seboe, Kelly/*Budd Elem Sch*	11
Sebring, Daniel/*Normandy Elem Sch*	40
Sechen, Mr/*Horizon Science Acad-Columbus [153]*	66
Seders, Angela/*Belden Leadership Sch*	184
Sedlak, Michael/*East Woods Sch*	193
Sedmock, Christin/*Allen Reading & Math Prep Sch*	184
Seeley, Crystal/*Horizon Sci Acad-Columbus Prim [153]*	3
Seevers, Lydia/*Tree of Life Christian Sch*	77
Seiberd, Eric/*Claymont Primary Sch*	202
Seifullah, Unique/*Life Skills HS of Columbus SE*	3
Seiling, Alexandra/*Worthington Hills Elem Sch*	76
Seislove, Marilyn/*Calvert Catholic Schools*	182
Seitz, Michelle/*Walnut Creek Elem Sch*	59
Self, Tricia/*T C Knapp Elem Sch*	188
Selgo, Jayson/*Ottawa-Glandorf High Sch*	170
Selm, Tiffany/*Pattison Elem Sch*	31
Selvaggio, Mark/*Wapakoneta Elem Sch*	16
Semple, Joe/*Monroe Central High Sch*	147
Senter, Joycelyn/*Evendale Elem Sch*	92
Seward, Bryan/*Nordonia Middle Sch*	193
Sexton, Ron/*Greenfield Middle Sch*	103
Seymour, Rob/*Mogadore Christian Academy*	196
Shafer, Cathy/*Chapel Hill Chrn School-North*	196
Shaffer, Amanda/*Rockway Elem Sch*	27
Shaffer, Samuel/*Northridge Elem Sch*	27
Shamblin, Bray/*South Gallia Middle Sch*	80
Shank, Scott/*Greenwood Early Learning Ctr*	185
Shanor, Ryan/*Norton High Sch*	193
Shantery, Traci/*Riverview Elem Sch*	114
Sharick, Alex/*Galion Intermediate Sch*	38
Sharosky, Brian/*Visintainer Middle Sch*	140

Ohio School Directory — PRINCIPAL INDEX

NAME/School	PAGE
Sharp, Darren/Elida High Sch	8
Sharp, Kari/Larchmont Elem Sch	129
Sharshan, Kimberly/Joshua Dixon Elem Sch	34
Shaver, Paul/Zanesville Christian Sch	158
Shea, David/Miami View Elem Sch	28
Shehee, Akisha/Westwood Elem Sch	149
Shelton, Derrick/Columbus Arts & Tech Academy [238]	1
Shelton, Derrick/Rose Hill Elem Sch	73
Shepherd-Smith, Amber/St Clairsville Elem Sch	18
Shepherd, Kim/New Hope Christian Academy	163
Sherman, Sue/St Marys Primary Sch	16
Sherwood, Teri/Bowsher High Sch	129
Shields, Matthew/Archbold Middle Sch	78
Shirley, David/Imac Academy	3
Shisler, Chris/Nativity of Our Lord Sch	95
Shoaf, Jessica/Horizon Sci Acad-Columbus ES [153]	3
Shockley, Lauren/College Hill Fundamental Acad	87
Shoemaker, Todd/Chillicothe Intermediate Sch	174
Shoemaker, Todd/Northwest Middle Sch	179
Shontz, Shannon/Hopewell Sch	36
Shope, Foresta/Sciotoville Elem Academy	5
Short, Erin/Solon High Sch	50
Short, Jessica/Dayton Regional STEM Sch	2
Short, Michael, Dr/Perrysburg High Sch	218
Short, Royal/Archbold High Sch	78
Short, Shane/Amelia Elem Sch	31
Shoultz, Jameica/Educational Acad-Boys & Girls [243]	2
Shoultz, Jameica/Moler Elem Sch	68
Shoup, Kevin/Van Buren High Sch	99
Shrock, Amy/Midnimo Cross Cultural CMS [243]	4
Shultz, Jason/Urbana Junior High Sch	26
Shumaker, Tara/Good Samaritan Sch	56
Shumate, Mike/Buckskin Elem Sch	103
Sich, Sean/Mahoning Unlimited Classroom	133
Sideris, Steve/Chca-Edyth B Lindner Elem Sch	96
Siefring, Matt/Van Cleve 6th Grade Sch	147
Sies, Tim/North College Hill Mid Sch	91
Sies, Timothy/North College Hill High Sch	91
Sigg, Greg/Plymouth High Sch	173
Sigman, Jenness/Bellbrook Middle Sch	83
Silcott, Jim/Our Lady of Peace Sch	76
Simko, Joe/Howland High Sch	198
Simmons, Anitra/Gahanna Christian Academy	77
Simmons, Basharus/Edison Elem Sch	149
Simmons, Danielle/Heritage Middle Sch	45
Simmons, Ericka/Mariemont Elem Sch	91
Simmons, Joella/Hope Learning Academy Toledo	127
Simmons, Leeanna/Colonial Preparatory Academy	1
Simmons, Leeanna/Middlebury Academy Charter Sch	4
Simmons, Whitney/Parker Woods Montessori Sch	88
Simon, Linda/Willetts Middle Sch	140
Simpson, Amber/Rothenberg Preparatory Academy	88
Simpson, Erin/Overlook Elem Sch	142
Simpson, Susan/Wilmington Christian Academy	33
Simpson, Tina/Stebbins High Sch	151
Sims, Jill/Circleville Elem Sch	162
Sims, Maryum/School of One	45
Sincel, Brenda/Barberton Elem Sch-West	192
Sinclair, James/Academy of Arts & Science	1
Sinclair, James/Lorain Preparatory Academy [238]	4
Singer, Heidi/Walls Elem Sch	166
Singh, Jaivir/Groveport Madison High Sch	71
Sinney, Jaren/Cans Sch	87
Sippel, Stephen/Fairview-Clifton German Sch	87
Sisco, Emily/James J Hilfiker Elem Sch	177
Skelton, Dave/Coshocton Elem Sch	37
Skinner, Heather/The Plains Elem Sch	14
Skrzyniecki, Bryan/Rossford Junior High Sch	218
Slamer, Dave/Carlisle High Sch	207
Slattery, Jeffrey/Hicksville Jr Sr High Sch	57
Sledge, Walter/Jefferson Jr Sr High Sch	150
Sledge, Walter/Snyder Park Elem Sch	28
Sledte, Walter/Blairwood Elem Sch	150
Slekar, Lori/Pymatuning Valley Primary Sch	13
Sleutz, Justin/St Clairsville High Sch	18
Sloat, Hilary/Hilliard Horizon Elem Sch	72
Slocum, Jessica/Lincoln High Sch	70
Smallwood, Jeffrey/Highland Elem Sch	22
Smathers, Paul/Whitehall Yearling High Sch	75
Smiley, Mark/Amity Elem Sch	89
Smiley, Mark/Taylor Middle High Sch	94
Smith-Benson, Natalie/Iowa Maple Elem Sch	43
Smith, Aaron/Oakview Elem Sch	150
Smith, Andrew/Valley Forge Elem Sch	69
Smith, Angie/Norwalk Catholic ECC	107
Smith, Bart/Glenwood Junior High Sch	134
Smith, Bridget/Stamm Elem Sch	177
Smith, Carnel, Dr/Scott High Sch	130
Smith, Casey, Dr/Lynchburg-Clay Middle Sch	103
Smith, Catherine/Bridges Cmty Academy	1
Smith, Chaundria/Cleveland Early College HS	43
Smith, Chris/Chesapeake High Sch	115
Smith, Christopher/Ontario High Sch	173
Smith, Cindy/Kettering ECC Center	150
Smith, Cory/Edison Middle Sch	60
Smith, Darren/St Pius X Sch	76
Smith, Dave/Cornerstone Community Sch	196
Smith, Doug/Adamsville Elem Sch	157
Smith, Gene/Gables Elem Sch	68
Smith, James/St Adalbert-Cleveland Sch	52
Smith, Jamie/Chestnut Elem Sch	113
Smith, Jamila/Old Brook High Sch	4
Smith, Janet/Johnstown Elem Sch	118
Smith, Jocelyn/Charles Dickens at Corlett	43
Smith, Kari/Christie Lane Sch	105
Smith, Kent/Rittman Academy	213
Smith, Kevin/Crooksville High Sch	161
Smith, Kevin/West Muskingum High Sch	157
Smith, Laurie/St Cecilia Sch	76
Smith, Lee/West Main Elem Sch	166
Smith, Lisa/Salem Township Elem Sch	208
Smith, Margarete/Archbishop Lyke-St Henry ES	52
Smith, Matt/Swanton Middle Sch	79
Smith, Miranda/South Elem Sch	206
Smith, Nate/Logan Elm High Sch	162
Smith, Patrick/Springfield High Sch	28
Smith, Rod/Margaretta High Sch	61
Smith, Sandy/Bloom-Vernon Elem Sch	178
Smith, Susan/Northwest High Sch	91
Smith, Teresa/New Albany Primary Sch	72
Smith, Tina/Broadway Elem Sch	146
Smith, Trond/Orange High Sch	59
Smith, Troy/Marr Cook Elem Sch	30
Smith, V Janice/Pleasant Elem Sch	106
Smithberger, Mark, Dr/Berea-Midpark High Sch	41
Smolen, Cassandre/Buckeye Elem Sch	114
Smoot, Nakita/Georgian Heights Elem Sch	68
Snider, Michael/Putman Elem Sch	32
Snider, Rachel/Benjamin Franklin Elem Sch	43
Snively, Jason/Hillsboro High Sch	103
Snyder, Brian/Kettering Middle Sch	150
Snyder, Connie/Immaculate Conception Sch	160
Snyder, Drew/Rolling Hills Elem Sch	27
Snyder, Kate/Robinson Achievement	130
Snyder, Kate/Westfield Achievement	130
Snyder, Kevin/Poland Seminary High Sch	135
Snyder, Lynda, Sr/Rosary Cathedral Sch	131
Snyder, Shawn/Fredericksburg Elem Sch	213
Snyder, Shawn/Holmesville Elem Sch	213
Snyder, Will/Wapakoneta Middle Sch	16
Solomon Gray, Tammy/Cheviot Elem Sch	87
Solomon, Diane/St Vincent De Paul Sch	196
Soltesz, Tricia/Starr Elem Sch	128
Sonty, Priya/Leap Academy	88
Sorg, Nate/Arlington Local Sch	97
Souder, Timothy/Bucyrus Elem Sch	38
Southers, Greg/Tippecanoe Middle Sch	146
Sovacool, Dave/Orrville Middle Sch	212
Sowders, Jamie/Sayler Park Sch	88
Sowers, Megan/Wellston High Sch	108

PRINCIPAL INDEX

Market Data Retrieval

NAME/School	PAGE
Sowers, Shelley/*Brook Intermediate Sch*	86
Spagnola, Leo/*Olmsted Falls High Sch*	48
Spagnola, Leo/*Parma Senior High Sch*	49
Sparks, Matthew/*Beacon Elem Sch*	72
Spaulding, Pia/*Ethel M Taylor Academy*	87
Speck, Tiffany/*Caldwell Elem Sch*	158
Spencer, David/*Turpin High Sch*	89
Spencer, Jason/*Minster Jr/Sr High Sch*	15
Spicer, Beth/*Holy Angels Sch*	183
Spinner, Todd/*Berlin High Sch*	59
Spondyl, Yianni/*Marlington High Sch*	186
Spotts-Hayes, Michelle/*Garfield Elem Sch*	124
Spradlin, Janeen/*Wheelersburg Elem Sch*	180
Sprague, Kristy/*Aurora Academy [238]*	127
Spreen, Jaime/*East Columbus Elem Sch*	67
Spreng, Cj/*Hiland Jr Sr High Sch*	104
Sprow, Sherry/*Lakota High Sch*	177
Spurlock, Laramie/*Oak Harbor Middle Sch*	158
Spurrier, Ann, Dr/*Shaker Hts HS-the IC*	50
Srithai, Tony/*Beachwood Middle Sch*	40
St Pierre, Keith, Dr/*St Pierre Education Center*	84
Stacho, Glen/*Edith Whitney Elem Sch*	51
Staffilino, Lou/*Columbus Torah Academy*	77
Stahl, Kelly/*Whittier Primary Sch*	98
Stahl, Tony/*Fort Recovery Elem Mid Sch*	144
Stallard, Mark/*Zane Grey Elem Sch*	157
Stamos, Lisa/*Sullivant Elem Sch*	69
Stanfill, Brandon/*Garfield Middle Sch*	22
Stankovich, Nickolas/*Ayers Elem Sch*	18
Stanley-Bryson, Kaye, Dr/*Windfall Sch*	139
Stant, Nathan/*St John Elem Sch*	10
Stanton, Tasha/*Upper Sandusky Senior High Sch*	219
Staph, Christopher/*Niles Intermediate Sch*	200
Stapleton, Donald/*Glenwood High Sch*	179
Starinski, Alyssa/*Rhodes College & Career Acad*	44
Stark, Dee/*Auburn Career Center*	112
Starkey, Jeff/*Labrae High Sch*	198
Starner, Michael/*Liberty High Sch*	59
Staton, Sam/*Ridgedale Elem Sch*	138
Staud, Sandra/*St Aloysius Gonzaga Sch*	95
Staudter, Joel/*Anna Middle High Sch*	182
Stauffer, Denise/*Lehman Catholic High Sch*	183
Staum, Susan/*Heritage Elem Sch*	59
Stec, David/*Padua Franciscan High Sch*	52
Steenrod, Becky/*Nelsonville-York Elem Sch*	15
Stein, Adam/*Shreve Elem Sch*	213
Steinmiller, Hilary/*Holland Elem Sch*	128
Stekli, John/*Fairlawn Middle High Sch*	182
Stephan, Elise/*Nelsonville-York High Sch*	15
Stephan, Jason/*Arcanum High Sch*	55
Stephens, Tracey/*Willard Elem Sch*	106
Stephenson, Jennifer/*H C Mines Elem Sch*	198
Stephenson, Lyndsey/*Chamberlin Hill Interm Sch*	98
Stern, Peter/*Johnnycake Corners Elem Sch*	59
Sternefeld, Margaret/*Hope Academy-Brown St Campus*	2
Stevens, Caitlin/*Middletown Prep & Fitness Acad [247]*	4
Stevens, Jonathan/*Early College Academy*	66
Stevens, Lynnette/*Bluestone Elem Sch*	46
Stevens, Richard/*Bloomfield Jr Sr High Sch*	197
Stewart, Julie/*Lima North Middle Sch*	9
Steyer, Gary/*Port Clinton High Sch*	159
Steyer, Leonard/*Southeastern High Sch*	175
Stickel, Ruth/*Fairfield Elem Sch*	64
Stidham, Cassy/*Summit Academy Alt Lrng-Xenia [248]*	83
Stipek, John/*St Joseph Parish Sch*	126
Stitt, James/*Mathews High Sch*	199
Stock, Dannon/*Lake Center Christian Sch*	190
Stockard, Maria/*Fairmoor Elem Sch*	68
Stockmaster, Randy/*Green Springs Elem Sch*	176
Stoffer, Todd/*Ridgewood High Sch*	37
Stokes, Joy/*Belle Haven Elem Sch*	149
Stokes, Tracey/*Antwerp Local Sch*	160
Stoll, Marisa/*St Barbara Sch*	189

NAME/School	PAGE
Stoll, Matt/*Southern Ohio Christian Sch*	103
Stone, Kim/*Cincinnati Christian High Sch*	24
Stone, Nelson/*David Ponitz Career Tech Ctr*	149
Stoops, Corey/*Guardian Angels Sch*	95
Stoops, Kathleen/*Holy Family Sch*	137
Storer, Erin/*Wilson Elem Sch*	89
Stotz, Andy/*Franklin Woods Interm Sch*	73
Stought, Jeffrey/*Millersport Jr Sr High Sch*	64
Stout, Jessie/*Northside Christian Sch*	77
Stover, Jill/*Ridgmont Jr Sr High Sch*	100
Stover, Jill/*Ridgemont Local Sch*	100
Stover, Jill/*Victory Garden Pre-School*	99
Stover, Kim/*St Mary Elem Sch*	174
Stowell, Ryan/*Bristol Elem Sch*	197
Strader, Karyl/*Park Layne Elem Sch*	29
Straight, Kelly/*Focus North High Sch [244]*	2
Straka, Jeff/*Jerusalem Elem Sch*	128
Stranges, Rick/*Rutherford B Hayes High Sch*	59
Stranges, Robert/*Fouse Elem Sch*	74
Strathern, Kari/*Magnificat High Sch*	52
Strathern, Kari/*Metro Catholic Sch*	52
Stratton, Nancy/*Monroe Elem Sch*	23
Straussdaugh, Steve/*Lake Academy*	112
Streber, Kathryn/*Fairfield Local Elem Sch*	102
Stringer, Dan/*St Francis DeSales Sch*	209
Strong, Mr/*Trinity Lutheran Sch*	99
Struckel, Kathy/*Miracle City Academy*	164
Stuhldreher, Stacy/*Menlo Park Academy*	39
Stull, Eileen/*Louisa May Alcott Elem Sch*	44
Stull, Gina/*St Mary Sch*	60
Stulley, Ashlee/*Waverly High Sch*	164
Stump, Nathan/*Mifflin Elem Sch*	172
Stupka, Janice/*St Joseph Catholic Sch*	39
Sturgeon, George/*Bethel-Tate High Sch*	30
Sturm, Jacki/*Sterling Morton Elem Sch*	113
Stutz, Joshua/*Triway Junior High Sch*	213
Styles, Libby/*Colerain Middle Sch*	91
Suber, V Rena/*Emmanuel Christian Academy*	196
Suber, Vincent/*Streetsboro Middle Sch*	167
Sulfsted, Michele/*Summit Elem Sch*	89
Sullen, Amanda/*Parkside Elem Sch*	50
Sullivan, Shane/*Midview East Intermediate Sch*	125
Sullivan, Thomas/*Newton Falls Elem Mid Sch*	200
Sumer, Fatih/*Horizon Sci Academy-Lorain [153]*	3
Summers, Kimberly/*Portage Path Cmty Lrng Ctr*	191
Sunderman, Jill/*Hyde Park Sch*	88
Sundermann, Tammy/*Bauer Elem Sch*	151
Surso, Megan/*Strongsville Early Learning PS*	51
Susie, Miss/*Weaver Child Development Ctr*	190
Sutherland, Sandra/*Richland Academy of Excellence*	171
Sutherland, Sandra/*Richland Sch of Academic Arts*	5
Sutliff, Jeff/*St Joseph Academy*	53
Suttell, Andrew/*Shiloh Middle Sch*	49
Suwannasing, Kim/*Mt Logan Learning Center*	175
Svec, Donald/*Olmsted Falls Intermediate Sch*	48
Svoboda, Janis/*Euclid City High Sch*	46
Swafford, Lori/*Northwestern Jr Sr High Sch*	28
Swaggerty, Steve/*Highland Elem Sch*	129
Swain, Jim/*McVay Elem Sch*	75
Swan, Janice/*Longcoy Elem Sch*	165
Swank, Stacey/*Bellville Elem Sch*	171
Swartz, Gary/*Norwalk Middle Sch*	106
Swartz, Gerry/*Education Alternative*	53
Swartz, Russ/*Mogadore Jr Sr High Sch*	166
Swartz, Victoria/*Findlay Learning Center*	98
Sweet, Jaimie/*Ferguson Hall Freshman Sch*	83
Swift, Dann/*Murray Ridge Sch*	122
Swoope, Lawrence/*Arlington Christian Academy*	196
Swope, Barret/*Bethel Middle High Sch*	145
Swope, Barrett/*Clinton-Massie High Sch*	33
Sycks, Jeanna/*East-West Elem Sch*	14
Szary, Jonathan/*Wilson Middle Sch*	22
Szendrey, Tom/*North Ridgeville High Sch*	125

Ohio School Directory — PRINCIPAL INDEX

NAME/School	PAGE
Szilvasi, Elizabeth, Sr/*St Anthony of Padua Sch*	195
Szolek, Dan/*South Range Middle Sch*	135
Szoyka, Tammy/*St John Lutheran Sch*	54

T

NAME/School	PAGE
Tackett, Jason/*Williamsburg Middle High Sch*	32
Tackett, Shon/*Pike Co Career Tech Center*	163
Taggart, Ryan/*Garaway 7-12 Sch*	202
Taggart, Tom/*Nelsonville-York Jr High Sch*	15
Talbot, Amanda/*Leap Sch*	196
Talbot, Eric/*Sandusky High Sch*	61
Tanchevski, Michael/*Watkins Memorial High Sch*	120
Tanner, Marilee/*Roy E Holmes Elem Sch*	33
Tanto, Karen/*Salem Christian Academy*	154
Tarazi, Mouhamed/*International Academy Columbus*	66
Tate, Norbert/*Eastland Performance Academy [247]*	2
Tausch, Larry/*Northwest High Sch*	187
Taylor-Ware, Teresa/*Oxford Elem Sch*	42
Taylor, Adam/*Bridgetown Middle Sch*	92
Taylor, Arika/*Sunview Elem Sch*	51
Taylor, Brent/*Warren Middle Sch*	210
Taylor, Jamie/*Trimble Elem Sch*	15
Taylor, Jamie/*Trimble Middle Sch*	15
Taylor, Jeff/*Rossford Elem Sch*	218
Taylor, Jennifer/*Citizens Academy East [239]*	39
Taylor, Joyce/*Central Christian Sch*	214
Taylor, Julie/*St Mary Sch*	215
Taylor, Katherine/*Navarre Elem Sch*	130
Taylor, Kimberly, Dr/*Steam Acad Warrensvlle Heights [238]*	5
Taylor, Lenelle/*Avalon Elem Sch*	67
Taylor, Maria/*Nightingale Montessori Sch*	29
Taylor, Scott/*Lakeview Elem Sch*	199
Taylor, Temujin/*East Technical High Sch*	43
Tect, Rachel/*North High Sch*	191
Tedeschi, Mark/*Willo-Hill Christian Sch*	115
Teis, Michelle/*Madison Plains High Sch*	133
Teis, Michelle/*Madison Plains Junior HS*	133
Telepak, Sarah/*Valley Christian Academy*	167
Tellier, Joseph/*Steele High Sch*	122
Templin, Steven/*Berne Union Elem Sch*	63
Tenbarge, Lisa/*Springdale Elem Sch*	92
Tennenbaum, Stacy/*Pickerington High Sch Central*	64
Tennyson, Kristin/*Linden Grove Sch*	96
Teske, Cindy/*Darby Creek Elem Sch*	72
Thacker, Kevin/*Clough Pike Elem Sch*	31
Thanos, Alexandros/*KIPP Columbus Sch [246]*	3
Thaxton, Ben/*ADA Sch*	99
Thayer, Jane/*Valley High Sch*	179
Theado, Andrew/*Upper Arlington High Sch*	74
Theis, Jennifer/*Bigelow Hill Intermediate Sch*	98
Theodore, Julie/*Crestline Sch*	38
Thiede, Phil/*Kelleys Island Local Sch*	61
Thiel, Ben/*Cory-Rawson Elem Sch*	97
Thobe, Brad/*Harry Russell Elem Sch*	153
Thobe, Kelli/*Fort Recovery Elem Mid Sch*	144
Thoma, Kate/*Gen Rosecrans Elem Sch*	58
Thomas, Aric/*Worthington Kilbourne High Sch*	76
Thomas, Cathy/*Cristo Rey Columbus High Sch*	77
Thomas, Derrick/*John H Morrison Elem Sch*	152
Thomas, Gail/*Byesville Elem Sch*	86
Thomas, Jana/*Waterford Elem Sch*	211
Thomas, Kelly/*Miamisburg Middle Sch*	151
Thomas, Kevin/*Shawnee Early Childhood Sch*	22
Thomas, Mari/*St Ursula Academy*	96
Thomas, Mary/*Shoreview Elem Sch*	46
Thomas, Mike/*Laurel Oaks Career Dev Campus*	89
Thomas, Nehemiah/*East Academy [238]*	2
Thomas, Nichole/*Valley View Junior High*	153
Thomas, Terrez/*Carson Sch*	87
Thomas, Valencia/*J F Kennedy Sch*	47
Thomas, Wendy/*Stambaugh Charter Academy [203]*	5
Thompson, Andrew/*Columbia Elem Sch*	111
Thompson, Ashley/*Tri Academy*	204
Thompson, Christopher/*Bedford High Sch*	41
Thompson, Danielle/*KIPP Columbus Sch [246]*	3
Thompson, David/*Steamm Academy at Hartford*	185
Thompson, Gary/*Toledo Technology Academy*	130
Thompson, Miguel/*Fredericktown Elem Sch*	111
Thompson, Rochelle/*David Smith Elem Sch*	58
Thompson, Sherry/*Woodlawn Elem Sch*	92
Thompson, Takiba/*John Dewey Elem Sch*	51
Thompson, Walter/*Imagine Akron Kinder Academy [245]*	3
Thorbahn, Jon/*Ottoville High Sch*	170
Thornburg, John/*Summit Country Day Sch*	96
Thorngate, Tony/*New Lexington Senior High Sch*	161
Thornsley, Chris/*Circleville High Sch*	162
Thorp, Lance/*Montpelier Sch*	215
Thorp, Sue/*Montpelier Sch*	215
Thorson, Erik, Dr/*Monroe Preparatory Academy [238]*	4
Threat, Jatina/*Edison Elem Sch*	114
Thrush, Chad/*Kenton High Sch*	100
Thurman, Allyson/*Kenwood Elem Sch*	28
Tidmore, Jason/*Harvey Rice Wraparound*	43
Tidwell, Nikita/*Main Preparatory Academy*	4
Tiley, Chelsea/*Brookville Elem Sch*	148
Timco, Joe/*Medina Christian Academy*	142
Tinker, Charmaine/*Medina Middle Sch*	68
Tinsman, Ray/*Church of God Academy*	56
Tipton, Eric/*Tinora High Sch*	57
Tisch, Wendy/*Lakeshore Primary Sch*	12
Tisher, Ronald/*Cloverleaf High Sch*	140
Toeller, John/*Crooksville Elem Sch*	161
Toeller, John/*Crooksville Middle Sch*	161
Tokarsky, Jim/*Norwalk Cath JHS-St Paul HS*	107
Tolley, Lynn/*Tree of Life Christian Sch*	77
Tolzda, Casey/*Beallsville High Sch*	147
Tomassetti, Cyndi/*Newbury Elem Sch*	82
Tomlin, Dru/*Heritage Middle Sch*	75
Tompkins, Laura/*Zanesville High Sch*	158
Tooman, Annette/*Lindbergh Elem Sch*	68
Toon, Scott/*Delhi Middle Sch*	92
Toppins, Kristi/*East Portsmouth Elem Sch*	179
Torrence, David/*Xenia High Sch*	85
Tracy, Christian/*William Henry Harrison Jr HS*	93
Travis, Casey/*Flatridge Elem Sch*	104
Travis, Casey/*Wise Elem Sch*	105
Tregoning, Brian/*Helke Elem Sch*	153
Trevathan, Catherine/*Little Miami High Sch*	208
Trifonoff, Ed/*River High Sch*	147
Triplet, Jaclyn/*South Elem Sch*	203
Triplet, Matt/*Bradford High Sch*	145
Trisler, Forrest/*Columbian Senior High Sch*	181
Trivelli, Beth/*Evamere Elem Sch*	193
Troehler, Stephen/*Maddux Elem Sch*	89
Trogdlon, Tracy/*Washington Primary Sch*	146
Troman, Julie/*Miller Elem Sch*	165
Trombitas, Matthew/*Hilliard Heritage Middle Sch*	72
Trotter, Andy/*United Local Elem Sch*	36
Troyer, Trent/*Rock of Ages Sch*	214
Truesdell, Erin/*Hunter Elem Sch*	207
Trujillo, Claire/*C R Towslee Elem Sch*	140
Trujillo, Daniel/*Lighthouse Community Sch*	3
Trumpower, Chastity/*Schreiber Reading & Math Prep*	185
Trunk, Karen/*Orchard Hollow Elem Sch*	113
Tubbs-Wallace, Belinda/*Rockdale Academy*	88
Tucker, Ralph/*Geo Voinovich Reclamation Acad [135]*	2
Tucker, Shannon/*Yorktown Middle Sch*	69
Tudor, Matt/*Edwin H Greene Interm Sch*	93
Tuite, Michelle/*Lincoln Pre-Kindergarten Ctr*	181
Turner, Anna/*Chapelside Cleveland Academy [238]*	1
Turner, Cheryl/*Merwin Elem Sch*	31
Turner, Daniel/*Chamberlain Middle Sch*	207
Turner, Danita/*Southwood Elem Sch*	69
Turner, Jeff/*Bertha Bradshaw Elem Sch*	166
Turner, Kaitlyn/*Grant Elem Sch*	47
Turner, Latasha/*Cedarwood Elem Sch*	67
Turner, Latasha/*Summit Road STEM Elem Sch*	73
Turner, Mary Ellis, Dr/*West Central Sch*	66
Turner, Michael/*Robert A Taft Info Tech HS*	88

PRINCIPAL INDEX

Market Data Retrieval

NAME/School	PAGE
Turner, Sara/*Waverly Primary Sch*	164
Turner, Sherie/*Franklin D Roosevelt Academy*	43
Turner, Tiffany/*McTigue Elem Sch*	130
Turner, Tim/*Liberty Union Middle Sch*	64
Turner, Tom/*Spaulding Elem Sch*	30
Turpeau, Ross/*Woodford Paideia Sch*	88
Turson, Brad/*Shiloh Middle Sch*	173
Tussing, Jennie/*St Louis Sch*	218
Tuttle, Renee/*Moreland Hills Elem Sch*	49
Tyburski, Josh/*McCord Junior High Sch*	129
Tyrrell, Terrence/*St Xavier High Sch*	96

U

Ulbrich, Mark/*Pickerington High School North*	64
Ulbricht, David/*Echo Hills Elem Sch*	194
Ulland, Jennifer/*Indian Hill Middle Sch*	90
Ullman, Shelia/*Pleasantview First Step Sch*	49
Ullum, Angela/*Robert L Stevenson Elem Sch*	71
Ulrich, Ann/*St Gabriel Sch*	115
Ulring, Mike/*Dublin Coffman High Sch*	69
Underwood, Jerry/*Georgetown Jr Sr High Sch*	20
Underwood, Sarah/*Columbiana Co Opportunity Ctr*	36
Unger, Matthew/*Wilmington High Sch*	33
Unger, Michelle/*New Albany Early Learning Ctr*	72
Unverferth, Tony/*Vantage Career Center High Sch*	206
Updegrove, Eileen/*St Charles Borromeo Sch*	53
Updike, Jennifer/*Clinton-Massie Elem Sch*	33
Updike, Timothy/*Buckeye Hills Career Center*	80
Urban, Rachel/*Normandy High Sch*	49
Urbic, Cynthia/*Elm Street Elem Sch*	113
Urig, Sharon/*St Mary School-Elyria*	126
Utley, Monica/*Fairview Elem Sch*	149

V

Vagedes, Mike/*L T Ball Intermediate Sch*	146
Valenti, Michael/*Middletown Middle Sch*	23
Valentine, Sue Ellen/*St Edward Elem Sch*	11
Van Doren, Kendra/*Bataan Memorial Primary Sch*	159
Van Horn, Lisa/*Central Elem Sch*	104
Van Kirk, Frank/*Roseville Elem Sch*	156
Van Loveren, Mary/*Montessori School-Centerville*	154
Vanarnhem, Chad/*Kirtland Elem Sch*	112
Vance, Andrea/*Early Childhood Learning Cmty*	125
Vance, Kevin/*St Ignatius Sch*	95
Vanderhoff, Steve/*Rushmore Academy*	138
Vanek, Jamie/*Independence Middle Sch*	47
VanKirk, Anne/*Symmes Elem Sch*	94
Vanscyoc, Cindy/*Shenandoah Elem Sch*	158
Vardon, Lisa/*Schrop Intermediate Sch*	194
Vargo, Jennifer/*Broadleigh Elem Sch*	67
Vargyas, Kevin/*Cuyahoga Falls High Sch*	192
Vargyas, Kevin/*Lincoln Elem Sch*	192
Vaughn, Anna Marie/*Columbiana Co Hi Unit*	33
Vaughn, Anna Marie/*Columbiana Co Orthopedic Unit*	33
Vaughn, Anna Marie/*Columbiana Co Pre-School Unit*	34
Vaughn, Anna Marie/*Columbiana Ed Service Center*	34
Vaughn, Rafiq/*Westwood Elem Sch*	51
Vega, Anne/*Good Shepherd Montessori Sch*	95
Vega, David/*Jackson-Milton Middle High Sch*	134
Vehre, Mark/*Mohawk Local Sch*	219
Velotta, Timothy/*Chardon Middle Sch*	82
Venne, Kristy/*Emerald Campus*	70
Vens, Kasey/*Southview High Sch*	129
Venzeio, Jacquelyn/*JFK Lower Campus*	201
Verhoff, Kathleen/*Kalida Elem Sch*	170
Verhoff, Steve/*Tippecanoe High Sch*	146
Verroco, Mark/*Shawnee High Sch*	9
Vertikoff, Paula/*Ervin Carlisle Elem Sch*	58
Vicha, Chris/*Lewis F Mayer Middle Sch*	46
Vicha, Christopher/*Fairview High Sch*	46
Vickroy, Derick/*Columbus Global Academy*	67
Viers, Melisa/*Arlington Elem Sch*	129
Vietmeier, Theresa/*Wauseon Elem Sch*	80

NAME/School	PAGE
Villa, Lynn/*Wilcox Primary Sch*	195
Vince, Jason/*Butler Middle Sch*	55
Vincent, Lee/*Cincinnati College Prep Acad*	1
Vincente, Philomena/*Leggett Cmty Learning Center*	191
Virgil, Matt/*Hudson Montessori Sch*	196
Viscounte, Cindy/*Reilly Elem Sch*	35
Vittardi, Edward/*St Albert the Great Sch*	52
Vivo, James/*Lordstown High Sch*	199
Vizzo, Eric/*Cornerstone Elem Sch*	213
Vogt, Don/*Seneca East Local Sch*	181
Vojtush, Gary/*Stockyard Cmty Elem Sch [242]*	40
Vojtush, Gary/*Stockyard Cmty Middle Sch [242]*	40
Voll, Harry/*Roselawn Condon Sch*	88
Vollmer, Mark/*Cardinal Mooney High Sch*	137
Vondrell, Leslie/*St Luke Sch*	85
Voress, Diane/*Sidney Middle Sch*	183
Voss, Cindy/*Hannah Crawford Elem Sch*	38
Votaw, Lisa/*Aiken High Sch*	87
Vroom, Craig/*Innovative Learning Hub*	72

W

Waddell, Jessica/*Beatty Park Elem Sch*	67
Waddell, Kevin/*West Elem Sch*	206
Wade, Kim/*Plains Junior High Sch*	22
Waechter, Jeff/*Cliff Park High Sch*	1
Wagner, Kyle/*Indian Lake High Sch*	121
Wagner, Matt/*Ebon C Hill Intermediate Sch*	30
Wagner, Susan/*Spencerville Elem Sch*	9
Wagoner, Katrina/*Russellville Elem Sch*	7
Wagoner, Missy/*Lake Elem Sch*	217
Wagonfield, Kathy/*Ridgeway Elem Sch*	22
Walczak, Jean, Sr/*St Richard Sch*	80
Walden, Leah/*Parma Community Middle Sch [242]*	40
Waldvogel, Jason/*Pettisville Elem Sch*	79
Waldy, James/*Mars Hill Academy*	209
Waler, Joseph/*Notre Dame Cathedral Latin Sch*	82
Walgate, Jacob/*La Croft Elem Sch*	35
Walgate, Jake/*Beaver Local Middle Sch*	34
Walk, Lisa/*Trebein Elem Sch*	83
Walker, Aaron/*Waterloo Elem Sch*	167
Walker, Bob/*Felicity-Franklin High Sch*	30
Walker, David/*Johnson Park Middle Sch*	68
Walker, Jennifer/*Wilson Elem Sch*	137
Walker, Juanita/*Ramah Junior Academy*	54
Walker, Michelle/*Melridge Elem Sch*	114
Walker, Michelle/*Parkside Elem Sch*	114
Walker, Paul/*Little Whippets Pre-School*	173
Walker, Stephanie/*Goshen High Sch*	30
Walker, Thomas/*Notre Dame Jr Sr High Sch*	180
Walker, Tonya/*Columbus Africentric EC 9-12*	67
Wallace, Brian/*West Clermont Virtual Academy*	31
Wallace, Danielle/*Winton Woods Primary Sch-South*	94
Wallace, Tami/*Mohawk Local Sch*	219
Wallace, Theodore/*Bishop Leibold Sch East*	154
Wallace, Theodore, Dr/*Bishop Leibold Sch W Campus*	154
Walland, Kelly/*Univ of Cleveland Prep Sch [238]*	5
Waller, Paul/*Oakwood High Sch*	152
Walter, Mark/*Lakewood High Sch*	47
Walter, Melanie/*Belmont High Sch*	149
Waltman, Susanne/*Strausser Elem Sch*	186
Walton, Kayla/*St Mary Sch*	76
Walton, Terrance/*New Day Academy*	4
Waluzak, Amanda/*Arts & College Prep Academy*	65
Wang, Michael/*James A Harmon Elem Sch*	73
Wank, Joe/*Eastwood Elem Sch*	216
Ward, Angela/*Adult Work Force Dev Center*	70
Ward, Chris/*Atkinson Elem Sch*	177
Ward, Dana/*Lakota Elem Sch*	177
Ward, Erica/*Westwood Elem Sch*	126
Ward, Jeremy/*Pennyroyal Elem Sch*	207
Ward, Jeremy/*Vinton Co Middle Sch*	206
Ward, Joe/*Monroe Jr High Sch*	23
Ward, Willie/*M Luther King Academy for Boys*	130

Ohio School Directory

PRINCIPAL INDEX

NAME/School	PAGE
Ware, Sherri/Jefferson Co Christian Sch	110
Warner, Brad/Edgewood Middle Sch	213
Warner, Melissa/Madison South Elem Sch	172
Warnimont, Chad, Dr/Frank Elem Sch	218
Warnock, Megan/Portsmouth STEM Academy	180
Warrell, Brenna/Lakewood Catholic Academy	52
Warren, Tiffane/Licking Heights High Sch	118
Waseman, Beverly/Orrville Elem Sch	212
Washburn, Kirk/Sheridan Middle Sch	161
Waskowitz, Bill/The Seven Hills Sch	96
Waterman, Kimberly/New Knoxville Sch	16
Waters, Merritt/Horace Mann Elem Sch	47
Watkins, Brad/Pleasant Run Middle Sch	91
Watkins, Brian/Claymont Middle Sch	202
Watkins, Kimberly/Schaefer Middle Sch	28
Watkins, Sharon, Dr/Life Skills Ctr of N Columbus	3
Watkins, Steven/Dalton Local Elem Middle Sch	212
Watry, Marcy/Regina Coeli Catholic Sch	189
Watson, Cheryl/Columbus Downtown High Sch	67
Watson, Stuart/Southridge Christian Academy	14
Watters, Melisa/Galion Primary Sch	38
Watterson, Karly/East Elem Sch	111
Watts, James/New Lexington Middle Sch	161
Watts, Mark/St Mary Magdalene Sch	76
Watts, Melissa/Robinson G Jones Elem Sch	45
Watts, Nance/Isham Memorial Elem Sch	141
Waugh, Mike/Lutheran High School West	54
Wayland, Lisa/Adena Elem Sch	174
Wayne, Eric/Washington Middle Sch	65
Weagley, Zach/North Olmsted High Sch	48
Weasner, Melanie/Harvest Temple Christian Acad	177
Weaver, Dustin/Chillicothe High Sch	174
Weaver, Teresa/Pleasant St Elem Sch	111
Weaver, Wes/Licking Valley High Sch	119
Webb, William/Clyde High Sch	176
Weber, Ashley/Malvern Elem Sch	25
Weeks, Mary/Herbert Mills Elem Sch	73
Weeman, Joselyn, Sr/Queen of Apostles Sch	131
Wehri, Jarrod/Allen East Middle Sch	7
Wehrman, Brad/Kirkersville Elem Sch	120
Weidig, Kathleen/Central Elem Sch	172
Weiler, Gretchen/Ashville Elem Sch	162
Weimer, Jill/Urbana Elem Sch	26
Weinberg, Lisa/Yavne High Sch	54
Weingart, Nicholas/Perry High Sch	9
Weirich, Sue/Ontario Middle Sch	173
Weisbrod, Jessica/Brookwood Elem Sch	22
Weisbrod, Jessica/Hamilton HS-Freshman Campus	22
Weisner, Janet/St Catharine Sch	76
Welch, Jill/Thomas Edison Center Pre-Sch	205
Welch, Shawna/Wright Brothers Middle Sch	149
Welker, Gay/Faircrest Memorial Middle Sch	185
Wells, Jeff/Green Middle Sch	185
Wells, Kathy/Fairway Sch	37
Wells, Nichole/Tinora Elem Sch	57
Wells, Ryan/Midvale Elem Sch	202
Welsh, Mary/St Charles Sch	137
Wendt, Stacie/St Gabriel Consolidated Sch	95
Wenning, Derek/Celina Intermediate Sch	143
Wensel, Deborah/Harter Reading & Math Prep Sch	185
Wertman, Ty/Zane Trace High Sch	176
Wesson, Dan/Shenandoah Elem Sch	158
West, Ernest/Independence High Sch	68
West, James/West Preparatory Academy	6
West, Scott/South Gallia High Sch	80
Westendorf, Joe/Sharpsburg Elem Sch	92
Westendorf, Stacey/Magsig Middle Sch	149
Westerlund, Craig/Licking County Christian Acad	120
Wetherholt, Doug/Geneva High Sch	13
Wharton, Scott/Triway High Sch	213
Wheat, Erin/Brookville Intermediate Sch	148
Wheeler, Ivy/Charles W Eliot Elem Sch	43
Wheeler, Ivy/Whitney M Young Gifted Campus	45
Wheeler, James/Upper Sandusky Middle Sch	219
Wheeler, Paul/Galion Middle Sch	38

NAME/School	PAGE
Wheeler, Ron/Buckeye Ranch Sch	73
Whelan, Lisa/St Angela Merici Sch	52
Whipkey, Heather/B L Miller Elem Sch	135
Whitaker, Robert/Ft Island Primary Sch	192
White, David/Trotwood-Madison Sr High Sch	153
White, Karen/Seton High Sch	95
White, Matt/Ashland Middle Sch	10
White, Mitch/Lake Ridge Academy	126
White, Shannon/Morton Middle Sch	153
White, Sue/Madison Christian Sch	77
Whiteley, Gerry/Communion of Saints Sch	52
Whitestone, Tim/Northridge High Sch	152
Whitis, Dianna/Preble Shawnee Jr/Sr High Sch	168
Whitlow, Shawnkeida/Valerie PK-6 Sch	149
Whitson, Nicolette/Bennett Venture Academy [203]	1
Whitt, Bethany/Western Elem Sch	164
Whitted, Matt/Sandy Valley High Sch	189
Whittemore, Jennifer/Mahoning Co High Sch	133
Wichtman, Joel/St Andrew Sch	76
Wickard, Nolan/Woodmore High Sch	159
Wielinski, Jenny/Brookside Elem Sch	75
Wigton, Erica, Dr/Canterbury Elem Sch	42
Wigton, Missy/Eastview Elem Sch	172
Wikel, Ryan/Sandusky Central Catholic Sch	62
Wilbarger, Jeff/Toledo Christian Sch	131
Wilburn, Tabatha/Annehurst Elem Sch	74
Wilch, Brian/Hudson High Sch	193
Wilcox, Peg/Cambridge High Sch	86
Wilde, Ryan/Napoleon Jr Sr High Sch	101
Wilds, Bob/Lawrence Co Academy	115
Wilhelm, John/Hamilton High Sch	22
Wilker, Nick/Marion Local Elem Sch	144
Wilkerson, Debra/Siebert Elem Sch	69
Wilkins, Darren/Spring Valley Academy	154
Wilkins, Kristel/Warner Girls Leadership Acad	45
Wilks, Allan/Parma Developmental Center	40
Will, Scott/Mt Vernon High Sch	111
Williams, Stephanie/Lima Central Catholic High Sch	10
Williams, Anthony/Wings Academy	6
Williams, Anthony/Wings Academy K-8	6
Williams, Anthony/Wings Academy Lower Sch	6
Williams, Barry/St Joseph Sch	95
Williams, Ben/Open Door Christian Sch	126
Williams, Brenda/Patriot Preparatory Academy	73
Williams, Brian/Newport Elem Sch	210
Williams, Brian, Dr/Delisle Options Center	42
Williams, Christene/Meadowvale Elem Sch	130
Williams, Courtney/Columbus Bilingual Acad-North [238]	1
Williams, Dakota/Cas-Jones Campus	53
Williams, Dakota/Cleveland Christian Home Ctr	53
Williams, Daphne/Imagine Hill Ave Environ Sch [245]	3
Williams, Don/Donnell Middle Sch	98
Williams, Dumaine, Dr/Bard HS Early College	43
Williams, Jasmine/E Prep & Village Prep-Willard [239]	2
Williams, Jay/Thomas A Wildey Sch	29
Williams, Jordan/Columbiana Co Career Tech Ctr	34
Williams, Kelli/Sherman Elem Sch	130
Williams, Larry/Shroder High Sch	88
Williams, Lisa/Falls-Lennox Primary Sch	48
Williams, Ranea/Barber Community Learning Ctr	190
Williams, Robert/Ohio College Preparatory Sch [238]	4
Williams, Ron/Galion High Sch	38
Williams, Sandy/North Road Intermediate Sch	198
Williams, Theresa/SS Peter & Paul Sch	214
Williams, Tiffany/North College Hill Elem Sch	91
Williams, Tom/Hillsdale Elem Sch	11
Williams, Trisha/Ransom H Barr Elem Sch	188
Williamson, Jamie/Marburn Academy	77
Williamson, Karl/Brush High Sch	51
Willian, Matthew/Sabina Elem Sch	33
Willig, Tara/Delshire Elem Sch	92
Willinston, Michael/Summit Academy Sch-Lorain [248]	122
Willis, Lauren/Waterloo Middle Sch	167
Willis, Rachel/Christian Community Sch	126
Willman, Ted/Calvert Catholic Schools	182

School Year 2019-2020   800-333-8802   OH-U29

PRINCIPAL INDEX

Market Data Retrieval

NAME/School	PAGE
Wills, Elizabeth/*Amanda-Clearcreek Elem Sch*	62
Wills, Mrs/*Southeastern Elem Sch*	175
Willson, Tom/*McCormick Elem Sch*	31
Wilson, Allen/*Ashland Co Cmty Academy*	10
Wilson, Carla/*Barrington Elem Sch*	74
Wilson, Elaine, Dr/*Phoenix Cmty Learning Center*	4
Wilson, India/*Eastgate Elem Sch*	67
Wilson, Jamie/*Hanna J Ashton Middle Sch*	73
Wilson, Kevin/*Wayne Trace Groverhill ES*	160
Wilson, Mike/*Lincoln Elem Sch*	28
Wilson, Paul/*Westlake High Sch*	52
Wiltse, Dale/*Toth Elem Sch*	218
Winchester, Jeffery/*Mississinawa Valley Jr Sr HS*	56
Windham, Lauren/*Scottish Corners Elem Sch*	70
Windon, Jason/*Regent High Sch*	4
Winer, Ellen/*Grand Valley Elem Sch*	13
Winfrey, Adrean/*Linden STEM Academy*	68
Wingler, William/*Brooklyn High Sch*	41
Wininger, Natalie/*McDowell Elem Sch*	193
Winkelfoos, Shawn/*Highland Elem Sch*	155
Winkle, Emily/*Oakdale Elem Sch*	92
Winkler, Thomas/*Lima West Middle Sch*	9
Winkler, Tricia/*Unity Elem Sch*	9
Winland, Erik/*Maysville Elem Sch*	157
Winner, Aaron/*Gahanna Middle School-West*	70
Winner, Dale/*Miami Valley Career Tech Ctr*	151
Winner, Tyler/*Holt Crossing Intermediate Sch*	73
Winslow, Jeff/*Bogan Elem Sch*	24
Winston, Monique/*Central Primary Sch*	41
Winter, Carol, Dr/*Palm Elem Sch*	124
Winterod, Brad/*Norwood High Sch*	92
Winters, Mark/*Springmyer Elem Sch*	92
Winters, Mike/*Bishop Hartley High Sch*	76
Wintersteller, Friederike/*St Mary Sch*	83
Winton, Rob/*Rocky River High Sch*	50
Wise, Brent/*McVey Innovative Learning Ctr*	72
Wise, Jeff/*Pandora Gilboa High Sch*	171
Wise, John/*Woodland Elem Sch*	23
Wise, Keven/*Margaretta Elem Sch*	61
Wise, Linda/*Chapel Hill Chrn School-South*	196
Wittig, Susann/*Deer Run Elem Sch*	69
Wohlgamuth, Kelly/*Jacobs Primary Sch*	98
Wojcik, Angela/*Gateway Middle Sch*	127
Wolf, Kevin/*York Elem Sch*	203
Wolfe, James/*Pickaway Elem Sch*	162
Wolfe, Jim/*Washington Elem Sch*	162
Wolfe, Kevin/*Edgerton High Sch*	214
Wolfel, Ed/*Somerset Elem Sch*	161
Wolfert, Hendrick/*Pymatuning Valley Middle Sch*	13
Wolgast, Brad/*Dixie High Sch*	152
Wolke, Jason/*Cridersville Elem Sch*	16
Wolph, Matt/*North Central Academy*	180
Woodard, Jennell/*Spring Garden Waldorf Sch*	196
Woodard, Jennifer/*Franklin Local Cmty Sch*	156
Woodin, Teresa/*Hollingsworth East Elem Sch*	168
Woodman, Jennifer/*St Hilary Sch*	195
Woods, Brian/*Parkway Middle Sch*	144
Woods, Denyse/*Huy Elem Sch*	68
Woods, Jeff/*West Holmes Middle Sch*	105
Woods, Jennifer/*Medill Elem Sch*	63
Woods, Renee/*Millersburg Elem Sch*	105
Woods, Susan/*Medlar View Elem Sch*	151
Woodward, Julie/*Scarlet Oaks Career Dev Campus*	89
Woodworth, Travis/*Robert F Schultz Elem Sch*	58
Woody, Jennifer/*Euclid Park Sch*	43
Worline, Laurie/*Millcreek-West Unity Local Sch*	215
Worsencroft, Paul/*Claggett Middle Sch*	141
Wotring, Kim/*Fairfield Compass Elem Sch*	21
Wray, Carrie/*Monac Elem Sch*	130
Wren, Dale/*Herman K Ankeney Middle Sch*	83
Wright, Casey/*Nordonia High Sch*	193
Wright, Denise/*Noble Elem Sch*	57
Wright, Kathy/*Hughes STEM High Sch*	88

NAME/School	PAGE
Wright, Michael/*The Miami Sch*	22
Wright, Mike/*Conotton Valley Elem Sch*	101
Wristen, Ellen/*Brookwood Academy*	1
Wulf, Jason/*Greensview Elem Sch*	74
Wushinske, Mandy/*Mansfield Christian Sch*	174
Wyandt, Beth/*Kleptz Early Learning Center*	152
Wyatt, Betsy/*Fairborn Intermediate Sch*	84
Wyckoff, Emory/*Montgomery Preparatory Academy [238]*	4
Wyland, Christopher/*Adlai Stevenson Elem Sch*	42

Y

NAME/School	PAGE
Yancey, Kurt/*Westerville North High Sch*	75
Yanchunas, Andrew/*Lakeview Intermediate Sch*	194
Yanni, Becca/*Walnut Springs Middle Sch*	75
Yates, Lin/*Norwood View Elem Sch*	92
Yates, Randy, Dr/*E Prep & Vlg Prep Cliffs Sch [239]*	2
Yates, Randy, Dr/*E Prep Cliffs Middle Campus*	2
Yeager, Bradly/*Memorial High Sch*	134
Yeagley, Brett/*Minerva High Sch*	187
Yenni, Kim/*Millersport Elem Sch*	64
Yenrick, Robert/*Oakdale Elem Sch*	130
Yetter, Eric/*New London High Sch*	106
Yetter, Eric/*New London Middle Sch*	106
Yingling, Crystal/*Summit Academy Mid Sch-Akron [248]*	5
Yobe, Bradilyn/*Hubbard High Sch*	198
Yocum, Mark/*C L Warstler Elem Sch*	188
York, Tom/*Talawanda High Sch*	24
Yost, Rusty/*Firelands Christian Academy*	62
Yost, Travis/*Arrowood Elem Sch*	84
Young, Blake/*Wauseon Primary Sch*	80
Young, Chad/*Bloom-Carroll Middle Sch*	63
Young, Chris/*Ripley-Union-Lewis-Huntngtn HS*	20
Young, H Danny/*Woodbury Elem Sch*	50
Young, Jen/*Worthington Park Elem Sch*	76
Young, Kathy/*Washington Preschool*	98
Young, Kevin/*Lexington High Sch*	172
Young, Laura/*Holgate Sch*	101
Young, Megan/*Toni Morrison Elem Sch*	124
Young, Scott/*E Central Ohio Ed Svc Center*	201
Young, Theresa/*St Mary Central Sch*	19
Young, William/*Cruiser Academy*	71
Young, William/*United Local High Sch*	36

Z

NAME/School	PAGE
Zabowski, Joe/*Evergreen Middle Sch*	78
Zaffini, Charles/*Veritas Academy*	78
Zapolnik, Jarred/*Massillon Intermediate Sch*	187
Zappitelli, Dawn/*Gateway Elem Sch*	12
Zawodny, Brian/*Greenmont Elem Sch*	150
Zeiders, Brenda/*Lancaster City Pre-School*	63
Zeller, Brian/*Fremont Ross High Sch*	177
Zeoli, Scott/*Albert Chapman Elem Sch*	69
Zesiger, Zachary/*East Elem Sch*	202
Zierden, Jennifer/*Cardington Interm Sch*	155
Zigarovich, Rich/*Lordstown Elem Sch*	199
Zimmerly, Brian/*Nashville Elem Sch*	105
Zimmerly, Doug/*Norwayne High Sch*	212
Zimmerman, Brad/*Piqua Catholic Sch*	147
Zinn, Duerk/*Margaret Rost Sch*	87
Zoccali, Michael/*Stadium Drive Elem Sch*	134
Zoller, James/*Clifton Area Neighborhd Sch*	87
Zollinger, Jamie/*Chippewa Intermediate Sch*	211
Zook, Rachel/*Valley Christian Academy*	167
Zucal, John/*Central Elem Sch*	203
Zuccola, Kristen/*Westside Christian Academy*	54
Zywczyk, Kelly/*Canal Winchester Middle Sch*	66

Ohio School Directory

DISTRICT & SCHOOL TELEPHONE INDEX

School/City/County DISTRICT/CITY/COUNTY	PID	TELEPHONE NUMBER	PAGE

A

School/City/County	PID	TELEPHONE	PAGE
A I Root Middle Sch/*Medina*/Medina	04368608	330/636-3500	141
A J Jordak Elem Sch/*Middlefield*/Geauga	00804143	440/632-0261	81
A Plus Arts Acad-Fair Campus/*Columbus*/Franklin	05381794	614/725-1305	1
A Plus Arts Acad-Maybury/*Columbus*/Franklin	04880694	614/626-2250	1
A Plus Arts Acad-Napoleon/*Columbus*/Franklin	12160959	614/338-0767	1
A Plus Children's Academy/*Columbus*/Franklin	12160806	614/491-8502	1
Aacs Early Lrng Center/*Ashtabula*/Ashtabula	04363294	440/992-1280	12
Abraham Lincoln Elem Sch/*Maple Heights*/Cuyahoga	00793673	216/438-6030	47
Acad Multilingual Immer Stud/*Cincinnati*/Hamilton	00805599	513/363-1800	87
Academic Enrichment Center/*Westerville*/Franklin	12313522	614/797-7450	74
Academy for Urban Scholars/*Youngstown*/Mahoning	12162945	330/744-9070	1
Academy for Urban Scholars HS/*Columbus*/Franklin	12162933	614/545-9890	1
Academy of Arts & Science/*Lorain*/Lorain	11448332	440/244-0156	1
Academy of Educ Excellence/*Toledo*/Lucas	12160765	419/382-2280	127
Academy of St Adalbert/*Berea*/Cuyahoga	00796027	440/234-5529	52
Academy of St Bartholomew/*Middlebrg HTS*/Cuyahoga	00796194	440/845-6660	52
Academy of World Languages/*Cincinnati*/Hamilton	00806127	513/363-7800	87
ACCESS/**CANFIELD**/**MAHONING**	04499465	330/702-7860	137
ACES/*Columbus*/Franklin	00800707	614/365-6000	67
Achieve Career Prep Academy/*Toledo*/Lucas	11553781	419/243-8559	1
Acs Early Learning Center/*Chauncey*/Athens	12038344	740/797-4589	14
ADA EXEMPTED VILLAGE SCH DIST/**ADA**/**HARDIN**	00810166	419/634-6421	99
ADA Sch/*Ada*/Hardin	00810178	419/634-6421	99
ADAMS CO OHIO VALLEY SCH DIST/**WEST UNION**/**ADAMS**	00783343	937/544-5586	6
Adams County Christian Sch/*West Union*/Adams	02165565	937/544-5502	7
Adamsville Elem Sch/*Adamsville*/Muskingum	00826452	740/796-2153	157
Addaville Elem Sch/*Gallipolis*/Gallia	00803943	740/367-7283	80
Adena Elem Sch/*Frankfort*/Ross	00830116	740/998-5293	174
Adena Elem Sch/*West Chester*/Butler	01829005	513/777-0100	22
Adena High Sch/*Frankfort*/Ross	00830099	740/998-2313	174
ADENA LOCAL SCH DIST/**FRANKFORT**/**ROSS**	00830087	740/998-4633	174
Adena Middle Sch/*Frankfort*/Ross	04448492	740/998-2313	174
Adlai Stevenson Elem Sch/*Cleveland*/Cuyahoga	00791077	216/838-5300	42
Admiral King Elem Sch/*Lorain*/Lorain	00816366	440/830-4120	124
Adrian Elem Sch/*Cleveland*/Cuyahoga	00794706	216/691-2170	51
Adult Center for Education/*Zanesville*/Muskingum	04800668	740/455-3111	157
Adult Work Force Dev Center/*Groveport*/Franklin	04797451	614/836-4541	70
Aiken High Sch/*Cincinnati*/Hamilton	00805317	513/363-6700	87
Aim Academy/*Canton*/Stark	12308046	330/456-3167	184
Akiva Academy/*Youngstown*/Mahoning	02949581	330/747-0452	137
Akron Alternative Academy/*Akron*/Summit	10003238	330/761-1609	190
Akron Digital Academy/*Akron*/Summit	05220126	330/237-2200	190
Akron Early College High Sch/*Akron*/Summit	11434915	330/972-6450	190
Akron Preparatory Sch/*Akron*/Summit	12114493	330/247-6232	1
AKRON PUBLIC SCHOOLS/**AKRON**/**SUMMIT**	00833833	330/761-1661	190
Akros Middle Sch/*Akron*/Summit	11566829	330/374-6704	190
AL Ihsan Islamic Sch/*Cleveland*/Cuyahoga	05363704	216/676-5006	53
AL Ihsan Sch/*Parma*/Cuyahoga	11223833	440/799-4875	53
Albert Chapman Elem Sch/*Powell*/Franklin	03236404	614/761-5864	69
Albert Einstein Acad-Westlake/*Westlake*/Cuyahoga	11927948	440/471-4982	39
Albion Elem Sch/*N Royalton*/Cuyahoga	00793934	440/582-9060	48
Alcott Elem Sch/*Westerville*/Franklin	05092462	614/797-7350	74
Alden R Brown Elem Sch/*Carlisle*/Warren	00838144	937/746-7610	206
Aldersgate Christian Academy/*Cincinnati*/Hamilton	00808010	513/763-6655	96
Alexander Elem Sch/*Albany*/Athens	00784983	740/698-8831	14
Alexander Jr Sr High Sch/*Albany*/Athens	00784995	740/698-8831	14
ALEXANDER LOCAL SCH DIST/**ALBANY**/**ATHENS**	00784971	740/698-8831	14
Alexandria Montessori Sch/*Centerville*/Montgomery	03063178	937/435-5392	154
Alfred Benesch Academy/*Cleveland*/Cuyahoga	00791273	216/838-1300	42
All Children of the World Acad/*Westerville*/Delaware	05099630	614/890-8985	60
All Saints Academy/*Columbus*/Franklin	00802793	614/231-3391	76
All Saints Catholic Sch/*Rossford*/Wood	00818302	419/661-2070	218
All Saints Sch/*Cincinnati*/Hamilton	00808101	513/792-4732	94
All Saints-St John Vianney Sch/*Wickliffe*/Lake	01539779	440/943-1395	114
ALLEN CO ED SERVICE CENTER/**LIMA**/**ALLEN**	00784098	419/222-1836	7
Allen Co Pre-School Unit/*Lima*/Allen	04026111	419/227-0600	7
Allen East Elem Sch/*Harrod*/Allen	00783551	419/648-3333	7
Allen East High Sch/*Harrod*/Allen	00783563	419/648-3333	7
ALLEN EAST LOCAL SCH DIST/**HARROD**/**ALLEN**	00783549	419/648-3333	7
Allen East Middle Sch/*Harrod*/Allen	12306945	419/648-3333	7
Allen Reading & Math Prep Sch/*Canton*/Stark	00832401	330/453-2782	184
Alliance Academy of Cincinnati/*Cincinnati*/Hamilton	05287150	513/751-5555	87
ALLIANCE CITY SCH DIST/**ALLIANCE**/**STARK**	00832190	330/821-2100	184
Alliance Early Learning Sch/*Alliance*/Stark	00832279	330/829-2266	184
Alliance High Sch/*Alliance*/Stark	00832205	330/829-2245	184
Alliance Middle Sch/*Alliance*/Stark	00832281	330/829-2254	184
Almira Academy/*Cleveland*/Cuyahoga	00791118	216/838-6150	42
Alpine Elem Sch/*Columbus*/Franklin	00799639	614/365-5359	67
Alton Darby Elem Sch/*Hilliard*/Franklin	04945074	614/921-5000	71
Alton Hall Elem Sch/*Galloway*/Franklin	00801828	614/801-8000	73
Alum Creek Elem Sch/*Lewis Center*/Delaware	04450196	740/657-4600	59
Amanda Elem Sch/*Middletown*/Butler	00786773	513/420-4542	23
Amanda-Clearcreek Elem Sch/*Amanda*/Fairfield	00798867	740/969-7253	62
Amanda-Clearcreek High Sch/*Amanda*/Fairfield	00798879	740/969-7251	62
AMANDA-CLEARCREEK LOCAL SD/**AMANDA**/**FAIRFIELD**	00798855	740/969-7250	62
Amanda-Clearcreek Middle Sch/*Amanda*/Fairfield	04368646	740/969-7252	62
Amanda-Clearcreek Primary Sch/*Amanda*/Fairfield	10011819	740/969-7254	63
Amelia Elem Sch/*Amelia*/Clermont	00788692	513/943-3800	31
Amesville Elem Sch/*Amesville*/Athens	00785119	740/448-2501	14
Amherst Elem Sch/*Massillon*/Stark	00832803	330/830-8024	186
AMHERST EXEMPTED VILLAGE SD/**AMHERST**/**LORAIN**	00815611	440/988-4406	122
Amherst Junior High Sch/*Amherst*/Lorain	05230561	440/988-0324	122
Amity Elem Sch/*Cincinnati*/Hamilton	00806373	513/891-5995	89
Anderson High Sch/*Cincinnati*/Hamilton	00806488	513/232-2772	89
Andrew J Rickoff Elem Sch/*Cleveland*/Cuyahoga	00791120	216/838-4150	42
Andrews Osborne Academy/*Willoughby*/Lake	00814069	440/942-3600	115
Angeline Sch/*Upper Sandsky*/Wyandot	02052736	419/294-4901	218
Ann Simpson Davis Middle Sch/*Dublin*/Franklin	03049421	614/761-5820	69
Anna Elem Sch/*Anna*/Shelby	00831847	937/394-2584	182
ANNA LOCAL SCH DIST/**ANNA**/**SHELBY**	00831811	937/394-2011	182
Anna Middle High Sch/*Anna*/Shelby	00831823	937/394-2011	182
Annehurst Elem Sch/*Westerville*/Franklin	00802262	614/797-7000	74
Annunciation Sch/*Cincinnati*/Hamilton	00808125	513/221-1230	94
Ansonia Elem Sch/*Ansonia*/Darke	00797473	937/337-5141	55
Ansonia Jr Sr High Sch/*Ansonia*/Darke	00797485	937/337-4000	55
ANSONIA LOCAL SCH DIST/**ANSONIA**/**DARKE**	00797461	937/337-4000	55
Anthony Wayne Early Chldhd Ctr/*Greenville*/Darke	02051782	937/548-8323	55
Anthony Wayne Elem Sch/*Franklin*/Warren	00838259	937/743-8640	207
Anthony Wayne High Sch/*Whitehouse*/Lucas	00816885	419/877-0466	127
Anthony Wayne Jr High Sch/*Whitehouse*/Lucas	04283151	419/877-5342	127
ANTHONY WAYNE LOCAL SCH DIST/**WHITEHOUSE**/**LUCAS**	00816873	419/877-5377	127
Anton Grdina Sch/*Cleveland*/Cuyahoga	00791144	216/838-1150	42
Antrim Mennonite Sch/*Freeport*/Harrison	11188453	740/489-5161	101
Antwerp Local Sch/*Antwerp*/Paulding	00827298	419/258-5421	160
ANTWERP LOCAL SCH DIST/**ANTWERP**/**PAULDING**	00827286	419/258-5421	160
Apex Academy/*E Cleveland*/Cuyahoga	10001034	216/451-1725	39
Apollo Career High Sch/*Lima*/Allen	01537680	419/998-2908	8
APOLLO JOINT VOC SCH DIST/**LIMA**/**ALLEN**	01537678	419/998-2911	8
Apostolic Christian Academy/*Toledo*/Lucas	04986810	419/885-5334	131

DISTRICT & SCHOOL TELEPHONE INDEX

Market Data Retrieval

School/City/County DISTRICT/CITY/COUNTY	PID	TELEPHONE NUMBER	PAGE
Apple Creek Elem Sch/*Apple Creek*/Wayne	00839368	330/698-3111	213
Applewood Elem Sch/*Brunswick*/Medina	00822121	330/273-0481	140
Applied Behavioral Services/*Dayton*/Montgomery	11223091	937/847-8750	154
Arbor Elem Sch/*Euclid*/Cuyahoga	11824621	216/797-6200	46
Arbor Hills Junior High Sch/*Sylvania*/Lucas	00817243	419/824-8640	129
ARCADIA LOCAL SCH DIST/ARCADIA/HANCOCK	00809739	419/894-6431	97
Arcadia Sch/*Arcadia*/Hancock	00809741	419/894-6431	97
ARCANUM BUTLER LOCAL SCH DIST/ARCANUM/DARKE	00797502	937/692-5174	55
Arcanum Early Learning Center/*Arcanum*/Darke	12038459	937/692-5092	55
Arcanum Elem Sch/*Arcanum*/Darke	00797514	937/692-5174	55
Arcanum High Sch/*Arcanum*/Darke	00797526	937/692-5174	55
Archbishop Alter High Sch/*Kettering*/Montgomery	00808113	937/434-4434	154
Archbishop Hoban High Sch/*Akron*/Summit	00795334	330/773-6658	195
Archbishop Lyke-St Henry ES/*Cleveland*/Cuyahoga	00796467	216/991-9644	52
Archbishop McNicholas HS/*Cincinnati*/Hamilton	00808474	513/231-3500	94
Archbishop Moeller High Sch/*Cincinnati*/Hamilton	00808498	513/791-1680	95
ARCHBOLD AREA LOCAL SCH DIST/ARCHBOLD/FULTON	00803503	419/445-5579	78
Archbold Elem Sch/*Archbold*/Fulton	00803515	419/446-2727	78
Archbold High Sch/*Archbold*/Fulton	00803527	419/445-5579	78
Archbold Middle Sch/*Archbold*/Fulton	00803541	419/446-2726	78
ARCHDIOCESE CINCINNATI ED OFF/CINCINNATI/HAMILTON	00808096	513/421-3131	94
Arlington Christian Academy/*Akron*/Summit	05256503	330/785-9116	196
Arlington Elem Sch/*Toledo*/Lucas	00817322	419/671-2550	129
Arlington Local Sch/*Arlington*/Hancock	00809777	419/365-5121	97
ARLINGTON LOCAL SCH DIST/ARLINGTON/HANCOCK	00809765	419/365-5121	97
Arrowhead Elem Sch/*Lewis Center*/Delaware	00798312	740/657-4650	59
Arrowhead Primary Sch/*Copley*/Summit	00834693	330/664-4885	192
Arrowood Elem Sch/*Xenia*/Greene	00804870	937/372-9251	84
Artemus Ward Sch/*Cleveland*/Cuyahoga	00791156	216/838-6200	43
Arts & College Prep Academy/*Columbus*/Franklin	05220205	614/986-9974	65
Arts Academy at Summit/*Canton*/Stark	11449283	330/452-6537	184
Arts Impact Middle Sch/*Columbus*/Franklin	00800123	614/365-5558	67
Asbury Elem Sch/*Columbus*/Franklin	00801490	614/833-2000	71
Ascension Sch/*Kettering*/Montgomery	00808137	937/254-5411	154
Ashland Christian Sch/*Ashland*/Ashland	01753834	419/289-6617	11
ASHLAND CITY SCH DIST/ASHLAND/ASHLAND	00784103	419/289-1117	10
Ashland Co Cmty Academy/*Ashland*/Ashland	11220776	419/903-0295	10
Ashland Co-W Holmes Career Ctr/*Ashland*/Ashland	00784361	419/289-3313	11
ASHLAND CO-WEST HOLMES JVSD/ASHLAND/ASHLAND	00784359	419/289-3313	10
Ashland High Sch/*Ashland*/Ashland	00784127	419/289-7968	10
Ashland Middle Sch/*Ashland*/Ashland	00784139	419/289-7966	10
ASHTABULA AREA CITY SCH DIST/ASHTABULA/ASHTABULA	00784385	440/992-1200	12
ASHTABULA CO ED SERVICE CENTER/ASHTABULA/ASHTABULA	00784957	440/576-9023	11
Ashtabula Co Educ Svc Ctr/*Ashtabula*/Ashtabula	04020844	440/576-4085	12
Ashtabula Co Tech & Career Ctr/*Jefferson*/Ashtabula	00784945	440/576-6015	12
ASHTABULA CO TECH & CAREER SD/JEFFERSON/ASHTABULA	00784933	440/576-6015	12
Ashville Elem Sch/*Ashville*/Pickaway	00827834	740/983-5066	162
Assumption Academy/*Broadview HTS*/Cuyahoga	00795360	440/526-4877	52
ATHENS CITY SCH DIST/THE PLAINS/ATHENS	00785028	740/797-4544	14
Athens High Sch/*The Plains*/Athens	00785030	740/797-4521	14
ATHENS MEIGS ED SERVICE CENTER/CHAUNCEY/ATHENS	02089105	740/797-0064	14
Athens Meigs ESC/*Chauncey*/Athens	04338861	740/593-8001	14
Athens Middle Sch/*Athens*/Athens	00785042	740/593-7107	14
Atkinson Elem Sch/*Fremont*/Sandusky	00830568	419/332-5361	177
Auburn Career Center/*Painesville*/Lake	00814112	440/357-7542	112
Auburn Elem Sch/*Shelby*/Richland	00829935	419/342-5456	173
AUBURN VOCATIONAL SCH DIST/PAINESVILLE/LAKE	00814100	440/357-7542	112
AUGLAIZE CO ED SERVICE CENTER/WAPAKONETA/AUGLAIZE	00785559	419/738-3422	15
Auglaize Co Educational Acad/*Lima*/Allen	05381823	419/738-4572	7
Aurora Academy/*Toledo*/Lucas	04880046	419/693-6841	127
AURORA CITY SCH DIST/AURORA/PORTAGE	00828163	330/562-6106	164
Aurora High Sch/*Aurora*/Portage	00828175	330/562-3501	165
Austinburg Elem Sch/*Austinburg*/Ashtabula	00784701	440/466-4831	13
Austintown Elem Sch/*Youngstown*/Mahoning	00819746	330/797-3901	134
Austintown Intermediate Sch/*Youngstown*/Mahoning	00819758	330/797-3901	134
AUSTINTOWN LOCAL SCH DIST/YOUNGSTOWN/MAHONING	00819708	330/797-3900	133
Austintown Middle Sch/*Youngstown*/Mahoning	00819710	330/797 3900	134
Autism Academy of Learning/*Toledo*/Lucas	05009037	419/865-7487	127
Autism Model Sch/*Toledo*/Lucas	04880072	419/897-4400	127
Avalon Elem Sch/*Columbus*/Franklin	01556521	614/365-5361	67
Avery Elem Sch/*Hilliard*/Franklin	00801725	614/921-5100	72
Avon Early Learning Center/*Avon*/Lorain	00815714	440/934-5124	123
Avon Heritage Elem Sch/*Avon*/Lorain	05070658	440/937-9660	123
Avon High Sch/*Avon*/Lorain	00815702	440/934-6171	123
AVON LAKE CITY SCH DIST/AVON LAKE/LORAIN	00815726	440/933-6210	122
Avon Lake High Sch/*Avon Lake*/Lorain	00815738	440/933-6290	122
AVON LOCAL SCH DIST/AVON/LORAIN	00815685	440/937-4680	122
Avon Middle Sch/*Avon*/Lorain	04801832	440/934-3800	123
Avondale Elem Sch/*Canton*/Stark	00833522	330/491-3720	188
Avondale Elem Sch/*Columbus*/Franklin	00799665	614/365-6511	67
Ayer Elem Sch/*Cincinnati*/Hamilton	00806505	513/474-3811	89
Ayers Elem Sch/*Martins Ferry*/Belmont	00785793	740/633-3754	18
Ayersville Elem Sch/*Defiance*/Defiance	00797849	419/395-1111	57
Ayersville High Sch/*Defiance*/Defiance	00797825	419/395-1111	57
AYERSVILLE LOCAL SCH DIST/DEFIANCE/DEFIANCE	00797813	419/395-1111	56
Ayersville Middle Sch/*Defiance*/Defiance	12367901	419/395-1111	57

B

B L Miller Elem Sch/*Sebring*/Mahoning	00820159	330/938-2025	135
Babeck Early Childhood Ctr/*Trenton*/Butler	00786292	513/867-3430	21
Badger Elem Sch/*Kinsman*/Trumbull	00836304	330/876-2860	198
Badger High Sch/*Kinsman*/Trumbull	00836299	330/876-2840	198
Badger Middle Sch/*Kinsman*/Trumbull	00836328	330/876-2840	198
Baker Elem Sch/*Vienna*/Trumbull	00836031	330/637-3500	199
Baker Middle Sch/*Fairborn*/Greene	00804648	937/878-4681	84
Ballard Brady Middle Sch/*Pepper Pike*/Cuyahoga	00794043	216/831-8600	49
Baltic Elem Sch/*Baltic*/Tuscarawas	00837229	330/897-7261	202
Barack Obama Sch/*Maple Heights*/Cuyahoga	00793697	216/438-6020	47
Barber Community Learning Ctr/*Akron*/Summit	00833845	330/761-7911	190
BARBERTON CITY SCH DIST/BARBERTON/SUMMIT	00834502	330/753-1025	192
Barberton Elem Sch-East/*Barberton*/Summit	00834540	330/745-5492	192
Barberton Elem Sch-West/*Barberton*/Summit	00834564	330/825-2183	192
Barberton High Sch/*Barberton*/Summit	00834526	330/753-1084	192
Barberton Middle Sch/*Barberton*/Summit	00834552	330/745-9950	192
Barberton Preschool/*Barberton*/Summit	12364674	330/753-1025	192
Bard HS Early Clg East Campus/*Cleveland*/Cuyahoga	12231417	216/838-4100	43
Bard HS Early College/*Cleveland*/Cuyahoga	12172495	216/838-9700	43
Barnesville Elem Sch/*Barnesville*/Belmont	00785573	740/425-3639	17
BARNESVILLE EXEMPTED VLG SD/BARNESVILLE/BELMONT	00785561	740/425-3615	17
Barnesville High Sch/*Barnesville*/Belmont	00785585	740/425-3617	17
Barnesville Ind Elem Sch/*Barnesville*/Belmont	11231543	740/425-3420	19
Barnesville Middle Sch/*Barnesville*/Belmont	04428624	740/425-3116	17
Barrington Elem Sch/*Upper Arlngtn*/Franklin	00802107	614/487-5180	74
Bascom Elem Sch/*Leavittsburg*/Trumbull	00836342	330/898-0800	198
Bataan Intermediate Sch/*Port Clinton*/Ottawa	00827200	419/734-3931	159
Bataan Memorial Primary Sch/*Port Clinton*/Ottawa	00827183	419/734-2815	159
Batavia Elem Sch/*Batavia*/Clermont	00788329	513/732-0780	29
Batavia High Sch/*Batavia*/Clermont	00788331	513/732-2341	29
BATAVIA LOCAL SCH DIST/BATAVIA/CLERMONT	00788317	513/732-2343	29
Batavia Middle Sch/*Batavia*/Clermont	04745410	513/732-9534	29
Bath Elem Sch/*Akron*/Summit	00835350	330/523-3802	194
Bath Elem Sch/*Lima*/Allen	00783599	419/221-1837	8
Bath High Sch/*Lima*/Allen	00783604	419/221-0366	8
BATH LOCAL SCH DIST/LIMA/ALLEN	00783587	419/221-0807	8
Bath Middle Sch/*Lima*/Allen	00783616	419/221-1839	8
Bauer Elem Sch/*Dayton*/Montgomery	00825252	937/434-9191	151

Ohio School Directory

DISTRICT & SCHOOL TELEPHONE INDEX

School/City/County DISTRICT/CITY/COUNTY	PID	TELEPHONE NUMBER	PAGE
Bay High Sch/*Bay Village*/Cuyahoga	00790413	440/617-7400	40
Bay Middle Sch/*Bay Village*/Cuyahoga	00790425	440/617-7600	40
BAY VILLAGE CITY SCH DIST/			
BAY VILLAGE/CUYAHOGA	00790401	440/617-7300	40
Beach Sch/*Rocky River*/Cuyahoga	12307016	440/356-6000	50
BEACHWOOD CITY SCH DIST/			
BEACHWOOD/CUYAHOGA	00790475	216/464-2600	40
Beachwood High Sch/*Beachwood*/Cuyahoga	00790487	216/831-2080	40
Beachwood Middle Sch/*Beachwood*/Cuyahoga	00790499	216/831-0355	40
Beacon Academy/*Canton*/Stark	12259524	330/941-5848	1
Beacon Elem Sch/*Hilliard*/Franklin	00801737	614/921-5200	72
Beacon Hill Community Sch/*Dundee*/Tuscarawas	11746574	330/359-5600	201
Beacon Sch/*Athens*/Athens	02051536	740/594-3539	14
Beallsville Elem Sch/*Beallsville*/Monroe	00823723	740/926-1302	147
Beallsville High Sch/*Beallsville*/Monroe	00823735	740/926-1302	147
Bear Elem Sch/*Miamisburg*/Montgomery	00825264	937/866-4691	151
Beatty Park Elem Sch/*Columbus*/Franklin	00799691	614/365-6074	67
Beaumont Sch/*Cleveland HTS*/Cuyahoga	00795372	216/321-2954	52
Beautiful Savior Luth Sch/*Cincinnati*/Hamilton	01874048	513/825-2290	96
Beautiful Savior Luth Sch/*Grove City*/Franklin	03101160	614/875-1147	77
Beaver Local Elem Sch/*E Liverpool*/Columbiana	00789153	330/386-8700	34
Beaver Local High Sch/*E Liverpool*/Columbiana	00789139	330/386-8700	34
Beaver Local Middle Sch/*E Liverpool*/Columbiana	00789141	330/386-8700	34
BEAVER LOCAL SCH DIST/E LIVERPOOL/			
COLUMBIANA	00789127	330/385-6831	34
BEAVERCREEK CITY SCH DIST/			
BEAVERCREEK/GREENE	00804466	937/426-1522	83
Beavercreek High Sch/*Beavercreek*/Greene	00804478	937/429-7547	83
Beavercreek Preschool Center/*Beavercreek*/Greene	12168690	937/458-2360	83
Beavertown Elem Sch/*Kettering*/Montgomery	00824844	937/499-1740	150
BEDFORD CITY SCH DIST/BEDFORD/			
CUYAHOGA	00790530	440/439-1500	40
Bedford High Sch/*Bedford*/Cuyahoga	00790554	440/439-4848	41
Beechcroft High Sch/*Columbus*/Franklin	01531844	614/365-5364	67
Beechwood Elem Sch/*Whitehall*/Franklin	00802432	614/417-5300	75
Belden Leadership Sch/*Canton*/Stark	00832425	330/453-6902	184
Bell Academy/*Reynoldsburg*/Franklin	11828861	614/501-4000	72
Bell Creek Intermediate Sch/*Bellbrook*/Greene	04447670	937/848-3777	83
Bellaire Elem Sch/*Bellaire*/Belmont	00785664	740/676-1272	17
Bellaire High Sch/*Bellaire*/Belmont	00785602	740/676-3652	17
BELLAIRE LOCAL SCH DIST/			
BELLAIRE/BELMONT	00785597	740/676-1826	17
Bellaire Middle Sch/*Bellaire*/Belmont	00785626	740/676-1635	17
Bellbrook High Sch/*Bellbrook*/Greene	00804777	937/848-3737	83
Bellbrook Middle Sch/*Bellbrook*/Greene	00804789	937/848-2141	83
BELLBROOK-SUGARCREEK SCHOOLS/			
BELLBROOK/GREENE	00804765	937/848-5001	83
Belle Aire Intermediate Sch/*Wshngtn Ct Hs*/Fayette	00799469	740/335-1810	65
Belle Haven Elem Sch/*Dayton*/Montgomery	00824105	937/542-4220	149
BELLEFONTAINE CITY SCH DIST/			
BELLEFONTAINE/LOGAN	00815362	937/593-9060	120
Bellefontaine Elem Sch/*Bellefontaine*/Logan	00815398	937/599-4431	121
Bellefontaine High Sch/*Bellefontaine*/Logan	00815386	937/593-0545	121
Bellefontaine Intermediate Sch/*Bellefontaine*/Logan	00815427	937/592-5646	121
Bellefontaine Middle Sch/*Bellefontaine*/Logan	00815374	937/593-9010	121
BELLEVUE CITY SCH DIST/BELLEVUE/			
HURON	00811457	419/484-5000	105
Bellevue Elem Sch/*Bellevue*/Huron	00811536	419/484-5050	105
Bellevue Middle Sch/*Bellevue*/Huron	00811471	419/484-5060	105
Bellevue Senior High Sch/*Bellevue*/Huron	00811469	419/484-5070	105
Bellflower Elem Sch/*Mentor*/Lake	00813364	440/255-4212	113
Bellville Elem Sch/*Bellville*/Richland	01557549	419/886-3244	171
Belmont Career Center/*St Clairsvle*/Belmont	00786010	740/695-9130	18
Belmont Co Alt Program/*St Clairsvle*/Belmont	04338873	740/695-9773	17
Belmont High Sch/*Dayton*/Montgomery	00824129	937/542-6460	149
BELMONT-HARRISON VOC SCH DIST/			
ST CLAIRSVLE/BELMONT	00786008	740/695-9130	17
Belpre Christian Academy/*Belpre*/Washington	03061326	740/423-7741	211
BELPRE CITY SCH DIST/BELPRE/			
WASHINGTON	00838572	740/423-9511	209
Belpre Elem Sch/*Belpre*/Washington	04941432	740/423-3010	209
Belpre High Sch/*Belpre*/Washington	00838596	740/423-3000	209
Ben Franklin Elem Sch/*Newark*/Licking	00814992	740/670-7340	119
Benedictine High Sch/*Cleveland*/Cuyahoga	00795384	216/421-2080	52
Benjamin Franklin Elem Sch/*Cleveland*/Cuyahoga	00791194	216/838-3150	43
Benjamin Harrison Elem Sch/*Marion*/Marion	00821842	740/223-4999	138
Benjamin Logan Elem Sch/*Bellefontaine*/Logan	00815441	937/592-4838	121
Benjamin Logan High Sch/*Bellefontaine*/Logan	00815489	937/592-1666	121
BENJAMIN LOGAN LOCAL SCH DIST/			
BELLEFONTAINE/LOGAN	00815439	937/593-9211	121
Benjamin Logan Middle Sch/*Bellefontaine*/Logan	00815491	937/599-2386	121
Bennett Venture Academy/*Toledo*/Lucas	10000999	419/269-2247	1
BENTON-CARROLL-SALEM LOCAL SD/			
OAK HARBOR/OTTAWA	00826983	419/898-6210	158
BEREA CITY SCH DIST/BEREA/			
CUYAHOGA	00790633	216/898-8300	41
Berea-Midpark High Sch/*Berea*/Cuyahoga	00790645	216/898-8900	41
Berea-Midpark Middle Sch/*Middlebrg HTS*/Cuyahoga	11927089	216/676-8400	41
Berkshire Jr Sr High Sch/*Burton*/Geauga	00804064	440/834-3380	81
BERKSHIRE LOCAL SCH DIST/			
BURTON/GEAUGA	00804052	440/834-3380	81
Berkshire Middle Sch/*Galena*/Delaware	11714765	740/657-5200	59
Berlin Elem Sch/*Berlin*/Holmes	00811287	330/893-2817	104
Berlin High Sch/*Delaware*/Delaware	12235839	740/657-5901	59
Berne Union Elem Sch/*Sugar Grove*/Fairfield	00798908	740/746-9668	63
Berne Union High Sch/*Sugar Grove*/Fairfield	04023949	740/746-9956	63
BERNE UNION LOCAL SCH DIST/			
SUGAR GROVE/FAIRFIELD	00798893	740/746-8341	63
Berry Intermediate Sch/*Lebanon*/Warren	05350147	513/934-5700	207
Bertha Bradshaw Elem Sch/*Rootstown*/Portage	00828606	330/325-7971	166
Berwick Alternative Elem Sch/*Columbus*/Franklin	00799744	614/365-6140	67
Bessie Kinsner Elem Sch/*Strongsville*/Cuyahoga	04806727	440/572-7120	51
Bethany Lutheran Sch/*Parma*/Cuyahoga	00795097	440/884-1010	53
Bethany Sch/*Cincinnati*/Hamilton	00807975	513/771-7462	96
Bethel Baptist Christian Acad/*Ravenna*/Portage	11224124	330/296-9845	167
Bethel Christian Academy/*Parma*/Cuyahoga	02123191	440/842-8575	53
Bethel Elem Sch/*Tipp City*/Miami	00823175	937/845-9439	145
BETHEL LOCAL SCH DIST/TIPP CITY/			
MIAMI	00823163	937/845-9414	145
Bethel Middle High Sch/*Tipp City*/Miami	12107402	937/845-9487	145
Bethel-Tate High Sch/*Bethel*/Clermont	00788355	513/734-2271	30
BETHEL-TATE LOCAL SCH DIST/			
BETHEL/CLERMONT	00788343	513/734-2271	30
Bethel-Tate Middle Sch/*Bethel*/Clermont	05070701	513/734-2271	30
Bethlehem Lutheran Sch/*Fairborn*/Greene	05103322	937/878-7050	85
Betty Jane Cmty Learning Ctr/*Akron*/Summit	00833871	330/794-4117	191
Beverly Elem Sch/*Toledo*/Lucas	00817346	419/671-2600	129
Beverly Gardens Elem Sch/*Riverside*/Montgomery	00825068	937/259-6620	151
Beverly-Center Elem Sch/*Beverly*/Washington	00838637	740/984-2371	210
BEXLEY CITY SCH DIST/BEXLEY/			
FRANKLIN	00799524	614/231-7611	66
Bexley High Sch/*Columbus*/Franklin	00799536	614/231-4591	66
Bexley Middle Sch/*Bexley*/Franklin	01399189	614/237-4277	66
Bible Believers Christian Sch/*Lima*/Allen	03342352	419/999-5517	10
Big Creek Elem Sch/*Middlebrg HTS*/Cuyahoga	00790762	216/898-8303	41
Big Walnut Elem Sch/*Sunbury*/Delaware	00798128	740/965-3902	58
Big Walnut High Sch/*Sunbury*/Delaware	00798116	740/965-3766	58
Big Walnut Intermediate Sch/*Sunbury*/Delaware	11823770	740/965-7800	58
BIG WALNUT LOCAL SCH DIST/			
SUNBURY/DELAWARE	00798104	740/965-3010	58
Big Walnut Middle Sch/*Sunbury*/Delaware	00798154	740/965-3006	58
Bigelow Hill Intermediate Sch/*Findlay*/Hancock	00809868	419/425-8317	98
Binns Elem Sch/*Columbus*/Franklin	00799756	614/365-5911	67
Bio-Med Science Academy/*Rootstown*/Portage	11849229	330/325-6186	1
Birch Primary Sch/*North Olmsted*/Cuyahoga	03320067	440/779-3570	48
Birchwood School of Hawken/*Cleveland*/Cuyahoga	03014684	216/251-2321	53
Birmingham Elem Sch/*Toledo*/Lucas	00817358	419/671-7700	129
Bishop Fenwick Elem Sch/*Zanesville*/Muskingum	00803448	740/454-9731	158
Bishop Fenwick High Sch/*Franklin*/Warren	00808280	513/423-0723	209

School Year 2019-2020   800-333-8802   OH-V3

DISTRICT & SCHOOL TELEPHONE INDEX

Market Data Retrieval

School/City/County DISTRICT/CITY/COUNTY	PID	TELEPHONE NUMBER	PAGE
Bishop Fenwick Middle Sch/*Zanesville/*Muskingum	00803345	740/453-2637	158
Bishop Flaget Sch/*Chillicothe*/Ross	00803266	740/774-2970	176
Bishop Hartley High Sch/*Columbus*/Franklin	00802731	614/237-5421	76
Bishop Leibold Sch East/*Dayton*/Montgomery	05359923	937/434-9343	154
Bishop Leibold Sch W Campus/*Miamisburg/*Montgomery	01600770	937/866-3021	154
Bishop Mussio Ctl Elem Sch/*Steubenville/*Jefferson	00812683	740/264-2550	110
Bishop Mussio Ctl Jr High Sch/*Steubenville/*Jefferson	00812712	740/346-0028	110
Bishop Ready High Sch/*Columbus*/Franklin	00802743	614/276-5263	76
Bishop Rosecrans High Sch/*Zanesville/*Muskingum	00802755	740/452-7504	158
Bishop Watterson High Sch/*Columbus/*Franklin	00802767	614/268-8671	76
Black River Education Center/*Sullivan/*Medina	00822078	419/736-2161	139
Black River High Sch/*Sullivan*/Medina	00822080	419/736-3303	140
BLACK RIVER LOCAL SCH DIST/ SULLIVAN/MEDINA	00822066	419/736-3300	139
Blacklick Elem Sch/*Blacklick*/Franklin	04282195	614/759 5100	70
Blairwood Elem Sch/*Dayton*/Montgomery	00824789	937/263-3504	150
Blanchard Valley Sch/*Findlay*/Hancock	02052047	419/422-8173	97
Blanchester High Sch/*Blanchester*/Clinton	00788886	937/783-2461	32
Blanchester Intermediate Sch/*Blanchester/*Clinton	10013350	937/783-2040	32
BLANCHESTER LOCAL SCH DIST/ BLANCHESTER/CLINTON	00788862	937/783-3523	32
Blanchester Middle Sch/*Blanchester*/Clinton	00788874	937/783-3642	32
Blendon Middle Sch/*Westerville*/Franklin	00802274	614/797-6400	74
Blessed Sacrament Sch/*Newark*/Licking	00802779	740/345-4125	120
Blessed Sacrament Sch/*Toledo*/Lucas	00818314	419/472-1121	131
Bloom-Carroll High Sch/*Carroll*/Fairfield	00798958	740/756-4317	63
Bloom-Carroll Intermediate Sch/*Lithopolis/*Fairfield	00798934	614/837-4044	63
BLOOM-CARROLL LOCAL SCH DIST/ CARROLL/FAIRFIELD	00798922	614/837-6560	63
Bloom-Carroll Middle Sch/*Carroll*/Fairfield	00798946	614/837-6205	63
Bloom-Carroll Primary/*Carroll*/Fairfield	00798960	740/756-4326	63
Bloom-Vernon Elem Sch/*South Webster*/Scioto	00830908	740/778-2339	178
BLOOM-VERNON LOCAL SCH DIST/ SOUTH WEBSTER/SCIOTO	00830867	740/778-2281	178
Bloomfield Jr Sr High Sch/*N Bloomfield/*Trumbull	00835831	440/685-4711	197
BLOOMFIELD-MESPO LOCAL SD/ N BLOOMFIELD/TRUMBULL	00835817	440/685-4711	197
Blott Guy Elem Sch/*Youngstown*/Trumbull	00836445	330/759-1733	199
Blue Ash Elem Charter Sch/*Cincinnati/*Hamilton	11833842	513/891-1723	1
Blue Ash Elem Sch/*Cincinnati*/Hamilton	00807779	513/686-1710	93
Bluestone Elem Sch/*Euclid*/Cuyahoga	11824619	216/797-6300	46
Bluffsview Elem Sch/*Columbus*/Franklin	03393284	614/450-5100	75
Bluffton Elem Sch/*Bluffton*/Allen	00783654	419/358-7951	8
BLUFFTON EXEMPTED VILLAGE SCH/ BLUFFTON/ALLEN	00783630	419/358-5901	8
Bluffton High Sch/*Bluffton*/Allen	00783666	419/358-7941	8
Bluffton Middle Sch/*Bluffton*/Allen	04840785	419/358-7961	8
Boardman Center Middle Sch/*Boardman/*Mahoning	00819813	330/726-3400	134
Boardman High Sch/*Boardman*/Mahoning	00819801	330/758-7511	134
BOARDMAN LOCAL SCH DIST/ BOARDMAN/MAHONING	00819796	330/726-3404	134
Bobbie B Fairfax Sch/*Cincinnati*/Hamilton	04008963	513/271-2313	87
Bobby F Grigsby Interm Sch/*Carlisle*/Warren	00838120	937/746-8969	206
Bogan Elem Sch/*Oxford*/Butler	10029397	513/273-3400	24
Bolich Middle Sch/*Cuyahoga FLS*/Summit	00834849	330/926-3801	192
Bolton Crossing Elem Sch/*Grove City/*Franklin	12168810	614/801-8275	73
Bolton Elem Sch/*Cleveland*/Cuyahoga	00791209	216/838-1200	43
Bond Hill Academy/*Cincinnati*/Hamilton	00805343	513/363-7900	87
Botkins Local Sch/*Botkins*/Shelby	00831873	937/693-4241	182
BOTKINS LOCAL SCH DIST/BOTKINS/ SHELBY	00831861	937/693-4241	182
Boulevard Elem Sch/*Cleveland HTS*/Cuyahoga	00792851	216/371-7140	42
Boulevard Elem Sch/*Shaker HTS*/Cuyahoga	00794512	216/295-4020	50
Bowling Green Chrn Academy/*Bowling Green/*Wood	04986779	419/354-2422	218
BOWLING GREEN CITY SCH DIST/ BOWLING GREEN/WOOD	00839942	419/352-3576	216
Bowling Green High Sch/*Bowling Green*/Wood	00839954	419/354-0100	216
Bowling Green Middle Sch/*Bowling Green/*Wood	00839966	419/354-0200	216
Bowling Green Pre-School/*Bowling Green/*Wood	11070284	419/354-0300	216
Bowman Primary Sch/*Lebanon*/Warren	00838390	513/934-5800	207
Bowsher High Sch/*Toledo*/Lucas	00817360	419/671-2000	129
Boyd E Smith Elem Sch/*Milford*/Clermont	02111045	513/575-1643	31
Boys Village Sch/*Wooster*/Wayne	00839502	330/262-3442	213
Bradford Elem Sch/*Bradford*/Miami	00823204	937/448-2811	145
BRADFORD EXEMPTED VILLAGE SD/ BRADFORD/MIAMI	00823199	937/448-2770	145
Bradford High Sch/*Bradford*/Miami	00823216	937/448-2719	145
Brantwood Elem Sch/*Dayton*/Montgomery	00825070	937/237-4270	151
BRECKSVILLE BROADVIEW HTS CSD/ BRECKSVILLE/CUYAHOGA	00790889	440/740-4000	41
Brecksville Broadview Hts HS/*Broadview HTS/*Cuyahoga	00790891	440/740-4700	41
Brecksville Broadview Hts MS/*Broadview HTS/*Cuyahoga	00790906	440/740-4400	41
Bremen Elem Sch/*Bremen*/Fairfield	01401110	740/569-4135	63
Brent Elem Sch/*Cincinnati*/Hamilton	04028274	513/728-3720	89
Briar Middle Sch/*Sandusky*/Erie	00798568	419/625-0132	61
Brice Christian Academy/*Brice*/Franklin	10013207	614/866-6789	77
Bridge Academy/*Cleveland*/Cuyahoga	12224701	216/965-8426	53
Bridge Gate Cmty Sch/*Columbus*/Franklin	12259641	614/501-3820	1
Bridgeport Elem Sch/*Bridgeport*/Belmont	00785729	740/635-0853	18
Bridgeport Elem Sch/*Hamilton*/Butler	00786448	513/868-5580	22
Bridgeport High Sch/*Bridgeport*/Belmont	00785705	740/635-0853	18
Bridgeport Middle Sch/*Bridgeport*/Belmont	05342140	740/635-0853	18
BRIDGEPORT SCH DIST/BRIDGEPORT/ BELMONT	00785690	740/635-1713	18
Bridges Cmty Academy/*Tiffin*/Seneca	05381847	419/455-9295	1
Bridges Learning Center/*Akron*/Summit	11453313	330/794-4191	191
Bridgetown Middle Sch/*Cincinnati*/Hamilton	00807353	513/574-3511	92
Bridgeway Academy/*Columbus*/Franklin	11978179	614/262-7520	77
Briggs High Sch/*Columbus*/Franklin	01399206	614/365-5915	67
Bright Beginnings Pre-School/*Cambridge/*Guernsey	04026056	740/435-0320	85
Bright Elem Sch/*Hillsboro*/Highland	00810922	937/927-7010	102
BRIGHT LOCAL SCH DIST/MOWRYSTOWN/ HIGHLAND	00810910	937/442-3114	102
Brimfield Elem Sch/*Kent*/Portage	00828321	330/673-8581	165
Bristol Elem Sch/*Bristolville*/Trumbull	01755519	330/889-2621	197
Bristol High Sch/*Bristolville*/Trumbull	00835879	330/889-2621	197
BRISTOL LOCAL SCH DIST/BRISTOLVILLE/ TRUMBULL	00835855	330/889-3882	197
Britton Elem Sch/*Hilliard*/Franklin	03246112	614/921-5300	72
Broadleigh Elem Sch/*Columbus*/Franklin	00799770	614/365-6144	67
Broadmoor Sch/*Mentor*/Lake	02052126	440/602-1000	112
Broadway Academy/*Cleveland*/Cuyahoga	04876021	216/271-7747	1
Broadway Elem Sch/*Tipp City*/Miami	00823541	937/667-6216	146
Brook Intermediate Sch/*Byesville*/Guernsey	02947595	740/685-2526	86
Brook Park Memorial Elem Sch/*Brookpark/*Cuyahoga	00790657	216/433-1350	41
Brookfield Elem Sch/*Brookfield*/Trumbull	00835922	330/619-5240	197
Brookfield High Sch/*Brookfield*/Trumbull	00835908	330/448-3001	197
BROOKFIELD LOCAL SCH DIST/ BROOKFIELD/TRUMBULL	00835881	330/448-4930	197
Brookfield Middle Sch/*Brookfield*/Trumbull	00835910	330/448-3003	197
BROOKLYN CITY SCH DIST/BROOKLYN/ CUYAHOGA	00790956	216/485-8100	41
Brooklyn High Sch/*Brooklyn*/Cuyahoga	00790968	216/485-8162	41
Brooklyn Sch/*Brooklyn*/Cuyahoga	00790970	216/485-8176	41
Brookpark Middle Sch/*Grove City*/Franklin	00801830	614/801-3500	73
Brooks Yates Sch/*Circleville*/Pickaway	02052396	740/474-1124	162
Brookside Elem Sch/*Columbus*/Franklin	00802511	614/450-5300	75
Brookside High Sch/*Sheffield VLG*/Lorain	00816706	440/949-4220	126
Brookside Intermediate Sch/*Sheffield VLG/*Lorain	00816691	440/949-4237	126
Brookside Middle Sch/*Sheffield VLG*/Lorain	00816732	440/949-4228	126
Brookview Elem Sch/*Brookpark*/Cuyahoga	00790669	216/676-4334	41
Brookville Elem Sch/*Brookville*/Montgomery	00823943	937/833-6796	148
Brookville High Sch/*Brookville*/Montgomery	00823929	937/833-6761	148
Brookville Intermediate Sch/*Brookville/*Montgomery	00823931	937/833-6731	148
BROOKVILLE LOCAL SCH DIST/ BROOKVILLE/MONTGOMERY	00823905	937/833-2181	148
Brookwood Academy/*Columbus*/Franklin	11925342	614/231-1199	1
Brookwood Elem Sch/*Rossville*/Butler	00786450	513/868-5590	22
BROWN CO ED SERVICE CENTER/ GEORGETOWN/BROWN	00786254	937/378-6118	19
Brown Elem Sch/*Hilliard*/Franklin	00801751	614/921-5400	72

OH-V4 **800-333-8802** **School Year 2019-2020**

Ohio School Directory
DISTRICT & SCHOOL TELEPHONE INDEX

School/City/County DISTRICT/CITY/COUNTY	PID	TELEPHONE NUMBER	PAGE
BROWN LOCAL SCH DIST/*Malvern*/ **CARROLL**	00787246	330/863-1355	25
Brown Middle Sch/*Ravenna*/Portage	00828515	330/296-3849	166
Bruce Elem Sch/*Eaton*/Preble	00828917	937/456-3874	168
BRUNSWICK CITY SCH DIST/ **BRUNSWICK/MEDINA**	00822119	330/225-7731	140
Brunswick High Sch/*Brunswick*/Medina	00822133	330/273-0496	140
Brush High Sch/*Lyndhurst*/Cuyahoga	00794732	216/691-2065	51
BRYAN CITY SCH DIST/*Bryan*/ **WILLIAMS**	00839643	419/636-6973	214
Bryan Elem Sch/*Bryan*/Williams	00839679	419/636-6931	214
Bryan Middle High Sch/*Bryan*/Williams	00839655	419/636-4536	214
Bryden Elem Sch/*Beachwood*/Cuyahoga	00790504	216/831-3933	40
Buchtel Community Learning Ctr/*Akron*/ Summit	00833895	330/761-7945	191
Buckeye Career Center/*New Phila*/Tuscarawas	01420362	330/339-2288	201
Buckeye Central Elem Sch/*New Washingtn*/ Crawford	00831718	419/492-1022	38
Buckeye Central High Sch/*New Washingtn*/ Crawford	00790023	419/492-2266	38
BUCKEYE CENTRAL LOCAL SCH DIST/ **NEW WASHINGTN/CRAWFORD**	00790011	419/492-2864	38
Buckeye Central Middle Sch/*New Washingtn*/ Crawford	00790035	419/492-1035	38
Buckeye Elem Sch/*Painesville*/Lake	00813546	440/352-2191	114
Buckeye Elem Sch/*Salem*/Columbiana	00789543	330/332-8917	35
Buckeye High Sch/*Medina*/Medina	00822200	330/722-8257	140
Buckeye Hills Career Center/*Rio Grande*/ Gallia	01417418	740/245-5334	80
Buckeye Intermediate Sch/*Medina*/Medina	00822236	330/722-8257	140
BUCKEYE JOINT VOC SCH DIST/ **NEW PHILA/TUSCARAWAS**	00837580	330/339-2288	201
Buckeye Junior High Sch/*Medina*/Medina	00822212	330/722-8257	140
Buckeye Local High Sch/*Rayland*/Jefferson	00812190	740/859-2196	108
Buckeye Local Jr High Sch/*Rayland*/ Jefferson	00812229	740/859-2196	108
BUCKEYE LOCAL SCH DIST/**ASHTABULA**/ **ASHTABULA**	00784529	440/998-4411	12
BUCKEYE LOCAL SCH DIST/**DILLONVALE**/ **JEFFERSON**	00812102	740/769-7395	108
BUCKEYE LOCAL SCH DIST/**MEDINA**/ **MEDINA**	00822195	330/722-8257	140
Buckeye Middle Sch/*Columbus*/Franklin	00799794	614/365-5417	67
Buckeye Online Sch-Success/*E Liverpool*/ Columbiana	05381859	330/385-1987	33
Buckeye Preparatory Academy/*Columbus*/ Franklin	12100557	614/300-3685	1
Buckeye Primary Sch/*Medina*/Medina	00822248	330/722-8257	140
Buckeye Ranch Sch/*Grove City*/Franklin	02857354	614/539-6456	73
Buckeye Trail Elem Sch/*Lore City*/Guernsey	00805252	740/489-5100	86
Buckeye Trail High Sch/*Lore City*/Guernsey	00805276	740/489-5005	86
Buckeye Trail Middle Sch/*Lore City*/ Guernsey	12037821	740/489-5005	86
Buckeye Valley East Elem Sch/*Ashley*/ Delaware	00798178	740/747-2266	58
Buckeye Valley High Sch/*Delaware*/Delaware	00798192	740/363-1349	58
BUCKEYE VALLEY LOCAL SCH DIST/ **DELAWARE/DELAWARE**	00798166	740/369-8735	58
Buckeye Valley Middle Sch/*Delaware*/ Delaware	00798219	740/363-6626	58
Buckeye Valley West Elem Sch/*Ostrander*/ Delaware	00798207	740/666-2731	58
Buckeye Woods Elem Sch/*Grove City*/Franklin	04366698	614/801-8025	73
Buckskin Elem Sch/*South Salem*/Highland	00810996	937/981-2673	103
BUCYRUS CITY SCH DIST/*Bucyrus*/ **CRAWFORD**	00790059	419/562-4045	38
Bucyrus Elem Sch/*Bucyrus*/Crawford	00790114	419/562-6089	38
Bucyrus Secondary Sch/*Bucyrus*/Crawford	00790061	419/562-7721	38
Budd Elem Sch/*Loudonville*/Ashland	00784268	419/994-3327	11
Buhrer Dual Language Elem Sch/*Cleveland*/ Cuyahoga	00791235	216/838-8350	43
Bulldog Online Academy/*Stow*/Summit	12172641	330/689-5443	194
Bundy Elem Sch/*Wellston*/Jackson	00812061	740/384-6245	108
Bunsold Middle Sch/*Marysville*/Union	00837695	937/578-6400	204
Burlington Elem Sch/*South Point*/Lawrence	00814461	740/894-4230	116
Burroughs Elem Sch/*Columbus*/Franklin	00799809	614/365-5923	67
Burroughs Elem Sch/*Toledo*/Lucas	00817372	419/671-2350	129
Burton Elem Sch/*Burton*/Geauga	00804076	440/834-3380	81
BUTLER CO ED SERVICE CENTER/ **HAMILTON/BUTLER**	00787234	513/887-3710	20
Butler Elem Sch/*Butler*/Richland	00829428	419/883-3451	171
Butler High Sch/*Vandalia*/Montgomery	00825642	937/415-6300	153
Butler Middle Sch/*Arcanum*/Darke	00797538	937/692-5174	55
Butler Tech Career Center/*Hamilton*/Butler	01483065	513/868-6300	21
BUTLER TECH CAREER DEV SCHS/ **HAMILTON/BUTLER**	01483053	513/868-6300	21
Byesville Elem Sch/*Byesville*/Guernsey	00805185	740/685-2523	86
Byrnedale Elem Sch/*Toledo*/Lucas	01531909	419/671-2200	129

C

School/City/County DISTRICT/CITY/COUNTY	PID	TELEPHONE NUMBER	PAGE
C F Holliday Elem Sch/*Dayton*/Montgomery	00825850	937/859-5121	153
C H Campbell Elem Sch/*Canfield*/Mahoning	00819930	330/533-5959	134
C L Warstler Elem Sch/*N Canton*/Stark	00833534	330/491-3770	188
C O Harrison Elem Sch/*Cincinnati*/Hamilton	00807365	513/922-1485	92
C R Towslee Elem Sch/*Brunswick*/Medina	00822145	330/273-0487	140
C Ray Williams Early Chldhd/*Columbus*/ Franklin	04450316	614/417-5680	75
C2RA at Lehman/*Canton*/Stark	00832566	330/456-1963	184
Caldwell Elem Sch/*Caldwell*/Noble	00826907	740/732-4614	158
CALDWELL EXEMPTED VILLAGE SD/ **CALDWELL/NOBLE**	00826878	740/732-5637	158
Caldwell High Sch/*Caldwell*/Noble	00826892	740/732-5634	158
Caledonia Elem Sch/*E Cleveland*/Cuyahoga	00793049	216/268-6690	45
Calumet Christian Sch/*Columbus*/Franklin	03184227	614/261-8136	77
Calvary Christian Sch/*Bellefontaine*/Logan	02165280	937/599-6847	121
Calvert Catholic Schools/*Tiffin*/Seneca	00818326	419/447-3844	182
CAMBRIDGE CITY SCH DIST/ **CAMBRIDGE/GUERNSEY**	00805018	740/439-5021	86
Cambridge High Sch/*Cambridge*/Guernsey	00805020	740/435-1100	86
Cambridge Interm Sch/*Cambridge*/Guernsey	00805068	740/435-1180	86
Cambridge Middle Sch/*Cambridge*/Guernsey	00805032	740/435-1140	86
Cambridge Primary Sch/*Cambridge*/Guernsey	00805070	740/439-7547	86
Camden Primary Sch/*Camden*/Preble	00828967	937/452-1204	168
CAMPBELL CITY SCH DIST/**CAMPBELL**/ **MAHONING**	00819875	330/799-8777	134
Campbell K-7 Sch/*Campbell*/Mahoning	00819904	330/799-5211	134
Campus International Sch North/*Cleveland*/ Cuyahoga	11697545	216/838-8000	43
Campus International Sch South/*Cleveland*/ Cuyahoga	12231390	216/838-8100	43
Canaan Middle Sch/*Plain City*/Madison	00819526	614/733-3975	132
Canal Winchester High Sch/*Canal Wnchstr*/ Franklin	04029371	614/833-2157	66
CANAL WINCHESTER LOCAL SD/ **CANAL WNCHSTR/FRANKLIN**	00799574	614/837-4533	66
Canal Winchester Middle Sch/*Canal Wnchstr*/ Franklin	04029383	614/833-2151	66
Canfield High Sch/*Canfield*/Mahoning	00819942	330/533-5507	134
CANFIELD LOCAL SCH DIST/ **CANFIELD/MAHONING**	00819928	330/533-3303	134
Canfield Village Middle Sch/*Canfield*/ Mahoning	00819954	330/533-4019	134
Cans Sch/*Cincinnati*/Hamilton	12231352	513/363-6500	87
Canterbury Elem Sch/*Cleveland HTS*/Cuyahoga	00792863	216/371-7470	42
CANTON CITY SCH DIST/**CANTON**/ **STARK**	00832396	330/438-2500	184
Canton College Prep Sch/*Canton*/Stark	12043430	330/455-0498	184
Canton Country Day Sch/*Canton*/Stark	00833821	330/453-8279	190
Canton Harbor High Sch/*Canton*/Stark	05382774	330/452-8414	1
CANTON LOCAL SCH DIST/**CANTON**/ **STARK**	00832308	330/484-8010	185
Canton South High Sch/*Canton*/Stark	00832310	330/484-8000	185
Capital High Sch/*Columbus*/Franklin	11746586	614/228-2854	1
Cardinal High Sch/*Middlefield*/Geauga	00804117	440/632-0264	81
CARDINAL LOCAL SCH DIST/ **MIDDLEFIELD/GEAUGA**	00804105	440/632-0261	81
Cardinal Middle Sch/*Middlefield*/Geauga	00804129	440/632-0261	81
Cardinal Mooney High Sch/*Youngstown*/ Mahoning	00820953	330/788-5007	137
Cardinal Pacelli Sch/*Cincinnati*/Hamilton	00808175	513/321-1048	95
Cardinal Stritch Cath HS-Acad/*Oregon*/Lucas	00818338	419/693-0465	131
Cardington Interm Sch/*Cardington*/Morrow	12101109	419/864-3152	155
Cardington-Lincoln Elem Sch/*Cardington*/ Morrow	00826115	419/864-6692	155
Cardington-Lincoln High Sch/*Cardington*/ Morrow	00826127	419/864-2691	155
CARDINGTON-LINCOLN LOCAL SD/ **CARDINGTON/MORROW**	00826103	419/864-3691	155
Cardington-Lincoln Middle Sch/*Cardington*/ Morrow	04428600	419/864-0609	155
Career Readiness Academy/*West Chester*/ Butler	12312982	513/682-4117	22
Career Tech Ed Ctr Licking Co/*Newark*/ Licking	00815336	740/364-2832	118

DISTRICT & SCHOOL TELEPHONE INDEX

Market Data Retrieval

School/City/County DISTRICT/CITY/COUNTY	PID	TELEPHONE NUMBER	PAGE
Cares Center/*Mentor*/Lake	12036994	440/257-5951	113
Carey Exempted Village Sch/*Carey*/Wyandot	00840563	419/396-7922	219
CAREY EXEMPTED VILLAGE SD/ CAREY/WYANDOT	00840551	419/396-7922	219
Carlin Elem Sch/*Ravenna*/Portage	00828527	330/296-6622	166
Carlisle High Sch/*Carlisle*/Warren	00838118	937/746-4481	207
CARLISLE LOCAL SCH DIST/ CARLISLE/WARREN	00838106	937/746-0710	206
Carlton Sch/*Syracuse*/Meigs	04014106	740/992-6683	142
Carroll Co Christian Academy/*Carrollton*/Carroll	02826343	330/627-5124	25
Carroll High Sch/*Dayton*/Greene	00808187	937/253-8188	85
Carroll Hills Sch/*Carrollton*/Carroll	02051586	330/627-7651	25
Carrollton Elem Sch/*Carrollton*/Carroll	00787296	330/627-4592	25
CARROLLTON EXEMPTED VILLAGE SD/ CARROLLTON/CARROLL	00787272	330/627-2181	25
Carrollton Middle High Sch/*Carrollton*/Carroll	00787301	330/627-2134	25
Carson Elem Sch/*Newark*/Licking	00814980	740/670-7300	119
Carson Sch/*Cincinnati*/Hamilton	04934714	513/363-9800	87
Carylwood Intermediate Sch/*Bedford*/Cuyahoga	00790566	440/439-4509	41
Cas-Gerson Sch/*Cleveland*/Cuyahoga	03051565	216/694-7200	53
Cas-Jones Campus/*Cleveland*/Cuyahoga	12368292	216/741-2241	53
Case Community Learning Ctr/*Akron*/Summit	00833900	330/761-1670	191
Case Elem Sch/*Cleveland*/Cuyahoga	00791261	216/838-1350	43
Cassady Elem Sch/*Columbus*/Franklin	00799823	614/365-5456	67
Cassingham Elem Sch/*Bexley*/Franklin	00799548	614/237-4266	66
Castle High Sch/*Cleveland*/Cuyahoga	11007471	216/583-5210	1
Catholic Central ES-Limestone/*Springfield*/Clark	00809569	937/399-5451	29
Catholic Central High Sch/*Steubenville*/Jefferson	00812695	740/264-5538	110
Catholic Central Jr Sr HS/*Springfield*/Clark	00808216	937/325-9204	29
Catholic Central Sch/*Springfield*/Clark	00808981	937/324-4551	29
CEDAR CLIFF LOCAL SCH DIST/ CEDARVILLE/GREENE	00804569	937/766-6000	84
Cedar Leadership Sch/*Canton*/Stark	00832463	330/580-3502	184
Cedarville Elem Sch/*Cedarville*/Greene	00804571	937/766-3811	84
Cedarville Middle High Sch/*Cedarville*/Greene	03247116	937/766-1871	84
Cedarwood Elem Sch/*Columbus*/Franklin	00799835	614/365-5421	67
Celeryville Christian Sch/*Willard*/Huron	00811873	419/935-3633	107
CELINA CITY SCH DIST/CELINA/ MERCER	00822793	419/586-8300	143
Celina Elem Sch/*Celina*/Mercer	00822846	419/586-8300	143
Celina High Sch/*Celina*/Mercer	00822808	419/586-8300	143
Celina Intermediate Sch/*Celina*/Mercer	04807355	419/586-8300	143
Celina Middle Sch/*Celina*/Mercer	00822810	419/586-8300	143
Celina Primary Sch/*Celina*/Mercer	00822822	419/586-8300	143
Centennial High Sch/*Columbus*/Franklin	01531856	614/365-5491	67
Centerburg Elem Sch/*Centerburg*/Knox	00812920	740/625-6488	110
Centerburg High Sch/*Centerburg*/Knox	00812932	740/625-6055	110
CENTERBURG LOCAL SCH DIST/ CENTERBURG/KNOX	00812918	740/625-6346	110
CENTERVILLE CITY SCH DIST/ CENTERVILLE/MONTGOMERY	00823955	937/433-8841	148
Centerville High Sch/*Centerville*/Montgomery	00823967	937/439-3500	148
Centerville Prim Vlg Sch North/*Centerville*/Montgomery	03391389	937/438-6062	148
Centerville Prim Vlg Sch South/*Centerville*/Montgomery	11075612	937/312-1273	148
Central Academy/*Middletown*/Butler	03327223	513/420-4537	23
Central Academy of Ohio/*Toledo*/Lucas	11135975	419/205-9800	1
Central Baptist Academy/*Cincinnati*/Hamilton	00807987	513/521-5481	96
Central Catholic High Sch/*Canton*/Stark	00820977	330/478-2131	189
Central Catholic High Sch/*Toledo*/Lucas	00818340	419/255-2280	131
Central Christian Sch/*Kidron*/Wayne	00839605	330/857-7311	214
Central College Christian Acad/*Westerville*/Franklin	05008904	614/882-2347	77
Central Crossing High Sch/*Grove City*/Franklin	05092486	614/801-6500	73
Central Elem Sch/*Lexington*/Richland	00829492	419/884-1308	172
Central Elem Sch/*Logan*/Hocking	00811251	740/380-4664	104
Central Elem Sch/*Mc Arthur*/Vinton	00838053	740/596-4386	206
Central Elem Sch/*New Phila*/Tuscarawas	00837346	330/364-0700	203
Central Elem Sch/*Reading*/Hamilton	00807585	513/554-1001	93
Central High Sch/*Columbus*/Franklin	12259653	614/362-7530	1
Central Intermediate Sch/*Wadsworth*/Medina	04916920	330/335-1480	141

School/City/County DISTRICT/CITY/COUNTY	PID	TELEPHONE NUMBER	PAGE
CENTRAL LOCAL SCH DIST/SHERWOOD/ DEFIANCE	00797851	419/658-2808	57
Central Middle Sch/*Euclid*/Cuyahoga	00793142	216/797-5300	46
Central Primary Sch/*Bedford*/Cuyahoga	00790578	440/439-4225	41
Central Trail Elem Sch/*Sylvania*/Lucas	00817217	419/824-8610	129
Cesar Chavez College Prep Sch/*Columbus*/Franklin	11016604	614/294-3020	1
Cesar Chavez North Sch/*Columbus*/Franklin	05010309	614/294-3020	65
CHAGRIN FALLS EXEMPTED VLG SD/ CHAGRIN FALLS/CUYAHOGA	00790994	440/247-5500	42
Chagrin Falls High Sch/*Chagrin Falls*/Cuyahoga	00791003	440/247-2583	42
Chagrin Falls Intermediate Sch/*Chagrin Falls*/Cuyahoga	04866076	440/893-7691	42
Chagrin Falls Middle Sch/*Chagrin Falls*/Cuyahoga	00791015	440/893-7695	42
Chamberlain Middle Sch/*Carlisle*/Warren	00838132	937/746-3227	207
Chamberlin Hill Interm Sch/*Findlay*/Hancock	00809882	419/425-8328	98
Chambers Elem Sch/*E Cleveland*/Cuyahoga	00793051	216/268-6640	45
Chaminade Julienne High Sch/*Dayton*/Montgomery	00808228	937/461-3740	154
Champion High Sch/*Warren*/Trumbull	00835960	330/847-2305	197
Champion K-8 Elementery Sch/*Warren*/Trumbull	00835958	330/847-2328	197
CHAMPION LOCAL SCH DIST/ WARREN/TRUMBULL	00835946	330/847-2330	197
Champion Middle Sch/*Columbus*/Franklin	00799859	614/365-6082	67
Chaney High Sch/*Youngstown*/Mahoning	00820484	330/744-8822	136
Chapel Hill Chrn School-North/*Cuyahoga FLS*/Summit	00835738	330/929-1901	196
Chapel Hill Chrn School-South/*Akron*/Summit	02123103	330/896-0852	196
Chapelfield Elem Sch/*Gahanna*/Franklin	00801402	614/478-5575	70
Chapelside Cleveland Academy/*Cleveland*/Cuyahoga	04815247	216/283-6589	1
Chardon High Sch/*Chardon*/Geauga	00804179	440/285-4057	82
Chardon Hills Magnet Sch/*Euclid*/Cuyahoga	11824645	216/797-6400	46
CHARDON LOCAL SCH DIST/CHARDON/ GEAUGA	00804167	440/285-4052	82
Chardon Middle Sch/*Chardon*/Geauga	00804181	440/285-4062	82
Charity Adams Earley Girl Acad/*Dayton*/Montgomery	10005303	937/542-5840	149
Charles A Mooney Sch/*Cleveland*/Cuyahoga	00791285	216/838-3200	43
Charles Dickens at Corlett/*Cleveland*/Cuyahoga	00791297	216/838-4200	43
Charles Huber Elem Sch/*Huber Heights*/Montgomery	00825795	937/237-6375	150
Charles Krout Elem Sch/*Tiffin*/Seneca	00831756	419/447-2652	181
Charles L Seipelt Elem Sch/*Milford*/Clermont	00788604	513/831-9460	31
Charles Sch at Ohio Dominican/*Columbus*/Franklin	11136084	614/258-8588	66
Charles W Eliot Elem Sch/*Cleveland*/Cuyahoga	00791314	216/838-5350	43
Chase Sch/*Cincinnati*/Hamilton	00805446	513/363-1300	87
Chase Stemm Academy/*Toledo*/Lucas	00817384	419/671-6650	129
Chaviva High Sch/*Cleveland*/Cuyahoga	12361335	216/303-9574	53
Chca-Edyth B Lindner Elem Sch/*Cincinnati*/Hamilton	11728845	513/247-0900	96
Chca-Founders Campus Upper Sch/*Cincinnati*/Hamilton	11728857	513/247-0900	96
Chca-Martha S Lindner High Sch/*Cincinnati*/Hamilton	03276260	513/247-0900	96
Chca-Otto Armleder Mem Ed Ctr/*Cincinnati*/Hamilton	11728869	513/721-2422	96
Cherokee Elem Sch/*Liberty Twp*/Butler	04282042	513/755-8200	22
Cherrington Elem Sch/*Westerville*/Franklin	00802298	614/797-7050	74
Cherry Hill Primary Sch/*Wshngtn Ct Hs*/Fayette	00799471	740/335-3370	65
Cherry Valley Elem Sch/*Newark*/Licking	00814966	740/670-7330	119
Chesapeake Elem Sch/*Chesapeake*/Lawrence	00814162	740/867-3448	115
Chesapeake High Sch/*Chesapeake*/Lawrence	00814148	740/867-5958	115
Chesapeake Middle Sch/*Chesapeake*/Lawrence	00814150	740/867-3972	115
CHESAPEAKE UNION EXEMPT VLG SD/ CHESAPEAKE/LAWRENCE	00814136	740/867-3135	115
Chesire Elem Sch/*Delaware*/Delaware	11552957	740/657-5750	59
Chess Christian Sch/*Centerville*/Montgomery	12113671	937/343-1130	154
Chestnut Elem Sch/*Painesville*/Lake	00813651	440/392-5350	113
Chestnut Intermediate Sch/*North Olmsted*/Cuyahoga	04941327	440/779-3641	48
Chestnut Ridge Elem Sch/*Berlin*/Holmes	00811304	330/893-2413	104
Cheviot Elem Sch/*Cincinnati*/Hamilton	00805458	513/363-1400	87
Chieftain Elem Sch/*Logan*/Hocking	00811225	740/385-1171	104

Ohio School Directory

DISTRICT & SCHOOL TELEPHONE INDEX

School/City/County DISTRICT/CITY/COUNTY	PID	TELEPHONE NUMBER	PAGE
Childhood League Center/*Columbus*/Franklin	02236580	614/253-6933	77
Children's Academy/*Columbus*/Franklin	04157291	614/491-3270	77
Children's Home Sch/*Cincinnati*/Hamilton	01464928	513/272-2800	96
Children's Mtng House Mont Sch/*Loveland*/ Clermont	02951132	513/683-4757	32
Children's Resource Center/*Bowling Green*/ Wood	04012237	419/352-7588	216
CHILLICOTHE CITY SCH DIST/ **CHILLICOTHE/ROSS**	00830128	740/775-4250	174
Chillicothe High Sch/*Chillicothe*/Ross	00830154	740/702-2287	174
Chillicothe Intermediate Sch/*Chillicothe*/ Ross	00830219	740/774-1119	174
Chillicothe Middle Sch/*Chillicothe*/Ross	00830207	740/773-2241	174
Chillicothe Primary Sch/*Chillicothe*/Ross	00830130	740/774-3307	175
Chippewa Elem Sch/*Brecksville*/Cuyahoga	00790918	440/740-4200	41
Chippewa Intermediate Sch/*Doylestown*/Wayne	00839021	330/658-2214	211
Chippewa Jr Sr High Sch/*Doylestown*/Wayne	00839019	330/658-6368	211
CHIPPEWA LOCAL SCH DIST/ **DOYLESTOWN/WAYNE**	00839007	330/658-6368	211
Choffin Career & Technical Ctr/*Youngstown*/ Mahoning	00820496	330/744-8700	136
Choices Alternative Sch/*Canton*/Stark	11449271	330/456-1189	184
Christ the King Sch/*Toledo*/Lucas	00818352	419/475-0909	131
Christian Academy Sch/*Sidney*/Shelby	02193718	937/492-7556	183
Christian Community Sch/*Grafton*/Lorain	04881193	440/748-6224	126
Christian Life Academy/*Jackson*/Jackson	02209123	740/286-1234	108
Christian Life Church Academy/*Westerville*/ Delaware	11460940	614/794-2529	60
Christian Star Academy/*Mount Vernon*/Knox	02951182	740/393-0251	111
Christie Lane Sch/*Norwalk*/Huron	02052073	419/668-8840	105
Church of God Academy/*Greenville*/Darke	11710719	937/316-7777	56
Cincinnati Christian Elem Sch/*Fairfield*/ Butler	01409629	513/874-8500	24
Cincinnati Christian High Sch/*Hamilton*/ Butler	05364801	513/892-8500	24
CINCINNATI CITY SCH DIST/ **CINCINNATI/HAMILTON**	00805290	513/363-0000	87
Cincinnati College Prep Acad/*Cincinnati*/ Hamilton	04880216	513/684-0777	1
Cincinnati Country Day Sch/*Cincinnati*/ Hamilton	03155630	513/561-7298	96
Cincinnati Digital Academy/*Cincinnati*/ Hamilton	11926839	513/363-2040	87
Cincinnati Hebrew Day Sch/*Cincinnati*/ Hamilton	00807999	513/351-7777	96
Cincinnati Junior Academy/*Cincinnati*/ Hamilton	00808008	513/751-1255	96
Cincinnati Waldorf Sch/*Cincinnati*/Hamilton	02653938	513/541-0220	96
Cinday Academy/*Springboro*/Warren	11714428	937/748-1991	209
CIRCLEVILLE CITY SCH DIST/ **CIRCLEVILLE/PICKAWAY**	00827664	740/474-4340	162
Circleville Elem Sch/*Circleville*/Pickaway	12031798	740/474-2495	162
Circleville High Sch/*Circleville*/Pickaway	00827688	740/474-4846	162
Circleville Middle Sch/*Circleville*/ Pickaway	00827690	740/474-2345	162
Citizens Academy/*Cleveland*/Cuyahoga	04870728	216/791-4195	39
Citizens Academy East/*Cleveland*/Cuyahoga	11915995	216/367-9392	39
Citizens Academy Southeast/*Cleveland*/ Cuyahoga	12230023	216/586-3887	39
Citizens Leadership Acad East/*Cleveland*/ Cuyahoga	12240054	216/352-5900	1
Citizens Leadership Academy/*Cleveland*/ Cuyahoga	11744069	216/229-8185	1
City Day Community Sch/*Dayton*/Montgomery	04880228	937/223-8130	1
Claggett Middle Sch/*Medina*/Medina	00822420	330/636-3600	141
Clara E Westropp Elem Sch/*Cleveland*/ Cuyahoga	00791352	216/267-3706	43
Clarendon Leadership Sch/*Canton*/Stark	00832475	330/453-7681	184
CLARK CO ED SERVICE CENTER/ **SPRINGFIELD/CLARK**	00788288	937/325-7671	27
Clark Elem Sch/*Cleveland*/Cuyahoga	00791376	216/838-7300	43
Clark Montessori Sch/*Cincinnati*/Hamilton	04754409	513/363-7100	87
Clark Pre-School/*Springfield*/Clark	11711103	937/505-4170	28
Clark Preparatory Academy/*Springfield*/ Clark	12160777	937/504-1175	1
CLARK-SHAWNEE LOCAL SCH DIST/ **SPRINGFIELD/CLARK**	00788226	937/328-5378	27
Clarksfield SDA Sch/*Wakeman*/Huron	01465087	419/929-7833	107
Clay High Sch/*Oregon*/Lucas	00817047	419/693-0665	128
Clay Local Sch/*Portsmouth*/Scioto	00830922	740/354-6644	178
CLAY LOCAL SCH DIST/PORTSMOUTH/ **SCIOTO**	00830910	740/354-6645	178
CLAYMONT CITY SCH DIST/DENNISON/ **TUSCARAWAS**	00837061	740/922-5478	201
Claymont Elem Sch/*Uhrichsville*/Tuscarawas	00837097	740/922-4641	202
Claymont High Sch/*Uhrichsville*/Tuscarawas	00837073	740/922-3471	202
Claymont Intermediate Sch/*Dennison*/ Tuscarawas	00837102	740/922-1901	202
Claymont Middle Sch/*Uhrichsville*/ Tuscarawas	00837085	740/922-5241	202
Claymont Preschool/*Dennison*/Tuscarawas	11072361	740/922-5888	202
Claymont Primary Sch/*Uhrichsville*/ Tuscarawas	00837138	740/922-5641	202
Clear Fork High Sch/*Bellville*/Richland	00829430	419/886-2601	171
Clear Fork Middle Sch/*Bellville*/Richland	04865072	419/886-3111	171
CLEAR FORK VLY LOCAL SCH DIST/ **BELLVILLE/RICHLAND**	00829404	419/886-3855	171
Clearcreek Elem Sch/*Springboro*/Warren	00838168	937/748-3958	208
Clearmount Elem Sch/*North Canton*/Stark	00833259	330/497-5640	187
Clearview High Sch/*Lorain*/Lorain	00815817	440/233-6313	123
CLEARVIEW LOCAL SCH DIST/ **LORAIN/LORAIN**	00815805	440/233-5412	123
CLERMONT CO ED SERVICE CENTER/ **BATAVIA/CLERMONT**	00788850	513/735-8300	29
Clermont Co Hearing Hndcp Unit/*Amelia*/ Clermont	04020727	513/943-8980	29
Clermont Educ Collaborative-N/*Milford*/ Clermont	12113372	513/735-8302	29
Clermont Educ Collaborative-S/*Williamsburg*/ Clermont	12113384	513/724-8555	29
Clermont Northeastern Elem Sch/*Batavia*/ Clermont	00788446	513/625-1211	30
Clermont Northeastern High Sch/*Batavia*/ Clermont	00788408	513/625-1211	30
CLERMONT NORTHEASTERN LOCAL SD/ **BATAVIA/CLERMONT**	00788393	513/625-1211	30
Clermont Northeastern Mid Sch/*Batavia*/ Clermont	00788422	513/625-1211	30
Cleveland Arts & Soc Sci Acad/*Cleveland*/ Cuyahoga	11223314	216/229-3000	1
Cleveland Central Catholic HS/*Cleveland*/ Cuyahoga	00795463	216/441-4700	52
Cleveland Christian Home Ctr/*Cleveland*/ Cuyahoga	12368307	216/416-4277	53
Cleveland College Prep/*Cleveland*/Cuyahoga	11566843	216/341-1347	39
Cleveland Early College HS/*Cleveland*/ Cuyahoga	05279969	216/838-8250	43
Cleveland Heights High Sch/*Cleveland HTS*/ Cuyahoga	10017643	216/371-7101	42
Cleveland HS for Digital Arts/*Cleveland*/ Cuyahoga	12168638	216/838-9650	43
CLEVELAND HTS-UNIV HTS CITY SD/ **UNIVERSITY HT/CUYAHOGA**	00792825	216/371-7171	42
CLEVELAND METRO SCH DIST/ **CLEVELAND/CUYAHOGA**	00791041	216/838-0000	42
Cleveland PK-6 Sch/*Dayton*/Montgomery	00824466	937/542-4340	149
Cleveland Preparatory Academy/*Cleveland*/ Cuyahoga	12259665	216/741-2991	1
Cleveland Sch of Arch & Design/*Cleveland*/ Cuyahoga	10029036	216/838-8200	43
Cleveland Sch of Science & Med/*Cleveland*/ Cuyahoga	10029048	216/838-8300	43
Cleveland School of the Arts/*Cleveland*/ Cuyahoga	02201004	216/838-9000	43
Cliff Park High Sch/*Springfield*/Clark	12160818	937/342-3006	1
Clifton Area Neighborhd Sch/*Cincinnati*/ Hamilton	12364624	513/363-2200	87
Clinton Elem Sch/*Columbus*/Franklin	00799897	614/365-6532	67
Clinton-Massie Elem Sch/*Clarksville*/ Clinton	11557610	937/289-2515	33
Clinton-Massie High Sch/*Clarksville*/ Clinton	00788953	937/289-2109	33
CLINTON-MASSIE LOCAL SCH DIST/ **CLARKSVILLE/CLINTON**	00788939	937/289-2471	33
Clinton-Massie Middle Sch/*Clarksville*/ Clinton	11560136	937/289-2932	33
Clintonville Academy/*Columbus*/Franklin	02148610	614/267-4799	77
Clough Pike Elem Sch/*Cincinnati*/Clermont	00788733	513/943-6700	31
Cloverleaf Elem Sch/*Seville*/Medina	00822303	330/302-0103	140
Cloverleaf High Sch/*Lodi*/Medina	00822274	330/948-2500	140
CLOVERLEAF LOCAL SCH DIST/ **LODI/MEDINA**	00822250	330/948-2500	140
Cloverleaf Middle Sch/*Seville*/Medina	00822286	330/302-0207	140
Clyde Elem Sch/*Clyde*/Sandusky	00830532	419/547-9868	176

School Year 2019-2020   800-333-8802   OH-V7

DISTRICT & SCHOOL TELEPHONE INDEX

Market Data Retrieval

School/City/County DISTRICT/CITY/COUNTY	PID	TELEPHONE NUMBER	PAGE
Clyde High Sch/*Clyde*/Sandusky	00830506	419/547-9511	176
CLYDE-GREEN SPGS EXMPT VLG SD/ **CLYDE/SANDUSKY**	00830491	419/547-0588	176
Coldwater Elem Sch/*Coldwater*/Mercer	03321554	419/678-2613	143
COLDWATER EXEMPTED VILLAGE SD/ **COLDWATER/MERCER**	00822858	419/678-2611	143
Coldwater High Sch/*Coldwater*/Mercer	00822860	419/678-4821	143
Coldwater Middle Sch/*Coldwater*/Mercer	04800929	419/678-3331	143
Colerain Elem Sch/*Cincinnati*/Hamilton	00807145	513/385-8740	91
Colerain High Sch/*Cincinnati*/Hamilton	00807157	513/385-6424	91
Colerain Middle Sch/*Cincinnati*/Hamilton	00807169	513/385-8490	91
Colerain Sch/*Columbus*/Franklin	00799914	614/365-6001	67
College Hill Fundamental Acad/*Cincinnati*/Hamilton	00805496	513/363-1600	87
Collins Career Center/*Chesapeake*/Lawrence	01548110	740/867-6641	116
Colonel Crawford High Sch/*N Robinson*/Crawford	00790152	419/562-4666	38
COLONEL CRAWFORD LOCAL SD/ **N ROBINSON/CRAWFORD**	00790140	419/562-6755	38
Colonial Hills Elem Sch/*Worthington*/Franklin	00802523	614/450-5400	75
Colonial Preparatory Academy/*Akron*/Summit	12043521	330/752-2792	1
Columbia Elem Sch/*Mount Vernon*/Knox	00813065	740/393-5975	111
Columbia High Sch/*Columbia Sta*/Lorain	00815879	440/236-5001	123
Columbia Intermediate Sch/*Kings Mills*/Warren	04747690	513/398-8050	207
COLUMBIA LOCAL SCH DIST/ **COLUMBIA STA/LORAIN**	00815855	440/236-5008	123
Columbia Middle Sch/*Columbia Sta*/Lorain	00815881	440/236-5741	123
Columbian Senior High Sch/*Tiffin*/Seneca	00831732	419/447-6331	181
Columbiana Co Career Tech Ctr/*Lisbon*/Columbiana	01601499	330/424-9561	34
Columbiana Co Ed Center/*Lisbon*/Columbiana	04338823	330/424-9591	33
COLUMBIANA CO ED SERVICE CTR/ **LISBON/COLUMBIANA**	02089131	330/424-9591	33
Columbiana Co Hi Unit/*Lisbon*/Columbiana	04338859	330/424-9591	33
Columbiana Co Opportunity Ctr/*Lisbon*/Columbiana	11225867	330/424-4047	36
Columbiana Co Orthopedic Unit/*Lisbon*/Columbiana	04338835	330/424-9591	33
Columbiana Co Pre-School Unit/*Lisbon*/Columbiana	04338847	330/424-9591	34
COLUMBIANA CO VOC SCH DIST/ **LISBON/COLUMBIANA**	01601487	330/424-9561	34
Columbiana Ed Service Center/*Lisbon*/Columbiana	04338811	330/424-9591	34
COLUMBIANA EXEMPTED VILLAGE SD/ **COLUMBIANA/COLUMBIANA**	00789191	330/482-5352	34
Columbiana High Sch/*Columbiana*/Columbiana	00789206	330/482-3818	34
Columbiana Middle Sch/*Columbiana*/Columbiana	00789220	330/482-5354	34
Columbus Academy/*Gahanna*/Franklin	00803498	614/475-2311	77
Columbus Adventist Academy/*Columbus*/Franklin	11227865	614/471-2083	77
Columbus Africentric EC 9-12/*Columbus*/Franklin	05346639	614/365-8675	67
Columbus Africentric EC K8 Sch/*Columbus*/Franklin	04459594	614/365-8675	67
Columbus Alternative High Sch/*Columbus*/Franklin	01841754	614/365-6006	67
Columbus Arts & Tech Academy/*Columbus*/Franklin	05381873	614/577-0900	1
Columbus Bilingual Acad-North/*Columbus*/Franklin	12162593	614/547-4500	1
Columbus City Prep Sch-Boys/*Columbus*/Franklin	11557490	614/365-6166	67
Columbus City Prep Sch-Girls/*Columbus*/Franklin	11557488	614/365-6113	67
COLUMBUS CITY SCH DIST/COLUMBUS/ **FRANKLIN**	00799603	614/365-5000	66
Columbus Collegiate Acad-Dana/*Columbus*/Franklin	12037120	614/545-9570	1
Columbus Collegiate Acad-Main/*Columbus*/Franklin	11156709	614/299-5284	1
Columbus Downtown High Sch/*Columbus*/Franklin	01556545	614/365-2283	67
Columbus Gifted Academy/*Columbus*/Franklin	12104917	614/365-6961	67
Columbus Global Academy/*Columbus*/Franklin	11102423	614/368-8472	67
Columbus Grove Elem Sch/*Columbus GRV*/Putnam	00829090	419/659-2631	169
Columbus Grove High Sch/*Columbus GRV*/Putnam	00829105	419/659-2156	169
COLUMBUS GROVE LOCAL SCH DIST/ **COLUMBUS GRV/PUTNAM**	00829088	419/659-2639	169
Columbus Humanties Arts & Tech/*Columbus*/Franklin	05381885	614/261-1200	1
Columbus Intermediate Sch/*Bedford HTS*/Cuyahoga	00790542	440/786-3322	41
Columbus Jewish Day Sch/*New Albany*/Franklin	04837946	614/939-5311	77
Columbus Mont Educational Ctr/*Columbus*/Franklin	03016096	614/231-3790	77
Columbus N International Sch/*Columbus*/Franklin	11557505	614/365-4054	67
Columbus Performance Academy/*Columbus*/Franklin	11566855	614/318-0720	66
Columbus Prep & Fitness Acad/*Columbus*/Franklin	10017526	614/318-0606	1
Columbus Preparatory Academy/*Columbus*/Franklin	10012174	614/275-3600	1
Columbus School for Girls/*Columbus*/Franklin	00802614	614/252-0781	77
Columbus Scioto/*Columbus*/Franklin	00799885	614/365-6085	67
Columbus Span Immersion Acad/*Columbus*/Franklin	04458526	614/365-8129	67
Columbus Torah Academy/*Columbus*/Franklin	00802626	614/864-0299	77
Communion of Saints Sch/*Cleveland HTS*/Cuyahoga	00796106	216/932-4177	52
Como Elem Sch/*Columbus*/Franklin	00799938	614/365-6013	67
Concord Elem Sch/*Troy*/Miami	00823606	937/332-6730	146
Conesville Elem Sch/*Conesville*/Coshocton	00789933	740/829-2334	37
CONNEAUT AREA CITY SCH DIST/ **CONNEAUT/ASHTABULA**	00784608	440/593-7200	12
Conneaut Elem Sch/*Bowling Green*/Wood	00839978	419/354-0300	216
Conneaut High Sch/*Conneaut*/Ashtabula	00784634	440/593-7210	12
Conneaut Middle Sch/*Conneaut*/Ashtabula	00784660	440/593-7240	12
CONNECT INFORMATION TECH CTR/ **ELYRIA/LORAIN**	04499491	440/324-3185	126
CONNECT INFORMATION TECH CTR/ **VALLEY VIEW/CUYAHOGA**	04499415	216/520-6900	54
Connections Academy/*Canton*/Stark	10028329	330/456-1189	184
Conotton Valley Elem Sch/*Bowerston*/Harrison	00810506	740/269-2141	101
Conotton Valley High Sch/*Bowerston*/Harrison	00810520	740/269-2711	101
CONOTTON VALLEY UNION LOCAL SD/ **SHERRODSVILLE/HARRISON**	00810491	740/269-2000	100
Continental Local Elem Sch/*Continental*/Putnam	00829131	419/596-3860	169
Continental Local High Sch/*Continental*/Putnam	00829143	419/596-3871	169
CONTINENTAL LOCAL SCH DIST/ **CONTINENTAL/PUTNAM**	00829129	419/596-3671	169
Cookson Elem Sch/*Troy*/Miami	00823618	937/332-6740	146
Coolville Elem Sch/*Coolville*/Athens	00785121	740/667-3121	14
Copley High Sch/*Copley*/Summit	00834708	330/664-4822	192
COPLEY-FAIRLAWN CITY SCH DIST/ **COPLEY/SUMMIT**	00834681	330/664-4800	192
Copley-Fairlawn Middle Sch/*Copley*/Summit	00834710	330/664-4875	192
Copopa Elem Sch/*Columbia Sta*/Lorain	00815893	440/236-5020	123
Cork Elem Sch/*Geneva*/Ashtabula	00784713	440/466-4831	13
Cornerstone Academy/*Westerville*/Franklin	05009116	614/775-0615	2
Cornerstone Christian Academy/*Willoughby*/Lake	12230011	440/943-9260	115
Cornerstone Community Sch/*Tallmadge*/Summit	05256735	330/686-8900	196
Cornerstone Elem Sch/*Wooster*/Wayne	00839497	330/988-1111	213
Corpus Christi Academy/*Cleveland*/Cuyahoga	12233685	440/449-4242	53
Corryville Catholic Elem Sch/*Cincinnati*/Hamilton	01539793	513/281-4856	95
Cory-Rawson Elem Sch/*Rawson*/Hancock	00809820	419/963-3415	97
Cory-Rawson High Sch/*Rawson*/Hancock	00809806	419/963-2611	97
CORY-RAWSON LOCAL SCH DIST/ **RAWSON/HANCOCK**	00809791	419/963-3415	97
Coshocton Christian Sch/*Coshocton*/Coshocton	10759009	740/622-5052	37
COSHOCTON CITY SCH DIST/ **COSHOCTON/COSHOCTON**	00789787	740/622-1901	36
Coshocton Co Career Center/*Coshocton*/Coshocton	01831591	740/622-0211	37
COSHOCTON CO JOINT VOC SD/ **COSHOCTON/COSHOCTON**	01831589	740/622-0211	37
Coshocton Elem Sch/*Coshocton*/Coshocton	00789816	740/622-5514	37
Coshocton High Sch/*Coshocton*/Coshocton	00789804	740/622-9433	37

Ohio School Directory

DISTRICT & SCHOOL TELEPHONE INDEX

School/City/County DISTRICT/CITY/COUNTY	PID	TELEPHONE NUMBER	PAGE
Coshocton Opportunity Sch/*Coshocton*/Coshocton	11547005	740/622-3600	2
Covedale Elem Sch/*Cincinnati*/Hamilton	00805525	513/363-1700	87
Coventry Elem Sch/*Akron*/Summit	00834813	330/644-8469	192
Coventry High Sch/*Akron*/Summit	04245147	330/644-3004	192
COVENTRY LOCAL SCH DIST/ AKRON/SUMMIT	00834758	330/644-8489	192
Coventry Middle Sch/*Akron*/Summit	00834772	330/644-2232	192
Covington Elem Sch/*Covington*/Miami	00823230	937/473-2252	145
COVINGTON EXEMPTED VILLAGE SD/ COVINGTON/MIAMI	00823228	937/473-2249	145
Covington High Sch/*Covington*/Miami	00823242	937/473-3746	145
Cox Elem Sch/*Xenia*/Greene	00804844	937/372-9201	85
Coy Elem Sch/*Oregon*/Lucas	00817059	419/693-0624	128
Cozaddale Baptist Academy/*Goshen*/Clermont	04987084	513/722-2064	32
Craddock Elem Sch/*Aurora*/Portage	00828187	330/562-3175	165
Cranbrook Elem Sch/*Columbus*/Franklin	00799952	614/365-5497	67
Crawford Woods Elem Sch/*Hamilton*/Butler	00786618	513/868-5600	22
Creekside Early Childhood Sch/*West Chester*/Butler	04747339	513/874-0175	22
Creekview Elem Sch/*Middletown*/Butler	00786802	513/420-4544	23
Creekview Intermediate Sch/*Marysville*/Union	04942187	937/578-6600	204
CRESTLINE EXEMPTED VILLAGE SD/ CRESTLINE/CRAWFORD	00790205	419/683-3647	38
Crestline Sch/*Crestline*/Crawford	00790217	419/683-3647	38
Crestview Elem Sch/*Ashland*/Richland	00829466	419/895-1700	171
Crestview Elem Sch/*Brunswick*/Medina	00822157	330/273-0482	140
Crestview Elem Sch/*Columbiana*/Columbiana	00789402	330/482-5370	34
Crestview High Sch/*Ashland*/Richland	00829454	419/895-1700	171
Crestview High Sch/*Columbiana*/Columbiana	00789426	330/482-4744	34
Crestview Local Sch/*Convoy*/Van Wert	00837839	419/749-9100	205
CRESTVIEW LOCAL SCH DIST/ ASHLAND/RICHLAND	00829442	419/895-1700	171
CRESTVIEW LOCAL SCH DIST/ COLUMBIANA/COLUMBIANA	00789397	330/482-5526	34
CRESTVIEW LOCAL SCH DIST/ CONVOY/VAN WERT	00837815	419/749-9100	205
Crestview Middle Sch/*Ashland*/Richland	04365656	419/895-1700	171
Crestview Middle Sch/*Columbiana*/Columbiana	00789414	330/482-4648	34
Crestwood Elem Sch/*Elyria*/Lorain	00815934	440/284-8002	123
Crestwood High Sch/*Mantua*/Portage	00828242	330/357-8205	165
Crestwood Intermediate Sch/*Mantua*/Portage	00828280	330/357-8203	165
CRESTWOOD LOCAL SCH DIST/ MANTUA/PORTAGE	00828230	330/357-8206	165
Crestwood Middle Sch/*Mantua*/Portage	00828266	330/357-8204	165
Crestwood Primary Sch/*Mantua*/Portage	00828278	330/357-8202	165
Cridersville Elem Sch/*Cridersville*/Auglaize	00785482	419/645-3000	16
Crim Elem Sch/*Bowling Green*/Wood	00839980	419/354-0400	216
Crissey Elem Sch/*Holland*/Lucas	00817152	419/867-5677	128
Cristo Rey Columbus High Sch/*Columbus*/Franklin	11914991	614/223-9261	77
Croghan Elem Sch/*Fremont*/Sandusky	00830570	419/332-1511	177
Crooksville Elem Sch/*Crooksville*/Perry	02125448	740/982-7010	161
CROOKSVILLE EXEMPTED VLG SD/ CROOKSVILLE/PERRY	00827418	740/982-7040	161
Crooksville High Sch/*Crooksville*/Perry	00827432	740/982-7015	161
Crooksville Middle Sch/*Crooksville*/Perry	12160703	740/982-7010	161
Crosby Elem Sch/*Harrison*/Hamilton	00807640	513/738-1717	93
Crossgates Pre-School/*Toledo*/Lucas	11716347	419/671-2750	129
Crossroads Christian Academy/*Circleville*/Pickaway	11225972	740/474-7265	163
Crossroads Day Treatment Ctr/*Mentor*/Lake	04020595	440/255-1700	112
Crouse Community Learning Ctr/*Akron*/Summit	00833936	330/761-1625	191
Cruiser Academy/*Groveport*/Franklin	11566958	614/237-8756	71
Currie Elem Sch/*Cortland*/Trumbull	00836043	330/637-3500	199
CUYAHOGA CO ED SERVICE CENTER/ INDEPENDENCE/CUYAHOGA	00795293	216/524-3000	39
CUYAHOGA FALLS CITY SCH DIST/ CUYAHOGA FLS/SUMMIT	00834825	330/926-3800	192
Cuyahoga Falls High Sch/*Cuyahoga FLS*/Summit	00834851	330/926-3808	192
Cuyahoga Heights Elem Sch/*Cleveland*/Cuyahoga	00793013	216/429-5880	45
Cuyahoga Heights High Sch/*Cleveland*/Cuyahoga	00793025	216/429-5707	45
CUYAHOGA HEIGHTS LOCAL SD/ CLEVELAND/CUYAHOGA	00793001	216/429-5700	45
Cuyahoga Heights Middle Sch/*Cleveland*/Cuyahoga	04028597	216/429-5757	45

School/City/County DISTRICT/CITY/COUNTY	PID	TELEPHONE NUMBER	PAGE
Cuyahoga Valley Career Center/*Brecksville*/Cuyahoga	00795281	440/526-5200	45
CUYAHOGA VLY CAREER CTR VOC SD/ BRECKSVILLE/CUYAHOGA	00795279	440/526-5200	45
Cuyahoga Vly Christian Academy/*Stow*/Summit	00835740	330/929-0575	196
Cypress Christian Sch/*Galloway*/Franklin	04885292	614/870-1181	77

D

Dale Roy Sch/*Ashland*/Ashland	02051512	419/289-7518	10
Dalton High Sch/*Dalton*/Wayne	00839069	330/828-2261	212
Dalton Local Elem Middle Sch/*Dalton*/Wayne	12031310	330/828-2405	212
DALTON LOCAL SCH DIST/DALTON/WAYNE	00839045	330/828-2267	211
Damascus Elem Sch/*Salem*/Mahoning	11078432	330/938-4500	136
Dan Emmett Elem Sch/*Mount Vernon*/Knox	00813077	740/393-5950	111
Danbury Local Sch/*Lksid Marblhd*/Ottawa	00827054	419/798-5185	159
DANBURY LOCAL SCH DIST/LKSID MARBLHD/OTTAWA	00827042	419/798-5185	159
Daniel E Morgan Elem Sch/*Cleveland*/Cuyahoga	00791431	216/838-1400	43
Daniel Wright Elem Sch/*Columbus*/Franklin	03236416	614/538-0464	69
Danville Elem Middle Sch/*Danville*/Knox	00812956	740/599-6116	110
Danville High Sch/*Danville*/Knox	00812968	740/599-6116	110
DANVILLE LOCAL SCH DIST/ DANVILLE/KNOX	00812944	740/599-6116	110
Darby Creek Elem Sch/*Hilliard*/Franklin	04753041	614/921-5500	72
Darby Woods Elem Sch/*Galloway*/Franklin	04367056	614/801-8075	73
Darbydale Elem Sch/*Darbydale*/Franklin	00801842	614/801-8050	73
DARKE CO ED SERVICE CENTER/ GREENVILLE/DARKE	00797801	937/548-4915	55
Dater Montessori Sch/*Cincinnati*/Hamilton	00805410	513/363-0900	87
Davey Elem Sch/*Kent*/Portage	00828436	330/676-7400	165
David Anderson Jr Sr High Sch/*Lisbon*/Columbiana	00789505	330/424-3215	35
David Hill Community Lrng Ctr/*Akron*/Summit	00834150	330/773-1129	191
David L Brown Youth Center/*Troy*/Miami	12161379	937/339-1858	145
David Ponitz Career Tech Ctr/*Dayton*/Montgomery	00824179	937/542-7180	149
David Smith Elem Sch/*Delaware*/Delaware	00798233	740/833-1350	58
Davis Aerospace & Maritime HS/*Cleveland*/Cuyahoga	12231405	216/838-2500	43
Daw Elem Sch/*Wellsville*/Columbiana	00789725	330/532-1372	36
Dawson-Bryant Elem Sch/*Ironton*/Lawrence	00814215	740/532-6898	115
Dawson-Bryant High Sch/*Coal Grove*/Lawrence	00814198	740/532-6345	115
DAWSON-BRYANT LOCAL SCH DIST/ COAL GROVE/LAWRENCE	00814174	740/532-6451	115
Dawson-Bryant Middle Sch/*Coal Grove*/Lawrence	00814203	740/533-6008	115
Dayton Christian Sch/*Miamisburg*/Montgomery	00825939	937/291-7201	154
Dayton Islamic Sch/*Dayton*/Montgomery	04987175	937/429-9477	154
Dayton Leadership Academy/*Dayton*/Montgomery	05009128	937/567-9426	2
Dayton Liberty Academy/*Dayton*/Montgomery	04880242	937/567-9426	2
DAYTON PUBLIC SCH DIST/DAYTON/MONTGOMERY	00824064	937/542-3000	149
Dayton Regional STEM Sch/*Dayton*/Montgomery	11930335	937/256-3777	2
Dayton Smart Bilingual Academy/*Dayton*/Montgomery	12160820	937/222-2812	2
Deca Prep/*Dayton*/Montgomery	12163133	937/610-0110	2
Decolores Mnt Jr High Farm Sch/*Greenville*/Darke	11647382	937/316-6104	56
Decolores Montessori Sch/*Greenville*/Darke	03016113	937/547-1334	56
DEER PARK CMTY SCH DIST/ CINCINNATI/HAMILTON	00806361	513/891-0222	89
Deer Park Jr Sr High Sch/*Cincinnati*/Hamilton	00806385	513/891-0010	89
Deer Run Elem Sch/*Dublin*/Franklin	02107044	614/764-5932	69
DEFIANCE CITY SCH DIST/DEFIANCE/DEFIANCE	00797916	419/782-0070	57
Defiance Elem Sch/*Defiance*/Defiance	00797928	419/785-2260	57
Defiance High Sch/*Defiance*/Defiance	00797954	419/784-2777	57
Defiance Middle Sch/*Defiance*/Defiance	00797966	419/782-0050	57
Delaware Area Career Ctr-North/*Delaware*/Delaware	00798350	740/363-1993	59
Delaware Area Career Ctr-South/*Delaware*/Delaware	04752188	740/548-0708	59
Delaware Christian Sch/*Delaware*/Delaware	01795997	740/363-8425	60
DELAWARE CITY SCH DIST/DELAWARE/DELAWARE	00798221	740/833-1100	58
DELAWARE JOINT VOC SCH DIST/ DELAWARE/DELAWARE	00798348	740/363-1993	59
Delhi Middle Sch/*Cincinnati*/Hamilton	00807389	513/922-8400	92

School Year 2019-2020   800-333-8802   OH-V9

DISTRICT & SCHOOL TELEPHONE INDEX

Market Data Retrieval

School/City/County DISTRICT/CITY/COUNTY	PID	TELEPHONE NUMBER	PAGE
Delisle Options Center/Cleveland/Cuyahoga	12109694	216/320-2390	42
DELPHOS CITY SCH DIST/DELPHOS/ ALLEN	00783678	419/692-2509	8
Delshire Elem Sch/Cincinnati/Hamilton	00807391	513/471-1766	92
Delta Elem Sch/Delta/Fulton	00803694	419/822-5630	79
Delta Middle Sch/Delta/Fulton	00803711	419/822-9118	79
Demmitt Elem Sch/Vandalia/Montgomery	00825654	937/415-6500	153
Dempsey Middle Sch/Delaware/Delaware	04918291	740/833-1800	58
Denison Elem Sch/Cleveland/Cuyahoga	00791455	216/838-3250	43
Dennis Elem Sch/Springboro/Warren	10024153	937/748-6070	208
Dentzler Elem Sch/Parma/Cuyahoga	00794122	440/885-2430	49
Denver Place Elem Sch/Wilmington/Clinton	00789036	937/382-2380	33
DePaul Cristo Rey High Sch/Cincinnati/ Hamilton	11708091	513/861-0600	96
Design Lab Early College HS/Cleveland/ Cuyahoga	11454202	216/838-8150	43
DeVeaux Elem Sch/Toledo/Lucas	00817449	419/671-3200	129
Devonshire Elem Sch/Columbus/Franklin	00799990	614/365-5335	67
Diamond Oaks Career Dev Campus/Cincinnati/ Hamilton	00810441	513/574-1300	89
Digital Academy/Canton/Stark	10013556	330/456-1189	184
Digital Academy/New London/Huron	12106733	419/929-8191	106
Dike School of the Arts/Cleveland/Cuyahoga	00791467	216/838-9150	43
Diley Middle Sch/Pickerington/Fairfield	04917649	614/830-2900	64
DIOCESE OF CLEVELAND ED OFFICE/ CLEVELAND/CUYAHOGA	00795308	216/696-6525	52
DIOCESE OF COLUMBUS ED OFFICE/ COLUMBUS/FRANKLIN	00802717	614/221-5829	76
DIOCESE OF STEUBENVILLE ED OFF/ STEUBENVILLE/JEFFERSON	00812671	740/282-3631	110
DIOCESE OF TOLEDO ED OFFICE/ TOLEDO/LUCAS	00818297	419/244-6711	131
DIOCESE OF YOUNGSTOWN ED OFF/ YOUNGSTOWN/MAHONING	00820915	330/744-8451	137
Discovery Academy/Toledo/Lucas	12043519	419/214-3266	2
Discovery Montessori Sch/Akron/Summit	11710111	330/867-6222	196
Discovery Sch/Mansfield/Richland	02148490	419/756-8880	174
Divine Mercy Elem Sch/Payne/Paulding	00818912	419/263-2114	161
Dixie Elem Sch/New Lebanon/Montgomery	00825367	937/687-3511	152
Dixie High Sch/New Lebanon/Montgomery	00825343	937/687-1366	152
Dixie Middle Sch/New Lebanon/Montgomery	00825355	937/687-3508	152
Dohn Cmty High Sch/Cincinnati/Hamilton	05009130	513/281-6100	87
Dohron Wilson Elem Sch/Mechanicsburg/ Champaign	00787428	937/834-2453	26
Dominion Middle Sch/Columbus/Franklin	00800006	614/365-6020	67
Donnell Middle Sch/Findlay/Hancock	12038071	419/425-8370	98
Donnelsville Elem Sch/Donnelsville/Clark	00787698	937/845-4540	29
Donovan Elem Sch/Lebanon/Warren	02890590	513/934-5400	207
Dorothy E Lewis Elem Sch/Solon/Cuyahoga	00794594	440/349-6225	50
Dorr Street Elem Sch/Toledo/Lucas	00817164	419/867-5666	128
Douglas MacArthur Girls Ldrshp/Cleveland/ Cuyahoga	10911087	216/838-8400	43
Dover Ave Elem Sch/Dover/Tuscarawas	00837152	330/364-7117	202
DOVER CITY SCH DIST/DOVER/ TUSCARAWAS	00837140	330/364-1906	202
Dover High Sch/Dover/Tuscarawas	01841900	330/364-7148	202
Dover Intermediate Sch/Westlake/Cuyahoga	00795059	440/835-5494	51
Dover Middle Sch/Dover/Tuscarawas	00837164	330/364-7121	202
Dowds Elem Sch/Shelby/Richland	00829959	419/342-4641	173
Downtown Educational Ctr/Cleveland/ Cuyahoga	11697571	216/443-4902	43
Dr Henry Karrer Middle Sch/Dublin/Franklin	04866064	614/873-0459	69
Dr John Hole Elem Sch/Centerville/ Montgomery	00823979	937/434-0725	148
Dresden Elem Sch/Dresden/Muskingum	00826476	740/754-4001	157
Driscoll Elem Sch/Dayton/Montgomery	00823981	937/434-0562	149
DUBLIN CITY SCH DIST/DUBLIN/ FRANKLIN	00802200	614/764-5913	69
Dublin Coffman High Sch/Dublin/Franklin	00802212	614/764-5900	69
Dublin Jerome High Sch/Dublin/Franklin	05345166	614/873-7377	69
Dublin Scioto High Sch/Dublin/Franklin	04366179	614/717-2464	70
Dueber Reading & Math Prep Sch/Canton/ Stark	00832499	330/580-3517	184
Dukes Digital Academy/Alliance/Stark	12365874	330/823-1000	186
Dunbar Early College HS/Dayton/Montgomery	00824193	937/542-6760	149
Dunbar Primary Sch/Tallmadge/Summit	00835611	330/633-4515	195
Duncan Falls Elem Sch/Duncan Falls/ Muskingum	00826529	740/674-5211	156
Dundee Elem Sch/Dundee/Tuscarawas	00837217	330/852-2022	202
Dunloe Elem Sch/Columbus/Franklin	00801517	614/833-2008	71
Durling Middle Sch/Lorain/Lorain	01171975	440/233-6869	123
Duxberry Park Elem Sch/Columbus/Franklin	00800020	614/365-6023	67

E

School/City/County DISTRICT/CITY/COUNTY	PID	TELEPHONE NUMBER	PAGE
E A Powell Elem Sch/N Baltimore/Wood	00840240	419/257-2124	217
E Central Ohio Ed Svc Center/New Phila/ Tuscarawas	04012718	330/308-9939	201
E Prep & Village Prep-Willard/Cleveland/ Cuyahoga	12230009	216/586-3892	2
E Prep & Vlg Prep Cliffs Sch/Cleveland/ Cuyahoga	11718216	216/456-2070	2
E Prep Cliffs Middle Campus/Cleveland/ Cuyahoga	11007299	216/456-2070	2
E Prep Woodland Hills Sch/Cleveland/ Cuyahoga	11916028	216/298-1164	2
Eakin Elem Sch/Columbus/Franklin	01841821	614/365-5928	67
Early Childhood Learning Cmty/N Ridgeville/ Lorain	04036570	440/353-1100	125
Early College Acad at Crenshaw/Canton/ Stark	00832487	330/454-7717	184
Early College Academy/Columbus/Franklin	11006829	614/298-4742	66
Early College High Sch/Elyria/Lorain	10002545	440/365-5222	123
Early Learning Center/Dayton/Montgomery	11020306	937/854-4511	153
East Academy/Cleveland/Cuyahoga	05299830	216/383-1214	2
East Bridge Acad of Excellence/Columbus/ Franklin	12240066	614/501-3822	2
East Broadway Elem Sch/Toledo/Lucas	01531911	419/671-7200	129
East Canton Elem Sch/East Canton/Stark	00833390	330/488-0392	188
East Canton High Sch/East Canton/Stark	00833405	330/488-0316	188
East Canton Middle Sch/East Canton/Stark	04170035	330/488-0334	188
EAST CENTRAL OHIO ESC-N PHIL/ NEW PHILA/TUSCARAWAS	00837592	330/308-9939	201
EAST CENTRAL OHIO ESC-ST CLAIR/ ST CLAIRSVLE/BELMONT	02089117	740/695-9773	17
East Clark Elem Sch/Cleveland/Cuyahoga	00791508	216/838-0650	43
EAST CLEVELAND CITY SCH DIST/ E CLEVELAND/CUYAHOGA	00793037	216/268-6600	45
East Clinton High Sch/Sabina/Clinton	00788991	937/584-2474	33
EAST CLINTON LOCAL SCH DIST/ SABINA/CLINTON	00788989	937/584-2461	33
East Clinton Middle Sch/Sabina/Clinton	04745484	937/584-9267	33
East Columbus Elem Sch/Columbus/Franklin	00800044	614/365-6147	67
East Community Learning Ctr/Akron/Summit	00833948	330/761-7928	191
East Dayton Christian Sch/Dayton/Greene	03155757	937/252-5400	85
East Elem Sch/Avon/Lorain	00815697	440/937-6015	123
East Elem Sch/Dover/Tuscarawas	00837176	330/364-7114	202
East Elem Sch/Mount Vernon/Knox	00813089	740/393-5985	111
East Elem Sch/New Phila/Tuscarawas	00837358	330/364-0715	203
East Elem Sch/Newcomerstown/Tuscarawas	00837449	740/498-6601	203
East Elem Sch/Upper Sandsky/Wyandot	03319197	419/294-2396	219
East End Elem Sch/Wilmington/Clinton	04032354	937/382-2443	33
East Franklin Elem Sch/Columbus/Franklin	12368022	614/801-8100	73
EAST GUERNSEY LOCAL SCH DIST/ LORE CITY/GUERNSEY	00805240	740/489-5190	86
East High Sch/Columbus/Franklin	00800056	614/365-6096	67
East High Sch/Youngstown/Mahoning	00820692	330/740-4005	136
EAST HOLMES LOCAL SCH DIST/ MILLERSBURG/HOLMES	00811275	330/893-2610	104
East Knox Elem Sch/Howard/Knox	00812982	740/599-7000	111
East Knox Junior Senior HS/Howard/Knox	00813003	740/599-7000	111
EAST KNOX LOCAL SCH DIST/ HOWARD/KNOX	00812970	740/599-7000	111
East Linden Elem Sch/Columbus/Franklin	00800068	614/365-5459	67
East Liverpool Christian Sch/E Liverpool/ Columbiana	01409631	330/385-5588	36
EAST LIVERPOOL CITY SCH DIST/ E LIVERPOOL/COLUMBIANA	00789232	330/385-7132	34
East Liverpool Jr Sr High Sch/E Liverpool/ Columbiana	00789268	330/386-8750	35
EAST MUSKINGUM LOCAL SCH DIST/ NEW CONCORD/MUSKINGUM	00826309	740/826-7655	156
East Muskingum Middle Sch/New Concord/ Muskingum	01417547	740/826-7631	156
EAST PALESTINE CITY SCH DIST/ E PALESTINE/COLUMBIANA	00789311	330/426-4191	35
East Palestine Elem Sch/E Palestine/ Columbiana	00789385	330/426-3638	35
East Palestine High Sch/E Palestine/ Columbiana	00789347	330/426-9401	35
East Palestine Middle Sch/E Palestine/ Columbiana	00789361	330/426-9451	35
East Portsmouth Elem Sch/Sciotoville/ Scioto	00831158	740/776-6444	179

Ohio School Directory

DISTRICT & SCHOOL TELEPHONE INDEX

School/City/County DISTRICT/CITY/COUNTY	PID	TELEPHONE NUMBER	PAGE
East Preparatory Academy/*Cleveland*/Cuyahoga	12039221	216/539-0595	39
East Richland Christian Sch/*St Clairsvle*/Belmont	02209185	740/695-2281	19
East Technical High Sch/*Cleveland*/Cuyahoga	11684964	216/838-1000	43
East Woods Sch/*Hudson*/Summit	00835142	330/653-1256	193
East-West Elem Sch/*Athens*/Athens	00785092	740/593-6866	14
Eastern Elem Sch/*Beaver*/Pike	05271412	740/226-6402	163
Eastern Elem Sch/*Lexington*/Richland	00829507	419/884-3610	172
Eastern Elem Sch/*Reedsville*/Meigs	00822561	740/985-3304	142
Eastern Heights Middle Sch/*Elyria*/Lorain	00815946	440/284-8015	123
Eastern High Sch/*Beaver*/Pike	00827975	740/226-1544	163
Eastern High Sch/*Reedsville*/Meigs	00822573	740/985-3329	142
Eastern Local High Sch/*Winchester*/Adams	00786072	937/695-0959	7
EASTERN LOCAL SCH DIST/BEAVER/PIKE	00827951	740/226-4851	163
EASTERN LOCAL SCH DIST/REEDSVILLE/MEIGS	00822559	740/667-6079	142
EASTERN LOCAL SCH DIST/WINCHESTER/ADAMS	00786046	937/695-9030	7
Eastern Middle Sch/*Beaver*/Pike	00827963	740/226-1544	163
Eastern Middle Sch/*Reedsville*/Meigs	12037481	740/985-3304	142
Eastern Middle Sch/*Winchester*/Adams	04797463	937/695-1249	7
Eastgate Elem Sch/*Columbus*/Franklin	00800824	614/365-6132	67
Eastgate Sch/*Louisville*/Stark	04012689	330/479-3440	184
Easthaven Elem Sch/*Columbus*/Franklin	00800082	614/365-6149	67
Eastlake Middle Sch/*Eastlake*/Lake	00813871	440/942-5696	114
Eastland Career Center/*Groveport*/Franklin	00802690	614/836-5725	70
Eastland Performance Academy/*Columbus*/Franklin	11567055	614/318-0602	2
Eastland Preparatory Academy/*Columbus*/Franklin	12319150	614/547-4493	2
EASTLAND-FFLD CAREER TECH VSD/GROVEPORT/FRANKLIN	00802688	614/836-4530	70
Eastmont Elem Sch/*Dayton*/Montgomery	00824210	937/542-4490	149
Eastmoor Academy/*Columbus*/Franklin	00800094	614/365-6158	67
Eastside Arts Academy/*Cleveland*/Cuyahoga	12102919	216/441-9830	2
Eastview Elem Sch/*Avon Lake*/Lorain	00815740	440/933-6283	122
Eastview Elem Sch/*Mansfield*/Richland	00829595	419/589-7335	172
Eastwood Elem Sch/*Oberlin*/Lorain	00816639	440/775-3473	125
Eastwood Elem Sch/*Pemberville*/Wood	00840082	419/833-2821	216
Eastwood Elem Sch/*Warrensvl HTS*/Cuyahoga	00794938	216/336-6546	51
Eastwood High Sch/*Pemberville*/Wood	00840056	419/833-3611	216
EASTWOOD LOCAL SCH DIST/PEMBERVILLE/WOOD	00840044	419/833-6411	216
Eastwood Middle Sch/*Pemberville*/Wood	00840068	419/833-6011	216
Eastwood SDA Junior Academy/*Westerville*/Franklin	01464796	614/794-6350	77
EATON CMTY SCH DIST/EATON/PREBLE	00828905	937/456-1107	168
Eaton High Sch/*Eaton*/Preble	00828943	937/456-1141	168
Eaton Middle Sch/*Eaton*/Preble	00828929	937/456-2286	168
Ebon C Hill Intermediate Sch/*Bethel*/Clermont	00788367	513/734-2271	30
Echo Hills Elem Sch/*Stow*/Summit	00835518	330/689-5450	194
Ecole Kenwood FR Immersion ES/*Columbus*/Franklin	00800434	614/365-5502	68
ED SERVICE CENTER LORAIN CO/ELYRIA/LORAIN	00816823	440/324-5777	122
ED SERVICE CTR LAKE ERIE WEST/TOLEDO/LUCAS	00818285	419/245-4150	127
ED SVC CENTER OF MEDINA CO/MEDINA/MEDINA	02089222	330/723-6393	139
Eden Grove Academy/*Cincinnati*/Hamilton	01409693	513/542-0643	96
Edge Academy/*Akron*/Summit	04879451	330/535-4581	190
Edgerton Elem Sch/*Edgerton*/Williams	00839710	419/298-2332	214
Edgerton High Sch/*Edgerton*/Williams	00839722	419/298-2331	214
EDGERTON LOCAL SCH DIST/EDGERTON/WILLIAMS	00839708	419/298-2112	214
Edgewater Elem Sch/*Toledo*/Lucas	00817475	419/671-6750	129
EDGEWOOD CITY SCH DIST/TRENTON/BUTLER	00786280	513/867-3400	21
Edgewood Elem Sch/*Marysville*/Union	00837671	937/578-6800	204
Edgewood Elem Sch/*Trenton*/Butler	00786307	513/867-3440	21
Edgewood High Sch/*Ashtabula*/Ashtabula	00784531	440/997-5301	12
Edgewood High Sch/*Trenton*/Butler	00786319	513/867-6300	21
Edgewood Middle Sch/*Trenton*/Butler	00786321	513/867-3450	21
Edgewood Middle Sch/*Wooster*/Wayne	00839514	330/988-1111	213
Edison Elem Sch/*Ashland*/Ashland	00784141	419/289-7965	10
Edison Elem Sch/*Dayton*/Montgomery	00824204	937/542-4540	149
Edison Elem Sch/*Milan*/Erie	00798415	419/499-4625	60
Edison Elem Sch/*Willoughby*/Lake	00813883	440/942-2099	114
Edison High Sch/*Milan*/Erie	00798403	419/499-4652	60
Edison Jr Sr High Sch/*Richmond*/Jefferson	00812322	740/765-4313	109
EDISON LOCAL SCH DIST/HAMMONDSVILLE/JEFFERSON	00812279	330/532-4590	109
EDISON LOCAL SCHOOLS DIST/MILAN/ERIE	00798374	419/499-3000	60
Edison Middle Sch/*Berlin HTS*/Erie	00798398	419/588-2079	60
Edison Middle Sch/*Massillon*/Stark	00833429	330/478-6167	188
Edith Whitney Elem Sch/*Strongsville*/Cuyahoga	00794859	440/572-7180	51
Edna Surrarrer Elem Sch/*Strongsville*/Cuyahoga	00794861	440/572-7170	51
Edon Northwest Local Sch/*Edon*/Williams	00839758	419/272-3213	215
EDON NORTHWEST LOCAL SCH DIST/EDON/WILLIAMS	00839746	419/272-3213	215
Education Alternative/*Brookpark*/Cuyahoga	11221524	216/332-9360	53
Education Alternatives/*Elyria*/Lorain	11226079	440/324-1168	126
Educational Acad-Boys & Girls/*Columbus*/Franklin	11016941	614/351-1774	2
EDUCATIONAL SERV CTR-CTL OHIO/COLUMBUS/FRANKLIN	00802705	614/445-3750	65
Educational Svc Ctr Pre-School/*Georgetown*/Brown	04009125	937/378-6118	19
Edwards Middle Sch/*Brunswick*/Medina	00822169	330/273-0488	140
Edwin H Greene Interm Sch/*Cincinnati*/Hamilton	00807822	513/686-1750	93
Edwin Joel Brown Mid Sch/*Dayton*/Montgomery	00824698	937/542-5740	149
Edwin Smith Elem Sch/*Dayton*/Montgomery	00825575	937/297-5335	152
Ehove Career Center/*Milan*/Erie	00798831	419/499-4663	60
EHOVE JOINT VOC SCH DIST/MILAN/ERIE	00798829	419/499-4663	60
Eisenhower Intermediate Sch/*Oregon*/Lucas	00817061	419/836-8498	128
Elda Elem Sch/*Hamilton*/Butler	00787076	513/738-1972	24
Elder High Sch/*Cincinnati*/Hamilton	00808266	513/921-3744	95
Elgin Elem Sch/*Marion*/Marion	00821684	740/223-4301	138
Elgin High Sch/*Marion*/Marion	00821660	740/223-4300	138
ELGIN LOCAL SCH DIST/MARION/MARION	00821658	740/382-1101	138
Elgin Middle Sch/*Marion*/Marion	00821672	740/223-4300	138
Eli Pinney Elem Sch/*Dublin*/Franklin	05090608	614/798-3570	70
Elida Elem Sch/*Elida*/Allen	00783733	419/331-7901	8
Elida High Sch/*Elida*/Allen	00783745	419/331-4115	8
ELIDA LOCAL SCH DIST/ELIDA/ALLEN	00783721	419/331-4155	8
Elida Middle Sch/*Elida*/Allen	02131760	419/331-2505	8
Eliza Northrop Elem Sch/*Medina*/Medina	11465615	330/636-4600	141
Elizabeth Price Elem Sch/*Cuyahoga FLS*/Summit	00834863	330/926-3806	192
Ella Canavan Elem Sch/*Medina*/Medina	00822391	330/636-4000	141
Ella P Stewart Acad for Girls/*Toledo*/Lucas	00817982	419/671-5350	129
Ellet High Sch/*Akron*/Summit	00833950	330/794-4120	191
Ellsworth Hill Elem Sch/*Hudson*/Summit	10904462	330/653-1236	193
Elm Primary Sch/*Wyoming*/Hamilton	00807913	513/206-7315	94
Elm Street Elem Sch/*Painesville*/Lake	00813675	440/392-5520	113
Elmhurst Elem Sch/*Toledo*/Lucas	00817487	419/671-3550	129
Elmwood Elem Sch/*Bloomdale*/Wood	00840123	419/655-2583	216
Elmwood Elem Sch/*Garfield HTS*/Cuyahoga	00793362	216/475-8110	46
Elmwood High Sch/*Bloomdale*/Wood	00840147	419/655-2583	216
ELMWOOD LOCAL SCH DIST/BLOOMDALE/WOOD	00840111	419/655-2583	216
Elmwood Middle Sch/*Bloomdale*/Wood	00840135	419/655-2583	216
Elmwood Place Elem Sch/*Elmwood Place*/Hamilton	00807729	513/482-7115	93
Elmwood Primary Sch/*Lima*/Allen	00784012	419/998-8090	9
Ely Elem Sch/*Elyria*/Lorain	00815972	440/284-8005	123
Elyria Catholic High Sch/*Elyria*/Lorain	00795487	440/365-1821	126
ELYRIA CITY SCH DIST/ELYRIA/LORAIN	00815908	440/284-8000	123
Elyria Cmty Elem Middle Sch/*Elyria*/Lorain	04951138	440/366-5225	122
Elyria Early Childhood Village/*Elyria*/Lorain	04802795	440/284-8000	123
Elyria High Sch/*Elyria*/Lorain	00815984	440/284-8300	123
Emerald Campus/*Dublin*/Franklin	12365836	614/764-5857	70
Emerson Academy of Dayton/*Dayton*/Montgomery	05382592	937/223-2889	148
Emerson Elem Sch/*Lakewood*/Cuyahoga	00793611	216/529-4254	47
Emerson Elem Sch/*Sidney*/Shelby	00832097	937/497-2261	183
Emerson Elementary/*Westerville*/Franklin	01823283	614/797-7080	74
Emmanuel Baptist Sch/*Lebanon*/Warren	11231440	513/932-5205	209
Emmanuel Christian Academy/*Akron*/Summit	04986963	330/836-7182	196
Emmanuel Christian Academy/*Springfield*/Clark	04987187	937/390-3777	29
Emmanuel Christian Sch/*Toledo*/Lucas	01465001	419/885-3558	131
Encore Academy/*Reynoldsburg*/Franklin	00801672	614/501-2300	73

DISTRICT & SCHOOL TELEPHONE INDEX

Market Data Retrieval

School/City/County DISTRICT/CITY/COUNTY	PID	TELEPHONE NUMBER	PAGE
Endeavor Elem Sch/*West Chester*/Butler	10908925	513/759-8300	22
Englewood Elem Sch/*Englewood*/Montgomery	00825408	937/832-5900	152
Englewood Hills Elem Sch/*Englewood*/ Montgomery	00825410	937/832-5950	152
Enon Primary Sch/*Enon*/Clark	00787636	937/864-7361	27
Erie Intermediate Sch/*Ashtabula*/Ashtabula	00784452	440/992-1260	12
Erieview Elem Sch/*Avon Lake*/Lorain	00815752	440/933-6282	122
Ervin Carlisle Elem Sch/*Delaware*/Delaware	00798245	740/833-1450	58
Esther Dennis MS at G Kennedy/*Dayton*/ Montgomery	00825525	937/275-6833	152
Ethel M Taylor Academy/*Cincinnati*/Hamilton	00805886	513/363-3600	87
Etna Elem Sch/*Pataskala*/Licking	00815283	740/927-5906	120
Etna Road Elem Sch/*Whitehall*/Franklin	00802456	614/417-5400	75
Euclid Child Dev Center/*Euclid*/Cuyahoga	04752102	216/322-2700	46
Euclid City High Sch/*Euclid*/Cuyahoga	00793154	216/797-7800	46
EUCLID CITY SCH DIST/**EUCLID**/ **CUYAHOGA**	00793128	216/261-2900	46
Euclid Park Sch/*Cleveland*/Cuyahoga	11697715	216/838-0700	43
Euclid Preparatory Sch/*Euclid*/Cuyahoga	12240078	216/750-2070	2
Evamere Elem Sch/*Hudson*/Summit	00835104	330/653-1226	193
Evangel Academy/*Dayton*/Montgomery	11229382	937/253-8342	154
Evanston Academy/*Cincinnati*/Hamilton	00805733	513/363-2700	87
Evendale Elem Sch/*Cincinnati*/Hamilton	00807444	513/864-1200	92
Evening Street Elem Sch/*Worthington*/ Franklin	00802535	614/450-4400	75
Everest High Sch/*Reynoldsburg*/Franklin	12160832	614/501-1033	73
Evergreen Elem Sch/*Metamora*/Fulton	00803589	419/644-9221	78
Evergreen High Sch/*Metamora*/Fulton	00803577	419/644-2951	78
EVERGREEN LOCAL SCH DIST/ **METAMORA/FULTON**	00803553	419/644-3521	78
Evergreen Middle Sch/*Metamora*/Fulton	00803565	419/644-2331	78
Evolve Academy/*Medina*/Medina	11465627	330/636-4213	141
Ewing Sch/*Marietta*/Washington	02052683	740/373-3781	209

F

School/City/County	PID	TELEPHONE NUMBER	PAGE
Facing History New Tech Sch/*Cleveland*/ Cuyahoga	11823782	216/838-8600	43
Fairbanks Elem Sch/*Milford CTR*/Union	00837621	937/349-9000	204
Fairbanks High Sch/*Milford CTR*/Union	00837619	937/349-3721	204
FAIRBANKS LOCAL SCH DIST/ **MILFORD CTR/UNION**	00837607	937/349-3731	204
Fairbanks Middle Sch/*Milford CTR*/Union	02200191	937/349-6841	204
FAIRBORN CITY SCH DIST/**FAIRBORN**/ **GREENE**	00804595	937/878-3961	84
Fairborn High Sch/*Fairborn*/Greene	00804650	937/879-3611	84
Fairborn Intermediate Sch/*Fairborn*/Greene	00804686	937/878-3969	84
Fairborn Primary Sch/*Fairborn*/Greene	00804662	937/878-8668	84
Fairbrook Elem Sch/*Dayton*/Greene	00804480	937/429-7616	83
Faircrest Memorial Middle Sch/*Canton*/Stark	00832322	330/484-8015	185
Fairfax Elem Sch/*Cleveland HTS*/Cuyahoga	00792887	216/371-7480	42
Fairfax Elem Sch/*Mentor*/Lake	00813390	440/255-7223	113
Fairfield Academy/*Fairfield*/Butler	12035419	513/858-7600	21
Fairfield Career Center/*Carroll*/Franklin	03011553	614/837-9443	70
Fairfield Central Elem Sch/*Fairfield*/ Butler	00786369	513/829-7979	21
Fairfield Christian Academy/*Lancaster*/ Fairfield	05330329	740/654-2889	65
FAIRFIELD CITY SCH DIST/ **FAIRFIELD/BUTLER**	00786357	513/829-6300	21
Fairfield Co Early Chldhd Ctr/*Lancaster*/ Fairfield	04009010	740/652-7225	62
FAIRFIELD CO ED SERVICE CENTER/ **LANCASTER/FAIRFIELD**	02089155	740/653-3193	62
Fairfield Compass Elem Sch/*Fairfield*/ Butler	12235358	513/858-8700	21
Fairfield Creekside Mid Sch/*Fairfield*/ Butler	01828984	513/829-4433	21
Fairfield Crossroads Mid Sch/*Fairfield*/ Butler	04748319	513/829-4504	21
Fairfield East Elem Sch/*Hamilton*/Butler	04747652	513/737-5000	21
Fairfield Elem Sch/*Maumee*/Lucas	00816952	419/893-9821	127
Fairfield Elem Sch/*Pickerington*/Fairfield	02126131	614/834-7600	64
Fairfield Freshman High Sch/*Fairfield*/ Butler	01828972	513/829-8300	21
Fairfield Local Elem Sch/*Leesburg*/Highland	00810960	937/780-2988	102
Fairfield Local High Sch/*Leesburg*/Highland	00810972	937/780-2966	102
Fairfield Local Middle Sch/*Leesburg*/ Highland	05026877	937/780-2977	102
FAIRFIELD LOCAL SCH DIST/ **LEESBURG/HIGHLAND**	00810958	937/780-2221	102
Fairfield North Elem Sch/*Hamilton*/Butler	00786395	513/868-0070	21

School/City/County	PID	TELEPHONE NUMBER	PAGE
Fairfield Senior High Sch/*Fairfield*/Butler	00786383	513/942-2999	21
Fairfield South Elem Sch/*Fairfield*/Butler	00786400	513/829-3078	21
Fairfield Union High Sch/*Lancaster*/ Fairfield	00798996	740/536-7306	63
FAIRFIELD UNION LOCAL SCH DIST/ **LANCASTER/FAIRFIELD**	00798972	740/536-7384	63
Fairfield West Elem Sch/*Fairfield*/Butler	00786412	513/868-3021	21
Fairhaven Sch/*London*/Madison	02052231	740/852-7052	132
Fairhaven Sch/*Niles*/Trumbull	02052592	330/652-5811	196
Fairland East Elem Sch/*Proctorville*/ Lawrence	00814241	740/886-3120	116
Fairland High Sch/*Proctorville*/Lawrence	00814253	740/886-3250	116
FAIRLAND LOCAL SCH DIST/ **PROCTORVILLE/LAWRENCE**	00814239	740/886-3100	116
Fairland Middle Sch/*Proctorville*/Lawrence	00814265	740/886-3200	116
Fairland West Elem Sch/*Proctorville*/ Lawrence	05273604	740/886-3150	116
Fairlawn Elem Sch/*Sidney*/Shelby	00831914	937/492-1654	182
FAIRLAWN LOCAL SCH DIST/ **SIDNEY/SHELBY**	00831902	937/492-1974	182
Fairlawn Middle High Sch/*Sidney*/Shelby	00831926	937/492-5930	182
Fairless Elem Sch/*Navarre*/Stark	00832724	330/767-3913	185
Fairless High Sch/*Navarre*/Stark	00832736	330/767-3444	185
FAIRLESS LOCAL SCH DIST/ **NAVARRE/STARK**	00832712	330/767-3577	185
Fairless Middle Sch/*Navarre*/Stark	10976477	330/767-4293	185
Fairmoor Elem Sch/*Columbus*/Franklin	00800159	614/365-6169	68
Fairmount Early Childhood Ctr/*Beachwood*/ Cuyahoga	00790516	216/464-2600	40
FAIRPORT HARBOR EXEMPT VLG SD/ **FAIRPORT HBR/LAKE**	00813209	440/354-5400	112
Fairview Elem Sch/*Dayton*/Montgomery	00824258	937/542-4590	149
Fairview Elem Sch/*Sherwood*/Defiance	00797875	419/658-2511	57
Fairview High Sch/*Fairview Park*/Cuyahoga	00793300	440/356-3500	46
Fairview High Sch/*Sherwood*/Defiance	00797863	419/658-2378	57
Fairview Middle Sch/*Sherwood*/Defiance	00797899	419/658-2331	57
FAIRVIEW PARK CITY SCH DIST/ **FAIRVIEW PARK/CUYAHOGA**	00793283	440/331-5500	46
Fairview-Clifton German Sch/*Cincinnati*/ Hamilton	00805628	513/363-2100	87
Fairway Sch/*Bucyrus*/Crawford	02051653	419/562-3321	37
Fairwood Elem Sch/*Columbus*/Franklin	00800161	614/365-6111	68
Fairwood Elem Sch/*Hamilton*/Butler	00786541	513/868-5610	22
Faith Islamic Elem Academy/*Cuyahoga FLS*/ Summit	05099678	330/926-9407	196
Fallen Timbers Middle Sch/*Whitehouse*/Lucas	00816902	419/877-0601	127
Falls Learning Academy/*Newton Falls*/ Trumbull	11721902	330/872-5121	200
Falls-Lennox Primary Sch/*Olmsted Falls*/ Cuyahoga	00793996	440/427-6400	48
Family Learning Center/*Tiffin*/Seneca	04012196	419/448-5079	180
Fassett Junior High Sch/*Oregon*/Lucas	00817073	419/693-0455	128
FAYETTE LOCAL SCH DIST/**FAYETTE**/ **FULTON**	00803618	419/237-2573	79
Fayette Progressive Sch/*Wshngtn Ct Hs*/ Fayette	02051859	740/335-1391	65
Fayette Sch/*Fayette*/Fulton	00803620	419/237-2114	79
Fayetteville Elem Sch/*Fayetteville*/Brown	00786113	513/875-2083	19
Fayetteville High Sch/*Fayetteville*/Brown	00786125	513/875-3520	19
Fayetteville Middle Sch/*Fayetteville*/Brown	01823245	513/875-2829	19
FAYETTEVILLE PERRY LOCAL SD/ **FAYETTEVILLE/BROWN**	00786101	513/875-2423	19
FEDERAL HOCKING LOCAL SCH DIST/ **STEWART/ATHENS**	00785107	740/662-6691	14
Federal Hocking Mid High Sch/*Stewart*/ Athens	00785133	740/662-6691	14
Felicity-Franklin Elem Sch/*Felicity*/ Clermont	00788460	513/876-2112	30
Felicity-Franklin High Sch/*Felicity*/ Clermont	00788472	513/876-2560	30
FELICITY-FRANKLIN LOCAL SD/ **FELICITY/CLERMONT**	00788458	513/876-2113	30
Felicity-Franklin Middle Sch/*Felicity*/ Clermont	04745719	513/876-2662	30
Ferguson Hall Freshman Sch/*Beavercreek*/ Greene	12168688	937/429-7533	83
Fernway Elem Sch/*Shaker HTS*/Cuyahoga	00794536	216/295-4040	50
Field High Sch/*Mogadore*/Portage	00828345	330/673-9591	165
FIELD LOCAL SCH DIST/**MOGADORE**/ **PORTAGE**	00828319	330/673-2659	165
Field Middle Sch/*Mogadore*/Portage	00828357	330/673-4176	165

Ohio School Directory

DISTRICT & SCHOOL TELEPHONE INDEX

School/City/County DISTRICT/CITY/COUNTY	PID	TELEPHONE NUMBER	PAGE
FINDLAY CITY SCH DIST/FINDLAY/ HANCOCK	00809832	419/427-5487	97
Findlay Digital Academy/Findlay/Hancock	10017435	419/425-3598	98
Findlay High Sch/Findlay/Hancock	00809909	419/425-8289	98
Findlay Learning Center/Findlay/Hancock	12171958	419/429-8938	98
Findley Community Learning Ctr/Akron/ Summit	00833998	330/761-7909	191
Finland Elem Sch/Columbus/Franklin	00801866	614/801-8125	73
Finland Middle Sch/Columbus/Franklin	00801878	614/801-3600	73
FINNEYTOWN LOCAL SCH DIST/ CINCINNATI/HAMILTON	00806414	513/728-3700	89
Finneytown Secondary Sch/Cincinnati/ Hamilton	00806440	513/931-0712	89
Firelands Christian Academy/Castalia/Erie	11227396	419/684-8642	62
Firelands Digital Academy/Oberlin/Lorain	12108951	440/965-4255	124
Firelands Elem Sch/Oberlin/Lorain	00816184	440/965-5381	124
Firelands High Sch/Oberlin/Lorain	00816172	440/965-4255	124
FIRELANDS LOCAL SCH DIST/ SOUTH AMHERST/LORAIN	00816146	440/965-5821	124
Firelands Montessori Academy/Huron/Erie	02655845	419/433-6181	62
Firestone Cmty Learning Center/Akron/ Summit	00834019	330/761-3270	191
Firestone Park Elem Sch/Akron/Summit	00834007	330/773-1308	191
First Baptist Christian Sch/Elyria/Lorain	01796044	440/458-5185	126
Fishcreek Elem Sch/Stow/Summit	00835520	330/689-5460	194
Fitch High Sch/Youngstown/Mahoning	00819734	330/797-3900	134
Five-Points Elememtary Sch/Centerville/ Warren	10030126	937/748-6090	208
Flatridge Elem Sch/Charm/Holmes	01486885	330/893-3156	104
Flex High Sch/Columbus/Franklin	12163339	614/610-9749	2
Flying Colors Pub Sch Pre-Sch/Newark/ Licking	04014120	740/349-1629	117
Focus Lrng Acad-E Columbus/Columbus/ Franklin	11016915	614/269-0150	2
Focus Lrng Acad-W Columbus/Columbus/ Franklin	11016903	614/545-2000	2
Focus North High Sch/Columbus/Franklin	11016927	614/310-0430	2
Forest Elem Sch/Troy/Miami	00823682	937/332-6746	146
Forest Hill Cmty Learning Ctr/Akron/Summit	00834021	330/761-1645	191
FOREST HILLS SCH DIST/CINCINNATI/ HAMILTON	00806476	513/231-3600	89
Forest Park Elem Sch/Columbus/Franklin	00800197	614/365-5337	68
Forest Primary Sch/North Olmsted/Cuyahoga	00793867	440/779-3527	48
Forest Rose Sch/Lancaster/Fairfield	02051847	740/652-7225	62
Forestlawn Elem Sch/Sheffield Lk/Lorain	00816718	440/949-4238	126
Fort Recovery Elem Mid Sch/Fort Recovery/ Mercer	00823060	419/375-2768	144
FOSTORIA CITY SCH DIST/FOSTORIA/ SENECA	00831457	419/435-8163	180
Fostoria Elem Sch/Fostoria/Seneca	00831471	419/436-4125	180
Fostoria Jr Sr High Sch/Fostoria/Seneca	00831495	419/436-4110	180
Foundation Academy/Mansfield/Richland	11016898	419/526-9540	2
Fountain City Christian Sch/Bryan/Williams	04852116	419/636-2333	216
Four Co Career Center/Archbold/Fulton	00810893	419/267-3331	79
Four Oaks Early Intervention/Xenia/Greene	02051990	937/562-6779	83
FOUR-CO JOINT VOC SCH DIST/ ARCHBOLD/FULTON	00810881	419/267-3331	79
Fouse Elem Sch/Westerville/Franklin	05092474	614/797-7400	74
Fox Run Sch/St Clairsvle/Belmont	05099680	740/695-2131	19
Foxfire East Academy/Cambridge/Guernsey	12161537	740/432-5457	86
Foxfire Schools/Zanesville/Muskingum	05300116	740/453-4509	2
Frank Elem Sch/Perrysburg/Wood	00840446	419/874-8721	218
Frank Jacinto Elem Sch/Lorain/Lorain	05361445	440/830-4130	124
FRANKLIN CITY SCH DIST/FRANKLIN/ WARREN	00838247	937/746-1699	207
Franklin D Roosevelt Academy/Cleveland/ Cuyahoga	00792019	216/838-2200	43
Franklin Elem Sch/Delphos/Allen	00783680	419/692-8766	8
Franklin Elem Sch/Elyria/Lorain	00816017	440/284-8007	123
Franklin Elem Sch/Massillon/Stark	00833077	330/830-3907	187
Franklin Elem Sch/Wadsworth/Medina	00822468	330/335-1470	141
Franklin Furnace Christn Acad/Frankln Frnce/ Scioto	11223869	740/354-9301	180
Franklin Heights High Sch/Columbus/ Franklin	00801880	614/801-3200	73
Franklin High Sch/Franklin/Warren	00838261	937/743-8610	207
Franklin Junior High Sch/Franklin/Warren	00838273	937/743-8630	207
Franklin Local Cmty Sch/Roseville/ Muskingum	05299907	740/697-7317	156
FRANKLIN LOCAL SCH DIST/ DUNCAN FALLS/MUSKINGUM	00826505	740/674-5203	156
Franklin School of Opportunity/Lakewood/ Cuyahoga	10017887	216/529-4037	47
Franklin Woods Interm Sch/Columbus/ Franklin	04931671	614/801-8600	73
Franklin-Monroe Elem Sch/Arcanum/Darke	00797552	937/947-1327	55
Franklin-Monroe Jr Sr High Sch/Arcanum/ Darke	00797564	937/937-1328	55
FRANKLIN-MONROE LOCAL SCH DIST/ ARCANUM/DARKE	00797540	937/947-1212	55
Franklinton Preparatory Acad/Columbus/ Franklin	12163327	614/636-3721	2
Frazer Elem Sch/Canton/Stark	00833558	330/491-3740	188
Frazeysburg Elem Sch/Frazeysburg/Muskingum	00826464	740/828-2781	157
Frederick Douglass Elem Sch/Cincinnati/ Hamilton	00805575	513/363-1900	87
Frederick Douglass High Sch/Cleveland/ Cuyahoga	12361426	216/273-3033	2
Fredericksburg Elem Sch/Fredericksbrg/ Wayne	00839370	330/695-2741	213
Fredericktown Elem Sch/Fredericktown/Knox	00813041	740/694-2781	111
Fredericktown High Sch/Fredericktown/Knox	00813027	740/694-2726	111
FREDERICKTOWN LOCAL SCH DIST/ FREDERICKTOWN/KNOX	00813015	740/694-2956	111
Fredericktown Middle Sch/Fredericktown/ Knox	00813039	740/694-2726	111
Freedom Elem Sch/Lima/Allen	00783915	419/996-3380	9
Freedom Elem Sch/West Chester/Butler	03049328	513/777-9787	22
Freedom Trail Elem Sch/Lewis Center/ Delaware	11512749	740/657-5700	59
FREMONT CITY SCH DIST/FREMONT/ SANDUSKY	00830556	419/332-6454	176
Fremont Middle Sch/Fremont/Sandusky	00830582	419/332-5569	177
Fremont Ross High Sch/Fremont/Sandusky	00830594	419/332-8221	177
French Run Elem Sch/Reynoldsburg/Franklin	00801646	614/367-1950	73
Frontier High Middle Sch/New Matamoras/ Washington	00838699	740/865-3441	210
FRONTIER LOCAL SCH DIST/ NEW MATAMORAS/WASHINGTON	00838687	740/865-3473	209
Ft Frye Jr Sr High Sch/Beverly/Washington	00838651	740/984-2376	210
FT FRYE LOCAL SCH DIST/BEVERLY/ WASHINGTON	00838625	740/984-2497	210
Ft Island Primary Sch/Fairlawn/Summit	00834722	330/664-4890	192
Ft Loramie Elem Sch/Fort Loramie/Shelby	00831952	937/295-2931	182
Ft Loramie Jr Sr High Sch/Fort Loramie/ Shelby	00831964	937/295-3342	182
FT LORAMIE LOCAL SCH DIST/ FORT LORAMIE/SHELBY	00831940	937/295-3931	182
Ft Meigs Elem Sch/Perrysburg/Wood	03393363	419/872-8822	218
Ft Miami Elem Sch/Maumee/Lucas	00816964	419/893-2201	127
Ft Recovery High Sch/Fort Recovery/Mercer	04243503	419/375-4111	144
FT RECOVERY LOCAL SCH DIST/ FORT RECOVERY/MERCER	00823046	419/375-4139	144
Fuchs Mizrachi Sch/Beachwood/Cuyahoga	02949995	216/932-0220	53
Fullerton Elem Sch/Cleveland/Cuyahoga	00791625	216/838-4400	43
Fulton Co Bd-Dev Disabilities/Wauseon/ Fulton	02051940	419/337-4575	78
Fulton Elem Sch/Springfield/Clark	00788006	937/505-4150	28
Furry Elem Sch/Sandusky/Erie	00798582	419/625-4352	61
G			
G A T E/Middletown/Butler	11222360	513/420-4617	24
Gables Elem Sch/Columbus/Franklin	01531870	614/365-5499	68
Gahanna Christian Academy/Columbus/ Franklin	02148608	614/471-9270	77
Gahanna Middle School-East/Gahanna/ Franklin	01396618	614/478-5550	70
Gahanna Middle School-South/Gahanna/ Franklin	04018047	614/337-3730	70
Gahanna Middle School-West/Gahanna/ Franklin	00801476	614/478-5570	70
GAHANNA-JEFFERSON PUBLIC SD/ GAHANNA/FRANKLIN	00801397	614/471-7065	70
GALION CITY SCH DIST/GALION/ CRAWFORD	00790255	419/468-3432	38
Galion High Sch/Galion/Crawford	00790281	419/468-6500	38
Galion Intermediate Sch/Galion/Crawford	11075832	419/468-3676	38
Galion Middle Sch/Galion/Crawford	00790293	419/468-3134	38
Galion Primary Sch/Galion/Crawford	11075820	419/478-4010	38
Gallia Academy High Sch/Gallipolis/Gallia	00803876	740/446-3212	81
Gallia Academy Middle Sch/Gallipolis/ Gallia	11635585	740/446-3214	81

School Year 2019-2020   800-333-8802   OH-V13

DISTRICT & SCHOOL TELEPHONE INDEX

Market Data Retrieval

DISTRICT/CITY/COUNTY School/City/County	PID	TELEPHONE NUMBER	PAGE
GALLIA CO LOCAL SCH DIST/			
PATRIOT/GALLIA	00803917	740/379-9085	80
GALLIA-JACKSON-VINTON JVSD/			
RIO GRANDE/GALLIA	00804038	740/245-5334	80
GALLIA-VINTON ED SVC CENTER/			
RIO GRANDE/GALLIA	00804040	740/245-0593	80
GALLIPOLIS CITY SCH DIST/			
GALLIPOLIS/GALLIA	00803852	740/446-3211	81
Galloway Ridge Interm Sch/*Galloway/*			
Franklin	04931700	614/801-8850	73
Garaway 7-12 Sch/*Sugarcreek/*Tuscarawas	01531959	330/852-4292	202
GARAWAY LOCAL SCH DIST/SUGARCREEK/			
TUSCARAWAS	00837205	330/852-2421	202
Garfield Academy/*Canton/*Stark	05220243	330/454-3128	2
Garfield East Elem Sch/*Steubenville/*			
Jefferson	00812578	740/282-5112	109
Garfield Elem Sch/*Cleveland/*Cuyahoga	11697727	216/838-6300	43
Garfield Elem Sch/*Heath/*Licking	00814679	740/238-7120	117
Garfield Elem Sch/*Lorain/*Lorain	10010932	440/830-4140	124
Garfield Elem Sch/*Marion/*Marion	00821763	740/223-4444	138
Garfield Elem Sch/*Medina/*Medina	00822406	330/636-4200	141
Garfield Elem Sch/*Toledo/*Lucas	00817530	419/671-7550	129
Garfield Elem Sch/*Wellsville/*Columbiana	00789749	330/532-3301	36
GARFIELD HEIGHTS CITY SD/			
GARFIELD HTS/CUYAHOGA	00793350	216/475-8100	46
Garfield Heights High Sch/*Cleveland/*			
Cuyahoga	00793374	216/662-2800	46
Garfield Heights Learning Ctr/*Cleveland/*			
Cuyahoga	12038186	216/475-8105	46
Garfield Heights Middle Sch/*Garfield HTS/*			
Cuyahoga	00793386	216/475-8105	46
Garfield Middle Sch/*Hamilton/*Butler	00786474	513/887-5035	22
Garfield Middle Sch/*Lakewood/*Cuyahoga	11135183	216/529-4241	47
Garrett Morgan Sch/*Cleveland/*Cuyahoga	02201016	216/838-8450	43
Gates Mills Elem Sch/*Gates Mills/*Cuyahoga	00793726	440/995-7500	47
Gateway Academy of Ohio/*Columbus/*Franklin	11456731	614/856-1149	2
Gateway Elem Sch/*Conneaut/*Ashtabula	00784646	440/593-7280	12
Gateway Middle Sch/*Maumee/*Lucas	00816976	419/893-3386	127
Gearity Professional Dev Sch/*University Ht/*			
Cuyahoga	00792849	216/371-6515	42
GEAUGA CO ED SERVICE CENTER/			
CHARDON/GEAUGA	00804454	440/279-1700	81
Gen Rosecrans Elem Sch/*Sunbury/*Delaware	03395957	740/965-8900	58
General Johnny Wilson Mid Sch/*Lorain/*			
Lorain	10010944	440/830-4240	124
General Sherman Jr High Sch/*Lancaster/*			
Fairfield	00799067	740/687-7344	63
GENEVA AREA CITY SCH DIST/			
GENEVA/ASHTABULA	00784696	440/466-4831	13
Geneva High Sch/*Geneva/*Ashtabula	00784737	440/466-4831	13
Geneva Middle Sch/*Geneva/*Ashtabula	10029646	440/466-4831	13
Geneva Platt R Spencer ES/*Geneva/*Ashtabula	00784725	440/415-9325	13
Genoa Area High Sch/*Genoa/*Ottawa	00827119	419/855-7741	159
GENOA AREA LOCAL SCH DIST/			
GENOA/OTTAWA	00827078	419/855-7741	159
Genoa Christian Academy/*Westerville/*			
Delaware	10013893	740/965-5433	60
Genoa Elem Sch/*Genoa/*Ottawa	00827080	419/855-7741	159
Genoa Elem Sch/*Massillon/*Stark	00833431	330/478-6171	188
Genoa Middle Sch/*Genoa/*Ottawa	00827121	419/855-7741	159
Genoa Middle Sch/*Westerville/*Franklin	04848268	614/797-6500	74
Geo Voinovich Reclamation Acad/*Cleveland/*			
Cuyahoga	12163315	216/273-3033	2
George G Dodge Interm Sch/*Twinsburg/*Summit	04872192	330/486-2200	195
George H Gerke Elem Sch/*Franklin/*Warren	00838285	937/743-8650	207
George McDowell Middle Sch/*Circleville/*			
Pickaway	00827767	740/474-7538	162
George W Carver-STEM Sch/*Cleveland/*			
Cuyahoga	00791649	216/838-1450	43
George Washington Elem Sch/*Marion/*Marion	00821880	740/223-3883	138
Georgetown Elem Sch/*Georgetown/*Brown	00786163	937/378-6235	20
GEORGETOWN EXEMPTED VILLAGE SD/			
GEORGETOWN/BROWN	00786137	937/378-3730	19
Georgetown Jr Sr High Sch/*Georgetown/*Brown	00786149	937/378-6730	20
Georgian Heights Elem Sch/*Columbus/*			
Franklin	00800240	614/365-5931	68
Gesu Catholic Sch/*University Ht/*Cuyahoga	00795504	216/932-0620	52
Gesu Sch/*Toledo/*Lucas	00818376	419/536-5634	131
Gibbs Leadership Sch/*Canton/*Stark	00832528	330/456-1521	184
GIBSONBURG EXEMPTED VILLAGE SD/			
GIBSONBURG/SANDUSKY	00830661	419/637-2479	177
Gibsonburg High Sch/*Gibsonburg/*Sandusky	00830685	419/637-2873	177
Gibsonburg Middle Sch/*Gibsonburg/*Sandusky	04748591	419/637-7954	177
Gilbert A Dater High Sch/*Cincinnati/*			
Hamilton	00805563	513/363-7200	87
Gilead Christian School-North/*Mount Gilead/*			
Morrow	02205323	419/947-5739	156
Gilead Christian School-South/*Mount Gilead/*			
Morrow	02661636	419/946-5900	156
Gilles-Sweet Elem Sch/*Fairview Park/*			
Cuyahoga	00793312	440/356-3525	46
Gilmour Academy/*Gates Mills/*Cuyahoga	00795516	440/442-1104	52
Ginn Academy/*Cleveland/*Cuyahoga	10911116	216/838-4466	43
GIRARD CITY SCH DIST/GIRARD/			
TRUMBULL	00836079	330/545-2596	197
Girard High Sch/*Girard/*Trumbull	11562641	330/545-5431	197
Girard Intermediate Sch/*Girard/*Trumbull	00836122	330/545-5219	197
Girard Junior High Sch/*Girard/*Trumbull	00836093	330/545-5431	197
Glacier Ridge Elem Sch/*Dublin/*Franklin	10021383	614/733-0012	70
Glandorf Elem Sch/*Glandorf/*Putnam	00829296	419/538-6880	170
Glass City Academy/*Toledo/*Lucas	10017540	419/720-6311	127
Glen Oak Elem Sch/*Lewis Center/*Delaware	10002674	740/657-5500	59
Glendale Elem Sch/*Cincinnati/*Hamilton	00807456	513/864-1300	92
Glendale Primary Sch/*Bedford/*Cuyahoga	00790607	440/439-4227	41
Glendale-Feilbach Elem Sch/*Toledo/*Lucas	01531923	419/671-2650	129
Glendening Elem Sch/*Groveport/*Franklin	00801531	614/836-4972	71
Glenford Elem Sch/*Glenford/*Perry	00827547	740/659-2209	161
Glenoak High Sch/*Canton/*Stark	00833560	330/491-3800	188
Glenville High Sch/*Cleveland/*Cuyahoga	11702310	216/838-2000	43
Glenwood Elem Sch/*Toledo/*Lucas	11453105	419/671-4600	129
Glenwood High Sch/*New Boston/*Scioto	00831031	740/456-4559	179
Glenwood Intermediate Sch/*Canton/*Stark	00833625	330/491-3780	188
Glenwood Junior High Sch/*Boardman/*Mahoning	00819825	330/726-3414	134
Glenwood Middle Sch/*Findlay/*Hancock	00809911	419/425-8373	98
Global Ambassadors Language CS/*Cleveland/*			
Cuyahoga	12259483	216/315-7942	2
Global Impact STEM Academy/*Springfield/*			
Clark	12240080	937/328-6600	2
Global Village Academy/*Parma/*Cuyahoga	11746598	216/767-5956	39
Gloria Dei Montessori Sch/*Dayton/*			
Montgomery	00825941	937/274-7195	154
Gloria S Friend Christian Acad/*Columbus/*			
Franklin	04986767	614/221-1518	77
Glover Community Learning Ctr/*Akron/*Summit	00834057	330/773-1245	191
Goal Digital Academy/*Mansfield/*Richland	05299995	419/521-9008	2
Golden Bridge Academy/*Lima/*Allen	05099707	419/222-6858	10
Golden Rule Sch/*Byesville/*Guernsey	02052009	740/439-4451	85
Goldwood Primary Sch/*Rocky River/*Cuyahoga	00794457	440/356-6720	50
Good Samaritan Sch/*Defiance/*Defiance	02051794	419/782-6621	56
Good Shepherd Montessori Sch/*Cincinnati/*			
Hamilton	10756174	513/271-4171	95
Gordon DeWitt Elem Sch/*Cuyahoga FLS/*Summit	00834875	330/926-3802	192
Gorrell Elem Sch/*Massillon/*Stark	00833089	330/830-3905	187
Gorsuch West Elem Sch/*Lancaster/*Fairfield	00799172	740/687-7332	63
Goshen High Sch/*Goshen/*Clermont	00788525	513/722-2227	30
Goshen Lane Elem Sch/*Gahanna/*Franklin	00801414	614/478-5580	70
GOSHEN LOCAL SCH DIST/GOSHEN/			
CLERMONT	00788484	513/722-2222	30
Goshen Middle Sch/*Goshen/*Clermont	00788501	513/722-2226	30
Grace Christian Sch/*Blacklick/*Franklin	02165292	614/861-0724	77
Grace Community Sch/*Delaware/*Delaware	11224679	740/363-5800	60
Grace L Roxbury Elem Sch/*Solon/*Cuyahoga	00794677	440/349-6220	50
Graduation Academy/*Canton/*Stark	10025171	330/456-1189	185
Graham Elem and Middle Sch/*Columbus/*			
Franklin	11746081	614/253-4000	66
Graham Elem Sch/*Saint Paris/*Champaign	00787387	937/663-4449	26
Graham High Sch/*Saint Paris/*Champaign	00787375	937/663-4127	26
GRAHAM LOCAL SCH DIST/SAINT PARIS/			
CHAMPAIGN	00787351	937/663-4123	25
Graham Middle Sch/*Saint Paris/*Champaign	00787404	937/663-5339	26
Graham Sch/*Columbus/*Franklin	05009142	614/262-1111	66
Granby Elem Sch/*Columbus/*Franklin	03049201	614/450-4500	75
Grand Lake Christian Sch/*Saint Marys/*			
Auglaize	04987242	419/300-9001	17
Grand River Academy/*Austinburg/*Ashtabula	00784969	440/275-2811	14
Grand Valley Elem Sch/*Orwell/*Ashtabula	00784775	440/805-4545	13
Grand Valley High Sch/*Orwell/*Ashtabula	00784799	440/805-4545	13
GRAND VALLEY LOCAL SCH DIST/			
ORWELL/ASHTABULA	00784763	440/805-4545	13
Grand Valley Middle Sch/*Orwell/*Ashtabula	01557525	440/805-4545	13
GRANDVIEW HEIGHTS CITY SD/			
COLUMBUS/FRANKLIN	00801294	614/485-4015	70
Grandview Heights High Sch/*Columbus/*			
Franklin	00801311	614/485-4000	71

School/City/County DISTRICT/CITY/COUNTY	PID	TELEPHONE	PAGE NUMBER
Granger Elem Sch/*Medina*/Medina	05342554	330/239-1901	141
Grant Elem Sch/*Lakewood*/Cuyahoga	00793518	216/529-4217	47
Grant Elem Sch/*Willoughby*/Lake	00813900	440/942-5944	114
Grant Middle Sch/*Marion*/Marion	00821725	740/223-4900	138
Granville Christian Academy/*Granville*/Licking	04795879	740/587-4423	120
Granville Elem Sch/*Granville*/Licking	00814617	740/587-8102	117
GRANVILLE EXEMPTED VILLAGE SD/ GRANVILLE/LICKING	00814605	740/587-8101	117
Granville High Sch/*Granville*/Licking	00814629	740/587-8105	117
Granville Intermediate Sch/*Granville*/Licking	05070622	740/587-8103	117
Granville Middle Sch/*Granville*/Licking	00814631	740/587-8104	117
GREAT OAKS CAREER CAMPUSES/ CINCINNATI/HAMILTON	00810439	513/771-8840	89
Greater Ohio Virtual Sch/*Lebanon*/Warren	10018025	513/695-2977	2
Greater Summit County ELC/*Akron*/Summit	11566996	234/718-2626	2
Green Elem Sch/*Frankln Frnce*/Scioto	00830960	740/354-9290	178
Green Elem Sch/*Gallipolis*/Gallia	00803888	740/446-3236	81
Green Elem Sch/*Logan*/Hocking	00811184	740/385-7789	104
Green Elem Sch/*Smithville*/Wayne	00839112	330/669-3501	212
Green High Sch/*Frankln Frnce*/Scioto	00830972	740/354-9150	178
Green High Sch/*Uniontown*/Summit	00835049	330/896-7575	185
Green Inspiration Academy/*Cleveland*/Cuyahoga	11934252	216/378-9573	2
Green Intermediate Sch/*Uniontown*/Summit	04450768	330/896-7700	185
GREEN LOCAL SCH DIST/*FRANKLN FRNCE*/ SCIOTO	00830958	740/354-9221	178
GREEN LOCAL SCH DIST/*SMITHVILLE*/ WAYNE	00839095	330/669-3921	212
GREEN LOCAL SCH DIST/*UNIONTOWN*/ SUMMIT	00835025	330/896-7500	185
Green Middle Sch/*Smithville*/Wayne	00839100	330/669-3165	212
Green Middle Sch/*Uniontown*/Summit	00835051	330/896-7710	185
Green Primary Sch/*Uniontown*/Summit	10031405	330/899-8700	185
Green Road Developmental Ctr/*Highland Hls*/Cuyahoga	02051718	216/931-7340	39
Green Springs Elem Sch/*Green Springs*/Sandusky	00830520	419/547-4902	176
Green Valley Elem Sch/*Parma*/Cuyahoga	00794158	440/885-2433	49
Greenbriar Middle Sch/*Parma*/Cuyahoga	00794160	440/885-2370	49
Greene Co Career Center/*Xenia*/Greene	00804997	937/372-6941	84
GREENE CO ED SERVICE CENTER/ YELLOW SPGS/GREENE	00805006	937/767-1303	83
GREENE CO VOC SCH DIST/*XENIA*/ GREENE	00804985	937/372-6941	84
Greeneview Elem Sch/*Jamestown*/Greene	05100459	937/675-6867	84
Greeneview High Sch/*Jamestown*/Greene	00804739	937/675-9711	84
GREENEVIEW LOCAL SCH DIST/ JAMESTOWN/GREENE	00804715	937/675-2728	84
Greeneview Middle Sch/*Jamestown*/Greene	00804727	937/675-9391	84
Greenfield Elem Sch/*Greenfield*/Highland	00811005	937/981-3241	103
GREENFIELD EXEMPTED VILLAGE SD/ GREENFIELD/HIGHLAND	00810984	937/981-2152	103
Greenfield Middle Sch/*Greenfield*/Highland	03397826	937/981-2197	103
Greenmont Elem Sch/*Kettering*/Montgomery	00824882	937/499-1850	150
Greenon Jr Sr High Sch/*Springfield*/Clark	00787648	937/340-6372	27
GREENON LOCAL SCH DIST/*ENON*/ CLARK	00787612	937/864-1202	27
Greensview Elem Sch/*Upper Arlngtn*/Franklin	00802133	614/487-5050	74
Greentown Intermediate Sch/*North Canton*/Stark	00833261	330/497-5645	187
Greenview Day Treatment Center/*Shaker HTS*/Cuyahoga	04008937	216/751-8453	39
Greenview Upper Elem Sch/*South Euclid*/Cuyahoga	03319769	216/691-2245	51
GREENVILLE CITY SCH DIST/ GREENVILLE/DARKE	00797576	937/548-3185	55
Greenville Elem Sch/*Greenville*/Darke	00797588	937/548-3185	55
Greenville Middle Sch/*Greenville*/Darke	00797617	937/548-3185	55
Greenville Senior High Sch/*Greenville*/Darke	00797605	937/548-4188	55
Greenwood Early Learning Ctr/*Uniontown*/Summit	00835075	330/896-7474	185
Greenwood Elem Sch/*Toledo*/Lucas	00818091	419/473-8263	130
Griffith Thomas Elem Sch/*Dublin*/Franklin	03049445	614/764-5970	70
Grindstone Elem Sch/*Berea*/Cuyahoga	00790798	216/898-8305	41
Gross Schechter Day Sch/*Pepper Pike*/Cuyahoga	02236748	216/763-1400	53
Grove City Christian Sch/*Grove City*/Franklin	03414058	614/875-3000	77
Grove City High Sch/*Grove City*/Franklin	00801907	614/801-3300	73
Grove Patterson Academy/*Toledo*/Lucas	04867161	419/671-3350	129
Groveport Elem Sch/*Groveport*/Franklin	00801543	614/836-4975	71
Groveport Madison High Sch/*Groveport*/Franklin	00801555	614/836-4964	71
GROVEPORT MADISON LOCAL SD/ GROVEPORT/FRANKLIN	00801488	614/492-2520	71
Groveport Madison MS Central/*Groveport*/Franklin	00801567	614/836-4957	71
Groveport Madison MS South/*Groveport*/Franklin	01399268	614/836-4953	71
Groveport Madison MS-North/*Columbus*/Franklin	01399270	614/837-5508	71
Guardian Angels Sch/*Cincinnati*/Hamilton	00808292	513/624-3141	95
Gurney Elem Sch/*Chagrin Falls*/Cuyahoga	00791027	440/893-4030	42
Guy Jr High Sch/*Youngstown*/Trumbull	00836471	330/759-3909	199

H

H B Booker Wraparound Sch/*Cleveland*/Cuyahoga	00791699	216/838-6350	43
H C Mines Elem Sch/*Warren*/Trumbull	00836201	330/856-8270	198
H G Blake Elem Sch/*Medina*/Medina	04943026	330/636-3900	141
Hadley E Watts Middle Sch/*Centerville*/Montgomery	00823993	937/434-0370	149
Hamersville Elem Sch/*Hamersville*/Brown	00786228	937/379-1144	20
Hamilton Christian Sch/*Hamilton*/Butler	03221875	513/863-3107	24
HAMILTON CITY SCH DIST/*HAMILTON*/ BUTLER	00786424	513/887-5000	21
HAMILTON CO ED SERVICE CENTER/ CINCINNATI/HAMILTON	00808084	513/674-4200	87
Hamilton Co Math & Sci Academy/*Cincinnati*/Hamilton	04951114	513/728-8620	87
HAMILTON COUNTY ESC/*CINCINNATI*/ HAMILTON	04499673	513/674-4200	97
Hamilton Elem Sch/*Columbus*/Franklin	00801359	614/491-8044	71
Hamilton High Sch/*Hamilton*/Butler	00786591	513/868-7700	22
Hamilton HS-Freshman Campus/*Hamilton*/Butler	00786620	513/896-3400	22
Hamilton Intermediate Sch/*Columbus*/Franklin	05271656	614/491-8044	71
HAMILTON LOCAL SCH DIST/ COLUMBUS/FRANKLIN	00801347	614/491-8044	71
Hamilton Middle Sch/*Columbus*/Franklin	00801373	614/491-8044	71
Hamilton STEM Academy/*Columbus*/Franklin	00800288	614/365-5568	68
Hamilton Twp High Sch/*Columbus*/Franklin	00801361	614/491-8044	71
HAMILTON-CLERMONT CO-OP OCA/ LOVELAND/CLERMONT	04499477	513/931-7120	32
Hamilton-Maineville Prim Sch/*Maineville*/Warren	11817343	513/899-4760	208
Hampton Bennett ECC/*Franklin*/Warren	11209708	937/743-5290	207
Hanby Elementary/*Westerville*/Franklin	04021745	614/797-7100	75
HANCOCK CO ED SERVICE CENTER/ FINDLAY/HANCOCK	00810154	419/422-7525	97
Hancock Co MH Unit/*Findlay*/Hancock	04025959	419/422-7525	97
Hancock Co SBH Unit/*Findlay*/Hancock	04025961	419/422-7525	97
Hancock Elem Sch/*Sandusky*/Erie	00798659	419/984-1210	61
Hanna J Ashton Middle Sch/*Reynoldsburg*/Franklin	00801684	614/367-1530	73
Hannah Crawford Elem Sch/*Crestline*/Crawford	00790188	419/562-5753	38
Hannah Gibbons STEM Sch/*Cleveland*/Cuyahoga	04752475	216/838-0750	43
Hannan Trace Elem Sch/*Crown City*/Gallia	00803929	740/256-6468	80
Happy Day Sch/*Ravenna*/Portage	02052425	330/678-2400	164
Happy Hearts Sch/*Ashtabula*/Ashtabula	02051524	440/224-2177	12
Harbor Education Serv Leap Prg/*Kent*/Portage	11222774	330/676-8674	167
Hardin Cmty Sch/*Kenton*/Hardin	12259495	419/673-3210	2
Hardin Northern Elem Sch/*Dola*/Hardin	00810207	419/759-3158	100
Hardin Northern High Sch/*Dola*/Hardin	04881208	419/759-3515	100
HARDIN NORTHERN LOCAL SCH DIST/ DOLA/HARDIN	00810192	419/759-2331	100
Hardin-Houston Local Sch/*Houston*/Shelby	00831990	937/295-3010	183
HARDIN-HOUSTON LOCAL SCH DIST/ HOUSTON/SHELBY	00831976	937/295-3010	182
Harding Elem Sch/*Youngstown*/Mahoning	00820563	330/744-7517	136
Harding High Sch/*Marion*/Marion	00821775	740/223-4700	138
Harding Middle High Sch/*Fairport Hbr*/Lake	00813211	440/354-3592	112
Harding Middle Sch/*Lakewood*/Cuyahoga	00793520	216/529-4261	47
Harding Middle Sch/*Steubenville*/Jefferson	00812542	740/282-3481	109
Harlan-Butlerville Prim Sch/*Blanchester*/Warren	11817331	513/899-5200	208
Harman Elem Sch/*Dayton*/Montgomery	00825551	937/297-5338	152
Harmar Elem Sch/*Marietta*/Washington	00838754	740/374-6510	210

DISTRICT & SCHOOL TELEPHONE INDEX

Market Data Retrieval

School/City/County DISTRICT/CITY/COUNTY	PID	TELEPHONE NUMBER	PAGE
Harmon Middle Sch/*Aurora*/Portage	00828199	330/562-3375	165
Harmon Middle Sch/*Pickerington*/Fairfield	02042987	614/835-2000	64
Harold Lewis Center/*Marysville*/Union	02180450	937/645-6733	204
Harold Schnell Elem Sch/*W Carrollton*/Montgomery	00825898	937/859-5121	153
Harris-Jackson Cmty Lrng Ctr/*Akron*/Summit	00834100	330/761-1315	191
Harrison Career Center/*Cadiz*/Belmont	01417391	740/942-2148	18
Harrison Centrl Jr Sr High Sch/*Cadiz*/Harrison	00810570	740/942-7700	101
Harrison Co Developmental Pgrm/*Cadiz*/Harrison	04009096	740/942-2158	100
Harrison East Elem Sch/*Hopedale*/Harrison	00810611	740/942-7550	101
Harrison Elem Sch/*Harrison*/Hamilton	00807664	513/367-4161	93
Harrison Elem Sch/*Lakewood*/Cuyahoga	00793532	216/529-4230	47
HARRISON HILLS CITY SCH DIST/**CADIZ/HARRISON**	00810544	740/942-7800	101
Harrison North Elem Sch/*Scio*/Harrison	00810635	740/942-7500	101
Harrison Street Elem Sch/*Sunbury*/Delaware	12031487	740/965-7850	58
Harry Russell Elem Sch/*W Carrollton*/Montgomery	00825874	937/859-5121	153
Harter Reading & Math Prep Sch/*Canton*/Stark	00832530	330/456-1001	185
Hartville Christian Sch/*Hartville*/Stark	00833778	330/877-2529	190
Hartwell Sch/*Cincinnati*/Hamilton	00805678	513/363-2300	88
Harvard Ave Performance Acad/*Cleveland*/Cuyahoga	12162971	216/283-5100	2
Harvard Elem Sch/*Toledo*/Lucas	00817607	419/671-2700	129
Harvest Preparatory Sch/*Canal Wnchstr*/Franklin	03184198	614/382-1111	77
Harvest Temple Christian Acad/*Clyde*/Sandusky	04836693	419/547-8251	177
Harvey Rice Wraparound/*Cleveland*/Cuyahoga	00791754	216/838-1500	43
Hastings Middle Sch/*Upper Arlngtn*/Franklin	00802145	614/487-5100	74
Hathaway Brown Sch/*Shaker HTS*/Cuyahoga	00797411	216/932-4214	54
Hatton Cmty Learning Center/*Akron*/Summit	00834112	330/761-7980	191
Hawken Lower-Middle Sch/*Cleveland*/Cuyahoga	04157203	440/423-2031	54
Hawken Sch/*Gates Mills*/Cuyahoga	00797423	440/423-4446	54
Hawkins Elem Sch/*Toledo*/Lucas	00817619	419/671-1550	129
Hawthorne Elem Sch/*Columbus*/Franklin	01171963	614/797-7130	75
Hawthorne Elem Sch/*Lorain*/Lorain	00816330	440/830-4150	124
Hayes Art & Academic HS/*Columbus*/Franklin	01531868	614/365-6681	68
Hayes Elem Sch/*Fremont*/Sandusky	00830609	419/332-6371	177
Hayes Elem Sch/*Lakewood*/Cuyahoga	00793544	216/529-4228	47
Hayes Elem Sch/*Marion*/Marion	00821854	740/223-4950	138
Hayes Intermediate Sch/*Grove City*/Franklin	05273185	614/801-6200	73
Hays-Porter Elem Sch/*Cincinnati*/Hamilton	00805680	513/363-1000	88
Hayward Middle Sch/*Springfield*/Clark	00788020	937/505-4190	28
Hazel Harvey Elem Sch/*Doylestown*/Wayne	00839033	330/658-2522	211
Heartland Christian Sch/*Columbiana*/Columbiana	04986987	330/482-2331	36
HEATH CITY SCH DIST/HEATH/**LICKING**	00814655	740/238-7110	117
Heath High Sch/*Heath*/Licking	00814681	740/238-7150	117
Heath Middle Sch/*Heath*/Licking	00814667	740/238-7140	117
Hebrew Academy of Cleveland/*Cleveland HTS*/Cuyahoga	00795140	216/321-5838	54
Hebron Elem Sch/*Hebron*/Licking	00814772	740/928-7126	118
Heir Force Cmty Sch/*Lima*/Allen	05382633	419/228-9241	7
Helen Arnold Cmty Lrng Center/*Akron*/Summit	10911659	330/376-0153	191
Helen Muraski Elem Sch/*Strongsville*/Cuyahoga	00794873	440/572-7160	51
Helen Steiner Rice Elem Sch/*Lorain*/Lorain	00816328	440/830-4160	124
Helke Elem Sch/*Vandalia*/Montgomery	00825666	937/415-3000	153
Henry Defer Intermediate Sch/*Streetsboro*/Portage	05092151	330/422-2480	167
Henry F Lamuth Middle Sch/*Painesville*/Lake	00813534	440/354-4394	114
Herberich Primary Sch/*Akron*/Summit	00834734	330/664-4991	192
Herbert Mills Elem Sch/*Reynoldsburg*/Franklin	00801660	614/367-2160	73
Heritage Christian Sch/*Brooklyn*/Cuyahoga	03061338	216/476-7976	54
Heritage Christian Sch/*Canton*/Stark	00833780	330/452-8271	190
Heritage Christian Sch/*Findlay*/Hancock	02198299	419/424-9511	99
Heritage Christian Sch/*Marion*/Marion	02826381	740/382-6248	139
Heritage Early Childhood Sch/*Liberty Twp*/Butler	04019780	513/863-7060	22
Heritage Elem Sch/*Lewis Center*/Delaware	11714753	740/657-5000	59
Heritage Elem Sch/*Lima*/Allen	00783812	419/996-3390	9
Heritage Elem Sch/*Marion*/Marion	00821995	740/725-5500	139
Heritage Elem Sch/*Medina*/Medina	01413838	330/636-4400	141
Heritage Elem Sch/*Pickerington*/Fairfield	04938057	614/833-6385	64
Heritage Hill Elem Sch/*Cincinnati*/Hamilton	00807468	513/864-1400	92
Heritage Middle Sch/*E Cleveland*/Cuyahoga	00793116	216/268-6610	45
Heritage Middle Sch/*Newark*/Licking	00815049	740/670-7110	119
Heritage Middle Sch/*Painesville*/Lake	00813728	440/392-5250	113
Heritage Middle Sch/*Westerville*/Franklin	03246954	614/797-6600	75
Herman K Ankeney Middle Sch/*Dayton*/Greene	00804507	937/429-7567	83
Hershey Montessori Sch/*Huntsburg*/Geauga	11234997	440/636-6290	83
Hershey Montessori Sch/*Painesville*/Lake	03121847	440/357-0918	115
Heskett Middle Sch/*Bedford HTS*/Cuyahoga	00790619	440/439-4450	41
Heywood Elem Sch/*Troy*/Miami	00823632	937/332-6750	147
Hiawatha Elem Sch/*Toledo*/Lucas	00818106	419/473-8268	130
Hickory Ridge Elem Sch/*Brunswick*/Medina	00822183	330/273-0483	140
Hicksville Elem Sch/*Hicksville*/Defiance	00798001	419/542-7475	57
HICKSVILLE EXEMPTED VILLAGE SD/**HICKSVILLE/DEFIANCE**	00797992	419/542-7665	57
Hicksville Jr Sr High Sch/*Hicksville*/Defiance	00798013	419/542-7636	57
High Point Elem Sch/*Gahanna*/Franklin	03047461	614/478-5545	70
High Street Christian Academy/*Columbus*/Franklin	11239284	614/888-5121	77
High Tech Academy/*Cleveland*/Cuyahoga	10016247	216/987-3549	43
Highland Co Pre-School Unit/*Hillsboro*/Highland	04025703	937/393-4237	102
Highland Community Lrng Ctr/*Columbus*/Franklin	11421217	614/210-0830	77
Highland Drive Elem Sch/*Brecksville*/Cuyahoga	00790920	440/740-4300	41
Highland Elem Sch/*Columbus*/Franklin	00800317	614/365-5935	68
Highland Elem Sch/*Hamilton*/Butler	00786462	513/868-5620	22
Highland Elem Sch/*Marengo*/Morrow	02846501	419/768-3040	155
Highland Elem Sch/*Stow*/Summit	00835532	330/689-5330	194
Highland Elem Sch/*Sylvania*/Lucas	00817255	419/824-8611	129
Highland High Sch/*Marengo*/Morrow	00826153	419/768-3101	155
Highland High Sch/*Medina*/Medina	00822341	330/239-1901	141
HIGHLAND LOCAL SCH DIST/**MARENGO/MORROW**	00826141	419/768-2206	155
HIGHLAND LOCAL SCH DIST/**MEDINA/MEDINA**	00822339	330/239-1901	141
Highland Middle Sch/*Marengo*/Morrow	00826165	419/768-2781	155
Highland Middle Sch/*Medina*/Medina	00822353	330/239-1901	141
Highland Park Elem Sch/*Grove City*/Franklin	00801921	614/801-8200	73
Highview 6th Grade Center/*Middletown*/Butler	00786993	513/420-4566	23
Hiland Jr Sr High Sch/*Berlin*/Holmes	00811316	330/893-2626	104
Hill View Elem Sch/*Sylvania*/Lucas	00817229	419/824-8612	129
Hillcrest Academy/*Cincinnati*/Hamilton	00805654	513/552-1200	2
Hillel Academy of Dayton/*Dayton*/Montgomery	00825953	937/277-8966	154
Hilliard Bradley High Sch/*Hilliard*/Franklin	11451597	614/921-7400	72
Hilliard City Pre-School/*Hilliard*/Franklin	10907488	614/921-5050	72
HILLIARD CITY SCH DIST/COLUMBUS/**FRANKLIN**	00801713	614/921-7000	71
Hilliard Crossing Elem Sch/*Hilliard*/Franklin	04035318	614/921-5600	72
Hilliard Darby High Sch/*Hilliard*/Franklin	04753039	614/921-7300	72
Hilliard Davidson High Sch/*Hilliard*/Franklin	00801775	614/921-7200	72
Hilliard Heritage Middle Sch/*Hilliard*/Franklin	00801787	614/921-7500	72
Hilliard Horizon Elem Sch/*Columbus*/Franklin	04449965	614/921-5800	72
Hilliard Memorial Middle Sch/*Hilliard*/Franklin	04945763	614/921-7600	72
Hilliard Station 6th Grade Sch/*Hilliard*/Franklin	03391602	614/921-6800	72
Hilliard Tharp 6th Grade Sch/*Hilliard*/Franklin	04945749	614/921-6900	72
Hilliard Weaver Middle Sch/*Hilliard*/Franklin	04286115	614/921-7500	72
Hills & Dales Training Center/*Hillsboro*/Highland	04009072	937/393-4237	102
Hills Elem Sch/*Mingo Jct*/Jefferson	00812449	740/283-2479	109
HILLSBORO CITY SCH DIST/**HILLSBORO/HIGHLAND**	00811043	937/393-3475	103
Hillsboro Elem Sch/*Hillsboro*/Highland	00811081	937/393-3132	103
Hillsboro High Sch/*Hillsboro*/Highland	00811055	937/393-3485	103
Hillsboro Middle Sch/*Hillsboro*/Highland	04917118	937/393-9877	103
Hillsdale Elem Sch/*Hayesville*/Ashland	00784220	419/368-4364	11
Hillsdale High Sch/*Jeromesville*/Ashland	00784232	419/368-6841	11
HILLSDALE LOCAL SCH DIST/**JEROMESVILLE/ASHLAND**	00784218	419/368-8231	11
Hillsdale Middle Sch/*Jeromesville*/Ashland	00784244	419/368-4911	11
Hillside Middle Sch/*Seven Hills*/Cuyahoga	00794184	440/885-2373	49
Hilltonia Middle Sch/*Columbus*/Franklin	00800329	614/365-5937	68

Ohio School Directory

DISTRICT & SCHOOL TELEPHONE INDEX

School/City/County DISTRICT/CITY/COUNTY	PID	TELEPHONE NUMBER	PAGE
Hilltop Elem Sch/*Beachwood*/Cuyahoga	00790528	216/831-7144	40
Hilltop Elem Sch/*Canfield*/Mahoning	00819966	330/533-9806	134
Hilltop Elem Sch/*Reading*/Hamilton	00807602	513/733-4322	93
Hilltop Primary Sch/*Wyoming*/Hamilton	00807925	513/206-7270	94
Hillview Elem Sch/*Newark*/Licking	00815037	740/670-7310	119
Hilton Elem Sch/*Brecksville*/Cuyahoga	00790932	440/740-4600	41
Hinckley Elem Sch/*Hinckley*/Medina	00822365	330/239-1901	141
Hocking Hills Elem Sch/*Logan*/Hocking	00811237	740/385-7071	104
Hoffman Trails Elem Sch/*Hilliard*/Franklin	04945062	614/921-5700	72
Holden Elem Sch/*Kent*/Portage	00828462	330/676-8400	165
HOLGATE LOCAL SCH DIST/HOLGATE/ HENRY	00810685	419/264-5141	101
Holgate Sch/*Holgate*/Henry	00810697	419/264-5141	101
Holland Elem Sch/*Holland*/Lucas	00817176	419/867-5655	128
Hollingsworth East Elem Sch/*Eaton*/Preble	00828931	937/456-5173	168
Holloway Elem Sch/*Holland*/Lucas	04282121	419/867-5703	128
Holly Hill Elem Sch/*Amelia*/Clermont	02175998	513/943-8900	31
Holmes Co Training Center/*Holmesville*/ Holmes	02052061	330/674-8045	104
Holmesville Elem Sch/*Holmesville*/Wayne	00839382	330/279-2341	213
Holt Crossing Intermediate Sch/*Grove City*/ Franklin	04931695	614/801-8700	73
Holy Angels Sch/*Dayton*/Montgomery	00808307	937/229-5959	154
Holy Angels Sch/*Sidney*/Shelby	00808319	937/492-9293	183
Holy Cross Cath Sch-Defiance/*Defiance*/ Defiance	00818936	419/784-2021	58
Holy Cross Lutheran Sch/*Cleveland*/Cuyahoga	02188579	216/941-2770	54
Holy Family Catholic Sch/*Cincinnati*/ Hamilton	00808345	513/921-8483	95
Holy Family Catholic Sch/*Parma*/Cuyahoga	00795542	440/842-7785	52
Holy Family Learning Center/*Lakewood*/ Cuyahoga	03448918	216/521-4352	52
Holy Family Sch/*Poland*/Mahoning	00820989	330/757-3713	137
Holy Family Sch/*Stow*/Summit	00795530	330/688-3816	195
Holy Name Elem Sch/*Cleveland*/Cuyahoga	00795566	216/341-0084	52
Holy Name High Sch/*Parma Heights*/Cuyahoga	00795786	440/886-0300	52
Holy Rosary Sch/*Saint Marys*/Auglaize	00808357	419/394-5291	17
Holy Spirit Sch/*Columbus*/Franklin	00802834	614/861-0475	76
Holy Trinity Christian Academy/*Warren*/ Trumbull	11231464	330/399-7642	201
Holy Trinity Sch/*Avon*/Lorain	00795592	440/937-6420	126
Holy Trinity Sch/*Somerset*/Perry	00802842	740/743-1324	162
Holy Trinity Sch/*Swanton*/Fulton	00819136	419/644-3971	80
Hook Elem Sch/*Troy*/Miami	00823644	937/332-6760	147
Hoover High Sch/*North Canton*/Stark	01534925	330/497-5620	187
Hope Academy for Autism/*Warren*/Trumbull	11832654	330/469-9501	201
Hope Academy Northwest/*Cleveland*/Cuyahoga	10017576	216/226-6800	2
Hope Academy-Brown St Campus/*Akron*/Summit	04814669	330/785-0180	2
Hope Academy-Northcoast/*Cleveland*/Cuyahoga	05220255	216/429-0232	2
Hope Academy-West/*Cleveland*/Cuyahoga	05009154	216/251-5450	2
Hope Haven Sch/*Jackson*/Jackson	02052085	740/286-6491	107
Hope Learning Academy Toledo/*Toledo*/Lucas	12160753	419/297-6313	127
Hopewell Early Childhood Sch/*West Chester*/ Butler	00786656	513/777-6128	22
Hopewell Junior High Sch/*West Chester*/ Butler	00786668	513/777-2258	22
Hopewell Sch/*Coshocton*/Coshocton	02051641	740/622-2032	36
Hopewell-Loudon Local Sch/*Bascom*/Seneca	00831550	419/937-2804	181
HOPEWELL-LOUDON LOCAL SD/ BASCOM/SENECA	00831548	419/937-2216	181
Hopkins Elem Sch/*Mentor*/Lake	00813429	440/255-6179	113
Horace Mann Elem Sch/*Dayton*/Montgomery	00824363	937/542-4890	149
Horace Mann Elem Sch/*Lakewood*/Cuyahoga	00793491	216/529-4257	47
Horace Mann Elem Sch/*Springfield*/Clark	00788109	937/505-4280	28
Horizon Sci Acad-Cincinnati/*Cincinnati*/ Hamilton	10017588	513/242-0099	2
Horizon Sci Acad-Cleveland HS/*Cleveland*/ Cuyahoga	04880280	216/432-3660	3
Horizon Sci Acad-Cleveland MS/*Cleveland*/ Cuyahoga	11915452	216/432-9940	39
Horizon Sci Acad-Columbus ES/*Columbus*/ Franklin	12163236	614/475-4585	3
Horizon Sci Acad-Columbus MS/*Columbus*/ Franklin	04880292	614/428-6564	3
Horizon Sci Acad-Columbus Prim/*Columbus*/ Franklin	12322688	614/532-3311	3
Horizon Sci Acad-Dayton Downtn/*Dayton*/ Montgomery	12163200	937/281-1980	3
Horizon Sci Acad-Dayton ES/*Dayton*/ Montgomery	11467417	937/277-1177	3
Horizon Sci Acad-Dayton HS/*Dayton*/ Montgomery	10017590	937/281-1480	3
Horizon Sci Acad-Sprngfld/*Toledo*/Lucas	10017617	419/535-0524	3
Horizon Sci Acad-Youngstwn/*Youngstown*/ Mahoning	11568138	330/782-3003	3
Horizon Sci Academy-Denison/*Cleveland*/ Cuyahoga	10017605	216/739-9911	39
Horizon Sci Academy-Lorain/*Lorain*/Lorain	12100698	440/282-4277	3
Horizon Sci Academy-Toledo/*Toledo*/Lucas	05382669	419/474-3350	3
Horizon Science Acad-Columbus/*Columbus*/ Franklin	12163614	614/846-7616	66
Houston Early Learning Center/*Cincinnati*/ Hamilton	00807171	513/385-8000	91
Howard Chapman Elem Sch/*Strongsville*/ Cuyahoga	00794885	440/572-7140	51
Howland Glen Primary Sch/*Warren*/Trumbull	00836160	330/856-8275	198
Howland High Sch/*Warren*/Trumbull	00836172	330/856-8220	198
HOWLAND LOCAL SCH DIST/WARREN/ TRUMBULL	00836146	330/856-8200	198
Howland Middle Sch/*Warren*/Trumbull	00836184	330/856-8250	198
Howland Springs Primary Sch/*Warren*/ Trumbull	00836196	330/856-8280	198
Hubbard Elem Sch/*Hubbard*/Trumbull	00836275	330/534-1921	198
HUBBARD EXEMPTED VILLAGE SD/ HUBBARD/TRUMBULL	00836237	330/534-1921	198
Hubbard High Sch/*Hubbard*/Trumbull	00836251	330/534-1921	198
Hubbard Mastery Sch/*Columbus*/Franklin	00800185	614/365-5564	68
Hubbard Middle Sch/*Hubbard*/Trumbull	00836263	330/534-1921	198
HUBER HEIGHTS CITY SCH DIST/ HUBER HEIGHTS/MONTGOMERY	00825721	937/237-6300	150
Huber Ridge Elem Sch/*Westerville*/Franklin	00802341	614/797-7150	75
HUDSON CITY SCH DIST/HUDSON/ SUMMIT	00835099	330/653-1200	193
Hudson High Sch/*Hudson*/Summit	00835128	330/653-1416	193
Hudson Middle Sch/*Hudson*/Summit	00835130	330/653-1316	193
Hudson Montessori Sch/*Hudson*/Summit	01754010	330/650-0424	196
Hughes STEM High Sch/*Cincinnati*/Hamilton	11451561	513/363-7400	88
Hull Prairie Interm Sch/*Perrysburg*/Wood	12233300	419/873-6293	218
Hunter Elem Sch/*Franklin*/Warren	00838302	937/743-8655	207
Huntington Elem Sch/*Brunswick*/Medina	02126741	330/273-0484	140
Huntington Elem Sch/*Chillicothe*/Ross	00830257	740/663-2191	175
Huntington High Sch/*Chillicothe*/Ross	04943789	740/663-2230	175
HUNTINGTON LOCAL SCH DIST/ CHILLICOTHE/ROSS	00830245	740/663-5892	175
Huntington Middle Sch/*Chillicothe*/Ross	04943777	740/663-6079	175
HURON CITY SCH DIST/HURON/ERIE	00798427	419/433-1234	60
Huron High Sch/*Huron*/Erie	00798439	419/433-1234	61
Huron Primary Sch/*Ashtabula*/Ashtabula	00784438	440/992-1230	12
Huy Elem Sch/*Columbus*/Franklin	00800367	614/365-5977	68
Hyatts Middle Sch/*Powell*/Delaware	10907531	740/657-5400	59
Hyde Park Sch/*Cincinnati*/Hamilton	11821150	513/363-2800	88
Hylen Souders Elem Sch/*Galena*/Delaware	00798142	740/965-3200	58
Hyre Cmty Learning Center/*Akron*/Summit	00834174	330/761-7930	191

I

I Promise Sch/*Akron*/Summit	12307212	330/761-1516	191
Ida Sue Sch/*Wooster*/Wayne	02052700	330/345-7251	211
Ilead Spring Meadows/*Holland*/Lucas	12259500	419/491-7423	3
Imac Academy/*Mansfield*/Richland	10017629	419/525-0105	3
Imagine Academy at Sullivant/*Columbus*/ Franklin	11453870	614/308-5991	3
Imagine Akron Kinder Academy/*Akron*/Summit	11816351	330/379-1034	3
Imagine Bella Acad Excellence/*Cleveland*/ Cuyahoga	11564613	216/481-1500	3
Imagine Clay Ave Cmty ES/*Toledo*/Lucas	11136010	419/727-9900	3
Imagine Columbus Primary Acad/*Columbus*/ Franklin	10017370	614/433-7510	3
Imagine Great Western Academy/*Columbus*/ Franklin	05382621	614/276-1028	66
Imagine Groveport Cmty ES/*Groveport*/ Franklin	11564663	614/574-4100	3
Imagine Groveport Prep Sch/*Groveport*/ Franklin	11564649	614/574-0037	3
Imagine Harrisburg PK Cmty Sch/*Columbus*/ Franklin	11564546	614/223-1510	3
Imagine Hill Ave Environ Sch/*Toledo*/Lucas	11818646	419/867-8167	3
Imagine Klepinger Rd Cmty Sch/*Dayton*/ Montgomery	11564687	937/610-1710	3
Imagine Madison Ave Sch-Arts/*Toledo*/Lucas	11458117	419/259-4000	3
Imagine Woodbury Academy/*Dayton*/Montgomery	11916494	937/610-1710	3
Immaculate Conception Academy/*Norwood*/ Hamilton	04883983	513/731-0154	96
Immaculate Conception Grd Sch/*Celina*/ Mercer	00808369	419/586-2379	144

School Year 2019-2020   800-333-8802   OH-V17

DISTRICT & SCHOOL TELEPHONE INDEX

Market Data Retrieval

School/City/County DISTRICT/CITY/COUNTY	PID	TELEPHONE NUMBER	PAGE
Immaculate Conception Sch/*Bellevue*/Huron	00818443	419/483-6066	107
Immaculate Conception Sch/*Columbus*/Franklin	00802858	614/267-6579	76
Immaculate Conception Sch/*Dayton*/Montgomery	00808371	937/253-8831	154
Immaculate Conception Sch/*Dennison*/Tuscarawas	00802860	740/922-3539	204
Immaculate Conception Sch/*Port Clinton*/Ottawa	00818431	419/734-3315	160
Immaculate Heart of Mary Sch/*Cincinnati*/Hamilton	00808383	513/388-4086	95
Immaculate Heart of Mary Sch/*Cuyahoga FLS*/Summit	00795657	330/923-1220	195
Immanuel Lutheran Sch/*Hamilton*/Butler	00787208	513/895-9212	24
Incarnate Word Academy/*Parma Heights*/Cuyahoga	00795671	440/842-6818	52
Incarnation Sch/*Dayton*/Montgomery	00808395	937/433-1051	154
Independence Elem Sch/*Liberty TWP*/Butler	04282054	513/755-8300	22
Independence Elem Sch/*Lima*/Allen	00783783	419/996-3330	9
Independence High Sch/*Columbus*/Franklin	01399218	614/365-5372	68
Independence High Sch/*Independence*/Cuyahoga	00793441	216/642-5860	46
INDEPENDENCE LOCAL SCH DIST/INDEPENDENCE/CUYAHOGA	00793439	216/642-5850	46
Independence Middle Sch/*Independence*/Cuyahoga	00793453	216/642-5865	47
Independence Primary Sch/*Independence*/Cuyahoga	00793465	216/642-5870	47
Indian Creek High Sch/*Wintersville*/Jefferson	00812499	740/264-1163	109
INDIAN CREEK LOCAL SCH DIST/WINTERSVILLE/JEFFERSON	00812396	740/264-3502	109
Indian Creek Middle Sch/*Mingo Jct*/Jefferson	00812413	740/282-0834	109
Indian Hill Elem Sch/*Cincinnati*/Hamilton	00806713	513/272-4703	90
INDIAN HILL EXEMPTED VLG SD/CINCINNATI/HAMILTON	00806696	513/272-4500	90
Indian Hill High Sch/*Cincinnati*/Hamilton	00806725	513/272-4550	90
Indian Hill Middle Sch/*Cincinnati*/Hamilton	00806737	513/272-4642	90
Indian Hill Primary Sch/*Cincinnati*/Hamilton	03247154	513/272-4754	90
Indian Lake Elem Sch/*Lewistown*/Logan	00815518	937/686-7323	121
Indian Lake High Sch/*Lewistown*/Logan	00815532	937/686-8851	121
INDIAN LAKE LOCAL SCH DIST/LEWISTOWN/LOGAN	00815506	937/686-8601	121
Indian Lake Middle Sch/*Lewistown*/Logan	00815544	937/686-8833	121
Indian Riffle Elem Sch/*Kettering*/Montgomery	00824894	937/499-1720	150
Indian River Sch/*Massillon*/Stark	04202169	330/837-4211	3
Indian Run Elem Sch/*Dublin*/Franklin	00802236	614/764-5928	70
Indian Springs Elem Sch/*Columbus*/Franklin	00800379	614/365-6032	68
Indian Springs Elem Sch/*Powell*/Delaware	05275236	740/657-4950	59
Indian Trail Elem Sch/*Canal Wnchstr*/Franklin	04864901	614/833-2154	66
Indian Trail Elem Sch/*Stow*/Summit	00835544	330/689-5320	194
Indian Valley Digital Academy/*Gnadenhutten*/Tuscarawas	12171427	740/561-4034	202
Indian Valley High Sch/*Gnadenhutten*/Tuscarawas	00837293	740/254-4262	202
Indian Valley Intermediate Sch/*Enon*/Clark	00787662	937/864-7348	27
INDIAN VALLEY LOCAL SCH DIST/GNADENHUTTEN/TUSCARAWAS	00837267	740/254-4334	202
Indian Valley Middle Sch/*Tuscarawas*/Tuscarawas	10911752	740/922-4226	202
Indianola K-8 Sch/*Columbus*/Franklin	00800381	614/365-5579	68
Innes Cmty Learning Ctr/*Akron*/Summit	00834186	330/761-7900	191
Innis Elem Sch/*Columbus*/Franklin	01399220	614/365-5462	68
Innovative Learning Hub/*Hilliard*/Franklin	12366397	614/921-4850	72
Int'l Academy of Cincinnati/*West Chester*/Butler	05099721	513/755-0169	24
Int'l Newcomers Acad-Jefferson/*Cleveland*/Cuyahoga	11718230	216/838-7150	43
Intergenerational Sch/*Cleveland*/Cuyahoga	05009178	216/721-0120	39
International Academy Columbus/*Columbus*/Franklin	05220267	614/794-0644	66
Invictus High Sch/*Cleveland*/Cuyahoga	12100789	216/539-7200	3
Iowa Maple Elem Sch/*Cleveland*/Cuyahoga	00791819	216/838-0800	43
IRONTON CITY SCH DIST/IRONTON/LAWRENCE	00814277	740/532-4133	116
Ironton Elem Sch/*Ironton*/Lawrence	00814320	740/532-2209	116
Ironton High Sch/*Ironton*/Lawrence	00814306	740/532-3911	116
Ironton Middle Sch/*Ironton*/Lawrence	00814318	740/532-3347	116

School/City/County DISTRICT/CITY/COUNTY	PID	TELEPHONE NUMBER	PAGE
Isham Memorial Elem Sch/*Wadsworth*/Medina	00822470	330/335-1440	141
Islamic Sch of Greater Toledo/*Perrysburg*/Wood	10013312	419/874-8820	218

J

J & G Snow Sch/*Berea*/Cuyahoga	03397319	440/260-8251	41
J C Sommer Elem Sch/*Grove City*/Franklin	00802030	614/801-8350	73
J E Prass Elem Sch/*Kettering*/Montgomery	00824997	937/499-1780	150
J F Burns Elem Sch/*Maineville*/Warren	00838209	513/398-8050	207
J F Kennedy Sch/*Maple Heights*/Cuyahoga	00793685	216/438-6010	47
J T Karaffa Elem Sch/*Toronto*/Jefferson	02180163	740/537-2471	109
J W Reason Elem Sch/*Hilliard*/Franklin	00801799	614/921-5900	72
Jackman Elem Sch/*Toledo*/Lucas	00818132	419/473-8274	130
JACKSON CENTER LOCAL SCH DIST/JACKSON CTR/SHELBY	00832009	937/596-6053	183
Jackson Center Sch/*Jackson CTR*/Shelby	00832011	937/596-6053	183
JACKSON CITY SCH DIST/JACKSON/JACKSON	00811897	740/286-6442	107
Jackson High Sch/*Jackson*/Jackson	00811926	740/286-7575	107
Jackson High Sch/*Massillon*/Stark	00832827	330/837-3501	186
Jackson Intermediate Sch/*Hebron*/Licking	00814813	740/928-1915	118
JACKSON LOCAL SCH DIST/MASSILLON/STARK	00832798	330/830-8000	186
Jackson Memorial Middle Sch/*Massillon*/Stark	01417561	330/830-8034	186
Jackson Middle Sch/*Grove City*/Franklin	00801971	614/801-3800	73
Jackson Middle Sch/*Jackson*/Jackson	00811940	740/286-7586	107
Jackson-Milton Elem Sch/*North Jackson*/Mahoning	00820018	330/538-2257	134
JACKSON-MILTON LOCAL SCH DIST/NORTH JACKSON/MAHONING	00819978	330/538-3232	134
Jackson-Milton Middle High Sch/*North Jackson*/Mahoning	00820006	330/538-3308	134
Jacob Coy Middle Sch/*Xenia*/Greene	00804492	937/429-7577	83
Jacobs Primary Sch/*Findlay*/Hancock	00809935	419/425-8299	98
James A Garfield Elem Sch/*Garrettsville*/Portage	00828383	330/527-2184	165
James A Garfield High Sch/*Garrettsville*/Portage	00828395	330/527-4341	165
JAMES A GARFIELD LOCAL SD/GARRETTSVILLE/PORTAGE	00828371	330/527-4336	165
James A Garfield Middle Sch/*Garrettsville*/Portage	00828400	330/527-2151	165
James A Harmon Elem Sch/*Grove City*/Franklin	00802042	614/801-8150	73
James Conger Elem Sch/*Delaware*/Delaware	00798269	740/833-1300	58
James F Rhodes High Sch/*Cleveland*/Cuyahoga	00791821	216/838-3000	43
James J Hilfiker Elem Sch/*Gibsonburg*/Sandusky	00830673	419/637-7249	177
James N Gamble Montessori ES/*Cincinnati*/Hamilton	12364636	513/363-9600	88
James N Gamble Montessori HS/*Cincinnati*/Hamilton	11079606	513/363-2600	88
Jane Addams Bus Career Center/*Cleveland*/Cuyahoga	00791833	216/838-9250	44
Jane Chance Elem Sch/*Miamisburg*/Montgomery	00825276	937/384-0510	151
Jasper Elem Sch/*Piketon*/Pike	00828008	740/289-2425	164
Jefferson Area Jr High Sch/*Jefferson*/Ashtabula	11556305	440/576-4731	13
JEFFERSON AREA LOCAL SD/JEFFERSON/ASHTABULA	00784828	440/576-9180	13
Jefferson Area Sr High Sch/*Jefferson*/Ashtabula	00784842	440/576-4736	13
Jefferson Avenue Elem Sch/*Shadyside*/Belmont	00785846	740/676-9669	18
Jefferson Co Alt Sch/*Steubenville*/Jefferson	11219002	740/283-8557	108
Jefferson Co Christian Sch/*Wintersville*/Jefferson	02165474	740/535-1337	110
JEFFERSON CO ED SERVICE CENTER/STEUBENVILLE/JEFFERSON	00812669	740/283-3347	108
Jefferson Co Joint Voc Sch/*Bloomingdale*/Jefferson	01417456	740/264-5545	109
JEFFERSON CO JT VOC SCH DIST/BLOOMINGDALE/JEFFERSON	01417444	740/264-5545	109
Jefferson Elem Sch/*Eastlake*/Lake	00813912	440/942-7244	114
Jefferson Elem Sch/*Gahanna*/Franklin	00801426	614/478-5560	70
Jefferson Elem Sch/*Jefferson*/Ashtabula	00784866	440/576-2646	13
Jefferson Jr Sr High Sch/*Dayton*/Montgomery	00824806	937/835-5691	150
Jefferson Junior High Sch/*Toledo*/Lucas	00818144	419/473-8482	130

Ohio School Directory

DISTRICT & SCHOOL TELEPHONE INDEX

School/City/County DISTRICT/CITY/COUNTY	PID	TELEPHONE NUMBER	PAGE
JEFFERSON LOCAL SCH DIST/			
W JEFFERSON/MADISON	00819461	614/879-7654	132
Jefferson Middle Sch/*Delphos*/Allen	00783707	419/695-2523	8
Jefferson PK-8 Sch/*Warren*/Trumbull	00836914	330/675-6960	200
Jefferson Primary Sch/*Findlay*/Hancock	00809947	419/425-8298	98
Jefferson Senior High Sch/*Delphos*/Allen	00783692	419/695-1786	8
JEFFERSON TWP LOCAL SCH DIST/			
DAYTON/MONTGOMERY	00824777	937/835-5682	150
Jennings Cmty Learning Ctr/*Akron*/Summit	00834203	330/761-2002	191
Jennings Local Sch/*Fort Jennings*/Putnam	00829179	419/286-2238	169
JENNINGS LOCAL SCH DIST/			
FORT JENNINGS/PUTNAM	00829155	419/286-2238	169
Jerusalem Elem Sch/*Curtice*/Lucas	00817085	419/836-6111	128
JFK E3Agle Academy/*Cleveland*/Cuyahoga	12180557	216/838-5150	44
JFK Lower Campus/*Warren*/Trumbull	00820939	330/372-2375	201
JFK-Pact Academy/*Cleveland*/Cuyahoga	12180569	216/838-5200	44
John Adams Clg & Career Acad/*Cleveland*/Cuyahoga	12320020	216/838-4050	44
John Adams High Sch/*Cleveland*/Cuyahoga	11702346	216/838-4000	44
John Clem Elem Sch/*Newark*/Licking	00814978	740/670-7130	119
John Dewey Elem Sch/*Warrensvl HTS*/Cuyahoga	00794940	216/755-8743	51
John E Gregg Elem Sch/*Bergholz*/Jefferson	00812334	740/768-2100	109
John F Kennedy Catholic Sch/*Warren*/Trumbull	00821050	330/369-1804	201
John F Kennedy Elem Sch/*Kettering*/Montgomery	00824909	937/499-1830	150
John Foster Dulles Elem Sch/*Cincinnati*/Hamilton	00807406	513/574-3443	92
John Glenn High Sch/*New Concord*/Muskingum	00826311	740/826-7641	156
John H Morrison Elem Sch/*Dayton*/Montgomery	00825501	937/276-8341	152
John Marshall-Civic & Business/*Cleveland*/Cuyahoga	12114302	216/838-6050	44
John Marshall-Engineering/*Cleveland*/Cuyahoga	12114314	216/838-6102	44
John Marshall-Info Tech/*Cleveland*/Cuyahoga	12114326	216/838-6850	44
John McIntire Elem Sch/*Zanesville*/Muskingum	00826725	740/453-2851	157
John Muir Elem Sch/*Parma*/Cuyahoga	00794201	440/885-2424	49
John P Parker Elem Sch/*Cincinnati*/Hamilton	00805824	513/363-2900	88
John Paul II Catholic Sch/*Cincinnati*/Hamilton	02095415	513/521-0860	95
John R Lea Middle Sch/*Apple Creek*/Wayne	00839394	330/698-3151	213
John Sells Middle Sch/*Dublin*/Franklin	00802224	614/764-5919	70
John XXIII Catholic Elem Sch/*Middletown*/Butler	00808400	513/424-1196	24
Johnnycake Corners Elem Sch/*Galena*/Delaware	10907517	740/657-5650	59
Johnson Park Middle Sch/*Columbus*/Franklin	00800410	614/365-6501	68
Johnstown Elem Sch/*Johnstown*/Licking	00814710	740/967-5461	118
Johnstown-Monroe High Sch/*Johnstown*/Licking	00814722	740/967-2721	118
JOHNSTOWN-MONROE LOCAL SD/			
JOHNSTOWN/LICKING	00814708	740/967-6846	118
Jonathan Alder High Sch/*Plain City*/Madison	00819538	614/873-4642	132
Jonathan Alder Junior High Sch/*Plain City*/Madison	10001216	614/873-4635	132
JONATHAN ALDER LOCAL SCH DIST/			
PLAIN CITY/MADISON	00819514	614/873-5621	132
Jones Leadership Academy/*Toledo*/Lucas	10910875	419/671-5400	129
Jones Middle Sch/*Upper Arlngtn*/Franklin	00802157	614/487-5080	74
Joseph & Florence Mandel Sch/*Beachwood*/Cuyahoga	00795073	216/464-4055	54
JOSEPH BADGER LOCAL SCH DIST/			
KINSMAN/TRUMBULL	00836287	330/876-2810	198
Joseph M Gallagher Elem Sch/*Cleveland*/Cuyahoga	00792693	216/838-6400	44
Joseph Welty Middle Sch/*New Phila*/Tuscarawas	00837401	330/364-0645	203
Joshua Dixon Elem Sch/*Columbiana*/Columbiana	00789218	330/482-5355	34
Judith A Resnik Cmty Lrng Ctr/*Akron*/Summit	00833986	330/873-3370	191
Juliann Lange Sch/*Dayton*/Montgomery	04914427	937/299-8730	152
Julie Billiart Sch/*Cleveland*/Cuyahoga	00795683	216/381-1191	52
Junction City Elem Sch/*Junction City*/Perry	00827494	740/987-3751	161

K

Kae Avenue Elem Sch/*Whitehall*/Franklin	00802468	614/417-5600	75
Kairos Academy/*Newark*/Licking	11231567	740/345-1995	120
Kalida Elem Sch/*Kalida*/Putnam	00829193	419/532-3845	170
Kalida High Sch/*Kalida*/Putnam	00829208	419/532-3529	170
KALIDA LOCAL SCH DIST/KALIDA/			
PUTNAM	00829181	419/532-3534	169

School/City/County DISTRICT/CITY/COUNTY	PID	TELEPHONE NUMBER	PAGE
Katherine Thomas Elem Sch/*Windham*/Portage	00828785	330/326-9800	167
Kean Elem Sch/*Wooster*/Wayne	00839552	330/345-6634	213
Keene Elem Sch/*Coshocton*/Coshocton	00789945	740/622-5884	37
Kelleys Island Local Sch/*Kelleys Is*/Erie	00798489	419/746-2730	61
KELLEYS ISLAND LOCAL SCH DIST/			
KELLEYS IS/ERIE	00798477	419/746-2730	61
Kemp PK-6 Sch/*Dayton*/Montgomery	00824430	937/542-5090	149
Kenmore-Garfield High Sch/*Akron*/Summit	00834215	330/848-4141	191
Kenneth Clement Boys Academy/*Cleveland*/Cuyahoga	10911104	216/838-8800	44
Kensington Intermediate Sch/*Rocky River*/Cuyahoga	00794469	440/356-6770	50
Kenston High Sch/*Chagrin Falls*/Geauga	00804258	440/543-9821	82
Kenston Intermediate Sch/*Chagrin Falls*/Geauga	10024177	440/543-9722	82
KENSTON LOCAL SCH DIST/CHAGRIN FALLS/			
GEAUGA	00804234	440/543-9677	82
Kenston Middle Sch/*Chagrin Falls*/Geauga	00804272	440/543-8241	82
KENT CITY SCH DIST/KENT/PORTAGE	00828412	330/673-6515	165
KENTON CITY SCH DIST/KENTON/			
HARDIN	00810221	419/673-0775	100
Kenton Elem Sch/*Kenton*/Hardin	00810245	419/673-7248	100
Kenton High Sch/*Kenton*/Hardin	00810269	419/673-1286	100
Kenton Middle Sch/*Kenton*/Hardin	00810271	419/673-1237	100
Kenton Ridge High Sch/*Springfield*/Clark	01522312	937/390-1274	27
Kenwood Elem Sch/*Bowling Green*/Wood	00839992	419/354-0500	216
Kenwood Elem Sch/*Springfield*/Clark	00788070	937/505-4220	28
KETTERING CITY SCH DIST/			
KETTERING/MONTGOMERY	00824832	937/499-1400	150
Kettering ECC Center/*Moraine*/Montgomery	12034908	937/499-1450	150
Kettering Fairmont High Sch/*Kettering*/Montgomery	00824935	937/499-1600	150
Kettering Middle Sch/*Kettering*/Montgomery	02198287	937/499-1550	150
Keyser Elem Sch/*Toledo*/Lucas	00817645	419/671-1450	129
Keystone Elem Sch/*Lagrange*/Lorain	00816249	440/355-2300	124
Keystone High Sch/*Lagrange*/Lorain	00816225	440/355-2400	124
KEYSTONE LOCAL SCH DIST/			
LAGRANGE/LORAIN	00816213	440/355-2424	124
Keystone Middle Sch/*Lagrange*/Lorain	00816237	440/355-2200	124
Kilbourne Middle Sch/*Worthington*/Franklin	04033528	614/450-4200	75
Kilgour Elem Sch/*Cincinnati*/Hamilton	00805771	513/363-3000	88
Killbuck Elem Sch/*Killbuck*/Holmes	00811380	330/276-2891	105
Kimpton Middle Sch/*Munroe Falls*/Summit	00835556	330/689-5288	194
Kinder Elem Sch/*Miamisburg*/Montgomery	11829968	937/866-4461	151
King Academy Cmty Sch/*Cincinnati*/Hamilton	02654619	513/421-7519	3
King Cmty Learning Center/*Akron*/Summit	00834239	330/761-7962	191
Kings High Sch/*Kings Mills*/Warren	00838211	513/398-8050	207
Kings Junior High Sch/*Kings Mills*/Warren	03046675	513/398-8050	207
KINGS LOCAL SCH DIST/KINGS MILLS/			
WARREN	00838194	513/459-2900	207
Kings Mills Elem Sch/*Kings Mills*/Warren	00838223	513/398-8050	207
Kings Preschool/*Kings Mills*/Warren	12173504	513/398-8050	207
Kingsville Elem Sch/*Kingsville*/Ashtabula	00784543	440/224-0281	12
KIPP Columbus Sch/*Columbus*/Franklin	11396741	614/263-6137	3
Kirkersville Elem Sch/*Kirkersville*/Licking	00815295	740/927-7281	120
Kirkmere Elem Sch/*Youngstown*/Mahoning	00820628	330/744-7725	136
Kirtland Elem Sch/*Kirtland*/Lake	00813261	440/256-3344	112
Kirtland High Sch/*Kirtland*/Lake	00813259	440/256-3366	112
KIRTLAND LOCAL SCH DIST/			
KIRTLAND/LAKE	00813235	440/256-3360	112
Kirtland Middle Sch/*Kirtland*/Lake	00813273	440/256-3358	112
Kiser Elem Sch/*Dayton*/Montgomery	00824442	937/542-6130	149
Kleptz Early Learning Center/*Clayton*/Montgomery	12042278	937/832-6750	152
Knollwood Elem Sch/*Sheffield Lk*/Lorain	00816720	440/949-4234	126
KNOX CO ED SERVICE CENTER/			
MOUNT VERNON/KNOX	02089193	740/393-6767	110
KNOX CO VOC SCH DIST/MOUNT VERNON/			
KNOX	00813170	740/397-5820	111
Knox County Career Center/*Mount Vernon*/Knox	00813182	740/397-5820	111
Knox County Head Start/*Mount Vernon*/Knox	02052114	740/397-9304	110
Knox Elem Sch/*Alliance*/Mahoning	00820367	330/938-1122	136
Kramer Elem Sch/*Oxford*/Butler	00787131	513/273-3500	24
Kyle Elem Sch/*Troy*/Miami	00823656	937/332-6770	147

L

L Hollingworth School for Tag/*Toledo*/Lucas	11567017	419/705-3411	3
L T Ball Intermediate Sch/*Tipp City*/Miami	00823577	937/667-3719	146
La Croft Elem Sch/*E Liverpool*/Columbiana	00789270	330/386-8774	35
La Salle High Sch/*Cincinnati*/Hamilton	00808412	513/741-3000	95
Labrae High Sch/*Leavittsburg*/Trumbull	00836354	330/898-0800	198

School Year 2019-2020 800-333-8802 OH-V19

DISTRICT & SCHOOL TELEPHONE INDEX

Market Data Retrieval

School/City/County DISTRICT/CITY/COUNTY	PID	TELEPHONE NUMBER	PAGE
Labrae Intermediate Sch/*Leavittsburg*/Trumbull	00836380	330/898-0800	198
LABRAE LOCAL SCH DIST/**LEAVITTSBURG**/**TRUMBULL**	00836330	330/898-0800	198
Labrae Middle Sch/*Leavittsburg*/Trumbull	00836366	330/898-0800	198
LACA-LICKING AREA CMOP ASSOC/**NEWARK/LICKING**	04499427	740/345-3400	120
Lagonda Elem Sch/*Springfield*/Clark	00788082	937/505-4240	28
Lake Academy/*Eastlake*/Lake	11231402	440/942-7401	112
Lake Cable Elem Sch/*Canton*/Stark	00832839	330/834-4673	186
Lake Catholic High Sch/*Mentor*/Lake	00795695	440/578-1020	114
Lake Center Christian Sch/*Hartville*/Stark	00833792	330/877-2049	190
Lake Elem Sch/*Hartville*/Stark	00832865	330/877-4276	186
Lake Elem Sch/*Mentor*/Lake	00813431	440/257-5953	113
Lake Elem Sch/*Millbury*/Wood	00840185	419/661-6680	217
Lake Erie International HS/*Cleveland*/Cuyahoga	12039087	216/539-7229	3
Lake Erie Preparatory Sch/*Cleveland*/Cuyahoga	12100208	216/453-4556	3
Lake High Sch/*Millbury*/Wood	00840197	419/661-6640	217
LAKE LOCAL SCH DIST/**MILLBURY**/**WOOD**	00840173	419/661-6690	217
LAKE LOCAL SCH DIST/**UNIONTOWN**/**STARK**	00832853	330/877-9383	186
Lake Middle High Sch/*Uniontown*/Stark	00832877	330/877-4282	186
Lake Middle Sch/*Millbury*/Wood	00840202	419/661-6660	217
Lake Primary Sch/*Uniontown*/Stark	00832891	330/877-4298	186
Lake Ridge Academy/*N Ridgeville*/Lorain	00816861	440/327-1175	126
Lakeland Academy Community Sch/*Freeport*/Harrison	12160935	740/658-1042	100
Lakeshore Intergenerationl Sch/*Cleveland*/Cuyahoga	12100765	216/586-3872	3
Lakeshore Primary Sch/*Conneaut*/Ashtabula	00784622	440/593-7250	12
Lakeside High Sch/*Ashtabula*/Ashtabula	00784402	440/993-2522	12
Lakeside Junior High Sch/*Ashtabula*/Ashtabula	00784426	440/993-2618	12
Lakeview Elem Sch/*Cortland*/Trumbull	00836407	330/638-2145	199
Lakeview High Sch/*Cortland*/Trumbull	00836421	330/637-4921	199
Lakeview Intermediate Sch/*Stow*/Summit	03048960	330/689-5250	194
Lakeview Junior High Sch/*Pickerington*/Fairfield	05272909	614/830-2200	64
LAKEVIEW LOCAL SCH DIST/**CORTLAND/TRUMBULL**	00836392	330/637-8741	198
Lakeview Middle Sch/*Cortland*/Trumbull	01823312	330/637-4360	199
Lakeville Elem Sch/*Lakeville*/Holmes	00811392	419/827-2006	105
Lakewood Catholic Academy/*Lakewood*/Cuyahoga	00796168	216/521-0559	52
LAKEWOOD CITY SCH DIST/**LAKEWOOD**/**CUYAHOGA**	00793477	216/529-4000	47
Lakewood High Sch/*Hebron*/Licking	00814796	740/928-4526	118
Lakewood High Sch/*Lakewood*/Cuyahoga	00793568	216/529-4028	47
LAKEWOOD LOCAL SCH DIST/**HEBRON/LICKING**	00814758	740/928-5878	118
Lakewood Lutheran Elem Sch/*Lakewood*/Cuyahoga	00795152	216/221-6941	54
Lakewood Middle Sch/*Hebron*/Licking	00814801	740/928-8340	118
Lakota East Freshman Campus/*Liberty TWP*/Butler	11077050	513/588-7700	22
Lakota East High Sch/*Liberty TWP*/Butler	04747341	513/755-7211	22
Lakota Elem Sch/*Kansas*/Sandusky	01755454	419/986-6640	177
Lakota High Sch/*Kansas*/Sandusky	00830740	419/986-6620	177
LAKOTA LOCAL SCH DIST/**KANSAS**/**SANDUSKY**	00830702	419/986-6650	177
LAKOTA LOCAL SCH DIST/**LIBERTY TWP**/**BUTLER**	00786644	513/874-5505	22
Lakota Middle Sch/*Kansas*/Sandusky	00830738	419/986-6630	177
Lakota West Freshman Campus/*West Chester*/Butler	04019778	513/874-8390	22
Lakota West High Sch/*West Chester*/Butler	00786670	513/874-5699	22
Lancaster City Pre-School/*Ashville*/Fairfield	12103793	740/687-7340	63
LANCASTER CITY SCH DIST/**LANCASTER/FAIRFIELD**	00799031	740/687-7300	63
Lancaster SDA Elem Sch/*Lancaster*/Fairfield	04986717	740/687-1741	65
Lancaster Senior High Sch/*Lancaster*/Fairfield	00799079	740/681-7500	63
Lander Elem Sch/*Mayfield HTS*/Cuyahoga	00793738	440/995-7350	47
Langston Middle Sch/*Oberlin*/Lorain	00816653	440/775-7961	125
Larchmont Elem Sch/*Toledo*/Lucas	00817683	419/671-3650	129
Larkmoor Elem Sch/*Lorain*/Lorain	00816378	440/830-4170	124
Larry Larson Middle Sch/*Columbus*/Franklin	12031401	614/485-4100	71
Larry Miller Intermediate Sch/*New Concord*/Muskingum	05272480	740/826-2271	156
Laura Woodward Elem Sch/*Delaware*/Delaware	00798295	740/833-1600	58
Laurel Oaks Career Dev Campus/*Wilmington*/Hamilton	00810453	937/382-1411	89
Laurel Sch/*Shaker HTS*/Cuyahoga	00797435	216/464-1441	54
Laurelville Elem Sch/*Laurelville*/Pickaway	00827779	740/332-2021	162
Lawrence Co Academy/*Chesapeake*/Lawrence	12160923	740/867-6641	115
LAWRENCE CO ED SERVICE CENTER/**IRONTON/LAWRENCE**	00814590	740/532-4223	115
LAWRENCE CO JOINT VOC SCH DIST/**CHESAPEAKE/LAWRENCE**	01548108	740/867 6641	116
Lawrence Lower Sch/*Broadview HTS*/Cuyahoga	01873991	440/526-0003	54
Lawrence Upper Sch/*Northfield*/Summit	11551408	440/832-7830	196
Le Chaperon Rouge Elem Sch/*Westlake*/Cuyahoga	11231476	440/899-9477	54
League Elem Sch/*Norwalk*/Huron	00811641	419/668-2450	106
Leap Academy/*Cincinnati*/Hamilton	12231376	513/363-1200	88
Leap Sch/*Akron*/Summit	11227750	330/899-9423	196
Learning Ctr at North Norwood/*Cincinnati*/Hamilton	04025985	513/396-5941	87
Learwood Middle Sch/*Avon Lake*/Lorain	00815764	440/933-8142	122
Leawood Elem Sch/*Columbus*/Franklin	00800458	614/365-6504	68
Lebanon Christian Sch/*Lebanon*/Warren	10014524	513/932-5590	209
LEBANON CITY SCH DIST/**LEBANON**/**WARREN**	00838340	513/934-5770	207
Lebanon High Sch/*Lebanon*/Warren	00838388	513/934-5100	207
Lebanon Junior High Sch/*Lebanon*/Warren	00838364	513/934-5300	207
Ledgemont Elem Sch/*Thompson*/Geauga	00804313	440/298-3341	81
Ledgeview Elem Sch/*Macedonia*/Summit	00835192	330/467-0583	193
Lee Burneson Middle Sch/*Westlake*/Cuyahoga	00795047	440/835-6340	52
Lee Eaton Elem Sch/*Northfield*/Summit	00835207	330/467-0582	193
LEETONIA EXEMPTED VILLAGE SD/**LEETONIA/COLUMBIANA**	00789438	330/427-6594	35
Leetonia Sch/*Leetonia*/Columbiana	00789452	330/427-2444	35
Legacy Christian Academy/*Xenia*/Greene	01464837	937/352-1640	85
Legacy Christian Sch/*Sugarcreek*/Tuscarawas	12115655	330/852-4322	204
Legend Elem Sch/*Newark*/Licking	00815099	740/670-7100	119
Leggett Cmty Learning Center/*Akron*/Summit	00834265	330/761-1735	191
Lehman Catholic High Sch/*Sidney*/Shelby	00808424	937/498-1161	183
Leighton Elem Sch/*Aurora*/Portage	04939013	330/562-2209	165
Leipsic High Sch/*Leipsic*/Putnam	05027285	419/943-2165	170
Leipsic Local Sch/*Leipsic*/Putnam	00829234	419/943-2165	170
LEIPSIC LOCAL SCH DIST/**LEIPSIC**/**PUTNAM**	00829210	419/943-2165	170
Leona Middle Sch/*Shadyside*/Belmont	00785858	740/676-9220	18
Leonard Kirtz Sch/*Austintown*/Mahoning	02052243	330/797-2847	133
Leverette Elem Sch/*Toledo*/Lucas	00817592	419/671-6200	129
Lewis F Mayer Middle Sch/*Fairview Park*/Cuyahoga	00793336	440/356-3510	46
Lexington Elem Sch/*Alliance*/Stark	00832982	330/823-7570	186
Lexington High Sch/*Lexington*/Richland	00829519	419/884-1111	172
Lexington Junior High Sch/*Lexington*/Richland	00829521	419/884-2112	172
LEXINGTON LOCAL SCH DIST/**LEXINGTON/RICHLAND**	00829480	419/884-2132	172
LGCA-LAKE GEAUGA OHIO OCA/**PAINESVILLE/LAKE**	04499489	440/357-9383	115
Lial Sch/*Whitehouse*/Lucas	02230574	419/877-5167	131
Liberty Arts Magnet Sch/*Lima*/Allen	00783795	419/996-3320	9
Liberty Bible Academy/*Mason*/Warren	04930562	513/754-1234	209
Liberty Center Elem Sch/*Liberty CTR*/Henry	00810726	419/533-2604	101
Liberty Center High Sch/*Liberty CTR*/Henry	00810738	419/533-6641	101
LIBERTY CENTER LOCAL SCH DIST/**LIBERTY CTR/HENRY**	00810714	419/533-5011	101
Liberty Center Middle Sch/*Liberty CTR*/Henry	12168779	419/533-0020	101
Liberty Christian Academy/*Pataskala*/Licking	11231555	740/964-2211	120
Liberty Christian Sch/*Lima*/Allen	04987228	419/229-6266	10
Liberty Early Childhood Sch/*Liberty Twp*/Butler	00786694	513/777-6194	22
Liberty Elem Sch/*Caledonia*/Marion	00822004	740/725-5600	139
Liberty Elem Sch/*Columbus*/Franklin	03396145	614/365-6482	68
Liberty Elem Sch/*Powell*/Franklin	02131423	614/450-5200	75
Liberty High Sch/*Dayton*/Montgomery	12259550	937/701-7945	3
Liberty High Sch/*Powell*/Delaware	05275224	740/657-4200	59
Liberty High Sch/*Youngstown*/Trumbull	00836457	330/759-2301	199
Liberty Junior High Sch/*Liberty TWP*/Butler	01538593	513/777-4420	22
LIBERTY LOCAL SCH DIST/**YOUNGSTOWN**/**TRUMBULL**	00836433	330/759-0807	199
Liberty Middle Sch/*Newark*/Licking	00815104	740/670-7320	119

Ohio School Directory

DISTRICT & SCHOOL TELEPHONE INDEX

School/City/County DISTRICT/CITY/COUNTY	PID	TELEPHONE NUMBER	PAGE
Liberty Middle Sch/*Powell*/Delaware	05008758	740/657-4400	59
Liberty Preparatory Sch/*Smithville*/Wayne	12163195	330/669-0055	211
Liberty Sch/*N Ridgeville*/Lorain	01522324	440/327-6767	125
Liberty Tree Elem Sch/*Powell*/Delaware	10907529	740/657-5600	59
Liberty Union Elem Sch/*Baltimore*/Fairfield	01823269	740/862-4143	64
Liberty Union High Sch/*Baltimore*/Fairfield	00799201	740/862-4107	64
Liberty Union Middle Sch/*Baltimore*/Fairfield	00799213	740/862-4126	64
LIBERTY UNION-THURSTN SCH DIST/ BALTIMORE/FAIRFIELD	00799184	740/862-4171	64
Liberty-Benton Elem Sch/*Findlay*/Hancock	00810025	419/422-9161	98
Liberty-Benton High Sch/*Findlay*/Hancock	04368036	419/424-5351	98
LIBERTY-BENTON LOCAL SCH DIST/ FINDLAY/HANCOCK	00810013	419/422-8526	98
Liberty-Benton Middle Sch/*Findlay*/Hancock	04368048	419/422-9166	98
LICKING CO ED SERVICE CENTER/ NEWARK/LICKING	02089208	740/349-6084	117
LICKING CO JOINT VOC SCH DIST/ NEWARK/LICKING	00815324	740/364-2832	118
Licking County Christian Acad/*Heath*/Licking	02826410	740/522-3600	120
Licking Heights Central MS/*Pataskala*/Licking	10031388	740/927-3365	118
Licking Heights High Sch/*Pataskala*/Licking	00814849	740/927-9046	118
LICKING HEIGHTS LOCAL SCH DIST/ PATASKALA/LICKING	00814825	740/927-6926	118
Licking Heights North Elem Sch/*Pataskala*/Licking	10031376	740/927-3268	118
Licking Heights South Elem Sch/*Pataskala*/Licking	00814851	740/964-1674	118
Licking Heights West Elem Sch/*Blacklick*/Licking	00814837	614/864-9089	118
Licking Valley Elem Sch/*Newark*/Licking	00814899	740/763-2865	119
Licking Valley High Sch/*Newark*/Licking	00814875	740/763-3721	119
LICKING VALLEY LOCAL SCH DIST/ NEWARK/LICKING	00814863	740/763-3525	118
Licking Valley Middle Sch/*Newark*/Licking	00814887	740/763-3396	119
Life Skills Center of Dayton/*Dayton*/Montgomery	11007483	937/274-2841	3
Life Skills Center of Elyria/*Elyria*/Lorain	05220310	440/324-1755	3
Life Skills Center of Toledo/*Toledo*/Lucas	05300051	419/241-5504	3
Life Skills Ctr of Cincinnati/*Cincinnati*/Hamilton	04907228	513/475-0222	3
Life Skills Ctr of N Columbus/*Columbus*/Franklin	05220281	614/891-9041	3
Life Skills HS of Columbus SE/*Columbus*/Franklin	05299878	614/863-9175	3
Life Skills HS of N Akron/*Akron*/Summit	05009192	330/510-5827	3
Lighthouse Community Sch/*Cincinnati*/Hamilton	05009025	513/561-7888	3
Lillian & Betty Ratner Sch/*Pepper Pike*/Cuyahoga	03184136	216/464-0033	54
Lima Central Catholic High Sch/*Lima*/Allen	00818481	419/222-4276	10
Lima Christian Academy/*Lima*/Allen	00784086	419/999-2219	10
LIMA CITY SCH DIST/LIMA/ALLEN	00783769	419/996-3400	9
Lima North Middle Sch/*Lima*/Allen	00783886	419/996-3100	9
Lima Senior High Sch/*Lima*/Allen	00783848	419/996-3030	9
Lima West Middle Sch/*Lima*/Allen	00783927	419/996-3150	9
Lincoln Elem Sch/*Cuyahoga FLS*/Summit	00834899	330/926-3803	192
Lincoln Elem Sch/*Findlay*/Hancock	00809959	419/425-8310	98
Lincoln Elem Sch/*Gahanna*/Franklin	00801438	614/478-5555	70
Lincoln Elem Sch/*Lakewood*/Cuyahoga	00793570	216/529-4232	47
Lincoln Elem Sch/*Springfield*/Clark	00788094	937/505-4260	28
Lincoln Elem Sch/*Wadsworth*/Medina	00822482	330/335-1460	142
Lincoln Heights Elem Sch/*Cincinnati*/Hamilton	00807470	513/864-2400	92
Lincoln High Sch/*Gahanna*/Franklin	00801440	614/478-5500	70
Lincoln Park Academy/*Cleveland*/Cuyahoga	04879463	216/263-7008	3
Lincoln Park Elem Sch/*Columbus*/Franklin	00800484	614/365-5524	68
Lincoln PK-8 Sch/*Warren*/Trumbull	00836885	330/373-4500	200
Lincoln Pre-Kindergarten Ctr/*Tiffin*/Seneca	12104852	419/455-9107	181
Lincoln Prepartory Academy/*Cleveland*/Cuyahoga	12100686	216/772-1336	3
Lincoln-West High Sch/*Cleveland*/Cuyahoga	11702401	216/838-7000	44
Lincoln-West HS Global Studies/*Cleveland*/Cuyahoga	12235554	216/838-7050	44
Lincoln-West Sch Sci & Health/*Cleveland*/Cuyahoga	12235566	216/838-7100	44
Lincolnview Elem Sch/*Van Wert*/Van Wert	00837865	419/968-2351	205
Lincolnview Jr Sr High Sch/*Van Wert*/Van Wert	05363780	419/968-2214	205
LINCOLNVIEW LOCAL SCH DIST/ VAN WERT/VAN WERT	00837853	419/968-2226	205
Lindbergh Elem Sch/*Columbus*/Franklin	03396157	614/365-6727	68
Linden Elem Sch/*Hamilton*/Butler	00786515	513/868-5630	22
Linden Grove Sch/*Cincinnati*/Hamilton	03017882	513/984-2215	96
Linden Park Ecec/*Columbus*/Franklin	12366957	614/365-7963	68
Linden STEM Academy/*Columbus*/Franklin	00800501	614/365-6537	68
Linden-McKinley STEM Academy/*Columbus*/Franklin	00800513	614/365-5583	68
Linworth Alternative High Sch/*Worthington*/Franklin	01539781	614/450-6900	75
Lippman Day Sch/*Akron*/Summit	00835752	330/836-0419	196
LISBON EXEMPTED VILLAGE SD/ LISBON/COLUMBIANA	00789490	330/424-7714	35
Litchfield Cmty Learning Ctr/*Akron*/Summit	00834289	330/761-2775	191
Little Hocking Elem Sch/*Little Hockng*/Washington	00838895	740/989-2000	210
Little Miami High Sch/*Morrow*/Warren	00838431	513/899-3781	208
Little Miami Intermediate Sch/*Maineville*/Warren	04934752	513/899-2334	208
Little Miami Junior High Sch/*Morrow*/Warren	03398179	513/899-3408	208
LITTLE MIAMI LOCAL SCH DIST/ MAINEVILLE/WARREN	00838405	513/899-2264	207
Little River Pre-School/*Mc Guffey*/Hardin	04009022	419/757-3231	99
Little Whippets Pre-School/*Shelby*/Richland	12166446	419/342-6593	173
Live Oaks Career Dev Campus/*Milford*/Hamilton	00810465	513/575-1900	89
Livingston Elem Sch/*Columbus*/Franklin	00800537	614/365-5527	68
Lockland Elem Sch/*Lockland*/Hamilton	00806799	513/563-5000	90
Lockland High Sch/*Lockland*/Hamilton	00806787	513/563-5000	90
Lockland Middle Sch/*Lockland*/Hamilton	11558987	513/563-5000	90
LOCKLAND SCH DIST/LOCKLAND/ HAMILTON	00806763	513/563-5000	90
Locust Corner Elem Sch/*Cincinnati*/Clermont	00788678	513/752-1432	31
Logan Christian Sch/*Logan*/Hocking	04986729	740/385-5360	104
Logan Elm High Sch/*Circleville*/Pickaway	00827781	740/474-7503	162
LOGAN ELM LOCAL SCH DIST/ CIRCLEVILLE/PICKAWAY	00827755	740/474-7501	162
Logan High Sch/*Logan*/Hocking	00811196	740/385-2069	104
LOGAN-HOCKING LOCAL SCH DIST/ LOGAN/HOCKING	00811146	740/385-8517	104
Logan-Hocking Middle Sch/*Logan*/Hocking	03389609	740/385-8764	104
Lohr Elem Sch/*Navarre*/Stark	00833443	330/484-3924	188
Lomond Elem Sch/*Shaker HTS*/Cuyahoga	00794548	216/295-4050	50
LONDON CITY SCH DIST/LONDON/ MADISON	00819564	740/852-5700	132
London Elem Sch/*London*/Madison	00819605	740/845-3272	132
London High Sch/*London*/Madison	00819590	740/852-5705	132
London Middle Sch/*London*/Madison	00819576	740/852-5701	132
Longcoy Elem Sch/*Kent*/Portage	00828474	330/676-8350	165
Longfellow Elem Sch/*Eastlake*/Lake	00813948	440/975-3720	114
Longfellow Elem Sch/*Sidney*/Shelby	00832102	937/497-2264	183
Longfellow Elem Sch/*Toledo*/Lucas	00817712	419/671-3800	129
Longfellow Elem Sch/*Westerville*/Franklin	12313510	614/797-7180	75
Longfellow Middle Sch/*Lorain*/Lorain	10011003	440/830-4220	124
Lorain Bilingual Academy/*Lorain*/Lorain	12361115	440/434-6320	4
LORAIN CITY SCH DIST/LORAIN/ LORAIN	00816263	440/233-2271	124
Lorain Cmty Elem Sch/*Lorain*/Lorain	05010373	440/204-2130	122
Lorain Cmty Middle Sch/*Lorain*/Lorain	11566946	440/242-2023	122
Lorain Co Joint Voc Sch/*Oberlin*/Lorain	00816859	440/774-1051	125
LORAIN CO JOINT VOC SCH DIST/ OBERLIN/LORAIN	00816847	440/774-1051	125
Lorain High Sch/*Lorain*/Lorain	00816354	440/233-2200	124
Lorain Preparatory Academy/*Lorain*/Lorain	11016800	440/282-3127	4
Lordstown Elem Sch/*Warren*/Trumbull	00836495	330/824-2572	199
Lordstown High Sch/*Warren*/Trumbull	00836512	330/824-2581	199
LORDSTOWN LOCAL SCH DIST/ WARREN/TRUMBULL	00836483	330/824-2534	199
Loudonville High Sch/*Loudonville*/Ashland	00784270	419/994-4101	11
LOUDONVILLE-PERRYSVILLE SD/ LOUDONVILLE/ASHLAND	00784256	419/994-3912	11
Louis Agassiz Elem Sch/*Cleveland*/Cuyahoga	00792007	216/838-6450	44
Louisa May Alcott Elem Sch/*Cleveland*/Cuyahoga	04752487	216/838-6500	44
Louise Troy Elem Sch/*Dayton*/Montgomery	00824131	937/542-4290	149
LOUISVILLE CITY SCH DIST/ LOUISVILLE/STARK	00832906	330/875-1666	186
Louisville Elem Sch/*Louisville*/Stark	00832920	330/875-1177	186
Louisville Middle Sch/*Louisville*/Stark	00832944	330/875-5597	186
Louisville Senior High Sch/*Louisville*/Stark	00832932	330/875-1438	186

DISTRICT & SCHOOL TELEPHONE INDEX

Market Data Retrieval

DISTRICT/CITY/COUNTY	PID	TELEPHONE NUMBER	PAGE
LOVELAND CITY SCH DIST/LOVELAND/ HAMILTON	00806804	513/683-5600	90
Loveland Early Childhood Ctr/Loveland/ Hamilton	00806830	513/683-4200	90
Loveland Elem Sch/Loveland/Hamilton	00806854	513/683-4333	90
Loveland High Sch/Loveland/Hamilton	00806828	513/683-1920	90
Loveland Intermediate Sch/Loveland/ Hamilton	04035095	513/697-3024	90
Loveland Middle Sch/Loveland/Hamilton	00806842	513/683-3100	90
Loveland Primary Sch/Loveland/Hamilton	04916786	513/683-3101	90
Lowell Elem Sch/Lowell/Washington	00838663	740/896-2523	210
Lowellville K-12 Sch/Lowellville/Mahoning	00820032	330/536-8426	135
LOWELLVILLE LOCAL SCH DIST/ LOWELLVILLE/MAHONING	00820020	330/536-8426	135
Lucas Co Pre-School Unit/Toledo/Lucas	04025844	419/245-4150	127
Lucas Elem Sch/Lucas/Richland	00829557	419/892-2338	172
Lucas Heritage Middle Sch/Lucas/Richland	02045264	419/892-2338	172
Lucas High Sch/Lucas/Richland	00829569	419/892-2338	172
LUCAS LOCAL SCH DIST/LUCAS/ RICHLAND	00829545	419/892-2338	172
Luis Munoz Marin Elem Sch/Cleveland/ Cuyahoga	00791962	216/838-3300	44
Luther E Ball High Sch/Cleveland/Cuyahoga	02051677	216/464-8200	4
Luther Memorial Sch/Cleveland/Cuyahoga	00795164	216/749-5300	54
Lutheran High School East/Cleveland/ Cuyahoga	00795176	216/382-6100	54
Lutheran High School West/Rocky River/ Cuyahoga	00795188	440/333-1660	54
Lutz Elem Sch/Fremont/Sandusky	00830611	419/332-0091	177
Lynchburg-Clay Elem Sch/Lynchburg/Highland	00811110	937/364-9119	103
Lynchburg-Clay High Sch/Lynchburg/Highland	00811122	937/364-2250	103
LYNCHBURG-CLAY LOCAL SCH DIST/ LYNCHBURG/HIGHLAND	00811093	937/364-2338	103
Lynchburg-Clay Middle Sch/Lynchburg/ Highland	04934790	937/364-2811	103

M

DISTRICT/CITY/COUNTY	PID	TELEPHONE NUMBER	PAGE
M Luther King Academy for Boys/Toledo/Lucas	00817700	419/671-4550	130
Mac-A-Cheek Learning Center/Bellefontaine/Logan	03409273	937/292-7956	120
Mad River Early Childhood Ctr/Riverside/Montgomery	11103738	937/259-6640	151
MAD RIVER LOCAL SCH DIST/ RIVERSIDE/MONTGOMERY	00825056	937/259-6606	151
Mad River Middle Sch/Dayton/Montgomery	00825109	937/237-4265	151
Maddux Elem Sch/Cincinnati/Hamilton	00806517	513/231-0780	89
Maddux-Lang Primary Sch/Miamisburg/Montgomery	11450701	937/847-2766	151
MADEIRA CITY SCH DIST/CINCINNATI/ HAMILTON	00806878	513/985-6070	90
Madeira Elem Sch/Cincinnati/Hamilton	00806880	513/985-6080	90
Madeira High Sch/Cincinnati/Hamilton	00806892	513/891-8222	90
Madeira Middle Sch/Cincinnati/Hamilton	00806919	513/561-5555	90
Madison Christian Sch/Groveport/Franklin	02165371	614/497-3456	77
Madison Cmty Elem Sch/Cleveland/Cuyahoga	05382700	216/651-5212	39
Madison Comprehensive High Sch/Mansfield/Richland	00829612	419/589-2112	172
Madison Elem Sch/Columbus/Franklin	00801579	614/833-2011	71
Madison Elem Sch/Middletown/Butler	00786735	513/420-4755	23
Madison High Sch/Madison/Lake	00813302	440/428-2161	112
Madison Junior Senior High Sch/Middletown/Butler	00786723	513/420-4760	23
MADISON LOCAL SCH DIST/MADISON/ LAKE	00813285	440/428-2166	112
MADISON LOCAL SCH DIST/MANSFIELD/ RICHLAND	00829571	419/589-2600	172
MADISON LOCAL SCH DIST/MIDDLETOWN/ BUTLER	00786711	513/420-4750	23
Madison Middle Sch/Madison/Lake	00813340	440/428-1196	112
Madison Middle Sch/Mansfield/Richland	00829624	419/522-0471	172
Madison Park Elem Sch/Trotwood/Montgomery	00825202	937/854-4456	153
Madison Plains Elem Sch/London/Madison	00819655	740/490-0610	133
Madison Plains High Sch/London/Madison	01823295	740/852-0364	133
Madison Plains Interm Sch/London/Madison	00819643	740/490-0610	133
Madison Plains Junior HS/London/Madison	11710795	740/852-1707	133
MADISON PLAINS LOCAL SCH DIST/ LONDON/MADISON	00819629	740/852-0290	133
Madison Pre-K/Madison/Lake	04921353	440/428-5111	112
Madison South Elem Sch/Madison/Lake	00813297	440/428-5121	112
Madison South Elem Sch/Mansfield/Richland	00829636	419/522-4319	172
MADISON-CHAMPAIGN ED SVC CTR/ URBANA/CHAMPAIGN	00787600	937/484-1557	25
Madisonville Smart Elem Sch/Cincinnati/Hamilton	12105519	513/241-1101	4
Magnificat High Sch/Rocky River/Cuyahoga	00795724	440/331-1572	52
Magsig Middle Sch/Centerville/Montgomery	01539808	937/433-0965	149
Mahoning Co Career Tech Ctr/Canfield/Mahoning	00820903	330/729-4000	135
MAHONING CO ED SERVICE CENTER/ CANFIELD/MAHONING	00820886	330/533-8755	133
Mahoning Co High Sch/Youngstown/Mahoning	11747009	330/965-2860	133
MAHONING CO JOINT VOC SCH DIST/ CANFIELD/MAHONING	00820898	330/729-4000	135
Mahoning Unlimited Classroom/Youngstown/Mahoning	05300104	330/533-8755	133
Main Elem Sch/Dayton/Greene	00804519	937/429-7588	83
Main Preparatory Academy/Akron/Summit	12028272	234/738-1925	4
Main Street Sch/Norwalk/Huron	05341689	419/660-1957	106
Maize Elem Sch/Columbus/Franklin	00800551	614/365-6040	68
Malabar Intermediate Sch/Mansfield/Richland	00829753	419/525-6374	172
Malcolm-Bain Center/Toledo/Lucas	12037259	419/473-8331	130
Malvern Elem Sch/Malvern/Carroll	01486859	330/863-1355	25
Malvern High Sch/Malvern/Carroll	04304999	330/863-1355	25
Malvern Middle Sch/Malvern/Carroll	12368486	330/863-1355	25
Manchester Elem Sch/Manchester/Adams	00783422	937/549-4777	7
Manchester High Sch/Akron/Summit	00834980	330/882-3291	193
Manchester Local High Sch/Manchester/Adams	00783434	937/549-4777	7
MANCHESTER LOCAL SCH DIST/ AKRON/SUMMIT	00834978	330/882-6926	193
MANCHESTER LOCAL SCH DIST/ MANCHESTER/ADAMS	05339375	937/549-4777	7
Manchester Middle Sch/Akron/Summit	00834992	330/882-3812	193
Mansfield Christian Sch/Mansfield/Richland	00830049	419/756-5651	174
MANSFIELD CITY SCHOOLS/MANSFIELD/ RICHLAND	00829674	419/525-6400	172
Mansfield Middle Sch/Mansfield/Richland	11563437	419/525-6307	172
Mansfield SDA Sch/Mansfield/Richland	04157318	419/756-9947	174
Mansfield Senior High Sch/Mansfield/Richland	00829686	419/525-6369	172
Mansion Day Sch/Columbus/Franklin	03463932	614/258-4449	77
Maple Dale Elem Sch/Cincinnati/Hamilton	00807781	513/686-1720	93
Maple Elem Sch/Painesville/Lake	00813716	440/392-5440	113
MAPLE HEIGHTS CITY SCH DIST/ MAPLE HEIGHTS/CUYAHOGA	00793623	216/587-6100	47
Maple Heights High Sch/Maple Heights/Cuyahoga	00793661	216/438-6400	47
Maple Intermediate Sch/North Olmsted/Cuyahoga	00793879	440/779-3533	48
Maple Leaf Elem Sch/Garfield HTS/Cuyahoga	04452039	216/662-3800	46
Maplehurst Elem Sch/Norwalk/Huron	00811653	419/668-6035	106
Mapleton Elem Sch/Ashland/Ashland	00784323	419/945-2188	11
Mapleton High Sch/Ashland/Ashland	11719351	419/945-2188	11
MAPLETON LOCAL SCH DIST/ ASHLAND/ASHLAND	00784309	419/945-2188	11
Mapleton Middle Sch/Ashland/Ashland	00784311	419/945-2188	11
Maplewood Career Center/Ravenna/Portage	00828814	330/296-2892	166
Maplewood Elem Sch/Cortland/Trumbull	00836562	330/583-2321	199
Maplewood Elem Sch/Sylvania/Lucas	00817231	419/824-8613	129
Maplewood High Sch/Cortland/Trumbull	00836548	330/637-8466	199
Maplewood Intermediate Sch/Lima/Allen	00783991	419/998-8076	9
MAPLEWOOD JT VOC SCH DIST/ RAVENNA/PORTAGE	00828802	330/296-2892	166
MAPLEWOOD LOCAL SCH DIST/ CORTLAND/TRUMBULL	00836524	330/637-7506	199
Marburn Academy/New Albany/Franklin	11832939	614/433-0822	77
Margaret Rost Sch/Cincinnati/Hamilton	04008975	513/574-2372	87
Margaretta Elem Sch/Castalia/Erie	00798518	419/684-5357	61
Margaretta High Sch/Castalia/Erie	00798520	419/684-5351	61
MARGARETTA LOCAL SCH DIST/ CASTALIA/ERIE	00798506	419/684-5322	61
Marie English ECC/Marion/Marion	02052267	740/387-1035	137
MARIEMONT CITY SCH DIST/ CINCINNATI/HAMILTON	00806921	513/272-7500	90
Mariemont Elem Sch/Cincinnati/Hamilton	00806969	513/272-7400	91
Mariemont High Sch/Cincinnati/Hamilton	00806957	513/272-7600	91
Mariemont Junior High Sch/Cincinnati/Hamilton	04473784	513/272-7300	91
Marietta Christian Sch/Marietta/Washington	02826379	740/373-5551	211
MARIETTA CITY SCH DIST/MARIETTA/ WASHINGTON	00838730	740/374-6500	210
Marietta High Sch/Marietta/Washington	00838766	740/374-6540	210

Ohio School Directory
DISTRICT & SCHOOL TELEPHONE INDEX

School/City/County DISTRICT/CITY/COUNTY	PID	TELEPHONE NUMBER	PAGE
Marietta Middle Sch/Marietta/Washington	00838778	740/374-6530	210
Marimor Sch/Lima/Allen	02051495	419/221-1262	7
Marion C Seltzer Elem Sch/Cleveland/Cuyahoga	00792045	216/838-6550	44
MARION CITY SCH DIST/MARION/MARION	00821713	740/387-3300	138
Marion Local Elem Sch/Maria Stein/Mercer	00822949	419/925-4595	144
Marion Local High Sch/Maria Stein/Mercer	00822937	419/925-4597	144
MARION LOCAL SCH DIST/MARIA STEIN/MERCER	00822913	419/925-4294	144
Marion Sterling Elem Sch/Cleveland/Cuyahoga	00792071	216/838-1550	44
Marion-Franklin High Sch/Columbus/Franklin	00800575	614/365-5432	68
Maritime Academy of Toledo/Toledo/Lucas	11016977	419/244-9999	127
Mark Twain Elem Sch/Miamisburg/Montgomery	00825288	937/866-2581	151
Mark Twain Elem Sch/Westerville/Franklin	00802389	614/797-7200	75
Marlington High Sch/Alliance/Stark	00833003	330/823-1300	186
MARLINGTON LOCAL SCH DIST/ALLIANCE/STARK	00832970	330/823-7458	186
Marlington Middle Sch/Alliance/Stark	00833015	330/823-7566	186
Marr Cook Elem Sch/Goshen/Clermont	00788513	513/722-2224	30
Mars Hill Academy/Mason/Warren	04906664	513/770-3223	209
Marsh Foundation Sch/Van Wert/Van Wert	00837891	419/238-1695	205
Marshall Elem Sch/Oxford/Butler	00787155	513/273-3600	24
Marshall Elem Sch/Toledo/Lucas	00817736	419/671-5700	130
Marshall High Sch/Middletown/Butler	11935646	513/318-7078	4
Martin L King Career Campus/Cleveland/Cuyahoga	02201028	216/838-9350	44
Martin Luther King Elem Sch/Youngstown/Mahoning	04838201	330/744-7823	136
Martins Ferry Christian Sch/Martins Ferry/Belmont	11238670	740/633-0199	19
MARTINS FERRY CITY SCH DIST/MARTINS FERRY/BELMONT	00785743	740/633-1732	18
Martins Ferry High Sch/Martins Ferry/Belmont	00785781	740/633-0684	18
Martins Ferry Middle Sch/Martins Ferry/Belmont	00785755	740/633-9741	18
Mary B Martin STEM Academy/Cleveland/Cuyahoga	00792100	216/838-1600	44
Mary Emma Bailey Elem Sch/Dublin/Franklin	04450134	614/717-6611	70
Mary L Evans Early Chldhd Ctr/North Canton/Stark	12178774	330/497-5608	187
Mary M Bethune Elem Sch/Cleveland/Cuyahoga	00792112	216/838-2250	44
Mary Queen of Peace Sch/Cleveland/Cuyahoga	00795839	216/741-3685	52
Maryland Ave Elem Sch/Bexley/Franklin	00799550	614/237-3280	66
Marysville Early College HS/Marysville/Union	12031786	937/578-7300	204
MARYSVILLE EXEMPTED VILLAGE SD/MARYSVILLE/UNION	00837657	937/578-6100	204
Marysville High Sch/Marysville/Union	00837683	937/578-6200	204
MASON CITY SCH DIST/MASON/WARREN	00838467	513/398-0474	208
Mason Cmty Learning Ctr/Akron/Summit	00834318	330/761-2237	191
Mason Early Childhood Center/Mason/Warren	04365046	513/398-3741	208
Mason Intermediate Sch/Mason/Warren	04804690	513/459-2850	208
Mason Leadership Sch/Canton/Stark	00832592	330/588-2156	185
Mason Middle Sch/Mason/Warren	00838479	513/398-9035	208
Mason Run High Sch/Columbus/Franklin	12164814	614/362-7540	4
Massillon Christian Sch/Massillon/Stark	01465128	330/833-1039	190
MASSILLON CITY SCH DIST/MASSILLON/STARK	00833039	330/830-3900	187
Massillon Digital Academy/Massillon/Stark	05299971	330/830-3900	187
Massillon Intermediate Sch/Massillon/Stark	11823354	330/830-3902	187
Massillon Junior High Sch/Massillon/Stark	00833041	330/830-3902	187
Massillon Washington High Sch/Massillon/Stark	00833144	330/830-3901	187
Matamoras Elem Sch/New Matamoras/Washington	00838716	740/865-3422	210
Mater Dei Academy/Columbus/Franklin	02147707	614/231-1984	77
Mater Dei Academy/Wickliffe/Lake	00795865	440/585-0800	114
Mathews High Sch/Vienna/Trumbull	00836055	330/637-3500	199
MATHEWS LOCAL SCH DIST/VIENNA/TRUMBULL	00836029	330/637-7000	199
MAUMEE CITY SCH DIST/MAUMEE/LUCAS	00816940	419/893-3200	127
Maumee High Sch/Maumee/Lucas	00816988	419/893-8778	128
Maumee Valley Country Day Sch/Toledo/Lucas	00818259	419/381-1313	131
Max S Hayes High Sch/Cleveland/Cuyahoga	00792124	216/838-9400	44
Mayfair Christian Sch/Uniontown/Stark	00833807	330/896-3184	190
Mayfair Elem Sch/Cleveland/Cuyahoga	00793087	216/268-6651	45
Mayfield Center Elem Sch/Mayfield VLG/Cuyahoga	00793740	440/995-7400	47
MAYFIELD CITY SCH DIST/MAYFIELD HTS/CUYAHOGA	00793714	440/995-6800	47
Mayfield Elem Sch/Middletown/Butler	00786888	513/420-4549	23
Mayfield High Sch/Mayfield VLG/Cuyahoga	00793752	440/995-6900	47
Mayfield Middle Sch/Mayfield HTS/Cuyahoga	03391353	440/995-7800	47
Maysville Elem Sch/Zanesville/Muskingum	00826438	740/454-4490	157
Maysville High Sch/Zanesville/Muskingum	00826397	740/454-7999	157
MAYSVILLE LOCAL SCH DIST/ZANESVILLE/MUSKINGUM	00826373	740/453-0754	156
Maysville Middle Sch/Zanesville/Muskingum	11463796	740/454-7982	157
MC2 STEM HS-Cleveland State/Cleveland/Cuyahoga	11718204	216/838-8500	44
MC2 STEM HS-GE Lighting/E Cleveland/Cuyahoga	11454214	216/838-8520	44
MC2 STEM HS-Grt Lakes Sci Ctr/Cleveland/Cuyahoga	11718199	216/838-8550	44
McClain High Sch/Greenfield/Highland	00811017	937/981-7731	103
McComb Elem Sch/Mc Comb/Hancock	00810063	419/293-3286	98
McComb High Sch/Mc Comb/Hancock	00810075	419/293-3853	98
MCCOMB LOCAL SCH DIST/MC COMB/HANCOCK	00810049	419/293-3979	98
McComb Middle Sch/Mc Comb/Hancock	00810051	419/293-3853	98
McCord Junior High Sch/Sylvania/Lucas	00817279	419/824-8650	129
McCord Middle Sch/Columbus/Franklin	02893231	614/450-4000	76
McCormick Elem Sch/Loveland/Clermont	05262203	513/575-0190	31
McCormick Junior High Sch/Huron/Erie	00798441	419/433-1234	61
McCormick Middle Sch/Wellington/Lorain	00816794	440/647-2342	126
McDonald High Sch/Mc Donald/Trumbull	00836586	330/530-8051	199
MCDONALD LOCAL SCH DIST/MC DONALD/TRUMBULL	00836574	330/530-8051	199
McDowell Elem Sch/Hudson/Summit	04017134	330/653-1246	193
McEbright Cmty Learning Center/Akron/Summit	00834320	330/761-7940	191
McEsc Learning Center East/Dayton/Montgomery	12311885	937/293-7559	148
McEsc Learning Center Presch/Dayton/Montgomery	12311873	937/225-4598	148
McEsc Learning Center West/Dayton/Montgomery	12311902	937/253-4178	148
McGregor Elem Sch/Toledo/Lucas	00818168	419/473-8279	130
McGregor Reading & Math Prep/Canton/Stark	00832607	330/452-7069	185
McGuffey Elem Sch/Newark/Licking	00815063	740/670-7140	119
McGuffey Montessori Sch/Oxford/Butler	02949593	513/523-7742	24
McGuffey PK-8 Sch/Warren/Trumbull	00836847	330/675-6980	200
McKinley Downtown Campus/Canton/Stark	00832657	330/438-2602	185
McKinley Elem Sch/Elyria/Lorain	00816067	440/284-8009	123
McKinley Elem Sch/Fairport Hbr/Lake	00813223	440/354-4982	112
McKinley Elem Sch/Lisbon/Columbiana	00789529	330/424-9869	35
McKinley Elem Sch/Marion/Marion	00821828	740/223-4600	138
McKinley Elem Sch/Xenia/Greene	00804856	937/372-1251	85
McKinley Sr High Sch/Canton/Stark	00832619	330/438-2712	185
McKinley Stemm Academy/Toledo/Lucas	00817762	419/671-3750	130
McMullen Elem Sch/Loudonville/Ashland	00784282	419/994-3913	11
McPherson Middle Sch/Clyde/Sandusky	00830518	419/547-9150	176
McTigue Elem Sch/Toledo/Lucas	00817774	419/671-1200	130
McVay Elem Sch/Westerville/Franklin	03246978	614/797-7230	75
McVey Innovative Learning Ctr/Hilliard/Franklin	12037209	614/921-4800	72
Meadowbrook High Sch/Byesville/Guernsey	00805214	740/685-2566	86
Meadowbrook Middle Sch/Byesville/Guernsey	03006118	740/685-2561	86
Meadowdale High Sch/Dayton/Montgomery	00824567	937/542-7030	149
Meadowlawn Intermediate Sch/Sandusky/Erie	00798594	419/625-0214	61
Meadowvale Elem Sch/Toledo/Lucas	00818170	419/473-8284	130
Meadowview Elem Sch/Milford/Clermont	00788549	513/831-9170	31
MECHANICSBURG EXEMPTED VLG SD/MECHANICSBURG/CHAMPAIGN	00787416	937/834-2453	26
Mechanicsburg Jr Sr High Sch/Mechanicsburg/Champaign	00787430	937/834-2453	26
Medill Elem Sch/Lancaster/Fairfield	00799081	740/687-7352	63
Medina Christian Academy/Medina/Medina	02236645	330/725-3227	142
MEDINA CITY SCH DIST/MEDINA/MEDINA	00822389	330/725-8831	141
Medina Co Career Center/Medina/Medina	00822547	330/725-8461	141
MEDINA CO JOINT VOC SCH DIST/MEDINA/MEDINA	00822535	330/725-8461	141
MEDINA CO SCH EDUCL SVCS CTR/MEDINA/MEDINA	02100943	330/723-4114	142
Medina High Sch/Medina/Medina	00822418	330/636-3200	141
Medina Middle Sch/Columbus/Franklin	00800628	614/365-6050	68
Medlar View Elem Sch/Miamisburg/Montgomery	04865761	937/865-5257	151
Meigs High Sch/Pomeroy/Meigs	00822638	740/992-2158	142
Meigs Intermediate ES/Middleport/Meigs	10773665	740/742-2666	143

DISTRICT & SCHOOL TELEPHONE INDEX

Market Data Retrieval

School/City/County DISTRICT/CITY/COUNTY	PID	TELEPHONE NUMBER	PAGE
MEIGS LOCAL SCH DIST/POMEROY/			
MEIGS	00822602	740/992-2153	142
Meigs Middle Sch/Pomeroy/Meigs	00822640	740/992-3058	143
Meigs Primary Elem Sch/Middleport/Meigs	00822614	740/742-3000	143
Melridge Elem Sch/Painesville/Lake	00813613	440/352-3854	114
Melrose Elem Sch/Wooster/Wayne	00839564	330/988-1111	214
Memorial Elem Sch/Brunswick/Medina	01841869	330/273-0486	140
Memorial High Sch/Campbell/Mahoning	00819899	330/799-1515	134
Memorial Junior High Sch/Cleveland/Cuyahoga	00794768	216/691-2141	51
Memorial Middle Sch/Mentor/Lake	00813443	440/974-2250	113
Memorial Year-Round Sch/Cleveland/Cuyahoga	00791481	216/838-0850	44
Menlo Park Academy/Cleveland/Cuyahoga	05382695	440/925-6365	39
Mentor Christian Sch/Mentor/Lake	00814071	440/257-3172	115
MENTOR EXEMPTED VILLAGE SD/ MENTOR/LAKE	00813352	440/255-4444	113
Mentor High Sch/Mentor/Lake	00813455	440/974-5300	113
Mercer Co Alternative Sch/Celina/Mercer	04848634	419/586-6722	4
MERCER CO ED SERVICE CENTER/ CELINA/MERCER	00823151	419/586-6628	143
Mercer Elem Sch/Cincinnati/Hamilton	00806555	513/232-7000	89
Mercer Elem Sch/Shaker HTS/Cuyahoga	00794574	216/295 4070	50
Mercy McAuley High Sch/Cincinnati/Hamilton	00808462	513/681-1800	95
Mercy Montessori Center Sch/Cincinnati/Hamilton	00808486	513/475-6700	95
Merwin Elem Sch/Cincinnati/Clermont	00788769	513/947-7800	31
Mesopotamia Elem Sch/Mesopotamia/Trumbull	00835843	440/693-4125	197
Messiah Lutheran Elem Sch/Fairview Park/Cuyahoga	00795190	440/331-6553	54
META SOLUTIONS/COLUMBUS/FRANKLIN	04499544	614/473-8300	78
META SOLUTIONS/MARION/MARION	04499506	740/389-4798	139
META SOLUTIONS BRANCH/DAYTON/ MARION	04499532	937/223-1112	154
Metro Catholic Sch/Cleveland/Cuyahoga	00797215	216/281-4044	52
Metro Early Clg Mid High Sch/Columbus/Franklin	11914989	614/259-6639	4
Metro Institute of Technology/Columbus/Franklin	12163872	614/797-4797	4
MIAMI CO ED SERVICE CENTER/ TROY/MIAMI	00823709	937/339-5100	144
Miami East Elem Sch/Casstown/Miami	00823280	937/335-5439	145
Miami East High Sch/Casstown/Miami	00823319	937/335-7070	145
Miami East Junior High Sch/Casstown/Miami	11927596	937/335-5439	145
MIAMI EAST LOCAL SCH DIST/ CASSTOWN/MIAMI	00823266	937/335-7505	145
Miami Montessori Sch/Troy/Miami	03056814	937/339-0025	147
Miami Trace Elem Sch/Wshngtn Ct Hs/Fayette	00799342	740/333-2400	65
Miami Trace High Sch/Wshngtn Ct Hs/Fayette	00799392	740/333-4700	65
MIAMI TRACE LOCAL SCH DIST/ WSHNGTN CT HS/FAYETTE	00799328	740/335-3010	65
Miami Trace Middle Sch/Wshngtn Ct Hs/Fayette	00799330	740/333-4900	65
Miami Valley Academies/Dayton/Montgomery	05220396	937/294-4522	4
Miami Valley Career Tech Ctr/Clayton/Montgomery	00825989	937/854-6291	151
MIAMI VALLEY CAREER TECH VSD/ ENGLEWOOD/MONTGOMERY	00825977	937/854-6291	151
Miami Valley Christian Academy/Cincinnati/Hamilton	04987149	513/272-6822	96
MIAMI VALLEY EDUCATIONAL CA/ YELLOW SPGS/GREENE	04499556	937/767-1468	85
Miami Valley Sch/Dayton/Montgomery	00826000	937/434-4444	154
Miami View Elem Sch/S Charleston/Clark	00787911	937/462-8364	28
MIAMISBURG CITY SCH DIST/ MIAMISBURG/MONTGOMERY	00825240	937/866-3381	151
Miamisburg High Sch/Miamisburg/Montgomery	00825290	937/866-0771	151
Miamisburg Middle Sch/Miamisburg/Montgomery	00825305	937/865-0011	151
Miamitown Elem Sch/Miamitown/Hamilton	00807690	513/353-1416	93
Michael R White STEM Sch/Cleveland/Cuyahoga	00792186	216/838-2300	44
Michigan Primary Sch/Ashtabula/Ashtabula	00784464	440/992-1250	12
Mid Ohio Pre-School/Mansfield/Richland	04020698	419/774-5556	171
MID-OHIO ED SERVICE CENTER/ MANSFIELD/RICHLAND	00830075	419/774-5520	171
Mid-Valley Christian Sch/Middleport/Meigs	11231581	740/992-6249	143
Middlebranch Elem Sch/Canton/Stark	10773926	330/491-3750	188
Middlebury Academy Charter Sch/Akron/Summit	12100234	330/752-2766	4
Middletown Christian Sch/Franklin/Warren	00787210	513/423-4542	209
MIDDLETOWN CITY SCH DIST/ MIDDLETOWN/BUTLER	00786761	513/423-0781	23
Middletown High Sch/Middletown/Butler	00786905	513/420-4500	23
Middletown Middle Sch/Middletown/Butler	00786826	513/420-4528	23
Middletown Prep & Fitness Acad/Middletown/Butler	05220358	513/424-6110	4
MIDEAST CAREER & TECH CTRS/ ZANESVILLE/MUSKINGUM	00826842	740/454-0105	157
Mideast CTC Buffalo Campus/Senecaville/Muskingum	00826854	740/685-2516	157
Mideast CTC Zanesville Campus/Zanesville/Muskingum	00826866	740/454-0101	157
Midnimo Cross Cultural CMS/Columbus/Franklin	11016616	614/261 7480	4
Midvale Elem Sch/Midvale/Tuscarawas	10901305	330/339-1191	202
Midview East Intermediate Sch/Grafton/Lorain	00816536	440/748-1851	125
Midview High Sch/Grafton/Lorain	00816550	440/748-2124	125
MIDVIEW LOCAL SCH DIST/GRAFTON/ LORAIN	00816483	440/748-5353	125
Midview Middle Sch/Grafton/Lorain	00816548	440/748-2122	125
Midview North Elem Sch/Grafton/Lorain	00816500	440/748-6869	125
Midview West Elem Sch/Grafton/Lorain	00816512	440/748-2305	125
Midway Elem Sch/Cincinnati/Hamilton	00805874	513/363-3500	88
MIDWEST REG ED SERVICE CENTER/ BELLEFONTAINE/LOGAN	00810489	937/599-5195	120
Mifflin Elem Sch/Mansfield/Richland	00829648	419/589-6517	172
Mifflin High Sch/Columbus/Franklin	01556533	614/365-5466	68
Mifflin Middle Sch/Columbus/Franklin	00800642	614/365-5474	68
Miles Elem Sch/Cleveland/Cuyahoga	00792162	216/838-5250	44
Miles Park Elem Sch/Cleveland/Cuyahoga	00792203	216/838-4450	44
Milford Christian Academy/Milford/Clermont	00788836	513/575-1708	32
MILFORD EXEMPTED VILLAGE SD/ MILFORD/CLERMONT	00788537	513/831-1314	30
Milford High Sch/Milford/Clermont	00788587	513/831-2990	31
Milford Junior High Sch/Milford/Clermont	00788563	513/831-1900	31
Milford Preschool/Milford/Clermont	11456250	513/728-7400	31
Milkovich Middle Sch/Maple Heights/Cuyahoga	00793659	216/438-6000	47
Mill Valley Elem Sch/Marysville/Union	04747688	937/578-6900	204
Millcreek Elem Sch/Corning/Perry	00827626	740/721-0522	161
Millcreek-West Unity Local Sch/West Unity/Williams	00839796	419/924-2366	215
MILLCREEK-WEST UNITY LOCAL SD/ WEST UNITY/WILLIAMS	00839784	419/924-2366	215
Millennium Community Sch/Columbus/Franklin	04880333	614/255-5585	66
Miller Avenue Elem Sch/Sugarcreek/Tuscarawas	00837243	330/852-2441	202
Miller City Elem Sch/Miller City/Putnam	00829258	419/876-3174	170
Miller City High Sch/Miller City/Putnam	00829260	419/876-3173	170
Miller City Middle Sch/Miller City/Putnam	00829272	419/876-3173	170
MILLER CITY-NEW CLEVELAND SD/ MILLER CITY/PUTNAM	00829246	419/876-3172	170
Miller Elem Sch/Aurora/Portage	00828204	330/562-6199	165
Miller High Sch/Corning/Perry	00827614	740/721-0521	161
Miller Ridge Elem Sch/Middletown/Butler	00786955	513/420-4559	23
Miller South School-Vpa/Akron/Summit	04143197	330/761-1765	191
Millersburg Elem Sch/Millersburg/Holmes	00811407	330/674-5681	105
Millersport Elem Sch/Millersport/Fairfield	00799287	740/467-2216	64
Millersport Jr Sr High Sch/Millersport/Fairfield	00799299	740/467-2929	64
Millridge Elem Sch/Highland Hgts/Cuyahoga	00793788	440/995-7250	48
Mills Elem Sch/Sandusky/Erie	00798685	419/984-1230	61
Mills Lawn Elem Sch/Yellow Spgs/Greene	00804959	937/767-7217	85
Millstream Career Center/Findlay/Hancock	10017447	419/425-8277	98
Milton-Union Elem Sch/West Milton/Miami	00823371	937/884-7920	146
MILTON-UNION EXEMPTED VLG SD/ WEST MILTON/MIAMI	00823333	937/884-7910	145
Milton-Union High Sch/West Milton/Miami	00823369	937/884-7940	146
Milton-Union Middle Sch/West Milton/Miami	00823357	937/884-7930	146
Mineral Ridge High Sch/Mineral Ridge/Trumbull	00837035	330/652-1451	201
Minerva Elem Sch/Minerva/Stark	00833182	330/868-4011	187
Minerva High Sch/Minerva/Stark	00833194	330/868-4134	187
MINERVA LOCAL SCH DIST/MINERVA/ STARK	00833170	330/868-4332	187
Minerva Middle Sch/Minerva/Stark	00833209	330/868-4497	187
Minford Elem Primary Sch/Minford/Scioto	00831017	740/820-2287	178
Minford High Sch/Minford/Scioto	00830996	740/820-3445	178
MINFORD LOCAL SCH DIST/MINFORD/ SCIOTO	00830984	740/820-3896	178
Minford Middle Sch/Minford/Scioto	00831005	740/820-2181	178
Minster Elem Sch/Minster/Auglaize	00785298	419/628-4174	15
Minster Jr/Sr High Sch/Minster/Auglaize	00785303	419/628-2324	15

Ohio School Directory

DISTRICT & SCHOOL TELEPHONE INDEX

School/City/County DISTRICT/CITY/COUNTY	PID	TELEPHONE NUMBER	PAGE
MINSTER LOCAL SCH DIST/*MINSTER*/ AUGLAIZE	00785286	419/628-3397	15
Miracle City Academy/*Piketon*/Pike	04987204	740/289-2787	164
Mississinawa Valley Elem Sch/*Union City*/ Darke	00797679	937/968-4464	56
Mississinawa Valley Jr Sr HS/*Union City*/ Darke	00797681	937/968-4464	56
MISSISSINAWA VALLEY SCH DIST/ UNION CITY/DARKE	00797667	937/968-5656	56
Mogadore Christian Academy/*Akron*/Summit	04986951	330/628-8482	196
Mogadore Jr Sr High Sch/*Mogadore*/Portage	00835166	330/628-9943	166
MOGADORE LOCAL SCH DIST/ MOGADORE/PORTAGE	00835154	330/628-9946	166
Mohawk Local Sch/*Sycamore*/Wyandot	00840604	419/927-2595	219
MOHAWK LOCAL SCH DIST/*SYCAMORE*/ WYANDOT	00840599	419/927-2595	219
Moler Elem Sch/*Columbus*/Franklin	00800678	614/365-5529	68
Monac Elem Sch/*Toledo*/Lucas	00818182	419/473-8289	130
Monarch Sch of Bellefaire Jcb/*Shaker HTS*/ Cuyahoga	12314667	216/320-8945	54
Monclova Christian Academy/*Monclova*/Lucas	11231426	419/866-7630	131
Monclova Primary Sch/*Monclova*/Lucas	00816914	419/865-9408	127
Monfort Heights Elem Sch/*Cincinnati*/ Hamilton	00807183	513/389-1570	91
Monroe Achievement Center/*Woodsfield*/ Monroe	04012794	740/472-1712	147
Monroe Central High Sch/*Woodsfield*/Monroe	00823888	740/472-0414	147
Monroe Elem Sch/*London*/Madison	00819540	614/873-8503	132
Monroe Elem Sch/*Monroe*/Butler	00786917	513/539-8101	23
Monroe Elem Sch/*New Richmond*/Clermont	00788628	513/553-3183	31
Monroe High Sch/*Monroe*/Butler	00786929	513/539-8471	23
Monroe Jr High Sch/*Monroe*/Butler	12231089	513/539-8471	23
MONROE LOCAL SCH DIST/*MONROE*/ BUTLER	04913801	513/539-2536	23
Monroe Preparatory Academy/*Sandusky*/Erie	12258972	567/998-7522	4
Monroe Primary Sch/*Monroe*/Butler	11072115	513/360-0700	23
Monroeville Elem Sch/*Monroeville*/Huron	00811550	419/465-2533	105
Monroeville High Sch/*Monroeville*/Huron	00811562	419/465-2531	105
MONROEVILLE LOCAL SCH DIST/ MONROEVILLE/HURON	00811548	419/465-2610	105
Monterey Elem Sch/*Grove City*/Franklin	00801945	614/801-8250	73
Montessori Academy Cincinnati/*Mason*/Warren	03077715	513/398-7773	209
Montessori Childrens Sch/*Westlake*/Cuyahoga	02188581	440/871-8773	54
Montessori HS-Univ Circle/*Cleveland*/ Cuyahoga	11545722	216/421-3033	54
Montessori Sch-Mahoning Valley/*Youngstown*/ Mahoning	03106952	330/788-4622	137
Montessori School-Centerville/*Huber Heights*/ Montgomery	02853164	937/435-4572	154
MONTGOMERY CO ED SERVICE CTR/ DAYTON/MONTGOMERY	00825991	937/225-4598	148
Montgomery Elem Sch/*Cincinnati*/Hamilton	00807793	513/686-1730	93
Montgomery Preparatory Academy/*Dayton*/ Montgomery	12361127	937/991-2900	4
Monticello Elem Sch/*Huber Heights*/ Montgomery	00825757	937/237-6360	150
Monticello Middle Sch/*Cleveland HTS*/ Cuyahoga	12367676	216/397-5967	42
MONTPELIER EXEMPTED VILLAGE SD/ MONTPELIER/WILLIAMS	00839825	419/485-3676	215
Montpelier Sch/*Montpelier*/Williams	00839849	419/485-6700	215
Montrose Elem Sch/*Bexley*/Franklin	00799562	614/237-4226	66
Moreland Hills Elem Sch/*Pepper Pike*/ Cuyahoga	00794055	216/831-8600	49
Morgan East Elem Sch/*McConnelsvle*/Morgan	00826024	740/962-3361	155
Morgan Elem Sch/*Hamilton*/Butler	00787088	513/738-1986	24
Morgan High Sch/*McConnelsvle*/Morgan	00826062	740/962-2944	155
Morgan Junior High Sch/*McConnelsvle*/Morgan	04941016	740/962-2833	155
MORGAN LOCAL SCH DIST/*MCCONNELSVLE*/ MORGAN	00826012	740/962-2377	154
Morgan South Elem Sch/*Stockport*/Morgan	00826036	740/559-2377	155
Morgan West Elem Sch/*Malta*/Morgan	00826048	740/342-4873	155
Morrison Elem Sch/*Athens*/Athens	00785078	740/593-5445	14
Morton Middle Sch/*Vandalia*/Montgomery	00825680	937/415-6600	153
Mother Maria Anna Brunner CS/*Dayton*/ Montgomery	00808632	937/277-2291	154
Mother Teresa Cath ES/*Middletown*/Butler	10019158	513/779-6585	24
Mound Elem Sch/*Miamisburg*/Montgomery	00825317	937/866-4641	151
Mound St Health Careers Acad/*Dayton*/ Montgomery	05220401	937/223-3041	4
Mound St Info & Tech Academy/*Dayton*/ Montgomery	05220413	937/223-3041	4
Mound St Tech Trade Military/*Dayton*/ Montgomery	05220425	937/223-3041	4
Mound-STEM Sch/*Cleveland*/Cuyahoga	00792215	216/838-1650	44
Mount Auburn Preparatory Acad/*Cincinnati*/ Hamilton	12320551	513/975-3391	4
Mount Vernon SDA Elem Sch/*Mount Vernon*/ Knox	00813168	740/393-7060	112
Mt Airy Elem Sch/*Cincinnati*/Hamilton	00805903	513/363-3700	88
Mt Eaton Elem Sch/*Mount Eaton*/Wayne	00839409	330/857-5313	213
MT GILEAD EXEMPTED VILLAGE SD/ MOUNT GILEAD/MORROW	00826191	419/946-1646	155
Mt Gilead High Sch/*Mount Gilead*/Morrow	00826220	419/947-6065	155
Mt Gilead Middle Sch/*Mount Gilead*/Morrow	00826232	419/947-9517	155
MT HEALTHY CITY SCH DIST/ CINCINNATI/HAMILTON	00806983	513/729-0077	91
Mt Healthy Jr Sr High Sch/*Cincinnati*/ Hamilton	00807030	513/729-0130	91
Mt Healthy Prep & Fitness Acad/*Cincinnati*/ Hamilton	11747023	513/587-6280	87
Mt Hope Elem Sch/*Mount Hope*/Holmes	00811330	330/674-0418	104
Mt Logan Learning Center/*Chillicothe*/Ross	00830142	740/773-2638	175
Mt Notre Dame High Sch/*Cincinnati*/Hamilton	00808515	513/821-3044	95
Mt Orab Elem Sch/*Mount Orab*/Brown	00786230	937/444-2528	20
Mt Orab Middle Sch/*Mount Orab*/Brown	04030588	937/444-2529	20
Mt Pleasant Elem Sch/*Lancaster*/Fairfield	00799055	740/687-7338	64
MT VERNON CITY SCH DIST/ MOUNT VERNON/KNOX	00813053	740/397-7422	111
Mt Vernon High Sch/*Mount Vernon*/Knox	00813118	740/393-5900	111
Mt Vernon Middle Sch/*Mount Vernon*/Knox	00813120	740/392-6867	111
Mt Washington Sch/*Cincinnati*/Hamilton	00805915	513/363-3800	88
Mulberry Elem Sch/*Milford*/Clermont	05271735	513/722-3588	31
Munroe Elem Sch/*Tallmadge*/Summit	00835623	330/633-5427	195
Munson Elem Sch/*Chardon*/Geauga	00804210	440/286-5901	82
Murray Ridge Sch/*Elyria*/Lorain	02052176	440/329-3760	122
MUSKINGUM VALLEY ESC/*ZANESVILLE*/ MUSKINGUM	02094708	740/452-4518	156
Mvctc Youth Connect Alt Sch/*Dayton*/ Montgomery	05091494	937/226-1741	151

N

Nagel Middle Sch/*Cincinnati*/Hamilton	04868529	513/474-5407	89
NAPOLEON AREA CITY SCH DIST/ NAPOLEON/HENRY	00810740	419/599-7015	101
Napoleon Elem Sch 3-6/*Napoleon*/Henry	00810764	419/592-6991	101
Napoleon Elem Sch PK-2/*Napoleon*/Henry	00810752	419/592-6991	101
Napoleon Jr Sr High Sch/*Napoleon*/Henry	00810790	419/599-1050	101
Nashport Elem Sch/*Nashport*/Muskingum	00826488	740/452-3977	157
Nashville Elem Sch/*Big Prairie*/Holmes	00811419	330/378-2111	105
Nathan Hale Elem Sch/*Cleveland*/Cuyahoga	00792265	216/838-4250	44
National Road Elem Sch/*Zanesville*/ Muskingum	00826737	740/450-1538	157
National Trail Elem Sch/*New Paris*/Preble	00828852	937/437-3333	168
National Trail High Sch/*New Paris*/Preble	00828876	937/437-3333	168
NATIONAL TRAIL LOCAL SCH DIST/ NEW PARIS/PREBLE	00828838	937/437-3333	168
National Trail Middle Sch/*New Paris*/Preble	00828864	937/437-3333	168
Nativity of Our Lord Sch/*Cincinnati*/ Hamilton	00808527	513/458-6767	95
Navarre Elem Sch/*Toledo*/Lucas	00817798	419/671-7600	130
Navin Elem Sch/*Marysville*/Union	05092955	937/578-7000	204
NCOCC-N CTRL OHIO CO-OP CA/ MANSFIELD/RICHLAND	04499568	419/747-8660	174
Near West Intergenerationl Sch/*Cleveland*/ Cuyahoga	11920249	216/961-4308	44
NELSONVILLE-YORK CITY SCH DIST/ NELSONVILLE/ATHENS	00785157	740/753-4441	15
Nelsonville-York Elem Sch/*Nelsonville*/ Athens	00785171	740/753-5145	15
Nelsonville-York High Sch/*Nelsonville*/ Athens	00785183	740/753-1964	15
Nelsonville-York Jr High Sch/*Nelsonville*/ Athens	00785195	740/753-1254	15
NEOMIN-NE OHIO MGMT INFO NET/ WARREN/TRUMBULL	04499570	330/847-6464	201
NEONET-NE OHIO ED TECH/*CUYAHOGA FLS*/ SUMMIT	04499439	330/926-3900	196
Nevin Coppock Elem Sch/*Tipp City*/Miami	00823565	937/667-2275	146
New Albany Early Learning Ctr/*New Albany*/ Franklin	05271670	614/413-8700	72
New Albany High Sch/*New Albany*/Franklin	00801622	614/413-8300	72
New Albany Interm Sch/*New Albany*/Franklin	12104840	614/413-3000	72
New Albany Middle Sch/*New Albany*/Franklin	00801610	614/413-8500	72

DISTRICT & SCHOOL TELEPHONE INDEX

Market Data Retrieval

School/City/County DISTRICT/CITY/COUNTY	PID	TELEPHONE NUMBER	PAGE
New Albany Primary Sch/New Albany/Franklin	00801608	614/413-8600	72
NEW ALBANY-PLAIN LOCAL SD/			
NEW ALBANY/FRANKLIN	00801593	614/855-2040	72
NEW BOSTON LOCAL SCH DIST/			
NEW BOSTON/SCIOTO	00831029	740/456-4626	178
New Bremen Elem Sch/New Bremen/Auglaize	00785327	419/629-3244	16
New Bremen High Sch/New Bremen/Auglaize	04867331	419/629-8606	16
NEW BREMEN LOCAL SCH DIST/			
NEW BREMEN/AUGLAIZE	00785315	419/629-8606	16
New Carlisle Elem Sch/New Carlisle/Clark	00787789	937/845-4480	29
New Concord Elem Sch/New Concord/Muskingum	00826323	740/826-4453	156
New Day Academy/Willowick/Lake	11016501	440/516-0866	4
New Franklin Christian Academy/Minerva/Stark	04987034	330/862-2491	190
New Hope Christian Academy/Circleville/Pickaway	04242391	740/477-6427	163
NEW KNOXVILLE LOCAL SCH DIST/			
NEW KNOXVILLE/AUGLAIZE	00785341	419/753-2431	16
New Knoxville Sch/New Knoxville/Auglaize	00785353	419/753-2431	16
NEW LEBANON LOCAL SCH DIST/			
NEW LEBANON/MONTGOMERY	00825331	937/687-1301	151
New Lexington Elem Sch/New Lexington/Perry	00827509	740/342-2556	161
New Lexington Middle Sch/New Lexington/Perry	01523536	740/342-4128	161
NEW LEXINGTON SCH DIST/NEW LEXINGTON/PERRY	00827470	740/342-4133	161
New Lexington Senior High Sch/New Lexington/Perry	00827511	740/342-3528	161
New London Elem Sch/New London/Huron	12314590	419/929-1586	106
New London High Sch/New London/Huron	00811586	419/929-1586	106
NEW LONDON LOCAL SCH DIST/			
NEW LONDON/HURON	00811574	419/929-8433	105
New London Middle Sch/New London/Huron	12314617	419/929-1586	106
New Miami Elem Sch/Hamilton/Butler	00787038	513/896-7153	23
NEW MIAMI LOCAL SCH DIST/			
HAMILTON/BUTLER	00787026	513/863-0833	23
New Miami Middle High Sch/Hamilton/Butler	11923772	513/863-4917	24
NEW PHILADELPHIA CITY SCH DIST/			
NEW PHILA/TUSCARAWAS	00837334	330/364-0600	202
New Philadelphia High Sch/New Phila/Tuscarawas	00837372	330/364-0644	203
NEW RICHMOND EXEMPTED VLG SD/			
NEW RICHMOND/CLERMONT	00788616	513/553-2616	31
New Richmond High Sch/New Richmond/Clermont	00788654	513/553-3191	31
New Richmond Middle Sch/New Richmond/Clermont	00788666	513/553-3161	31
New Riegel K-12 Sch/New Riegel/Seneca	00831598	419/595-2265	181
NEW RIEGEL LOCAL SCH DIST/			
NEW RIEGEL/SENECA	00831574	419/595-2256	181
New School Montessori/Cincinnati/Hamilton	02236762	513/281-7999	96
New Tech Collinwood/Cleveland/Cuyahoga	00791388	216/838-0500	44
New Tech High School-East/Cleveland/Cuyahoga	11684990	216/838-8650	44
New Tech High School-West/Cleveland/Cuyahoga	11696931	216/838-8700	44
New Vienna Elem Sch/New Vienna/Clinton	00789000	937/987-2448	33
Newark Catholic High Sch/Newark/Licking	00802896	740/344-3594	120
NEWARK CITY SCH DIST/NEWARK/LICKING	00814930	740/670-7000	119
Newark Digital Academy/Newark/Licking	05300037	740/328-2022	119
Newark High Sch/Newark/Licking	00815087	740/670-7400	119
Newark SDA Sch/Heath/Licking	02147745	740/323-4222	120
Newbridge Math Reading Academy/Columbus/Franklin	12100404	614/279-6000	4
Newbury Elem Sch/Newbury/Geauga	00804351	440/564-2282	82
Newbury Jr Sr High Sch/Newbury/Geauga	04504541	440/564-2281	82
NEWBURY LOCAL SCH DIST/NEWBURY/GEAUGA	00804337	440/564-5501	82
NEWCOMERSTOWN EXEMPTED VLG SD/			
NEWCOMERSTOWN/TUSCARAWAS	00837437	740/498-8373	203
Newcomerstown High Sch/Newcomerstown/Tuscarawas	00837451	740/498-5111	203
Newcomerstown Middle Sch/Newcomerstown/Tuscarawas	00837463	740/498-8151	203
Newport Elem Sch/Newport/Washington	00838728	740/473-2667	210
Newton D Baker School of Arts/Cleveland/Cuyahoga	00792289	216/838-6650	44
Newton Elem Sch/Newark/Licking	00815178	740/745-5982	119
Newton Falls Elem Mid Sch/Newton Falls/Trumbull	00836615	330/872-0695	200
NEWTON FALLS EXEMPTED VLG SD/			
NEWTON FALLS/TRUMBULL	00836603	330/872-5445	200
Newton Falls High Sch/Newton Falls/Trumbull	00836627	330/872-5121	200
Newton Falls Junior High Sch/Newton Falls/Trumbull	00836639	330/872-0905	200
NEWTON LOCAL SCH DIST/PLEASANT HILL/MIAMI	00823383	937/676-2002	146
Newton Sch/Pleasant Hill/Miami	00823395	937/676-2002	146
Nightingale Montessori Sch/Springfield/Clark	02646894	937/324-0336	29
Nihf STEM High Sch/Akron/Summit	11824906	330/761-7965	191
Nihf STEM Middle Sch/Akron/Summit	11464348	330/761-3195	191
NILES CITY SCH DIST/NILES/TRUMBULL	00836653	330/989-5095	200
Niles Intermediate Sch/Niles/Trumbull	00836732	330/989-5093	200
Niles McKinley High Sch/Niles/Trumbull	00836720	330/652-9968	200
Niles Middle Sch/Niles/Trumbull	00836677	330/652-5656	200
Niles Primary Sch/Niles/Trumbull	00836665	330/989-5091	200
Noble Academy Cleveland/Euclid/Cuyahoga	10025224	216/486-8866	4
Noble Academy-Columbus/Columbus/Franklin	11016537	614/326-0687	4
Noble Elem Sch/Cleveland HTS/Cuyahoga	00792930	216/371-6535	42
Noble Elem Sch/Defiance/Defiance	00798037	419/782-7941	57
Noble Elem Sch/Tiffin/Seneca	00831770	419/447-1566	181
NOBLE LOCAL SCH DIST/SARAHSVILLE/NOBLE	00826921	740/732-4120	158
NOECA-NORTHERN OHIO ED CA/			
SANDUSKY/ERIE	04499582	419/627-1439	62
Nolley Elem Sch/Akron/Summit	00835013	330/882-4133	193
Nordonia High Sch/Macedonia/Summit	00835221	330/468-4601	193
NORDONIA HILLS CITY SCH DIST/			
NORTHFIELD/SUMMIT	00835180	330/467-0580	193
Nordonia Middle Sch/Northfield/Summit	00835233	330/467-0584	193
Normandy Elem Sch/Bay Village/Cuyahoga	00790451	440/617-7350	40
Normandy Elem Sch/Dayton/Montgomery	00824014	937/434-0917	149
Normandy High Sch/Parma/Cuyahoga	00794213	440/885-2400	49
North Adams Elem Sch/Seaman/Adams	00783472	937/386-2516	6
North Adams Jr Sr High Sch/Seaman/Adams	00783446	937/386-2528	6
North Avondale Montessori Sch/Cincinnati/Hamilton	00805927	513/363-3900	88
North Baltimore Jr Sr High Sch/N Baltimore/Wood	00840276	419/257-3464	217
NORTH BALTIMORE LOCAL SCH DIST/			
N BALTIMORE/WOOD	00840238	419/257-3531	217
NORTH CANTON CITY SCH DIST/			
NORTH CANTON/STARK	00833247	330/497-5600	187
North Canton Middle Sch/North Canton/Stark	00833285	330/497-5635	187
North Central Academy/Tiffin/Seneca	11747035	419/448-5786	180
North Central Local Sch/Pioneer/Williams	00839875	419/737-2366	215
NORTH CENTRAL LOCAL SCH DIST/			
PIONEER/WILLIAMS	00839863	419/737-2392	215
NORTH CENTRAL OHIO ED SVC CTR/			
MARION/MARION	02089210	740/387-6625	137
NORTH COAST ED MEDIA CENTER/			
VALLEY VIEW/CUYAHOGA	02100840	216/901-4233	54
NORTH COLLEGE HILL CITY SD/			
CINCINNATI/HAMILTON	00807078	513/931-8181	91
North College Hill Elem Sch/Cincinnati/Hamilton	00807080	513/728-4787	91
North College Hill High Sch/Cincinnati/Hamilton	00807119	513/728-4783	91
North College Hill Mid Sch/Cincinnati/Hamilton	11556343	513/728-4785	91
NORTH CTRL OHIO ED SERVICE CTR/			
TIFFIN/SENECA	00830855	419/447-2927	180
North Dayton Sch of Discovery/Dayton/Montgomery	05220437	937/278-6671	148
North East Center/Gahanna/Franklin	04008884	614/476-0530	66
North Elem Sch/Brilliant/Jefferson	00812126	740/598-4589	108
North Elem Sch/Cincinnati/Hamilton	00807016	513/742-6004	91
North Elem Sch/E Liverpool/Columbiana	00789282	330/386-8772	35
North Elem Sch/Madison/Lake	00813338	440/428-2151	113
NORTH FORK LOCAL SCH DIST/			
UTICA/LICKING	00815142	740/892-3666	119
North High Sch/Akron/Summit	00834332	330/761-2665	191
North High Sch/Eastlake/Lake	00813962	440/975-3666	114
North Linden Elem Sch/Columbus/Franklin	00800719	614/365-6055	68
North Nimishillen Elem Sch/Louisville/Stark	00832956	330/875-2661	186
NORTH OLMSTED CITY SCH DIST/			
NORTH OLMSTED/CUYAHOGA	00793817	440/588-5300	48

Ohio School Directory

DISTRICT & SCHOOL TELEPHONE INDEX

School/City/County DISTRICT/CITY/COUNTY	PID	TELEPHONE NUMBER	PAGE
North Olmsted High Sch/*North Olmsted*/Cuyahoga	00793881	440/779-8825	48
North Olmsted Middle Sch/*North Olmsted*/Cuyahoga	00793893	440/588-5700	48
NORTH POINT ED SVC CTR/SANDUSKY/ERIE	00798843	419/627-3900	60
North Ridgeville Academic Ctr/*N Ridgeville*/Lorain	00816603	440/353-1180	125
NORTH RIDGEVILLE CITY SCH DIST/N RIDGEVILLE/LORAIN	00816562	440/327-4444	125
North Ridgeville High Sch/*N Ridgeville*/Lorain	00816598	440/327-1992	125
North Road Intermediate Sch/*Warren*/Trumbull	00836225	330/856-8265	198
NORTH ROYALTON CITY SCH DIST/N ROYALTON/CUYAHOGA	00793922	440/237-8800	48
North Royalton High Sch/*N Royalton*/Cuyahoga	00793946	440/582-7801	48
North Royalton Middle Sch/*N Royalton*/Cuyahoga	03235498	440/582-9120	48
North Union Elem Sch/*Richwood*/Union	00837736	740/943-3113	205
North Union High Sch/*Richwood*/Union	00837762	740/943-3012	205
NORTH UNION LOCAL SCH DIST/RICHWOOD/UNION	00837712	740/943-2509	204
North Union Middle Sch/*Richwood*/Union	00837774	740/943-2369	205
NORTH WEST OHIO ED SERVICE CTR/ARCHBOLD/FULTON	00803840	567/444-4807	78
Northeast Ohio College Prep/*Cleveland*/Cuyahoga	11567043	216/965-0580	4
Northeastern High Sch/*Springfield*/Clark	00787820	937/328-6575	27
NORTHEASTERN LOCAL SCH DIST/DEFIANCE/DEFIANCE	00798025	419/497-3461	57
NORTHEASTERN LOCAL SCH DIST/SPRINGFIELD/CLARK	00787791	937/325-7615	27
Northern Career Institute/*Willoughby*/Lake	00814021	440/946-7085	114
NORTHERN LOCAL SCH DIST/THORNVILLE/PERRY	00827535	740/743-1303	161
Northfield Bapt Christian Sch/*Northfield*/Summit	04986884	330/467-8918	196
Northfield Elem Sch/*Northfield*/Summit	04363127	330/467-2010	193
Northgate Intermediate Sch/*Columbus*/Franklin	12168808	614/365-8815	68
Northland High Sch/*Columbus*/Franklin	00800721	614/365-5342	68
Northland Prep & Fitness Acad/*Columbus*/Franklin	05382736	614/318-0600	4
NORTHMONT CITY SCH DIST/ENGLEWOOD/MONTGOMERY	00825379	937/832-5000	152
Northmont High Sch/*Clayton*/Montgomery	00825422	937/832-6000	152
Northmont Middle Sch/*Clayton*/Montgomery	00825434	937/832-6500	152
Northmoor Elem Sch/*Englewood*/Montgomery	00825446	937/832-6800	152
NORTHMOR LOCAL SCH DIST/GALION/MORROW	00826256	419/946-8861	155
Northmor Sch/*Galion*/Morrow	00826268	419/946-3946	156
Northridge Elem Sch/*Springfield*/Clark	00787832	937/342-4627	27
Northridge High Sch/*Dayton*/Montgomery	00825513	937/275-7469	152
Northridge High Sch/*Johnstown*/Licking	00815269	740/967-6651	119
Northridge Intermediate Sch/*Johnstown*/Licking	11130494	740/967-1401	119
NORTHRIDGE LOCAL SCH DIST/DAYTON/MONTGOMERY	00825484	937/278-5885	152
NORTHRIDGE LOCAL SCH DIST/JOHNSTOWN/LICKING	00815219	740/967-6631	119
Northridge Middle Sch/*Johnstown*/Licking	04029333	740/967-6671	120
Northridge Middle Sch/*Springfield*/Clark	05271498	937/399-2852	27
Northridge Primary Sch/*Alexandria*/Licking	00815221	740/924-2691	120
Northside Christian Sch/*Westerville*/Franklin	02148581	614/882-1493	77
Northside Intermediate Sch/*Alliance*/Stark	00832229	330/829-2269	184
Northtowne Elem Sch/*Columbus*/Franklin	00800745	614/365-5488	68
Northview Elem Sch/*Jackson*/Jackson	00811952	740/286-2390	107
Northview High Sch/*Sylvania*/Lucas	00817267	419/824-8570	129
Northview Primary Sch/*Findlay*/Hancock	00809973	419/425-8290	98
Northview Sch/*Dayton*/Montgomery	02052308	937/890-0730	148
Northwest Elem Sch/*Mc Dermott*/Scioto	04281165	740/259-2250	179
Northwest High Sch/*Canal Fulton*/Stark	00833364	330/854-2205	187
Northwest High Sch/*Cincinnati*/Hamilton	00807195	513/851-7300	91
Northwest High Sch/*Mc Dermott*/Scioto	00831093	740/259-2366	179
NORTHWEST LOCAL SCH DIST/CANAL FULTON/STARK	00833326	330/854-2291	187
NORTHWEST LOCAL SCH DIST/CINCINNATI/HAMILTON	00807121	513/923-1000	91
NORTHWEST LOCAL SCH DIST/MC DERMOTT/SCIOTO	00831067	740/259-5558	179
Northwest Middle Sch/*Canal Fulton*/Stark	00833352	330/854-3303	188
Northwest Middle Sch/*Mc Dermott*/Scioto	04281177	740/259-2528	179
NORTHWEST OHIO COMPUTER ASSOC/ARCHBOLD/FULTON	04499594	419/267-5565	80
NORTHWEST OHIO COMPUTER CO-OP/LIMA/ALLEN	04499453	419/228-7417	10
NORTHWEST OHIO ED TECH/BOWLING GREEN/WOOD	02101052	419/372-7033	218
Northwest Primary/*Canal Fulton*/Stark	00833338	330/854-5405	188
Northwestern Elem Sch/*Springfield*/Clark	00787870	937/964-3240	28
Northwestern Elem Sch/*West Salem*/Wayne	00839203	419/846-3519	212
Northwestern High Sch/*West Salem*/Wayne	00839227	419/846-3833	212
Northwestern Jr Sr High Sch/*Springfield*/Clark	00787882	937/964-1324	28
NORTHWESTERN LOCAL SCH DIST/SPRINGFIELD/CLARK	00787868	937/964-1318	27
NORTHWESTERN LOCAL SCH DIST/WEST SALEM/WAYNE	00839198	419/846-3151	212
Northwestern Middle Sch/*West Salem*/Wayne	00839215	419/846-3974	212
Northwood Elem Sch/*Dayton*/Montgomery	00825458	937/832-6240	152
Northwood Elem Sch/*Marysville*/Union	10903755	937/578-7100	204
Northwood Elem Sch/*North Canton*/Stark	00833297	330/497-5650	187
Northwood Elem Sch/*Northwood*/Wood	00840317	419/691-4621	217
Northwood Elem Sch/*Sidney*/Shelby	00832126	937/497-2231	183
Northwood High Sch/*Northwood*/Wood	00840305	419/691-4651	217
NORTHWOOD LOCAL SCH DIST/NORTHWOOD/WOOD	00840288	419/691-3888	217
Northwood Middle Sch/*Elyria*/Lorain	00816079	440/284-8016	123
NORTON CITY SCH DIST/NORTON/SUMMIT	00835269	330/825-0863	193
Norton Elem Sch/*Norton*/Summit	00835271	330/825-3828	193
Norton High Sch/*Norton*/Summit	00835295	330/825-7300	193
Norton Middle Sch/*Columbus*/Franklin	00801969	614/801-3700	74
Norton Middle Sch/*Norton*/Summit	00835312	330/825-5607	194
Norton Primary Sch/*Norton*/Summit	00835324	330/825-5133	194
Norwalk Cath JHS-St Paul HS/*Norwalk*/Huron	00819291	419/668-3005	107
Norwalk Catholic ECC/*Norwalk*/Huron	00819095	419/668-8480	107
Norwalk Catholic Elem Sch/*Norwalk*/Huron	00819289	419/668-6091	107
NORWALK CITY SCH DIST/NORWALK/HURON	00811615	419/668-2779	106
Norwalk High Sch/*Norwalk*/Huron	00811677	419/660-6500	106
Norwalk Middle Sch/*Norwalk*/Huron	00811665	419/668-8370	106
Norwayne Elem Sch/*Creston*/Wayne	00839150	330/435-6383	212
Norwayne High Sch/*Creston*/Wayne	00839174	330/435-6384	212
NORWAYNE LOCAL SCH DIST/CRESTON/WAYNE	00839148	330/435-6382	212
Norwayne Middle Sch/*Creston*/Wayne	00839162	330/435-1195	212
Norwich Elem Sch/*Hilliard*/Franklin	04035320	614/921-6000	72
NORWOOD CITY SCH DIST/NORWOOD/HAMILTON	00807262	513/924-2500	92
Norwood Elem Sch/*W Jefferson*/Madison	00819497	614/879-7642	132
Norwood High Sch/*Norwood*/Hamilton	00807298	513/924-2800	92
Norwood Middle Sch/*Norwood*/Hamilton	00807303	513/924-2700	92
Norwood View Elem Sch/*Norwood*/Hamilton	00807315	513/924-2610	92
Notre Dame Academy/*Toledo*/Lucas	00818534	419/475-9359	131
Notre Dame Cathedral Latin Sch/*Chardon*/Geauga	00795803	440/286-6226	82
Notre Dame Elem Sch/*Chardon*/Geauga	00795798	440/279-1127	83
Notre Dame Elem Sch/*Portsmouth*/Scioto	00802949	740/353-2354	180
Notre Dame Jr Sr High Sch/*Portsmouth*/Scioto	00802901	740/353-2354	180

O

O H Somers Elem Sch/*Mogadore*/Portage	00835178	330/628-9947	166
Oak Creek Elem Sch/*Lewis Center*/Delaware	04917857	740/657-4700	59
Oak Harbor High Sch/*Oak Harbor*/Ottawa	01420350	419/898-6216	158
Oak Harbor Middle Sch/*Oak Harbor*/Ottawa	00827016	419/898-6217	158
Oak Hill Elem Sch/*Oak Hill*/Jackson	00812047	740/682-7096	107
Oak Hill Middle High Sch/*Oak Hill*/Jackson	00812035	740/682-7055	107
OAK HILL UNION LOCAL SCH DIST/OAK HILL/JACKSON	00811988	740/682 7595	107
Oak Hills High Sch/*Cincinnati*/Hamilton	00807418	513/922-2300	92
OAK HILLS LOCAL SCH DIST/CINCINNATI/HAMILTON	00807341	513/574-3200	92
Oak Intermediate Sch/*New Boston*/Scioto	00831043	740/456-4559	179
Oakdale Elem Sch/*Cincinnati*/Hamilton	00807420	513/574-1100	92
Oakdale Elem Sch/*Toledo*/Lucas	00817815	419/671-7350	130
Oakland Park Elem Sch/*Columbus*/Franklin	00800769	614/365-6058	68
Oakmont Elem Sch/*Columbus*/Franklin	00800771	614/365-5385	68
Oakstone Academy/*Columbus*/Franklin	05008772	614/890-7854	77

School Year 2019-2020   800-333-8802   OH-V27

DISTRICT & SCHOOL TELEPHONE INDEX

Market Data Retrieval

School/City/County DISTRICT/CITY/COUNTY	PID	TELEPHONE NUMBER	PAGE
Oakstone Academy Mid High Sch/Westerville/Franklin	11222516	614/865-0400	77
Oakstone Cmty Sch/Columbus/Franklin	05382748	614/458-1085	66
Oakview Elem Sch/Kettering/Montgomery	00824973	937/499-1870	150
OAKWOOD CITY SCH DIST/OAKWOOD/MONTGOMERY	00825549	937/297-5332	152
Oakwood Elem Sch/Elyria/Lorain	00816081	440/284-8010	123
Oakwood Elem Sch/Oakwood/Paulding	00827339	419/594-3346	160
Oakwood High Sch/Oakwood/Montgomery	00825563	937/297-5325	152
Oakwood Junior High Sch/Dayton/Montgomery	04745434	937/297-5328	152
Oakwood Middle Sch/Canton/Stark	00833572	330/491-3790	188
OBERLIN CITY SCH DIST/OBERLIN/LORAIN	00816627	440/774-1458	125
Oberlin High Sch/Oberlin/Lorain	00816641	440/774-1295	125
Ohdela Academy/Akron/Summit	05220152	330/253-8680	4
Ohio Avenue Elem Sch/Columbus/Franklin	00800783	614/365-6130	68
Ohio Christian Academy/Middletown/Butler	12258996	513/594-4334	25
Ohio College Preparatory Sch/Maple Heights/Cuyahoga	12100791	216/453-4550	4
Ohio Connections Academy/Worthington/Franklin	05300099	216/361-9460	4
Ohio Construction Academy/Columbus/Franklin	12163145	614/532-1863	4
OHIO DEPARTMENT OF EDUCATION/COLUMBUS/FRANKLIN	00783331	877/644-6338	1
Ohio Hi-Point Career Center/Bellefontaine/Logan	00815609	937/599-3010	121
OHIO HI-POINT JOINT VOC SD/BELLEFONTAINE/LOGAN	00815594	937/599-3010	121
OHIO MID-EASTERN RESA/STEUBENVILLE/JEFFERSON	04499609	740/283-2050	110
Ohio School for the Deaf/Columbus/Franklin	02051861	614/728-4030	4
Ohio State Sch for the Blind/Columbus/Franklin	02051873	614/752-1152	4
Ohio Valley Career Tech Ctr/West Union/Adams	01538995	937/544-2336	6
Ohio Valley Christian Sch/Gallipolis/Gallia	02119281	740/446-0374	81
OHIO VALLEY ED SERVICE CENTER/CAMBRIDGE/GUERNSEY	00805288	740/439-3558	85
OHIO VALLEY ED SERVICE CTR/MARIETTA/WASHINGTON	00838998	740/373-6669	209
Ohio Valley Educ ESC/Marietta/Washington	04012720	740/374-5873	209
Ohio Virtual Academy/Maumee/Lucas	05220164	419/482-0948	4
Old Brook High Sch/Cleveland/Cuyahoga	12259574	216/721-0845	4
Old Brooklyn Cmty Elem Sch/Cleveland/Cuyahoga	04815235	216/661-7888	4
Old Brooklyn Cmty Middle Sch/Cleveland/Cuyahoga	11566922	216/351-0280	4
Old Fort Elem Sch/Bettsville/Seneca	00831627	419/986-5166	181
Old Fort High Sch/Tiffin/Seneca	00831639	419/992-4291	181
OLD FORT LOCAL SCH DIST/TIFFIN/SENECA	00831615	419/992-4291	181
Old Orchard Elem Sch/Toledo/Lucas	00817827	419/671-3700	130
Old Trail Sch/Akron/Summit	00835790	330/666-1118	196
Old West End Academy/Toledo/Lucas	05011652	419/671-4700	130
Olde Orchard Elem Sch/Columbus/Franklin	00800795	614/365-5388	68
Olde Sawmill Elem Sch/Dublin/Franklin	02127159	614/764-5936	70
Olentangy High Sch/Lewis Center/Delaware	00798324	740/657-4100	59
OLENTANGY LOCAL SCH DIST/LEWIS CENTER/DELAWARE	00798300	740/657-4050	59
Olentangy Meadows Elem Sch/Lewis Center/Delaware	10751514	740/657-5550	59
Olentangy Spec Needs Pre-Sch/Powell/Delaware	05350123	740/657-4350	59
Oliver Hazard Perry Academy/Cleveland/Cuyahoga	00792318	216/838-0090	44
Oliver Sch/West Union/Adams	02051483	937/544-2574	6
OLMSTED FALLS CITY SCH DIST/OLMSTED FALLS/CUYAHOGA	00793972	440/427-6000	48
Olmsted Falls Early Chldhd Ctr/Olmsted Falls/Cuyahoga	11445653	440/427-6360	48
Olmsted Falls High Sch/Olmsted Falls/Cuyahoga	00794017	440/427-6100	48
Olmsted Falls Intermediate Sch/Olmsted Falls/Cuyahoga	00793984	440/427-6500	48
Olmsted Falls Middle Sch/Olmsted Falls/Cuyahoga	00794029	440/427-6200	48
Olney Friends Sch/Barnesville/Belmont	00786034	740/425-3655	19
On Course/Springfield/Clark	11918258	937/505-4120	28
Onaway Elem Sch/Shaker HTS/Cuyahoga	00794598	216/295-4080	50
Ontario Elem Sch/Sandusky/Erie	00798702	419/984-1250	61
Ontario High Sch/Ontario/Richland	00830013	419/529-3969	173
ONTARIO LOCAL SCH DIST/ONTARIO/RICHLAND	00829997	419/747-4311	173
Ontario Middle Sch/Mansfield/Richland	00830025	419/529-5507	173
Ontario Primary Sch/Ashtabula/Ashtabula	00784440	440/992-1240	12
Open Door Christian Sch/Elyria/Lorain	01874062	440/322-6386	126
Open Door Sch/Ironton/Lawrence	02052140	740/532-1234	115
ORANGE CITY SCH DIST/PEPPER PIKE/CUYAHOGA	00794031	216/831-8600	48
Orange High Sch/Lewis Center/Delaware	11073688	740/657-5100	59
Orange High Sch/Pepper Pike/Cuyahoga	00794067	216/831-8600	49
Orange Inclusive Pre-School/Pepper Pike/Cuyahoga	11450440	216/831-8600	49
Orange Middle Sch/Lewis Center/Delaware	05350111	740/657-5300	59
Orchard Hill Intermediate Sch/North Canton/Stark	00833302	330/497-5655	187
Orchard Hollow Elem Sch/Mentor/Lake	00813479	440/257-5955	113
Orchard Middle Sch/Solon/Cuyahoga	00794665	440/349-7252	50
Orchard Park Elem Sch/Kettering/Montgomery	00824985	937/499-1910	150
Orchard STEM Sch/Cleveland/Cuyahoga	00792320	216/838-7350	44
OREGON CITY SCH DIST/OREGON/LUCAS	00817023	419/693-0661	128
Oregon Eagle Learning Center/Oregon/Lucas	11007330	419/720-2003	128
Orion Academy/Cincinnati/Hamilton	05362190	513/251-6000	87
ORRVILLE CITY SCH DIST/ORRVILLE/WAYNE	00839241	330/682-5811	212
Orrville Elem Sch/Orrville/Wayne	00839253	330/682-1851	212
Orrville High Sch/Orrville/Wayne	00839289	330/682-4661	212
Orrville Middle Sch/Orrville/Wayne	00839291	330/682-1791	212
Osborne Elem Sch/Sandusky/Erie	00798714	419/984-1270	61
OSNABURG LOCAL SCH DIST/EAST CANTON/STARK	00833388	330/488-1609	188
Otis Elem Sch/Fremont/Sandusky	00830623	419/332-8964	177
Otsego Elem Sch/Bowling Green/Wood	00840343	419/823-4381	217
Otsego High Sch/Bowling Green/Wood	00840379	419/823-4381	217
Otsego Junior High Sch/Bowling Green/Wood	00840355	419/823-4381	217
OTSEGO LOCAL SCH DIST/BOWLING GREEN/WOOD	00840331	419/823-4381	217
Ottawa Co Christian Academy/Oak Harbor/Ottawa	12225157	419/898-3888	160
Ottawa Elem Sch/Ottawa/Putnam	00829301	419/523-4290	170
Ottawa Hills Elem Sch/Toledo/Lucas	00817126	419/536-8329	128
Ottawa Hills Jr Sr High Sch/Ottawa Hills/Lucas	00817138	419/534-5376	128
OTTAWA HILLS LOCAL SCH DIST/TOLEDO/LUCAS	00817114	419/536-6371	128
Ottawa River Elem Sch/Toledo/Lucas	00817839	419/671-6350	130
Ottawa-Glandorf High Sch/Ottawa/Putnam	00829313	419/523-5702	170
OTTAWA-GLANDORF LOCAL SCH DIST/OTTAWA/PUTNAM	00829284	419/523-5261	170
Ottoville Elem Sch/Ottoville/Putnam	00829337	419/453-3357	170
Ottoville High Sch/Ottoville/Putnam	11458399	419/453-3358	170
OTTOVILLE LOCAL SCH DIST/OTTOVILLE/PUTNAM	00829325	419/453-3356	170
Our Lady Mt Carmel Sch/Cleveland/Cuyahoga	00795877	216/281-7146	52
Our Lady of Angels Sch/Cleveland/Cuyahoga	00795827	216/251-6841	52
Our Lady of Bethlehem Sch/Columbus/Franklin	02949933	614/459-8285	76
Our Lady of Consolation Sch/Carey/Wyandot	00818546	419/396-6166	219
Our Lady of Grace Sch/Cincinnati/Hamilton	00808929	513/931-3070	95
Our Lady of Lourdes Sch/Cincinnati/Hamilton	00808541	513/347-2660	95
Our Lady of Peace Sch/Canton/Stark	00821098	330/492-0622	189
Our Lady of Peace Sch/Columbus/Franklin	00802913	614/267-4535	76
Our Lady of the Elms Elem Sch/Akron/Summit	00795918	330/864-7210	195
Our Lady of the Elms Sch/Akron/Summit	00795906	330/867-0880	195
Our Lady of the Lake/Euclid/Cuyahoga	00795528	216/481-6824	52
Our Lady of the Rosary Sch/Dayton/Montgomery	00808589	937/222-7231	154
Our Lady of Victory Sch/Cincinnati/Hamilton	00808618	513/347-2072	95
Our Lady of Visitation Sch/Cincinnati/Hamilton	00808606	513/347-2222	95
Our Lady-Perpetual Help Sch/Grove City/Franklin	00802925	614/875-6779	76
Our Lady-Perpetual Help Sch/Toledo/Lucas	00818560	419/382-5696	131
Our Shepherd Lutheran Sch/Painesville/Lake	02214087	440/357-7776	115
Overlook Elem Sch/Wadsworth/Medina	00822494	330/335-1420	142
Oxford Elem Sch/Cleveland HTS/Cuyahoga	00792954	216/371-6525	42
Oyler Sch/Cincinnati/Hamilton	00805965	513/363-4100	88

Ohio School Directory

DISTRICT & SCHOOL TELEPHONE INDEX

School/City/County DISTRICT/CITY/COUNTY	PID	TELEPHONE NUMBER	PAGE
P			
Padre Pio Academy/*Lakewood*/Cuyahoga	05355989	216/226-4854	54
Padua Franciscan High Sch/*Parma*/Cuyahoga	00795920	440/845-2444	52
PAINESVILLE CITY LOCAL SD/			
PAINESVILLE/LAKE	00813649	440/392-5060	113
Paint Valley Elem Sch/*Bainbridge*/Ross	00830283	740/634-3454	175
Paint Valley High Sch/*Bainbridge*/Ross	00830295	740/634-3582	175
PAINT VALLEY LOCAL SCH DIST/			
BAINBRIDGE/ROSS	00830271	740/634-2826	175
Paint Valley Middle Sch/*Bainbridge*/Ross	00830300	740/634-3512	175
Palm Elem Sch/*Lorain*/Lorain	10010920	440/830-4180	124
Pandora Gilboa Elem Sch/*Pandora*/Putnam	00829375	419/384-3225	171
Pandora Gilboa High Sch/*Pandora*/Putnam	00829387	419/384-3225	171
PANDORA GILBOA LOCAL SCH DIST/			
PANDORA/PUTNAM	00829351	419/384-3225	170
Pandora Gilboa Middle Sch/*Pandora*/Putnam	00829363	419/384-3225	171
Par Excellence Academy/*Newark*/Licking	00815051	740/344-7279	119
Parc Lane Training Center/*Paulding*/Paulding	02052360	419/399-4800	160
Park Avenue Elem Sch/*Mount Gilead*/Morrow	00826244	419/946-5736	155
Park Elem Sch/*Chardon*/Geauga	00804222	440/285-4067	82
Park Layne Elem Sch/*New Carlisle*/Clark	00787765	937/845-4470	29
Park Street Intermediate Sch/*Grove City*/Franklin	04931683	614/801-8800	74
Parker Woods Montessori Sch/*Cincinnati*/Hamilton	04288266	513/363-6200	88
Parkmoor Elem Sch/*Columbus*/Franklin	00800800	614/365-5349	68
Parkside Elem Sch/*Painesville*/Lake	00813560	440/352-8822	114
Parkside Elem Sch/*Solon*/Cuyahoga	04012421	440/349-2175	50
Parkview Early Education Ctr/*Fairview Park*/Cuyahoga	11134127	440/356-3515	46
Parkview Elem Sch/*Wooster*/Wayne	00839576	330/262-3821	214
Parkway Elem Sch/*Alliance*/Stark	00832255	330/829-2264	184
Parkway Elem Sch/*Rockford*/Mercer	00823010	419/363-3045	144
Parkway High Sch/*Rockford*/Mercer	00823034	419/363-3045	144
PARKWAY LOCAL SCH DIST/ROCKFORD/			
MERCER	00823008	419/363-3045	144
Parkway Middle Sch/*Rockford*/Mercer	00823022	419/363-3045	144
Parkwood Elem Sch/*Beavercreek*/Greene	00804521	937/429-7604	83
PARMA CITY SCH DIST/PARMA/			
CUYAHOGA	00794081	440/842-5300	49
Parma Cmty Elem Sch/*Parma*/Cuyahoga	05010165	440/888-5490	39
Parma Cmty Elem Sch/*Parma*/Cuyahoga	11566893	440/887-0319	40
Parma Cmty Pearl Rd Elem Sch/*Cleveland*/Cuyahoga	12099910	440/345-5960	40
Parma Community Middle Sch/*Parma*/Cuyahoga	11566908	440/845-2587	40
Parma Developmental Center/*Parma*/Cuyahoga	02051768	216/362-6450	40
Parma Heights Chrn Academy/*Parma Heights*/Cuyahoga	02147771	440/845-8668	54
Parma Park Elem Sch/*Parma Heights*/Cuyahoga	00794249	440/885-2390	49
Parma Senior High Sch/*Parma*/Cuyahoga	00794237	440/885-2300	49
Parsons Elem Sch/*Columbus*/Franklin	00800886	614/365-5099	68
Passages Sch/*Canton*/Stark	05343572	330/456-1189	185
Pataskala Elem Sch/*Pataskala*/Licking	00815300	740/927-3861	120
Pathway School of Discovery/*Dayton*/Montgomery	05287162	937/235-5498	148
Pathways to Success/*Oberlin*/Lorain	11434898	440/775-0276	122
Patrick Henry Elem Sch/*Hamler*/Henry	00810829	419/274-3015	102
Patrick Henry High Sch/*Hamler*/Henry	00810855	419/274-3015	102
PATRICK HENRY LOCAL SCH DIST/			
HAMLER/HENRY	00810817	419/274-5451	102
Patrick Henry Middle Sch/*Hamler*/Henry	00810831	419/274-3015	102
Patrick Henry Sch/*Cleveland*/Cuyahoga	00792344	216/838-2350	44
Patriot Preparatory Academy/*Columbus*/Franklin	11663001	614/864-5332	73
Pattison Elem Sch/*Milford*/Clermont	00788599	513/831-6570	31
Paul C Bunn Elem Sch/*Youngstown*/Mahoning	00820472	330/744-8963	136
Paul L Dunbar Elem Sch/*Cleveland*/Cuyahoga	00792368	216/838-7400	44
Paulding Elem Sch/*Paulding*/Paulding	00827341	419/399-4656	160
PAULDING EXEMPTED VILLAGE SD/			
PAULDING/PAULDING	00827315	419/399-4656	160
Paulding High Sch/*Paulding*/Paulding	01486938	419/399-4656	160
Paulding Middle Sch/*Paulding*/Paulding	00827353	419/399-4656	160
Payne Elem Sch/*Payne*/Paulding	00827389	419/263-2512	160
Pearl Academy/*Cleveland*/Cuyahoga	11722217	216/741-2991	4
Peebles Elem Sch/*Peebles*/Adams	00783458	937/587-2611	6
Peebles High Sch/*Peebles*/Adams	00783460	937/587-2681	6
Pennyroyal Elem Sch/*Franklin*/Warren	00838326	937/743-8660	207
Penta Career Center/*Perrysburg*/Wood	00840525	419/666-1120	217
PENTA CO JT VOC SCH DIST/			
PERRYSBURG/WOOD	00840513	419/666-1120	217
Perkins High Sch/*Sandusky*/Erie	00798609	419/625-1252	61
PERKINS LOCAL SCH DIST/SANDUSKY/			
ERIE	00798556	419/625-0484	61
Perrin Woods Elem Sch/*Springfield*/Clark	00788135	937/505-4310	28
Perry Elem Sch/*Lima*/Allen	00783965	419/221-2771	9
Perry Elem Sch/*Perry*/Lake	00813742	440/599-9600	113
Perry Elem Sch/*Zanesville*/Muskingum	00826347	740/872-3436	156
Perry High Sch/*Lima*/Allen	00783977	419/221-2773	9
Perry High Sch/*Massillon*/Stark	00833455	330/477-3486	188
Perry High Sch/*Perry*/Lake	00813766	440/599-9300	113
PERRY LOCAL SCH DIST/LIMA/ALLEN	00783953	419/221-2770	9
PERRY LOCAL SCH DIST/MASSILLON/			
STARK	00833417	330/477-8121	188
PERRY LOCAL SCH DIST/PERRY/LAKE	00813730	440/259-9200	113
Perry Middle Sch/*Perry*/Lake	00813778	440/599-9500	113
PERRYSBURG EXEMPTED VILLAGE SD/			
PERRYSBURG/WOOD	00840408	419/874-9131	218
Perrysburg High Sch/*Perrysburg*/Wood	00840422	419/874-3181	218
Perrysburg Junior High Sch/*Perrysburg*/Wood	00840434	419/874-9193	218
Pettisville Elem Sch/*Pettisville*/Fulton	00803668	419/446-2705	79
Pettisville Jr Sr High Sch/*Pettisville*/Fulton	00803670	419/446-2705	79
PETTISVILLE LOCAL SCH DIST/			
PETTISVILLE/FULTON	00803656	419/446-2705	79
Pfeiffer Elem Sch/*Akron*/Summit	00834356	330/848-5244	191
Pfeiffer Intermediate Sch/*Massillon*/Stark	01417573	330/478-6163	188
Phillips Elem Sch/*Marietta*/Washington	00838819	740/374-6514	210
Philo High Sch/*Duncan Falls*/Muskingum	00826555	740/674-4355	156
Philo Junior High Sch/*Philo*/Muskingum	00826543	740/674-5210	156
Phoenix Cmty Learning Center/*Cincinnati*/Hamilton	05010177	513/351-5801	4
Phoenix Middle Sch/*Worthington*/Franklin	00802559	614/450-4100	76
Phoenix Sch/*Akron*/Summit	03112303	330/784-0408	196
PICKAWAY CO ED SERVICE CENTER/			
CIRCLEVILLE/PICKAWAY	00827949	740/474-7529	162
Pickaway Elem Sch/*Circleville*/Pickaway	00827793	740/474-3877	162
Pickaway-Ross Career Tech Ctr/*Chillicothe*/Ross	00830477	740/642-1200	175
PICKAWAY-ROSS CO JT VOC SD/			
CHILLICOTHE/ROSS	00830465	740/642-1200	175
Pickerington Alternative Sch/*Pickerington*/Fairfield	11747059	614/830-2797	64
Pickerington Elem Sch/*Pickerington*/Fairfield	00799237	614/548-1400	64
Pickerington High Sch Central/*Pickerington*/Fairfield	00799249	614/548-1800	64
Pickerington High School North/*Pickerington*/Fairfield	05272894	614/830-2700	64
PICKERINGTON LOCAL SCH DIST/			
PICKERINGTON/FAIRFIELD	00799225	614/833-2110	64
Pickett Academy/*Toledo*/Lucas	00817853	419/671-5600	130
PIKE CO AREA JT VOC SCH DIST/			
PIKETON/PIKE	00828137	740/289-2721	163
Pike Co Career Tech Center/*Piketon*/Pike	00828149	740/289-2721	163
Pike Co Early Childhood Center/*Piketon*/Pike	04020648	740/289-1681	163
Pike Elem Sch/*Cambridge*/Muskingum	10001084	740/439-1645	156
Pike-Delta-York High Sch/*Delta*/Fulton	00803709	419/822-8247	79
PIKE-DELTA-YORK LOCAL SCH DIST/			
DELTA/FULTON	00803682	419/822-3391	79
Piketon Jr Sr High Sch/*Piketon*/Pike	00828022	740/289-2254	164
Pine Intermediate Sch/*North Olmsted*/Cuyahoga	00793908	440/779-3536	48
Pinnacle Academy/*Euclid*/Cuyahoga	05382750	216/731-0127	40
Pioneer Career & Tech Center/*Shelby*/Richland	00830063	419/347-7744	173
Pioneer Center/*Chillicothe*/Ross	02052475	740/773-2165	174
PIONEER JOINT VOC SCH DIST/			
SHELBY/RICHLAND	00830051	419/347-7926	173
Piqua Catholic Sch/*Piqua*/Miami	00809430	937/773-1564	147
Piqua Central Interm Sch/*Piqua*/Miami	12109852	937/773-2017	146
PIQUA CITY SCH DIST/PIQUA/MIAMI	00823412	937/773-4321	146
Piqua High Sch/*Piqua*/Miami	00823436	937/773-6314	146
Piqua Junior High Sch/*Piqua*/Miami	04875649	937/778-2997	146
Piqua SDA Christian Sch/*Piqua*/Miami	01560534	937/778-0223	147
Plain City Elem Sch/*Plain City*/Madison	00819552	614/873-4608	132
PLAIN LOCAL SCH DIST/CANTON/			
STARK	00833510	330/492-3500	188
Plains Junior High Sch/*Liberty Twp*/Butler	05272674	513/644-1130	22
Pleasant Cmty Digital Academy/*Marion*/Marion	10017928	740/389-4815	138
Pleasant Elem Sch/*Marion*/Marion	00821907	740/389-4815	138
Pleasant Elem Sch/*Norwalk*/Huron	00811689	419/668-4134	106

School Year 2019-2020   800-333-8802   OH-V29

DISTRICT & SCHOOL TELEPHONE INDEX

Market Data Retrieval

School/City/County DISTRICT/CITY/COUNTY	PID	TELEPHONE NUMBER	PAGE
Pleasant High Sch/*Marion*/Marion	00821919	740/389-2389	138
Pleasant Hill Academy/*Cincinnati*/Hamilton	00806000	513/363-4300	88
PLEASANT LOCAL SCH DIST/ MARION/MARION	00821892	740/389-4479	138
Pleasant Middle Sch/*Marion*/Marion	00821921	740/389-5167	138
Pleasant Ridge Montessori Sch/*Cincinnati*/ Hamilton	00806012	513/363-4400	88
Pleasant Run Elem Sch/*Cincinnati*/Hamilton	00807200	513/825-7070	91
Pleasant Run Middle Sch/*Cincinnati*/ Hamilton	00807212	513/851-2400	91
Pleasant St Elem Sch/*Mount Vernon*/Knox	00813132	740/393-5990	111
Pleasant Valley Elem Sch/*Parma*/Cuyahoga	00794093	440/885-2380	49
Pleasant View Middle Sch/*Grove City*/ Franklin	00801995	614/801-3900	74
Pleasantview First Step Sch/*Parma*/Cuyahoga	04033217	440/885-8665	49
Pleasantville Elem Sch/*Pleasantville*/ Fairfield	00799017	740/468-2181	63
Plymouth High Sch/*Plymouth*/Richland	05116094	419/687-8200	173
PLYMOUTH-SHILOH LOCAL SCH DIST/ PLYMOUTH/RICHLAND	00829882	419/687-4733	173
Pointview Elem Sch/*Westerville*/Franklin	00802377	614/797-7250	75
POLAND LOCAL SCH DIST/POLAND/ MAHONING	00820056	330/757-7000	135
Poland MS-McKinley Elem Sch/*Poland*/ Mahoning	00820082	330/757-7003	135
Poland Seminary High Sch/*Poland*/Mahoning	00820109	330/757-7018	135
Polaris Career Ctr High Sch/*Middlebrg HTS*/ Cuyahoga	01484837	440/891-7600	49
Polaris Christian Academy/*Lewis Center*/ Delaware	02209006	614/431-6888	60
POLARIS JOINT VOC SCH DIST/ MIDDLEBRG HTS/CUYAHOGA	01484825	440/891-7600	49
PORT CLINTON CITY SCH DIST/ PORT CLINTON/OTTAWA	00827171	419/732-2103	159
Port Clinton High Sch/*Port Clinton*/Ottawa	00827212	419/734-2147	159
Port Clinton Middle Sch/*Port Clinton*/ Ottawa	00827224	419/734-4448	159
Port Washington Elem Sch/*Prt Washingtn*/ Tuscarawas	00837310	740/498-8389	202
PORTAGE CO ED SERVICE CENTER/ RAVENNA/PORTAGE	00828826	330/297-1436	164
Portage Collaborative Mont Sch/*Canton*/ Stark	04368610	330/966-1912	185
Portage Lakes Career Center/*Uniontown*/ Stark	01601566	330/896-8200	189
PORTAGE LAKES JOINT VOC SD/ UNIONTOWN/STARK	01601554	330/896-8200	189
Portage Path Cmty Lrng Ctr/*Akron*/Summit	00834368	330/761-2795	191
PORTSMOUTH CITY SCH DIST/ PORTSMOUTH/SCIOTO	00831122	740/354-5663	179
Portsmouth Elem Sch/*Portsmouth*/Scioto	00831196	740/353-6719	179
Portsmouth High Sch/*Portsmouth*/Scioto	00831213	740/353-2398	179
Portsmouth STEM Academy/*Portsmouth*/Scioto	12045177	740/351-0591	180
Portsmouth West Elem Sch/*W Portsmouth*/ Scioto	00831316	740/858-1116	180
Portsmouth West High Sch/*W Portsmouth*/ Scioto	00831354	740/858-1103	180
Portsmouth West Middle Sch/*W Portsmouth*/ Scioto	00831342	740/858-6668	180
Possum Elem Sch/*Springfield*/Clark	00788238	937/328-5383	27
Powers Elem Sch/*Amherst*/Lorain	05262021	440/988-8670	122
Powhatan Elem Sch/*Powhatan Pt*/Monroe	00823826	740/795-5665	147
Prairie Lincoln Elem Sch/*Columbus*/Franklin	00802004	614/801-8300	74
Prairie Norton Elem Sch/*Columbus*/Franklin	00802016	614/801-8450	74
PREBLE CO ED SERVICE CENTER/ EATON/PREBLE	00829076	937/456-1187	168
Preble Shawnee Jr/Sr High Sch/*Camden*/ Preble	00828981	937/787-3541	168
PREBLE-SHAWNEE LOCAL SCH DIST/ CAMDEN/PREBLE	00828955	937/452-1283	168
Preschool Early Learning Ctr/*Westerville*/ Franklin	12313534	614/797-7450	75
Preston Elem Sch/*Cuyahoga FLS*/Summit	00834916	330/926-3805	192
Primrose Sch of Lewis Center/*Powell*/ Delaware	11223534	740/548-5808	60
PRINCETON CITY SCH DIST/ CINCINNATI/HAMILTON	00807432	513/864-1000	92
Princeton Cmty Middle Sch/*Cincinnati*/ Hamilton	00807494	513/864-2000	92
Princeton High Sch/*Cincinnati*/Hamilton	00807482	513/864-1500	92
Promise Academy/*Cleveland*/Cuyahoga	11007287	216/443-0500	44
Prospect Elem Sch/*Elyria*/Lorain	00816093	440/284-8011	123
Prospect Elem Sch/*Girard*/Trumbull	00836110	330/545-3854	197
Prospect Elem Sch/*Mansfield*/Richland	00829789	419/525-6313	172
Prospect Elem Sch/*Oberlin*/Lorain	00816677	440/774-4421	125
Purcell Marian High Sch/*Cincinnati*/ Hamilton	00808644	513/751-1230	95
Puritas Cmty Elememtary Sch/*Cleveland*/ Cuyahoga	10017942	216/688-0680	40
Puritas Cmty Middle Sch/*Cleveland*/Cuyahoga	11703338	216/251-1596	40
PUT-IN-BAY LOCAL SCH DIST/ PUT IN BAY/OTTAWA	00827248	419/285-3614	159
Put-In-Bay Sch/*Put In Bay*/Ottawa	00827262	419/285-3614	159
Putman Elem Sch/*Blanchester*/Clinton	00788927	937/783-2681	32
PUTNAM CO ED SERVICE CENTER/ OTTAWA/PUTNAM	02089260	419/523-5951	169
Putnam Elem Sch/*Marietta*/Washington	00838821	740/374-6516	210
Pymatuning Valley High Sch/*Andover*/ Ashtabula	00784919	440/293-6263	13
PYMATUNING VALLEY LOCAL SD/ ANDOVER/ASHTABULA	00784880	440/293-6488	13
Pymatuning Valley Middle Sch/*Andover*/ Ashtabula	00784907	440/293-6981	13
Pymatuning Valley Primary Sch/*Andover*/ Ashtabula	00784892	440/293-6206	13

Q

School/City/County	PID	TELEPHONE NUMBER	PAGE
Quaker Digital Academy/*New Phila*/ Tuscarawas	05300025	866/968-7032	203
Queen of Apostles Sch/*Toledo*/Lucas	00818467	419/241-7829	131
Queen of Peace Elem Sch/*Hamilton*/Butler	00808204	513/863-8705	24

R

School/City/County	PID	TELEPHONE NUMBER	PAGE
R B Chamberlin Middle Sch/*Twinsburg*/Summit	00835685	330/486-2281	195
R C Waters Elem Sch/*Oak Harbor*/Ottawa	00827028	419/898-6219	158
R G Drage Career Tech Center/*Massillon*/ Stark	01601542	330/832-9856	189
Ragersville Elem Sch/*Sugarcreek*/Tuscarawas	00837255	330/897-5021	202
Rainsboro Elem Sch/*Bainbridge*/Highland	00811029	937/365-1271	103
Ralph Waite Elem Sch/*Medina*/Medina	11465603	330/636-4500	141
Ramah Junior Academy/*Cleveland*/Cuyahoga	01464708	216/581-2626	54
Ranger High-Tech Academy/*N Ridgeville*/ Lorain	12241383	440/353-1178	125
Ransom H Barr Elem Sch/*Canton*/Stark	00833613	330/491-3730	188
Rapid Run Middle Sch/*Cincinnati*/Hamilton	04876538	513/467-0300	92
Ravenna Early Childhood Ctr/*Ravenna*/ Portage	12171611	330/297-4139	166
Ravenna High Sch/*Ravenna*/Portage	00828541	330/296-3844	166
RAVENNA SCH DIST/RAVENNA/PORTAGE	00828503	330/296-9679	166
Rayen Early College Interm Sch/*Youngstown*/ Mahoning	11453143	330/744-7602	137
Raymer Elem Sch/*Toledo*/Lucas	00817877	419/671-7650	130
Raymond Elem Sch/*Raymond*/Union	00837700	937/578-7200	204
RE-Education Aspire Access/*Mentor*/Lake	12239641	440/257-3131	115
Reach Academy/*Toledo*/Lucas	05009075	419/691-4876	4
READING CMTY CITY SCH DIST/ READING/HAMILTON	00807573	513/554-1800	93
Reading High Sch/*Reading*/Hamilton	00807614	513/733-4422	93
Reading Middle Sch/*Reading*/Hamilton	11558999	513/842-5151	93
Reagan Elem Sch/*Ashland*/Ashland	12108377	419/289-7967	10
Red Raiders Pre-School/*Painesville*/Lake	12110083	440/392-5612	113
Redeemer Christian Sch/*Cuyahoga FLS*/Summit	00835764	330/923-1445	196
Redwood Elem Sch/*Avon Lake*/Lorain	00815776	440/933-5145	122
Rees E Price Academy/*Cincinnati*/Hamilton	00806309	513/363-6000	88
Regent High Sch/*Cleveland*/Cuyahoga	12160894	216/512-0076	4
Regina Coeli Catholic Sch/*Alliance*/Stark	00821103	330/823-9239	189
Regina Coeli Sch/*Toledo*/Lucas	00818572	419/476-0920	131
Reid Sch/*Springfield*/Clark	00788240	937/328-5380	27
Reilly Elem Sch/*Salem*/Columbiana	00789579	330/332-8921	35
Renaissance Academy/*Columbus*/Franklin	11565693	614/235-1900	4
Renwood Elem Sch/*Parma*/Cuyahoga	00794287	440/885-2338	49
Resurrection of Our Lord Sch/*Cincinnati*/ Hamilton	00808670	513/471-6600	95
Revere High Sch/*Richfield*/Summit	00835386	330/523-3202	194
REVERE LOCAL SCH DIST/RICHFIELD/ SUMMIT	00835348	330/659-6111	194
Revere Middle Sch/*Bath*/Summit	00835362	330/523-3403	194
Reynolds Elem Sch/*Toledo*/Lucas	00817889	419/671-1500	130
Reynolds HS-HS2 STEM Academy/*Reynoldsburg*/ Franklin	11828873	614/501-4030	73
REYNOLDSBURG CITY SCH DIST/ REYNOLDSBURG/FRANKLIN	00801634	614/501-1020	72

Ohio School Directory

DISTRICT & SCHOOL TELEPHONE INDEX

School/City/County DISTRICT/CITY/COUNTY	PID	TELEPHONE NUMBER	PAGE
Reynoldsburg HS-E STEM Academy/*Reynoldsburg*/Franklin	11828859	614/501-2310	73
Rhodes College & Career Acad/*Cleveland*/Cuyahoga	12231443	216/838-3050	44
Rhodes Sch Environmental Study/*Cleveland*/Cuyahoga	12231431	216/838-3100	44
Rich Center for Autism/*Youngstown*/Mahoning	11237779	330/941-1927	137
Richard Allen Academy-Hamilton/*Hamilton*/Butler	05367891	513/795-6549	4
Richard Allen Prep-Dayton/*Dayton*/Montgomery	04889107	937/723-7721	4
Richard Allen Prep-Downtown/*Dayton*/Montgomery	05220449	937/951-2800	4
Richard Avenue Elem Sch/*Grove City*/Franklin	00802028	614/801-8325	74
Richardson Elem Sch/*Cuyahoga FLS*/Summit	00834928	330/926-3807	192
Richfield Elem Sch/*Richfield*/Summit	00835374	330/523-3603	194
Richland Academy of Excellence/*Mansfield*/Richland	12100399	419/522-8224	171
Richland Sch of Academic Arts/*Mansfield*/Richland	12259512	419/522-7273	5
Richland-New Hope Sch/*Mansfield*/Richland	02052463	419/774-4277	171
Richmond Heights Elem Sch/*Richmond HTS*/Cuyahoga	00794392	216/692-0099	49
RICHMOND HEIGHTS LOCAL SD/ RICHMOND HTS/CUYAHOGA	00794380	216/692-0086	49
Richmond Heights Secondary Sch/*Richmond HTS*/Cuyahoga	00794407	216/692-0094	49
Ridge Elem Sch/*Mentor*/Lake	00813376	440/255-5400	113
Ridge Junior High Sch/*West Chester*/Butler	04747353	513/777-0552	22
Ridge-Brook Elem Sch/*Parma*/Cuyahoga	00794299	440/885-2350	49
Ridgedale Elem Sch/*Morral*/Marion	01486914	740/383-2020	138
Ridgedale Jr Sr High Sch/*Morral*/Marion	00821971	740/383-2167	138
RIDGEDALE LOCAL SCH DIST/ MORRAL/MARION	00821933	740/382-6065	138
Ridgemont Jr Sr High Sch/*Ridgeway*/Hardin	00810336	937/363-2701	100
Ridgemont Local Sch/*Mount Victory*/Hardin	00810324	937/354-2141	100
RIDGEMONT LOCAL SCH DIST/ MOUNT VICTORY/HARDIN	00810312	937/354-2141	100
Ridgeview Elem Sch/*Ashtabula*/Ashtabula	00784581	440/997-7321	12
Ridgeview Middle Sch/*Columbus*/Franklin	00800850	614/365-5506	68
Ridgeview STEM Junior High Sch/*Pickerington*/Fairfield	03389673	614/548-1700	64
Ridgeway Elem Sch/*Hamilton*/Butler	00786565	513/868-5640	22
Ridgewood Elem Sch/*Hilliard*/Franklin	00801804	614/921-6100	72
Ridgewood Elem Sch/*W Lafayette*/Coshocton	04866351	740/545-5312	37
Ridgewood High Sch/*W Lafayette*/Coshocton	00789907	740/545-6345	37
RIDGEWOOD LOCAL SCH DIST/ W LAFAYETTE/COSHOCTON	00789866	740/545-6354	37
Ridgewood Middle Sch/*W Lafayette*/Coshocton	00789919	740/545-6335	37
Ridgewood Sch/*Springfield*/Clark	00788276	937/399-8900	29
Rimer Cmty Learning Ctr/*Akron*/Summit	00834382	330/761-7905	191
Rio Grande Elem Sch/*Rio Grande*/Gallia	00803890	740/245-5333	81
Ripley-Union-Lewis-Huntngtn ES/*Ripley*/Brown	00786199	937/392-1141	20
Ripley-Union-Lewis-Huntngtn HS/*Ripley*/Brown	00786204	937/392-4384	20
Ripley-Union-Lewis-Huntngtn MS/*Aberdeen*/Brown	05363297	937/795-8001	20
RIPLEY-UNION-LEWIS-HUNTNGTN SD/ RIPLEY/BROWN	00786175	937/392-4396	20
Rise & Shine Academy/*Toledo*/Lucas	12163157	419/244-9900	127
Risen Christ Lutheran Sch/*Springfield*/Clark	04213302	937/323-3688	29
Rising Stars Academy/*Cincinnati*/Hamilton	12168640	513/363-6500	88
Rittman Academy/*Rittman*/Wayne	12160882	330/927-7162	213
Rittman Elem Sch/*Rittman*/Wayne	00839344	330/927-7460	213
RITTMAN EXEMPTED VILLAGE SD/ RITTMAN/WAYNE	00839306	330/927-7400	212
Rittman High Sch/*Rittman*/Wayne	00839320	330/927-7140	213
Rittman Middle Sch/*Rittman*/Wayne	00839332	330/927-7100	213
Ritzman Cmty Learning Ctr/*Akron*/Summit	00834394	330/761-7903	191
River Elem Sch/*Hannibal*/Monroe	00823785	740/483-1358	147
River Gate High Sch/*Warren*/Trumbull	12162517	330/647-6500	5
River High Sch/*Hannibal*/Monroe	00823838	740/483-1358	147
River Valley High Sch/*Bidwell*/Gallia	00803931	740/446-2926	80
River Valley High Sch/*Caledonia*/Marion	00822028	740/725-5800	139
RIVER VALLEY LOCAL SCH DIST/ CALEDONIA/MARION	00821983	740/725-5400	139
River Valley Middle Sch/*Bidwell*/Gallia	00803955	740/446-8399	80
River Valley Middle Sch/*Caledonia*/Marion	00822030	740/725-5700	139
River View High Sch/*Warsaw*/Coshocton	00789969	740/824-3522	37
River View Junior High Sch/*Warsaw*/Coshocton	02108012	740/824-3523	37
RIVER VIEW LOCAL SCH DIST/ WARSAW/COSHOCTON	00789921	740/824-3521	37
Riverdale Elem Sch/*Mt Blanchard*/Hancock	00810362	419/694-2211	98
Riverdale Local High Sch/*Mt Blanchard*/Hancock	00810374	419/694-2211	98
RIVERDALE LOCAL SCH DIST/ MT BLANCHARD/HANCOCK	00810348	419/694-4994	98
Riverdale Middle Sch/*Mt Blanchard*/Hancock	00810350	419/694-2211	98
Rivers Edge Mont Elem Sch/*Dayton*/Montgomery	00824284	937/542-4640	149
Riverside Academy/*Cincinnati*/Hamilton	04880668	513/921-7777	5
Riverside Campus/*Painesville*/Lake	00813625	440/352-3341	114
Riverside Elem Sch/*De Graff*/Logan	00815568	937/585-5981	121
Riverside Elem Sch/*Dublin*/Franklin	02223076	614/764-5940	70
Riverside Elem Sch/*Toledo*/Lucas	00817891	419/671-6700	130
Riverside Jr Sr High Sch/*De Graff*/Logan	00815570	937/585-5981	121
RIVERSIDE LOCAL SCH DIST/ DE GRAFF/LOGAN	00815556	937/585-5981	121
RIVERSIDE LOCAL SCH DIST/ PAINESVILLE/LAKE	00813522	440/352-0668	113
Riverside of Miami Co Sch/*Troy*/Miami	02052293	937/339-8313	145
Riverside Sch/*Cleveland*/Cuyahoga	00792411	216/838-6700	44
Riverview East Academy/*Cincinnati*/Hamilton	00805848	513/363-3400	88
Riverview Elem Sch/*Hamilton*/Butler	00786503	513/887-5650	22
Riverview Elem Sch/*Munroe Falls*/Summit	00835568	330/689-5310	194
Riverview Elem Sch/*Painesville*/Lake	00813601	440/352-0688	114
Road to Success Academy/*Columbus*/Franklin	12164838	614/252-4656	66
Robert A Taft Info Tech HS/*Cincinnati*/Hamilton	00806220	513/363-8200	88
Robert Bycroft Sch/*Lisbon*/Columbiana	02051639	330/424-7787	34
Robert C Lindsey Elem Sch/*Chesterland*/Geauga	00804404	440/729-5980	82
Robert F Schultz Elem Sch/*Delaware*/Delaware	04428595	740/833-1400	58
Robert Frost Elem Sch/*Westerville*/Franklin	00802315	614/797-7280	75
Robert H Jamison Sch/*Cleveland*/Cuyahoga	04144397	216/838-5400	45
Robert L Stevenson Elem Sch/*Columbus*/Franklin	00801323	614/485-4200	71
Robert Taft Elem Sch/*Canton*/Stark	10773938	330/491-3760	188
Roberts Middle Sch/*Cuyahoga FLS*/Summit	00834930	330/926-3809	193
Roberts Paideia Academy/*Cincinnati*/Hamilton	00806050	513/363-4600	88
Robinson Achievement/*Toledo*/Lucas	11823380	419/671-4200	130
Robinson Cmty Learning Center/*Akron*/Summit	00834409	330/761-2785	191
Robinson Elem Sch/*Toledo*/Lucas	00817906	419/671-4200	130
Robinson G Jones Elem Sch/*Cleveland*/Cuyahoga	00792447	216/838-6750	45
Robinwood Lane Elem Sch/*Boardman*/Mahoning	00819849	330/782-3164	134
Rock Creek Elem Sch/*Rock Creek*/Ashtabula	00784878	440/563-3820	13
Rock Hill Elem Sch/*Ironton*/Lawrence	00814411	740/532-7016	116
Rock Hill High Sch/*Ironton*/Lawrence	00814423	740/532-7012	116
ROCK HILL LOCAL SCH DIST/ IRONTON/LAWRENCE	00814370	740/532-7030	116
Rock Hill Middle Sch/*Ironton*/Lawrence	00814435	740/532-7026	116
Rock of Ages Sch/*Apple Creek*/Wayne	11231531	330/698-2298	214
Rockdale Academy/*Cincinnati*/Hamilton	00806062	513/363-4700	88
Rockhill Elem Sch/*Alliance*/Stark	00832267	330/829-2260	184
Rockway Elem Sch/*Springfield*/Clark	00788252	937/328-5385	27
Rockwern Academy/*Cincinnati*/Hamilton	00808072	513/984-3770	96
ROCKY RIVER CITY SCH DIST/ ROCKY RIVER/CUYAHOGA	00794421	440/356-6000	50
Rocky River High Sch/*Rocky River*/Cuyahoga	00794471	440/356-6800	50
Rocky River Middle Sch/*Rocky River*/Cuyahoga	00794483	440/356-6870	50
Roger Bacon High Sch/*Cincinnati*/Hamilton	00808694	513/641-1300	95
Rogers High Sch/*Toledo*/Lucas	00817918	419/671-1000	130
Roll Hill Sch/*Cincinnati*/Hamilton	00805939	513/363-4000	88
Rolling Hills Elem Sch/*Springfield*/Clark	00787844	937/399-2250	27
ROLLING HILLS LOCAL SCH DIST/ CAMBRIDGE/GUERNSEY	00805159	740/432-6952	86
Roosevelt Elem Sch/*Dayton*/Montgomery	00824612	937/542-5340	149
Roosevelt Elem Sch/*Lakewood*/Cuyahoga	00793609	216/529-4224	47
Roosevelt Elem Sch/*Mc Donald*/Trumbull	00836598	330/530-8051	200
Roosevelt High Sch/*Kent*/Portage	00828486	330/676-8700	166
Roosevelt Middle Sch/*Springfield*/Clark	00788147	937/505-4370	28
Rootstown High Sch/*Rootstown*/Portage	00828618	330/325-7911	166
ROOTSTOWN LOCAL SCH DIST/ ROOTSTOWN/PORTAGE	00828591	330/325-9911	166
Rootstown Middle Sch/*Rootstown*/Portage	00828620	330/325-9956	166

DISTRICT & SCHOOL TELEPHONE INDEX

Market Data Retrieval

School/City/County DISTRICT/CITY/COUNTY	PID	TELEPHONE NUMBER	PAGE
Rosa Parks Early Learning Ctr/*Dayton*/Montgomery	00824167	937/542-4390	149
Rosa Parks Elem Sch/*Middletown*/Butler	00786838	513/420-4552	23
Rosa Parks Elem Sch/*Toledo*/Lucas	00817396	419/671-4350	130
Rosary Cathedral Sch/*Toledo*/Lucas	00818584	419/243-4396	131
Rose Hill Elem Sch/*Reynoldsburg*/Franklin	00801701	614/367-2380	73
Roselawn Condon Sch/*Cincinnati*/Hamilton	00806098	513/363-4800	88
Rosemont Center/*Columbus*/Franklin	00802963	614/471-2626	77
Rosemore Middle Sch/*Whitehall*/Franklin	00802482	614/417-5200	75
Roseville Elem Sch/*Roseville*/Muskingum	00826579	740/697-7216	156
Ross Co Christian Academy/*Chillicothe*/Ross	12180533	740/772-4532	176
Ross High Sch/*Hamilton*/Butler	00787090	513/863-1252	24
ROSS LOCAL SCH DIST/HAMILTON/BUTLER	00787064	513/863-1253	24
Ross Middle Sch/*Hamilton*/Butler	00787105	513/863-1251	24
ROSS-PIKE CO ED SERVICE CENTER/CHILLICOTHE/ROSS	00830489	740/702-3120	174
Rossford Elem Sch/*Rossford*/Wood	00840460	419/666-8130	218
ROSSFORD EXEMPTED VILLAGE SD/ROSSFORD/WOOD	00840458	419/666-2010	218
Rossford High Sch/*Rossford*/Wood	00840501	419/666-5262	218
Rossford Junior High Sch/*Rossford*/Wood	03046326	419/666-5254	218
Rothenberg Preparatory Academy/*Cincinnati*/Hamilton	00806103	513/363-5700	88
Rowland Elem Sch/*South Euclid*/Cuyahoga	00794782	216/691-2200	51
Roxboro Elem Sch/*Cleveland HTS*/Cuyahoga	00792978	216/371-7115	42
Roxboro Middle Sch/*Cleveland HTS*/Cuyahoga	12232344	216/371-7440	42
Roy E Holmes Elem Sch/*Wilmington*/Clinton	00789050	937/382-2750	33
Royal Manor Elem Sch/*Gahanna*/Franklin	00801464	614/478-5585	70
Royal Redeemer Lutheran Sch/*N Royalton*/Cuyahoga	10019213	440/237-7988	54
Royalmont Academy/*Mason*/Warren	11708106	513/754-0555	209
Royalview Elem Sch/*N Royalton*/Cuyahoga	00793958	440/582-9080	48
Royalview Elem Sch/*Willowick*/Lake	00813986	440/944-3130	114
Ruffing Mont Rocky River Sch/*Rocky River*/Cuyahoga	01409679	440/333-2250	54
Ruffing Montessori Ingalls Sch/*Cleveland HTS*/Cuyahoga	02147824	216/321-7571	54
Rushmore Academy/*Marion*/Marion	11559008	740/387-2043	138
Rushmore Elem Sch/*Huber Heights*/Montgomery	00825769	937/237-6365	150
Rushville Middle Sch/*Lancaster*/Fairfield	00799029	740/536-7249	63
Rushwood Elem Sch/*Northfield*/Summit	00835257	330/467-0581	193
Ruskin Elem Sch/*Dayton*/Montgomery	11131187	937/542-5680	149
Russellville Elem Sch/*Russellville*/Adams	00786058	937/377-4771	7
Russia Local Sch/*Russia*/Shelby	00832047	937/526-3156	183
RUSSIA LOCAL SCH DIST/RUSSIA/SHELBY	00832035	937/526-3156	183
Rutherford B Hayes High Sch/*Delaware*/Delaware	00798283	740/833-1010	59

S

School/City/County	PID	TELEPHONE NUMBER	PAGE
Sabina Elem Sch/*Sabina*/Clinton	00789012	937/584-5421	33
Sacred Heart of Jesus Sch/*Fairfield*/Butler	01600768	513/858-4215	24
Sacred Heart Parish Sch/*Wadsworth*/Medina	00795968	330/334-6272	142
Sacred Heart Sch/*Coshocton*/Coshocton	00802987	740/622-3728	37
Sacred Heart Sch/*Shelby*/Richland	00818596	419/342-2797	173
Sacred Heart Sch-Bshp Hoffman/*Fremont*/Sandusky	00818613	419/332-7102	177
Sailorway Middle Sch/*Vermilion*/Erie	01538610	440/204-1702	62
Salem Christian Academy/*Clayton*/Montgomery	03191165	937/836-9910	154
SALEM CITY SCH DIST/SALEM/COLUMBIANA	00789531	330/332-0316	35
Salem Elem Sch/*Columbus*/Franklin	00800874	614/365-5351	68
Salem High Sch/*Salem*/Columbiana	00789593	330/332-8905	35
Salem Junior High Sch/*Salem*/Columbiana	00789581	330/332-8914	35
Salem Liberty Elem Sch/*Lower Salem*/Washington	00838675	740/585-2252	210
Salem Township Elem Sch/*Morrow*/Warren	11070272	513/899-5275	208
Salem Wesleyan Academy/*Salem*/Columbiana	11231189	330/332-4819	36
Salt Creek Intermediate Sch/*Kingston*/Pickaway	00827808	740/332-4212	162
Sam Salem Cmty Learning Center/*Akron*/Summit	00834148	330/848-5231	191
Samuel Bissell Elem Sch/*Twinsburg*/Summit	00835697	330/486-2100	195
Sands Montessori Sch/*Cincinnati*/Hamilton	00806115	513/363-5000	88
Sandusky Central Catholic Sch/*Sandusky*/Erie	00818625	419/626-1892	62
SANDUSKY CITY SCH DIST/SANDUSKY/ERIE	00798611	419/626-6940	61
Sandusky High Sch/*Sandusky*/Erie	00798726	419/984-1068	61
Sandusky Middle Sch/*Sandusky*/Erie	00798623	419/984-1182	61

School/City/County	PID	TELEPHONE NUMBER	PAGE
Sandy Valley Elem Sch/*Magnolia*/Stark	00833651	330/866-9225	189
Sandy Valley High Sch/*Magnolia*/Stark	00833675	330/866-9371	189
SANDY VALLEY LOCAL SCH DIST/MAGNOLIA/STARK	00833649	330/866-3339	189
Sandy Valley Middle Sch/*Magnolia*/Stark	11458088	330/866-9416	189
Sardinia Elem Sch/*Sardinia*/Adams	00786096	937/446-2250	7
Sauder Elem Sch/*Massillon*/Stark	00832841	330/830-8028	186
Saville Elem Sch/*Riverside*/Montgomery	00825135	937/259-6625	151
Sayler Park Sch/*Cincinnati*/Hamilton	00806139	513/363-5100	88
Scarlet Oaks Career Dev Campus/*Cincinnati*/Hamilton	00810477	513/771-8810	89
Scenic Ridge Christian Sch/*Joromesville*/Ashland	11475593	419/368-0307	11
Sch for Creative Perform Arts/*Cincinnati*/Hamilton	00805551	513/363-8000	88
Schaefer Middle Sch/*Springfield*/Clark	00788159	937/505-4390	28
Schilling Sch-Gifted Children/*Cincinnati*/Hamilton	04987137	513/489-8940	96
Schnee Learning Center/*Cuyahoga FLS*/Summit	11016965	330/922-1966	193
School of Bright Promise/*Steubenville*/Jefferson	02052097	740/264-7176	108
School of Hope/*Fremont*/Sandusky	02052487	419/332-9296	176
School of One/*Cleveland*/Cuyahoga	11911420	216/838-8850	45
School of Possibilities/*Dayton*/Montgomery	12171398	937/438-6092	149
Schreiber Reading & Math Prep/*Canton*/Stark	00832683	330/452-1672	185
Schrop Intermediate Sch/*Akron*/Summit	00835439	330/798-1007	194
Schumacher Cmty Learning Ctr/*Akron*/Summit	00834411	330/761-7934	191
Scioto Co Career Tech Center/*Lucasville*/Scioto	00831407	740/259-5522	179
SCIOTO CO JOINT VOCATIONAL SD/LUCASVILLE/SCIOTO	00831392	740/259-5522	179
Scioto Darby Elem Sch/*Hilliard*/Franklin	00801763	614/921-6300	72
Scioto Elem Sch/*Commercial Pt*/Pickaway	00827846	740/983-5059	162
Scioto Ridge Elem Sch/*Powell*/Delaware	04803036	740/657-4800	59
SCIOTO VALLEY LOCAL SCH DIST/PIKETON/PIKE	00827999	740/289-4456	164
Sciotoville Cmty East High Sch/*Portsmouth*/Scioto	01755466	740/776-6777	5
Sciotoville Elem Academy/*Portsmouth*/Scioto	11462455	740/776-2920	5
Scott High Sch/*Toledo*/Lucas	00817932	419/617-4000	130
Scottish Corners Elem Sch/*Dublin*/Franklin	03003233	614/764-5963	70
Scottwood Elem Sch/*Columbus*/Franklin	00800898	614/365-6507	68
Scranton Elem Sch/*Cleveland*/Cuyahoga	00792473	216/838-7450	45
SE OHIO VOLUNTARY ED CO-OP/ATHENS/ATHENS	04499611	740/594-7663	15
Seaborn Elem Sch/*Mineral Ridge*/Trumbull	00837047	330/652-9695	201
SEBRING LOCAL SCH DIST/SEBRING/MAHONING	00820123	330/938-6165	135
Sebring McKinley Jr/Sr High/*Sebring*/Mahoning	00820147	330/938-2963	135
Secrest Elem Sch/*Senecaville*/Guernsey	02947466	740/685-2504	86
Sedalia Elem Sch/*Columbus*/Franklin	00801581	614/833-2014	71
Seiberling Cmty Learning Ctr/*Akron*/Summit	00834423	330/761-7956	191
Seneca Co Opportunity Ctr/*Tiffin*/Seneca	02052504	419/447-7521	180
Seneca East Local Sch/*Attica*/Seneca	00831689	419/426-7041	181
SENECA EAST LOCAL SCH DIST/ATTICA/SENECA	00831641	419/426-7041	181
Sentinel Career Center/*Tiffin*/Sandusky	02894091	419/448-1212	177
Seton Catholic Sch/*Hudson*/Summit	04785496	330/342-4200	195
Seton High Sch/*Cincinnati*/Hamilton	00808826	513/471-2600	95
Seven Hills Sch-Doherty Campus/*Cincinnati*/Hamilton	01874024	513/272-5180	96
Seven Mile Elem Sch/*Seven Mile*/Butler	00786333	513/867-3420	21
Shady Lane Elem Sch/*Columbus*/Franklin	00800915	614/365-5391	69
Shadyside High Sch/*Shadyside*/Belmont	00785872	740/676-3235	18
SHADYSIDE LOCAL SCH DIST/SHADYSIDE/BELMONT	00785834	740/676-3235	18
SHAKER HEIGHTS CITY SCH DIST/SHAKER HTS/CUYAHOGA	00794500	216/295-1400	50
Shaker Heights High Sch/*Shaker HTS*/Cuyahoga	00794603	216/295-4200	50
Shaker Heights Middle Sch/*Shaker HTS*/Cuyahoga	00794524	216/295-4100	50
Shaker Hts HS-the IC/*Shaker HTS*/Cuyahoga	12366311	216/295-6272	50
Shanahan Middle Sch/*Lewis Center*/Delaware	00798336	740/657-4300	59
Sharon Elem Sch/*Sharon Center*/Medina	00822377	330/239-1901	141
Sharonville Elem Sch/*Cincinnati*/Hamilton	00807535	513/864-2600	92
Sharpsburg Elem Sch/*Norwood*/Hamilton	00807327	513/924-2600	92
Shaw Elem Sch/*Beavercreek*/Greene	00804533	937/429-7610	83
Shaw High Sch/*E Cleveland*/Cuyahoga	05273563	216/268-6887	45
Shawnee Early Childhood Sch/*Cincinnati*/Butler	03317709	513/779-3014	22

Ohio School Directory

DISTRICT & SCHOOL TELEPHONE INDEX

School/City/County DISTRICT/CITY/COUNTY	PID	TELEPHONE NUMBER	PAGE
Shawnee Elem Sch/*Huron*/Erie	11072103	419/433-1234	61
Shawnee Elem Sch/*Xenia*/Greene	00804882	937/372-6461	85
Shawnee High Sch/*Lima*/Allen	00784000	419/998-8000	9
Shawnee High Sch/*Springfield*/Clark	00788264	937/325-9296	27
SHAWNEE LOCAL SCH DIST/LIMA/ALLEN	00783989	419/998-8031	9
Shawnee Middle Sch/*Lima*/Allen	00784024	419/998-8057	9
Shawnee Middle Sch/*Springfield*/Clark	12235774	937/328-5378	27
SHEFFIELD-SHEFFIELD LAKE CSD/SHEFFIELD VLG/LORAIN	00816689	440/949-6181	125
Shekinah Christian Sch/*Plain City*/Madison	04433100	614/873-3130	133
SHELBY CITY SCH DIST/SHELBY/RICHLAND	00829923	419/342-3520	173
Shelby High Sch/*Shelby*/Richland	00829961	419/342-5065	173
Shelby Middle Sch/*Shelby*/Richland	00829973	419/347-5451	173
Shenandoah Elem Sch/*Sarahsville*/Noble	00826957	740/732-5661	158
Shenandoah High Sch/*Sarahsville*/Noble	00826969	740/732-2361	158
Shepherd Christian Sch/*Columbus*/Franklin	12315582	614/471-0859	77
Sheridan High Sch/*Thornville*/Perry	00827559	740/743-1335	161
Sheridan Middle Sch/*Thornville*/Perry	00827561	740/743-1315	161
Sherman Elem Sch/*Mansfield*/Richland	00829820	419/525-6337	172
Sherman Elem Sch/*Toledo*/Lucas	00817944	419/671-6550	130
Sherwood Elem Sch/*Cincinnati*/Hamilton	00806531	513/231-7565	89
Sherwood Middle Sch/*Columbus*/Franklin	00800941	614/365-5393	69
Shiloh Elem Sch/*Shiloh*/Richland	00829911	419/687-8200	173
Shiloh Middle Sch/*Parma*/Cuyahoga	03401910	440/885-8485	49
Shiloh Middle Sch/*Plymouth*/Richland	00829909	419/687-8200	173
Shore Middle Sch/*Mentor*/Lake	00813467	440/257-8750	113
Shoreland Elem Sch/*Toledo*/Lucas	00818194	419/473-8294	130
Shoreview Elem Sch/*Euclid*/Cuyahoga	11824633	216/797-6500	46
Shreve Elem Sch/*Shreve*/Wayne	00839447	330/567-2837	213
Shroder High Sch/*Cincinnati*/Hamilton	00806165	513/363-6900	88
SIDNEY CITY SCH DIST/SIDNEY/SHELBY	00832061	937/497-2200	183
Sidney Fenn Elem Sch/*Medina*/Medina	00822432	330/636-4100	141
Sidney High Sch/*Sidney*/Shelby	00832164	937/497-2238	183
Sidney Middle Sch/*Sidney*/Shelby	00832073	937/497-2225	183
Siebert Elem Sch/*Columbus*/Franklin	00800953	614/365-6613	69
Silver Lake Elem Sch/*Cuyahoga FLS*/Summit	00834966	330/926-3811	193
Silverton Paideia Academy/*Cincinnati*/Hamilton	00806177	513/363-5400	88
Simon Kenton Elem Sch/*Springfield*/Clark	00788068	937/505-4210	28
Simon Kenton Sch/*Kenton*/Hardin	04009101	419/674-4158	99
Skyvue Elem Sch/*Graysville*/Monroe	00823852	740/567-3312	147
Slate Hill Elem Sch/*Worthington*/Franklin	03393296	614/450-5000	76
Slate Ridge Elem Sch/*Reynoldsburg*/Franklin	10012289	614/501-5500	73
Smith Middle Sch/*Dayton*/Montgomery	00825678	937/415-7000	153
Smithville High Sch/*Smithville*/Wayne	00839136	330/669-3165	212
Snowhill Elem Sch/*Springfield*/Clark	00788161	937/505-4410	28
Snyder Park Elem Sch/*Springfield*/Clark	00788173	937/505-4430	28
Solomon Lutheran Sch/*Woodville*/Sandusky	00830829	419/849-3600	177
SOLON CITY SCH DIST/SOLON/CUYAHOGA	00794639	440/248-1600	50
Solon High Sch/*Solon*/Cuyahoga	00794689	440/349-6230	50
Solon Middle Sch/*Solon*/Cuyahoga	00794641	440/349-3848	50
Solon Pre-Chool/*Solon*/Cuyahoga	12171934	440/349-6210	50
Somerset Elem Sch/*Somerset*/Perry	04366301	740/743-1454	161
Sonshine Christian Academy/*Columbus*/Franklin	02209018	614/498-0082	77
South Amherst Middle Sch/*South Amherst*/Lorain	00816770	440/986-7021	124
South Avondale Elem Sch/*Cincinnati*/Hamilton	00806189	513/363-5500	88
South Bloomfield Elem Sch/*Ashville*/Pickaway	11563774	740/983-5003	163
South Central Elem Sch/*Greenwich*/Huron	00811706	419/752-5021	106
South Central High Sch/*Greenwich*/Huron	00811720	419/752-3354	106
SOUTH CENTRAL LOCAL SCH DIST/GREENWICH/HURON	00811691	419/752-3815	106
South Central Middle Sch/*Greenwich*/Huron	12309428	419/752-0011	106
SOUTH CENTRAL OHIO ED SVC CTR/NEW BOSTON/SCIOTO	00831419	740/354-7761	178
South Columbus Prep Acad/*Columbus*/Franklin	12259548	614/986-0116	5
South Community Yph/*Dayton*/Montgomery	11223546	937/252-0100	154
South Elem Sch/*Cincinnati*/Hamilton	00807004	513/728-4683	91
South Elem Sch/*Dover*/Tuscarawas	00837190	330/364-7111	202
South Elem Sch/*Hamden*/Vinton	00838065	740/384-2731	206
South Elem Sch/*New Phila*/Tuscarawas	01171999	330/364-0725	203
South Elem Sch/*Tiltonsville*/Jefferson	00812231	740/859-2800	108
South Elem Sch/*Upper Sandusky*/Wyandot	00840707	419/294-2304	219
SOUTH EUCLID-LYNDHURST CITY SD/LYNDHURST/CUYAHOGA	00794691	216/691-2000	50
South Gallia High Sch/*Crown City*/Gallia	04451516	740/256-1054	80
South Gallia Middle Sch/*Crown City*/Gallia	11464374	740/256-1054	80
South High Sch/*Columbus*/Franklin	00800977	614/365-5541	69
South High Sch/*Willoughby*/Lake	00814007	440/975-3648	114
South Lebanon Elem Sch/*Maineville*/Warren	00838235	513/398-8050	207
South Mifflin STEM Academy/*Columbus*/Franklin	00800989	614/365-6135	69
South Point Elem Sch/*South Point*/Lawrence	00814497	740/377-2756	116
South Point High Sch/*South Point*/Lawrence	02202357	740/377-4323	116
SOUTH POINT LOCAL SCH DIST/SOUTH POINT/LAWRENCE	00814447	740/377-4315	116
South Point Middle Sch/*South Point*/Lawrence	00814502	740/377-4343	116
South Range Elem Sch/*Canfield*/Mahoning	00820173	330/549-5578	135
South Range High Sch/*Canfield*/Mahoning	00820185	330/549-2163	135
SOUTH RANGE LOCAL SCH DIST/CANFIELD/MAHONING	00820161	330/549-5226	135
South Range Middle Sch/*Canfield*/Mahoning	00820197	330/549-4071	135
South Science Tech Magnet Sch/*Lima*/Allen	00783903	419/996-3190	9
South Scioto Perform Academy/*Columbus*/Franklin	10751851	614/445-7684	66
South Side Academy/*Youngstown*/Mahoning	11596484	330/774-5562	5
South Suburban Montessori Sch/*Brecksville*/Cuyahoga	02828224	440/526-1966	54
South Vienna Elem Sch/*South Vienna*/Clark	00787856	937/346-0840	27
South Vienna Middle Sch/*South Vienna*/Clark	05271503	937/346-0880	27
South Webster Jr Sr High Sch/*South Webster*/Scioto	03047849	740/778-2320	178
South Western Preschool/*Grove City*/Franklin	11452450	614/801-8448	74
South-Western Career Academy/*Grove City*/Franklin	00801983	614/801-3400	74
SOUTH-WESTERN CITY SCH DIST/GROVE CITY/FRANKLIN	00801816	614/801-3000	73
Southdale Elem Sch/*Kettering*/Montgomery	00825032	937/499-1890	150
Southeast Elem Sch/*Salem*/Columbiana	00789608	330/332-8925	35
Southeast High Sch/*Ravenna*/Portage	00828656	330/654-1960	167
Southeast Intermediate Sch/*Ravenna*/Portage	04914269	330/654-1940	167
SOUTHEAST LOCAL SCH DIST/APPLE CREEK/WAYNE	00839356	330/698-3001	213
SOUTHEAST LOCAL SCH DIST/RAVENNA/PORTAGE	00828632	330/654-5841	166
Southeast Middle Sch/*Diamond*/Portage	01823300	330/654-1950	167
Southeast Primary Sch/*Ravenna*/Portage	00828644	330/654-1930	167
Southeastern Elem Sch/*Chillicothe*/Ross	00830336	740/774-2003	175
Southeastern High Sch/*Chillicothe*/Ross	00830362	740/774-2003	175
Southeastern Jr Sr High Sch/*S Charleston*/Clark	00787923	937/462-8308	28
SOUTHEASTERN LOCAL SCH DIST/CHILLICOTHE/ROSS	00830312	740/774-2003	175
SOUTHEASTERN LOCAL SCH DIST/S CHARLESTON/CLARK	00787909	216/462-8388	28
Southeastern Middle Sch/*Chillicothe*/Ross	00830350	740/774-2003	175
Southern Elem Sch/*Racine*/Meigs	00822717	740/949-4222	143
Southern Elem Sch/*Salineville*/Columbiana	10014823	330/679-2305	36
Southern High Sch/*Racine*/Meigs	00822755	740/949-4222	143
Southern Hills Career Tech Ctr/*Georgetown*/Brown	00786278	937/378-6131	20
SOUTHERN HILLS JOINT VOC SD/GEORGETOWN/BROWN	00786266	937/378-6131	20
Southern Local Jr Sr HS/*Salineville*/Columbiana	00789660	330/679-2305	36
SOUTHERN LOCAL SCH DIST/CORNING/PERRY	00827597	740/394-2402	161
SOUTHERN LOCAL SCH DIST/RACINE/MEIGS	00822705	740/949-2669	143
SOUTHERN LOCAL SCH DIST/SALINEVILLE/COLUMBIANA	00789610	330/679-2343	35
Southern Ohio Christian Sch/*Leesburg*/Highland	11748429	937/780-5470	103
SOUTHERN OHIO ED SERV CTR/WILMINGTON/CLINTON	00789115	937/382-6921	32
Southgate Sch/*Canton*/Stark	02094150	330/484-2547	184
Southington Local Sch/*Southington*/Trumbull	00836768	330/898-7480	200
SOUTHINGTON LOCAL SCH DIST/SOUTHINGTON/TRUMBULL	00836756	330/898-7480	200
Southridge Christian Academy/*Conneaut*/Ashtabula	03409285	440/593-4657	14
Southview Child & Family Ctr/*Dayton*/Montgomery	02052310	937/258-1446	148
Southview Elem Sch/*Jackson*/Jackson	00811902	740/286-1831	107
Southview High Sch/*Sylvania*/Lucas	01530503	419/824-8580	129

School Year 2019-2020   800-333-8802   OH-V33

DISTRICT & SCHOOL TELEPHONE INDEX

Market Data Retrieval

School/City/County DISTRICT/CITY/COUNTY	PID	TELEPHONE NUMBER	PAGE
Southview Middle Sch/*Lorain*/Lorain	12172512	440/830-4280	124
Southwest Licking ELC/*Pataskala*/Licking	12234304	740/927-5437	120
SOUTHWEST LICKING LOCAL SD/ PATASKALA/LICKING	00815271	740/927-3941	120
SOUTHWEST LOCAL SCH DIST/ HARRISON/HAMILTON	00807638	513/367-4139	93
SOUTHWEST OHIO OCA/HAMILTON/ BUTLER	04499623	513/867-1028	25
Southwest Ohio Prep Sch/*Cincinnati*/ Hamilton	12259471	513/975-4946	5
Southwestern Elem Sch/*Patriot*/Gallia	02845856	740/379-2532	80
Southwood Elem Sch/*Columbus*/Franklin	00800848	614/365-5553	69
Spanish Immersion Sch/*Mansfield*/Richland	11148142	419/525-6321	173
SPARCC/NORTH CANTON/STARK	04499635	330/492-8136	190
Spaulding Elem Sch/*Goshen*/Clermont	05264914	513/722-2225	30
Spencer Ctr-Gifted/*Cincinnati*/Hamilton	12231364	513/363-5800	88
Spencerville Elem Sch/*Spencerville*/Allen	00784050	419/647-4113	9
Spencerville High Sch/*Spencerville*/Allen	00784062	419/647-4111	9
SPENCERVILLE LOCAL SCH DIST/ SPENCERVILLE/ALLEN	00784036	419/647-4111	9
Spencerville Middle Sch/*Spencerville*/Allen	00784074	419/647-4112	9
Spinning Hills Middle Sch/*Dayton*/ Montgomery	00825147	937/259-6635	151
Spring Elem Sch/*Toledo*/Lucas	11453088	419/671-6600	130
Spring Garden Waldorf Sch/*Copley*/Summit	03184148	330/666-0574	196
Spring Hill Elem Sch/*Akron*/Summit	00835441	330/798-1006	194
Spring Valley Academy/*Centerville*/ Montgomery	00825965	937/433-0790	154
SPRINGBORO CMTY SCH DIST/ SPRINGBORO/WARREN	00838156	937/748-3960	208
Springboro High Sch/*Springboro*/Warren	01880918	937/748-3950	208
Springboro Intermediate Sch/*Springboro*/ Warren	04918423	937/748-4113	208
Springboro Junior High Sch/*Springboro*/ Warren	00838182	937/748-3953	208
Springcreek Primary Sch/*Piqua*/Miami	00823498	937/773-6540	146
Springdale Elem Sch/*Cincinnati*/Hamilton	00807547	513/864-2700	92
Springer School and Center/*Cincinnati*/ Hamilton	02236475	513/871-6080	96
Springfield Christian Sch/*Springfield*/ Clark	02123165	937/325-3113	29
SPRINGFIELD CITY SCH DIST/ SPRINGFIELD/CLARK	00787935	937/505-2800	28
Springfield Elem Sch/*New Middletwn*/ Mahoning	00820214	330/542-3722	136
Springfield High Sch/*Akron*/Summit	00835489	330/798-1002	194
Springfield High Sch/*Holland*/Lucas	00817188	419/867-5633	128
Springfield High Sch/*New Middletwn*/ Mahoning	00820238	330/542-3626	136
Springfield High Sch/*Springfield*/Clark	00788185	937/505-4320	28
Springfield Local Interm Sch/*New Middletwn*/ Mahoning	00820240	330/542-3626	136
SPRINGFIELD LOCAL SCH DIST/ AKRON/SUMMIT	00835403	330/798-1111	194
SPRINGFIELD LOCAL SCH DIST/ HOLLAND/LUCAS	00817140	419/867-5600	128
SPRINGFIELD LOCAL SCH DIST/ NEW MIDDLETWN/MAHONING	00820202	330/542-2929	135
Springfield Middle Sch/*Holland*/Lucas	00817190	419/867-5644	128
Springfield Prep-Fitness Acad/*Springfield*/ Clark	10017980	937/323-6250	5
Springfield-Clark Career Tech/*Springfield*/ Clark	00788305	937/325-7368	28
SPRINGFIELD-CLARK CO JVSD/ SPRINGFIELD/CLARK	00788290	937/325-7368	28
Springmill STEM Elem Sch/*Mansfield*/ Richland	12173205	419/525-6348	173
Springmyer Elem Sch/*Cincinnati*/Hamilton	00807377	513/574-1205	92
Spruce Primary Sch/*North Olmsted*/Cuyahoga	00793910	440/779-3541	48
SS Agatha & Aloysius Sch/*Cleveland*/ Cuyahoga	00796077	216/451-2050	52
SS Andrew-Elizabeth Seton Sch/*Milford*/ Clermont	00808278	513/575-0093	32
SS Joseph & John Sch/*Strongsville*/Cuyahoga	00796675	440/238-4877	52
SS Peter & Paul Academy/*Cincinnati*/ Hamilton	11066192	513/761-7772	96
SS Peter & Paul Cath Sch/*Wellston*/Jackson	00803008	740/384-6354	108
SS Peter & Paul Sch/*Doylestown*/Wayne	00796003	330/658-2804	214
SS Peter & Paul Sch/*Ottawa*/Putnam	00818649	419/523-3697	171
SS Philip & James Sch/*Canal Fulton*/Stark	00821165	330/854-2823	189
SS Robert & William Sch/*Euclid*/Cuyahoga	00797332	216/731-3060	52

School/City/County DISTRICT/CITY/COUNTY	PID	TELEPHONE NUMBER	PAGE
St Adalbert-Cleveland Sch/*Cleveland*/ Cuyahoga	00796039	216/881-6250	52
St Agatha Sch/*Columbus*/Franklin	00803010	614/488-9000	76
St Albert the Great Sch/*Kettering*/ Montgomery	00808876	937/293-9452	154
St Albert the Great Sch/*N Royalton*/ Cuyahoga	00796065	440/237-1032	52
St Aloysius Educational Center/*Cincinnati*/ Hamilton	00808905	513/242-7600	96
St Aloysius Gonzaga Sch/*Cincinnati*/ Hamilton	00808890	513/574-4035	95
St Aloysius Sch/*Bowling Green*/Wood	00818675	419/352-8614	218
St Ambrose Sch/*Brunswick*/Medina	00796089	330/225-2116	142
St Andrew Sch/*Columbus*/Franklin	00803046	614/451-1626	76
St Angela Merici Sch/*Fairview Park*/ Cuyahoga	00796091	440/333-2126	52
St Ann Catholic Sch/*Hamilton*/Butler	00808931	513/863-0604	24
St Anselm Sch/*Chesterland*/Geauga	00796118	440/729-7806	83
St Anthony Catholic Sch/*Dayton*/Montgomery	00808955	937/253-6251	154
St Anthony of Padua Sch/*Akron*/Summit	00796156	330/253-6918	195
St Anthony of Padua Sch/*Columbus GRV*/ Putnam	00818728	419/659-2103	171
St Anthony of Padua Sch/*Lorain*/Lorain	00796120	440/288-2155	126
St Anthony Padua Elem Sch/*Parma*/Cuyahoga	00796132	440/845-3444	52
St Anthony Sch/*Columbus*/Franklin	00803058	614/888-4268	76
St Antoninus Sch/*Cincinnati*/Hamilton	00808711	513/922-2500	95
St Augustine Sch/*Barberton*/Summit	00796170	330/753-6435	195
St Augustine Sch/*Napoleon*/Henry	00818730	419/592-3641	102
St Barbara Sch/*Massillon*/Stark	00821218	330/833-9510	189
St Barnabas Parish Sch/*Northfield*/Summit	00796182	330/467-7921	195
St Benedict Catholic Sch/*Garfield HTS*/ Cuyahoga	00796986	216/662-9380	52
St Benedict Catholic Sch/*Toledo*/Lucas	00818493	419/536-1194	131
St Benedict Sch/*Cambridge*/Guernsey	00812762	740/432-6751	86
St Benedict the Moor Cath Sch/*Dayton*/ Montgomery	00808682	937/268-6391	154
St Bernadette Sch/*Amelia*/Clermont	00808979	513/753-4744	32
St Bernadette Sch/*Lancaster*/Fairfield	00803072	740/654-3137	65
St Bernadette Sch/*Westlake*/Cuyahoga	00796211	440/734-7717	52
St Bernard Elem Sch/*New Washingtn*/Crawford	00818742	419/492-2693	39
St Bernard Elem Sch/*Saint Bernard*/Hamilton	00807755	513/482-7110	93
St Bernard Taylor Creek Sch/*Cincinnati*/ Hamilton	00808993	513/353-4224	95
St Bernard-Elmwood Place HS/*Saint Bernard*/ Hamilton	00807731	513/482-7100	93
ST BERNARD-ELMWOOD PLACE SCHS/ SAINT BERNARD/HAMILTON	00807717	513/482-7121	93
St Boniface Catholic Sch/*Oak Harbor*/Ottawa	00818754	419/898-1340	160
St Boniface Sch/*Cincinnati*/Hamilton	00808735	513/541-5122	95
St Brendan Sch/*Hilliard*/Franklin	00803084	614/876-6132	76
St Brendan Sch/*North Olmsted*/Cuyahoga	00796247	440/777-8433	52
St Bridget of Kildare Sch/*Parma*/Cuyahoga	00796259	440/886-1468	53
St Brigid of Kildare Elem Sch/*Dublin*/ Franklin	04472792	614/718-5825	76
St Brigid Sch/*Xenia*/Greene	00808747	937/372-3222	85
St Catharine Sch/*Cincinnati*/Hamilton	00809026	513/481-7683	95
St Catharine Sch/*Columbus*/Franklin	00803096	614/235-1396	76
St Catherine of Siena ECC/*Toledo*/Lucas	12314693	419/478-9900	131
St Cecilia Sch/*Cincinnati*/Hamilton	00809038	513/533-6060	95
St Cecilia Sch/*Columbus*/Franklin	00803101	614/878-3555	76
St Charles Borremo Sch/*Lima*/Allen	00818778	419/222-2536	10
St Charles Borromeo Sch/*Dayton*/Montgomery	00809040	937/434-4933	154
St Charles Borromeo Sch/*Parma*/Cuyahoga	00796285	440/886-5546	53
St Charles Preparatory Sch/*Columbus*/ Franklin	00803113	614/252-6714	76
St Charles Sch/*Boardman*/Mahoning	00821244	330/758-6689	137
St Christine Sch/*Youngstown*/Mahoning	00821268	330/792-4544	137
St Christopher Sch/*Rocky River*/Cuyahoga	00796302	440/331-3075	53
St Christopher Sch/*Vandalia*/Montgomery	00809064	937/898-5104	154
St Clairsville Elem Sch/*St Clairsvle*/ Belmont	00785901	740/695-0884	18
St Clairsville High Sch/*St Clairsvle*/ Belmont	00785913	740/695-1584	18
St Clairsville Middle Sch/*St Clairsvle*/ Belmont	00785925	740/695-1591	18
ST CLAIRSVILLE-RICHLAND CSD/ ST CLAIRSVLE/BELMONT	00785884	740/695-1624	18
St Clement Sch/*Cincinnati*/Hamilton	00809088	513/641-2137	95
St Columban Sch/*Loveland*/Clermont	00809090	513/683-7903	32
St Columbkille Sch/*Parma*/Cuyahoga	00796338	216/524-4816	53
St Dominic Sch/*Beachwood*/Cuyahoga	00796340	216/561-4400	53
St Dominic Sch/*Cincinnati*/Hamilton	00809105	513/251-1276	95

Ohio School Directory

DISTRICT & SCHOOL TELEPHONE INDEX

School/City/County DISTRICT/CITY/COUNTY	PID	TELEPHONE NUMBER	PAGE
St Edmund Campion Academy/*Cincinnati*/Hamilton	05355977	513/871-0331	96
St Edward Elem Sch/*Ashland*/Ashland	00796364	419/289-7456	11
St Edward High Sch/*Lakewood*/Cuyahoga	00796352	216/221-3776	53
St Francis DeSales Elem Sch/*Newark*/Licking	00803137	740/345-4049	120
St Francis DeSales High Sch/*Columbus*/Franklin	00802810	614/267-7808	76
St Francis DeSales High Sch/*Toledo*/Lucas	00818821	419/531-1618	131
St Francis DeSales Sch/*Akron*/Summit	00796390	330/644-0638	195
St Francis DeSales Sch/*Cincinnati*/Hamilton	00809129	513/961-1953	95
St Francis DeSales Sch/*Lebanon*/Warren	00809117	513/932-6501	209
St Francis of Assisi Sch/*Gates Mills*/Cuyahoga	00796405	440/442-7450	53
St Francis School-Cleveland/*Cleveland*/Cuyahoga	00796417	216/361-4858	53
St Francis Seraph Sch/*Cincinnati*/Hamilton	00808759	513/721-7778	95
St Francis Xavier Sch/*Medina*/Medina	00796429	330/725-3345	142
St Francis Xavier Sch/*Willard*/Huron	00818857	419/935-4744	107
St Gabriel Consolidated Sch/*Cincinnati*/Hamilton	00809143	513/771-5220	95
St Gabriel Sch/*Mentor*/Lake	00796431	440/352-6169	115
St Gerard Sch/*Lima*/Allen	00818869	419/222-0431	10
St Gertrude Sch/*Cincinnati*/Hamilton	00809167	513/561-8020	95
St Helen Sch/*Newbury*/Geauga	00796455	440/564-7125	83
St Helen Sch/*Riverside*/Greene	00809179	937/256-1761	85
ST HENRY CONS LOCAL SCH DIST/ **SAINT HENRY/MERCER**	00823101	419/678-4834	144
St Henry Elem Sch/*Saint Henry*/Mercer	00823125	419/678-4834	144
St Henry High Sch/*Saint Henry*/Mercer	00823137	419/678-4834	144
St Henry Middle Sch/*Saint Henry*/Mercer	00823149	419/678-4834	144
St Hilary Sch/*Fairlawn*/Summit	00796479	330/867-8720	195
St Ignatius High Sch/*Cleveland*/Cuyahoga	00796508	216/651-0222	53
St Ignatius of Antioch ES/*Cleveland*/Cuyahoga	00796493	216/671-0535	53
St Ignatius Sch/*Cincinnati*/Hamilton	00809193	513/389-3242	95
St James Sch/*Waynesburg*/Stark	00821323	330/866-9556	189
St James the Greater Sch/*Cincinnati*/Hamilton	00809222	513/741-5333	95
St James the Less Sch/*Columbus*/Franklin	00803151	614/268-3311	76
St Jerome Elem Sch/*Cleveland*/Cuyahoga	00796522	216/486-3587	53
St Joan of Arc Sch/*Canton*/Stark	00821335	330/477-2972	189
St Joan of Arc Sch/*Chagrin Falls*/Cuyahoga	00796534	440/247-6530	53
St Joan of Arc Sch/*Toledo*/Lucas	02113445	419/866-6177	131
St John Baptist Sch/*Harrison*/Hamilton	00809246	513/367-6826	95
St John Central Academy/*Bellaire*/Belmont	00812798	740/676-4932	19
St John Central Sch/*Marietta*/Washington	00812815	740/896-2697	211
St John Elem Sch/*Delphos*/Allen	00818948	419/692-8561	10
St John Lutheran Sch/*Cleveland*/Cuyahoga	00795205	216/531-8204	54
St John Lutheran Sch/*Defiance*/Defiance	00798087	419/782-6166	58
St John Lutheran Sch/*Napoleon*/Henry	00810867	419/598-8702	102
St John Lutheran Sch/*South Euclid*/Cuyahoga	00795229	216/381-8595	54
St John Sch/*Ashtabula*/Ashtabula	00821074	440/997-5531	14
St John Sch/*Logan*/Hocking	00803163	740/385-2767	104
St John the Baptist Sch/*Cincinnati*/Hamilton	00809234	513/385-7970	95
St John's High Sch/*Delphos*/Allen	00818950	419/692-5371	10
St John's Jesuit High Sch/*Toledo*/Lucas	00818962	419/865-5743	131
St John's Lutheran Sch/*Marysville*/Union	00837786	937/644-5540	205
St Joseph Academy/*Cleveland*/Cuyahoga	00796596	216/251-6788	53
St Joseph Catholic Sch/*Crestline*/Crawford	00819019	419/683-1284	39
St Joseph Catholic Sch/*Galion*/Crawford	00818998	419/468-5436	39
St Joseph Consolidated Sch/*Hamilton*/Butler	00809296	513/863-8758	24
St Joseph Ctl Cath Jr Sr HS/*Fremont*/Sandusky	00818986	419/332-9947	177
St Joseph High Sch/*Ironton*/Lawrence	00812827	740/532-0485	117
St Joseph Montessori Sch/*Columbus*/Franklin	00803175	614/291-8601	76
St Joseph Parish Sch/*Avon Lake*/Lorain	00796663	440/933-6233	126
St Joseph Sch/*Amherst*/Lorain	00796649	440/988-4244	126
St Joseph Sch/*Cincinnati*/Hamilton	00809272	513/381-2126	95
St Joseph Sch/*Maumee*/Lucas	00819057	419/893-3304	131
St Joseph Sch/*Monroeville*/Huron	00819021	419/465-2625	107
St Joseph Sch/*Sylvania*/Lucas	00819045	419/882-6670	131
St Joseph Sch-Cuyahoga Falls/*Cuyahoga FLS*/Summit	00796651	330/928-2151	195
St Joseph School-Randolph/*Mogadore*/Portage	00821385	330/628-9555	167
St Joseph the Provider Sch/*Youngstown*/Mahoning	00821438	330/259-0353	137
St Jude Sch/*Cincinnati*/Hamilton	00809301	513/598-2100	95
St Jude Sch/*Elyria*/Lorain	00796699	440/366-1681	126
St Lawrence Elem Sch/*Ironton*/Lawrence	00812841	740/532-5052	117
St Lawrence Sch/*Cincinnati*/Hamilton	00809313	513/921-4996	95
St Leo the Great Sch/*Cleveland*/Cuyahoga	00796728	216/661-2120	53
St Louis Sch/*Custar*/Wood	00819071	419/669-1875	218
St Louis Sch/*Louisville*/Stark	00821440	330/875-1467	189
St Louis Sch/*Owensville*/Clermont	00809337	513/732-0636	32
St Luke Sch/*Beavercreek*/Greene	00809349	937/426-8551	85
St Margaret of York Sch/*Loveland*/Clermont	03266150	513/697-3100	32
St Mark Sch/*Cleveland*/Cuyahoga	00796778	216/521-4115	53
St Mark's Lutheran Sch/*Milford*/Clermont	11816777	513/575-3354	32
St Martin De Porres High Sch/*Cleveland*/Cuyahoga	10000200	216/881-1689	54
St Martin of Tours Sch/*Cincinnati*/Hamilton	00809399	513/661-7609	95
St Mary Asumption Catholic ES/*Van Wert*/Van Wert	00819174	419/238-5186	206
St Mary Byzantine Sch/*Cleveland*/Cuyahoga	00796936	216/749-7980	53
St Mary Catholic Sch/*Berea*/Cuyahoga	00796807	440/243-4555	53
St Mary Catholic Sch/*Vermilion*/Erie	00819148	440/967-7911	62
St Mary Central Sch/*Martins Ferry*/Belmont	00812853	740/633-5424	19
St Mary Central Sch/*St Clairsvle*/Belmont	00812865	740/695-3189	19
St Mary Elem Sch/*Shelby*/Richland	00819203	419/342-2626	174
St Mary Magdalene Sch/*Columbus*/Franklin	00803254	614/279-9935	76
St Mary of the Assumption Sch/*Mentor*/Lake	00796869	440/255-9781	115
St Mary of the Falls Sch/*Olmsted Falls*/Cuyahoga	00796845	440/235-4580	53
St Mary of the Imm Concep Sch/*Wooster*/Wayne	00796821	330/262-8671	214
St Mary Sch/*Akron*/Summit	00796819	330/253-1233	195
St Mary Sch/*Chardon*/Geauga	00796900	440/286-3590	83
St Mary Sch/*Cincinnati*/Hamilton	00809404	513/321-0703	95
St Mary Sch/*Columbus*/Franklin	00803307	614/444-8994	76
St Mary Sch/*Delaware*/Delaware	00803280	740/362-8961	60
St Mary Sch/*Edgerton*/Williams	00819124	419/298-2531	215
St Mary Sch/*Greenville*/Darke	00808773	937/548-2345	56
St Mary Sch/*Hillsboro*/Highland	05326081	937/840-9932	103
St Mary Sch/*Lancaster*/Fairfield	00803242	740/654-1632	65
St Mary Sch/*Leipsic*/Putnam	00819198	419/943-2801	171
St Mary Sch/*Mansfield*/Richland	00819162	419/589-2114	174
St Mary Sch/*Marietta*/Washington	01600392	740/374-8181	211
St Mary Sch/*Marion*/Marion	00803278	740/382-1607	139
St Mary Sch/*Massillon*/Stark	00821476	330/832-9355	189
St Mary School-Avon/*Avon*/Lorain	00795619	440/934-6246	126
St Mary School-Elyria/*Elyria*/Lorain	00796871	440/322-2808	126
ST MARY'S CITY SCH DIST/ **SAINT MARYS/AUGLAIZE**	00785365	419/394-4312	16
St Marys Intermediate Sch/*Saint Marys*/Auglaize	00785432	419/394-2016	16
St Marys Memorial High Sch/*Saint Marys*/Auglaize	00785406	419/394-4011	16
St Marys Middle Sch/*Saint Marys*/Auglaize	00785391	419/394-2112	16
St Marys Primary Sch/*Saint Marys*/Auglaize	00785389	419/394-2616	16
St Matthew Parish Sch/*Akron*/Summit	00796948	330/784-1711	195
St Matthew Sch/*Gahanna*/Franklin	00803319	614/471-4930	76
St Matthias Sch/*Columbus*/Franklin	00803321	614/268-3030	76
St Michael Sch/*Canton*/Stark	00821490	330/492-2657	190
St Michael Sch/*Findlay*/Hancock	00819253	419/423-2738	99
St Michael Sch/*Independence*/Cuyahoga	00796974	216/524-6405	53
St Michael Sch/*Ripley*/Brown	00808785	937/392-4202	20
St Michael Sch/*Sharonville*/Hamilton	00808797	513/554-3555	95
St Michael Sch/*Worthington*/Franklin	00803333	614/885-3149	76
St Nicholas Academy/*Cincinnati*/Hamilton	00809258	513/686-2727	96
St Nicholas Sch/*Struthers*/Mahoning	00821505	330/755-2128	137
St Paschal Baylon Sch/*Highland Hgts*/Cuyahoga	00797007	440/442-6766	53
St Patrick Catholic Sch/*Troy*/Miami	00809454	937/339-3705	147
St Patrick Sch/*Bryan*/Williams	00819277	419/636-3592	215
St Patrick Sch/*Kent*/Portage	00821517	330/673-7232	167
St Patrick Sch/*London*/Madison	00803357	740/852-0161	133
St Patrick-Heatherdowns Sch/*Toledo*/Lucas	00819265	419/381-1775	131
St Paul Lutheran Sch/*Milford CTR*/Union	00788848	937/349-5939	205
St Paul Lutheran Sch/*Napoleon*/Henry	00810879	419/592-5536	102
St Paul Lutheran Sch/*Westlake*/Cuyahoga	00795243	440/835-3051	54
St Paul Sch/*North Canton*/Stark	00821555	330/494-0223	190
St Paul Sch/*Salem*/Columbiana	00821567	330/337-3451	36
St Paul Sch/*Westerville*/Delaware	00803369	614/882-2710	60
St Paul's Lutheran Sch/*Columbus*/Franklin	00802652	614/444-4216	77
St Peter Catholic Sch/*Huron*/Erie	00819318	419/433-4640	62
St Peter Catholic Sch/*Upper Sandsky*/Wyandot	00819306	419/294-1395	219
St Peter Elem Sch/*Mansfield*/Richland	00819320	419/524-2572	174
St Peter In Chains Sch/*Hamilton*/Butler	00809478	513/863-0685	24
St Peter Jr Sr High Sch/*Mansfield*/Richland	00819332	419/524-0979	174
St Peter Sch/*Canton*/Stark	00821579	330/452-0125	190
St Peter Sch/*Huber Heights*/Montgomery	00809466	937/233-8710	154
St Peter Sch/*N Ridgeville*/Lorain	00797057	440/327-3212	126

School Year 2019-2020   800-333-8802   OH-V35

DISTRICT & SCHOOL TELEPHONE INDEX

Market Data Retrieval

School/City/County DISTRICT/CITY/COUNTY	PID	TELEPHONE NUMBER	PAGE
St Peter School-Lorain/*Lorain*/Lorain	00797071	440/282-9909	126
St Pierre Education Center/*Bellbrook*/Greene	11556991	937/848-5001	84
St Pius X Sch/*Reynoldsburg*/Franklin	00803395	614/866-6050	76
St Pius X Sch/*Toledo*/Lucas	00819344	419/535-7688	131
St Raphael Sch/*Bay Village*/Cuyahoga	00797112	440/871-6760	53
St Richard Sch/*Swanton*/Fulton	00819356	419/826-5041	80
St Rita Sch/*Solon*/Cuyahoga	00797136	440/248-1350	53
St Rita School for the Deaf/*Cincinnati*/Hamilton	00809521	513/771-7600	96
St Rocco Sch/*Cleveland*/Cuyahoga	00797150	216/961-8557	53
St Rose Catholic Sch/*Lima*/Allen	00819368	419/223-6361	10
St Rose of Lima Sch/*New Lexington*/Perry	00803400	740/342-3043	162
St Rose Sch/*Girard*/Trumbull	00821593	330/545-1163	201
St Rose Sch/*Perrysburg*/Wood	00819370	419/874-5631	218
St Sebastian Parish Sch/*Akron*/Summit	00797174	330/836-9107	196
St Stanislaus Elem Sch/*Cleveland*/Cuyahoga	00797186	216/883-3307	53
St Susanna Sch/*Mason*/Warren	00809545	513/398-3821	209
St Sylvester Sch/*Woodsfield*/Monroe	00812906	740/472-0321	148
St Teresa of Avila Sch/*Cincinnati*/Hamilton	00809557	513/471-4530	96
St Thomas Aquinas Mid High Sch/*Louisville*/Stark	00821622	330/875-1631	190
St Thomas Aquinas Sch/*Cleveland*/Cuyahoga	00797239	216/421-4668	53
St Thomas More Sch/*Brooklyn*/Cuyahoga	00797241	216/749-1660	53
St Thomas More Sch/*Cincinnati*/Clermont	00809571	513/753-2540	32
St Timothy Sch/*Columbus*/Franklin	00803436	614/451-1405	77
St Ursula Academy/*Cincinnati*/Hamilton	00809583	513/961-3410	96
St Ursula Academy/*Toledo*/Lucas	00819411	419/531-1693	131
St Ursula Villa Sch/*Cincinnati*/Hamilton	00809595	513/871-7218	96
St Veronica Sch/*Cincinnati*/Hamilton	01484435	513/528-0442	96
St Vincent De Paul Sch/*Akron*/Summit	00797291	330/762-5912	196
St Vincent De Paul Sch/*Mount Vernon*/Knox	00803450	740/393-3611	111
St Vincent Family Center/*Columbus*/Franklin	02051897	614/252-0731	77
St Vincent Ferrer Sch/*Cincinnati*/Hamilton	00809612	513/791-6320	96
St Vincent St Mary HS/*Akron*/Summit	00796924	330/253-9113	196
St Vivian Sch/*Cincinnati*/Hamilton	00808814	513/522-6858	96
St Wendelin Catholic Sch/*Fostoria*/Seneca	00819435	419/435-8144	182
St William Sch/*Cincinnati*/Hamilton	00809624	513/471-2989	96
St Xavier High Sch/*Cincinnati*/Hamilton	00809636	513/761-7600	96
Stadium Drive Elem Sch/*Boardman*/Mahoning	00819851	330/726-3428	134
Stambaugh Charter Academy/*Youngstown*/Mahoning	11016549	330/792-4806	5
Stamm Elem Sch/*Fremont*/Sandusky	00830647	419/332-5538	177
Stanton Elem Sch/*Hammondsville*/Jefferson	00812384	740/282-5501	109
Stanton Middle Sch/*Kent*/Portage	00828448	330/676-8600	166
Stanton Primary Sch/*New Boston*/Scioto	00831055	740/456-4559	179
Star Academy of Toledo/*Toledo*/Lucas	11016953	419/720-6330	127
STARK CO AREA VOC SCH DIST/MASSILLON/STARK	01601530	330/832-1591	189
STARK CO ED SERVICE CENTER/CANTON/STARK	00833819	330/492-8136	184
Stark High Sch/*Canton*/Stark	12259469	234/214-4140	5
Starlight Sch/*New Phila*/Tuscarawas	02052607	330/339-3577	201
Starlight Sch/*Zanesville*/Muskingum	02052346	740/455-4176	156
Starling STEM PK-8 Sch/*Columbus*/Franklin	00801012	614/365-5945	69
Starr Elem Sch/*Oregon*/Lucas	00817097	419/693-0589	128
Start High Sch/*Toledo*/Lucas	00817970	419/671-3000	130
STATE SUPPORT TEAM 3/INDEPENDENCE/CUYAHOGA	02228208	216/524-3000	54
STATE SUPPORT TEAM 11/COLUMBUS/FRANKLIN	02228193	614/753-4690	78
STATE SUPPORT TEAM-REGION 1/TOLEDO/LUCAS	02228301	419/720-8999	132
STATE SUPPORT TEAM-REGION 2/ELYRIA/LORAIN	02228296	440/324-5777	126
STATE SUPPORT TEAM-REGION 4/CONCORD TWP/LAKE	00814124	440/350-2563	112
STATE SUPPORT TEAM-REGION 5/CANFIELD/MAHONING	02228284	330/533-8755	137
STATE SUPPORT TEAM-REGION 6/WAPAKONETA/AUGLAIZE	02228349	419/738-9224	17
STATE SUPPORT TEAM-REGION 7/MANSFIELD/RICHLAND	02228272	419/747-4808	174
STATE SUPPORT TEAM-REGION 8/CUYAHOGA FLS/SUMMIT	02228260	330/929-6634	196
STATE SUPPORT TEAM-REGION 9/NORTH CANTON/STARK	02228246	330/492-8136	190
STATE SUPPORT TEAM-REGION 10/DAYTON/GREENE	02228258	937/236-9965	85
STATE SUPPORT TEAM-REGION 12/BYESVILLE/GUERNSEY	02228210	740/439-9383	86
STATE SUPPORT TEAM-REGION 13/CINCINNATI/HAMILTON	02228337	513/674-4200	97
STATE SUPPORT TEAM-REGION 14/HILLSBORO/HIGHLAND	02228234	937/393-1904	103
STATE SUPPORT TEAM-REGION 16/CHAUNCEY/ATHENS	02228325	740/797-0150	15
Steam Acad Warrensvlle Heights/*Cleveland*/Cuyahoga	12162476	216/595-2866	5
Steam Academy of Akron/*Akron*/Summit	12162488	330/773-1100	5
Steam Academy of Warren/*Warren*/Trumbull	11721603	330/394-3200	5
Steamm Academy at Hartford/*Canton*/Stark	00832542	330/453-6012	185
Stebbins High Sch/*Dayton*/Montgomery	00825159	937/237-4250	151
Steele High Sch/*Amherst*/Lorain	00815647	440/988-4433	122
STEM Academy/*Steubenville*/Jefferson	12038306	740/284-5613	109
STEM Middle at Baldwin Rd JHS/*Reynoldsburg*/Franklin	00801696	614/367-1600	73
Stephen Bell Elem Sch/*Bellbrook*/Greene	00804791	937/848-7831	84
Stephen T Badin High Sch/*Hamilton*/Butler	00809648	513/863-3993	24
Stepstone Academy/*Cleveland*/Cuyahoga	12042204	440/260-6400	5
Sterling Morton Elem Sch/*Mentor*/Lake	00813510	440/257-5954	113
STEUBENVILLE CITY SCH DIST/STEUBENVILLE/JEFFERSON	00812504	740/283-3767	109
Steubenville High Sch/*Steubenville*/Jefferson	00812580	740/282-9741	109
Stevan Dohanos Elem Sch/*Lorain*/Lorain	00816419	440/830-4190	124
Stevenson Elem Sch/*Heath*/Licking	04746684	740/238-7130	118
Stewart Alternative Elem Sch/*Columbus*/Franklin	00801024	614/365-5556	69
Stewart Early Learning Center/*Akron*/Summit	12108121	330/873-3396	191
Stewart Elem Sch/*Cincinnati*/Hamilton	00807559	513/864-2800	92
Stiles Elem Sch/*Columbus*/Franklin	00802054	614/801-8375	74
Stingel Elem Sch/*Ontario*/Richland	00830037	419/529-4955	173
Stingley Elem Sch/*Centerville*/Montgomery	00824026	937/434-1054	149
Stivers School for Arts/*Dayton*/Montgomery	01755428	937/542-7380	149
Stockyard Cmty Elem Sch/*Cleveland*/Cuyahoga	05364461	216/651-5143	40
Stockyard Cmty Middle Sch/*Cleveland*/Cuyahoga	12036281	216/961-5052	40
Stone Reading & Math Prep Sch/*Canton*/Stark	00832437	330/452-6521	185
Stonebrook Montessori Sch/*Cleveland*/Cuyahoga	12231429	216/644-3012	45
STOW-MUNROE FALLS CITY SD/STOW/SUMMIT	00835506	330/689-5445	194
Stow-Munroe Falls High Sch/*Stow*/Summit	03009225	330/689-5300	194
Stranahan Elem Sch/*Toledo*/Lucas	00817281	419/824-8614	129
Strasburg Franklin Elem Sch/*Strasburg*/Tuscarawas	00837504	330/878-6503	203
Strasburg Franklin High Sch/*Strasburg*/Tuscarawas	00837516	330/878-5571	203
STRASBURG FRANKLIN LOCAL SD/STRASBURG/TUSCARAWAS	00837499	330/878-5571	203
Strausser Elem Sch/*Massillon*/Stark	05035127	330/830-8056	186
STREETSBORO CITY SCH DIST/STREETSBORO/PORTAGE	00828668	330/626-4900	167
Streetsboro Elem Sch/*Streetsboro*/Portage	00828670	330/626-4907	167
Streetsboro High Sch/*Streetsboro*/Portage	00828682	330/626-4902	167
Streetsboro Middle Sch/*Streetsboro*/Portage	00828694	330/626-4905	167
STRONGSVILLE CITY SCH DIST/STRONGSVILLE/CUYAHOGA	00794823	440/572-7010	51
Strongsville Early Learning PS/*Strongsville*/Cuyahoga	10004878	440/572-7046	51
Strongsville High Sch/*Strongsville*/Cuyahoga	00794914	440/572-7100	51
Strongsville Middle Sch/*Strongsville*/Cuyahoga	00794835	440/572-7090	51
Struble Elem Sch/*Cincinnati*/Hamilton	00807224	513/522-2700	91
STRUTHERS CITY SCH DIST/STRUTHERS/MAHONING	00820252	330/750-1061	136
Struthers Elem Sch/*Struthers*/Mahoning	00820264	330/750-1065	136
Struthers High Sch/*Struthers*/Mahoning	00820329	330/750-1062	136
Struthers Middle Sch/*Struthers*/Mahoning	00820276	330/750-1064	136
Stryker Elem Sch/*Stryker*/Williams	00839916	419/682-2841	215
Stryker High Sch/*Stryker*/Williams	00839928	419/682-4591	215
STRYKER LOCAL SCH DIST/STRYKER/WILLIAMS	00839904	419/682-2841	215
Studebaker Pre-School/*Huber Heights*/Montgomery	12037003	937/237-6345	150
Success Academy/*Milford*/Clermont	12037118	513/576-8943	31
Suffield Elem Sch/*Mogadore*/Portage	00828369	330/552-5252	165
Sugar Creek Christian Academy/*Ironton*/Lawrence	11227621	740/533-2215	117
Sullivant Elem Sch/*Columbus*/Franklin	00801048	614/365-6524	69
Summerside Elem Sch/*Cincinnati*/Clermont	00788771	513/947-7900	31

Ohio School Directory

DISTRICT & SCHOOL TELEPHONE INDEX

School/City/County DISTRICT/CITY/COUNTY	PID	TELEPHONE NUMBER	PAGE
Summit Acad Alt Lrng-Lorain/*Lorain*/Lorain	11734222	440/277-4110	122
Summit Acad Alt Lrng-Middleton/*Middletown*/Butler	11739272	513/422-8540	20
Summit Acad Cmty Sch-Columbus/*Columbus*/Franklin	05382798	614/237-5497	5
Summit Acad Cmty Sch-Painsvlle/*Painesville*/Lake	10017992	440/358-0877	112
Summit Acad Sch-Cincinnati/*Cincinnati*/Hamilton	05382786	513/321-0561	87
Summit Acad Sec Sch-Middletown/*Middletown*/Butler	05010218	513/420-9767	5
Summit Acad Sec Sch-Youngstown/*Youngstown*/Mahoning	05382865	234/228-8235	133
Summit Acad Trans HS-Columbus/*Columbus*/Franklin	11136072	614/880-0714	5
Summit Academy Alt Lrng-Canton/*Canton*/Stark	05010220	330/458-0393	5
Summit Academy Alt Lrng-Warren/*Warren*/Trumbull	11544132	330/399-1692	5
Summit Academy Alt Lrng-Xenia/*Xenia*/Greene	05010256	937/372-5210	83
Summit Academy Cmty Sch-Dayton/*Dayton*/Montgomery	05382815	937/278-4298	148
Summit Academy Cmty Sch-Parma/*Parma*/Cuyahoga	05010244	440/888-5407	40
Summit Academy Cmty Sch-Warren/*Warren*/Trumbull	05362279	330/369-4233	196
Summit Academy Elem Sch-Akron/*Akron*/Summit	05220451	330/253-7441	5
Summit Academy Elem Sch-Toledo/*Toledo*/Lucas	11446140	419/476-0784	127
Summit Academy Mid Sch-Akron/*Akron*/Summit	05010270	330/252-1510	5
Summit Academy Sch-Lorain/*Lorain*/Lorain	05010232	440/288-0448	122
Summit Academy Sec Sch-Akron/*Akron*/Summit	05382827	330/434-2343	5
Summit Academy Sec Sch-Canton/*Canton*/Stark	11150121	330/453-8547	184
Summit Academy Trans HS-Cinn/*Cincinnati*/Hamilton	11136060	513/541-4000	5
Summit Academy Trans HS-Dayton/*Dayton*/Montgomery	11136058	937/813-8592	5
Summit Academy Youngstown/*Youngstown*/Mahoning	11544259	330/743-9235	5
Summit Academy-Toledo/*Toledo*/Lucas	05382803	419/243-1815	5
Summit Academy-Youngstown/*Youngstown*/Mahoning	05010268	330/259-0421	5
Summit Christian Sch/*Cuyahoga FLS*/Summit	02209032	330/762-3382	196
SUMMIT CO ED SERVICE CENTER/ **CUYAHOGA FLS/SUMMIT**	00835788	330/945-5600	190
SUMMIT CO EDUCATIONAL SVC CTR/ **CUYAHOGA FLS/SUMMIT**	02100993	330/945-5600	196
Summit Country Day Sch/*Cincinnati*/Hamilton	00809662	513/871-4700	96
Summit Elem Sch/*Cincinnati*/Hamilton	00806543	513/474-2270	89
Summit Road STEM Elem Sch/*Reynoldsburg*/Franklin	11712810	614/501-5530	73
Sunbeam Sch/*Cleveland*/Cuyahoga	00792526	216/838-1700	45
Sunbridge Sch/*Toledo*/Lucas	11818751	419/725-5437	131
Sunrise Academy/*Hilliard*/Franklin	04986664	614/527-0465	77
Sunview Elem Sch/*Lyndhurst*/Cuyahoga	00794809	216/691-2225	51
Super Learning Center/*Lakemore*/Summit	11831337	330/889-4119	196
Superior Elem Sch/*E Cleveland*/Cuyahoga	00793104	216/268-6670	46
Superior Intermediate Sch/*Ashtabula*/Ashtabula	00784476	440/992-1270	12
Sutter Park Pre-School/*Powell*/Franklin	02893229	614/450-4900	76
Swanton Elem Sch/*Swanton*/Fulton	00803761	419/826-8991	79
Swanton High Sch/*Swanton*/Fulton	00803785	419/826-3045	79
SWANTON LOCAL SCH DIST/SWANTON/ **FULTON**	00803747	419/826-7085	79
Swanton Middle Sch/*Swanton*/Fulton	00803759	419/826-4016	79
Swiss Hills Career Center/*Woodsfield*/Monroe	01537771	740/472-0722	148
SWITZERLAND OF OHIO LOCAL SD/ **WOODSFIELD/MONROE**	00823711	740/472-5801	147
SYCAMORE CMTY SCH DIST/CINCINNATI/ **HAMILTON**	00807767	513/686-1700	93
Sycamore Creek Elem Sch/*Pickerington*/Fairfield	11456523	614/834-6200	64
Sycamore High Sch/*Cincinnati*/Hamilton	00807810	513/686-1770	93
Sycamore Junior High Sch/*Cincinnati*/Hamilton	00807808	513/686-1760	93
Sylvan Elem Sch/*Sylvania*/Lucas	00817293	419/824-8615	129
SYLVANIA CITY SCH DIST/SYLVANIA/ **LUCAS**	00817205	419/824-8500	128
Symmes Elem Sch/*Loveland*/Hamilton	03236868	513/686-1740	94
Symmes Valley Elem Sch/*Willow Wood*/Lawrence	00814538	740/643-0023	117
Symmes Valley High Sch/*Willow Wood*/Lawrence	00814540	740/643-2371	117
SYMMES VALLEY LOCAL SCH DIST/ **WILLOW WOOD/LAWRENCE**	00814526	740/643-2451	117
Synergy Learning Center/*Van Wert*/Van Wert	04934805	419/623-5380	205

T

School/City/County DISTRICT/CITY/COUNTY	PID	TELEPHONE NUMBER	PAGE
T C Knapp Elem Sch/*Canton*/Stark	00833481	330/478-6174	188
T Squared Honors Academy/*Warrensvl HTS*/Cuyahoga	12179168	216/510-5458	5
T W Harvey High Sch/*Painesville*/Lake	00813663	440/392-5110	113
Taft Elem Sch/*Marion*/Marion	00821751	740/223-4500	138
Taft Elem Sch/*Youngstown*/Mahoning	00820769	330/744-7973	137
Taft Intermediate Sch/*Ashland*/Ashland	00784206	419/289-7969	10
Talawanda High Sch/*Oxford*/Butler	00787193	513/273-3200	24
Talawanda Middle Sch/*Oxford*/Butler	03247283	513/273-3300	24
TALAWANDA SCH DIST/OXFORD/BUTLER	00787117	513/273-3100	24
TALLMADGE CITY SCH DIST/ **TALLMADGE/SUMMIT**	00835594	330/633-3291	194
Tallmadge Elem Sch/*Lancaster*/Fairfield	00799134	740/687-7336	64
Tallmadge High Sch/*Tallmadge*/Summit	00835659	330/633-5505	195
Tallmadge Middle Sch/*Tallmadge*/Summit	00835647	330/633-4994	195
Tarhe Trails Elem Sch/*Lancaster*/Fairfield	00799146	740/687-7330	64
Taylor Elem Sch/*Cincinnati*/Hamilton	00807236	513/825-3000	91
Taylor Middle High Sch/*Cleves*/Hamilton	00807872	513/467-3200	94
Taylor Road Elem Sch/*Reynoldsburg*/Franklin	04281945	614/367-2930	73
TCCSA-TRI-CO COMP SVCS/WOOSTER/ **WAYNE**	04499647	330/264-6047	214
Tcp World Academy/*Cincinnati*/Hamilton	05010282	513/531-9500	5
Teays Valley East Middle Sch/*Ashville*/Pickaway	02857122	740/983-5078	163
Teays Valley High Sch/*Ashville*/Pickaway	00827858	740/983-5053	163
TEAYS VALLEY LOCAL SCH DIST/ **ASHVILLE/PICKAWAY**	00827822	740/983-5000	162
Teays Valley West Middle Sch/*Commercial Pt*/Pickaway	11485392	740/983-5000	163
Tecumseh Elem Sch/*Xenia*/Greene	00804909	937/372-3321	85
Tecumseh High Sch/*New Carlisle*/Clark	00787777	937/845-4500	29
TECUMSEH LOCAL SCH DIST/ **NEW CARLISLE/CLARK**	00787686	937/845-3576	28
Tecumseh Middle Sch/*New Carlisle*/Clark	00787739	937/845-4465	29
Temple Christian Academy/*Fremont*/Sandusky	02826355	419/332-6114	177
Temple Christian Sch/*Dayton*/Montgomery	01409760	937/253-5288	154
Temple Christian Sch/*Lima*/Allen	03061986	419/227-1644	10
Temple Christian Sch/*Mansfield*/Richland	01465099	419/589-9707	174
Terrace Park Elem Sch/*Terrace Park*/Hamilton	00806971	513/272-7700	91
The Alternate Learning Center/*Toledo*/Lucas	04444329	419/473-3442	127
The Antioch Sch/*Yellow Spgs*/Greene	00804973	937/767-7642	85
The Lyceum/*Cleveland*/Cuyahoga	12174132	216/707-1121	54
The Miami Sch/*Hamilton*/Butler	12226187	513/887-5197	22
The Plains Elem Sch/*The Plains*/Athens	00785080	740/797-4572	14
The Seven Hills Sch/*Cincinnati*/Hamilton	00809715	513/728-2400	96
The Steel Academy/*Akron*/Summit	12042280	330/633-1383	5
The Tomorrow Center/*Cardington*/Morrow	12178164	419/718-4242	5
Third Street Sch/*W Alexandria*/Preble	04020624	937/839-3128	168
Thomas A Edison Interm Sch/*Columbus*/Franklin	00801335	614/485-4100	71
Thomas A Wildey Sch/*Batavia*/Clermont	02051615	513/732-7015	29
Thomas Edison Center Pre-Sch/*Van Wert*/Van Wert	02052633	419/238-4019	205
Thomas Ewing Jr High Sch/*Lancaster*/Fairfield	00799158	740/687-7347	64
Thomas Worthington High Sch/*Worthington*/Franklin	00802597	614/450-6200	76
Thoreau Park Elem Sch/*Parma*/Cuyahoga	00794354	440/885-2351	49
Thornville Elem Sch/*Thornville*/Perry	00827585	740/246-6636	161
Three Rivers Elem Sch/*Cleves*/Hamilton	00807860	513/467-3210	94
THREE RIVERS LOCAL SCH DIST/ **CLEVES/HAMILTON**	00807834	513/941-6400	94
Thurgood Marshall STEM HS/*Dayton*/Montgomery	00824155	937/542-6610	149
TIFFIN CITY SCH DIST/TIFFIN/ **SENECA**	00831706	419/447-2515	181
Tiffin Middle Sch/*Tiffin*/Seneca	00831794	419/447-3358	181
Timberlane Learning Center/*Dayton*/Montgomery	00825537	937/278-0689	152
Timberstone Junior High Sch/*Sylvania*/Lucas	04754306	419/824-8680	129
Timken Early College HS/*Canton*/Stark	10025169	330/458-3950	185
Timmons Elem Sch/*Chagrin Falls*/Geauga	00804260	440/543-9380	82
Tinora Elem Sch/*Defiance*/Defiance	00798049	419/497-1022	57
Tinora High Sch/*Defiance*/Defiance	00798063	419/497-2621	57

School Year 2019-2020 800-333-8802 OH-V37

DISTRICT & SCHOOL TELEPHONE INDEX

Market Data Retrieval

School/City/County DISTRICT/CITY/COUNTY	PID	TELEPHONE NUMBER	PAGE
Tinora Junior High Sch/*Defiance*/Defiance	00798075	419/497-2361	57
Tipp City Enrichment Center/*Tipp City*/Miami	11223558	937/667-8800	147
TIPP CITY EXEMPTED VILLAGE SD/ TIPP CITY/MIAMI	00823539	937/667-8444	146
Tippecanoe High Sch/*Tipp City*/Miami	00823589	937/667-8448	146
Tippecanoe Middle Sch/*Tipp City*/Miami	00823653	937/667-8454	146
Titan Tikes Pre-School/*Ottawa*/Putnam	04034572	419/523-6464	170
Toledo Christian Sch/*Toledo*/Lucas	02147862	419/389-8700	131
Toledo Early College High Sch/*Toledo*/Lucas	10027739	419/530-3003	130
Toledo Islamic Academy/*Sylvania*/Lucas	04937558	419/882-3339	131
Toledo Junior Academy/*Toledo*/Lucas	00818273	419/841-0082	131
Toledo Prep & Fitness Academy/*Toledo*/Lucas	11747114	419/535-3700	5
TOLEDO PUBLIC SCHOOLS/TOLEDO/ LUCAS	00817310	419/671-0001	129
Toledo School for the Arts/*Toledo*/Lucas	04879449	419/246-8732	5
Toledo Smart Elem Sch/*Toledo*/Lucas	12100636	419/214-3290	5
Toledo Technology Academy/*Toledo*/Lucas	05012993	419/671-3900	130
Toll Gate Elem Sch/*Pickerington*/Fairfield	11456509	614/834-6300	64
Toll Gate Middle Sch/*Pickerington*/Fairfield	11456511	614/834-6400	64
Tolles Career & Tech Center/*Plain City*/Madison	01417470	614/873-4666	133
TOLLES CAREER & TECH SCH DIST/ PLAIN CITY/MADISON	01417468	614/873-4666	133
Toni Morrison Elem Sch/*Lorain*/Lorain	11434903	440/830-4200	124
TORONTO CITY SCH DIST/TORONTO/ JEFFERSON	00812607	740/537-2456	109
Toronto High Sch/*Toronto*/Jefferson	00812657	740/537-2442	110
Toth Elem Sch/*Perrysburg*/Wood	00840410	419/874-3123	218
Tower Heights Middle Sch/*Centerville*/Montgomery	00824038	937/434-0383	149
Townsend Cmty Sch/*Castalia*/Erie	11747126	419/684-5402	61
Towpath Trail High Sch/*Akron*/Summit	04880319	234/542-0102	5
Trebein Elem Sch/*Xenia*/Greene	11927572	937/458-2300	83
Treca Digital Academy/*Marion*/Marion	05009063	740/389-4798	5
Tree of Life Christian Sch/*Columbus*/Franklin	02123141	614/263-2688	77
Tree of Life Christian Sch/*Columbus*/Franklin	02198378	614/299-4906	77
Tree of Life Christian Sch/*Dublin*/Franklin	11235185	614/792-2671	77
Tremont Elem Sch/*Upper Arlngtn*/Franklin	00802169	614/487-5170	74
Tremont Montessori Sch/*Cleveland*/Cuyahoga	00792564	216/838-9850	45
Trevitt Elem Sch/*Columbus*/Franklin	00801074	614/365-6137	69
Tri Academy/*Marysville*/Union	12226058	937/578-6191	204
Tri County Pre-School/*Ashland*/Ashland	04009151	419/281-4239	10
Tri-Co Career Center/*Nelsonville*/Athens	00785274	740/753-3511	15
TRI-CO ED SERVICE CENTER/ WOOSTER/WAYNE	00839631	330/345-6771	211
TRI-CO JOINT VOC SCH DIST/ NELSONVILLE/ATHENS	00785262	740/753-3511	15
Tri-Co North Elem Sch/*Lewisburg*/Preble	00829026	937/962-2673	168
Tri-Co North High Sch/*Lewisburg*/Preble	00829038	937/833-4830	168
Tri-Co North Middle Sch/*Lewisburg*/Preble	00829052	937/962-2675	168
TRI-CO NORTH SCH DIST/LEWISBURG/ PREBLE	02199487	937/962-2671	168
Tri-County International Acad/*Wooster*/Wayne	11545710	330/345-4000	211
Tri-County Pre-School Unit/*Holmesville*/Holmes	04025911	330/674-0246	104
Tri-Rivers Career Center HS/*Marion*/Marion	01417494	740/389-4681	139
TRI-RIVERS JOINT VOC SCH DIST/ MARION/MARION	01417482	740/389-4681	139
Tri-Valley High Sch/*Dresden*/Muskingum	00826490	740/754-2921	157
TRI-VALLEY LOCAL SCH DIST/ DRESDEN/MUSKINGUM	00826440	740/754-1442	157
Tri-Valley Middle Sch/*Dresden*/Muskingum	03241825	740/754-3531	157
TRI-VILLAGE LOCAL SCH DIST/ NEW MADISON/DARKE	00797708	937/996-6261	56
Tri-Village Sch/*New Madison*/Darke	00797746	937/996-6261	56
Triad Elem Sch/*N Lewisburg*/Champaign	00787466	937/826-3102	26
Triad High Sch/*N Lewisburg*/Champaign	00787478	937/826-3771	26
TRIAD LOCAL SCH DIST/N LEWISBURG/ CHAMPAIGN	00787442	937/826-4961	26
Triad Middle Sch/*N Lewisburg*/Champaign	05027132	937/826-3071	26
Trimble Elem Sch/*Glouster*/Athens	00785248	740/767-2810	15
Trimble High Sch/*Glouster*/Athens	01486835	740/767-3434	15
TRIMBLE LOCAL SCH DIST/GLOUSTER/ ATHENS	00785224	740/767-4444	15
Trimble Middle Sch/*Glouster*/Athens	00785236	740/767-2810	15
Trinity Cath Elem Sch/*Columbus*/Franklin	00803125	614/488-7650	77
Trinity Christian Academy/*Norwalk*/Huron	11223974	419/668-2011	107
Trinity High Sch/*Garfield HTS*/Cuyahoga	00795748	216/581-1644	53
Trinity Lutheran Sch/*Jenera*/Hancock	01409710	419/326-4685	99
Trinity Lutheran Sch/*Marysville*/Union	00837798	937/642-1726	205
Trinity Lutheran Sch/*Toledo*/Lucas	01409722	419/385-2301	131
Triway High Sch/*Wooster*/Wayne	00839459	330/264-8685	213
Triway Junior High Sch/*Wooster*/Wayne	00839461	330/264-2114	213
TRIWAY LOCAL SCH DIST/WOOSTER/ WAYNE	00839423	330/264-9491	213
Trotwood Prep & Fitness Acad/*Trotwood*/Montgomery	05220463	937/854-4100	5
TROTWOOD-MADISON CITY SD/ TROTWOOD/MONTGOMERY	00825161	937/854-3050	152
Trotwood-Madison Middle Sch/*Trotwood*/Montgomery	11927807	937/854-0017	153
Trotwood-Madison Sr High Sch/*Trotwood*/Montgomery	00825197	937/854-0878	153
Troy Christian Schools/*Troy*/Miami	02123232	937/339-5692	147
TROY CITY SCH DIST/TROY/MIAMI	00823591	937/332-6700	146
Troy High Sch/*Troy*/Miami	00823668	937/332-6710	147
Troy Intermediate Sch/*Avon Lake*/Lorain	04364858	440/933-2701	122
Troy Junior High Sch/*Troy*/Miami	00823670	937/332-6720	147
Trumbull Career & Tech Center/*Warren*/Trumbull	05361550	330/847-0503	196
TRUMBULL CO ED SERVICE CENTER/ NILES/TRUMBULL	00837059	330/505-2800	196
Truth Christian Academy/*Wheelersburg*/Scioto	04486195	740/574-8449	180
Turpin High Sch/*Cincinnati*/Hamilton	01525338	513/232-7770	89
Tuscarawas Central Catholic HS/*New Phila*/Tuscarawas	00802781	330/343-3302	204
Tuscarawas Ctrl Catholic ES/*Dover*/Tuscarawas	00803204	330/343-9134	204
TUSCARAWAS VALLEY LOCAL SD/ ZOARVILLE/TUSCARAWAS	00837528	330/859-2213	203
Tuscarawas Valley Primary Sch/*Mineral City*/Tuscarawas	00837542	330/859-2461	203
Tuscarawas Vly Interm Sch/*Bolivar*/Tuscarawas	00837530	330/874-3234	203
Tuscarawas Vly Middle Sch/*Zoarville*/Tuscarawas	04448088	330/859-2427	203
Tuscarawas Vly Senior High Sch/*Zoarville*/Tuscarawas	00837566	330/859-2421	203
Tuslaw Elem Sch/*Massillon*/Stark	00833754	330/837-7809	189
Tuslaw High Sch/*Massillon*/Stark	10000224	330/837-7800	189
TUSLAW LOCAL SCH DIST/MASSILLON/ STARK	00833699	330/837-7813	189
Tuslaw Middle Sch/*Massillon*/Stark	00833742	330/837-7807	189
Tussing Elem Sch/*Reynoldsburg*/Fairfield	04449472	614/834-2600	64
Twin Oak Elem Sch/*Mount Vernon*/Knox	00813091	740/393-5970	111
TWIN VALLEY CMTY LOCAL SD/ W ALEXANDRIA/PREBLE	00829002	937/839-4688	169
Twin Valley Middle High Sch/*W Alexandria*/Preble	00829014	937/839-4693	169
Twin Valley South Elem Sch/*W Alexandria*/Preble	05027089	937/839-4315	169
TWINSBURG CITY SCH DIST/ TWINSBURG/SUMMIT	00835661	330/486-2000	195
Twinsburg High Sch/*Twinsburg*/Summit	00835673	330/486-2400	195
Tyler Run Elem Sch/*Powell*/Delaware	05008746	740/657-4900	59

U

U S Grant Career Center/*Bethel*/Clermont	01537719	513/734-6222	31
U S GRANT CAREER SCH DIST/ BETHEL/CLERMONT	01537707	513/734-6222	31
Union Elem Sch/*Poland*/Mahoning	03006209	330/757-7014	135
Union Elem Sch/*Union*/Montgomery	00825472	937/832-6700	152
Union Elem Sch/*Upper Sandsky*/Wyandot	00840719	419/294-5721	219
Union Elem Sch/*West Chester*/Butler	00786709	513/777-2201	22
Union Furnace Elem Sch/*Union Furnace*/Hocking	00811249	740/380-6881	104
Union Local Elem Sch/*Belmont*/Belmont	00785949	740/782-1384	19
Union Local High Sch/*Belmont*/Belmont	00785999	740/782-1181	19
Union Local Middle Sch/*Belmont*/Belmont	00785975	740/782-1388	19
UNION LOCAL SCH DIST/BELMONT/ BELMONT	00785937	740/782-1208	18
UNION SCIOTO LOCAL SCH DIST/ CHILLICOTHE/ROSS	00830374	740/773-4102	175
Unioto Elem Sch/*Chillicothe*/Ross	00830386	740/773-4103	176
Unioto High Sch/*Chillicothe*/Ross	04357714	740/773-4105	176
Unioto Junior High Sch/*Chillicothe*/Ross	00830415	740/773-5211	176

Ohio School Directory

DISTRICT & SCHOOL TELEPHONE INDEX

School/City/County DISTRICT/CITY/COUNTY	PID	TELEPHONE NUMBER	PAGE
United Local Elem Sch/*Hanoverton*/Columbiana	05243362	330/223-8001	36
United Local High Sch/*Hanoverton*/Columbiana	00789696	330/223-7102	36
UNITED LOCAL SCH DIST/**HANOVERTON**/**COLUMBIANA**	00789684	330/223-1521	36
United Preparatory Acad-East/*Columbus*/Franklin	12363046	614/586-1228	5
United Preparatory Acad-State/*Columbus*/Franklin	12100674	614/453-8993	5
Unity Elem Sch/*Lima*/Allen	00783771	419/996-3300	9
Univ of Cleveland Prep Sch/*Cleveland*/Cuyahoga	11735862	216/361-9720	5
University Academy/*Akron*/Summit	04814657	330/535-7728	5
University High Sch/*Chagrin Falls*/Cuyahoga	00797447	216/831-2200	54
University Sch-Shaker Campus/*Shaker HTS*/Cuyahoga	01874000	216/321-8260	54
UPPER ARLINGTON CITY SCH DIST/**UPPER ARLNGTN**/**FRANKLIN**	00802092	614/487-5000	74
Upper Arlington High Sch/*Upper Arlngtn*/Franklin	00802171	614/487-5200	74
UPPER SANDUSKY EXEMPTED VLG SD/**UPPER SANDSKY**/**WYANDOT**	00840642	419/294-2306	219
Upper Sandusky Middle Sch/*Upper Sandsky*/Wyandot	11709409	419/294-5721	219
Upper Sandusky Senior High Sch/*Upper Sandsky*/Wyandot	00840721	419/294-2308	219
UPPER SCIOTO VALLEY LOCAL SD/**MC GUFFEY**/**HARDIN**	00810398	419/757-3231	100
Upper Scioto Valley Sch/*Mc Guffey*/Hardin	00810427	419/757-3231	100
Upper Valley Career Center/*Piqua*/Miami	01417535	937/778-1980	147
UPPER VALLEY JT VOC SCH DIST/**PIQUA**/**MIAMI**	01417523	937/778-1980	147
URBANA CITY SCH DIST/**URBANA**/**CHAMPAIGN**	00787492	937/653-1402	26
Urbana Elem Sch/*Urbana*/Champaign	00787507	937/653-1453	26
Urbana High Sch/*Urbana*/Champaign	00787545	937/653-1412	26
Urbana Junior High Sch/*Urbana*/Champaign	00787533	937/653-1439	26
Ursuline Academy/*Cincinnati*/Hamilton	00809674	513/791-5791	96
Ursuline High Sch/*Youngstown*/Mahoning	00821634	330/744-4563	137
Utica Elem Sch/*Utica*/Licking	00815180	740/892-2551	119
Utica Junior High Sch/*Utica*/Licking	00815207	740/892-2691	119
Utica Senior High Sch/*Utica*/Licking	00815192	740/892-2855	119
Utica Shale Academy of Ohio/*Salineville*/Columbiana	12162995	330/420-5353	34

V

School/City/County	PID	TELEPHONE	PAGE
Valerie PK-6 Sch/*Dayton*/Montgomery	00824686	937/542-5390	149
Valley Christian Academy/*Aurora*/Portage	02147587	330/562-8191	167
Valley Christian Sch/*Youngstown*/Mahoning	01874074	330/788-8088	137
Valley Elem Sch/*Beavercreek*/Greene	00804545	937/429-7597	83
Valley Elem Sch/*Lucasville*/Scioto	00831275	740/259-2611	179
Valley Forge Elem Sch/*Columbus*/Franklin	03396133	614/365-5648	69
Valley Forge Elem Sch/*Huber Heights*/Montgomery	00825800	937/237-6380	150
Valley Forge High Sch/*Parma Heights*/Cuyahoga	00794366	440/885-2330	49
Valley High Sch/*Lucasville*/Scioto	00831287	740/259-5551	179
VALLEY LOCAL SCH DIST/**LUCASVILLE**/**SCIOTO**	00831251	740/259-3115	179
Valley Middle Sch/*Lucasville*/Scioto	00831299	740/259-2651	179
Valley STEM and ME2 Academy/*Canfield*/Mahoning	12262753	330/729-4000	135
Valley View Boys Ldrshp Acad/*Cleveland*/Cuyahoga	10911128	216/838-8900	45
Valley View Elem Sch/*Wadsworth*/Medina	00822509	330/335-1430	142
Valley View High Sch/*Germantown*/Montgomery	00825628	937/855-4116	153
Valley View Intermediate Sch/*Germantown*/Montgomery	00825604	937/855-4203	153
Valley View Junior High/*Farmersville*/Montgomery	00825616	937/696-2591	153
VALLEY VIEW LOCAL SCH DIST/**GERMANTOWN**/**MONTGOMERY**	00825587	937/855-6581	153
Valley View Primary Sch/*Germantown*/Montgomery	00825599	937/855-6571	153
Valley Vista Elem Sch/*N Royalton*/Cuyahoga	00793960	440/582-9101	48
Valleyview Elem Sch/*Columbus*/Franklin	03267087	614/365-6312	69
Van Buren Elem Sch/*Van Buren*/Hancock	00810099	419/299-3416	99
Van Buren High Sch/*Van Buren*/Hancock	04940402	419/299-3384	99
VAN BUREN LOCAL SCH DIST/**VAN BUREN**/**HANCOCK**	00810087	419/299-3578	99
Van Buren Middle Sch/*Kettering*/Montgomery	00825044	937/499-1800	150
Van Buren Middle Sch/*Van Buren*/Hancock	00810104	419/299-3384	99
Van Cleve 6th Grade Sch/*Troy*/Miami	10020901	937/332-6780	147
Van Gorden Elem Sch/*Liberty Twp*/Butler	05270092	513/644-1150	23
VAN WERT CITY SCH DIST/**VAN WERT**/**VAN WERT**	00837932	419/238-0648	205
Van Wert Early Childhood Ctr/*Van Wert*/Van Wert	11828586	419/238-0384	205
Van Wert Elem Sch/*Van Wert*/Van Wert	00837956	419/238-1761	205
Van Wert High Sch/*Van Wert*/Van Wert	00838003	419/238-3350	206
Van Wert Middle Sch/*Van Wert*/Van Wert	00837982	419/238-0727	206
VANDALIA BUTLER CITY SCH DIST/**VANDALIA**/**MONTGOMERY**	00825630	937/415-6400	153
Vanguard Technology Center/*Fremont*/Sandusky	04449202	419/332-2626	177
VANGUARD-SENTINEL JT VOC SD/**FREMONT**/**SANDUSKY**	00830831	419/332-2626	177
Vanlue Local Sch/*Vanlue*/Hancock	00810128	419/387-7724	99
VANLUE LOCAL SCH DIST/**VANLUE**/**HANCOCK**	00810116	419/387-7724	99
Vantage Career Center High Sch/*Van Wert*/Van Wert	01537812	419/238-5411	206
VANTAGE CAREER CENTER SCH DIST/**VAN WERT**/**VAN WERT**	01537800	419/238-5411	206
Venice Heights Elem Sch/*Sandusky*/Erie	00798740	419/984-1290	61
Veritas Academy/*Worthington*/Franklin	11229241	614/885-2810	78
Veritas Classical Academy/*Marietta*/Washington	12232411	740/885-2033	211
Vermilion Elem Sch/*Vermilion*/Erie	00798805	440/204-1703	62
Vermilion High Sch/*Vermilion*/Erie	00798790	440/204-1701	62
VERMILION LOCAL SCH DIST/**VERMILION**/**ERIE**	00798752	440/204-1700	62
Vermont Primary Sch/*Wyoming*/Hamilton	00807949	513/206-7345	94
Vern Riffe Sch/*Portsmouth*/Scioto	02052499	740/353-1876	178
Versailles Elem Sch/*Versailles*/Darke	00797772	937/526-4681	56
VERSAILLES EXEMPTED VILLAGE SD/**VERSAILLES**/**DARKE**	00797758	937/526-4773	56
Versailles High Sch/*Versailles*/Darke	00797784	937/526-4427	56
Versailles Middle Sch/*Versailles*/Darke	00797796	937/526-4426	56
Victory Christian Sch/*Niles*/Trumbull	02165383	330/539-9827	201
Victory Christian Sch/*Urbana*/Champaign	02188555	937/652-1133	26
Victory Garden Pre-School/*Mount Victory*/Hardin	04009034	937/354-2141	99
Villa Angela-St Joseph HS/*Cleveland*/Cuyahoga	00796637	216/481-8414	53
Village Academy/*Powell*/Delaware	03414137	614/841-0050	60
Village Christian Sch/*Pleasant PLN*/Warren	04987096	513/877-2014	209
Village Prep Sch-Woodland/*Cleveland*/Cuyahoga	11916030	216/298-1164	5
Vincent Elem Sch/*Lorain*/Lorain	01171987	440/233-7113	123
Vinton Co High Sch/*Mc Arthur*/Vinton	00838089	740/596-5258	206
VINTON CO LOCAL SCH DIST/**MC ARTHUR**/**VINTON**	00838039	740/596-5218	206
Vinton Co Middle Sch/*Mc Arthur*/Vinton	03338131	740/596-5243	206
Vinton Elem Sch/*Vinton*/Gallia	00803993	740/388-8261	80
Violet Elem Sch/*Pickerington*/Fairfield	00799251	614/548-1500	64
Virginia Stevenson Elem Sch/*Riverside*/Montgomery	00825082	937/259-6630	151
Virtual High Sch/*Cincinnati*/Hamilton	05100552	513/363-2060	88
Visintainer Middle Sch/*Brunswick*/Medina	04941250	330/273-0402	140
Volney Rogers Elem Sch/*Youngstown*/Mahoning	12036712	330/744-8845	137
Voris Cmty Learning Center/*Akron*/Summit	00834473	330/773-6926	191

W

School/City/County	PID	TELEPHONE	PAGE
W C Schenck Elem Sch/*Franklin*/Warren	00838338	937/743-8665	207
W O Cline Elem Sch/*Centerville*/Montgomery	01523524	937/435-1315	149
W-E School of Innovation/*Willoughby*/Lake	12105040	440/942-1525	114
Wade Park Elem Sch/*Cleveland*/Cuyahoga	00792617	216/838-1750	45
WADSWORTH CITY SCH DIST/**WADSWORTH**/**MEDINA**	00822444	330/336-3571	141
Wadsworth High Sch/*Wadsworth*/Medina	00822511	330/335-1400	142
Wadsworth Middle Sch/*Wadsworth*/Medina	00822456	330/335-1410	142
Waggoner Rd Junior High Sch/*Reynoldsburg*/Franklin	10901525	614/501-5700	73
Waggoner Road Middle Sch/*Reynoldsburg*/Franklin	10012291	614/501-5600	73
Waite High Sch/*Toledo*/Lucas	00818003	419/671-7000	130
Walbridge Elem Sch/*Toledo*/Lucas	00818015	419/671-5650	130
Walker Elem Sch/*Canton*/Stark	00832384	330/484-8020	185
Wallace H Braden Middle Sch/*Ashtabula*/Ashtabula	00784593	440/998-0550	12
Walls Elem Sch/*Kent*/Portage	00828498	330/676-8300	166
Walnut Creek Elem Sch/*Galena*/Delaware	05275248	740/657-4750	59

School Year 2019-2020   800-333-8802   OH-V39

DISTRICT & SCHOOL TELEPHONE INDEX

Market Data Retrieval

School/City/County DISTRICT/CITY/COUNTY	PID	TELEPHONE NUMBER	PAGE
Walnut Creek Elem Sch/*Walnut Creek*/Holmes	00811342	330/893-2213	104
Walnut Elem Sch/*Ashville*/Pickaway	00827872	740/983-5061	163
Walnut Hills High Sch/*Cincinnati*/Hamilton	00806244	513/363-8400	88
Walnut Ridge High Sch/*Columbus*/Franklin	00801127	614/365-5400	69
Walnut Springs Middle Sch/*Westerville*/Franklin	00802391	614/797-6700	75
WALNUT TWP LOCAL SCH DIST/ MILLERSPORT/FAIRFIELD	00799275	740/467-2802	64
Walsh Jesuit High Sch/*Cuyahoga FLS*/Summit	00797370	330/929-4205	196
Walter G Nord Middle Sch/*Amherst*/Lorain	00815661	440/988-4441	122
Walter Kidder Elem Sch/*Brunswick*/Medina	00822171	330/273-0485	140
Walter Shade Early Chldhd Ctr/*W Carrollton*/Montgomery	00825886	937/859-5121	153
Walton Elem Sch/*Cleveland*/Cuyahoga	00792629	216/838-7500	45
WAPAKONETA CITY SCH DIST/ WAPAKONETA/AUGLAIZE	00785444	419/739-2900	16
Wapakoneta Elem Sch/*Wapakoneta*/Auglaize	00785494	419/739-5000	16
Wapakoneta High Sch/*Wapakoneta*/Auglaize	00785511	419/739-5200	16
Wapakoneta Middle Sch/*Wapakoneta*/Auglaize	00785456	419/739-5100	16
Warder Park Wayne Elem Sch/*Springfield*/Clark	00788202	937/505-4450	28
Warner Girls Leadership Acad/*Cleveland*/Cuyahoga	10911099	216/838-8950	45
Warner Middle Sch/*Xenia*/Greene	00804911	937/376-9488	85
WARREN CITY SCH SCH/WARREN/ TRUMBULL	00836782	330/841-2321	200
Warren Co Career Center/*Lebanon*/Warren	01537836	513/932-5677	208
WARREN CO ED SERVICE CENTER/ LEBANON/WARREN	00838560	513/695-2900	206
WARREN CO VOC SCH DIST/LEBANON/ WARREN	01537824	513/932-5677	208
Warren Elem Sch/*Marietta*/Washington	00838900	740/445-5300	210
Warren G Harding High Sch/*Warren*/Trumbull	00836873	330/841-2316	200
Warren High Sch/*Vincent*/Washington	00838912	740/678-2393	210
WARREN LOCAL SCH DIST/VINCENT/ WASHINGTON	00838857	740/678-2366	210
Warren Middle Sch/*Vincent*/Washington	12108963	740/678-2395	210
WARRENSVILLE HEIGHTS CITY SD/ WARRENSVL HTS/CUYAHOGA	00794926	216/295-7710	51
Warrensville Heights High Sch/*Warrensvl HTS*/Cuyahoga	00794964	216/336-6651	51
Warrensville Heights Mid Sch/*Warrensvl HTS*/Cuyahoga	00794976	216/336-6575	51
Warrior Academy/*Beloit*/Mahoning	12109565	330/938-2183	136
Warsaw Elem Sch/*Warsaw*/Coshocton	00789995	740/824-3727	37
Washington Co Career Center/*Marietta*/Washington	00838974	740/373-2766	210
WASHINGTON CO JT VOC SCH DIST/ MARIETTA/WASHINGTON	00838962	740/373-2766	210
WASHINGTON COURT HOUSE CITY SD/ WSHNGTN CT HS/FAYETTE	00799457	740/335-6620	65
Washington Elem Sch/*Alliance*/Stark	00833027	330/823-7586	186
Washington Elem Sch/*Circleville*/Pickaway	00827810	740/474-2851	162
Washington Elem Sch/*Dublin*/Franklin	10907490	614/921-6200	72
Washington Elem Sch/*Gallipolis*/Gallia	00803905	740/446-3213	81
Washington Elem Sch/*Lindsey*/Sandusky	00830659	419/665-2327	177
Washington Elem Sch/*Lorain*/Lorain	00816469	440/830-4210	124
Washington Elem Sch/*Marietta*/Washington	00838845	740/374-6520	210
Washington Elem Sch/*Tiffin*/Seneca	00831782	419/447-1072	181
Washington High Sch/*Wshngtn Ct Hs*/Fayette	00799500	740/636-4221	65
Washington Junior High Sch/*Toledo*/Lucas	00818211	419/473-8449	131
WASHINGTON LOCAL SCH DIST/ TOLEDO/LUCAS	00818089	419/473-8220	130
Washington Middle Sch/*Wshngtn Ct Hs*/Fayette	00799512	740/335-0291	65
Washington Park Cmty Sch/*Newburgh HTS*/Cuyahoga	05010294	216/271-6055	40
Washington Park Env Stud Acad/*Cleveland*/Cuyahoga	11718228	216/838-9200	45
Washington Preschool/*Findlay*/Hancock	12178762	419/425-8231	98
Washington Primary Sch/*Piqua*/Miami	00823448	937/773-8472	146
WASHINGTON-NILE LOCAL SCH DIST/ W PORTSMOUTH/SCIOTO	00831304	740/858-1111	179
Waterford Elem Sch/*Waterford*/Washington	00838936	740/984-2342	211
Waterford High Sch/*Waterford*/Washington	00838948	740/984-2373	211
Waterloo Elem Sch/*Atwater*/Portage	00828759	330/947-2153	167
Waterloo High Sch/*Atwater*/Portage	00828735	330/947-2124	167
WATERLOO LOCAL SCH DIST/ ATWATER/PORTAGE	00828723	330/947-2664	167
Waterloo Middle Sch/*Atwater*/Portage	00828747	330/947-0033	167
Waterville Primary Sch/*Waterville*/Lucas	00816926	419/878-2436	127
Watkins Elem Sch/*Columbus*/Franklin	00799873	614/365-6411	69

School/City/County DISTRICT/CITY/COUNTY	PID	TELEPHONE NUMBER	PAGE
Watkins Memorial High Sch/*Pataskala*/Licking	00815312	740/927-3846	120
Watkins Middle Sch/*Pataskala*/Licking	01401122	740/927-5767	120
Watson Elem Sch/*Massillon*/Stark	00833493	330/832-8100	188
Wauseon Elem Sch/*Wauseon*/Fulton	00803826	419/335-6581	80
WAUSEON EXEMPTED VILLAGE SD/ WAUSEON/FULTON	00803802	419/335-6616	79
Wauseon High Sch/*Wauseon*/Fulton	00803838	419/335-5756	80
Wauseon Middle Sch/*Wauseon*/Fulton	00803814	419/335-2701	80
Wauseon Primary Sch/*Wauseon*/Fulton	04839255	419/335-4000	80
WAVERLY CITY SCH DIST/WAVERLY/ PIKE	00828034	740/947 4770	164
Waverly High Sch/*Waverly*/Pike	00828060	740/947-7701	164
Waverly Intermediate Sch/*Waverly*/Pike	00828072	740/947-5173	164
Waverly Junior High Sch/*Waverly*/Pike	00828058	740/947-4527	164
Waverly Primary Sch/*Waverly*/Pike	00828046	740/947-2813	164
Waverly Sch/*Cleveland*/Cuyahoga	00792681	216/838-7550	45
WAYNE CO JOINT VOC SCH DIST/ SMITHVILLE/WAYNE	00839617	330/669-2134	213
Wayne Co Schools Career Center/*Smithville*/Wayne	00839629	330/669-2134	213
Wayne High Sch/*Huber Heights*/Montgomery	00825824	937/233-6431	150
WAYNE LOCAL SCH DIST/WAYNESVILLE/ WARREN	00838510	513/897-6971	208
Wayne Trace Groverhill ES/*Grover Hill*/Paulding	00827377	419/587-3414	160
Wayne Trace Jr Sr High Sch/*Haviland*/Paulding	00827391	419/622-5171	160
WAYNE TRACE LOCAL SCH DIST/ HAVILAND/PAULDING	00827365	419/622-6300	160
Wayne Trail Elem Sch/*Maumee*/Lucas	00817011	419/893-2851	128
Waynedale High Sch/*Apple Creek*/Wayne	00839411	330/698-3071	213
Waynesfield-Goshen Elem Sch/*Waynesfield*/Auglaize	00785547	419/568-9100	16
WAYNESFIELD-GOSHEN LOCAL SD/ WAYNESFIELD/AUGLAIZE	00785523	419/568-9100	16
Waynesfield-Goshen Mid/Hi Sch/*Waynesfield*/Auglaize	11926889	419/568-9100	16
Waynesville Elem Sch/*Waynesville*/Warren	00838522	513/897-2761	209
Waynesville High Sch/*Waynesville*/Warren	00838534	513/897-2776	209
Waynesville Middle Sch/*Waynesville*/Warren	00838546	513/897-4706	209
Wayside Christian Sch/*Bucyrus*/Crawford	01464514	419/562-5930	39
WEATHERSFIELD LOCAL SCH DIST/ MINERAL RIDGE/TRUMBULL	00837011	330/652-0287	200
Weaver Child Development Ctr/*Canton*/Stark	02663438	330/433-8881	190
Wedgewood Middle Sch/*Columbus*/Franklin	00801153	614/365-5947	69
Weinland Park Elem Sch/*Columbus*/Franklin	00800903	614/365-5321	69
Weisenborn Junior High Sch/*Huber Heights*/Montgomery	00825836	937/237-6350	150
Weller Elem Sch/*Centerville*/Montgomery	00824052	937/885-3273	149
WELLINGTON EXEMPTED VILLAGE SD/ WELLINGTON/LORAIN	00816782	440/647-4286	126
Wellington High Sch/*Wellington*/Lorain	00816809	440/647-3734	126
Wellington Sch/*Columbus*/Franklin	02236798	614/457-7883	78
Wells Academy/*Steubenville*/Jefferson	00812530	740/282-1651	109
WELLSTON CITY SCH DIST/WELLSTON/ JACKSON	00812059	740/384-2152	108
Wellston High Sch/*Wellston*/Jackson	00812097	740/384-2162	108
Wellston Intermediate Sch/*Wellston*/Jackson	00812085	740/384-2060	108
Wellston Middle Sch/*Wellston*/Jackson	00812073	740/384-2251	108
Wellsville Jr Sr High Sch/*Wellsville*/Columbiana	00789763	330/532-1188	36
WELLSVILLE LOCAL SCH DIST/ WELLSVILLE/COLUMBIANA	00789713	330/532-2643	36
Welsh Hills Sch/*Granville*/Licking	02236803	740/522-2020	120
Wernert Elem Sch/*Toledo*/Lucas	00818223	419/473-8218	131
West Boulevard Elem Sch/*Boardman*/Mahoning	00819863	330/726-3427	134
West Branch High Sch/*Beloit*/Mahoning	00820393	330/938-2183	136
WEST BRANCH LOCAL SCH DIST/ BELOIT/MAHONING	00820331	330/938-9324	136
West Branch Middle Sch/*Beloit*/Mahoning	03392929	330/938-4300	136
West Broad Elem Sch/*Columbus*/Franklin	00801177	614/365-5964	69
WEST CARROLLTON CITY SCH DIST/ W CARROLLTON/MONTGOMERY	00825848	937/859-5121	153
West Carrollton High Sch/*W Carrollton*/Montgomery	00825903	937/859-5121	153
West Carrollton Middle Sch/*W Carrollton*/Montgomery	00825915	937/859-5121	153
West Central Learning Academy/*Lima*/Allen	11704265	419/227-9252	5
West Central Sch/*Columbus*/Franklin	04008872	614/276-8231	66
West Clermont High Sch/*Batavia*/Clermont	10968028	513/947-7600	31

Ohio School Directory

DISTRICT & SCHOOL TELEPHONE INDEX

School/City/County DISTRICT/CITY/COUNTY	PID	TELEPHONE NUMBER	PAGE
WEST CLERMONT LOCAL SCH DIST/ **CINCINNATI/CLERMONT**	00788680	513/943-5000	31
West Clermont Middle Sch/*Batavia*/Clermont	00788707	513/947-7400	31
West Clermont Virtual Academy/*Batavia*/Clermont	12037223	513/943-5075	31
West Elem Sch/*Adena*/Jefferson	00812114	740/546-3331	108
West Elem Sch/*Mc Arthur*/Vinton	00838041	740/596-5236	206
West Elem Sch/*New Phila*/Tuscarawas	00837413	330/364-0755	203
West Elem Sch/*Newcomerstown*/Tuscarawas	00837475	740/498-4151	203
West Elkton Intermediate Sch/*West Elkton*/Preble	00828993	937/787-4102	168
West Franklin Elem Sch/*Columbus*/Franklin	00802078	614/801-8400	74
West Geauga High Sch/*Chesterland*/Geauga	00804428	440/729-5950	82
WEST GEAUGA LOCAL SCH DIST/ **CHESTERLAND/GEAUGA**	00804387	440/729-5900	82
West Geauga Middle Sch/*Chesterland*/Geauga	00804430	440/729-5940	82
West High Sch/*Columbus*/Franklin	00801189	614/365-5956	69
West Holmes High Sch/*Millersburg*/Holmes	00811421	330/674-6085	105
WEST HOLMES LOCAL SCH DIST/ **MILLERSBURG/HOLMES**	00811378	330/674-3546	105
West Holmes Middle Sch/*Millersburg*/Holmes	00811433	330/674-4761	105
West Jefferson High Sch/*W Jefferson*/Madison	00819502	614/879-7681	132
West Jefferson Middle Sch/*W Jefferson*/Madison	00819485	614/879-8345	132
West Lake Elem Sch/*Westlake*/Cuyahoga	00795009	440/250-1200	52
WEST LIBERTY-SALEM LOCAL SD/ **WEST LIBERTY/CHAMPAIGN**	00787569	937/465-1075	26
West Liberty-Salem Sch/*West Liberty*/Champaign	00787571	937/465-1075	26
West Main Elem Sch/*Ravenna*/Portage	00828565	330/296-6522	166
West Mound Sch/*Columbus*/Franklin	00801191	614/365-5968	69
West Muskingum Elem Sch/*Zanesville*/Muskingum	00826593	740/455-4058	157
West Muskingum High Sch/*Zanesville*/Muskingum	00826634	740/452-6312	157
WEST MUSKINGUM LOCAL SCH DIST/ **ZANESVILLE/MUSKINGUM**	00826581	740/455-4052	157
West Muskingum Middle Sch/*Zanesville*/Muskingum	00826646	740/455-4055	157
West Park Academy/*Cleveland*/Cuyahoga	12163341	216/251-5450	6
West Park Elem Sch/*Ravenna*/Portage	00828577	330/297-1744	166
West Preparatory Academy/*Cleveland*/Cuyahoga	12043492	216/772-1340	6
West Pugleise Elem Sch/*Steubenville*/Jefferson	00812516	740/346-0903	109
West Shore Career & Tech Sch/*Lakewood*/Cuyahoga	11135195	216/529-4163	47
West Side Montessori/*Toledo*/Lucas	02147898	419/866-1931	131
West Union Elem Sch/*West Union*/Adams	00783513	937/544-2951	6
West Union High Sch/*West Union*/Adams	00783525	937/544-5553	6
Westbrooke Village Elem Sch/*Trotwood*/Montgomery	12032405	937/854-3196	153
Westerly Elem Sch/*Bay Village*/Cuyahoga	00790463	440/617-7550	40
Western Brown High Sch/*Mount Orab*/Brown	00786242	937/444-2544	20
WESTERN BROWN LOCAL SCH DIST/ **MOUNT ORAB/BROWN**	00786216	937/444-2044	20
WESTERN BUCKEYE ED SERVICE CTR/ **PAULDING/PAULDING**	00829399	419/399-4711	160
WESTERN BUCKEYE ED SERVICE CTR/ **VAN WERT/VAN WERT**	00838027	419/238-4746	205
Western Elem Sch/*Latham*/Pike	00828113	740/493-2881	164
Western Elem Sch/*Lexington*/Richland	00829533	419/884-2765	172
Western Elem Sch/*Mason*/Warren	00838493	513/398-5821	208
Western High Sch/*Latham*/Pike	00828125	740/493-2514	164
Western Hills Univ High Sch/*Cincinnati*/Hamilton	05100526	513/363-8900	88
WESTERN LOCAL SCH DIST/LATHAM/PIKE	00828084	740/493-3113	164
Western Reserve Academy/*Hudson*/Summit	00835805	330/650-4400	196
Western Reserve Elem Sch/*Collins*/Huron	00811756	419/660-9824	106
Western Reserve High Sch/*Collins*/Huron	00811770	419/668-8470	106
Western Reserve Local Sch/*Berlin Center*/Mahoning	00820410	330/547-4100	136
WESTERN RESERVE LOCAL SCH DIST/ **BERLIN CENTER/MAHONING**	00820408	330/547-4100	136
WESTERN RESERVE LOCAL SCH DIST/ **COLLINS/HURON**	00811744	419/660-8508	106
Western Reserve Middle Sch/*Collins*/Huron	00811782	419/668-8470	106
Westerville Central High Sch/*Westerville*/Franklin	05273575	614/797-6800	75
WESTERVILLE CITY SCH DIST/ **WESTERVILLE/FRANKLIN**	00802250	614/797-5700	74
Westerville North High Sch/*Westerville*/Franklin	01399294	614/797-6200	75
Westerville South High Sch/*Westerville*/Franklin	00802406	614/797-6000	75
Westfall Elem Sch/*Williamsport*/Pickaway	00827896	740/986-4008	163
Westfall High Sch/*Williamsport*/Pickaway	00827925	740/986-2911	163
WESTFALL LOCAL SCH DIST/ **WILLIAMSPORT/PICKAWAY**	00827884	740/986-3671	163
Westfall Middle Sch/*Williamsport*/Pickaway	00827937	740/986-2941	163
Westfield Achievement/*Toledo*/Lucas	11823392	419/725-5008	130
Westgate Elem Sch/*Columbus*/Franklin	00801206	614/365-5971	69
Westgate Middle Sch/*E Liverpool*/Columbiana	11075753	330/386-8765	35
WESTLAKE CITY SCH DIST/WESTLAKE/CUYAHOGA	00794990	440/871-7300	51
Westlake High Sch/*Westlake*/Cuyahoga	00795061	440/835-6352	52
Westland High Sch/*Galloway*/Franklin	00802080	614/851-7000	74
Westmoor Middle Sch/*Columbus*/Franklin	00801218	614/365-5974	69
Westpark Cmty Elem Sch/*Cleveland*/Cuyahoga	05010335	216/688-0271	40
Westpark Cmty Middle Sch/*Cleveland*/Cuyahoga	11566881	216/251-7200	40
Westside Academy/*Columbus*/Franklin	11007562	614/272-9392	6
Westside Christian Academy/*Westlake*/Cuyahoga	04927852	440/331-1300	54
Westside Cmty Sch of the Arts/*Cleveland*/Cuyahoga	11016496	216/688-1900	6
Westside Montessori Middle Sch/*Toledo*/Lucas	10025121	419/843-5703	131
Westview Elem Sch/*Avon Lake*/Lorain	00815790	440/933-8131	122
Westview Elem Sch/*Jackson*/Jackson	00811938	740/286-2790	107
Westwood Elem Sch/*Cleveland*/Cuyahoga	12235334	216/865-4934	51
Westwood Elem Sch/*Dayton*/Montgomery	00824416	937/542-4990	149
Westwood Elem Sch/*Novelty*/Geauga	00804442	440/729-5990	82
Westwood Elem Sch/*Wellington*/Lorain	00816811	440/647-3636	126
Westwood Middle Sch/*Elyria*/Lorain	00816122	440/284-8017	123
Westwood Preparatory Academy/*Columbus*/Franklin	12259562	330/510-5400	6
Westwood Sch/*Cincinnati*/Hamilton	00806294	513/363-5900	88
Wheelersburg Elem Sch/*Wheelersburg*/Scioto	00831378	740/574-8130	180
Wheelersburg High Sch/*Wheelersburg*/Scioto	00831380	740/574-2527	180
WHEELERSBURG LOCAL SCH DIST/ **WHEELERSBURG/SCIOTO**	00831366	740/574-8484	180
Wheelersburg Middle Sch/*Wheelersburg*/Scioto	11568102	740/574-2515	180
Whetstone High Sch/*Columbus*/Franklin	00801220	614/365-6060	69
Whetstone Sch/*Mount Gilead*/Morrow	02052334	419/947-7045	155
Whipple Heights Elem Sch/*Canton*/Stark	00833508	330/478-6177	188
Whitaker Elem Sch/*Cincinnati*/Hamilton	00806464	513/728-3737	89
White Oak Middle Sch/*Cincinnati*/Hamilton	00807250	513/741-4300	91
Whiteford Elem Sch/*Toledo*/Lucas	00817308	419/824-8616	129
WHITEHALL CITY SCH DIST/ **WHITEHALL/FRANKLIN**	00802420	614/417-5000	75
Whitehall Prep & Fitness Acad/*Columbus*/Franklin	11547031	614/324-4585	6
Whitehall Yearling High Sch/*Whitehall*/Franklin	00802494	614/417-5100	75
Whitehouse Primary Sch/*Whitehouse*/Lucas	00816938	419/877-0543	127
Whiteoak Jr Sr High Sch/*Mowrystown*/Highland	00810946	937/442-2241	102
Whitewater Valley Elem Sch/*Harrison*/Hamilton	03321413	513/367-5577	93
Whitmer Career & Tech Center/*Toledo*/Lucas	01539030	419/473-8339	131
Whitmer High Sch/*Toledo*/Lucas	00818247	419/473-8490	131
Whitney M Young Gifted Campus/*Cleveland*/Cuyahoga	00792710	216/838-5500	45
Whittier Elem Sch/*Massillon*/Stark	00833156	330/830-3904	187
Whittier Elem Sch/*Sidney*/Shelby	00832176	937/497-2275	183
Whittier Elem Sch/*Toledo*/Lucas	00818065	419/671-3600	130
Whittier Elem Sch/*Westerville*/Franklin	00802418	614/797-7300	75
Whittier Primary Sch/*Findlay*/Hancock	00810001	419/425-8358	98
WICKLIFFE CITY SCH DIST/ **WICKLIFFE/LAKE**	00813780	440/943-6900	114
Wickliffe Elem Sch/*Upper Arlngtn*/Franklin	00802183	614/487-5150	74
Wickliffe Elem Sch/*Wickliffe*/Lake	00813792	440/943-0320	114
Wickliffe High Sch/*Wickliffe*/Lake	00813819	440/944-0800	114
Wickliffe Middle Sch/*Wickliffe*/Lake	00813821	440/943-3220	114
Wiggin St Elem Sch/*Gambier*/Knox	00813106	740/427-4262	111
Wilbur Wright Sch/*Cleveland*/Cuyahoga	00792722	216/838-6800	45
Wilcox Primary Sch/*Twinsburg*/Summit	00835714	330/486-2030	195
Wilder Elem Sch/*Westerville*/Franklin	03246966	614/797-7330	75
Wildwood Elem Sch/*Middletown*/Butler	00787002	513/420-4564	23

DISTRICT & SCHOOL TELEPHONE INDEX

Market Data Retrieval

School/City/County DISTRICT/CITY/COUNTY	PID	TELEPHONE NUMBER	PAGE
Wildwood Environmental Acad K5/*Maumee*/Lucas	10018037	419/868-9885	6
WILLARD CITY SCH DIST/**WILLARD**/**HURON**	00811794	419/935-1541	106
Willard Elem Sch/*Willard*/Huron	00811809	419/935-5341	106
Willard Grizzell Middle Sch/*Dublin*/Franklin	04278546	614/798-3569	70
Willard Middle High Sch/*Willard*/Huron	00811861	419/935-0181	106
Willard PK-8 Sch/*Warren*/Trumbull	00836861	330/675-8700	200
Willetts Middle Sch/*Brunswick*/Medina	02199889	330/273-0489	140
William Bick Primary Sch/*Bethel*/Clermont	00788379	513/734-2271	30
William Crawford Interm Sch/*Crestline*/Crawford	01486861	419/562-7529	38
William Cullen Bryant Sch/*Cleveland*/Cuyahoga	00792746	216/838-3350	45
William Foster Elem Sch/*Garfield HTS*/Cuyahoga	00793427	216/475-8123	46
William H Taft Elem Sch/*Cincinnati*/Hamilton	00806218	513/363-5600	88
William Henry Harrison HS/*Harrison*/Hamilton	00807705	513/367-4169	93
William Henry Harrison Jr HS/*Harrison*/Hamilton	00807676	513/367-4831	93
William Holmes McGuffey ES/*Youngstown*/Mahoning	00820800	330/744-7999	137
William Mason High Sch/*Mason*/Warren	00838508	513/398-5025	208
William Patrick Day EC Center/*Cleveland*/Cuyahoga	02051756	216/736-2920	40
William Rainey Harper Sch/*Cleveland*/Cuyahoga	12309387	216/838-3400	45
William S Stinson Elem Sch/*Canal Fulton*/Stark	00833376	330/854-4646	188
William V Fisher Catholic HS/*Lancaster*/Fairfield	00803486	740/654-1231	65
Williams Avenue Elem Sch/*Norwood*/Hamilton	00807339	513/924-2520	92
Williamsburg Elem Sch/*Williamsburg*/Clermont	00788812	513/724-2241	32
WILLIAMSBURG LOCAL SCH DIST/**WILLIAMSBURG/CLERMONT**	00788800	513/724-2211	32
Williamsburg Middle High Sch/*Williamsburg*/Clermont	00788824	513/724-2211	32
Williamson Elem Sch/*Youngstown*/Mahoning	00820836	330/744-7155	137
Willis C Adams Middle Sch/*Johnstown*/Licking	00814746	740/967-8766	118
Willo-Hill Christian Sch/*Willoughby*/Lake	01796020	440/951-5391	115
Willoughby Middle Sch/*Willoughby*/Lake	00814045	440/975-3600	114
WILLOUGHBY-EASTLAKE CITY SD/**EASTLAKE/LAKE**	00813845	440/946-5000	114
Willoughby-Eastlake Preschool/*Eastlake*/Lake	10004969	440/283-2220	114
Willow Sch/*Cleveland*/Cuyahoga	00792784	216/838-1800	45
Willowick Middle Sch/*Willowick*/Lake	00814057	440/943-2950	114
Willowville Elem Sch/*Batavia*/Clermont	00788783	513/943-6800	31
Willson Elem Sch/*Cleveland*/Cuyahoga	11701392	216/838-1850	45
Willyard Elem Sch/*Ravenna*/Portage	00828589	330/296-6481	166
Wilmington Christian Academy/*Wilmington*/Clinton	10910306	937/383-1319	33
WILMINGTON CITY SCH DIST/**WILMINGTON/CLINTON**	00789024	937/382-1641	33
Wilmington High Sch/*Wilmington*/Clinton	00789103	937/382-7716	33
Wilmington Middle Sch/*Wilmington*/Clinton	00789062	937/382-7556	33
Wilson Elem Sch/*Cincinnati*/Hamilton	00806567	513/231-3240	89
Wilson Elem Sch/*Youngstown*/Mahoning	00820599	330/744-8002	137
Wilson Hill Elem Sch/*Worthington*/Franklin	00802561	614/450-4800	76
Wilson Middle Sch/*Hamilton*/Butler	00786632	513/887-5170	22
Wilson Middle Sch/*Newark*/Licking	00815128	740/670-7120	119
Wilson Vance Intermediate Sch/*Findlay*/Hancock	00809997	419/425-8332	98
Winchester Trail Elem Sch/*Canal Wnchstr*/Franklin	05096640	614/833-2150	66
Windemere Cmty Learning Center/*Akron*/Summit	00834497	330/761-7937	191
Windermere Elem Sch/*Upper Arlngtn*/Franklin	00802195	614/487-5060	74
Windfall Sch/*Medina*/Medina	02052279	330/725-7751	139
WINDHAM EXEMPTED VLG SCH DIST/**WINDHAM/PORTAGE**	00828761	330/326-2711	167
Windham High Sch/*Windham*/Portage	00828797	330/326-2711	167
Windham Junior High Sch/*Windham*/Portage	01878240	330/326-3490	167
Windsor Elem Sch/*Elyria*/Lorain	00816134	440/284-8014	123
Windsor-STEM Academy/*Columbus*/Franklin	00801244	614/365-5906	69
Winesburg Elem Sch/*Winesburg*/Holmes	00811354	330/359-5059	105
Wings Academy/*Cleveland*/Cuyahoga	11007536	216/812-0244	6
Wings Academy K-8/*Cleveland*/Cuyahoga	12259586	216/812-0244	6
Wings Academy Lower Sch/*Cleveland*/Cuyahoga	12259598	216/812-0244	6
Winterfield Venture Academy/*Toledo*/Lucas	10001058	419/531-3285	127
Winterset Elem Sch/*Columbus*/Franklin	00801256	614/365-5510	69
Wintersville Elem Sch/*Wintersville*/Jefferson	00812487	740/264-1691	109
Winton Hills Academy/*Cincinnati*/Hamilton	00806323	513/363-6300	88
Winton Place Baptist Academy/*Cincinnati*/Hamilton	11231177	513/681-9480	96
Winton Preparatory Academy/*Cincinnati*/Hamilton	12043480	513/276-4166	6
WINTON WOODS CITY SCH DIST/**CINCINNATI/HAMILTON**	00806579	513/619-2300	94
Winton Woods Elem Sch/*Cincinnati*/Hamilton	00806684	513/619-2490	94
Winton Woods HS-Global Studies/*Cincinnati*/Hamilton	12037833	513/619-2420	94
Winton Woods HS-New Tech Acad/*Cincinnati*/Hamilton	00806610	513/619-2420	94
Winton Woods Interm Sch/*Cincinnati*/Hamilton	00806660	513/619-2450	94
Winton Woods Middle Sch/*Cincinnati*/Hamilton	00806622	513/619-2440	94
Winton Woods Primary Sch-North/*Cincinnati*/Hamilton	00806581	513/619-2390	94
Winton Woods Primary Sch-South/*Cincinnati*/Hamilton	00806672	513/619-2470	94
Wise Elem Sch/*Charm*/Holmes	00811366	330/893-2505	105
Withamsville-Tobasco Elem Sch/*Cincinnati*/Clermont	00788795	513/943-6900	31
Withrow University High Sch/*Cincinnati*/Hamilton	05100538	513/363-9200	88
WOCO-W OHIO COMPUTER ORG/**SIDNEY/SHELBY**	04499518	937/498-2161	183
Wogaman Middle Sch/*Dayton*/Montgomery	00824569	937/542-5890	149
WOLF CREEK LOCAL SCH DIST/**WATERFORD/WASHINGTON**	00838924	740/984-2373	211
WOOD CO ED SERVICE CENTER/**BOWLING GREEN/WOOD**	00840549	419/354-9010	216
Wood Lane Sch/*Bowling Green*/Wood	02052724	419/352-9577	216
Woodbury Elem Sch/*Shaker HTS*/Cuyahoga	00794627	216/295-4150	50
Woodcrest Elem Sch/*Columbus*/Franklin	04943739	614/365-6747	69
Woodford Paideia Sch/*Cincinnati*/Hamilton	01556583	513/363-6400	88
Woodland Elem Sch/*Liberty TWP*/Butler	03317711	513/779-7775	23
Woodland Elem Sch/*Mansfield*/Richland	00829870	419/525-6325	173
Woodland Elem Sch/*Perrysburg*/Wood	01880932	419/874-8736	218
Woodland Elem Sch/*Stow*/Summit	00835582	330/689-5470	194
Woodlands Intermediate Sch/*Huron*/Erie	00798465	419/433-1234	61
Woodlawn Elem Sch/*Cincinnati*/Hamilton	00807561	513/864-2900	92
Woodmore Elementary/Middle Sch/*Woodville*/Ottawa	00830817	419/862-1070	159
Woodmore High Sch/*Elmore*/Ottawa	00830790	419/862-2721	159
WOODMORE LOCAL SCH DIST/**ELMORE/OTTAWA**	00830776	419/862-1060	159
Woodridge Elem Sch/*Peninsula*/Summit	02125424	330/928-1223	195
Woodridge High Sch/*Peninsula*/Summit	00834679	330/929-3191	195
WOODRIDGE LOCAL SCH DIST/**PENINSULA/SUMMIT**	00834643	330/928-9074	195
Woodridge Middle Sch/*Peninsula*/Summit	02125436	330/928-7420	195
Woodsfield Elem Sch/*Woodsfield*/Monroe	00823876	740/472-0953	148
Woodward Career Tech High Sch/*Cincinnati*/Hamilton	05100540	513/363-9300	88
Woodward High Sch/*Toledo*/Lucas	00818077	419/671-6000	130
Woodward Park Middle Sch/*Columbus*/Franklin	00801270	614/365-5354	69
Wooster Christian Sch/*Wooster*/Wayne	03417050	330/345-6436	214
WOOSTER CITY SCH DIST/**WOOSTER**/**WAYNE**	00839485	330/264-0869	213
Wooster High Sch/*Wooster*/Wayne	00839590	330/988-1111	214
Wooster Twp Elem Sch/*Wooster*/Wayne	00839473	330/264-6252	213
Worley Reading & Math Prep Sch/*Canton*/Stark	00832695	330/452-5748	185
Worthington Academy/*Worthington*/Franklin	12312310	614/450-6000	76
Worthington Adventist Academy/*Worthington*/Franklin	11223780	614/885-9525	78
Worthington Christian High Sch/*Columbus*/Franklin	01464772	614/431-8210	78
Worthington Christian Mid Sch/*Westerville*/Franklin	02203820	614/431-8230	78
Worthington Chrstn Westview ES/*Columbus*/Franklin	02147630	614/431-8240	78
Worthington Estates Elem Sch/*Worthington*/Franklin	00802573	614/450-4600	76

Ohio School Directory

DISTRICT & SCHOOL TELEPHONE INDEX

School/City/County DISTRICT/CITY/COUNTY	PID	TELEPHONE NUMBER	PAGE
Worthington Hills Elem Sch/*Columbus*/Franklin	00802585	614/450-4700	76
Worthington Kilbourne High Sch/*Columbus*/Franklin	03393301	614/450-6400	76
Worthington Park Elem Sch/*Westerville*/Franklin	03049213	614/450-5500	76
WORTHINGTON SCH DIST/WORTHINGTON/FRANKLIN	00802509	614/450-6000	75
Worthingway Middle Sch/*Worthington*/Franklin	00802602	614/450-4300	76
Wright Brothers Elem Sch/*Huber Heights*/Montgomery	03400564	937/237-6392	150
Wright Brothers Middle Sch/*Dayton*/Montgomery	00824571	937/542-5940	149
Wright Preparatory Academy/*Canton*/Stark	12259536	234/207-5455	6
Wyandot Early Childhood Sch/*Liberty TWP*/Butler	10908949	513/759-8100	23
Wyandot Elem Sch/*Dublin*/Franklin	03049433	614/761-5840	70
Wyandot Run Elem Sch/*Powell*/Delaware	04028690	740/657-4850	59
Wynford Elem Sch/*Bucyrus*/Crawford	00790346	419/562-4619	39
Wynford High Sch/*Bucyrus*/Crawford	00790384	419/562-7828	39
WYNFORD LOCAL SCH DIST/BUCYRUS/CRAWFORD	00790334	419/562-7828	39
Wynn Center/*Oregon*/Lucas	12109577	419/698-8003	128
WYOMING CITY SCH DIST/WYOMING/HAMILTON	00807901	513/206-7000	94
Wyoming High Sch/*Wyoming*/Hamilton	00807951	513/206-7050	94
Wyoming Middle Sch/*Wyoming*/Hamilton	00807963	513/206-7170	94

X

School/City/County	PID	TELEPHONE	PAGE
Xavier Univ Montessori Lab Sch/*Cincinnati*/Hamilton	02655417	513/745-3424	96
XENIA COMMUNITY SCH DIST/XENIA/GREENE	00804818	937/376-2961	84
Xenia High Sch/*Xenia*/Greene	00804923	937/372-6983	85
Xenia Preschool/*Xenia*/Greene	12168157	937/562-9706	85

Y

School/City/County	PID	TELEPHONE	PAGE
Yavne High Sch/*Beachwood*/Cuyahoga	11009211	216/691-5838	54
YELLOW SPRINGS EXEMPTED VLG SD/YELLOW SPGS/GREENE	00804935	937/767-7381	85
Yellow Springs High Sch/*Yellow Spgs*/Greene	00804961	937/767-7224	85
Yeshiva Derech Ha Torah/*Cleveland*/Cuyahoga	02856544	216/321-1547	54
Yeshiva Derech Ha Torah/*Cleveland*/Cuyahoga	02856556	216/382-6248	54
York Elem Sch/*New Phila*/Tuscarawas	00837425	330/364-0770	203
Yorktown Middle Sch/*Columbus*/Franklin	00801282	614/365-5408	69
Young Elem Sch/*Akron*/Summit	00835491	330/798-1008	194
Young Scholars Prep Sch/*Columbus*/Franklin	12042345	614/653-2116	6
Youngstown Acad of Excellence/*Youngstown*/Mahoning	10018063	330/746-3970	6
YOUNGSTOWN CITY SCH DIST/YOUNGSTOWN/MAHONING	00820446	330/744-6900	136
Youngstown Community Sch/*Youngstown*/Mahoning	04880670	330/746-2240	6
Youngstown Early College HS/*Youngstown*/Mahoning	05378187	330/744-7923	137
Youngstown Virtual Academy/*Youngstown*/Mahoning	12368072	330/744-8700	137
Youthbuild Columbus Cmty Sch/*Columbus*/Franklin	05010347	614/291-0805	6
Youtz Leadership Sch/*Canton*/Stark	00832700	330/452-7601	185

Z

School/City/County	PID	TELEPHONE	PAGE
Zane Grey Elem Sch/*Zanesville*/Muskingum	00826816	740/453-0576	157
Zane Trace Elem Sch/*Chillicothe*/Ross	00830439	740/775-1304	176
Zane Trace High Sch/*Chillicothe*/Ross	00830441	740/775-1809	176
ZANE TRACE LOCAL SCH DIST/CHILLICOTHE/ROSS	00830427	740/775-1355	176
Zane Trace Middle Sch/*Chillicothe*/Ross	00830453	740/773-5842	176
Zanesville Christian Sch/*Zanesville*/Muskingum	01796070	740/454-2509	158
ZANESVILLE CITY SCH DIST/ZANESVILLE/MUSKINGUM	00826658	740/454-9751	157
Zanesville Community High Sch/*Zanesville*/Muskingum	04370223	740/588-5685	158
Zanesville High Sch/*Zanesville*/Muskingum	00826828	740/453-0335	158
Zanesville Middle Sch/*Zanesville*/Muskingum	00826787	740/453-0711	158
Zanesville SDA Sch/*Zanesville*/Muskingum	01465075	740/453-6050	158
Zenith Academy East/*Columbus*/Franklin	11915505	614/577-0997	6
Zenith Academy North/*Columbus*/Franklin	10760008	614/589-8497	6
Zenith Academy West/*Columbus*/Franklin	12259639	614/272-6300	6
Zion Lutheran Sch/*Toledo*/Lucas	01409734	419/531-1507	132

Ohio School Directory

DISTRICT URL INDEX

DISTRICT	URL	PAGE
ADA Exempted Village Sch Dist	ada.k12.oh.us/	99
Adams Co Ohio Valley Sch Dist	ohiovalley.k12.oh.us/	6
Adena Local School Dist	adena.k12.oh.us/	174
Akron Public Schools	akronschools.com	190
Alexander Local School Dist	alexanderschools.org/	14
Allen East Local School Dist	ae.k12.oh.us/	7
Alliance City School Dist	alliancecityschools.org/	184
Amanda-Clearcreek Local SD	amanda.k12.oh.us/	62
Amherst Exempted Village SD	amherst.k12.oh.us	122
Anna Local School Dist	anna.k12.oh.us	182
Ansonia Local School Dist	ansonia.k12.oh.us	55
Anthony Wayne Local Sch Dist	anthonywayneschools.org/	127
Antwerp Local School Dist	antwerpschools.org/	160
Apollo Joint Voc School Dist	apollocareercenter.com/	8
Arcadia Local School Dist	arcadia.noacsc.org/	97
Arcanum Butler Local Sch Dist	arcanum-butler.k12.oh.us/	55
Archbold Area Local Sch Dist	archbold.k12.oh.us	78
Arlington Local School Dist	arlingtonlocalschools.com/	97
Ashland City School Dist	ashland-city.k12.oh.us/	10
Ashland Co-West Holmes JVSD	acwhcc-jvs.k12.oh.us/	10
Ashtabula Area City Sch Dist	aacs.net/	12
Ashtabula Co Tech & Career SD	atech.edu/	12
Athens City School Dist	athenscsd.org/	14
Auburn Vocational School Dist	auburncc.org/	112
Aurora City School Dist	aurora-schools.org/	164
Austintown Local School Dist	austintownschools.org/	133
Avon Lake City School Dist	avonlakecityschools.com/	122
Avon Local School Dist	avonlocalschools.org/	122
Ayersville Local School Dist	ayersville.org/	56
Barberton City School Dist	barbertonschools.org/	192
Barnesville Exempted Vlg SD	barnesville.k12.oh.us/	17
Batavia Local School Dist	bataviaschools.org	29
Bath Local School Dist	bathwildcats.org/	8
Bay Village City School Dist	bayvillageschools.com/	40
Beachwood City School Dist	beachwoodschools.org/	40
Beaver Local School Dist	beaver.k12.oh.us/	34
Beavercreek City School Dist	beavercreek.k12.oh.us	83
Bedford City School Dist	bedford.k12.oh.us/bcsd	40
Bellaire Local School Dist	bellaire.k12.oh.us/	17
Bellbrook-Sugarcreek Schools	sugarcreek.k12.oh.us/	83
Bellefontaine City School Dist	bellefontaine.k12.oh.us/	120
Bellevue City School Dist	bellevueschools.org	105
Belmont-Harrison Voc Sch Dist	bhccenters.com/	17
Belpre City School Dist	belpre.k12.oh.us	209
Benjamin Logan Local Sch Dist	benlogan.k12.oh.us	121
Benton-Carroll-Salem Local SD	bcs.k12.oh.us	158
Berea City School Dist	berea.k12.oh.us	41
Berkshire Local School Dist	berkshire.k12.oh.us/	81
Berne Union Local School Dist	berne-union.k12.oh.us/	63
Bethel Local School Dist	bethel.k12.oh.us/	145
Bethel-Tate Local School Dist	betheltate.org/	30
Bexley City School Dist	bexleyschools.org/	66
Big Walnut Local School Dist	bigwalnut.k12.oh.us/	58
Black River Local School Dist	blackriver.k12.oh.us/	139
Blanchester Local School Dist	blanschools.org/	32
Bloom-Carroll Local Sch Dist	bloom-carroll.k12.oh.us/	63
Bloom-Vernon Local Sch Dist	bv.k12.oh.us/	178
Bloomfield-Mespo Local SD	bloomfield-mespo.org/	197
Bluffton Exempted Village Sch	bluffton.noacsc.org/	8
Boardman Local School Dist	boardman.k12.oh.us/	134
Botkins Local School Dist	botkins.k12.oh.us	182
Bowling Green City Sch Dist	bgcs.k12.oh.us/	216
Bradford Exempted Village SD	bradford.k12.oh.us/	145
Brecksville Broadview Hts CSD	bbhcsd.org/	41
Bridgeport School Dist	bevs.k12.oh.us/	18
Bright Local School Dist	bright.k12.oh.us/	102
Bristol Local School Dist	bristol.k12.oh.us/	197
Brookfield Local School Dist	brookfield.k12.oh.us/	197
Brooklyn City School Dist	brooklyn.k12.oh.us/	41
Brookville Local School Dist	brookville.k12.oh.us	148
Brown Local School Dist	brownlocalschools.com/	25
Brunswick City School Dist	brunswickschools.org/	140
Bryan City School Dist	bryan.k12.oh.us/	214

School Year 2019-2020   800-333-8802   OH-W1

DISTRICT URL INDEX

Market Data Retrieval

DISTRICT	URL	PAGE
Buckeye Central Local Sch Dist	buckeye-central.k12.oh.us	38
Buckeye Joint Voc School Dist	buckeyecareercenter.org/	201
Buckeye Local School Dist	buckeyeschools.info/	12
Buckeye Local School Dist	omeresa.net/schools/buckeye/	108
Buckeye Local School Dist	buckeye.k12.oh.us/	140
Buckeye Valley Local Sch Dist	buckeyevalley.k12.oh.us/	58
Bucyrus City School Dist	bucyrusschools.org/	38
Butler Tech Career Dev Schs	butlertech.org/	21
Caldwell Exempted Village SD	caldwell.k12.oh.us/	158
Cambridge City School Dist	cambridge.k12.oh.us/	86
Campbell City School Dist	campbell.k12.oh.us/	134
Canal Winchester Local SD	cwschools.org/	66
Canfield Local School Dist	canfield.access-k12.org/	134
Canton City School Dist	ccsdistrict.org	184
Canton Local School Dist	cantonlocal.org/	185
Cardinal Local School Dist	cardinal.k12.oh.us/	81
Cardington-Lincoln Local SD	cardington.k12.oh.us	155
Carey Exempted Village SD	careyschools.org/	219
Carlisle Local School Dist	carlisleindians.org/	206
Carrollton Exempted Village SD	carrollton.k12.oh.us/	25
Cedar Cliff Local School Dist	cedarcliffschools.org/	84
Celina City School Dist	celinaschools.org/	143
Centerburg Local School Dist	centerburgschools.org/	110
Centerville City School Dist	centerville.k12.oh.us/	148
Central Local School Dist	centrallocal.k12.oh.us/	57
Chagrin Falls Exempted Vlg SD	chagrin-falls.k12.oh.us	42
Champion Local School Dist	championlocal.org/	197
Chardon Local School Dist	chardon.k12.oh.us/	82
Chesapeake Union Exempt Vlg SD	peake.k12.oh.us/	115
Chillicothe City School Dist	chillicothe.k12.oh.us/	174
Chippewa Local School Dist	chippewa.k12.oh.us	211
Cincinnati City School Dist	cps-k12.org/	87
Circleville City School Dist	circlevillecityschools.org/district/	162
Clark-Shawnee Local Sch Dist	clark-shawnee.k12.oh.us/	27
Clay Local School Dist	clay.k12.oh.us/	178
Claymont City School Dist	claymontschools.org/district/contact.html	201
Clear Fork Vly Local Sch Dist	clearfork.k12.oh.us	171
Clearview Local School Dist	clearview.k12.oh.us/	123
Clermont Northeastern Local SD	cneschools.org	30
Cleveland Hts-Univ Hts City SD	chuh.org	42
Cleveland Metro School Dist	clevelandmetroschools.org	42
Clinton-Massie Local Sch Dist	clinton-massie.k12.oh.us	33
Cloverleaf Local School Dist	cloverleaflocal.org/	140
Clyde-Green Spgs Exmpt Vlg SD	clyde.k12.oh.us/	176
Coldwater Exempted Village SD	cw.noacsc.org/	143
Colonel Crawford Local SD	colonel-crawford.k12.oh.us/	38
Columbia Local School Dist	columbia.k12.oh.us/	123
Columbiana Co Voc Sch Dist	ccctc.k12.oh.us/	34
Columbiana Exempted Village SD	columbiana.k12.oh.us/	34
Columbus City School Dist	ccsoh.us/	66
Columbus Grove Local Sch Dist	cg.noacsc.org/	169
Conneaut Area City Sch Dist	cacsk12.org/	12
Conotton Valley Union Local SD	conottonvalley.k12.oh.us/	100
Continental Local School Dist	continentalpirates.org/	169
Copley-Fairlawn City Sch Dist	copley-fairlawn.org/	192
Cory-Rawson Local School Dist	cory-rawson.k12.oh.us/	97
Coshocton City School Dist	coshoctonredskins.com/	36
Coshocton Co Joint Voc SD	coshoctoncareers.org/	37
Coventry Local School Dist	coventryschools.org/	192
Covington Exempted Village SD	covington.k12.oh.us/	145
Crestline Exempted Village SD	crestline.k12.oh.us/	38
Crestview Local School Dist	crestview-richland.k12.oh.us/	171
Crestview Local School Dist	crestviewrebels.org/	34
Crestview Local School Dist	crestviewknights.com	205
Crestwood Local School Dist	crestwood.sparcc.org/	165
Crooksville Exempted Vlg SD	crooksville.k12.oh.us/	161
Cuyahoga Falls City Sch Dist	cfalls.summit.k12.oh.us/	192
Cuyahoga Heights Local SD	cuyhts.k12.oh.us	45
Cuyahoga Vly Career Ctr Voc SD	cvccworks.edu	45
Dalton Local School Dist	dalton.k12.oh.us/	211
Danbury Local School Dist	danbury.k12.oh.us/	159
Danville Local School Dist	danville.k12.oh.us/	110
Dawson-Bryant Local Sch Dist	db.k12.oh.us/	115
Dayton Public School Dist	dps.k12.oh.us	149

OH-W2   800-333-8802   School Year 2019-2020

Ohio School Directory

DISTRICT URL INDEX

DISTRICT	URL	PAGE
Deer Park Cmty School Dist	deerparkcityschools.org	89
Defiance City School Dist	defiancecityschools.org	57
Delaware City School Dist	dcs.k12.oh.us/	58
Delaware Joint Voc Sch Dist	delawareareacc.org/	59
Delphos City School Dist	delphoscityschools.org/	8
Dover City School Dist	dover.k12.oh.us	202
Dublin City School Dist	dublinschools.net/	69
East Cleveland City Sch Dist	east-cleveland.k12.oh.us/	45
East Clinton Local School Dist	east-clinton.k12.oh.us/	33
East Guernsey Local Sch Dist	eguernsey.k12.oh.us/	86
East Holmes Local School Dist	eastholmes.k12.oh.us/	104
East Knox Local School Dist	eastknox.k12.oh.us	111
East Liverpool City Sch Dist	elcsd.k12.oh.us/	34
East Muskingum Local Sch Dist	east-muskingum.k12.oh.us/	156
East Palestine City Sch Dist	myepschools.org/	35
Eastern Local School Dist	easternlocal.com/	142
Eastern Local School Dist	eb.k12.oh.us/	7
Eastern Local School Dist	ep.k12.oh.us/	163
Eastland-Ffld Career Tech VSD	eastlandfairfield.com/	70
Eastwood Local School Dist	eastwoodschools.org/	216
Eaton Cmty School Dist	eatoncommunityschools.org/	168
Edgerton Local School Dist	edgerton.k12.oh.us/	214
Edgewood City School Dist	edgewoodschools.com/	21
Edison Local School Dist	edisonlocal.k12.oh.us/	109
Edison Local Schools District	edisonchargers.org/	60
Edon Northwest Local Sch Dist	edon.k12.oh.us/	215
Ehove Joint Voc School Dist	ehove-jvs.k12.oh.us/	60
Elgin Local School Dist	elginschools.org/	138
Elida Local School Dist	home.elida.k12.oh.us/	8
Elmwood Local School Dist	elmwood.k12.oh.us	216
Elyria City School Dist	elyriaschools.org/	123
Euclid City School Dist	euclidschools.org	46
Evergreen Local School Dist	evergreen.k12.oh.us	78
Fairbanks Local School Dist	fairbanks.k12.oh.us/	204
Fairborn City School Dist	fairborn.k12.oh.us	84
Fairfield City School Dist	fairfieldcityschools.com/	21
Fairfield Local Sch Dist	fairfieldlocal.org/index.aspx	102
Fairfield Union Local Sch Dist	fairfield-union.k12.oh.us	63
Fairland Local School Dist	fairland.k12.oh.us/	116
Fairlawn Local School Dist	fairlawn.k12.oh.us/	182
Fairless Local School Dist	falcon.stark.k12.oh.us/	185
Fairport Harbor Exempt Vlg SD	fhevs.org/	112
Fairview Park City Sch Dist	fairviewparkschools.org/	46
Fayette Local Sch Dist	fayettesch.org/	79
Fayetteville Perry Local SD	fp.k12.oh.us	19
Federal Hocking Local Sch Dist	fedhock.com/	14
Felicity-Franklin Local SD	felicityschools.org/	30
Field Local School Dist	fieldlocalschools.org/	165
Findlay City School Dist	findlaycityschools.org	97
Finneytown Local School Dist	finneytown.org	89
Firelands Local School Dist	firelandsschools.org	124
Forest Hills School Dist	foresthills.edu	89
Fostoria City School Dist	fostoria.k12.oh.us/	180
Four-Co Joint Voc School Dist	fourcounty.net/	79
Franklin City School Dist	franklincityschools.com	207
Franklin Local School Dist	franklin-local.k12.oh.us/	156
Franklin-Monroe Local Sch Dist	franklin-monroe.k12.oh.us/	55
Fredericktown Local Sch Dist	fredericktownschools.com/	111
Fremont City School Dist	fremont.k12.oh.us/	176
Frontier Local School Dist	flsd.k12.oh.us/	209
Ft Frye Local School Dist	fortfrye.k12.oh.us/	210
Ft Loramie Local School Dist	loramie.k12.oh.us/	182
Ft Recovery Local School Dist	fortrecoveryschools.org/	144
Gahanna-Jefferson Public SD	gahannaschools.org/	70
Galion City School Dist	galionschools.org	38
Gallia Co Local School Dist	gallialocal.org/	80
Gallia-Jackson-Vinton JVSD	bhcc.k12.oh.us/	80
Gallipolis City School Dist	gallipoliscityschools.k12.oh.us/	81
Garaway Local School Dist	garaway.org/	202
Garfield Heights City SD	garfieldheightscityschools.com/	46
Geneva Area City School Dist	genevaschools.org	13
Genoa Area Local School Dist	genoaschools.com/	159
Georgetown Exempted Village SD	gtown.k12.oh.us/	19
Gibsonburg Exempted Village SD	gibsonburg.k12.oh.us/	177

School Year 2019-2020 800-333-8802 OH-W3

DISTRICT URL INDEX

Market Data Retrieval

DISTRICT	URL	PAGE
Girard City School Dist	girardcityschools.org/wp/	197
Goshen Local School Dist	goshenlocalschools.org/	30
Graham Local School Dist	grahamlocalschools.org/	25
Grand Valley Local School Dist	grand-valley.k12.oh.us/	13
Grandview Heights City SD	grandviewschools.org	70
Granville Exempted Village SD	granville.k12.oh.us/	117
Great Oaks Career Campuses	greatoaks.com/	89
Green Local School Dist	green.k12.oh.us/	178
Green Local School Dist	greenlocalschools.org/	185
Green Local School Dist	green-local.k12.oh.us/	212
Greene Co Voc School Dist	greeneccc.com/	84
Greeneview Local School Dist	greeneview.k12.oh.us/	84
Greenfield Exempted Village SD	greenfield.k12.oh.us/	103
Greenon Local School Dist	greenon.k12.oh.us/	27
Greenville City School Dist	greenville.k12.oh.us	55
Groveport Madison Local SD	gocruisers.org/	71
Hamilton City School Dist	hamiltoncityschools.com/	21
Hamilton Local School Dist	hamilton-local.k12.oh.us	71
Hardin Northern Local Sch Dist	hn.k12.oh.us/	100
Hardin-Houston Local Sch Dist	houston.k12.oh.us/	182
Harrison Hills City Sch Dist	hhcsd.org/	101
Heath City School Dist	heath.k12.oh.us	117
Hicksville Exempted Village SD	hicksvilleschools.org/	57
Highland Local School Dist	highlandschools.org/	141
Highland Local School Dist	highland.k12.oh.us/	155
Hilliard City School Dist	hilliardschools.org/	71
Hillsboro City School Dist	hillsboro.k12.oh.us/	103
Hillsdale Local School Dist	hillsdale.k12.oh.us/	11
Holgate Local School Dist	holgate.k12.oh.us/	101
Hopewell-Loudon Local SD	hopewell-loudon.k12.oh.us/	181
Howland Local School Dist	howlandschools.com/	198
Hubbard Exempted Village SD	hubbard.k12.oh.us/	198
Huber Heights City School Dist	huberheightscityschools.org/	150
Hudson City School Dist	hudson.k12.oh.us	193
Huntington Local School Dist	huntsmen.org/	175
Huron City School Dist	huronhs.com	60
Independence Local School Dist	independence.k12.oh.us/	46
Indian Creek Local Sch Dist	indian-creek.k12.oh.us/	109
Indian Hill Exempted Vlg SD	ih.k12.oh.us	90
Indian Lake Local School Dist	indianlake.k12.oh.us	121
Indian Valley Local Sch Dist	ivtv.k12.oh.us/	202
Ironton City School Dist	tigertown.com/	116
Jackson Center Local Sch Dist	jackson-center.k12.oh.us/	183
Jackson City School Dist	jcs.k12.oh.us/	107
Jackson Local School Dist	jackson.stark.k12.oh.us/	186
Jackson-Milton Local Sch Dist	jacksonmilton.k12.oh.us	134
James A Garfield Local SD	garfield.sparcc.org/	165
Jefferson Area Local SD	jalsd.org	13
Jefferson Co JT Voc Sch Dist	jeffjvs.org/	109
Jefferson Local School Dist	west-jefferson.k12.oh.us/	132
Jefferson Twp Local Sch Dist	jeffersontwp.k12.oh.us/	150
Jennings Local School Dist	jenningslocal.org/	169
Johnstown-Monroe Local SD	johnstown.k12.oh.us/	118
Jonathan Alder Local Sch Dist	alder.k12.oh.us	132
Joseph Badger Local Sch Dist	badgerbraves.org/	198
Kalida Local School Dist	kalida.k12.oh.us	169
Kelleys Island Local Sch Dist	kelleys.k12.oh.us/	61
Kenston Local School Dist	kenstonlocal.com/	82
Kent City School Dist	kent.k12.oh.us/	165
Kenton City School Dist	kentoncityschools.org/	100
Kettering City School Dist	ketteringschools.org/	150
Keystone Local School Dist	keystonelocalschools.org/	124
Kings Local School Dist	kingslocal.net/	207
Kirtland Local School Dist	kirtlandschools.org/	112
Knox Co Voc School Dist	knoxcc.org/	111
Labrae Local School Dist	labrae.k12.oh.us/	198
Lake Local School Dist	lakelocal.org/	186
Lake Local School Dist	lakeschools.org/	217
Lakeview Local School Dist	lakeviewlocal.org/	198
Lakewood City School Dist	lakewoodcityschools.org/	47
Lakewood Local School Dist	lakewoodlocal.k12.oh.us/	118
Lakota Local School Dist	lakotaonline.com/	22
Lakota Local School Dist	lakota-sandusky.k12.oh.us/	177
Lancaster City School Dist	lancaster.k12.oh.us	63

Ohio School Directory

DISTRICT URL INDEX

DISTRICT	URL	PAGE
Lawrence Co Joint Voc Sch Dist	collins-cc.k12.oh.us/	116
Lebanon City School Dist	lebanonschools.org/	207
Leetonia Exempted Village SD	leetonia.k12.oh.us/	35
Leipsic Local School Dist	llsdk12.org/	170
Lexington Local School Dist	lexington.k12.oh.us/	172
Liberty Center Local Sch Dist	libertycenter.k12.oh.us	101
Liberty Local School Dist	liberty.k12.oh.us/	199
Liberty Union-Thurstn Sch Dist	libertyunion.org/	64
Liberty-Benton Local Sch Dist	liberty-benton.org/	98
Licking Co Joint Voc Sch Dist	c-tec.edu/	118
Licking Heights Local Sch Dist	licking-heights.k12.oh.us/	118
Licking Valley Local Sch Dist	lickingvalley.k12.oh.us/	118
Lima City School Dist	limacityschools.org/	9
Lincolnview Local School Dist	lincolnview.k12.oh.us/	205
Lisbon Exempted Village SD	lisbon.k12.oh.us/	35
Little Miami Local School Dist	littlemiamischools.com/	207
Lockland School Dist	locklandschools.org/	90
Logan Elm Local School Dist	loganelmschools.com/	162
Logan-Hocking Local Sch Dist	loganhocking.k12.oh.us/	104
London City School Dist	london.k12.oh.us	132
Lorain City School Dist	lorainschools.org/	124
Lorain Co Joint Voc Sch Dist	lcjvs.com/	125
Lordstown Local School Dist	lordstown.k12.oh.us/	199
Loudonville-Perrysville SD	lpschools.k12.oh.us/	11
Louisville City School Dist	louisvillecityschools.org/	186
Loveland City School Dist	lovelandschools.org/	90
Lowellville Local School Dist	lowellville.k12.oh.us/	135
Lucas Local School Dist	lucascubs.org	172
Lynchburg-Clay Local Sch Dist	lynchclay.k12.oh.us/	103
Mad River Local School Dist	madriver.k12.oh.us/	151
Madeira City School Dist	madeiracityschools.org/	90
Madison Local School Dist	madisonmohawks.org/	23
Madison Local School Dist	madisonschools.net/	112
Madison Local School Dist	mlsd.net/	172
Madison Plains Local Sch Dist	mplsd.org/	133
Mahoning Co Joint Voc Sch Dist	mahoningctc.com/	135
Manchester Local School Dist	mlsd.us/	7
Manchester Local School Dist	panthercountry.org/	193
Mansfield City Schools	mansfieldschools.org/	172
Maple Heights City School Dist	mapleschools.com/	47
Mapleton Local School Dist	mapleton.k12.oh.us	11
Maplewood JT Voc School Dist	mwood.cc/	166
Maplewood Local School Dist	maplewood.k12.oh.us/	199
Margaretta Local School Dist	margaretta.k12.oh.us/	61
Mariemont City School Dist	mariemontschools.org/	90
Marietta City School Dist	mariettacityschools.k12.oh.us/	210
Marion City School Dist	marioncityschools.org/	138
Marion Local School Dist	marionlocal.org/	144
Marlington Local School Dist	marlingtonlocal.org/	186
Martins Ferry City School Dist	mfcsd.k12.oh.us/	18
Marysville Exempted Village SD	marysville.k12.oh.us/	204
Mason City School Dist	masonohioschools.com	208
Massillon City School Dist	massillonschools.org/	187
Mathews Local School Dist	mathews.k12.oh.us/	199
Maumee City School Dist	maumee.k12.oh.us/	127
Mayfield City School Dist	mayfieldschools.org/	47
Maysville Local School Dist	maysville.k12.oh.us/	156
McComb Local School Dist	mccomblocalschools.org/	98
McDonald Local School Dist	mcdonald.k12.oh.us/	199
Mechanicsburg Exempted Vlg SD	mechanicsburg.k12.oh.us/	26
Medina City School Dist	medinabees.org/Medina	141
Medina Co Joint Voc Sch Dist	mcjvs.edu/ui/	141
Meigs Local School Dist	ml.k12.oh.us/	142
Mentor Exempted Village SD	mentorschools.net/	113
Miami East Local School Dist	miamieast.k12.oh.us/	145
Miami Trace Local School Dist	miamitrace.k12.oh.us/	65
Miami Valley Career Tech VSD	mvctc.com/	151
Miamisburg City School Dist	miamisburgcityschools.org/	151
Middletown City School Dist	middletowncityschools.com/	23
Mideast Career & Tech Ctrs	mid-east.k12.oh.us	157
Midview Local School Dist	midviewk12.org/	125
Milford Exempted Village SD	milfordschools.org/	30
Millcreek-West Unity Local SD	hilltop.k12.oh.us	215
Miller City-New Cleveland SD	web.ml.noacsc.org	170

School Year 2019-2020 800-333-8802

DISTRICT URL INDEX

DISTRICT	URL	PAGE
Milton-Union Exempted Vlg SD	milton-union.k12.oh.us/	145
Minerva Local School Dist	mlsd.sparcc.org/	187
Minford Local School Dist	minford.k12.oh.us/	178
Minster Local School Dist	minsterschools.org/	15
Mississinawa Valley Sch Dist	mississinawa.k12.oh.us/	56
Mogadore Local School Dist	mogadore.net/	166
Mohawk Local School Dist	mohawk.k12.oh.us/	219
Monroe Local School Dist	monroelocalschools.com/	23
Monroeville Local School Dist	monroevilleschools.org/	105
Montpelier Exempted Village SD	montpelier.k12.oh.us	215
Morgan Local School Dist	mlsd.k12.oh.us/	154
Mt Gilead Exempted Village SD	mtgilead.k12.oh.us/	155
Mt Healthy City School Dist	mthcs.org/	91
Mt Vernon City School Dist	mt-vernon.k12.oh.us	111
Napoleon Area City School Dist	napoleon.k12.oh.us/	101
National Trail Local Sch Dist	nationaltrail.k12.oh.us/	168
Nelsonville-York City Sch Dist	nelsonvilleyork.k12.oh.us/	15
New Albany-Plain Local SD	napls.us/site/default.aspx?PageID=1	72
New Boston Local School Dist	newboston.k12.oh.us/	178
New Bremen Local School Dist	bremen.k12.oh.us/	16
New Knoxville Local Sch Dist	nk.k12.oh.us/	16
New Lebanon Local School Dist	newlebanon.k12.oh.us/	151
New Lexington School Dist	nlpanthers.org	161
New London Local School Dist	nlschools.org/	105
New Miami Local School Dist	new-miami.k12.oh.us/	23
New Philadelphia City Sch Dist	npschools.org/	202
New Richmond Exempted Vlg SD	nrschools.org	31
New Riegel Local School Dist	newriegelschools.org/	181
Newark City School Dist	newarkcity.k12.oh.us/	119
Newbury Local School Dist	newburyschools.org/	82
Newcomerstown Exempted Vlg SD	nctschools.org	203
Newton Falls Exempted Vlg SD	newton-falls.k12.oh.us/	200
Newton Local School Dist	newton.k12.oh.us/	146
Niles City School Dist	nilescityschools.org	200
Noble Local School Dist	gozeps.org	158
Nordonia Hills City Sch Dist	nordoniaschools.org/	193
North Baltimore Local Sch Dist	northbaltimoreschools.org/	217
North Canton City School Dist	northcantonschools.org	187
North Central Local Sch Dist	ncschool.k12.oh.us/	215
North College Hill City SD	nchcityschools.org/	91
North Fork Local School Dist	northfork.k12.oh.us/	119
North Olmsted City School Dist	northolmstedschools.org/	48
North Ridgeville City Sch Dist	nrcs.k12.oh.us/	125
North Royalton City Sch Dist	northroyaltonsd.org/	48
North Union Local School Dist	n-union.k12.oh.us/	204
Northeastern Local School Dist	northeastern.k12.oh.us/	27
Northeastern Local School Dist	tinora.k12.oh.us/	57
Northern Local School Dist	nlsd.k12.oh.us/	161
Northmont City School Dist	northmontschools.com/	152
Northmor Local School Dist	northmor.k12.oh.us/	155
Northridge Local School Dist	northridge.k12.oh.us	119
Northridge Local School Dist	northridgeschools.org/	152
Northwest Local School Dist	nwlsd.org	91
Northwest Local School Dist	northwest.k12.oh.us/	179
Northwest Local School Dist	northwest.sparcc.org/	187
Northwestern Local School Dist	northwestern.k12.oh.us/	27
Northwestern Local School Dist	northwestern-wayne.k12.oh.us	212
Northwood Local School Dist	northwood.k12.oh.us/	217
Norton City School Dist	nortonschools.org/	193
Norwalk City School Dist	norwalk-city.k12.oh.us/	106
Norwayne Local School Dist	northcentral.k12.oh.us/	212
Norwood City School Dist	norwoodschools.org/	92
Oak Hill Union Local Sch Dist	oakhill.k12.oh.us/	107
Oak Hills Local School Dist	ohlsd.us/	92
Oakwood City School Dist	oakwoodschools.org/	152
Oberlin City School Dist	oberlinschools.net/	125
Ohio Hi-Point Joint Voc SD	ohp.k12.oh.us/	121
Old Fort Local School Dist	old-fort.k12.oh.us/	181
Olentangy Local School Dist	olentangy.k12.oh.us/	59
Olmsted Falls City School Dist	ofcs.k12.oh.us/	48
Ontario Local School Dist	ontarioschools.org/	173
Orange City School Dist	orangeschools.org/	48
Oregon City School Dist	oregoncityschools.org/	128
Orrville City School Dist	orrville.k12.oh.us/	212

Ohio School Directory

DISTRICT URL INDEX

DISTRICT	URL	PAGE
Osnaburg Local School Dist	ecweb.sparcc.org/	188
Otsego Local School Dist	otsego.k12.oh.us	217
Ottawa Hills Local Sch Dist	ohschools.k12.oh.us	128
Ottawa-Glandorf Local Sch Dist	ottawaglandorf.org/	170
Ottoville Local School Dist	ottovilleschools.org/	170
Painesville City Local SD	painesville-city.k12.oh.us/	113
Paint Valley Local School Dist	paintvalleylocalschools.org/	175
Pandora Gilboa Local Sch Dist	pg.noacsc.org	170
Parkway Local School Dist	parkwayschools.org	144
Parma City School Dist	parmacityschools.org/	49
Patrick Henry Local Sch Dist	patrickhenry.k12.oh.us/	102
Paulding Exempted Village SD	pauldingschools.org/	160
Penta Co JT Voc School Dist	pentacareercenter.org/	217
Perkins Local School Dist	perkinsschools.org/	61
Perry Local School Dist	mycommodores.org/	9
Perry Local School Dist	perry-lake.org/	113
Perry Local School Dist	perrylocal.org/	188
Perrysburg Exempted Village SD	perrysburg.k12.oh.us/	218
Pettisville Local School Dist	blackbirds.pettisville.k12.oh.us/	79
Pickaway-Ross Co JT Voc SD	pickawayross.com	175
Pickerington Local School Dist	pickerington.k12.oh.us/	64
Pike Co Area JT Voc Sch Dist	pikectc.org/	163
Pike-Delta-York Local Sch Dist	pdy.k12.oh.us/	79
Pioneer Joint Voc School Dist	pctc.k12.oh.us/	173
Piqua City School Dist	piqua.org/	146
Plain Local School Dist	plainlocal.org/	188
Pleasant Local School Dist	pleasantlocalschools.org/	138
Plymouth-Shiloh Local Sch Dist	plymouth.schoolwires.com/	173
Poland Local School Dist	polandbulldogs.com/	135
Polaris Joint Voc School Dist	polaris.edu	49
Port Clinton City School Dist	pccsd.net/	159
Portage Lakes Joint Voc SD	plcc.k12.oh.us/	189
Portsmouth City School Dist	portsmouth.k12.oh.us	179
Preble-Shawnee Local Sch Dist	preble-shawnee.k12.oh.us/	168
Princeton City School Dist	princetonschools.net/	92
Put-In-Bay Local School Dist	put-in-bay.k12.oh.us/	159
Pymatuning Valley Local SD	pvschools.org/	13
Ravenna School Dist	ravennaschools.us/home	166
Reading Cmty City School Dist	readingschools.org/	93
Revere Local School Dist	revere.k12.oh.us/	194
Reynoldsburg City School Dist	reyn.org/	72
Richmond Heights Local SD	richmondheightsschools.org/	49
Ridgedale Local School Dist	ridgedale.k12.oh.us/	138
Ridgemont Local School Dist	ridgemont.k12.oh.us/	100
Ridgewood Local School Dist	ridgewood.k12.oh.us	37
Ripley-Union-Lewis-Huntngtn SD	ripley.k12.oh.us	20
Rittman Exempted Village SD	rittman.k12.oh.us/	212
River Valley Local School Dist	rvk12.org/	139
River View Local School Dist	river-view.k12.oh.us/	37
Riverdale Local School Dist	riverdale.k12.oh.us	98
Riverside Local School Dist	riverside.k12.oh.us/	121
Riverside Local School Dist	painesville-township.k12.oh.us/	113
Rock Hill Local School Dist	rockhill.org	116
Rocky River City School Dist	rrcs.org/	50
Rolling Hills Local Sch Dist	rollinghills.k12.oh.us/	86
Rootstown Local School Dist	rootstown.sparcc.org/	166
Ross Local School Dist	rossrams.com/	24
Rossford Exempted Village SD	rossfordschools.org/	218
Russia Local School Dist	russiaschool.org/home	183
Salem City School Dist	salem.k12.oh.us/	35
Sandusky City School Dist	sandusky-city.k12.oh.us/	61
Sandy Valley Local School Dist	sandyvalleylocal.org/	189
Scioto Co Joint Vocational SD	sciototech.org/	179
Scioto Valley Local Sch Dist	piketon.k12.oh.us/	164
Sebring Local School Dist	sebring.k12.oh.us	135
Seneca East Local School Dist	seneca-east.k12.oh.us/	181
Shadyside Local School Dist	shadysideschools.com/	18
Shaker Heights City Sch Dist	shaker.org/	50
Shawnee Local School Dist	limashawnee.com/	9
Sheffield-Sheffield Lake CSD	sheffield.k12.oh.us/	125
Shelby City School Dist	shelby-city.k12.oh.us/	173
Sidney City School Dist	sidney.k12.oh.us/	183
Solon City School Dist	solonschools.org/	50
South Central Local Sch Dist	south-central.k12.oh.us	106

School Year 2019-2020 800-333-8802 OH-W7

DISTRICT URL INDEX

Market Data Retrieval

DISTRICT	URL	PAGE
South Euclid-Lyndhurst City SD	sel.k12.oh.us/	50
South Point Local School Dist	southpoint.k12.oh.us/	116
South Range Local School Dist	southrange.k12.oh.us/	135
South-Western City School Dist	swcsd.us/	73
Southeast Local School Dist	southeast.k12.oh.us/	213
Southeast Local School Dist	sepirates.org/contactus.aspx	166
Southeastern Local Sch Dist	sepanthers.k12.oh.us/	175
Southeastern Local School Dist	sels.us/	28
Southern Hills Joint Voc SD	shctc.k12.oh.us/	20
Southern Local School Dist	southern.k12.oh.us	35
Southern Local School Dist	southernlocalmeigs.org/	143
Southern Local School Dist	spsd.k12.oh.us	161
Southington Local School Dist	southington.k12.oh.us/	200
Southwest Licking Local SD	swl.k12.oh.us/	120
Southwest Local School Dist	southwestschools.org	93
Spencerville Local School Dist	noacsc.org/allen/sv/sv_home.htm	9
Springboro Cmty School Dist	springboro.org/	208
Springfield City School Dist	scsdoh.org/	28
Springfield Local School Dist	springfieldspartans.org/	194
Springfield Local School Dist	springfield-schools.org/	128
Springfield Local School Dist	springfield.k12.oh.us/	135
Springfield-Clark Co JVSD	scctc.org/	28
St Bernard-Elmwood Place Schs	sbepschools.org/	93
St Clairsville-Richland CSD	stcs.k12.oh.us	18
St Henry Cons Local Sch Dist	sthenryschools.org/	144
St Mary's City School Dist	smriders.net/	16
Stark Co Area Voc Sch Dist	drage.stark.k12.oh.us/	189
Steubenville City School Dist	steubenville.k12.oh.us/	109
Stow-Munroe Falls City SD	smfschools.org/	194
Strasburg Franklin Local SD	strasburg.k12.oh.us/	203
Streetsboro City School Dist	scsrockets.org/	167
Strongsville City School Dist	strongnet.org/Page/214	51
Struthers City School Dist	strutherscityschools.org/struthers/	136
Stryker Local School Dist	stryker.k12.oh.us/index.php?section=1	215
Swanton Local School Dist	swantonschools.org/	79
Switzerland of Ohio Local SD	swissohio.k12.oh.us/	147
Sycamore Cmty School Dist	sycamoreschools.org/	93
Sylvania City School Dist	sylvania.k12.oh.us/	128
Symmes Valley Local Sch Dist	symmesvalley.k12.oh.us/	117
Talawanda School Dist	talawanda.net/	24
Tallmadge City School Dist	tallmadgeschools.org/	194
Teays Valley Local School Dist	tvsd.us/	162
Tecumseh Local School Dist	tecumseh.k12.oh.us/	28
Three Rivers Local School Dist	threeriversschools.org	94
Tiffin City School Dist	tiffin.k12.oh.us/	181
Tipp City Exempted Village SD	tippcityschools.com/	146
Toledo Public Schools	tps.org	129
Tolles Career & Tech Sch Dist	tollestech.com	133
Toronto City School Dist	torontocityschools.k12.oh.us/	109
Tri-Co Joint Voc Sch Dist	tricountyhightech.com/	15
Tri-Co North School Dist	tcnschools.com	168
Tri-Rivers Joint Voc Sch Dist	tririvers.com/	139
Tri-Valley Local School Dist	tri-valley.k12.oh.us/	157
Tri-Village Local Sch Dist	tri-village.k12.oh.us/	56
Triad Local School Dist	triad.k12.oh.us/	26
Trimble Local School Dist	trimble.k12.oh.us/	15
Triway Local School Dist	triway.k12.oh.us/	213
Trotwood-Madison City SD	trotwood.k12.oh.us/	152
Troy City School Dist	troy.k12.oh.us	146
Tuscarawas Valley Local SD	tvtrojans.org/	203
Tuslaw Local School Dist	tuslaw.sparcc.org/	189
Twin Valley Cmty Local SD	tvs.k12.oh.us/	169
Twinsburg City School Dist	twinsburg.k12.oh.us	195
U S Grant Career School Dist	grantcareer.com/	31
Union Local School Dist	ulschools.com/	18
Union Scioto Local Sch Dist	unioto.k12.oh.us/	175
United Local School Dist	united.k12.oh.us/	36
Upper Arlington City Sch Dist	uaschools.org/	74
Upper Sandusky Exempted Vlg SD	usevs.org/	219
Upper Scioto Valley Local SD	usv.k12.oh.us/	100
Upper Valley JT Voc Sch Dist	uppervalleycc.org/	147
Urbana City School Dist	urbanacityschools.org/	26
Valley Local School Dist	valley.k12.oh.us/	179
Valley View Local School Dist	valleyview.k12.oh.us/	153

OH-W8   800-333-8802   School Year 2019-2020

Ohio School Directory

DISTRICT URL INDEX

DISTRICT	URL	PAGE
Van Buren Local School Dist	VBSCHOOLS.NET	99
Van Wert City School Dist	vwcs.net/	205
Vandalia Butler City Sch Dist	vbcsd.com/	153
Vanguard-Sentinel JT Voc SD	vscc.k12.oh.us/	177
Vanlue Local School Dist	vanlueschool.org/	99
Vantage Career Center Sch Dist	vantagecareercenter.com/	206
Vermilion Local School Dist	vermilionschools.org/	62
Versailles Exempted Village SD	versailles.k12.oh.us/	56
Vinton Co Local School Dist	vinton.k12.oh.us	206
Wadsworth City School Dist	wadsworth.k12.oh.us/	141
Walnut Twp Local School Dist	walnuttsd.org/	64
Wapakoneta City School Dist	wapak.org/	16
Warren City School Dist	warrenschools.k12.oh.us/	200
Warren Co Voc School Dist	mywccc.org/	208
Warren Local School Dist	warrenlocal.org/	210
Warrensville Heights City SD	warrensville.k12.oh.us/	51
Washington Co JT Voc Sch Dist	washingtoncocareerctr.com/	210
Washington Court House City SD	washingtonch.k12.oh.us/	65
Washington Local School Dist	wls4kids.org/	130
Washington-Nile Local Sch Dist	west.k12.oh.us/	179
Waterloo Local School Dist	viking.portage.k12.oh.us/	167
Wauseon Exempted Village SD	sites.google.com/a/wauseonindians.org/wevs2/	79
Waverly City School Dist	waverly.k12.oh.us/	164
Wayne Co Joint Voc School Dist	wayne-jvs.k12.oh.us/	213
Wayne Local School Dist	wayne-local.com/	208
Wayne Trace Local School Dist	waynetrace.org/	160
Waynesfield-Goshen Local SD	wgschools.org/	16
Weathersfield Local Sch Dist	weathersfield.k12.oh.us/	200
Wellington Exempted Village SD	wellington.k12.oh.us/	126
Wellston City School Dist	wcs.k12.oh.us/	108
Wellsville Local Sch Dist	wellsville.k12.oh.us/	36
West Branch Local School Dist	westbranch.k12.oh.us/	136
West Carrollton City Sch Dist	westcarrolltonschools.com/	153
West Clermont Local Sch Dist	westcler.k12.oh.us	31
West Geauga Local School Dist	westg.org/	82
West Holmes Local School Dist	westholmes.k12.oh.us/	105
West Liberty-Salem Local SD	wls.k12.oh.us/	26
West Muskingum Local Sch Dist	westm.k12.oh.us/	157
Western Brown Local Sch Dist	wb.k12.oh.us/	20
Western Local School Dist	westernlocalschools.com/	164
Western Reserve Local Sch Dist	western-reserve.org/	106
Western Reserve Local Sch Dist	westernreserve.k12.oh.us	136
Westerville City School Dist	westerville.k12.oh.us	74
Westfall Local School Dist	westfall.k12.oh.us/	163
Westlake City School Dist	wlake.org/	51
Wheelersburg Local School Dist	burg.k12.oh.us/	180
Whitehall City School Dist	whitehallcityschools.org/	75
Wickliffe City School Dist	wickliffe-city.k12.oh.us/	114
Willard City School Dist	willard.k12.oh.us/	106
Williamsburg Local School Dist	williamsburg.k12.oh.us/	32
Willoughby-Eastlake City SD	weschools.org/	114
Wilmington City School Dist	wilmington.k12.oh.us/	33
Windham Exempted Vlg Sch Dist	windham-schools.org/	167
Winton Woods City School Dist	wintonwoods.org/	94
Wolf Creek Local School Dist	wolfcreek.k12.oh.us	211
Woodmore Local School Dist	woodmore.k12.oh.us/	159
Woodridge Local School Dist	woodridge.k12.oh.us/	195
Wooster City School Dist	woostercityschools.org	213
Worthington School Dist	worthington.k12.oh.us/	75
Wynford Local School Dist	wynford.k12.oh.us/	39
Wyoming City School Dist	wyomingcityschools.org/	94
Xenia Community School Dist	xenia.k12.oh.us/	84
Yellow Springs Exempted Vlg SD	yellow-springs.k12.oh.us/	85
Youngstown City School Dist	youngstown.k12.oh.us	136
Zane Trace Local School Dist	zanetrace.org/	176
Zanesville City School Dist	zanesville.k12.oh.us	157

MDR School Directory

CHARTER MANAGEMENT ORGANIZATION (CMO) INDEX

CMO No.	PID	CMO Name	Address	Phone
001	11912383	Estem Public Charter Schools	200 River Market Ave Ste 225, Little Rock AR 72201	(501) 324-9200
002	11916092	KIPP Delta Public Schools	415 Ohio, Helena AR 72342	(870) 753-9035
003	12319502	Lisa Academy Foundation	10825 Financial Centre Pkwy, Little Rock AR 72211	(501) 916-9450
004	11912826	Academy of Tucson Inc	10720 E 22nd St, Tucson AZ 85748	(520) 733-0096
005	11914305	Accelerated Learning Ctr	4105 E Shea Blvd, Phoenix AZ 85028	(602) 485-0309
006	11914288	Allen-Cochran Enterprises	1700 E Elliot Rd Ste 9, Tempe AZ 85284	(480) 632-1940
007	11914264	American Basic Schools LLC	131 E Southern Ave, Mesa AZ 85210	(480) 655-7868
008	11928033	American Leadership Acad Inc	2250 E Germann Rd Ste 14, Chandler AZ 85286	(480) 420-2101
009	11912761	Arizona Agribus&Equine Ctr Org	315 E Mulberry Dr, Phoenix AZ 85012	(602) 297-8500
010	11912759	Arizona Charter Schools	5704 E Grant Rd, Tucson AZ 85712	(520) 545-0575
011	11912723	Basis School Inc	7975 N Hayden Rd Ste B202, Scottsdale AZ 85258	(480) 289-2088
012	11914525	Benjamin Franklin Chtr Schools	690 E Warner Rd, Gilbert AZ 85296	(480) 264-3710
013	11912668	Blueprint Education	5651 W Talavi Blvd Ste 170, Glendale AZ 85306	(602) 674-5555
014	11914226	Bright Beginnings School Inc	400 N Andersen Blvd, Chandler AZ 85224	(480) 821-1404
015	11912620	CAFA Inc	4055 E Warner Rd, Gilbert AZ 85296	(480) 635-1900
016	11913387	Career Success Schools	3816 N 27th Ave, Phoenix AZ 85017	(602) 285-5525
017	11913351	Center for Academic Success	1843 Paseo San Luis, Sierra Vista AZ 85635	(520) 458-9309
018	11914173	Compass High School Inc	PO Box 17810, Tucson AZ 85731	(520) 296-4070
019	11914159	Cornerstone Charter School Inc	7107 N Black Canyon Hwy, Phoenix AZ 85021	(602) 595-2198
020	11914147	Country Gardens Educl Svcs	6313 W Southern Ave, Laveen AZ 85339	(602) 237-3741
021	11914111	Eastpointe High School Inc	8495 E Broadway Blvd, Tucson AZ 85710	(520) 731-8180
022	11914068	Educational Impact Inc	1950 E Placita Sin Nombre, Tucson AZ 85718	(520) 407-1200
023	11914044	Eduprize Schools Inc	4567 W Roberts Rd, Queen Creek AZ 85142	(480) 888-1610
024	11912395	Espiritu Community Development	4848 S 2nd St, Phoenix AZ 85040	(602) 243-7788
025	11914032	GAR LLC	8253 W Thunderbird Rd Ste 105, Peoria AZ 85381	(602) 334-4104
026	11913234	Great Hearts Academies	4801 E Washington St Ste 250, Phoenix AZ 85034	(602) 438-7045
027	11913985	Heritage Academy Inc	32 S Center St, Mesa AZ 85210	(480) 969-5641
028	11914434	Humanities & Sciences Acad US	5201 N 7th St, Phoenix AZ 85014	(602) 650-1333
029	11911781	Imagine Southwest Regional	1843 W 16th Ave, Apache Jct AZ 85120	(480) 355-0502
030	11913179	Kingman Academy of Learning	3410 N Burbank St, Kingman AZ 86409	(928) 681-2400
031	11913167	Leading Edge Charter Solutions	633 E Ray Rd Ste 132, Gilbert AZ 85296	(480) 633-0414
032	11913143	Learning Matters Educl Group	4744 W Grovers Ave, Glendale AZ 85308	(602) 439-5026
033	11913959	Legacy Traditional Schools	3125 S Gilbert Rd, Chandler AZ 85286	(480) 270-5438
034	11914599	Leona Group LLC-AZ	7878 N 16th St Ste 150, Phoenix AZ 85020	(602) 953-2933
035	11914381	Mgrm Pinnacle Education Inc	2224 W Southern Ave Ste 1, Tempe AZ 85282	(480) 755-8222
036	11913911	Montessori Schoolhouse Tucson	1301 E Fort Lowell Rd, Tucson AZ 85719	(520) 319-8668
037	11913923	Montessori Schools Flagstaff	2212 E Cedar Ave, Flagstaff AZ 86004	(928) 774-1600
038	12305874	Pima Prevention Partnership	924 N Alvernon Way, Tucson AZ 85711	(520) 791-2711
039	12306309	Plc Charter Schools	2504 S 91st Ave, Tolleson AZ 85353	(623) 474-2120
040	11912101	Pointe Educational Services	10215 N 43rd Ave, Phoenix AZ 85051	(602) 843-2014
041	11913519	PPEP and Affiliates	802 E 46th St, Tucson AZ 85713	(520) 622-3553
042	11913856	Rose Management Group	3686 W Orange Grove Rd Ste 192, Tucson AZ 85741	(520) 797-4884
043	11913832	Self Development Chtr Sch Org	1709 N Greenfield Rd, Mesa AZ 85205	(480) 641-2640
044	11913337	Sequoia Schools-Edkey Inc	1460 S Horne Bldg 6, Mesa AZ 85204	(480) 461-3200
045	11912979	Skyline Education	7450 S 40th St 7500, Phoenix AZ 85042	(877) 225-2118
046	11913349	Sonoran Schools Inc	1489 W Elliot Rd Ste 103, Gilbert AZ 85233	(480) 940-5440
047	11913806	Southern Arizona Cmty Acad Inc	2470 N Tucson Blvd, Tucson AZ 85716	(520) 319-6113
048	11912929	The Charter Foundation Inc	1150 N Country Club Rd Ste 100, Tucson AZ 85716	(520) 296-1100
049	11911901	The Edge School Inc	2555 E 1st St, Tucson AZ 85716	(520) 881-1389
050	11912890	Tucson International Academy	2700 W Broadway Blvd, Tucson AZ 85745	(520) 792-3255
051	11912802	Albert Einstein Academies	3035 Ash St, San Diego CA 92102	(619) 795-1190
052	11913686	Alliance College-Ready Pub Sch	601 S Figueroa St Fl 4, Los Angeles CA 90017	(213) 943-4930
053	12305812	Alpha Public Schools	PO Box 21366, San Jose CA 95151	(408) 455-6355
054	12262961	Alta Public Schools	2410 Broadway, Huntington Pk CA 90255	(323) 923-0383
055	11912785	American Indian Model Schools	171 12th St, Oakland CA 94607	(510) 893-8701
056	12262911	Amethod Public Schools	2101 Livingston St, Oakland CA 94606	(510) 436-0172
057	11913648	Aspire Public Schools	1001 22nd Ave Ste 100, Oakland CA 94606	(510) 434-5000
058	11912656	Bright Star Education Group	600 S La Fayette Park Pl, Los Angeles CA 90057	(323) 954-9957
059	11913404	California Montessori Projects	5330A Gibbons Dr Ste 700, Carmichael CA 95608	(916) 971-2432
060	11913399	Camino Nuevo Charter Academy	3435 W Temple St, Los Angeles CA 90026	(213) 417-3400

CHARTER MANAGEMENT ORGANIZATION (CMO) INDEX — Market Data Retrieval

CMO No.	PID	CMO Name	Address	Phone
061	11912709	Ceiba Public Schools	260 W Riverside Dr, Watsonville CA 95076	(831) 740-8800
062	12260028	Citizens of the World Chtr Sch	5371 Wilshire Blvd Ste 210, Los Angeles CA 90036	(323) 634-7109
063	11912565	Civicorps Schools	101 Myrtle St, Oakland CA 94607	(510) 992-7800
064	11912539	Community Learning Center Schs	1900 3rd St, Alameda CA 94501	(510) 263-9266
065	11912527	Core-Cmty Options Resources Ed	321 16th St, Marysville CA 95901	(530) 742-2786
066	12110435	Downtown College Prep	1400 Parkmoor Ave Ste 206, San Jose CA 95126	(408) 271-8120
067	12261486	Ednovate Inc	3939 S Vermont Ave, Los Angeles CA 90037	(213) 454-0599
068	11912436	Education for Change	333 Hegenberger Rd Ste 600, Oakland CA 94621	(510) 568-7936
069	11912412	Environmental Charter Schools	2625 Manhattn Bch Blvd Ste 100, Redondo Beach CA 90278	(310) 214-3408
070	11913301	Envision Education	111 Myrtle St Ste 203, Oakland CA 94607	(510) 451-2415
071	12179015	Equitas Academy Chtr Sch Inc	1700 W Pico Blvd, Los Angeles CA 90015	(213) 201-0440
072	12305824	Fenton Charter Public Schools	8928 Sunland Blvd, Sun Valley CA 91352	(818) 962-3630
073	11912357	Five Keys Charter Schools Inc	70 Oak Grove St, San Francisco CA 94107	(415) 734-3310
074	12262935	Fortune School of Education	2890 Gateway Oaks Dr Ste 100, Sacramento CA 95833	(916) 924-8633
075	11913258	Gateway Community Charters	5112 Arnold Ave Ste A, McClellan CA 95652	(916) 286-5129
076	11912319	Golden Valley Charter Schools	3585 Maple St Ste 101, Ventura CA 93003	(805) 642-3435
077	11913595	Green Dot Public Schools	1149 S Hill St Ste 600, Los Angeles CA 90015	(323) 565-1600
078	12239598	Grimmway Schools	5080 California Ave Ste 100, Bakersfield CA 93309	(661) 432-7880
079	11912280	High Desert Partnsp Acad Excel	17500 Mana Rd, Apple Valley CA 92307	(760) 946-5414
080	11913222	High Tech High	2861 Womble Rd, San Diego CA 92106	(619) 243-5000
081	11913583	ICEF Public Schools	3855 W Slauson Ave, Los Angeles CA 90043	(323) 290-6900
082	11912266	Innovative Education Managemnt	4535 Missouri Flat Rd Ste 1A, Placerville CA 95667	(800) 979-4436
083	11913375	Isana Academies	3580 Wilshire Blvd Ste 1130, Los Angeles CA 90010	(323) 291-1211
084	11913181	King-Chavez Neighborhood Schs	415 31st St, San Diego CA 92102	(619) 525-7320
085	11916054	KIPP Bay Area Public Schools	1000 Broadway Ste 460, Oakland CA 94607	(510) 465-5477
086	11913571	KIPP Foundation	135 Main St Ste 1700, San Francisco CA 94105	(415) 399-1556
087	11916169	KIPP LA Public Schools	3601 E 1st St, Los Angeles CA 90063	(213) 489-4461
088	12115045	KIPP San Diego Clg Prep Public	1475 6th Ave, San Diego CA 92101	(619) 233-3242
089	11913155	Leadership Public Schools	99 Linden St, Oakland CA 94607	(510) 830-3780
090	12260030	Los Angeles Education Corps	3635 Atlantic Ave, Long Beach CA 90807	(562) 216-1790
091	11913557	Magnolia Ed & Research Fdn	250 E 1st St Ste 1500, Los Angeles CA 90012	(213) 628-3634
092	11912187	National Univ Academy System	2030 University Dr, Vista CA 92083	(760) 630-4080
093	12262777	Navigator Schools	650 San Benito St Ste 230, Hollister CA 95023	(831) 217-4880
094	12361373	Olive Grove Charter Schools	2353 S Broadway, Santa Maria CA 93454	(805) 623-1111
095	11935907	Opportunities for Learning	320 N Halstead St Ste 220, Pasadena CA 91107	(888) 207-1119
096	11913052	Options for Youth Inc	320 N Halstead St Ste 280, Pasadena CA 91107	(888) 389-9992
097	12262923	Pacific Charter Institute	1401 El Camino Ave Ste 510, Sacramento CA 95815	(866) 992-9033
098	11912125	Para Los Ninos PCS	5000 Hollywood Blvd, Los Angeles CA 90027	(213) 250-4800
099	11913521	Partnerships to Uplift Cmty	1405 N San Fernando Blvd 303, Burbank CA 91504	(818) 559-7699
100	11912060	Real Journey Academies	1425 W Foothill Blvd Ste 100, Upland CA 91786	(909) 888-8458
101	11912046	Roads Education Organization	2999 Cleveland Ave Ste D, Santa Rosa CA 95403	(707) 843-4676
102	11912034	Rocketship Education	350 Twin Dolphin Dr Ste 109, Redwood City CA 94065	(877) 806-0920
103	11911872	Rocklin Academy Charter Schs	2204 Plaza Dr Ste 200, Rocklin CA 95765	(916) 778-4544
104	11912008	Semillas Sociedad Civil	4736 Huntington Dr S, Los Angeles CA 90032	(323) 352-3148
105	11911987	St Hope Public Schools	PO Box 5038, Sacramento CA 95817	(916) 649-7900
106	12101381	Summit Public Schools	780 Broadway St, Redwood City CA 94063	(650) 257-9880
107	11911925	The Accelerated School	116 E Mlk Jr Blvd, Los Angeles CA 90011	(323) 235-6343
108	11911884	The Learner-Centered School	3325 Hacienda Way, Antioch CA 94509	(925) 755-7311
109	11911846	Tracy Learning Center	51 E Beverly Pl, Tracy CA 95376	(209) 290-0511
110	11911822	Value Schools	680 Wilshire Pl Ste 315, Los Angeles CA 90005	(213) 388-8676
111	12306244	Western Sierra Charter Schools	41267 Highway 41, Oakhurst CA 93644	(559) 642-1422
112	12262791	Ypi Charter Schools	10660 White Oak Ave B101, Granada Hills CA 91344	(818) 834-5805
113	12321684	Colorado Early College Network	4405 N Chestnut St Ste E, Colorado Spgs CO 80907	(719) 955-4685
114	12322432	Global Village Charter Collab	10701 Melody Dr Ste 610, Denver CO 80234	(720) 353-4113
115	11916078	KIPP Colorado	1390 Lawrence St Ste 200, Denver CO 80204	(303) 934-3245
116	12305886	Rocky Mountain Prep Schools	7808 Cherry Creek Dr S, Denver CO 80231	(720) 863-8920
117	12110356	Strive Preparatory Schools	2480 W 26th Ave Ste 360B, Denver CO 80211	(720) 772-4300
118	12322626	Tatonka Education Services	10375 Park Meadows Dr Ste 230, Lone Tree CO 80124	(303) 296-6500
119	11913090	The New America Schools Netwk	925 S Niagara St Ste 140/400, Denver CO 80224	(303) 800-0058
120	11913698	Achievement First Network	370 James St Ste 404, New Haven CT 06513	(203) 773-3223

MDR School Directory — CHARTER MANAGEMENT ORGANIZATION (CMO) INDEX

CMO No.	PID	CMO Name	Address	Phone
121	11915414	Jumoke Academy Inc	999 Asylum Ave Ste 200, Hartford CT 06105	(860) 216-9636
122	11913650	Aspira Educl Management Org	1220 L St NW Ste 701, Washington DC 20005	(202) 835-3600
123	11913363	Center City Public Charter Sch	900 2nd St NE Ste 221, Washington DC 20002	(202) 589-0202
124	11912591	Cesar Chavez Public Chtr Schs	709 12th St SE, Washington DC 20003	(202) 547-3975
125	11912503	DC Prep	707 Edgewood St NE, Washington DC 20017	(202) 635-4590
126	11913260	Friendship Public Charter Sch	111 O St NW, Washington DC 20001	(202) 281-1700
127	11914836	KIPP DC	2600 Virginia Ave NW Ste 900, Washington DC 20037	(202) 223-4505
128	11912010	See Forever Foundation	600 Pnnsylvnia Ave SE Ste 210, Washington DC 20003	(202) 797-8250
129	11911860	The Seed Foundation	1730 Rh Isl Ave NW Ste 1102, Washington DC 20036	(202) 785-4123
130	11914680	Academica	6340 Sunset Dr, Miami FL 33143	(305) 669-2906
131	11914549	Accelerated Learning Solutions	5850 T G Lee Blvd Ste 345, Orlando FL 32822	(888) 437-9353
132	11914496	Charter School Associates Inc	5471 N University Dr, Coral Springs FL 33067	(954) 414-5767
133	11914678	Charter Schools USA	800 Corporate Dr Ste 700, Ft Lauderdale FL 33334	(954) 202-3500
134	11912541	Cmty & Eco Dev Org Gadsden Co	20 E Washington St, Quincy FL 32351	(850) 627-7656
135	11914630	Edisonlearning Inc	1 E Broward Blvd Ste 1111, Ft Lauderdale FL 33301	(877) 890-7088
136	12261709	Forza Education Management LLC	7815 111th Ter E, Parrish FL 34219	(727) 642-9319
137	11916420	Imagine South Florida Regional	13790 NW 4th St Ste 108, Sunrise FL 33325	(954) 870-5023
138	11916406	Imagine Southeast Regional	755 Town Center Blvd, Palm Coast FL 32164	(888) 709-8010
139	11916157	KIPP Jacksonville Schools	1440 McDuff Ave N, Jacksonville FL 32254	(904) 683-6643
140	12179651	Lake Wales Charter Schools	130 E Central Ave, Lake Wales FL 33853	(863) 679-6560
141	11913569	Lighthouse Academies	29140 Chapel Park Dr Bldg 5A, Wesley Chapel FL 33543	(800) 901-6943
142	11913947	LII Licensing Inc	6710 86th Ave N, Pinellas Park FL 33782	(727) 768-0989
143	11914379	Rader Group	101A Business Centre Dr, Miramar Beach FL 32550	(850) 650-3984
144	11913789	Superior Schools	861 N Hercules Ave, Clearwater FL 33765	(727) 799-1200
145	11916224	KIPP Metro Atlanta Schools	504 Fair St SW Ste 300, Atlanta GA 30313	(404) 924-6310
146	12240195	Mountain Ed Chtr High School	1963 Tom Bell Rd, Cleveland GA 30528	(706) 219-4664
147	12259990	Gem Innovation Schools	PO Box 86, Deary ID 83823	(208) 238-1388
148	11913466	Acero Charter Schools Inc	209 W Jackson Blvd Ste 500, Chicago IL 60606	(312) 637-3900
149	11913662	American Quality Schools Corp	1315 Butterfield Rd Ste 224, Chicago IL 60615	(312) 226-3355
150	11912670	Betty Shabazz Intl Chtr Sch	7822 S Dobson Ave, Chicago IL 60619	(773) 651-1221
151	11912606	Catalyst Schools	6727 S California Ave, Chicago IL 60629	(773) 295-7001
152	11912553	Civitas Education Partners	901 W Jackson Blvd Ste 205, Chicago IL 60607	(312) 733-6790
153	11913636	Concept Schools	1336 Basswood Rd, Schaumburg IL 60173	(847) 824-3380
154	11912333	Galapagos Charter	3051 Rotary Rd, Rockford IL 61109	(779) 368-0852
155	11914812	KIPP Chicago	2007 S Halsted St, Chicago IL 60608	(312) 733-8108
156	12110447	Lawndale Educ & Reg Network	3021 W Carroll Ave, Chicago IL 60612	(773) 584-4399
157	11913545	Noble Network of Charter Sch	1 N State St Ste 700, Chicago IL 60602	(312) 521-5287
158	11913038	Perspectives Charter Schools	1530 S State St Ste 200, Chicago IL 60605	(312) 604-2200
159	12260016	Regeneration Schools	1816 W Garfield Blvd, Chicago IL 60609	(773) 778-9455
160	11913246	GEO Foundation	1630 N Meridian St Ste 350, Indianapolis IN 46202	(317) 536-1027
161	12315427	Goodwill Education Initiatives	1635 W Michigan St, Indianapolis IN 46222	(317) 524-4265
162	11916145	KIPP Indy Public Schools	1740 E 30th St, Indianapolis IN 46218	(317) 547-5477
163	12179027	Tindley Accelerated Schools	3960 Meadows Dr, Indianapolis IN 46205	(317) 545-1745
164	11913430	Algiers Charter School Assoc	2401 Westbend Pkwy Ste 2001, New Orleans LA 70114	(504) 302-7001
165	12115203	Collegiate Academies	7301 Dwyer Rd, New Orleans LA 70126	(504) 503-0008
166	11930816	Crescent City Schools	3811 N Galvez St, New Orleans LA 70117	(504) 708-4136
167	11912369	Firstline Schools Inc	300 N Broad St Ste 207, New Orleans LA 70119	(504) 267-9038
168	11930725	Friends of King Schools	1617 Caffin Ave, New Orleans LA 70117	(504) 940-2243
169	12179039	Inspirenola Charter Schools	2401 Westbend Pkwy Ste 4040, New Orleans LA 70114	(504) 227-3057
170	12259213	Jcfa Charter Schools	475 Manhattan Blvd, Harvey LA 70058	(504) 410-3121
171	11916250	KIPP New Orleans Schools	1307 Oretha Castle Haley Blvd, New Orleans LA 70113	(504) 373-6269
172	11912058	Renew Schools Inc	1607 S Carrollton Ave, New Orleans LA 70118	(504) 367-3307
173	11911913	The Choice Foundation	3201 Live Oak St, New Orleans LA 70118	(504) 861-8370
174	12110411	The Einstein Group Inc	5316 Michoud Blvd, New Orleans LA 70129	(504) 324-7450
175	11913296	Excel Academy	58 Moore St, East Boston MA 02128	(617) 874-4080
176	11916171	KIPP Massachusetts Pub CH Schs	90 High Rock St, Lynn MA 01902	(781) 598-1609
177	12306086	The Community Group	190 Hampshire St Ste 2, Lawrence MA 01840	(978) 682-6628
178	12260004	Up Education Network	90 Canal St Ste 600, Boston MA 02114	(617) 307-5980
179	11913428	Baltimore Curriculum Project	2707 E Fayette St, Baltimore MD 21224	(410) 675-7000
180	11912577	City Neighbors Inc	4301 Raspe Ave, Baltimore MD 21206	(410) 325-2627

CHARTER MANAGEMENT ORGANIZATION (CMO) INDEX — Market Data Retrieval

CMO No.	PID	CMO Name	Address	Phone
181	11914666	Connections Academy	10960 Grantchester Way, Columbia MD 21044	(443) 529-1000
182	11916470	Imagine Mid-Atlantic Regional	4415 Nicole Dr Ste C, Lanham MD 20706	(301) 316-1802
183	11915830	KIPP Baltimore	4701 Greenspring Ave Rm 115, Baltimore MD 21209	(410) 367-0807
184	11912228	Living Classrooms Foundation	802 S Caroline St, Baltimore MD 21231	(410) 685-0295
185	11914252	American Institutional Mgmt	5728 Schaefer Rd Ste 200, Dearborn MI 48126	(313) 624-2000
186	11914240	Bardwell Group	19800 Beech Daly Rd, Redford MI 48240	(313) 450-0642
187	11914501	Charter School Admin Services	20820 Greenfield Rd, Oak Park MI 48237	(248) 569-7787
188	11914484	Choice Schools Associates LLC	5251 Clyde Park Ave SW, Wyoming MI 49509	(616) 785-8440
189	11911858	Cornerstone Education Group	306 E 4th St, Royal Oak MI 48067	(248) 439-6228
190	11914642	CS Partners LLC	869 S Old US 23 Ste 500, Brighton MI 48114	(810) 229-5145
191	11914094	EdTec Central LLC	10 S Main St Ste 100, Mount Clemens MI 48043	(248) 582-8100
192	11914343	Education Enrichmnet Services	19236 W 11 Mile Rd, Lathrup Vlg MI 48076	(248) 905-5030
193	11914070	Education Management&Networks	27704 Franklin Rd, Southfield MI 48034	(248) 327-7673
194	11912345	Foundation for Behavioral Res	600 S Lincoln St, Augusta MI 49012	(269) 731-5796
195	11914446	Global Educational Excellence	2455 S Industrial Hwy Ste A, Ann Arbor MI 48104	(734) 369-9500
196	11914018	Hamadeh Educational Services	PO Box 1440, Dearborn MI 48121	(313) 565-0507
197	11914006	Hanley-Harper Group Inc	20542 Harper Ave, Harper Woods MI 48225	(313) 347-0026
198	11913973	Innovative Teaching Solutions	18470 W 10 Mile Rd Ste 100, Southfield MI 48075	(248) 799-2780
199	11913961	Lakeshore Educl Management	12955 Robins Ridge Rd, Charlevoix MI 49720	(231) 547-4264
200	11916597	Leona Group LLC-Midwest	2125 University Park Dr, Okemos MI 48864	(517) 333-9030
201	11912204	Midland Charter Initiative	4653 Bailey Bridge Rd, Midland MI 48640	(989) 496-2404
202	11913935	MJ Management Services Inc	PO Box 1014, Flat Rock MI 48134	(734) 675-5505
203	11914575	National Heritage Academies	3850 Broadmoor Ave SE Ste 201, Grand Rapids MI 49512	(877) 223-6402
204	11913868	PrepNet LLC	3755 36th St SE Ste 250, Grand Rapids MI 49512	(616) 726-8900
205	12038734	Promise Schools	15000 Trojan St, Detroit MI 48235	(313) 964-2339
206	11914367	Romine Group LLC	7877 Stead St Ste 100, Utica MI 48317	(586) 731-5300
207	11913818	Solid Rock Management Company	3031 W Grand Blvd Ste 524, Detroit MI 48202	(313) 873-7625
208	11913753	Technical Academy Group LLC	4801 Oakman Blvd, Dearborn MI 48126	(313) 625-4700
209	11911793	Youth Visions Solutions	1450 25th St, Detroit MI 48216	(313) 558-9022
210	12262284	Harvest Network of Schools	1300 Olson Memorial Hwy, Minneapolis MN 55411	(612) 876-4105
211	12262301	Hiawatha Academies	1611 E 46th St, Minneapolis MN 55407	(612) 455-4004
212	12115033	KIPP Minnesota Public Schools	5034 Oliver Ave N, Minneapolis MN 55430	(612) 287-9700
213	12262387	MN Transitions Charter Schs	2872 26th Ave S, Minneapolis MN 55406	(612) 722-9013
214	11914355	Sabis Educational Systems	6385 Beach Rd, Eden Prairie MN 55344	(952) 918-1850
215	12261462	Confluence Academies	611 N 10th St Ste 525, Saint Louis MO 63101	(314) 588-8554
216	12115021	KIPP Kansas City	2700 E 18th St Ste 155B, Kansas City MO 64127	(816) 241-3994
217	11916303	KIPP St Louis Public Schools	1310 Papin St Ste 203, Saint Louis MO 63103	(314) 349-1388
218	12115019	KIPP Charlotte Public Schools	931 Wilann Dr, Charlotte NC 28215	(704) 537-2044
219	11916119	KIPP Enc College Prep Pub Schs	320 Pleasant Hill Rd, Gaston NC 27832	(252) 308-6932
220	12179431	Teamcfa	9935D Rea Rd Ste 167, Charlotte NC 28277	(704) 774-3038
221	12309351	The Roger Bacon Academy	3610 Thaddeus Lott Ln NE, Leland NC 28451	(910) 655-3600
222	12306593	College Achieve Ctl CS Network	365 Emerson Ave, Plainfield NJ 07062	(908) 625-1879
223	12110332	Ilearn Schools Inc	33-00 Broadway Ste 301, Fair Lawn NJ 07410	(201) 773-9140
224	11916327	KIPP New Jersey	60 Park Pl Ste 802, Newark NJ 07102	(973) 622-0905
225	11912694	Beginning with Children Fndn	217 Havemeyer St Ste 2, Brooklyn NY 11211	(212) 750-9320
226	11912644	Brighter Choice Charter Schs	250 Central Ave, Albany NY 12206	(518) 694-4100
227	11912498	Democracy Prep Public Schools	1767 Park Ave Fl 4, New York NY 10035	(212) 281-1248
228	12262894	Excellence Community Schools	2090 7th Ave Ste 605, New York NY 10027	(212) 222-5071
229	11912371	Explore Schools Inc	20 Jay St Ste 211, Brooklyn NY 11201	(718) 989-6730
230	12161604	Great Oaks Foundation	200 Broadway 3rd Fl, New York NY 10038	(917) 239-3641
231	11912292	Harlem Village Academies	15 Penn Plz Ste 15, New York NY 10001	(646) 812-9501
232	12114986	KIPP Albany Public Schools	321 Northern Blvd, Albany NY 12210	(518) 694-9494
233	11914824	KIPP NYC Public Schools	1501 Broadway Ste 1000, New York NY 10036	(212) 991-2610
234	11912084	Public Prep Network Inc	441 E 148th St, Bronx NY 10455	(212) 346-6000
235	11912943	Success Academy Charter Schls	95 Pine St Fl 6, New York NY 10005	(646) 597-4641
236	11913478	Uncommon Schools	826 Broadway Fl 9, New York NY 10003	(212) 844-3584
237	11914563	Victory Education Partners	135 W 40 St Fl 5, New York NY 10036	(212) 786-7900
238	12179819	Accel Schools	4700 Rockside Rd Ste 345, Independence OH 44131	(216) 583-5230
239	11913416	Breakthrough Charter Schools	3615 Superior Ave E Ste 4403A, Cleveland OH 44114	(216) 456-2086
240	11912632	Buckeye on-Line School Success	119 E 5th St, E Liverpool OH 43920	(330) 385-1987

MDR School Directory

CHARTER MANAGEMENT ORGANIZATION (CMO) INDEX

CMO No.	PID	CMO Name	Address	Phone
241	12106575	Carpe Diem Learning Systems	301 N Breiel Blvd Ste B, Middletown OH 45042	(513) 217-3400
242	11914654	Constellation Schools	5730 Broadview Rd, Parma OH 44134	(216) 712-7600
243	12319069	Educational Solutions	1500 W 3rd Ave Ste 125, Columbus OH 43212	(614) 299-1007
244	11914460	Eschool Consultants	4480 Refugee Rd, Columbus OH 43232	(614) 322-7996
245	11916509	Imagine Ohio Regional	11518 Banning Rd, Mount Vernon OH 43050	(614) 930-1184
246	11916066	KIPP Columbus	2980 Inspire Dr, Columbus OH 43224	(614) 263-6137
247	11914393	Performance Academies LLC	2 Easton Oval Ste 525, Columbus OH 43219	(614) 512-2151
248	11913480	Summit Academy Management	2791 Mogadore Rd, Akron OH 44312	(330) 670-8470
249	12363034	United Schools Network	1469 E Main St, Columbus OH 43205	(614) 299-5284
250	12305745	KIPP Okc Public Schools	PO Box 776, Oklahoma City OK 73101	(405) 425-4622
251	12115069	KIPP Tulsa Public Charter Schs	1661 E Virgin St, Tulsa OK 74106	(918) 794-8652
252	12361452	Santa Fe South Public Schools	4825 S Shields Blvd, Oklahoma City OK 73129	(405) 601-5440
253	11913117	Mastery Lrng Inst-Arthur Acad	13717 SE Division St, Portland OR 97236	(503) 762-6061
254	11914185	Charter School Management Inc	419 Avenue of the States, Chester PA 19013	(610) 447-0200
255	11912448	EdSys Inc	201 Stanwix St Ste 100, Pittsburgh PA 15222	(412) 690-2489
256	11916274	KIPP Philadelphia Public Schs	5070 Parkside Ave Ste 3500D, Philadelphia PA 19131	(215) 294-8596
257	11913129	Mastery Charter Schools	5700 Wayne Ave, Philadelphia PA 19144	(215) 866-9000
258	11914408	Omnivest Properties Management	115 Pheasant Run Ste 210, Newtown PA 18940	(215) 497-8301
259	11913026	Propel Schools	3447 E Carson St Ste 200, Pittsburgh PA 15203	(412) 325-7305
260	11912888	Universal Companies Inc	800 S 15th St, Philadelphia PA 19146	(215) 391-4161
261	12312499	Charter Institute at Erskine	1201 Main St Ste 300, Columbia SC 29201	(803) 849-2464
262	12161719	Capstone Education Group	PO Box 22569, Memphis TN 38122	(901) 416-3640
263	11914628	Chancelight Behavioral Hlth-Ed	1321 Murfreesboro Pike Ste 702, Nashville TN 37217	(615) 361-4000
264	12319629	Freedom Prep Academy Network	778 Parkrose Ave, Memphis TN 38109	(901) 881-1149
265	12038813	Gestalt Community Schools	2650 Thsnd Oaks Blvd Ste 1400, Memphis TN 38118	(901) 213-5161
266	12305850	Green Dot Pub Schs-Tennessee	4950 Fairley Rd, Memphis TN 38109	(901) 730-8160
267	11916200	KIPP Memphis Collegiate Schs	2670 Union Avenue Ext Ste 1100, Memphis TN 38112	(901) 452-2682
268	11916236	KIPP Nashville	123 Douglas Ave, Nashville TN 37207	(615) 226-4484
269	12038825	Lead Public Schools	2835 Brick Church Pike, Nashville TN 37207	(615) 815-1264
270	12110461	Republic Schools	3307 Brick Church Pike, Nashville TN 37207	(615) 921-6620
271	11911896	The Influence 1 Foundation	665 Madison Ave, Memphis TN 38103	(901) 526-1944
272	11912993	A Plus Charter Schools	8225 Bruton Rd, Dallas TX 75217	(214) 381-3226
273	12315738	Arrow Academy	PO Box 12207, College Sta TX 77842	(979) 703-8820
274	11913105	Baker-Ripley	PO Box 271389, Houston TX 77277	(713) 667-9400
275	11912618	Calvin Nelms Charter Schools	20625 Clay Rd, Katy TX 77449	(281) 398-8031
276	11912486	Democratic Schools Research	410 Bethel Ln, Bryan TX 77802	(979) 775-2152
277	11912450	East Waco Innovative Sch Dev	1020 Elm St Ste 100, Waco TX 76704	(254) 754-8000
278	11913325	Educational Leadership Inc	3333 Bering Dr Ste 200, Houston TX 77057	(713) 784-6345
279	12361414	Evolution Academy Charter Schs	1101 S Sherman St, Richardson TX 75081	(972) 907-3755
280	11913284	Faith Family Academy Chtr Schs	1608 Osprey Dr, Desoto TX 75115	(972) 224-4110
281	11912321	Golden Rule Schools Inc	2602 W Illinois Ave, Dallas TX 75233	(214) 333-9330
282	12160947	Great Hearts Texas	824 Broadway St Ste 101, San Antonio TX 78215	(210) 888-9475
283	11912307	Gulf Coast Council of La Raza	4129 Greenwood Dr, Corp Christi TX 78416	(361) 881-9988
284	11913624	Harmony Pub Schs-Cosmos Found	9321 W Sam Houston Pkwy S, Houston TX 77099	(713) 343-3333
285	11913193	Jubilee Academic Center Inc	4434 Roland Rd, San Antonio TX 78222	(210) 333-6227
286	11915828	KIPP Texas Public Schs Austin	8509 FM 969 Ste 513, Austin TX 78724	(512) 501-3643
287	11916080	KIPP Texas Public Schs Dallas	1545 S Ewing Ave, Dallas TX 75216	(972) 323-4200
288	11916133	KIPP Texas Public Schs Houston	10711 Kipp Way Dr, Houston TX 77099	(832) 328-1051
289	11916298	KIPP Texas Public Schs Sa	731 Fredericksburg Rd, San Antonio TX 78201	(210) 787-3197
290	11913131	Life School	132 E Ovilla Rd Ste 1A, Red Oak TX 75154	(469) 850-5433
291	11912163	New Frontiers Public Schools	138 Fair Ave, San Antonio TX 78223	(210) 519-3900
292	11913040	Orenda Education	2951 Williams Dr, Georgetown TX 78628	(512) 869-3020
293	11912137	Panola Charter Schools	PO Box 610, Carthage TX 75633	(903) 693-6355
294	11912096	Por Vida Inc	1135 Mission Rd, San Antonio TX 78210	(210) 532-8816
295	12113918	Priority Charter Schools	275 FM 2483, Morgans Point TX 76513	(254) 206-2013
296	11913014	Raul Yzaguirre Sch-Success Org	2950 Broadway St, Houston TX 77017	(713) 640-3700
297	12233855	Responsive Education Solutions	PO Box 292730, Lewisville TX 75029	(972) 316-3663
298	11913507	Richard Milburn Academy Inc	1263 Terminal Loop Rd, Mc Queeney TX 78123	(830) 557-6181
299	11913002	Riverwalk Education Foundation	5300 Wurzbach Rd, San Antonio TX 78238	(210) 957-1955
300	11912981	Salvaging Teens at Risk Inc	4601 N Interstate 35, Denton TX 76207	(940) 383-6655

CHARTER MANAGEMENT ORGANIZATION (CMO) INDEX

Market Data Retrieval

CMO No.	PID	CMO Name	Address	Phone
301	11911999	South Texas Educ Technologies	2402 E Business 83, Weslaco TX 78596	(956) 969-3092
302	11912967	Southwest Winners Foundation	1258 Austin Hwy, San Antonio TX 78209	(210) 829-8017
303	11912955	Student Alternatives Program	PO Box 15644, San Antonio TX 78212	(210) 227-0295
304	11912931	Tekoa Academy Accel Studies	326 Thomas Blvd, Port Arthur TX 77640	(409) 982-5400
305	11913674	Texans Can Academies	325 W 12th St, Dallas TX 75208	(214) 944-1985
306	11911937	Texas Center for Arts & Acad	3901 S Hulen St, Fort Worth TX 76109	(817) 766-2390
307	11912905	Trinity Charter Schools	8305 Cross Park Dr, Austin TX 78754	(512) 706-7564
308	11911834	Two Dimensions Prep Chtr Acad	12121 Veterans Memorial Dr, Houston TX 77067	(281) 227-4700
309	11913454	Uplift Education	1825 Market Ctr Blvd Ste 500, Dallas TX 75207	(469) 621-8500
310	11911810	Varnett Public School Inc	5025 S Willow Dr, Houston TX 77035	(713) 667-4051
311	11912876	Winfree Academy Charter Schs	1555 Valwood Pkwy Ste 160, Carrollton TX 75006	(972) 869-3250
312	11912864	YES Prep Public Schools	5515 South Loop E Ste B, Houston TX 77033	(713) 967-9000
313	11914616	Imagine Schools Inc	1900 Gallows Rd Ste 250, Vienna VA 22182	(703) 527-2600
314	11914604	K12 Inc	2300 Corporate Park Dr, Herndon VA 20171	(866) 283-0300
315	12305836	Green Dot Pub Schs-Washington	4800 S 188th St Ste 250, Seatac WA 98188	(253) 382-2400
316	12306000	Seeds of Health Inc	1445 S 32nd St, Milwaukee WI 53215	(414) 672-3430